Calculus

Concepts and Contexts | 4e

A Preview of Calculus

Calculus is fundamentally different from the mathematics that you have studied previously: calculus is less static and more dynamic. It is concerned with change and motion; it deals with quantities that approach other quantities. For that reason it may be useful to have an overview of the subject before beginning its intensive study. Here we give a glimpse of some of the main ideas of calculus by showing how the concept of a limit arises when we attempt to solve a variety of problems.

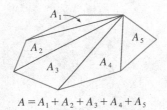

$$A = A_1 + A_2 + A_3 + A_4 + A_5$$

FIGURE 1

The Area Problem

The origins of calculus go back at least 2500 years to the ancient Greeks, who found areas using the "method of exhaustion." They knew how to find the area A of any polygon by dividing it into triangles as in Figure 1 and adding the areas of these triangles.

It is a much more difficult problem to find the area of a curved figure. The Greek method of exhaustion was to inscribe polygons in the figure and circumscribe polygons about the figure and then let the number of sides of the polygons increase. Figure 2 illustrates this process for the special case of a circle with inscribed regular polygons.

     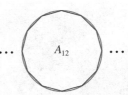

FIGURE 2

Let A_n be the area of the inscribed polygon with n sides. As n increases, it appears that A_n becomes closer and closer to the area of the circle. We say that the area of the circle is the *limit* of the areas of the inscribed polygons, and we write

$$A = \lim_{n \to \infty} A_n$$

TEC In the Preview Visual, you can see how inscribed and circumscribed polygons approximate the area of a circle.

The Greeks themselves did not use limits explicitly. However, by indirect reasoning, Eudoxus (fifth century BC) used exhaustion to prove the familiar formula for the area of a circle: $A = \pi r^2$.

We will use a similar idea in Chapter 5 to find areas of regions of the type shown in Figure 3. We will approximate the desired area A by areas of rectangles (as in Figure 4), let the width of the rectangles decrease, and then calculate A as the limit of these sums of areas of rectangles.

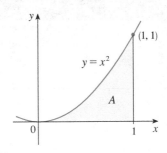 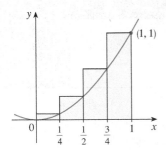 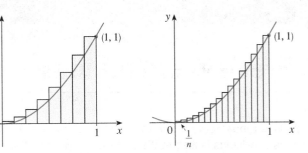

FIGURE 3   **FIGURE 4**

The area problem is the central problem in the branch of calculus called *integral calculus*. The techniques that we will develop in Chapter 5 for finding areas will also enable us to compute the volume of a solid, the length of a curve, the force of water against a dam, the mass and center of gravity of a rod, and the work done in pumping water out of a tank.

The Tangent Problem

Consider the problem of trying to find an equation of the tangent line t to a curve with equation $y = f(x)$ at a given point P. (We will give a precise definition of a tangent line in

Calculus

Volume 2 - Math 253 and 254

Custom Edition for Portland Community College

James Stewart

CENGAGE
Learning

Australia Brazil Japan • Korea • Mexico • Singapore • Spain • United Kingdom • United States

Calculus
Volume 2 - Math 253 and 254
Custom Edition for Portland Community College

Calculus: Concepts and Contexts, Fourth Edition
James Stewart

© 2010, 2005 Cengage Learning. All rights reserved.

Library of Congress Control Number: 2008941257

Senior Project Development Manager:
Linda deStefano

Market Development Manager:
Heather Kramer

Senior Production/Manufacturing Manager:
Donna M. Brown

Production Editorial Manager:
Kim Fry

Sr. Rights Acquisition Account Manager:
Todd Osborne

For product information and technology assistance, contact us at
Cengage Learning Customer & Sales Support, 1-800-354-9706

For permission to use material from this text or product,
submit all requests online at **cengage.com/permissions**
Further permissions questions can be emailed to
permissionrequest@cengage.com

This book contains select works from existing Cengage Learning resources and was produced by Cengage Learning Custom Solutions for collegiate use. As such, those adopting and/or contributing to this work are responsible for editorial content accuracy, continuity and completeness.

Compilation © 2013 Cengage Learning

ISBN-13: 978-1-285-88061-7

ISBN-10: 1-285-88061-7

Cengage Learning
5191 Natorp Boulevard
Mason, Ohio 45040
USA
Cengage Learning is a leading provider of customized learning solutions with office locations around the globe, including Singapore, the United Kingdom, Australia, Mexico, Brazil, and Japan. Locate your local office at:
international.cengage.com/region.

Cengage Learning products are represented in Canada by Nelson Education, Ltd.
For your lifelong learning solutions, visit **www.cengage.com/custom.**
Visit our corporate website at **www.cengage.com.**

Printed in the United States of America

Contents

Student Solutions Manual

DOCUMENTATION STANDARDS FOR MATHEMATICS

All work in this course will be evaluated for your ability to meet the following writing objectives as well as for "mathematical content."

1. Every solution must be written in such a way that the question that was asked is clear.

2. Any table or graph that appears in the original problem must also appear somewhere in your solution.

3. All graphs that appear in your solution must have a figure number, a caption, and contain axis names and scales. When the graph is referenced in your written work, the reference must be by figure number. For applied problems, variables on each axis must be well defined and include units.

4. All tables that appear in your solution must have well-defined column headings, an assigned table number, and a brief caption (description). When the table is referenced in your written work, the reference must be by table number.

5. A brief introduction to the problem is almost always appropriate.

6. In applied problems, all variables and constants must be defined.

7. If you used the graph or table feature of your calculator in the problem solving process, you must include the graph or table in your written solution.

8. If you used some other non-trivial feature of your calculator (e.g., SOLVER), you must state this in your solution.

9. All (relevant) information given in the problem must be stated somewhere in your solution.

10. A sentence that orients the reader to the purpose of the mathematics should precede symbolic mathematical work.

11. Your conclusion shall not be encased in a box, but rather stated at the end of your solution in complete sentence form.

12. Remember to line up your equal signs.

13. If work is word-processed, all mathematical symbols must be generated with a math equation editor.

SHOWING YOUR WORK AND PROPER SYNTAX

On written work, you are expected to show the math and processes you followed to reach the answer. Merely providing the answer is not sufficient. In fact, how you present the steps that lead to the answer is as important as the answer itself. You will be evaluated not only on your ability to get the correct answers and perform the correct steps, but also on the accuracy of your presentation and the proper use of mathematical symbols.

1. Solve the differential equation $\frac{dy}{dx} = xy$.

   Solution

   The work below will show how to solve the differential equation $\frac{dy}{dx} = xy$.

   Case 1 Assume that $y \neq 0$. First, separate the variables.

   $$\frac{dy}{dx} = xy$$

   $$\left(\frac{1}{y}\frac{dy}{dx}\right) dx = x\,dx$$

   Next, integrate both sides of the equation.

   $$\int \left(\frac{1}{y}\frac{dy}{dx}\right) dx = \int x\,dx$$

   $$\int \frac{1}{y}\,dy = \int x\,dx$$

   $$\ln|y| = \frac{1}{2}x^2 + C$$

   Finally, solve for y.

   $$e^{\ln|y|} = e^{\frac{1}{2}x^2 + C}$$

   $$|y| = e^C\, e^{\frac{1}{2}x^2}$$

   $$y = k\, e^{\frac{1}{2}x^2} \tag{1}$$

   where in (1), k is an arbitrary nonzero constant (equal to e^C or $-e^C$).

   Case 2 Assume that $y = 0$; clearly this implies $\frac{dy}{dx} = 0$ and we have to verify that this function satisfies the differential equation, i.e

   $$\frac{dy}{dx} \overset{?}{=} xy$$

   $$0 \overset{?}{=} x \cdot 0$$

   $$0 = 0 \quad \checkmark$$

   So $y = 0$ is in fact also a solution to the differential equation. This removes the nonzero constraint for k in Case 1.

   Therefore the solution set to the differential equation $\frac{dy}{dx} = xy$ is the family of functions of the form $y = k\, e^{\frac{1}{2}x^2}$, where k is an arbitrary constant.

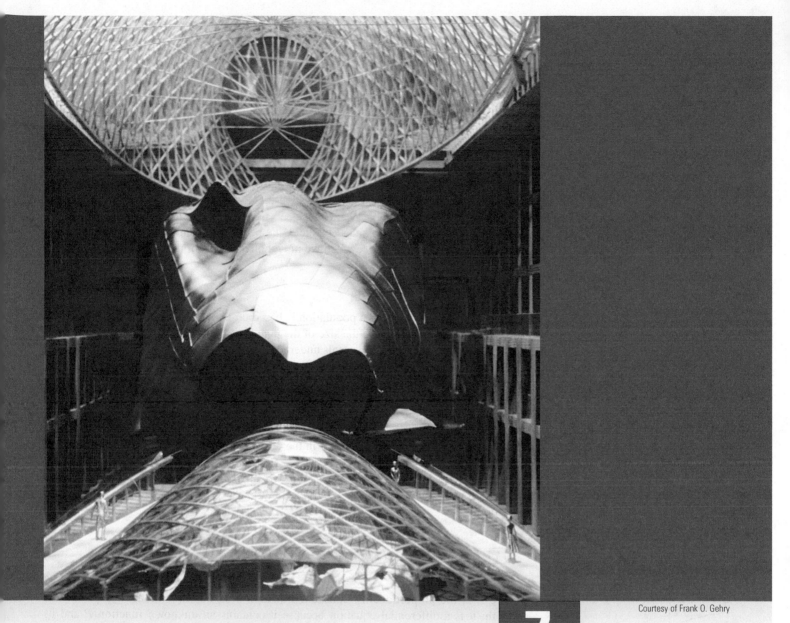

Differential Equations

7

Perhaps the most important of all the applications of calculus is to differential equations. When physical scientists or social scientists use calculus, more often than not it is to analyze a differential equation that has arisen in the process of modeling some phenomenon that they are studying. Although it is often impossible to find an explicit formula for the solution of a differential equation, we will see that graphical and numerical approaches provide the needed information.

7.1 Modeling with Differential Equations

Now is a good time to read (or reread) the discussion of mathematical modeling on page 25.

In describing the process of modeling in Section 1.2, we talked about formulating a mathematical model of a real-world problem either through intuitive reasoning about the phenomenon or from a physical law based on evidence from experiments. The mathematical model often takes the form of a *differential equation,* that is, an equation that contains an unknown function and some of its derivatives. This is not surprising because in a real-world problem we often notice that changes occur and we want to predict future behavior on the basis of how current values change. Let's begin by examining several examples of how differential equations arise when we model physical phenomena.

Models of Population Growth

One model for the growth of a population is based on the assumption that the population grows at a rate proportional to the size of the population. That is a reasonable assumption for a population of bacteria or animals under ideal conditions (unlimited environment, adequate nutrition, absence of predators, immunity from disease).

Let's identify and name the variables in this model:

$$t = \text{time} \quad \text{(the independent variable)}$$

$$P = \text{the number of individuals in the population} \quad \text{(the dependent variable)}$$

The rate of growth of the population is the derivative dP/dt. So our assumption that the rate of growth of the population is proportional to the population size is written as the equation

1
$$\frac{dP}{dt} = kP$$

where k is the proportionality constant. Equation 1 is our first model for population growth; it is a differential equation because it contains an unknown function P and its derivative dP/dt.

Having formulated a model, let's look at its consequences. If we rule out a population of 0, then $P(t) > 0$ for all t. So, if $k > 0$, then Equation 1 shows that $P'(t) > 0$ for all t. This means that the population is always increasing. In fact, as $P(t)$ increases, Equation 1 shows that dP/dt becomes larger. In other words, the growth rate increases as the population increases.

Let's try to think of a solution of Equation 1. This equation asks us to find a function whose derivative is a constant multiple of itself. We know that exponential functions have that property. In fact, if we let $P(t) = Ce^{kt}$, then

$$P'(t) = C(ke^{kt}) = k(Ce^{kt}) = kP(t)$$

Thus any exponential function of the form $P(t) = Ce^{kt}$ is a solution of Equation 1. When we study this equation in detail in Section 7.4, we will see that there is no other solution.

Allowing C to vary through all the real numbers, we get the *family* of solutions $P(t) = Ce^{kt}$ whose graphs are shown in Figure 1. But populations have only positive values and so we are interested only in the solutions with $C > 0$. And we are probably concerned only with values of t greater than the initial time $t = 0$. Figure 2 shows the physi-

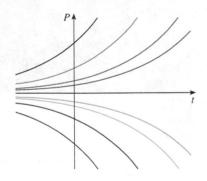

FIGURE 1
The family of solutions of $dP/dt = kP$

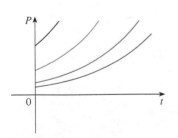

FIGURE 2
The family of solutions $P(t) = Ce^{kt}$
with $C > 0$ and $t \geq 0$

cally meaningful solutions. Putting $t = 0$, we get $P(0) = Ce^{k(0)} = C$, so the constant C turns out to be the initial population, $P(0)$.

Equation 1 is appropriate for modeling population growth under ideal conditions, but we have to recognize that a more realistic model must reflect the fact that a given environment has limited resources. Many populations start by increasing in an exponential manner, but the population levels off when it approaches its *carrying capacity M* (or decreases toward M if it ever exceeds M). For a model to take into account both trends, we make two assumptions:

■ $\dfrac{dP}{dt} \approx kP$ if P is small   (Initially, the growth rate is proportional to P.)

■ $\dfrac{dP}{dt} < 0$ if $P > M$ (P decreases if it ever exceeds M.)

A simple expression that incorporates both assumptions is given by the equation

$$\boxed{2} \qquad\qquad \frac{dP}{dt} = kP\left(1 - \frac{P}{M}\right)$$

Notice that if P is small compared with M, then P/M is close to 0 and so $dP/dt \approx kP$. If $P > M$, then $1 - P/M$ is negative and so $dP/dt < 0$.

Equation 2 is called the *logistic differential equation* and was proposed by the Dutch mathematical biologist Pierre-François Verhulst in the 1840s as a model for world population growth. We will develop techniques that enable us to find explicit solutions of the logistic equation in Section 7.5, but for now we can deduce qualitative characteristics of the solutions directly from Equation 2. We first observe that the constant functions $P(t) = 0$ and $P(t) = M$ are solutions because, in either case, one of the factors on the right side of Equation 2 is zero. (This certainly makes physical sense: If the population is ever either 0 or at the carrying capacity, it stays that way.) These two constant solutions are called *equilibrium solutions*.

If the initial population $P(0)$ lies between 0 and M, then the right side of Equation 2 is positive, so $dP/dt > 0$ and the population increases. But if the population exceeds the carrying capacity $(P > M)$, then $1 - P/M$ is negative, so $dP/dt < 0$ and the population decreases. Notice that, in either case, if the population approaches the carrying capacity $(P \to M)$, then $dP/dt \to 0$, which means the population levels off. So we expect that the solutions of the logistic differential equation have graphs that look something like the ones in Figure 3. Notice that the graphs move away from the equilibrium solution $P = 0$ and move toward the equilibrium solution $P = M$.

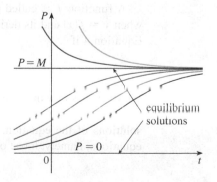

FIGURE 3
Solutions of the logistic equation

A Model for the Motion of a Spring

Let's now look at an example of a model from the physical sciences. We consider the motion of an object with mass m at the end of a vertical spring (as in Figure 4). In Section 6.6 we discussed Hooke's Law, which says that if the spring is stretched (or compressed) x units from its natural length, then it exerts a force that is proportional to x:

$$\text{restoring force} = -kx$$

where k is a positive constant (called the *spring constant*). If we ignore any external resisting forces (due to air resistance or friction) then, by Newton's Second Law (force equals mass times acceleration), we have

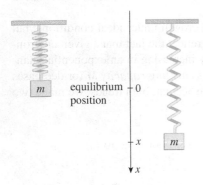

FIGURE 4

$$\boxed{3} \qquad m\frac{d^2x}{dt^2} = -kx$$

This is an example of what is called a *second-order differential equation* because it involves second derivatives. Let's see what we can guess about the form of the solution directly from the equation. We can rewrite Equation 3 in the form

$$\frac{d^2x}{dt^2} = -\frac{k}{m}x$$

which says that the second derivative of x is proportional to x but has the opposite sign. We know two functions with this property, the sine and cosine functions. In fact, it turns out that all solutions of Equation 3 can be written as combinations of certain sine and cosine functions (see Exercise 4). This is not surprising; we expect the spring to oscillate about its equilibrium position and so it is natural to think that trigonometric functions are involved.

General Differential Equations

In general, a **differential equation** is an equation that contains an unknown function and one or more of its derivatives. The **order** of a differential equation is the order of the highest derivative that occurs in the equation. Thus Equations 1 and 2 are first-order equations and Equation 3 is a second-order equation. In all three of those equations the independent variable is called t and represents time, but in general the independent variable doesn't have to represent time. For example, when we consider the differential equation

$$\boxed{4} \qquad y' = xy$$

it is understood that y is an unknown function of x.

A function f is called a **solution** of a differential equation if the equation is satisfied when $y = f(x)$ and its derivatives are substituted into the equation. Thus f is a solution of Equation 4 if

$$f'(x) = xf(x)$$

for all values of x in some interval.

When we are asked to *solve* a differential equation we are expected to find all possible solutions of the equation. We have already solved some particularly simple differential equations, namely, those of the form

$$y' = f(x)$$

For instance, we know that the general solution of the differential equation

$$y' = x^3$$

is given by

$$y = \frac{x^4}{4} + C$$

where C is an arbitrary constant.

But, in general, solving a differential equation is not an easy matter. There is no systematic technique that enables us to solve all differential equations. In Section 7.2, however, we will see how to draw rough graphs of solutions even when we have no explicit formula. We will also learn how to find numerical approximations to solutions.

V EXAMPLE 1 Verifying solutions of a differential equation Show that every member of the family of functions

$$y = \frac{1 + ce^t}{1 - ce^t}$$

is a solution of the differential equation $y' - \frac{1}{2}(y^2 - 1)$.

SOLUTION We use the Quotient Rule to differentiate the expression for y:

$$y' - \frac{(1 - ce^t)(ce^t) - (1 + ce^t)(-ce^t)}{(1 - ce^t)^2}$$

$$= \frac{ce^t - c^2e^{2t} + ce^t + c^2e^{2t}}{(1 - ce^t)^2} = \frac{2ce^t}{(1 - ce^t)^2}$$

The right side of the differential equation becomes

$$\frac{1}{2}(y^2 - 1) = \frac{1}{2}\left[\left(\frac{1 + ce^t}{1 - ce^t}\right)^2 - 1\right]$$

$$= \frac{1}{2}\left[\frac{(1 + ce^t)^2 - (1 - ce^t)^2}{(1 - ce^t)^2}\right]$$

$$= \frac{1}{2}\frac{4ce^t}{(1 - ce^t)^2} = \frac{2ce^t}{(1 - ce^t)^2}$$

Therefore, for every value of c, the given function is a solution of the differential equation.

Figure 5 shows graphs of seven members of the family in Example 1. The differential equation shows that if $y \approx \pm1$, then $y' \approx 0$. That is borne out by the flatness of the graphs near $y = 1$ and $y = -1$.

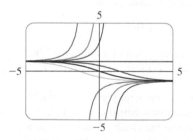

FIGURE 5

When applying differential equations, we are usually not as interested in finding a family of solutions (the *general solution*) as we are in finding a solution that satisfies some additional requirement. In many physical problems we need to find the particular solution that satisfies a condition of the form $y(t_0) = y_0$. This is called an **initial condition**, and the problem of finding a solution of the differential equation that satisfies the initial condition is called an **initial-value problem**.

Geometrically, when we impose an initial condition, we look at the family of solution curves and pick the one that passes through the point (t_0, y_0). Physically, this corresponds to measuring the state of a system at time t_0 and using the solution of the initial-value problem to predict the future behavior of the system.

V EXAMPLE 2 Find a solution of the differential equation $y' = \frac{1}{2}(y^2 - 1)$ that satisfies the initial condition $y(0) = 2$.

SOLUTION Substituting the values $t = 0$ and $y = 2$ into the formula

$$y = \frac{1 + ce^t}{1 - ce^t}$$

from Example 1, we get

$$2 = \frac{1 + ce^0}{1 - ce^0} = \frac{1 + c}{1 - c}$$

Solving this equation for c, we get $2 - 2c = 1 + c$, which gives $c = \frac{1}{3}$. So the solution of the initial-value problem is

$$y = \frac{1 + \frac{1}{3}e^t}{1 - \frac{1}{3}e^t} = \frac{3 + e^t}{3 - e^t}$$

7.1 Exercises

1. Show that $y = \frac{2}{3}e^x + e^{-2x}$ is a solution of the differential equation $y' + 2y = 2e^x$.

2. Verify that $y = -t \cos t - t$ is a solution of the initial-value problem

$$t\frac{dy}{dt} = y + t^2 \sin t \qquad y(\pi) = 0$$

3. (a) For what values of r does the function $y = e^{rx}$ satisfy the differential equation $2y'' + y' - y = 0$?
   (b) If r_1 and r_2 are the values of r that you found in part (a), show that every member of the family of functions $y = ae^{r_1 x} + be^{r_2 x}$ is also a solution.

4. (a) For what values of k does the function $y = \cos kt$ satisfy the differential equation $4y'' = -25y$?
   (b) For those values of k, verify that every member of the family of functions $y = A \sin kt + B \cos kt$ is also a solution.

5. Which of the following functions are solutions of the differential equation $y'' + y = \sin x$?
   (a) $y = \sin x$ (b) $y = \cos x$
   (c) $y = \frac{1}{2}x \sin x$ (d) $y = -\frac{1}{2}x \cos x$

6. (a) Show that every member of the family of functions $y = (\ln x + C)/x$ is a solution of the differential equation $x^2 y' + xy = 1$.

   (b) Illustrate part (a) by graphing several members of the family of solutions on a common screen.
   (c) Find a solution of the differential equation that satisfies the initial condition $y(1) = 2$.
   (d) Find a solution of the differential equation that satisfies the initial condition $y(2) = 1$.

7. (a) What can you say about a solution of the equation $y' = -y^2$ just by looking at the differential equation?
   (b) Verify that all members of the family $y = 1/(x + C)$ are solutions of the equation in part (a).
   (c) Can you think of a solution of the differential equation $y' = -y^2$ that is not a member of the family in part (b)?
   (d) Find a solution of the initial-value problem

$$y' = -y^2 \qquad y(0) = 0.5$$

8. (a) What can you say about the graph of a solution of the equation $y' = xy^3$ when x is close to 0? What if x is large?
   (b) Verify that all members of the family $y = (c - x^2)^{-1/2}$ are solutions of the differential equation $y' = xy^3$.
   (c) Graph several members of the family of solutions on a common screen. Do the graphs confirm what you predicted in part (a)?
   (d) Find a solution of the initial-value problem

$$y' = xy^3 \qquad y(0) = 2$$

9. A population is modeled by the differential equation

$$\frac{dP}{dt} = 1.2P\left(1 - \frac{P}{4200}\right)$$

   (a) For what values of P is the population increasing?
   (b) For what values of P is the population decreasing?
   (c) What are the equilibrium solutions?

10. A function $y(t)$ satisfies the differential equation

$$\frac{dy}{dt} = y^4 - 6y^3 + 5y^2$$

   (a) What are the constant solutions of the equation?

(b) For what values of y is y increasing?

(c) For what values of y is y decreasing?

11. Explain why the functions with the given graphs *can't* be solutions of the differential equation

$$\frac{dy}{dt} = e^t(y - 1)^2$$

(a)

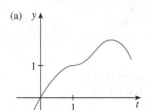

(b)

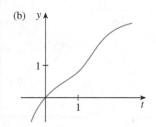

12. The function with the given graph is a solution of one of the following differential equations. Decide which is the correct equation and justify your answer.

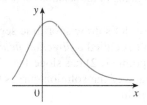

A. $y' = 1 + xy$ **B.** $y' = -2xy$ **C.** $y' = 1 - 2xy$

13. Match the differential equations with the solution graphs labeled I–IV. Give reasons for your choices.

(a) $y' = 1 + x^2 + y^2$ (b) $y' = xe^{-x^2-y^2}$

(c) $y' = \dfrac{1}{1 + e^{x^2+y^2}}$ (d) $y' = \sin(xy)\cos(xy)$

I

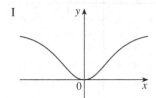

II

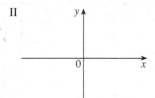

III

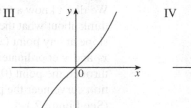

IV

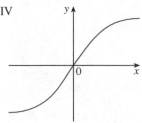

14. Suppose you have just poured a cup of freshly brewed coffee with temperature 95°C in a room where the temperature is 20°C.

(a) When do you think the coffee cools most quickly? What happens to the rate of cooling as time goes by? Explain.

(b) **Newton's Law of Cooling** states that the rate of cooling of an object is proportional to the temperature difference between the object and its surroundings, provided that this difference is not too large. Write a differential equation that expresses Newton's Law of Cooling for this particular situation. What is the initial condition? In view of your answer to part (a), do you think this differential equation is an appropriate model for cooling?

(c) Make a rough sketch of the graph of the solution of the initial-value problem in part (b).

15. Psychologists interested in learning theory study **learning curves**. A learning curve is the graph of a function $P(t)$, the performance of someone learning a skill as a function of the training time t. The derivative dP/dt represents the rate at which performance improves.

(a) When do you think P increases most rapidly? What happens to dP/dt as t increases? Explain.

(b) If M is the maximum level of performance of which the learner is capable, explain why the differential equation

$$\frac{dP}{dt} = k(M - P) \qquad k \text{ a positive constant}$$

is a reasonable model for learning.

(c) Make a rough sketch of a possible solution of this differential equation.

7.2 Direction Fields and Euler's Method

Unfortunately, it's impossible to solve most differential equations in the sense of obtaining an explicit formula for the solution. In this section we show that, despite the absence of an explicit solution, we can still learn a lot about the solution through a graphical approach (direction fields) or a numerical approach (Euler's method).

Direction Fields

Suppose we are asked to sketch the graph of the solution of the initial-value problem

$$y' = x + y \qquad y(0) = 1$$

We don't know a formula for the solution, so how can we possibly sketch its graph? Let's think about what the differential equation means. The equation $y' = x + y$ tells us that the slope at any point (x, y) on the graph (called the *solution curve*) is equal to the sum of the x- and y-coordinates of the point (see Figure 1). In particular, because the curve passes through the point $(0, 1)$, its slope there must be $0 + 1 = 1$. So a small portion of the solution curve near the point $(0, 1)$ looks like a short line segment through $(0, 1)$ with slope 1. (See Figure 2.)

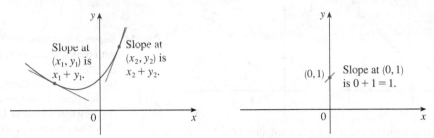

FIGURE 1
A solution of $y' = x + y$

FIGURE 2
Beginning of the solution curve through $(0, 1)$

As a guide to sketching the rest of the curve, let's draw short line segments at a number of points (x, y) with slope $x + y$. The result is called a *direction field* and is shown in Figure 3. For instance, the line segment at the point $(1, 2)$ has slope $1 + 2 = 3$. The direction field allows us to visualize the general shape of the solution curves by indicating the direction in which the curves proceed at each point.

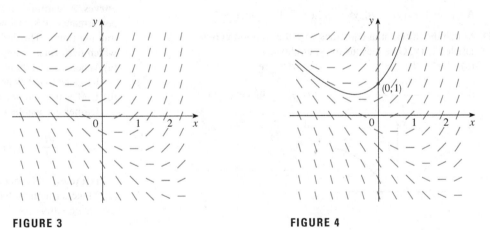

FIGURE 3
Direction field for $y' = x + y$

FIGURE 4
The solution curve through $(0, 1)$

Now we can sketch the solution curve through the point $(0, 1)$ by following the direction field as in Figure 4. Notice that we have drawn the curve so that it is parallel to nearby line segments.

In general, suppose we have a first-order differential equation of the form

$$y' = F(x, y)$$

where $F(x, y)$ is some expression in x and y. The differential equation says that the slope of a solution curve at a point (x, y) on the curve is $F(x, y)$. If we draw short line segments with slope $F(x, y)$ at several points (x, y), the result is called a **direction field** (or **slope field**). These line segments indicate the direction in which a solution curve is heading, so the direction field helps us visualize the general shape of these curves.

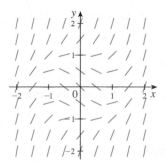

FIGURE 5

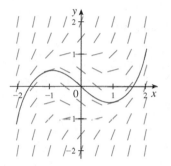

FIGURE 6

TEC Module 7.2A shows direction fields and solution curves for a variety of differential equations.

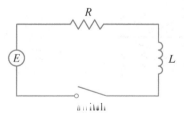

FIGURE 9

V   EXAMPLE 1   Using a direction field to sketch a solution curve

(a) Sketch the direction field for the differential equation $y' = x^2 + y^2 - 1$.

(b) Use part (a) to sketch the solution curve that passes through the origin.

SOLUTION

(a) We start by computing the slope at several points in the following chart:

x	-2	-1	0	1	2	-2	-1	0	1	2	$\ldots$
y	0	0	0	0	0	1	1	1	1	1	$\ldots$
$y' = x^2 + y^2 - 1$	3	0	-1	0	3	4	1	0	1	4	$\ldots$

Now we draw short line segments with these slopes at these points. The result is the direction field shown in Figure 5.

(b) We start at the origin and move to the right in the direction of the line segment (which has slope -1). We continue to draw the solution curve so that it moves parallel to the nearby line segments. The resulting solution curve is shown in Figure 6. Returning to the origin, we draw the solution curve to the left as well. ▬

The more line segments we draw in a direction field, the clearer the picture becomes. Of course, it's tedious to compute slopes and draw line segments for a huge number of points by hand, but computers are well suited for this task. Figure 7 shows a more detailed, computer-drawn direction field for the differential equation in Example 1. It enables us to draw, with reasonable accuracy, the solution curves shown in Figure 8 with y-intercepts $-2, -1, 0, 1,$ and 2.

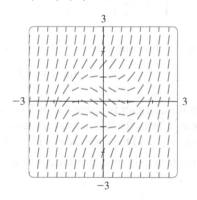

FIGURE 7

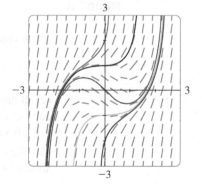

FIGURE 8

Now let's see how direction fields give insight into physical situations. The simple electric circuit shown in Figure 9 contains an electromotive force (usually a battery or generator) that produces a voltage of $E(t)$ volts (V) and a current of $I(t)$ amperes (A) at time t. The circuit also contains a resistor with a resistance of R ohms (Ω) and an inductor with an inductance of L henries (H).

Ohm's Law gives the drop in voltage due to the resistor as RI. The voltage drop due to the inductor is $L(dI/dt)$. One of Kirchhoff's laws says that the sum of the voltage drops is equal to the supplied voltage $E(t)$. Thus we have

$$\boxed{1} \qquad\qquad L\frac{dI}{dt} + RI = E(t)$$

which is a first-order differential equation that models the current I at time t.

V EXAMPLE 2 Suppose that in the simple circuit of Figure 9 the resistance is 12 Ω, the inductance is 4 H, and a battery gives a constant voltage of 60 V.
(a) Draw a direction field for Equation 1 with these values.
(b) What can you say about the limiting value of the current?
(c) Identify any equilibrium solutions.
(d) If the switch is closed when $t = 0$ so the current starts with $I(0) = 0$, use the direction field to sketch the solution curve.

SOLUTION
(a) If we put $L = 4$, $R = 12$, and $E(t) = 60$ in Equation 1, we get

$$4\frac{dI}{dt} + 12I = 60 \qquad \text{or} \qquad \frac{dI}{dt} = 15 - 3I$$

The direction field for this differential equation is shown in Figure 10.

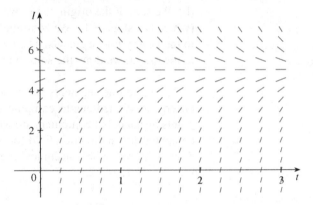

FIGURE 10

(b) It appears from the direction field that all solutions approach the value 5 A, that is,

$$\lim_{t \to \infty} I(t) = 5$$

(c) It appears that the constant function $I(t) = 5$ is an equilibrium solution. Indeed, we can verify this directly from the differential equation $dI/dt = 15 - 3I$. If $I(t) = 5$, then the left side is $dI/dt = 0$ and the right side is $15 - 3(5) = 0$.

(d) We use the direction field to sketch the solution curve that passes through $(0, 0)$, as shown in red in Figure 11.

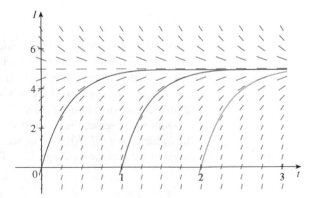

FIGURE 11

Notice from Figure 10 that the line segments along any horizontal line are parallel. That is because the independent variable t does not occur on the right side of the equation

$I' = 15 - 3I$. In general, a differential equation of the form

$$y' = f(y)$$

in which the independent variable is missing from the right side, is called **autonomous**. For such an equation, the slopes corresponding to two different points with the same y-coordinate must be equal. This means that if we know one solution to an autonomous differential equation, then we can obtain infinitely many others just by shifting the graph of the known solution to the right or left. In Figure 11 we have shown the solutions that result from shifting the solution curve of Example 2 one and two time units (namely, seconds) to the right. They correspond to closing the switch when $t = 1$ or $t = 2$.

Euler's Method

The basic idea behind direction fields can be used to find numerical approximations to solutions of differential equations. We illustrate the method on the initial-value problem that we used to introduce direction fields:

$$y' = x + y \qquad y(0) = 1$$

The differential equation tells us that $y'(0) = 0 + 1 = 1$, so the solution curve has slope 1 at the point $(0, 1)$. As a first approximation to the solution we could use the linear approximation $L(x) = x + 1$. In other words, we could use the tangent line at $(0, 1)$ as a rough approximation to the solution curve (see Figure 12).

Euler's idea was to improve on this approximation by proceeding only a short distance along this tangent line and then making a midcourse correction by changing direction as indicated by the direction field. Figure 13 shows what happens if we start out along the tangent line but stop when $x = 0.5$. (This horizontal distance traveled is called the *step size*.) Since $L(0.5) = 1.5$, we have $y(0.5) \approx 1.5$ and we take $(0.5, 1.5)$ as the starting point for a new line segment. The differential equation tells us that $y'(0.5) = 0.5 + 1.5 = 2$, so we use the linear function

$$y = 1.5 + 2(x - 0.5) = 2x + 0.5$$

as an approximation to the solution for $x > 0.5$ (the green segment in Figure 13). If we decrease the step size from 0.5 to 0.25, we get the better Euler approximation shown in Figure 14.

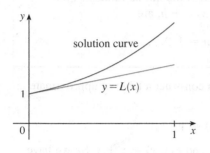

FIGURE 12
First Euler approximation

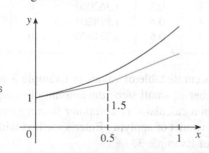

FIGURE 13
Euler approximation with step size 0.5

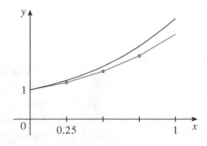

FIGURE 14
Euler approximation with step size 0.25

In general, Euler's method says to start at the point given by the initial value and proceed in the direction indicated by the direction field. Stop after a short time, look at the slope at the new location, and proceed in that direction. Keep stopping and changing direction according to the direction field. Euler's method does not produce the exact solution to an initial-value problem—it gives approximations. But by decreasing the step size (and therefore increasing the number of midcourse corrections), we obtain successively better approximations to the exact solution. (Compare Figures 12, 13, and 14.)

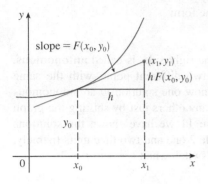

FIGURE 15

For the general first-order initial-value problem $y' = F(x, y)$, $y(x_0) = y_0$, our aim is to find approximate values for the solution at equally spaced numbers x_0, $x_1 = x_0 + h$, $x_2 = x_1 + h, \ldots$, where h is the step size. The differential equation tells us that the slope at (x_0, y_0) is $y' = F(x_0, y_0)$, so Figure 15 shows that the approximate value of the solution when $x = x_1$ is

$$y_1 = y_0 + hF(x_0, y_0)$$

Similarly,

$$y_2 = y_1 + hF(x_1, y_1)$$

In general,

$$y_n = y_{n-1} + hF(x_{n-1}, y_{n-1})$$

Euler's Method Approximate values for the solution of the initial-value problem $y' = F(x, y)$, $y(x_0) = y_0$, with step size h, at $x_n = x_{n-1} + h$, are

$$y_n = y_{n-1} + hF(x_{n-1}, y_{n-1}) \qquad n = 1, 2, 3, \ldots$$

EXAMPLE 3   Use Euler's method with step size 0.1 to construct a table of approximate values for the solution of the initial-value problem

$$y' = x + y \qquad y(0) = 1$$

SOLUTION We are given that $h = 0.1$, $x_0 = 0$, $y_0 = 1$, and $F(x, y) = x + y$. So we have

$$y_1 = y_0 + hF(x_0, y_0) = 1 + 0.1(0 + 1) = 1.1$$

$$y_2 = y_1 + hF(x_1, y_1) = 1.1 + 0.1(0.1 + 1.1) = 1.22$$

$$y_3 = y_2 + hF(x_2, y_2) = 1.22 + 0.1(0.2 + 1.22) = 1.362$$

This means that if $y(x)$ is the exact solution, then $y(0.3) \approx 1.362$.

TEC Module 7.2B shows how Euler's method works numerically and visually for a variety of differential equations and step sizes.

Proceeding with similar calculations, we get the values in the table:

n	x_n	y_n	n	x_n	y_n
1	0.1	1.100000	6	0.6	1.943122
2	0.2	1.220000	7	0.7	2.197434
3	0.3	1.362000	8	0.8	2.487178
4	0.4	1.528200	9	0.9	2.815895
5	0.5	1.721020	10	1.0	3.187485

For a more accurate table of values in Example 3 we could decrease the step size. But for a large number of small steps the amount of computation is considerable and so we need to program a calculator or computer to carry out these calculations. The following table shows the results of applying Euler's method with decreasing step size to the initial-value problem of Example 3.

Computer software packages that produce numerical approximations to solutions of differential equations use methods that are refinements of Euler's method. Although Euler's method is simple and not as accurate, it is the basic idea on which the more accurate methods are based.

Step size	Euler estimate of $y(0.5)$	Euler estimate of $y(1)$
0.500	1.500000	2.500000
0.250	1.625000	2.882813
0.100	1.721020	3.187485
0.050	1.757789	3.306595
0.020	1.781212	3.383176
0.010	1.789264	3.409628
0.005	1.793337	3.423034
0.001	1.796619	3.433848

Notice that the Euler estimates in the table seem to be approaching limits, namely, the true values of $y(0.5)$ and $y(1)$. Figure 16 shows graphs of the Euler approximations with step sizes 0.5, 0.25, 0.1, 0.05, 0.02, 0.01, and 0.005. They are approaching the exact solution curve as the step size h approaches 0.

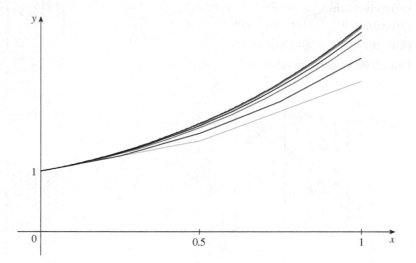

FIGURE 16

Euler approximations
approaching the exact solution

V EXAMPLE 4 In Example 2 we discussed a simple electric circuit with resistance
12 Ω, inductance 4 H, and a battery with voltage 60 V. If the switch is closed when
$t = 0$, we modeled the current I at time t by the initial-value problem

$$\frac{dI}{dt} = 15 - 3I \qquad I(0) = 0$$

Estimate the current in the circuit half a second after the switch is closed.

SOLUTION We use Euler's method with $F(t, I) = 15 - 3I$, $t_0 = 0$, $I_0 = 0$, and step size
$h = 0.1$ second:

$$I_1 = 0 + 0.1(15 - 3 \cdot 0) = 1.5$$

$$I_2 = 1.5 + 0.1(15 - 3 \cdot 1.5) = 2.55$$

$$I_3 = 2.55 + 0.1(15 - 3 \cdot 2.55) = 3.285$$

$$I_4 = 3.285 + 0.1(15 - 3 \cdot 3.285) = 3.7995$$

$$I_5 = 3.7995 + 0.1(15 - 3 \cdot 3.7995) = 4.15965$$

So the current after 0.5 s is

$$I(0.5) \approx 4.16 \text{ A}$$

7.2 Exercises

1. A direction field for the differential equation $y' = x \cos \pi y$ is shown.
   (a) Sketch the graphs of the solutions that satisfy the given initial conditions.
      (i) $y(0) = 0$ (ii) $y(0) = 0.5$
      (iii) $y(0) = 1$ (iv) $y(0) = 1.6$
   (b) Find all the equilibrium solutions.

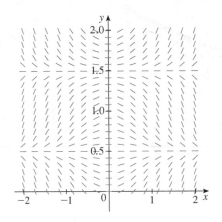

2. A direction field for the differential equation $y' = \tan\left(\frac{1}{2}\pi y\right)$ is shown.
   (a) Sketch the graphs of the solutions that satisfy the given initial conditions.
      (i) $y(0) = 1$ (ii) $y(0) = 0.2$
      (iii) $y(0) = 2$ (iv) $y(1) = 3$
   (b) Find all the equilibrium solutions.

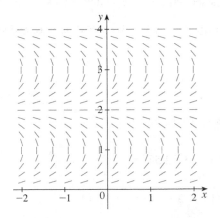

3–6 Match the differential equation with its direction field (labeled I–IV). Give reasons for your answer.

3. $y' = 2 - y$ 4. $y' = x(2 - y)$

5. $y' = x + y - 1$ 6. $y' = \sin x \sin y$

I
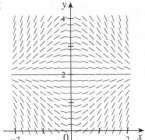

II
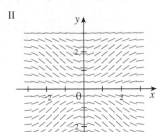

III
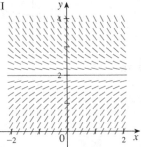

IV
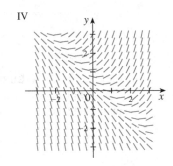

7. Use the direction field labeled II (above) to sketch the graphs of the solutions that satisfy the given initial conditions.
   (a) $y(0) = 1$ (b) $y(0) = 2$ (c) $y(0) = -1$

8. Use the direction field labeled IV (above) to sketch the graphs of the solutions that satisfy the given initial conditions.
   (a) $y(0) = -1$ (b) $y(0) = 0$ (c) $y(0) = 1$

9–10 Sketch a direction field for the differential equation. Then use it to sketch three solution curves.

9. $y' = \frac{1}{2}y$ 10. $y' = x - y + 1$

11–14 Sketch the direction field of the differential equation. Then use it to sketch a solution curve that passes through the given point.

11. $y' = y - 2x, \quad (1, 0)$ 12. $y' = xy - x^2, \quad (0, 1)$

13. $y' = y + xy, \quad (0, 1)$ 14. $y' = x + y^2, \quad (0, 0)$

CAS **15–16** Use a computer algebra system to draw a direction field for the given differential equation. Get a printout and sketch on it the solution curve that passes through $(0, 1)$. Then use the CAS to draw the solution curve and compare it with your sketch.

15. $y' = x^2 \sin y$ 16. $y' = x(y^2 - 4)$

CAS **17.** Use a computer algebra system to draw a direction field for the differential equation $y' = y^3 - 4y$. Get a printout and sketch on it solutions that satisfy the initial condition $y(0) = c$ for various values of c. For what values of c does $\lim_{t\to\infty} y(t)$ exist? What are the possible values for this limit?

18. Make a rough sketch of a direction field for the autonomous differential equation $y' = f(y)$, where the graph of f is as shown. How does the limiting behavior of solutions depend on the value of $y(0)$?

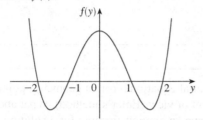

19. (a) Use Euler's method with each of the following step sizes to estimate the value of $y(0.4)$, where y is the solution of the initial-value problem $y' = y$, $y(0) = 1$.
   (i) $h = 0.4$ (ii) $h = 0.2$ (iii) $h = 0.1$
   (b) We know that the exact solution of the initial-value problem in part (a) is $y = e^x$. Draw, as accurately as you can, the graph of $y = e^x$, $0 \le x \le 0.4$, together with the Euler approximations using the step sizes in part (a). (Your sketches should resemble Figures 12, 13, and 14.) Use your sketches to decide whether your estimates in part (a) are underestimates or overestimates.
   (c) The error in Euler's method is the difference between the exact value and the approximate value. Find the errors made in part (a) in using Euler's method to estimate the true value of $y(0.4)$, namely $e^{0.4}$. What happens to the error each time the step size is halved?

20. A direction field for a differential equation is shown. Draw, with a ruler, the graphs of the Euler approximations to the solution curve that passes through the origin. Use step sizes $h = 1$ and $h = 0.5$. Will the Euler estimates be underestimates or overestimates? Explain.

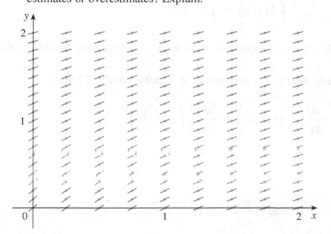

21. Use Euler's method with step size 0.5 to compute the approximate y-values y_1, y_2, y_3, and y_4 of the solution of the initial-value problem $y' = y - 2x$, $y(1) = 0$.

22. Use Euler's method with step size 0.2 to estimate $y(1)$, where $y(x)$ is the solution of the initial-value problem $y' = xy - x^2$, $y(0) = 1$.

23. Use Euler's method with step size 0.1 to estimate $y(0.5)$, where $y(x)$ is the solution of the initial-value problem $y' = y + xy$, $y(0) = 1$.

24. (a) Use Euler's method with step size 0.2 to estimate $y(0.4)$, where $y(x)$ is the solution of the initial-value problem $y' = x + y^2$, $y(0) = 0$.
   (b) Repeat part (a) with step size 0.1.

25. (a) Program a calculator or computer to use Euler's method to compute $y(1)$, where $y(x)$ is the solution of the initial-value problem

$$\frac{dy}{dx} + 3x^2 y = 6x^2 \qquad y(0) = 3$$

   (i) $h = 1$ (ii) $h = 0.1$
   (iii) $h = 0.01$ (iv) $h = 0.001$
   (b) Verify that $y = 2 + e^{-x^3}$ is the exact solution of the differential equation
   (c) Find the errors in using Euler's method to compute $y(1)$ with the step sizes in part (a). What happens to the error when the step size is divided by 10?

CAS **26.** (a) Program your computer algebra system, using Euler's method with step size 0.01, to calculate $y(2)$, where y is the solution of the initial-value problem

$$y' = x^3 - y^3 \qquad y(0) = 1$$

   (b) Check your work by using the CAS to draw the solution curve.

27. The figure shows a circuit containing an electromotive force, a capacitor with a capacitance of C farads (F), and a resistor with a resistance of R ohms (Ω). The voltage drop across the capacitor is Q/C, where Q is the charge (in coulombs, C), so in this case Kirchhoff's Law gives

$$RI + \frac{Q}{C} = E(t)$$

But $I = dQ/dt$, so we have

$$R\frac{dQ}{dt} + \frac{1}{C}Q = E(t)$$

Suppose the resistance is 5 Ω, the capacitance is 0.05 F, and a battery gives a constant voltage of 60 V.
   (a) Draw a direction field for this differential equation
   (b) What is the limiting value of the charge?
   (c) Is there an equilibrium solution?
   (d) If the initial charge is $Q(0) = 0$ C, use the direction field to sketch the solution curve.

(e) If the initial charge is $Q(0) = 0$ C, use Euler's method with step size 0.1 to estimate the charge after half a second.

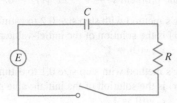

28. In Exercise 14 in Section 7.1 we considered a 95°C cup of coffee in a 20°C room. Suppose it is known that the coffee cools at a rate of 1°C per minute when its temperature is 70°C.
  (a) What does the differential equation become in this case?
  (b) Sketch a direction field and use it to sketch the solution curve for the initial-value problem. What is the limiting value of the temperature?
  (c) Use Euler's method with step size $h = 2$ minutes to estimate the temperature of the coffee after 10 minutes.

7.3 Separable Equations

We have looked at first-order differential equations from a geometric point of view (direction fields) and from a numerical point of view (Euler's method). What about the symbolic point of view? It would be nice to have an explicit formula for a solution of a differential equation. Unfortunately, that is not always possible. But in this section we examine a certain type of differential equation that *can* be solved explicitly.

A **separable equation** is a first-order differential equation in which the expression for dy/dx can be factored as a function of x times a function of y. In other words, it can be written in the form

$$\frac{dy}{dx} = g(x)f(y)$$

The name *separable* comes from the fact that the expression on the right side can be "separated" into a function of x and a function of y. Equivalently, if $f(y) \neq 0$, we could write

$$\boxed{1} \qquad \frac{dy}{dx} = \frac{g(x)}{h(y)}$$

where $h(y) = 1/f(y)$. To solve this equation we rewrite it in the differential form

$$h(y)\, dy = g(x)\, dx$$

so that all y's are on one side of the equation and all x's are on the other side. Then we integrate both sides of the equation:

$$\boxed{2} \qquad \int h(y)\, dy = \int g(x)\, dx$$

Equation 2 defines y implicitly as a function of x. In some cases we may be able to solve for y in terms of x.

We use the Chain Rule to justify this procedure: If h and g satisfy (2), then

$$\frac{d}{dx}\left(\int h(y)\, dy \right) = \frac{d}{dx}\left(\int g(x)\, dx \right)$$

so

$$\frac{d}{dy}\left(\int h(y)\, dy \right)\frac{dy}{dx} = g(x)$$

and

$$h(y)\frac{dy}{dx} = g(x)$$

Thus Equation 1 is satisfied.

The technique for solving separable differential equations was first used by James Bernoulli (in 1690) in solving a problem about pendulums and by Leibniz (in a letter to Huygens in 1691). John Bernoulli explained the general method in a paper published in 1694.

EXAMPLE 1 **Solving a separable equation**

(a) Solve the differential equation $\dfrac{dy}{dx} = \dfrac{x^2}{y^2}$.

(b) Find the solution of this equation that satisfies the initial condition $y(0) = 2$.

SOLUTION

(a) We write the equation in terms of differentials and integrate both sides:

$$y^2\, dy = x^2\, dx$$

$$\int y^2\, dy = \int x^2\, dx$$

$$\tfrac{1}{3}y^3 = \tfrac{1}{3}x^3 + C$$

where C is an arbitrary constant. (We could have used a constant C_1 on the left side and another constant C_2 on the right side. But then we could combine these constants by writing $C = C_2 - C_1$.)

Solving for y, we get

$$y = \sqrt[3]{x^3 + 3C}$$

We could leave the solution like this or we could write it in the form

$$y = \sqrt[3]{x^3 + K}$$

where $K = 3C$. (Since C is an arbitrary constant, so is K.)

(b) If we put $x = 0$ in the general solution in part (a), we get $y(0) = \sqrt[3]{K}$. To satisfy the initial condition $y(0) = 2$, we must have $\sqrt[3]{K} = 2$ and so $K = 8$. Thus the solution of the initial-value problem is

$$y = \sqrt[3]{x^3 + 8}$$

Figure 1 shows graphs of several members of the family of solutions of the differential equation in Example 1. The solution of the initial-value problem in part (b) is shown in red.

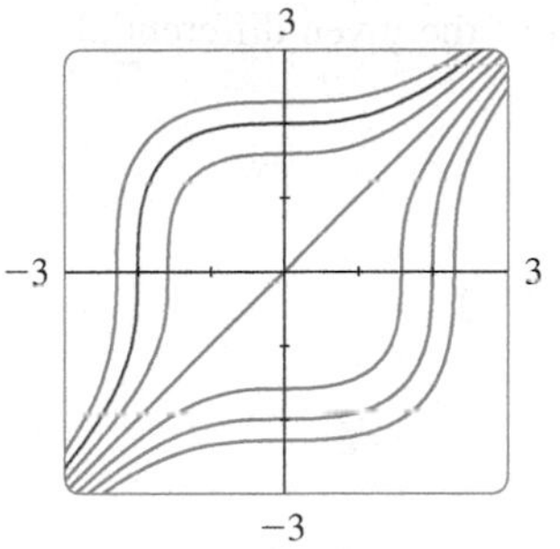

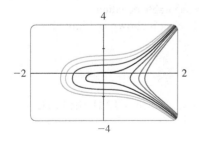

FIGURE 1

V **EXAMPLE 2** **A separable equation with an implicit solution**

Solve the differential equation $\dfrac{dy}{dx} = \dfrac{6x^2}{2y + \cos y}$.

SOLUTION Writing the equation in differential form and integrating both sides, we have

$$(2y + \cos y)\, dy = 6x^2\, dx$$

$$\int (2y + \cos y)\, dy = \int 6x^2\, dx$$

$$\boxed{3} \qquad y^2 + \sin y = 2x^3 + C$$

where C is a constant. Equation 3 gives the general solution implicitly. In this case it's impossible to solve the equation to express y explicitly as a function of x.

Some computer algebra systems can plot curves defined by implicit equations. Figure 2 shows the graphs of several members of the family of solutions of the differential equation in Example 2. As we look at the curves from left to right, the values of C are 3, 2, 1, 0, −1, −2, and −3.

FIGURE 2

EXAMPLE 3 Solve the equation $y' = x^2 y$.

SOLUTION First we rewrite the equation using Leibniz notation:

$$\frac{dy}{dx} = x^2 y$$

If a solution y is a function that satisfies $y(x) \neq 0$ for some x, it follows from a uniqueness theorem for solutions of differential equations that $y(x) \neq 0$ for all x.

If $y \neq 0$, we can rewrite it in differential notation and integrate:

$$\frac{dy}{y} = x^2 \, dx \qquad y \neq 0$$

$$\int \frac{dy}{y} = \int x^2 \, dx$$

$$\ln|y| = \frac{x^3}{3} + C$$

This equation defines y implicitly as a function of x. But in this case we can solve explicitly for y as follows:

$$|y| = e^{\ln|y|} = e^{(x^3/3)+C} = e^C e^{x^3/3}$$

so

$$y = \pm e^C e^{x^3/3}$$

We can easily verify that the function $y = 0$ is also a solution of the given differential equation. So we can write the general solution in the form

$$y = A e^{x^3/3}$$

where A is an arbitrary constant ($A = e^C$, or $A = -e^C$, or $A = 0$).

Figure 3 shows a direction field for the differential equation in Example 3. Compare it with Figure 4, in which we use the equation $y = A e^{x^3/3}$ to graph solutions for several values of A. If you use the direction field to sketch solution curves with y-intercepts 5, 2, 1, -1, and -2, they will resemble the curves in Figure 4.

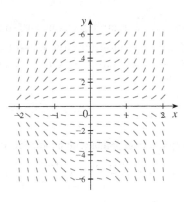

FIGURE 3

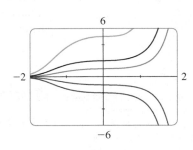

FIGURE 4

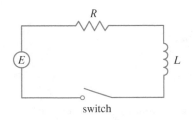

FIGURE 5

▧ **EXAMPLE 4** **Finding the current in a circuit by solving a separable equation**
In Section 7.2 we modeled the current $I(t)$ in the electric circuit shown in Figure 5 by the differential equation

$$L \frac{dI}{dt} + RI = E(t)$$

Find an expression for the current in a circuit where the resistance is 12 Ω, the inductance is 4 H, a battery gives a constant voltage of 60 V, and the switch is turned on when $t = 0$. What is the limiting value of the current?

SOLUTION With $L = 4$, $R = 12$, and $E(t) = 60$, the equation becomes

$$4 \frac{dI}{dt} + 12I = 60 \qquad \text{or} \qquad \frac{dI}{dt} = 15 - 3I$$

and the initial-value problem is

$$\frac{dI}{dt} = 15 - 3I \qquad I(0) = 0$$

We recognize this equation as being separable, and we solve it as follows:

$$\int \frac{dI}{15 - 3I} = \int dt \qquad (15 - 3I \neq 0)$$

$$-\tfrac{1}{3} \ln |15 - 3I| = t + C$$

$$|15 - 3I| = e^{-3(t+C)}$$

$$15 - 3I = \pm e^{-3C} e^{-3t} = A e^{-3t}$$

$$I = 5 - \tfrac{1}{3} A e^{-3t}$$

Since $I(0) = 0$, we have $5 - \tfrac{1}{3} A = 0$, so $A = 15$ and the solution is

$$I(t) = 5 - 5e^{-3t}$$

The limiting current, in amperes, is

$$\lim_{t \to \infty} I(t) = \lim_{t \to \infty} (5 - 5e^{-3t}) = 5 - 5 \lim_{t \to \infty} e^{-3t} = 5 - 0 = 5$$

Figure 6 shows how the solution in Example 4 (the current) approaches its limiting value. Comparison with Figure 11 in Section 7.2 shows that we were able to draw a fairly accurate solution curve from the direction field.

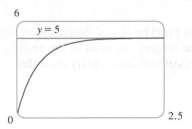

FIGURE 6

Orthogonal Trajectories

An **orthogonal trajectory** of a family of curves is a curve that intersects each curve of the family orthogonally, that is, at right angles (see Figure 7). For instance, each member of the family $y = mx$ of straight lines through the origin is an orthogonal trajectory of the family $x^2 + y^2 = r^2$ of concentric circles with center the origin (see Figure 8). We say that the two families are orthogonal trajectories of each other.

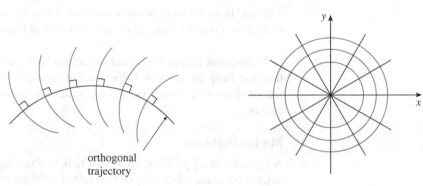

orthogonal
trajectory

FIGURE 7   **FIGURE 8**

▼ **EXAMPLE 5** Find the orthogonal trajectories of the family of curves $x = ky^2$, where k is an arbitrary constant.

SOLUTION The curves $x = ky^2$ form a family of parabolas whose axis of symmetry is the x-axis. The first step is to find a single differential equation that is satisfied by all members of the family. If we differentiate $x = ky^2$, we get

$$1 = 2ky\frac{dy}{dx} \qquad \text{or} \qquad \frac{dy}{dx} = \frac{1}{2ky}$$

This differential equation depends on k, but we need an equation that is valid for all values of k simultaneously. To eliminate k we note that, from the equation of the given general parabola $x = ky^2$, we have $k = x/y^2$ and so the differential equation can be written as

$$\frac{dy}{dx} = \frac{1}{2ky} = \frac{1}{2\dfrac{x}{y^2}\,y}$$

or

$$\frac{dy}{dx} = \frac{y}{2x}$$

This means that the slope of the tangent line at any point (x, y) on one of the parabolas is $y' = y/(2x)$. On an orthogonal trajectory the slope of the tangent line must be the negative reciprocal of this slope. Therefore the orthogonal trajectories must satisfy the differential equation

$$\frac{dy}{dx} = -\frac{2x}{y}$$

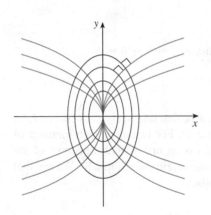

FIGURE 9

This differential equation is separable, and we solve it as follows:

$$\int y\,dy = -\int 2x\,dx$$

$$\frac{y^2}{2} = -x^2 + C$$

$$\boxed{4} \qquad x^2 + \frac{y^2}{2} = C$$

where C is an arbitrary positive constant. Thus the orthogonal trajectories are the family of ellipses given by Equation 4 and sketched in Figure 9.

Orthogonal trajectories occur in various branches of physics. For example, in an electrostatic field the lines of force are orthogonal to the lines of constant potential. Also, the streamlines in aerodynamics are orthogonal trajectories of the velocity-equipotential curves.

Mixing Problems

A typical mixing problem involves a tank of fixed capacity filled with a thoroughly mixed solution of some substance, such as salt. A solution of a given concentration enters the tank at a fixed rate and the mixture, thoroughly stirred, leaves at a fixed rate, which may differ from the entering rate. If $y(t)$ denotes the amount of substance in the tank at time t, then $y'(t)$ is the rate at which the substance is being added minus the rate at which it is being removed. The mathematical description of this situation often leads to a first-order separable differential equation. We can use the same type of reasoning to model a variety of phenomena: chemical reactions, discharge of pollutants into a lake, injection of a drug into the bloodstream.

EXAMPLE 6 A tank contains 20 kg of salt dissolved in 5000 L of water. Brine that contains 0.03 kg of salt per liter of water enters the tank at a rate of 25 L/min. The solution is kept thoroughly mixed and drains from the tank at the same rate. How much salt remains in the tank after half an hour?

SOLUTION Let $y(t)$ be the amount of salt (in kilograms) after t minutes. We are given that $y(0) = 20$ and we want to find $y(30)$. We do this by finding a differential equation satisfied by $y(t)$. Note that dy/dt is the rate of change of the amount of salt, so

$$\boxed{5} \qquad \frac{dy}{dt} = (\text{rate in}) - (\text{rate out})$$

where (rate in) is the rate at which salt enters the tank and (rate out) is the rate at which salt leaves the tank. We have

$$\text{rate in} = \left(0.03 \frac{\text{kg}}{\text{L}}\right)\left(25 \frac{\text{L}}{\text{min}}\right) = 0.75 \frac{\text{kg}}{\text{min}}$$

The tank always contains 5000 L of liquid, so the concentration at time t is $y(t)/5000$ (measured in kilograms per liter). Since the brine flows out at a rate of 25 L/min, we have

$$\text{rate out} = \left(\frac{y(t)}{5000} \frac{\text{kg}}{\text{L}}\right)\left(25 \frac{\text{L}}{\text{min}}\right) = \frac{y(t)}{200} \frac{\text{kg}}{\text{min}}$$

Thus, from Equation 5, we get

$$\frac{dy}{dt} = 0.75 - \frac{y(t)}{200} = \frac{150 - y(t)}{200}$$

Solving this separable differential equation, we obtain

$$\int \frac{dy}{150 - y} = \int \frac{dt}{200}$$

$$-\ln|150 - y| = \frac{t}{200} + C$$

Since $y(0) = 20$, we have $-\ln 130 = C$, so

$$-\ln|150 - y| = \frac{t}{200} - \ln 130$$

Therefore

$$|150 - y| = 130e^{-t/200}$$

Since $y(t)$ is continuous and $y(0) = 20$ and the right side is never 0, we deduce that $150 - y(t)$ is always positive. Thus $|150 - y| = 150 - y$ and so

$$y(t) = 150 - 130e^{-t/200}$$

The amount of salt after 30 min is

$$y(30) = 150 - 130e^{-30/200} \approx 38.1 \text{ kg}$$

Figure 10 shows the graph of the function $y(t)$ of Example 6. Notice that, as time goes by, the amount of salt approaches 150 kg.

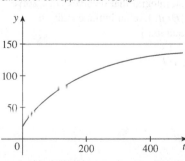

FIGURE 10

7.3 Exercises

1–10 Solve the differential equation.

1. $\dfrac{dy}{dx} = xy^2$

2. $\dfrac{dy}{dx} = xe^{-y}$

3. $(x^2 + 1)y' = xy$

4. $(y^2 + xy^2)y' = 1$

5. $(y + \sin y)y' = x + x^3$

6. $\dfrac{du}{dr} = \dfrac{1 + \sqrt{r}}{1 + \sqrt{u}}$

7. $\dfrac{dy}{dt} = \dfrac{te^t}{y\sqrt{1 + y^2}}$

8. $\dfrac{dy}{d\theta} = \dfrac{e^y \sin^2\theta}{y \sec \theta}$

9. $\dfrac{du}{dt} = 2 + 2u + t + tu$

10. $\dfrac{dz}{dt} + e^{t+z} = 0$

11–18 Find the solution of the differential equation that satisfies the given initial condition.

11. $\dfrac{dy}{dx} = \dfrac{x}{y}, \quad y(0) = -3$

12. $\dfrac{dy}{dx} = \dfrac{\ln x}{xy}, \quad y(1) = 2$

13. $\dfrac{du}{dt} = \dfrac{2t + \sec^2 t}{2u}, \quad u(0) = -5$

14. $y' = \dfrac{xy \sin x}{y + 1}, \quad y(0) = 1$

15. $x \ln x = y\left(1 + \sqrt{3 + y^2}\right)y', \quad y(1) = 1$

16. $\dfrac{dP}{dt} = \sqrt{Pt}, \quad P(1) = 2$

17. $y' \tan x = a + y, \quad y(\pi/3) = a, \quad 0 < x < \pi/2$

18. $\dfrac{dL}{dt} = kL^2 \ln t, \quad L(1) = -1$

19. Find an equation of the curve that passes through the point $(0, 1)$ and whose slope at (x, y) is xy.

20. Find the function f such that $f'(x) = f(x)(1 - f(x))$ and $f(0) = \frac{1}{2}$.

21. Solve the differential equation $y' = x + y$ by making the change of variable $u = x + y$.

22. Solve the differential equation $xy' = y + xe^{y/x}$ by making the change of variable $v = y/x$.

23. (a) Solve the differential equation $y' = 2x\sqrt{1 - y^2}$.
 (b) Solve the initial-value problem $y' = 2x\sqrt{1 - y^2}$, $y(0) = 0$, and graph the solution.
 (c) Does the initial-value problem $y' = 2x\sqrt{1 - y^2}$, $y(0) = 2$, have a solution? Explain.

24. Solve the equation $e^{-y}y' + \cos x = 0$ and graph several members of the family of solutions. How does the solution curve change as the constant C varies?

25. Solve the initial-value problem $y' = (\sin x)/\sin y$, $y(0) = \pi/2$, and graph the solution (if your CAS does implicit plots).

26. Solve the equation $y' = x\sqrt{x^2 + 1}/(ye^y)$ and graph several members of the family of solutions (if your CAS does implicit plots). How does the solution curve change as the constant C varies?

27–28
 (a) Use a computer algebra system to draw a direction field for the differential equation. Get a printout and use it to sketch some solution curves without solving the differential equation.
 (b) Solve the differential equation.
 (c) Use the CAS to draw several members of the family of solutions obtained in part (b). Compare with the curves from part (a).

27. $y' = y^2$

28. $y' = xy$

29–32 Find the orthogonal trajectories of the family of curves. Use a graphing device to draw several members of each family on a common screen.

29. $x^2 + 2y^2 = k^2$

30. $y^2 = kx^3$

31. $y = \dfrac{k}{x}$

32. $y = \dfrac{x}{1 + kx}$

33–35 An **integral equation** is an equation that contains an unknown function $y(x)$ and an integral that involves $y(x)$. Solve the given integral equation. [*Hint*: Use an initial condition obtained from the integral equation.]

33. $y(x) = 2 + \displaystyle\int_2^x [t - ty(t)]\, dt$

34. $y(x) = 2 + \displaystyle\int_1^x \dfrac{dt}{ty(t)}, \quad x > 0$

35. $y(x) = 4 + \displaystyle\int_0^x 2t\sqrt{y(t)}\, dt$

---

36. Find a function f such that $f(3) = 2$ and

$$(t^2 + 1)f'(t) + [f(t)]^2 + 1 = 0 \qquad t \neq 1$$

[*Hint*: Use the addition formula for $\tan(x + y)$ on Reference Page 2.]

37. Solve the initial-value problem in Exercise 27 in Section 7.2 to find an expression for the charge at time t. Find the limiting value of the charge.

38. In Exercise 28 in Section 7.2 we discussed a differential equation that models the temperature of a 95°C cup of coffee in a 20°C room. Solve the differential equation to find an expression for the temperature of the coffee at time t.

39. In Exercise 15 in Section 7.1 we formulated a model for learning in the form of the differential equation

$$\frac{dP}{dt} = k(M - P)$$

where $P(t)$ measures the performance of someone learning a skill after a training time t, M is the maximum level of performance, and k is a positive constant. Solve this differential equation to find an expression for $P(t)$. What is the limit of this expression?

40. In an elementary chemical reaction, single molecules of two reactants A and B form a molecule of the product C: $A + B \rightarrow C$. The law of mass action states that the rate of reaction is proportional to the product of the concentrations of A and B:

$$\frac{d[C]}{dt} = k[A][B]$$

(See Example 4 in Section 3.8.) Thus, if the initial concentrations are $[A] = a$ moles/L and $[B] = b$ moles/L and we write $x = [C]$, then we have

$$\frac{dx}{dt} = k(a - x)(b - x)$$

CAS   (a) Assuming that $a \neq b$, find x as a function of t. Use the fact that the initial concentration of C is 0.
(b) Find $x(t)$ assuming that $a = b$. How does this expression for $x(t)$ simplify if it is known that $[C] = \frac{1}{2}a$ after 20 seconds?

41. In contrast to the situation of Exercise 40, experiments show that the reaction $H_2 + Br_2 \rightarrow 2HBr$ satisfies the rate law

$$\frac{d[HBr]}{dt} = k[H_2][Br_2]^{1/2}$$

and so for this reaction the differential equation becomes

$$\frac{dx}{dt} = k(a - x)(b - x)^{1/2}$$

where $x = [HBr]$ and a and b are the initial concentrations of hydrogen and bromine.
(a) Find x as a function of t in the case where $a = b$. Use the fact that $x(0) = 0$.

(b) If $a > b$, find t as a function of x. [*Hint*: In performing the integration, make the substitution $u = \sqrt{b - x}$.]

42. A sphere with radius 1 m has temperature 15°C. It lies inside a concentric sphere with radius 2 m and temperature 25°C. The temperature $T(r)$ at a distance r from the common center of the spheres satisfies the differential equation

$$\frac{d^2T}{dr^2} + \frac{2}{r}\frac{dT}{dr} = 0$$

If we let $S = dT/dr$, then S satisfies a first-order differential equation. Solve it to find an expression for the temperature $T(r)$ between the spheres.

43. A glucose solution is administered intravenously into the bloodstream at a constant rate r. As the glucose is added, it is converted into other substances and removed from the bloodstream at a rate that is proportional to the concentration at that time. Thus a model for the concentration $C = C(t)$ of the glucose solution in the bloodstream is

$$\frac{dC}{dt} = r - kC$$

where k is a positive constant.
(a) Suppose that the concentration at time $t = 0$ is C_0. Determine the concentration at any time t by solving the differential equation.
(b) Assuming that $C_0 < r/k$, find $\lim_{t \to \infty} C(t)$ and interpret your answer.

44. A certain small country has $10 billion in paper currency in circulation, and each day $50 million comes into the country's banks. The government decides to introduce new currency by having the banks replace old bills with new ones whenever old currency comes into the banks. Let $x = x(t)$ denote the amount of new currency in circulation at time t, with $x(0) = 0$.
(a) Formulate a mathematical model in the form of an initial-value problem that represents the "flow" of the new currency into circulation.
(b) Solve the initial-value problem found in part (a).
(c) How long will it take for the new bills to account for 90% of the currency in circulation?

45. A tank contains 1000 L of brine with 15 kg of dissolved salt. Pure water enters the tank at a rate of 10 L/min. The solution is kept thoroughly mixed and drains from the tank at the same rate. How much salt is in the tank (a) after t minutes and (b) after 20 minutes?

46. The air in a room with volume 180 m^3 contains 0.15% carbon dioxide initially. Fresher air with only 0.05% carbon dioxide flows into the room at a rate of 2 m^3/min and the mixed air flows out at the same rate. Find the percentage of carbon dioxide in the room as a function of time. What happens in the long run?

47. A vat with 500 gallons of beer contains 4% alcohol (by volume). Beer with 6% alcohol is pumped into the vat at a rate of 5 gal/min and the mixture is pumped out at the same rate. What is the percentage of alcohol after an hour?

48. A tank contains 1000 L of pure water. Brine that contains 0.05 kg of salt per liter of water enters the tank at a rate of 5 L/min. Brine that contains 0.04 kg of salt per liter of water enters the tank at a rate of 10 L/min. The solution is kept thoroughly mixed and drains from the tank at a rate of 15 L/min. How much salt is in the tank (a) after t minutes and (b) after one hour?

49. When a raindrop falls, it increases in size and so its mass at time t is a function of t, namely $m(t)$. The rate of growth of the mass is $km(t)$ for some positive constant k. When we apply Newton's Law of Motion to the raindrop, we get $(mv)' = gm$, where v is the velocity of the raindrop (directed downward) and g is the acceleration due to gravity. The *terminal velocity* of the raindrop is $\lim_{t \to \infty} v(t)$. Find an expression for the terminal velocity in terms of g and k.

50. An object of mass m is moving horizontally through a medium which resists the motion with a force that is a function of the velocity; that is,

$$m \frac{d^2 s}{dt^2} = m \frac{dv}{dt} = f(v)$$

where $v = v(t)$ and $s = s(t)$ represent the velocity and position of the object at time t, respectively. For example, think of a boat moving through the water.
(a) Suppose that the resisting force is proportional to the velocity, that is, $f(v) = -kv$, k a positive constant. (This model is appropriate for small values of v.) Let $v(0) = v_0$ and $s(0) = s_0$ be the initial values of v and s. Determine v and s at any time t. What is the total distance that the object travels from time $t = 0$?
(b) For larger values of v a better model is obtained by supposing that the resisting force is proportional to the square of the velocity, that is, $f(v) = -kv^2$, $k > 0$. (This model was first proposed by Newton.) Let v_0 and s_0 be the initial values of v and s. Determine v and s at any time t. What is the total distance that the object travels in this case?

51. *Allometric growth* in biology refers to relationships between sizes of parts of an organism (skull length and body length, for instance). If $L_1(t)$ and $L_2(t)$ are the sizes of two organs in an organism of age t, then L_1 and L_2 satisfy an allometric law if their specific growth rates are proportional:

$$\frac{1}{L_1} \frac{dL_1}{dt} = k \frac{1}{L_2} \frac{dL_2}{dt}$$

where k is a constant.
(a) Use the allometric law to write a differential equation relating L_1 and L_2 and solve it to express L_1 as a function of L_2.
(b) In a study of several species of unicellular algae, the proportionality constant in the allometric law relating B (cell biomass) and V (cell volume) was found to be $k = 0.0794$. Write B as a function of V.

52. *Homeostasis* refers to a state in which the nutrient content of a consumer is independent of the nutrient content of its food. In the absence of homeostasis, a model proposed by Sterner and Elser is given by

$$\frac{dy}{dx} = \frac{1}{\theta} \frac{y}{x}$$

where x and y represent the nutrient content of the food and the consumer, respectively, and θ is a constant with $\theta \geqslant 1$.
(a) Solve the differential equation.
(b) What happens when $\theta = 1$? What happens when $\theta \to \infty$?

53. Let $A(t)$ be the area of a tissue culture at time t and let M be the final area of the tissue when growth is complete. Most cell divisions occur on the periphery of the tissue and the number of cells on the periphery is proportional to $\sqrt{A(t)}$. So a reasonable model for the growth of tissue is obtained by assuming that the rate of growth of the area is jointly proportional to $\sqrt{A(t)}$ and $M - A(t)$.
(a) Formulate a differential equation and use it to show that the tissue grows fastest when $A(t) = \frac{1}{3} M$.

CAS
(b) Solve the differential equation to find an expression for $A(t)$. Use a computer algebra system to perform the integration.

54. According to Newton's Law of Universal Gravitation, the gravitational force on an object of mass m that has been projected vertically upward from the earth's surface is

$$F = \frac{mgR^2}{(x + R)^2}$$

where $x = x(t)$ is the object's distance above the surface at time t, R is the earth's radius, and g is the acceleration due to gravity. Also, by Newton's Second Law, $F = ma = m(dv/dt)$ and so

$$m \frac{dv}{dt} = -\frac{mgR^2}{(x + R)^2}$$

(a) Suppose a rocket is fired vertically upward with an initial velocity v_0. Let h be the maximum height above the surface reached by the object. Show that

$$v_0 = \sqrt{\frac{2gRh}{R + h}}$$

[*Hint:* By the Chain Rule, $m(dv/dt) = mv(dv/dx)$.]
(b) Calculate $v_e = \lim_{h \to \infty} v_0$. This limit is called the *escape velocity* for the earth.
(c) Use $R = 3960$ mi and $g = 32$ ft/s^2 to calculate v_e in feet per second and in miles per second.

How Fast Does a Tank Drain?

If water (or other liquid) drains from a tank, we expect that the flow will be greatest at first (when the water depth is greatest) and will gradually decrease as the water level decreases. But we need a more precise mathematical description of how the flow decreases in order to answer the kinds of questions that engineers ask: How long does it take for a tank to drain completely? How much water should a tank hold in order to guarantee a certain minimum water pressure for a sprinkler system?

Let $h(t)$ and $V(t)$ be the height and volume of water in a tank at time t. If water drains through a hole with area a at the bottom of the tank, then Torricelli's Law says that

$$\boxed{1} \qquad \frac{dV}{dt} = -a\sqrt{2gh}$$

where g is the acceleration due to gravity. So the rate at which water flows from the tank is proportional to the square root of the water height.

1. (a) Suppose the tank is cylindrical with height 6 ft and radius 2 ft and the hole is circular with radius 1 inch. If we take $g = 32$ ft/s^2, show that h satisfies the differential equation

$$\frac{dh}{dt} = -\frac{1}{72}\sqrt{h}$$

   (b) Solve this equation to find the height of the water at time t, assuming the tank is full at time $t = 0$.

   (c) How long will it take for the water to drain completely?

2. Because of the rotation and viscosity of the liquid, the theoretical model given by Equation 1 isn't quite accurate. Instead, the model

$$\boxed{2} \qquad \frac{dh}{dt} = k\sqrt{h}$$

   is often used and the constant k (which depends on the physical properties of the liquid) is determined from data concerning the draining of the tank.

   (a) Suppose that a hole is drilled in the side of a cylindrical bottle and the height h of the water (above the hole) decreases from 10 cm to 3 cm in 68 seconds. Use Equation 2 to find an expression for $h(t)$. Evaluate $h(t)$ for $t = 10, 20, 30, 40, 50, 60$.

   (b) Drill a 4-mm hole near the bottom of the cylindrical part of a two-liter plastic soft-drink bottle. Attach a strip of masking tape marked in centimeters from 0 to 10, with 0 corresponding to the top of the hole. With one finger over the hole, fill the bottle with water to the 10-cm mark. Then take your finger off the hole and record the values of $h(t)$ for $t = 10, 20, 30, 40, 50, 60$ seconds. (You will probably find that it takes 68 seconds for the level to decrease to $h = 3$ cm.) Compare your data with the values of $h(t)$ from part (a). How well did the model predict the actual values?

3. In many parts of the world, the water for sprinkler systems in large hotels and hospitals is supplied by gravity from cylindrical tanks on or near the roofs of the buildings. Suppose such a tank has radius 10 ft and the diameter of the outlet is 2.5 inches. An engineer has to guarantee that the water pressure will be at least 2160 lb/ft^2 for a period of 10 minutes. (When a fire happens, the electrical system might fail and it could take up to 10 minutes for the emergency generator and fire pump to be activated.) What height should the engineer specify for the tank in order to make such a guarantee? (Use the fact that the water pressure at a depth of d feet is $P = 62.5d$. See Section 6.6.)

This part of the project is best done as a classroom demonstration or as a group project with three students in each group: a timekeeper to call out seconds, a bottle keeper to estimate the height every 10 seconds, and a record keeper to record these values.

4. Not all water tanks are shaped like cylinders. Suppose a tank has cross-sectional area $A(h)$ at height h. Then the volume of water up to height h is $V = \int_0^h A(u)\,du$ and so the Fundamental Theorem of Calculus gives $dV/dh = A(h)$. It follows that

$$\frac{dV}{dt} = \frac{dV}{dh}\frac{dh}{dt} = A(h)\frac{dh}{dt}$$

and so Torricelli's Law becomes

$$A(h)\frac{dh}{dt} = -a\sqrt{2gh}$$

(a) Suppose the tank has the shape of a sphere with radius 2 m and is initially half full of water. If the radius of the circular hole is 1 cm and we take $g = 10$ m/s^2, show that h satisfies the differential equation

$$(4h - h^2)\frac{dh}{dt} = -0.0001\sqrt{20h}$$

(b) How long will it take for the water to drain completely?

APPLIED PROJECT   **Which Is Faster, Going Up or Coming Down?**

Suppose you throw a ball into the air. Do you think it takes longer to reach its maximum height or to fall back to earth from its maximum height? We will solve the problem in this project but, before getting started, think about that situation and make a guess based on your physical intuition.

In modeling force due to air resistance, various functions have been used, depending on the physical characteristics and speed of the ball. Here we use a linear model, $-pv$, but a quadratic model ($-pv^2$ on the way up and pv^2 on the way down) is another possibility for higher speeds (see Exercise 50 in Section 7.3). For a golf ball, experiments have shown that a good model is $-pv^{1.3}$ going up and $p|v|^{1.3}$ coming down. But no matter which force function $-f(v)$ is used [where $f(v) > 0$ for $v > 0$ and $f(v) < 0$ for $v < 0$], the answer to the question remains the same. See F. Brauer, "What Goes Up Must Come Down, Eventually," *Amer. Math. Monthly* 108 (2001), pp. 437–440.

1. A ball with mass m is projected vertically upward from the earth's surface with a positive initial velocity v_0. We assume the forces acting on the ball are the force of gravity and a retarding force of air resistance with direction opposite to the direction of motion and with magnitude $p|v(t)|$, where p is a positive constant and $v(t)$ is the velocity of the ball at time t. In both the ascent and the descent, the total force acting on the ball is $-pv - mg$. [During ascent, $v(t)$ is positive and the resistance acts downward; during descent, $v(t)$ is negative and the resistance acts upward.] So, by Newton's Second Law, the equation of motion is

$$mv' = -pv - mg$$

Solve this differential equation to show that the velocity is

$$v(t) = \left(v_0 + \frac{mg}{p}\right)e^{-pt/m} - \frac{mg}{p}$$

2. Show that the height of the ball, until it hits the ground, is

$$y(t) = \left(v_0 + \frac{mg}{p}\right)\frac{m}{p}(1 - e^{-pt/m}) - \frac{mgt}{p}$$

3. Let t_1 be the time that the ball takes to reach its maximum height. Show that

$$t_1 = \frac{m}{p}\ln\left(\frac{mg + pv_0}{mg}\right)$$

Find this time for a ball with mass 1 kg and initial velocity 20 m/s. Assume the air resistance is $\frac{1}{10}$ of the speed.

4. Let t_2 be the time at which the ball falls back to earth. For the particular ball in Problem 3, estimate t_2 by using a graph of the height function $y(t)$. Which is faster, going up or coming down?

5. In general, it's not easy to find t_2 because it's impossible to solve the equation $y(t) = 0$ explicitly. We can, however, use an indirect method to determine whether ascent or descent is faster; we determine whether $y(2t_1)$ is positive or negative. Show that

$$y(2t_1) = \frac{m^2 g}{p^2}\left(x - \frac{1}{x} - 2\ln x\right)$$

where $x = e^{pt_1/m}$. Then show that $x > 1$ and the function

$$f(x) = x - \frac{1}{x} - 2\ln x$$

is increasing for $x > 1$. Use this result to decide whether $y(2t_1)$ is positive or negative. What can you conclude? Is ascent or descent faster?

◢ Graphing calculator or computer with graphing software required.

7.4 Exponential Growth and Decay

One of the models for population growth that we considered in Section 7.1 was based on the assumption that the population grows at a rate proportional to the size of the population:

$$\frac{dP}{dt} = kP$$

Is that a reasonable assumption? Suppose we have a population (of bacteria, for instance) with size $P = 1000$ and at a certain time it is growing at a rate of $P' = 300$ bacteria per hour. Now let's take another 1000 bacteria of the same type and put them with the first population. Each half of the new population was growing at a rate of 300 bacteria per hour. We would expect the total population of 2000 to increase at a rate of 600 bacteria per hour initially (provided there's enough room and nutrition). So if we double the size, we double the growth rate. In general, it seems reasonable that the growth rate should be proportional to the size.

The same assumption applies in other situations as well. In nuclear physics, the mass of a radioactive substance decays at a rate proportional to the mass. In chemistry, the rate of a unimolecular first-order reaction is proportional to the concentration of the substance. In finance, the value of a savings account with continuously compounded interest increases at a rate proportional to that value.

In general, if $y(t)$ is the value of a quantity y at time t and if the rate of change of y with respect to t is proportional to its size $y(t)$ at any time, then

$$\boxed{1} \qquad\qquad \frac{dy}{dt} = ky$$

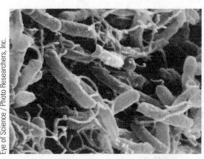

E. coli bacteria are about 2 micrometers (μm) long and 0.75 μm wide. The image was produced with a scanning electron microscope.

where k is a constant. Equation 1 is sometimes called the **law of natural growth** (if $k > 0$) or the **law of natural decay** (if $k < 0$). Because it is a separable differential equation we can solve it by the methods of Section 7.3:

$$\int \frac{dy}{y} = \int k \, dt$$

$$\ln |y| = kt + C$$

$$|y| = e^{kt+C} = e^C e^{kt}$$

$$y = Ae^{kt}$$

where A ($= \pm e^C$ or 0) is an arbitrary constant. To see the significance of the constant A, we observe that

$$y(0) = Ae^{k \cdot 0} = A$$

Therefore A is the initial value of the function.

Because Equation 1 occurs so frequently in nature, we summarize what we have just proved for future use.

---

2 The solution of the initial-value problem

$$\frac{dy}{dt} = ky \qquad y(0) = y_0$$

is

$$y(t) = y_0 e^{kt}$$

Population Growth

What is the significance of the proportionality constant k? In the context of population growth, we can write

3
$$\frac{dP}{dt} = kP \qquad \text{or} \qquad \frac{1}{P} \frac{dP}{dt} = k$$

The quantity

$$\frac{1}{P} \frac{dP}{dt}$$

is the growth rate divided by the population size; it is called the **relative growth rate**. According to (3), instead of saying "the growth rate is proportional to population size" we could say "the relative growth rate is constant." Then (2) says that a population with constant relative growth rate must grow exponentially. Notice that the relative growth rate k appears as the coefficient of t in the exponential function $y_0 e^{kt}$. For instance, if

$$\frac{dP}{dt} = 0.02P$$

and t is measured in years, then the relative growth rate is $k = 0.02$ and the population grows at a relative rate of 2% per year. If the population at time 0 is P_0, then the expression for the population is

$$P(t) = P_0 e^{0.02t}$$

TABLE 1

Year	Population (millions)
1900	1650
1910	1750
1920	1860
1930	2070
1940	2300
1950	2560
1960	3040
1970	3710
1980	4450
1990	5280
2000	6080

EXAMPLE 1 Modeling world population with the law of natural growth   Assuming that the growth rate is proportional to population size, use the data in Table 1 to model the population of the world in the 20th century. What is the relative growth rate? How well does the model fit the data?

SOLUTION We measure the time t in years and let $t = 0$ in the year 1900. We measure the population $P(t)$ in millions of people. Then the initial condition is $P(0) = 1650$. We are assuming that the growth rate is proportional to population size, so the initial-value problem is

$$\frac{dP}{dt} = kP \qquad P(0) = 1650$$

From (2) we know that the solution is

$$P(t) = 1650e^{kt}$$

One way to estimate the relative growth rate k is to use the fact that the population in 1950 was 2560 million. Therefore

$$P(50) = 1650e^{k(50)} = 2560$$

We solve this equation for k:

$$e^{50k} = \frac{2560}{1650}$$

$$k = \frac{1}{50} \ln \frac{2560}{1650} \approx 0.0087846$$

Thus the relative growth rate is about 0.88% per year and the model becomes

$$P(t) = 1650e^{0.0087846t}$$

TABLE 2

Year	Model	Population
1900	1650	1650
1910	1802	1750
1920	1967	1860
1930	2148	2070
1940	2345	2300
1950	2560	2560
1960	2795	3040
1970	3052	3710
1980	3332	4450
1990	3638	5280
2000	3972	6080

In Section 1.5 we modeled the same data with an exponential function, but there we used the method of least squares.

Table 2 and Figure 1 allow us to compare the predictions of this model with the actual data. You can see that the predictions become quite inaccurate after about 60 years.

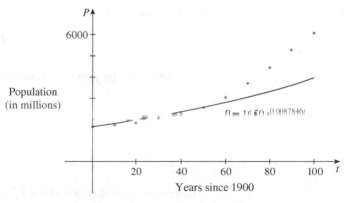

FIGURE 1 A possible model for world population growth

Looking at Figure 1, we might think that we would get a better model by using the given population for 1970, instead of 1950, to estimate k. Then

$$P(70) = 1650e^{70k} = 3710$$

$$k = \frac{1}{70} \ln \frac{3710}{1650} \approx 0.0115751$$

The estimate for the relative growth rate is now 1.16% per year and the model is

$$P(t) = 1650e^{0.0115751t}$$

Figure 2 illustrates the second model. This exponential model is more accurate after 1970 but less accurate before 1950.

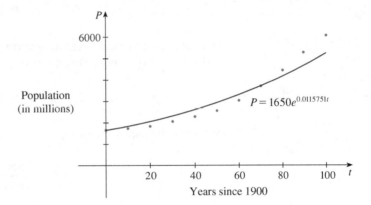

FIGURE 2
Another model for world
population growth

EXAMPLE 2   **Estimating and predicting from an exponential growth model**   Use the data in Table 1 to model the population of the world in the second half of the 20th century. Use the model to estimate the population in 1993 and to predict the population in the year 2015.

SOLUTION Here we let $t = 0$ in the year 1950. Then the initial-value problem is

$$\frac{dP}{dt} = kP \qquad P(0) = 2560$$

and the solution is

$$P(t) = 2560e^{kt}$$

Let's estimate k by using the population in 1960:

$$P(10) = 2560e^{10k} = 3040$$

$$k = \frac{1}{10} \ln \frac{3040}{2560} \approx 0.017185$$

The relative growth rate is about 1.7% per year and the model is

$$P(t) = 2560e^{0.017185t}$$

We estimate that the world population in 1993 was

$$P(43) = 2560e^{0.017185(43)} \approx 5360 \text{ million}$$

The model predicts that the population in 2015 will be

$$P(60) = 2560e^{0.017185(65)} \approx 7822 \text{ million}$$

The graph in Figure 3 shows that the model is fairly accurate to the turn of the century, so the estimate for 1993 is quite reliable. But the prediction for 2015 is much riskier.

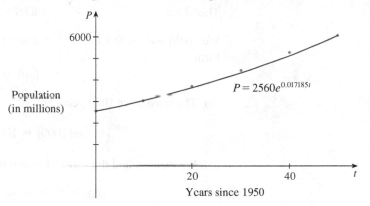

FIGURE 3

A model for world population growth in the second half of the 20th century

Radioactive Decay

Radioactive substances decay by spontaneously emitting radiation. If $m(t)$ is the mass remaining from an initial mass m_0 of the substance after time t, then the relative decay rate

$$-\frac{1}{m}\frac{dm}{dt}$$

has been found experimentally to be constant. (Since dm/dt is negative, the relative decay rate is positive.) It follows that

$$\frac{dm}{dt} = km$$

where k is a negative constant. In other words, radioactive substances decay at a rate proportional to the remaining mass. This means that we can use (2) to show that the mass decays exponentially:

$$m(t) = m_0 e^{kt}$$

Physicists express the rate of decay in terms of **half-life**, the time required for half of any given quantity to decay.

▼ **EXAMPLE 3** The half-life of radium-226 is 1590 years.
(a) A sample of radium-226 has a mass of 100 mg. Find a formula for the mass of $_{88}^{226}\text{Ra}$ that remains after t years.
(b) Find the mass after 1000 years correct to the nearest milligram.
(c) When will the mass be reduced to 30 mg?

SOLUTION
(a) Let $m(t)$ be the mass of radium-226 (in milligrams) that remains after t years. Then $dm/dt = km$ and $y(0) = 100$, so (2) gives

$$m(t) = m(0)e^{kt} = 100e^{kt}$$

In order to determine the value of k, we use the fact that $y(1590) = \frac{1}{2}(100)$. Thus

$$100e^{1590k} = 50 \qquad \text{so} \qquad e^{1590k} = \tfrac{1}{2}$$

and

$$1590k = \ln \tfrac{1}{2} = -\ln 2$$

$$k = -\frac{\ln 2}{1590}$$

Therefore

$$m(t) = 100e^{-(\ln 2)t/1590}$$

We could use the fact that $e^{\ln 2} = 2$ to write the expression for $m(t)$ in the alternative form

$$m(t) = 100 \times 2^{-t/1590}$$

(b) The mass after 1000 years is

$$m(1000) = 100e^{-(\ln 2)1000/1590} \approx 65 \text{ mg}$$

(c) We want to find the value of t such that $m(t) = 30$, that is,

$$100e^{-(\ln 2)t/1590} = 30 \qquad \text{or} \qquad e^{-(\ln 2)t/1590} = 0.3$$

We solve this equation for t by taking the natural logarithm of both sides:

$$-\frac{\ln 2}{1590}\,t = \ln 0.3$$

Thus

$$t = -1590\,\frac{\ln 0.3}{\ln 2} \approx 2762 \text{ years}$$

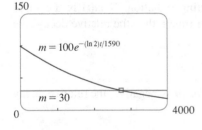

$$m = 100e^{-(\ln 2)t/1590}$$

$$m = 30$$

FIGURE 4

As a check on our work in Example 3, we use a graphing device to draw the graph of $m(t)$ in Figure 4 together with the horizontal line $m = 30$. These curves intersect when $t \approx 2800$, and this agrees with the answer to part (c).

Newton's Law of Cooling

Newton's Law of Cooling states that the rate of cooling of an object is proportional to the temperature difference between the object and its surroundings, provided that this difference is not too large. (This law also applies to warming.) If we let $T(t)$ be the temperature of the object at time t and T_s be the temperature of the surroundings, then we can formulate Newton's Law of Cooling as a differential equation:

$$\frac{dT}{dt} = k(T - T_s)$$

where k is a constant. We could solve this equation as a separable differential equation by the method of Section 7.3, but an easier method is to make the change of variable $y(t) = T(t) - T_s$. Because T_s is constant, we have $y'(t) = T'(t)$ and so the equation becomes

$$\frac{dy}{dt} = ky$$

We can then use (2) to find an expression for y, from which we can find T.

EXAMPLE 4 **Using Newton's Law of Cooling to predict temperatures** A bottle of soda pop at room temperature (72°F) is placed in a refrigerator where the temperature is 44°F. After half an hour the soda pop has cooled to 61°F.
(a) What is the temperature of the soda pop after another half hour?
(b) How long does it take for the soda pop to cool to 50°F?

SOLUTION
(a) Let $T(t)$ be the temperature of the soda after t minutes. The surrounding temperature is $T_s = 44°F$, so Newton's Law of Cooling states that

$$\frac{dT}{dt} = k(T - 44)$$

If we let $y = T - 44$, then $y(0) = T(0) - 44 = 72 - 44 = 28$, so y is a solution of the initial-value problem

$$\frac{dy}{dt} = ky \qquad y(0) = 28$$

and by (2) we have

$$y(t) = y(0)e^{kt} = 28e^{kt}$$

We are given that $T(30) = 61$, so $y(30) = 61 - 44 = 17$ and

$$28e^{30k} = 17 \qquad e^{30k} = \tfrac{17}{28}$$

Taking logarithms, we have

$$k = \frac{\ln\left(\frac{17}{28}\right)}{30} \approx -0.01663$$

Thus

$$y(t) = 28e^{-0.01663t}$$

$$T(t) = 44 + 28e^{-0.01663t}$$

$$T(60) = 44 + 28e^{-0.01663(60)} \approx 54.3$$

So after another half hour the pop has cooled to about 54°F.
(b) We have $T(t) = 50$ when

$$44 + 28e^{-0.01663t} = 50$$

$$e^{-0.01663t} = \tfrac{6}{28}$$

$$t = \frac{\ln\left(\frac{6}{28}\right)}{-0.01663} \approx 92.6$$

The pop cools to 50°F after about 1 hour 33 minutes.

Notice that in Example 4, we have

$$\lim_{t \to \infty} T(t) = \lim_{t \to \infty} (44 + 28e^{-0.01663t}) = 44 + 28 \cdot 0 = 44$$

which is to be expected. The graph of the temperature function is shown in Figure 5.

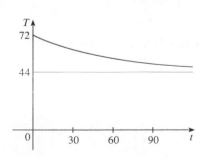

FIGURE 5

Continuously Compounded Interest

EXAMPLE 5   If $1000 is invested at 6% interest, compounded annually, then after 1 year the investment is worth $1000(1.06) = $1060, after 2 years it's worth $[1000(1.06)]1.06 = $1123.60, and after t years it's worth $1000(1.06)^t. In general, if an amount A_0 is invested at an interest rate r ($r = 0.06$ in this example), then after t years it's worth $A_0(1 + r)^t$. Usually, however, interest is compounded more frequently, say, n times a year. Then in each compounding period the interest rate is r/n and there are nt compounding periods in t years, so the value of the investment is

$$A_0\left(1 + \frac{r}{n}\right)^{nt}$$

For instance, after 3 years at 6% interest a $1000 investment will be worth

$$\$1000(1.06)^3 = \$1191.02 \quad \text{with annual compounding}$$

$$\$1000(1.03)^6 = \$1194.05 \quad \text{with semiannual compounding}$$

$$\$1000(1.015)^{12} = \$1195.62 \quad \text{with quarterly compounding}$$

$$\$1000(1.005)^{36} = \$1196.68 \quad \text{with monthly compounding}$$

$$\$1000\left(1 + \frac{0.06}{365}\right)^{365 \cdot 3} = \$1197.20 \quad \text{with daily compounding}$$

You can see that the interest paid increases as the number of compounding periods (n) increases. If we let $n \to \infty$, then we will be compounding the interest **continuously** and the value of the investment will be

$$A(t) = \lim_{n \to \infty} A_0\left(1 + \frac{r}{n}\right)^{nt}$$

$$= \lim_{n \to \infty} A_0\left[\left(1 + \frac{r}{n}\right)^{n/r}\right]^{rt}$$

$$= A_0\left[\lim_{n \to \infty} \left(1 + \frac{r}{n}\right)^{n/r}\right]^{rt}$$

$$= A_0\left[\lim_{m \to \infty} \left(1 + \frac{1}{m}\right)^{m}\right]^{rt} \qquad \text{(where } m = n/r)$$

But the limit in this expression is equal to the number e (see Equation 3.7.6). So with continuous compounding of interest at interest rate r, the amount after t years is

$$A(t) = A_0 e^{rt}$$

If we differentiate this equation, we get

$$\frac{dA}{dt} = rA_0 e^{rt} = rA(t)$$

which says that, with continuous compounding of interest, the rate of increase of an investment is proportional to its size.

Returning to the example of $1000 invested for 3 years at 6% interest, we see that with continuous compounding of interest the value of the investment will be

$$A(3) = \$1000e^{(0.06)3}$$

$$= \$1000e^{0.18} = \$1197.22$$

Notice how close this is to the amount we calculated for daily compounding, $1197.20. But the amount is easier to compute if we use continuous compounding.

7.4 Exercises

1. A population of protozoa develops with a constant relative growth rate of 0.7944 per member per day. On day zero the population consists of two members. Find the population size after six days.

2. A common inhabitant of human intestines is the bacterium *Escherichia coli*. A cell of this bacterium in a nutrient-broth medium divides into two cells every 20 minutes. The initial population of a culture is 60 cells.
(a) Find the relative growth rate.
(b) Find an expression for the number of cells after t hours.
(c) Find the number of cells after 8 hours.
(d) Find the rate of growth after 8 hours.
(e) When will the population reach 20,000 cells?

3. A bacteria culture initially contains 100 cells and grows at a rate proportional to its size. After an hour the population has increased to 420.
(a) Find an expression for the number of bacteria after t hours.
(b) Find the number of bacteria after 3 hours.
(c) Find the rate of growth after 3 hours.
(d) When will the population reach 10,000?

4. A bacteria culture grows with constant relative growth rate. The bacteria count was 400 after 2 hours and 25,600 after 6 hours.
(a) What is the relative growth rate? Express your answer as a percentage.
(b) What was the intitial size of the culture?
(c) Find an expression for the number of bacteria after t hours.
(d) Find the number of cells after 4.5 hours.
(e) Find the rate of growth after 4.5 hours.
(f) When will the population reach 50,000?

5. The table gives estimates of the world population, in millions, from 1750 to 2000.
(a) Use the exponential model and the population figures for 1750 and 1800 to predict the world population in 1900 and 1950. Compare with the actual figures.

(b) Use the exponential model and the population figures for 1850 and 1900 to predict the world population in 1950. Compare with the actual population.
(c) Use the exponential model and the population figures for 1900 and 1950 to predict the world population in 2000. Compare with the actual population and try to explain the discrepancy.

Year	Population	Year	Population
1750	790	1900	1650
1800	980	1950	2560
1850	1260	2000	6080

6. The table gives the population of India, in millions, for the second half of the 20th century.

Year	Population
1951	361
1961	439
1971	548
1981	683
1991	846
2001	1029

(a) Use the exponential model and the census figures for 1951 and 1961 to predict the population in 2001. Compare with the actual figure.
(b) Use the exponential model and the census figures for 1961 and 1981 to predict the population in 2001. Compare with the actual population. Then use this model to predict the population in the years 2010 and 2020.
(c) Graph both of the exponential functions in parts (a) and (b) together with a plot of the actual population. Are these models reasonable ones?

7. Experiments show that if the chemical reaction

$$N_2O_5 \rightarrow 2NO_2 + \tfrac{1}{2}O_2$$

Graphing calculator or computer with graphing software required   **1.** Homework Hints available in TEC

takes place at 45°C, the rate of reaction of dinitrogen pent-oxide is proportional to its concentration as follows:

$$-\frac{d[\text{N}_2\text{O}_5]}{dt} = 0.0005[\text{N}_2\text{O}_5]$$

(See Example 4 in Section 3.8.)
(a) Find an expression for the concentration $[\text{N}_2\text{O}_5]$ after t seconds if the initial concentration is C.
(b) How long will the reaction take to reduce the concentration of N_2O_5 to 90% of its original value?

8. Strontium-90 has a half-life of 28 days.
(a) A sample has a mass of 50 mg initially. Find a formula for the mass remaining after t days.
(b) Find the mass remaining after 40 days.
(c) How long does it take the sample to decay to a mass of 2 mg?
(d) Sketch the graph of the mass function.

9. The half-life of cesium-137 is 30 years. Suppose we have a 100-mg sample.
(a) Find the mass that remains after t years.
(b) How much of the sample remains after 100 years?
(c) After how long will only 1 mg remain?

10. A sample of tritium-3 decayed to 94.5% of its original amount after a year.
(a) What is the half-life of tritium-3?
(b) How long would it take the sample to decay to 20% of its original amount?

11. Scientists can determine the age of ancient objects by the method of *radiocarbon dating*. The bombardment of the upper atmosphere by cosmic rays converts nitrogen to a radioactive isotope of carbon, ^{14}C, with a half-life of about 5730 years. Vegetation absorbs carbon dioxide through the atmosphere and animal life assimilates ^{14}C through food chains. When a plant or animal dies, it stops replacing its carbon and the amount of ^{14}C begins to decrease through radioactive decay. Therefore the level of radioactivity must also decay exponentially.

A parchment fragment was discovered that had about 74% as much ^{14}C radioactivity as does plant material on the earth today. Estimate the age of the parchment.

12. A curve passes through the point $(0, 5)$ and has the property that the slope of the curve at every point P is twice the y-coordinate of P. What is the equation of the curve?

13. A roast turkey is taken from an oven when its temperature has reached 185°F and is placed on a table in a room where the temperature is 75°F.
(a) If the temperature of the turkey is 150°F after half an hour, what is the temperature after 45 minutes?
(b) When will the turkey have cooled to 100°F?

14. In a murder investigation, the temperature of the corpse was 32.5°C at 1:30 PM and 30.3°C an hour later. Normal body temperature is 37.0°C and the temperature of the surroundings was 20.0°C. When did the murder take place?

15. When a cold drink is taken from a refrigerator, its temperature is 5°C. After 25 minutes in a 20°C room its temperature has increased to 10°C.
(a) What is the temperature of the drink after 50 minutes?
(b) When will its temperature be 15°C?

16. A freshly brewed cup of coffee has temperature 95°C in a 20°C room. When its temperature is 70°C, it is cooling at a rate of 1°C per minute. When does this occur?

17. The rate of change of atmospheric pressure P with respect to altitude h is proportional to P, provided that the temperature is constant. At 15°C the pressure is 101.3 kPa at sea level and 87.14 kPa at $h = 1000$ m.
(a) What is the pressure at an altitude of 3000 m?
(b) What is the pressure at the top of Mount McKinley, at an altitude of 6187 m?

18. (a) If $1000 is borrowed at 8% interest, find the amounts due at the end of 3 years if the interest is compounded (i) annually, (ii) quarterly, (iii) monthly, (iv) weekly, (v) daily, (vi) hourly, and (vii) continuously.
(b) Suppose $1000 is borrowed and the interest is compounded continuously. If $A(t)$ is the amount due after t years, where $0 \le t \le 3$, graph $A(t)$ for each of the interest rates 6%, 8%, and 10% on a common screen.

19. (a) If $3000 is invested at 5% interest, find the value of the investment at the end of 5 years if the interest is compounded (i) annually, (ii) semiannually, (iii) monthly, (iv) weekly, (v) daily, and (vi) continuously.
(b) If $A(t)$ is the amount of the investment at time t for the case of continuous compounding, write a differential equation and an initial condition satisfied by $A(t)$.

20. (a) How long will it take an investment to double in value if the interest rate is 6% compounded continuously?
(b) What is the equivalent annual interest rate?

21. Consider a population $P = P(t)$ with constant relative birth and death rates α and β, respectively, and a constant emigration rate m, where α, β, and m are positive constants. Assume that $\alpha > \beta$. Then the rate of change of the population at time t is modeled by the differential equation

$$\frac{dP}{dt} = kP - m \qquad \text{where } k = \alpha - \beta$$

(a) Find the solution of this equation that satisfies the initial condition $P(0) = P_0$.
(b) What condition on m will lead to an exponential expansion of the population?
(c) What condition on m will result in a constant population? A population decline?
(d) In 1847, the population of Ireland was about 8 million and the difference between the relative birth and death rates was 1.6% of the population. Because of the potato famine in the 1840s and 1850s, about 210,000 inhabitants per year emigrated from Ireland. Was the population expanding or declining at that time?

22. Let c be a positive number. A differential equation of the form

$$\frac{dy}{dt} = ky^{1+c}$$

where k is a positive constant, is called a *doomsday equation* because the exponent in the expression ky^{1+c} is larger than the exponent 1 for natural growth.

(a) Determine the solution that satisfies the initial condition $y(0) = y_0$.

(b) Show that there is a finite time $t = T$ (doomsday) such that $\lim_{t \to T^-} y(t) = \infty$.

(c) An especially prolific breed of rabbits has the growth term $ky^{1.01}$. If 2 such rabbits breed initially and the warren has 16 rabbits after three months, then when is doomsday?

| APPLIED PROJECT | **Calculus and Baseball** |

In this project we explore three of the many applications of calculus to baseball. The physical interactions of the game, especially the collision of ball and bat, are quite complex and their models are discussed in detail in a book by Robert Adair, *The Physics of Baseball*, 3d ed. (New York, 2002).

1. It may surprise you to learn that the collision of baseball and bat lasts only about a thousandth of a second. Here we calculate the average force on the bat during this collision by first computing the change in the ball's momentum.

The *momentum* p of an object is the product of its mass m and its velocity v, that is, $p = mv$. Suppose an object, moving along a straight line, is acted on by a force $F = F(t)$ that is a continuous function of time.

(a) Show that the change in momentum over a time interval $[t_0, t_1]$ is equal to the integral of F from t_0 to t_1; that is, show that

$$p(t_1) - p(t_0) = \int_{t_0}^{t_1} F(t)\, dt$$

This integral is called the *impulse* of the force over the time interval.

(b) A pitcher throws a 90-mi/h fastball to a batter, who hits a line drive directly back to the pitcher. The ball is in contact with the bat for 0.001 s and leaves the bat with velocity 110 mi/h. A baseball weighs 5 oz and, in US Customary units, its mass is measured in slugs: $m = w/g$ where $g = 32$ ft/s^2.
  (i) Find the change in the ball's momentum.
  (ii) Find the average force on the bat.

Batter's box

An overhead view of the position of a baseball bat, shown every fiftieth of a second during a typical swing. (Adapted from *The Physics of Baseball*)

2. In this problem we calculate the work required for a pitcher to throw a 90-mi/h fastball by first considering kinetic energy.

The *kinetic energy* K of an object of mass m and velocity v is given by $K = \frac{1}{2}mv^2$. Suppose an object of mass m, moving in a straight line, is acted on by a force $F = F(s)$ that depends on its position s. According to Newton's Second Law

$$F(s) = ma = m\frac{dv}{dt}$$

where a and v denote the acceleration and velocity of the object.

(a) Show that the work done in moving the object from a position s_0 to a position s_1 is equal to the change in the object's kinetic energy, that is, show that

$$W = \int_{s_0}^{s_1} F(s)\, ds = \tfrac{1}{2}mv_1^2 - \tfrac{1}{2}mv_0^2$$

Graphing calculator or computer with graphing software required.

where $v_0 = v(s_0)$ and $v_1 = v(s_1)$ are the velocities of the object at the positions s_0 and s_1. *Hint:* By the Chain Rule,

$$m\frac{dv}{dt} = m\frac{dv}{ds}\frac{ds}{dt} = mv\frac{dv}{ds}$$

(b) How many foot-pounds of work does it take to throw a baseball at a speed of 90 mi/h?

3. (a) An outfielder fields a baseball 280 ft away from home plate and throws it directly to the catcher with an initial velocity of 100 ft/s. Assume that the velocity $v(t)$ of the ball after t seconds satisfies the differential equation $dv/dt = -\frac{1}{10}v$ because of air resistance. How long does it take for the ball to reach home plate? (Ignore any vertical motion of the ball.)

(b) The manager of the team wonders whether the ball will reach home plate sooner if it is relayed by an infielder. The shortstop can position himself directly between the outfielder and home plate, catch the ball thrown by the outfielder, turn, and throw the ball to the catcher with an initial velocity of 105 ft/s. The manager clocks the relay time of the shortstop (catching, turning, throwing) at half a second. How far from home plate should the shortstop position himself to minimize the total time for the ball to reach home plate? Should the manager encourage a direct throw or a relayed throw? What if the shortstop can throw at 115 ft/s?

(c) For what throwing velocity of the shortstop does a relayed throw take the same time as a direct throw?

7.5 The Logistic Equation

In this section we discuss in detail a model for population growth, the logistic model, that is more sophisticated than exponential growth. In doing so we use all the tools at our disposal—direction fields and Euler's method from Section 7.2 and the explicit solution of separable differential equations from Section 7.3. In the exercises we investigate other possible models for population growth, some of which take into account harvesting and seasonal growth.

The Logistic Model

As we discussed in Section 7.1, a population often increases exponentially in its early stages but levels off eventually and approaches its carrying capacity because of limited resources. If $P(t)$ is the size of the population at time t, we assume that

$$\frac{dP}{dt} \approx kP \qquad \text{if } P \text{ is small}$$

This says that the growth rate is initially close to being proportional to size. In other words, the relative growth rate is almost constant when the population is small. But we also want to reflect the fact that the relative growth rate decreases as the population P increases and becomes negative if P ever exceeds its **carrying capacity** M, the maximum population that the environment is capable of sustaining in the long run. The simplest expression for the relative growth rate that incorporates these assumptions is

$$\frac{1}{P}\frac{dP}{dt} = k\left(1 - \frac{P}{M}\right)$$

Multiplying by P, we obtain the model for population growth known as the **logistic differential equation**:

$$\boxed{1} \qquad \frac{dP}{dt} = kP\left(1 - \frac{P}{M}\right)$$

Notice from Equation 1 that if P is small compared with M, then P/M is close to 0 and so $dP/dt \approx kP$. However, if $P \to M$ (the population approaches its carrying capacity), then $P/M \to 1$, so $dP/dt \to 0$. We can deduce information about whether solutions increase or decrease directly from Equation 1. If the population P lies between 0 and M, then the right side of the equation is positive, so $dP/dt > 0$ and the population increases. But if the population exceeds the carrying capacity ($P > M$), then $1 - P/M$ is negative, so $dP/dt < 0$ and the population decreases.

Direction Fields

Let's start our more detailed analysis of the logistic differential equation by looking at a direction field.

V EXAMPLE 1 What a direction field tells us about solutions of the logistic equation
Draw a direction field for the logistic equation with $k = 0.08$ and carrying capacity $M = 1000$. What can you deduce about the solutions?

SOLUTION In this case the logistic differential equation is

$$\frac{dP}{dt} = 0.08P\left(1 - \frac{P}{1000}\right)$$

A direction field for this equation is shown in Figure 1. We show only the first quadrant because negative populations aren't meaningful and we are interested only in what happens after $t = 0$.

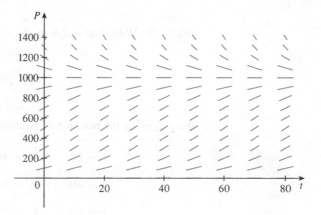

FIGURE 1
Direction field for the logistic
equation in Example 1

The logistic equation is autonomous (dP/dt depends only on P, not on t), so the slopes are the same along any horizontal line. As expected, the slopes are positive for $0 < P < 1000$ and negative for $P > 1000$.

The slopes are small when P is close to 0 or 1000 (the carrying capacity). Notice that the solutions move away from the equilibrium solution $P = 0$ and move toward the equilibrium solution $P = 1000$.

In Figure 2 we use the direction field to sketch solution curves with initial populations $P(0) = 100$, $P(0) = 400$, and $P(0) = 1300$. Notice that solution curves that start below $P = 1000$ are increasing and those that start above $P = 1000$ are decreasing. The slopes are greatest when $P \approx 500$ and therefore the solution curves that start below $P = 1000$ have inflection points when $P \approx 500$. In fact we can prove that all solution curves that start below $P = 500$ have an inflection point when P is exactly 500. (See Exercise 11.)

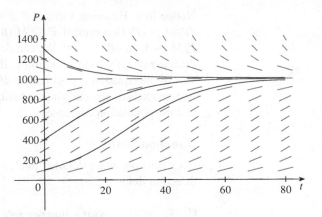

FIGURE 2

Solution curves for the logistic equation in Example 1

Euler's Method

Next let's use Euler's method to obtain numerical estimates for solutions of the logistic differential equation at specific times.

☑ EXAMPLE 2   Use Euler's method with step sizes 20, 10, 5, 1, and 0.1 to estimate the population sizes $P(40)$ and $P(80)$, where P is the solution of the initial-value problem

$$\frac{dP}{dt} = 0.08P\left(1 - \frac{P}{1000}\right) \qquad P(0) = 100$$

SOLUTION   With step size $h = 20$, $t_0 = 0$, $P_0 = 100$, and

$$F(t, P) = 0.08P\left(1 - \frac{P}{1000}\right)$$

we get, using the notation of Section 7.2,

$$t = 20: \qquad P_1 = 100 + 20F(0, 100) = 244$$

$$t = 40: \qquad P_2 = 244 + 20F(20, 244) \approx 539.14$$

$$t = 60: \qquad P_3 = 539.14 + 20F(40, 539.14) \approx 936.69$$

$$t = 80: \qquad P_4 = 936.69 + 20F(60, 936.69) \approx 1031.57$$

Thus our estimates for the population sizes at times $t = 40$ and $t = 80$ are

$$P(40) \approx 539 \qquad P(80) \approx 1032$$

For smaller step sizes we need to program a calculator or computer. The table gives the results.

Step size	Euler estimate of $P(40)$	Euler estimate of $P(80)$
20	539	1032
10	647	997
5	695	991
1	725	986
0.1	731	985

Figure 3 shows a graph of the Euler approximations with step sizes $h = 10$ and $h = 1$. We see that the Euler approximation with $h = 1$ looks very much like the lower solution curve that we drew using a direction field in Figure 2.

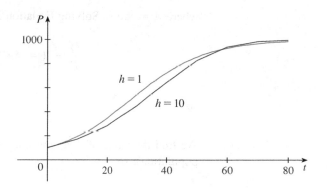

FIGURE 3
Euler approximations of the
solution curve in Example 2

The Analytic Solution

The logistic equation (1) is separable and so we can solve it explicitly using the method of Section 7.3. Since

$$\frac{dP}{dt} = kP\left(1 - \frac{P}{M}\right)$$

we have

2
$$\int \frac{dP}{P(1 - P/M)} = \int k\, dt$$

To evaluate the integral on the left side, we write

$$\frac{1}{P(1 - P/M)} = \frac{M}{P(M - P)}$$

Using partial fractions (see Section 5.7), we get

$$\frac{M}{P(M - P)} = \frac{1}{P} + \frac{1}{M - P}$$

This enables us to rewrite Equation 2:

$$\int \left(\frac{1}{P} + \frac{1}{M - P} \right) dP = \int k \, dt$$

$$\ln |P| - \ln |M - P| = kt + C$$

$$\ln \left| \frac{M - P}{P} \right| = -kt - C$$

$$\left| \frac{M - P}{P} \right| = e^{-kt-C} = e^{-C} e^{-kt}$$

3
$$\frac{M - P}{P} = A e^{-kt}$$

where $A = \pm e^{-C}$. Solving Equation 3 for P, we get

$$\frac{M}{P} - 1 = A e^{-kt} \quad \Rightarrow \quad \frac{P}{M} = \frac{1}{1 + A e^{-kt}}$$

so
$$P = \frac{M}{1 + A e^{-kt}}$$

We find the value of A by putting $t = 0$ in Equation 3. If $t = 0$, then $P = P_0$ (the initial population), so

$$\frac{M - P_0}{P_0} = A e^0 = A$$

Thus the solution to the logistic equation is

4
$$P(t) = \frac{M}{1 + A e^{-kt}} \quad \text{where} \quad A = \frac{M - P_0}{P_0}$$

Using the expression for $P(t)$ in Equation 4, we see that

$$\lim_{t \to \infty} P(t) = M$$

which is to be expected.

EXAMPLE 3   An explicit solution of the logistic equation   Write the solution of the initial-value problem

$$\frac{dP}{dt} = 0.08 P \left(1 - \frac{P}{1000} \right) \qquad P(0) = 100$$

and use it to find the population sizes $P(40)$ and $P(80)$. At what time does the population reach 900?

SOLUTION   The differential equation is a logistic equation with $k = 0.08$, carrying capacity $M = 1000$, and initial population $P_0 = 100$. So Equation 4 gives the population at time t as

$$P(t) = \frac{1000}{1 + Ae^{-0.08t}} \qquad \text{where } A = \frac{1000 - 100}{100} = 9$$

Thus

$$P(t) = \frac{1000}{1 + 9e^{-0.08t}}$$

So the population sizes when $t = 40$ and 80 are

Compare these values with the Euler estimates from Example 2:

$P(40) \approx 731 \qquad P(80) \approx 985$

$$P(40) = \frac{1000}{1 + 9e^{-3.2}} \approx 731.6 \qquad P(80) = \frac{1000}{1 + 9e^{-6.4}} \approx 985.3$$

The population reaches 900 when

$$\frac{1000}{1 + 9e^{-0.08t}} = 900$$

Solving this equation for t, we get

Compare the solution curve in Figure 4 with the lowest solution curve we drew from the direction field in Figure 2.

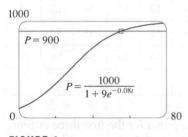

FIGURE 4

$$1 + 9e^{-0.08t} = \tfrac{10}{9}$$

$$e^{-0.08t} = \tfrac{1}{81}$$

$$-0.08t = \ln \tfrac{1}{81} = -\ln 81$$

$$t = \frac{\ln 81}{0.08} \approx 54.9$$

So the population reaches 900 when t is approximately 55. As a check on our work, we graph the population curve in Figure 4 and observe where it intersects the line $P = 900$. The cursor indicates that $t \approx 55$.

Comparison of the Natural Growth and Logistic Models

In the 1930s the biologist G. F. Gause conducted an experiment with the protozoan *Paramecium* and used a logistic equation to model his data. The table gives his daily count of the population of protozoa. He estimated the initial relative growth rate to be 0.7944 and the carrying capacity to be 64.

t (days)	0	1	2	3	4	5	6	7	8	9	10	11	12	13	14	15	16
P (observed)	2	3	22	16	39	52	54	47	50	76	69	51	57	70	53	59	57

V **EXAMPLE 4** Find the exponential and logistic models for Gause's data. Compare the predicted values with the observed values and comment on the fit.

SOLUTION Given the relative growth rate $k = 0.7944$ and the initial population $P_0 = 2$, the exponential model is

$$P(t) = P_0 e^{kt} = 2e^{0.7944t}$$

Gause used the same value of k for his logistic model. [This is reasonable because $P_0 = 2$ is small compared with the carrying capacity ($M = 64$). The equation

$$\frac{1}{P_0} \frac{dP}{dt}\bigg|_{t=0} = k\left(1 - \frac{2}{64}\right) \approx k$$

shows that the value of k for the logistic model is very close to the value for the exponential model.]

Then the solution of the logistic equation in Equation 4 gives

$$P(t) = \frac{M}{1 + Ae^{-kt}} = \frac{64}{1 + Ae^{-0.7944t}}$$

where

$$A = \frac{M - P_0}{P_0} = \frac{64 - 2}{2} = 31$$

So

$$P(t) = \frac{64}{1 + 31e^{-0.7944t}}$$

We use these equations to calculate the predicted values (rounded to the nearest integer) and compare them in the following table.

t (days)	0	1	2	3	4	5	6	7	8	9	10	11	12	13	14	15	16
P (observed)	2	3	22	16	39	52	54	47	50	76	69	51	57	70	53	59	57
P (logistic model)	2	4	9	17	28	40	51	57	61	62	63	64	64	64	64	64	64
P (exponential model)	2	4	10	22	48	106	$\cdots$										

We notice from the table and from the graph in Figure 5 that for the first three or four days the exponential model gives results comparable to those of the more sophisticated logistic model. For $t \geq 5$, however, the exponential model is hopelessly inaccurate, but the logistic model fits the observations reasonably well.

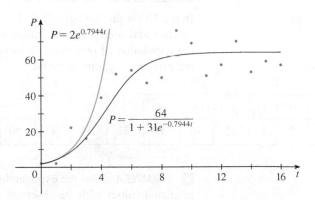

FIGURE 5

The exponential and logistic models for the *Paramecium* data

Many countries that formerly experienced exponential growth are now finding that their rates of population growth are declining and the logistic model provides a better model.

t	$B(t)$	t	$B(t)$
1980	9,847	1992	10,036
1982	9,856	1994	10,109
1984	9,855	1996	10,152
1986	9,862	1998	10,175
1988	9,884	2000	10,186
1990	9,962		

The table in the margin shows midyear values of $B(t)$, the population of Belgium, in thousands, at time t, from 1980 to 2000. Figure 6 shows these data points together with a shifted logistic function obtained from a calculator with the ability to fit a logistic function to these points by regression. We see that the logistic model provides a very good fit.

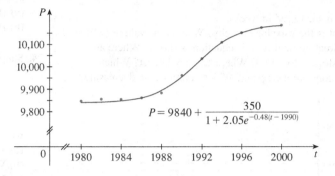

FIGURE 6

Logistic model for
the population of Belgium

$$P = 9840 + \frac{350}{1 + 2.05e^{-0.48(t - 1990)}}$$

Other Models for Population Growth

The Law of Natural Growth and the logistic differential equation are not the only equations that have been proposed to model population growth. In Exercise 18 we look at the Gompertz growth function and in Exercises 19 and 20 we investigate seasonal-growth models.

Two of the other models are modifications of the logistic model. The differential equation

$$\frac{dP}{dt} = kP\left(1 - \frac{P}{M}\right) - c$$

has been used to model populations that are subject to "harvesting" of one sort or another. (Think of a population of fish being caught at a constant rate.) This equation is explored in Exercises 15 and 16.

For some species there is a minimum population level m below which the species tends to become extinct. (Adults may not be able to find suitable mates.) Such populations have been modeled by the differential equation

$$\frac{dP}{dt} = kP\left(1 - \frac{P}{M}\right)\left(1 - \frac{m}{P}\right)$$

where the extra factor, $1 - m/P$, takes into account the consequences of a sparse population (see Exercise 17).

7.5 Exercises

1. Suppose that a population develops according to the logistic equation

$$\frac{dP}{dt} = 0.05P - 0.0005P^2$$

where t is measured in weeks.
(a) What is the carrying capacity? What is the value of k?
(b) A direction field for this equation is shown. Where are the slopes close to 0? Where are they largest? Which solutions are increasing? Which solutions are decreasing?

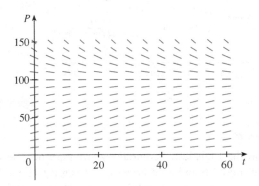

(c) Use the direction field to sketch solutions for initial populations of 20, 40, 60, 80, 120, and 140. What do these solutions have in common? How do they differ? Which solutions have inflection points? At what population levels do they occur?
(d) What are the equilibrium solutions? How are the other solutions related to these solutions?

2. Suppose that a population grows according to a logistic model with carrying capacity 6000 and $k = 0.0015$ per year.
(a) Write the logistic differential equation for these data.
(b) Draw a direction field (either by hand or with a computer algebra system). What does it tell you about the solution curves?
(c) Use the direction field to sketch the solution curves for initial populations of 1000, 2000, 4000, and 8000. What can you say about the concavity of these curves? What is the significance of the inflection points?
(d) Program a calculator or computer to use Euler's method with step size $h = 1$ to estimate the population after 50 years if the initial population is 1000.
(e) If the initial population is 1000, write a formula for the population after t years. Use it to find the population after 50 years and compare with your estimate in part (d).
(f) Graph the solution in part (e) and compare with the solution curve you sketched in part (c).

3. The Pacific halibut fishery has been modeled by the differential equation

$$\frac{dy}{dt} = ky\left(1 - \frac{y}{M}\right)$$

where $y(t)$ is the biomass (the total mass of the members of the population) in kilograms at time t (measured in years), the carrying capacity is estimated to be $M = 8 \times 10^7$ kg, and $k = 0.71$ per year.
(a) If $y(0) = 2 \times 10^7$ kg, find the biomass a year later.
(b) How long will it take for the biomass to reach 4×10^7 kg?

4. Suppose a population $P(t)$ satisfies

$$\frac{dP}{dt} = 0.4P - 0.001P^2 \qquad P(0) = 50$$

where t is measured in years.
(a) What is the carrying capacity?
(b) What is $P'(0)$?
(c) When will the population reach 50% of the carrying capacity?

5. Suppose a population grows according to a logistic model with initial population 1000 and carrying capacity 10,000. If the population grows to 2500 after one year, what will the population be after another three years?

6. The table gives the number of yeast cells in a new laboratory culture.

Time (hours)	Yeast cells	Time (hours)	Yeast cells
0	18	10	509
2	39	12	597
4	80	14	640
6	171	16	664
8	336	18	672

(a) Plot the data and use the plot to estimate the carrying capacity for the yeast population.
(b) Use the data to estimate the initial relative growth rate.
(c) Find both an exponential model and a logistic model for these data.
(d) Compare the predicted values with the observed values, both in a table and with graphs. Comment on how well your models fit the data.
(e) Use your logistic model to estimate the number of yeast cells after 7 hours.

7. The population of the world was about 5.3 billion in 1990. Birth rates in the 1990s ranged from 35 to 40 million per year and death rates ranged from 15 to 20 million per year. Let's assume that the carrying capacity for world population is 100 billion.
(a) Write the logistic differential equation for these data. (Because the initial population is small compared to the

---

carrying capacity, you can take k to be an estimate of the initial relative growth rate.)

(b) Use the logistic model to estimate the world population in the year 2000 and compare with the actual population of 6.1 billion.

(c) Use the logistic model to predict the world population in the years 2100 and 2500.

(d) What are your predictions if the carrying capacity is 50 billion?

8. (a) Make a guess as to the carrying capacity for the US population. Use it and the fact that the population was 250 million in 1990 to formulate a logistic model for the US population.

(b) Determine the value of k in your model by using the fact that the population in 2000 was 275 million.

(c) Use your model to predict the US population in the years 2100 and 2200.

(d) Use your model to predict the year in which the US population will exceed 350 million.

9. One model for the spread of a rumor is that the rate of spread is proportional to the product of the fraction y of the population who have heard the rumor and the fraction who have not heard the rumor.

(a) Write a differential equation that is satisfied by y.

(b) Solve the differential equation.

(c) A small town has 1000 inhabitants. At 8 AM, 80 people have heard a rumor. By noon half the town has heard it. At what time will 90% of the population have heard the rumor?

10. Biologists stocked a lake with 400 fish and estimated the carrying capacity (the maximal population for the fish of that species in that lake) to be 10,000. The number of fish tripled in the first year.

(a) Assuming that the size of the fish population satisfies the logistic equation, find an expression for the size of the population after t years.

(b) How long will it take for the population to increase to 5000?

11. (a) Show that if P satisfies the logistic equation (1), then

$$\frac{d^2P}{dt^2} = k^2P\left(1 - \frac{P}{M}\right)\left(1 - \frac{2P}{M}\right)$$

(b) Deduce that a population grows fastest when it reaches half its carrying capacity.

12. For a fixed value of M (say $M = 10$), the family of logistic functions given by Equation 4 depends on the initial value P_0 and the proportionality constant k. Graph several members of this family. How does the graph change when P_0 varies? How does it change when k varies?

13. The table gives the midyear population of Japan, in thousands, from 1960 to 2005.

Year	Population	Year	Population
1960	94,092	1985	120,754
1965	98,883	1990	123,537
1970	104,345	1995	125,341
1975	111,573	2000	126,700
1980	116,807	2005	127,417

Use a graphing calculator to fit both an exponential function and a logistic function to these data. Graph the data points and both functions, and comment on the accuracy of the models. [*Hint:* Subtract 94,000 from each of the population figures. Then, after obtaining a model from your calculator, add 94,000 to get your final model. It might be helpful to choose $t = 0$ to correspond to 1960 or 1980.]

14. The table gives the midyear population of Spain, in thousands, from 1955 to 2000.

Year	Population	Year	Population
1955	29,319	1980	37,488
1960	30,641	1985	38,535
1965	32,085	1990	39,351
1970	33,876	1995	39,750
1975	35,564	2000	40,016

Use a graphing calculator to fit both an exponential function and a logistic function to these data. Graph the data points and both functions, and comment on the accuracy of the models. [*Hint:* Subtract 29,000 from each of the population figures. Then, after obtaining a model from your calculator, add 29,000 to get your final model. It might be helpful to choose $t = 0$ to correspond to 1955 or 1975.]

15. Let's modify the logistic differential equation of Example 1 as follows:

$$\frac{dP}{dt} = 0.08P\left(1 - \frac{P}{1000}\right) - 15$$

(a) Suppose $P(t)$ represents a fish population at time t, where t is measured in weeks. Explain the meaning of the final term in the equation (-15).

(b) Draw a direction field for this differential equation.

(c) What are the equilibrium solutions?

(d) Use the direction field to sketch several solution curves. Describe what happens to the fish population for various initial populations.

(e) Solve this differential equation explicitly, either by using partial fractions or with a computer algebra system. Use the initial populations 200 and 300. Graph the solutions and compare with your sketches in part (d).

CAS **16.** Consider the differential equation

$$\frac{dP}{dt} = 0.08P\left(1 - \frac{P}{1000}\right) - c$$

as a model for a fish population, where t is measured in weeks and c is a constant.

(a) Use a CAS to draw direction fields for various values of c.

(b) From your direction fields in part (a), determine the values of c for which there is at least one equilibrium solution. For what values of c does the fish population always die out?

(c) Use the differential equation to prove what you discovered graphically in part (b).

(d) What would you recommend for a limit to the weekly catch of this fish population?

17. There is considerable evidence to support the theory that for some species there is a minimum population m such that the species will become extinct if the size of the population falls below m. This condition can be incorporated into the logistic equation by introducing the factor $(1 - m/P)$. Thus the modified logistic model is given by the differential equation

$$\frac{dP}{dt} = kP\left(1 - \frac{P}{M}\right)\left(1 - \frac{m}{P}\right)$$

(a) Use the differential equation to show that any solution is increasing if $m < P < M$ and decreasing if $0 < P < m$.

(b) For the case where $k = 0.08$, $M = 1000$, and $m = 200$, draw a direction field and use it to sketch several solution curves. Describe what happens to the population for various initial populations. What are the equilibrium solutions?

(c) Solve the differential equation explicitly, either by using partial fractions or with a computer algebra system. Use the initial population P_0.

(d) Use the solution in part (c) to show that if $P_0 < m$, then the species will become extinct. [*Hint:* Show that the numerator in your expression for $P(t)$ is 0 for some value of t.]

18. Another model for a growth function for a limited population is given by the **Gompertz function**, which is a solution of the differential equation

$$\frac{dP}{dt} = c \ln\left(\frac{M}{P}\right)P$$

where c is a constant and M is the carrying capacity.

(a) Solve this differential equation.

(b) Compute $\lim_{t\to\infty} P(t)$.

(c) Graph the Gompertz growth function for $M = 1000$, $P_0 = 100$, and $c = 0.05$, and compare it with the logistic function in Example 3. What are the similarities? What are the differences?

(d) We know from Exercise 11 that the logistic function grows fastest when $P = M/2$. Use the Gompertz differential equation to show that the Gompertz function grows fastest when $P = M/e$.

19. In a **seasonal-growth model**, a periodic function of time is introduced to account for seasonal variations in the rate of growth. Such variations could, for example, be caused by seasonal changes in the availability of food.

(a) Find the solution of the seasonal-growth model

$$\frac{dP}{dt} = kP\cos(rt - \phi) \qquad P(0) = P_0$$

where k, r, and ϕ are positive constants.

(b) By graphing the solution for several values of k, r, and ϕ, explain how the values of k, r, and ϕ affect the solution. What can you say about $\lim_{t\to\infty} P(t)$?

20. Suppose we alter the differential equation in Exercise 19 as follows:

$$\frac{dP}{dt} = kP\cos^2(rt - \phi) \qquad P(0) = P_0$$

(a) Solve this differential equation with the help of a table of integrals or a CAS.

(b) Graph the solution for several values of k, r, and ϕ. How do the values of k, r, and ϕ affect the solution? What can you say about $\lim_{t\to\infty} P(t)$ in this case?

7.6 Predator-Prey Systems

We have looked at a variety of models for the growth of a single species that lives alone in an environment. In this section we consider more realistic models that take into account the interaction of two species in the same habitat. We will see that these models take the form of a pair of linked differential equations.

We first consider the situation in which one species, called the *prey,* has an ample food supply and the second species, called the *predators,* feeds on the prey. Examples of prey and predators include rabbits and wolves in an isolated forest, food fish and sharks, aphids and ladybugs, and bacteria and amoebas. Our model will have two dependent variables and both are functions of time. We let $R(t)$ be the number of prey (using R for rabbits) and $W(t)$ be the number of predators (with W for wolves) at time t.

In the absence of predators, the ample food supply would support exponential growth of the prey, that is,

$$\frac{dR}{dt} = kR \qquad \text{where } k \text{ is a positive constant}$$

In the absence of prey, we assume that the predator population would decline at a rate proportional to itself, that is,

$$\frac{dW}{dt} = -rW \qquad \text{where } r \text{ is a positive constant}$$

With both species present, however, we assume that the principal cause of death among the prey is being eaten by a predator, and the birth and survival rates of the predators depend on their available food supply, namely, the prey. We also assume that the two species encounter each other at a rate that is proportional to both populations and is therefore proportional to the product RW. (The more there are of either population, the more encounters there are likely to be.) A system of two differential equations that incorporates these assumptions is as follows:

W represents the predator.

R represents the prey.

$$\boxed{1} \qquad \frac{dR}{dt} = kR - aRW \qquad \frac{dW}{dt} = -rW + bRW$$

where k, r, a, and b are positive constants. Notice that the term $-aRW$ decreases the natural growth rate of the prey and the term bRW increases the natural growth rate of the predators.

The Lotka-Volterra equations were proposed as a model to explain the variations in the shark and food-fish populations in the Adriatic Sea by the Italian mathematician Vito Volterra (1860–1940).

The equations in (1) are known as the **predator-prey equations**, or the **Lotka-Volterra equations**. A **solution** of this system of equations is a pair of functions $R(t)$ and $W(t)$ that describe the populations of prey and predator as functions of time. Because the system is coupled (R and W occur in both equations), we can't solve one equation and then the other; we have to solve them simultaneously. Unfortunately, it is usually impossible to find explicit formulas for R and W as functions of t. We can, however, use graphical methods to analyze the equations.

V **EXAMPLE 1** Suppose that populations of rabbits and wolves are described by the Lotka-Volterra equations (1) with $k = 0.08$, $a = 0.001$, $r = 0.02$, and $b = 0.00002$. The time t is measured in months.
(a) Find the constant solutions (called the **equilibrium solutions**) and interpret the answer.
(b) Use the system of differential equations to find an expression for dW/dR.
(c) Draw a direction field for the resulting differential equation in the RW-plane. Then use that direction field to sketch some solution curves.
(d) Suppose that, at some point in time, there are 1000 rabbits and 40 wolves. Draw the corresponding solution curve and use it to describe the changes in both population levels.
(e) Use part (d) to make sketches of R and W as functions of t.

SOLUTION
(a) With the given values of k, a, r, and b, the Lotka-Volterra equations become

$$\frac{dR}{dt} = 0.08R - 0.001RW$$

$$\frac{dW}{dt} = -0.02W + 0.00002RW$$

Both R and W will be constant if both derivatives are 0, that is,

$$R' = R(0.08 - 0.001W) = 0$$

$$W' = W(-0.02 + 0.00002R) = 0$$

One solution is given by $R = 0$ and $W = 0$. (This makes sense: If there are no rabbits or wolves, the populations are certainly not going to increase.) The other constant solution is

$$W = \frac{0.08}{0.001} = 80 \qquad R = \frac{0.02}{0.00002} = 1000$$

So the equilibrium populations consist of 80 wolves and 1000 rabbits. This means that 1000 rabbits are just enough to support a constant wolf population of 80. There are neither too many wolves (which would result in fewer rabbits) nor too few wolves (which would result in more rabbits).

(b) We use the Chain Rule to eliminate t:

$$\frac{dW}{dt} = \frac{dW}{dR}\frac{dR}{dt}$$

so

$$\frac{dW}{dR} = \frac{\dfrac{dW}{dt}}{\dfrac{dR}{dt}} = \frac{-0.02W + 0.00002RW}{0.08R - 0.001RW}$$

(c) If we think of W as a function of R, we have the differential equation

$$\frac{dW}{dR} = \frac{-0.02W + 0.00002RW}{0.08R - 0.001RW}$$

We draw the direction field for this differential equation in Figure 1 and we use it to sketch several solution curves in Figure 2. If we move along a solution curve, we observe how the relationship between R and W changes as time passes. Notice that the curves appear to be closed in the sense that if we travel along a curve, we always return to the same point. Notice also that the point (1000, 80) is inside all the solution curves. That point is called an *equilibrium point* because it corresponds to the equilibrium solution $R = 1000$, $W = 80$.

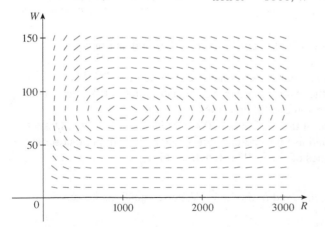

FIGURE 1   Direction field for the predator-prey system

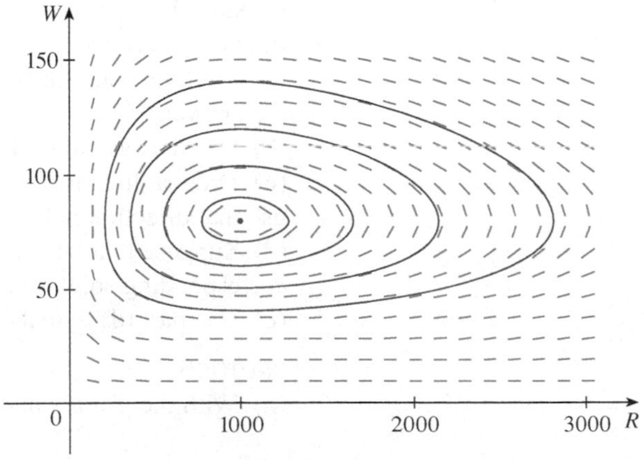

FIGURE 2   Phase portrait of the system

When we represent solutions of a system of differential equations as in Figure 2, we refer to the RW-plane as the **phase plane**, and we call the solution curves **phase trajectories**. So a phase trajectory is a path traced out by solutions (R, W) as time goes by.

A **phase portrait** consists of equilibrium points and typical phase trajectories, as shown in Figure 2.

(d) Starting with 1000 rabbits and 40 wolves corresponds to drawing the solution curve through the point $P_0(1000, 40)$. Figure 3 shows this phase trajectory with the direction field removed. Starting at the point P_0 at time $t = 0$ and letting t increase, do we move clockwise or counterclockwise around the phase trajectory? If we put $R = 1000$ and $W = 40$ in the first differential equation, we get

$$\frac{dR}{dt} = 0.08(1000) - 0.001(1000)(40) = 80 - 40 = 40$$

Since $dR/dt > 0$, we conclude that R is increasing at P_0 and so we move counter-clockwise around the phase trajectory.

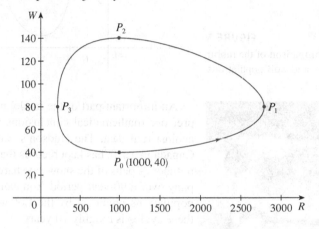

FIGURE 3
Phase trajectory through $(1000, 40)$

We see that at P_0 there aren't enough wolves to maintain a balance between the populations, so the rabbit population increases. That results in more wolves and eventually there are so many wolves that the rabbits have a hard time avoiding them. So the number of rabbits begins to decline (at P_1, where we estimate that R reaches its maximum population of about 2800). This means that at some later time the wolf population starts to fall (at P_2, where $R = 1000$ and $W \approx 140$). But this benefits the rabbits, so their population later starts to increase (at P_3, where $W = 80$ and $R \approx 210$). As a consequence, the wolf population eventually starts to increase as well. This happens when the populations return to their initial values of $R = 1000$ and $W = 40$, and the entire cycle begins again.

(e) From the description in part (d) of how the rabbit and wolf populations rise and fall, we can sketch the graphs of $R(t)$ and $W(t)$. Suppose the points P_1, P_2, and P_3 in Figure 3 are reached at times t_1, t_2, and t_3. Then we can sketch graphs of R and W as in Figure 4.

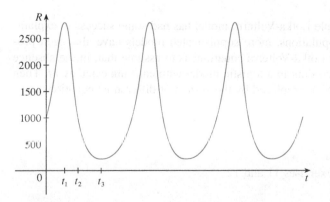

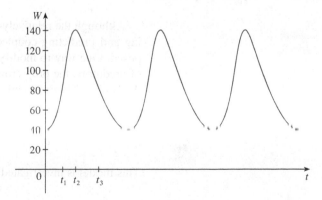

FIGURE 4 Graphs of the rabbit and wolf populations as functions of time

TEC In Module 7.6 you can change the coefficients in the Lotka-Volterra equations and observe the resulting changes in the phase trajectory and graphs of the rabbit and wolf populations.

To make the graphs easier to compare, we draw the graphs on the same axes but with different scales for R and W, as in Figure 5. Notice that the rabbits reach their maximum populations about a quarter of a cycle before the wolves.

FIGURE 5

Comparison of the rabbit and wolf populations

An important part of the modeling process, as we discussed in Section 1.2, is to interpret our mathematical conclusions as real-world predictions and to test the predictions against real data. The Hudson's Bay Company, which started trading in animal furs in Canada in 1670, has kept records that date back to the 1840s. Figure 6 shows graphs of the number of pelts of the snowshoe hare and its predator, the Canada lynx, traded by the company over a 90-year period. You can see that the coupled oscillations in the hare and lynx populations predicted by the Lotka-Volterra model do actually occur and the period of these cycles is roughly 10 years.

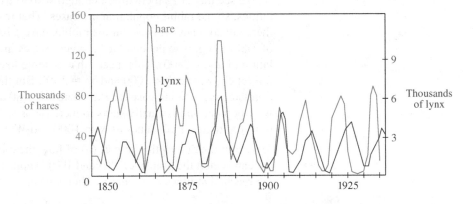

FIGURE 6

Relative abundance of hare and lynx from Hudson's Bay Company records

Although the relatively simple Lotka-Volterra model has had some success in explaining and predicting coupled populations, more sophisticated models have also been proposed. One way to modify the Lotka-Volterra equations is to assume that, in the absence of predators, the prey grow according to a logistic model with carrying capacity M. Then the Lotka-Volterra equations (1) are replaced by the system of differential equations

$$\frac{dR}{dt} = kR\left(1 - \frac{R}{M}\right) - aRW \qquad \frac{dW}{dt} = -rW + bRW$$

This model is investigated in Exercises 11 and 12.

Models have also been proposed to describe and predict population levels of two or more species that compete for the same resources or cooperate for mutual benefit. Such models are explored in Exercises 2–4.

7.6 Exercises

1. For each predator-prey system, determine which of the variables, x or y, represents the prey population and which represents the predator population. Is the growth of the prey restricted just by the predators or by other factors as well? Do the predators feed only on the prey or do they have additional food sources? Explain.

   (a) $\dfrac{dx}{dt} = -0.05x + 0.0001xy$

   $\dfrac{dy}{dt} = 0.1y - 0.005xy$

   (b) $\dfrac{dx}{dt} = 0.2x - 0.0002x^2 - 0.006xy$

   $\dfrac{dy}{dt} = -0.015y + 0.00008xy$

2. Each system of differential equations is a model for two species that either compete for the same resources or cooperate for mutual benefit (flowering plants and insect pollinators, for instance). Decide whether each system describes competition or cooperation and explain why it is a reasonable model. (Ask yourself what effect an increase in one species has on the growth rate of the other.)

   (a) $\dfrac{dx}{dt} = 0.12x - 0.0006x^2 + 0.00001xy$

   $\dfrac{dy}{dt} = 0.08x + 0.00004xy$

   (b) $\dfrac{dx}{dt} = 0.15x - 0.0002x^2 - 0.0006xy$

   $\dfrac{dy}{dt} = 0.2y - 0.00008y^2 - 0.0002xy$

3. The system of differential equations

   $$\dfrac{dx}{dt} = 0.5x - 0.004x^2 - 0.001xy$$

   $$\dfrac{dy}{dt} = 0.4y - 0.001y^2 - 0.002xy$$

   is a model for the populations of two species.
   (a) Does the model describe cooperation, or competition, or a predator-prey relationship?
   (b) Find the equilibrium solutions and explain their significance.

4. Flies, frogs, and crocodiles coexist in an environment. To survive, frogs need to eat flies and crocodiles need to eat frogs. In the absence of frogs, the fly population will grow exponentially and the crocodile population will decay exponentially. In the absence of crocodiles and flies, the frog population will decay exponentially. If $P(t)$, $Q(t)$, and $R(t)$ represent the populations of these three species at time t, write a system of differential equations as a model for their evolution. If the constants in your equation are all positive, explain why you have used plus or minus signs.

5–6 A phase trajectory is shown for populations of rabbits (R) and foxes (F).
(a) Describe how each population changes as time goes by.
(b) Use your description to make a rough sketch of the graphs of R and F as functions of time.

5.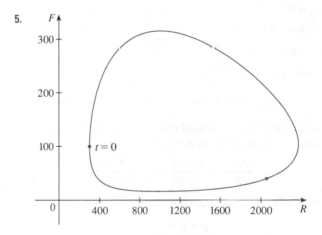

6.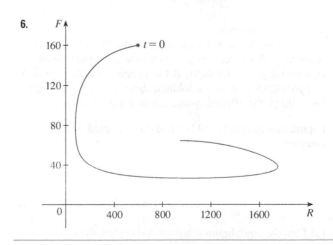

7–8 Graphs of populations of two species are shown. Use them to sketch the corresponding phase trajectory.

7.

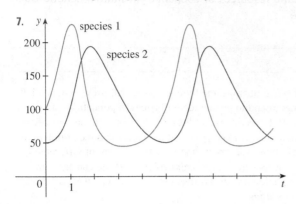

8.

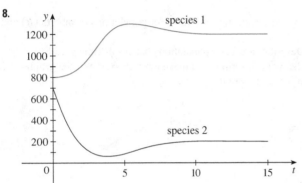

9. In Example 1(b) we showed that the rabbit and wolf populations satisfy the differential equation

$$\frac{dW}{dR} = \frac{-0.02W + 0.00002RW}{0.08R - 0.001RW}$$

By solving this separable differential equation, show that

$$\frac{R^{0.02}W^{0.08}}{e^{0.00002R}e^{0.001W}} = C$$

where C is a constant.

It is impossible to solve this equation for W as an explicit function of R (or vice versa). If you have a computer algebra system that graphs implicitly defined curves, use this equation and your CAS to draw the solution curve that passes through the point $(1000, 40)$ and compare with Figure 3.

10. Populations of aphids and ladybugs are modeled by the equations

$$\frac{dA}{dt} = 2A - 0.01AL$$

$$\frac{dL}{dt} = -0.5L + 0.0001AL$$

(a) Find the equilibrium solutions and explain their significance.
(b) Find an expression for dL/dA.

(c) The direction field for the differential equation in part (b) is shown. Use it to sketch a phase portrait. What do the phase trajectories have in common?

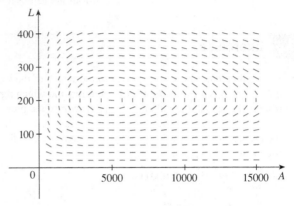

(d) Suppose that at time $t = 0$ there are 1000 aphids and 200 ladybugs. Draw the corresponding phase trajectory and use it to describe how both populations change.
(e) Use part (d) to make rough sketches of the aphid and ladybug populations as functions of t. How are the graphs related to each other?

11. In Example 1 we used Lotka-Volterra equations to model populations of rabbits and wolves. Let's modify those equations as follows:

$$\frac{dR}{dt} = 0.08R(1 - 0.0002R) - 0.001RW$$

$$\frac{dW}{dt} = -0.02W + 0.00002RW$$

(a) According to these equations, what happens to the rabbit population in the absence of wolves?
(b) Find all the equilibrium solutions and explain their significance.
(c) The figure shows the phase trajectory that starts at the point $(1000, 40)$. Describe what eventually happens to the rabbit and wolf populations.

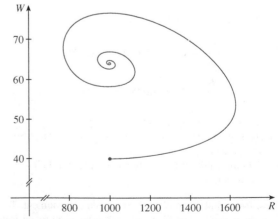

(d) Sketch graphs of the rabbit and wolf populations as functions of time.

CAS **12.** In Exercise 10 we modeled populations of aphids and lady-bugs with a Lotka-Volterra system. Suppose we modify those equations as follows:

$$\frac{dA}{dt} = 2A(1 - 0.0001A) - 0.01AL$$

$$\frac{dL}{dt} = -0.5L + 0.0001AL$$

(a) In the absence of ladybugs, what does the model predict about the aphids?

(b) Find the equilibrium solutions.
(c) Find an expression for dL/dA.
(d) Use a computer algebra system to draw a direction field for the differential equation in part (c). Then use the direction field to sketch a phase portrait. What do the phase trajectories have in common?
(e) Suppose that at time $t = 0$ there are 1000 aphids and 200 ladybugs. Draw the corresponding phase trajectory and use it to describe how both populations change.
(f) Use part (e) to make rough sketches of the aphid and ladybug populations as functions of t. How are the graphs related to each other?

7 Review

Concept Check

1. (a) What is a differential equation?
(b) What is the order of a differential equation?
(c) What is an initial condition?

2. What can you say about the solutions of the equation $y' = x^2 + y^2$ just by looking at the differential equation?

3. What is a direction field for the differential equation $y' = F(x, y)$?

4. Explain how Euler's method works.

5. What is a separable differential equation? How do you solve it?

6. (a) Write a differential equation that expresses the law of natural growth. What does it say in terms of relative growth rate?

(b) Under what circumstances is this an appropriate model for population growth?
(c) What are the solutions of this equation?

7. (a) Write the logistic equation.
(b) Under what circumstances is this an appropriate model for population growth?

8. (a) Write Lotka-Volterra equations to model populations of food fish (F) and sharks (S).
(b) What do these equations say about each population in the absence of the other?

True-False Quiz

Determine whether the statement is true or false. If it is true, explain why. If it is false, explain why or give an example that disproves the statement.

1. All solutions of the differential equation $y' = -1 - y^4$ are decreasing functions.

2. The function $f(x) = (\ln x)/x$ is a solution of the differential equation $x^2y' + xy = 1$.

3. The equation $y' - x + y$ is separable.

4. The equation $y' = 3y - 2x + 6xy - 1$ is separable.

5. If y is the solution of the initial-value problem

$$\frac{dy}{dt} = 2y\left(1 - \frac{y}{5}\right) \qquad y(0) = 1$$

then $\lim_{t \to \infty} y = 5$.

Exercises

1. (a) A direction field for the differential equation
$y' = y(y - 2)(y - 4)$ is shown. Sketch the graphs of the
solutions that satisfy the given initial conditions.
   - (i) $y(0) = -0.3$ (ii) $y(0) = 1$
   - (iii) $y(0) = 3$ (iv) $y(0) = 4.3$
   (b) If the initial condition is $y(0) = c$, for what values of
   c is $\lim_{t \to \infty} y(t)$ finite? What are the equilibrium solutions?

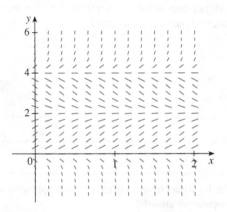

2. (a) Sketch a direction field for the differential equation
$y' = x/y$. Then use it to sketch the four solutions that
satisfy the initial conditions $y(0) = 1$, $y(0) = -1$,
$y(2) = 1$, and $y(-2) = 1$.
   (b) Check your work in part (a) by solving the differential
   equation explicitly. What type of curve is each solution
   curve?

3. (a) A direction field for the differential equation $y' = x^2 - y^2$
is shown. Sketch the solution of the initial-value problem

$$y' = x^2 - y^2 \qquad y(0) = 1$$

Use your graph to estimate the value of $y(0.3)$.

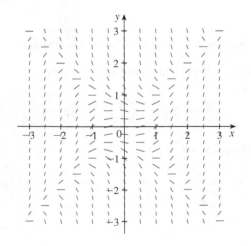

(b) Use Euler's method with step size 0.1 to estimate $y(0.3)$,
where $y(x)$ is the solution of the initial-value problem in
part (a). Compare with your estimate from part (a).
(c) On what lines are the centers of the horizontal line
segments of the direction field in part (a) located? What
happens when a solution curve crosses these lines?

4. (a) Use Euler's method with step size 0.2 to estimate $y(0.4)$,
where $y(x)$ is the solution of the initial-value problem

$$y' = 2xy^2 \qquad y(0) = 1$$

   (b) Repeat part (a) with step size 0.1.
   (c) Find the exact solution of the differential equation and
   compare the value at 0.4 with the approximations in
   parts (a) and (b).

5–6 Solve the differential equation.

5. $2ye^{y^2}y' = 2x + 3\sqrt{x}$ **6.** $\dfrac{dx}{dt} = 1 - t + x - tx$

7–8 Solve the initial-value problem.

7. $\dfrac{dr}{dt} + 2tr = r, \quad r(0) = 5$

8. $(1 + \cos x)y' = (1 + e^{-y})\sin x, \quad y(0) = 0$

9–10 Find the orthogonal trajectories of the family of curves.

9. $y = ke^x$ **10.** $y = e^{kx}$

11. A bacteria culture contains 200 cells initially and grows at a
rate proportional to its size. After half an hour the population
has increased to 360 cells.
   (a) Find the number of bacteria after t hours.
   (b) Find the number of bacteria after 4 hours.
   (c) Find the rate of growth after 4 hours.
   (d) When will the population reach 10,000?

12. Cobalt-60 has a half-life of 5.24 years.
   (a) Find the mass that remains from a 100-mg sample after
   20 years.
   (b) How long would it take for the mass to decay to 1 mg?

13. Let $C(t)$ be the concentration of a drug in the bloodstream. As
the body eliminates the drug, $C(t)$ decreases at a rate that is
proportional to the amount of the drug that is present at the
time. Thus $C'(t) = -kC(t)$, where k is a positive number called
the *elimination constant* of the drug.
   (a) If C_0 is the concentration at time $t = 0$, find the concentration at time t.
   (b) If the body eliminates half the drug in 30 hours, how long
   does it take to eliminate 90% of the drug?

14. A cup of hot chocolate has temperature 80°C in a room kept at 20°C. After half an hour the hot chocolate cools to 60°C.
(a) What is the temperature of the chocolate after another half hour?
(b) When will the chocolate have cooled to 40°C?

15. (a) Write the solution of the initial-value problem

$$\frac{dP}{dt} = 0.1P\left(1 - \frac{P}{2000}\right) \qquad P(0) = 100$$

and use it to find the population when $t = 20$.
(b) When does the population reach 1200?

16. (a) The population of the world was 5.28 billion in 1990 and 6.07 billion in 2000. Find an exponential model for these data and use the model to predict the world population in the year 2020.
(b) According to the model in part (a), when will the world population exceed 10 billion?
(c) Use the data in part (a) to find a logistic model for the population. Assume a carrying capacity of 100 billion. Then use the logistic model to predict the population in 2020. Compare with your prediction from the exponential model.
(d) According to the logistic model, when will the world population exceed 10 billion? Compare with your prediction in part (b).

17. The von Bertalanffy growth model is used to predict the length $L(t)$ of a fish over a period of time. If L_∞ is the largest length for a species, then the hypothesis is that the rate of growth in length is proportional to $L_\infty - L$, the length yet to be achieved.
(a) Formulate and solve a differential equation to find an expression for $L(t)$.
(b) For the North Sea haddock it has been determined that $L_\infty = 53$ cm, $L(0) = 10$ cm, and the constant of proportionality is 0.2. What does the expression for $L(t)$ become with these data?

18. The Brentano-Stevens Law in psychology models the way that a subject reacts to a stimulus. It states that if R represents the reaction to an amount S of stimulus, then the relative rates of increase are proportional:

$$\frac{1}{R}\frac{dR}{dt} = \frac{k}{S}\frac{dS}{dt}$$

where k is a positive constant. Find R as a function of S.

19. One model for the spread of an epidemic is that the rate of spread is jointly proportional to the number of infected people and the number of uninfected people. In an isolated town of 5000 inhabitants, 160 people have a disease at the beginning of the week and 1200 have it at the end of the week. How long does it take for 80% of the population to become infected?

20. A tank contains 100 L of pure water. Brine that contains 0.1 kg of salt per liter enters the tank at a rate of 10 L/min. The solution is kept thoroughly mixed and drains from the tank at the same rate. How much salt is in the tank after 6 minutes?

21. The transport of a substance across a capillary wall in lung physiology has been modeled by the differential equation

$$\frac{dh}{dt} = -\frac{R}{V}\left(\frac{h}{k + h}\right)$$

where h is the hormone concentration in the bloodstream, t is time, R is the maximum transport rate, V is the volume of the capillary, and k is a positive constant that measures the affinity between the hormones and the enzymes that assist the process. Solve this differential equation to find a relationship between h and t.

22. Populations of birds and insects are modeled by the equations

$$\frac{dx}{dt} = 0.4x - 0.002xy$$

$$\frac{dy}{dt} = -0.2y + 0.000008xy$$

(a) Which of the variables, x or y, represents the bird population and which represents the insect population? Explain.
(b) Find the equilibrium solutions and explain their significance.
(c) Find an expression for dy/dx.
(d) The direction field for the differential equation in part (c) is shown. Use it to sketch the phase trajectory corresponding to initial populations of 100 birds and 40,000 insects. Then use the phase trajectory to describe how both populations change.

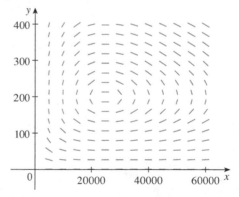

(e) Use part (d) to make rough sketches of the bird and insect populations as functions of time. How are these graphs related to each other?

23. Suppose the model of Exercise 22 is replaced by the equations

$$\frac{dx}{dt} = 0.4x(1 - 0.000005x) - 0.002xy$$

$$\frac{dy}{dt} = -0.2y + 0.000008xy$$

(a) According to these equations, what happens to the insect population in the absence of birds?
(b) Find the equilibrium solutions and explain their significance.

(c) The figure at the right shows the phase trajectory that starts with 100 birds and 40,000 insects. Describe what eventually happens to the bird and insect populations.

(d) Sketch graphs of the bird and insect populations as functions of time.

24. Barbara weighs 60 kg and is on a diet of 1600 calories per day, of which 850 are used automatically by basal metabolism. She spends about 15 cal/kg/day times her weight doing exercise. If 1 kg of fat contains 10,000 cal and we assume that the storage of calories in the form of fat is 100% efficient, formulate a differential equation and solve it to find her weight as a function of time. Does her weight ultimately approach an equilibrium weight?

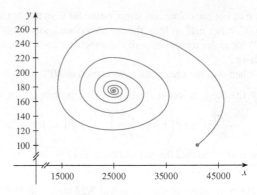

FIGURE FOR EXERCISE 23

Focus on Problem Solving

1. Find all functions f such that f' is continuous and

$$[f(x)]^2 = 100 + \int_0^x \{[f(t)]^2 + [f'(t)]^2\}\, dt \qquad \text{for all real } x$$

2. A student forgot the Product Rule for differentiation and made the mistake of thinking that $(fg)' = f'g'$. However, he was lucky and got the correct answer. The function f that he used was $f(x) = e^{x^2}$ and the domain of his problem was the interval $(\frac{1}{2}, \infty)$. What was the function g?

3. Let f be a function with the property that $f(0) = 1$, $f'(0) = 1$, and $f(a + b) = f(a)f(b)$ for all real numbers a and b. Show that $f'(x) = f(x)$ for all x and deduce that $f(x) = e^x$.

4. Find all functions f that satisfy the equation

$$\left(\int f(x)\, dx \right) \left(\int \frac{1}{f(x)}\, dx \right) = -1$$

5. Find the curve $y = f(x)$ such that $f(x) \geq 0$, $f(0) = 0$, $f(1) = 1$, and the area under the graph of f from 0 to x is proportional to the $(n + 1)$st power of $f(x)$.

6. A *subtangent* is a portion of the x-axis that lies directly beneath the segment of a tangent line from the point of contact to the x-axis. Find the curves that pass through the point $(c, 1)$ and whose subtangents all have length c.

7. A peach pie is taken out of the oven at 5:00 PM. At that time it is piping hot, 100°C. At 5:10 PM its temperature is 80°C; at 5:20 PM it is 65°C. What is the temperature of the room?

8. Snow began to fall during the morning of February 2 and continued steadily into the afternoon. At noon a snowplow began removing snow from a road at a constant rate. The plow traveled 6 km from noon to 1 PM but only 3 km from 1 PM to 2 PM. When did the snow begin to fall? [*Hints:* To get started, let t be the time measured in hours after noon; let $x(t)$ be the distance traveled by the plow at time t; then the speed of the plow is dx/dt. Let b be the number of hours before noon that it began to snow. Find an expression for the height of the snow at time t. Then use the given information that the rate of removal R (in m³/h) is constant.]

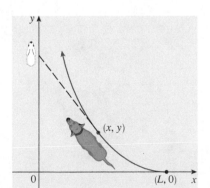

FIGURE FOR PROBLEM 9

9. A dog sees a rabbit running in a straight line across an open field and gives chase. In a rectangular coordinate system (as shown in the figure), assume:

   (i) The rabbit is at the origin and the dog is at the point $(L, 0)$ at the instant the dog first sees the rabbit.

   (ii) The rabbit runs up the y-axis and the dog always runs straight for the rabbit.

   (iii) The dog runs at the same speed as the rabbit.

(a) Show that the dog's path is the graph of the function $y = f(x)$, where y satisfies the differential equation

$$x \frac{d^2y}{dx^2} = \sqrt{1 + \left(\frac{dy}{dx} \right)^2}$$

(b) Determine the solution of the equation in part (a) that satisfies the initial conditions $y = y' = 0$ when $x = L$. [*Hint:* Let $z = dy/dx$ in the differential equation and solve the resulting first-order equation to find z; then integrate z to find y.]

(c) Does the dog ever catch the rabbit?

10. (a) Suppose that the dog in Problem 9 runs twice as fast as the rabbit. Find a differential equation for the path of the dog. Then solve it to find the point where the dog catches the rabbit.

(b) Suppose the dog runs half as fast as the rabbit. How close does the dog get to the rabbit? What are their positions when they are closest?

11. A planning engineer for a new alum plant must present some estimates to his company regarding the capacity of a silo designed to contain bauxite ore until it is processed into alum. The ore resembles pink talcum powder and is poured from a conveyor at the top of the silo. The silo is a cylinder 100 ft high with a radius of 200 ft. The conveyor carries $60{,}000\pi$ ft^3/h and the ore maintains a conical shape whose radius is 1.5 times its height.

(a) If, at a certain time t, the pile is 60 ft high, how long will it take for the pile to reach the top of the silo?

(b) Management wants to know how much room will be left in the floor area of the silo when the pile is 60 ft high. How fast is the floor area of the pile growing at that height?

(c) Suppose a loader starts removing the ore at the rate of $20{,}000\pi$ ft^3/h when the height of the pile reaches 90 ft. Suppose, also, that the pile continues to maintain its shape. How long will it take for the pile to reach the top of the silo under these conditions?

12. Find the curve that passes through the point $(3, 2)$ and has the property that if the tangent line is drawn at any point P on the curve, then the part of the tangent line that lies in the first quadrant is bisected at P.

13. Recall that the normal line to a curve at a point P on the curve is the line that passes through P and is perpendicular to the tangent line at P. Find the curve that passes through the point $(3, 2)$ and has the property that if the normal line is drawn at any point on the curve, then the y-intercept of the normal line is always 6.

14. Find all curves with the property that if the normal line is drawn at any point P on the curve, then the part of the normal line between P and the x-axis is bisected by the y-axis.

Infinite Sequences and Series

8

Infinite sequences and series were introduced briefly in *A Preview of Calculus* in connection with Zeno's paradoxes and the decimal representation of numbers. Their importance in calculus stems from Newton's idea of representing functions as sums of infinite series. For instance, in finding areas he often integrated a function by first expressing it as a series and then integrating each term of the series. We will pursue his idea in Section 8.7 in order to integrate such functions as e^{-x^2}. (Recall that we have previously been unable to do this.) Many of the functions that arise in mathematical physics and chemistry, such as Bessel functions, are defined as sums of series, so it is important to be familiar with the basic concepts of convergence of infinite sequences and series.

Physicists also use series in another way, as we will see in Section 8.8. In studying fields as diverse as optics, special relativity, and electromagnetism, they analyze phenomena by replacing a function with the first few terms in the series that represents it.

8.1 Sequences

A **sequence** can be thought of as a list of numbers written in a definite order:

$$a_1, \ a_2, \ a_3, \ a_4, \ \ldots, \ a_n, \ldots$$

The number a_1 is called the *first term,* a_2 is the *second term,* and in general a_n is the *nth term.* We will deal exclusively with infinite sequences and so each term a_n will have a successor a_{n+1}.

Notice that for every positive integer n there is a corresponding number a_n and so a sequence can be defined as a function whose domain is the set of positive integers. But we usually write a_n instead of the function notation $f(n)$ for the value of the function at the number n.

Notation: The sequence $\{a_1, a_2, a_3, \ldots\}$ is also denoted by

$$\{a_n\} \qquad \text{or} \qquad \{a_n\}_{n=1}^{\infty}$$

EXAMPLE 1 Describing sequences Some sequences can be defined by giving a formula for the nth term. In the following examples we give three descriptions of the sequence: one by using the preceding notation, another by using the defining formula, and a third by writing out the terms of the sequence. Notice that n doesn't have to start at 1.

(a) $\left\{\dfrac{n}{n+1}\right\}_{n=1}^{\infty}$ $\qquad a_n = \dfrac{n}{n+1}$ $\qquad \left\{\dfrac{1}{2}, \dfrac{2}{3}, \dfrac{3}{4}, \dfrac{4}{5}, \ldots, \dfrac{n}{n+1}, \ldots\right\}$

(b) $\left\{\dfrac{(-1)^n(n+1)}{3^n}\right\}$ $\qquad a_n = \dfrac{(-1)^n(n+1)}{3^n}$ $\qquad \left\{-\dfrac{2}{3}, \dfrac{3}{9}, -\dfrac{4}{27}, \dfrac{5}{81}, \ldots, \dfrac{(-1)^n(n+1)}{3^n}, \ldots\right\}$

(c) $\left\{\sqrt{n-3}\right\}_{n=3}^{\infty}$ $\qquad a_n = \sqrt{n-3}, \ n \geqslant 3$ $\qquad \left\{0, 1, \sqrt{2}, \sqrt{3}, \ldots, \sqrt{n-3}, \ldots\right\}$

(d) $\left\{\cos\dfrac{n\pi}{6}\right\}_{n=0}^{\infty}$ $\qquad a_n = \cos\dfrac{n\pi}{6}, \ n \geqslant 0$ $\qquad \left\{1, \dfrac{\sqrt{3}}{2}, \dfrac{1}{2}, 0, \ldots, \cos\dfrac{n\pi}{6}, \ldots\right\}$

V EXAMPLE 2 Find a formula for the general term a_n of the sequence

$$\left\{\dfrac{3}{5}, -\dfrac{4}{25}, \dfrac{5}{125}, -\dfrac{6}{625}, \dfrac{7}{3125}, \ldots\right\}$$

assuming that the pattern of the first few terms continues.

SOLUTION We are given that

$$a_1 = \dfrac{3}{5} \qquad a_2 = -\dfrac{4}{25} \qquad a_3 = \dfrac{5}{125} \qquad a_4 = -\dfrac{6}{625} \qquad a_5 = \dfrac{7}{3125}$$

Notice that the numerators of these fractions start with 3 and increase by 1 whenever we go to the next term. The second term has numerator 4, the third term has numerator 5; in general, the nth term will have numerator $n + 2$. The denominators are the powers of 5, so a_n has denominator 5^n. The signs of the terms are alternately positive and negative, so we need to multiply by a power of -1. In Example 1(b) the factor $(-1)^n$ meant we started with a negative term. Here we want to start with a positive term and so we use $(-1)^{n-1}$ or $(-1)^{n+1}$. Therefore

$$a_n = (-1)^{n-1} \frac{n+2}{5^n}$$

EXAMPLE 3 Here are some sequences that don't have simple defining equations.

(a) The sequence $\{p_n\}$, where p_n is the population of the world as of January 1 in the year n.

(b) If we let a_n be the digit in the nth decimal place of the number e, then $\{a_n\}$ is a well-defined sequence whose first few terms are

$$\{7, 1, 8, 2, 8, 1, 8, 2, 8, 4, 5, \ldots\}$$

(c) The **Fibonacci sequence** $\{f_n\}$ is defined recursively by the conditions

$$f_1 = 1 \qquad f_2 = 1 \qquad f_n = f_{n-1} + f_{n-2} \qquad n \geqslant 3$$

Each term is the sum of the two preceding terms. The first few terms are

$$\{1, 1, 2, 3, 5, 8, 13, 21, \ldots\}$$

This sequence arose when the 13th-century Italian mathematician known as Fibonacci solved a problem concerning the breeding of rabbits (see Exercise 47).

A sequence such as the one in Example 1(a), $a_n = n/(n+1)$, can be pictured either by plotting its terms on a number line, as in Figure 1, or by plotting its graph, as in Figure 2. Note that, since a sequence is a function whose domain is the set of positive integers, its graph consists of isolated points with coordinates

$$(1, a_1) \qquad (2, a_2) \qquad (3, a_3) \qquad \ldots \qquad (n, a_n) \qquad \ldots$$

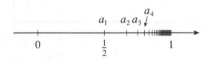

FIGURE 1

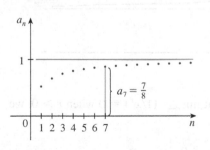

FIGURE 2

From Figure 1 or Figure 2 it appears that the terms of the sequence $a_n = n/(n+1)$ are approaching 1 as n becomes large. In fact, the difference

$$1 - \frac{n}{n+1} = \frac{1}{n+1}$$

can be made as small as we like by taking n sufficiently large. We indicate this by writing

$$\lim_{n \to \infty} a_n = \lim_{n \to \infty} \frac{n}{n+1} = 1$$

In general, the notation

$$\lim_{n \to \infty} a_n = L$$

means that the terms of the sequence $\{a_n\}$ approach L as n becomes large. Notice that the following definition of the limit of a sequence is very similar to the definition of a limit of a function at infinity given in Section 2.5.

A more precise definition of the limit of a sequence is given in Appendix D.

---

1 **Definition**   A sequence $\{a_n\}$ has the **limit** L and we write

$$\lim_{n \to \infty} a_n = L \qquad \text{or} \qquad a_n \to L \text{ as } n \to \infty$$

if we can make the terms a_n as close to L as we like by taking n sufficiently large. If $\lim_{n\to\infty} a_n$ exists, we say the sequence **converges** (or is **convergent**). Otherwise, we say the sequence **diverges** (or is **divergent**).

Figure 3 illustrates Definition 1 by showing the graphs of two sequences that have the limit L.

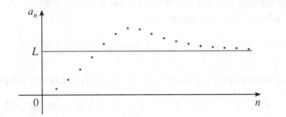
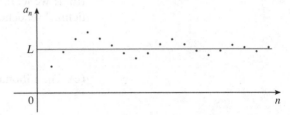

FIGURE 3
Graphs of two sequences with $\lim\limits_{n \to \infty} a_n = L$

If you compare Definition 1 with Definition 2.5.4 you will see that the only difference between $\lim_{n\to\infty} a_n = L$ and $\lim_{x\to\infty} f(x) = L$ is that n is required to be an integer. Thus we have the following theorem, which is illustrated by Figure 4.

---

2 **Theorem**   If $\lim_{x\to\infty} f(x) = L$ and $f(n) = a_n$ when n is an integer, then $\lim_{n\to\infty} a_n = L$.

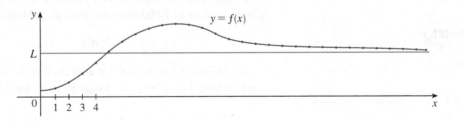

FIGURE 4

In particular, since we know from Section 2.5 that $\lim_{x\to\infty} (1/x^r) = 0$ when $r > 0$, we have

3 $$\lim_{n \to \infty} \frac{1}{n^r} = 0 \qquad \text{if } r > 0$$

If a_n becomes large as n becomes large, we use the notation

$$\lim_{n \to \infty} a_n = \infty$$

In this case the sequence $\{a_n\}$ is divergent, but in a special way. We say that $\{a_n\}$ diverges to ∞.

The Limit Laws given in Section 2.3 also hold for the limits of sequences and their proofs are similar.

Limit Laws for Sequences

If $\{a_n\}$ and $\{b_n\}$ are convergent sequences and c is a constant, then

$$\lim_{n \to \infty} (a_n + b_n) = \lim_{n \to \infty} a_n + \lim_{n \to \infty} b_n$$

$$\lim_{n \to \infty} (a_n - b_n) = \lim_{n \to \infty} a_n - \lim_{n \to \infty} b_n$$

$$\lim_{n \to \infty} ca_n = c \lim_{n \to \infty} a_n \qquad\qquad \lim_{n \to \infty} c = c$$

$$\lim_{n \to \infty} (a_n b_n) = \lim_{n \to \infty} a_n \cdot \lim_{n \to \infty} b_n$$

$$\lim_{n \to \infty} \frac{a_n}{b_n} = \frac{\lim\limits_{n \to \infty} a_n}{\lim\limits_{n \to \infty} b_n} \quad \text{if } \lim_{n \to \infty} b_n \neq 0$$

$$\lim_{n \to \infty} a_n^p = \left[\lim_{n \to \infty} a_n \right]^p \quad \text{if } p > 0 \text{ and } a_n > 0$$

The Squeeze Theorem can also be adapted for sequences as follows (see Figure 5).

Squeeze Theorem for Sequences

If $a_n \leqslant b_n \leqslant c_n$ for $n \geqslant n_0$ and $\lim\limits_{n \to \infty} a_n = \lim\limits_{n \to \infty} c_n = L$, then $\lim\limits_{n \to \infty} b_n = L$.

Another useful fact about limits of sequences is given by the following theorem, which follows from the Squeeze Theorem because $-|a_n| \leqslant a_n \leqslant |a_n|$.

4 Theorem If $\lim\limits_{n \to \infty} |a_n| = 0$, then $\lim\limits_{n \to \infty} a_n = 0$.

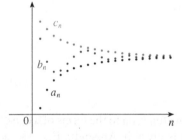

FIGURE 5
The sequence $\{b_n\}$ is squeezed between the sequences $\{a_n\}$ and $\{c_n\}$.

EXAMPLE 4 Find $\lim\limits_{n \to \infty} \dfrac{n}{n + 1}$.

SOLUTION The method is similar to the one we used in Section 2.5: Divide numerator and denominator by the highest power of n that occurs in the denominator and then use the Limit Laws.

$$\lim_{n \to \infty} \frac{n}{n + 1} = \lim_{n \to \infty} \frac{1}{1 + \dfrac{1}{n}} = \frac{\lim\limits_{n \to \infty} 1}{\lim\limits_{n \to \infty} 1 + \lim\limits_{n \to \infty} \dfrac{1}{n}}$$

$$= \frac{1}{1 + 0} = 1$$

This shows that the guess we made earlier from Figures 1 and 2 was correct.

Here we used Equation 3 with $r = 1$.

EXAMPLE 5 **Applying l'Hospital's Rule to a related function** Calculate $\lim\limits_{n \to \infty} \dfrac{\ln n}{n}$.

SOLUTION Notice that both numerator and denominator approach infinity as $n \to \infty$. We can't apply l'Hospital's Rule directly because it applies not to sequences but to functions of a real variable. However, we can apply l'Hospital's Rule to the related function $f(x) = (\ln x)/x$ and obtain

$$\lim_{x \to \infty} \frac{\ln x}{x} = \lim_{x \to \infty} \frac{1/x}{1} = 0$$

Therefore, by Theorem 2, we have

$$\lim_{n \to \infty} \frac{\ln n}{n} = 0$$

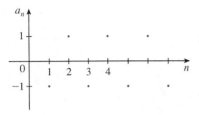

FIGURE 6

EXAMPLE 6 Determine whether the sequence $a_n = (-1)^n$ is convergent or divergent.

SOLUTION If we write out the terms of the sequence, we obtain

$$\{-1, 1, -1, 1, -1, 1, -1, \ldots\}$$

The graph of this sequence is shown in Figure 6. Since the terms oscillate between 1 and -1 infinitely often, a_n does not approach any number. Thus $\lim_{n \to \infty} (-1)^n$ does not exist; that is, the sequence $\{(-1)^n\}$ is divergent.

The graph of the sequence in Example 7 is shown in Figure 7 and supports the answer.

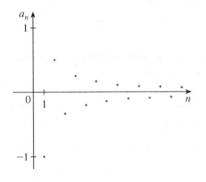

FIGURE 7

EXAMPLE 7 Evaluate $\lim_{n \to \infty} \dfrac{(-1)^n}{n}$ if it exists.

SOLUTION We first calculate the limit of the absolute value:

$$\lim_{n \to \infty} \left| \frac{(-1)^n}{n} \right| = \lim_{n \to \infty} \frac{1}{n} = 0$$

Therefore, by Theorem 4,

$$\lim_{n \to \infty} \frac{(-1)^n}{n} = 0$$

The following theorem says that if we apply a continuous function to the terms of a convergent sequence, the result is also convergent. The proof is given in Appendix E.

---

5 **Theorem** If $\lim\limits_{n \to \infty} a_n = L$ and the function f is continuous at L, then

$$\lim_{n \to \infty} f(a_n) = f(L)$$

EXAMPLE 8 Find $\lim\limits_{n \to \infty} \sin(\pi/n)$.

SOLUTION Because the sine function is continuous at 0, Theorem 5 enables us to write

$$\lim_{n \to \infty} \sin(\pi/n) = \sin\left(\lim_{n \to \infty} (\pi/n) \right) = \sin 0 = 0$$

▼ EXAMPLE 9 **Using the Squeeze Theorem** Discuss the convergence of the sequence $a_n = n!/n^n$, where $n! = 1 \cdot 2 \cdot 3 \cdot \cdots \cdot n$.

SOLUTION Both numerator and denominator approach infinity as $n \to \infty$ but here we have no corresponding function for use with l'Hospital's Rule ($x!$ is not defined when x is not an integer). Let's write out a few terms to get a feeling for what happens to a_n

Creating Graphs of Sequences

Some computer algebra systems have special commands that enable us to create sequences and graph them directly. With most graphing calculators, however, sequences can be graphed by using parametric equations. For instance, the sequence in Example 9 can be graphed by entering the parametric equations

$$x = t \qquad y = t!/t^t$$

and graphing in dot mode, starting with $t = 1$ and setting the t-step equal to 1. The result is shown in Figure 8.

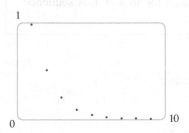

FIGURE 8

as n gets large:

$$a_1 = 1 \qquad a_2 = \frac{1 \cdot 2}{2 \cdot 2} \qquad a_3 = \frac{1 \cdot 2 \cdot 3}{3 \cdot 3 \cdot 3}$$

$$\boxed{6} \qquad\qquad a_n = \frac{1 \cdot 2 \cdot 3 \cdot \,\cdots\, \cdot n}{n \cdot n \cdot n \cdot \,\cdots\, \cdot n}$$

It appears from these expressions and the graph in Figure 8 that the terms are decreasing and perhaps approach 0. To confirm this, observe from Equation 6 that

$$a_n = \frac{1}{n} \left(\frac{2 \cdot 3 \cdot \,\cdots\, \cdot n}{n \cdot n \cdot \,\cdots\, \cdot n} \right)$$

Notice that the expression in parentheses is at most 1 because the numerator is less than (or equal to) the denominator. So

$$0 < a_n \leqslant \frac{1}{n}$$

We know that $1/n \to 0$ as $n \to \infty$. Therefore $a_n \to 0$ as $n \to \infty$ by the Squeeze Theorem.

▼ EXAMPLE 10 **Limit of a geometric sequence** For what values of r is the sequence $\{r^n\}$ convergent?

SOLUTION We know from Section 2.5 and the graphs of the exponential functions in Section 1.5 that $\lim_{x \to \infty} a^x = \infty$ for $a > 1$ and $\lim_{x \to \infty} a^x = 0$ for $0 < a < 1$. Therefore, putting $a = r$ and using Theorem 2, we have

$$\lim_{n \to \infty} r^n = \begin{cases} \infty & \text{if } r > 1 \\ 0 & \text{if } 0 < r < 1 \end{cases}$$

For the cases $r = 1$ and $r = 0$ we have

$$\lim_{n \to \infty} 1^n = \lim_{n \to \infty} 1 = 1 \qquad \text{and} \qquad \lim_{n \to \infty} 0^n = \lim_{n \to \infty} 0 = 0$$

If $-1 < r < 0$, then $0 < |r| < 1$, so

$$\lim_{n \to \infty} |r^n| = \lim_{n \to \infty} |r|^n = 0$$

and therefore $\lim_{n \to \infty} r^n = 0$ by Theorem 4. If $r \leqslant -1$, then $\{r^n\}$ diverges as in Example 6. Figure 9 shows the graphs for various values of r. (The case $r = -1$ is shown in Figure 6.)

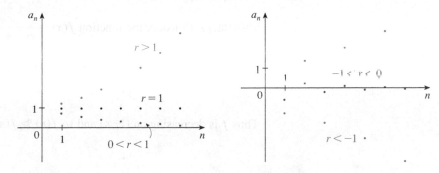

FIGURE 9

The sequence $a_n = r^n$

The results of Example 10 are summarized for future use as follows.

$\boxed{7}$ The sequence $\{r^n\}$ is convergent if $-1 < r \le 1$ and divergent for all other values of r.

$$\lim_{n \to \infty} r^n = \begin{cases} 0 & \text{if } -1 < r < 1 \\ 1 & \text{if } r = 1 \end{cases}$$

Definition A sequence $\{a_n\}$ is called **increasing** if $a_n < a_{n+1}$ for all $n \ge 1$, that is, $a_1 < a_2 < a_3 < \cdots$. It is called **decreasing** if $a_n > a_{n+1}$ for all $n \ge 1$. A sequence is **monotonic** if it is either increasing or decreasing.

EXAMPLE 11 The sequence $\left\{ \dfrac{3}{n+5} \right\}$ is decreasing because

The right side is smaller because it has a larger denominator.

$$\frac{3}{n+5} > \frac{3}{(n+1)+5} = \frac{3}{n+6}$$

and so $a_n > a_{n+1}$ for all $n \ge 1$.

EXAMPLE 12 Show that the sequence $a_n = \dfrac{n}{n^2+1}$ is decreasing.

SOLUTION 1 We must show that $a_{n+1} < a_n$, that is,

$$\frac{n+1}{(n+1)^2+1} < \frac{n}{n^2+1}$$

This inequality is equivalent to the one we get by cross-multiplication:

$$\frac{n+1}{(n+1)^2+1} < \frac{n}{n^2+1} \iff (n+1)(n^2+1) < n[(n+1)^2+1]$$

$$\iff n^3 + n^2 + n + 1 < n^3 + 2n^2 + 2n$$

$$\iff 1 < n^2 + n$$

Since $n \ge 1$, we know that the inequality $n^2 + n > 1$ is true. Therefore $a_{n+1} < a_n$ and so $\{a_n\}$ is decreasing.

SOLUTION 2 Consider the function $f(x) = \dfrac{x}{x^2+1}$.

$$f'(x) = \frac{x^2+1-2x^2}{(x^2+1)^2} = \frac{1-x^2}{(x^2+1)^2} < 0 \qquad \text{whenever } x^2 > 1$$

Thus f is decreasing on $(1, \infty)$ and so $f(n) > f(n+1)$. Therefore $\{a_n\}$ is decreasing.

> **Definition** A sequence $\{a_n\}$ is **bounded above** if there is a number M such that
>
> $$a_n \leqslant M \qquad \text{for all } n \geqslant 1$$
>
> It is **bounded below** if there is a number m such that
>
> $$m \leqslant a_n \qquad \text{for all } n \geqslant 1$$
>
> If it is bounded above and below, then $\{a_n\}$ is a **bounded sequence**.

For instance, the sequence $a_n = n$ is bounded below $(a_n > 0)$ but not above. The sequence $a_n = n/(n + 1)$ is bounded because $0 < a_n < 1$ for all n.

We know that not every bounded sequence is convergent [for instance, the sequence $a_n = (-1)^n$ satisfies $-1 \leqslant a_n \leqslant 1$ but is divergent, from Example 6] and not every monotonic sequence is convergent $(a_n = n \to \infty)$. But if a sequence is both bounded *and* monotonic, then it must be convergent. This fact is stated without proof as Theorem 8, but intuitively you can understand why it is true by looking at Figure 10. If $\{a_n\}$ is increasing and $a_n \leqslant M$ for all n, then the terms are forced to crowd together and approach some number L.

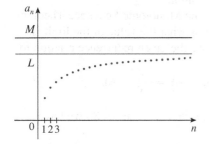

FIGURE 10

> $\boxed{8}$ **Monotonic Sequence Theorem** Every bounded, monotonic sequence is convergent.

EXAMPLE 13 **The limit of a recursively defined sequence**   Investigate the sequence $\{a_n\}$ defined by the *recurrence relation*

$$a_1 = 2 \qquad a_{n+1} = \tfrac{1}{2}(a_n + 6) \qquad \text{for } n = 1, 2, 3, \ldots$$

SOLUTION We begin by computing the first several terms:

$$a_1 = 2 \qquad\qquad a_2 = \tfrac{1}{2}(2 + 6) = 4 \qquad a_3 = \tfrac{1}{2}(4 + 6) = 5$$

$$a_4 = \tfrac{1}{2}(5 + 6) = 5.5 \qquad a_5 = 5.75 \qquad\qquad a_6 = 5.875$$

$$a_7 = 5.9375 \qquad\qquad a_8 = 5.96875 \qquad\qquad a_9 = 5.984375$$

Mathematical induction is often used in dealing with recursive sequences. See page 84 for a discussion of the Principle of Mathematical Induction.

These initial terms suggest that the sequence is increasing and the terms are approaching 6. To confirm that the sequence is increasing, we use mathematical induction to show that $a_{n+1} > a_n$ for all $n \geqslant 1$. This is true for $n = 1$ because $a_2 = 4 > a_1$. If we assume that it is true for $n = k$, then we have

$$a_{k+1} > a_k$$

so

$$a_{k+1} + 6 > a_k + 6$$

and

$$\tfrac{1}{2}(a_{k+1} + 6) > \tfrac{1}{2}(a_k + 6)$$

Thus

$$a_{k+2} > a_{k+1}$$

We have deduced that $a_{n+1} > a_n$ is true for $n = k + 1$. Therefore the inequality is true for all n by induction.

Next we verify that $\{a_n\}$ is bounded by showing that $a_n < 6$ for all n. (Since the sequence is increasing, we already know that it has a lower bound: $a_n \geqslant a_1 = 2$ for all n.) We know that $a_1 < 6$, so the assertion is true for $n = 1$. Suppose it is true for $n = k$. Then

$$a_k < 6$$

so

$$a_k + 6 < 12$$

and

$$\tfrac{1}{2}(a_k + 6) < \tfrac{1}{2}(12) = 6$$

Thus

$$a_{k+1} < 6$$

This shows, by mathematical induction, that $a_n < 6$ for all n.

Since the sequence $\{a_n\}$ is increasing and bounded, the Monotonic Sequence Theorem guarantees that it has a limit. The theorem doesn't tell us what the value of the limit is. But now that we know $L = \lim_{n \to \infty} a_n$ exists, we can use the given recurrence relation to write

$$\lim_{n \to \infty} a_{n+1} = \lim_{n \to \infty} \tfrac{1}{2}(a_n + 6) = \tfrac{1}{2}\left(\lim_{n \to \infty} a_n + 6\right) = \tfrac{1}{2}(L + 6)$$

Since $a_n \to L$, it follows that $a_{n+1} \to L$ too (as $n \to \infty$, $n + 1 \to \infty$ also). So we have

$$L = \tfrac{1}{2}(L + 6)$$

Solving this equation for L, we get $L = 6$, as we predicted.

8.1 Exercises

1. (a) What is a sequence?
   (b) What does it mean to say that $\lim_{n \to \infty} a_n = 8$?
   (c) What does it mean to say that $\lim_{n \to \infty} a_n = \infty$?

2. (a) What is a convergent sequence? Give two examples.
   (b) What is a divergent sequence? Give two examples.

3. List the first six terms of the sequence defined by

$$a_n = \frac{n}{2n + 1}$$

Does the sequence appear to have a limit? If so, find it.

4. List the first nine terms of the sequence $\{\cos(n\pi/3)\}$. Does this sequence appear to have a limit? If so, find it. If not, explain why.

5–10 Find a formula for the general term a_n of the sequence, assuming that the pattern of the first few terms continues.

5. $\left\{1, \tfrac{1}{3}, \tfrac{1}{5}, \tfrac{1}{7}, \tfrac{1}{9}, \ldots\right\}$

6. $\left\{1, \tfrac{1}{3}, \tfrac{1}{9}, \tfrac{1}{27}, \tfrac{1}{81}, \ldots\right\}$

7. $\{2, 7, 12, 17, \ldots\}$

8. $\left\{-\tfrac{1}{4}, \tfrac{2}{9}, -\tfrac{3}{16}, \tfrac{4}{25}, \ldots\right\}$

9. $\left\{1, -\tfrac{2}{3}, \tfrac{4}{9}, -\tfrac{8}{27}, \ldots\right\}$

10. $\{5, 1, 5, 1, 5, 1, \ldots\}$

11–34 Determine whether the sequence converges or diverges. If it converges, find the limit.

11. $a_n = \dfrac{3 + 5n^2}{n + n^2}$

12. $a_n = \dfrac{n^3}{n^3 + 1}$

13. $a_n = 1 - (0.2)^n$

14. $a_n = \dfrac{n^3}{n + 1}$

15. $a_n = e^{1/n}$

16. $a_n = \dfrac{3^{n+2}}{5^n}$

17. $a_n = \tan\left(\dfrac{2n\pi}{1 + 8n}\right)$

18. $a_n = \sqrt{\dfrac{n + 1}{9n + 1}}$

19. $a_n = \dfrac{(-1)^{n-1}n}{n^2 + 1}$

20. $a_n = \dfrac{(-1)^n n^3}{n^3 + 2n^2 + 1}$

21. $\left\{\dfrac{e^n + e^{-n}}{e^{2n} - 1}\right\}$

22. $a_n = \cos(2/n)$

---

23. $\{n^2 e^{-n}\}$

24. $\{\arctan 2n\}$

25. $a_n = \dfrac{\cos^2 n}{2^n}$

26. $\{n \cos n\pi\}$

27. $a_n = \left(1 + \dfrac{2}{n}\right)^n$

28. $a_n = \sqrt[n]{2^{1+3n}}$

29. $\left\{\dfrac{(2n-1)!}{(2n+1)!}\right\}$

30. $a_n = \dfrac{\sin 2n}{1 + \sqrt{n}}$

31. $\{0, 1, 0, 0, 1, 0, 0, 0, 1, \ldots\}$

32. $a_n = \dfrac{(\ln n)^2}{n}$

33. $a_n = \ln(2n^2 + 1) - \ln(n^2 + 1)$

34. $a_n = \dfrac{(-3)^n}{n!}$

35-40 Use a graph of the sequence to decide whether the sequence is convergent or divergent. If the sequence is convergent, guess the value of the limit from the graph and then prove your guess. (See the margin note on page 559 for advice on graphing sequences.)

35. $a_n = 1 + (-2/e)^n$

36. $a_n = \sqrt{n}\,\sin(\pi/\sqrt{n})$

37. $a_n = \sqrt{\dfrac{3 + 2n^2}{8n^2 + n}}$

38. $a_n = \sqrt[n]{3^n + 5^n}$

39. $a_n = \dfrac{n^2 \cos n}{1 + n^2}$

40. $a_n = \dfrac{1 \cdot 3 \cdot 5 \cdot \cdots \cdot (2n-1)}{(2n)^n}$

41. If \$1000 is invested at 6% interest, compounded annually, then after n years the investment is worth $a_n = 1000(1.06)^n$ dollars.
(a) Find the first five terms of the sequence $\{a_n\}$.
(b) Is the sequence convergent or divergent? Explain.

42. If you deposit \$100 at the end of every month into an account that pays 3% interest per year compounded monthly, the amount of interest accumulated after n months is given by the sequence

$$I_n = 100\left(\dfrac{1.0025^n - 1}{0.0025} - n\right)$$

(a) Find the first six terms of the sequence.
(b) How much interest will you have earned after two years?

43. A fish farmer has 5000 catfish in his pond. The number of catfish increases by 8% per month and the farmer harvests 300 catfish per month.
(a) Show that the catfish population P_n after n months is given recursively by

$$P_n = 1.08 P_{n-1} - 300 \qquad P_0 = 5000$$

(b) How many catfish are in the pond after six months?

44. Find the first 40 terms of the sequence defined by

$$a_{n+1} = \begin{cases} \frac{1}{2} a_n & \text{if } a_n \text{ is an even number} \\ 3a_n + 1 & \text{if } a_n \text{ is an odd number} \end{cases}$$

and $a_1 = 11$. Do the same if $a_1 = 25$. Make a conjecture about this type of sequence.

45. (a) Determine whether the sequence defined as follows is convergent or divergent:

$$a_1 = 1 \qquad a_{n+1} = 4 - a_n \quad \text{for } n \geqslant 1$$

(b) What happens if the first term is $a_1 = 2$?

46. (a) If $\lim_{n\to\infty} a_n = L$, what is the value of $\lim_{n\to\infty} a_{n+1}$?
(b) A sequence $\{a_n\}$ is defined by

$$a_1 = 1 \qquad a_{n+1} = 1/(1 + a_n) \quad \text{for } n \geqslant 1$$

Find the first ten terms of the sequence correct to five decimal places. Does it appear that the sequence is convergent? If so, estimate the value of the limit to three decimal places.
(c) Assuming that the sequence in part (b) has a limit, use part (a) to find its exact value. Compare with your estimate from part (b).

47. (a) Fibonacci posed the following problem: Suppose that rabbits live forever and that every month each pair produces a new pair which becomes productive at age 2 months. If we start with one newborn pair, how many pairs of rabbits will we have in the nth month? Show that the answer is f_n, where $\{f_n\}$ is the Fibonacci sequence defined in Example 3(c).
(b) Let $a_n = f_{n+1}/f_n$ and show that $a_{n-1} = 1 + 1/a_{n-2}$. Assuming that $\{a_n\}$ is convergent, find its limit.

48. Find the limit of the sequence

$$\left\{\sqrt{2}, \sqrt{2\sqrt{2}}, \sqrt{2\sqrt{2\sqrt{2}}}, \ldots\right\}$$

49-52 Determine whether the sequence is increasing, decreasing, or not monotonic. Is the sequence bounded?

49. $a_n = \dfrac{1}{2n + 3}$

50. $a_n = \dfrac{2n - 3}{3n + 4}$

51. $a_n = n(-1)^n$

52. $a_n = n + \dfrac{1}{n}$

---

53. Suppose you know that $\{a_n\}$ is a decreasing sequence and all its terms lie between the numbers 5 and 8. Explain why the sequence has a limit. What can you say about the value of the limit?

54. A sequence $\{a_n\}$ is given by $a_1 = \sqrt{2}$, $a_{n+1} = \sqrt{2 + a_n}$.
(a) By induction or otherwise, show that $\{a_n\}$ is increasing and bounded above by 3. Apply the Monotonic Sequence Theorem to show that $\lim_{n\to\infty} a_n$ exists.
(b) Find $\lim_{n\to\infty} a_n$.

55. Show that the sequence defined by

$$a_1 = 1 \qquad a_{n+1} = 3 - \frac{1}{a_n}$$

is increasing and $a_n < 3$ for all n. Deduce that $\{a_n\}$ is convergent and find its limit.

56. Show that the sequence defined by

$$a_1 = 2 \qquad a_{n+1} = \frac{1}{3 - a_n}$$

satisfies $0 < a_n \leq 2$ and is decreasing. Deduce that the sequence is convergent and find its limit.

57. We know that $\lim_{n \to \infty} (0.8)^n = 0$ [from (7) with $r = 0.8$]. Use logarithms to determine how large n has to be so that $(0.8)^n < 0.000001$.

58. (a) Let $a_1 = a$, $a_2 = f(a)$, $a_3 = f(a_2) = f(f(a))$, ..., $a_{n+1} = f(a_n)$, where f is a continuous function. If $\lim_{n \to \infty} a_n = L$, show that $f(L) = L$.
(b) Illustrate part (a) by taking $f(x) = \cos x$, $a = 1$, and estimating the value of L to five decimal places.

59. The size of an undisturbed fish population has been modeled by the formula

$$p_{n+1} = \frac{bp_n}{a + p_n}$$

where p_n is the fish population after n years and a and b are positive constants that depend on the species and its environment. Suppose that the population in year 0 is $p_0 > 0$.
(a) Show that if $\{p_n\}$ is convergent, then the only possible values for its limit are 0 and $b - a$.
(b) Show that $p_{n+1} < (b/a)p_n$.
(c) Use part (b) to show that if $a > b$, then $\lim_{n \to \infty} p_n = 0$; in other words, the population dies out.
(d) Now assume that $a < b$. Show that if $p_0 < b - a$, then $\{p_n\}$ is increasing and $0 < p_n < b - a$. Show also that if $p_0 > b - a$, then $\{p_n\}$ is decreasing and $p_n > b - a$. Deduce that if $a < b$, then $\lim_{n \to \infty} p_n = b - a$.

60. A sequence is defined recursively by

$$a_1 = 1 \qquad a_{n+1} = 1 + \frac{1}{1 + a_n}$$

Find the first eight terms of the sequence $\{a_n\}$. What do you notice about the odd terms and the even terms? By considering the odd and even terms separately, show that $\{a_n\}$ is convergent and deduce that

$$\lim_{n \to \infty} a_n = \sqrt{2}$$

This gives the **continued fraction expansion**

$$\sqrt{2} = 1 + \cfrac{1}{2 + \cfrac{1}{2 + \cdots}}$$

LABORATORY PROJECT   [CAS] **Logistic Sequences**

A sequence that arises in ecology as a model for population growth is defined by the **logistic difference equation**

$$p_{n+1} = kp_n(1 - p_n)$$

where p_n measures the size of the population of the nth generation of a single species. To keep the numbers manageable, p_n is a fraction of the maximal size of the population, so $0 \leq p_n \leq 1$. Notice that the form of this equation is similar to the logistic differential equation in Section 7.5. The discrete model—with sequences instead of continuous functions—is preferable for modeling insect populations, where mating and death occur in a periodic fashion.

An ecologist is interested in predicting the size of the population as time goes on, and asks these questions: Will it stabilize at a limiting value? Will it change in a cyclical fashion? Or will it exhibit random behavior?

Write a program to compute the first n terms of this sequence starting with an initial population p_0, where $0 < p_0 < 1$. Use this program to do the following.

1. Calculate 20 or 30 terms of the sequence for $p_0 = \frac{1}{2}$ and for two values of k such that $1 < k < 3$. Graph each sequence. Do the sequences appear to converge? Repeat for a different value of p_0 between 0 and 1. Does the limit depend on the choice of p_0? Does it depend on the choice of k?

2. Calculate terms of the sequence for a value of k between 3 and 3.4 and plot them. What do you notice about the behavior of the terms?

[CAS] Computer algebra system required

3. Experiment with values of k between 3.4 and 3.5. What happens to the terms?

4. For values of k between 3.6 and 4, compute and plot at least 100 terms and comment on the behavior of the sequence. What happens if you change p_0 by 0.001? This type of behavior is called *chaotic* and is exhibited by insect populations under certain conditions.

8.2 | Series

What do we mean when we express a number as an infinite decimal? For instance, what does it mean to write

$$\pi = 3.14159\ 26535\ 89793\ 23846\ 26433\ 83279\ 50288\ldots$$

The current record (2011) is that π has been computed to more than ten trillion decimal places by Shigeru Kondo and Alexander Yee.

The convention behind our decimal notation is that any number can be written as an infinite sum. Here it means that

$$\pi = 3 + \frac{1}{10} + \frac{4}{10^2} + \frac{1}{10^3} + \frac{5}{10^4} + \frac{9}{10^5} + \frac{2}{10^6} + \frac{6}{10^7} + \frac{5}{10^8} + \cdots$$

where the three dots $(\cdots)$ indicate that the sum continues forever, and the more terms we add, the closer we get to the actual value of π.

In general, if we try to add the terms of an infinite sequence $\{a_n\}_{n=1}^{\infty}$ we get an expression of the form

$$\boxed{1} \qquad a_1 + a_2 + a_3 + \cdots + a_n + \cdots$$

which is called an **infinite series** (or just a **series**) and is denoted, for short, by the symbol

$$\sum_{n=1}^{\infty} a_n \qquad \text{or} \qquad \sum a_n$$

Does it make sense to talk about the sum of infinitely many terms?

It would be impossible to find a finite sum for the series

$$1 + 2 + 3 + 4 + 5 + \cdots + n + \cdots$$

because if we start adding the terms we get the cumulative sums 1, 3, 6, 10, 15, 21, ... and, after the nth term, we get $n(n + 1)/2$, which becomes very large as n increases.

However, if we start to add the terms of the series

$$\frac{1}{2} + \frac{1}{4} + \frac{1}{8} + \frac{1}{16} + \frac{1}{32} + \frac{1}{64} + \cdots + \frac{1}{2^n} + \cdots$$

n	Sum of first n terms
1	0.50000000
2	0.75000000
3	0.87500000
4	0.93750000
5	0.96875000
6	0.98437500
7	0.99218750
10	0.99902344
15	0.99996948
20	0.99999905
25	0.99999997

we get $\frac{1}{2}, \frac{3}{4}, \frac{7}{8}, \frac{15}{16}, \frac{31}{32}, \frac{63}{64}, \ldots, 1 - 1/2^n, \ldots$ The table shows that as we add more and more terms, these *partial sums* become closer and closer to 1. (See also Figure 11 in *A Preview of Calculus*, page 6.) In fact, by adding sufficiently many terms of the series we can make the partial sums as close as we like to 1. So it seems reasonable to say that the sum of this infinite series is 1 and to write

$$\sum_{n=1}^{\infty} \frac{1}{2^n} = \frac{1}{2} + \frac{1}{4} + \frac{1}{8} + \frac{1}{16} + \cdots + \frac{1}{2^n} + \cdots = 1$$

We use a similar idea to determine whether or not a general series (1) has a sum. We consider the **partial sums**

$$s_1 = a_1$$

$$s_2 = a_1 + a_2$$

$$s_3 = a_1 + a_2 + a_3$$

$$s_4 = a_1 + a_2 + a_3 + a_4$$

and, in general,

$$s_n = a_1 + a_2 + a_3 + \cdots + a_n = \sum_{i=1}^{n} a_i$$

These partial sums form a new sequence $\{s_n\}$, which may or may not have a limit. If $\lim_{n \to \infty} s_n = s$ exists (as a finite number), then, as in the preceding example, we call it the sum of the infinite series $\Sigma \, a_n$.

---

2 **Definition** Given a series $\sum_{n=1}^{\infty} a_n = a_1 + a_2 + a_3 + \cdots$, let s_n denote its nth partial sum:

$$s_n = \sum_{i=1}^{n} a_i = a_1 + a_2 + \cdots + a_n$$

If the sequence $\{s_n\}$ is convergent and $\lim_{n \to \infty} s_n = s$ exists as a real number, then the series $\Sigma \, a_n$ is called **convergent** and we write

$$a_1 + a_2 + \cdots + a_n + \cdots = s \qquad \text{or} \qquad \sum_{n=1}^{\infty} a_n = s$$

The number s is called the **sum** of the series. If the sequence $\{s_n\}$ is divergent, then the series is called **divergent**.

Thus the sum of a series is the limit of the sequence of partial sums. So when we write $\sum_{n=1}^{\infty} a_n = s$ we mean that by adding sufficiently many terms of the series we can get as close as we like to the number s. Notice that

$$\sum_{n=1}^{\infty} a_n = \lim_{n \to \infty} \sum_{i=1}^{n} a_i$$

Compare with the improper integral

$$\int_{1}^{\infty} f(x)\, dx = \lim_{t \to \infty} \int_{1}^{t} f(x)\, dx$$

To find this integral we integrate from 1 to t and then let $t \to \infty$. For a series, we sum from 1 to n and then let $n \to \infty$.

EXAMPLE 1 An important example of an infinite series is the **geometric series**

$$a + ar + ar^2 + ar^3 + \cdots + ar^{n-1} + \cdots = \sum_{n=1}^{\infty} ar^{n-1} \qquad a \neq 0$$

Each term is obtained from the preceding one by multiplying it by the **common ratio** r. (We have already considered the special case where $a = \frac{1}{2}$ and $r = \frac{1}{2}$ on page 565.)

If $r = 1$, then $s_n = a + a + \cdots + a = na \to \pm\infty$. Since $\lim_{n \to \infty} s_n$ doesn't exist, the geometric series diverges in this case.

If $r \neq 1$, we have

$$s_n = a + ar + ar^2 + \cdots + ar^{n-1}$$

and

$$rs_n = \qquad ar + ar^2 + \cdots + ar^{n-1} + ar^n$$

Figure 1 provides a geometric demonstration of the result in Example 1. If the triangles are constructed as shown and s is the sum of the series, then, by similar triangles,

$$\frac{s}{a} = \frac{a}{a - ar} \qquad \text{so} \qquad s = \frac{a}{1 - r}$$

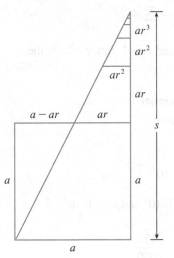

FIGURE 1

In words: The sum of a convergent geometric series is

$$\frac{\text{first term}}{1 - \text{common ratio}}$$

Subtracting these equations, we get

$$s_n - rs_n = a - ar^n$$

$$\boxed{3} \qquad s_n = \frac{a(1 - r^n)}{1 - r}$$

If $-1 < r < 1$, we know from (8.1.7) that $r^n \to 0$ as $n \to \infty$, so

$$\lim_{n \to \infty} s_n = \lim_{n \to \infty} \frac{a(1 - r^n)}{1 - r} = \frac{a}{1 - r} - \frac{a}{1 - r} \lim_{n \to \infty} r^n = \frac{a}{1 - r}$$

Thus when $|r| < 1$ the geometric series is convergent and its sum is $a/(1 - r)$.

If $r \leq -1$ or $r > 1$, the sequence $\{r^n\}$ is divergent by (8.1.7) and so, by Equation 3, $\lim_{n \to \infty} s_n$ does not exist. Therefore the geometric series diverges in those cases.

We summarize the results of Example 1 as follows.

---

4 The geometric series

$$\sum_{n=1}^{\infty} ar^{n-1} = a + ar + ar^2 + \cdots$$

is convergent if $|r| < 1$ and its sum is

$$\sum_{n=1}^{\infty} ar^{n-1} = \frac{a}{1 - r} \qquad |r| < 1$$

If $|r| \geq 1$, the geometric series is divergent.

V EXAMPLE 2 Find the sum of the geometric series

$$5 - \frac{10}{3} + \frac{20}{9} - \frac{40}{27} + \cdots$$

SOLUTION The first term is $a = 5$ and the common ratio is $r = -\frac{2}{3}$. Since $|r| = \frac{2}{3} < 1$, the series is convergent by (4) and its sum is

$$5 - \frac{10}{3} + \frac{20}{9} - \frac{40}{27} + \cdots = \frac{5}{1 - \left(-\frac{2}{3}\right)} = \frac{5}{\frac{5}{3}} = 3$$

What do we really mean when we say that the sum of the series in Example 2 is 3? Of course, we can't literally add an infinite number of terms, one by one. But, according to Definition 2, the total sum is the limit of the sequence of partial sums. So, by taking the sum of sufficiently many terms, we can get as close as we like to the number 3. The table shows the first ten partial sums s_n and the graph in Figure 2 shows how the sequence of partial sums approaches 3.

n	s_n
1	5.000000
2	1.666667
3	3.888889
4	2.407407
5	3.395062
6	2.736626
7	3.175583
8	2.882945
9	3.078037
10	2.947975

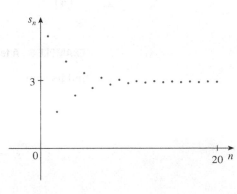

FIGURE 2

EXAMPLE 3 Is the series $\displaystyle\sum_{n=1}^{\infty} 2^{2n}3^{1-n}$ convergent or divergent?

SOLUTION Let's rewrite the nth term of the series in the form ar^{n-1}:

$$\sum_{n=1}^{\infty} 2^{2n}3^{1-n} = \sum_{n=1}^{\infty} (2^2)^n 3^{-(n-1)} = \sum_{n=1}^{\infty} \frac{4^n}{3^{n-1}} = \sum_{n=1}^{\infty} 4\left(\tfrac{4}{3}\right)^{n-1}$$

Another way to identify a and r is to write out the first few terms:

$$4 + \tfrac{16}{3} + \tfrac{64}{9} + \cdots$$

We recognize this series as a geometric series with $a = 4$ and $r = \frac{4}{3}$. Since $r > 1$, the series diverges by (4).

▼ EXAMPLE 4 **Expressing a repeating decimal as a rational number**
Write the number $2.3\overline{17} = 2.3171717\ldots$ as a ratio of integers.
SOLUTION

$$2.3171717\ldots = 2.3 + \frac{17}{10^3} + \frac{17}{10^5} + \frac{17}{10^7} + \cdots$$

After the first term we have a geometric series with $a = 17/10^3$ and $r = 1/10^2$. Therefore

$$2.3\overline{17} = 2.3 + \frac{\dfrac{17}{10^3}}{1 - \dfrac{1}{10^2}} = 2.3 + \frac{\dfrac{17}{1000}}{\dfrac{99}{100}}$$

$$= \frac{23}{10} + \frac{17}{990} = \frac{1147}{495}$$

EXAMPLE 5 **A series with variable terms** Find the sum of the series $\displaystyle\sum_{n=0}^{\infty} x^n$, where $|x| < 1$.

SOLUTION Notice that this series starts with $n = 0$ and so the first term is $x^0 = 1$. (With series, we adopt the convention that $x^0 = 1$ even when $x = 0$.) Thus

$$\sum_{n=0}^{\infty} x^n = 1 + x + x^2 + x^3 + x^4 + \cdots$$

TEC Module 8.2 explores a series that depends on an angle θ in a triangle and enables you to see how rapidly the series converges when θ varies.

This is a geometric series with $a = 1$ and $r = x$. Since $|r| = |x| < 1$, it converges and (4) gives

$$\boxed{5} \qquad\qquad \sum_{n=0}^{\infty} x^n = \frac{1}{1 - x}$$

EXAMPLE 6 **A telescoping sum** Show that the series $\displaystyle\sum_{n=1}^{\infty} \frac{1}{n(n+1)}$ is convergent, and find its sum.

SOLUTION This is not a geometric series, so we go back to the definition of a convergent series and compute the partial sums.

$$s_n = \sum_{i=1}^{n} \frac{1}{i(i+1)} = \frac{1}{1 \cdot 2} + \frac{1}{2 \cdot 3} + \frac{1}{3 \cdot 4} + \cdots + \frac{1}{n(n+1)}$$

We can simplify this expression if we use the partial fraction decomposition

$$\frac{1}{i(i + 1)} = \frac{1}{i} - \frac{1}{i + 1}$$

(see Section 5.7). Thus we have

$$s_n = \sum_{i=1}^{n} \frac{1}{i(i + 1)} = \sum_{i=1}^{n} \left(\frac{1}{i} - \frac{1}{i + 1} \right)$$

$$= \left(1 - \frac{1}{2} \right) + \left(\frac{1}{2} - \frac{1}{3} \right) + \left(\frac{1}{3} - \frac{1}{4} \right) + \cdots + \left(\frac{1}{n} - \frac{1}{n + 1} \right)$$

$$= 1 - \frac{1}{n + 1}$$

and so

$$\lim_{n \to \infty} s_n = \lim_{n \to \infty} \left(1 - \frac{1}{n + 1} \right) = 1 - 0 = 1$$

Therefore the given series is convergent and

$$\sum_{n=1}^{\infty} \frac{1}{n(n + 1)} = 1$$

V EXAMPLE 7 Show that the **harmonic series**

$$\sum_{n=1}^{\infty} \frac{1}{n} = 1 + \frac{1}{2} + \frac{1}{3} + \frac{1}{4} + \cdots$$

is divergent.

SOLUTION For this particular series it's convenient to consider the partial sums s_2, s_4, s_8, s_{16}, s_{32}, . . . and show that they become large.

$$s_2 = 1 + \tfrac{1}{2}$$

$$s_4 = 1 + \tfrac{1}{2} + \left(\tfrac{1}{3} + \tfrac{1}{4} \right) > 1 + \tfrac{1}{2} + \left(\tfrac{1}{4} + \tfrac{1}{4} \right) = 1 + \tfrac{2}{2}$$

$$s_8 = 1 + \tfrac{1}{2} + \left(\tfrac{1}{3} + \tfrac{1}{4} \right) + \left(\tfrac{1}{5} + \tfrac{1}{6} + \tfrac{1}{7} + \tfrac{1}{8} \right)$$

$$> 1 + \tfrac{1}{2} + \left(\tfrac{1}{4} + \tfrac{1}{4} \right) + \left(\tfrac{1}{8} + \tfrac{1}{8} + \tfrac{1}{8} + \tfrac{1}{8} \right)$$

$$= 1 + \tfrac{1}{2} + \tfrac{1}{2} + \tfrac{1}{2} = 1 + \tfrac{3}{2}$$

$$s_{16} = 1 + \tfrac{1}{2} + \left(\tfrac{1}{3} + \tfrac{1}{4} \right) + \left(\tfrac{1}{5} + \cdots + \tfrac{1}{8} \right) + \left(\tfrac{1}{9} + \cdots + \tfrac{1}{16} \right)$$

$$> 1 + \tfrac{1}{2} + \left(\tfrac{1}{4} + \tfrac{1}{4} \right) + \left(\tfrac{1}{8} + \cdots + \tfrac{1}{8} \right) + \left(\tfrac{1}{16} + \cdots + \tfrac{1}{16} \right)$$

$$= 1 + \tfrac{1}{2} + \tfrac{1}{2} + \tfrac{1}{2} + \tfrac{1}{2} = 1 + \tfrac{4}{2}$$

Similarly, $s_{32} > 1 + \tfrac{5}{2}$, $s_{64} > 1 + \tfrac{6}{2}$, and in general

$$s_{2^n} > 1 + \frac{n}{2}$$

This shows that $s_{2^n} \to \infty$ as $n \to \infty$ and so $\{s_n\}$ is divergent. Therefore the harmonic series diverges.

Notice that the terms cancel in pairs. This is an example of a **telescoping sum**: Because of all the cancellations, the sum collapses (like a pirate's collapsing telescope) into just two terms.

Figure 3 illustrates Example 6 by showing the graphs of the sequence of terms $a_n = 1/[n(n + 1)]$ and the sequence $\{s_n\}$ of partial sums. Notice that $a_n \to 0$ and $s_n \to 1$. See Exercises 56 and 57 for two geometric interpretations of Example 6.

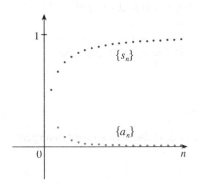

FIGURE 3

Thu method used in Example 7 for showing that the harmonic series diverges is due to the French scholar Nicole Oresme (1323–1382).

> **6** **Theorem** If the series $\sum_{n=1}^{\infty} a_n$ is convergent, then $\lim_{n \to \infty} a_n = 0$.

PROOF Let $s_n = a_1 + a_2 + \cdots + a_n$. Then $a_n = s_n - s_{n-1}$. Since $\Sigma\, a_n$ is convergent, the sequence $\{s_n\}$ is convergent. Let $\lim_{n \to \infty} s_n = s$. Since $n - 1 \to \infty$ as $n \to \infty$, we also have $\lim_{n \to \infty} s_{n-1} = s$. Therefore

$$\lim_{n \to \infty} a_n = \lim_{n \to \infty} (s_n - s_{n-1}) = \lim_{n \to \infty} s_n - \lim_{n \to \infty} s_{n-1}$$
$$= s - s = 0$$

Note 1: With any *series* $\Sigma\, a_n$ we associate two *sequences:* the sequence $\{s_n\}$ of its partial sums and the sequence $\{a_n\}$ of its terms. If $\Sigma\, a_n$ is convergent, then the limit of the sequence $\{s_n\}$ is s (the sum of the series) and, as Theorem 6 asserts, the limit of the sequence $\{a_n\}$ is 0.

Note 2: The converse of Theorem 6 is not true in general. If $\lim_{n \to \infty} a_n = 0$, we cannot conclude that $\Sigma\, a_n$ is convergent. Observe that for the harmonic series $\Sigma\, 1/n$ we have $a_n = 1/n \to 0$ as $n \to \infty$, but we showed in Example 7 that $\Sigma\, 1/n$ is divergent.

> **7** **The Test for Divergence** If $\lim_{n \to \infty} a_n$ does not exist or if $\lim_{n \to \infty} a_n \neq 0$, then the series $\sum_{n=1}^{\infty} a_n$ is divergent.

The Test for Divergence follows from Theorem 6 because, if the series is not divergent, then it is convergent, and so $\lim_{n \to \infty} a_n = 0$.

EXAMPLE 8 **Using the Test for Divergence** Show that the series $\sum_{n=1}^{\infty} \dfrac{n^2}{5n^2 + 4}$ diverges.

SOLUTION

$$\lim_{n \to \infty} a_n = \lim_{n \to \infty} \frac{n^2}{5n^2 + 4} = \lim_{n \to \infty} \frac{1}{5 + 4/n^2} = \frac{1}{5} \neq 0$$

So the series diverges by the Test for Divergence.

Note 3: If we find that $\lim_{n \to \infty} a_n \neq 0$, we know that $\Sigma\, a_n$ is divergent. If we find that $\lim_{n \to \infty} a_n = 0$, we know *nothing* about the convergence or divergence of $\Sigma\, a_n$. Remember the warning in Note 2: If $\lim_{n \to \infty} a_n = 0$, the series $\Sigma\, a_n$ might converge or it might diverge.

> **8** **Theorem** If $\Sigma\, a_n$ and $\Sigma\, b_n$ are convergent series, then so are the series $\Sigma\, ca_n$ (where c is a constant), $\Sigma\, (a_n + b_n)$, and $\Sigma\, (a_n - b_n)$, and
>
> (i) $\displaystyle\sum_{n=1}^{\infty} ca_n = c \sum_{n=1}^{\infty} a_n$ $\qquad\qquad$ (ii) $\displaystyle\sum_{n=1}^{\infty} (a_n + b_n) = \sum_{n=1}^{\infty} a_n + \sum_{n=1}^{\infty} b_n$
>
> (iii) $\displaystyle\sum_{n=1}^{\infty} (a_n - b_n) = \sum_{n=1}^{\infty} a_n - \sum_{n=1}^{\infty} b_n$

These properties of convergent series follow from the corresponding Limit Laws for Sequences in Section 8.1. For instance, here is how part (ii) of Theorem 8 is proved:
Let

$$s_n = \sum_{i=1}^{n} a_i \qquad s = \sum_{n=1}^{\infty} a_n \qquad t_n = \sum_{i=1}^{n} b_i \qquad t = \sum_{n=1}^{\infty} b_n$$

The nth partial sum for the series $\sum (a_n + b_n)$ is

$$u_n = \sum_{i=1}^{n} (a_i + b_i)$$

and, using Equation 5.2.10, we have

$$\lim_{n \to \infty} u_n = \lim_{n \to \infty} \sum_{i=1}^{n} (a_i + b_i) = \lim_{n \to \infty} \left(\sum_{i=1}^{n} a_i + \sum_{i=1}^{n} b_i \right)$$

$$= \lim_{n \to \infty} \sum_{i=1}^{n} a_i + \lim_{n \to \infty} \sum_{i=1}^{n} b_i$$

$$= \lim_{n \to \infty} s_n + \lim_{n \to \infty} t_n = s + t$$

Therefore $\sum (a_n + b_n)$ is convergent and its sum is

$$\sum_{n=1}^{\infty} (a_n + b_n) = s + t = \sum_{n=1}^{\infty} a_n + \sum_{n=1}^{\infty} b_n$$

EXAMPLE 9 Find the sum of the series $\displaystyle\sum_{n=1}^{\infty} \left(\frac{3}{n(n+1)} + \frac{1}{2^n} \right)$.

SOLUTION The series $\sum 1/2^n$ is a geometric series with $a = \frac{1}{2}$ and $r = \frac{1}{2}$, so

$$\sum_{n=1}^{\infty} \frac{1}{2^n} = \frac{\frac{1}{2}}{1 - \frac{1}{2}} = 1$$

In Example 6 we found that

$$\sum_{n=1}^{\infty} \frac{1}{n(n+1)} = 1$$

So, by Theorem 8, the given series is convergent and

$$\sum_{n=1}^{\infty} \left(\frac{3}{n(n+1)} + \frac{1}{2^n} \right) = 3 \sum_{n=1}^{\infty} \frac{1}{n(n+1)} + \sum_{n=1}^{\infty} \frac{1}{2^n}$$

$$= 3 \cdot 1 + 1 = 4$$

Note 4: A finite number of terms doesn't affect the convergence or divergence of a series. For instance, suppose that we were able to show that the series

$$\sum_{n=4}^{\infty} \frac{n}{n^3 + 1}$$

is convergent. Since

$$\sum_{n=1}^{\infty} \frac{n}{n^3 + 1} = \frac{1}{2} + \frac{2}{9} + \frac{3}{28} + \sum_{n=4}^{\infty} \frac{n}{n^3 + 1}$$

it follows that the entire series $\sum_{n=1}^{\infty} n/(n^3 + 1)$ is convergent. Similarly, if it is known that the series $\sum_{n=N+1}^{\infty} a_n$ converges, then the full series

$$\sum_{n=1}^{\infty} a_n = \sum_{n=1}^{N} a_n + \sum_{n=N+1}^{\infty} a_n$$

is also convergent.

8.2 Exercises

1. (a) What is the difference between a sequence and a series?
(b) What is a convergent series? What is a divergent series?

2. Explain what it means to say that $\sum_{n=1}^{\infty} a_n = 5$.

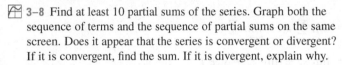 **3–8** Find at least 10 partial sums of the series. Graph both the sequence of terms and the sequence of partial sums on the same screen. Does it appear that the series is convergent or divergent? If it is convergent, find the sum. If it is divergent, explain why.

3. $\displaystyle\sum_{n=1}^{\infty} \frac{12}{(-5)^n}$

4. $\displaystyle\sum_{n=1}^{\infty} \cos n$

5. $\displaystyle\sum_{n=1}^{\infty} \frac{n}{\sqrt{n^2 + 4}}$

6. $\displaystyle\sum_{n=1}^{\infty} \frac{7^{n+1}}{10^n}$

7. $\displaystyle\sum_{n=1}^{\infty} \left(\frac{1}{\sqrt{n}} - \frac{1}{\sqrt{n+1}} \right)$

8. $\displaystyle\sum_{n=2}^{\infty} \frac{1}{n(n+2)}$

9. Let $a_n = \dfrac{2n}{3n+1}$.
(a) Determine whether $\{a_n\}$ is convergent.
(b) Determine whether $\sum_{n=1}^{\infty} a_n$ is convergent.

10. (a) Explain the difference between

$$\sum_{i=1}^{n} a_i \quad \text{and} \quad \sum_{j=1}^{n} a_j$$

(b) Explain the difference between

$$\sum_{i=1}^{n} a_i \quad \text{and} \quad \sum_{i=1}^{n} a_j$$

11–18 Determine whether the geometric series is convergent or divergent. If it is convergent, find its sum.

11. $3 - 4 + \frac{16}{3} - \frac{64}{9} + \cdots$

12. $4 + 3 + \frac{9}{4} + \frac{27}{16} + \cdots$

13. $10 - 2 + 0.4 - 0.08 + \cdots$

14. $1 + 0.4 + 0.16 + 0.064 + \cdots$

15. $\displaystyle\sum_{n=1}^{\infty} 6(0.9)^{n-1}$

16. $\displaystyle\sum_{n=1}^{\infty} \frac{10^n}{(-9)^{n-1}}$

17. $\displaystyle\sum_{n=0}^{\infty} \frac{\pi^n}{3^{n+1}}$

18. $\displaystyle\sum_{n=0}^{\infty} \frac{1}{(\sqrt{2})^n}$

19–30 Determine whether the series is convergent or divergent. If it is convergent, find its sum.

19. $\displaystyle\sum_{n=1}^{\infty} \frac{n-1}{3n-1}$

20. $\displaystyle\sum_{k=1}^{\infty} \frac{k(k+2)}{(k+3)^2}$

21. $\displaystyle\sum_{k=2}^{\infty} \frac{k^2}{k^2 - 1}$

22. $\displaystyle\sum_{n=1}^{\infty} \cos \frac{1}{n}$

23. $\displaystyle\sum_{n=1}^{\infty} \frac{1 + 2^n}{3^n}$

24. $\displaystyle\sum_{n=1}^{\infty} \frac{1 + 3^n}{2^n}$

25. $\displaystyle\sum_{n=1}^{\infty} \sqrt[n]{2}$

26. $\displaystyle\sum_{k=1}^{\infty} (\cos 1)^k$

27. $\displaystyle\sum_{n=1}^{\infty} \arctan n$

28. $\displaystyle\sum_{n=1}^{\infty} [(0.8)^{n-1} - (0.3)^n]$

29. $\displaystyle\sum_{n=1}^{\infty} \left(\frac{1}{e^n} + \frac{1}{n(n+1)} \right)$

30. $\displaystyle\sum_{n=1}^{\infty} \left(\frac{3}{5^n} + \frac{2}{n} \right)$

31–34 Determine whether the series is convergent or divergent by expressing s_n as a telescoping sum (as in Example 6). If it is convergent, find its sum.

31. $\displaystyle\sum_{n=2}^{\infty} \frac{2}{n^2 - 1}$

32. $\displaystyle\sum_{n=1}^{\infty} \frac{2}{n^2 + 4n + 3}$

33. $\displaystyle\sum_{n=1}^{\infty} \frac{3}{n(n+3)}$

34. $\displaystyle\sum_{n=1}^{\infty} \ln \frac{n}{n+1}$

35. Let $x = 0.99999 \ldots$.
(a) Do you think that $x < 1$ or $x = 1$?
(b) Sum a geometric series to find the value of x.
(c) How many decimal representations does the number 1 have?
(d) Which numbers have more than one decimal representation?

36–40 Express the number as a ratio of integers.

36. $0.\overline{73} = 0.73737373 \ldots$

37. $0.\overline{2} = 0.2222 \ldots$

38. $6.2\overline{54} = 6.2545454\ldots$

39. $1.5\overline{342}$

40. $7.\overline{12345}$

41–43 Find the values of x for which the series converges. Find the sum of the series for those values of x.

41. $\sum_{n=1}^{\infty} \dfrac{x^n}{3^n}$

42. $\sum_{n=0}^{\infty} \dfrac{(x+3)^n}{2^n}$

43. $\sum_{n=0}^{\infty} \dfrac{\cos^n x}{2^n}$

---

44. We have seen that the harmonic series is a divergent series whose terms approach 0. Show that

$$\sum_{n=1}^{\infty} \ln\left(1 + \frac{1}{n}\right)$$

is another series with this property.

CAS **45–46** Use the partial fraction command on your CAS to find a convenient expression for the partial sum, and then use this expression to find the sum of the series. Check your answer by using the CAS to sum the series directly.

45. $\sum_{n=1}^{\infty} \dfrac{3n^2 + 3n + 1}{(n^2 + n)^3}$

46. $\sum_{n=2}^{\infty} \dfrac{1}{n^3 - n}$

---

47. If the nth partial sum of a series $\sum_{n=1}^{\infty} a_n$ is

$$s_n = \frac{n-1}{n+1}$$

find a_n and $\sum_{n=1}^{\infty} a_n$.

48. If the nth partial sum of a series $\sum_{n=1}^{\infty} a_n$ is $s_n = 3 - n2^{-n}$, find a_n and $\sum_{n=1}^{\infty} a_n$.

49. A patient is prescribed a drug and is told to take one 100-mg pill every eight hours. After eight hours, about 5% of the drug remains in the body.
(a) What quantity of the drug remains in the body after the patient takes three pills?
(b) What quantity remains after n pills are taken?
(c) What happens in the long run?

50. To control an agricultural pest called the medfly (Mediterranean fruit fly), N sterilized male flies are released into the general fly population every day. If s is the proportion of these sterilized flies that survive a given day, then Ns^k will survive for k days.
(a) How many sterile flies are there after n days? What happens in the long run?

(b) If $s = 0.9$ and 10,000 sterilized males are needed to control the medfly population in a given area, how many should be released every day?

51. When money is spent on goods and services, those who receive the money also spend some of it. The people receiving some of the twice-spent money will spend some of that, and so on. Economists call this chain reaction the *multiplier effect*. In a hypothetical isolated community, the local government begins the process by spending D dollars. Suppose that each recipient of spent money spends $100c\%$ and saves $100s\%$ of the money that he or she receives. The values c and s are called the *marginal propensity to consume* and the *marginal propensity to save* and, of course, $c + s = 1$.
(a) Let S_n be the total spending that has been generated after n transactions. Find an equation for S_n.
(b) Show that $\lim_{n \to \infty} S_n = kD$, where $k = 1/s$. The number k is called the *multiplier*. What is the multiplier if the marginal propensity to consume is 80%?

Note: The federal government uses this principle to justify deficit spending. Banks use this principle to justify lending a large percentage of the money that they receive in deposits.

52. A certain ball has the property that each time it falls from a height h onto a hard, level surface, it rebounds to a height rh, where $0 < r < 1$. Suppose that the ball is dropped from an initial height of H meters.
(a) Assuming that the ball continues to bounce indefinitely, find the total distance that it travels.
(b) Calculate the total time that the ball travels. (Use the fact that the ball falls $\frac{1}{2}gt^2$ meters in t seconds.)
(c) Suppose that each time the ball strikes the surface with velocity v it rebounds with velocity $-kv$, where $0 < k < 1$. How long will it take for the ball to come to rest?

53. Find the value of c if

$$\sum_{n=2}^{\infty} (1 + c)^{-n} = 2$$

54. Find the value of c such that

$$\sum_{n=0}^{\infty} e^{nc} = 10$$

55. In Example 7 we showed that the harmonic series is divergent. Here we outline another method, making use of the fact that $e^x > 1 + x$ for any $x > 0$. (See Exercise 4.3.62.)
If s_n is the nth partial sum of the harmonic series, show that $e^{s_n} > n + 1$. Why does this imply that the harmonic series is divergent?

56. Graph the curves $y = x^n$, $0 \le x \le 1$, for $n = 0, 1, 2, 3, 4, \ldots$ on a common screen. By finding the areas between successive curves, give a geometric demonstration of the fact, shown in Example 6, that

$$\sum_{n=1}^{\infty} \frac{1}{n(n+1)} = 1$$

57. The figure shows two circles C and D of radius 1 that touch at P. T is a common tangent line; C_1 is the circle that touches C, D, and T; C_2 is the circle that touches C, D, and C_1; C_3 is the circle that touches C, D, and C_2. This procedure can be continued indefinitely and produces an infinite sequence of circles $\{C_n\}$. Find an expression for the diameter of C_n and thus provide another geometric demonstration of Example 6.

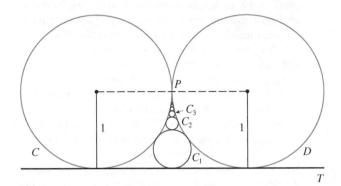

58. A right triangle ABC is given with $\angle A = \theta$ and $|AC| = b$. CD is drawn perpendicular to AB, DE is drawn perpendicular to BC, $EF \perp AB$, and this process is continued indefinitely, as shown in the figure. Find the total length of all the perpendiculars

$$|CD| + |DE| + |EF| + |FG| + \cdots$$

in terms of b and θ.

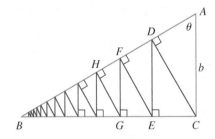

59. What is wrong with the following calculation?

$$0 = 0 + 0 + 0 + \cdots$$
$$= (1 - 1) + (1 - 1) + (1 - 1) + \cdots$$
$$= 1 - 1 + 1 - 1 + 1 - 1 + \cdots$$
$$= 1 + (-1 + 1) + (-1 + 1) + (-1 + 1) + \cdots$$
$$= 1 + 0 + 0 + 0 + \cdots = 1$$

(Guido Ubaldus thought that this proved the existence of God because "something has been created out of nothing.")

60. Suppose that $\sum_{n=1}^{\infty} a_n \ (a_n \neq 0)$ is known to be a convergent series. Prove that $\sum_{n=1}^{\infty} 1/a_n$ is a divergent series.

61. If $\Sigma \, a_n$ is convergent and $\Sigma \, b_n$ is divergent, show that the series $\Sigma \, (a_n + b_n)$ is divergent. [*Hint:* Argue by contradiction.]

62. If $\Sigma \, a_n$ and $\Sigma \, b_n$ are both divergent, is $\Sigma \, (a_n + b_n)$ necessarily divergent?

63. Suppose that a series $\Sigma \, a_n$ has positive terms and its partial sums s_n satisfy the inequality $s_n \leq 1000$ for all n. Explain why $\Sigma \, a_n$ must be convergent.

64. The Fibonacci sequence was defined in Section 8.1 by the equations

$$f_1 = 1, \quad f_2 = 1, \quad f_n = f_{n-1} + f_{n-2} \quad n \geq 3$$

Show that each of the following statements is true.

(a) $\dfrac{1}{f_{n-1}f_{n+1}} = \dfrac{1}{f_{n-1}f_n} - \dfrac{1}{f_n f_{n+1}}$

(b) $\displaystyle\sum_{n=2}^{\infty} \dfrac{1}{f_{n-1}f_{n+1}} = 1$

(c) $\displaystyle\sum_{n=2}^{\infty} \dfrac{f_n}{f_{n-1}f_{n+1}} = 2$

65. The **Cantor set**, named after the German mathematician Georg Cantor (1845–1918), is constructed as follows. We start with the closed interval $[0, 1]$ and remove the open interval $\left(\frac{1}{3}, \frac{2}{3}\right)$. That leaves the two intervals $\left[0, \frac{1}{3}\right]$ and $\left[\frac{2}{3}, 1\right]$ and we remove the open middle third of each. Four intervals remain and again we remove the open middle third of each of them. We continue this procedure indefinitely, at each step removing the open middle third of every interval that remains from the preceding step. The Cantor set consists of the numbers that remain in $[0, 1]$ after all those intervals have been removed.

(a) Show that the total length of all the intervals that are removed is 1. Despite that, the Cantor set contains infinitely many numbers. Give examples of some numbers in the Cantor set.

(b) The **Sierpinski carpet** is a two-dimensional counterpart of the Cantor set. It is constructed by removing the center one-ninth of a square of side 1, then removing the centers of the eight smaller remaining squares, and so on. (The figure shows the first three steps of the construction.) Show that the sum of the areas of the removed squares is 1. This implies that the Sierpinski carpet has area 0.

 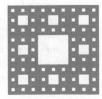

66. (a) A sequence $\{a_n\}$ is defined recursively by the equation
   $a_n = \frac{1}{2}(a_{n-1} + a_{n-2})$ for $n \geq 3$, where a_1 and a_2 can be any
   real numbers. Experiment with various values of a_1 and a_2
   and use your calculator to guess the limit of the sequence.
   (b) Find $\lim_{n \to \infty} a_n$ in terms of a_1 and a_2 by expressing
   $a_{n+1} - a_n$ in terms of $a_2 - a_1$ and summing a series.

67. Consider the series $\sum_{n=1}^{\infty} n/(n+1)!$.
   (a) Find the partial sums s_1, s_2, s_3, and s_4. Do you recognize the
   denominators? Use the pattern to guess a formula for s_n.
   (b) Use mathematical induction to prove your guess.
   (c) Show that the given infinite series is convergent, and find
   its sum.

68. In the figure there are infinitely many circles approaching the
   vertices of an equilateral triangle, each circle touching other

circles and sides of the triangle. If the triangle has sides of
length 1, find the total area occupied by the circles.

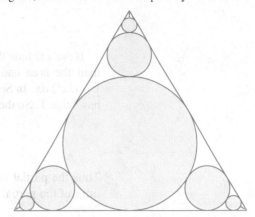

8.3   The Integral and Comparison Tests; Estimating Sums

In general, it is difficult to find the exact sum of a series. We were able to accomplish this
for geometric series and the series $\sum 1/[n(n+1)]$ because in each of those cases we could
find a simple formula for the nth partial sum s_n. But usually it isn't easy to compute
$\lim_{n \to \infty} s_n$. Therefore in this section and the next we develop tests that enable us to
determine whether a series is convergent or divergent without explicitly finding its sum.
In some cases, however, our methods will enable us to find good estimates of the sum.

In this section we deal only with series with positive terms, so the partial sums are increasing. In view of the Monotonic Sequence Theorem, to decide whether a series is convergent or divergent, we need to determine whether the partial sums are bounded or not.

Testing with an Integral

Let's investigate the series whose terms are the reciprocals of the squares of the positive
integers:

$$\sum_{n=1}^{\infty} \frac{1}{n^2} = \frac{1}{1^2} + \frac{1}{2^2} + \frac{1}{3^2} + \frac{1}{4^2} + \frac{1}{5^2} + \cdots$$

There's no simple formula for the sum s_n of the first n terms, but the computer-generated
table of values given in the margin suggests that the partial sums are approaching a number near 1.64 as $n \to \infty$ and so it looks as if the series is convergent.

We can confirm this impression with a geometric argument. Figure 1 shows the curve
$y = 1/x^2$ and rectangles that lie below the curve. The base of each rectangle is an interval
of length 1; the height is equal to the value of the function $y = 1/x^2$ at the right endpoint
of the interval.

n	$s_n = \displaystyle\sum_{i=1}^{n} \frac{1}{i^2}$
5	1.4636
10	1.5498
50	1.6251
100	1.6350
500	1.6429
1000	1.6439
5000	1.6447

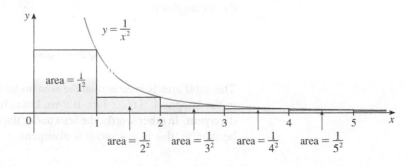

FIGURE 1

So the sum of the areas of the rectangles is

$$\frac{1}{1^2} + \frac{1}{2^2} + \frac{1}{3^2} + \frac{1}{4^2} + \frac{1}{5^2} + \cdots = \sum_{n=1}^{\infty} \frac{1}{n^2}$$

If we exclude the first rectangle, the total area of the remaining rectangles is smaller than the area under the curve $y = 1/x^2$ for $x \geqslant 1$, which is the value of the integral $\int_1^{\infty} (1/x^2) \, dx$. In Section 5.10 we discovered that this improper integral is convergent and has value 1. So the picture shows that all the partial sums are less than

$$\frac{1}{1^2} + \int_1^{\infty} \frac{1}{x^2} \, dx = 2$$

Thus the partial sums are bounded and the series converges. The sum of the series (the limit of the partial sums) is also less than 2:

$$\sum_{n=1}^{\infty} \frac{1}{n^2} = \frac{1}{1^2} + \frac{1}{2^2} + \frac{1}{3^2} + \frac{1}{4^2} + \cdots < 2$$

[The exact sum of this series was found by the Swiss mathematician Leonhard Euler (1707–1783) to be $\pi^2/6$, but the proof of this fact is beyond the scope of this book.]

Now let's look at the series

$$\sum_{n=1}^{\infty} \frac{1}{\sqrt{n}} = \frac{1}{\sqrt{1}} + \frac{1}{\sqrt{2}} + \frac{1}{\sqrt{3}} + \frac{1}{\sqrt{4}} + \frac{1}{\sqrt{5}} + \cdots$$

n	$s_n = \displaystyle\sum_{i=1}^{n} \frac{1}{\sqrt{i}}$
5	3.2317
10	5.0210
50	12.7524
100	18.5896
500	43.2834
1000	61.8010
5000	139.9681

The table of values of s_n suggests that the partial sums aren't approaching a finite number, so we suspect that the given series may be divergent. Again we use a picture for confirmation. Figure 2 shows the curve $y = 1/\sqrt{x}$, but this time we use rectangles whose tops lie *above* the curve.

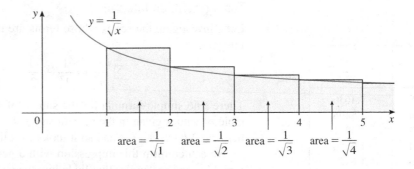

FIGURE 2

The base of each rectangle is an interval of length 1. The height is equal to the value of the function $y = 1/\sqrt{x}$ at the *left* endpoint of the interval. So the sum of the areas of all the rectangles is

$$\frac{1}{\sqrt{1}} + \frac{1}{\sqrt{2}} + \frac{1}{\sqrt{3}} + \frac{1}{\sqrt{4}} + \frac{1}{\sqrt{5}} + \cdots = \sum_{n=1}^{\infty} \frac{1}{\sqrt{n}}$$

This total area is greater than the area under the curve $y = 1/\sqrt{x}$ for $x \geqslant 1$, which is equal to the integral $\int_1^{\infty} (1/\sqrt{x}) \, dx$. But we know from Section 5.10 that this improper integral is divergent. In other words, the area under the curve is infinite. So the sum of the series must be infinite, that is, the series is divergent.

The same sort of geometric reasoning that we used for these two series can be used to prove the following test.

The Integral Test Suppose f is a continuous, positive, decreasing function on $[1, \infty)$ and let $a_n = f(n)$. Then the series $\sum_{n=1}^{\infty} a_n$ is convergent if and only if the improper integral $\int_1^{\infty} f(x)\, dx$ is convergent. In other words:

(a) If $\int_1^{\infty} f(x)\, dx$ is convergent, then $\displaystyle\sum_{n=1}^{\infty} a_n$ is convergent.

(b) If $\int_1^{\infty} f(x)\, dx$ is divergent, then $\displaystyle\sum_{n=1}^{\infty} a_n$ is divergent.

Note: When we use the Integral Test it is not necessary to start the series or the integral at $n = 1$. For instance, in testing the series

$$\sum_{n=4}^{\infty} \frac{1}{(n-3)^2} \qquad \text{we use} \qquad \int_4^{\infty} \frac{1}{(x-3)^2}\, dx$$

Also, it is not necessary that f be always decreasing. What is important is that f be *ultimately* decreasing, that is, decreasing for x larger than some number N. Then $\sum_{n=N}^{\infty} a_n$ is convergent, so $\sum_{n=1}^{\infty} a_n$ is convergent by Note 4 of Section 8.2.

V EXAMPLE 1 Using the Integral Test

Determine whether the series $\displaystyle\sum_{n=1}^{\infty} \frac{\ln n}{n}$ converges or diverges.

SOLUTION The function $f(x) = (\ln x)/x$ is positive and continuous for $x > 1$ because the logarithm function is continuous. But it is not obvious whether or not f is decreasing, so we compute its derivative:

$$f'(x) = \frac{x(1/x) - \ln x}{x^2} = \frac{1 - \ln x}{x^2}$$

Thus $f'(x) < 0$ when $\ln x > 1$, that is, $x > e$. It follows that f is decreasing when $x > e$ and so we can apply the Integral Test:

$$\int_1^{\infty} \frac{\ln x}{x}\, dx = \lim_{t \to \infty} \int_1^t \frac{\ln x}{x}\, dx = \lim_{t \to \infty} \frac{(\ln x)^2}{2} \bigg]_1^t$$

$$= \lim_{t \to \infty} \frac{(\ln t)^2}{2} = \infty$$

Since this improper integral is divergent, the series $\sum (\ln n)/n$ is also divergent by the Integral Test. ∎

V EXAMPLE 2 Convergence of the p-series

For what values of p is the series $\displaystyle\sum_{n=1}^{\infty} \frac{1}{n^p}$ convergent?

SOLUTION If $p < 0$, then $\lim_{n \to \infty} (1/n^p) = \infty$. If $p = 0$, then $\lim_{n \to \infty} (1/n^p) = 1$. In either case $\lim_{n \to \infty} (1/n^p) \neq 0$, so the given series diverges by the Test for Divergence [see (8.2.7)].

In order to use the Integral Test we need to be able to evaluate $\int_1^\infty f(x)\,dx$ and therefore we have to be able to find an antiderivative of f. Frequently this is difficult or impossible, so we need other tests for convergence too.

If $p > 0$, then the function $f(x) = 1/x^p$ is clearly continuous, positive, and decreasing on $[1, \infty)$. We found in Chapter 5 [see (5.10.2)] that

$$\int_1^\infty \frac{1}{x^p}\,dx \quad \text{converges if } p > 1 \text{ and diverges if } p \le 1$$

It follows from the Integral Test that the series $\Sigma\, 1/n^p$ converges if $p > 1$ and diverges if $0 < p \le 1$. (For $p = 1$, this series is the harmonic series discussed in Example 7 in Section 8.2.)

The series in Example 2 is called the **p-series**. It is important in the rest of this chapter, so we summarize the results of Example 2 for future reference as follows.

$\boxed{1}$ The p-series $\displaystyle\sum_{n=1}^{\infty} \frac{1}{n^p}$ is convergent if $p > 1$ and divergent if $p \le 1$.

For instance, the series

$$\sum_{n=1}^{\infty} \frac{1}{n^3} = \frac{1}{1^3} + \frac{1}{2^3} + \frac{1}{3^3} + \frac{1}{4^3} + \cdots$$

is convergent because it is a p-series with $p = 3 > 1$. But the series

$$\sum_{n=1}^{\infty} \frac{1}{n^{1/3}} = \sum_{n=1}^{\infty} \frac{1}{\sqrt[3]{n}} = 1 + \frac{1}{\sqrt[3]{2}} + \frac{1}{\sqrt[3]{3}} + \frac{1}{\sqrt[3]{4}} + \cdots$$

is divergent because it is a p-series with $p = \frac{1}{3} < 1$.

Testing by Comparing

The series

$\boxed{2}$
$$\sum_{n=1}^{\infty} \frac{1}{2^n + 1}$$

reminds us of the series $\sum_{n=1}^{\infty} 1/2^n$, which is a geometric series with $a = \frac{1}{2}$ and $r = \frac{1}{2}$ and is therefore convergent. Because the series (2) is so similar to a convergent series, we have the feeling that it too must be convergent. Indeed, it is. The inequality

$$\frac{1}{2^n + 1} < \frac{1}{2^n}$$

shows that our given series (2) has smaller terms than those of the geometric series and therefore all its partial sums are also smaller than 1 (the sum of the geometric series). This means that its partial sums form a bounded increasing sequence, which is convergent. It also follows that the sum of the series is less than the sum of the geometric series:

$$\sum_{n=1}^{\infty} \frac{1}{2^n + 1} < 1$$

Similar reasoning can be used to prove the following test, which applies only to series whose terms are positive. The first part says that if we have a series whose terms are *smaller* than those of a known *convergent* series, then our series is also convergent. The second part says that if we start with a series whose terms are *larger* than those of a known *divergent* series, then it too is divergent.

The Comparison Test   Suppose that $\Sigma\, a_n$ and $\Sigma\, b_n$ are series with positive terms.

(a) If $\Sigma\, b_n$ is convergent and $a_n \leqslant b_n$ for all n, then $\Sigma\, a_n$ is also convergent.

(b) If $\Sigma\, b_n$ is divergent and $a_n \geqslant b_n$ for all n, then $\Sigma\, a_n$ is also divergent.

Standard Series for Use with the Comparison Test

In using the Comparison Test we must, of course, have some known series $\Sigma\, b_n$ for the purpose of comparison. Most of the time we use one of these series:

- A *p*-series $\left[\Sigma\, 1/n^p \text{ converges if } p > 1 \text{ and diverges if } p \leqslant 1; \text{ see (1)}\right]$
- A geometric series $\left[\Sigma\, ar^{n-1} \text{ converges if } |r| < 1 \text{ and diverges if } |r| \geqslant 1; \text{ see (8.2.4)}\right]$

V EXAMPLE 3   Using the Comparison Test

Determine whether the series $\displaystyle\sum_{n=1}^{\infty} \frac{5}{2n^2 + 4n + 3}$ converges or diverges.

SOLUTION For large n the dominant term in the denominator is $2n^2$, so we compare the given series with the series $\Sigma\, 5/(2n^2)$. Observe that

$$\frac{5}{2n^2 + 4n + 3} < \frac{5}{2n^2}$$

because the left side has a bigger denominator. (In the notation of the Comparison Test, a_n is the left side and b_n is the right side.) We know that

$$\sum_{n=1}^{\infty} \frac{5}{2n^2} = \frac{5}{2} \sum_{n=1}^{\infty} \frac{1}{n^2}$$

is convergent because it's a constant times a *p*-series with $p = 2 > 1$. Therefore

$$\sum_{n=1}^{\infty} \frac{5}{2n^2 + 4n + 3}$$

is convergent by part (a) of the Comparison Test.

Although the condition $a_n \leqslant b_n$ or $a_n \geqslant b_n$ in the Comparison Test is given for all n, we need verify only that it holds for $n \geqslant N$, where N is some fixed integer, because the convergence of a series is not affected by a finite number of terms. This is illustrated in the next example.

V EXAMPLE 4   Test the series $\displaystyle\sum_{n=1}^{\infty} \frac{\ln n}{n}$ **for convergence or divergence.**

SOLUTION We used the Integral Test to test this series in Example 1, but we can also test it by comparing it with the harmonic series. Observe that $\ln n > 1$ for $n \geqslant 3$ and so

$$\frac{\ln n}{n} > \frac{1}{n} \qquad n \geqslant 3$$

We know that $\Sigma\, 1/n$ is divergent (*p*-series with $p = 1$). Thus the given series is divergent by the Comparison Test.

Note: The terms of the series being tested must be smaller than those of a convergent series or larger than those of a divergent series. If the terms are larger than the terms of a convergent series or smaller than those of a divergent series, then the Comparison Test doesn't apply. Consider, for instance, the series

$$\sum_{n=1}^{\infty} \frac{1}{2^n - 1}$$

The inequality

$$\frac{1}{2^n - 1} > \frac{1}{2^n}$$

is useless as far as the Comparison Test is concerned because $\Sigma\, b_n = \Sigma\left(\frac{1}{2}\right)^n$ is convergent and $a_n > b_n$. Nonetheless, we have the feeling that $\Sigma\, 1/(2^n - 1)$ ought to be convergent because it is very similar to the convergent geometric series $\Sigma\left(\frac{1}{2}\right)^n$. In such cases the following test can be used.

The Limit Comparison Test Suppose that $\Sigma\, a_n$ and $\Sigma\, b_n$ are series with positive terms. If

$$\lim_{n \to \infty} \frac{a_n}{b_n} = c$$

where c is a finite number and $c > 0$, then either both series converge or both diverge.

Although we won't prove the Limit Comparison Test, it seems reasonable because for large n, $a_n \approx cb_n$.

EXAMPLE 5 **Using the Limit Comparison Test**

Test the series $\displaystyle\sum_{n=1}^{\infty} \frac{1}{2^n - 1}$ for convergence or divergence.

SOLUTION We use the Limit Comparison Test with

$$a_n = \frac{1}{2^n - 1} \qquad b_n = \frac{1}{2^n}$$

and obtain

$$\lim_{n \to \infty} \frac{a_n}{b_n} = \lim_{n \to \infty} \frac{1/(2^n - 1)}{1/2^n} = \lim_{n \to \infty} \frac{2^n}{2^n - 1} = \lim_{n \to \infty} \frac{1}{1 - 1/2^n} = 1 > 0$$

Since this limit exists and $\Sigma\, 1/2^n$ is a convergent geometric series, the given series converges by the Limit Comparison Test.

Estimating the Sum of a Series

Suppose we have been able to use the Integral Test to show that a series $\Sigma\, a_n$ is convergent and we now want to find an approximation to the sum s of the series. Of course, any partial sum s_n is an approximation to s because $\lim_{n \to \infty} s_n = s$. But how good is such an approximation? To find out, we need to estimate the size of the **remainder**

$$R_n = s - s_n = a_{n+1} + a_{n+2} + a_{n+3} + \cdots$$

The remainder R_n is the error made when s_n, the sum of the first n terms, is used as an approximation to the total sum.

We use the same notation and ideas as in the Integral Test, assuming that f is decreasing on $[n, \infty)$. Comparing the areas of the rectangles with the area under $y = f(x)$ for $x > n$ in Figure 3, we see that

$$R_n = a_{n+1} + a_{n+2} + \cdots \leq \int_n^\infty f(x)\, dx$$

Similarly, we see from Figure 4 that

$$R_n = a_{n+1} + a_{n+2} + \cdots \geq \int_{n+1}^\infty f(x)\, dx$$

So we have proved the following error estimate.

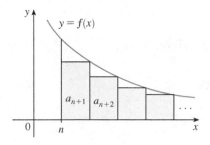

FIGURE 3

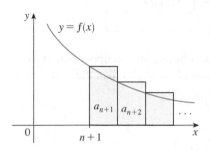

FIGURE 4

---

3 **Remainder Estimate for the Integral Test** Suppose $f(k) = a_k$, where f is a continuous, positive, decreasing function for $x \geq n$ and $\Sigma\, a_n$ is convergent. If $R_n = s - s_n$, then

$$\int_{n+1}^\infty f(x)\, dx \leq R_n \leq \int_n^\infty f(x)\, dx$$

▼ **EXAMPLE 6** **Estimating the sum of a series**
(a) Approximate the sum of the series $\Sigma\, 1/n^3$ by using the sum of the first 10 terms. Estimate the error involved in this approximation.
(b) How many terms are required to ensure that the sum is accurate to within 0.0005?

SOLUTION In both parts (a) and (b) we need to know $\int_n^\infty f(x)\, dx$. With $f(x) = 1/x^3$, which satisfies the conditions of the Integral Test, we have

$$\int_n^\infty \frac{1}{x^3}\, dx = \lim_{t \to \infty} \left[-\frac{1}{2x^2} \right]_n^t = \lim_{t \to \infty} \left(-\frac{1}{2t^2} + \frac{1}{2n^2} \right) = \frac{1}{2n^2}$$

(a) Approximating the sum of the series by the 10th partial sum, we have

$$\sum_{n=1}^\infty \frac{1}{n^3} \approx s_{10} = \frac{1}{1^3} + \frac{1}{2^3} + \frac{1}{3^3} + \cdots + \frac{1}{10^3} \approx 1.1975$$

According to the remainder estimate in (3), we have

$$R_{10} \leq \int_{10}^\infty \frac{1}{x^3}\, dx = \frac{1}{2(10)^2} = \frac{1}{200}$$

So the size of the error is at most 0.005.

(b) Accuracy to within 0.0005 means that we have to find a value of n such that $R_n \leq 0.0005$. Since

$$R_n \leq \int_n^\infty \frac{1}{x^3}\, dx = \frac{1}{2n^2}$$

we want

$$\frac{1}{2n^2} < 0.0005$$

Solving this inequality, we get

$$n^2 > \frac{1}{0.001} = 1000 \qquad \text{or} \qquad n > \sqrt{1000} \approx 31.6$$

We need 32 terms to ensure accuracy to within 0.0005.

If we add s_n to each side of the inequalities in (3), we get

$$\boxed{4} \qquad \qquad s_n + \int_{n+1}^{\infty} f(x)\, dx \leqslant s \leqslant s_n + \int_{n}^{\infty} f(x)\, dx$$

because $s_n + R_n = s$. The inequalities in (4) give a lower bound and an upper bound for s. They provide a more accurate approximation to the sum of the series than the partial sum s_n does.

EXAMPLE 7   An improved estimate

Use (4) with $n = 10$ to estimate the sum of the series $\sum_{n=1}^{\infty} \frac{1}{n^3}$.

SOLUTION   The inequalities in (4) become

$$s_{10} + \int_{11}^{\infty} \frac{1}{x^3}\, dx \leqslant s \leqslant s_{10} + \int_{10}^{\infty} \frac{1}{x^3}\, dx$$

From Example 6 we know that

$$\int_{n}^{\infty} \frac{1}{x^3}\, dx = \frac{1}{2n^2}$$

so

$$s_{10} + \frac{1}{2(11)^2} \leqslant s \leqslant s_{10} + \frac{1}{2(10)^2}$$

Using $s_{10} \approx 1.197532$, we get

$$1.201664 \leqslant s \leqslant 1.202532$$

If we approximate s by the midpoint of this interval, then the error is at most half the length of the interval. So

$$\sum_{n=1}^{\infty} \frac{1}{n^3} \approx 1.2021 \qquad \text{with error} < 0.0005$$

If we compare Example 7 with Example 6, we see that the improved estimate in (4) can be much better than the estimate $s \approx s_n$. To make the error smaller than 0.0005 we had to use 32 terms in Example 6 but only 10 terms in Example 7.

If we have used the Comparison Test to show that a series $\Sigma\, a_n$ converges by comparison with a series $\Sigma\, b_n$, then we may be able to estimate the sum $\Sigma\, a_n$ by comparing remainders, as the following example shows.

V EXAMPLE 8 Use the sum of the first 100 terms to approximate the sum of the series $\Sigma\, 1/(n^3 + 1)$. Estimate the error involved in this approximation.

SOLUTION Since

$$\frac{1}{n^3 + 1} < \frac{1}{n^3}$$

the given series is convergent by the Comparison Test. The remainder T_n for the comparison series $\Sigma\, 1/n^3$ was estimated in Example 6. There we found that

$$T_n \le \int_n^\infty \frac{1}{x^3}\, dx = \frac{1}{2n^2}$$

Therefore the remainder R_n for the given series satisfies

$$R_n \le T_n \le \frac{1}{2n^2}$$

With $n = 100$ we have

$$R_{100} \le \frac{1}{2(100)^2} = 0.00005$$

Using a programmable calculator or a computer, we find that

$$\sum_{n-1}^{\infty} \frac{1}{n^3 + 1} \approx \sum_{n-1}^{100} \frac{1}{n^3 + 1} \approx 0.6864538$$

with error less than 0.00005.

8.3 Exercises

1. Draw a picture to show that

$$\sum_{n=2}^{\infty} \frac{1}{n^{1.3}} < \int_1^\infty \frac{1}{x^{1.3}}\, dx$$

What can you conclude about the series?

2. Suppose f is a continuous positive decreasing function for $x \ge 1$ and $a_n = f(n)$. By drawing a picture, rank the following three quantities in increasing order:

$$\int_1^6 f(x)\, dx \qquad \sum_{i=1}^{5} a_i \qquad \sum_{i=2}^{6} a_i$$

3. Suppose $\Sigma\, a_n$ and $\Sigma\, b_n$ are series with positive terms and $\Sigma\, b_n$ is known to be convergent.
(a) If $a_n > b_n$ for all n, what can you say about $\Sigma\, a_n$? Why?
(b) If $a_n < b_n$ for all n, what can you say about $\Sigma\, a_n$? Why?

4. Suppose $\Sigma\, a_n$ and $\Sigma\, b_n$ are series with positive terms and $\Sigma\, b_n$ is known to be divergent.
(a) If $a_n > b_n$ for all n, what can you say about $\Sigma\, a_n$? Why?
(b) If $a_n < b_n$ for all n, what can you say about $\Sigma\, a_n$? Why?

5. It is important to distinguish between

$$\sum_{n=1}^{\infty} n^b \qquad \text{and} \qquad \sum_{n=1}^{\infty} b^n$$

What name is given to the first series? To the second? For what values of b does the first series converge? For what values of b does the second series converge?

6–8 Use the Integral Test to determine whether the series is convergent or divergent.

6. $\displaystyle\sum_{n=1}^{\infty} \frac{1}{n^5}$

7. $\displaystyle\sum_{n=1}^{\infty} \frac{1}{\sqrt[5]{n}}$

8. $\displaystyle\sum_{n=1}^{\infty} \frac{1}{\sqrt{n+4}}$

9–10 Use the Comparison Test to determine whether the series is convergent or divergent.

9. $\displaystyle\sum_{n=1}^{\infty} \frac{n}{2n^3 + 1}$

10. $\displaystyle\sum_{n=2}^{\infty} \frac{n^3}{n^4 - 1}$

---

1. Homework Hints available in TEC

11–30 Determine whether the series is convergent or divergent.

11. $\displaystyle\sum_{n=1}^{\infty} \frac{2}{n^{0.85}}$

12. $\displaystyle\sum_{n=1}^{\infty} (n^{-1.4} + 3n^{-1.2})$

13. $\displaystyle 1 + \frac{1}{8} + \frac{1}{27} + \frac{1}{64} + \frac{1}{125} + \cdots$

14. $\displaystyle 1 + \frac{1}{2\sqrt{2}} + \frac{1}{3\sqrt{3}} + \frac{1}{4\sqrt{4}} + \frac{1}{5\sqrt{5}} + \cdots$

15. $\displaystyle\sum_{n=1}^{\infty} ne^{-n}$ **16.** $\displaystyle\sum_{n=1}^{\infty} \frac{n^2}{n^3 + 1}$

17. $\displaystyle\sum_{n=2}^{\infty} \frac{1}{n \ln n}$ **18.** $\displaystyle\sum_{n=1}^{\infty} \frac{1}{n^2 + 9}$

19. $\displaystyle\sum_{n=1}^{\infty} \frac{\cos^2 n}{n^2 + 1}$ **20.** $\displaystyle\sum_{n=1}^{\infty} \frac{n^2 - 1}{3n^4 + 1}$

21. $\displaystyle\sum_{n=1}^{\infty} \frac{n - 1}{n4^n}$ **22.** $\displaystyle\sum_{n=1}^{\infty} \frac{4 + 3^n}{2^n}$

23. $\displaystyle 1 + \frac{1}{3} + \frac{1}{5} + \frac{1}{7} + \frac{1}{9} + \cdots$

24. $\displaystyle \frac{1}{5} + \frac{1}{8} + \frac{1}{11} + \frac{1}{14} + \frac{1}{17} + \cdots$

25. $\displaystyle\sum_{n=1}^{\infty} \frac{1 + 4^n}{1 + 3^n}$ **26.** $\displaystyle\sum_{n=1}^{\infty} \frac{1}{\sqrt{n^3 + 1}}$

27. $\displaystyle\sum_{n=1}^{\infty} \frac{2 + (-1)^n}{n\sqrt{n}}$ **28.** $\displaystyle\sum_{n=0}^{\infty} \frac{1 + \sin n}{10^n}$

29. $\displaystyle\sum_{n=1}^{\infty} \sin\left(\frac{1}{n}\right)$ **30.** $\displaystyle\sum_{n=1}^{\infty} \frac{n^2 - 5n}{n^3 + n + 1}$

31. Find the values of p for which the following series is convergent.

$$\sum_{n=2}^{\infty} \frac{1}{n(\ln n)^p}$$

32. (a) Find the partial sum s_{10} of the series $\sum_{n=1}^{\infty} 1/n^4$. Estimate the error in using s_{10} as an approximation to the sum of the series.
(b) Use (4) with $n = 10$ to give an improved estimate of the sum.
(c) Find a value of n so that s_n is within 0.00001 of the sum.

33. (a) Use the sum of the first 10 terms to estimate the sum of the series $\sum_{n=1}^{\infty} 1/n^2$. How good is this estimate?
(b) Improve this estimate using (4) with $n = 10$.
(c) Find a value of n that will ensure that the error in the approximation $s \approx s_n$ is less than 0.001.

34. Find the sum of the series $\sum_{n=1}^{\infty} 1/n^5$ correct to three decimal places.

35. Estimate $\sum_{n=1}^{\infty} (2n + 1)^{-6}$ correct to five decimal places.

36. How many terms of the series $\sum_{n=2}^{\infty} 1/[n(\ln n)^2]$ would you need to add to find its sum to within 0.01?

37–38 Use the sum of the first 10 terms to approximate the sum of the series. Estimate the error.

37. $\displaystyle\sum_{n=1}^{\infty} \frac{1}{\sqrt{n^4 + 1}}$ **38.** $\displaystyle\sum_{n=1}^{\infty} \frac{\sin^2 n}{n^3}$

39. (a) Use a graph of $y = 1/x$ to show that if s_n is the nth partial sum of the harmonic series, then

$$s_n \leq 1 + \ln n$$

(b) The harmonic series diverges, but very slowly. Use part (a) to show that the sum of the first million terms is less than 15 and the sum of the first billion terms is less than 22.

40. Show that if we want to approximate the sum of the series $\sum_{n=1}^{\infty} n^{-1.001}$ so that the error is less than 5 in the ninth decimal place, then we need to add more than $10^{11,301}$ terms!

41. The meaning of the decimal representation of a number $0.d_1 d_2 d_3 \ldots$ (where the digit d_i is one of the numbers 0, 1, 2, $\ldots$, 9) is that

$$0.d_1 d_2 d_3 d_4 \ldots = \frac{d_1}{10} + \frac{d_2}{10^2} + \frac{d_3}{10^3} + \frac{d_4}{10^4} + \cdots$$

Show that this series always converges.

42. Show that if $a_n > 0$ and $\sum a_n$ is convergent, then $\sum \ln(1 + a_n)$ is convergent.

43. If $\sum a_n$ is a convergent series with positive terms, is it true that $\sum \sin(a_n)$ is also convergent?

44. Find all positive values of b for which the series $\sum_{n=1}^{\infty} b^{\ln n}$ converges.

45. Show that if $a_n > 0$ and $\lim_{n \to \infty} na_n \neq 0$, then $\sum a_n$ is divergent.

46. Find all values of c for which the following series converges.

$$\sum_{n=1}^{\infty} \left(\frac{c}{n} - \frac{1}{n + 1}\right)$$

8.4 Other Convergence Tests

The convergence tests that we have looked at so far apply only to series with positive terms. In this section we learn how to deal with series whose terms are not necessarily positive.

Alternating Series

An **alternating series** is a series whose terms are alternately positive and negative. Here are two examples:

$$1 - \frac{1}{2} + \frac{1}{3} - \frac{1}{4} + \frac{1}{5} - \frac{1}{6} + \cdots = \sum_{n=1}^{\infty} (-1)^{n-1} \frac{1}{n}$$

$$-\frac{1}{2} + \frac{2}{3} - \frac{3}{4} + \frac{4}{5} - \frac{5}{6} + \frac{6}{7} - \cdots = \sum_{n=1}^{\infty} (-1)^{n} \frac{n}{n+1}$$

We see from these examples that the nth term of an alternating series is of the form

$$a_n = (-1)^{n-1} b_n \qquad \text{or} \qquad a_n = (-1)^{n} b_n$$

where b_n is a positive number. $\big($In fact, $b_n = |a_n|.\big)$

The following test says that if the terms of an alternating series decrease to 0 in absolute value, then the series converges.

The Alternating Series Test If the alternating series

$$\sum_{n=1}^{\infty} (-1)^{n-1} b_n = b_1 - b_2 + b_3 - b_4 + b_5 - b_6 + \cdots \qquad b_n > 0$$

satisfies

(i) $b_{n+1} \leq b_n$ \qquad for all n

(ii) $\lim_{n \to \infty} b_n = 0$

then the series is convergent.

We won't present a formal proof of this test, but Figure 1 gives a picture of the idea behind the proof.

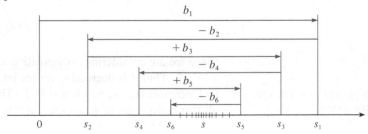

FIGURE 1

We first plot $s_1 = b_1$ on a number line. To find s_2 we subtract b_2, so s_2 is to the left of s_1. Then to find s_3 we add b_3, so s_3 is to the right of s_2. But, since $b_3 < b_2$, s_3 is to the left of s_1. Continuing in this manner, we see that the partial sums oscillate back and forth. Since $b_n \to 0$, the successive steps are becoming smaller and smaller. The even partial sums s_2, s_4, s_6, ... are increasing and the odd partial sums s_1, s_3, s_5, ... are decreasing. Thus it seems plausible that both are converging to some number s, which is the sum of the series.

Figure 2 illustrates Example 1 by showing the graphs of the terms $a_n = (-1)^{n-1}/n$ and the partial sums s_n. Notice how the values of s_n zigzag across the limiting value, which appears to be about 0.7. In fact, it can be proved that the exact sum of the series is $\ln 2 \approx 0.693$.

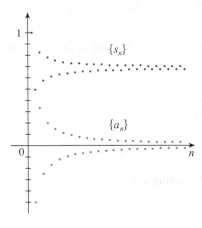

FIGURE 2

V   EXAMPLE 1   Using the Alternating Series Test   The alternating harmonic series

$$1 - \frac{1}{2} + \frac{1}{3} - \frac{1}{4} + \cdots = \sum_{n=1}^{\infty} \frac{(-1)^{n-1}}{n}$$

satisfies

(i) $b_{n+1} < b_n$ because $\dfrac{1}{n+1} < \dfrac{1}{n}$

(ii) $\lim\limits_{n \to \infty} b_n = \lim\limits_{n \to \infty} \dfrac{1}{n} = 0$

so the series is convergent by the Alternating Series Test.

V   EXAMPLE 2   An alternating series for which the Alternating Series Test fails

The series $\sum\limits_{n=1}^{\infty} \dfrac{(-1)^n 3n}{4n - 1}$ is alternating, but

$$\lim_{n \to \infty} b_n = \lim_{n \to \infty} \frac{3n}{4n - 1} = \lim_{n \to \infty} \frac{3}{4 - \dfrac{1}{n}} = \frac{3}{4}$$

so condition (ii) is not satisfied. Instead, we look at the limit of the nth term of the series:

$$\lim_{n \to \infty} a_n = \lim_{n \to \infty} \frac{(-1)^n 3n}{4n - 1}$$

This limit does not exist, so the series diverges by the Test for Divergence.

EXAMPLE 3   Test the series $\sum\limits_{n=1}^{\infty} (-1)^{n+1} \dfrac{n^2}{n^3 + 1}$ for convergence or divergence.

SOLUTION   The given series is alternating so we try to verify conditions (i) and (ii) of the Alternating Series Test.

Unlike the situation in Example 1, it is not obvious that the sequence given by $b_n = n^2/(n^3 + 1)$ is decreasing. However, if we consider the related function $f(x) = x^2/(x^3 + 1)$, we find that

$$f'(x) = \frac{x(2 - x^3)}{(x^3 + 1)^2}$$

Instead of verifying condition (i) of the Alternating Series Test by computing a derivative, we could verify that $b_{n+1} < b_n$ directly by using the technique of Solution 1 of Example 12 in Section 8.1.

Since we are considering only positive x, we see that $f'(x) < 0$ if $2 - x^3 < 0$, that is, $x > \sqrt[3]{2}$. Thus f is decreasing on the interval $\left(\sqrt[3]{2}, \infty \right)$. This means that $f(n + 1) < f(n)$ and therefore $b_{n+1} < b_n$ when $n \geq 2$. (The inequality $b_2 < b_1$ can be verified directly but all that really matters is that the sequence $\{b_n\}$ is eventually decreasing.)

Condition (ii) is readily verified:

$$\lim_{n \to \infty} b_n = \lim_{n \to \infty} \frac{n^2}{n^3 + 1} = \lim_{n \to \infty} \frac{\dfrac{1}{n}}{1 + \dfrac{1}{n^3}} = 0$$

Thus the given series is convergent by the Alternating Series Test.

The error involved in using the partial sum s_n as an approximation to the total sum s is the remainder $R_n = s - s_n$. The next theorem says that for series that satisfy the conditions of the Alternating Series Test, the size of the error is smaller than b_{n+1}, which is the absolute value of the first neglected term.

Alternating Series Estimation Theorem If $s = \Sigma\,(-1)^{n-1}b_n$ is the sum of an alternating series that satisfies

$$(i)\ \ b_{n+1} \leqslant b_n \qquad \text{and} \qquad (ii)\ \lim_{n \to \infty} b_n = 0$$

then

$$|R_n| = |s - s_n| \leqslant b_{n+1}$$

You can see geometrically why this is true by looking at Figure 1. Notice that $s - s_4 < b_5,\ |s - s_5| < b_6$, and so on.

V EXAMPLE 4 Using the Alternating Series Estimation Theorem

By definition, $0! = 1$.

Find the sum of the series $\displaystyle\sum_{n=0}^{\infty} \frac{(-1)^n}{n!}$ correct to three decimal places.

SOLUTION We first observe that the series is convergent by the Alternating Series Test because

$$(i)\quad b_{n+1} = \frac{1}{(n+1)!} = \frac{1}{n!(n+1)} < \frac{1}{n!} = b_n$$

$$(ii)\quad 0 < \frac{1}{n!} < \frac{1}{n} \to 0 \quad \text{so} \quad b_n = \frac{1}{n!} \to 0 \ \text{ as } n \to \infty$$

To get a feel for how many terms we need to use in our approximation, let's write out the first few terms of the series:

$$s = \frac{1}{0!} - \frac{1}{1!} + \frac{1}{2!} - \frac{1}{3!} + \frac{1}{4!} - \frac{1}{5!} + \frac{1}{6!} - \frac{1}{7!} + \cdots$$

$$= 1 - 1 + \tfrac{1}{2} - \tfrac{1}{6} + \tfrac{1}{24} - \tfrac{1}{120} + \tfrac{1}{720} - \tfrac{1}{5040} + \cdots$$

Notice that

$$b_7 = \tfrac{1}{5040} < \tfrac{1}{5000} = 0.0002$$

and

$$s_6 = 1 - 1 + \tfrac{1}{2} - \tfrac{1}{6} + \tfrac{1}{24} - \tfrac{1}{120} + \tfrac{1}{720} \approx 0.368056$$

By the Alternating Series Estimation Theorem we know that

$$|s - s_6| \leqslant b_7 < 0.0002$$

In Section 8.7 we will prove that $e^x = \sum_{n=0}^{\infty} x^n/n!$ for all x, so what we have obtained in Example 4 is actually an approximation to the number e^{-1}.

This error of less than 0.0002 does not affect the third decimal place, so we have $s \approx 0.368$ correct to three decimal places. ∎

Note: The rule that the error (in using s_n to approximate s) is smaller than the first neglected term is, in general, valid only for alternating series that satisfy the conditions of the Alternating Series Estimation Theorem. The rule does not apply to other types of series.

Absolute Convergence

Given any series $\Sigma\, a_n$, we can consider the corresponding series

$$\sum_{n=1}^{\infty} |a_n| = |a_1| + |a_2| + |a_3| + \cdots$$

whose terms are the absolute values of the terms of the original series.

We have convergence tests for series with positive terms and for alternating series. But what if the signs of the terms switch back and forth irregularly? We will see in Example 7 that the idea of absolute convergence sometimes helps in such cases.

> **Definition**   A series $\Sigma\, a_n$ is called **absolutely convergent** if the series of absolute values $\Sigma\, |a_n|$ is convergent.

Notice that if $\Sigma\, a_n$ is a series with positive terms, then $|a_n| = a_n$ and so absolute convergence is the same as convergence in this case.

EXAMPLE 5   **Determining absolute convergence**   The series

$$\sum_{n=1}^{\infty} \frac{(-1)^{n-1}}{n^2} = 1 - \frac{1}{2^2} + \frac{1}{3^2} - \frac{1}{4^2} + \cdots$$

is absolutely convergent because

$$\sum_{n=1}^{\infty} \left| \frac{(-1)^{n-1}}{n^2} \right| = \sum_{n=1}^{\infty} \frac{1}{n^2} = 1 + \frac{1}{2^2} + \frac{1}{3^2} + \frac{1}{4^2} + \cdots$$

is a convergent p-series ($p = 2$).

EXAMPLE 6   **A series that is convergent but not absolutely convergent**
We know that the alternating harmonic series

$$\sum_{n=1}^{\infty} \frac{(-1)^{n-1}}{n} = 1 - \frac{1}{2} + \frac{1}{3} - \frac{1}{4} + \cdots$$

is convergent (see Example 1), but it is not absolutely convergent because the corresponding series of absolute values is

$$\sum_{n=1}^{\infty} \left| \frac{(-1)^{n-1}}{n} \right| = \sum_{n=1}^{\infty} \frac{1}{n} = 1 + \frac{1}{2} + \frac{1}{3} + \frac{1}{4} + \cdots$$

which is the harmonic series (p-series with $p = 1$) and is therefore divergent.

Example 6 shows that it is possible for a series to be convergent but not absolutely convergent. However, Theorem 1 shows that absolute convergence implies convergence.

> **1**   **Theorem**   If a series $\Sigma\, a_n$ is absolutely convergent, then it is convergent.

To see why Theorem 1 is true, observe that the inequality

$$0 \leqslant a_n + |a_n| \leqslant 2|a_n|$$

is true because $|a_n|$ is either a_n or $-a_n$. If $\Sigma\, a_n$ is absolutely convergent, then $\Sigma\, |a_n|$ is convergent, so $\Sigma\, 2|a_n|$ is convergent. Therefore, by the Comparison Test, $\Sigma\, (a_n + |a_n|)$ is convergent. Then

$$\Sigma\, a_n = \Sigma\, (a_n + |a_n|) - \Sigma\, |a_n|$$

is the difference of two convergent series and is therefore convergent.

▼ EXAMPLE 7 Determine whether the series

$$\sum_{n=1}^{\infty} \frac{\cos n}{n^2} = \frac{\cos 1}{1^2} + \frac{\cos 2}{2^2} + \frac{\cos 3}{3^2} + \cdots$$

is convergent or divergent.

Figure 3 shows the graphs of the terms a_n and partial sums s_n of the series in Example 7. Notice that the series is not alternating but has positive and negative terms.

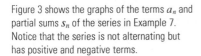
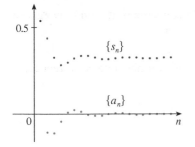

FIGURE 3

SOLUTION This series has both positive and negative terms, but it is not alternating. (The first term is positive, the next three are negative, and the following three are positive. The signs change irregularly.) We can apply the Comparison Test to the series of absolute values

$$\sum_{n=1}^{\infty} \left| \frac{\cos n}{n^2} \right| = \sum_{n=1}^{\infty} \frac{|\cos n|}{n^2}$$

Since $|\cos n| \leq 1$ for all n, we have

$$\frac{|\cos n|}{n^2} \leq \frac{1}{n^2}$$

We know that $\Sigma\, 1/n^2$ is convergent (p-series with $p = 2$) and therefore $\Sigma\, |\cos n|/n^2$ is convergent by the Comparison Test. Thus the given series $\Sigma\, (\cos n)/n^2$ is absolutely convergent and therefore convergent by Theorem 1.

The Ratio Test

The following test is very useful in determining whether a given series is absolutely convergent.

The Ratio Test

(i) If $\displaystyle\lim_{n\to\infty} \left| \frac{a_{n+1}}{a_n} \right| = L < 1$, then the series $\displaystyle\sum_{n=1}^{\infty} a_n$ is absolutely convergent (and therefore convergent).

(ii) If $\displaystyle\lim_{n\to\infty} \left| \frac{a_{n+1}}{a_n} \right| = L > 1$ or $\displaystyle\lim_{n\to\infty} \left| \frac{a_{n+1}}{a_n} \right| = \infty$, then the series $\displaystyle\sum_{n=1}^{\infty} a_n$ is divergent.

(iii) If $\displaystyle\lim_{n\to\infty} \left| \frac{a_{n+1}}{a_n} \right| = 1$, the Ratio Test is inconclusive; that is, no conclusion can be drawn about the convergence or divergence of $\Sigma\, a_n$.

The Ratio Test can be proved by comparing the given series to a geometric series. It's understandable that geometric series are involved because, for those series, the ratio r of consecutive terms is constant and the series converges if $|r| < 1$. In part (i) of the Ratio Test, the ratio of consecutive terms isn't constant but $|a_{n+1}/a_n| \to L$ so, for large n, $|a_{n+1}/a_n|$ is almost constant and the series converges if $L < 1$.

Note: Part (iii) of the Ratio Test says that if $\lim_{n\to\infty} |a_{n+1}/a_n| = 1$, the test gives no information. For instance, for the convergent series $\Sigma\, 1/n^2$ we have

$$\left|\frac{a_{n+1}}{a_n}\right| = \frac{\dfrac{1}{(n+1)^2}}{\dfrac{1}{n^2}} = \frac{n^2}{(n+1)^2} = \frac{1}{\left(1+\dfrac{1}{n}\right)^2} \to 1 \qquad \text{as } n \to \infty$$

whereas for the divergent series $\Sigma\, 1/n$ we have

$$\left|\frac{a_{n+1}}{a_n}\right| = \frac{\dfrac{1}{n+1}}{\dfrac{1}{n}} = \frac{n}{n+1} = \frac{1}{1+\dfrac{1}{n}} \to 1 \qquad \text{as } n \to \infty$$

Therefore, if $\lim_{n\to\infty} |a_{n+1}/a_n| = 1$, the series $\Sigma\, a_n$ might converge or it might diverge. In this case the Ratio Test fails and we must use some other test.

EXAMPLE 8   Using the Ratio Test   Test the series $\displaystyle\sum_{n=1}^{\infty} (-1)^n \frac{n^3}{3^n}$ for absolute convergence.

SOLUTION We use the Ratio Test with $a_n = (-1)^n n^3/3^n$:

$$\left|\frac{a_{n+1}}{a_n}\right| = \left|\frac{\dfrac{(-1)^{n+1}(n+1)^3}{3^{n+1}}}{\dfrac{(-1)^n n^3}{3^n}}\right| = \frac{(n+1)^3}{3^{n+1}} \cdot \frac{3^n}{n^3}$$

$$= \frac{1}{3}\left(\frac{n+1}{n}\right)^3 = \frac{1}{3}\left(1+\frac{1}{n}\right)^3 \to \frac{1}{3} < 1$$

Thus, by the Ratio Test, the given series is absolutely convergent and therefore convergent.

EXAMPLE 9   Test the convergence of the series $\displaystyle\sum_{n=1}^{\infty} \frac{n^n}{n!}$.

Series that involve factorials or other products (including a constant raised to the nth power) are often conveniently tested using the Ratio Test.

SOLUTION Since the terms $a_n = n^n/n!$ are positive, we don't need the absolute value signs.

$$\frac{a_{n+1}}{a_n} = \frac{(n+1)^{n+1}}{(n+1)!} \cdot \frac{n!}{n^n}$$

$$= \frac{(n+1)(n+1)^n}{(n+1)n!} \cdot \frac{n!}{n^n}$$

$$= \left(\frac{n+1}{n}\right)^n = \left(1+\frac{1}{n}\right)^n \to e \qquad \text{as } n \to \infty$$

(see Equation 3.7.6). Since $e > 1$, the given series is divergent by the Ratio Test.

www.stewartcalculus.com
We now have several tests for convergence
of series. So, given a series, how do you
know which test to use? For advice, click on
Additional Topics and then on *Strategy for
Testing Series*.

Note: Although the Ratio Test works in Example 9, another method is to use the Test for Divergence. Since

$$a_n = \frac{n^n}{n!} = \frac{n \cdot n \cdot n \cdot \cdots \cdot n}{1 \cdot 2 \cdot 3 \cdot \cdots \cdot n} \geq n$$

it follows that a_n does not approach 0 as $n \to \infty$. Therefore the given series is divergent by the Test for Divergence.

8.4 Exercises

1. (a) What is an alternating series?
 (b) Under what conditions does an alternating series converge?
 (c) If these conditions are satisfied, what can you say about the remainder after n terms?

2. What can you say about the series $\Sigma\, a_n$ in each of the following cases?

 (a) $\lim_{n\to\infty} \left| \frac{a_{n+1}}{a_n} \right| = 8$ (b) $\lim_{n\to\infty} \left| \frac{a_{n+1}}{a_n} \right| = 0.8$

 (c) $\lim_{n\to\infty} \left| \frac{a_{n+1}}{a_n} \right| = 1$

3–10 Test the series for convergence or divergence.

3. $\frac{4}{7} - \frac{4}{8} + \frac{4}{9} - \frac{4}{10} + \frac{4}{11} - \cdots$

4. $-\frac{3}{4} + \frac{5}{5} - \frac{7}{6} + \frac{9}{7} - \frac{11}{8} + \cdots$

5. $\sum_{n=1}^{\infty} \frac{(-1)^{n-1}}{2n+1}$ **6.** $\sum_{n=1}^{\infty} \frac{(-1)^{n-1}}{\ln(n+4)}$

7. $\sum_{n=1}^{\infty} (-1)^n \frac{3n-1}{2n+1}$ **8.** $\sum_{n=1}^{\infty} (-1)^n \frac{n}{\sqrt{n^3+2}}$

9. $\sum_{n=1}^{\infty} (-1)^{n+1} \frac{n}{n^2+9}$ **10.** $\sum_{n=1}^{\infty} (-1)^n \cos\left(\frac{\pi}{n}\right)$

11. Is the 50th partial sum s_{50} of the alternating series $\sum_{n=1}^{\infty} (-1)^{n-1}/n$ an overestimate or an underestimate of the total sum? Explain.

12. Calculate the first 10 partial sums of the series

$$\sum_{n=1}^{\infty} \frac{(-1)^{n-1}}{n^3}$$

and graph both the sequence of terms and the sequence of partial sums on the same screen. Estimate the error in using the 10th partial sum to approximate the total sum.

13. For what values of p is the following series convergent?

$$\sum_{n=1}^{\infty} \frac{(-1)^{n-1}}{n^p}$$

14–16 Show that the series is convergent. How many terms of the series do we need to add in order to find the sum to the indicated accuracy?

14. $\sum_{n=1}^{\infty} \frac{(-1)^n}{n\,5^n}$ ($|\,\text{error}\,| < 0.0001$)

15. $\sum_{n=1}^{\infty} \frac{(-1)^{n+1}}{n^6}$ ($|\,\text{error}\,| < 0.00005$)

16. $\sum_{n=1}^{\infty} (-1)^{n-1} n e^{-n}$ ($|\,\text{error}\,| < 0.01$)

17–18 Graph both the sequence of terms and the sequence of partial sums on the same screen. Use the graph to make a rough estimate of the sum of the series. Then use the Alternating Series Estimation Theorem to estimate the sum correct to four decimal places.

17. $\sum_{n=1}^{\infty} \frac{(-0.8)^n}{n!}$ **18.** $\sum_{n=1}^{\infty} (-1)^{n-1} \frac{n}{8^n}$

19–20 Approximate the sum of the series correct to four decimal places.

19. $\sum_{n=1}^{\infty} \frac{(-1)^{n-1} n^2}{10^n}$ **20.** $\sum_{n=1}^{\infty} \frac{(-1)^n}{3^n n!}$

21–34 Determine whether the series is absolutely convergent.

21. $\sum_{n=1}^{\infty} \frac{(-3)^n}{n^3}$ **22.** $\sum_{n=1}^{\infty} \frac{n!}{100^n}$

23. $\sum_{n=1}^{\infty} \frac{(-10)^n}{n!}$ **24.** $\sum_{n=1}^{\infty} (-1)^{n-1} \frac{\sqrt{n}}{n+1}$

25. $\sum_{k=1}^{\infty} k\left(\tfrac{2}{3}\right)^k$ **26.** $\sum_{n=1}^{\infty} \frac{n^2}{2^n}$

Graphing calculator or computer with graphing software required   **1.** Homework Hints available in TEC

27. $\displaystyle\sum_{n=1}^{\infty} \frac{(-1)^{n-1}}{\sqrt{n}}$

28. $\displaystyle\sum_{n=1}^{\infty} (-1)^{n-1} \frac{2^n}{n^4}$

29. $\displaystyle\sum_{n=1}^{\infty} \frac{10^n}{(n+1)4^{2n+1}}$

30. $\displaystyle\sum_{n=1}^{\infty} \frac{\sin 4n}{4^n}$

31. $\displaystyle\sum_{n=1}^{\infty} \frac{(-1)^n \arctan n}{n^2}$

32. $\displaystyle\sum_{n=1}^{\infty} \frac{(-2)^n n!}{(2n)!}$

33. $1 - \dfrac{1 \cdot 3}{3!} + \dfrac{1 \cdot 3 \cdot 5}{5!} - \dfrac{1 \cdot 3 \cdot 5 \cdot 7}{7!} + \cdots$

$\qquad + (-1)^{n-1} \dfrac{1 \cdot 3 \cdot 5 \cdot \cdots \cdot (2n-1)}{(2n-1)!} + \cdots$

34. $\dfrac{2}{5} + \dfrac{2 \cdot 6}{5 \cdot 8} + \dfrac{2 \cdot 6 \cdot 10}{5 \cdot 8 \cdot 11} + \dfrac{2 \cdot 6 \cdot 10 \cdot 14}{5 \cdot 8 \cdot 11 \cdot 14} + \cdots$

35. The terms of a series are defined recursively by the equations

$$a_1 = 2 \qquad a_{n+1} = \frac{5n+1}{4n+3} a_n$$

Determine whether $\Sigma\, a_n$ converges or diverges.

36. A series $\Sigma\, a_n$ is defined by the equations

$$a_1 = 1 \qquad a_{n+1} = \frac{2 + \cos n}{\sqrt{n}} a_n$$

Determine whether $\Sigma\, a_n$ converges or diverges.

37. For which of the following series is the Ratio Test inconclusive (that is, it fails to give a definite answer)?

(a) $\displaystyle\sum_{n=1}^{\infty} \frac{1}{n^3}$

(b) $\displaystyle\sum_{n=1}^{\infty} \frac{n}{2^n}$

(c) $\displaystyle\sum_{n=1}^{\infty} \frac{(-3)^{n-1}}{\sqrt{n}}$

(d) $\displaystyle\sum_{n=1}^{\infty} \frac{\sqrt{n}}{1+n^2}$

38–39 Let

$$\lim_{n\to\infty} \sqrt[n]{|a_n|} = L$$

The **Root Test** says the following:

(i) If $L < 1$, then $\Sigma\, a_n$ is absolutely convergent.

(ii) If $L > 1$ (or $L = \infty$), then $\Sigma\, a_n$ is divergent.

(iii) If $L = 1$, then the Root Test is inconclusive.

(Like the Ratio Test, the Root Test is proved by comparison with a geometric series.) Determine whether the given series is absolutely convergent.

38. $\displaystyle\sum_{n=2}^{\infty} \left(\frac{-2n}{n+1} \right)^{5n}$

39. $\displaystyle\sum_{n=1}^{\infty} \left(\frac{n^2+1}{2n^2+1} \right)^n$

40. For which positive integers k is the following series convergent?

$$\sum_{n=1}^{\infty} \frac{(n!)^2}{(kn)!}$$

41. (a) Show that $\sum_{n=0}^{\infty} x^n/n!$ converges for all x.

(b) Deduce that $\lim_{n\to\infty} x^n/n! = 0$ for all x.

42. Around 1910, the Indian mathematician Srinivasa Ramanujan discovered the formula

$$\frac{1}{\pi} = \frac{2\sqrt{2}}{9801} \sum_{n=0}^{\infty} \frac{(4n)!(1103 + 26390n)}{(n!)^4 396^{4n}}$$

William Gosper used this series in 1985 to compute the first 17 million digits of π.

(a) Verify that the series is convergent.

(b) How many correct decimal places of π do you get if you use just the first term of the series? What if you use two terms?

8.5 Power Series

A **power series** is a series of the form

$$\boxed{1} \qquad \sum_{n=0}^{\infty} c_n x^n = c_0 + c_1 x + c_2 x^2 + c_3 x^3 + \cdots$$

where x is a variable and the c_n's are constants called the **coefficients** of the series. For each fixed x, the series (1) is a series of constants that we can test for convergence or divergence. A power series may converge for some values of x and diverge for other values of x. The sum of the series is a function

$$f(x) = c_0 + c_1 x + c_2 x^2 + \cdots + c_n x^n + \cdots$$

whose domain is the set of all x for which the series converges. Notice that f resembles a polynomial. The only difference is that f has infinitely many terms.

Trigonometric Series

A power series is a series in which each term is a power function. A **trigonometric series**

$$\sum_{n=0}^{\infty} (a_n \cos nx + b_n \sin nx)$$

is a series whose terms are trigonometric functions. This type of series is discussed on the website

www.stewartcalculus.com

Click on *Additional Topics* and then on *Fourier Series*.

For instance, if we take $c_n = 1$ for all n, the power series becomes the geometric series

$$\sum_{n=0}^{\infty} x^n = 1 + x + x^2 + \cdots + x^n + \cdots$$

which converges when $-1 < x < 1$ and diverges when $|x| \geq 1$. (See Equation 8.2.5.)

More generally, a series of the form

$$\boxed{2} \qquad \sum_{n=0}^{\infty} c_n(x - a)^n = c_0 + c_1(x - a) + c_2(x - a)^2 + \cdots$$

is called a **power series in** $(x - a)$ or a **power series centered at** a or a **power series about** a. Notice that in writing out the term corresponding to $n = 0$ in Equations 1 and 2 we have adopted the convention that $(x - a)^0 = 1$ even when $x = a$. Notice also that when $x = a$ all of the terms are 0 for $n \geq 1$ and so the power series (2) always converges when $x = a$.

V EXAMPLE 1 **A power series that converges only at its center**

For what values of x is the series $\sum_{n=0}^{\infty} n! \, x^n$ convergent?

SOLUTION We use the Ratio Test. If we let a_n, as usual, denote the nth term of the series, then $a_n = n! \, x^n$. If $x \neq 0$, we have

Notice that
$$(n + 1)! = (n + 1)n(n - 1) \cdot \cdots \cdot 3 \cdot 2 \cdot 1$$
$$= (n + 1)n!$$

$$\lim_{n \to \infty} \left| \frac{a_{n+1}}{a_n} \right| = \lim_{n \to \infty} \left| \frac{(n + 1)! \, x^{n+1}}{n! \, x^n} \right| = \lim_{n \to \infty} (n + 1)|x| = \infty$$

By the Ratio Test, the series diverges when $x \neq 0$. Thus the given series converges only when $x = 0$.

V EXAMPLE 2 **Using the Ratio Test to determine where a power series converges**

For what values of x does the series $\sum_{n=1}^{\infty} \frac{(x - 3)^n}{n}$ converge?

SOLUTION Let $a_n = (x - 3)^n/n$. Then

$$\left| \frac{a_{n+1}}{a_n} \right| = \left| \frac{(x - 3)^{n+1}}{n + 1} \cdot \frac{n}{(x - 3)^n} \right|$$

$$= \frac{1}{1 + \dfrac{1}{n}} |x - 3| \to |x - 3| \qquad \text{as } n \to \infty$$

By the Ratio Test, the given series is absolutely convergent, and therefore convergent, when $|x - 3| < 1$ and divergent when $|x - 3| > 1$. Now

$$|x - 3| < 1 \iff -1 < x - 3 < 1 \iff 2 < x < 4$$

so the series converges when $2 < x < 4$ and diverges when $x < 2$ or $x > 4$.

The Ratio Test gives no information when $|x - 3| = 1$ so we must consider $x = 2$ and $x = 4$ separately. If we put $x = 4$ in the series, it becomes $\Sigma \, 1/n$, the harmonic series, which is divergent. If $x = 2$, the series is $\Sigma \, (-1)^n/n$, which converges by the Alternating Series Test. Thus the given power series converges for $2 \leq x < 4$.

Notice how closely the computer-generated model (which involves Bessel functions and cosine functions) matches the photograph of a vibrating rubber membrane.

We will see that the main use of a power series is that it provides a way to represent some of the most important functions that arise in mathematics, physics, and chemistry. In particular, the sum of the power series in the next example is called a **Bessel function**, after the German astronomer Friedrich Bessel (1784–1846), and the function given in Exercise 29 is another example of a Bessel function. In fact, these functions first arose when Bessel solved Kepler's equation for describing planetary motion. Since that time, these functions have been applied in many different physical situations, including the temperature distribution in a circular plate and the shape of a vibrating drumhead.

EXAMPLE 3 **A power series that converges for all values of x** Find the domain of the Bessel function of order 0 defined by

$$J_0(x) = \sum_{n=0}^{\infty} \frac{(-1)^n x^{2n}}{2^{2n}(n!)^2}$$

SOLUTION Let $a_n = (-1)^n x^{2n}/[2^{2n}(n!)^2]$. Then

$$\left| \frac{a_{n+1}}{a_n} \right| = \left| \frac{(-1)^{n+1} x^{2(n+1)}}{2^{2(n+1)}[(n+1)!]^2} \cdot \frac{2^{2n}(n!)^2}{(-1)^n x^{2n}} \right|$$

$$= \frac{x^{2n+2}}{2^{2n+2}(n+1)^2(n!)^2} \cdot \frac{2^{2n}(n!)^2}{x^{2n}}$$

$$= \frac{x^2}{4(n+1)^2} \to 0 < 1 \qquad \text{for all } x$$

Thus, by the Ratio Test, the given series converges for all values of x. In other words, the domain of the Bessel function J_0 is $(-\infty, \infty) = \mathbb{R}$.

Recall that the sum of a series is equal to the limit of the sequence of partial sums. So when we define the Bessel function in Example 3 as the sum of a series we mean that, for every real number x,

$$J_0(x) = \lim_{n \to \infty} s_n(x) \qquad \text{where} \qquad s_n(x) = \sum_{i=0}^{n} \frac{(-1)^i x^{2i}}{2^{2i}(i!)^2}$$

The first few partial sums are

$$s_0(x) = 1 \qquad s_1(x) = 1 - \frac{x^2}{4} \qquad s_2(x) = 1 - \frac{x^2}{4} + \frac{x^4}{64}$$

$$s_3(x) = 1 - \frac{x^2}{4} + \frac{x^4}{64} - \frac{x^6}{2304} \qquad s_4(x) = 1 - \frac{x^2}{4} + \frac{x^4}{64} - \frac{x^6}{2304} + \frac{x^8}{147,456}$$

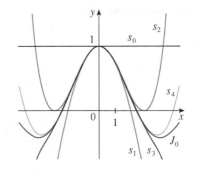

FIGURE 1

Partial sums of the Bessel function J_0

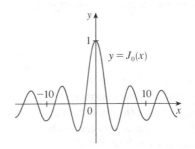

FIGURE 2

Figure 1 shows the graphs of these partial sums, which are polynomials. They are all approximations to the function J_0, but notice that the approximations become better when more terms are included. Figure 2 shows a more complete graph of the Bessel function.

For the power series that we have looked at so far, the set of values of x for which the series is convergent has always turned out to be an interval [a finite interval for the geometric series and the series in Example 2, the infinite interval $(-\infty, \infty)$ in Example 3, and a collapsed interval $[0, 0] = \{0\}$ in Example 1]. The following theorem, which we won't prove, says that this is true in general.

> **3 Theorem** For a given power series $\sum_{n=0}^{\infty} c_n(x - a)^n$ there are only three possibilities:
>
> (i) The series converges only when $x = a$.
>
> (ii) The series converges for all x.
>
> (iii) There is a positive number R such that the series converges if $|x - a| < R$ and diverges if $|x - a| > R$.

The number R in case (iii) is called the **radius of convergence** of the power series. By convention, the radius of convergence is $R = 0$ in case (i) and $R = \infty$ in case (ii). The **interval of convergence** of a power series is the interval that consists of all values of x for which the series converges. In case (i) the interval consists of just a single point a. In case (ii) the interval is $(-\infty, \infty)$. In case (iii) note that the inequality $|x - a| < R$ can be rewritten as $a - R < x < a + R$. When x is an *endpoint* of the interval, that is, $x = a \pm R$, anything can happen—the series might converge at one or both endpoints or it might diverge at both endpoints. Thus in case (iii) there are four possibilities for the interval of convergence:

$$(a - R, a + R) \qquad (a - R, a + R] \qquad [a - R, a + R) \qquad [a - R, a + R]$$

The situation is illustrated in Figure 3.

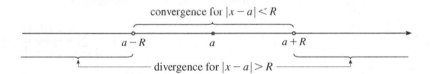

FIGURE 3

We summarize here the radius and interval of convergence for each of the examples already considered in this section.

	Series	Radius of convergence	Interval of convergence
Geometric series	$\sum_{n=0}^{\infty} x^n$	$R = 1$	$(-1, 1)$
Example 1	$\sum_{n=0}^{\infty} n!\, x^n$	$R = 0$	$\{0\}$
Example 2	$\sum_{n=1}^{\infty} \dfrac{(x - 3)^n}{n}$	$R = 1$	$[2, 4)$
Example 3	$\sum_{n=0}^{\infty} \dfrac{(-1)^n x^{2n}}{2^{2n}(n!)^2}$	$R = \infty$	$(-\infty, \infty)$

The Ratio Test can be used to determine the radius of convergence R in most cases. The Ratio Test always fails when x is an endpoint of the interval of convergence, so the endpoints must be checked with some other test.

EXAMPLE 4 Find the radius of convergence and interval of convergence of the series

$$\sum_{n=0}^{\infty} \frac{(-3)^n x^n}{\sqrt{n+1}}$$

SOLUTION Let $a_n = (-3)^n x^n / \sqrt{n+1}$. Then

$$\left| \frac{a_{n+1}}{a_n} \right| = \left| \frac{(-3)^{n+1} x^{n+1}}{\sqrt{n+2}} \cdot \frac{\sqrt{n+1}}{(-3)^n x^n} \right| = \left| -3x \sqrt{\frac{n+1}{n+2}} \right|$$

$$= 3 \sqrt{\frac{1 + (1/n)}{1 + (2/n)}} |x| \rightarrow 3|x| \qquad \text{as } n \rightarrow \infty$$

By the Ratio Test, the given series converges if $3|x| < 1$ and diverges if $3|x| > 1$. Thus it converges if $|x| < \frac{1}{3}$ and diverges if $|x| > \frac{1}{3}$. This means that the radius of convergence is $R = \frac{1}{3}$.

We know the series converges in the interval $\left(-\frac{1}{3}, \frac{1}{3}\right)$, but we must now test for convergence at the endpoints of this interval. If $x = -\frac{1}{3}$, the series becomes

$$\sum_{n=0}^{\infty} \frac{(-3)^n \left(-\frac{1}{3}\right)^n}{\sqrt{n+1}} = \sum_{n=0}^{\infty} \frac{1}{\sqrt{n+1}} = \frac{1}{\sqrt{1}} + \frac{1}{\sqrt{2}} + \frac{1}{\sqrt{3}} + \frac{1}{\sqrt{4}} + \cdots$$

which diverges. (Use the Integral Test or simply observe that it is a p-series with $p = \frac{1}{2} < 1$.) If $x = \frac{1}{3}$, the series is

$$\sum_{n=0}^{\infty} \frac{(-3)^n \left(\frac{1}{3}\right)^n}{\sqrt{n+1}} = \sum_{n=0}^{\infty} \frac{(-1)^n}{\sqrt{n+1}}$$

which converges by the Alternating Series Test. Therefore the given power series converges when $-\frac{1}{3} < x \leq \frac{1}{3}$, so the interval of convergence is $\left(-\frac{1}{3}, \frac{1}{3}\right]$.

V EXAMPLE 5 Find the radius of convergence and interval of convergence of the series

$$\sum_{n=0}^{\infty} \frac{n(x+2)^n}{3^{n+1}}$$

SOLUTION If $a_n = n(x+2)^n / 3^{n+1}$, then

$$\left| \frac{a_{n+1}}{a_n} \right| = \left| \frac{(n+1)(x+2)^{n+1}}{3^{n+2}} \cdot \frac{3^{n+1}}{n(x+2)^n} \right|$$

$$= \left(1 + \frac{1}{n} \right) \frac{|x+2|}{3} \rightarrow \frac{|x+2|}{3} \qquad \text{as } n \rightarrow \infty$$

Using the Ratio Test, we see that the series converges if $|x+2|/3 < 1$ and it diverges if $|x+2|/3 > 1$. So it converges if $|x+2| < 3$ and diverges if $|x+2| > 3$. Thus the radius of convergence is $R = 3$.

The inequality $|x+2| < 3$ can be written as $-5 < x < 1$, so we test the series at the endpoints -5 and 1. When $x = -5$, the series is

$$\sum_{n=0}^{\infty} \frac{n(-3)^n}{3^{n+1}} = \frac{1}{3} \sum_{n=0}^{\infty} (-1)^n n$$

which diverges by the Test for Divergence [$(-1)^n n$ doesn't converge to 0]. When $x = 1$, the series is

$$\sum_{n=0}^{\infty} \frac{n(3)^n}{3^{n+1}} = \tfrac{1}{3} \sum_{n=0}^{\infty} n$$

which also diverges by the Test for Divergence. Thus the series converges only when $-5 < x < 1$, so the interval of convergence is $(-5, 1)$.

8.5 Exercises

1. What is a power series?

2. (a) What is the radius of convergence of a power series? How do you find it?
(b) What is the interval of convergence of a power series? How do you find it?

3–24 Find the radius of convergence and interval of convergence of the series.

3. $\displaystyle\sum_{n=1}^{\infty} \frac{x^n}{\sqrt{n}}$

4. $\displaystyle\sum_{n=0}^{\infty} \frac{(-1)^n x^n}{n+1}$

5. $\displaystyle\sum_{n=1}^{\infty} \frac{(-1)^{n-1} x^n}{n^3}$

6. $\displaystyle\sum_{n=1}^{\infty} \sqrt{n}\, x^n$

7. $\displaystyle\sum_{n=0}^{\infty} \frac{x^n}{n!}$

8. $\displaystyle\sum_{n=1}^{\infty} \frac{10^n x^n}{n^3}$

9. $\displaystyle\sum_{n=1}^{\infty} (-1)^n \frac{n^2 x^n}{2^n}$

10. $\displaystyle\sum_{n=0}^{\infty} (-1)^n \frac{x^{2n}}{(2n)!}$

11. $\displaystyle\sum_{n=1}^{\infty} \frac{(-2)^n x^n}{\sqrt[4]{n}}$

12. $\displaystyle\sum_{n=1}^{\infty} \frac{(2n)!}{2^n} x^n$

13. $\displaystyle\sum_{n=0}^{\infty} \frac{(x-2)^n}{n^2+1}$

14. $\displaystyle\sum_{n=0}^{\infty} (-1)^n \frac{(x-3)^n}{2n+1}$

15. $\displaystyle\sum_{n=1}^{\infty} \frac{3^n (x+4)^n}{\sqrt{n}}$

16. $\displaystyle\sum_{n=1}^{\infty} \frac{n}{4^n} (x+1)^n$

17. $\displaystyle\sum_{n=1}^{\infty} \frac{(4x+1)^n}{n^2}$

18. $\displaystyle\sum_{n=1}^{\infty} \frac{n(x-4)^n}{n^3+1}$

19. $\displaystyle\sum_{n=1}^{\infty} n!(2x-1)^n$

20. $\displaystyle\sum_{n=1}^{\infty} \frac{(3x-2)^n}{n\,3^n}$

21. $\displaystyle\sum_{n=1}^{\infty} \frac{n}{b^n} (x-a)^n, \quad b > 0$

22. $\displaystyle\sum_{n=2}^{\infty} \frac{x^n}{n(\ln n)^2}$

23. $\displaystyle\sum_{n=1}^{\infty} \frac{x^n}{1 \cdot 3 \cdot 5 \cdot \,\cdots\, \cdot (2n-1)}$

24. $\displaystyle\sum_{n=1}^{\infty} \frac{n^2 x^n}{2 \cdot 4 \cdot 6 \cdot \,\cdots\, \cdot (2n)}$

25. If $\sum_{n=0}^{\infty} c_n 4^n$ is convergent, does it follow that the following series are convergent?

(a) $\displaystyle\sum_{n=0}^{\infty} c_n(-2)^n$

(b) $\displaystyle\sum_{n=0}^{\infty} c_n(-4)^n$

26. Suppose that $\sum_{n=0}^{\infty} c_n x^n$ converges when $x = -4$ and diverges when $x = 6$. What can be said about the convergence or divergence of the following series?

(a) $\displaystyle\sum_{n=0}^{\infty} c_n$

(b) $\displaystyle\sum_{n=0}^{\infty} c_n 8^n$

(c) $\displaystyle\sum_{n=0}^{\infty} c_n(-3)^n$

(d) $\displaystyle\sum_{n=0}^{\infty} (-1)^n c_n 9^n$

27. If k is a positive integer, find the radius of convergence of the series

$$\sum_{n=0}^{\infty} \frac{(n!)^k}{(kn)!} x^n$$

28. Graph the first several partial sums $s_n(x)$ of the series $\sum_{n=0}^{\infty} x^n$, together with the sum function $f(x) = 1/(1-x)$, on a common screen. On what interval do these partial sums appear to be converging to $f(x)$?

29. The function J_1 defined by

$$J_1(x) = \sum_{n=0}^{\infty} \frac{(-1)^n x^{2n+1}}{n!(n+1)!\,2^{2n+1}}$$

is called the *Bessel function of order 1*.

(a) Find its domain.

(b) Graph the first several partial sums on a common screen.

(c) If your CAS has built-in Bessel functions, graph J_1 on the same screen as the partial sums in part (b) and observe how the partial sums approximate J_1.

⊞ Graphing calculator or computer with graphing software required   CAS Computer algebra system required   **1.** Homework Hints available in TEC

30. The function A defined by

$$A(x) = 1 + \frac{x^3}{2 \cdot 3} + \frac{x^6}{2 \cdot 3 \cdot 5 \cdot 6} + \frac{x^9}{2 \cdot 3 \cdot 5 \cdot 6 \cdot 8 \cdot 9} + \cdots$$

is called the *Airy function* after the English mathematician and astronomer Sir George Airy (1801–1892).
(a) Find the domain of the Airy function.
(b) Graph the first several partial sums on a common screen.
(c) If your CAS has built-in Airy functions, graph A on the same screen as the partial sums in part (b) and observe how the partial sums approximate A.

31. A function f is defined by

$$f(x) = 1 + 2x + x^2 + 2x^3 + x^4 + \cdots$$

that is, its coefficients are $c_{2n} = 1$ and $c_{2n+1} = 2$ for all $n \geq 0$. Find the interval of convergence of the series and find an explicit formula for $f(x)$.

32. If $f(x) = \sum_{n=0}^{\infty} c_n x^n$, where $c_{n+4} = c_n$ for all $n \geq 0$, find the interval of convergence of the series and a formula for $f(x)$.

33. Suppose the series $\Sigma\, c_n x^n$ has radius of convergence 2 and the series $\Sigma\, d_n x^n$ has radius of convergence 3. What is the radius of convergence of the series $\Sigma\, (c_n + d_n)x^n$?

34. Suppose that the radius of convergence of the power series $\Sigma\, c_n x^n$ is R. What is the radius of convergence of the power series $\Sigma\, c_n x^{2n}$?

35. Is it possible to find a power series whose interval of convergence is $[0, \infty)$? Explain.

36. Let p and q be real numbers with $p < q$. Find a power series whose interval of convergence is
(a) (p, q) (b) $(p, q]$
(c) $[p, q)$ (d) $[p, q]$

8.6 Representations of Functions as Power Series

In this section we learn how to represent certain types of functions as sums of power series by manipulating geometric series or by differentiating or integrating such a series. You might wonder why we would ever want to express a known function as a sum of infinitely many terms. This strategy is useful for integrating functions that don't have elementary antiderivatives, for solving differential equations, and for approximating functions by polynomials. (Scientists do this to simplify the expressions they deal with; computer scientists do this to represent functions on calculators and computers.)

We start with an equation that we have seen before:

A geometric illustration of Equation 1 is shown in Figure 1. Because the sum of a series is the limit of the sequence of partial sums, we have

$$\frac{1}{1-x} = \lim_{n \to \infty} s_n(x)$$

where

$$s_n(x) = 1 + x + x^2 + \cdots + x^n$$

is the nth partial sum. Notice that as n increases, $s_n(x)$ becomes a better approximation to $f(x)$ for $-1 < x < 1$.

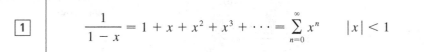

$$\boxed{\quad \frac{1}{1-x} = 1 + x + x^2 + x^3 + \cdots = \sum_{n=0}^{\infty} x^n \qquad |x| < 1 \quad}$$
1

We first encountered this equation in Example 5 in Section 8.2, where we obtained it by observing that the series is a geometric series with $a = 1$ and $r = x$. But here our point of view is different. We now regard Equation 1 as expressing the function $f(x) = 1/(1-x)$ as a sum of a power series.

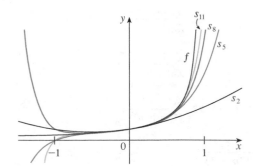

FIGURE 1

$f(x) = \dfrac{1}{1-x}$ and some partial sums

V̄ EXAMPLE 1 Finding a new power series from an old one   Express $1/(1 + x^2)$ as the sum of a power series and find the interval of convergence.

SOLUTION   Replacing x by $-x^2$ in Equation 1, we have

$$\frac{1}{1 + x^2} = \frac{1}{1 - (-x^2)} = \sum_{n=0}^{\infty} (-x^2)^n$$

$$= \sum_{n=0}^{\infty} (-1)^n x^{2n} = 1 - x^2 + x^4 - x^6 + x^8 - \cdots$$

Because this is a geometric series, it converges when $\left|-x^2\right| < 1$, that is, $x^2 < 1$, or $|x| < 1$. Therefore the interval of convergence is $(-1, 1)$. (Of course, we could have determined the radius of convergence by applying the Ratio Test, but that much work is unnecessary here.) ▬

EXAMPLE 2   Find a power series representation for $1/(x + 2)$.

SOLUTION   In order to put this function in the form of the left side of Equation 1 we first factor a 2 from the denominator:

$$\frac{1}{2 + x} = \frac{1}{2\left(1 + \dfrac{x}{2}\right)} = \frac{1}{2\left[1 - \left(-\dfrac{x}{2}\right)\right]}$$

$$= \frac{1}{2} \sum_{n=0}^{\infty} \left(-\frac{x}{2}\right)^n = \sum_{n=0}^{\infty} \frac{(-1)^n}{2^{n+1}} x^n$$

This series converges when $\left|-x/2\right| < 1$, that is, $|x| < 2$. So the interval of convergence is $(-2, 2)$. ▬

EXAMPLE 3   Find a power series representation of $x^3/(x + 2)$.

SOLUTION   Since this function is just x^3 times the function in Example 2, all we have to do is to multiply that series by x^3:

It's legitimate to move x^3 across the sigma sign because it doesn't depend on n. [Use Theorem 8.2.8(i) with $c = x^3$.]

$$\frac{x^3}{x + 2} = x^3 \cdot \frac{1}{x + 2} = x^3 \sum_{n=0}^{\infty} \frac{(-1)^n}{2^{n+1}} x^n = \sum_{n=0}^{\infty} \frac{(-1)^n}{2^{n+1}} x^{n+3}$$

$$= \tfrac{1}{2} x^3 - \tfrac{1}{4} x^4 + \tfrac{1}{8} x^5 - \tfrac{1}{16} x^6 + \cdots$$

Another way of writing this series is as follows:

$$\frac{x^3}{x + 2} = \sum_{n=3}^{\infty} \frac{(-1)^{n-1}}{2^{n-2}} x^n$$

As in Example 2, the interval of convergence is $(-2, 2)$. ▬

Differentiation and Integration of Power Series

The sum of a power series is a function $f(x) = \sum_{n=0}^{\infty} c_n (x - a)^n$ whose domain is the interval of convergence of the series. We would like to be able to differentiate and integrate such functions, and the following theorem (which we won't prove) says that we can do so by differentiating or integrating each individual term in the series, just as we would for a polynomial. This is called **term-by-term differentiation and integration**.

$\boxed{2}$ **Theorem** If the power series $\Sigma\, c_n(x - a)^n$ has radius of convergence $R > 0$, then the function f defined by

$$f(x) = c_0 + c_1(x - a) + c_2(x - a)^2 + \cdots = \sum_{n=0}^{\infty} c_n(x - a)^n$$

is differentiable (and therefore continuous) on the interval $(a - R, a + R)$ and

(i) $f'(x) = c_1 + 2c_2(x - a) + 3c_3(x - a)^2 + \cdots = \displaystyle\sum_{n=1}^{\infty} nc_n(x - a)^{n-1}$

(ii) $\displaystyle\int f(x)\, dx = C + c_0(x - a) + c_1 \frac{(x - a)^2}{2} + c_2 \frac{(x - a)^3}{3} + \cdots$

$$= C + \sum_{n=0}^{\infty} c_n \frac{(x - a)^{n+1}}{n + 1}$$

The radii of convergence of the power series in Equations (i) and (ii) are both R.

In part (ii), $\int c_0\, dx = c_0 x + C_1$ is written as $c_0(x - a) + C$, where $C = C_1 + ac_0$, so all the terms of the series have the same form.

Note 1: Equations (i) and (ii) in Theorem 2 can be rewritten in the form

(iii) $\displaystyle\frac{d}{dx}\left[\sum_{n=0}^{\infty} c_n(x - a)^n\right] = \sum_{n=0}^{\infty} \frac{d}{dx}\left[c_n(x - a)^n\right]$

(iv) $\displaystyle\int \left[\sum_{n=0}^{\infty} c_n(x - a)^n\right] dx = \sum_{n=0}^{\infty} \int c_n(x - a)^n\, dx$

www.stewartcalculus.com

The idea of differentiating a power series term by term is the basis for a powerful method for solving differential equations. Click on *Additional Topics* and then on *Using Series to Solve Differential Equations.*

We know that, for finite sums, the derivative of a sum is the sum of the derivatives and the integral of a sum is the sum of the integrals. Equations (iii) and (iv) assert that the same is true for infinite sums, provided we are dealing with *power series*. (For other types of series of functions the situation is not as simple; see Exercise 36.)

Note 2: Although Theorem 2 says that the radius of convergence remains the same when a power series is differentiated or integrated, this does not mean that the *interval* of convergence remains the same. It may happen that the original series converges at an endpoint, whereas the differentiated series diverges there. (See Exercise 37.)

EXAMPLE 4 **Differentiating a power series** In Example 3 in Section 8.5 we saw that the Bessel function

$$J_0(x) = \sum_{n=0}^{\infty} \frac{(-1)^n x^{2n}}{2^{2n}(n!)^2}$$

is defined for all x. Thus, by Theorem 2, J_0 is differentiable for all x and its derivative is found by term-by-term differentiation as follows:

$$J_0'(x) = \sum_{n=0}^{\infty} \frac{d}{dx} \frac{(-1)^n x^{2n}}{2^{2n}(n!)^2} = \sum_{n=1}^{\infty} \frac{(-1)^n 2n x^{2n-1}}{2^{2n}(n!)^2}$$

▼ **EXAMPLE 5** Express $1/(1 - x)^2$ as a power series by differentiating Equation 1. What is the radius of convergence?

SOLUTION Differentiating each side of the equation

$$\frac{1}{1-x} = 1 + x + x^2 + x^3 + \cdots = \sum_{n=0}^{\infty} x^n$$

we get

$$\frac{1}{(1-x)^2} = 1 + 2x + 3x^2 + \cdots = \sum_{n=1}^{\infty} nx^{n-1}$$

If we wish, we can replace n by $n + 1$ and write the answer as

$$\frac{1}{(1-x)^2} = \sum_{n=0}^{\infty} (n + 1)x^n$$

According to Theorem 2, the radius of convergence of the differentiated series is the same as the radius of convergence of the original series, namely, $R = 1$. ▬

EXAMPLE 6 **Finding a new power series by integrating an old one** Find a power series representation for $\ln(1 + x)$ and its radius of convergence.

SOLUTION We notice that the derivative of this function is $1/(1 + x)$. From Equation 1 we have

$$\frac{1}{1+x} = \frac{1}{1-(-x)} = 1 - x + x^2 - x^3 + \cdots \qquad |x| < 1$$

Integrating both sides of this equation, we get

$$\ln(1 + x) = \int \frac{1}{1+x}\, dx = \int (1 - x + x^2 - x^3 + \cdots)\, dx$$

$$= x - \frac{x^2}{2} + \frac{x^3}{3} - \frac{x^4}{4} + \cdots + C$$

$$= \sum_{n=1}^{\infty} (-1)^{n-1} \frac{x^n}{n} + C \qquad |x| < 1$$

To determine the value of C we put $x = 0$ in this equation and obtain $\ln(1 + 0) = C$. Thus $C = 0$ and

$$\ln(1 + x) = x - \frac{x^2}{2} + \frac{x^3}{3} - \frac{x^4}{4} + \cdots = \sum_{n=1}^{\infty} (-1)^{n-1} \frac{x^n}{n} \qquad |x| < 1$$

The radius of convergence is the same as for the original series: $R = 1$. ▬

▼ **EXAMPLE 7** Find a power series representation for $f(x) = \tan^{-1}x$.

SOLUTION We observe that $f'(x) = 1/(1 + x^2)$ and find the required series by integrating the power series for $1/(1 + x^2)$ found in Example 1.

$$\tan^{-1}x = \int \frac{1}{1+x^2}\, dx = \int (1 - x^2 + x^4 - x^6 + \cdots)\, dx$$

$$= C + x - \frac{x^3}{3} + \frac{x^5}{5} - \frac{x^7}{7} + \cdots$$

The power series for $\tan^{-1}x$ obtained in Example 7 is called *Gregory's series* after the Scottish mathematician James Gregory (1638–1675), who had anticipated some of Newton's discoveries. We have shown that Gregory's series is valid when $-1 < x < 1$, but it turns out (although it isn't easy to prove) that it is also valid when $x = \pm 1$. Notice that when $x = 1$ the series becomes

$$\frac{\pi}{4} = 1 - \frac{1}{3} + \frac{1}{5} - \frac{1}{7} + \cdots$$

This beautiful result is known as the Leibniz formula for π.

To find C we put $x = 0$ and obtain $C = \tan^{-1}0 = 0$. Therefore

$$\tan^{-1}x = x - \frac{x^3}{3} + \frac{x^5}{5} - \frac{x^7}{7} + \cdots = \sum_{n=0}^{\infty} (-1)^n \frac{x^{2n+1}}{2n+1}$$

Since the radius of convergence of the series for $1/(1 + x^2)$ is 1, the radius of convergence of this series for $\tan^{-1}x$ is also 1.

EXAMPLE 8
(a) Evaluate $\int [1/(1 + x^7)]\,dx$ as a power series.
(b) Use part (a) to approximate $\int_0^{0.5} [1/(1 + x^7)]\,dx$ correct to within 10^{-7}.

SOLUTION
(a) The first step is to express the integrand, $1/(1 + x^7)$, as the sum of a power series. As in Example 1, we start with Equation 1 and replace x by $-x^7$:

$$\frac{1}{1 + x^7} = \frac{1}{1 - (-x^7)} = \sum_{n=0}^{\infty} (-x^7)^n$$

$$= \sum_{n=0}^{\infty} (-1)^n x^{7n} = 1 - x^7 + x^{14} - \cdots$$

This example demonstrates one way in which power series representations are useful. Integrating $1/(1 + x^7)$ by hand is incredibly difficult. Different computer algebra systems return different forms of the answer, but they are all extremely complicated. (If you have a CAS, try it yourself.) The infinite series answer that we obtain in Example 8(a) is actually much easier to deal with than the finite answer provided by a CAS.

Now we integrate term by term:

$$\int \frac{1}{1 + x^7}\,dx = \int \sum_{n=0}^{\infty} (-1)^n x^{7n}\,dx = C + \sum_{n=0}^{\infty} (-1)^n \frac{x^{7n+1}}{7n+1}$$

$$= C + x - \frac{x^8}{8} + \frac{x^{15}}{15} - \frac{x^{22}}{22} + \cdots$$

This series converges for $|-x^7| < 1$, that is, for $|x| < 1$.

(b) In applying the Evaluation Theorem it doesn't matter which antiderivative we use, so let's use the antiderivative from part (a) with $C = 0$:

$$\int_0^{0.5} \frac{1}{1 + x^7}\,dx = \left[x - \frac{x^8}{8} + \frac{x^{15}}{15} - \frac{x^{22}}{22} + \cdots \right]_0^{1/2}$$

$$= \frac{1}{2} - \frac{1}{8 \cdot 2^8} + \frac{1}{15 \cdot 2^{15}} - \frac{1}{22 \cdot 2^{22}} + \cdots + \frac{(-1)^n}{(7n+1)2^{7n+1}} + \cdots$$

This infinite series is the exact value of the definite integral, but since it is an alternating series, we can approximate the sum using the Alternating Series Estimation Theorem. If we stop adding after the term with $n = 3$, the error is smaller than the term with $n = 4$:

$$\frac{1}{29 \cdot 2^{29}} \approx 6.4 \times 10^{-11}$$

So we have

$$\int_0^{0.5} \frac{1}{1 + x^7}\,dx \approx \frac{1}{2} - \frac{1}{8 \cdot 2^8} + \frac{1}{15 \cdot 2^{15}} - \frac{1}{22 \cdot 2^{22}} \approx 0.49951374$$

8.6 Exercises

1. If the radius of convergence of the power series $\sum_{n=0}^{\infty} c_n x^n$ is 10, what is the radius of convergence of the series $\sum_{n=1}^{\infty} nc_n x^{n-1}$? Why?

2. Suppose you know that the series $\sum_{n=0}^{\infty} b_n x^n$ converges for $|x| < 2$. What can you say about the following series? Why?

$$\sum_{n=0}^{\infty} \frac{b_n}{n+1} x^{n+1}$$

3–10 Find a power series representation for the function and determine the interval of convergence.

3. $f(x) = \dfrac{1}{1+x}$ **4.** $f(x) = \dfrac{3}{1-x^4}$

5. $f(x) = \dfrac{2}{3-x}$ **6.** $f(x) = \dfrac{1}{x+10}$

7. $f(x) = \dfrac{x}{9+x^2}$ **8.** $f(x) = \dfrac{x}{2x^2+1}$

9. $f(x) = \dfrac{1+x}{1-x}$ **10.** $f(x) = \dfrac{x^2}{a^3-x^3}$

11. (a) Use differentiation to find a power series representation for

$$f(x) = \frac{1}{(1+x)^2}$$

     What is the radius of convergence?
    (b) Use part (a) to find a power series for

$$f(x) = \frac{1}{(1+x)^3}$$

    (c) Use part (b) to find a power series for

$$f(x) = \frac{x^2}{(1+x)^3}$$

12. (a) Use Equation 1 to find a power series representation for $f(x) = \ln(1-x)$. What is the radius of convergence?
    (b) Use part (a) to find a power series for $f(x) = x \ln(1-x)$.
    (c) By putting $x = \frac{1}{2}$ in your result from part (a), express $\ln 2$ as the sum of an infinite series.

13–18 Find a power series representation for the function and determine the radius of convergence.

13. $f(x) = \ln(5-x)$ **14.** $f(x) = x^2 \tan^{-1}(x^3)$

15. $f(x) = \dfrac{x}{(1+4x)^2}$ **16.** $f(x) = \left(\dfrac{x}{2-x}\right)^3$

17. $f(x) = \dfrac{1+x}{(1-x)^2}$ **18.** $f(x) = \dfrac{x^2+x}{(1-x)^3}$

19–22 Find a power series representation for f, and graph f and several partial sums $s_n(x)$ on the same screen. What happens as n increases?

19. $f(x) = \dfrac{x}{x^2+16}$ **20.** $f(x) = \ln(x^2+4)$

21. $f(x) = \ln\left(\dfrac{1+x}{1-x}\right)$ **22.** $f(x) = \tan^{-1}(2x)$

23–26 Evaluate the indefinite integral as a power series. What is the radius of convergence?

23. $\displaystyle\int \frac{t}{1-t^8}\, dt$ **24.** $\displaystyle\int \frac{\ln(1-t)}{t}\, dt$

25. $\displaystyle\int \frac{x - \tan^{-1}x}{x^3}\, dx$ **26.** $\displaystyle\int \tan^{-1}(x^2)\, dx$

27–30 Use a power series to approximate the definite integral to six decimal places.

27. $\displaystyle\int_0^{0.2} \frac{1}{1+x^5}\, dx$ **28.** $\displaystyle\int_0^{0.4} \ln(1+x^4)\, dx$

29. $\displaystyle\int_0^{0.1} x \arctan(3x)\, dx$ **30.** $\displaystyle\int_0^{0.3} \frac{x^2}{1+x^4}\, dx$

31. Use the result of Example 7 to compute arctan 0.2 correct to five decimal places.

32. Show that the function

$$f(x) = \sum_{n=0}^{\infty} \frac{(-1)^n x^{2n}}{(2n)!}$$

is a solution of the differential equation

$$f''(x) + f(x) = 0$$

33. (a) Show that J_0 (the Bessel function of order 0 given in Example 4) satisfies the differential equation

$$x^2 J_0''(x) + x J_0'(x) + x^2 J_0(x) = 0$$

    (b) Evaluate $\int_0^1 J_0(x)\, dx$ correct to three decimal places.

Graphing calculator or computer with graphing software required   **1.** Homework Hints available in TEC

34. The Bessel function of order 1 is defined by

$$J_1(x) = \sum_{n=0}^{\infty} \frac{(-1)^n x^{2n+1}}{n!(n+1)!2^{2n+1}}$$

(a) Show that J_1 satisfies the differential equation

$$x^2 J_1''(x) + x J_1'(x) + (x^2 - 1)J_1(x) = 0$$

(b) Show that $J_0'(x) = -J_1(x)$.

35. (a) Show that the function

$$f(x) = \sum_{n=0}^{\infty} \frac{x^n}{n!}$$

is a solution of the differential equation

$$f'(x) = f(x)$$

(b) Show that $f(x) = e^x$.

36. Let $f_n(x) = (\sin nx)/n^2$. Show that the series $\Sigma f_n(x)$ converges for all values of x but the series of derivatives $\Sigma f_n'(x)$ diverges when $x = 2n\pi$, n an integer. For what values of x does the series $\Sigma f_n''(x)$ converge?

37. Let

$$f(x) = \sum_{n=1}^{\infty} \frac{x^n}{n^2}$$

Find the intervals of convergence for f, f', and f''.

38. (a) Starting with the geometric series $\Sigma_{n=0}^{\infty} x^n$, find the sum of the series

$$\sum_{n=1}^{\infty} n x^{n-1} \qquad |x| < 1$$

(b) Find the sum of each of the following series.

(i) $\displaystyle\sum_{n=1}^{\infty} n x^n$, $|x| < 1$ (ii) $\displaystyle\sum_{n=1}^{\infty} \frac{n}{2^n}$

(c) Find the sum of each of the following series.

(i) $\displaystyle\sum_{n=2}^{\infty} n(n-1)x^n$, $|x| < 1$

(ii) $\displaystyle\sum_{n=2}^{\infty} \frac{n^2 - n}{2^n}$ (iii) $\displaystyle\sum_{n=1}^{\infty} \frac{n^2}{2^n}$

39. Use the power series for $\tan^{-1} x$ to prove the following expression for π as the sum of an infinite series:

$$\pi = 2\sqrt{3} \sum_{n=0}^{\infty} \frac{(-1)^n}{(2n+1)3^n}$$

40. (a) By completing the square, show that

$$\int_0^{1/2} \frac{dx}{x^2 - x + 1} = \frac{\pi}{3\sqrt{3}}$$

(b) By factoring $x^3 + 1$ as a sum of cubes, rewrite the integral in part (a). Then express $1/(x^3 + 1)$ as the sum of a power series and use it to prove the following formula for π:

$$\pi = \frac{3\sqrt{3}}{4} \sum_{n=0}^{\infty} \frac{(-1)^n}{8^n} \left(\frac{2}{3n+1} + \frac{1}{3n+2} \right)$$

8.7 Taylor and Maclaurin Series

In the preceding section we were able to find power series representations for a certain restricted class of functions. Here we investigate more general problems: Which functions have power series representations? How can we find such representations?

We start by supposing that f is any function that can be represented by a power series

$$\boxed{1} \quad f(x) = c_0 + c_1(x - a) + c_2(x - a)^2 + c_3(x - a)^3 + c_4(x - a)^4 + \cdots \qquad |x - a| < R$$

Let's try to determine what the coefficients c_n must be in terms of f. To begin, notice that if we put $x = a$ in Equation 1, then all terms after the first one are 0 and we get

$$f(a) = c_0$$

By Theorem 8.6.2, we can differentiate the series in Equation 1 term by term:

$$\boxed{2} \quad f'(x) = c_1 + 2c_2(x - a) + 3c_3(x - a)^2 + 4c_4(x - a)^3 + \cdots \qquad |x - a| < R$$

and substitution of $x = a$ in Equation 2 gives

$$f'(a) = c_1$$

Now we differentiate both sides of Equation 2 and obtain

$$\boxed{3}\quad f''(x) = 2c_2 + 2 \cdot 3c_3(x - a) + 3 \cdot 4c_4(x - a)^2 + \cdots \qquad |x - a| < R$$

Again we put $x = a$ in Equation 3. The result is

$$f''(a) = 2c_2$$

Let's apply the procedure one more time. Differentiation of the series in Equation 3 gives

$$\boxed{4}\quad f'''(x) = 2 \cdot 3c_3 + 2 \cdot 3 \cdot 4c_4(x - a) + 3 \cdot 4 \cdot 5c_5(x - a)^2 + \cdots \qquad |x - a| < R$$

and substitution of $x = a$ in Equation 4 gives

$$f'''(a) = 2 \cdot 3c_3 = 3!c_3$$

By now you can see the pattern. If we continue to differentiate and substitute $x = a$, we obtain

$$f^{(n)}(a) = 2 \cdot 3 \cdot 4 \cdot \cdots \cdot nc_n = n!c_n$$

Solving this equation for the nth coefficient c_n, we get

$$c_n = \frac{f^{(n)}(a)}{n!}$$

This formula remains valid even for $n = 0$ if we adopt the conventions that $0! = 1$ and $f^{(0)} = f$. Thus we have proved the following theorem.

$\boxed{5}$ **Theorem** If f has a power series representation (expansion) at a, that is, if

$$f(x) = \sum_{n=0}^{\infty} c_n(x - a)^n \qquad |x - a| < R$$

then its coefficients are given by the formula

$$c_n = \frac{f^{(n)}(a)}{n!}$$

Substituting this formula for c_n back into the series, we see that *if f has a power series expansion at a, then it must be of the following form.*

$$\boxed{6}\quad f(x) = \sum_{n=0}^{\infty} \frac{f^{(n)}(a)}{n!} (x - a)^n$$

$$= f(a) + \frac{f'(a)}{1!}(x - a) + \frac{f''(a)}{2!}(x - a)^2 + \frac{f'''(a)}{3!}(x - a)^3 + \cdots$$

The series in Equation 6 is called the **Taylor series of the function f at a** (or **about a** or **centered at a**).

Taylor and Maclaurin

The Taylor series is named after the English mathematician Brook Taylor (1685–1731) and the Maclaurin series is named in honor of the Scottish mathematician Colin Maclaurin (1698–1746) despite the fact that the Maclaurin series is really just a special case of the Taylor series. But the idea of representing particular functions as sums of power series goes back to Newton, and the general Taylor series was known to the Scottish mathematician James Gregory in 1668 and to the Swiss mathematician John Bernoulli in the 1690s. Taylor was apparently unaware of the work of Gregory and Bernoulli when he published his discoveries on series in 1715 in his book *Methodus incrementorum directa et inversa*. Maclaurin series are named after Colin Maclaurin because he popularized them in his calculus textbook *Treatise of Fluxions* published in 1742.

For the special case $a = 0$ the Taylor series becomes

$$\boxed{7} \qquad f(x) = \sum_{n=0}^{\infty} \frac{f^{(n)}(0)}{n!} x^n = f(0) + \frac{f'(0)}{1!} x + \frac{f''(0)}{2!} x^2 + \cdots$$

This case arises frequently enough that it is given the special name **Maclaurin series**.

Note: We have shown that *if* f can be represented as a power series about a, then f is equal to the sum of its Taylor series. But there exist functions that are not equal to the sum of their Taylor series. An example of such a function is given in Exercise 68.

V EXAMPLE 1 Maclaurin series for the exponential function   Find the Maclaurin series of the function $f(x) = e^x$ and its radius of convergence.

SOLUTION If $f(x) = e^x$, then $f^{(n)}(x) = e^x$, so $f^{(n)}(0) = e^0 = 1$ for all n. Therefore the Taylor series for f at 0 (that is, the Maclaurin series) is

$$\sum_{n=0}^{\infty} \frac{f^{(n)}(0)}{n!} x^n = \sum_{n=0}^{\infty} \frac{x^n}{n!} = 1 + \frac{x}{1!} + \frac{x^2}{2!} + \frac{x^3}{3!} + \cdots$$

To find the radius of convergence we let $a_n = x^n/n!$. Then

$$\left| \frac{a_{n+1}}{a_n} \right| = \left| \frac{x^{n+1}}{(n+1)!} \cdot \frac{n!}{x^n} \right| = \frac{|x|}{n+1} \to 0 < 1$$

so, by the Ratio Test, the series converges for all x and the radius of convergence is $R = \infty$.

The conclusion we can draw from Theorem 5 and Example 1 is that *if* e^x has a power series expansion at 0, then

$$e^x = \sum_{n=0}^{\infty} \frac{x^n}{n!}$$

So how can we determine whether e^x *does* have a power series representation?

Let's investigate the more general question: Under what circumstances is a function equal to the sum of its Taylor series? In other words, if f has derivatives of all orders, when is it true that

$$f(x) = \sum_{n=0}^{\infty} \frac{f^{(n)}(a)}{n!} (x - a)^n$$

As with any convergent series, this means that $f(x)$ is the limit of the sequence of partial sums. In the case of the Taylor series, the partial sums are

$$T_n(x) = \sum_{i=0}^{n} \frac{f^{(i)}(a)}{i!} (x - a)^i$$

$$= f(a) + \frac{f'(a)}{1!} (x - a) + \frac{f''(a)}{2!} (x - a)^2 + \cdots + \frac{f^{(n)}(a)}{n!} (x - a)^n$$

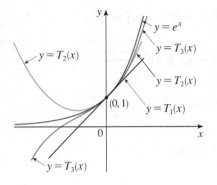

FIGURE 1

As n increases, $T_n(x)$ appears to approach e^x in Figure 1. This suggests that e^x is equal to the sum of its Taylor series.

Notice that T_n is a polynomial of degree n called the **nth-degree Taylor polynomial of f at a**. For instance, for the exponential function $f(x) = e^x$, the result of Example 1 shows that the Taylor polynomials at 0 (or Maclaurin polynomials) with $n = 1$, 2, and 3 are

$$T_1(x) = 1 + x \qquad T_2(x) = 1 + x + \frac{x^2}{2!} \qquad T_3(x) = 1 + x + \frac{x^2}{2!} + \frac{x^3}{3!}$$

The graphs of the exponential function and these three Taylor polynomials are drawn in Figure 1.

In general, $f(x)$ is the sum of its Taylor series if

$$f(x) = \lim_{n \to \infty} T_n(x)$$

If we let

$$R_n(x) = f(x) - T_n(x) \qquad \text{so that} \qquad f(x) = T_n(x) + R_n(x)$$

then $R_n(x)$ is called the **remainder** of the Taylor series. If we can somehow show that $\lim_{n \to \infty} R_n(x) = 0$, then it follows that

$$\lim_{n \to \infty} T_n(x) = \lim_{n \to \infty} [f(x) - R_n(x)] = f(x) - \lim_{n \to \infty} R_n(x) = f(x)$$

We have therefore proved the following.

---

8 **Theorem** If $f(x) = T_n(x) + R_n(x)$, where T_n is the nth-degree Taylor polynomial of f at a and

$$\lim_{n \to \infty} R_n(x) = 0$$

for $|x - a| < R$, then f is equal to the sum of its Taylor series on the interval $|x - a| < R$.

In trying to show that $\lim_{n \to \infty} R_n(x) = 0$ for a specific function f, we usually use the following fact.

---

9 **Taylor's Inequality** If $|f^{(n+1)}(x)| \leq M$ for $|x - a| \leq d$, then the remainder $R_n(x)$ of the Taylor series satisfies the inequality

$$|R_n(x)| \leq \frac{M}{(n + 1)!} |x - a|^{n+1} \qquad \text{for } |x - a| \leq d$$

To see why this is true for $n = 1$, we assume that $|f''(x)| \leq M$. In particular, we have $f''(x) \leq M$, so for $a \leq x \leq a + d$ we have

$$\int_a^x f''(t)\, dt \leq \int_a^x M\, dt$$

An antiderivative of f'' is f', so by the Evaluation Theorem, we have

$$f'(x) - f'(a) \leq M(x - a) \qquad \text{or} \qquad f'(x) \leq f'(a) + M(x - a)$$

Formulas for the Taylor Remainder Term

As alternatives to Taylor's Inequality, we have the following formulas for the remainder term. If $f^{(n+1)}$ is continuous on an interval I and $x \in I$, then

$$R_n(x) = \frac{1}{n!} \int_a^x (x-t)^n f^{(n+1)}(t)\, dt$$

This is called the *integral form of the remainder term*. Another formula, called *Lagrange's form of the remainder term*, states that there is a number z between x and a such that

$$R_n(x) = \frac{f^{(n+1)}(z)}{(n+1)!} (x-a)^{n+1}$$

This version is an extension of the Mean Value Theorem (which is the case $n = 0$).

Proofs of these formulas, together with discussions of how to use them to solve the examples of Sections 8.7 and 8.8, are given on the website

www.stewartcalculus.com

Click on *Additional Topics* and then on *Formulas for the Remainder Term in Taylor series*.

Thus

$$\int_a^x f'(t)\, dt \leqslant \int_a^x [f'(a) + M(t-a)]\, dt$$

$$f(x) - f(a) \leqslant f'(a)(x-a) + M \frac{(x-a)^2}{2}$$

$$f(x) - f(a) - f'(a)(x-a) \leqslant \frac{M}{2}(x-a)^2$$

But $R_1(x) = f(x) - T_1(x) = f(x) - f(a) - f'(a)(x-a)$. So

$$R_1(x) \leqslant \frac{M}{2}(x-a)^2$$

A similar argument, using $f''(x) \geqslant -M$, shows that

$$R_1(x) \geqslant -\frac{M}{2}(x-a)^2$$

So

$$|R_1(x)| \leqslant \frac{M}{2}|x-a|^2$$

Although we have assumed that $x > a$, similar calculations show that this inequality is also true for $x < a$.

This proves Taylor's Inequality for the case where $n = 1$. The result for any n is proved in a similar way by integrating $n + 1$ times. (See Exercise 67 for the case $n = 2$.)

Note: In Section 8.8 we will explore the use of Taylor's Inequality in approximating functions. Our immediate use of it is in conjunction with Theorem 8.

In applying Theorems 8 and 9 it is often helpful to make use of the following fact.

$$\boxed{10} \qquad \lim_{n \to \infty} \frac{x^n}{n!} = 0 \qquad \text{for every real number } x$$

This is true because we know from Example 1 that the series $\sum x^n/n!$ converges for all x and so its nth term approaches 0.

V EXAMPLE 2 Prove that e^x is equal to the sum of its Maclaurin series.

SOLUTION If $f(x) = e^x$, then $f^{(n+1)}(x) = e^x$ for all n. If d is any positive number and $|x| \leqslant d$, then $|f^{(n+1)}(x)| = e^x \leqslant e^d$. So Taylor's Inequality, with $a = 0$ and $M = e^d$, says that

$$|R_n(x)| \leqslant \frac{e^d}{(n+1)!}|x|^{n+1} \qquad \text{for } |x| \leqslant d$$

Notice that the same constant $M = e^d$ works for every value of n. But, from Equation 10, we have

$$\lim_{n \to \infty} \frac{e^d}{(n+1)!}|x|^{n+1} = e^d \lim_{n \to \infty} \frac{|x|^{n+1}}{(n+1)!} = 0$$

It follows from the Squeeze Theorem that $\lim_{n\to\infty} |R_n(x)| = 0$ and therefore $\lim_{n\to\infty} R_n(x) = 0$ for all values of x. By Theorem 8, e^x is equal to the sum of its Maclaurin series, that is,

$$\boxed{11} \qquad e^x = \sum_{n=0}^{\infty} \frac{x^n}{n!} \qquad \text{for all } x$$

In particular, if we put $x = 1$ in Equation 11, we obtain the following expression for the number e as a sum of an infinite series:

$$\boxed{12} \qquad e = \sum_{n=0}^{\infty} \frac{1}{n!} = 1 + \frac{1}{1!} + \frac{1}{2!} + \frac{1}{3!} + \cdots$$

In 1748 Leonard Euler used Equation 12 to find the value of e correct to 23 digits. In 2003 Shigeru Kondo, again using the series in (12), computed e to more than 50 billion decimal places. The special techniques employed to speed up the computation are explained on the web page

numbers.computation.free.fr

EXAMPLE 3 Find the Taylor series for $f(x) = e^x$ at $a = 2$.

SOLUTION We have $f^{(n)}(2) = e^2$ and so, putting $a = 2$ in the definition of a Taylor series (6), we get

$$\sum_{n=0}^{\infty} \frac{f^{(n)}(2)}{n!} (x-2)^n = \sum_{n=0}^{\infty} \frac{e^2}{n!} (x-2)^n$$

Again it can be verified, as in Example 1, that the radius of convergence is $R = \infty$. As in Example 2 we can verify that $\lim_{n\to\infty} R_n(x) = 0$, so

$$\boxed{13} \qquad e^x = \sum_{n=0}^{\infty} \frac{e^2}{n!} (x-2)^n \qquad \text{for all } x$$

We have two power series expansions for e^x, the Maclaurin series in Equation 11 and the Taylor series in Equation 13. The first is better if we are interested in values of x near 0 and the second is better if x is near 2.

EXAMPLE 4 Find the Maclaurin series for $\sin x$ and prove that it represents $\sin x$ for all x.

SOLUTION We arrange our computation in two columns as follows:

$$f(x) = \sin x \qquad\qquad f(0) = 0$$
$$f'(x) = \cos x \qquad\qquad f'(0) = 1$$
$$f''(x) = -\sin x \qquad\qquad f''(0) = 0$$
$$f'''(x) = -\cos x \qquad\qquad f'''(0) = -1$$
$$f^{(4)}(x) = \sin x \qquad\qquad f^{(4)}(0) = 0$$

Since the derivatives repeat in a cycle of four, we can write the Maclaurin series as follows:

$$f(0) + \frac{f'(0)}{1!} x + \frac{f''(0)}{2!} x^2 + \frac{f'''(0)}{3!} x^3 + \cdots$$

$$= x - \frac{x^3}{3!} + \frac{x^5}{5!} - \frac{x^7}{7!} + \cdots = \sum_{n=0}^{\infty} (-1)^n \frac{x^{2n+1}}{(2n+1)!}$$

Figure 2 shows the graph of $\sin x$ together with its Taylor (or Maclaurin) polynomials

$$T_1(x) = x$$

$$T_3(x) = x - \frac{x^3}{3!}$$

$$T_5(x) = x - \frac{x^3}{3!} + \frac{x^5}{5!}$$

Notice that, as n increases, $T_n(x)$ becomes a better approximation to $\sin x$.

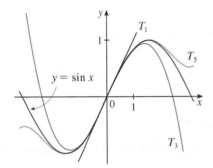

FIGURE 2

Since $f^{(n+1)}(x)$ is $\pm\sin x$ or $\pm\cos x$, we know that $\left| f^{(n+1)}(x) \right| \leq 1$ for all x. So we can take $M = 1$ in Taylor's Inequality:

$$\boxed{14} \qquad |R_n(x)| \leq \frac{M}{(n+1)!} |x^{n+1}| = \frac{|x|^{n+1}}{(n+1)!}$$

By Equation 10 the right side of this inequality approaches 0 as $n \to \infty$, so $|R_n(x)| \to 0$ by the Squeeze Theorem. It follows that $R_n(x) \to 0$ as $n \to \infty$, so $\sin x$ is equal to the sum of its Maclaurin series by Theorem 8.

We state the result of Example 4 for future reference.

$$\boxed{15} \qquad \sin x = x - \frac{x^3}{3!} + \frac{x^5}{5!} - \frac{x^7}{7!} + \cdots$$

$$= \sum_{n=0}^{\infty} (-1)^n \frac{x^{2n+1}}{(2n+1)!} \qquad \text{for all } x$$

EXAMPLE 5   **Obtaining a Maclaurin series by differentiating a known series**
Find the Maclaurin series for $\cos x$.

SOLUTION   We could proceed directly as in Example 4, but it's easier to differentiate the Maclaurin series for $\sin x$ given by Equation 15:

$$\cos x = \frac{d}{dx}(\sin x) = \frac{d}{dx}\left(x - \frac{x^3}{3!} + \frac{x^5}{5!} - \frac{x^7}{7!} + \cdots \right)$$

$$= 1 - \frac{3x^2}{3!} + \frac{5x^4}{5!} - \frac{7x^6}{7!} + \cdots = 1 - \frac{x^2}{2!} + \frac{x^4}{4!} - \frac{x^6}{6!} + \cdots$$

The Maclaurin series for e^x, $\sin x$, and $\cos x$ that we found in Examples 2, 4, and 5 were discovered, using different methods, by Newton. These equations are remarkable because they say we know everything about each of these functions if we know all its derivatives at the single number 0.

Since the Maclaurin series for $\sin x$ converges for all x, Theorem 2 in Section 8.6 tells us that the differentiated series for $\cos x$ also converges for all x. Thus

$$\boxed{16} \qquad \cos x = 1 - \frac{x^2}{2!} + \frac{x^4}{4!} - \frac{x^6}{6!} + \cdots$$

$$= \sum_{n=0}^{\infty} (-1)^n \frac{x^{2n}}{(2n)!} \qquad \text{for all } x$$

EXAMPLE 6   **A shortcut for obtaining a Maclaurin series**   Find the Maclaurin series for the function $f(x) = x \cos x$.

SOLUTION   Instead of computing derivatives and substituting in Equation 7, it's easier to multiply the series for $\cos x$ (Equation 16) by x:

$$x \cos x = x \sum_{n=0}^{\infty} (-1)^n \frac{x^{2n}}{(2n)!} = \sum_{n=0}^{\infty} (-1)^n \frac{x^{2n+1}}{(2n)!}$$

The power series that we obtained by indirect methods in Examples 5 and 6 and in Section 8.6 are indeed the Taylor or Maclaurin series of the given functions because

Theorem 5 asserts that, no matter how a power series representation $f(x) = \Sigma \, c_n(x - a)^n$ is obtained, it is always true that $c_n = f^{(n)}(a)/n!$. In other words, the coefficients are uniquely determined.

EXAMPLE 7 Represent $f(x) = \sin x$ as the sum of its Taylor series centered at $\pi/3$.

SOLUTION Arranging our work in columns, we have

$$f(x) = \sin x \qquad f\left(\frac{\pi}{3}\right) = \frac{\sqrt{3}}{2}$$

$$f'(x) = \cos x \qquad f'\left(\frac{\pi}{3}\right) = \frac{1}{2}$$

$$f''(x) = -\sin x \qquad f''\left(\frac{\pi}{3}\right) = -\frac{\sqrt{3}}{2}$$

$$f'''(x) = -\cos x \qquad f'''\left(\frac{\pi}{3}\right) = -\frac{1}{2}$$

and this pattern repeats indefinitely. Therefore the Taylor series at $\pi/3$ is

$$f\left(\frac{\pi}{3}\right) + \frac{f'\left(\frac{\pi}{3}\right)}{1!}\left(x - \frac{\pi}{3}\right) + \frac{f''\left(\frac{\pi}{3}\right)}{2!}\left(x - \frac{\pi}{3}\right)^2 + \frac{f'''\left(\frac{\pi}{3}\right)}{3!}\left(x - \frac{\pi}{3}\right)^3 + \cdots$$

$$= \frac{\sqrt{3}}{2} + \frac{1}{2 \cdot 1!}\left(x - \frac{\pi}{3}\right) - \frac{\sqrt{3}}{2 \cdot 2!}\left(x - \frac{\pi}{3}\right)^2 - \frac{1}{2 \cdot 3!}\left(x - \frac{\pi}{3}\right)^3 + \cdots$$

We have obtained two different series representations for $\sin x$, the Maclaurin series in Example 4 and the Taylor series in Example 7. It is best to use the Maclaurin series for values of x near 0 and the Taylor series for x near $\pi/3$. Notice that the third Taylor polynomial T_3 in Figure 3 is a good approximation to $\sin x$ near $\pi/3$ but not as good near 0. Compare it with the third Maclaurin polynomial T_3 in Figure 2, where the opposite is true.

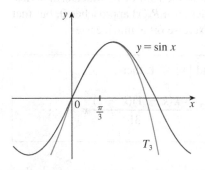

FIGURE 3

The proof that this series represents $\sin x$ for all x is very similar to that in Example 4. [Just replace x by $x - \pi/3$ in (14).] We can write the series in sigma notation if we separate the terms that contain $\sqrt{3}$:

$$\sin x = \sum_{n=0}^{\infty} \frac{(-1)^n \sqrt{3}}{2(2n)!}\left(x - \frac{\pi}{3}\right)^{2n} + \sum_{n=0}^{\infty} \frac{(-1)^n}{2(2n+1)!}\left(x - \frac{\pi}{3}\right)^{2n+1}$$

EXAMPLE 8 Find the Maclaurin series for $f(x) = (1 + x)^k$, where k is any real number.

SOLUTION Arranging our work in columns, we have

$$f(x) = (1 + x)^k \qquad\qquad f(0) = 1$$

$$f'(x) = k(1 + x)^{k-1} \qquad\qquad f'(0) = k$$

$$f''(x) = k(k - 1)(1 + x)^{k-2} \qquad\qquad f''(0) = k(k - 1)$$

$$f'''(x) = k(k - 1)(k - 2)(1 + x)^{k-3} \qquad\qquad f'''(0) = k(k - 1)(k - 2)$$

$$\vdots \qquad\qquad\qquad\qquad \vdots$$

$$f^{(n)}(x) = k(k - 1) \cdots (k - n + 1)(1 + x)^{k-n} \qquad f^{(n)}(0) = k(k - 1) \cdots (k - n + 1)$$

Therefore the Maclaurin series of $f(x) = (1 + x)^k$ is

$$\sum_{n=0}^{\infty} \frac{f^{(n)}(0)}{n!} x^n = \sum_{n=0}^{\infty} \frac{k(k-1)\cdots(k-n+1)}{n!} x^n$$

This series is called the **binomial series**. If its nth term is a_n, then

$$\left| \frac{a_{n+1}}{a_n} \right| = \left| \frac{k(k-1)\cdots(k-n+1)(k-n)x^{n+1}}{(n+1)!} \cdot \frac{n!}{k(k-1)\cdots(k-n+1)x^n} \right|$$

$$= \frac{|k-n|}{n+1}|x| = \frac{\left|1 - \dfrac{k}{n}\right|}{1 + \dfrac{1}{n}}|x| \to |x| \qquad \text{as } n \to \infty$$

Thus, by the Ratio Test, the binomial series converges if $|x| < 1$ and diverges if $|x| > 1$.

The traditional notation for the coefficients in the binomial series is

$$\binom{k}{n} = \frac{k(k-1)(k-2)\cdots(k-n+1)}{n!}$$

and these numbers are called the **binomial coefficients**.

The following theorem states that $(1 + x)^k$ is equal to the sum of its Maclaurin series. It is possible to prove this by showing that the remainder term $R_n(x)$ approaches 0, but that turns out to be quite difficult. The proof outlined in Exercise 69 is much easier.

> **17** **The Binomial Series** If k is any real number and $|x| < 1$, then
>
> $$(1 + x)^k = \sum_{n=0}^{\infty} \binom{k}{n} x^n = 1 + kx + \frac{k(k-1)}{2!}x^2 + \frac{k(k-1)(k-2)}{3!}x^3 + \cdots$$

Although the binomial series always converges when $|x| < 1$, the question of whether or not it converges at the endpoints, ± 1, depends on the value of k. It turns out that the series converges at 1 if $-1 < k \le 0$ and at both endpoints if $k \ge 0$. Notice that if k is a positive integer and $n > k$, then the expression for $\binom{k}{n}$ contains a factor $(k - k)$, so $\binom{k}{n} = 0$ for $n > k$. This means that the series terminates and reduces to the ordinary Binomial Theorem when k is a positive integer. (See Reference Page 1.)

V EXAMPLE 9 **Using a binomial series to obtain a Maclaurin series**

Find the Maclaurin series for the function $f(x) = \dfrac{1}{\sqrt{4-x}}$ and its radius of convergence.

SOLUTION We rewrite $f(x)$ in a form where we can use the binomial series:

$$\frac{1}{\sqrt{4-x}} = \frac{1}{\sqrt{4\left(1 - \dfrac{x}{4}\right)}} = \frac{1}{2\sqrt{1 - \dfrac{x}{4}}} = \frac{1}{2}\left(1 - \frac{x}{4}\right)^{-1/2}$$

Using the binomial series with $k = -\frac{1}{2}$ and with x replaced by $-x/4$, we have

$$\frac{1}{\sqrt{4-x}} = \frac{1}{2}\left(1 - \frac{x}{4}\right)^{-1/2} = \frac{1}{2}\sum_{n=0}^{\infty}\binom{-\frac{1}{2}}{n}\left(-\frac{x}{4}\right)^n$$

$$= \frac{1}{2}\left[1 + \left(-\frac{1}{2}\right)\left(-\frac{x}{4}\right) + \frac{\left(-\frac{1}{2}\right)\left(-\frac{3}{2}\right)}{2!}\left(-\frac{x}{4}\right)^2 + \frac{\left(-\frac{1}{2}\right)\left(-\frac{3}{2}\right)\left(-\frac{5}{2}\right)}{3!}\left(-\frac{x}{4}\right)^3\right.$$

$$\left. + \cdots + \frac{\left(-\frac{1}{2}\right)\left(-\frac{3}{2}\right)\left(-\frac{5}{2}\right)\cdots\left(-\frac{1}{2} - n + 1\right)}{n!}\left(-\frac{x}{4}\right)^n + \cdots\right]$$

$$= \frac{1}{2}\left[1 + \frac{1}{8}x + \frac{1\cdot 3}{2!8^2}x^2 + \frac{1\cdot 3\cdot 5}{3!8^3}x^3 + \cdots + \frac{1\cdot 3\cdot 5\cdot\cdots\cdot(2n-1)}{n!8^n}x^n + \cdots\right]$$

We know from (17) that this series converges when $|-x/4| < 1$, that is, $|x| < 4$, so the radius of convergence is $R = 4$.

We collect in the following table, for future reference, some important Maclaurin series that we have derived in this section and the preceding one.

TABLE 1

Important Maclaurin Series and Their Radii of Convergence

$\dfrac{1}{1-x} = \displaystyle\sum_{n=0}^{\infty} x^n = 1 + x + x^2 + x^3 + \cdots$	$R = 1$
$e^x = \displaystyle\sum_{n=0}^{\infty} \frac{x^n}{n!} = 1 + \frac{x}{1!} + \frac{x^2}{2!} + \frac{x^3}{3!} + \cdots$	$R = \infty$
$\sin x = \displaystyle\sum_{n=0}^{\infty}(-1)^n \frac{x^{2n+1}}{(2n+1)!} = x - \frac{x^3}{3!} + \frac{x^5}{5!} - \frac{x^7}{7!} + \cdots$	$R = \infty$
$\cos x = \displaystyle\sum_{n=0}^{\infty}(-1)^n \frac{x^{2n}}{(2n)!} = 1 - \frac{x^2}{2!} + \frac{x^4}{4!} - \frac{x^6}{6!} + \cdots$	$R = \infty$
$\tan^{-1}x = \displaystyle\sum_{n=0}^{\infty}(-1)^n \frac{x^{2n+1}}{2n+1} = x - \frac{x^3}{3} + \frac{x^5}{5} - \frac{x^7}{7} + \cdots$	$R = 1$
$\ln(1+x) = \displaystyle\sum_{n=1}^{\infty}(-1)^{n-1} \frac{x^n}{n} = x - \frac{x^2}{2} + \frac{x^3}{3} - \frac{x^4}{4} + \cdots$	$R = 1$
$(1+x)^k = \displaystyle\sum_{n=0}^{\infty}\binom{k}{n}x^n = 1 + kx + \frac{k(k-1)}{2!}x^2 + \frac{k(k-1)(k-2)}{3!}x^3 + \cdots$	$R = 1$

EXAMPLE 10 Find the sum of the series $\dfrac{1}{1\cdot 2} - \dfrac{1}{2\cdot 2^2} + \dfrac{1}{3\cdot 2^3} - \dfrac{1}{4\cdot 2^4} + \cdots$.

SOLUTION With sigma notation we can write the given series as

$$\sum_{n=1}^{\infty}(-1)^{n-1}\frac{1}{n\cdot 2^n} = \sum_{n=1}^{\infty}(-1)^{n-1}\frac{\left(\frac{1}{2}\right)^n}{n}$$

Then from Table 1 we see that this series matches the entry for $\ln(1 + x)$ with $x = \frac{1}{2}$. So

$$\sum_{n=1}^{\infty}(-1)^{n-1}\frac{1}{n \cdot 2^n} = \ln\left(1 + \tfrac{1}{2}\right) = \ln \tfrac{3}{2}$$

TEC Module 8.7/8.8 enables you to see how successive Taylor polynomials approach the original function.

One reason that Taylor series are important is that they enable us to integrate functions that we couldn't previously handle. In fact, in the introduction to this chapter we mentioned that Newton often integrated functions by first expressing them as power series and then integrating the series term by term. The function $f(x) = e^{-x^2}$ can't be integrated by techniques discussed so far because its antiderivative is not an elementary function (see Section 5.8). In the following example we use Newton's idea to integrate this function.

V EXAMPLE 11   Using a series to evaluate an integral

(a) Evaluate $\int e^{-x^2}\,dx$ as an infinite series.

(b) Evaluate $\int_0^1 e^{-x^2}\,dx$ correct to within an error of 0.001.

SOLUTION

(a) First we find the Maclaurin series for $f(x) = e^{-x^2}$. Although it's possible to use the direct method, let's find it simply by replacing x with $-x^2$ in the series for e^x given in Table 1. Thus, for all values of x,

$$e^{-x^2} = \sum_{n=0}^{\infty}\frac{(-x^2)^n}{n!} = \sum_{n=0}^{\infty}(-1)^n\frac{x^{2n}}{n!} = 1 - \frac{x^2}{1!} + \frac{x^4}{2!} - \frac{x^6}{3!} + \cdots$$

Now we integrate term by term:

$$\int e^{-x^2}\,dx = \int\left(1 - \frac{x^2}{1!} + \frac{x^4}{2!} - \frac{x^6}{3!} + \cdots + (-1)^n\frac{x^{2n}}{n!} + \cdots\right)dx$$

$$= C + x - \frac{x^3}{3 \cdot 1!} + \frac{x^5}{5 \cdot 2!} - \frac{x^7}{7 \cdot 3!} + \cdots + (-1)^n\frac{x^{2n+1}}{(2n + 1)n!} + \cdots$$

This series converges for all x because the original series for e^{-x^2} converges for all x.

(b) The Evaluation Theorem gives

We can take $C = 0$ in the antiderivative in part (a).

$$\int_0^1 e^{-x^2}\,dx = \left[x - \frac{x^3}{3 \cdot 1!} + \frac{x^5}{5 \cdot 2!} - \frac{x^7}{7 \cdot 3!} + \frac{x^9}{9 \cdot 4!} - \cdots\right]_0^1$$

$$= 1 - \tfrac{1}{3} + \tfrac{1}{10} - \tfrac{1}{42} + \tfrac{1}{216} - \cdots$$

$$\approx 1 - \tfrac{1}{3} + \tfrac{1}{10} - \tfrac{1}{42} + \tfrac{1}{216} \approx 0.7475$$

The Alternating Series Estimation Theorem shows that the error involved in this approximation is less than

$$\frac{1}{11 \cdot 5!} = \frac{1}{1320} < 0.001$$

Another use of Taylor series is illustrated in the next example. The limit could be found with l'Hospital's Rule, but instead we use a series.

EXAMPLE 12 **Using a series to evaluate a limit** Evaluate $\lim\limits_{x \to 0} \dfrac{e^x - 1 - x}{x^2}$.

SOLUTION Using the Maclaurin series for e^x, we have

$$\lim_{x \to 0} \frac{e^x - 1 - x}{x^2} = \lim_{x \to 0} \frac{\left(1 + \dfrac{x}{1!} + \dfrac{x^2}{2!} + \dfrac{x^3}{3!} + \cdots\right) - 1 - x}{x^2}$$

$$= \lim_{x \to 0} \frac{\dfrac{x^2}{2!} + \dfrac{x^3}{3!} + \dfrac{x^4}{4!} + \cdots}{x^2}$$

Some computer algebra systems compute limits in this way.

$$= \lim_{x \to 0} \left(\frac{1}{2} + \frac{x}{3!} + \frac{x^2}{4!} + \frac{x^3}{5!} + \cdots\right) = \frac{1}{2}$$

because power series are continuous functions.

Multiplication and Division of Power Series

If power series are added or subtracted, they behave like polynomials (Theorem 8.2.8 shows this). In fact, as the following example illustrates, they can also be multiplied and divided like polynomials. We find only the first few terms because the calculations for the later terms become tedious and the initial terms are the most important ones.

EXAMPLE 13 **Finding Maclaurin series by multiplication and division** Find the first three nonzero terms in the Maclaurin series for (a) $e^x \sin x$ and (b) $\tan x$.

SOLUTION
(a) Using the Maclaurin series for e^x and $\sin x$ in Table 1, we have

$$e^x \sin x = \left(1 + \frac{x}{1!} + \frac{x^2}{2!} + \frac{x^3}{3!} + \cdots\right)\left(x - \frac{x^3}{3!} + \cdots\right)$$

We multiply these expressions, collecting like terms just as for polynomials:

$$
\begin{array}{r}
1 + x + \frac{1}{2}x^2 + \frac{1}{6}x^3 + \cdots \\
\times \qquad x \qquad\quad - \frac{1}{6}x^3 + \cdots \\
\hline
x + \ x^2 + \frac{1}{2}x^3 + \frac{1}{6}x^4 + \cdots \\
+ \qquad\qquad\quad - \frac{1}{6}x^3 - \frac{1}{6}x^4 - \cdots \\
\hline
x + \ x^2 + \frac{1}{3}x^3 + \cdots
\end{array}
$$

Thus $\qquad\qquad e^x \sin x = x + x^2 + \frac{1}{3}x^3 + \cdots$

(b) Using the Maclaurin series in Table 1, we have

$$\tan x = \frac{\sin x}{\cos x} = \frac{x - \dfrac{x^3}{3!} + \dfrac{x^5}{5!} - \cdots}{1 - \dfrac{x^2}{2!} + \dfrac{x^4}{4!} - \cdots}$$

We use a procedure like long division:

$$x + \tfrac{1}{3}x^3 + \tfrac{2}{15}x^5 + \cdots$$

$$1 - \tfrac{1}{2}x^2 + \tfrac{1}{24}x^4 - \cdots \overline{)\,x - \tfrac{1}{6}x^3 + \tfrac{1}{120}x^5 - \cdots}$$

$$\underline{x - \tfrac{1}{2}x^3 + \tfrac{1}{24}x^5 - \cdots}$$

$$\tfrac{1}{3}x^3 - \tfrac{1}{30}x^5 + \cdots$$

$$\underline{\tfrac{1}{3}x^3 - \tfrac{1}{6}x^5 + \cdots}$$

$$\tfrac{2}{15}x^5 + \cdots$$

Thus $\tan x = x + \tfrac{1}{3}x^3 + \tfrac{2}{15}x^5 + \cdots$

Although we have not attempted to justify the formal manipulations used in Example 13, they are legitimate. There is a theorem which states that if both $f(x) = \Sigma\, c_n x^n$ and $g(x) = \Sigma\, b_n x^n$ converge for $|x| < R$ and the series are multiplied as if they were polynomials, then the resulting series also converges for $|x| < R$ and represents $f(x)g(x)$. For division we require $b_0 \neq 0$; the resulting series converges for sufficiently small $|x|$.

8.7 Exercises

1. If $f(x) = \sum_{n=0}^{\infty} b_n(x - 5)^n$ for all x, write a formula for b_8.

2. The graph of f is shown.

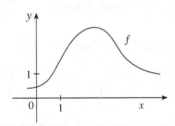

(a) Explain why the series

$$1.6 - 0.8(x - 1) + 0.4(x - 1)^2 - 0.1(x - 1)^3 + \cdots$$

is *not* the Taylor series of f centered at 1.
(b) Explain why the series

$$2.8 + 0.5(x - 2) + 1.5(x - 2)^2 - 0.1(x - 2)^3 + \cdots$$

is *not* the Taylor series of f centered at 2.

3. If $f^{(n)}(0) = (n + 1)!$ for $n = 0, 1, 2, \ldots$, find the Maclaurin series for f and its radius of convergence.

4. Find the Taylor series for f centered at 4 if

$$f^{(n)}(4) = \frac{(-1)^n\, n!}{3^n(n + 1)}$$

What is the radius of convergence of the Taylor series?

5–10 Find the Maclaurin series for $f(x)$ using the definition of a Maclaurin series. [Assume that f has a power series expansion. Do not show that $R_n(x) \to 0$.] Also find the associated radius of convergence.

5. $f(x) = (1 - x)^{-2}$ **6.** $f(x) = \ln(1 + x)$

7. $f(x) = \sin \pi x$ **8.** $f(x) = \cos 3x$

9. $f(x) = e^{5x}$ **10.** $f(x) = xe^x$

11–18 Find the Taylor series for $f(x)$ centered at the given value of a. [Assume that f has a power series expansion. Do not show that $R_n(x) \to 0$.]

11. $f(x) = x^4 - 3x^2 + 1, \quad a = 1$

12. $f(x) = x - x^3, \quad a = -2$

13. $f(x) = e^x, \quad a = 3$ **14.** $f(x) = 1/x, \quad a = -3$

15. $f(x) = \cos x, \quad a = \pi$ **16.** $f(x) = \sin x, \quad a = \pi/2$

17. $f(x) = 1/\sqrt{x}, \quad a = 9$ **18.** $f(x) = x^{-2}, \quad a = 1$

19. Prove that the series obtained in Exercise 7 represents $\sin \pi x$ for all x.

20. Prove that the series obtained in Exercise 16 represents $\sin x$ for all x.

⊞ Graphing calculator or computer with graphing software required   **1.** Homework Hints available in TEC

21–24 Use the binomial series to expand the function as a power series. State the radius of convergence.

21. $\sqrt{1 + x}$

22. $\dfrac{1}{(1 + x)^4}$

23. $\dfrac{1}{(2 + x)^3}$

24. $(1 - x)^{2/3}$

25–34 Use a Maclaurin series in Table 1 to obtain the Maclaurin series for the given function.

25. $f(x) = \sin \pi x$

26. $f(x) = \cos(\pi x/2)$

27. $f(x) = e^x + e^{2x}$

28. $f(x) = e^x + 2e^{-x}$

29. $f(x) = x \cos(\tfrac{1}{2}x^2)$

30. $f(x) = x^2 \ln(1 + x^3)$

31. $f(x) = \dfrac{x}{\sqrt{4 + x^2}}$

32. $f(x) = \dfrac{x^2}{\sqrt{2 + x}}$

33. $f(x) = \sin^2 x$ $\left[\textit{Hint:} \text{ Use } \sin^2 x = \tfrac{1}{2}(1 - \cos 2x).\right]$

34. $f(x) = \begin{cases} \dfrac{x - \sin x}{x^3} & \text{if } x \neq 0 \\ \tfrac{1}{6} & \text{if } x = 0 \end{cases}$

35–38 Find the Maclaurin series of f (by any method) and its radius of convergence. Graph f and its first few Taylor polynomials on the same screen. What do you notice about the relationship between these polynomials and f?

35. $f(x) = \cos(x^2)$

36. $f(x) = e^{-x^2} + \cos x$

37. $f(x) = xe^{-x}$

38. $f(x) = \ln(1 + x^2)$

---

39. Use the Maclaurin series for e^x to calculate $e^{-0.2}$ correct to five decimal places.

40. Use the Maclaurin series for $\sin x$ to compute $\sin 3°$ correct to five decimal places.

41. (a) Use the binomial series to expand $1/\sqrt{1 - x^2}$.
    (b) Use part (a) to find the Maclaurin series for $\sin^{-1}x$.

42. (a) Expand $1/\sqrt[4]{1 + x}$ as a power series.
    (b) Use part (a) to estimate $1/\sqrt[4]{1.1}$ correct to three decimal places.

43–46 Evaluate the indefinite integral as an infinite series.

43. $\displaystyle\int x \cos(x^3)\, dx$

44. $\displaystyle\int \dfrac{e^x - 1}{x}\, dx$

45. $\displaystyle\int \dfrac{\cos x - 1}{x}\, dx$

46. $\displaystyle\int \arctan(x^3)\, dx$

47–50 Use series to approximate the definite integral to within the indicated accuracy.

47. $\displaystyle\int_0^1 x \cos(x^3)\, dx$ (three decimal places)

48. $\displaystyle\int_0^{0.2} [\tan^{-1}(x^3) + \sin(x^3)]\, dx$ (five decimal places)

49. $\displaystyle\int_0^{0.4} \sqrt{1 + x^4}\, dx$ $\left(|\,\text{error}\,| < 5 \times 10^{-6}\right)$

50. $\displaystyle\int_0^{0.5} x^2 e^{-x^2}\, dx$ $\left(|\,\text{error}\,| < 0.001\right)$

51–53 Use series to evaluate the limit.

51. $\displaystyle\lim_{x \to 0} \dfrac{x - \ln(1 + x)}{x^2}$

52. $\displaystyle\lim_{x \to 0} \dfrac{1 - \cos x}{1 + x - e^x}$

53. $\displaystyle\lim_{x \to 0} \dfrac{\sin x - x + \tfrac{1}{6}x^3}{x^5}$

---

54. Use the series in Example 13(b) to evaluate

$$\lim_{x \to 0} \dfrac{\tan x - x}{x^3}$$

We found this limit in Example 4 in Section 4.5 using l'Hospital's Rule three times. Which method do you prefer?

55–58 Use multiplication or division of power series to find the first three nonzero terms in the Maclaurin series for each function.

55. $y = e^{-x^2} \cos x$

56. $y = \sec x$

57. $y = \dfrac{x}{\sin x}$

58. $y = e^x \ln(1 + x)$

59–66 Find the sum of the series.

59. $\displaystyle\sum_{n=0}^{\infty} (-1)^n \dfrac{x^{4n}}{n!}$

60. $\displaystyle\sum_{n=0}^{\infty} \dfrac{(-1)^n \pi^{2n}}{6^{2n}(2n)!}$

61. $\displaystyle\sum_{n=1}^{\infty} (-1)^{n-1} \dfrac{3^n}{n\,5^n}$

62. $\displaystyle\sum_{n=0}^{\infty} \dfrac{3^n}{5^n n!}$

63. $\displaystyle\sum_{n=0}^{\infty} \dfrac{(-1)^n \pi^{2n+1}}{4^{2n+1}(2n + 1)!}$

64. $1 - \ln 2 + \dfrac{(\ln 2)^2}{2!} - \dfrac{(\ln 2)^3}{3!} + \cdots$

65. $3 + \dfrac{9}{2!} + \dfrac{27}{3!} + \dfrac{81}{4!} + \cdots$

66. $\dfrac{1}{1 \cdot 2} - \dfrac{1}{3 \cdot 2^3} + \dfrac{1}{5 \cdot 2^5} - \dfrac{1}{7 \cdot 2^7} + \cdots$

---

67. Prove Taylor's Inequality for $n = 2$, that is, prove that if $|f'''(x)| \leq M$ for $|x - a| \leq d$, then

$$|R_2(x)| \leq \frac{M}{6}|x - a|^3 \qquad \text{for } |x - a| \leq d$$

68. (a) Show that the function defined by

$$f(x) = \begin{cases} e^{-1/x^2} & \text{if } x \neq 0 \\ 0 & \text{if } x = 0 \end{cases}$$

is not equal to its Maclaurin series.

(b) Graph the function in part (a) and comment on its behavior near the origin.

69. Use the following steps to prove (17).

(a) Let $g(x) = \sum_{n=0}^{\infty} \binom{k}{n} x^n$. Differentiate this series to show that

$$g'(x) = \frac{kg(x)}{1 + x} \qquad -1 < x < 1$$

(b) Let $h(x) = (1 + x)^{-k} g(x)$ and show that $h'(x) = 0$.

(c) Deduce that $g(x) = (1 + x)^k$.

70. In Exercise 31 in Section 6.4 it was shown that the length of the ellipse $x = a \sin \theta$, $y = b \cos \theta$, where $a > b > 0$, is

$$L = 4a \int_0^{\pi/2} \sqrt{1 - e^2 \sin^2 \theta}\ d\theta$$

where $e = \sqrt{a^2 - b^2}/a$ is the eccentricity of the ellipse. Expand the integrand as a binomial series and use the result of Exercise 38 in Section 5.6 to express L as a series in powers of the eccentricity up to the term in e^6.

LABORATORY PROJECT   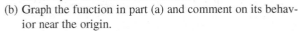 CAS **An Elusive Limit**

This project deals with the function

$$f(x) = \frac{\sin(\tan x) - \tan(\sin x)}{\arcsin(\arctan x) - \arctan(\arcsin x)}$$

1. Use your computer algebra system to evaluate $f(x)$ for $x = 1, 0.1, 0.01, 0.001,$ and 0.0001. Does it appear that f has a limit as $x \to 0$?

2. Use the CAS to graph f near $x = 0$. Does it appear that f has a limit as $x \to 0$?

3. Try to evaluate $\lim_{x \to 0} f(x)$ with l'Hospital's Rule, using the CAS to find derivatives of the numerator and denominator. What do you discover? How many applications of l'Hospital's Rule are required?

4. Evaluate $\lim_{x \to 0} f(x)$ by using the CAS to find sufficiently many terms in the Taylor series of the numerator and denominator. (Use the command `taylor` in Maple or `Series` in Mathematica.)

5. Use the limit command on your CAS to find $\lim_{x \to 0} f(x)$ directly. (Most computer algebra systems use the method of Problem 4 to compute limits.)

6. In view of the answers to Problems 4 and 5, how do you explain the results of Problems 1 and 2?

CAS Computer algebra system required

WRITING PROJECT   **How Newton Discovered the Binomial Series**

The Binomial Theorem, which gives the expansion of $(a + b)^k$, was known to Chinese mathematicians many centuries before the time of Newton for the case where the exponent k is a positive integer. In 1665, when he was 22, Newton was the first to discover the infinite series expansion of $(a + b)^k$ when k is a fractional exponent (positive or negative). He didn't publish his discovery, but he stated it and gave examples of how to use it in a letter (now called the *epistola prior*) dated June 13, 1676, that he sent to Henry Oldenburg, secretary of the Royal Society of London, to transmit to Leibniz. When Leibniz replied, he asked how Newton had discovered the binomial series. Newton wrote a second letter, the *epistola posterior* of October 24, 1676, in which he explained in great detail how he arrived at his discovery by a very indirect route. He was investigating the areas under the curves $y = (1 - x^2)^{n/2}$ from 0 to x for $n = 0, 1, 2, 3, 4, \ldots$. These are easy to calculate if n is even. By observing patterns and interpolating, Newton was able to guess the answers for odd values of n. Then he realized he could get the same answers by expressing $(1 - x^2)^{n/2}$ as an infinite series.

Write a report on Newton's discovery of the binomial series. Start by giving the statement of the binomial series in Newton's notation (see the *epistola prior* on page 285 of [4] or page 402 of [2]). Explain why Newton's version is equivalent to Theorem 17 on page 612. Then read Newton's *epistola posterior* (page 287 in [4] or page 404 in [2]) and explain the patterns that Newton discovered in the areas under the curves $y = (1 - x^2)^{n/2}$. Show how he was able to guess the areas under the remaining curves and how he verified his answers. Finally, explain how these discoveries led to the binomial series. The books by Edwards [1] and Katz [3] contain commentaries on Newton's letters.

1. C. H. Edwards, *The Historical Development of the Calculus* (New York: Springer-Verlag, 1979), pp. 178–187.

2. John Fauvel and Jeremy Gray, eds., *The History of Mathematics: A Reader* (London: MacMillan Press, 1987).

3. Victor Katz, *A History of Mathematics: An Introduction* (New York: HarperCollins, 1993), pp. 463–466.

4. D. J. Struik, ed., *A Sourcebook in Mathematics, 1200–1800* (Princeton, NJ: Princeton University Press, 1969).

8.8 Applications of Taylor Polynomials

In this section we explore two types of applications of Taylor polynomials. First we look at how they are used to approximate functions—computer scientists like them because polynomials are the simplest of functions. Then we investigate how physicists and engineers use them in such fields as relativity, optics, blackbody radiation, electric dipoles, and building highways across a desert.

Approximating Functions by Polynomials

Suppose that $f(x)$ is equal to the sum of its Taylor series at a:

$$f(x) = \sum_{n=0}^{\infty} \frac{f^{(n)}(a)}{n!}(x - a)^n$$

In Section 8.7 we introduced the notation $T_n(x)$ for the nth partial sum of this series and called it the nth-degree Taylor polynomial of f at a. Thus

$$T_n(x) = \sum_{i=0}^{n} \frac{f^{(i)}(a)}{i!}(x - a)^i$$

$$= f(a) + \frac{f'(a)}{1!}(x - a) + \frac{f''(a)}{2!}(x - a)^2 + \cdots + \frac{f^{(n)}(a)}{n!}(x - a)^n$$

Since f is the sum of its Taylor series, we know that $T_n(x) \to f(x)$ as $n \to \infty$ and so T_n can be used as an approximation to f: $f(x) \approx T_n(x)$.

Notice that the first-degree Taylor polynomial

$$T_1(x) = f(a) + f'(a)(x - a)$$

is the same as the linearization of f at a that we discussed in Section 3.9. Notice also that T_1 and its derivative have the same values at a that f and f' have. In general, it can be shown that the derivatives of T_n at a agree with those of f up to and including derivatives of order n.

To illustrate these ideas let's take another look at the graphs of $y = e^x$ and its first few Taylor polynomials, as shown in Figure 1. The graph of T_1 is the tangent line to $y = e^x$ at $(0, 1)$; this tangent line is the best linear approximation to e^x near $(0, 1)$. The graph of T_2 is the parabola $y = 1 + x + x^2/2$, and the graph of T_3 is the cubic curve $y = 1 + x + x^2/2 + x^3/6$, which is a closer fit to the exponential curve $y = e^x$ than T_2. The next Taylor polynomial T_4 would be an even better approximation, and so on.

The values in the table give a numerical demonstration of the convergence of the Taylor polynomials $T_n(x)$ to the function $y = e^x$. We see that when $x = 0.2$ the convergence is very rapid, but when $x = 3$ it is somewhat slower. In fact, the farther x is from 0, the more slowly $T_n(x)$ converges to e^x.

When using a Taylor polynomial T_n to approximate a function f, we have to ask the questions: How good an approximation is it? How large should we take n to be in order to achieve a desired accuracy? To answer these questions we need to look at the absolute value of the remainder:

$$\left| R_n(x) \right| = \left| f(x) - T_n(x) \right|$$

There are three possible methods for estimating the size of the error:

1. If a graphing device is available, we can use it to graph $\left| R_n(x) \right|$ and thereby estimate the error.

2. If the series happens to be an alternating series, we can use the Alternating Series Estimation Theorem.

3. In all cases we can use Taylor's Inequality (Theorem 8.7.9), which says that if $\left| f^{(n+1)}(x) \right| \leqslant M$, then

$$\left| R_n(x) \right| \leqslant \frac{M}{(n + 1)!} \left| x - a \right|^{n+1}$$

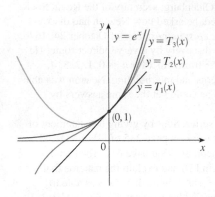

FIGURE 1

	$x = 0.2$	$x = 3.0$
$T_2(x)$	1.220000	8.500000
$T_4(x)$	1.221400	16.375000
$T_6(x)$	1.221403	19.412500
$T_8(x)$	1.221403	20.009152
$T_{10}(x)$	1.221403	20.079665
e^x	1.221403	20.085537

☑ **EXAMPLE 1 Approximating a root function by a quadratic function**
(a) Approximate the function $f(x) = \sqrt[3]{x}$ by a Taylor polynomial of degree 2 at $a = 8$.
(b) How accurate is this approximation when $7 \leqslant x \leqslant 9$?

SOLUTION
(a)
$$f(x) = \sqrt[3]{x} = x^{1/3} \qquad f(8) = 2$$

$$f'(x) = \tfrac{1}{3}x^{-2/3} \qquad f'(8) = \tfrac{1}{12}$$

$$f''(x) = -\tfrac{2}{9}x^{-5/3} \qquad f''(8) = -\tfrac{1}{144}$$

$$f'''(x) = \tfrac{10}{27}x^{-8/3}$$

Thus the second-degree Taylor polynomial is

$$T_2(x) = f(8) + \frac{f'(8)}{1!}(x-8) + \frac{f''(8)}{2!}(x-8)^2$$

$$= 2 + \tfrac{1}{12}(x-8) - \tfrac{1}{288}(x-8)^2$$

The desired approximation is

$$\sqrt[3]{x} \approx T_2(x) = 2 + \tfrac{1}{12}(x-8) - \tfrac{1}{288}(x-8)^2$$

(b) The Taylor series is not alternating when $x < 8$, so we can't use the Alternating Series Estimation Theorem in this example. But we can use Taylor's Inequality with $n = 2$ and $a = 8$:

$$|R_2(x)| \le \frac{M}{3!}|x-8|^3$$

where $|f'''(x)| \le M$. Because $x \ge 7$, we have $x^{8/3} \ge 7^{8/3}$ and so

$$f'''(x) = \frac{10}{27} \cdot \frac{1}{x^{8/3}} \le \frac{10}{27} \cdot \frac{1}{7^{8/3}} < 0.0021$$

Therefore we can take $M = 0.0021$. Also $7 \le x \le 9$, so $-1 \le x - 8 \le 1$ and $|x - 8| \le 1$. Then Taylor's Inequality gives

$$|R_2(x)| \le \frac{0.0021}{3!} \cdot 1^3 = \frac{0.0021}{6} < 0.0004$$

Thus, if $7 \le x \le 9$, the approximation in part (a) is accurate to within 0.0004. ▬

Let's use a graphing device to check the calculation in Example 1. Figure 2 shows that the graphs of $y = \sqrt[3]{x}$ and $y = T_2(x)$ are very close to each other when x is near 8. Figure 3 shows the graph of $|R_2(x)|$ computed from the expression

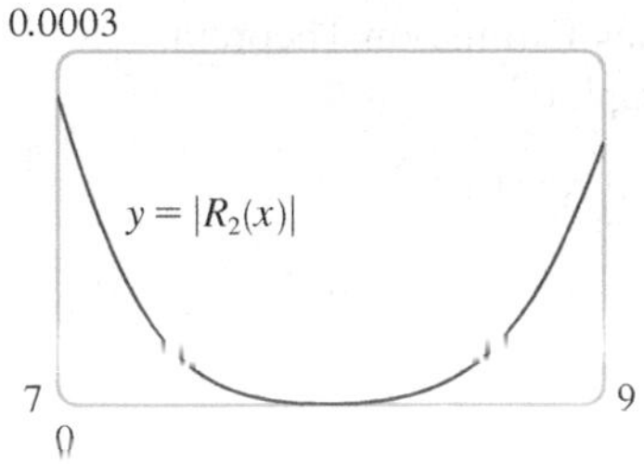

$$|R_2(x)| = |\sqrt[3]{x} - T_2(x)|$$

We see from the graph that

$$|R_2(x)| < 0.0003$$

when $7 \le x \le 9$. Thus the error estimate from graphical methods is slightly better than the error estimate from Taylor's Inequality in this case.

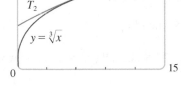

FIGURE 2

FIGURE 3

V **EXAMPLE 2** **Approximating sin x by a fifth-degree Taylor polynomial**
(a) What is the maximum error possible in using the approximation

$$\sin x \approx x - \frac{x^3}{3!} + \frac{x^5}{5!}$$

when $-0.3 \le x \le 0.3$? Use this approximation to find $\sin 12°$ correct to six decimal places.
(b) For what values of x is this approximation accurate to within 0.00005?

SOLUTION

(a) Notice that the Maclaurin series

$$\sin x = x - \frac{x^3}{3!} + \frac{x^5}{5!} - \frac{x^7}{7!} + \cdots$$

is alternating for all nonzero values of x, and the successive terms decrease in size because $|x| < 1$, so we can use the Alternating Series Estimation Theorem. The error in approximating $\sin x$ by the first three terms of its Maclaurin series is at most

$$\left|\frac{x^7}{7!}\right| = \frac{|x|^7}{5040}$$

If $-0.3 \leqslant x \leqslant 0.3$, then $|x| \leqslant 0.3$, so the error is smaller than

$$\frac{(0.3)^7}{5040} \approx 4.3 \times 10^{-8}$$

To find $\sin 12°$ we first convert to radian measure:

$$\sin 12° = \sin\left(\frac{12\pi}{180}\right) = \sin\left(\frac{\pi}{15}\right)$$

$$\approx \frac{\pi}{15} - \left(\frac{\pi}{15}\right)^3 \frac{1}{3!} + \left(\frac{\pi}{15}\right)^5 \frac{1}{5!} \approx 0.20791169$$

Thus, correct to six decimal places, $\sin 12° \approx 0.207912$.

(b) The error will be smaller than 0.00005 if

$$\frac{|x|^7}{5040} < 0.00005$$

Solving this inequality for x, we get

$$|x|^7 < 0.252 \qquad \text{or} \qquad |x| < (0.252)^{1/7} \approx 0.821$$

So the given approximation is accurate to within 0.00005 when $|x| < 0.82$.

What if we use Taylor's Inequality to solve Example 2? Since $f^{(7)}(x) = -\cos x$, we have $|f^{(7)}(x)| \leqslant 1$ and so

$$|R_6(x)| \leqslant \frac{1}{7!}|x|^7$$

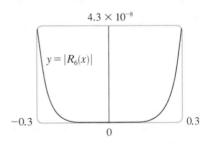

FIGURE 4

So we get the same estimates as with the Alternating Series Estimation Theorem.

What about graphical methods? Figure 4 shows the graph of

$$|R_6(x)| = \left|\sin x - \left(x - \tfrac{1}{6}x^3 + \tfrac{1}{120}x^5\right)\right|$$

and we see from it that $|R_6(x)| < 4.3 \times 10^{-8}$ when $|x| \leqslant 0.3$. This is the same estimate that we obtained in Example 2. For part (b) we want $|R_6(x)| < 0.00005$, so we graph both $y = |R_6(x)|$ and $y = 0.00005$ in Figure 5. By placing the cursor on the right intersection point we find that the inequality is satisfied when $|x| < 0.82$. Again this is the same estimate that we obtained in the solution to Example 2.

If we had been asked to approximate $\sin 72°$ instead of $\sin 12°$ in Example 2, it would have been wise to use the Taylor polynomials at $a = \pi/3$ (instead of $a = 0$) because they

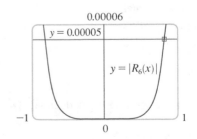

FIGURE 5

are better approximations to $\sin x$ for values of x close to $\pi/3$. Notice that $72°$ is close to $60°$ (or $\pi/3$ radians) and the derivatives of $\sin x$ are easy to compute at $\pi/3$.

Figure 6 shows the graphs of the Maclaurin polynomial approximations

$$T_1(x) = x \qquad\qquad T_3(x) = x - \frac{x^3}{3!}$$

$$T_5(x) = x - \frac{x^3}{3!} + \frac{x^5}{5!} \qquad T_7(x) = x - \frac{x^3}{3!} + \frac{x^5}{5!} - \frac{x^7}{7!}$$

to the sine curve. You can see that as n increases, $T_n(x)$ is a good approximation to $\sin x$ on a larger and larger interval.

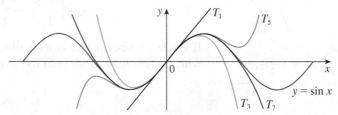

FIGURE 6

One use of the type of calculation done in Examples 1 and 2 occurs in calculators and computers. For instance, when you press the sin or e^x key on your calculator, or when a computer programmer uses a subroutine for a trigonometric or exponential or Bessel function, in many machines a polynomial approximation is calculated. The polynomial is often a Taylor polynomial that has been modified so that the error is spread more evenly throughout an interval.

Applications to Physics

Taylor polynomials are also used frequently in physics. In order to gain insight into an equation, a physicist often simplifies a function by considering only the first two or three terms in its Taylor series. In other words, the physicist uses a Taylor polynomial as an approximation to the function. Taylor's Inequality can then be used to gauge the accuracy of the approximation. The following example shows one way in which this idea is used in special relativity.

Ⅴ **EXAMPLE 3** **Using Taylor to compare Einstein and Newton**   In Einstein's theory of special relativity the mass of an object moving with velocity v is

$$m = \frac{m_0}{\sqrt{1 - v^2/c^2}}$$

where m_0 is the mass of the object when at rest and c is the speed of light. The kinetic energy of the object is the difference between its total energy and its energy at rest:

$$K = mc^2 - m_0 c^2$$

(a) Show that when v is very small compared with c, this expression for K agrees with classical Newtonian physics: $K = \frac{1}{2}m_0 v^2$.

(b) Use Taylor's Inequality to estimate the difference in these expressions for K when $|v| \leqslant 100$ m/s.

SOLUTION

(a) Using the expressions given for K and m, we get

$$K = mc^2 - m_0 c^2 = \frac{m_0 c^2}{\sqrt{1 - v^2/c^2}} - m_0 c^2 = m_0 c^2 \left[\left(1 - \frac{v^2}{c^2}\right)^{-1/2} - 1 \right]$$

The upper curve in Figure 7 is the graph of the expression for the kinetic energy K of an object with velocity v in special relativity. The lower curve shows the function used for K in classical Newtonian physics. When v is much smaller than the speed of light, the curves are practically identical.

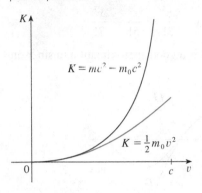

FIGURE 7

With $x = -v^2/c^2$, the Maclaurin series for $(1 + x)^{-1/2}$ is most easily computed as a binomial series with $k = -\frac{1}{2}$. (Notice that $|x| < 1$ because $v < c$.) Therefore we have

$$(1 + x)^{-1/2} = 1 - \frac{1}{2}x + \frac{(-\frac{1}{2})(-\frac{3}{2})}{2!}x^2 + \frac{(-\frac{1}{2})(-\frac{3}{2})(-\frac{5}{2})}{3!}x^3 + \cdots$$

$$= 1 - \frac{1}{2}x + \frac{3}{8}x^2 - \frac{5}{16}x^3 + \cdots$$

and

$$K = m_0 c^2 \left[\left(1 + \frac{1}{2}\frac{v^2}{c^2} + \frac{3}{8}\frac{v^4}{c^4} + \frac{5}{16}\frac{v^6}{c^6} + \cdots \right) - 1 \right]$$

$$= m_0 c^2 \left(\frac{1}{2}\frac{v^2}{c^2} + \frac{3}{8}\frac{v^4}{c^4} + \frac{5}{16}\frac{v^6}{c^6} + \cdots \right)$$

If v is much smaller than c, then all terms after the first are very small when compared with the first term. If we omit them, we get

$$K \approx m_0 c^2 \left(\frac{1}{2}\frac{v^2}{c^2} \right) = \frac{1}{2}m_0 v^2$$

(b) If $x = -v^2/c^2$, $f(x) = m_0 c^2 [(1 + x)^{-1/2} - 1]$, and M is a number such that $|f''(x)| \leq M$, then we can use Taylor's Inequality to write

$$|R_1(x)| \leq \frac{M}{2!}x^2$$

We have $f''(x) = \frac{3}{4}m_0 c^2 (1 + x)^{-5/2}$ and we are given that $|v| \leq 100$ m/s, so

$$|f''(x)| = \frac{3m_0 c^2}{4(1 - v^2/c^2)^{5/2}} \leq \frac{3m_0 c^2}{4(1 - 100^2/c^2)^{5/2}} \quad (= M)$$

Thus, with $c = 3 \times 10^8$ m/s,

$$|R_1(x)| \leq \frac{1}{2} \cdot \frac{3m_0 c^2}{4(1 - 100^2/c^2)^{5/2}} \cdot \frac{100^4}{c^4} < (4.17 \times 10^{-10})m_0$$

So when $|v| \leq 100$ m/s, the magnitude of the error in using the Newtonian expression for kinetic energy is at most $(4.2 \times 10^{-10})m_0$.

Another application to physics occurs in optics. Figure 8 is adapted from *Optics*, 4th ed., by Eugene Hecht (San Francisco, 2002), page 153. It depicts a wave from the point source S meeting a spherical interface of radius R centered at C. The ray SA is refracted toward P.

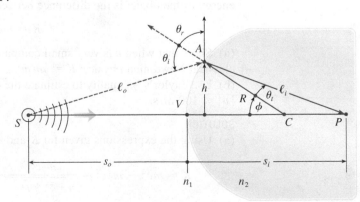

FIGURE 8

Refraction at a spherical interface

Using Fermat's principle that light travels so as to minimize the time taken, Hecht derives the equation

$$\boxed{1} \qquad \frac{n_1}{\ell_o} + \frac{n_2}{\ell_i} = \frac{1}{R}\left(\frac{n_2 s_i}{\ell_i} - \frac{n_1 s_o}{\ell_o}\right)$$

where n_1 and n_2 are indexes of refraction and ℓ_o, ℓ_i, s_o, and s_i are the distances indicated in Figure 8. By the Law of Cosines, applied to triangles ACS and ACP, we have

$$\boxed{2} \qquad \ell_o = \sqrt{R^2 + (s_o + R)^2 - 2R(s_o + R)\cos\phi}$$

$$\ell_i = \sqrt{R^2 + (s_i - R)^2 + 2R(s_i - R)\cos\phi}$$

Here we use the identity
$$\cos(\pi - \phi) = -\cos\phi$$

Because Equation 1 is cumbersome to work with, Gauss, in 1841, simplified it by using the linear approximation $\cos\phi \approx 1$ for small values of ϕ. (This amounts to using the Taylor polynomial of degree 1.) Then Equation 1 becomes the following simpler equation [as you are asked to show in Exercise 28(a)]:

$$\boxed{3} \qquad \frac{n_1}{s_o} + \frac{n_2}{s_i} = \frac{n_2 - n_1}{R}$$

The resulting optical theory is known as *Gaussian optics,* or *first-order optics,* and has become the basic theoretical tool used to design lenses.

A more accurate theory is obtained by approximating $\cos\phi$ by its Taylor polynomial of degree 3 (which is the same as the Taylor polynomial of degree 2). This takes into account rays for which ϕ is not so small, that is, rays that strike the surface at greater distances h above the axis. In Exercise 28(b) you are asked to use this approximation to derive the more accurate equation

$$\boxed{4} \qquad \frac{n_1}{s_o} + \frac{n_2}{s_i} = \frac{n_2 - n_1}{R} + h^2\left[\frac{n_1}{2s_o}\left(\frac{1}{s_o} + \frac{1}{R}\right)^2 + \frac{n_2}{2s_i}\left(\frac{1}{R} - \frac{1}{s_i}\right)^2\right]$$

The resulting optical theory is known as *third-order optics.*

Other applications of Taylor polynomials to physics and engineering are explored in Exercises 29–32 and in the Applied Project on page 627.

8.8   Exercises

1. (a) Find the Taylor polynomials up to degree 6 for $f(x) = \cos x$ centered at $a = 0$. Graph f and these polynomials on a common screen.
   (b) Evaluate f and these polynomials at $x = \pi/4$, $\pi/2$, and π.
   (c) Comment on how the Taylor polynomials converge to $f(x)$.

2. (a) Find the Taylor polynomials up to degree 3 for $f(x) = 1/x$ centered at $a = 1$. Graph f and these polynomials on a common screen.
   (b) Evaluate f and these polynomials at $x = 0.9$ and 1.3.
   (c) Comment on how the Taylor polynomials converge to $f(x)$.

3–8 Find the Taylor polynomial $T_3(x)$ for the function f at the number a. Graph f and T_3 on the same screen.

3. $f(x) = 1/x, \quad a = 2$

4. $f(x) = x + e^{-x}, \quad a = 0$

5. $f(x) = \cos x, \quad a = \pi/2$

6. $f(x) = \dfrac{\ln x}{x}, \quad a = 1$

7. $f(x) = xe^{-2x}, \quad a = 0$

8. $f(x) = \tan^{-1}x, \quad a = 1$

Graphing calculator or computer with graphing software required   CAS Computer algebra system required   **1.** Homework Hints available in TEC

CAS **9–10** Use a computer algebra system to find the Taylor polynomials T_n centered at a for $n = 2, 3, 4, 5$. Then graph these polynomials and f on the same screen.

9. $f(x) = \cot x$, $a = \pi/4$

10. $f(x) = \sqrt[3]{1 + x^2}$, $a = 0$

11–18

(a) Approximate f by a Taylor polynomial with degree n at the number a.

(b) Use Taylor's Inequality to estimate the accuracy of the approximation $f(x) \approx T_n(x)$ when x lies in the given interval.

(c) Check your result in part (b) by graphing $|R_n(x)|$.

11. $f(x) = \sqrt{x}$, $a = 4$, $n = 2$, $4 \leqslant x \leqslant 4.2$

12. $f(x) = x^{-2}$, $a = 1$, $n = 2$, $0.9 \leqslant x \leqslant 1.1$

13. $f(x) = x^{2/3}$, $a = 1$, $n = 3$, $0.8 \leqslant x \leqslant 1.2$

14. $f(x) = \sin x$, $a = \pi/6$, $n = 4$, $0 \leqslant x \leqslant \pi/3$

15. $f(x) = e^{x^2}$, $a = 0$, $n = 3$, $0 \leqslant x \leqslant 0.1$

16. $f(x) = \ln(1 + 2x)$, $a = 1$, $n = 3$, $0.5 \leqslant x \leqslant 1.5$

17. $f(x) = x \sin x$, $a = 0$, $n = 4$, $-1 \leqslant x \leqslant 1$

18. $f(x) = x \ln x$, $a = 1$, $n = 3$, $0.5 \leqslant x \leqslant 1.5$

---

19. Use the information from Exercise 5 to estimate $\cos 80°$ correct to five decimal places.

20. Use the information from Exercise 14 to estimate $\sin 38°$ correct to five decimal places.

21. Use Taylor's Inequality to determine the number of terms of the Maclaurin series for e^x that should be used to estimate $e^{0.1}$ to within 0.00001.

22. How many terms of the Maclaurin series for $\ln(1 + x)$ do you need to use to estimate $\ln 1.4$ to within 0.001?

23–25 Use the Alternating Series Estimation Theorem or Taylor's Inequality to estimate the range of values of x for which the given approximation is accurate to within the stated error. Check your answer graphically.

23. $\sin x \approx x - \dfrac{x^3}{6}$ $(|\text{error}| < 0.01)$

24. $\cos x \approx 1 - \dfrac{x^2}{2} + \dfrac{x^4}{24}$ $(|\text{error}| < 0.005)$

25. $\arctan x \approx x - \dfrac{x^3}{3} + \dfrac{x^5}{5}$ $(|\text{error}| < 0.05)$

26. Suppose you know that

$$f^{(n)}(4) = \frac{(-1)^n n!}{3^n (n + 1)}$$

and the Taylor series of f centered at 4 converges to $f(x)$ for all x in the interval of convergence. Show that the fifth-degree Taylor polynomial approximates $f(5)$ with error less than 0.0002.

27. A car is moving with speed 20 m/s and acceleration 2 m/s² at a given instant. Using a second-degree Taylor polynomial, estimate how far the car moves in the next second. Would it be reasonable to use this polynomial to estimate the distance traveled during the next minute?

28. (a) Derive Equation 3 for Gaussian optics from Equation 1 by approximating $\cos \phi$ in Equation 2 by its first-degree Taylor polynomial.

(b) Show that if $\cos \phi$ is replaced by its third-degree Taylor polynomial in Equation 2, then Equation 1 becomes Equation 4 for third-order optics. [*Hint:* Use the first two terms in the binomial series for ℓ_o^{-1} and ℓ_i^{-1}. Also, use $\phi \approx \sin \phi$.]

29. An electric dipole consists of two electric charges of equal magnitude and opposite sign. If the charges are q and $-q$ and are located at a distance d from each other, then the electric field E at the point P in the figure is

$$E = \frac{q}{D^2} - \frac{q}{(D + d)^2}$$

By expanding this expression for E as a series in powers of d/D, show that E is approximately proportional to $1/D^3$ when P is far away from the dipole.

30. The resistivity ρ of a conducting wire is the reciprocal of the conductivity and is measured in units of ohm-meters (Ω-m). The resistivity of a given metal depends on the temperature according to the equation

$$\rho(t) = \rho_{20} e^{\alpha(t - 20)}$$

where t is the temperature in °C. There are tables that list the values of α (called the temperature coefficient) and ρ_{20} (the resistivity at 20°C) for various metals. Except at very low temperatures, the resistivity varies almost linearly with temperature and so it is common to approximate the expression for $\rho(t)$ by its first- or second-degree Taylor polynomial at $t = 20$.

(a) Find expressions for these linear and quadratic approximations.

(b) For copper, the tables give $\alpha = 0.0039/°C$ and $\rho_{20} = 1.7 \times 10^{-8}$ Ω-m. Graph the resistivity of copper and the linear and quadratic approximations for $-250°C \leq t \leq 1000°C$.

(c) For what values of t does the linear approximation agree with the exponential expression to within one percent?

31. If a surveyor measures differences in elevation when making plans for a highway across a desert, corrections must be made for the curvature of the earth.

(a) If R is the radius of the earth and L is the length of the highway, show that the correction is

$$C = R \sec(L/R) - R$$

(b) Use a Taylor polynomial to show that

$$C \approx \frac{L^2}{2R} + \frac{5L^4}{24R^3}$$

(c) Compare the corrections given by the formulas in parts (a) and (b) for a highway that is 100 km long. (Take the radius of the earth to be 6370 km.)

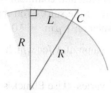

32. The period of a pendulum with length L that makes a maximum angle θ_0 with the vertical is

$$T = 4\sqrt{\frac{L}{g}} \int_0^{\pi/2} \frac{dx}{\sqrt{1 - k^2 \sin^2 x}}$$

where $k = \sin\left(\frac{1}{2}\theta_0\right)$ and g is the acceleration due to gravity. (In Exercise 34 in Section 5.9 we approximated this integral using Simpson's Rule.)

(a) Expand the integrand as a binomial series and use the result of Exercise 38 in Section 5.6 to show that

$$T = 2\pi\sqrt{\frac{L}{g}} \left[1 + \frac{1^2}{2^2}k^2 + \frac{1^2 3^2}{2^2 4^2}k^4 + \frac{1^2 3^2 5^2}{2^2 4^2 6^2}k^6 + \cdots \right]$$

If θ_0 is not too large, the approximation $T \approx 2\pi\sqrt{L/g}$, obtained by using only the first term in the series, is often used. A better approximation is obtained by using two terms:

$$T \approx 2\pi\sqrt{\frac{L}{g}} \left(1 + \tfrac{1}{4}k^2\right)$$

(b) Notice that all the terms in the series after the first one have coefficients that are at most $\frac{1}{4}$. Use this fact to compare this series with a geometric series and show that

$$2\pi\sqrt{\frac{L}{g}} \left(1 + \tfrac{1}{4}k^2\right) \leq T \leq 2\pi\sqrt{\frac{L}{g}} \frac{4 - 3k^2}{4 - 4k^2}$$

(c) Use the inequalities in part (b) to estimate the period of a pendulum with $L = 1$ meter and $\theta_0 = 10°$. How does it compare with the estimate $T \approx 2\pi\sqrt{L/g}$? What if $\theta_0 = 42°$?

33. In Section 4.7 we considered Newton's method for approximating a root r of the equation $f(x) = 0$, and from an initial approximation x_1 we obtained successive approximations $x_2, x_3, \ldots$, where

$$x_{n+1} = x_n - \frac{f(x_n)}{f'(x_n)}$$

Use Taylor's Inequality with $n = 1$, $a = x_n$, and $x = r$ to show that if $f''(x)$ exists on an interval I containing r, x_n, and x_{n+1}, and $|f''(x)| \leq M$, $|f'(x)| \geq K$ for all $x \in I$, then

$$|x_{n+1} - r| \leq \frac{M}{2K}|x_n - r|^2$$

[This means that if x_n is accurate to d decimal places, then x_{n+1} is accurate to about $2d$ decimal places. More precisely, if the error at stage n is at most 10^{-m}, then the error at stage $n + 1$ is at most $(M/2K)10^{-2m}$.]

APPLIED PROJECT   Radiation from the Stars

Any object emits radiation when heated. A *blackbody* is a system that absorbs all the radiation that falls on it. For instance, a matte black surface or a large cavity with a small hole in its wall (like a blastfurnace) is a blackbody and emits blackbody radiation. Even the radiation from the sun is close to being blackbody radiation.

Proposed in the late 19th century, the Rayleigh-Jeans Law expresses the energy density of blackbody radiation of wavelength λ as

$$f(\lambda) = \frac{8\pi kT}{\lambda^4}$$

where λ is measured in meters, T is the temperature in kelvins (K), and k is Boltzmann's constant. The Rayleigh-Jeans Law agrees with experimental measurements for long wavelengths

Graphing calculator or computer with graphing software required

but disagrees drastically for short wavelengths. [The law predicts that $f(\lambda) \to \infty$ as $\lambda \to 0^+$ but experiments have shown that $f(\lambda) \to 0$.] This fact is known as the *ultraviolet catastrophe*.

In 1900 Max Planck found a better model (known now as Planck's Law) for blackbody radiation:

$$f(\lambda) = \frac{8\pi hc\lambda^{-5}}{e^{hc/(\lambda kT)} - 1}$$

where λ is measured in meters, T is the temperature (in kelvins), and

$$h = \text{Planck's constant} = 6.6262 \times 10^{-34} \text{ J·s}$$

$$c = \text{speed of light} = 2.997925 \times 10^8 \text{ m/s}$$

$$k = \text{Boltzmann's constant} = 1.3807 \times 10^{-23} \text{ J/K}$$

1. Use l'Hospital's Rule to show that

$$\lim_{\lambda \to 0^+} f(\lambda) = 0 \quad \text{and} \quad \lim_{\lambda \to \infty} f(\lambda) = 0$$

for Planck's Law. So this law models blackbody radiation better than the Rayleigh-Jeans Law for short wavelengths.

2. Use a Taylor polynomial to show that, for large wavelengths, Planck's Law gives approximately the same values as the Rayleigh-Jeans Law.

3. Graph f as given by both laws on the same screen and comment on the similarities and differences. Use $T = 5700$ K (the temperature of the sun). (You may want to change from meters to the more convenient unit of micrometers: $1 \ \mu m = 10^{-6}$ m.)

4. Use your graph in Problem 3 to estimate the value of λ for which $f(\lambda)$ is a maximum under Planck's Law.

5. Investigate how the graph of f changes as T varies. (Use Planck's Law.) In particular, graph f for the stars Betelgeuse ($T = 3400$ K), Procyon ($T = 6400$ K), and Sirius ($T = 9200$ K), as well as the sun. How does the total radiation emitted (the area under the curve) vary with T? Use the graph to comment on why Sirius is known as a blue star and Betelgeuse as a red star.

8 Review

Concept Check

1. (a) What is a convergent sequence?
   (b) What is a convergent series?
   (c) What does $\lim_{n \to \infty} a_n = 3$ mean?
   (d) What does $\sum_{n=1}^{\infty} a_n = 3$ mean?

2. (a) What is a bounded sequence?
   (b) What is a monotonic sequence?
   (c) What can you say about a bounded monotonic sequence?

3. (a) What is a geometric series? Under what circumstances is it convergent? What is its sum?
   (b) What is a p-series? Under what circumstances is it convergent?

4. Suppose $\Sigma a_n = 3$ and s_n is the nth partial sum of the series. What is $\lim_{n \to \infty} a_n$? What is $\lim_{n \to \infty} s_n$?

5. State the following.
   (a) The Test for Divergence
   (b) The Integral Test
   (c) The Comparison Test
   (d) The Limit Comparison Test
   (e) The Alternating Series Test
   (f) The Ratio Test

6. (a) What is an absolutely convergent series?
   (b) What can you say about such a series?

7. (a) If a series is convergent by the Integral Test, how do you estimate its sum?
   (b) If a series is convergent by the Comparison Test, how do you estimate its sum?

(c) If a series is convergent by the Alternating Series Test, how do you estimate its sum?

8. (a) Write the general form of a power series.
(b) What is the radius of convergence of a power series?
(c) What is the interval of convergence of a power series?

9. Suppose $f(x)$ is the sum of a power series with radius of convergence R.
(a) How do you differentiate f? What is the radius of convergence of the series for f'?
(b) How do you integrate f? What is the radius of convergence of the series for $\int f(x)\,dx$?

10. (a) Write an expression for the nth-degree Taylor polynomial of f centered at a.

(b) Write an expression for the Taylor series of f centered at a.
(c) Write an expression for the Maclaurin series of f.
(d) How do you show that $f(x)$ is equal to the sum of its Taylor series?
(e) State Taylor's Inequality.

11. Write the Maclaurin series and the interval of convergence for each of the following functions.
(a) $1/(1-x)$ (b) e^x
(c) $\sin x$ (d) $\cos x$
(e) $\tan^{-1}x$ (f) $\ln(1+x)$

12. Write the binomial series expansion of $(1+x)^k$. What is the radius of convergence of this series?

True-False Quiz

Determine whether the statement is true or false. If it is true, explain why. If it is false, explain why or give an example that disproves the statement.

1. If $\lim_{n\to\infty} a_n = 0$, then $\Sigma\, a_n$ is convergent.

2. The series $\sum_{n=1}^{\infty} n^{-\sin 1}$ is convergent.

3. If $\lim_{n\to\infty} a_n = L$, then $\lim_{n\to\infty} a_{2n+1} = L$.

4. If $\Sigma\, c_n 6^n$ is convergent, then $\Sigma\, c_n(-2)^n$ is convergent.

5. If $\Sigma\, c_n 6^n$ is convergent, then $\Sigma\, c_n(-6)^n$ is convergent.

6. If $\Sigma\, c_n x^n$ diverges when $x=6$, then it diverges when $x=10$.

7. The Ratio Test can be used to determine whether $\Sigma\, 1/n^3$ converges.

8. The Ratio Test can be used to determine whether $\Sigma\, 1/n!$ converges.

9. If $0 \le a_n \le b_n$ and $\Sigma\, b_n$ diverges, then $\Sigma\, a_n$ diverges.

10. $\displaystyle\sum_{n=0}^{\infty} \frac{(-1)^n}{n!} = \frac{1}{e}$

11. If $-1 < \alpha < 1$, then $\lim_{n\to\infty} \alpha^n = 0$.

12. If $\Sigma\, a_n$ is divergent, then $\Sigma\, |a_n|$ is divergent.

13. If $f(x) = 2x - x^2 + \frac{1}{3}x^3 - \cdots$ converges for all x, then $f'''(0) = 2$.

14. If $\{a_n\}$ and $\{b_n\}$ are divergent, then $\{a_n + b_n\}$ is divergent.

15. If $\{a_n\}$ and $\{b_n\}$ are divergent, then $\{a_n b_n\}$ is divergent.

16. If $\{a_n\}$ is decreasing and $a_n > 0$ for all n, then $\{a_n\}$ is convergent.

17. If $a_n > 0$ and $\Sigma\, a_n$ converges, then $\Sigma\, (-1)^n a_n$ converges.

18. If $a_n > 0$ and $\lim_{n\to\infty} (a_{n+1}/a_n) < 1$, then $\lim_{n\to\infty} a_n = 0$.

19. $0.99999\ldots = 1$

20. If $\lim_{n\to\infty} a_n = 2$, then $\lim_{n\to\infty} (a_{n+3} - a_n) = 0$.

Exercises

1–7 Determine whether the sequence is convergent or divergent. If it is convergent, find its limit.

1. $a_n = \dfrac{2+n^3}{1+2n^3}$ **2.** $a_n = \dfrac{9^{n+1}}{10^n}$

3. $a_n = \dfrac{n^3}{1+n^2}$ **4.** $a_n = \cos(n\pi/2)$

5. $a_n = \dfrac{n\sin n}{n^2+1}$ **6.** $a_n = \dfrac{\ln n}{\sqrt{n}}$

7. $\{(1+3/n)^{4n}\}$

8. A sequence is defined recursively by the equations $a_1 = 1$, $a_{n+1} = \frac{1}{3}(a_n + 4)$. Show that $\{a_n\}$ is increasing and $a_n < 2$ for all n. Deduce that $\{a_n\}$ is convergent and find its limit.

9–18 Determine whether the series is convergent or divergent.

9. $\displaystyle\sum_{n=1}^{\infty} \frac{n}{n^3+1}$ **10.** $\displaystyle\sum_{n=1}^{\infty} \frac{n^2+1}{n^3+1}$

11. $\displaystyle\sum_{n=1}^{\infty} \frac{n^3}{5^n}$ **12.** $\displaystyle\sum_{n=1}^{\infty} \frac{(-1)^n}{\sqrt{n+1}}$

13. $\displaystyle\sum_{n=2}^{\infty} \frac{1}{n\sqrt{\ln n}}$ **14.** $\displaystyle\sum_{n=1}^{\infty} \ln\!\left(\frac{n}{3n+1}\right)$

15. $\displaystyle\sum_{n=1}^{\infty} (-1)^{n-1} \frac{\sqrt{n}}{n+1}$

16. $\displaystyle\sum_{n=1}^{\infty} \frac{\cos 3n}{1 + (1.2)^n}$

17. $\displaystyle\sum_{n=1}^{\infty} \frac{1 \cdot 3 \cdot 5 \cdot \cdots \cdot (2n-1)}{5^n n!}$

18. $\displaystyle\sum_{n=1}^{\infty} \frac{(-5)^{2n}}{n^2 9^n}$

19–22 Find the sum of the series.

19. $\displaystyle\sum_{n=1}^{\infty} \frac{(-3)^{n-1}}{2^{3n}}$

20. $\displaystyle\sum_{n=0}^{\infty} \frac{(-1)^n \pi^n}{3^{2n}(2n)!}$

21. $\displaystyle\sum_{n=1}^{\infty} [\tan^{-1}(n+1) - \tan^{-1}n]$

22. $1 - e + \dfrac{e^2}{2!} - \dfrac{e^3}{3!} + \dfrac{e^4}{4!} - \cdots$

23. Express the repeating decimal $1.2345345345\ldots$ as a fraction.

24. For what values of x does the series $\sum_{n=1}^{\infty} (\ln x)^n$ converge?

25. Find the sum of the series $\displaystyle\sum_{n=1}^{\infty} \frac{(-1)^{n+1}}{n^5}$ correct to four decimal places.

26. (a) Find the partial sum s_5 of the series $\sum_{n=1}^{\infty} 1/n^6$ and estimate the error in using it as an approximation to the sum of the series.
(b) Find the sum of this series correct to five decimal places.

27. Use the sum of the first eight terms to approximate the sum of the series $\sum_{n=1}^{\infty} (2 + 5^n)^{-1}$. Estimate the error involved in this approximation.

28. (a) Show that the series $\displaystyle\sum_{n=1}^{\infty} \frac{n^n}{(2n)!}$ is convergent.

(b) Deduce that $\displaystyle\lim_{n \to \infty} \frac{n^n}{(2n)!} = 0$.

29. Prove that if the series $\sum_{n=1}^{\infty} a_n$ is absolutely convergent, then the series

$$\sum_{n=1}^{\infty} \left(\frac{n+1}{n}\right) a_n$$

is also absolutely convergent.

30–33 Find the radius of convergence and interval of convergence of the series.

30. $\displaystyle\sum_{n=1}^{\infty} (-1)^n \frac{x^n}{n^2 5^n}$

31. $\displaystyle\sum_{n=1}^{\infty} \frac{(x+2)^n}{n\,4^n}$

32. $\displaystyle\sum_{n=1}^{\infty} \frac{2^n(x-2)^n}{(n+2)!}$

33. $\displaystyle\sum_{n=0}^{\infty} \frac{2^n(x-3)^n}{\sqrt{n+3}}$

34. Find the radius of convergence of the series

$$\sum_{n=1}^{\infty} \frac{(2n)!}{(n!)^2} x^n$$

35. Find the Taylor series of $f(x) = \sin x$ at $a = \pi/6$.

36. Find the Taylor series of $f(x) = \cos x$ at $a = \pi/3$.

37–44 Find the Maclaurin series for f and its radius of convergence. You may use either the direct method (definition of a Maclaurin series) or known series such as geometric series, binomial series, or the Maclaurin series for e^x, $\sin x$, and $\tan^{-1}x$.

37. $f(x) = \dfrac{x^2}{1+x}$

38. $f(x) = \tan^{-1}(x^2)$

39. $f(x) = \ln(4 - x)$

40. $f(x) = xe^{2x}$

41. $f(x) = \sin(x^4)$

42. $f(x) = 10^x$

43. $f(x) = 1/\sqrt[4]{16 - x}$

44. $f(x) = (1 - 3x)^{-5}$

45. Evaluate $\displaystyle\int \frac{e^x}{x}\, dx$ as an infinite series.

46. Use series to approximate $\int_0^1 \sqrt{1 + x^4}\, dx$ correct to two decimal places.

47–48
(a) Approximate f by a Taylor polynomial with degree n at the number a.
(b) Graph f and T_n on a common screen.
(c) Use Taylor's Inequality to estimate the accuracy of the approximation $f(x) \approx T_n(x)$ when x lies in the given interval.
(d) Check your result in part (c) by graphing $|R_n(x)|$.

47. $f(x) = \sqrt{x}, \quad a = 1, \quad n = 3, \quad 0.9 \le x \le 1.1$

48. $f(x) = \sec x, \quad a = 0, \quad n = 2, \quad 0 \le x \le \pi/6$

49. Use series to evaluate the following limit.

$$\lim_{x \to 0} \frac{\sin x - x}{x^3}$$

50. The force due to gravity on an object with mass m at a height h above the surface of the earth is

$$F = \frac{mgR^2}{(R + h)^2}$$

where R is the radius of the earth and g is the acceleration due to gravity.
(a) Express F as a series in powers of h/R.
(b) Observe that if we approximate F by the first term in the series, we get the expression $F \approx mg$ that is usually used when h is much smaller than R. Use the Alternating Series Estimation Theorem to estimate the range of values of h for which the approximation $F \approx mg$ is accurate to within one percent. (Use $R = 6400$ km.)

Focus on Problem Solving

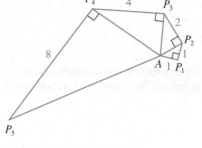

FIGURE FOR PROBLEM 2

1. If $f(x) = \sin(x^3)$, find $f^{(15)}(0)$.

2. Let $\{P_n\}$ be a sequence of points determined as in the figure. Thus $|AP_1| = 1$, $|P_nP_{n+1}| = 2^{n-1}$, and angle AP_nP_{n+1} is a right angle. Find $\lim_{n\to\infty} \angle P_nAP_{n+1}$.

3. To construct the **snowflake curve**, start with an equilateral triangle with sides of length 1. Step 1 in the construction is to divide each side into three equal parts, construct an equilateral triangle on the middle part, and then delete the middle part (see the figure). Step 2 is to repeat step 1 for each side of the resulting polygon. This process is repeated at each succeeding step. The snowflake curve is the curve that results from repeating this process indefinitely.

   (a) Let s_n, l_n, and p_n represent the number of sides, the length of a side, and the total length of the nth approximating curve (the curve obtained after step n of the construction), respectively. Find formulas for s_n, l_n, and p_n.

   (b) Show that $p_n \to \infty$ as $n \to \infty$.

   (c) Sum an infinite series to find the area enclosed by the snowflake curve.

   Note: Parts (b) and (c) show that the snowflake curve is infinitely long but encloses only a finite area.

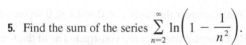

4. Find the sum of the series

$$1 + \frac{1}{2} + \frac{1}{3} + \frac{1}{4} + \frac{1}{6} + \frac{1}{8} + \frac{1}{9} + \frac{1}{12} + \cdots$$

where the terms are the reciprocals of the positive integers whose only prime factors are 2s and 3s.

5. Find the sum of the series $\displaystyle\sum_{n=2}^{\infty} \ln\left(1 - \frac{1}{n^2}\right)$.

6. Suppose you have a large supply of books, all the same size, and you stack them at the edge of a table, with each book extending farther beyond the edge of the table than the one beneath it. Show that it is possible to do this so that the top book extends entirely beyond the table. In fact, show that the top book can extend any distance at all beyond the edge of the table if the stack is high enough. Use the following method of stacking: The top book extends half its length beyond the second book. The second book extends a quarter of its length beyond the third. The third extends one-sixth of its length beyond the fourth, and so on. (Try it yourself with a deck of cards.) Consider centers of mass.

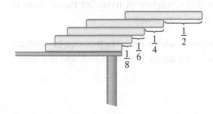

FIGURE FOR PROBLEM 6

7. Let

$$u = 1 + \frac{x^3}{3!} + \frac{x^6}{6!} + \frac{x^9}{9!} + \cdots$$

$$v = x + \frac{x^4}{4!} + \frac{x^7}{7!} + \frac{x^{10}}{10!} + \cdots$$

$$w = \frac{x^2}{2!} + \frac{x^5}{5!} + \frac{x^8}{8!} + \cdots$$

Show that $u^3 + v^3 + w^3 - 3uvw = 1$.

8. If $p > 1$, evaluate the expression

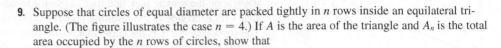

$$\frac{1 + \dfrac{1}{2^p} + \dfrac{1}{3^p} + \dfrac{1}{4^p} + \cdots}{1 - \dfrac{1}{2^p} + \dfrac{1}{3^p} - \dfrac{1}{4^p} + \cdots}$$

9. Suppose that circles of equal diameter are packed tightly in n rows inside an equilateral triangle. (The figure illustrates the case $n = 4$.) If A is the area of the triangle and A_n is the total area occupied by the n rows of circles, show that

$$\lim_{n \to \infty} \frac{A_n}{A} = \frac{\pi}{2\sqrt{3}}$$

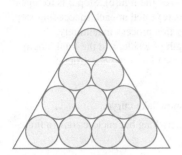

FIGURE FOR PROBLEM 9

10. A sequence $\{a_n\}$ is defined recursively by the equations

$$a_0 = a_1 = 1 \qquad n(n-1)a_n = (n-1)(n-2)a_{n-1} - (n-3)a_{n-2}$$

Find the sum of the series $\sum_{n=0}^{\infty} a_n$.

11. Find the sum of the series $\displaystyle\sum_{n=1}^{\infty} \frac{(-1)^n}{(2n+1)3^n}$.

12. Starting with the vertices $P_1(0, 1)$, $P_2(1, 1)$, $P_3(1, 0)$, $P_4(0, 0)$ of a square, we construct further points as shown in the figure: P_5 is the midpoint of P_1P_2, P_6 is the midpoint of P_2P_3, P_7 is the midpoint of P_3P_4, and so on. The polygonal spiral path $P_1P_2P_3P_4P_5P_6P_7 \ldots$ approaches a point P inside the square.
(a) If the coordinates of P_n are (x_n, y_n), show that $\frac{1}{2}x_n + x_{n+1} + x_{n+2} + x_{n+3} = 2$ and find a similar equation for the y-coordinates.
(b) Find the coordinates of P.

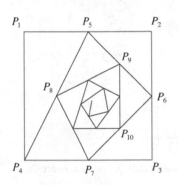

FIGURE FOR PROBLEM 12

13. Find all the solutions of the equation

$$1 + \frac{x}{2!} + \frac{x^2}{4!} + \frac{x^3}{6!} + \frac{x^4}{8!} + \cdots = 0$$

Hint: Consider the cases $x \geqslant 0$ and $x < 0$ separately.

14. Right-angled triangles are constructed as in the figure. Each triangle has height 1 and its base is the hypotenuse of the preceding triangle. Show that this sequence of triangles makes indefinitely many turns around P by showing that $\Sigma \, \theta_n$ is a divergent series.

15. Consider the series whose terms are the reciprocals of the positive integers that can be written in base 10 notation without using the digit 0. Show that this series is convergent and the sum is less than 90.

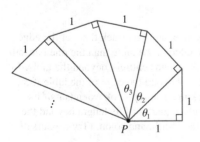

FIGURE FOR PROBLEM 14

16. (a) Show that the Maclaurin series of the function

$$f(x) = \frac{x}{1 - x - x^2} \qquad \text{is} \qquad \sum_{n=1}^{\infty} f_n x^n$$

where f_n is the nth Fibonacci number, that is, $f_1 = 1$, $f_2 = 1$, and $f_n = f_{n-1} + f_{n-2}$ for $n \geqslant 3$. [*Hint:* Write $x/(1 - x - x^2) = c_0 + c_1 x + c_2 x^2 + \cdots$ and multiply both sides of this equation by $1 - x - x^2$.]
(b) By writing $f(x)$ as a sum of partial fractions and thereby obtaining the Maclaurin series in a different way, find an explicit formula for the nth Fibonacci number.

Vectors and the Geometry of Space | 9

In this chapter we introduce vectors and coordinate systems for three-dimensional space. This is the setting for the study of functions of two variables because the graph of such a function is a surface in space. Vectors provide particularly simple descriptions of lines and planes in space as well as velocities and accelerations of objects that move in space.

633

9.1 Three-Dimensional Coordinate Systems

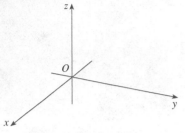

FIGURE 1
Coordinate axes

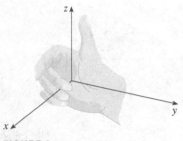

FIGURE 2
Right-hand rule

To locate a point in a plane, two numbers are necessary. We know that any point in the plane can be represented as an ordered pair (a, b) of real numbers, where a is the x-coordinate and b is the y-coordinate. For this reason, a plane is called two-dimensional. To locate a point in space, three numbers are required. We represent any point in space by an ordered triple (a, b, c) of real numbers.

In order to represent points in space, we first choose a fixed point O (the origin) and three directed lines through O that are perpendicular to each other, called the **coordinate axes** and labeled the x-axis, y-axis, and z-axis. Usually we think of the x- and y-axes as being horizontal and the z-axis as being vertical, and we draw the orientation of the axes as in Figure 1. The direction of the z-axis is determined by the **right-hand rule** as illustrated in Figure 2: If you curl the fingers of your right hand around the z-axis in the direction of a $90°$ counterclockwise rotation from the positive x-axis to the positive y-axis, then your thumb points in the positive direction of the z-axis.

The three coordinate axes determine the three **coordinate planes** illustrated in Figure 3(a). The xy-plane is the plane that contains the x- and y-axes; the yz-plane contains the y- and z-axes; the xz-plane contains the x- and z-axes. These three coordinate planes divide space into eight parts, called **octants**. The **first octant**, in the foreground, is determined by the positive axes.

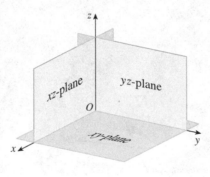

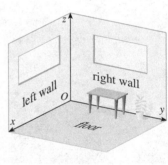

FIGURE 3   (a) Coordinate planes   (b)

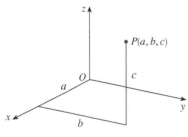

FIGURE 4

Because many people have some difficulty visualizing diagrams of three-dimensional figures, you may find it helpful to do the following [see Figure 3(b)]. Look at any bottom corner of a room and call the corner the origin. The wall on your left is in the xz-plane, the wall on your right is in the yz-plane, and the floor is in the xy-plane. The x-axis runs along the intersection of the floor and the left wall. The y-axis runs along the intersection of the floor and the right wall. The z-axis runs up from the floor toward the ceiling along the intersection of the two walls. You are situated in the first octant, and you can now imagine seven other rooms situated in the other seven octants (three on the same floor and four on the floor below), all connected by the common corner point O.

Now if P is any point in space, let a be the (directed) distance from the yz-plane to P, let b be the distance from the xz-plane to P, and let c be the distance from the xy-plane to P. We represent the point P by the ordered triple (a, b, c) of real numbers and we call a, b, and c the **coordinates** of P; a is the x-coordinate, b is the y-coordinate, and c is the z-coordinate. Thus, to locate the point (a, b, c), we can start at the origin O and move a units along the x-axis, then b units parallel to the y-axis, and then c units parallel to the z-axis as in Figure 4.

The point $P(a, b, c)$ determines a rectangular box as in Figure 5. If we drop a perpendicular from P to the xy-plane, we get a point Q with coordinates $(a, b, 0)$ called the **projection** of P onto the xy-plane. Similarly, $R(0, b, c)$ and $S(a, 0, c)$ are the projections of P onto the yz-plane and xz-plane, respectively.

As numerical illustrations, the points $(-4, 3, -5)$ and $(3, -2, -6)$ are plotted in Figure 6.

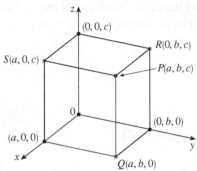

FIGURE 5

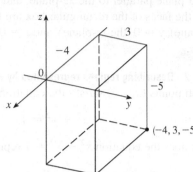

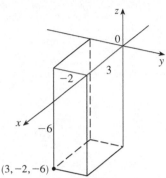

FIGURE 6

The Cartesian product $\mathbb{R} \times \mathbb{R} \times \mathbb{R} = \{(x, y, z) \mid x, y, z \in \mathbb{R}\}$ is the set of all ordered triples of real numbers and is denoted by $\mathbb{R}^3$. We have given a one-to-one correspondence between points P in space and ordered triples (a, b, c) in $\mathbb{R}^3$. It is called a **three-dimensional rectangular coordinate system**. Notice that, in terms of coordinates, the first octant can be described as the set of points whose coordinates are all positive.

In two-dimensional analytic geometry, the graph of an equation involving x and y is a curve in $\mathbb{R}^2$. In three-dimensional analytic geometry, an equation in x, y, and z represents a *surface* in $\mathbb{R}^3$.

V EXAMPLE 1 Graphing equations

What surfaces in $\mathbb{R}^3$ are represented by the following equations?

(a) $z = 3$ (b) $y = 5$

SOLUTION

(a) The equation $z = 3$ represents the set $\{(x, y, z) \mid z = 3\}$, which is the set of all points in $\mathbb{R}^3$ whose z-coordinate is 3. This is the horizontal plane that is parallel to the xy-plane and three units above it as in Figure 7(a).

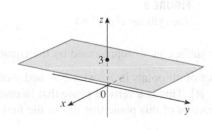

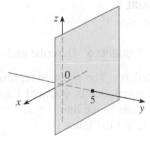

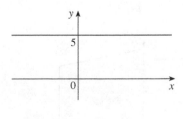

FIGURE 7   (a) $z = 3$, a plane in $\mathbb{R}^3$ (b) $y = 5$, a plane in $\mathbb{R}^3$ (c) $y = 5$, a line in $\mathbb{R}^2$

(b) The equation $y = 5$ represents the set of all points in $\mathbb{R}^3$ whose y-coordinate is 5. This is the vertical plane that is parallel to the xz-plane and five units to the right of it as in Figure 7(b).

Note: When an equation is given, we must understand from the context whether it represents a curve in $\mathbb{R}^2$ or a surface in $\mathbb{R}^3$. In Example 1, $y = 5$ represents a plane in $\mathbb{R}^3$, but of course $y = 5$ can also represent a line in $\mathbb{R}^2$ if we are dealing with two-dimensional analytic geometry. See Figure 7(b) and (c).

In general, if k is a constant, then $x = k$ represents a plane parallel to the yz-plane, $y = k$ is a plane parallel to the xz-plane, and $z = k$ is a plane parallel to the xy-plane. In Figure 5, the faces of the rectangular box are formed by the three coordinate planes $x = 0$ (the yz-plane), $y = 0$ (the xz-plane), and $z = 0$ (the xy-plane), and the planes $x = a$, $y = b$, and $z = c$.

EXAMPLE 2   Describing regions represented by equations
(a) Which points (x, y, z) satisfy the equations

$$x^2 + y^2 = 1 \qquad \text{and} \qquad z = 3$$

(b) What does the equation $x^2 + y^2 = 1$ represent as a surface in $\mathbb{R}^3$?

SOLUTION
(a) Because $z = 3$, the points lie in the horizontal plane $z = 3$ from Example 1(a). Because $x^2 + y^2 = 1$, the points lie on the circle with radius 1 and center on the z-axis. See Figure 8.

(b) Given that $x^2 + y^2 = 1$, with no restrictions on z, we see that the point (x, y, z) could lie on a circle in any horizontal plane $z = k$. So the surface $x^2 + y^2 = 1$ in $\mathbb{R}^3$ consists of all possible horizontal circles $x^2 + y^2 = 1$, $z = k$, and is therefore the circular cylinder with radius 1 whose axis is the z-axis. See Figure 9.

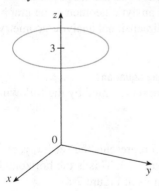

FIGURE 8
The circle $x^2 + y^2 = 1$, $z = 3$

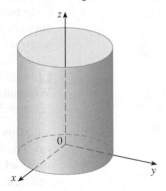

FIGURE 9
The cylinder $x^2 + y^2 = 1$

▼ EXAMPLE 3 Describe and sketch the surface in $\mathbb{R}^3$ represented by the equation $y = x$.

SOLUTION The equation represents the set of all points in $\mathbb{R}^3$ whose x- and y-coordinates are equal, that is, $\{(x, x, z) \mid x \in \mathbb{R}, z \in \mathbb{R}\}$. This is a vertical plane that intersects the xy-plane in the line $y = x$, $z = 0$. The portion of this plane that lies in the first octant is sketched in Figure 10.

The familiar formula for the distance between two points in a plane is easily extended to the following three-dimensional formula.

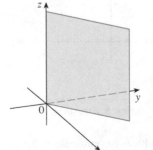

FIGURE 10
The plane $y = x$

> **Distance Formula in Three Dimensions**   The distance $|P_1P_2|$ between the points $P_1(x_1, y_1, z_1)$ and $P_2(x_2, y_2, z_2)$ is
>
> $$|P_1P_2| = \sqrt{(x_2 - x_1)^2 + (y_2 - y_1)^2 + (z_2 - z_1)^2}$$

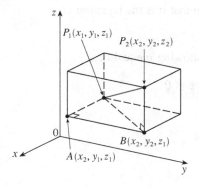

FIGURE 11

To see why this formula is true, we construct a rectangular box as in Figure 11, where P_1 and P_2 are opposite vertices and the faces of the box are parallel to the coordinate planes. If $A(x_2, y_1, z_1)$ and $B(x_2, y_2, z_1)$ are the vertices of the box indicated in the figure, then

$$|P_1A| = |x_2 - x_1| \qquad |AB| = |y_2 - y_1| \qquad |BP_2| = |z_2 - z_1|$$

Because triangles P_1BP_2 and P_1AB are both right-angled, two applications of the Pythagorean Theorem give

$$|P_1P_2|^2 = |P_1B|^2 + |BP_2|^2$$

and

$$|P_1B|^2 = |P_1A|^2 + |AB|^2$$

Combining these equations, we get

$$|P_1P_2|^2 = |P_1A|^2 + |AB|^2 + |BP_2|^2$$
$$= |x_2 - x_1|^2 + |y_2 - y_1|^2 + |z_2 - z_1|^2$$
$$= (x_2 - x_1)^2 + (y_2 - y_1)^2 + (z_2 - z_1)^2$$

Therefore $\qquad |P_1P_2| = \sqrt{(x_2 - x_1)^2 + (y_2 - y_1)^2 + (z_2 - z_1)^2}$

EXAMPLE 4 The distance from the point $P(2, -1, 7)$ to the point $Q(1, -3, 5)$ is

$$|PQ| = \sqrt{(1 - 2)^2 + (-3 + 1)^2 + (5 - 7)^2} = \sqrt{1 + 4 + 4} = 3$$

▼ EXAMPLE 5 Find an equation of a sphere with radius r and center $C(h, k, l)$.

SOLUTION By definition, a sphere is the set of all points $P(x, y, z)$ whose distance from C is r. (See Figure 12.) Thus P is on the sphere if and only if $|PC| = r$. Squaring both sides, we have $|PC|^2 = r^2$ or

$$(x - h)^2 + (y - k)^2 + (z - l)^2 = r^2$$

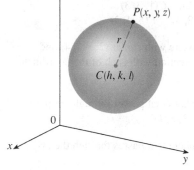

FIGURE 12

The result of Example 5 is worth remembering.

Equation of a Sphere An equation of a sphere with center $C(h, k, l)$ and radius r is

$$(x - h)^2 + (y - k)^2 + (z - l)^2 = r^2$$

In particular, if the center is the origin O, then an equation of the sphere is

$$x^2 + y^2 + z^2 = r^2$$

EXAMPLE 6 Finding the center and radius of a sphere
Show that $x^2 + y^2 + z^2 + 4x - 6y + 2z + 6 = 0$ is the equation of a sphere, and find its center and radius.

SOLUTION We can rewrite the given equation in the form of an equation of a sphere if we complete squares:

$$(x^2 + 4x + 4) + (y^2 - 6y + 9) + (z^2 + 2z + 1) = -6 + 4 + 9 + 1$$
$$(x + 2)^2 + (y - 3)^2 + (z + 1)^2 = 8$$

Comparing this equation with the standard form, we see that it is the equation of a sphere with center $(-2, 3, -1)$ and radius $\sqrt{8} = 2\sqrt{2}$.

EXAMPLE 7   What region in $\mathbb{R}^3$ is represented by the following inequalities?

$$1 \leqslant x^2 + y^2 + z^2 \leqslant 4 \qquad z \leqslant 0$$

SOLUTION   The inequalities

$$1 \leqslant x^2 + y^2 + z^2 \leqslant 4$$

can be rewritten as

$$1 \leqslant \sqrt{x^2 + y^2 + z^2} \leqslant 2$$

so they represent the points (x, y, z) whose distance from the origin is at least 1 and at most 2. But we are also given that $z \leqslant 0$, so the points lie on or below the xy-plane. Thus the given inequalities represent the region that lies between (or on) the spheres $x^2 + y^2 + z^2 = 1$ and $x^2 + y^2 + z^2 = 4$ and beneath (or on) the xy-plane. It is sketched in Figure 13.

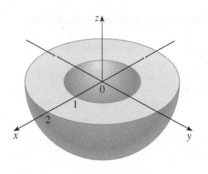

FIGURE 13

9.1 Exercises

1. Suppose you start at the origin, move along the x-axis a distance of 4 units in the positive direction, and then move downward a distance of 3 units. What are the coordinates of your position?

2. Sketch the points $(0, 5, 2)$, $(4, 0, -1)$, $(2, 4, 6)$, and $(1, -1, 2)$ on a single set of coordinate axes.

3. Which of the points $P(6, 2, 3)$, $Q(-5, -1, 4)$, and $R(0, 3, 8)$ is closest to the xz-plane? Which point lies in the yz-plane?

4. What are the projections of the point $(2, 3, 5)$ on the xy-, yz-, and xz-planes? Draw a rectangular box with the origin and $(2, 3, 5)$ as opposite vertices and with its faces parallel to the coordinate planes. Label all vertices of the box. Find the length of the diagonal of the box.

5. Describe and sketch the surface in $\mathbb{R}^3$ represented by the equation $x + y = 2$.

6. (a) What does the equation $x = 4$ represent in $\mathbb{R}^2$? What does it represent in $\mathbb{R}^3$? Illustrate with sketches.
(b) What does the equation $y = 3$ represent in $\mathbb{R}^3$? What does $z = 5$ represent? What does the pair of equations $y = 3$, $z = 5$ represent? In other words, describe the set of points (x, y, z) such that $y = 3$ and $z = 5$. Illustrate with a sketch.

7. Find the lengths of the sides of the triangle PQR. Is it a right triangle? Is it an isosceles triangle?
(a) $P(3, -2, -3)$, $Q(7, 0, 1)$, $R(1, 2, 1)$
(b) $P(2, -1, 0)$, $Q(4, 1, 1)$, $R(4, -5, 4)$

8. Find the distance from $(3, 7, -5)$ to each of the following.
(a) The xy-plane   (b) The yz-plane
(c) The xz-plane   (d) The x-axis
(e) The y-axis   (f) The z-axis

9. Determine whether the points lie on straight line.
(a) $A(2, 4, 2)$, $B(3, 7, -2)$, $C(1, 3, 3)$
(b) $D(0, -5, 5)$, $E(1, -2, 4)$, $F(3, 4, 2)$

10. Find an equation of the sphere with center $(2, -6, 4)$ and radius 5. Describe its intersection with each of the coordinate planes.

11. Find an equation of the sphere that passes through the point $(4, 3, -1)$ and has center $(3, 8, 1)$.

12. Find an equation of the sphere that passes through the origin and whose center is $(1, 2, 3)$.

13–16 Show that the equation represents a sphere, and find its center and radius.

13. $x^2 + y^2 + z^2 - 6x + 4y - 2z = 11$

14. $x^2 + y^2 + z^2 + 8x - 6y + 2z + 17 = 0$

15. $2x^2 + 2y^2 + 2z^2 = 8x - 24z + 1$

16. $3x^2 + 3y^2 + 3z^2 = 10 + 6y + 12z$

---

1. Homework Hints available in TEC

17. (a) Prove that the midpoint of the line segment from $P_1(x_1, y_1, z_1)$ to $P_2(x_2, y_2, z_2)$ is

$$\left(\frac{x_1 + x_2}{2}, \frac{y_1 + y_2}{2}, \frac{z_1 + z_2}{2} \right)$$

   (b) Find the lengths of the medians of the triangle with vertices $A(1, 2, 3)$, $B(-2, 0, 5)$, and $C(4, 1, 5)$.

18. Find an equation of a sphere if one of its diameters has endpoints $(2, 1, 4)$ and $(4, 3, 10)$.

19. Find equations of the spheres with center $(2, -3, 6)$ that touch (a) the xy-plane, (b) the yz-plane, (c) the xz-plane.

20. Find an equation of the largest sphere with center $(5, 4, 9)$ that is contained in the first octant.

21–32 Describe in words the region of $\mathbb{R}^3$ represented by the equations or inequalities.

21. $x = 5$ 22. $y = -2$

23. $y < 8$ 24. $x \geqslant -3$

25. $0 \leqslant z \leqslant 6$ 26. $z^2 = 1$

27. $x^2 + y^2 = 4, \quad z = -1$ 28. $y^2 + z^2 = 16$

29. $x^2 + y^2 + z^2 \leqslant 3$ 30. $r = z$

31. $x^2 + z^2 \leqslant 9$ 32. $x^2 + y^2 + z^2 > 2z$

33–36 Write inequalities to describe the region.

33. The region between the yz-plane and the vertical plane $x = 5$

34. The solid cylinder that lies on or below the plane $z = 8$ and on or above the disk in the xy-plane with center the origin and radius 2

35. The region consisting of all points between (but not on) the spheres of radius r and R centered at the origin, where $r < R$

36. The solid upper hemisphere of the sphere of radius 2 centered at the origin

---

37. The figure shows a line L_1 in space and a second line L_2, which is the projection of L_1 on the xy-plane. (In other words, the points on L_2 are directly beneath, or above, the points on L_1.)

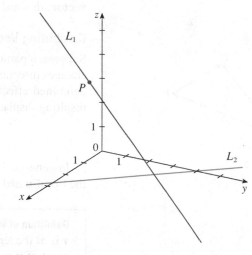

   (a) Find the coordinates of the point P on the line L_1.
   (b) Locate on the diagram the points A, B, and C, where the line L_1 intersects the xy-plane, the yz-plane, and the xz-plane, respectively.

38. Consider the points P such that the distance from P to $A(-1, 5, 3)$ is twice the distance from P to $B(6, 2, -2)$. Show that the set of all such points is a sphere, and find its center and radius.

39. Find an equation of the set of all points equidistant from the points $A(-1, 5, 3)$ and $B(6, 2, -2)$. Describe the set.

40. Find the volume of the solid that lies inside both of the spheres

$$x^2 + y^2 + z^2 + 4x - 2y + 4z + 5 = 0$$

and

$$x^2 + y^2 + z^2 = 4$$

41. Find the distance between the spheres $x^2 + y^2 + z^2 = 4$ and $x^2 + y^2 + z^2 = 4x + 4y + 4z - 11$.

42. Describe and sketch a solid with the following properties. When illuminated by rays parallel to the z-axis, its shadow is a circular disk. If the rays are parallel to the y-axis, its shadow is a square. If the rays are parallel to the x-axis, its shadow is an isosceles triangle.

9.2 Vectors

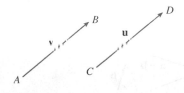

FIGURE 1
Equivalent vectors

The term **vector** is used by scientists to indicate a quantity (such as displacement or velocity or force) that has both magnitude and direction. A vector is often represented by an arrow or a directed line segment. The length of the arrow represents the magnitude of the vector and the arrow points in the direction of the vector. We denote a vector by printing a letter in boldface (**v**) or by putting an arrow above the letter ($\vec{v}$).

For instance, suppose a particle moves along a line segment from point A to point B. The corresponding **displacement vector** $\mathbf{v}$, shown in Figure 1, has **initial point** A (the tail) and **terminal point** B (the tip) and we indicate this by writing $\mathbf{v} = \overrightarrow{AB}$. Notice that the vector $\mathbf{u} = \overrightarrow{CD}$ has the same length and the same direction as $\mathbf{v}$ even though it is in a different position. We say that $\mathbf{u}$ and $\mathbf{v}$ are **equivalent** (or **equal**) and we write $\mathbf{u} = \mathbf{v}$. The **zero vector**, denoted by $\mathbf{0}$, has length 0. It is the only vector with no specific direction.

Combining Vectors

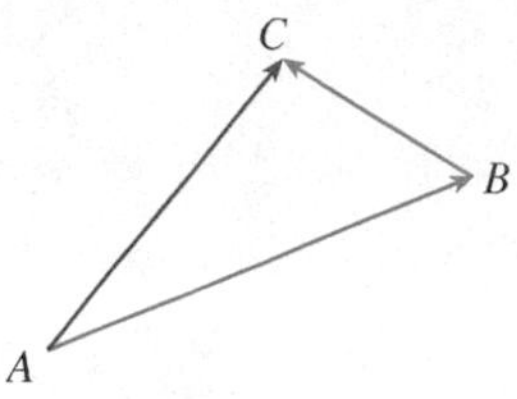

Suppose a particle moves from A to B, so its displacement vector is $\overrightarrow{AB}$. Then the particle changes direction and moves from B to C, with displacement vector $\overrightarrow{BC}$ as in Figure 2. The combined effect of these displacements is that the particle has moved from A to C. The resulting displacement vector $\overrightarrow{AC}$ is called the *sum* of $\overrightarrow{AB}$ and $\overrightarrow{BC}$ and we write

$$\overrightarrow{AC} = \overrightarrow{AB} + \overrightarrow{BC}$$

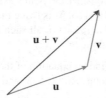

FIGURE 2

In general, if we start with vectors $\mathbf{u}$ and $\mathbf{v}$, we first move $\mathbf{v}$ so that its tail coincides with the tip of $\mathbf{u}$ and define the sum of $\mathbf{u}$ and $\mathbf{v}$ as follows.

> **Definition of Vector Addition**   If $\mathbf{u}$ and $\mathbf{v}$ are vectors positioned so the initial point of $\mathbf{v}$ is at the terminal point of $\mathbf{u}$, then the **sum** $\mathbf{u} + \mathbf{v}$ is the vector from the initial point of $\mathbf{u}$ to the terminal point of $\mathbf{v}$.

The definition of vector addition is illustrated in Figure 3. You can see why this definition is sometimes called the **Triangle Law**.

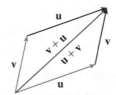

FIGURE 3   The Triangle Law   **FIGURE 4**   The Parallelogram Law

In Figure 4 we start with the same vectors $\mathbf{u}$ and $\mathbf{v}$ as in Figure 3 and draw another copy of $\mathbf{v}$ with the same initial point as $\mathbf{u}$. Completing the parallelogram, we see that $\mathbf{u} + \mathbf{v} = \mathbf{v} + \mathbf{u}$. This also gives another way to construct the sum: If we place $\mathbf{u}$ and $\mathbf{v}$ so they start at the same point, then $\mathbf{u} + \mathbf{v}$ lies along the diagonal of the parallelogram with $\mathbf{u}$ and $\mathbf{v}$ as sides. (This is called the **Parallelogram Law**.)

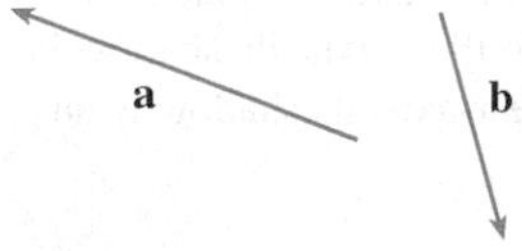

V **EXAMPLE 1**   Draw the sum of the vectors $\mathbf{a}$ and $\mathbf{b}$ shown in Figure 5.

SOLUTION   First we translate $\mathbf{b}$ and place its tail at the tip of $\mathbf{a}$, being careful to draw a copy of $\mathbf{b}$ that has the same length and direction. Then we draw the vector $\mathbf{a} + \mathbf{b}$ [see Figure 6(a)] starting at the initial point of $\mathbf{a}$ and ending at the terminal point of the copy of $\mathbf{b}$.

Alternatively, we could place $\mathbf{b}$ so it starts where $\mathbf{a}$ starts and construct $\mathbf{a} + \mathbf{b}$ by the Parallelogram Law as in Figure 6(b).

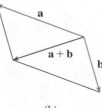

FIGURE 5

TEC Visual 9.2 shows how the Triangle and Parallelogram Laws work for various vectors $\mathbf{a}$ and $\mathbf{b}$.

FIGURE 6   (a)   (b)

It is possible to multiply a vector by a real number c. (In this context we call the real number c a **scalar** to distinguish it from a vector.) For instance, we want $2\mathbf{v}$ to be the same vector as $\mathbf{v} + \mathbf{v}$, which has the same direction as $\mathbf{v}$ but is twice as long. In general, we multiply a vector by a scalar as follows.

> **Definition of Scalar Multiplication** If c is a scalar and $\mathbf{v}$ is a vector, then the **scalar multiple** $c\mathbf{v}$ is the vector whose length is $|c|$ times the length of $\mathbf{v}$ and whose direction is the same as $\mathbf{v}$ if $c > 0$ and is opposite to $\mathbf{v}$ if $c < 0$. If $c = 0$ or $\mathbf{v} = \mathbf{0}$, then $c\mathbf{v} = \mathbf{0}$.

This definition is illustrated in Figure 7. We see that real numbers work like scaling factors here; that's why we call them scalars. Notice that two nonzero vectors are **parallel** if they are scalar multiples of one another. In particular, the vector $-\mathbf{v} = (-1)\mathbf{v}$ has the same length as $\mathbf{v}$ but points in the opposite direction. We call it the **negative** of $\mathbf{v}$.

By the **difference** $\mathbf{u} - \mathbf{v}$ of two vectors we mean

$$\mathbf{u} - \mathbf{v} = \mathbf{u} + (-\mathbf{v})$$

So we can construct $\mathbf{u} - \mathbf{v}$ by first drawing the negative of $\mathbf{v}$, $-\mathbf{v}$, and then adding it to $\mathbf{u}$ by the Parallelogram Law as in Figure 8(a). Alternatively, since $\mathbf{v} + (\mathbf{u} - \mathbf{v}) = \mathbf{u}$, the vector $\mathbf{u} - \mathbf{v}$, when added to $\mathbf{v}$, gives $\mathbf{u}$. So we could construct $\mathbf{u} - \mathbf{v}$ as in Figure 8(b) by means of the Triangle Law.

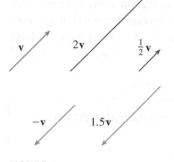

FIGURE 7

Scalar multiples of $\mathbf{v}$

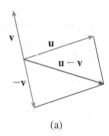

FIGURE 8

Drawing $\mathbf{u} - \mathbf{v}$

(a)   (b)

FIGURE 9

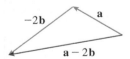

FIGURE 10

EXAMPLE 2 If $\mathbf{a}$ and $\mathbf{b}$ are the vectors shown in Figure 9, draw $\mathbf{a} - 2\mathbf{b}$.

SOLUTION We first draw the vector $-2\mathbf{b}$ pointing in the direction opposite to $\mathbf{b}$ and twice as long. We place it with its tail at the tip of $\mathbf{a}$ and then use the Triangle Law to draw $\mathbf{a} + (-2\mathbf{b})$ as in Figure 10. ▬

Components

For some purposes it's best to introduce a coordinate system and treat vectors algebraically. If we place the initial point of a vector $\mathbf{a}$ at the origin of a rectangular coordinate system, then the terminal point of $\mathbf{a}$ has coordinates of the form (a_1, a_2) or (a_1, a_2, a_3), depending on whether our coordinate system is two- or three-dimensional (see Figure 11).

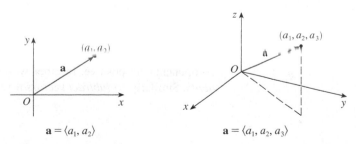

FIGURE 11

$\mathbf{a} = \langle a_1, a_2 \rangle$ $\mathbf{a} = \langle a_1, a_2, a_3 \rangle$

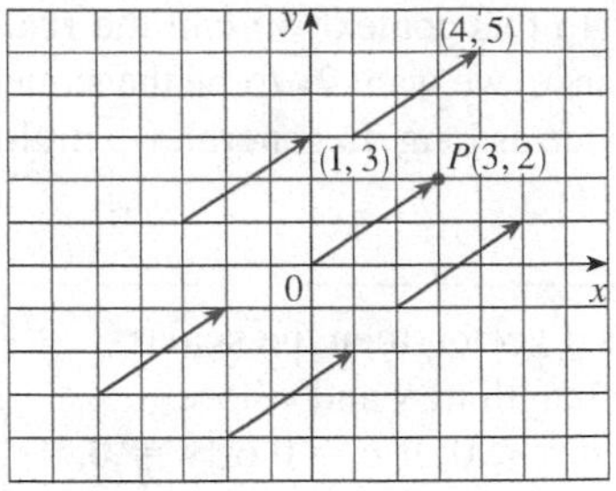

FIGURE 12
Representations of the vector $\mathbf{a} = \langle 3, 2 \rangle$

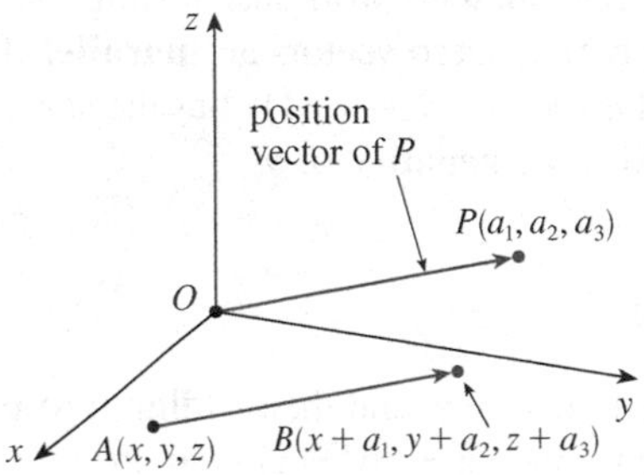

FIGURE 13
Representations of $\mathbf{a} = \langle a_1, a_2, a_3 \rangle$

These coordinates are called the **components** of **a** and we write

$$\mathbf{a} = \langle a_1, a_2 \rangle \qquad \text{or} \qquad \mathbf{a} = \langle a_1, a_2, a_3 \rangle$$

We use the notation $\langle a_1, a_2 \rangle$ for the ordered pair that refers to a vector so as not to confuse it with the ordered pair (a_1, a_2) that refers to a point in the plane.

For instance, the vectors shown in Figure 12 are all equivalent to the vector $\overrightarrow{OP} = \langle 3, 2 \rangle$ whose terminal point is $P(3, 2)$. What they have in common is that the terminal point is reached from the initial point by a displacement of three units to the right and two upward. We can think of all these geometric vectors as **representations** of the algebraic vector $\mathbf{a} = \langle 3, 2 \rangle$. The particular representation $\overrightarrow{OP}$ from the origin to the point $P(3, 2)$ is called the **position vector** of the point P.

In three dimensions, the vector $\mathbf{a} = \overrightarrow{OP} = \langle a_1, a_2, a_3 \rangle$ is the **position vector** of the point $P(a_1, a_2, a_3)$. (See Figure 13.) Let's consider any other representation $\overrightarrow{AB}$ of **a**, where the initial point is $A(x_1, y_1, z_1)$ and the terminal point is $B(x_2, y_2, z_2)$. Then we must have $x_1 + a_1 = x_2$, $y_1 + a_2 = y_2$, and $z_1 + a_3 = z_2$ and so $a_1 = x_2 - x_1$, $a_2 = y_2 - y_1$, and $a_3 = z_2 - z_1$. Thus we have the following result.

1 Given the points $A(x_1, y_1, z_1)$ and $B(x_2, y_2, z_2)$, the vector **a** with representation $\overrightarrow{AB}$ is

$$\mathbf{a} = \langle x_2 - x_1, y_2 - y_1, z_2 - z_1 \rangle$$

V EXAMPLE 3 Representing the displacement vector from one point to another
Find the vector represented by the directed line segment with initial point $A(2, -3, 4)$ and terminal point $B(-2, 1, 1)$.

SOLUTION By (1), the vector corresponding to $\overrightarrow{AB}$ is

$$\mathbf{a} = \langle -2 - 2, 1 - (-3), 1 - 4 \rangle = \langle -4, 4, -3 \rangle$$

The **magnitude** or **length** of the vector **v** is the length of any of its representations and is denoted by the symbol $|\mathbf{v}|$ or $\|\mathbf{v}\|$. By using the distance formula to compute the length of a segment OP, we obtain the following formulas.

The length of the two-dimensional vector $\mathbf{a} = \langle a_1, a_2 \rangle$ is

$$|\mathbf{a}| = \sqrt{a_1^2 + a_2^2}$$

The length of the three-dimensional vector $\mathbf{a} = \langle a_1, a_2, a_3 \rangle$ is

$$|\mathbf{a}| = \sqrt{a_1^2 + a_2^2 + a_3^2}$$

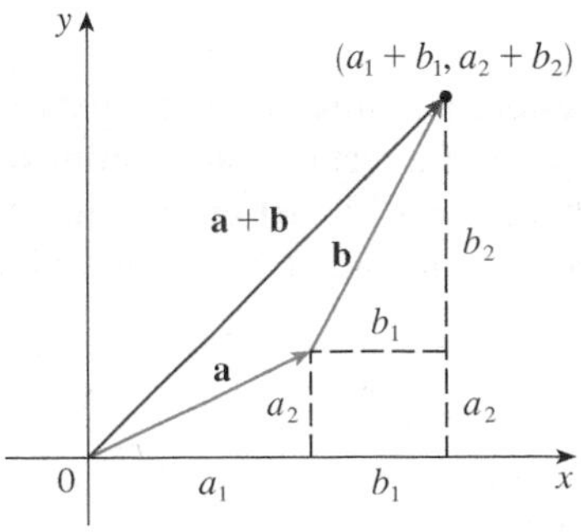

FIGURE 14

How do we add vectors algebraically? Figure 14 shows that if $\mathbf{a} = \langle a_1, a_2 \rangle$ and $\mathbf{b} = \langle b_1, b_2 \rangle$, then the sum is $\mathbf{a} + \mathbf{b} = \langle a_1 + b_1, a_2 + b_2 \rangle$, at least for the case where the components are positive. In other words, *to add algebraic vectors we add their components*. Similarly, *to subtract vectors we subtract components*. From the similar triangles in

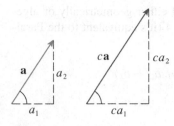

FIGURE 15

Figure 15 we see that the components of $c\mathbf{a}$ are ca_1 and ca_2. So *to multiply a vector by a scalar we multiply each component by that scalar.*

If $\mathbf{a} = \langle a_1, a_2 \rangle$ and $\mathbf{b} = \langle b_1, b_2 \rangle$, then

$$\mathbf{a} + \mathbf{b} = \langle a_1 + b_1, a_2 + b_2 \rangle \qquad \mathbf{a} - \mathbf{b} = \langle a_1 - b_1, a_2 - b_2 \rangle$$

$$c\mathbf{a} = \langle ca_1, ca_2 \rangle$$

Similarly, for three-dimensional vectors,

$$\langle a_1, a_2, a_3 \rangle + \langle b_1, b_2, b_3 \rangle = \langle a_1 + b_1, a_2 + b_2, a_3 + b_3 \rangle$$

$$\langle a_1, a_2, a_3 \rangle - \langle b_1, b_2, b_3 \rangle = \langle a_1 - b_1, a_2 - b_2, a_3 - b_3 \rangle$$

$$c\langle a_1, a_2, a_3 \rangle = \langle ca_1, ca_2, ca_3 \rangle$$

V EXAMPLE 4 Operations on vectors If $\mathbf{a} = \langle 4, 0, 3 \rangle$ and $\mathbf{b} = \langle -2, 1, 5 \rangle$, find $|\mathbf{a}|$ and the vectors $\mathbf{a} + \mathbf{b}$, $\mathbf{a} - \mathbf{b}$, $3\mathbf{b}$, and $2\mathbf{a} + 5\mathbf{b}$.

SOLUTION
$$|\mathbf{a}| = \sqrt{4^2 + 0^2 + 3^2} = \sqrt{25} = 5$$

$$\mathbf{a} + \mathbf{b} = \langle 4, 0, 3 \rangle + \langle -2, 1, 5 \rangle$$
$$= \langle 4 + (-2), 0 + 1, 3 + 5 \rangle = \langle 2, 1, 8 \rangle$$

$$\mathbf{a} - \mathbf{b} = \langle 4, 0, 3 \rangle - \langle -2, 1, 5 \rangle$$
$$= \langle 4 - (-2), 0 - 1, 3 - 5 \rangle = \langle 6, -1, -2 \rangle$$

$$3\mathbf{b} = 3\langle -2, 1, 5 \rangle = \langle 3(-2), 3(1), 3(5) \rangle = \langle -6, 3, 15 \rangle$$

$$2\mathbf{a} + 5\mathbf{b} = 2\langle 4, 0, 3 \rangle + 5\langle -2, 1, 5 \rangle$$
$$= \langle 8, 0, 6 \rangle + \langle -10, 5, 25 \rangle = \langle -2, 5, 31 \rangle$$

We denote by V_2 the set of all two-dimensional vectors and by V_3 the set of all three-dimensional vectors. More generally, we will later need to consider the set V_n of all n-dimensional vectors. An n-dimensional vector is an ordered n-tuple:

$$\mathbf{a} = \langle a_1, a_2, \ldots, a_n \rangle$$

Vectors in n dimensions are used to list various quantities in an organized way. For instance, the components of a six-dimensional vector

$$\mathbf{p} = \langle p_1, p_2, p_3, p_4, p_5, p_6 \rangle$$

might represent the prices of six different ingredients required to make a particular product. Four-dimensional vectors $\langle x, y, z, t \rangle$ are used in relativity theory, where the first three components specify a position in space and the fourth represents time.

where $a_1, a_2, \ldots, a_n$ are real numbers that are called the components of $\mathbf{a}$. Addition and scalar multiplication are defined in terms of components just as for the cases $n = 2$ and $n = 3$.

Properties of Vectors If $\mathbf{a}$, $\mathbf{b}$, and $\mathbf{c}$ are vectors in V_n and c and d are scalars, then

1. $\mathbf{a} + \mathbf{b} = \mathbf{b} + \mathbf{a}$ 2. $\mathbf{a} + (\mathbf{b} + \mathbf{c}) = (\mathbf{a} + \mathbf{b}) + \mathbf{c}$

3. $\mathbf{a} + \mathbf{0} = \mathbf{a}$ 4. $\mathbf{a} + (-\mathbf{a}) = \mathbf{0}$

5. $c(\mathbf{a} + \mathbf{b}) = c\mathbf{a} + c\mathbf{b}$ 6. $(c + d)\mathbf{a} = c\mathbf{a} + d\mathbf{a}$

7. $(cd)\mathbf{a} = c(d\mathbf{a})$ 8. $1\mathbf{a} = \mathbf{a}$

These eight properties of vectors can be readily verified either geometrically or algebraically. For instance, Property 1 can be seen from Figure 4 (it's equivalent to the Parallelogram Law) or as follows for the case $n = 2$:

$$\mathbf{a} + \mathbf{b} = \langle a_1, a_2 \rangle + \langle b_1, b_2 \rangle = \langle a_1 + b_1, a_2 + b_2 \rangle$$

$$= \langle b_1 + a_1, b_2 + a_2 \rangle = \langle b_1, b_2 \rangle + \langle a_1, a_2 \rangle$$

$$= \mathbf{b} + \mathbf{a}$$

We can see why Property 2 (the associative law) is true by looking at Figure 16 and applying the Triangle Law several times: The vector $\overrightarrow{PQ}$ is obtained either by first constructing $\mathbf{a} + \mathbf{b}$ and then adding $\mathbf{c}$ or by adding $\mathbf{a}$ to the vector $\mathbf{b} + \mathbf{c}$.

Three vectors in V_3 play a special role. Let

$$\mathbf{i} = \langle 1, 0, 0 \rangle \qquad \mathbf{j} = \langle 0, 1, 0 \rangle \qquad \mathbf{k} = \langle 0, 0, 1 \rangle$$

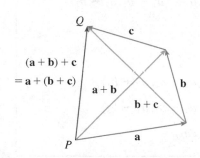

FIGURE 16

Then $\mathbf{i}$, $\mathbf{j}$, and $\mathbf{k}$ are vectors that have length 1 and point in the directions of the positive x-, y-, and z-axes. Similarly, in two dimensions we define $\mathbf{i} = \langle 1, 0 \rangle$ and $\mathbf{j} = \langle 0, 1 \rangle$. (See Figure 17.)

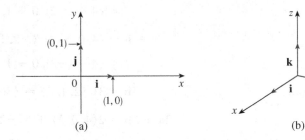

(a)

(b)

FIGURE 17

Standard basis vectors in V_2 and V_3

If $\mathbf{a} = \langle a_1, a_2, a_3 \rangle$, then we can write

$$\mathbf{a} = \langle a_1, a_2, a_3 \rangle = \langle a_1, 0, 0 \rangle + \langle 0, a_2, 0 \rangle + \langle 0, 0, a_3 \rangle$$

$$= a_1 \langle 1, 0, 0 \rangle + a_2 \langle 0, 1, 0 \rangle + a_3 \langle 0, 0, 1 \rangle$$

$$\boxed{2} \qquad \mathbf{a} = a_1 \mathbf{i} + a_2 \mathbf{j} + a_3 \mathbf{k}$$

Thus any vector in V_3 can be expressed in terms of the **standard basis vectors i, j, and k**. For instance,

$$\langle 1, -2, 6 \rangle = \mathbf{i} - 2\mathbf{j} + 6\mathbf{k}$$

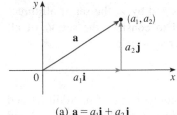

(a) $\mathbf{a} = a_1 \mathbf{i} + a_2 \mathbf{j}$

Similarly, in two dimensions, we can write

$$\boxed{3} \qquad \mathbf{a} = \langle a_1, a_2 \rangle = a_1 \mathbf{i} + a_2 \mathbf{j}$$

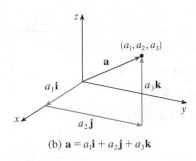

(b) $\mathbf{a} = a_1 \mathbf{i} + a_2 \mathbf{j} + a_3 \mathbf{k}$

FIGURE 18

See Figure 18 for the geometric interpretation of Equations 3 and 2 and compare with Figure 17.

EXAMPLE 5 If $\mathbf{a} = \mathbf{i} + 2\mathbf{j} - 3\mathbf{k}$ and $\mathbf{b} = 4\mathbf{i} + 7\mathbf{k}$, express the vector $2\mathbf{a} + 3\mathbf{b}$ in terms of $\mathbf{i}$, $\mathbf{j}$, and $\mathbf{k}$.

SOLUTION Using Properties 1, 2, 5, 6, and 7 of vectors, we have

$$2\mathbf{a} + 3\mathbf{b} = 2(\mathbf{i} + 2\mathbf{j} - 3\mathbf{k}) + 3(4\mathbf{i} + 7\mathbf{k})$$
$$= 2\mathbf{i} + 4\mathbf{j} - 6\mathbf{k} + 12\mathbf{i} + 21\mathbf{k} = 14\mathbf{i} + 4\mathbf{j} + 15\mathbf{k}$$

A **unit vector** is a vector whose length is 1. For instance, $\mathbf{i}$, $\mathbf{j}$, and $\mathbf{k}$ are all unit vectors. In general, if $\mathbf{a} \neq \mathbf{0}$, then the unit vector that has the same direction as $\mathbf{a}$ is

$$\boxed{4} \qquad \mathbf{u} = \frac{1}{|\mathbf{a}|}\mathbf{a} = \frac{\mathbf{a}}{|\mathbf{a}|}$$

In order to verify this, we let $c = 1/|\mathbf{a}|$. Then $\mathbf{u} = c\mathbf{a}$ and c is a positive scalar, so $\mathbf{u}$ has the same direction as $\mathbf{a}$. Also

$$|\mathbf{u}| = |c\mathbf{a}| = |c||\mathbf{a}| = \frac{1}{|\mathbf{a}|}|\mathbf{a}| = 1$$

EXAMPLE 6 Find the unit vector in the direction of the vector $2\mathbf{i} - \mathbf{j} - 2\mathbf{k}$.

SOLUTION The given vector has length

$$|2\mathbf{i} - \mathbf{j} - 2\mathbf{k}| = \sqrt{2^2 + (-1)^2 + (-2)^2} = \sqrt{9} = 3$$

so, by Equation 4, the unit vector with the same direction is

$$\tfrac{1}{3}(2\mathbf{i} - \mathbf{j} - 2\mathbf{k}) = \tfrac{2}{3}\mathbf{i} - \tfrac{1}{3}\mathbf{j} - \tfrac{2}{3}\mathbf{k}$$

Applications

Vectors are useful in many aspects of physics and engineering. In Chapter 10 we will see how they describe the velocity and acceleration of objects moving in space. Here we look at forces.

A force is represented by a vector because it has both a magnitude (measured in pounds or newtons) and a direction. If several forces are acting on an object, the **resultant force** experienced by the object is the vector sum of these forces.

EXAMPLE 7 A 100-lb weight hangs from two wires as shown in Figure 19. Find the tensions (forces) $\mathbf{T}_1$ and $\mathbf{T}_2$ in both wires and the magnitudes of the tensions.

SOLUTION We first express $\mathbf{T}_1$ and $\mathbf{T}_2$ in terms of their horizontal and vertical components. From Figure 20 we see that

$$\boxed{5} \qquad \mathbf{T}_1 = -|\mathbf{T}_1|\cos 50° \,\mathbf{i} + |\mathbf{T}_1|\sin 50° \,\mathbf{j}$$

$$\boxed{6} \qquad \mathbf{T}_2 = |\mathbf{T}_2|\cos 32° \,\mathbf{i} + |\mathbf{T}_2|\sin 32° \,\mathbf{j}$$

The resultant $\mathbf{T}_1 + \mathbf{T}_2$ of the tensions counterbalances the weight $\mathbf{w}$ and so we must have

$$\mathbf{T}_1 + \mathbf{T}_2 = -\mathbf{w} = 100\,\mathbf{j}$$

Thus

$$\left(-|\mathbf{T}_1|\cos 50° + |\mathbf{T}_2|\cos 32°\right)\mathbf{i} + \left(|\mathbf{T}_1|\sin 50° + |\mathbf{T}_2|\sin 32°\right)\mathbf{j} = 100\,\mathbf{j}$$

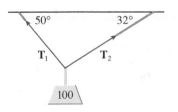

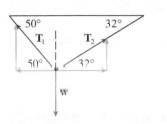

FIGURE 19

FIGURE 20

Equating components, we get

$$-|\mathbf{T}_1|\cos 50° + |\mathbf{T}_2|\cos 32° = 0$$

$$|\mathbf{T}_1|\sin 50° + |\mathbf{T}_2|\sin 32° = 100$$

Solving the first of these equations for $|\mathbf{T}_2|$ and substituting into the second, we get

$$|\mathbf{T}_1|\sin 50° + \frac{|\mathbf{T}_1|\cos 50°}{\cos 32°}\sin 32° = 100$$

So the magnitudes of the tensions are

$$|\mathbf{T}_1| = \frac{100}{\sin 50° + \tan 32° \cos 50°} \approx 85.64 \text{ lb}$$

and

$$|\mathbf{T}_2| = \frac{|\mathbf{T}_1|\cos 50°}{\cos 32°} \approx 64.91 \text{ lb}$$

Substituting these values in (5) and (6), we obtain the tension vectors

$$\mathbf{T}_1 \approx -55.05\,\mathbf{i} + 65.60\,\mathbf{j} \qquad \mathbf{T}_2 \approx 55.05\,\mathbf{i} + 34.40\,\mathbf{j}$$

9.2 Exercises

1. Are the following quantities vectors or scalars? Explain.
   (a) The cost of a theater ticket
   (b) The current in a river
   (c) The initial flight path from Houston to Dallas
   (d) The population of the world

2. What is the relationship between the point $(4, 7)$ and the vector $\langle 4, 7\rangle$? Illustrate with a sketch.

3. Name all the equal vectors in the parallelogram shown.

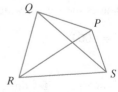

4. Write each combination of vectors as a single vector.
   (a) $\overrightarrow{PQ} + \overrightarrow{QR}$
   (b) $\overrightarrow{RP} + \overrightarrow{PS}$
   (c) $\overrightarrow{QS} - \overrightarrow{PS}$
   (d) $\overrightarrow{RS} + \overrightarrow{SP} + \overrightarrow{PQ}$

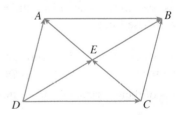

5. Copy the vectors in the figure and use them to draw the following vectors.
   (a) $\mathbf{u} + \mathbf{v}$ (b) $\mathbf{u} - \mathbf{v}$
   (c) $\mathbf{v} + \mathbf{w}$ (d) $\mathbf{w} + \mathbf{v} + \mathbf{u}$

6. Copy the vectors in the figure and use them to draw the following vectors.
   (a) $\mathbf{a} + \mathbf{b}$ (b) $\mathbf{a} - \mathbf{b}$
   (c) $\frac{1}{2}\mathbf{a}$ (d) $-3\mathbf{b}$
   (e) $\mathbf{a} + 2\mathbf{b}$ (f) $2\mathbf{b} - \mathbf{a}$

7–10 Find a vector $\mathbf{a}$ with representation given by the directed line segment $\overrightarrow{AB}$. Draw $\overrightarrow{AB}$ and the equivalent representation starting at the origin.

7. $A(-1, 3)$, $B(2, 2)$ **8.** $A(2, 1)$, $B(0, 6)$

9. $A(0, 3, 1)$, $B(2, 3, -1)$ **10.** $A(4, 0, -2)$, $B(4, 2, 1)$

---

1. Homework Hints available in TEC

11–14 Find the sum of the given vectors and illustrate geometrically.

11. $\langle -1, 4\rangle$, $\langle 6, -2\rangle$ **12.** $\langle -2, -1\rangle$, $\langle 5, 7\rangle$

13. $\langle 0, 1, 2\rangle$, $\langle 0, 0, -3\rangle$ **14.** $\langle -1, 0, 2\rangle$, $\langle 0, 4, 0\rangle$

15–18 Find $\mathbf{a} + \mathbf{b}$, $2\mathbf{a} + 3\mathbf{b}$, $|\mathbf{a}|$, and $|\mathbf{a} - \mathbf{b}|$.

15. $\mathbf{a} = \langle 5, -12\rangle$, $\mathbf{b} = \langle -3, -6\rangle$

16. $\mathbf{a} = 4\mathbf{i} + \mathbf{j}$, $\mathbf{b} = \mathbf{i} - 2\mathbf{j}$

17. $\mathbf{a} = \mathbf{i} + 2\mathbf{j} - 3\mathbf{k}$, $\mathbf{b} = -2\mathbf{i} - \mathbf{j} + 5\mathbf{k}$

18. $\mathbf{a} = 2\mathbf{i} - 4\mathbf{j} + 4\mathbf{k}$, $\mathbf{b} = 2\mathbf{j} - \mathbf{k}$

19–21 Find a unit vector that has the same direction as the given vector.

19. $-3\mathbf{i} + 7\mathbf{j}$ **20.** $\langle -4, 2, 4\rangle$

21. $8\mathbf{i} - \mathbf{j} + 4\mathbf{k}$

22. Find a vector that has the same direction as $\langle -2, 4, 2\rangle$ but has length 6.

23. If $\mathbf{v}$ lies in the first quadrant and makes an angle $\pi/3$ with the positive x-axis and $|\mathbf{v}| = 4$, find $\mathbf{v}$ in component form.

24. If a child pulls a sled through the snow on a level path with a force of 50 N exerted at an angle of 38° above the horizontal, find the horizontal and vertical components of the force.

25. A quarterback throws a football with angle of elevation 40° and speed 60 ft/s. Find the horizontal and vertical components of the velocity vector.

26–27 Find the magnitude of the resultant force and the angle it makes with the positive x-axis.

26.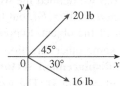

27.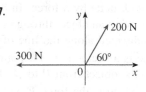

28. The magnitude of a velocity vector is called *speed*. Suppose that a wind is blowing from the direction N45°W at a speed of 50 km/h. (This means that the direction from which the wind blows is 45° west of the northerly direction.) A pilot is steering a plane in the direction N60°E at an airspeed (speed in still air) of 250 km/h. The *true course*, or *track*, of the plane is the direction of the resultant of the velocity vectors of the plane and the wind. The *ground speed* of the plane is the magnitude of the resultant. Find the true course and the ground speed of the plane.

29. A woman walks due west on the deck of a ship at 3 mi/h. The ship is moving north at a speed of 22 mi/h. Find the speed and direction of the woman relative to the surface of the water.

30. Ropes 3 m and 5 m in length are fastened to a holiday decoration that is suspended over a town square. The decoration has a mass of 5 kg. The ropes, fastened at different heights, make angles of 52° and 40° with the horizontal. Find the tension in each wire and the magnitude of each tension.

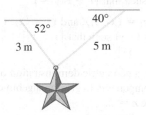

31. A clothesline is tied between two poles, 8 m apart. The line is quite taut and has negligible sag. When a wet shirt with a mass of 0.8 kg is hung at the middle of the line, the midpoint is pulled down 8 cm. Find the tension in each half of the clothesline.

32. The tension $\mathbf{T}$ at each end of the chain has magnitude 25 N (see the figure). What is the weight of the chain?

33. Find the unit vectors that are parallel to the tangent line to the parabola $y = x^2$ at the point $(2, 4)$.

34. (a) Find the unit vectors that are parallel to the tangent line to the curve $y = 2 \sin x$ at the point $(\pi/6, 1)$.
(b) Find the unit vectors that are perpendicular to the tangent line.
(c) Sketch the curve $y = 2 \sin x$ and the vectors in parts (a) and (b), all starting at $(\pi/6, 1)$.

35. (a) Draw the vectors $\mathbf{a} = \langle 3, 2\rangle$, $\mathbf{b} = \langle 2, -1\rangle$, and $\mathbf{c} = \langle 7, 1\rangle$.
(b) Show, by means of a sketch, that there are scalars s and t such that $\mathbf{c} = s\mathbf{a} + t\mathbf{b}$.
(c) Use the sketch to estimate the values of s and t.
(d) Find the exact values of s and t.

36. Suppose that $\mathbf{a}$ and $\mathbf{b}$ are nonzero vectors that are not parallel and $\mathbf{c}$ is any vector in the plane determined by $\mathbf{a}$ and $\mathbf{b}$. Give a geometric argument to show that $\mathbf{c}$ can be written as $\mathbf{c} = s\mathbf{a} + t\mathbf{b}$ for suitable scalars s and t. Then give an argument using components.

37. Suppose $\mathbf{a}$ is a three-dimensional unit vector in the first octant that starts at the origin and makes angles of 60° and 72° with the positive x- and y-axes, respectively. Express $\mathbf{a}$ in terms of its components.

38. Suppose a vector **a** makes angles α, β, and γ with the positive x-, y-, and z-axes, respectively. Find the components of **a** and show that
$$\cos^2\alpha + \cos^2\beta + \cos^2\gamma = 1$$
(The numbers $\cos \alpha$, $\cos \beta$, and $\cos \gamma$ are called the *direction cosines* of **a**.)

39. If $\mathbf{r} = \langle x, y, z \rangle$ and $\mathbf{r}_0 = \langle x_0, y_0, z_0 \rangle$, describe the set of all points (x, y, z) such that $|\mathbf{r} - \mathbf{r}_0| = 1$.

40. If $\mathbf{r} = \langle x, y \rangle$, $\mathbf{r}_1 = \langle x_1, y_1 \rangle$, and $\mathbf{r}_2 = \langle x_2, y_2 \rangle$, describe the set of all points (x, y) such that $|\mathbf{r} - \mathbf{r}_1| + |\mathbf{r} - \mathbf{r}_2| = k$, where $k > |\mathbf{r}_1 - \mathbf{r}_2|$.

41. Figure 16 gives a geometric demonstration of Property 2 of vectors. Use components to give an algebraic proof of this fact for the case $n = 2$.

42. Prove Property 5 of vectors algebraically for the case $n = 3$. Then use similar triangles to give a geometric proof.

43. Use vectors to prove that the line joining the midpoints of two sides of a triangle is parallel to the third side and half its length.

44. Suppose the three coordinate planes are all mirrored and a light ray given by the vector $\mathbf{a} = \langle a_1, a_2, a_3 \rangle$ first strikes the xz-plane, as shown in the figure. Use the fact that the angle of incidence equals the angle of reflection to show that the direction of the reflected ray is given by $\mathbf{b} = \langle a_1, -a_2, a_3 \rangle$. Deduce that, after being reflected by all three mutually perpendicular mirrors, the resulting ray is parallel to the initial ray. (American space scientists used this principle, together with laser beams and an array of corner mirrors on the moon, to calculate very precisely the distance from the earth to the moon.)

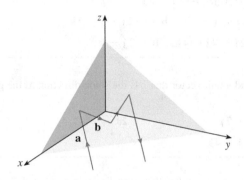

9.3   The Dot Product

So far we have added two vectors and multiplied a vector by a scalar. The question arises: Is it possible to multiply two vectors so that their product is a useful quantity? One such product is the dot product, which we consider in this section. Another is the cross product, which is discussed in the next section.

Work and the Dot Product

An example of a situation in physics and engineering where we need to combine two vectors occurs in calculating the work done by a force. In Section 6.5 we defined the work done by a constant force F in moving an object through a distance d as $W = Fd$, but this applies only when the force is directed along the line of motion of the object. Suppose, however, that the constant force is a vector $\mathbf{F} = \overrightarrow{PR}$ pointing in some other direction, as in Figure 1. If the force moves the object from P to Q, then the **displacement vector** is $\mathbf{D} = \overrightarrow{PQ}$. So here we have two vectors: the force **F** and the displacement **D**. The **work** done by **F** is defined as the magnitude of the displacement, $|\mathbf{D}|$, multiplied by the magnitude of the applied force in the direction of the motion, which, from Figure 1, is
$$|\overrightarrow{PS}| = |\mathbf{F}| \cos \theta$$

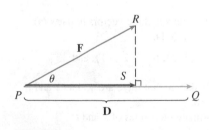

FIGURE 1

So the work done by **F** is defined to be

$$W = |\mathbf{D}|\left(|\mathbf{F}| \cos \theta\right) = |\mathbf{F}||\mathbf{D}| \cos \theta$$

Notice that work is a scalar quantity; it has no direction. But its value depends on the angle θ between the force and displacement vectors.

We use the expression in Equation 1 to define the dot product of two vectors even when they don't represent force or displacement.

> **Definition** The **dot product** of two nonzero vectors **a** and **b** is the number
>
> $$\mathbf{a} \cdot \mathbf{b} = |\mathbf{a}||\mathbf{b}| \cos \theta$$
>
> where θ is the angle between **a** and **b**, $0 \le \theta \le \pi$. (So θ is the smaller angle between the vectors when they are drawn with the same initial point.) If either **a** or **b** is **0**, we define $\mathbf{a} \cdot \mathbf{b} = 0$.

This product is called the **dot product** because of the dot in the notation $\mathbf{a} \cdot \mathbf{b}$. The result of computing $\mathbf{a} \cdot \mathbf{b}$ is not a vector. It is a real number, that is, a scalar. For this reason, the dot product is sometimes called the **scalar product**.

In the example of finding the work done by a force **F** in moving an object through a displacement $\mathbf{D} = \overrightarrow{PQ}$ by calculating $\mathbf{F} \cdot \mathbf{D} = |\mathbf{F}||\mathbf{D}| \cos \theta$, it makes no sense for the angle θ between **F** and **D** to be $\pi/2$ or larger because movement from P to Q couldn't take place. We make no such restriction in our general definition of $\mathbf{a} \cdot \mathbf{b}$, however, and allow θ to be any angle from 0 to π.

EXAMPLE 1   Computing a dot product from lengths and the contained angle   If the vectors **a** and **b** have lengths 4 and 6, and the angle between them is $\pi/3$, find $\mathbf{a} \cdot \mathbf{b}$.

SOLUTION   According to the definition,

$$\mathbf{a} \cdot \mathbf{b} = |\mathbf{a}||\mathbf{b}| \cos(\pi/3) = 4 \cdot 6 \cdot \tfrac{1}{2} = 12$$

EXAMPLE 2   A wagon is pulled a distance of 100 m along a horizontal path by a constant force of 70 N. The handle of the wagon is held at an angle of 35° above the horizontal. Find the work done by the force.

SOLUTION   If **F** and **D** are the force and displacement vectors, as pictured in Figure 2, then the work done is

$$W = \mathbf{F} \cdot \mathbf{D} = |\mathbf{F}||\mathbf{D}| \cos 35°$$

$$= (70)(100) \cos 35° \approx 5734 \text{ N·m} = 5734 \text{ J}$$

Two nonzero vectors **a** and **b** are called **perpendicular** or **orthogonal** if the angle between them is $\theta = \pi/2$. For such vectors we have

$$\mathbf{a} \cdot \mathbf{b} = |\mathbf{a}||\mathbf{b}| \cos(\pi/2) = 0$$

and conversely if $\mathbf{a} \cdot \mathbf{b} = 0$, then $\cos \theta = 0$, so $\theta = \pi/2$. The zero vector **0** is considered to be perpendicular to all vectors. Therefore

> 2   Two vectors **a** and **b** are orthogonal if and only if $\mathbf{a} \cdot \mathbf{b} = 0$.

Because $\cos \theta > 0$ if $0 \le \theta < \pi/2$ and $\cos \theta < 0$ if $\pi/2 < \theta \le \pi$, we see that $\mathbf{a} \cdot \mathbf{b}$ is positive for $\theta < \pi/2$ and negative for $\theta > \pi/2$. We can think of $\mathbf{a} \cdot \mathbf{b}$ as measuring the extent to which **a** and **b** point in the same direction. The dot product $\mathbf{a} \cdot \mathbf{b}$ is positive if **a**

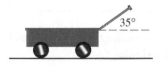
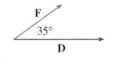

FIGURE 2

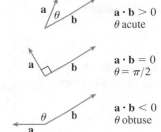

FIGURE 3

TEC Visual 9.3A shows an animation of Figure 3.

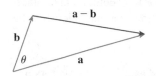

FIGURE 4

and **b** point in the same general direction, 0 if they are perpendicular, and negative if they point in generally opposite directions (see Figure 3). In the extreme case where **a** and **b** point in exactly the same direction, we have $\theta = 0$, so $\cos \theta = 1$ and

$$\mathbf{a} \cdot \mathbf{b} = |\mathbf{a}||\mathbf{b}|$$

If **a** and **b** point in exactly opposite directions, then $\theta = \pi$ and so $\cos \theta = -1$ and $\mathbf{a} \cdot \mathbf{b} = -|\mathbf{a}||\mathbf{b}|$.

The Dot Product in Component Form

Suppose we are given two vectors in component form:

$$\mathbf{a} = \langle a_1, a_2, a_3 \rangle \qquad \mathbf{b} = \langle b_1, b_2, b_3 \rangle$$

We want to find a convenient expression for $\mathbf{a} \cdot \mathbf{b}$ in terms of these components. If we apply the Law of Cosines to the triangle in Figure 4, we get

$$|\mathbf{a} - \mathbf{b}|^2 = |\mathbf{a}|^2 + |\mathbf{b}|^2 - 2|\mathbf{a}||\mathbf{b}| \cos \theta = |\mathbf{a}|^2 + |\mathbf{b}|^2 - 2\mathbf{a} \cdot \mathbf{b}$$

Solving for the dot product, we obtain

$$\begin{aligned} \mathbf{a} \cdot \mathbf{b} &= \tfrac{1}{2} \left(|\mathbf{a}|^2 + |\mathbf{b}|^2 - |\mathbf{a} - \mathbf{b}|^2 \right) \\ &= \tfrac{1}{2} \left[a_1^2 + a_2^2 + a_3^2 + b_1^2 + b_2^2 + b_3^2 - (a_1 - b_1)^2 - (a_2 - b_2)^2 - (a_3 - b_3)^2 \right] \\ &= a_1 b_1 + a_2 b_2 + a_3 b_3 \end{aligned}$$

The dot product of $\mathbf{a} = \langle a_1, a_2, a_3 \rangle$ and $\mathbf{b} = \langle b_1, b_2, b_3 \rangle$ is

$$\mathbf{a} \cdot \mathbf{b} = a_1 b_1 + a_2 b_2 + a_3 b_3$$

Thus, to find the dot product of **a** and **b**, we multiply corresponding components and add. The dot product of two-dimensional vectors is found in a similar fashion:

$$\langle a_1, a_2 \rangle \cdot \langle b_1, b_2 \rangle = a_1 b_1 + a_2 b_2$$

▼ EXAMPLE 3 Computing dot products from components

$$\langle 2, 4 \rangle \cdot \langle 3, -1 \rangle = 2(3) + 4(-1) = 2$$

$$\langle -1, 7, 4 \rangle \cdot \langle 6, 2, -\tfrac{1}{2} \rangle = (-1)(6) + 7(2) + 4\left(-\tfrac{1}{2}\right) = 6$$

$$(\mathbf{i} + 2\mathbf{j} - 3\mathbf{k}) \cdot (2\mathbf{j} - \mathbf{k}) = 1(0) + 2(2) + (-3)(-1) = 7$$

EXAMPLE 4 Testing for orthogonality Show that $2\mathbf{i} + 2\mathbf{j} - \mathbf{k}$ is perpendicular to $5\mathbf{i} - 4\mathbf{j} + 2\mathbf{k}$.

SOLUTION Since

$$(2\mathbf{i} + 2\mathbf{j} - \mathbf{k}) \cdot (5\mathbf{i} - 4\mathbf{j} + 2\mathbf{k}) = 2(5) + 2(-4) + (-1)(2) = 0$$

these vectors are perpendicular by (2).

V **EXAMPLE 5** Find the angle between the vectors $\mathbf{a} = \langle 2, 2, -1 \rangle$ and $\mathbf{b} = \langle 5, -3, 2 \rangle$.

SOLUTION Let θ be the required angle. Since

$$|\mathbf{a}| = \sqrt{2^2 + 2^2 + (-1)^2} = 3 \qquad \text{and} \qquad |\mathbf{b}| = \sqrt{5^2 + (-3)^2 + 2^2} = \sqrt{38}$$

and since

$$\mathbf{a} \cdot \mathbf{b} = 2(5) + 2(-3) + (-1)(2) = 2$$

we have, from the definition of the dot product

$$\cos \theta = \frac{\mathbf{a} \cdot \mathbf{b}}{|\mathbf{a}||\mathbf{b}|} = \frac{2}{3\sqrt{38}}$$

So the angle between $\mathbf{a}$ and $\mathbf{b}$ is

$$\theta = \cos^{-1}\left(\frac{2}{3\sqrt{38}}\right) \approx 1.46 \quad (\text{or } 84°)$$

EXAMPLE 6 A force is given by a vector $\mathbf{F} = 3\mathbf{i} + 4\mathbf{j} + 5\mathbf{k}$ and moves a particle from the point $P(2, 1, 0)$ to the point $Q(4, 6, 2)$. Find the work done.

SOLUTION The displacement vector is $\mathbf{D} = \overrightarrow{PQ} = \langle 2, 5, 2 \rangle$, so the work done is

$$W = \mathbf{F} \cdot \mathbf{D} = \langle 3, 4, 5 \rangle \cdot \langle 2, 5, 2 \rangle = 6 + 20 + 10 = 36$$

If the unit of length is meters and the magnitude of the force is measured in newtons, then the work done is 36 J.

The dot product obeys many of the laws that hold for ordinary products of real numbers. These are stated in the following theorem.

Properties of the Dot Product If $\mathbf{a}$, $\mathbf{b}$, and $\mathbf{c}$ are vectors in V_3 and c is a scalar, then

1. $\mathbf{a} \cdot \mathbf{a} = |\mathbf{a}|^2$
2. $\mathbf{a} \cdot \mathbf{b} = \mathbf{b} \cdot \mathbf{a}$
3. $\mathbf{a} \cdot (\mathbf{b} + \mathbf{c}) = \mathbf{a} \cdot \mathbf{b} + \mathbf{a} \cdot \mathbf{c}$
4. $(c\mathbf{a}) \cdot \mathbf{b} = c(\mathbf{a} \cdot \mathbf{b}) = \mathbf{a} \cdot (c\mathbf{b})$
5. $\mathbf{0} \cdot \mathbf{a} = 0$

Properties 1, 2, and 5 are immediate consequences of the definition of a dot product. Property 3 is best proved using components:

$$\begin{aligned}
\mathbf{a} \cdot (\mathbf{b} + \mathbf{c}) &= \langle a_1, a_2, a_3 \rangle \cdot \langle b_1 + c_1, b_2 + c_2, b_3 + c_3 \rangle \\
&= a_1(b_1 + c_1) + a_2(b_2 + c_2) + a_3(b_3 + c_3) \\
&= a_1 b_1 + a_1 c_1 + a_2 b_2 + a_2 c_2 + a_3 b_3 + a_3 c_3 \\
&= (a_1 b_1 + a_2 b_2 + a_3 b_3) + (a_1 c_1 + a_2 c_2 + a_3 c_3) \\
&= \mathbf{a} \cdot \mathbf{b} + \mathbf{a} \cdot \mathbf{c}
\end{aligned}$$

The proof of Property 4 is left as Exercise 47.

TEC Visual 9.3B shows how Figure 5 changes when we vary **a** and **b**.

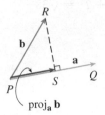

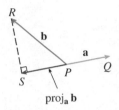

FIGURE 5
Vector projections

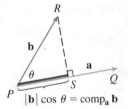

$|\mathbf{b}| \cos \theta = \text{comp}_{\mathbf{a}} \mathbf{b}$

FIGURE 6
Scalar projection

Projections

Figure 5 shows representations $\overrightarrow{PQ}$ and $\overrightarrow{PR}$ of two vectors **a** and **b** with the same initial point P. If S is the foot of the perpendicular from R to the line containing $\overrightarrow{PQ}$, then the vector with representation $\overrightarrow{PS}$ is called the **vector projection** of **b** onto **a** and is denoted by $\text{proj}_{\mathbf{a}} \mathbf{b}$. (You can think of it as a shadow of **b**).

The **scalar projection** of **b** onto **a** (also called the **component of b along a**) is defined to be the signed magnitude of the vector projection, which is the number $|\mathbf{b}| \cos \theta$, where θ is the angle between **a** and **b**. (See Figure 6.) This is denoted by $\text{comp}_{\mathbf{a}} \mathbf{b}$. Observe that it is negative if $\pi/2 < \theta \leq \pi$. (Note that we used the component of the force **F** along the displacement **D**, $\text{comp}_{\mathbf{D}} \mathbf{F}$, at the beginning of this section.)

The equation

$$\mathbf{a} \cdot \mathbf{b} = |\mathbf{a}||\mathbf{b}| \cos \theta = |\mathbf{a}|(|\mathbf{b}| \cos \theta)$$

shows that the dot product of **a** and **b** can be interpreted as the length of **a** times the scalar projection of **b** onto **a**. Since

$$|\mathbf{b}| \cos \theta = \frac{\mathbf{a} \cdot \mathbf{b}}{|\mathbf{a}|} = \frac{\mathbf{a}}{|\mathbf{a}|} \cdot \mathbf{b}$$

the component of **b** along **a** can be computed by taking the dot product of **b** with the unit vector in the direction of **a**. We summarize these ideas as follows.

Scalar projection of **b** onto **a**: $\text{comp}_{\mathbf{a}} \mathbf{b} = \dfrac{\mathbf{a} \cdot \mathbf{b}}{|\mathbf{a}|}$

Vector projection of **b** onto **a**: $\text{proj}_{\mathbf{a}} \mathbf{b} = \left(\dfrac{\mathbf{a} \cdot \mathbf{b}}{|\mathbf{a}|} \right) \dfrac{\mathbf{a}}{|\mathbf{a}|} = \dfrac{\mathbf{a} \cdot \mathbf{b}}{|\mathbf{a}|^2} \mathbf{a}$

V EXAMPLE 7 Find the scalar projection and vector projection of $\mathbf{b} = \langle 1, 1, 2 \rangle$ onto $\mathbf{a} = \langle -2, 3, 1 \rangle$.

SOLUTION Since $|\mathbf{a}| = \sqrt{(-2)^2 + 3^2 + 1^2} = \sqrt{14}$, the scalar projection of **b** onto **a** is

$$\text{comp}_{\mathbf{a}} \mathbf{b} = \frac{\mathbf{a} \cdot \mathbf{b}}{|\mathbf{a}|} = \frac{(-2)(1) + 3(1) + 1(2)}{\sqrt{14}} = \frac{3}{\sqrt{14}}$$

The vector projection is this scalar projection times the unit vector in the direction of **a**:

$$\text{proj}_{\mathbf{a}} \mathbf{b} = \frac{3}{\sqrt{14}} \frac{\mathbf{a}}{|\mathbf{a}|} = \frac{3}{14} \mathbf{a} = \left\langle -\frac{3}{7}, \frac{9}{14}, \frac{3}{14} \right\rangle$$

At the beginning of this section we saw one use of projections in physics—we used a scalar projection of a force vector in defining work. Other uses of projections occur in three-dimensional geometry. In Exercise 41 you are asked to use a projection to find the distance from a point to a line, and in Section 9.5 we use a projection to find the distance from a point to a plane.

9.3 Exercises

1. Which of the following expressions are meaningful? Which are meaningless? Explain.
   (a) $(\mathbf{a} \cdot \mathbf{b}) \cdot \mathbf{c}$
   (b) $(\mathbf{a} \cdot \mathbf{b})\mathbf{c}$
   (c) $|\mathbf{a}|(\mathbf{b} \cdot \mathbf{c})$
   (d) $\mathbf{a} \cdot (\mathbf{b} + \mathbf{c})$
   (e) $\mathbf{a} \cdot \mathbf{b} + \mathbf{c}$
   (f) $|\mathbf{a}| \cdot (\mathbf{b} + \mathbf{c})$

2–10 Find $\mathbf{a} \cdot \mathbf{b}$.

2. $|\mathbf{a}| = 3$, $|\mathbf{b}| = \sqrt{6}$, the angle between $\mathbf{a}$ and $\mathbf{b}$ is $45°$

3. $|\mathbf{a}| = 6$, $|\mathbf{b}| = 5$, the angle between $\mathbf{a}$ and $\mathbf{b}$ is $2\pi/3$

4. $\mathbf{a} = \langle -2, 3 \rangle$, $\mathbf{b} = \langle 0.7, 1.2 \rangle$

5. $\mathbf{a} = \langle -2, \frac{1}{3} \rangle$, $\mathbf{b} = \langle -5, 12 \rangle$

6. $\mathbf{a} = \langle 6, -2, 3 \rangle$, $\mathbf{b} = \langle 2, 5, -1 \rangle$

7. $\mathbf{a} = \langle 4, 1, \frac{1}{4} \rangle$, $\mathbf{b} = \langle 6, -3, -8 \rangle$

8. $\mathbf{a} = \langle p, -p, 2p \rangle$, $\mathbf{b} = \langle 2q, q, -q \rangle$

9. $\mathbf{a} = 2\mathbf{i} + \mathbf{j}$, $\mathbf{b} = \mathbf{i} - \mathbf{j} + \mathbf{k}$

10. $\mathbf{a} = 3\mathbf{i} + 2\mathbf{j} - \mathbf{k}$, $\mathbf{b} = 4\mathbf{i} + 5\mathbf{k}$

11–12 If $\mathbf{u}$ is a unit vector, find $\mathbf{u} \cdot \mathbf{v}$ and $\mathbf{u} \cdot \mathbf{w}$.

11.
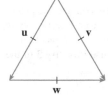

12.
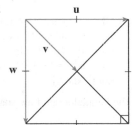

13. (a) Show that $\mathbf{i} \cdot \mathbf{j} = \mathbf{j} \cdot \mathbf{k} = \mathbf{k} \cdot \mathbf{i} = 0$.
   (b) Show that $\mathbf{i} \cdot \mathbf{i} = \mathbf{j} \cdot \mathbf{j} = \mathbf{k} \cdot \mathbf{k} = 1$.

14. A street vendor sells a hamburgers, b hot dogs, and c soft drinks on a given day. He charges $2 for a hamburger, $1.50 for a hot dog, and $1 for a soft drink. If $\mathbf{A} = \langle a, b, c \rangle$ and $\mathbf{P} = \langle 2, 1.5, 1 \rangle$, what is the meaning of the dot product $\mathbf{A} \cdot \mathbf{P}$?

15–18 Find the angle between the vectors. (First find an exact expression and then approximate to the nearest degree.)

15. $\mathbf{a} = \langle -8, 6 \rangle$, $\mathbf{b} = \langle \sqrt{7}, 3 \rangle$

16. $\mathbf{a} = \langle \sqrt{3}, 1 \rangle$, $\mathbf{b} = \langle 0, 5 \rangle$

17. $\mathbf{a} = \mathbf{j} + \mathbf{k}$, $\mathbf{b} = \mathbf{i} + 2\mathbf{j} - 3\mathbf{k}$

18. $\mathbf{a} = \mathbf{i} + 2\mathbf{j} - 2\mathbf{k}$, $\mathbf{b} = 4\mathbf{i} - 3\mathbf{k}$

19–20 Find, correct to the nearest degree, the three angles of the triangle with the given vertices.

19. $A(1, 0)$, $B(3, 6)$, $C(-1, 4)$

20. $D(0, 1, 1)$, $E(-2, 4, 3)$, $F(1, 2, -1)$

21–22 Determine whether the given vectors are orthogonal, parallel, or neither.

21. (a) $\mathbf{a} = \langle -5, 3, 7 \rangle$, $\mathbf{b} = \langle 6, -8, 2 \rangle$
   (b) $\mathbf{a} = \langle 4, 6 \rangle$, $\mathbf{b} = \langle -3, 2 \rangle$
   (c) $\mathbf{a} = -\mathbf{i} + 2\mathbf{j} + 5\mathbf{k}$, $\mathbf{b} = 3\mathbf{i} + 4\mathbf{j} - \mathbf{k}$
   (d) $\mathbf{a} = 2\mathbf{i} + 6\mathbf{j} - 4\mathbf{k}$, $\mathbf{b} = -3\mathbf{i} - 9\mathbf{j} + 6\mathbf{k}$

22. (a) $\mathbf{u} = \langle -3, 9, 6 \rangle$, $\mathbf{v} = \langle 4, -12, -8 \rangle$
   (b) $\mathbf{u} = \mathbf{i} - \mathbf{j} + 2\mathbf{k}$, $\mathbf{v} = 2\mathbf{i} - \mathbf{j} + \mathbf{k}$
   (c) $\mathbf{u} = \langle a, b, c \rangle$, $\mathbf{v} = \langle -b, a, 0 \rangle$

23. Use vectors to decide whether the triangle with vertices $P(1, -3, -2)$, $Q(2, 0, -4)$, and $R(6, -2, -5)$ is right-angled.

24. For what values of b are the vectors $\langle -6, b, 2 \rangle$ and $\langle b, b^2, b \rangle$ orthogonal?

25. Find a unit vector that is orthogonal to both $\mathbf{i} + \mathbf{j}$ and $\mathbf{i} + \mathbf{k}$.

26. Find two unit vectors that make an angle of $60°$ with $\mathbf{v} = \langle 3, 4 \rangle$.

27–28 Find the acute angle between the lines.

27. $2x - y = 3$, $3x + y = 7$

28. $x + 2y = 7$, $5x - y = 2$

29–32 Find the scalar and vector projections of $\mathbf{b}$ onto $\mathbf{a}$.

29. $\mathbf{a} = \langle 3, -4 \rangle$, $\mathbf{b} = \langle 5, 0 \rangle$

30. $\mathbf{a} = \langle 1, 2 \rangle$, $\mathbf{b} = \langle -4, 1 \rangle$

31. $\mathbf{a} = 2\mathbf{i} - \mathbf{j} + 4\mathbf{k}$, $\mathbf{b} = \mathbf{j} + \frac{1}{2}\mathbf{k}$

32. $\mathbf{a} = \mathbf{i} + \mathbf{j} + \mathbf{k}$, $\mathbf{b} = \mathbf{i} - \mathbf{j} + \mathbf{k}$

33. Show that the vector $\text{orth}_\mathbf{a}\,\mathbf{b} = \mathbf{b} - \text{proj}_\mathbf{a}\,\mathbf{b}$ is orthogonal to $\mathbf{a}$. (It is called an **orthogonal projection** of $\mathbf{b}$.)

34. For the vectors in Exercise 30, find $\text{orth}_\mathbf{a}\,\mathbf{b}$ and illustrate by drawing the vectors $\mathbf{a}$, $\mathbf{b}$, $\text{proj}_\mathbf{a}\,\mathbf{b}$, and $\text{orth}_\mathbf{a}\,\mathbf{b}$.

35. If $\mathbf{a} = \langle 3, 0, -1 \rangle$, find a vector $\mathbf{b}$ such that $\text{comp}_\mathbf{a}\,\mathbf{b} = 2$.

36. Suppose that $\mathbf{a}$ and $\mathbf{b}$ are nonzero vectors.
   (a) Under what circumstances is $\text{comp}_\mathbf{a}\,\mathbf{b} = \text{comp}_\mathbf{b}\,\mathbf{a}$?
   (b) Under what circumstances is $\text{proj}_\mathbf{a}\,\mathbf{b} = \text{proj}_\mathbf{b}\,\mathbf{a}$?

---

1. Homework Hints available in TEC

37. Find the work done by a force $\mathbf{F} = 8\,\mathbf{i} - 6\,\mathbf{j} + 9\,\mathbf{k}$ that moves an object from the point $(0, 10, 8)$ to the point $(6, 12, 20)$ along a straight line. The distance is measured in meters and the force in newtons.

38. A tow truck drags a stalled car along a road. The chain makes an angle of $30°$ with the road and the tension in the chain is 1500 N. How much work is done by the truck in pulling the car 1 km?

39. A sled is pulled along a level path through snow by a rope. A 30-lb force acting at an angle of $40°$ above the horizontal moves the sled 80 ft. Find the work done by the force.

40. A boat sails south with the help of a wind blowing in the direction S36°E with magnitude 400 lb. Find the work done by the wind as the boat moves 120 ft.

41. Use a scalar projection to show that the distance from a point $P_1(x_1, y_1)$ to the line $ax + by + c = 0$ is

$$\frac{|ax_1 + by_1 + c|}{\sqrt{a^2 + b^2}}$$

Use this formula to find the distance from the point $(-2, 3)$ to the line $3x - 4y + 5 = 0$.

42. If $\mathbf{r} = \langle x, y, z \rangle$, $\mathbf{a} = \langle a_1, a_2, a_3 \rangle$, and $\mathbf{b} = \langle b_1, b_2, b_3 \rangle$, show that the vector equation $(\mathbf{r} - \mathbf{a}) \cdot (\mathbf{r} - \mathbf{b}) = 0$ represents a sphere, and find its center and radius.

43. Find the angle between a diagonal of a cube and one of its edges.

44. Find the angle between a diagonal of a cube and a diagonal of one of its faces.

45. A molecule of methane, CH_4, is structured with the four hydrogen atoms at the vertices of a regular tetrahedron and the carbon atom at the centroid. The *bond angle* is the angle formed by the H—C—H combination; it is the angle between the lines that join the carbon atom to two of the hydrogen atoms. Show that the bond angle is about $109.5°$. [*Hint:* Take the vertices of the tetrahedron to be the points $(1, 0, 0)$, $(0, 1, 0)$,

$(0, 0, 1)$, and $(1, 1, 1)$, as shown in the figure. Then the centroid is $\left(\frac{1}{2}, \frac{1}{2}, \frac{1}{2}\right)$.]

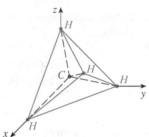

46. If $\mathbf{c} = |\mathbf{a}|\,\mathbf{b} + |\mathbf{b}|\,\mathbf{a}$, where $\mathbf{a}$, $\mathbf{b}$, and $\mathbf{c}$ are all nonzero vectors, show that $\mathbf{c}$ bisects the angle between $\mathbf{a}$ and $\mathbf{b}$.

47. Prove Property 4 of the dot product. Use either the definition of a dot product (considering the cases $c > 0$, $c = 0$, and $c < 0$ separately) or the component form.

48. Suppose that all sides of a quadrilateral are equal in length and opposite sides are parallel. Use vector methods to show that the diagonals are perpendicular.

49. Prove the Cauchy-Schwarz Inequality:

$$|\mathbf{a} \cdot \mathbf{b}| \leqslant |\mathbf{a}|\,|\mathbf{b}|$$

50. The Triangle Inequality for vectors is

$$|\mathbf{a} + \mathbf{b}| \leqslant |\mathbf{a}| + |\mathbf{b}|$$

(a) Give a geometric interpretation of the Triangle Inequality.
(b) Use the Cauchy-Schwarz Inequality from Exercise 49 to prove the Triangle Inequality. [*Hint:* Use the fact that $|\mathbf{a} + \mathbf{b}|^2 = (\mathbf{a} + \mathbf{b}) \cdot (\mathbf{a} + \mathbf{b})$ and use Property 3 of the dot product.]

51. The Parallelogram Law states that

$$|\mathbf{a} + \mathbf{b}|^2 + |\mathbf{a} - \mathbf{b}|^2 = 2|\mathbf{a}|^2 + 2|\mathbf{b}|^2$$

(a) Give a geometric interpretation of the Parallelogram Law.
(b) Prove the Parallelogram Law. (See the hint in Exercise 50.)

52. Show that if $\mathbf{u} + \mathbf{v}$ and $\mathbf{u} - \mathbf{v}$ are orthogonal, then the vectors $\mathbf{u}$ and $\mathbf{v}$ must have the same length.

9.4 The Cross Product

The **cross product** $\mathbf{a} \times \mathbf{b}$ of two vectors $\mathbf{a}$ and $\mathbf{b}$, unlike the dot product, is a vector. For this reason it is also called the **vector product**. We will see that $\mathbf{a} \times \mathbf{b}$ is useful in geometry because it is perpendicular to both $\mathbf{a}$ and $\mathbf{b}$. But we introduce this product by looking at a situation where it arises in physics and engineering.

Torque and the Cross Product

If we tighten a bolt by applying a force to a wrench as in Figure 1, we produce a turning effect called a *torque* $\boldsymbol{\tau}$. The magnitude of the torque depends on two things:

- The distance from the axis of the bolt to the point where the force is applied. This is $|\mathbf{r}|$, the length of the position vector $\mathbf{r}$.

FIGURE 1

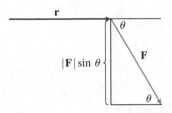

FIGURE 2

- The scalar component of the force **F** in the direction perpendicular to **r**. This is the only component that can cause a rotation and, from Figure 2, we see that it is

$$|\mathbf{F}|\sin\theta$$

where θ is the angle between the vectors **r** and **F**.

We define the magnitude of the torque vector to be the product of these two factors:

$$|\boldsymbol{\tau}| = |\mathbf{r}||\mathbf{F}|\sin\theta$$

The direction is along the axis of rotation. If **n** is a unit vector that points in the direction in which a right-threaded bolt moves (see Figure 1), we define the **torque** to be the vector

$$\boxed{1} \qquad \boldsymbol{\tau} = (|\mathbf{r}||\mathbf{F}|\sin\theta)\mathbf{n}$$

We denote this torque vector by $\boldsymbol{\tau} = \mathbf{r} \times \mathbf{F}$ and we call it the *cross product* or *vector product* of **r** and **F**.

The type of expression in Equation 1 occurs so frequently in the study of fluid flow, planetary motion, and other areas of physics and engineering, that we define and study the cross product of *any* pair of three-dimensional vectors **a** and **b**.

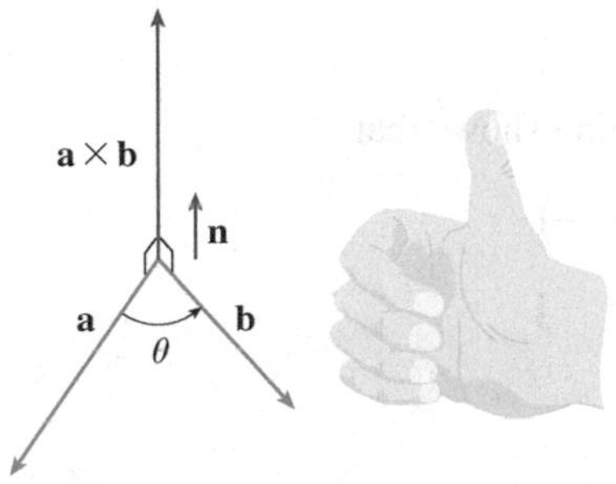

> **Definition** If **a** and **b** are nonzero three-dimensional vectors, the **cross product** of **a** and **b** is the vector
>
> $$\mathbf{a} \times \mathbf{b} = (|\mathbf{a}||\mathbf{b}|\sin\theta)\mathbf{n}$$
>
> where θ is the angle between **a** and **b**, $0 \le \theta \le \pi$, and **n** is a unit vector perpendicular to both **a** and **b** and whose direction is given by the **right-hand rule**: If the fingers of your right hand curl through the angle θ from **a** to **b**, then your thumb points in the direction of **n**. (See Figure 3.)

FIGURE 3
The right-hand rule gives
the direction of $\mathbf{a} \times \mathbf{b}$.

TEC Visual 9.4 shows how $\mathbf{a} \times \mathbf{b}$ changes as **b** changes.

If either **a** or **b** is **0**, then we define $\mathbf{a} \times \mathbf{b}$ to be **0**.
Because $\mathbf{a} \times \mathbf{b}$ is a scalar multiple of **n**, it has the same direction as **n** and so

$$\mathbf{a} \times \mathbf{b} \text{ is orthogonal to both } \mathbf{a} \text{ and } \mathbf{b}.$$

In particular, any vector **a** is parallel to itself, so

$$\mathbf{a} \times \mathbf{a} = \mathbf{0}$$

Notice that two nonzero vectors **a** and **b** are parallel if and only if the angle between them is 0 or π. In either case, $\sin\theta = 0$ and so $\mathbf{a} \times \mathbf{b} = \mathbf{0}$.

$$\text{Two nonzero vectors } \mathbf{a} \text{ and } \mathbf{b} \text{ are parallel if and only if } \mathbf{a} \times \mathbf{b} = \mathbf{0}.$$

This makes sense in the torque interpretation: If we pull or push the wrench in the direction of its handle (so **F** is parallel to **r**), we produce no torque.

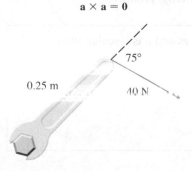

FIGURE 4

EXAMPLE 1 A bolt is tightened by applying a 40 N force to a 0.25 m wrench, as shown in Figure 4. Find the magnitude of the torque about the center of the bolt.

SOLUTION The magnitude of the torque vector is

$$|\boldsymbol{\tau}| = |\mathbf{r} \times \mathbf{F}| = |\mathbf{r}||\mathbf{F}|\sin 75°|\mathbf{n}| = (0.25)(40)\sin 75°$$
$$= 10\sin 75° \approx 9.66 \text{ N·m}$$

If the bolt is right-threaded, then the torque vector itself is

$$\tau = |\tau| \, \mathbf{n} \approx 9.66\mathbf{n}$$

where $\mathbf{n}$ is a unit vector directed down into the page.

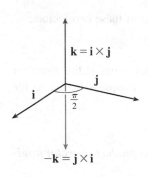

FIGURE 5

EXAMPLE 2 **Cross product of standard basis vectors** Find $\mathbf{i} \times \mathbf{j}$ and $\mathbf{j} \times \mathbf{i}$.

SOLUTION The standard basis vectors $\mathbf{i}$ and $\mathbf{j}$ both have length 1 and the angle between them is $\pi/2$. By the right-hand rule, the unit vector perpendicular to $\mathbf{i}$ and $\mathbf{j}$ is $\mathbf{n} = \mathbf{k}$ (see Figure 5), so

$$\mathbf{i} \times \mathbf{j} = \left(|\mathbf{i}||\mathbf{j}| \sin(\pi/2)\right)\mathbf{k} = \mathbf{k}$$

But if we apply the right-hand rule to the vectors $\mathbf{j}$ and $\mathbf{i}$ (in that order), we see that $\mathbf{n}$ points downward and so $\mathbf{n} = -\mathbf{k}$. Thus

$$\mathbf{j} \times \mathbf{i} = -\mathbf{k}$$

From Example 2 we see that

$$\mathbf{i} \times \mathbf{j} \neq \mathbf{j} \times \mathbf{i}$$

so the cross product is not commutative. Similar reasoning shows that

$$\mathbf{j} \times \mathbf{k} = \mathbf{i} \qquad \mathbf{k} \times \mathbf{j} = -\mathbf{i}$$

$$\mathbf{k} \times \mathbf{i} = \mathbf{j} \qquad \mathbf{i} \times \mathbf{k} = -\mathbf{j}$$

In general, the right-hand rule shows that

⊘
$$\mathbf{b} \times \mathbf{a} = -\mathbf{a} \times \mathbf{b}$$

Another algebraic law that fails for the cross product is the associative law for multiplication; that is, in general,

⊘
$$(\mathbf{a} \times \mathbf{b}) \times \mathbf{c} \neq \mathbf{a} \times (\mathbf{b} \times \mathbf{c})$$

For instance, if $\mathbf{a} = \mathbf{i}$, $\mathbf{b} = \mathbf{i}$, and $\mathbf{c} = \mathbf{j}$, then

$$(\mathbf{i} \times \mathbf{i}) \times \mathbf{j} = \mathbf{0} \times \mathbf{j} = \mathbf{0}$$

whereas

$$\mathbf{i} \times (\mathbf{i} \times \mathbf{j}) = \mathbf{i} \times \mathbf{k} = -\mathbf{j}$$

However, some of the usual laws of algebra *do* hold for cross products:

Properties of the Cross Product If $\mathbf{a}$, $\mathbf{b}$, and $\mathbf{c}$ are vectors and c is a scalar, then

1. $\mathbf{a} \times \mathbf{b} = -\mathbf{b} \times \mathbf{a}$

2. $(c\mathbf{a}) \times \mathbf{b} = c(\mathbf{a} \times \mathbf{b}) = \mathbf{a} \times (c\mathbf{b})$

3. $\mathbf{a} \times (\mathbf{b} + \mathbf{c}) = \mathbf{a} \times \mathbf{b} + \mathbf{a} \times \mathbf{c}$

4. $(\mathbf{a} + \mathbf{b}) \times \mathbf{c} = \mathbf{a} \times \mathbf{c} + \mathbf{b} \times \mathbf{c}$

Property 2 is proved by applying the definition of a cross product to each of the three expressions. Properties 3 and 4 (the Vector Distributive Laws) are more difficult to establish (see Exercise 41).

A geometric interpretation of the length of the cross product can be seen by looking at Figure 6. If **a** and **b** are represented by directed line segments with the same initial point, then they determine a parallelogram with base $|\mathbf{a}|$, altitude $|\mathbf{b}|\sin\theta$, and area

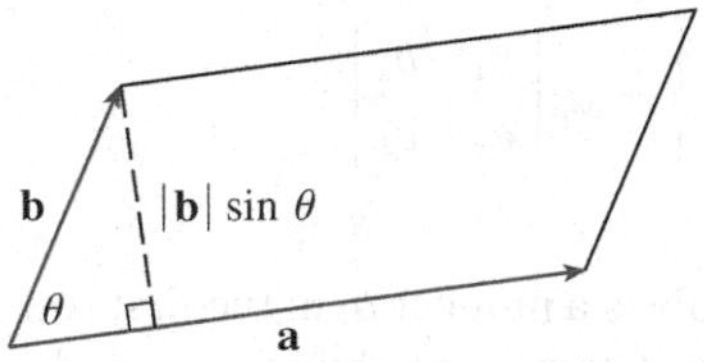

$$A = |\mathbf{a}|\,(|\mathbf{b}|\sin\theta) = |\mathbf{a} \times \mathbf{b}|$$

FIGURE 6

The length of the cross product $\mathbf{a} \times \mathbf{b}$ is equal to the area of the parallelogram determined by **a** and **b**.

The Cross Product in Component Form

Suppose **a** and **b** are given in component form:

$$\mathbf{a} = a_1\mathbf{i} + a_2\mathbf{j} + a_3\mathbf{k} \qquad \mathbf{b} = b_1\mathbf{i} + b_2\mathbf{j} + b_3\mathbf{k}$$

We can express $\mathbf{a} \times \mathbf{b}$ in component form by using the Vector Distributive Laws together with the results from Example 2:

$$\mathbf{a} \times \mathbf{b} = (a_1\mathbf{i} + a_2\mathbf{j} + a_3\mathbf{k}) \times (b_1\mathbf{i} + b_2\mathbf{j} + b_3\mathbf{k})$$

$$= a_1b_1\mathbf{i} \times \mathbf{i} + a_1b_2\mathbf{i} \times \mathbf{j} + a_1b_3\mathbf{i} \times \mathbf{k}$$

$$+ a_2b_1\mathbf{j} \times \mathbf{i} + a_2b_2\mathbf{j} \times \mathbf{j} + a_2b_3\mathbf{j} \times \mathbf{k}$$

$$+ a_3b_1\mathbf{k} \times \mathbf{i} + a_3b_2\mathbf{k} \times \mathbf{j} + a_3b_3\mathbf{k} \times \mathbf{k}$$

$$= a_1b_2\mathbf{k} + a_1b_3(-\mathbf{j}) + a_2b_1(-\mathbf{k}) + a_2b_3\mathbf{i} + a_3b_1\mathbf{j} + a_3b_2(-\mathbf{i})$$

$$= (a_2b_3 - a_3b_2)\mathbf{i} + (a_3b_1 - a_1b_3)\mathbf{j} + (a_1b_2 - a_2b_1)\mathbf{k}$$

Note that
$$\mathbf{i} \times \mathbf{i} = \mathbf{0} \quad \mathbf{j} \times \mathbf{j} = \mathbf{0} \quad \mathbf{k} \times \mathbf{k} = \mathbf{0}$$

$\boxed{2}$ If $\mathbf{a} = \langle a_1, a_2, a_3 \rangle$ and $\mathbf{b} = \langle b_1, b_2, b_3 \rangle$, then

$$\mathbf{a} \times \mathbf{b} = \langle a_2b_3 - a_3b_2, a_3b_1 - a_1b_3, a_1b_2 - a_2b_1 \rangle$$

In order to make this expression for $\mathbf{a} \times \mathbf{b}$ easier to remember, we use the notation of determinants. A **determinant of order 2** is defined by

$$\begin{vmatrix} a & b \\ c & d \end{vmatrix} = ad - bc$$

For example,

$$\begin{vmatrix} 2 & 1 \\ -6 & 4 \end{vmatrix} = 2(4) - 1(-6) = 14$$

A **determinant of order 3** can be defined in terms of second-order determinants as follows:

$$\boxed{3} \qquad \begin{vmatrix} a_1 & a_2 & a_3 \\ b_1 & b_2 & b_3 \\ c_1 & c_2 & c_3 \end{vmatrix} = a_1 \begin{vmatrix} b_2 & b_3 \\ c_2 & c_3 \end{vmatrix} - a_2 \begin{vmatrix} b_1 & b_3 \\ c_1 & c_3 \end{vmatrix} + a_3 \begin{vmatrix} b_1 & b_2 \\ c_1 & c_2 \end{vmatrix}$$

Observe that each term on the right side of Equation 3 involves a number a_i in the first row of the determinant, and a_i is multiplied by the second-order determinant obtained from the left side by deleting the row and column in which a_i appears. Notice also the minus sign in the second term. For example,

$$\begin{vmatrix} 1 & 2 & -1 \\ 3 & 0 & 1 \\ -5 & 4 & 2 \end{vmatrix} = 1 \begin{vmatrix} 0 & 1 \\ 4 & 2 \end{vmatrix} - 2 \begin{vmatrix} 3 & 1 \\ -5 & 2 \end{vmatrix} + (-1) \begin{vmatrix} 3 & 0 \\ -5 & 4 \end{vmatrix}$$

$$= 1(0 - 4) - 2(6 + 5) + (-1)(12 - 0) = -38$$

If we now rewrite the expression for $\mathbf{a} \times \mathbf{b}$ in (2) using second-order determinants and the standard basis vectors $\mathbf{i}$, $\mathbf{j}$, and $\mathbf{k}$, we see that the cross product of the vectors $\mathbf{a} = a_1\mathbf{i} + a_2\mathbf{j} + a_3\mathbf{k}$ and $\mathbf{b} = b_1\mathbf{i} + b_2\mathbf{j} + b_3\mathbf{k}$ is

$$\boxed{4} \qquad \mathbf{a} \times \mathbf{b} = \begin{vmatrix} a_2 & a_3 \\ b_2 & b_3 \end{vmatrix} \mathbf{i} - \begin{vmatrix} a_1 & a_3 \\ b_1 & b_3 \end{vmatrix} \mathbf{j} + \begin{vmatrix} a_1 & a_2 \\ b_1 & b_2 \end{vmatrix} \mathbf{k}$$

In view of the similarity between Equations 3 and 4, we often write

$$\boxed{5} \qquad \mathbf{a} \times \mathbf{b} = \begin{vmatrix} \mathbf{i} & \mathbf{j} & \mathbf{k} \\ a_1 & a_2 & a_3 \\ b_1 & b_2 & b_3 \end{vmatrix}$$

Although the first row of the symbolic determinant in Equation 5 consists of vectors, if we expand it as if it were an ordinary determinant using the rule in Equation 3, we obtain Equation 4. The symbolic formula in Equation 5 is probably the easiest way of remembering and computing cross products.

V **EXAMPLE 3** **Cross product of vectors in component form**
If $\mathbf{a} = \langle 1, 3, 4 \rangle$ and $\mathbf{b} = \langle 2, 7, -5 \rangle$, then, from Equation 5, we have

$$\mathbf{a} \times \mathbf{b} = \begin{vmatrix} \mathbf{i} & \mathbf{j} & \mathbf{k} \\ 1 & 3 & 4 \\ 2 & 7 & -5 \end{vmatrix}$$

$$= \begin{vmatrix} 3 & 4 \\ 7 & -5 \end{vmatrix} \mathbf{i} - \begin{vmatrix} 1 & 4 \\ 2 & -5 \end{vmatrix} \mathbf{j} + \begin{vmatrix} 1 & 3 \\ 2 & 7 \end{vmatrix} \mathbf{k}$$

$$= (-15 - 28)\,\mathbf{i} - (-5 - 8)\,\mathbf{j} + (7 - 6)\,\mathbf{k} = -43\mathbf{i} + 13\mathbf{j} + \mathbf{k} \qquad \blacksquare$$

EXAMPLE 4 Find a vector perpendicular to the plane that passes through the points $P(1, 4, 6)$, $Q(-2, 5, -1)$, and $R(1, -1, 1)$.

SOLUTION The vector $\vec{PQ} \times \vec{PR}$ is perpendicular to both $\vec{PQ}$ and $\vec{PR}$ and is therefore perpendicular to the plane through P, Q, and R. We know from (9.2.1) that

$$\vec{PQ} = (-2 - 1)\mathbf{i} + (5 - 4)\mathbf{j} + (-1 - 6)\mathbf{k} = -3\mathbf{i} + \mathbf{j} - 7\mathbf{k}$$

$$\vec{PR} = (1 - 1)\mathbf{i} + (-1 - 4)\mathbf{j} + (1 - 6)\mathbf{k} = -5\mathbf{j} - 5\mathbf{k}$$

We compute the cross product of these vectors:

$$\vec{PQ} \times \vec{PR} = \begin{vmatrix} \mathbf{i} & \mathbf{j} & \mathbf{k} \\ -3 & 1 & -7 \\ 0 & -5 & -5 \end{vmatrix}$$

$$= (-5 - 35)\mathbf{i} - (15 - 0)\mathbf{j} + (15 - 0)\mathbf{k} = -40\mathbf{i} - 15\mathbf{j} + 15\mathbf{k}$$

So the vector $\langle -40, -15, 15 \rangle$ is perpendicular to the given plane. Any nonzero scalar multiple of this vector, such as $\langle -8, -3, 3 \rangle$, is also perpendicular to the plane. ▬

EXAMPLE 5 Find the area of the triangle with vertices $P(1, 4, 6)$, $Q(-2, 5, -1)$, and $R(1, -1, 1)$.

SOLUTION In Example 4 we computed that $\vec{PQ} \times \vec{PR} = \langle -40, -15, 15 \rangle$. The area of the parallelogram with adjacent sides PQ and PR is the length of this cross product:

$$|\vec{PQ} \times \vec{PR}| = \sqrt{(-40)^2 + (-15)^2 + 15^2} = 5\sqrt{82}$$

The area A of the triangle PQR is half the area of this parallelogram, that is, $\frac{5}{2}\sqrt{82}$. ▬

Triple Products

The product $\mathbf{a} \cdot (\mathbf{b} \times \mathbf{c})$ is called the **scalar triple product** of the vectors $\mathbf{a}$, $\mathbf{b}$, and $\mathbf{c}$. Its geometric significance can be seen by considering the parallelepiped determined by the vectors $\mathbf{a}$, $\mathbf{b}$, and $\mathbf{c}$. (See Figure 7.) The area of the base parallelogram is $A = |\mathbf{b} \times \mathbf{c}|$. If θ is the angle between the vectors $\mathbf{a}$ and $\mathbf{b} \times \mathbf{c}$, then the height h of the parallelepiped is $h = |\mathbf{a}||\cos\theta|$. (We must use $|\cos\theta|$ instead of $\cos\theta$ in case $\theta > \pi/2$.) Thus the volume of the parallelepiped is

$$V = Ah = |\mathbf{b} \times \mathbf{c}||\mathbf{a}||\cos\theta| = |\mathbf{a} \cdot (\mathbf{b} \times \mathbf{c})|$$

Therefore we have proved the following:

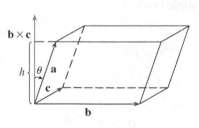

FIGURE 7

> The volume of the parallelepiped determined by the vectors $\mathbf{a}$, $\mathbf{b}$, and $\mathbf{c}$ is the magnitude of their scalar triple product:
>
> $$V = |\mathbf{a} \cdot (\mathbf{b} \times \mathbf{c})|$$

Instead of thinking of the parallelepiped as having its base parallelogram determined by $\mathbf{b}$ and $\mathbf{c}$, we can think of it with base parallelogram determined by $\mathbf{a}$ and $\mathbf{b}$. In this way, we see that

$$\mathbf{a} \cdot (\mathbf{b} \times \mathbf{c}) = \mathbf{c} \cdot (\mathbf{a} \times \mathbf{b})$$

But the dot product is commutative, so we can write

$$\boxed{6} \qquad \mathbf{a} \cdot (\mathbf{b} \times \mathbf{c}) = (\mathbf{a} \times \mathbf{b}) \cdot \mathbf{c}$$

Suppose that $\mathbf{a}$, $\mathbf{b}$, and $\mathbf{c}$ are given in component form:

$$\mathbf{a} = a_1 \mathbf{i} + a_2 \mathbf{j} + a_3 \mathbf{k} \qquad \mathbf{b} = b_1 \mathbf{i} + b_2 \mathbf{j} + b_3 \mathbf{k} \qquad \mathbf{c} = c_1 \mathbf{i} + c_2 \mathbf{j} + c_3 \mathbf{k}$$

Then

$$\mathbf{a} \cdot (\mathbf{b} \times \mathbf{c}) = \mathbf{a} \cdot \left[\begin{vmatrix} b_2 & b_3 \\ c_2 & c_3 \end{vmatrix} \mathbf{i} - \begin{vmatrix} b_1 & b_3 \\ c_1 & c_3 \end{vmatrix} \mathbf{j} + \begin{vmatrix} b_1 & b_2 \\ c_1 & c_2 \end{vmatrix} \mathbf{k} \right]$$

$$= a_1 \begin{vmatrix} b_2 & b_3 \\ c_2 & c_3 \end{vmatrix} - a_2 \begin{vmatrix} b_1 & b_3 \\ c_1 & c_3 \end{vmatrix} + a_3 \begin{vmatrix} b_1 & b_2 \\ c_1 & c_2 \end{vmatrix}$$

This shows that we can write the scalar triple product of $\mathbf{a}$, $\mathbf{b}$, and $\mathbf{c}$ as the determinant whose rows are the components of these vectors:

$$\boxed{7} \qquad \mathbf{a} \cdot (\mathbf{b} \times \mathbf{c}) = \begin{vmatrix} a_1 & a_2 & a_3 \\ b_1 & b_2 & b_3 \\ c_1 & c_2 & c_3 \end{vmatrix}$$

V **EXAMPLE 6** **Coplanar vectors** Use the scalar triple product to show that the vectors $\mathbf{a} = \langle 1, 4, -7 \rangle$, $\mathbf{b} = \langle 2, -1, 4 \rangle$, and $\mathbf{c} = \langle 0, -9, 18 \rangle$ are coplanar; that is, they lie in the same plane.

SOLUTION We use Equation 7 to compute their scalar triple product:

$$\mathbf{a} \cdot (\mathbf{b} \times \mathbf{c}) = \begin{vmatrix} 1 & 4 & -7 \\ 2 & -1 & 4 \\ 0 & -9 & 18 \end{vmatrix}$$

$$= 1 \begin{vmatrix} -1 & 4 \\ -9 & 18 \end{vmatrix} - 4 \begin{vmatrix} 2 & 4 \\ 0 & 18 \end{vmatrix} - 7 \begin{vmatrix} 2 & -1 \\ 0 & -9 \end{vmatrix}$$

$$= 1(18) - 4(36) - 7(-18) = 0$$

Therefore the volume of the parallelepiped determined by $\mathbf{a}$, $\mathbf{b}$, and $\mathbf{c}$ is 0. This means that $\mathbf{a}$, $\mathbf{b}$, and $\mathbf{c}$ are coplanar. ▬

The product $\mathbf{a} \times (\mathbf{b} \times \mathbf{c})$ is called the **vector triple product** of $\mathbf{a}$, $\mathbf{b}$, and $\mathbf{c}$. The proof of the following formula for the vector triple product is left as Exercise 36.

$$\boxed{8} \qquad \mathbf{a} \times (\mathbf{b} \times \mathbf{c}) = (\mathbf{a} \cdot \mathbf{c})\mathbf{b} - (\mathbf{a} \cdot \mathbf{b})\mathbf{c}$$

Formula 8 will be used to derive Kepler's First Law of planetary motion in Chapter 10.

9.4 Exercises

1. State whether each expression is meaningful. If not, explain why. If so, state whether it is a vector or a scalar.
(a) $\mathbf{a} \cdot (\mathbf{b} \times \mathbf{c})$ (b) $\mathbf{a} \times (\mathbf{b} \cdot \mathbf{c})$
(c) $\mathbf{a} \times (\mathbf{b} \times \mathbf{c})$ (d) $(\mathbf{a} \cdot \mathbf{b}) \times \mathbf{c}$
(e) $(\mathbf{a} \cdot \mathbf{b}) \times (\mathbf{c} \cdot \mathbf{d})$ (f) $(\mathbf{a} \times \mathbf{b}) \cdot (\mathbf{c} \times \mathbf{d})$

2–3 Find $|\mathbf{u} \times \mathbf{v}|$ and determine whether $\mathbf{u} \times \mathbf{v}$ is directed into the page or out of the page.

2.
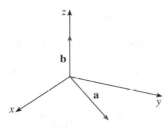
$|\mathbf{v}| = 5$
$45°$
$|\mathbf{u}| = 4$

3.
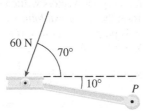
$|\mathbf{v}| = 16$
$|\mathbf{u}| = 12$
$120°$

4. The figure shows a vector $\mathbf{a}$ in the xy-plane and a vector $\mathbf{b}$ in the direction of $\mathbf{k}$. Their lengths are $|\mathbf{a}| = 3$ and $|\mathbf{b}| = 2$.
(a) Find $|\mathbf{a} \times \mathbf{b}|$.
(b) Use the right-hand rule to decide whether the components of $\mathbf{a} \times \mathbf{b}$ are positive, negative, or 0.

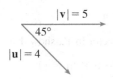

5. A bicycle pedal is pushed by a foot with a 60-N force as shown. The shaft of the pedal is 18 cm long. Find the magnitude of the torque about P.

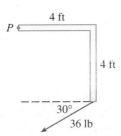
60 N
$70°$
$10°$
P

6. Find the magnitude of the torque about P if a 36-lb force is applied as shown.

P
4 ft
4 ft
$30°$
36 lb

7–13 Find the cross product $\mathbf{a} \times \mathbf{b}$ and verify that it is orthogonal to both $\mathbf{a}$ and $\mathbf{b}$.

7. $\mathbf{a} = \langle 6, 0, -2 \rangle$, $\mathbf{b} = \langle 0, 8, 0 \rangle$

8. $\mathbf{a} = \langle 1, 1, -1 \rangle$, $\mathbf{b} = \langle 2, 4, 6 \rangle$

9. $\mathbf{a} = \mathbf{i} + 3\mathbf{j} - 2\mathbf{k}$, $\mathbf{b} = -\mathbf{i} + 5\mathbf{k}$

10. $\mathbf{a} = \mathbf{j} + 7\mathbf{k}$, $\mathbf{b} = 2\mathbf{i} - \mathbf{j} + 4\mathbf{k}$

11. $\mathbf{a} = \mathbf{i} - \mathbf{j} - \mathbf{k}$, $\mathbf{b} = \frac{1}{2}\mathbf{i} + \mathbf{j} + \frac{1}{2}\mathbf{k}$

12. $\mathbf{a} = \mathbf{i} + e^t\mathbf{j} + e^{-t}\mathbf{k}$, $\mathbf{b} = 2\mathbf{i} + e^t\mathbf{j} - e^{-t}\mathbf{k}$

13. $\mathbf{a} = \langle t, t^2, t^3 \rangle$, $\mathbf{b} = \langle 1, 2t, 3t^2 \rangle$

14. If $\mathbf{a} = \mathbf{i} - 2\mathbf{k}$ and $\mathbf{b} = \mathbf{j} + \mathbf{k}$, find $\mathbf{a} \times \mathbf{b}$. Sketch $\mathbf{a}$, $\mathbf{b}$, and $\mathbf{a} \times \mathbf{b}$ as vectors starting at the origin.

15–18 Find the vector, not with determinants, but by using properties of cross products.

15. $(\mathbf{i} \times \mathbf{j}) \times \mathbf{k}$ **16.** $\mathbf{k} \times (\mathbf{i} - 2\mathbf{j})$

17. $(\mathbf{j} - \mathbf{k}) \times (\mathbf{k} - \mathbf{i})$ **18.** $(\mathbf{i} + \mathbf{j}) \times (\mathbf{i} - \mathbf{j})$

19. Find two unit vectors orthogonal to both $\langle 1, -1, 1 \rangle$ and $\langle 0, 4, 4 \rangle$.

20. Find two unit vectors orthogonal to both $\mathbf{i} + \mathbf{j} + \mathbf{k}$ and $2\mathbf{i} + \mathbf{k}$.

21. Find the area of the parallelogram with vertices $A(-2, 1)$, $B(0, 4)$, $C(4, 2)$, and $D(2, -1)$.

22. Find the area of the parallelogram with vertices $K(1, 2, 3)$, $L(1, 3, 6)$, $M(3, 8, 6)$, and $N(3, 7, 3)$.

23–24 (a) Find a nonzero vector orthogonal to the plane through the points P, Q, and R, and (b) find the area of triangle PQR.

23. $P(0, -2, 0)$, $Q(4, 1, -2)$, $R(5, 3, 1)$

24. $P(-1, 3, 1)$, $Q(0, 5, 2)$, $R(4, 3, -1)$

25. A wrench 30 cm long lies along the positive y-axis and grips a bolt at the origin. A force is applied in the direction $\langle 0, 3, -4 \rangle$ at the end of the wrench. Find the magnitude of the force needed to supply 100 N·m of torque to the bolt.

26. Let $\mathbf{v} = 5\mathbf{j}$ and let $\mathbf{u}$ be a vector with length 3 that starts at the origin and rotates in the xy-plane. Find the maximum and minimum values of the length of the vector $\mathbf{u} \times \mathbf{v}$. In what direction does $\mathbf{u} \times \mathbf{v}$ point?

27–28 Find the volume of the parallelepiped determined by the vectors $\mathbf{a}$, $\mathbf{b}$, and $\mathbf{c}$.

27. $\mathbf{a} = \langle 6, 3, -1 \rangle$, $\mathbf{b} = \langle 0, 1, 2 \rangle$, $\mathbf{c} = \langle 4, -2, 5 \rangle$

28. $\mathbf{a} = \mathbf{i} + \mathbf{j} - \mathbf{k}$, $\mathbf{b} = \mathbf{i} - \mathbf{j} + \mathbf{k}$, $\mathbf{c} = -\mathbf{i} + \mathbf{j} + \mathbf{k}$

1. Homework Hints available in TEC

29–30 Find the volume of the parallelepiped with adjacent edges PQ, PR, and PS.

29. $P(2, 0, -1)$, $Q(4, 1, 0)$, $R(3, -1, 1)$, $S(2, -2, 2)$

30. $P(3, 0, 1)$, $Q(-1, 2, 5)$, $R(5, 1, -1)$, $S(0, 4, 2)$

---

31. Use the scalar triple product to verify that the vectors $\mathbf{u} = \mathbf{i} + 5\mathbf{j} - 2\mathbf{k}$, $\mathbf{v} = 3\mathbf{i} - \mathbf{j}$, and $\mathbf{w} = 5\mathbf{i} + 9\mathbf{j} - 4\mathbf{k}$ are coplanar.

32. Use the scalar triple product to determine whether the points $A(1, 3, 2)$, $B(3, -1, 6)$, $C(5, 2, 0)$, and $D(3, 6, -4)$ lie in the same plane.

33. (a) Let P be a point not on the line L that passes through the points Q and R. Show that the distance d from the point P to the line L is
$$d = \frac{|\mathbf{a} \times \mathbf{b}|}{|\mathbf{a}|}$$
where $\mathbf{a} = \overrightarrow{QR}$ and $\mathbf{b} = \overrightarrow{QP}$.
(b) Use the formula in part (a) to find the distance from the point $P(1, 1, 1)$ to the line through $Q(0, 6, 8)$ and $R(-1, 4, 7)$.

34. (a) Let P be a point not on the plane that passes through the points Q, R, and S. Show that the distance d from P to the plane is
$$d = \frac{|\mathbf{a} \cdot (\mathbf{b} \times \mathbf{c})|}{|\mathbf{a} \times \mathbf{b}|}$$
where $\mathbf{a} = \overrightarrow{QR}$, $\mathbf{b} = \overrightarrow{QS}$, and $\mathbf{c} = \overrightarrow{QP}$.
(b) Use the formula in part (a) to find the distance from the point $P(2, 1, 4)$ to the plane through the points $Q(1, 0, 0)$, $R(0, 2, 0)$, and $S(0, 0, 3)$.

35. Prove that $(\mathbf{a} - \mathbf{b}) \times (\mathbf{a} + \mathbf{b}) = 2(\mathbf{a} \times \mathbf{b})$.

36. Prove the following formula (8) for the vector triple product:
$$\mathbf{a} \times (\mathbf{b} \times \mathbf{c}) = (\mathbf{a} \cdot \mathbf{c})\mathbf{b} - (\mathbf{a} \cdot \mathbf{b})\mathbf{c}$$

37. Use Exercise 36 to prove that
$$\mathbf{a} \times (\mathbf{b} \times \mathbf{c}) + \mathbf{b} \times (\mathbf{c} \times \mathbf{a}) + \mathbf{c} \times (\mathbf{a} \times \mathbf{b}) = \mathbf{0}$$

38. Prove that
$$(\mathbf{a} \times \mathbf{b}) \cdot (\mathbf{c} \times \mathbf{d}) = \begin{vmatrix} \mathbf{a} \cdot \mathbf{c} & \mathbf{b} \cdot \mathbf{c} \\ \mathbf{a} \cdot \mathbf{d} & \mathbf{b} \cdot \mathbf{d} \end{vmatrix}$$

39. Suppose that $\mathbf{a} \neq \mathbf{0}$.
(a) If $\mathbf{a} \cdot \mathbf{b} = \mathbf{a} \cdot \mathbf{c}$, does it follow that $\mathbf{b} = \mathbf{c}$?
(b) If $\mathbf{a} \times \mathbf{b} = \mathbf{a} \times \mathbf{c}$, does it follow that $\mathbf{b} = \mathbf{c}$?
(c) If $\mathbf{a} \cdot \mathbf{b} = \mathbf{a} \cdot \mathbf{c}$ and $\mathbf{a} \times \mathbf{b} = \mathbf{a} \times \mathbf{c}$, does it follow that $\mathbf{b} = \mathbf{c}$?

40. (a) If $\mathbf{u}$ is a unit vector and $\mathbf{a}$ is orthogonal to $\mathbf{u}$, show that
$$\mathbf{u} \times (\mathbf{u} \times \mathbf{a}) = -\mathbf{a}$$
(b) If $\mathbf{u}$ is a unit vector and $\mathbf{v}$ is any vector in V_3, show that
$$\mathbf{u} \times (\mathbf{u} \times (\mathbf{u} \times (\mathbf{u} \times \mathbf{v}))) = -\mathbf{u} \times (\mathbf{u} \times \mathbf{v})$$

41. (a) If $\mathbf{u} \cdot \mathbf{r} = \mathbf{v} \cdot \mathbf{r}$ for every vector $\mathbf{r}$ in V_3, show that $\mathbf{u} = \mathbf{v}$.
(b) Prove Property 3 of the cross product
$$\mathbf{a} \times (\mathbf{b} + \mathbf{c}) = \mathbf{a} \times \mathbf{b} + \mathbf{a} \times \mathbf{c}$$
by showing that
$$[\mathbf{a} \times (\mathbf{b} + \mathbf{c})] \cdot \mathbf{r} = [\mathbf{a} \times \mathbf{b} + \mathbf{a} \times \mathbf{c}] \cdot \mathbf{r}$$
for every vector $\mathbf{r}$ in V_3.

42. If $\mathbf{v}_1$, $\mathbf{v}_2$, and $\mathbf{v}_3$ are noncoplanar vectors, let
$$\mathbf{k}_1 = \frac{\mathbf{v}_2 \times \mathbf{v}_3}{\mathbf{v}_1 \cdot (\mathbf{v}_2 \times \mathbf{v}_3)} \qquad \mathbf{k}_2 = \frac{\mathbf{v}_3 \times \mathbf{v}_1}{\mathbf{v}_1 \cdot (\mathbf{v}_2 \times \mathbf{v}_3)}$$
$$\mathbf{k}_3 = \frac{\mathbf{v}_1 \times \mathbf{v}_2}{\mathbf{v}_1 \cdot (\mathbf{v}_2 \times \mathbf{v}_3)}$$
(These vectors occur in the study of crystallography. Vectors of the form $n_1\mathbf{v}_1 + n_2\mathbf{v}_2 + n_3\mathbf{v}_3$, where each n_i is an integer, form a *lattice* for a crystal. Vectors written similarly in terms of $\mathbf{k}_1$, $\mathbf{k}_2$, and $\mathbf{k}_3$ form the *reciprocal lattice*.)
(a) Show that $\mathbf{k}_i$ is perpendicular to $\mathbf{v}_j$ if $i \neq j$.
(b) Show that $\mathbf{k}_i \cdot \mathbf{v}_i = 1$ for $i = 1, 2, 3$.
(c) Show that $\mathbf{k}_1 \cdot (\mathbf{k}_2 \times \mathbf{k}_3) = \dfrac{1}{\mathbf{v}_1 \cdot (\mathbf{v}_2 \times \mathbf{v}_3)}$.

DISCOVERY PROJECT   **The Geometry of a Tetrahedron**

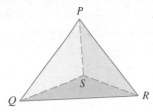

A tetrahedron is a solid with four vertices, P, Q, R, and S, and four triangular faces, as shown in the figure.

1. Let $\mathbf{v}_1$, $\mathbf{v}_2$, $\mathbf{v}_3$, and $\mathbf{v}_4$ be vectors with lengths equal to the areas of the faces opposite the vertices P, Q, R, and S, respectively, and directions perpendicular to the respective faces and pointing outward. Show that
$$\mathbf{v}_1 + \mathbf{v}_2 + \mathbf{v}_3 + \mathbf{v}_4 = \mathbf{0}$$

2. The volume V of a tetrahedron is one-third the distance from a vertex to the opposite face, times the area of that face.
    (a) Find a formula for the volume of a tetrahedron in terms of the coordinates of its vertices P, Q, R, and S.
    (b) Find the volume of the tetrahedron whose vertices are $P(1, 1, 1)$, $Q(1, 2, 3)$, $R(1, 1, 2)$, and $S(3, -1, 2)$.

3. Suppose the tetrahedron in the figure has a trirectangular vertex S. (This means that the three angles at S are all right angles.) Let A, B, and C be the areas of the three faces that meet at S, and let D be the area of the opposite face PQR. Using the result of Problem 1, or otherwise, show that

$$D^2 = A^2 + B^2 + C^2$$

(This is a three-dimensional version of the Pythagorean Theorem.)

9.5 Equations of Lines and Planes

A line in the xy-plane is determined when a point on the line and the direction of the line (its slope or angle of inclination) are given. The equation of the line can then be written using the point-slope form.

Likewise, a line L in three-dimensional space is determined when we know a point $P_0(x_0, y_0, z_0)$ on L and the direction of L. In three dimensions the direction of a line is conveniently described by a vector, so we let $\mathbf{v}$ be a vector parallel to L. Let $P(x, y, z)$ be an arbitrary point on L and let $\mathbf{r}_0$ and $\mathbf{r}$ be the position vectors of P_0 and P (that is, they have representations $\overrightarrow{OP_0}$ and $\overrightarrow{OP}$). If $\mathbf{a}$ is the vector with representation $\overrightarrow{P_0P}$, as in Figure 1, then the Triangle Law for vector addition gives $\mathbf{r} = \mathbf{r}_0 + \mathbf{a}$. But, since $\mathbf{a}$ and $\mathbf{v}$ are parallel vectors, there is a scalar t such that $\mathbf{a} = t\mathbf{v}$. Thus

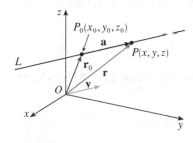

FIGURE 1

$$\boxed{1} \qquad \boxed{\mathbf{r} = \mathbf{r}_0 + t\mathbf{v}}$$

which is a **vector equation** of L. Each value of the **parameter** t gives the position vector $\mathbf{r}$ of a point on L. In other words, as t varies, the line is traced out by the tip of the vector $\mathbf{r}$. As Figure 2 indicates, positive values of t correspond to points on L that lie on one side of P_0, whereas negative values of t correspond to points that lie on the other side of P_0.

If the vector $\mathbf{v}$ that gives the direction of the line L is written in component form as $\mathbf{v} = \langle a, b, c \rangle$, then we have $t\mathbf{v} = \langle ta, tb, tc \rangle$. We can also write $\mathbf{r} = \langle x, y, z \rangle$ and $\mathbf{r}_0 = \langle x_0, y_0, z_0 \rangle$, so the vector equation (1) becomes

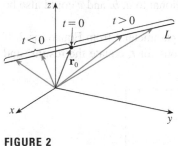

FIGURE 2

$$\langle x, y, z \rangle = \langle x_0 + ta, y_0 + tb, z_0 + tc \rangle$$

Two vectors are equal if and only if corresponding components are equal. Therefore we have the three scalar equations:

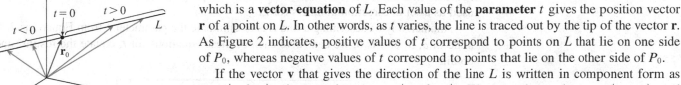

$$\boxed{2} \qquad x = x_0 + at \qquad y = y_0 + bt \qquad z = z_0 + ct$$

where $t \in \mathbb{R}$. These equations are called **parametric equations** of the line L through the point $P_0(x_0, y_0, z_0)$ and parallel to the vector $\mathbf{v} = \langle a, b, c \rangle$. Each value of the parameter t gives a point (x, y, z) on L.

Figure 3 shows the line L in Example 1 and its relation to the given point and to the vector that gives its direction.

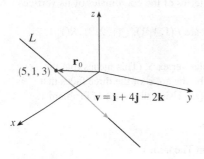

FIGURE 3

EXAMPLE 1   Equations of a line with a given direction
(a) Find a vector equation and parametric equations for the line that passes through the point $(5, 1, 3)$ and is parallel to the vector $\mathbf{i} + 4\mathbf{j} - 2\mathbf{k}$.
(b) Find two other points on the line.

SOLUTION
(a) Here $\mathbf{r}_0 = \langle 5, 1, 3 \rangle = 5\mathbf{i} + \mathbf{j} + 3\mathbf{k}$ and $\mathbf{v} = \mathbf{i} + 4\mathbf{j} - 2\mathbf{k}$, so the vector equation (1) becomes

$$\mathbf{r} = (5\mathbf{i} + \mathbf{j} + 3\mathbf{k}) + t(\mathbf{i} + 4\mathbf{j} - 2\mathbf{k})$$

or

$$\mathbf{r} = (5 + t)\mathbf{i} + (1 + 4t)\mathbf{j} + (3 - 2t)\mathbf{k}$$

Parametric equations are

$$x = 5 + t \qquad y = 1 + 4t \qquad z = 3 - 2t$$

(b) Choosing the parameter value $t = 1$ gives $x = 6$, $y = 5$, and $z = 1$, so $(6, 5, 1)$ is a point on the line. Similarly, $t = -1$ gives the point $(4, -3, 5)$.

The vector equation and parametric equations of a line are not unique. If we change the point or the parameter or choose a different parallel vector, then the equations change. For instance, if, instead of $(5, 1, 3)$, we choose the point $(6, 5, 1)$ in Example 1, then the parametric equations of the line become

$$x = 6 + t \qquad y = 5 + 4t \qquad z = 1 - 2t$$

Or, if we stay with the point $(5, 1, 3)$ but choose the parallel vector $2\mathbf{i} + 8\mathbf{j} - 4\mathbf{k}$, we arrive at the equations

$$x = 5 + 2t \qquad y = 1 + 8t \qquad z = 3 - 4t$$

In general, if a vector $\mathbf{v} = \langle a, b, c \rangle$ is used to describe the direction of a line L, then the numbers a, b, and c are called **direction numbers** of L. Since any vector parallel to $\mathbf{v}$ could also be used, we see that any three numbers proportional to a, b, and c could also be used as a set of direction numbers for L.

Another way of describing a line L is to eliminate the parameter t from Equations 2. If none of a, b, or c is 0, we can solve each of these equations for t, equate the results, and obtain

3
$$\frac{x - x_0}{a} = \frac{y - y_0}{b} = \frac{z - z_0}{c}$$

These equations are called **symmetric equations** of L. Notice that the numbers a, b, and c that appear in the denominators of Equations 3 are direction numbers of L, that is, components of a vector parallel to L. If one of a, b, or c is 0, we can still eliminate t. For instance, if $a = 0$, we could write the equations of L as

$$x = x_0 \qquad \frac{y - y_0}{b} = \frac{z - z_0}{c}$$

This means that L lies in the vertical plane $x = x_0$.

Figure 4 shows the line L in Example 2 and the point P where it intersects the xy-plane.

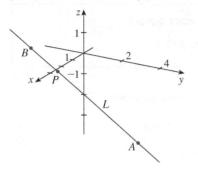

FIGURE 4

EXAMPLE 2 **Equations of a line through two points**

(a) Find parametric equations and symmetric equations of the line that passes through the points $A(2, 4, -3)$ and $B(3, -1, 1)$.

(b) At what point does this line intersect the xy-plane?

SOLUTION

(a) We are not explicitly given a vector parallel to the line, but observe that the vector $\mathbf{v}$ with representation $\overrightarrow{AB}$ is parallel to the line and

$$\mathbf{v} = \langle 3 - 2, -1 - 4, 1 - (-3) \rangle = \langle 1, -5, 4 \rangle$$

Thus direction numbers are $a = 1$, $b = -5$, and $c = 4$. Taking the point $(2, 4, -3)$ as P_0, we see that parametric equations (2) are

$$x = 2 + t \qquad y = 4 - 5t \qquad z = -3 + 4t$$

and symmetric equations (3) are

$$\frac{x - 2}{1} = \frac{y - 4}{-5} = \frac{z + 3}{4}$$

(b) The line intersects the xy-plane when $z = 0$, so we put $z = 0$ in the symmetric equations and obtain

$$\frac{x - 2}{1} = \frac{y - 4}{-5} = \frac{3}{4}$$

This gives $x = \frac{11}{4}$ and $y = \frac{1}{4}$, so the line intersects the xy-plane at the point $\left(\frac{11}{4}, \frac{1}{4}, 0\right)$.

In general, the procedure of Example 2 shows that direction numbers of the line L through the points $P_0(x_0, y_0, z_0)$ and $P_1(x_1, y_1, z_1)$ are $x_1 - x_0$, $y_1 - y_0$, and $z_1 - z_0$ and so symmetric equations of L are

$$\frac{x - x_0}{x_1 - x_0} = \frac{y - y_0}{y_1 - y_0} = \frac{z - z_0}{z_1 - z_0}$$

Often, we need a description, not of an entire line, but of just a line segment. How, for instance, could we describe the line segment AB in Example 2? If we put $t = 0$ in the parametric equations in Example 2(a), we get the point $(2, 4, -3)$ and if we put $t = 1$ we get $(3, -1, 1)$. So the line segment AB is described by the parametric equations

$$x = 2 + t \qquad y = 4 - 5t \qquad z = -3 + 4t \qquad 0 \le t \le 1$$

or by the corresponding vector equation

$$\mathbf{r}(t) = \langle 2 + t, 4 - 5t, -3 + 4t \rangle \qquad 0 \le t \le 1$$

In general, we know from Equation 1 that the vector equation of a line through the (tip of the) vector $\mathbf{r}_0$ in the direction of a vector $\mathbf{v}$ is $\mathbf{r} = \mathbf{r}_0 + t\mathbf{v}$. If the line also passes through (the tip of) $\mathbf{r}_1$, then we can take $\mathbf{v} = \mathbf{r}_1 - \mathbf{r}_0$ and so its vector equation is

$$\mathbf{r} = \mathbf{r}_0 + t(\mathbf{r}_1 - \mathbf{r}_0) = (1 - t)\mathbf{r}_0 + t\mathbf{r}_1$$

The line segment from $\mathbf{r}_0$ to $\mathbf{r}_1$ is given by the parameter interval $0 \leqslant t \leqslant 1$.

---

4   The line segment from $\mathbf{r}_0$ to $\mathbf{r}_1$ is given by the vector equation

$$\mathbf{r}(t) = (1 - t)\mathbf{r}_0 + t\mathbf{r}_1 \qquad 0 \leqslant t \leqslant 1$$

The lines L_1 and L_2 in Example 3, shown in Figure 5, are skew lines.

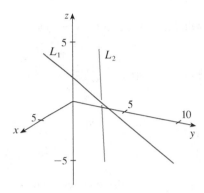

FIGURE 5

☑ EXAMPLE 3   Show that the lines L_1 and L_2 with parametric equations

$$x = 1 + t \qquad y = -2 + 3t \qquad z = 4 - t$$

$$x = 2s \qquad y = 3 + s \qquad z = -3 + 4s$$

are **skew lines**; that is, they do not intersect and are not parallel (and therefore do not lie in the same plane).

SOLUTION   The lines are not parallel because the corresponding vectors $\langle 1, 3, -1 \rangle$ and $\langle 2, 1, 4 \rangle$ are not parallel. (Their components are not proportional.) If L_1 and L_2 had a point of intersection, there would be values of t and s such that

$$1 + t = 2s$$

$$-2 + 3t = 3 + s$$

$$4 - t = -3 + 4s$$

But if we solve the first two equations, we get $t = \frac{11}{5}$ and $s = \frac{8}{5}$, and these values don't satisfy the third equation. Therefore there are no values of t and s that satisfy the three equations, so L_1 and L_2 do not intersect. Thus L_1 and L_2 are skew lines.   ∎

Planes

Although a line in space is determined by a point and a direction, a plane in space is more difficult to describe. A single vector parallel to a plane is not enough to convey the "direction" of the plane, but a vector perpendicular to the plane does completely specify its direction. Thus a plane in space is determined by a point $P_0(x_0, y_0, z_0)$ in the plane and a vector $\mathbf{n}$ that is orthogonal to the plane. This orthogonal vector $\mathbf{n}$ is called a **normal vector**. Let $P(x, y, z)$ be an arbitrary point in the plane, and let $\mathbf{r}_0$ and $\mathbf{r}$ be the position vectors of P_0 and P. Then the vector $\mathbf{r} - \mathbf{r}_0$ is represented by $\overrightarrow{P_0P}$. (See Figure 6.) The normal vector $\mathbf{n}$ is orthogonal to every vector in the given plane. In particular, $\mathbf{n}$ is orthogonal to $\mathbf{r} - \mathbf{r}_0$ and so we have

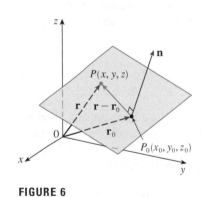

FIGURE 6

5
$$\mathbf{n} \cdot (\mathbf{r} - \mathbf{r}_0) = 0$$

which can be rewritten as

6
$$\mathbf{n} \cdot \mathbf{r} = \mathbf{n} \cdot \mathbf{r}_0$$

Either Equation 5 or Equation 6 is called a **vector equation of the plane**.

To obtain a scalar equation for the plane, we write $\mathbf{n} = \langle a, b, c \rangle$, $\mathbf{r} = \langle x, y, z \rangle$, and $\mathbf{r}_0 = \langle x_0, y_0, z_0 \rangle$. Then the vector equation (5) becomes

$$\langle a, b, c \rangle \cdot \langle x - x_0, y - y_0, z - z_0 \rangle = 0$$

or

7 $\boxed{a(x - x_0) + b(y - y_0) + c(z - z_0) = 0}$

Equation 7 is the **scalar equation of the plane through** $P_0(x_0, y_0, z_0)$ **with normal vector** $\mathbf{n} = \langle a, b, c \rangle$.

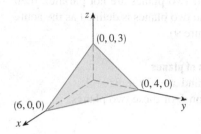

(0, 0, 3)

(0, 4, 0)

(6, 0, 0)

FIGURE 7

V **EXAMPLE 4** Find an equation of the plane through the point $(2, 4, -1)$ with normal vector $\mathbf{n} = \langle 2, 3, 4 \rangle$. Find the intercepts and sketch the plane.

SOLUTION Putting $a = 2$, $b = 3$, $c = 4$, $x_0 = 2$, $y_0 = 4$, and $z_0 = -1$ in Equation 7, we see that an equation of the plane is

$$2(x - 2) + 3(y - 4) + 4(z + 1) = 0$$

or

$$2x + 3y + 4z = 12$$

To find the x-intercept we set $y = z = 0$ in this equation and obtain $x = 6$. Similarly, the y-intercept is 4 and the z-intercept is 3. This enables us to sketch the portion of the plane that lies in the first octant (see Figure 7).

By collecting terms in Equation 7 as we did in Example 4, we can rewrite the equation of a plane as

8 $\boxed{ax + by + cz + d = 0}$

where $d = -(ax_0 + by_0 + cz_0)$. Equation 8 is called a **linear equation** in x, y, and z. Conversely, it can be shown that if a, b, and c are not all 0, then the linear equation (8) represents a plane with normal vector $\langle a, b, c \rangle$. (See Exercise 63.)

Figure 8 shows the portion of the plane in Example 5 that is enclosed by triangle PQR.

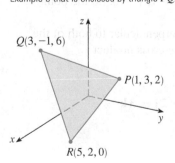

$Q(3, -1, 6)$

$P(1, 3, 2)$

$R(5, 2, 0)$

FIGURE 8

EXAMPLE 5 **The plane through three points** Find an equation of the plane that passes through the points $P(1, 3, 2)$, $Q(3, -1, 6)$, and $R(5, 2, 0)$.

SOLUTION The vectors $\mathbf{a}$ and $\mathbf{b}$ corresponding to $\overrightarrow{PQ}$ and $\overrightarrow{PR}$ are

$$\mathbf{a} = \langle 2, -4, 4 \rangle \qquad \mathbf{b} = \langle 4, -1, -2 \rangle$$

Since both $\mathbf{a}$ and $\mathbf{b}$ lie in the plane, their cross product $\mathbf{a} \times \mathbf{b}$ is orthogonal to the plane and can be taken as the normal vector. Thus

$$\mathbf{n} = \mathbf{a} \times \mathbf{b} = \begin{vmatrix} \mathbf{i} & \mathbf{j} & \mathbf{k} \\ 2 & -4 & 4 \\ 4 & -1 & -2 \end{vmatrix} = 12\mathbf{i} + 20\mathbf{j} + 14\mathbf{k}$$

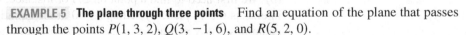

With the point $P(1, 3, 2)$ and the normal vector $\mathbf{n}$, an equation of the plane is

$$12(x - 1) + 20(y - 3) + 14(z - 2) = 0$$

or

$$6x + 10y + 7z = 50$$

EXAMPLE 6 Find the point at which the line with parametric equations $x = 2 + 3t$, $y = -4t$, $z = 5 + t$ intersects the plane $4x + 5y - 2z = 18$.

SOLUTION We substitute the expressions for x, y, and z from the parametric equations into the equation of the plane:

$$4(2 + 3t) + 5(-4t) - 2(5 + t) = 18$$

This simplifies to $-10t = 20$, so $t = -2$. Therefore the point of intersection occurs when the parameter value is $t = -2$. Then $x = 2 + 3(-2) = -4$, $y = -4(-2) = 8$, $z = 5 - 2 = 3$ and so the point of intersection is $(-4, 8, 3)$. ▬

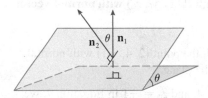

FIGURE 9

Two planes are **parallel** if their normal vectors are parallel. For instance, the planes $x + 2y - 3z = 4$ and $2x + 4y - 6z = 3$ are parallel because their normal vectors are $\mathbf{n}_1 = \langle 1, 2, -3 \rangle$ and $\mathbf{n}_2 = \langle 2, 4, -6 \rangle$ and $\mathbf{n}_2 = 2\mathbf{n}_1$. If two planes are not parallel, then they intersect in a straight line and the angle between the two planes is defined as the acute angle between their normal vectors (see angle θ in Figure 9).

Figure 10 shows the planes in Example 7 and their line of intersection L.

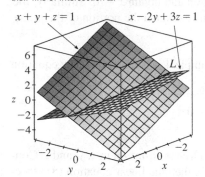

FIGURE 10

EXAMPLE 7 **Angle between planes; line of intersection of planes**
(a) Find the angle between the planes $x + y + z = 1$ and $x - 2y + 3z = 1$.
(b) Find symmetric equations for the line of intersection L of these two planes.

SOLUTION
(a) The normal vectors of these planes are

$$\mathbf{n}_1 = \langle 1, 1, 1 \rangle \qquad \mathbf{n}_2 = \langle 1, -2, 3 \rangle$$

and so, if θ is the angle between the planes,

$$\cos \theta = \frac{\mathbf{n}_1 \cdot \mathbf{n}_2}{|\mathbf{n}_1||\mathbf{n}_2|} = \frac{1(1) + 1(-2) + 1(3)}{\sqrt{1 + 1 + 1}\,\sqrt{1 + 4 + 9}} = \frac{2}{\sqrt{42}}$$

$$\theta = \cos^{-1}\left(\frac{2}{\sqrt{42}}\right) \approx 72°$$

(b) We first need to find a point on L. For instance, we can find the point where the line intersects the xy-plane by setting $z = 0$ in the equations of both planes. This gives the equations $x + y = 1$ and $x - 2y = 1$, whose solution is $x = 1$, $y = 0$. So the point $(1, 0, 0)$ lies on L.

Now we observe that, since L lies in both planes, it is perpendicular to both of the normal vectors. Thus a vector $\mathbf{v}$ parallel to L is given by the cross product

Another way to find the line of intersection is to solve the equations of the planes for two of the variables in terms of the third, which can be taken as the parameter.

$$\mathbf{v} = \mathbf{n}_1 \times \mathbf{n}_2 = \begin{vmatrix} \mathbf{i} & \mathbf{j} & \mathbf{k} \\ 1 & 1 & 1 \\ 1 & -2 & 3 \end{vmatrix} = 5\mathbf{i} - 2\mathbf{j} - 3\mathbf{k}$$

and so the symmetric equations of L can be written as

$$\frac{x - 1}{5} = \frac{y}{-2} = \frac{z}{-3}$$

▬

Note: Since a linear equation in x, y, and z represents a plane and two nonparallel planes intersect in a line, it follows that two linear equations can represent a line. The

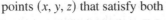

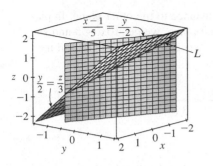

FIGURE 11

Figure 11 shows how the line L in Example 7 can also be regarded as the line of intersection of planes derived from its symmetric equations.

points (x, y, z) that satisfy both

$$a_1 x + b_1 y + c_1 z + d_1 = 0 \quad \text{and} \quad a_2 x + b_2 y + c_2 z + d_2 = 0$$

lie on both of these planes, and so the pair of linear equations represents the line of intersection of the planes (if they are not parallel). For instance, in Example 7 the line L was given as the line of intersection of the planes $x + y + z = 1$ and $x - 2y + 3z = 1$. The symmetric equations that we found for L could be written as

$$\frac{x-1}{5} = \frac{y}{-2} \quad \text{and} \quad \frac{y}{-2} = \frac{z}{-3}$$

which is again a pair of linear equations. They exhibit L as the line of intersection of the planes $(x - 1)/5 = y/(-2)$ and $y/(-2) = z/(-3)$. (See Figure 11.)

In general, when we write the equations of a line in the symmetric form

$$\frac{x - x_0}{a} = \frac{y - y_0}{b} = \frac{z - z_0}{c}$$

we can regard the line as the line of intersection of the two planes

$$\frac{x - x_0}{a} = \frac{y - y_0}{b} \quad \text{and} \quad \frac{y - y_0}{b} = \frac{z - z_0}{c}$$

EXAMPLE 8   Find a formula for the distance D from a point $P_1(x_1, y_1, z_1)$ to the plane $ax + by + cz + d = 0$.

SOLUTION   Let $P_0(x_0, y_0, z_0)$ be any point in the given plane and let $\mathbf{b}$ be the vector corresponding to $\overrightarrow{P_0 P_1}$. Then

$$\mathbf{b} = \langle x_1 - x_0, y_1 - y_0, z_1 - z_0 \rangle$$

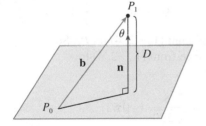

FIGURE 12

From Figure 12 you can see that the distance D from P_1 to the plane is equal to the absolute value of the scalar projection of $\mathbf{b}$ onto the normal vector $\mathbf{n} = \langle a, b, c \rangle$. (See Section 9.3.) Thus

$$D = |\operatorname{comp}_{\mathbf{n}} \mathbf{b}| = \frac{|\mathbf{n} \cdot \mathbf{b}|}{|\mathbf{n}|}$$

$$= \frac{|a(x_1 - x_0) + b(y_1 - y_0) + c(z_1 - z_0)|}{\sqrt{a^2 + b^2 + c^2}}$$

$$= \frac{|(ax_1 + by_1 + cz_1) - (ax_0 + by_0 + cz_0)|}{\sqrt{a^2 + b^2 + c^2}}$$

Since P_0 lies in the plane, its coordinates satisfy the equation of the plane and so we have $ax_0 + by_0 + cz_0 + d = 0$. Thus the formula for D can be written as

9
$$D = \frac{|ax_1 + by_1 + cz_1 + d|}{\sqrt{a^2 + b^2 + c^2}}$$

EXAMPLE 9   Distance between planes   Find the distance between the parallel planes $10x + 2y - 2z = 5$ and $5x + y - z = 1$.

SOLUTION   First we note that the planes are parallel because their normal vectors $\langle 10, 2, -2 \rangle$ and $\langle 5, 1, -1 \rangle$ are parallel. To find the distance D between the planes, we choose any point on one plane and calculate its distance to the other plane. In particular, if we put $y = z = 0$ in the equation of the first plane, we get $10x = 5$ and so $\left(\frac{1}{2}, 0, 0\right)$ is a point in this plane. By Formula 9, the distance between $\left(\frac{1}{2}, 0, 0\right)$ and the plane $5x + y - z - 1 = 0$ is

$$D = \frac{\left|5\left(\frac{1}{2}\right) + 1(0) - 1(0) - 1\right|}{\sqrt{5^2 + 1^2 + (-1)^2}} = \frac{\frac{3}{2}}{3\sqrt{3}} = \frac{\sqrt{3}}{6}$$

So the distance between the planes is $\sqrt{3}/6$.

EXAMPLE 10 **Distance between lines** In Example 3 we showed that the lines

$$L_1: \quad x = 1 + t \qquad y = -2 + 3t \qquad z = 4 - t$$

$$L_2: \quad x = 2s \qquad y = 3 + s \qquad z = -3 + 4s$$

are skew. Find the distance between them.

SOLUTION Since the two lines L_1 and L_2 are skew, they can be viewed as lying on two parallel planes P_1 and P_2. The distance between L_1 and L_2 is the same as the distance between P_1 and P_2, which can be computed as in Example 9. The common normal vector to both planes must be orthogonal to both $\mathbf{v}_1 = \langle 1, 3, -1 \rangle$ (the direction of L_1) and $\mathbf{v}_2 = \langle 2, 1, 4 \rangle$ (the direction of L_2). So a normal vector is

$$\mathbf{n} = \mathbf{v}_1 \times \mathbf{v}_2 = \begin{vmatrix} \mathbf{i} & \mathbf{j} & \mathbf{k} \\ 1 & 3 & -1 \\ 2 & 1 & 4 \end{vmatrix} = 13\mathbf{i} - 6\mathbf{j} - 5\mathbf{k}$$

If we put $s = 0$ in the equations of L_2, we get the point $(0, 3, -3)$ on L_2 and so an equation for P_2 is

$$13(x - 0) - 6(y - 3) - 5(z + 3) = 0 \qquad \text{or} \qquad 13x - 6y - 5z + 3 = 0$$

If we now set $t = 0$ in the equations for L_1, we get the point $(1, -2, 4)$ on P_1. So the distance between L_1 and L_2 is the same as the distance from $(1, -2, 4)$ to $13x - 6y - 5z + 3 = 0$. By Formula 9, this distance is

$$D = \frac{\left|13(1) - 6(-2) - 5(4) + 3\right|}{\sqrt{13^2 + (-6)^2 + (-5)^2}} = \frac{8}{\sqrt{230}} \approx 0.53$$

9.5 Exercises

1. Determine whether each statement is true or false.
   (a) Two lines parallel to a third line are parallel.
   (b) Two lines perpendicular to a third line are parallel.
   (c) Two planes parallel to a third plane are parallel.
   (d) Two planes perpendicular to a third plane are parallel.
   (e) Two lines parallel to a plane are parallel.
   (f) Two lines perpendicular to a plane are parallel.
   (g) Two planes parallel to a line are parallel.
   (h) Two planes perpendicular to a line are parallel.
   (i) Two planes either intersect or are parallel.
   (j) Two lines either intersect or are parallel.
   (k) A plane and a line either intersect or are parallel.

2–5 Find a vector equation and parametric equations for the line.

2. The line through the point $(6, -5, 2)$ and parallel to the vector $\langle 1, 3, -\frac{2}{3} \rangle$

3. The line through the point $(2, 2.4, 3.5)$ and parallel to the vector $3\mathbf{i} + 2\mathbf{j} - \mathbf{k}$

4. The line through the point $(0, 14, -10)$ and parallel to the line $x = -1 + 2t, y = 6 - 3t, z = 3 + 9t$

---

5. The line through the point $(1, 0, 6)$ and perpendicular to the plane $x + 3y + z = 5$

6–10 Find parametric equations and symmetric equations for the line.

6. The line through the points $(6, 1, -3)$ and $(2, 4, 5)$

7. The line through the points $\left(0, \frac{1}{2}, 1\right)$ and $(2, 1, -3)$

8. The line through $(2, 1, 0)$ and perpendicular to both $\mathbf{i} + \mathbf{j}$ and $\mathbf{j} + \mathbf{k}$

9. The line through $(1, -1, 1)$ and parallel to the line $x + 2 = \frac{1}{2}y = z - 3$

10. The line of intersection of the planes $x + 2y + 3z = 1$ and $x - y + z = 1$

---

11. Is the line through $(-4, -6, 1)$ and $(-2, 0, -3)$ parallel to the line through $(10, 18, 4)$ and $(5, 3, 14)$?

12. Is the line through $(4, 1, -1)$ and $(2, 5, 3)$ perpendicular to the line through $(-3, 2, 0)$ and $(5, 1, 4)$?

13. (a) Find symmetric equations for the line that passes through the point $(1, -5, 6)$ and is parallel to the vector $\langle -1, 2, -3 \rangle$.
(b) Find the points in which the required line in part (a) intersects the coordinate planes.

14. (a) Find parametric equations for the line through $(2, 4, 6)$ that is perpendicular to the plane $x - y + 3z = 7$.
(b) In what points does this line intersect the coordinate planes?

15. Find a vector equation for the line segment from $(2, -1, 4)$ to $(4, 6, 1)$.

16. Find parametric equations for the line segment from $(10, 3, 1)$ to $(5, 6, -3)$.

17–20 Determine whether the lines L_1 and L_2 are parallel, skew, or intersecting. If they intersect, find the point of intersection.

17. L_1: $x = -6t$, $y = 1 + 9t$, $z = -3t$
L_2: $x = 1 + 2s$, $y = 4 - 3s$, $z = s$

18. L_1: $x = 1 + 2t$, $y = 3t$, $z = 2 - t$
L_2: $x = -1 + s$, $y = 4 + s$, $z = 1 + 3s$

19. L_1: $\dfrac{x}{1} = \dfrac{y-1}{2} = \dfrac{z-2}{3}$

L_2: $\dfrac{x-3}{-4} = \dfrac{y-2}{-3} = \dfrac{z-1}{2}$

20. L_1: $\dfrac{x-1}{2} = \dfrac{y-3}{2} = \dfrac{z-2}{-1}$

L_2: $\dfrac{x-2}{1} = \dfrac{y-6}{-1} = \dfrac{z+2}{3}$

21–32 Find an equation of the plane.

21. The plane through the point $(6, 3, 2)$ and perpendicular to the vector $\langle -2, 1, 5 \rangle$

22. The plane through the point $(4, 0, -3)$ and with normal vector $\mathbf{j} + 2\mathbf{k}$

23. The plane through the point $(4, -2, 3)$ and parallel to the plane $3x - 7z = 12$

24. The plane that contains the line $x = 1 + t$, $y = 2 - t$, $z = 4 - 3t$ and is parallel to the plane $5x + 2y + z = 1$

25. The plane through the points $(0, 1, 1)$, $(1, 0, 1)$, and $(1, 1, 0)$

26. The plane through the origin and the points $(2, -4, 6)$ and $(5, 1, 3)$

27. The plane that passes through the point $(6, 0, -2)$ and contains the line $x = 4 - 2t$, $y = 3 + 5t$, $z = 7 + 4t$

28. The plane that passes through the point $(1, -1, 1)$ and contains the line with symmetric equations $x = 2y = 3z$

29. The plane that passes through the point $(-1, 2, 1)$ and contains the line of intersection of the planes $x + y - z = 2$ and $2x - y + 3z = 1$

30. The plane that passes through the points $(0, -2, 5)$ and $(-1, 3, 1)$ and is perpendicular to the plane $2z = 5x + 4y$

31. The plane that passes through the point $(1, 5, 1)$ and is perpendicular to the planes $2x + y - 2z = 2$ and $x + 3z = 4$

32. The plane that passes through the line of intersection of the planes $x - z = 1$ and $y + 2z = 3$ and is perpendicular to the plane $x + y - 2z = 1$

33–36 Use intercepts to help sketch the plane.

33. $2x + 5y + z = 10$ **34.** $3x + y + 2z = 6$

35. $6x - 3y + 4z = 6$ **36.** $6x + 5y - 3z = 15$

---

37. Find the point at which the line $x = 3 - t$, $y = 2 + t$, $z = 5t$ intersects the plane $x - y + 2z = 9$.

38. Where does the line through $(1, 0, 1)$ and $(4, -2, 2)$ intersect the plane $x + y + z = 6$?

39–42 Determine whether the planes are parallel, perpendicular, or neither. If neither, find the angle between them.

39. $x + 4y - 3z = 1$, $-3x + 6y + 7z = 0$

40. $x + 2y + 2z = 1$, $2x - y + 2z = 1$

41. $x + y + z = 1$, $x - y + z = 1$

42. $2z = 4y - x$, $3x - 12y + 6z = 1$

43–44 (a) Find parametric equations for the line of intersection of the planes and (b) find the angle between the planes.

43. $x + y + z = 1$, $x + 2y + 2z = 1$

44. $3x - 2y + z = 1$, $2x + y - 3z = 3$

45. Find symmetric equations for the line of intersection of the planes $5x - 2y - 2z = 1$ and $4x + y + z = 6$.

46. Find an equation for the plane consisting of all points that are equidistant from the points $(2, 5, 5)$ and $(-6, 3, 1)$.

47. Find an equation of the plane with x-intercept a, y-intercept b, and z-intercept c.

48. (a) Find the point at which the given lines intersect:

$$\mathbf{r} = \langle 1, 1, 0 \rangle + t\langle 1, -1, 2 \rangle$$

$$\mathbf{r} = \langle 2, 0, 2 \rangle + s\langle -1, 1, 0 \rangle$$

(b) Find an equation of the plane that contains these lines.

49. Find parametric equations for the line through the point $(0, 1, 2)$ that is parallel to the plane $x + y + z = 2$ and perpendicular to the line $x = 1 + t, y = 1 - t, z = 2t$.

50. Find parametric equations for the line through the point $(0, 1, 2)$ that is perpendicular to the line $x = 1 + t$, $y = 1 - t, z = 2t$ and intersects this line.

51. Which of the following four planes are parallel? Are any of them identical?

P_1: $3x + 6y - 3z = 6$ P_2: $4x - 12y + 8z = 5$

P_3: $9y = 1 + 3x + 6z$ P_4: $z = x + 2y - 2$

52. Which of the following four lines are parallel? Are any of them identical?

L_1: $x = 1 + 6t$, $y = 1 - 3t$, $z = 12t + 5$

L_2: $x = 1 + 2t$, $y = t$, $z = 1 + 4t$

L_3: $2x - 2 = 4 - 4y = z + 1$

L_4: $\mathbf{r} = \langle 3, 1, 5 \rangle + t\langle 4, 2, 8 \rangle$

53–54 Use the formula in Exercise 33 in Section 9.4 to find the distance from the point to the given line.

53. $(4, 1, -2)$; $x = 1 + t, y = 3 - 2t, z = 4 - 3t$

54. $(0, 1, 3)$; $x = 2t, y = 6 - 2t, z = 3 + t$

55–56 Find the distance from the point to the given plane.

55. $(1, -2, 4)$, $3x + 2y + 6z = 5$

56. $(-6, 3, 5)$, $x - 2y - 4z = 8$

57–58 Find the distance between the given parallel planes.

57. $2x - 3y + z = 4$, $4x - 6y + 2z = 3$

58. $6z = 4y - 2x$, $9z = 1 - 3x + 6y$

59. Show that the distance between the parallel planes $ax + by + cz + d_1 = 0$ and $ax + by + cz + d_2 = 0$ is

$$D = \frac{|d_1 - d_2|}{\sqrt{a^2 + b^2 + c^2}}$$

60. Find equations of the planes that are parallel to the plane $x + 2y - 2z = 1$ and two units away from it.

61. Show that the lines with symmetric equations $x = y = z$ and $x + 1 = y/2 = z/3$ are skew, and find the distance between these lines.

62. Find the distance between the skew lines with parametric equations $x = 1 + t, y = 1 + 6t, z = 2t$, and $x = 1 + 2s$, $y = 5 + 15s, z = -2 + 6s$.

63. If a, b, and c are not all 0, show that the equation $ax + by + cz + d = 0$ represents a plane and $\langle a, b, c \rangle$ is a normal vector to the plane.
   Hint: Suppose $a \neq 0$ and rewrite the equation in the form

$$a\left(x + \frac{d}{a}\right) + b(y - 0) + c(z - 0) = 0$$

64. Give a geometric description of each family of planes.
   (a) $x + y + z = c$ (b) $x + y + cz = 1$
   (c) $y \cos\theta + z \sin\theta = 1$

LABORATORY PROJECT | **Putting 3D in Perspective**

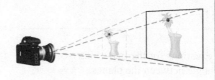

Computer graphics programmers face the same challenge as the great painters of the past: how to represent a three-dimensional scene as a flat image on a two-dimensional plane (a screen or a canvas). To create the illusion of perspective, in which closer objects appear larger than those farther away, three-dimensional objects in the computer's memory are projected onto a rectangular screen window from a viewpoint where the eye, or camera, is located. The viewing volume—the portion of space that will be visible—is the region contained by the four planes that pass through the viewpoint and an edge of the screen window. If objects in the scene extend beyond these four planes, they must be truncated before pixel data are sent to the screen. These planes are therefore called *clipping planes*.

1. Suppose the screen is represented by a rectangle in the yz-plane with vertices $(0, \pm 400, 0)$ and $(0, \pm 400, 600)$, and the camera is placed at $(1000, 0, 0)$. A line L in the scene passes through the points $(230, -285, 102)$ and $(860, 105, 264)$. At what points should L be clipped by the clipping planes?

2. If the clipped line segment is projected on the screen window, identify the resulting line segment.

3. Use parametric equations to plot the edges of the screen window, the clipped line segment, and its projection on the screen window. Then add sight lines connecting the viewpoint to each end of the clipped segments to verify that the projection is correct.

4. A rectangle with vertices $(621, -147, 206)$, $(563, 31, 242)$, $(657, -111, 86)$, and $(599, 67, 122)$ is added to the scene. The line L intersects this rectangle. To make the rectangle appear opaque, a programmer can use *hidden line rendering,* which removes portions of objects that are behind other objects. Identify the portion of L that should be removed.

9.6 Functions and Surfaces

In this section we take a first look at functions of two variables and their graphs, which are surfaces in three-dimensional space. We will give a much more thorough treatment of such functions in Chapter 11.

Functions of Two Variables

The temperature T at a point on the surface of the earth at any given time depends on the longitude x and latitude y of the point. We can think of T as being a function of the two variables x and y, or as a function of the pair (x, y). We indicate this functional dependence by writing $T = f(x, y)$.

The volume V of a circular cylinder depends on its radius r and its height h. In fact, we know that $V = \pi r^2 h$. We say that V is a function of r and h, and we write $V(r, h) = \pi r^2 h$.

> **Definition** A **function f of two variables** is a rule that assigns to each ordered pair of real numbers (x, y) in a set D a unique real number denoted by $f(x, y)$. The set D is the **domain** of f and its **range** is the set of values that f takes on, that is, $\{f(x, y) \mid (x, y) \in D\}$.

We often write $z = f(x, y)$ to make explicit the value taken on by f at the general point (x, y). The variables x and y are **independent variables** and z is the **dependent variable**. [Compare this with the notation $y = f(x)$ for functions of a single variable.]

The domain is a subset of $\mathbb{R}^2$, the xy-plane. We can think of the domain as the set of all possible inputs and the range as the set of all possible outputs. If a function f is given by a formula and no domain is specified, then the domain of f is understood to be the set of all pairs (x, y) for which the given expression is a well-defined real number.

EXAMPLE 1   Domain and range   If $f(x, y) = 4x^2 + y^2$, then $f(x, y)$ is defined for all possible ordered pairs of real numbers (x, y), so the domain is $\mathbb{R}^2$, the entire xy-plane. The range of f is the set $[0, \infty)$ of all nonnegative real numbers. [Notice that $x^2 \geq 0$ and $y^2 \geq 0$, so $f(x, y) \geq 0$ for all x and y.]

EXAMPLE 2   **Sketching domains**   For each of the following functions, evaluate $f(3, 2)$ and find and sketch the domain.

(a) $f(x, y) = \dfrac{\sqrt{x + y + 1}}{x - 1}$

(b) $f(x, y) = x \ln(y^2 - x)$

SOLUTION

(a)
$$f(3, 2) = \frac{\sqrt{3 + 2 + 1}}{3 - 1} = \frac{\sqrt{6}}{2}$$

The expression for f makes sense if the denominator is not 0 and the quantity under the square root sign is nonnegative. So the domain of f is

$$D = \{(x, y) \mid x + y + 1 \geqslant 0, \ x \neq 1\}$$

The inequality $x + y + 1 \geqslant 0$, or $y \geqslant -x - 1$, describes the points that lie on or above the line $y = -x - 1$, while $x \neq 1$ means that the points on the line $x = 1$ must be excluded from the domain. (See Figure 1.)

(b)
$$f(3, 2) = 3 \ln(2^2 - 3) = 3 \ln 1 = 0$$

Since $\ln(y^2 - x)$ is defined only when $y^2 - x > 0$, that is, $x < y^2$, the domain of f is $D = \{(x, y) \mid x < y^2\}$. This is the set of points to the left of the parabola $x = y^2$. (See Figure 2.)

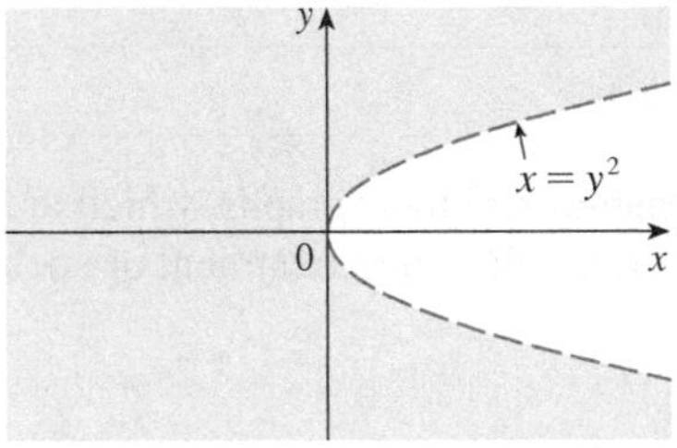

Not all functions can be represented by explicit formulas. The function in the next example is described verbally and by numerical estimates of its values.

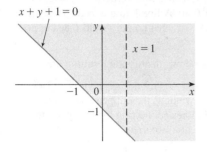

$x + y + 1 = 0$

$x = 1$

FIGURE 1
Domain of $f(x, y) = \dfrac{\sqrt{x + y + 1}}{x - 1}$

$x = y^2$

FIGURE 2
Domain of $f(x, y) = x \ln(y^2 - x)$

EXAMPLE 3   **Wave height as a function of wind speed and time**   The wave heights h (in feet) in the open sea depend mainly on the speed v of the wind (in knots) and the length of time t (in hours) that the wind has been blowing at that speed. So h is a function of v and t and we can write $h = f(v, t)$. Observations and measurements have been made by meteorologists and oceanographers and are recorded in Table 1.

TABLE 1
Wave heights (in feet) produced by different wind speeds for various lengths of time

	Duration (hours)						
v \ t	5	10	15	20	30	40	50
10	2	2	2	2	2	2	2
15	4	4	5	5	5	5	5
20	5	7	8	8	9	9	9
30	9	13	16	17	18	19	19
40	14	21	25	28	31	33	33
50	19	29	36	40	45	48	50
60	24	37	47	54	62	67	69

Wind speed (knots)

For instance, the table indicates that if the wind has been blowing at 50 knots for 30 hours, then the wave heights are estimated to be 45 ft, so

$$f(50, 30) \approx 45$$

The domain of this function h is given by $v \geq 0$ and $t \geq 0$. Although there is no exact formula for h in terms of v and t, we will see that the operations of calculus can still be carried out for such an experimentally defined function.

Graphs

One way of visualizing the behavior of a function of two variables is to consider its graph.

Definition If f is a function of two variables with domain D, then the **graph** of f is the set of all points (x, y, z) in $\mathbb{R}^3$ such that $z = f(x, y)$ and (x, y) is in D.

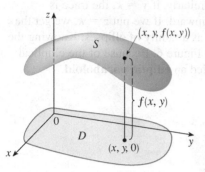

FIGURE 3

Just as the graph of a function f of one variable is a curve C with equation $y = f(x)$, so the graph of a function f of two variables is a surface S with equation $z = f(x, y)$. We can visualize the graph S of f as lying directly above or below its domain D in the xy-plane (see Figure 3).

EXAMPLE 4 **Graphing a linear function** Sketch the graph of the function $f(x, y) = 6 - 3x - 2y$.

SOLUTION The graph of f has the equation $z = 6 - 3x - 2y$, or $3x + 2y + z = 6$, which represents a plane. To graph the plane we first find the intercepts. Putting $y = z = 0$ in the equation, we get $x = 2$ as the x-intercept. Similarly, the y-intercept is 3 and the z-intercept is 6. This helps us sketch the portion of the graph that lies in the first octant in Figure 4.

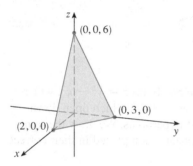

FIGURE 4

The function in Example 4 is a special case of the function

$$f(x, y) = ax + by + c$$

which is called a **linear function**. The graph of such a function has the equation

$$z = ax + by + c \qquad \text{or} \qquad ax + by - z + c = 0$$

so it is a plane. In much the same way that linear functions of one variable are important in single-variable calculus, we will see that linear functions of two variables play a central role in multivariable calculus.

☑ EXAMPLE 5 Sketch the graph of the function $f(x, y) = x^2$.

SOLUTION Notice that, no matter what value we give y, the value of $f(x, y)$ is always x^2. The equation of the graph is $z = x^2$, which doesn't involve y. This means that any vertical plane with equation $y = k$ (parallel to the xz-plane) intersects the graph in a curve with equation $z = x^2$, that is, a parabola. Figure 5 shows how the graph is formed by taking the parabola $z = x^2$ in the xz-plane and moving it in the direction of the y-axis. So the graph is a surface, called a **parabolic cylinder**, made up of infinitely many shifted copies of the same parabola.

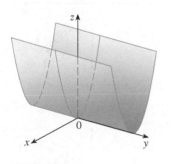

FIGURE 5
The graph of $f(x, y) = x^2$ is the parabolic cylinder $z = x^2$.

In sketching the graphs of functions of two variables, it's often useful to start by determining the shapes of cross-sections (slices) of the graph. For example, if we keep x fixed by putting $x = k$ (a constant) and letting y vary, the result is a function of one variable $z = f(k, y)$, whose graph is the curve that results when we intersect the surface $z = f(x, y)$ with the vertical plane $x = k$. In a similar fashion we can slice the surface with the vertical plane $y = k$ and look at the curves $z = f(x, k)$. We can also slice with horizontal planes $z = k$. All three types of curves are called **traces** (or cross-sections) of the surface $z = f(x, y)$.

EXAMPLE 6 Use traces to sketch the graph of the function $f(x, y) = 4x^2 + y^2$.

SOLUTION The equation of the graph is $z = 4x^2 + y^2$. If we put $x = 0$, we get $z = y^2$, so the yz-plane intersects the surface in a parabola. If we put $x = k$ (a constant), we get $z = y^2 + 4k^2$. This means that if we slice the graph with any plane parallel to the yz-plane, we obtain a parabola that opens upward. Similarly, if $y = k$, the trace is $z = 4x^2 + k^2$, which is again a parabola that opens upward. If we put $z = k$, we get the horizontal traces $4x^2 + y^2 = k$, which we recognize as a family of ellipses. Knowing the shapes of the traces, we can sketch the graph of f in Figure 6. Because of the elliptical and parabolic traces, the surface $z = 4x^2 + y^2$ is called an **elliptic paraboloid**.

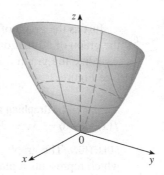

FIGURE 6
The graph of $f(x, y) = 4x^2 + y^2$ is
the elliptic paraboloid $z = 4x^2 + y^2$.
Horizontal traces are ellipses;
vertical traces are parabolas.

EXAMPLE 7 Sketch the graph of $f(x, y) = y^2 - x^2$.

SOLUTION The traces in the vertical planes $x = k$ are the parabolas $z = y^2 - k^2$, which open upward. The traces in $y = k$ are the parabolas $z = -x^2 + k^2$, which open downward. The horizontal traces are $y^2 - x^2 = k$, a family of hyperbolas. We draw the families of traces in Figure 7 and we show how the traces appear when placed in their correct planes in Figure 8.

FIGURE 7
Vertical traces are parabolas;
horizontal traces are hyperbolas.
All traces are labeled with the
value of k.

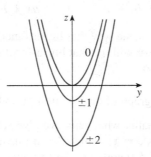

Traces in $x = k$ are $z = y^2 - k^2$

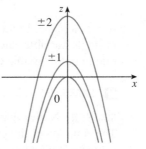

Traces in $y = k$ are $z = -x^2 + k^2$

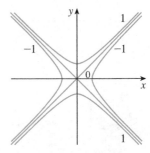

Traces in $z = k$ are $y^2 - x^2 = k$

FIGURE 8
Traces moved to their
correct planes

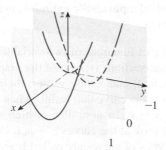

Traces in $x = k$

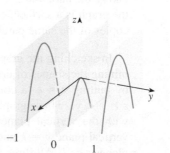

Traces in $y = k$

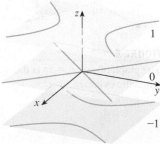

Traces in $z = k$

In Figure 9 we fit together the traces from Figure 8 to form the surface $z = y^2 - x^2$, a **hyperbolic paraboloid**. Notice that the shape of the surface near the origin resembles that of a saddle. This surface will be investigated further in Section 11.7 when we discuss saddle points.

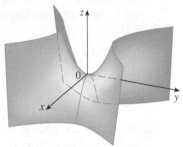

FIGURE 9

The graph of $f(x, y) = y^2 - x^2$ is the hyperbolic paraboloid $z = y^2 - x^2$.

The idea of using traces to draw a surface is employed in three-dimensional graphing software for computers. In most such software, traces in the vertical planes $x = k$ and $y = k$ are drawn for equally spaced values of k and parts of the graph are eliminated using hidden line removal. Figure 10 shows computer-generated graphs of several functions. Notice that we get an especially good picture of a function when rotation is used to give views from different vantage points. In parts (a) and (b) the graph of f is very flat and close to the xy-plane except near the origin; this is because $e^{-x^2 - y^2}$ is very small when x or y is large.

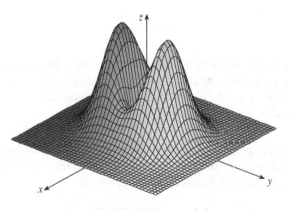

(a) $f(x, y) = (x^2 + 3y^2)e^{-x^2 - y^2}$

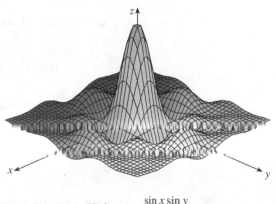

(b) $f(x, y) = (x^2 + 3y^2)e^{-x^2 - y^2}$

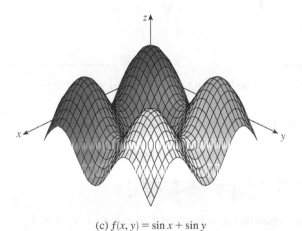

(c) $f(x, y) = \sin x + \sin y$

(d) $f(x, y) = \dfrac{\sin x \sin y}{xy}$

FIGURE 10

Quadric Surfaces

The graph of a second-degree equation in three variables x, y, and z is called a **quadric surface**. We have already sketched the quadric surfaces $z = 4x^2 + y^2$ (an elliptic paraboloid) and $z = y^2 - x^2$ (a hyperbolic paraboloid) in Figures 6 and 9. In the next example we investigate a quadric surface called an *ellipsoid*.

EXAMPLE 8   Sketch the quadric surface with equation

$$x^2 + \frac{y^2}{9} + \frac{z^2}{4} = 1$$

SOLUTION   The trace in the xy-plane ($z = 0$) is $x^2 + y^2/9 = 1$, which we recognize as an equation of an ellipse. In general, the horizontal trace in the plane $z = k$ is

$$x^2 + \frac{y^2}{9} = 1 - \frac{k^2}{4} \qquad z = k$$

which is an ellipse, provided that $k^2 < 4$, that is, $-2 < k < 2$.

Similarly, the vertical traces are also ellipses:

$$\frac{y^2}{9} + \frac{z^2}{4} = 1 - k^2 \qquad x = k \qquad \text{(if } -1 < k < 1)$$

$$x^2 + \frac{z^2}{4} = 1 - \frac{k^2}{9} \qquad y = k \qquad \text{(if } -3 < k < 3)$$

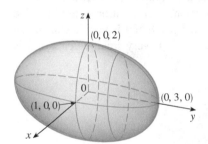

FIGURE 11

The ellipsoid $x^2 + \dfrac{y^2}{9} + \dfrac{z^2}{4} = 1$

Figure 11 shows how drawing some traces indicates the shape of the surface. It's called an **ellipsoid** because all of its traces are ellipses. Notice that it is symmetric with respect to each coordinate plane; this symmetry is a reflection of the fact that its equation involves only even powers of x, y, and z.

The ellipsoid in Example 8 is *not* the graph of a function because some vertical lines (such as the z-axis) intersect it more than once. But the top and bottom halves *are* graphs of functions. In fact, if we solve the equation of the ellipsoid for z, we get

$$z^2 = 4\left(1 - x^2 - \frac{y^2}{9}\right) \qquad z = \pm 2\sqrt{1 - x^2 - \frac{y^2}{9}}$$

So the graphs of the functions

$$f(x, y) = 2\sqrt{1 - x^2 - \frac{y^2}{9}} \qquad \text{and} \qquad g(x, y) = -2\sqrt{1 - x^2 - \frac{y^2}{9}}$$

are the top and bottom halves of the ellipsoid (see Figure 12). The domain of both f and g is the set of all points (x, y) such that

$$1 - x^2 - \frac{y^2}{9} \geqslant 0 \quad \Longleftrightarrow \quad x^2 + \frac{y^2}{9} \leqslant 1$$

so the domain is the set of all points that lie on or inside the ellipse $x^2 + y^2/9 = 1$.

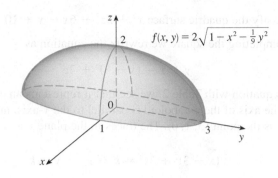

$f(x, y) = 2\sqrt{1 - x^2 - \frac{1}{9}y^2}$

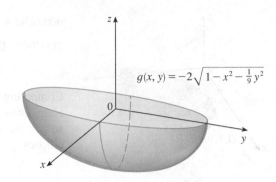

$g(x, y) = -2\sqrt{1 - x^2 - \frac{1}{9}y^2}$

FIGURE 12

TEC In Module 9.6B you can see how changing a, b, and c in Table 2 affects the shape of the quadric surface.

Table 2 shows computer-drawn graphs of the six basic types of quadric surfaces in standard form. All surfaces are symmetric with respect to the z-axis. If a quadric surface is symmetric about a different axis, its equation changes accordingly.

TABLE 2 Graphs of quadric surfaces

Surface	Equation	Surface	Equation
Ellipsoid	$\dfrac{x^2}{a^2} + \dfrac{y^2}{b^2} + \dfrac{z^2}{c^2} = 1$ All traces are ellipses. If $a = b = c$, the ellipsoid is a sphere.	Cone	$\dfrac{z^2}{c^2} = \dfrac{x^2}{a^2} + \dfrac{y^2}{b^2}$ Horizontal traces are ellipses. Vertical traces in the planes $x = k$ and $y = k$ are hyperbolas if $k \neq 0$ but are pairs of lines if $k = 0$.
Elliptic Paraboloid	$\dfrac{z}{c} = \dfrac{x^2}{a^2} + \dfrac{y^2}{b^2}$ Horizontal traces are ellipses. Vertical traces are parabolas. The variable raised to the first power indicates the axis of the paraboloid.	Hyperboloid of One Sheet	$\dfrac{x^2}{a^2} + \dfrac{y^2}{b^2} - \dfrac{z^2}{c^2} = 1$ Horizontal traces are ellipses. Vertical traces are hyperbolas. The axis of symmetry corresponds to the variable whose coefficient is negative.
Hyperbolic Paraboloid	$\dfrac{z}{c} = \dfrac{x^2}{a^2} - \dfrac{y^2}{b^2}$ Horizontal traces are hyperbolas. Vertical traces are parabolas. The case where $c < 0$ is illustrated.	Hyperboloid of Two Sheets	$-\dfrac{x^2}{a^2} - \dfrac{y^2}{b^2} + \dfrac{z^2}{c^2} = 1$ Horizontal traces in $z = k$ are ellipses if $k > c$ or $k < -c$. Vertical traces are hyperbolas. The two minus signs indicate two sheets.

EXAMPLE 9 Classify the quadric surface $x^2 + 2z^2 - 6x - y + 10 = 0$.

SOLUTION By completing the square we rewrite the equation as

$$y - 1 = (x - 3)^2 + 2z^2$$

Comparing this equation with Table 2, we see that it represents an elliptic paraboloid. Here, however, the axis of the paraboloid is parallel to the y-axis, and it has been shifted so that its vertex is the point $(3, 1, 0)$. The traces in the plane $y = k$ $(k > 1)$ are the ellipses

$$(x - 3)^2 + 2z^2 = k - 1 \qquad y = k$$

The trace in the xy-plane is the parabola with equation $y = 1 + (x - 3)^2$, $z = 0$. The paraboloid is sketched in Figure 13.

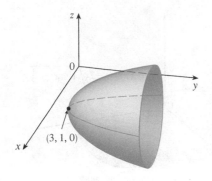

FIGURE 13
$x^2 + 2z^2 - 6x - y + 10 = 0$

9.6 Exercises

1. In Example 3 we considered the function $h = f(v, t)$, where h is the height of waves produced by wind at speed v for a time t. Use Table 1 to answer the following questions.
(a) What is the value of $f(40, 15)$? What is its meaning?
(b) What is the meaning of the function $h = f(30, t)$? Describe the behavior of this function.
(c) What is the meaning of the function $h = f(v, 30)$? Describe the behavior of this function.

2. Let $f(x, y) = y^4 e^{x/y}$.
(a) Evaluate $f(0, 2)$.
(b) Find the domain of f.
(c) Find the range of f.

3. Let $g(x, y) = \cos(x + 2y)$.
(a) Evaluate $g(2, -1)$.
(b) Find the domain of g.
(c) Find the range of g.

4. Let $F(x, y) = 1 + \sqrt{4 - y^2}$.
(a) Evaluate $F(3, 1)$.
(b) Find and sketch the domain of F.
(c) Find the range of F.

5–8 Find and sketch the domain of the function.

5. $f(x, y) = \dfrac{\sqrt{y - x^2}}{1 - x^2}$

6. $f(x, y) = \sqrt{xy}$

7. $f(x, y) = \sqrt{1 - x^2} - \sqrt{1 - y^2}$

8. $f(x, y) = \ln(x^2 + y^2 - 2)$

9–13 Sketch the graph of the function.

9. $f(x, y) = 3$

10. $f(x, y) = y$

11. $f(x, y) = 6 - 3x - 2y$

12. $f(x, y) = \cos x$

13. $f(x, y) = y^2 + 1$

14. (a) Find the traces of the function $f(x, y) = x^2 + y^2$ in the planes $x = k$, $y = k$, and $z = k$. Use these traces to sketch the graph.
(b) Sketch the graph of $g(x, y) = -x^2 - y^2$. How is it related to the graph of f?
(c) Sketch the graph of $h(x, y) = 3 - x^2 - y^2$. How is it related to the graph of g?

15. Match the function with its graph (labeled I–VI). Give reasons for your choices.
(a) $f(x, y) = |x| + |y|$
(b) $f(x, y) = |xy|$
(c) $f(x, y) = \dfrac{1}{1 + x^2 + y^2}$
(d) $f(x, y) = (x^2 - y^2)^2$
(e) $f(x, y) = (x - y)^2$
(f) $f(x, y) = \sin(|x| + |y|)$

I
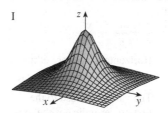

II
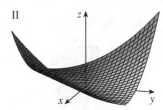

III
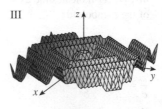

IV
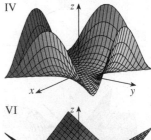

V
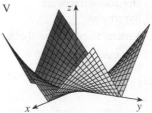

VI
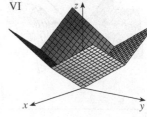

 Graphing calculator or computer with graphing software required   **1.** Homework Hints available in TEC

16–18 Use traces to sketch the graph of the function.

16. $f(x, y) = \sqrt{16 - x^2 - 16y^2}$

17. $f(x, y) = \sqrt{4x^2 + y^2}$

18. $f(x, y) = x^2 - y^2$

19–20 Use traces to sketch the surface.

19. $y = z^2 - x^2$ **20.** $x = y^2 + 4z^2$

21–22 Classify the surface by comparing with one of the standard forms in Table 2. Then sketch its graph.

21. $4x^2 + y^2 + 4z^2 - 4y - 24z + 36 = 0$

22. $4y^2 + z^2 - x - 16y - 4z + 20 = 0$

23. (a) What does the equation $x^2 + y^2 = 1$ represent as a curve in $\mathbb{R}^2$?
 (b) What does it represent as a surface in $\mathbb{R}^3$?
 (c) What does the equation $x^2 + z^2 = 1$ represent?

24. (a) Identify the traces of the surface $z^2 = x^2 + y^2$.
 (b) Sketch the surface.
 (c) Sketch the graphs of the functions $f(x, y) = \sqrt{x^2 + y^2}$ and $g(x, y) = -\sqrt{x^2 + y^2}$.

25. (a) Find and identify the traces of the quadric surface $x^2 + y^2 - z^2 = 1$ and explain why the graph looks like the graph of the hyperboloid of one sheet in Table 2.
 (b) If we change the equation in part (a) to $x^2 - y^2 + z^2 = 1$, how is the graph affected?
 (c) What if we change the equation in part (a) to $x^2 + y^2 + 2y - z^2 = 0$?

26. (a) Find and identify the traces of the quadric surface $-x^2 - y^2 + z^2 = 1$ and explain why the graph looks like the graph of the hyperboloid of two sheets in Table 2.
 (b) If the equation in part (a) is changed to $x^2 - y^2 - z^2 = 1$, what happens to the graph? Sketch the new graph.

27. The figure shows vertical traces for a function $z = f(x, y)$. Which one of the graphs I–IV has these traces? Explain.

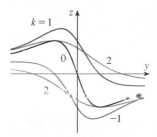

Traces in $x = k$

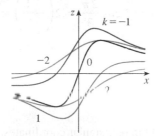

Traces in $y = k$

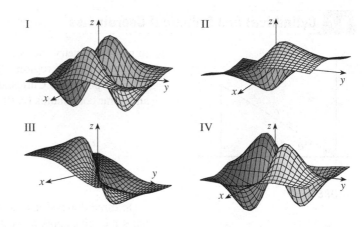

28–29 Use a computer to graph the function using various domains and viewpoints. Get a printout that gives a good view of the "peaks and valleys." Would you say that the function has a maximum value? Can you identify any points on the graph that you might consider to be "local maximum points"? What about "local minimum points"?

28. $f(x, y) = x^2 y^2 e^{x - 4x^2 - 4y^2}$

29. $f(x, y) = xy e^{x + 2y - 9x^2 - 9y^2}$

30. Use a computer to graph the function using various domains and viewpoints. Comment on the limiting behavior of the function. What happens as both x and y become large? What happens as (x, y) approaches the origin?

 (a) $f(x, y) = \dfrac{x + y}{x^2 + y^2}$ (b) $f(x, y) = \dfrac{xy}{x^2 + y^2}$

31. Graph the surfaces $z = x^2 + y^2$ and $z = 1 - y^2$ on a common screen using the domain $|x| \leqslant 1.2$, $|y| \leqslant 1.2$ and observe the curve of intersection of these surfaces. Show that the projection of this curve onto the xy-plane is an ellipse.

32. Show that the curve of intersection of the surfaces $x^2 + 2y^2 - z^2 + 3x = 1$ and $2x^2 + 4y^2 - 2z^2 - 5y = 0$ lies in a plane.

33. Show that if the point (a, b, c) lies on the hyperbolic paraboloid $z = y^2 - x^2$, then the lines with parametric equations $x = a + t$, $y = b + t$, $z = c + 2(b - a)t$ and $x = a + t$, $y = b - t$, $z = c - 2(b + a)t$ both lie entirely on this paraboloid. (This shows that the hyperbolic paraboloid is what is called a **ruled surface**; that is, it can be generated by the motion of a straight line. In fact, this exercise shows that through each point on the hyperbolic paraboloid there are two generating lines. The only other quadric surfaces that are ruled surfaces are cylinders, cones, and hyperboloids of one sheet.)

34. Find an equation for the surface consisting of all points P for which the distance from P to the x-axis is twice the distance from P to the yz-plane. Identify the surface.

9.7 Cylindrical and Spherical Coordinates

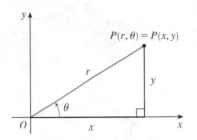

FIGURE 1

In plane geometry the polar coordinate system is used to give a convenient description of certain curves and regions. (See Appendix H.) Figure 1 enables us to recall the connection between polar and Cartesian coordinates. If the point P has Cartesian coordinates (x, y) and polar coordinates (r, θ), then, from the figure,

$$x = r \cos \theta \qquad y = r \sin \theta$$

$$r^2 = x^2 + y^2 \qquad \tan \theta = \frac{y}{x}$$

In three dimensions there are two coordinate systems that are similar to polar coordinates and give convenient descriptions of some commonly occurring surfaces and solids. They will be especially useful in Chapter 12 when we compute volumes and triple integrals.

Cylindrical Coordinates

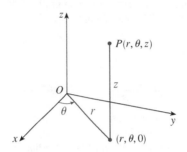

FIGURE 2
The cylindrical coordinates of a point

In the **cylindrical coordinate system**, a point P in three-dimensional space is represented by the ordered triple (r, θ, z), where r and θ are polar coordinates of the projection of P onto the xy-plane and z is the directed distance from the xy-plane to P. (See Figure 2.)

To convert from cylindrical to rectangular coordinates, we use the equations

1
$$x = r \cos \theta \qquad y = r \sin \theta \qquad z = z$$

whereas to convert from rectangular to cylindrical coordinates, we use

2
$$r^2 = x^2 + y^2 \qquad \tan \theta = \frac{y}{x} \qquad z = z$$

EXAMPLE 1 **Converting between cylindrical and rectangular coordinates**
(a) Plot the point with cylindrical coordinates $(2, 2\pi/3, 1)$ and find its rectangular coordinates.
(b) Find cylindrical coordinates of the point with rectangular coordinates $(3, -3, -7)$.

SOLUTION
(a) The point with cylindrical coordinates $(2, 2\pi/3, 1)$ is plotted in Figure 3. From Equations 1, its rectangular coordinates are

$$x = 2 \cos \frac{2\pi}{3} = 2\left(-\frac{1}{2}\right) = -1$$

$$y = 2 \sin \frac{2\pi}{3} = 2\left(\frac{\sqrt{3}}{2}\right) = \sqrt{3}$$

$$z = 1$$

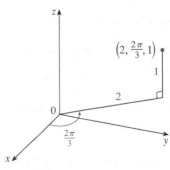

FIGURE 3

Thus the point is $\left(-1, \sqrt{3}, 1\right)$ in rectangular coordinates.

(b) From Equations 2 we have

$$r = \sqrt{3^2 + (-3)^2} = 3\sqrt{2}$$

$$\tan\theta = \frac{-3}{3} = -1 \qquad \text{so} \qquad \theta = \frac{7\pi}{4} + 2n\pi$$

$$z = -7$$

Therefore one set of cylindrical coordinates is $\left(3\sqrt{2}, 7\pi/4, -7\right)$. Another is $\left(3\sqrt{2}, -\pi/4, -7\right)$. As with polar coordinates, there are infinitely many choices.

Cylindrical coordinates are useful in problems that involve symmetry about an axis, and the z-axis is chosen to coincide with this axis of symmetry. For instance, the axis of the circular cylinder with Cartesian equation $x^2 + y^2 = c^2$ is the z-axis. In cylindrical coordinates this cylinder has the very simple equation $r = c$. (See Figure 4.) This is the reason for the name "cylindrical" coordinates.

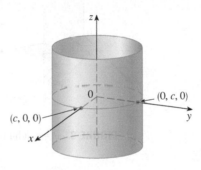

FIGURE 4
$r = c$, a cylinder

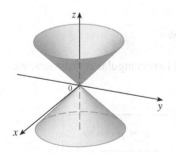

FIGURE 5
$z = r$, a cone

V   EXAMPLE 2   Describe the surface whose equation in cylindrical coordinates is $z = r$.

SOLUTION   The equation says that the z-value, or height, of each point on the surface is the same as r, the distance from the point to the z-axis. Because θ doesn't appear, it can vary. So any horizontal trace in the plane $z = k$ ($k > 0$) is a circle of radius k. These traces suggest that the surface is a cone. This prediction can be confirmed by converting the equation into rectangular coordinates. From the first equation in (2) we have

$$z^2 = r^2 = x^2 + y^2$$

We recognize the equation $z^2 = x^2 + y^2$ (by comparison with Table 2 in Section 9.6) as being a circular cone whose axis is the z-axis (see Figure 5).

EXAMPLE 3   A cylindrical equation for an ellipsoid   Find an equation in cylindrical coordinates for the ellipsoid $4x^2 + 4y^2 + z^2 = 1$.

SOLUTION   Since $r^2 = x^2 + y^2$ from Equations 2, we have

$$z^2 = 1 - 4(x^2 + y^2) = 1 - 4r^2$$

So an equation of the ellipsoid in cylindrical coordinates is $z^2 = 1 - 4r^2$.

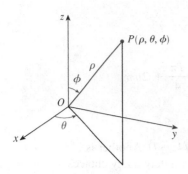

FIGURE 6
The spherical coordinates of a point

Spherical Coordinates

The **spherical coordinates** (ρ, θ, ϕ) of a point P in space are shown in Figure 6, where $\rho = |OP|$ is the distance from the origin to P, θ is the same angle as in cylindrical coordinates, and ϕ is the angle between the positive z-axis and the line segment OP. Note that

$$\rho \geqslant 0 \qquad 0 \leqslant \phi \leqslant \pi$$

The spherical coordinate system is especially useful in problems where there is symmetry about a point, and the origin is placed at this point. For example, the sphere with center the origin and radius c has the simple equation $\rho = c$ (see Figure 7); this is the reason for the name "spherical" coordinates. The graph of the equation $\theta = c$ is a vertical half-plane (see Figure 8), and the equation $\phi = c$ represents a half-cone with the z-axis as its axis (see Figure 9).

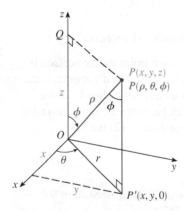

FIGURE 7 $\rho = c$, a sphere

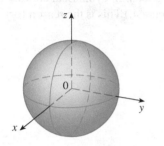

FIGURE 8 $\theta = c$, a half-plane

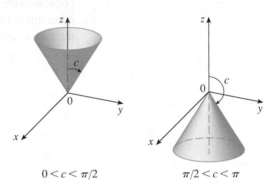

$$0 < c < \pi/2 \qquad\qquad \pi/2 < c < \pi$$

FIGURE 9 $\phi = c$, a half-cone

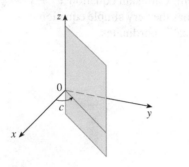

FIGURE 10

The relationship between rectangular and spherical coordinates can be seen from Figure 10. From triangles OPQ and OPP' we have

$$z = \rho \cos \phi \qquad r = \rho \sin \phi$$

But $x = r \cos \theta$ and $y = r \sin \theta$, so to convert from spherical to rectangular coordinates, we use the equations

$$\boxed{3} \qquad \boxed{\quad x = \rho \sin \phi \cos \theta \qquad y = \rho \sin \phi \sin \theta \qquad z = \rho \cos \phi \quad}$$

Also, the distance formula shows that

$$\boxed{4} \qquad \boxed{\quad \rho^2 = x^2 + y^2 + z^2 \quad}$$

We use this equation in converting from rectangular to spherical coordinates.

▶ EXAMPLE 4 **Converting from spherical to rectangular coordinates**
The point $(2, \pi/4, \pi/3)$ is given in spherical coordinates. Plot the point and find its rectangular coordinates.

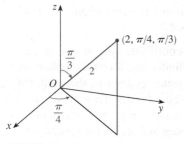

FIGURE 11

SOLUTION We plot the point in Figure 11. From Equations 3 we have

$$x = \rho \sin \phi \cos \theta = 2 \sin \frac{\pi}{3} \cos \frac{\pi}{4} = 2\left(\frac{\sqrt{3}}{2}\right)\left(\frac{1}{\sqrt{2}}\right) = \sqrt{\frac{3}{2}}$$

$$y = \rho \sin \phi \sin \theta = 2 \sin \frac{\pi}{3} \sin \frac{\pi}{4} = 2\left(\frac{\sqrt{3}}{2}\right)\left(\frac{1}{\sqrt{2}}\right) = \sqrt{\frac{3}{2}}$$

$$z = \rho \cos \phi = 2 \cos \frac{\pi}{3} = 2(\tfrac{1}{2}) = 1$$

Thus the point $(2, \pi/4, \pi/3)$ is $\left(\sqrt{3/2}, \sqrt{3/2}, 1\right)$ in rectangular coordinates.

▼ EXAMPLE 5 Converting from rectangular to spherical coordinates
The point $\left(0, 2\sqrt{3}, -2\right)$ is given in rectangular coordinates. Find spherical coordinates for this point.

SOLUTION From Equation 4 we have

$$\rho = \sqrt{x^2 + y^2 + z^2} = \sqrt{0 + 12 + 4} = 4$$

⊘ **Warning:** There is not universal agreement on the notation for spherical coordinates. Most books on physics reverse the meanings of θ and ϕ and use r in place of ρ.

and so Equations 3 give

$$\cos \phi = \frac{z}{\rho} = \frac{-2}{4} = -\frac{1}{2} \qquad \phi = \frac{2\pi}{3}$$

$$\cos \theta = \frac{x}{\rho \sin \phi} = 0 \qquad \theta = \frac{\pi}{2}$$

$\left(\text{Note that } \theta \neq 3\pi/2 \text{ because } y = 2\sqrt{3} > 0.\right)$ Therefore spherical coordinates of the given point are $(4, \pi/2, 2\pi/3)$.

EXAMPLE 6   A spherical equation for a hyperboloid   Find an equation in spherical coordinates for the hyperboloid of two sheets with equation $x^2 - y^2 - z^2 = 1$.

SOLUTION Substituting the expressions in Equations 3 into the given equation, we have

TEC In Module 9.7 you can investigate families of surfaces in cylindrical and spherical coordinates.

$$\rho^2 \sin^2\phi \, \cos^2\theta - \rho^2 \sin^2\phi \, \sin^2\theta - \rho^2 \cos^2\phi = 1$$

$$\rho^2[\sin^2\phi \, (\cos^2\theta - \sin^2\theta) - \cos^2\phi] = 1$$

or

$$\rho^2(\sin^2\phi \, \cos 2\theta - \cos^2\phi) = 1$$

EXAMPLE 7   Find a rectangular equation for the surface whose spherical equation is $\rho = \sin \theta \sin \phi$.

SOLUTION From Equations 4 and 3 we have

$$x^2 + y^2 + z^2 = \rho^2 = \rho \sin \theta \sin \phi = y$$

or

$$x^2 + \left(y - \tfrac{1}{2}\right)^2 + z^2 = \tfrac{1}{4}$$

which is the equation of a sphere with center $\left(0, \tfrac{1}{2}, 0\right)$ and radius $\tfrac{1}{2}$.

EXAMPLE 8 Use a computer to draw a picture of the solid that remains when a hole of radius 3 is drilled through the center of a sphere of radius 4.

SOLUTION To keep the equations simple, let's choose the coordinate system so that the center of the sphere is at the origin and the axis of the cylinder that forms the hole is the z-axis. We could use either cylindrical or spherical coordinates to describe the solid, but the description is somewhat simpler if we use cylindrical coordinates. Then the equation of the cylinder is $r = 3$ and the equation of the sphere is $x^2 + y^2 + z^2 = 16$, or $r^2 + z^2 = 16$. The points in the solid lie outside the cylinder and inside the sphere, so they satisfy the inequalities

Most three-dimensional graphing programs can graph surfaces whose equations are given in cylindrical or spherical coordinates. As Example 8 demonstrates, this is often the most convenient way of drawing a solid.

$$3 \le r \le \sqrt{16 - z^2}$$

To ensure that the computer graphs only the appropriate parts of these surfaces, we find where they intersect by solving the equations $r = 3$ and $r = \sqrt{16 - z^2}$:

$$\sqrt{16 - z^2} = 3 \quad \Rightarrow \quad 16 - z^2 = 9 \quad \Rightarrow \quad z^2 = 7 \quad \Rightarrow \quad z = \pm\sqrt{7}$$

The solid lies between $z = -\sqrt{7}$ and $z = \sqrt{7}$, so we ask the computer to graph the surfaces with the following equations and domains:

$$r = 3 \qquad\qquad 0 \le \theta \le 2\pi \qquad\qquad -\sqrt{7} \le z \le \sqrt{7}$$

$$r = \sqrt{16 - z^2} \qquad\qquad 0 \le \theta \le 2\pi \qquad\qquad -\sqrt{7} \le z \le \sqrt{7}$$

FIGURE 12

The resulting picture, shown in Figure 12, is exactly what we want.

9.7 Exercises

1. What are cylindrical coordinates? For what types of surfaces do they provide convenient descriptions?

2. What are spherical coordinates? For what types of surfaces do they provide convenient descriptions?

3–4 Plot the point whose cylindrical coordinates are given. Then find the rectangular coordinates of the point.

3. (a) $(2, \pi/4, 1)$ (b) $(4, -\pi/3, 5)$

4. (a) $(1, \pi, e)$ (b) $(1, 3\pi/2, 2)$

5–6 Change from rectangular to cylindrical coordinates.

5. (a) $(1, -1, 4)$ (b) $(-1, -\sqrt{3}, 2)$

6. (a) $(2\sqrt{3}, 2, -1)$ (b) $(4, -3, 2)$

7–8 Plot the point whose spherical coordinates are given. Then find the rectangular coordinates of the point.

7. (a) $(1, 0, 0)$ (b) $(2, \pi/3, \pi/4)$

8. (a) $(5, \pi, \pi/2)$ (b) $(4, 3\pi/4, \pi/3)$

9–10 Change from rectangular to spherical coordinates.

9. (a) $(1, \sqrt{3}, 2\sqrt{3})$ (b) $(0, -1, -1)$

10. (a) $(0, \sqrt{3}, 1)$ (b) $(-1, 1, \sqrt{6})$

11–14 Describe in words the surface whose equation is given.

11. $\theta = \pi/4$ **12.** $r = 5$

13. $\phi = \pi/3$ **14.** $\rho = 3$

15–20 Identify the surface whose equation is given.

15. $z = 4 - r^2$ **16.** $\rho \sin \phi = 2$

17. $r = 2 \cos \theta$ **18.** $2r^2 + z^2 = 1$

19. $\rho = \sin \theta \sin \phi$ **20.** $\rho^2(\sin^2\phi \, \sin^2\theta + \cos^2\phi) = 9$

⌂ Graphing calculator or computer with graphing software required   **1.** Homework Hints available in TEC

21–24 Write the equation (a) in cylindrical coordinates and (b) in spherical coordinates.

21. $x^2 + y^2 = 2y$

22. $x^2 + y^2 + z^2 = 2$

23. $3x + 2y + z = 6$

24. $x^2 - 2x + y^2 + z^2 = 0$

25–30 Sketch the solid described by the given inequalities.

25. $0 \le r \le 2, \quad -\pi/2 \le \theta \le \pi/2, \quad 0 \le z \le 1$

26. $0 \le \theta \le \pi/2, \quad r \le z \le 2$

27. $\rho \le 2, \quad 0 \le \phi \le \pi/2, \quad 0 \le \theta \le \pi/2$

28. $2 \le \rho \le 3, \quad \pi/2 \le \phi \le \pi$

29. $\rho \le 1, \quad 3\pi/4 \le \phi \le \pi$

30. $\rho \le 2, \quad \rho \le \csc \phi$

31. A cylindrical shell is 20 cm long, with inner radius 6 cm and outer radius 7 cm. Write inequalities that describe the shell in an appropriate coordinate system. Explain how you have positioned the coordinate system with respect to the shell.

32. (a) Find inequalities that describe a hollow ball with diameter 30 cm and thickness 0.5 cm. Explain how you have positioned the coordinate system that you have chosen.
(b) Suppose the ball is cut in half. Write inequalities that describe one of the halves.

33. A solid lies above the cone $z = \sqrt{x^2 + y^2}$ and below the sphere $x^2 + y^2 + z^2 = z$. Write a description of the solid in terms of inequalities involving spherical coordinates.

34. Use a graphing device to draw the solid enclosed by the paraboloids $z = x^2 + y^2$ and $z = 5 - x^2 - y^2$.

35. Use a graphing device to draw a silo consisting of a cylinder with radius 3 and height 10 surmounted by a hemisphere.

36. The latitude and longitude of a point P in the Northern Hemisphere are related to spherical coordinates ρ, θ, ϕ as follows. We take the origin to be the center of the earth and the positive z-axis to pass through the North Pole. The positive x-axis passes through the point where the prime meridian (the meridian through Greenwich, England) intersects the equator. Then the latitude of P is $\alpha = 90° - \phi°$ and the longitude is $\beta = 360° - \theta°$. Find the great-circle distance from Los Angeles (lat. 34.06° N, long. 118.25° W) to Montréal (lat. 45.50° N, long. 73.60° W). Take the radius of the earth to be 3960 mi. (A *great circle* is the circle of intersection of a sphere and a plane through the center of the sphere.)

LABORATORY PROJECT   Families of Surfaces

In this project you will discover the interesting shapes that members of families of surfaces can take. You will also see how the shape of the surface evolves as you vary the constants.

1. Use a computer to investigate the family of functions

$$f(x, y) = (ax^2 + by^2)e^{-x^2-y^2}$$

How does the shape of the graph depend on the numbers a and b?

2. Use a computer to investigate the family of surfaces $z = x^2 + y^2 + cxy$. In particular, you should determine the transitional values of c for which the surface changes from one type of quadric surface to another.

3. Members of the family of surfaces given in spherical coordinates by the equation

$$\rho = 1 + 0.2 \sin m\theta \sin n\phi$$

have been suggested as models for tumors and have been called *bumpy spheres* and *wrinkled spheres*. Use a computer to investigate this family of surfaces, assuming that m and n are positive integers. What roles do the values of m and n play in the shape of the surface?

 Graphing calculator or computer with graphing software required

9 | Review

Concept Check

1. What is the difference between a vector and a scalar?

2. How do you add two vectors geometrically? How do you add them algebraically?

3. If **a** is a vector and c is a scalar, how is c**a** related to **a** geometrically? How do you find c**a** algebraically?

4. How do you find the vector from one point to another?

5. How do you find the dot product **a** · **b** of two vectors if you know their lengths and the angle between them? What if you know their components?

6. How are dot products useful?

7. Write expressions for the scalar and vector projections of **b** onto **a**. Illustrate with diagrams.

8. How do you find the cross product **a** × **b** of two vectors if you know their lengths and the angle between them? What if you know their components?

9. How are cross products useful?

10. (a) How do you find the area of the parallelogram determined by **a** and **b**?
    (b) How do you find the volume of the parallelepiped determined by **a**, **b**, and **c**?

11. How do you find a vector perpendicular to a plane?

12. How do you find the angle between two intersecting planes?

13. Write a vector equation, parametric equations, and symmetric equations for a line.

14. Write a vector equation and a scalar equation for a plane.

15. (a) How do you tell if two vectors are parallel?
    (b) How do you tell if two vectors are perpendicular?
    (c) How do you tell if two planes are parallel?

16. (a) Describe a method for determining whether three points P, Q, and R lie on the same line.
    (b) Describe a method for determining whether four points P, Q, R, and S lie in the same plane.

17. (a) How do you find the distance from a point to a line?
    (b) How do you find the distance from a point to a plane?
    (c) How do you find the distance between two lines?

18. How do you sketch the graph of a function of two variables?

19. Write equations in standard form of the six types of quadric surfaces.

20. (a) Write the equations for converting from cylindrical to rectangular coordinates. In what situation would you use cylindrical coordinates?
    (b) Write the equations for converting from spherical to rectangular coordinates. In what situation would you use spherical coordinates?

True-False Quiz

Determine whether the statement is true or false. If it is true, explain why. If it is false, explain why or give an example that disproves the statement.

1. For any vectors **u** and **v** in V_3, **u** · **v** = **v** · **u**.

2. For any vectors **u** and **v** in V_3, **u** × **v** = **v** × **u**.

3. For any vectors **u** and **v** in V_3, $|\mathbf{u} \times \mathbf{v}| = |\mathbf{v} \times \mathbf{u}|$.

4. For any vectors **u** and **v** in V_3 and any scalar k,
   $k(\mathbf{u} \cdot \mathbf{v}) = (k\mathbf{u}) \cdot \mathbf{v}$.

5. For any vectors **u** and **v** in V_3 and any scalar k,
   $k(\mathbf{u} \times \mathbf{v}) = (k\mathbf{u}) \times \mathbf{v}$.

6. For any vectors **u**, **v**, and **w** in V_3,
   $(\mathbf{u} + \mathbf{v}) \times \mathbf{w} = \mathbf{u} \times \mathbf{w} + \mathbf{v} \times \mathbf{w}$.

7. For any vectors **u**, **v**, and **w** in V_3,
   $\mathbf{u} \cdot (\mathbf{v} \times \mathbf{w}) = (\mathbf{u} \times \mathbf{v}) \cdot \mathbf{w}$.

8. For any vectors **u**, **v**, and **w** in V_3,
   $\mathbf{u} \times (\mathbf{v} \times \mathbf{w}) = (\mathbf{u} \times \mathbf{v}) \times \mathbf{w}$.

9. For any vectors **u** and **v** in V_3, $(\mathbf{u} \times \mathbf{v}) \cdot \mathbf{u} = 0$.

10. For any vectors **u** and **v** in V_3, $(\mathbf{u} + \mathbf{v}) \times \mathbf{v} = \mathbf{u} \times \mathbf{v}$.

11. The cross product of two unit vectors is a unit vector.

12. A linear equation $Ax + By + Cz + D = 0$ represents a line in space.

13. The set of points $\{(x, y, z) \mid x^2 + y^2 = 1\}$ is a circle.

14. If $\mathbf{u} = \langle u_1, u_2 \rangle$ and $\mathbf{v} = \langle v_1, v_2 \rangle$, then $\mathbf{u} \cdot \mathbf{v} = \langle u_1 v_1, u_2 v_2 \rangle$.

15. If **u** · **v** = 0, then **u** = **0** or **v** = **0**.

16. If **u** × **v** = **0**, then **u** = **0** or **v** = **0**.

17. If **u** · **v** = 0 and **u** × **v** = **0**, then **u** = **0** or **v** = **0**.

18. If **u** and **v** are in V_3, then $|\mathbf{u} \cdot \mathbf{v}| \leq |\mathbf{u}||\mathbf{v}|$.

Exercises

1. (a) Find an equation of the sphere that passes through the point $(6, -2, 3)$ and has center $(-1, 2, 1)$.
(b) Find the curve in which this sphere intersects the yz-plane.
(c) Find the center and radius of the sphere

$$x^2 + y^2 + z^2 - 8x + 2y + 6z + 1 = 0$$

2. Copy the vectors in the figure and use them to draw each of the following vectors.
(a) $\mathbf{a} + \mathbf{b}$ (b) $\mathbf{a} - \mathbf{b}$ (c) $-\frac{1}{2}\mathbf{a}$ (d) $2\mathbf{a} + \mathbf{b}$

3. If $\mathbf{u}$ and $\mathbf{v}$ are the vectors shown in the figure, find $\mathbf{u} \cdot \mathbf{v}$ and $|\mathbf{u} \times \mathbf{v}|$. Is $\mathbf{u} \times \mathbf{v}$ directed into the page or out of it?

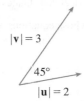

4. Calculate the given quantity if

$$\mathbf{a} = \mathbf{i} + \mathbf{j} - 2\mathbf{k}$$
$$\mathbf{b} = 3\mathbf{i} - 2\mathbf{j} + \mathbf{k}$$
$$\mathbf{c} = \mathbf{j} - 5\mathbf{k}$$

(a) $2\mathbf{a} + 3\mathbf{b}$ (b) $|\mathbf{b}|$
(c) $\mathbf{a} \cdot \mathbf{b}$ (d) $\mathbf{a} \times \mathbf{b}$
(e) $|\mathbf{b} \times \mathbf{c}|$ (f) $\mathbf{a} \cdot (\mathbf{b} \times \mathbf{c})$
(g) $\mathbf{c} \times \mathbf{c}$ (h) $\mathbf{a} \times (\mathbf{b} \times \mathbf{c})$
(i) $\text{comp}_{\mathbf{a}} \mathbf{b}$ (j) $\text{proj}_{\mathbf{a}} \mathbf{b}$
(k) The angle between $\mathbf{a}$ and $\mathbf{b}$ (correct to the nearest degree)

5. Find the values of x such that the vectors $\langle 3, 2, x \rangle$ and $\langle 2x, 4, x \rangle$ are orthogonal.

6. Find two unit vectors that are orthogonal to both $\mathbf{j} + 2\mathbf{k}$ and $\mathbf{i} - 2\mathbf{j} + 3\mathbf{k}$.

7. Suppose that $\mathbf{u} \cdot (\mathbf{v} \times \mathbf{w}) = 2$. Find
(a) $(\mathbf{u} \times \mathbf{v}) \cdot \mathbf{w}$ (b) $\mathbf{u} \cdot (\mathbf{w} \times \mathbf{v})$
(c) $\mathbf{v} \cdot (\mathbf{u} \times \mathbf{w})$ (d) $(\mathbf{u} \times \mathbf{v}) \cdot \mathbf{v}$

8. Show that if $\mathbf{a}$, $\mathbf{b}$, and $\mathbf{c}$ are in V_3, then

$$(\mathbf{a} \times \mathbf{b}) \cdot [(\mathbf{b} \times \mathbf{c}) \times (\mathbf{c} \times \mathbf{a})] = [\mathbf{a} \cdot (\mathbf{b} \times \mathbf{c})]^2$$

9. Find the acute angle between two diagonals of a cube.

10. Given the points $A(1, 0, 1)$, $B(2, 3, 0)$, $C(-1, 1, 4)$, and $D(0, 3, 2)$, find the volume of the parallelepiped with adjacent edges AB, AC, and AD.

11. (a) Find a vector perpendicular to the plane through the points $A(1, 0, 0)$, $B(2, 0, -1)$, and $C(1, 4, 3)$.
(b) Find the area of triangle ABC.

12. A constant force $\mathbf{F} = 3\mathbf{i} + 5\mathbf{j} + 10\mathbf{k}$ moves an object along the line segment from $(1, 0, 2)$ to $(5, 3, 8)$. Find the work done if the distance is measured in meters and the force in newtons.

13. A boat is pulled onto shore using two ropes, as shown in the diagram. If a force of 255 N is needed, find the magnitude of the force in each rope.

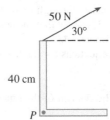

14. Find the magnitude of the torque about P if a 50-N force is applied as shown.

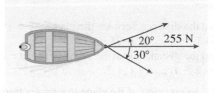

15–17 Find parametric equations for the line.

15. The line through $(4, -1, 2)$ and $(1, 1, 5)$

16. The line through $(1, 0, -1)$ and parallel to the line $\frac{1}{3}(x - 4) = \frac{1}{2}y = z + 2$

17. The line through $(-2, 2, 4)$ and perpendicular to the plane $2x - y + 5z = 12$

18–21 Find an equation of the plane.

18. The plane through $(2, 1, 0)$ and parallel to $x + 4y - 3z = 1$

19. The plane through $(3, -1, 1)$, $(4, 0, 2)$, and $(6, 3, 1)$

20. The plane through $(1, 2, -2)$ that contains the line $x = 2t$, $y = 3 - t$, $z = 1 + 3t$

21. The plane through the line of intersection of the planes $x - z = 1$ and $y + 2z = 3$ and perpendicular to the plane $x + y - 2z = 1$

22. Find the point in which the line with parametric equations $x = 2 - t$, $y = 1 + 3t$, $z = 4t$ intersects the plane $2x - y + z = 2$.

23. Determine whether the lines given by the symmetric equations

$$\frac{x - 1}{2} = \frac{y - 2}{3} = \frac{z - 3}{4}$$

and

$$\frac{x + 1}{6} = \frac{y - 3}{-1} = \frac{z + 5}{2}$$

are parallel, skew, or intersecting.

24. (a) Show that the planes $x + y - z = 1$ and $2x - 3y + 4z = 5$ are neither parallel nor perpendicular.
(b) Find, correct to the nearest degree, the angle between these planes.

25. (a) Find the distance between the planes $3x + y - 4z = 2$ and $3x + y - 4z = 24$.
(b) Find the distance from the origin to the line $x = 1 + t$, $y = 2 - t$, $z = -1 + 2t$.

26. (a) Find an equation of the plane that passes through the points $A(2, 1, 1)$, $B(-1, -1, 10)$, and $C(1, 3, -4)$.
(b) Find symmetric equations for the line through B that is perpendicular to the plane in part (a).
(c) A second plane passes through $(2, 0, 4)$ and has normal vector $\langle 2, -4, -3 \rangle$. Show that the acute angle between the planes is approximately $43°$.
(d) Find parametric equations for the line of intersection of the two planes.

27–28 Find and sketch the domain of the function.

27. $f(x, y) = x \ln(x - y^2)$

28. $f(x, y) = \sqrt{\sin \pi(x^2 + y^2)}$

29–32 Sketch the graph of the function.

29. $f(x, y) = 6 - 2x - 3y$ **30.** $f(x, y) = \cos y$

31. $f(x, y) = 4 - x^2 - 4y^2$

32. $f(x, y) = \sqrt{4 - x^2 - 4y^2}$

33–36 Identify and sketch the graph of the surface. Include several traces in your sketch.

33. $y^2 + z^2 = 1 - 4x^2$ **34.** $y^2 + z^2 = x$

35. $y^2 + z^2 = 1$ **36.** $y^2 + z^2 = 1 + x^2$

37. The cylindrical coordinates of a point are $(2\sqrt{3}, \pi/3, 2)$. Find the rectangular and spherical coordinates of the point.

38. The rectangular coordinates of a point are $(2, 2, -1)$. Find the cylindrical and spherical coordinates of the point.

39. The spherical coordinates of a point are $(8, \pi/4, \pi/6)$. Find the rectangular and cylindrical coordinates of the point.

40. Identify the surfaces whose equations are given.
(a) $\theta = \pi/4$ (b) $\phi = \pi/4$

41–42 Write the equation in cylindrical coordinates and in spherical coordinates.

41. $x^2 + y^2 + z^2 = 4$ **42.** $x^2 + y^2 = 4$

43. The parabola $z = 4y^2$, $x = 0$ is rotated about the z-axis. Write an equation of the resulting surface in cylindrical coordinates.

44. Sketch the solid consisting of all points with spherical coordinates (ρ, θ, ϕ) such that $0 \leq \theta \leq \pi/2$, $0 \leq \phi \leq \pi/6$, and $0 \leq \rho \leq 2 \cos \phi$.

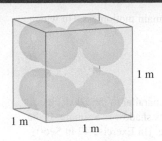

FIGURE FOR PROBLEM 1

Focus on Problem Solving

1. Each edge of a cubical box has length 1 m. The box contains nine spherical balls with the same radius r. The center of one ball is at the center of the cube and it touches the other eight balls. Each of the other eight balls touches three sides of the box. Thus the balls are tightly packed in the box. (See the figure.) Find r. (If you have trouble with this problem, read about the problem-solving strategy entitled *Use Analogy* on page 83.)

2. Let B be a solid box with length L, width W, and height H. Let S be the set of all points that are a distance at most 1 from some point of B. Express the volume of S in terms of L, W, and H.

3. Let L be the line of intersection of the planes $cx + y + z = c$ and $x - cy + cz = -1$, where c is a real number.
   (a) Find symmetric equations for L.
   (b) As the number c varies, the line L sweeps out a surface S. Find an equation for the curve of intersection of S with the horizontal plane $z = t$ (the trace of S in the plane $z = t$).
   (c) Find the volume of the solid bounded by S and the planes $z = 0$ and $z = 1$.

4. A plane is capable of flying at a speed of 180 km/h in still air. The pilot takes off from an airfield and heads due north according to the plane's compass. After 30 minutes of flight time, the pilot notices that, due to the wind, the plane has actually traveled 80 km at an angle $5°$ east of north.
   (a) What is the wind velocity?
   (b) In what direction should the pilot have headed to reach the intended destination?

5. Suppose $\mathbf{v}_1$ and $\mathbf{v}_2$ are vectors with $|\mathbf{v}_1| = 2$, $|\mathbf{v}_2| = 3$, and $\mathbf{v}_1 \cdot \mathbf{v}_2 = 5$. Let $\mathbf{v}_3 = \text{proj}_{\mathbf{v}_1}\mathbf{v}_2$, $\mathbf{v}_4 = \text{proj}_{\mathbf{v}_2}\mathbf{v}_3$, $\mathbf{v}_5 = \text{proj}_{\mathbf{v}_3}\mathbf{v}_4$, and so on. Compute $\sum_{n=1}^{\infty} |\mathbf{v}_n|$.

6. Find an equation of the largest sphere that passes through the point $(-1, 1, 4)$ and is such that each of the points (x, y, z) inside the sphere satisfies the condition

$$x^2 + y^2 + z^2 < 136 + 2(x + 2y + 3z)$$

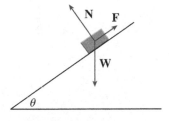

FIGURE FOR PROBLEM 7

7. Suppose a block of mass m is placed on an inclined plane, as shown in the figure. The block's descent down the plane is slowed by friction; if θ is not too large, friction will prevent the block from moving at all. The forces acting on the block are the weight $\mathbf{W}$, where $|\mathbf{W}| = mg$ (g is the acceleration due to gravity); the normal force $\mathbf{N}$ (the normal component of the reactionary force of the plane on the block), where $|\mathbf{N}| = n$; and the force $\mathbf{F}$ due to friction, which acts parallel to the inclined plane, opposing the direction of motion. If the block is at rest and θ is increased, $|\mathbf{F}|$ must also increase until ultimately $|\mathbf{F}|$ reaches its maximum, beyond which the block begins to slide. At this angle θ_s, it has been observed that $|\mathbf{F}|$ is proportional to n. Thus, when $|\mathbf{F}|$ is maximal, we can say that $|\mathbf{F}| = \mu_s n$, where μ_s is called the *coefficient of static friction* and depends on the materials that are in contact.
   (a) Observe that $\mathbf{N} + \mathbf{F} + \mathbf{W} = \mathbf{0}$ and deduce that $\mu_s = \tan(\theta_s)$.
   (b) Suppose that, for $\theta > \theta_s$, an additional outside force $\mathbf{H}$ is applied to the block, horizontally from the left, and let $|\mathbf{H}| = h$. If h is small, the block may still slide down the plane; if h is large enough, the block will move up the plane. Let $h_{\min}$ be the smallest value of h that allows the block to remain motionless (so that $|\mathbf{F}|$ is maximal).
   By choosing the coordinate axes so that $\mathbf{F}$ lies along the x-axis, resolve each force into components parallel and perpendicular to the inclined plane and show that

$$h_{\min} \sin\theta + mg\cos\theta = n \quad \text{and} \quad h_{\min}\cos\theta + \mu_s n = mg\sin\theta$$

   (c) Show that
$$h_{\min} = mg\tan(\theta - \theta_s)$$

   Does this equation seem reasonable? Does it make sense for $\theta = \theta_s$? As $\theta \to 90°$? Explain.

(d) Let $h_{\max}$ be the largest value of h that allows the block to remain motionless. (In which direction is **F** heading?) Show that

$$h_{\max} = mg \tan(\theta + \theta_s)$$

Does this equation seem reasonable? Explain.

8. A solid has the following properties. When illuminated by rays parallel to the z-axis, its shadow is a circular disk. If the rays are parallel to the y-axis, its shadow is a square. If the rays are parallel to the x-axis, its shadow is an isosceles triangle. (In Exercise 42 in Section 9.1 you were asked to describe and sketch an example of such a solid, but there are many such solids.) Assume that the projection onto the xz-plane is a square whose sides have length 1.
(a) What is the volume of the largest such solid?
(b) Is there a smallest volume?

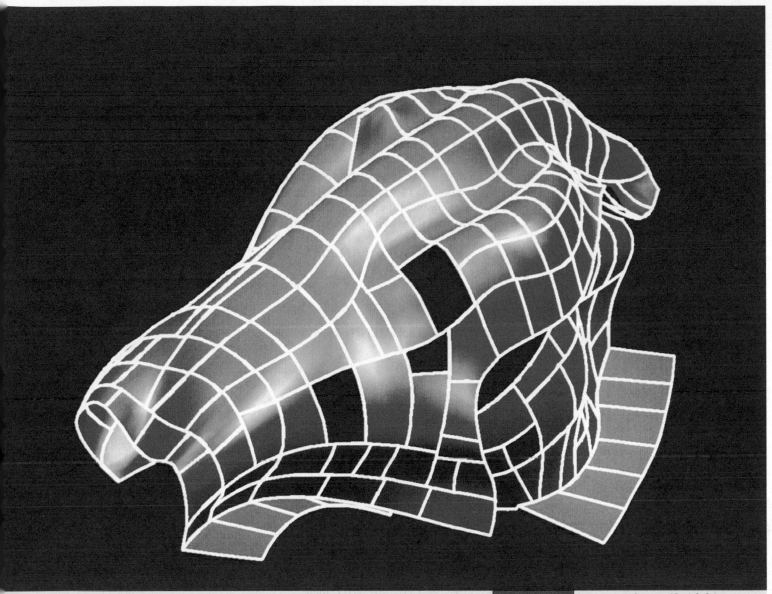

Vector Functions

10

The functions that we have been using so far have been real-valued functions. We now study functions whose values are vectors because such functions are needed to describe curves and surfaces in space. We will also use vector-valued functions to describe the motion of objects through space. In particular, we will use them to derive Kepler's laws of planetary motion.

10.1 Vector Functions and Space Curves

In general, a function is a rule that assigns to each element in the domain an element in the range. A **vector-valued function**, or **vector function**, is simply a function whose domain is a set of real numbers and whose range is a set of vectors. We are most interested in vector functions **r** whose values are three-dimensional vectors. This means that for every number t in the domain of **r** there is a unique vector in V_3 denoted by $\mathbf{r}(t)$. If $f(t)$, $g(t)$, and $h(t)$ are the components of the vector $\mathbf{r}(t)$, then f, g, and h are real-valued functions called the **component functions** of **r** and we can write

$$\mathbf{r}(t) = \langle f(t), g(t), h(t) \rangle = f(t)\,\mathbf{i} + g(t)\,\mathbf{j} + h(t)\,\mathbf{k}$$

We use the letter t to denote the independent variable because it represents time in most applications of vector functions.

EXAMPLE 1 **Domain of a vector function**

If
$$\mathbf{r}(t) = \langle t^3, \ln(3 - t), \sqrt{t} \rangle$$

then the component functions are

$$f(t) = t^3 \qquad g(t) = \ln(3 - t) \qquad h(t) = \sqrt{t}$$

By our usual convention, the domain of **r** consists of all values of t for which the expression for $\mathbf{r}(t)$ is defined. The expressions t^3, $\ln(3 - t)$, and $\sqrt{t}$ are all defined when $3 - t > 0$ and $t \geq 0$. Therefore the domain of **r** is the interval $[0, 3)$. ∎

The **limit** of a vector function **r** is defined by taking the limits of its component functions as follows.

If $\lim_{t \to a} \mathbf{r}(t) = \mathbf{L}$, this definition is equivalent to saying that the length and direction of the vector $\mathbf{r}(t)$ approach the length and direction of the vector **L**.

---

1 If $\mathbf{r}(t) = \langle f(t), g(t), h(t) \rangle$, then

$$\lim_{t \to a} \mathbf{r}(t) = \left\langle \lim_{t \to a} f(t), \lim_{t \to a} g(t), \lim_{t \to a} h(t) \right\rangle$$

provided the limits of the component functions exist.

Limits of vector functions obey the same rules as limits of real-valued functions (see Exercise 45).

EXAMPLE 2 Find $\lim_{t \to 0} \mathbf{r}(t)$, where $\mathbf{r}(t) = (1 + t^3)\,\mathbf{i} + te^{-t}\,\mathbf{j} + \dfrac{\sin t}{t}\,\mathbf{k}$.

SOLUTION According to Definition 1, the limit of **r** is the vector whose components are the limits of the component functions of **r**:

$$\lim_{t \to 0} \mathbf{r}(t) = \left[\lim_{t \to 0} (1 + t^3) \right]\mathbf{i} + \left[\lim_{t \to 0} te^{-t} \right]\mathbf{j} + \left[\lim_{t \to 0} \frac{\sin t}{t} \right]\mathbf{k}$$

$$= \mathbf{i} + \mathbf{k} \qquad \text{(by Equation 3.3.2)} \qquad \blacksquare$$

A vector function $\mathbf{r}$ is **continuous at a** if

$$\lim_{t \to a} \mathbf{r}(t) = \mathbf{r}(a)$$

In view of Definition 1, we see that $\mathbf{r}$ is continuous at a if and only if its component functions f, g, and h are continuous at a.

There is a close connection between continuous vector functions and space curves. Suppose that f, g, and h are continuous real-valued functions on an interval I. Then the set C of all points (x, y, z) in space, where

$$\boxed{2} \qquad x = f(t) \qquad y = g(t) \qquad z = h(t)$$

and t varies throughout the interval I, is called a **space curve**. The equations in (2) are called **parametric equations of C** and t is called a **parameter**. We can think of C as being traced out by a moving particle whose position at time t is $(f(t), g(t), h(t))$. If we now consider the vector function $\mathbf{r}(t) = \langle f(t), g(t), h(t) \rangle$, then $\mathbf{r}(t)$ is the position vector of the point $P(f(t), g(t), h(t))$ on C. Thus any continuous vector function $\mathbf{r}$ defines a space curve C that is traced out by the tip of the moving vector $\mathbf{r}(t)$, as shown in Figure 1.

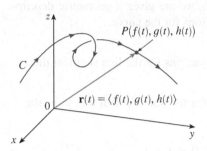

FIGURE 1

C is traced out by the tip of a moving position vector $\mathbf{r}(t)$.

◢ EXAMPLE 3 Describe the curve defined by the vector function

$$\mathbf{r}(t) = \langle 1 + t, 2 + 5t, -1 + 6t \rangle$$

SOLUTION The corresponding parametric equations are

$$x = 1 + t \qquad y = 2 + 5t \qquad z = -1 + 6t$$

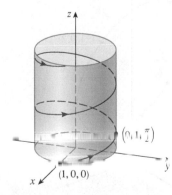

TEC Visual 10.1A shows several curves being traced out by position vectors, including those in Figures 1 and 2.

which we recognize from Equations 9.5.2 as parametric equations of a line passing through the point $(1, 2, -1)$ and parallel to the vector $\langle 1, 5, 6 \rangle$. Alternatively, we could observe that the function can be written as $\mathbf{r} = \mathbf{r}_0 + t\mathbf{v}$, where $\mathbf{r}_0 = \langle 1, 2, -1 \rangle$ and $\mathbf{v} = \langle 1, 5, 6 \rangle$, and this is the vector equation of a line as given by Equation 9.5.1. ▬

Plane curves can also be represented in vector notation. For instance, the curve given by the parametric equations $x = t^2 - 2t$ and $y = t + 1$ (see Example 1 in Section 1.7) could also be described by the vector equation

$$\mathbf{r}(t) = \langle t^2 - 2t, t + 1 \rangle = (t^2 - 2t)\,\mathbf{i} + (t + 1)\,\mathbf{j}$$

where $\mathbf{i} = \langle 1, 0 \rangle$ and $\mathbf{j} = \langle 0, 1 \rangle$.

◢ EXAMPLE 4 Sketching a helix   Sketch the curve whose vector equation is

$$\mathbf{r}(t) = \cos t\,\mathbf{i} + \sin t\,\mathbf{j} + t\,\mathbf{k}$$

SOLUTION The parametric equations for this curve are

$$x = \cos t \qquad y = \sin t \qquad z = t$$

FIGURE 2

Since $x^2 + y^2 = \cos^2 t + \sin^2 t = 1$, the curve must lie on the circular cylinder $x^2 + y^2 = 1$. The point (x, y, z) lies directly above the point $(x, y, 0)$, which moves counterclockwise around the circle $x^2 + y^2 = 1$ in the xy-plane. (The projection of the curve onto the xy-plane has vector equation $\mathbf{r}(t) = \langle \cos t, \sin t, 0 \rangle$. See Example 2 in Section 1.7.) Since $z = t$, the curve spirals upward around the cylinder as t increases. The curve, shown in Figure 2, is called a **helix**. ▬

FIGURE 3
A double helix

Figure 4 shows the line segment PQ in Example 5.

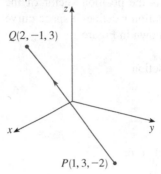

FIGURE 4

The corkscrew shape of the helix in Example 4 is familiar from its occurrence in coiled springs. It also occurs in the model of DNA (deoxyribonucleic acid, the genetic material of living cells). In 1953 James Watson and Francis Crick showed that the structure of the DNA molecule is that of two linked, parallel helixes that are intertwined as in Figure 3.

In Examples 3 and 4 we were given vector equations of curves and asked for a geometric description or sketch. In the next two examples we are given a geometric description of a curve and are asked to find parametric equations for the curve.

EXAMPLE 5   Find a vector equation and parametric equations for the line segment that joins the point $P(1, 3, -2)$ to the point $Q(2, -1, 3)$.

SOLUTION   In Section 9.5 we found a vector equation for the line segment that joins the tip of the vector $\mathbf{r}_0$ to the tip of the vector $\mathbf{r}_1$:

$$\mathbf{r}(t) = (1 - t)\mathbf{r}_0 + t\mathbf{r}_1 \qquad 0 \leq t \leq 1$$

(See Equation 9.5.4.) Here we take $\mathbf{r}_0 = \langle 1, 3, -2 \rangle$ and $\mathbf{r}_1 = \langle 2, -1, 3 \rangle$ to obtain a vector equation of the line segment from P to Q:

$$\mathbf{r}(t) = (1 - t)\langle 1, 3, -2 \rangle + t\langle 2, -1, 3 \rangle \qquad 0 \leq t \leq 1$$

or $$\mathbf{r}(t) = \langle 1 + t, 3 - 4t, -2 + 5t \rangle \qquad 0 \leq t \leq 1$$

The corresponding parametric equations are

$$x = 1 + t \qquad y = 3 - 4t \qquad z = -2 + 5t \qquad 0 \leq t \leq 1 \qquad \blacksquare$$

V **EXAMPLE 6**   **The intersection of two surfaces is a space curve**   Find a vector function that represents the curve of intersection of the cylinder $x^2 + y^2 = 1$ and the plane $y + z = 2$.

SOLUTION   Figure 5 shows how the plane and the cylinder intersect, and Figure 6 shows the curve of intersection C, which is an ellipse.

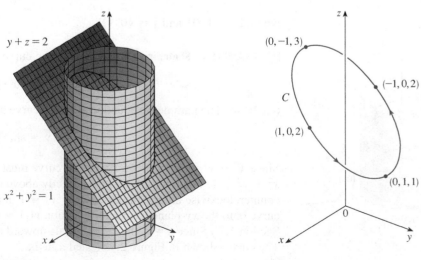

FIGURE 5   **FIGURE 6**

The projection of C onto the xy-plane is the circle $x^2 + y^2 = 1$, $z = 0$. So we know from Example 2 in Section 1.7 that we can write

$$x = \cos t \qquad y = \sin t \qquad 0 \le t \le 2\pi$$

From the equation of the plane, we have

$$z = 2 - y = 2 - \sin t$$

So we can write parametric equations for C as

$$x = \cos t \qquad y = \sin t \qquad z = 2 - \sin t \qquad 0 \le t \le 2\pi$$

The corresponding vector equation is

$$\mathbf{r}(t) = \cos t\,\mathbf{i} + \sin t\,\mathbf{j} + (2 - \sin t)\,\mathbf{k} \qquad 0 \le t \le 2\pi$$

This equation is called a *parametrization* of the curve C. The arrows in Figure 6 indicate the direction in which C is traced as the parameter t increases.

Using Computers to Draw Space Curves

Space curves are inherently more difficult to draw by hand than plane curves; for an accurate representation we need to use technology. For instance, Figure 7 shows a computer-generated graph of the curve with parametric equations

$$x = (4 + \sin 20t)\cos t \qquad y = (4 + \sin 20t)\sin t \qquad z = \cos 20t$$

It's called a **toroidal spiral** because it lies on a torus. Another interesting curve, the **trefoil knot**, with equations

$$x = (2 + \cos 1.5t)\cos t \qquad y = (2 + \cos 1.5t)\sin t \qquad z = \sin 1.5t$$

is graphed in Figure 8. It wouldn't be easy to plot either of these curves by hand.

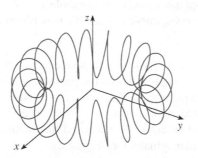

FIGURE 7 A toroidal spiral

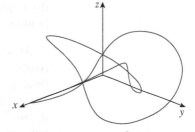

FIGURE 8 A trefoil knot

Even when a computer is used to draw a space curve, optical illusions make it difficult to get a good impression of what the curve really looks like. (This is especially true in Figure 8. See Exercise 46.) The next example shows how to cope with this problem.

EXAMPLE 7 Use a computer to draw the curve with vector equation $\mathbf{r}(t) = \langle t, t^2, t^3 \rangle$. This curve is called a **twisted cubic**.

SOLUTION We start by using the computer to plot the curve with parametric equations $x = t$, $y = t^2$, $z = t^3$ for $-2 \le t \le 2$. The result is shown in Figure 9(a), but it's hard to see the true nature of the curve from that graph alone. Most three-dimensional computer graphing programs allow the user to enclose a curve or surface in a box instead of displaying the coordinate axes. When we look at the same curve in a box in Figure 9(b), we have a much clearer picture of the curve. We can see that it climbs from a lower corner of the box to the upper corner nearest us, and it twists as it climbs.

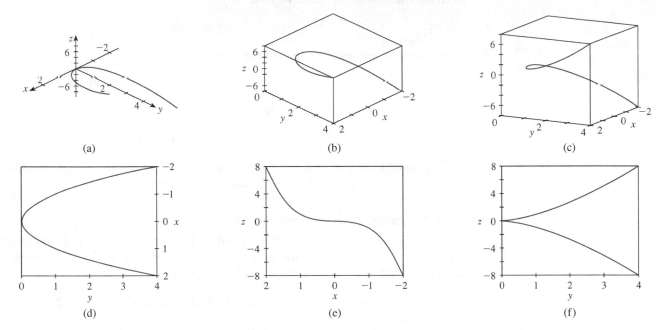

(a)

(b)

(c)

(d)

(e)

(f)

FIGURE 9 Views of the twisted cubic

TEC In Visual 10.1B you can rotate the box in Figure 9 to see the curve from any viewpoint.

We get an even better idea of the curve when we view it from different vantage points. Part (c) shows the result of rotating the box to give another viewpoint. Parts (d), (e), and (f) show the views we get when we look directly at a face of the box. In particular, part (d) shows the view from directly above the box. It is the projection of the curve on the xy-plane, namely, the parabola $y = x^2$. Part (e) shows the projection on the xz-plane, the cubic curve $z = x^3$. It's now obvious why the given curve is called a twisted cubic.

Another method of visualizing a space curve is to draw it on a surface. For instance, the twisted cubic in Example 7 lies on the parabolic cylinder $y = x^2$. (Eliminate the parameter from the first two parametric equations, $x = t$ and $y = t^2$.) Figure 10 shows both the cylinder and the twisted cubic, and we see that the curve moves upward from the origin along the surface of the cylinder. We also used this method in Example 4 to visualize the helix lying on the circular cylinder (see Figure 2).

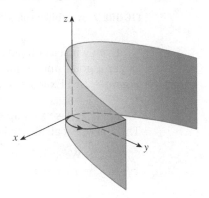

FIGURE 10

A third method for visualizing the twisted cubic is to realize that it also lies on the cylinder $z = x^3$. So it can be viewed as the curve of intersection of the cylinders $y = x^2$ and $z = x^3$. (See Figure 11.)

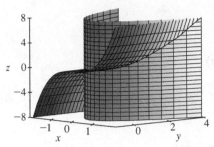

FIGURE 11

Some computer algebra systems provide us with a clearer picture of a space curve by enclosing it in a tube. Such a plot enables us to see whether one part of a curve passes in front of or behind another part of the curve. For example, Figure 13 shows the curve of Figure 12(b) as rendered by the `tubeplot` command in Maple.

We have seen that an interesting space curve, the helix, occurs in the model of DNA. Another notable example of a space curve in science is the trajectory of a positively charged particle in orthogonally oriented electric and magnetic fields $\mathbf{E}$ and $\mathbf{B}$. Depending on the initial velocity given the particle at the origin, the path of the particle is either a space curve whose projection on the horizontal plane is the cycloid we studied in Section 1.7 [Figure 12(a)] or a curve whose projection is the trochoid investigated in Exercise 38 in Section 1.7 [Figure 12(b)].

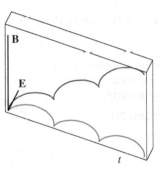

(a) $\mathbf{r}(t) = \langle t - \sin t, 1 - \cos t, t \rangle$

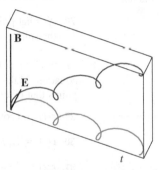

(b) $\mathbf{r}(t) = \langle t - \frac{3}{2} \sin t, 1 - \frac{3}{2} \cos t, t \rangle$

FIGURE 12

Motion of a charged particle in orthogonally oriented electric and magnetic fields

FIGURE 13

For further details concerning the physics involved and animations of the trajectories of the particles, see the following web sites:

- www.phy.ntnu.edu.tw/java/emField/emField.html
- www.physics.ucla.edu/plasma-exp/Beam/

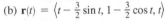

10.1 Exercises

1–2 Find the domain of the vector function.

1. $\mathbf{r}(t) = \langle \sqrt{4 - t^2}, e^{-3t}, \ln(t + 1) \rangle$

2. $\mathbf{r}(t) = \dfrac{t - 2}{t + 2}\,\mathbf{i} + \sin t\,\mathbf{j} + \ln(9 - t^2)\,\mathbf{k}$

3–4 Find the limit.

3. $\displaystyle \lim_{t \to \infty} \left\langle \frac{1 + t^2}{1 - t^2}, \tan^{-1} t, \frac{1 - e^{-2t}}{t} \right\rangle$

4. $\displaystyle \lim_{t \to 0} \left\langle \frac{e^t - 1}{t}, \frac{\sqrt{1 + t} - 1}{t}, \frac{3}{1 + t} \right\rangle$

Graphing calculator or computer with graphing software required   **1.** Homework Hints available in TEC

5–12 Sketch the curve with the given vector equation. Indicate with an arrow the direction in which t increases.

5. $\mathbf{r}(t) = \langle \sin t, t \rangle$

6. $\mathbf{r}(t) = \langle t^3, t^2 \rangle$

7. $\mathbf{r}(t) = \langle t, 2 - t, 2t \rangle$

8. $\mathbf{r}(t) = \langle \sin \pi t, t, \cos \pi t \rangle$

9. $\mathbf{r}(t) = \langle 1, \cos t, 2 \sin t \rangle$

10. $\mathbf{r}(t) = t^2 \mathbf{i} + t \mathbf{j} + 2 \mathbf{k}$

11. $\mathbf{r}(t) = t^2 \mathbf{i} + t^4 \mathbf{j} + t^6 \mathbf{k}$

12. $\mathbf{r}(t) = \cos t \,\mathbf{i} - \cos t \,\mathbf{j} + \sin t \,\mathbf{k}$

13–14 Draw the projections of the curve on the three coordinate planes. Use these projections to help sketch the curve.

13. $\mathbf{r}(t) = \langle t, \sin t, 2 \cos t \rangle$

14. $\mathbf{r}(t) = \langle t, t, t^2 \rangle$

15–18 Find a vector equation and parametric equations for the line segment that joins P to Q.

15. $P(0, 0, 0)$, $Q(1, 2, 3)$

16. $P(1, 0, 1)$, $Q(2, 3, 1)$

17. $P(1, -1, 2)$, $Q(4, 1, 7)$

18. $P(-2, 4, 0)$, $Q(6, -1, 2)$

19–24 Match the parametric equations with the graphs (labeled I–VI). Give reasons for your choices.

I
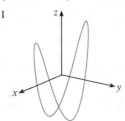

II
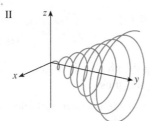

III
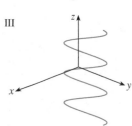

IV
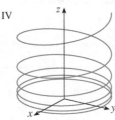

V

VI

19. $x = t \cos t$, $y = t$, $z = t \sin t$, $t \geq 0$

20. $x = \cos t$, $y = \sin t$, $z = 1/(1 + t^2)$

21. $x = t$, $y = 1/(1 + t^2)$, $z = t^2$

22. $x = \cos t$, $y = \sin t$, $z = \cos 2t$

23. $x = \cos 8t$, $y = \sin 8t$, $z = e^{0.8t}$, $t \geq 0$

24. $x = \cos^2 t$, $y = \sin^2 t$, $z = t$

---

25. Show that the curve with parametric equations $x = t \cos t$, $y = t \sin t$, $z = t$ lies on the cone $z^2 = x^2 + y^2$, and use this fact to help sketch the curve.

26. Show that the curve with parametric equations $x = \sin t$, $y = \cos t$, $z = \sin^2 t$ is the curve of intersection of the surfaces $z = x^2$ and $x^2 + y^2 = 1$. Use this fact to help sketch the curve.

27. At what points does the curve $\mathbf{r}(t) = t \mathbf{i} + (2t - t^2) \mathbf{k}$ intersect the paraboloid $z = x^2 + y^2$?

28. At what points does the helix $\mathbf{r}(t) = \langle \sin t, \cos t, t \rangle$ intersect the sphere $x^2 + y^2 + z^2 = 5$?

29–31 Use a computer to graph the curve with the given vector equation. Make sure you choose a parameter domain and viewpoints that reveal the true nature of the curve.

29. $\mathbf{r}(t) = \langle \cos t \sin 2t, \sin t \sin 2t, \cos 2t \rangle$

30. $\mathbf{r}(t) = \langle t, e^t, \cos t \rangle$

31. $\mathbf{r}(t) = \langle \cos 2t, \cos 3t, \cos 4t \rangle$

---

32. Graph the curve with parametric equations $x = \sin t$, $y = \sin 2t$, $z = \cos 4t$. Explain its shape by graphing its projections onto the three coordinate planes.

33. Graph the curve with parametric equations

$$x = (1 + \cos 16t) \cos t$$
$$y = (1 + \cos 16t) \sin t$$
$$z = 1 + \cos 16t$$

Explain the appearance of the graph by showing that it lies on a cone.

34. Graph the curve with parametric equations

$$x = \sqrt{1 - 0.25 \cos^2 10t} \, \cos t$$
$$y = \sqrt{1 - 0.25 \cos^2 10t} \, \sin t$$
$$z = 0.5 \cos 10t$$

Explain the appearance of the graph by showing that it lies on a sphere.

35. Show that the curve with parametric equations $x = t^2$, $y = 1 - 3t$, $z = 1 + t^3$ passes through the points $(1, 4, 0)$ and $(9, -8, 28)$ but not through the point $(4, 7, -6)$.

36–40 Find a vector function that represents the curve of intersection of the two surfaces.

36. The cylinder $x^2 + y^2 = 4$ and the surface $z = xy$

37. The cone $z = \sqrt{x^2 + y^2}$ and the plane $z = 1 + y$

38. The paraboloid $z = 4x^2 + y^2$ and the parabolic cylinder $y = x^2$

39. The hyperboloid $z = x^2 - y^2$ and the cylinder $x^2 + y^2 = 1$

40. The semiellipsoid $x^2 + y^2 + 4z^2 = 4$, $y \geq 0$, and the cylinder $x^2 + z^2 = 1$

41. Try to sketch by hand the curve of intersection of the circular cylinder $x^2 + y^2 = 4$ and the parabolic cylinder $z = x^2$. Then find parametric equations for this curve and use these equations and a computer to graph the curve.

42. Try to sketch by hand the curve of intersection of the parabolic cylinder $y = x^2$ and the top half of the ellipsoid $x^2 + 4y^2 + 4z^2 = 16$. Then find parametric equations for this curve and use these equations and a computer to graph the curve.

43. If two objects travel through space along two different curves, it's often important to know whether they will collide. (Will a missile hit its moving target? Will two aircraft collide?) The curves might intersect, but we need to know whether the objects are in the same position *at the same time*. Suppose the trajectories of two particles are given by the vector functions

$$\mathbf{r}_1(t) = \langle t^2, 7t - 12, t^2 \rangle \qquad \mathbf{r}_2(t) = \langle 4t - 3, t^2, 5t - 6 \rangle$$

for $t \geq 0$. Do the particles collide?

44. Two particles travel along the space curves

$$\mathbf{r}_1(t) = \langle t, t^2, t^3 \rangle \qquad \mathbf{r}_2(t) = \langle 1 + 2t, 1 + 6t, 1 + 14t \rangle$$

Do the particles collide? Do their paths intersect?

45. Suppose $\mathbf{u}$ and $\mathbf{v}$ are vector functions that possess limits as $t \to a$ and let c be a constant. Prove the following properties of limits.

(a) $\lim\limits_{t \to a} [\mathbf{u}(t) + \mathbf{v}(t)] = \lim\limits_{t \to a} \mathbf{u}(t) + \lim\limits_{t \to a} \mathbf{v}(t)$

(b) $\lim\limits_{t \to a} c\mathbf{u}(t) = c \lim\limits_{t \to a} \mathbf{u}(t)$

(c) $\lim\limits_{t \to a} [\mathbf{u}(t) \cdot \mathbf{v}(t)] = \lim\limits_{t \to a} \mathbf{u}(t) \cdot \lim\limits_{t \to a} \mathbf{v}(t)$

(d) $\lim\limits_{t \to a} [\mathbf{u}(t) \times \mathbf{v}(t)] = \lim\limits_{t \to a} \mathbf{u}(t) \times \lim\limits_{t \to a} \mathbf{v}(t)$

46. The view of the trefoil knot shown in Figure 8 is accurate, but it doesn't reveal the whole story. Use the parametric equations

$$x = (2 + \cos 1.5t) \cos t$$
$$y = (2 + \cos 1.5t) \sin t$$
$$z = \sin 1.5t$$

to sketch the curve by hand as viewed from above, with gaps indicating where the curve passes over itself. Start by showing that the projection of the curve onto the xy-plane has polar coordinates $r = 2 + \cos 1.5t$ and $\theta = t$, so r varies between 1 and 3. Then show that z has maximum and minimum values when the projection is halfway between $r = 1$ and $r = 3$.

When you have finished your sketch, use a computer to draw the curve with viewpoint directly above and compare with your sketch. Then use the computer to draw the curve from several other viewpoints. You can get a better impression of the curve if you plot a tube with radius 0.2 around the curve. (Use the `tubeplot` command in Maple or the `tubecurve` or `Tube` command in Mathematica.)

10.2 Derivatives and Integrals of Vector Functions

Later in this chapter we are going to use vector functions to describe the motion of planets and other objects through space. Here we prepare the way by developing the calculus of vector functions.

Derivatives

The **derivative** $\mathbf{r}'$ of a vector function $\mathbf{r}$ is defined in much the same way as for real-valued functions:

$$\boxed{1} \qquad \frac{d\mathbf{r}}{dt} = \mathbf{r}'(t) = \lim\limits_{h \to 0} \frac{\mathbf{r}(t + h) - \mathbf{r}(t)}{h}$$

if this limit exists. The geometric significance of this definition is shown in Figure 1. If the points P and Q have position vectors $\mathbf{r}(t)$ and $\mathbf{r}(t + h)$, then $\overrightarrow{PQ}$ represents the vector $\mathbf{r}(t + h) - \mathbf{r}(t)$, which can therefore be regarded as a secant vector. If $h > 0$, the scalar multiple $(1/h)(\mathbf{r}(t + h) - \mathbf{r}(t))$ has the same direction as $\mathbf{r}(t + h) - \mathbf{r}(t)$. As $h \to 0$, it appears that this vector approaches a vector that lies on the tangent line. For this reason, the vector $\mathbf{r}'(t)$ is called the **tangent vector** to the curve defined by $\mathbf{r}$ at the point P, provided that $\mathbf{r}'(t)$ exists and $\mathbf{r}'(t) \neq \mathbf{0}$. The **tangent line** to C at P is defined to be the line through P parallel to the tangent vector $\mathbf{r}'(t)$. We will also have occasion to consider the **unit tangent vector**, which is

$$\mathbf{T}(t) = \frac{\mathbf{r}'(t)}{|\mathbf{r}'(t)|}$$

TEC Visual 10.2 shows an animation of Figure 1.

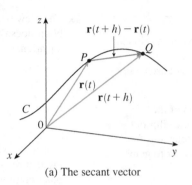

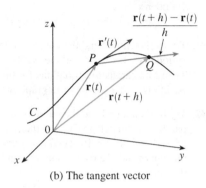

FIGURE 1   (a) The secant vector   (b) The tangent vector

The following theorem gives us a convenient method for computing the derivative of a vector function $\mathbf{r}$: just differentiate each component of $\mathbf{r}$.

---

2   Theorem   If $\mathbf{r}(t) = \langle f(t), g(t), h(t) \rangle = f(t)\,\mathbf{i} + g(t)\,\mathbf{j} + h(t)\,\mathbf{k}$, where f, g, and h are differentiable functions, then

$$\mathbf{r}'(t) = \langle f'(t), g'(t), h'(t) \rangle = f'(t)\,\mathbf{i} + g'(t)\,\mathbf{j} + h'(t)\,\mathbf{k}$$

PROOF

$$\mathbf{r}'(t) = \lim_{\Delta t \to 0} \frac{1}{\Delta t}\,[\mathbf{r}(t + \Delta t) - \mathbf{r}(t)]$$

$$= \lim_{\Delta t \to 0} \frac{1}{\Delta t}\,[\langle f(t + \Delta t), g(t + \Delta t), h(t + \Delta t) \rangle - \langle f(t), g(t), h(t) \rangle]$$

$$= \lim_{\Delta t \to 0} \left\langle \frac{f(t + \Delta t) - f(t)}{\Delta t}, \frac{g(t + \Delta t) - g(t)}{\Delta t}, \frac{h(t + \Delta t) - h(t)}{\Delta t} \right\rangle$$

$$= \left\langle \lim_{\Delta t \to 0} \frac{f(t + \Delta t) - f(t)}{\Delta t}, \lim_{\Delta t \to 0} \frac{g(t + \Delta t) - g(t)}{\Delta t}, \lim_{\Delta t \to 0} \frac{h(t + \Delta t) - h(t)}{\Delta t} \right\rangle$$

$$= \langle f'(t), g'(t), h'(t) \rangle$$

⚡ EXAMPLE 1 **Finding a unit tangent vector**
(a) Find the derivative of $\mathbf{r}(t) = (1 + t^3)\mathbf{i} + te^{-t}\mathbf{j} + \sin 2t\,\mathbf{k}$.
(b) Find the unit tangent vector at the point where $t = 0$.

SOLUTION
(a) According to Theorem 2, we differentiate each component of $\mathbf{r}$:

$$\mathbf{r}'(t) = 3t^2\mathbf{i} + (1 - t)e^{-t}\mathbf{j} + 2\cos 2t\,\mathbf{k}$$

(b) Since $\mathbf{r}(0) = \mathbf{i}$ and $\mathbf{r}'(0) = \mathbf{j} + 2\mathbf{k}$, the unit tangent vector at the point $(1, 0, 0)$ is

$$\mathbf{T}(0) = \frac{\mathbf{r}'(0)}{|\mathbf{r}'(0)|} = \frac{\mathbf{j} + 2\mathbf{k}}{\sqrt{1 + 4}} = \frac{1}{\sqrt{5}}\mathbf{j} + \frac{2}{\sqrt{5}}\mathbf{k}$$

EXAMPLE 2 For the curve $\mathbf{r}(t) = \sqrt{t}\,\mathbf{i} + (2 - t)\mathbf{j}$, find $\mathbf{r}'(t)$ and sketch the position vector $\mathbf{r}(1)$ and the tangent vector $\mathbf{r}'(1)$.

SOLUTION We have

$$\mathbf{r}'(t) = \frac{1}{2\sqrt{t}}\mathbf{i} - \mathbf{j} \qquad \text{and} \qquad \mathbf{r}'(1) = \frac{1}{2}\mathbf{i} - \mathbf{j}$$

The curve is a plane curve and elimination of the parameter from the equations $x = \sqrt{t}$, $y = 2 - t$ gives $y = 2 - x^2$, $x \geq 0$. In Figure 2 we draw the position vector $\mathbf{r}(1) = \mathbf{i} + \mathbf{j}$ starting at the origin and the tangent vector $\mathbf{r}'(1)$ starting at the corresponding point $(1, 1)$.

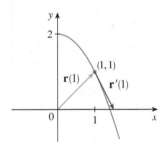

FIGURE 2

Notice from Figure 2 that the tangent vector points in the direction of increasing t. (See Exercise 54.)

⚡ EXAMPLE 3 **Finding a tangent line to a space curve** Find parametric equations for the tangent line to the helix with parametric equations

$$x = 2\cos t \qquad y = \sin t \qquad z = t$$

at the point $(0, 1, \pi/2)$.

SOLUTION The vector equation of the helix is $\mathbf{r}(t) = \langle 2\cos t, \sin t, t\rangle$, so

$$\mathbf{r}'(t) = \langle -2\sin t, \cos t, 1\rangle$$

The parameter value corresponding to the point $(0, 1, \pi/2)$ is $t = \pi/2$, so the tangent vector there is $\mathbf{r}'(\pi/2) = \langle -2, 0, 1\rangle$. The tangent line is the line through $(0, 1, \pi/2)$ parallel to the vector $\langle -2, 0, 1\rangle$, so by Equations 9.5.2 its parametric equations are

$$x = -2t \qquad y = 1 \qquad z = \frac{\pi}{2} + t$$

The helix and the tangent line in Example 3 are shown in Figure 3.

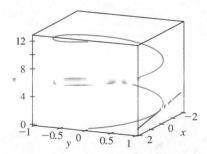

FIGURE 3

In Section 10.4 we will see how $\mathbf{r}'(t)$ and $\mathbf{r}''(t)$ can be interpreted as the velocity and acceleration vectors of a particle moving through space with position vector $\mathbf{r}(t)$ at time t.

Just as for real-valued functions, the **second derivative** of a vector function $\mathbf{r}$ is the derivative of $\mathbf{r}'$, that is, $\mathbf{r}'' = (\mathbf{r}')'$. For instance, the second derivative of the function in Example 3 is

$$\mathbf{r}''(t) = \langle -2 \cos t, -\sin t, 0 \rangle$$

Differentiation Rules

The next theorem shows that the differentiation formulas for real-valued functions have their counterparts for vector-valued functions.

---

3 **Theorem** Suppose $\mathbf{u}$ and $\mathbf{v}$ are differentiable vector functions, c is a scalar, and f is a real-valued function. Then

1. $\dfrac{d}{dt}[\mathbf{u}(t) + \mathbf{v}(t)] = \mathbf{u}'(t) + \mathbf{v}'(t)$

2. $\dfrac{d}{dt}[c\mathbf{u}(t)] = c\mathbf{u}'(t)$

3. $\dfrac{d}{dt}[f(t)\mathbf{u}(t)] = f'(t)\mathbf{u}(t) + f(t)\mathbf{u}'(t)$

4. $\dfrac{d}{dt}[\mathbf{u}(t) \cdot \mathbf{v}(t)] = \mathbf{u}'(t) \cdot \mathbf{v}(t) + \mathbf{u}(t) \cdot \mathbf{v}'(t)$

5. $\dfrac{d}{dt}[\mathbf{u}(t) \times \mathbf{v}(t)] = \mathbf{u}'(t) \times \mathbf{v}(t) + \mathbf{u}(t) \times \mathbf{v}'(t)$

6. $\dfrac{d}{dt}[\mathbf{u}(f(t))] = f'(t)\mathbf{u}'(f(t))$ (Chain Rule)

This theorem can be proved either directly from Definition 1 or by using Theorem 2 and the corresponding differentiation formulas for real-valued functions. The proof of Formula 4 follows; the remaining proofs are left as exercises.

PROOF OF FORMULA 4 Let

$$\mathbf{u}(t) = \langle f_1(t), f_2(t), f_3(t) \rangle \qquad \mathbf{v}(t) = \langle g_1(t), g_2(t), g_3(t) \rangle$$

Then

$$\mathbf{u}(t) \cdot \mathbf{v}(t) = f_1(t)g_1(t) + f_2(t)g_2(t) + f_3(t)g_3(t) = \sum_{i=1}^{3} f_i(t)g_i(t)$$

so the ordinary Product Rule gives

$$\frac{d}{dt}[\mathbf{u}(t) \cdot \mathbf{v}(t)] = \frac{d}{dt} \sum_{i=1}^{3} f_i(t)g_i(t) = \sum_{i=1}^{3} \frac{d}{dt}[f_i(t)g_i(t)]$$

$$= \sum_{i=1}^{3} [f_i'(t)g_i(t) + f_i(t)g_i'(t)]$$

$$= \sum_{i=1}^{3} f_i'(t)g_i(t) + \sum_{i=1}^{3} f_i(t)g_i'(t)$$

$$= \mathbf{u}'(t) \cdot \mathbf{v}(t) + \mathbf{u}(t) \cdot \mathbf{v}'(t)$$

EXAMPLE 4 **The position and tangent vectors are orthogonal if $\mathbf{r}(t)$ has constant length**
Show that if $|\mathbf{r}(t)| = c$ (a constant), then $\mathbf{r}'(t)$ is orthogonal to $\mathbf{r}(t)$ for all t.

SOLUTION Since

$$\mathbf{r}(t) \cdot \mathbf{r}(t) = |\mathbf{r}(t)|^2 = c^2$$

and c^2 is a constant, Formula 4 of Theorem 3 gives

$$0 = \frac{d}{dt}[\mathbf{r}(t) \cdot \mathbf{r}(t)] = \mathbf{r}'(t) \cdot \mathbf{r}(t) + \mathbf{r}(t) \cdot \mathbf{r}'(t) = 2\mathbf{r}'(t) \cdot \mathbf{r}(t)$$

Thus $\mathbf{r}'(t) \cdot \mathbf{r}(t) = 0$, which says that $\mathbf{r}'(t)$ is orthogonal to $\mathbf{r}(t)$.

Geometrically, this result says that if a curve lies on a sphere with center the origin, then the tangent vector $\mathbf{r}'(t)$ is always perpendicular to the position vector $\mathbf{r}(t)$. ▬

Integrals

The **definite integral** of a continuous vector function $\mathbf{r}(t)$ can be defined in much the same way as for real-valued functions except that the integral is a vector. But then we can express the integral of $\mathbf{r}$ in terms of the integrals of its component functions f, g, and h as follows. (We use the notation of Chapter 5.)

$$\int_a^b \mathbf{r}(t)\, dt = \lim_{n \to \infty} \sum_{i=1}^{n} \mathbf{r}(t_i^*)\, \Delta t$$

$$= \lim_{n \to \infty} \left[\left(\sum_{i=1}^{n} f(t_i^*)\, \Delta t \right) \mathbf{i} + \left(\sum_{i=1}^{n} g(t_i^*)\, \Delta t \right) \mathbf{j} + \left(\sum_{i=1}^{n} h(t_i^*)\, \Delta t \right) \mathbf{k} \right]$$

and so

$$\int_a^b \mathbf{r}(t)\, dt = \left(\int_a^b f(t)\, dt \right) \mathbf{i} + \left(\int_a^b g(t)\, dt \right) \mathbf{j} + \left(\int_a^b h(t)\, dt \right) \mathbf{k}$$

This means that we can evaluate an integral of a vector function by integrating each component function.

We can extend the Fundamental Theorem of Calculus to continuous vector functions as follows:

$$\int_a^b \mathbf{r}(t)\, dt = \mathbf{R}(t)\big]_a^b = \mathbf{R}(b) - \mathbf{R}(a)$$

where $\mathbf{R}$ is an antiderivative of $\mathbf{r}$, that is, $\mathbf{R}'(t) = \mathbf{r}(t)$. We use the notation $\int \mathbf{r}(t)\, dt$ for indefinite integrals (antiderivatives).

EXAMPLE 5 **Integral of a vector function** If $\mathbf{r}(t) = 2\cos t\, \mathbf{i} + \sin t\, \mathbf{j} + 2t\, \mathbf{k}$, then

$$\int \mathbf{r}(t)\, dt = \left(\int 2\cos t\, dt \right) \mathbf{i} + \left(\int \sin t\, dt \right) \mathbf{j} + \left(\int 2t\, dt \right) \mathbf{k}$$

$$= 2\sin t\, \mathbf{i} - \cos t\, \mathbf{j} + t^2\, \mathbf{k} + \mathbf{C}$$

where $\mathbf{C}$ is a vector constant of integration, and

$$\int_0^{\pi/2} \mathbf{r}(t)\, dt = \left[2\sin t\, \mathbf{i} - \cos t\, \mathbf{j} + t^2\, \mathbf{k} \right]_0^{\pi/2} = 2\mathbf{i} + \mathbf{j} + \frac{\pi^2}{4}\, \mathbf{k}$$ ▬

10.2 Exercises

1. The figure shows a curve C given by a vector function $\mathbf{r}(t)$.
   (a) Draw the vectors $\mathbf{r}(4.5) - \mathbf{r}(4)$ and $\mathbf{r}(4.2) - \mathbf{r}(4)$.
   (b) Draw the vectors

   $$\frac{\mathbf{r}(4.5) - \mathbf{r}(4)}{0.5} \quad \text{and} \quad \frac{\mathbf{r}(4.2) - \mathbf{r}(4)}{0.2}$$

   (c) Write expressions for $\mathbf{r}'(4)$ and the unit tangent vector $\mathbf{T}(4)$.
   (d) Draw the vector $\mathbf{T}(4)$.

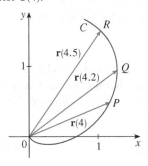

2. (a) Make a large sketch of the curve described by the vector function $\mathbf{r}(t) = \langle t^2, t \rangle$, $0 \leq t \leq 2$, and draw the vectors $\mathbf{r}(1)$, $\mathbf{r}(1.1)$, and $\mathbf{r}(1.1) - \mathbf{r}(1)$.
   (b) Draw the vector $\mathbf{r}'(1)$ starting at $(1, 1)$, and compare it with the vector

   $$\frac{\mathbf{r}(1.1) - \mathbf{r}(1)}{0.1}$$

   Explain why these vectors are so close to each other in length and direction.

3–8
(a) Sketch the plane curve with the given vector equation.
(b) Find $\mathbf{r}'(t)$.
(c) Sketch the position vector $\mathbf{r}(t)$ and the tangent vector $\mathbf{r}'(t)$ for the given value of t.

3. $\mathbf{r}(t) = \langle t - 2, t^2 + 1 \rangle$, $t = -1$

4. $\mathbf{r}(t) = \langle 1 + t, \sqrt{t} \rangle$, $t = 1$

5. $\mathbf{r}(t) = \sin t\, \mathbf{i} + 2 \cos t\, \mathbf{j}$, $t = \pi/4$

6. $\mathbf{r}(t) = e^t\, \mathbf{i} + e^{-t}\, \mathbf{j}$, $t = 0$

7. $\mathbf{r}(t) = e^t\, \mathbf{i} + e^{3t}\, \mathbf{j}$, $t = 0$

8. $\mathbf{r}(t) = (1 + \cos t)\, \mathbf{i} + (2 + \sin t)\, \mathbf{j}$, $t = \pi/6$

9–14 Find the derivative of the vector function.

9. $\mathbf{r}(t) = \langle t \sin t, t^2, t \cos 2t \rangle$

10. $\mathbf{r}(t) = \langle \tan t, \sec t, 1/t^2 \rangle$

11. $\mathbf{r}(t) = e^{t^2}\mathbf{i} - \mathbf{j} + \ln(1 + 3t)\, \mathbf{k}$

12. $\mathbf{r}(t) = at \cos 3t\, \mathbf{i} + b \sin^3 t\, \mathbf{j} + c \cos^3 t\, \mathbf{k}$

13. $\mathbf{r}(t) = \mathbf{a} + t\, \mathbf{b} + t^2\, \mathbf{c}$

14. $\mathbf{r}(t) = t\, \mathbf{a} \times (\mathbf{b} + t\, \mathbf{c})$

15–18 Find the unit tangent vector $\mathbf{T}(t)$ at the point with the given value of the parameter t.

15. $\mathbf{r}(t) = \langle te^{-t}, 2 \arctan t, 2e^t \rangle$, $t = 0$

16. $\mathbf{r}(t) = 4\sqrt{t}\, \mathbf{i} + t^2\, \mathbf{j} + t\, \mathbf{k}$, $t = 1$

17. $\mathbf{r}(t) = \cos t\, \mathbf{i} + 3t\, \mathbf{j} + 2 \sin 2t\, \mathbf{k}$, $t = 0$

18. $\mathbf{r}(t) = 2 \sin t\, \mathbf{i} + 2 \cos t\, \mathbf{j} + \tan t\, \mathbf{k}$, $t = \pi/4$

19. If $\mathbf{r}(t) = \langle t, e^t, te^t \rangle$, find $\mathbf{r}'(t)$, $\mathbf{T}(0)$, $\mathbf{r}''(t)$, and $\mathbf{r}'(t) \cdot \mathbf{r}''(t)$.

20. If $\mathbf{r}(t) = \langle \cos t, 3 \sin t, 4t \rangle$, find $\mathbf{T}(0)$, $\mathbf{r}''(t)$, and $\mathbf{r}'(t) \times \mathbf{r}''(t)$.

21–24 Find parametric equations for the tangent line to the curve with the given parametric equations at the specified point.

21. $x = 1 + 2\sqrt{t}$, $y = t^3 - t$, $z = t^3 + t$; $(3, 0, 2)$

22. $x = e^t$, $y = te^t$, $z = te^{t^2}$; $(1, 0, 0)$

23. $x = e^{-t} \cos t$, $y = e^{-t} \sin t$, $z = e^{-t}$; $(1, 0, 1)$

24. $x = \ln t$, $y = 2\sqrt{t}$, $z = t^2$; $(0, 2, 1)$

25. Find a vector equation for the tangent line to the curve of intersection of the cylinders $x^2 + y^2 = 25$ and $y^2 + z^2 = 20$ at the point $(3, 4, 2)$.

26. Find the point on the curve $\mathbf{r}(t) = \langle 2 \cos t, 2 \sin t, e^t \rangle$, $0 \leq t \leq \pi$, where the tangent line is parallel to the plane $\sqrt{3}x + y = 1$.

27–29 Find parametric equations for the tangent line to the curve with the given parametric equations at the specified point. Illustrate by graphing both the curve and the tangent line on a common screen.

27. $x = t$, $y = e^{-t}$, $z = 2t - t^2$; $(0, 1, 0)$

28. $x = 2 \cos t$, $y = 2 \sin t$, $z = 4 \cos 2t$; $(\sqrt{3}, 1, 2)$

29. $x = t \cos t$, $y = t$, $z = t \sin t$; $(-\pi, \pi, 0)$

30. (a) Find the point of intersection of the tangent lines to the curve $\mathbf{r}(t) = \langle \sin \pi t, 2 \sin \pi t, \cos \pi t \rangle$ at the points where $t = 0$ and $t = 0.5$.
    (b) Illustrate by graphing the curve and both tangent lines.

31. The curves $\mathbf{r}_1(t) = \langle t, t^2, t^3 \rangle$ and $\mathbf{r}_2(t) = \langle \sin t, \sin 2t, t \rangle$ intersect at the origin. Find their angle of intersection correct to the nearest degree.

32. At what point do the curves $\mathbf{r}_1(t) = \langle t, 1 - t, 3 + t^2 \rangle$ and $\mathbf{r}_2(s) = \langle 3 - s, s - 2, s^2 \rangle$ intersect? Find their angle of intersection correct to the nearest degree.

Graphing calculator or computer with graphing software required   **1.** Homework Hints available in TEC

33–38 Evaluate the integral.

33. $\int_0^1 (16t^3 \mathbf{i} - 9t^2 \mathbf{j} + 25t^4 \mathbf{k}) \, dt$

34. $\int_0^1 \left(\dfrac{4}{1 + t^2} \mathbf{j} + \dfrac{2t}{1 + t^2} \mathbf{k} \right) dt$

35. $\int_0^{\pi/2} (3 \sin^2 t \cos t \, \mathbf{i} + 3 \sin t \cos^2 t \, \mathbf{j} + 2 \sin t \cos t \, \mathbf{k}) \, dt$

36. $\int_1^2 (t^2 \mathbf{i} + t\sqrt{t - 1} \, \mathbf{j} + t \sin \pi t \, \mathbf{k}) \, dt$

37. $\int (\sec^2 t \, \mathbf{i} + t(t^2 + 1)^3 \mathbf{j} + t^2 \ln t \, \mathbf{k}) \, dt$

38. $\int \left(te^{2t} \mathbf{i} + \dfrac{t}{1 - t} \mathbf{j} + \dfrac{1}{\sqrt{1 - t^2}} \mathbf{k} \right) dt$

39. Find $\mathbf{r}(t)$ if $\mathbf{r}'(t) = 2t \mathbf{i} + 3t^2 \mathbf{j} + \sqrt{t} \, \mathbf{k}$ and $\mathbf{r}(1) = \mathbf{i} + \mathbf{j}$.

40. Find $\mathbf{r}(t)$ if $\mathbf{r}'(t) = t \mathbf{i} + e^t \mathbf{j} + te^t \mathbf{k}$ and $\mathbf{r}(0) = \mathbf{i} + \mathbf{j} + \mathbf{k}$.

41. Prove Formula 1 of Theorem 3.

42. Prove Formula 3 of Theorem 3.

43. Prove Formula 5 of Theorem 3.

44. Prove Formula 6 of Theorem 3.

45. If $\mathbf{u}(t) = \langle \sin t, \cos t, t \rangle$ and $\mathbf{v}(t) = \langle t, \cos t, \sin t \rangle$, use Formula 4 of Theorem 3 to find
$$\frac{d}{dt} [\mathbf{u}(t) \cdot \mathbf{v}(t)]$$

46. If $\mathbf{u}$ and $\mathbf{v}$ are the vector functions in Exercise 45, use Formula 5 of Theorem 3 to find
$$\frac{d}{dt} [\mathbf{u}(t) \times \mathbf{v}(t)]$$

47. Find $f'(2)$, where $f(t) = \mathbf{u}(t) \cdot \mathbf{v}(t)$, $\mathbf{u}(2) = \langle 1, 2, -1 \rangle$, $\mathbf{u}'(2) = \langle 3, 0, 4 \rangle$, and $\mathbf{v}(t) = \langle t, t^2, t^3 \rangle$.

48. If $\mathbf{r}(t) = \mathbf{u}(t) \times \mathbf{v}(t)$, where $\mathbf{u}$ and $\mathbf{v}$ are the vector functions in Exercise 47, find $\mathbf{r}'(2)$.

49. Show that if $\mathbf{r}$ is a vector function such that $\mathbf{r}''$ exists, then
$$\frac{d}{dt} [\mathbf{r}(t) \times \mathbf{r}'(t)] = \mathbf{r}(t) \times \mathbf{r}''(t)$$

50. Find an expression for $\dfrac{d}{dt} [\mathbf{u}(t) \cdot (\mathbf{v}(t) \times \mathbf{w}(t))]$.

51. If $\mathbf{r}(t) \neq \mathbf{0}$, show that $\dfrac{d}{dt} |\mathbf{r}(t)| = \dfrac{1}{|\mathbf{r}(t)|} \mathbf{r}(t) \cdot \mathbf{r}'(t)$.

$[\textit{Hint: } |\mathbf{r}(t)|^2 = \mathbf{r}(t) \cdot \mathbf{r}(t)]$

52. If a curve has the property that the position vector $\mathbf{r}(t)$ is always perpendicular to the tangent vector $\mathbf{r}'(t)$, show that the curve lies on a sphere with center the origin.

53. If $\mathbf{u}(t) = \mathbf{r}(t) \cdot [\mathbf{r}'(t) \times \mathbf{r}''(t)]$, show that
$$\mathbf{u}'(t) = \mathbf{r}(t) \cdot [\mathbf{r}'(t) \times \mathbf{r}'''(t)]$$

54. Show that the tangent vector to a curve defined by a vector function $\mathbf{r}(t)$ points in the direction of increasing t. [*Hint:* Refer to Figure 1 and consider the cases $h > 0$ and $h < 0$ separately.]

10.3 Arc Length and Curvature

In Section 6.4 we defined the length of a plane curve with parametric equations $x = f(t)$, $y = g(t)$, $a \leq t \leq b$, as the limit of lengths of inscribed polygons and, for the case where f' and g' are continuous, we arrived at the formula

$$\boxed{1} \qquad L = \int_a^b \sqrt{[f'(t)]^2 + [g'(t)]^2} \, dt = \int_a^b \sqrt{\left(\frac{dx}{dt} \right)^2 + \left(\frac{dy}{dt} \right)^2} \, dt$$

The length of a space curve is defined in exactly the same way (see Figure 1). Suppose that the curve has the vector equation $\mathbf{r}(t) = \langle f(t), g(t), h(t) \rangle$, $a \leq t \leq b$, or, equivalently, the parametric equations $x = f(t)$, $y = g(t)$, $z = h(t)$, where f', g', and h' are continuous. If the curve is traversed exactly once as t increases from a to b, then it can be shown that its length is

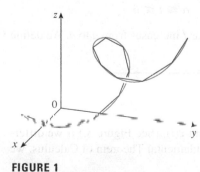

FIGURE 1
The length of a space curve is the limit of lengths of inscribed polygons.

$$\boxed{2} \qquad L = \int_a^b \sqrt{[f'(t)]^2 + [g'(t)]^2 + [h'(t)]^2} \, dt$$
$$= \int_a^b \sqrt{\left(\frac{dx}{dt} \right)^2 + \left(\frac{dy}{dt} \right)^2 + \left(\frac{dz}{dt} \right)^2} \, dt$$

Notice that both of the arc length formulas (1) and (2) can be put into the more compact form

$$\boxed{3} \qquad L = \int_a^b |\mathbf{r}'(t)|\, dt$$

because, for plane curves $\mathbf{r}(t) = f(t)\,\mathbf{i} + g(t)\,\mathbf{j}$,

$$|\mathbf{r}'(t)| = |f'(t)\,\mathbf{i} + g'(t)\,\mathbf{j}| = \sqrt{[f'(t)]^2 + [g'(t)]^2}$$

and for space curves $\mathbf{r}(t) = f(t)\,\mathbf{i} + g(t)\,\mathbf{j} + h(t)\,\mathbf{k}$,

$$|\mathbf{r}'(t)| = |f'(t)\,\mathbf{i} + g'(t)\,\mathbf{j} + h'(t)\,\mathbf{k}| = \sqrt{[f'(t)]^2 + [g'(t)]^2 + [h'(t)]^2}$$

Figure 2 shows the arc of the helix whose length is computed in Example 1.

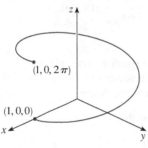

FIGURE 2

☑ **EXAMPLE 1** Find the length of the arc of the circular helix with vector equation $\mathbf{r}(t) = \cos t\,\mathbf{i} + \sin t\,\mathbf{j} + t\,\mathbf{k}$ from the point $(1, 0, 0)$ to the point $(1, 0, 2\pi)$.

SOLUTION Since $\mathbf{r}'(t) = -\sin t\,\mathbf{i} + \cos t\,\mathbf{j} + \mathbf{k}$, we have

$$|\mathbf{r}'(t)| = \sqrt{(-\sin t)^2 + \cos^2 t + 1} = \sqrt{2}$$

The arc from $(1, 0, 0)$ to $(1, 0, 2\pi)$ is described by the parameter interval $0 \le t \le 2\pi$ and so, from Formula 3, we have

$$L = \int_0^{2\pi} |\mathbf{r}'(t)|\, dt = \int_0^{2\pi} \sqrt{2}\, dt = 2\sqrt{2}\,\pi$$

A single curve C can be represented by more than one vector function. For instance, the twisted cubic

$$\boxed{4} \qquad \mathbf{r}_1(t) = \langle t, t^2, t^3 \rangle \qquad 1 \le t \le 2$$

could also be represented by the function

$$\boxed{5} \qquad \mathbf{r}_2(u) = \langle e^u, e^{2u}, e^{3u} \rangle \qquad 0 \le u \le \ln 2$$

where the connection between the parameters t and u is given by $t = e^u$. We say that Equations 4 and 5 are **parametrizations** of the curve C. If we were to use Equation 3 to compute the length of C using Equations 4 and 5, we would get the same answer. In general, it can be shown that when Equation 3 is used to compute arc length, the answer is independent of the parametrization that is used.

Now we suppose that C is a curve given by a vector function

$$\mathbf{r}(t) = f(t)\,\mathbf{i} + g(t)\,\mathbf{j} + h(t)\,\mathbf{k} \qquad a \le t \le b$$

where $\mathbf{r}'$ is continuous and C is traversed exactly once as t increases from a to b. We define its **arc length function** s by

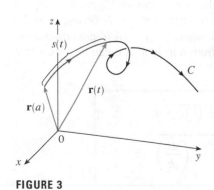

FIGURE 3

$$\boxed{6} \qquad s(t) = \int_a^t |\mathbf{r}'(u)|\, du = \int_a^t \sqrt{\left(\frac{dx}{du}\right)^2 + \left(\frac{dy}{du}\right)^2 + \left(\frac{dz}{du}\right)^2}\, du$$

Thus $s(t)$ is the length of the part of C between $\mathbf{r}(a)$ and $\mathbf{r}(t)$. (See Figure 3.) If we differentiate both sides of Equation 6 using Part 1 of the Fundamental Theorem of Calculus, we obtain

$$\boxed{7} \qquad \frac{ds}{dt} = |\mathbf{r}'(t)|$$

It is often useful to **parametrize a curve with respect to arc length** because arc length arises naturally from the shape of the curve and does not depend on a particular coordinate system. If a curve $\mathbf{r}(t)$ is already given in terms of a parameter t and $s(t)$ is the arc length function given by Equation 6, then we may be able to solve for t as a function of s: $t = t(s)$. Then the curve can be reparametrized in terms of s by substituting for t: $\mathbf{r} = \mathbf{r}(t(s))$. Thus, if $s = 3$ for instance, $\mathbf{r}(t(3))$ is the position vector of the point 3 units of length along the curve from its starting point.

EXAMPLE 2 Finding an arc length parametrization

Reparametrize the helix $\mathbf{r}(t) = \cos t\,\mathbf{i} + \sin t\,\mathbf{j} + t\,\mathbf{k}$ with respect to arc length measured from $(1, 0, 0)$ in the direction of increasing t.

SOLUTION The initial point $(1, 0, 0)$ corresponds to the parameter value $t = 0$. From Example 1 we have

$$\frac{ds}{dt} = |\,\mathbf{r}'(t)\,| = \sqrt{2}$$

and so

$$s = s(t) = \int_0^t |\,\mathbf{r}'(u)\,|\,du = \int_0^t \sqrt{2}\,du = \sqrt{2}\,t$$

Therefore $t = s/\sqrt{2}$ and the required reparametrization is obtained by substituting for t:

$$\mathbf{r}(t(s)) = \cos\!\left(s/\sqrt{2}\right)\mathbf{i} + \sin\!\left(s/\sqrt{2}\right)\mathbf{j} + \left(s/\sqrt{2}\right)\mathbf{k}$$

Curvature

A parametrization $\mathbf{r}(t)$ is called **smooth** on an interval I if $\mathbf{r}'$ is continuous and $\mathbf{r}'(t) \neq \mathbf{0}$ on I. A curve is called **smooth** if it has a smooth parametrization. A smooth curve has no sharp corners or cusps; when the tangent vector turns, it does so continuously.

If C is a smooth curve defined by the vector function $\mathbf{r}$, recall that the unit tangent vector $\mathbf{T}(t)$ is given by

$$\mathbf{T}(t) = \frac{\mathbf{r}'(t)}{|\,\mathbf{r}'(t)\,|}$$

and indicates the direction of the curve. From Figure 4 you can see that $\mathbf{T}(t)$ changes direction very slowly when C is fairly straight, but it changes direction more quickly when C bends or twists more sharply.

The curvature of C at a given point is a measure of how quickly the curve changes direction at that point. Specifically, we define it to be the magnitude of the rate of change of the unit tangent vector with respect to arc length. (We use arc length so that the curvature will be independent of the parametrization.)

8 **Definition** The **curvature** of a curve is

$$\kappa = \left|\frac{d\mathbf{T}}{ds}\right|$$

where $\mathbf{T}$ is the unit tangent vector.

The curvature is easier to compute if it is expressed in terms of the parameter t instead of s, so we use the Chain Rule (Theorem 10.2.3, Formula 6) to write

$$\frac{d\mathbf{T}}{dt} = \frac{d\mathbf{T}}{ds}\frac{ds}{dt} \qquad \text{and} \qquad \kappa = \left|\frac{d\mathbf{T}}{ds}\right| = \left|\frac{d\mathbf{T}/dt}{ds/dt}\right|$$

TEC Visual 10.3A shows animated unit tangent vectors, like those in Figure 4, for a variety of plane curves and space curves.

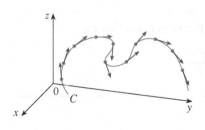

FIGURE 4

Unit tangent vectors at equally spaced points on C

But $ds/dt = |\mathbf{r}'(t)|$ from Equation 7, so the curvature can be written as

$$\boxed{9} \qquad \kappa(t) = \frac{|\mathbf{T}'(t)|}{|\mathbf{r}'(t)|}$$

V EXAMPLE 3 **A circle has constant curvature** Show that the curvature of a circle of radius a is $1/a$.

SOLUTION We can take the circle to have center the origin, and then a parametrization is

$$\mathbf{r}(t) = a \cos t \, \mathbf{i} + a \sin t \, \mathbf{j}$$

Therefore $\qquad \mathbf{r}'(t) = -a \sin t \, \mathbf{i} + a \cos t \, \mathbf{j} \qquad$ and $\qquad |\mathbf{r}'(t)| = a$

so $\qquad \mathbf{T}(t) = \dfrac{\mathbf{r}'(t)}{|\mathbf{r}'(t)|} = -\sin t \, \mathbf{i} + \cos t \, \mathbf{j}$

and $\qquad \mathbf{T}'(t) = -\cos t \, \mathbf{i} - \sin t \, \mathbf{j}$

This gives $|\mathbf{T}'(t)| = 1$, so using Equation 9, we have

$$\kappa(t) = \frac{|\mathbf{T}'(t)|}{|\mathbf{r}'(t)|} = \frac{1}{a}$$

The result of Example 3 shows that small circles have large curvature and large circles have small curvature, in accordance with our intuition. We can see directly from the definition of curvature that the curvature of a straight line is always 0 because the tangent vector is constant.

Although Formula 9 can be used in all cases to compute the curvature, the formula given by the following theorem is often more convenient to apply.

> $\boxed{10}$ **Theorem** The curvature of the curve given by the vector function $\mathbf{r}$ is
>
> $$\kappa(t) = \frac{|\mathbf{r}'(t) \times \mathbf{r}''(t)|}{|\mathbf{r}'(t)|^3}$$

PROOF Since $\mathbf{T} = \mathbf{r}'/|\mathbf{r}'|$ and $|\mathbf{r}'| = ds/dt$, we have

$$\mathbf{r}' = |\mathbf{r}'|\mathbf{T} = \frac{ds}{dt}\mathbf{T}$$

so the Product Rule (Theorem 10.2.3, Formula 3) gives

$$\mathbf{r}'' = \frac{d^2s}{dt^2}\mathbf{T} + \frac{ds}{dt}\mathbf{T}'$$

Using the fact that $\mathbf{T} \times \mathbf{T} = \mathbf{0}$ (see Section 9.4), we have

$$\mathbf{r}' \times \mathbf{r}'' = \left(\frac{ds}{dt}\right)^2 (\mathbf{T} \times \mathbf{T}')$$

Now $|\mathbf{T}(t)| = 1$ for all t, so $\mathbf{T}$ and $\mathbf{T}'$ are orthogonal by Example 4 in Section 10.2. Therefore, by the definition of a cross product,

$$|\mathbf{r}' \times \mathbf{r}''| = \left(\frac{ds}{dt}\right)^2 |\mathbf{T} \times \mathbf{T}'| = \left(\frac{ds}{dt}\right)^2 |\mathbf{T}||\mathbf{T}'| = \left(\frac{ds}{dt}\right)^2 |\mathbf{T}'|$$

Thus

$$|\mathbf{T}'| = \frac{|\mathbf{r}' \times \mathbf{r}''|}{(ds/dt)^2} = \frac{|\mathbf{r}' \times \mathbf{r}''|}{|\mathbf{r}'|^2}$$

and

$$\kappa = \frac{|\mathbf{T}'|}{|\mathbf{r}'|} = \frac{|\mathbf{r}' \times \mathbf{r}''|}{|\mathbf{r}'|^3}$$

EXAMPLE 4 Find the curvature of the twisted cubic $\mathbf{r}(t) = \langle t, t^2, t^3 \rangle$ at a general point and at $(0, 0, 0)$.

SOLUTION We first compute the required ingredients:

$$\mathbf{r}'(t) = \langle 1, 2t, 3t^2 \rangle \qquad \mathbf{r}''(t) = \langle 0, 2, 6t \rangle$$

$$|\mathbf{r}'(t)| = \sqrt{1 + 4t^2 + 9t^4}$$

$$\mathbf{r}'(t) \times \mathbf{r}''(t) = \begin{vmatrix} \mathbf{i} & \mathbf{j} & \mathbf{k} \\ 1 & 2t & 3t^2 \\ 0 & 2 & 6t \end{vmatrix} = 6t^2\,\mathbf{i} - 6t\,\mathbf{j} + 2\,\mathbf{k}$$

$$|\mathbf{r}'(t) \times \mathbf{r}''(t)| = \sqrt{36t^4 + 36t^2 + 4} = 2\sqrt{9t^4 + 9t^2 + 1}$$

Theorem 10 then gives

$$\kappa(t) = \frac{|\mathbf{r}'(t) \times \mathbf{r}''(t)|}{|\mathbf{r}'(t)|^3} = \frac{2\sqrt{1 + 9t^2 + 9t^4}}{(1 + 4t^2 + 9t^4)^{3/2}}$$

At the origin, where $t = 0$, the curvature is $\kappa(0) = 2$.

For the special case of a plane curve with equation $y = f(x)$, we choose x as the parameter and write $\mathbf{r}(x) = x\,\mathbf{i} + f(x)\,\mathbf{j}$. Then $\mathbf{r}'(x) = \mathbf{i} + f'(x)\,\mathbf{j}$ and $\mathbf{r}''(x) = f''(x)\,\mathbf{j}$. Since $\mathbf{i} \times \mathbf{j} = \mathbf{k}$ and $\mathbf{j} \times \mathbf{j} = \mathbf{0}$, it follows that $\mathbf{r}'(x) \times \mathbf{r}''(x) = f''(x)\,\mathbf{k}$. We also have $|\mathbf{r}'(x)| = \sqrt{1 + [f'(x)]^2}$ and so, by Theorem 10,

11

$$\kappa(x) = \frac{|f''(x)|}{[1 + (f'(x))^2]^{3/2}}$$

EXAMPLE 5 Find the curvature of the parabola $y = x^2$ at the points $(0, 0)$, $(1, 1)$, and $(2, 4)$.

SOLUTION Since $y' = 2x$ and $y'' = 2$, Formula 11 gives

$$\kappa(x) = \frac{|y''|}{[1 + (y')^2]^{3/2}} = \frac{2}{(1 + 4x^2)^{3/2}}$$

The curvature at $(0, 0)$ is $\kappa(0) = 2$. At $(1, 1)$ it is $\kappa(1) = 2/5^{3/2} \approx 0.18$. At $(2, 4)$ it is $\kappa(2) = 2/17^{3/2} \approx 0.03$. Observe from the expression for $\kappa(x)$ or the graph of κ in Figure 5 that $\kappa(x) \to 0$ as $x \to \pm\infty$. This corresponds to the fact that the parabola appears to become flatter as $x \to \pm\infty$.

FIGURE 5

The parabola $y = x^2$ and its curvature function

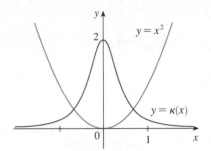

The Normal and Binormal Vectors

We can think of the normal vector as indicating the direction in which the curve is turning at each point.

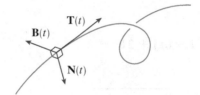

FIGURE 6

At a given point on a smooth space curve $\mathbf{r}(t)$, there are many vectors that are orthogonal to the unit tangent vector $\mathbf{T}(t)$. We single out one by observing that, because $|\mathbf{T}(t)| = 1$ for all t, we have $\mathbf{T}(t) \cdot \mathbf{T}'(t) = 0$ by Example 4 in Section 10.2, so $\mathbf{T}'(t)$ is orthogonal to $\mathbf{T}(t)$. Note that $\mathbf{T}'(t)$ is itself not a unit vector. But at any point where $\kappa \neq 0$ we can define the **principal unit normal vector** $\mathbf{N}(t)$ (or simply **unit normal**) as

$$\mathbf{N}(t) = \frac{\mathbf{T}'(t)}{|\mathbf{T}'(t)|}$$

The vector $\mathbf{B}(t) = \mathbf{T}(t) \times \mathbf{N}(t)$ is called the **binormal vector**. It is perpendicular to both $\mathbf{T}$ and $\mathbf{N}$ and is also a unit vector. (See Figure 6.)

Figure 7 illustrates Example 6 by showing the vectors $\mathbf{T}$, $\mathbf{N}$, and $\mathbf{B}$ at two locations on the helix. In general, the vectors $\mathbf{T}$, $\mathbf{N}$, and $\mathbf{B}$, starting at the various points on a curve, form a set of orthogonal vectors, called the **TNB** frame, that moves along the curve as t varies. This **TNB** frame plays an important role in the branch of mathematics known as differential geometry and in its applications to the motion of spacecraft.

EXAMPLE 6   Find the unit normal and binormal vectors for the circular helix

$$\mathbf{r}(t) = \cos t \, \mathbf{i} + \sin t \, \mathbf{j} + t \, \mathbf{k}$$

SOLUTION   We first compute the ingredients needed for the unit normal vector:

$$\mathbf{r}'(t) = -\sin t \, \mathbf{i} + \cos t \, \mathbf{j} + \mathbf{k} \qquad |\mathbf{r}'(t)| = \sqrt{2}$$

$$\mathbf{T}(t) = \frac{\mathbf{r}'(t)}{|\mathbf{r}'(t)|} = \frac{1}{\sqrt{2}}(-\sin t \, \mathbf{i} + \cos t \, \mathbf{j} + \mathbf{k})$$

$$\mathbf{T}'(t) = \frac{1}{\sqrt{2}}(-\cos t \, \mathbf{i} - \sin t \, \mathbf{j}) \qquad |\mathbf{T}'(t)| = \frac{1}{\sqrt{2}}$$

$$\mathbf{N}(t) = \frac{\mathbf{T}'(t)}{|\mathbf{T}'(t)|} = -\cos t \, \mathbf{i} - \sin t \, \mathbf{j} = \langle -\cos t, -\sin t, 0 \rangle$$

This shows that the normal vector at a point on the helix is horizontal and points toward the z-axis. The binormal vector is

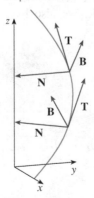

FIGURE 7

$$\mathbf{B}(t) = \mathbf{T}(t) \times \mathbf{N}(t) = \frac{1}{\sqrt{2}} \begin{bmatrix} \mathbf{i} & \mathbf{j} & \mathbf{k} \\ -\sin t & \cos t & 1 \\ -\cos t & -\sin t & 0 \end{bmatrix} = \frac{1}{\sqrt{2}} \langle \sin t, -\cos t, 1 \rangle$$

The plane determined by the normal and binormal vectors **N** and **B** at a point P on a curve C is called the **normal plane** of C at P. It consists of all lines that are orthogonal to the tangent vector **T**. The plane determined by the vectors **T** and **N** is called the **osculating plane** of C at P. The name comes from the Latin *osculum*, meaning "kiss." It is the plane that comes closest to containing the part of the curve near P. (For a plane curve, the osculating plane is simply the plane that contains the curve.)

The circle that lies in the osculating plane of C at P, has the same tangent as C at P, lies on the concave side of C (toward which **N** points), and has radius $\rho = 1/\kappa$ (the reciprocal of the curvature) is called the **osculating circle** (or the **circle of curvature**) of C at P. It is the circle that best describes how C behaves near P; it shares the same tangent, normal, and curvature at P.

V **EXAMPLE 7** Find the equations of the normal plane and osculating plane of the helix in Example 6 at the point $P(0, 1, \pi/2)$.

Figure 8 shows the helix and the osculating plane in Example 7.

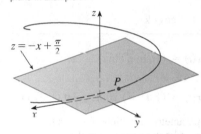

$$z = -x + \frac{\pi}{2}$$

FIGURE 8

SOLUTION The normal plane at P has normal vector $\mathbf{r}'(\pi/2) = \langle -1, 0, 1 \rangle$, so an equation is

$$-1(x - 0) + 0(y - 1) + 1\left(z - \frac{\pi}{2}\right) = 0 \qquad \text{or} \qquad z = x + \frac{\pi}{2}$$

The osculating plane at P contains the vectors **T** and **N**, so its normal vector is $\mathbf{T} \times \mathbf{N} = \mathbf{B}$. From Example 6 we have

$$\mathbf{B}(t) = \frac{1}{\sqrt{2}} \langle \sin t, -\cos t, 1 \rangle \qquad \mathbf{B}\left(\frac{\pi}{2}\right) = \left\langle \frac{1}{\sqrt{2}}, 0, \frac{1}{\sqrt{2}} \right\rangle$$

A simpler normal vector is $\langle 1, 0, 1 \rangle$, so an equation of the osculating plane is

$$1(x - 0) + 0(y - 1) + 1\left(z - \frac{\pi}{2}\right) = 0 \qquad \text{or} \qquad z = -x + \frac{\pi}{2}$$

EXAMPLE 8 Find and graph the osculating circle of the parabola $y = x^2$ at the origin.

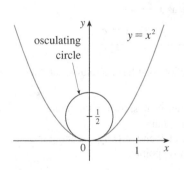

osculating circle

$y = x^2$

$\frac{1}{2}$

FIGURE 9

SOLUTION From Example 5, the curvature of the parabola at the origin is $\kappa(0) = 2$. So the radius of the osculating circle at the origin is $1/\kappa = \frac{1}{2}$ and its center is $\left(0, \frac{1}{2}\right)$. Its equation is therefore

$$x^2 + \left(y - \tfrac{1}{2}\right)^2 = \tfrac{1}{4}$$

For the graph in Figure 9 we use parametric equations of this circle:

$$x = \tfrac{1}{2} \cos t \qquad y = \tfrac{1}{2} + \tfrac{1}{2} \sin t$$

We summarize here the formulas for unit tangent, unit normal and binormal vectors, and curvature.

$$\mathbf{T}(t) = \frac{\mathbf{r}'(t)}{|\mathbf{r}'(t)|} \qquad \mathbf{N}(t) = \frac{\mathbf{T}'(t)}{|\mathbf{T}'(t)|} \qquad \mathbf{B}(t) = \mathbf{T}(t) \times \mathbf{N}(t)$$

$$\kappa = \left| \frac{d\mathbf{T}}{ds} \right| = \frac{|\mathbf{T}'(t)|}{|\mathbf{r}'(t)|} = \frac{|\mathbf{r}'(t) \times \mathbf{r}''(t)|}{|\mathbf{r}'(t)|^3}$$

10.3 Exercises

1–6 Find the length of the curve.

1. $\mathbf{r}(t) = \langle 2 \sin t, 5t, 2 \cos t \rangle, \quad -10 \leq t \leq 10$

2. $\mathbf{r}(t) = \langle 2t, t^2, \frac{1}{3}t^3 \rangle, \quad 0 \leq t \leq 1$

3. $\mathbf{r}(t) = \sqrt{2}\,t\,\mathbf{i} + e^t\,\mathbf{j} + e^{-t}\,\mathbf{k}, \quad 0 \leq t \leq 1$

4. $\mathbf{r}(t) = \cos t\,\mathbf{i} + \sin t\,\mathbf{j} + \ln \cos t\,\mathbf{k}, \quad 0 \leq t \leq \pi/4$

5. $\mathbf{r}(t) = \mathbf{i} + t^2\,\mathbf{j} + t^3\,\mathbf{k}, \quad 0 \leq t \leq 1$

6. $\mathbf{r}(t) = 12t\,\mathbf{i} + 8t^{3/2}\,\mathbf{j} + 3t^2\,\mathbf{k}, \quad 0 \leq t \leq 1$

7–9 Find the length of the curve correct to four decimal places. (Use your calculator to approximate the integral.)

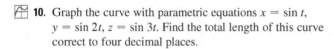

7. $\mathbf{r}(t) = \langle \sqrt{t}, t, t^2 \rangle, \quad 1 \leq t \leq 4$

8. $\mathbf{r}(t) = \langle t, \ln t, t \ln t \rangle, \quad 1 \leq t \leq 2$

9. $\mathbf{r}(t) = \langle \sin t, \cos t, \tan t \rangle, \quad 0 \leq t \leq \pi/4$

10. Graph the curve with parametric equations $x = \sin t$, $y = \sin 2t$, $z = \sin 3t$. Find the total length of this curve correct to four decimal places.

11. Let C be the curve of intersection of the parabolic cylinder $x^2 = 2y$ and the surface $3z = xy$. Find the exact length of C from the origin to the point $(6, 18, 36)$.

12. Find, correct to four decimal places, the length of the curve of intersection of the cylinder $4x^2 + y^2 = 4$ and the plane $x + y + z = 2$.

13–14 Reparametrize the curve with respect to arc length measured from the point where $t = 0$ in the direction of increasing t.

13. $\mathbf{r}(t) = 2t\,\mathbf{i} + (1 - 3t)\,\mathbf{j} + (5 + 4t)\,\mathbf{k}$

14. $\mathbf{r}(t) = e^{2t} \cos 2t\,\mathbf{i} + 2\,\mathbf{j} + e^{2t} \sin 2t\,\mathbf{k}$

15. Suppose you start at the point $(0, 0, 3)$ and move 5 units along the curve $x = 3 \sin t$, $y = 4t$, $z = 3 \cos t$ in the positive direction. Where are you now?

16. Reparametrize the curve

$$\mathbf{r}(t) = \left(\frac{2}{t^2 + 1} - 1 \right) \mathbf{i} + \frac{2t}{t^2 + 1}\,\mathbf{j}$$

with respect to arc length measured from the point $(1, 0)$ in the direction of increasing t. Express the reparametrization in its simplest form. What can you conclude about the curve?

17–20
(a) Find the unit tangent and unit normal vectors $\mathbf{T}(t)$ and $\mathbf{N}(t)$.
(b) Use Formula 9 to find the curvature.

17. $\mathbf{r}(t) = \langle 2 \sin t, 5t, 2 \cos t \rangle$

18. $\mathbf{r}(t) = \langle t^2, \sin t - t \cos t, \cos t + t \sin t \rangle, \quad t > 0$

19. $\mathbf{r}(t) = \langle \sqrt{2}\,t, e^t, e^{-t} \rangle$

20. $\mathbf{r}(t) = \langle t, \frac{1}{2}t^2, t^2 \rangle$

21–23 Use Theorem 10 to find the curvature.

21. $\mathbf{r}(t) = t^3\,\mathbf{j} + t^2\,\mathbf{k}$

22. $\mathbf{r}(t) = t\,\mathbf{i} + t^2\,\mathbf{j} + e^t\,\mathbf{k}$

23. $\mathbf{r}(t) = 3t\,\mathbf{i} + 4 \sin t\,\mathbf{j} + 4 \cos t\,\mathbf{k}$

24. Find the curvature of $\mathbf{r}(t) = \langle t^2, \ln t, t \ln t \rangle$ at the point $(1, 0, 0)$.

25. Find the curvature of $\mathbf{r}(t) = \langle t, t^2, t^3 \rangle$ at the point $(1, 1, 1)$.

26. Graph the curve with parametric equations $x = \cos t$, $y = \sin t$, $z = \sin 5t$ and find the curvature at the point $(1, 0, 0)$.

27–29 Use Formula 11 to find the curvature.

27. $y = x^4$ **28.** $y = \tan x$ **29.** $y = xe^x$

30–31 At what point does the curve have maximum curvature? What happens to the curvature as $x \to \infty$?

30. $y = \ln x$ **31.** $y = e^x$

32. Find an equation of a parabola that has curvature 4 at the origin.

33. (a) Is the curvature of the curve C shown in the figure greater at P or at Q? Explain.
(b) Estimate the curvature at P and at Q by sketching the osculating circles at those points.

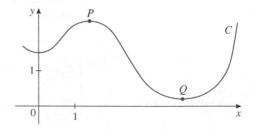

34–35 Use a graphing calculator or computer to graph both the curve and its curvature function $\kappa(x)$ on the same screen. Is the graph of κ what you would expect?

34. $y = x^4 - 2x^2$ **35.** $y = x^{-2}$

36–37 Two graphs, a and b, are shown. One is a curve $y = f(x)$ and the other is the graph of its curvature function $y = \kappa(x)$. Identify each curve and explain your choices.

36.

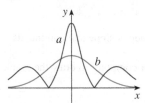

37.

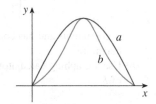

CAS **38.** (a) Graph the curve $\mathbf{r}(t) = \langle \sin 3t, \sin 2t, \sin 3t \rangle$. At how many points on the curve does it appear that the curvature has a local or absolute maximum?
(b) Use a CAS to find and graph the curvature function. Does this graph confirm your conclusion from part (a)?

CAS **39.** The graph of $\mathbf{r}(t) = \langle t - \frac{3}{2}\sin t, 1 - \frac{3}{2}\cos t, t \rangle$ is shown in Figure 12(b) in Section 10.1. Where do you think the curvature is largest? Use a CAS to find and graph the curvature function. For which values of t is the curvature largest?

40. Use Theorem 10 to show that the curvature of a plane parametric curve $x = f(t)$, $y = g(t)$ is

$$\kappa = \frac{|\dot{x}\ddot{y} - \dot{y}\ddot{x}|}{[\dot{x}^2 + \dot{y}^2]^{3/2}}$$

where the dots indicate derivatives with respect to t.

41–43 Use the formula in Exercise 40 to find the curvature.

41. $x = t^2$, $y = t^3$

42. $x = a \cos \omega t$, $y = b \sin \omega t$

43. $x = e^t \cos t$, $y = e^t \sin t$

---

44. Consider the curvature at $x = 0$ for each member of the family of functions $f(x) = e^{cx}$. For which members is $\kappa(0)$ largest?

45–46 Find the vectors $\mathbf{T}$, $\mathbf{N}$, and $\mathbf{B}$ at the given point.

45. $\mathbf{r}(t) = \langle t^2, \frac{2}{3}t^3, t \rangle$, $(1, \frac{2}{3}, 1)$

46. $\mathbf{r}(t) = \langle \cos t, \sin t, \ln \cos t \rangle$, $(1, 0, 0)$

47–48 Find equations of the normal plane and osculating plane of the curve at the given point.

47. $x = 2 \sin 3t$, $y = t$, $z = 2 \cos 3t$; $(0, \pi, -2)$

48. $x = t$, $y = t^2$, $z = t^3$; $(1, 1, 1)$

49. Find equations of the osculating circles of the ellipse $9x^2 + 4y^2 = 36$ at the points $(2, 0)$ and $(0, 3)$. Use a graphing calculator or computer to graph the ellipse and both osculating circles on the same screen.

50. Find equations of the osculating circles of the parabola $y = \frac{1}{2}x^2$ at the points $(0, 0)$ and $(1, \frac{1}{2})$. Graph both osculating circles and the parabola on the same screen.

51. At what point on the curve $x = t^3$, $y = 3t$, $z = t^4$ is the normal plane parallel to the plane $6x + 6y - 8z = 1$?

CAS **52.** Is there a point on the curve in Exercise 51 where the osculating plane is parallel to the plane $x + y + z = 1$? [*Note:* You will need a CAS for differentiating, for simplifying, and for computing a cross product.]

53. Find equations of the normal and osculating planes of the curve of intersection of the parabolic cylinders $x = y^2$ and $z = x^2$ at the point $(1, 1, 1)$.

54. Show that the osculating plane at every point on the curve $\mathbf{r}(t) = \langle t + 2, 1 - t, \frac{1}{2}t^2 \rangle$ is the same plane. What can you conclude about the curve?

55. Show that the curvature κ is related to the tangent and normal vectors by the equation

$$\frac{d\mathbf{T}}{ds} = \kappa \mathbf{N}$$

56. Show that the curvature of a plane curve is $\kappa = |d\phi/ds|$, where ϕ is the angle between $\mathbf{T}$ and $\mathbf{i}$; that is, ϕ is the angle of inclination of the tangent line.

57. (a) Show that $d\mathbf{B}/ds$ is perpendicular to $\mathbf{B}$.
(b) Show that $d\mathbf{B}/ds$ is perpendicular to $\mathbf{T}$.
(c) Deduce from parts (a) and (b) that $d\mathbf{B}/ds = -\tau(s)\mathbf{N}$ for some number $\tau(s)$ called the **torsion** of the curve. (The torsion measures the degree of twisting of a curve.)
(d) Show that for a plane curve the torsion is $\tau(s) = 0$.

58. The following formulas, called the **Frenet-Serret formulas**, are of fundamental importance in differential geometry:

1. $d\mathbf{T}/ds = \kappa \mathbf{N}$

2. $d\mathbf{N}/ds = -\kappa\mathbf{T} + \tau\mathbf{B}$

3. $d\mathbf{B}/ds = -\tau\mathbf{N}$

(Formula 1 comes from Exercise 55 and Formula 3 comes from Exercise 57.) Use the fact that $\mathbf{N} = \mathbf{B} \times \mathbf{T}$ to deduce Formula 2 from Formulas 1 and 3.

59. Use the Frenet-Serret formulas to prove each of the following. (Primes denote derivatives with respect to t. Start as in the proof of Theorem 10.)

(a) $\mathbf{r}'' = s''\mathbf{T} + \kappa(s')^2\mathbf{N}$

(b) $\mathbf{r}' \times \mathbf{r}'' = \kappa(s')^3\mathbf{B}$

(c) $\mathbf{r}''' = [s''' - \kappa^2(s')^3]\mathbf{T} + [3\kappa s's'' + \kappa'(s')^2]\mathbf{N} + \kappa\tau(s')^3\mathbf{B}$

(d) $\tau = \dfrac{(\mathbf{r}' \times \mathbf{r}'') \cdot \mathbf{r}'''}{|\mathbf{r}' \times \mathbf{r}''|^2}$

60. Show that the circular helix $\mathbf{r}(t) = \langle a \cos t, a \sin t, bt \rangle$, where a and b are positive constants, has constant curvature and constant torsion. [Use the result of Exercise 59(d).]

61. The DNA molecule has the shape of a double helix (see Figure 3 on page 696). The radius of each helix is about 10 angstroms (1 Å = 10^{-8} cm). Each helix rises about 34 Å

during each complete turn, and there are about 2.9×10^8 complete turns. Estimate the length of each helix.

62. Let's consider the problem of designing a railroad track to make a smooth transition between sections of straight track. Existing track along the negative x-axis is to be joined smoothly to a track along the line $y = 1$ for $x \geq 1$.

(a) Find a polynomial $P = P(x)$ of degree 5 such that the function F defined by

$$F(x) = \begin{cases} 0 & \text{if } x \leq 0 \\ P(x) & \text{if } 0 < x < 1 \\ 1 & \text{if } x \geq 1 \end{cases}$$

is continuous and has continuous slope and continuous curvature.

(b) Use a graphing calculator or computer to draw the graph of F.

10.4 | Motion in Space: Velocity and Acceleration

In this section we show how the ideas of tangent and normal vectors and curvature can be used in physics to study the motion of an object, including its velocity and acceleration, along a space curve. In particular, we follow in the footsteps of Newton by using these methods to derive Kepler's First Law of planetary motion.

Suppose a particle moves through space so that its position vector at time t is $\mathbf{r}(t)$. Notice from Figure 1 that, for small values of h, the vector

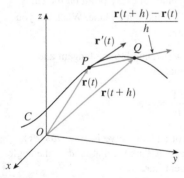

$$\boxed{1} \qquad \frac{\mathbf{r}(t + h) - \mathbf{r}(t)}{h}$$

FIGURE 1

approximates the direction of the particle moving along the curve $\mathbf{r}(t)$. Its magnitude measures the size of the displacement vector per unit time. The vector (1) gives the average velocity over a time interval of length h and its limit is the **velocity vector** $\mathbf{v}(t)$ at time t:

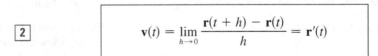

$$\boxed{2} \qquad \mathbf{v}(t) = \lim_{h \to 0} \frac{\mathbf{r}(t + h) - \mathbf{r}(t)}{h} = \mathbf{r}'(t)$$

Thus the velocity vector is also the tangent vector and points in the direction of the tangent line.

The **speed** of the particle at time t is the magnitude of the velocity vector, that is, $|\mathbf{v}(t)|$. This is appropriate because, from (2) and from Equation 10.3.7, we have

$$|\mathbf{v}(t)| = |\mathbf{r}'(t)| = \frac{ds}{dt} = \text{rate of change of distance with respect to time}$$

As in the case of one-dimensional motion, the **acceleration** of the particle is defined as the derivative of the velocity:

$$\mathbf{a}(t) = \mathbf{v}'(t) = \mathbf{r}''(t)$$

EXAMPLE 1   Finding acceleration, given position   The position vector of an object moving in a plane is given by $\mathbf{r}(t) = t^3\,\mathbf{i} + t^2\,\mathbf{j}$. Find its velocity, speed, and acceleration when $t = 1$ and illustrate geometrically.

SOLUTION   The velocity and acceleration at time t are

$$\mathbf{v}(t) = \mathbf{r}'(t) = 3t^2\,\mathbf{i} + 2t\,\mathbf{j}$$

$$\mathbf{a}(t) = \mathbf{r}''(t) = 6t\,\mathbf{i} + 2\,\mathbf{j}$$

and the speed is

$$|\mathbf{v}(t)| = \sqrt{(3t^2)^2 + (2t)^2} = \sqrt{9t^4 + 4t^2}$$

When $t = 1$, we have

$$\mathbf{v}(1) = 3\,\mathbf{i} + 2\,\mathbf{j} \qquad \mathbf{a}(1) = 6\,\mathbf{i} + 2\,\mathbf{j} \qquad |\mathbf{v}(1)| = \sqrt{13}$$

These velocity and acceleration vectors are shown in Figure 2.

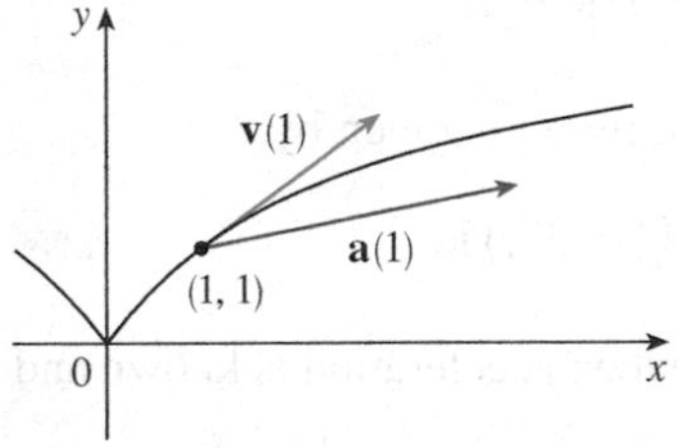

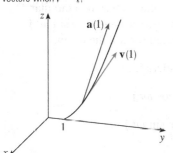

FIGURE 2

TEC Visual 10.4 shows animated velocity and acceleration vectors for objects moving along various curves.

Figure 3 shows the path of the particle in Example 2 with the velocity and acceleration vectors when $t = 1$.

FIGURE 3

EXAMPLE 2   Find the velocity, acceleration, and speed of a particle with position vector $\mathbf{r}(t) = \langle t^2, e^t, te^t \rangle$.

SOLUTION

$$\mathbf{v}(t) = \mathbf{r}'(t) = \langle 2t, e^t, (1 + t)e^t \rangle$$

$$\mathbf{a}(t) = \mathbf{v}'(t) = \langle 2, e^t, (2 + t)e^t \rangle$$

$$|\mathbf{v}(t)| = \sqrt{4t^2 + e^{2t} + (1 + t)^2 e^{2t}}$$

The vector integrals that were introduced in Section 10.2 can be used to find position vectors when velocity or acceleration vectors are known, as in the next example.

EXAMPLE 3   Finding position, given acceleration   A moving particle starts at an initial position $\mathbf{r}(0) = \langle 1, 0, 0 \rangle$ with initial velocity $\mathbf{v}(0) = \mathbf{i} - \mathbf{j} + \mathbf{k}$. Its acceleration is $\mathbf{a}(t) = 4t\,\mathbf{i} + 6t\,\mathbf{j} + \mathbf{k}$. Find its velocity and position at time t.

SOLUTION   Since $\mathbf{a}(t) = \mathbf{v}'(t)$, we have

$$\mathbf{v}(t) = \int \mathbf{a}(t)\,dt = \int (4t\,\mathbf{i} + 6t\,\mathbf{j} + \mathbf{k})\,dt$$

$$= 2t^2\,\mathbf{i} + 3t^2\,\mathbf{j} + t\,\mathbf{k} + \mathbf{C}$$

To determine the value of the constant vector $\mathbf{C}$ we use the fact that $\mathbf{v}(0) = \mathbf{i} - \mathbf{j} + \mathbf{k}$. The preceding equation gives $\mathbf{v}(0) = \mathbf{C}$, so $\mathbf{C} = \mathbf{i} - \mathbf{j} + \mathbf{k}$ and

$$\mathbf{v}(t) = 2t^2\,\mathbf{i} + 3t^2\,\mathbf{j} + t\,\mathbf{k} + \mathbf{i} - \mathbf{j} + \mathbf{k}$$

$$= (2t^2 + 1)\,\mathbf{i} + (3t^2 - 1)\,\mathbf{j} + (t + 1)\,\mathbf{k}$$

The expression for $\mathbf{r}(t)$ that we obtained in Example 3 was used to plot the path of the particle in Figure 4 for $0 \leqslant t \leqslant 3$.

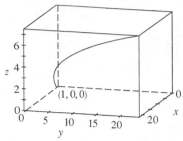

FIGURE 4

Since $\mathbf{v}(t) = \mathbf{r}'(t)$, we have

$$\mathbf{r}(t) = \int \mathbf{v}(t)\, dt$$

$$= \int [(2t^2 + 1)\,\mathbf{i} + (3t^2 - 1)\,\mathbf{j} + (t + 1)\,\mathbf{k}]\, dt$$

$$= \left(\tfrac{2}{3}t^3 + t\right)\mathbf{i} + (t^3 - t)\,\mathbf{j} + \left(\tfrac{1}{2}t^2 + t\right)\mathbf{k} + \mathbf{D}$$

Putting $t = 0$, we find that $\mathbf{D} = \mathbf{r}(0) = \mathbf{i}$, so the position at time t is given by

$$\mathbf{r}(t) = \left(\tfrac{2}{3}t^3 + t + 1\right)\mathbf{i} + (t^3 - t)\,\mathbf{j} + \left(\tfrac{1}{2}t^2 + t\right)\mathbf{k}$$

In general, vector integrals allow us to recover velocity when acceleration is known and position when velocity is known:

$$\mathbf{v}(t) = \mathbf{v}(t_0) + \int_{t_0}^{t} \mathbf{a}(u)\, du \qquad \mathbf{r}(t) = \mathbf{r}(t_0) + \int_{t_0}^{t} \mathbf{v}(u)\, du$$

If the force that acts on a particle is known, then the acceleration can be found from **Newton's Second Law of Motion**. The vector version of this law states that if, at any time t, a force $\mathbf{F}(t)$ acts on an object of mass m producing an acceleration $\mathbf{a}(t)$, then

$$\mathbf{F}(t) = m\mathbf{a}(t)$$

EXAMPLE 4 **Uniform circular motion**   An object with mass m that moves in a circular path with constant angular speed ω has position vector $\mathbf{r}(t) = a \cos \omega t\, \mathbf{i} + a \sin \omega t\, \mathbf{j}$. Find the force acting on the object and show that it is directed toward the origin.

The angular speed of the object moving with position P is $\omega = d\theta/dt$, where θ is the angle shown in Figure 5.

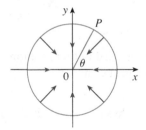

FIGURE 5

SOLUTION   To find the force, we first need to know the acceleration:

$$\mathbf{v}(t) = \mathbf{r}'(t) = -a\omega \sin \omega t\, \mathbf{i} + a\omega \cos \omega t\, \mathbf{j}$$

$$\mathbf{a}(t) = \mathbf{v}'(t) = -a\omega^2 \cos \omega t\, \mathbf{i} - a\omega^2 \sin \omega t\, \mathbf{j}$$

Therefore Newton's Second Law gives the force as

$$\mathbf{F}(t) = m\mathbf{a}(t) = -m\omega^2(a \cos \omega t\, \mathbf{i} + a \sin \omega t\, \mathbf{j})$$

Notice that $\mathbf{F}(t) = -m\omega^2\, \mathbf{r}(t)$. This shows that the force acts in the direction opposite to the radius vector $\mathbf{r}(t)$ and therefore points toward the origin (see Figure 5). Such a force is called a *centripetal* (center-seeking) force.

V   EXAMPLE 5 **Motion of a projectile**   A projectile is fired with angle of elevation α and initial velocity $\mathbf{v}_0$. (See Figure 6.) Assuming that air resistance is negligible and the only external force is due to gravity, find the position function $\mathbf{r}(t)$ of the projectile. What value of α maximizes the range (the horizontal distance traveled)?

SOLUTION   We set up the axes so that the projectile starts at the origin. Since the force due to gravity acts downward, we have

$$\mathbf{F} = m\mathbf{a} = -mg\,\mathbf{j}$$

where $g = |\mathbf{a}| \approx 9.8 \text{ m/s}^2$. Thus

$$\mathbf{a} = -g\,\mathbf{j}$$

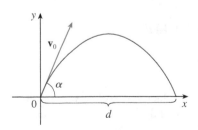

FIGURE 6

Since $\mathbf{v}'(t) = \mathbf{a}$, we have

$$\mathbf{v}(t) = -gt\,\mathbf{j} + \mathbf{C}$$

where $\mathbf{C} = \mathbf{v}(0) = \mathbf{v}_0$. Therefore

$$\mathbf{r}'(t) = \mathbf{v}(t) = -gt\,\mathbf{j} + \mathbf{v}_0$$

Integrating again, we obtain

$$\mathbf{r}(t) = -\tfrac{1}{2}gt^2\,\mathbf{j} + t\,\mathbf{v}_0 + \mathbf{D}$$

But $\mathbf{D} = \mathbf{r}(0) = \mathbf{0}$, so the position vector of the projectile is given by

$$\boxed{3} \qquad\qquad \mathbf{r}(t) = -\tfrac{1}{2}gt^2\,\mathbf{j} + t\,\mathbf{v}_0$$

If we write $|\mathbf{v}_0| = v_0$ (the initial speed of the projectile), then

$$\mathbf{v}_0 = v_0 \cos \alpha\,\mathbf{i} + v_0 \sin \alpha\,\mathbf{j}$$

and Equation 3 becomes

$$\mathbf{r}(t) = (v_0 \cos \alpha)t\,\mathbf{i} + \left[(v_0 \sin \alpha)t - \tfrac{1}{2}gt^2\right]\mathbf{j}$$

The parametric equations of the trajectory are therefore

<table>
<tr><td>$\boxed{4}$</td><td>$x = (v_0 \cos \alpha)t \qquad y = (v_0 \sin \alpha)t - \tfrac{1}{2}gt^2$</td></tr>
</table>

If you eliminate t from Equations 4, you will see that y is a quadratic function of x. So the path of the projectile is part of a parabola.

The horizontal distance d is the value of x when $y = 0$. Setting $y = 0$, we obtain $t = 0$ or $t = (2v_0 \sin \alpha)/g$. This second value of t then gives

$$d = x = (v_0 \cos \alpha)\,\frac{2v_0 \sin \alpha}{g} = \frac{v_0^2(2 \sin \alpha \cos \alpha)}{g} = \frac{v_0^2 \sin 2\alpha}{g}$$

Clearly, d has its maximum value when $\sin 2\alpha = 1$, that is, $\alpha = \pi/4$.

V EXAMPLE 6 A projectile is fired with muzzle speed 150 m/s and angle of elevation 45° from a position 10 m above ground level. Where does the projectile hit the ground, and with what speed?

SOLUTION If we place the origin at ground level, then the initial position of the projectile is $(0, 10)$ and so we need to adjust Equations 4 by adding 10 to the expression for y. With $v_0 = 150$ m/s, $\alpha = 45°$, and $g = 9.8$ m/s², we have

$$x = 150 \cos(\pi/4)t = 75\sqrt{2}\,t$$

$$y = 10 + 150 \sin(\pi/4)t - \tfrac{1}{2}(9.8)t^2 = 10 + 75\sqrt{2}\,t - 4.9t^2$$

Impact occurs when $y = 0$, that is, $4.9t^2 - 75\sqrt{2}\,t - 10 = 0$. Solving this quadratic equation (and using only the positive value of t), we get

$$t = \frac{75\sqrt{2} + \sqrt{11{,}250 + 196}}{9.8} \approx 21.74$$

Then $x \approx 75\sqrt{2}\,(21.74) \approx 2306$, so the projectile hits the ground about 2306 m away.

The velocity of the projectile is

$$\mathbf{v}(t) = \mathbf{r}'(t) = 75\sqrt{2}\,\mathbf{i} + \left(75\sqrt{2} - 9.8t\right)\mathbf{j}$$

So its speed at impact is

$$\left|\,\mathbf{v}(21.74)\,\right| = \sqrt{\left(75\sqrt{2}\right)^2 + \left(75\sqrt{2} - 9.8 \cdot 21.74\right)^2} \approx 151 \text{ m/s}$$

Tangential and Normal Components of Acceleration

When we study the motion of a particle, it is often useful to resolve the acceleration into two components, one in the direction of the tangent and the other in the direction of the normal. If we write $v = |\mathbf{v}|$ for the speed of the particle, then

$$\mathbf{T}(t) = \frac{\mathbf{r}'(t)}{|\mathbf{r}'(t)|} = \frac{\mathbf{v}(t)}{|\mathbf{v}(t)|} = \frac{\mathbf{v}}{v}$$

and so
$$\mathbf{v} = v\mathbf{T}$$

If we differentiate both sides of this equation with respect to t, we get

$$\boxed{5} \qquad \mathbf{a} = \mathbf{v}' = v'\mathbf{T} + v\mathbf{T}'$$

If we use the expression for the curvature given by Equation 10.3.9, then we have

$$\boxed{6} \qquad \kappa = \frac{|\mathbf{T}'|}{|\mathbf{r}'|} = \frac{|\mathbf{T}'|}{v} \qquad \text{so} \qquad |\mathbf{T}'| = \kappa v$$

The unit normal vector was defined in the preceding section as $\mathbf{N} = \mathbf{T}'/|\mathbf{T}'|$, so (6) gives

$$\mathbf{T}' = |\mathbf{T}'|\mathbf{N} = \kappa v\mathbf{N}$$

and Equation 5 becomes

$$\boxed{7} \qquad \boxed{\mathbf{a} = v'\mathbf{T} + \kappa v^2\mathbf{N}}$$

Writing a_T and a_N for the tangential and normal components of acceleration, we have

$$\mathbf{a} = a_T\mathbf{T} + a_N\mathbf{N}$$

where

$$\boxed{8} \qquad a_T = v' \qquad \text{and} \qquad a_N = \kappa v^2$$

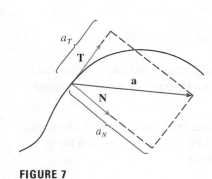

FIGURE 7

This resolution is illustrated in Figure 7.

Let's look at what Formula 7 says. The first thing to notice is that the binormal vector $\mathbf{B}$ is absent. No matter how an object moves through space, its acceleration always lies in the plane of $\mathbf{T}$ and $\mathbf{N}$ (the osculating plane). (Recall that $\mathbf{T}$ gives the direction of motion and $\mathbf{N}$ points in the direction the curve is turning.) Next we notice that the tangential component of acceleration is v', the rate of change of speed, and the normal component of acceleration is κv^2, the curvature times the square of the speed. This makes sense if we think of a passenger in a car—a sharp turn in a road means a large value of the curvature κ, so the component of the acceleration perpendicular to the motion is large and the passenger is thrown against a car door. High speed around the turn has the same effect; in fact, if you double your speed, a_N is increased by a factor of 4.

Although we have expressions for the tangential and normal components of acceleration in Equations 8, it's desirable to have expressions that depend only on $\mathbf{r}$, $\mathbf{r}'$, and $\mathbf{r}''$. To this end we take the dot product of $\mathbf{v} = v\mathbf{T}$ with $\mathbf{a}$ as given by Equation 7:

$$\mathbf{v} \cdot \mathbf{a} = v\mathbf{T} \cdot (v'\mathbf{T} + \kappa v^2 \mathbf{N})$$

$$= vv'\mathbf{T} \cdot \mathbf{T} + \kappa v^3 \mathbf{T} \cdot \mathbf{N}$$

$$= vv' \qquad\qquad \text{(since } \mathbf{T} \cdot \mathbf{T} = 1 \text{ and } \mathbf{T} \cdot \mathbf{N} = 0)$$

Therefore

$$\boxed{9} \qquad a_T = v' = \frac{\mathbf{v} \cdot \mathbf{a}}{v} = \frac{\mathbf{r}'(t) \cdot \mathbf{r}''(t)}{|\mathbf{r}'(t)|}$$

Using the formula for curvature given by Theorem 10.3.10, we have

$$\boxed{10} \qquad a_N = \kappa v^2 = \frac{|\mathbf{r}'(t) \times \mathbf{r}''(t)|}{|\mathbf{r}'(t)|^3} |\mathbf{r}'(t)|^2 = \frac{|\mathbf{r}'(t) \times \mathbf{r}''(t)|}{|\mathbf{r}'(t)|}$$

EXAMPLE 7 A particle moves with position function $\mathbf{r}(t) = \langle t^2, t^2, t^3 \rangle$. Find the tangential and normal components of acceleration.

SOLUTION
$$\mathbf{r}(t) = t^2\,\mathbf{i} + t^2\,\mathbf{j} + t^3\,\mathbf{k}$$

$$\mathbf{r}'(t) = 2t\,\mathbf{i} + 2t\,\mathbf{j} + 3t^2\,\mathbf{k}$$

$$\mathbf{r}''(t) = 2\,\mathbf{i} + 2\,\mathbf{j} + 6t\,\mathbf{k}$$

$$|\mathbf{r}'(t)| = \sqrt{8t^2 + 9t^4}$$

Therefore Equation 9 gives the tangential component as

$$a_T = \frac{\mathbf{r}'(t) \cdot \mathbf{r}''(t)}{|\mathbf{r}'(t)|} = \frac{8t + 18t^3}{\sqrt{8t^2 + 9t^4}}$$

Since
$$\mathbf{r}'(t) \times \mathbf{r}''(t) = \begin{vmatrix} \mathbf{i} & \mathbf{j} & \mathbf{k} \\ 2t & 2t & 3t^2 \\ 2 & 2 & 6t \end{vmatrix} = 6t^2\,\mathbf{i} - 6t^2\,\mathbf{j}$$

Equation 10 gives the normal component as

$$a_N = \frac{|\mathbf{r}'(t) \times \mathbf{r}''(t)|}{|\mathbf{r}'(t)|} = \frac{6\sqrt{2}\,t^2}{\sqrt{8t^2 + 9t^4}}$$

Kepler's Laws of Planetary Motion

We now describe one of the great accomplishments of calculus by showing how the material of this chapter can be used to prove Kepler's laws of planetary motion. After 20 years of studying the astronomical observations of the Danish astronomer Tycho Brahe, the German mathematician and astronomer Johannes Kepler (1571–1630) formulated the following three laws.

Kepler's Laws

1. A planet revolves around the sun in an elliptical orbit with the sun at one focus.

2. The line joining the sun to a planet sweeps out equal areas in equal times.

3. The square of the period of revolution of a planet is proportional to the cube of the length of the major axis of its orbit.

In his book *Principia Mathematica* of 1687, Sir Isaac Newton was able to show that these three laws are consequences of two of his own laws, the Second Law of Motion and the Law of Universal Gravitation. In what follows we prove Kepler's First Law. The remaining laws are left as exercises (with hints).

Since the gravitational force of the sun on a planet is so much larger than the forces exerted by other celestial bodies, we can safely ignore all bodies in the universe except the sun and one planet revolving about it. We use a coordinate system with the sun at the origin and we let $\mathbf{r} = \mathbf{r}(t)$ be the position vector of the planet. (Equally well, $\mathbf{r}$ could be the position vector of the moon or a satellite moving around the earth or a comet moving around a star.) The velocity vector is $\mathbf{v} = \mathbf{r}'$ and the acceleration vector is $\mathbf{a} = \mathbf{r}''$. We use the following laws of Newton:

$$\text{Second Law of Motion:} \quad \mathbf{F} = m\mathbf{a}$$

$$\text{Law of Gravitation:} \quad \mathbf{F} = -\frac{GMm}{r^3}\mathbf{r} = -\frac{GMm}{r^2}\mathbf{u}$$

where $\mathbf{F}$ is the gravitational force on the planet, m and M are the masses of the planet and the sun, G is the gravitational constant, $r = |\mathbf{r}|$, and $\mathbf{u} = (1/r)\mathbf{r}$ is the unit vector in the direction of $\mathbf{r}$.

We first show that the planet moves in one plane. By equating the expressions for $\mathbf{F}$ in Newton's two laws, we find that

$$\mathbf{a} = -\frac{GM}{r^3}\mathbf{r}$$

and so $\mathbf{a}$ is parallel to $\mathbf{r}$. It follows that $\mathbf{r} \times \mathbf{a} = \mathbf{0}$. We use Formula 5 in Theorem 10.2.3 to write

$$\frac{d}{dt}(\mathbf{r} \times \mathbf{v}) = \mathbf{r}' \times \mathbf{v} + \mathbf{r} \times \mathbf{v}'$$

$$= \mathbf{v} \times \mathbf{v} + \mathbf{r} \times \mathbf{a} = \mathbf{0} + \mathbf{0} = \mathbf{0}$$

Therefore
$$\mathbf{r} \times \mathbf{v} = \mathbf{h}$$

where $\mathbf{h}$ is a constant vector. (We may assume that $\mathbf{h} \neq \mathbf{0}$; that is, $\mathbf{r}$ and $\mathbf{v}$ are not parallel.) This means that the vector $\mathbf{r} = \mathbf{r}(t)$ is perpendicular to $\mathbf{h}$ for all values of t, so the planet always lies in the plane through the origin perpendicular to $\mathbf{h}$. Thus the orbit of the planet is a plane curve.

To prove Kepler's First Law we rewrite the vector $\mathbf{h}$ as follows:

$$\mathbf{h} = \mathbf{r} \times \mathbf{v} = \mathbf{r} \times \mathbf{r}' = r\mathbf{u} \times (r\mathbf{u})'$$

$$= r\mathbf{u} \times (r\mathbf{u}' + r'\mathbf{u}) = r^2(\mathbf{u} \times \mathbf{u}') + rr'(\mathbf{u} \times \mathbf{u})$$

$$= r^2(\mathbf{u} \times \mathbf{u}')$$

Then

$$\mathbf{a} \times \mathbf{h} = \frac{-GM}{r^2} \mathbf{u} \times (r^2 \mathbf{u} \times \mathbf{u}') = -GM \mathbf{u} \times (\mathbf{u} \times \mathbf{u}')$$

$$= -GM[(\mathbf{u} \cdot \mathbf{u}')\mathbf{u} - (\mathbf{u} \cdot \mathbf{u})\mathbf{u}'] \quad \text{(by Formula 9.4.8)}$$

But $\mathbf{u} \cdot \mathbf{u} = |\mathbf{u}|^2 = 1$ and, since $|\mathbf{u}(t)| = 1$, it follows from Example 4 in Section 10.2 that $\mathbf{u} \cdot \mathbf{u}' = 0$. Therefore

$$\mathbf{a} \times \mathbf{h} = GM \mathbf{u}'$$

and so

$$(\mathbf{v} \times \mathbf{h})' = \mathbf{v}' \times \mathbf{h} = \mathbf{a} \times \mathbf{h} = GM \mathbf{u}'$$

Integrating both sides of this equation, we get

$$\boxed{11} \qquad \mathbf{v} \times \mathbf{h} = GM \mathbf{u} + \mathbf{c}$$

where $\mathbf{c}$ is a constant vector.

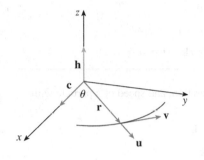

FIGURE 8

At this point it is convenient to choose the coordinate axes so that the standard basis vector $\mathbf{k}$ points in the direction of the vector $\mathbf{h}$. Then the planet moves in the xy-plane. Since both $\mathbf{v} \times \mathbf{h}$ and $\mathbf{u}$ are perpendicular to $\mathbf{h}$, Equation 11 shows that $\mathbf{c}$ lies in the xy-plane. This means that we can choose the x- and y-axes so that the vector $\mathbf{i}$ lies in the direction of $\mathbf{c}$, as shown in Figure 8.

If θ is the angle between $\mathbf{c}$ and $\mathbf{r}$, then (r, θ) are polar coordinates of the planet. From Equation 11 we have

$$\mathbf{r} \cdot (\mathbf{v} \times \mathbf{h}) = \mathbf{r} \cdot (GM \mathbf{u} + \mathbf{c}) = GM \mathbf{r} \cdot \mathbf{u} + \mathbf{r} \cdot \mathbf{c}$$

$$= GMr \mathbf{u} \cdot \mathbf{u} + |\mathbf{r}||\mathbf{c}| \cos \theta = GMr + rc \cos \theta$$

where $c = |\mathbf{c}|$. Then

$$r = \frac{\mathbf{r} \cdot (\mathbf{v} \times \mathbf{h})}{GM + c \cos \theta} = \frac{1}{GM} \frac{\mathbf{r} \cdot (\mathbf{v} \times \mathbf{h})}{1 + e \cos \theta}$$

where $e = c/(GM)$. But

$$\mathbf{r} \cdot (\mathbf{v} \times \mathbf{h}) = (\mathbf{r} \times \mathbf{v}) \cdot \mathbf{h} = \mathbf{h} \cdot \mathbf{h} = |\mathbf{h}|^2 = h^2$$

where $h = |\mathbf{h}|$. So

$$r = \frac{h^2/(GM)}{1 + e \cos \theta} = \frac{eh^2/c}{1 + e \cos \theta}$$

Writing $d = h^2/c$, we obtain the equation

$$\boxed{12} \qquad r = \frac{ed}{1 + e \cos \theta}$$

In Appendix H it is shown that Equation 12 is the polar equation of a conic section with focus at the origin and eccentricity e. We know that the orbit of a planet is a closed curve and so the conic must be an ellipse.

This completes the derivation of Kepler's First Law. We will guide you through the derivation of the Second and Third Laws in the Applied Project on page 726. The proofs of these three laws show that the methods of this chapter provide a powerful tool for describing some of the laws of nature.

10.4 Exercises

1. The table gives coordinates of a particle moving through space along a smooth curve.
   (a) Find the average velocities over the time intervals [0, 1], [0.5, 1], [1, 2], and [1, 1.5].
   (b) Estimate the velocity and speed of the particle at $t = 1$.

t	x	y	z
0	2.7	9.8	3.7
0.5	3.5	7.2	3.3
1.0	4.5	6.0	3.0
1.5	5.9	6.4	2.8
2.0	7.3	7.8	2.7

2. The figure shows the path of a particle that moves with position vector $\mathbf{r}(t)$ at time t.
   (a) Draw a vector that represents the average velocity of the particle over the time interval $2 \leqslant t \leqslant 2.4$.
   (b) Draw a vector that represents the average velocity over the time interval $1.5 \leqslant t \leqslant 2$.
   (c) Write an expression for the velocity vector $\mathbf{v}(2)$.
   (d) Draw an approximation to the vector $\mathbf{v}(2)$ and estimate the speed of the particle at $t = 2$.

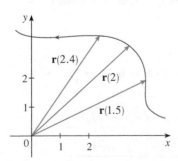

3–8 Find the velocity, acceleration, and speed of a particle with the given position function. Sketch the path of the particle and draw the velocity and acceleration vectors for the specified value of t.

3. $\mathbf{r}(t) = \langle -\frac{1}{2}t^2, t \rangle$, $\quad t = 2$

4. $\mathbf{r}(t) = \langle 2 - t, 4\sqrt{t} \rangle$, $\quad t = 1$

5. $\mathbf{r}(t) = 3 \cos t\,\mathbf{i} + 2 \sin t\,\mathbf{j}$, $\quad t = \pi/3$

6. $\mathbf{r}(t) = e^t\,\mathbf{i} + e^{2t}\,\mathbf{j}$, $\quad t = 0$

7. $\mathbf{r}(t) = t\,\mathbf{i} + t^2\,\mathbf{j} + 2\,\mathbf{k}$, $\quad t = 1$

8. $\mathbf{r}(t) = t\,\mathbf{i} + 2 \cos t\,\mathbf{j} + \sin t\,\mathbf{k}$, $\quad t = 0$

9–12 Find the velocity, acceleration, and speed of a particle with the given position function.

9. $\mathbf{r}(t) = \sqrt{2}\,t\,\mathbf{i} + e^t\,\mathbf{j} + e^{-t}\,\mathbf{k}$

10. $\mathbf{r}(t) = t^2\,\mathbf{i} + 2t\,\mathbf{j} + \ln t\,\mathbf{k}$

11. $\mathbf{r}(t) = e^t(\cos t\,\mathbf{i} + \sin t\,\mathbf{j} + t\,\mathbf{k})$

12. $\mathbf{r}(t) = \langle t^2, \sin t - t \cos t, \cos t + t \sin t \rangle$, $\quad t \geqslant 0$

13–14 Find the velocity and position vectors of a particle that has the given acceleration and the given initial velocity and position.

13. $\mathbf{a}(t) = \mathbf{i} + 2\,\mathbf{j}$, $\quad \mathbf{v}(0) = \mathbf{k}$, $\quad \mathbf{r}(0) = \mathbf{i}$

14. $\mathbf{a}(t) = 2\,\mathbf{i} + 6t\,\mathbf{j} + 12t^2\,\mathbf{k}$, $\quad \mathbf{v}(0) = \mathbf{i}$, $\quad \mathbf{r}(0) = \mathbf{j} - \mathbf{k}$

15–16
(a) Find the position vector of a particle that has the given acceleration and the specified initial velocity and position.
(b) Use a computer to graph the path of the particle.

15. $\mathbf{a}(t) = 2t\,\mathbf{i} + \sin t\,\mathbf{j} + \cos 2t\,\mathbf{k}$, $\quad \mathbf{v}(0) = \mathbf{i}$, $\quad \mathbf{r}(0) = \mathbf{j}$

16. $\mathbf{a}(t) = t\,\mathbf{i} + e^t\,\mathbf{j} + e^{-t}\,\mathbf{k}$, $\quad \mathbf{v}(0) = \mathbf{k}$, $\quad \mathbf{r}(0) = \mathbf{j} + \mathbf{k}$

17. The position function of a particle is given by $\mathbf{r}(t) = \langle t^2, 5t, t^2 - 16t \rangle$. When is the speed a minimum?

18. What force is required so that a particle of mass m has the position function $\mathbf{r}(t) = t^3\,\mathbf{i} + t^2\,\mathbf{j} + t^3\,\mathbf{k}$?

19. A force with magnitude 20 N acts directly upward from the xy-plane on an object with mass 4 kg. The object starts at the origin with initial velocity $\mathbf{v}(0) = \mathbf{i} - \mathbf{j}$. Find its position function and its speed at time t.

Graphing calculator or computer with graphing software required   **1.** Homework Hints available in TEC

20. Show that if a particle moves with constant speed, then the velocity and acceleration vectors are orthogonal.

21. A projectile is fired with an initial speed of 200 m/s and angle of elevation 60°. Find (a) the range of the projectile, (b) the maximum height reached, and (c) the speed at impact.

22. Rework Exercise 21 if the projectile is fired from a position 100 m above the ground.

23. A ball is thrown at an angle of 45° to the ground. If the ball lands 90 m away, what was the initial speed of the ball?

24. A gun is fired with angle of elevation 30°. What is the muzzle speed if the maximum height of the shell is 500 m?

25. A gun has muzzle speed 150 m/s. Find two angles of elevation that can be used to hit a target 800 m away.

26. A batter hits a baseball 3 ft above the ground toward the center field fence, which is 10 ft high and 400 ft from home plate. The ball leaves the bat with speed 115 ft/s at an angle 50° above the horizontal. Is it a home run? (In other words, does the ball clear the fence?)

27. A medieval city has the shape of a square and is protected by walls with length 500 m and height 15 m. You are the commander of an attacking army and the closest you can get to the wall is 100 m. Your plan is to set fire to the city by catapulting heated rocks over the wall (with an initial speed of 80 m/s). At what range of angles should you tell your men to set the catapult? (Assume the path of the rocks is perpendicular to the wall.)

28. A ball with mass 0.8 kg is thrown southward into the air with a speed of 30 m/s at an angle of 30° to the ground. A west wind applies a steady force of 4 N to the ball in an easterly direction. Where does the ball land and with what speed?

29. Water traveling along a straight portion of a river normally flows fastest in the middle, and the speed slows to almost zero at the banks. Consider a long straight stretch of river flowing north, with parallel banks 40 m apart. If the maximum water speed is 3 m/s, we can use a quadratic function as a basic model for the rate of water flow x units from the west bank: $f(x) = \frac{3}{400} x(40 - x)$.
  (a) A boat proceeds at a constant speed of 5 m/s from a point A on the west bank while maintaining a heading perpendicular to the bank. How far down the river on the opposite bank will the boat touch shore? Graph the path of the boat.
  (b) Suppose we would like to pilot the boat to land at the point B on the east bank directly opposite A. If we maintain a constant speed of 5 m/s and a constant heading, find the angle at which the boat should head. Then graph the actual path the boat follows. Does the path seem realistic?

30. Another reasonable model for the water speed of the river in Exercise 29 is a sine function: $f(x) = 3 \sin(\pi x/40)$. If a boater would like to cross the river from A to B with constant heading and a constant speed of 5 m/s, determine the angle at which the boat should head.

31. A particle has position function $\mathbf{r}(t)$. If $\mathbf{r}'(t) = \mathbf{c} \times \mathbf{r}(t)$, where $\mathbf{c}$ is a constant vector, describe the path of the particle.

32. (a) If a particle moves along a straight line, what can you say about its acceleration vector?
  (b) If a particle moves with constant speed along a curve, what can you say about its acceleration vector?

33–36 Find the tangential and normal components of the acceleration vector.

33. $\mathbf{r}(t) = t^3\,\mathbf{i} + t^2\,\mathbf{j}$

34. $\mathbf{r}(t) = (1 + t)\,\mathbf{i} + (t^2 - 2t)\,\mathbf{j}$

35. $\mathbf{r}(t) = \cos t\,\mathbf{i} + \sin t\,\mathbf{j} + t\,\mathbf{k}$

36. $\mathbf{r}(t) = t\,\mathbf{i} + t^2\,\mathbf{j} + 3t\,\mathbf{k}$

37. The magnitude of the acceleration vector $\mathbf{a}$ is 10 cm/s². Use the figure to estimate the tangential and normal components of $\mathbf{a}$.

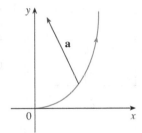

38. If a particle with mass m moves with position vector $\mathbf{r}(t)$, then its **angular momentum** is defined as $\mathbf{L}(t) = m\mathbf{r}(t) \times \mathbf{v}(t)$ and its **torque** as $\boldsymbol{\tau}(t) = m\mathbf{r}(t) \times \mathbf{a}(t)$. Show that $\mathbf{L}'(t) = \boldsymbol{\tau}(t)$. Deduce that if $\boldsymbol{\tau}(t) = \mathbf{0}$ for all t, then $\mathbf{L}(t)$ is constant. (This is the *law of conservation of angular momentum.*)

39. The position function of a spaceship is

$$\mathbf{r}(t) = (3 + t)\,\mathbf{i} + (2 + \ln t)\,\mathbf{j} + \left(7 - \frac{4}{t^2 + 1}\right)\mathbf{k}$$

and the coordinates of a space station are $(6, 4, 9)$. The captain wants the spaceship to coast into the space station. When should the engines be turned off?

40. A rocket burning its onboard fuel while moving through space has velocity $\mathbf{v}(t)$ and mass $m(t)$ at time t. If the exhaust gases escape with velocity $\mathbf{v}_e$ relative to the rocket, it can be deduced from Newton's Second Law of Motion that

$$m\frac{d\mathbf{v}}{dt} = \frac{dm}{dt}\mathbf{v}_e$$

  (a) Show that $\mathbf{v}(t) = \mathbf{v}(0) - \ln\dfrac{m(0)}{m(t)}\,\mathbf{v}_e$.
  (b) For the rocket to accelerate in a straight line from rest to twice the speed of its own exhaust gases, what fraction of its initial mass would the rocket have to burn as fuel?

APPLIED PROJECT | **Kepler's Laws**

Johannes Kepler stated the following three laws of planetary motion on the basis of masses of data on the positions of the planets at various times.

> **Kepler's Laws**
> 1. A planet revolves around the sun in an elliptical orbit with the sun at one focus.
> 2. The line joining the sun to a planet sweeps out equal areas in equal times.
> 3. The square of the period of revolution of a planet is proportional to the cube of the length of the major axis of its orbit.

Kepler formulated these laws because they fitted the astronomical data. He wasn't able to see why they were true or how they related to each other. But Sir Isaac Newton, in his *Principia Mathematica* of 1687, showed how to deduce Kepler's three laws from two of Newton's own laws, the Second Law of Motion and the Law of Universal Gravitation. In Section 10.4 we proved Kepler's First Law using the calculus of vector functions. In this project we guide you through the proofs of Kepler's Second and Third Laws and explore some of their consequences.

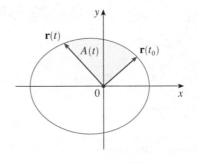

1. Use the following steps to prove Kepler's Second Law. The notation is the same as in the proof of the First Law in Section 10.4. In particular, use polar coordinates so that
$$\mathbf{r} = (r\cos\theta)\,\mathbf{i} + (r\sin\theta)\,\mathbf{j}.$$

   (a) Show that $\mathbf{h} = r^2 \dfrac{d\theta}{dt}\,\mathbf{k}.$

   (b) Deduce that $r^2 \dfrac{d\theta}{dt} = h.$

   (c) If $A = A(t)$ is the area swept out by the radius vector $\mathbf{r} = \mathbf{r}(t)$ in the time interval $[t_0, t]$ as in the figure, show that
$$\frac{dA}{dt} = \tfrac{1}{2}r^2 \frac{d\theta}{dt}$$

   (d) Deduce that
$$\frac{dA}{dt} = \tfrac{1}{2}h = \text{constant}$$

   This says that the rate at which A is swept out is constant and proves Kepler's Second Law.

2. Let T be the period of a planet about the sun; that is, T is the time required for it to travel once around its elliptical orbit. Suppose that the lengths of the major and minor axes of the ellipse are $2a$ and $2b$.

   (a) Use part (d) of Problem 1 to show that $T = 2\pi ab/h$.

   (b) Show that $\dfrac{h^2}{GM} = ed = \dfrac{b^2}{a}.$

   (c) Use parts (a) and (b) to show that $T^2 = \dfrac{4\pi^2}{GM}a^3.$

   This proves Kepler's Third Law. [Notice that the proportionality constant $4\pi^2/(GM)$ is independent of the planet.]

3. The period of the earth's orbit is approximately 365.25 days. Use this fact and Kepler's Third Law to find the length of the major axis of the earth's orbit. You will need the mass of the sun, $M = 1.99 \times 10^{30}$ kg, and the gravitational constant, $G = 6.67 \times 10^{-11}$ N·m²/kg².

4. It's possible to place a satellite into orbit about the earth so that it remains fixed above a given location on the equator. Compute the altitude that is needed for such a satellite. The earth's mass is 5.98×10^{24} kg; its radius is 6.37×10^6 m. (This orbit is called the Clarke Geosynchronous Orbit after Arthur C. Clarke, who first proposed the idea in 1945. The first such satellite, *Syncom II*, was launched in July 1963.)

10.5 Parametric Surfaces

In Section 9.6 we looked at surfaces that are graphs of functions of two variables. Here we use vector functions to discuss more general surfaces, called *parametric surfaces*.

In much the same way that we describe a space curve by a vector function $\mathbf{r}(t)$ of a single parameter t, we can describe a surface by a vector function $\mathbf{r}(u, v)$ of two parameters u and v. We suppose that

$$\boxed{1} \qquad \mathbf{r}(u, v) = x(u, v)\, \mathbf{i} + y(u, v)\, \mathbf{j} + z(u, v)\, \mathbf{k}$$

is a vector-valued function defined on a region D in the uv-plane. So x, y, and z, the component functions of $\mathbf{r}$, are functions of the two variables u and v with domain D. The set of all points (x, y, z) in $\mathbb{R}^3$ such that

$$\boxed{2} \qquad x = x(u, v) \qquad y = y(u, v) \qquad z = z(u, v)$$

and (u, v) varies throughout D, is called a **parametric surface** S and Equations 2 are called **parametric equations** of S. Each choice of u and v gives a point on S; by making all choices, we get all of S. In other words, the surface S is traced out by the tip of the position vector $\mathbf{r}(u, v)$ as (u, v) moves throughout the region D. (See Figure 1.)

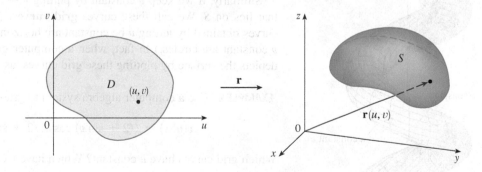

FIGURE 1
A parametric surface

EXAMPLE 1 Identify and sketch the surface with vector equation

$$\mathbf{r}(u, v) = 2\cos u\, \mathbf{i} + v\, \mathbf{j} + 2\sin u\, \mathbf{k}$$

SOLUTION The parametric equations for this surface are

$$x = 2\cos u \qquad y = v \qquad z = 2\sin u$$

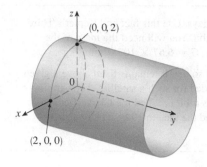

FIGURE 2

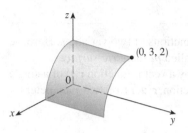

FIGURE 3

TEC Visual 10.5 shows animated versions of Figures 4 and 5, with moving grid curves, for several parametric surfaces.

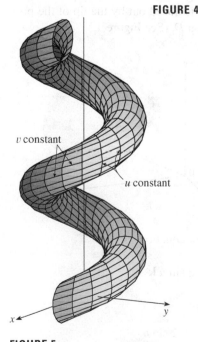

v constant

u constant

FIGURE 5

So for any point (x, y, z) on the surface, we have

$$x^2 + z^2 = 4\cos^2 u + 4\sin^2 u = 4$$

This means that vertical cross-sections parallel to the xz-plane (that is, with y constant) are all circles with radius 2. Since $y = v$ and no restriction is placed on v, the surface is a circular cylinder with radius 2 whose axis is the y-axis (see Figure 2).

In Example 1 we placed no restrictions on the parameters u and v and so we got the entire cylinder. If, for instance, we restrict u and v by writing the parameter domain as

$$0 \leqslant u \leqslant \pi/2 \qquad 0 \leqslant v \leqslant 3$$

then $x \geqslant 0, z \geqslant 0, 0 \leqslant y \leqslant 3$, and we get the quarter-cylinder with length 3 illustrated in Figure 3.

If a parametric surface S is given by a vector function $\mathbf{r}(u, v)$, then there are two useful families of curves that lie on S, one family with u constant and the other with v constant. These families correspond to vertical and horizontal lines in the uv-plane. If we keep u constant by putting $u = u_0$, then $\mathbf{r}(u_0, v)$ becomes a vector function of the single parameter v and defines a curve C_1 lying on S. (See Figure 4.)

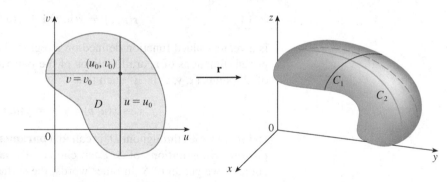

FIGURE 4

Similarly, if we keep v constant by putting $v = v_0$, we get a curve C_2 given by $\mathbf{r}(u, v_0)$ that lies on S. We call these curves **grid curves**. (In Example 1, for instance, the grid curves obtained by letting u be constant are horizontal lines whereas the grid curves with v constant are circles.) In fact, when a computer graphs a parametric surface, it usually depicts the surface by plotting these grid curves, as we see in the following example.

EXAMPLE 2   Use a computer algebra system to graph the surface

$$\mathbf{r}(u, v) = \langle (2 + \sin v)\cos u, (2 + \sin v)\sin u, u + \cos v \rangle$$

Which grid curves have u constant? Which have v constant?

SOLUTION We graph the portion of the surface with parameter domain $0 \leqslant u \leqslant 4\pi$, $0 \leqslant v \leqslant 2\pi$ in Figure 5. It has the appearance of a spiral tube. To identify the grid curves, we write the corresponding parametric equations:

$$x = (2 + \sin v)\cos u \qquad y = (2 + \sin v)\sin u \qquad z = u + \cos v$$

If v is constant, then $\sin v$ and $\cos v$ are constant, so the parametric equations resemble those of the helix in Example 4 in Section 10.1. Thus the grid curves with v constant are the spiral curves in Figure 5. We deduce that the grid curves with u constant must be the curves that look like circles in the figure. Further evidence for this assertion is that if u is kept constant, $u = u_0$, then the equation $z = u_0 + \cos v$ shows that the z-values vary from $u_0 - 1$ to $u_0 + 1$.

In Examples 1 and 2 we were given a vector equation and asked to graph the corresponding parametric surface. In the following examples, however, we are given the more challenging problem of finding a vector function to represent a given surface. In later chapters we will often need to do exactly that.

EXAMPLE 3 Parametric equations for a plane Find a vector function that represents the plane that passes through the point P_0 with position vector $\mathbf{r}_0$ and that contains two non-parallel vectors $\mathbf{a}$ and $\mathbf{b}$.

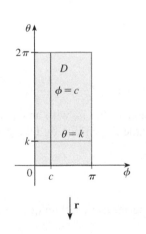

FIGURE 6

SOLUTION If P is any point in the plane, we can get from P_0 to P by moving a certain distance in the direction of $\mathbf{a}$ and another distance in the direction of $\mathbf{b}$. So there are scalars u and v such that $\overrightarrow{P_0P} = u\mathbf{a} + v\mathbf{b}$. (Figure 6 illustrates how this works, by means of the Parallelogram Law, for the case where u and v are positive. See also Exercise 36 in Section 9.2.) If $\mathbf{r}$ is the position vector of P, then

$$\mathbf{r} = \overrightarrow{OP_0} + \overrightarrow{P_0P} = \mathbf{r}_0 + u\mathbf{a} + v\mathbf{b}$$

So the vector equation of the plane can be written as

$$\mathbf{r}(u, v) = \mathbf{r}_0 + u\mathbf{a} + v\mathbf{b}$$

where u and v are real numbers.

If we write $\mathbf{r} = \langle x, y, z \rangle$, $\mathbf{r}_0 = \langle x_0, y_0, z_0 \rangle$, $\mathbf{a} = \langle a_1, a_2, a_3 \rangle$, and $\mathbf{b} = \langle b_1, b_2, b_3 \rangle$, then we can write the parametric equations of the plane through the point (x_0, y_0, z_0) as follows:

$$x = x_0 + ua_1 + vb_1 \qquad y = y_0 + ua_2 + vb_2 \qquad z = z_0 + ua_3 + vb_3$$

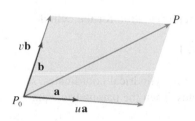

EXAMPLE 4 Parametrizing a sphere Find a parametric representation of the sphere

$$x^2 + y^2 + z^2 = a^2$$

SOLUTION The sphere has a simple representation $\rho = a$ in spherical coordinates, so let's choose the angles ϕ and θ in spherical coordinates as the parameters (see Section 9.7). Then, putting $\rho = a$ in the equations for conversion from spherical to rectangular coordinates (Equations 9.7.3), we obtain

$$x = a \sin\phi \cos\theta \qquad y = a \sin\phi \sin\theta \qquad z = a \cos\phi$$

as the parametric equations of the sphere. The corresponding vector equation is

$$\mathbf{r}(\phi, \theta) = a \sin\phi \cos\theta\, \mathbf{i} + a \sin\phi \sin\theta\, \mathbf{j} + a \cos\phi\, \mathbf{k}$$

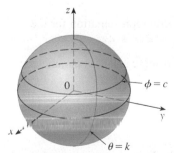

FIGURE 7

We have $0 \leq \phi \leq \pi$ and $0 \leq \theta \leq 2\pi$, so the parameter domain is the rectangle $D = [0, \pi] \times [0, 2\pi]$. The grid curves with ϕ constant are the circles of constant latitude (including the equator). The grid curves with θ constant are the meridians (semicircles), which connect the north and south poles (see Figure 7).

One of the uses of parametric surfaces is in computer graphics. Figure 8 shows the result of trying to graph the sphere $x^2 + y^2 + z^2 = 1$ by solving the equation for z and graphing the top and bottom hemispheres separately. Part of the sphere appears to be missing because of the rectangular grid system used by the computer. The much better picture in Figure 9 was produced by a computer using the parametric equations found in Example 4.

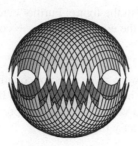

FIGURE 8

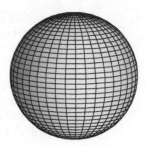

FIGURE 9

EXAMPLE 5   Parametrizing a cylinder   Find a parametric representation for the cylinder

$$x^2 + y^2 = 4 \qquad 0 \leqslant z \leqslant 1$$

SOLUTION   The cylinder has a simple representation $r = 2$ in cylindrical coordinates, so we choose as parameters θ and z in cylindrical coordinates. Then the parametric equations of the cylinder are

$$x = 2 \cos \theta \qquad y = 2 \sin \theta \qquad z = z$$

where $0 \leqslant \theta \leqslant 2\pi$ and $0 \leqslant z \leqslant 1$.

▼ EXAMPLE 6   Find a vector function that represents the elliptic paraboloid $z = x^2 + 2y^2$.

SOLUTION   If we regard x and y as parameters, then the parametric equations are simply

$$x = x \qquad y = y \qquad z = x^2 + 2y^2$$

and the vector equation is

$$\mathbf{r}(x, y) = x\,\mathbf{i} + y\,\mathbf{j} + (x^2 + 2y^2)\,\mathbf{k}$$

TEC In Module 10.5 you can investigate several families of parametric surfaces.

In general, a surface given as the graph of a function of x and y, that is, with an equation of the form $z = f(x, y)$, can always be regarded as a parametric surface by taking x and y as parameters and writing the parametric equations as

$$x = x \qquad y = y \qquad z = f(x, y)$$

Parametric representations (also called parametrizations) of surfaces are not unique. The next example shows two ways to parametrize a cone.

EXAMPLE 7   Two ways to parametrize a cone   Find a parametric representation for the surface $z = 2\sqrt{x^2 + y^2}$, that is, the top half of the cone $z^2 = 4x^2 + 4y^2$.

SOLUTION 1   One possible representation is obtained by choosing x and y as parameters:

$$x = x \qquad y = y \qquad z = 2\sqrt{x^2 + y^2}$$

So the vector equation is

$$\mathbf{r}(x, y) = x\,\mathbf{i} + y\,\mathbf{j} + 2\sqrt{x^2 + y^2}\,\mathbf{k}$$

For some purposes the parametric representations in Solutions 1 and 2 are equally good, but Solution 2 might be preferable in certain situations. If we are interested only in the part of the cone that lies below the plane $z = 1$, for instance, all we have to do in Solution 2 is change the parameter domain to

$$0 \leqslant r \leqslant \tfrac{1}{2} \quad 0 \leqslant \theta \leqslant 2\pi$$

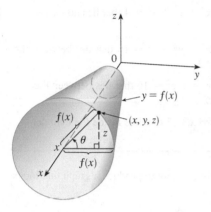

FIGURE 10

FIGURE 11

SOLUTION 2 Another representation results from choosing as parameters the polar coordinates r and θ. A point (x, y, z) on the cone satisfies $x = r \cos \theta$, $y = r \sin \theta$, and $z = 2\sqrt{x^2 + y^2} = 2r$. So a vector equation for the cone is

$$\mathbf{r}(r, \theta) = r \cos \theta \, \mathbf{i} + r \sin \theta \, \mathbf{j} + 2r \, \mathbf{k}$$

where $r \geqslant 0$ and $0 \leqslant \theta \leqslant 2\pi$. ∎

Surfaces of Revolution

Surfaces of revolution can be represented parametrically and thus graphed using a computer. For instance, let's consider the surface S obtained by rotating the curve $y = f(x)$, $a \leqslant x \leqslant b$, about the x-axis, where $f(x) \geqslant 0$. Let θ be the angle of rotation as shown in Figure 10. If (x, y, z) is a point on S, then

$$\boxed{3} \qquad x = x \qquad y = f(x) \cos \theta \qquad z = f(x) \sin \theta$$

Therefore we take x and θ as parameters and regard Equations 3 as parametric equations of S. The parameter domain is given by $a \leqslant x \leqslant b, 0 \leqslant \theta \leqslant 2\pi$.

EXAMPLE 8 **Graphing a surface of revolution** Find parametric equations for the surface generated by rotating the curve $y = \sin x$, $0 \leqslant x \leqslant 2\pi$, about the x-axis. Use these equations to graph the surface of revolution.

SOLUTION From Equations 3, the parametric equations are

$$x = x \qquad y = \sin x \cos \theta \qquad z = \sin x \sin \theta$$

and the parameter domain is $0 \leqslant x \leqslant 2\pi, 0 \leqslant \theta \leqslant 2\pi$. Using a computer to plot these equations and rotate the image, we obtain the graph in Figure 11. ∎

We can adapt Equations 3 to represent a surface obtained through revolution about the y- or z-axis. (See Exercise 30.)

10.5 Exercises

1–2 Determine whether the points P and Q lie on the given surface.

1. $\mathbf{r}(u, v) = \langle 2u + 3v, 1 + 5u - v, 2 + u + v \rangle$
$P(7, 10, 4)$, $Q(5, 22, 5)$

2. $\mathbf{r}(u, v) = \langle u + v, u^2 - v, u + v^2 \rangle$
$P(3, -1, 5)$, $Q(-1, 3, 4)$

3–6 Identify the surface with the given vector equation.

3. $\mathbf{r}(u, v) = (u + v)\,\mathbf{i} + (3 - v)\,\mathbf{j} + (1 + 4u + 5v)\,\mathbf{k}$

4. $\mathbf{r}(u, v) = 2 \sin u \, \mathbf{i} + 3 \cos u \, \mathbf{j} + v\,\mathbf{k}, \quad 0 \leqslant v \leqslant 2$

5. $\mathbf{r}(s, t) = \langle s, t, t^2 - s^2 \rangle$

6. $\mathbf{r}(s, t) = \langle s \sin 2t, s^2, s \cos 2t \rangle$

⊞ **7–12** Use a computer to graph the parametric surface. Get a printout and indicate on it which grid curves have u constant and which have v constant.

7. $\mathbf{r}(u, v) = \langle u^2 + 1, v^3 + 1, u + v \rangle$,
$-1 \leqslant u \leqslant 1, \ -1 \leqslant v \leqslant 1$

8. $\mathbf{r}(u, v) = \langle u + v, u^2, v^2 \rangle$, $\quad -1 \leqslant u \leqslant 1, -1 \leqslant v \leqslant 1$

9. $\mathbf{r}(u, v) = \langle u \cos v, u \sin v, u^5 \rangle$, $\quad -1 \leqslant u \leqslant 1, 0 \leqslant v \leqslant 2\pi$

⊞ Graphing calculator or computer with graphing software required   [CAS] Computer algebra system required   **1.** Homework Hints available in TEC

10. $\mathbf{r}(u, v) = \langle \cos u \sin v, \sin u \sin v, \cos v + \ln \tan(v/2) \rangle$,
$0 \le u \le 2\pi$, $0.1 \le v \le 6.2$

11. $x = \sin v$, $y = \cos u \sin 4v$, $z = \sin 2u \sin 4v$,
$0 \le u \le 2\pi$, $-\pi/2 \le v \le \pi/2$

12. $x = u \sin u \cos v$, $y = u \cos u \cos v$, $z = u \sin v$

13–18 Match the equations with the graphs labeled I–VI and give reasons for your answers. Determine which families of grid curves have u constant and which have v constant.

13. $\mathbf{r}(u, v) = u \cos v\, \mathbf{i} + u \sin v\, \mathbf{j} + v\, \mathbf{k}$

14. $\mathbf{r}(u, v) = u \cos v\, \mathbf{i} + u \sin v\, \mathbf{j} + \sin u\, \mathbf{k}$, $-\pi \le u \le \pi$

15. $\mathbf{r}(u, v) = \sin v\, \mathbf{i} + \cos u \sin 2v\, \mathbf{j} + \sin u \sin 2v\, \mathbf{k}$

16. $x = (1 - u)(3 + \cos v) \cos 4\pi u$,
$y = (1 - u)(3 + \cos v) \sin 4\pi u$,
$z = 3u + (1 - u) \sin v$

17. $x = \cos^3 u \cos^3 v$, $y = \sin^3 u \cos^3 v$, $z = \sin^3 v$

18. $x = (1 - |u|) \cos v$, $y = (1 - |u|) \sin v$, $z = u$

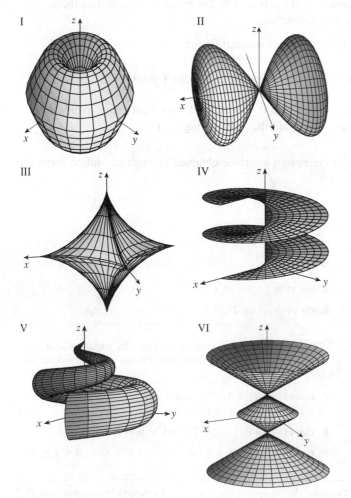

19–26 Find a parametric representation for the surface.

19. The plane that passes through the point $(1, 2, -3)$ and contains the vectors $\mathbf{i} + \mathbf{j} - \mathbf{k}$ and $\mathbf{i} - \mathbf{j} + \mathbf{k}$

20. The lower half of the ellipsoid $2x^2 + 4y^2 + z^2 = 1$

21. The part of the hyperboloid $x^2 + y^2 - z^2 = 1$ that lies to the right of the xz-plane

22. The part of the elliptic paraboloid $x + y^2 + 2z^2 = 4$ that lies in front of the plane $x = 0$

23. The part of the sphere $x^2 + y^2 + z^2 = 4$ that lies above the cone $z = \sqrt{x^2 + y^2}$

24. The part of the sphere $x^2 + y^2 + z^2 = 16$ that lies between the planes $z = -2$ and $z = 2$

25. The part of the cylinder $y^2 + z^2 = 16$ that lies between the planes $x = 0$ and $x = 5$

26. The part of the plane $z = x + 3$ that lies inside the cylinder $x^2 + y^2 = 1$

[CAS] **27–28** Use a computer algebra system to produce a graph that looks like the given one.

27.

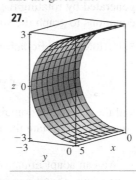

28.

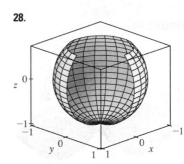

⊞ **29.** Find parametric equations for the surface obtained by rotating the curve $y = e^{-x}$, $0 \le x \le 3$, about the x-axis and use them to graph the surface.

⊞ **30.** Find parametric equations for the surface obtained by rotating the curve $x = 4y^2 - y^4$, $-2 \le y \le 2$, about the y-axis and use them to graph the surface.

31. (a) Show that the parametric equations $x = a \sin u \cos v$, $y = b \sin u \sin v$, $z = c \cos u$, $0 \le u \le \pi$, $0 \le v \le 2\pi$, represent an ellipsoid.

⊞ (b) Use the parametric equations in part (a) to graph the ellipsoid for the case $a = 1$, $b = 2$, $c = 3$.

⊞ **32.** The surface with parametric equations

$$x = 2 \cos \theta + r \cos(\theta/2)$$
$$y = 2 \sin \theta + r \cos(\theta/2)$$
$$z = r \sin(\theta/2)$$

where $-\tfrac{1}{2} \le r \le \tfrac{1}{2}$ and $0 \le \theta \le 2\pi$, is called a **Möbius strip**. Graph this surface with several viewpoints. What is unusual about it?

33. (a) What happens to the spiral tube in Example 2 (see Figure 5) if we replace cos u by sin u and sin u by cos u?
    (b) What happens if we replace cos u by cos $2u$ and sin u by sin $2u$?

34. (a) Find a parametric representation for the torus obtained by rotating about the z-axis the circle in the xz-plane with center $(b, 0, 0)$ and radius $a < b$. [*Hint:* Take as parameters the angles θ and α shown in the figure.]
    (b) Use the parametric equations found in part (a) to graph the torus for several values of a and b.

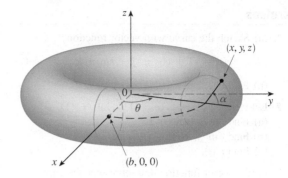

---

10 Review

Concept Check

1. What is a vector function? How do you find its derivative and its integral?

2. What is the connection between vector functions and space curves?

3. How do you find the tangent vector to a smooth curve at a point? How do you find the tangent line? The unit tangent vector?

4. If **u** and **v** are differentiable vector functions, c is a scalar, and f is a real-valued function, write the rules for differentiating the following vector functions.
   (a) $\mathbf{u}(t) + \mathbf{v}(t)$ (b) $c\mathbf{u}(t)$ (c) $f(t)\mathbf{u}(t)$
   (d) $\mathbf{u}(t) \cdot \mathbf{v}(t)$ (e) $\mathbf{u}(t) \times \mathbf{v}(t)$ (f) $\mathbf{u}(f(t))$

5. How do you find the length of a space curve given by a vector function $\mathbf{r}(t)$?

6. (a) What is the definition of curvature?
   (b) Write a formula for curvature in terms of $\mathbf{r}'(t)$ and $\mathbf{T}'(t)$.
   (c) Write a formula for curvature in terms of $\mathbf{r}'(t)$ and $\mathbf{r}''(t)$.
   (d) Write a formula for the curvature of a plane curve with equation $y = f(x)$.

7. (a) Write formulas for the unit normal and binormal vectors of a smooth space curve $\mathbf{r}(t)$.
   (b) What is the normal plane of a curve at a point? What is the osculating plane? What is the osculating circle?

8. (a) How do you find the velocity, speed, and acceleration of a particle that moves along a space curve?
   (b) Write the acceleration in terms of its tangential and normal components.

9. State Kepler's Laws.

10. What is a parametric surface? What are its grid curves?

True-False Quiz

Determine whether the statement is true or false. If it is true, explain why. If it is false, explain why or give an example that disproves the statement.

1. The curve with vector equation $\mathbf{r}(t) = t^3\mathbf{i} + 2t^3\mathbf{j} + 3t^3\mathbf{k}$ is a line.

2. The derivative of a vector function is obtained by differentiating each component function.

3. If $\mathbf{u}(t)$ and $\mathbf{v}(t)$ are differentiable vector functions, then
$$\frac{d}{dt}[\mathbf{u}(t) \times \mathbf{v}(t)] = \mathbf{u}'(t) \times \mathbf{v}'(t)$$

4. If $\mathbf{r}(t)$ is a differentiable vector function, then
$$\frac{d}{dt}|\mathbf{r}(t)| = |\mathbf{r}'(t)|$$

5. If $\mathbf{T}(t)$ is the unit tangent vector of a smooth curve, then the curvature is $\kappa = |d\mathbf{T}/dt|$.

6. The binormal vector is $\mathbf{B}(t) = \mathbf{N}(t) \times \mathbf{T}(t)$.

7. Suppose f is twice continuously differentiable. At an inflection point of the curve $y = f(x)$, the curvature is 0.

8. If $\kappa(t) = 0$ for all t, the curve is a straight line.

9. If $|\mathbf{r}(t)| = 1$ for all t, then $|\mathbf{r}'(t)|$ is a constant.

10. If $|\mathbf{r}(t)| = 1$ for all t, then $\mathbf{r}'(t)$ is orthogonal to $\mathbf{r}(t)$ for all t.

11. The osculating circle of a curve C at a point has the same tangent vector, normal vector, and curvature as C at that point.

12. Different parametrizations of the same curve result in identical tangent vectors at a given point on the curve.

Exercises

1. (a) Sketch the curve with vector function

$$\mathbf{r}(t) = t\,\mathbf{i} + \cos \pi t\,\mathbf{j} + \sin \pi t\,\mathbf{k} \qquad t \geq 0$$

   (b) Find $\mathbf{r}'(t)$ and $\mathbf{r}''(t)$.

2. Let $\mathbf{r}(t) = \langle \sqrt{2-t}, (e^t - 1)/t, \ln(t+1) \rangle$.
   (a) Find the domain of $\mathbf{r}$.
   (b) Find $\lim_{t \to 0} \mathbf{r}(t)$.
   (c) Find $\mathbf{r}'(t)$.

3. Find a vector function that represents the curve of intersection of the cylinder $x^2 + y^2 = 16$ and the plane $x + z = 5$.

4. Find parametric equations for the tangent line to the curve $x = 2 \sin t$, $y = 2 \sin 2t$, $z = 2 \sin 3t$ at the point $\left(1, \sqrt{3}, 2\right)$. Graph the curve and the tangent line on a common screen.

5. If $\mathbf{r}(t) = t^2\,\mathbf{i} + t \cos \pi t\,\mathbf{j} + \sin \pi t\,\mathbf{k}$, evaluate $\int_0^1 \mathbf{r}(t)\,dt$.

6. Let C be the curve with equations $x = 2 - t^3$, $y = 2t - 1$, $z = \ln t$. Find (a) the point where C intersects the xz-plane, (b) parametric equations of the tangent line at $(1, 1, 0)$, and (c) an equation of the normal plane to C at $(1, 1, 0)$.

7. Use Simpson's Rule with $n = 6$ to estimate the length of the arc of the curve with equations $x = t^2$, $y = t^3$, $z = t^4$, $0 \leq t \leq 3$.

8. Find the length of the curve $\mathbf{r}(t) = \langle 2t^{3/2}, \cos 2t, \sin 2t \rangle$, $0 \leq t \leq 1$.

9. The helix $\mathbf{r}_1(t) = \cos t\,\mathbf{i} + \sin t\,\mathbf{j} + t\,\mathbf{k}$ intersects the curve $\mathbf{r}_2(t) = (1 + t)\mathbf{i} + t^2\mathbf{j} + t^3\mathbf{k}$ at the point $(1, 0, 0)$. Find the angle of intersection of these curves.

10. Reparametrize the curve $\mathbf{r}(t) = e^t\,\mathbf{i} + e^t \sin t\,\mathbf{j} + e^t \cos t\,\mathbf{k}$ with respect to arc length measured from the point $(1, 0, 1)$ in the direction of increasing t.

11. For the curve given by $\mathbf{r}(t) = \langle \frac{1}{3}t^3, \frac{1}{2}t^2, t \rangle$, find
   (a) the unit tangent vector,
   (b) the unit normal vector, and
   (c) the curvature.

12. Find the curvature of the ellipse $x = 3 \cos t$, $y = 4 \sin t$ at the points $(3, 0)$ and $(0, 4)$.

13. Find the curvature of the curve $y = x^4$ at the point $(1, 1)$.

14. Find an equation of the osculating circle of the curve $y = x^4 - x^2$ at the origin. Graph both the curve and its osculating circle.

15. Find an equation of the osculating plane of the curve $x = \sin 2t$, $y = t$, $z = \cos 2t$ at the point $(0, \pi, 1)$.

16. The figure shows the curve C traced by a particle with position vector $\mathbf{r}(t)$ at time t.
   (a) Draw a vector that represents the average velocity of the particle over the time interval $3 \leq t \leq 3.2$.
   (b) Write an expression for the velocity $\mathbf{v}(3)$.
   (c) Write an expression for the unit tangent vector $\mathbf{T}(3)$ and draw it.

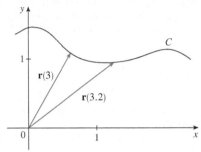

17. A particle moves with position function $\mathbf{r}(t) = t \ln t\,\mathbf{i} + t\,\mathbf{j} + e^{-t}\,\mathbf{k}$. Find the velocity, speed, and acceleration of the particle.

18. A particle starts at the origin with initial velocity $\mathbf{i} - \mathbf{j} + 3\mathbf{k}$. Its acceleration is $\mathbf{a}(t) = 6t\,\mathbf{i} + 12t^2\,\mathbf{j} - 6t\,\mathbf{k}$. Find its position function.

19. An athlete throws a shot at an angle of $45°$ to the horizontal at an initial speed of 43 ft/s. It leaves his hand 7 ft above the ground.
   (a) Where is the shot 2 seconds later?
   (b) How high does the shot go?
   (c) Where does the shot land?

20. Find the tangential and normal components of the acceleration vector of a particle with position function

$$\mathbf{r}(t) = t\,\mathbf{i} + 2t\,\mathbf{j} + t^2\,\mathbf{k}$$

21. Find a parametric representation for the part of the sphere $x^2 + y^2 + z^2 = 4$ that lies between the planes $z = 1$ and $z = -1$.

22. Use a computer to graph the surface with vector equation

$$\mathbf{r}(u, v) = \langle (1 - \cos u) \sin v, u, (u - \sin u) \cos v \rangle$$

Get a printout that gives a good view of the surface and indicate on it which grid curves have u constant and which have v constant.

23. Find the curvature of the curve with parametric equations

$$x = \int_0^t \sin\left(\tfrac{1}{2}\pi\theta^2\right) d\theta \qquad y = \int_0^t \cos\left(\tfrac{1}{2}\pi\theta^2\right) d\theta$$

Graphing calculator or computer with graphing software required   **1.** Homework Hints available in TEC

Focus on Problem Solving

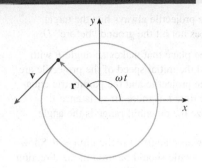

FIGURE FOR PROBLEM 1

1. A particle P moves with constant angular speed ω around a circle whose center is at the origin and whose radius is R. The particle is said to be in *uniform circular motion*. Assume that the motion is counterclockwise and that the particle is at the point $(R, 0)$ when $t = 0$. The position vector at time $t \geqslant 0$ is $\mathbf{r}(t) = R \cos \omega t \, \mathbf{i} + R \sin \omega t \, \mathbf{j}$.
   (a) Find the velocity vector $\mathbf{v}$ and show that $\mathbf{v} \cdot \mathbf{r} = 0$. Conclude that $\mathbf{v}$ is tangent to the circle and points in the direction of the motion.
   (b) Show that the speed $|\mathbf{v}|$ of the particle is the constant ωR. The *period* T of the particle is the time required for one complete revolution. Conclude that

$$T = \frac{2\pi R}{|\mathbf{v}|} = \frac{2\pi}{\omega}$$

   (c) Find the acceleration vector $\mathbf{a}$. Show that it is proportional to $\mathbf{r}$ and that it points toward the origin. An acceleration with this property is called a *centripetal acceleration*. Show that the magnitude of the acceleration vector is $|\mathbf{a}| = R\omega^2$.
   (d) Suppose that the particle has mass m. Show that the magnitude of the force $\mathbf{F}$ that is required to produce this motion, called a *centripetal force*, is

$$|\mathbf{F}| = \frac{m|\mathbf{v}|^2}{R}$$

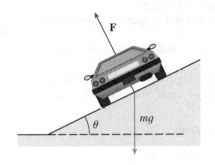

FIGURE FOR PROBLEM 2

2. A circular curve of radius R on a highway is banked at an angle θ so that a car can safely traverse the curve without skidding when there is no friction between the road and the tires. The loss of friction could occur, for example, if the road is covered with a film of water or ice. The rated speed v_R of the curve is the maximum speed that a car can attain without skidding. Suppose a car of mass m is traversing the curve at the rated speed v_R. Two forces are acting on the car: the vertical force, mg, due to the weight of the car, and a force $\mathbf{F}$ exerted by, and normal to, the road (see the figure).

   The vertical component of $\mathbf{F}$ balances the weight of the car, so that $|\mathbf{F}| \cos \theta = mg$. The horizontal component of $\mathbf{F}$ produces a centripetal force on the car so that, by Newton's Second Law and part (d) of Problem 1,

$$|\mathbf{F}| \sin \theta = \frac{mv_R^2}{R}$$

   (a) Show that $v_R^2 = Rg \tan \theta$.
   (b) Find the rated speed of a circular curve with radius 400 ft that is banked at an angle of 12°.
   (c) Suppose the design engineers want to keep the banking at 12°, but wish to increase the rated speed by 50%. What should the radius of the curve be?

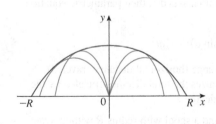

3. A projectile is fired from the origin with angle of elevation α and initial speed v_0. Assuming that air resistance is negligible and that the only force acting on the projectile is gravity, g, we showed in Example 5 in Section 10.4 that the position vector of the projectile is

$$\mathbf{r}(t) = (v_0 \cos \alpha)t \, \mathbf{i} + \left[(v_0 \sin \alpha)t - \tfrac{1}{2}gt^2\right] \mathbf{j}$$

We also showed that the maximum horizontal distance of the projectile is achieved when $\alpha = 45°$ and in this case the range is $R = v_0^2/g$.
   (a) At what angle should the projectile be fired to achieve maximum height and what is the maximum height?
   (b) Fix the initial speed v_0 and consider the parabola $x^2 + 2Ry - R^2 = 0$, whose graph is shown in the figure. Show that the projectile can hit any target inside or on the boundary of the region bounded by the parabola and the x-axis, and that it can't hit any target outside this region.
   (c) Suppose that the gun is elevated to an angle of inclination α in order to aim at a target that is suspended at a height h directly over a point D units downrange. The target is

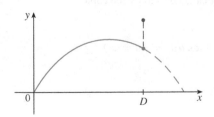

FIGURE FOR PROBLEM 3

⌂ Graphing calculator or computer with graphing software required

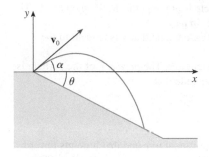

FIGURE FOR PROBLEM 4

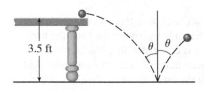

FIGURE FOR PROBLEM 5

released at the instant the gun is fired. Show that the projectile always hits the target, regardless of the value v_0, provided the projectile does not hit the ground "before" D.

4. (a) A projectile is fired from the origin down an inclined plane that makes an angle θ with the horizontal. The angle of elevation of the gun and the initial speed of the projectile are α and v_0, respectively. Find the position vector of the projectile and the parametric equations of the path of the projectile as functions of the time t. (Ignore air resistance.)

   (b) Show that the angle of elevation α that will maximize the downhill range is the angle halfway between the plane and the vertical.

   (c) Suppose the projectile is fired up an inclined plane whose angle of inclination is θ. Show that, in order to maximize the (uphill) range, the projectile should be fired in the direction halfway between the plane and the vertical.

   (d) In a paper presented in 1686, Edmond Halley summarized the laws of gravity and projectile motion and applied them to gunnery. One problem he posed involved firing a projectile to hit a target a distance R up an inclined plane. Show that the angle at which the projectile should be fired to hit the target but use the least amount of energy is the same as the angle in part (c). (Use the fact that the energy needed to fire the projectile is proportional to the square of the initial speed, so minimizing the energy is equivalent to minimizing the initial speed.)

5. A ball rolls off a table with a speed of 2 ft/s. The table is 3.5 ft high.

   (a) Determine the point at which the ball hits the floor and find its speed at the instant of impact.

   (b) Find the angle θ between the path of the ball and the vertical line drawn through the point of impact (see the figure).

   (c) Suppose the ball rebounds from the floor at the same angle with which it hits the floor, but loses 20% of its speed due to energy absorbed by the ball on impact. Where does the ball strike the floor on the second bounce?

6. Investigate the shape of the surface with parametric equations

$$x = \sin u \qquad y = \sin v \qquad z = \sin(u + v)$$

Start by graphing the surface from several points of view. Explain the appearance of the graphs by determining the traces in the horizontal planes $z = 0$, $z = \pm 1$, and $z = \pm \frac{1}{2}$.

7. If a projectile is fired with angle of elevation α and initial speed v, then parametric equations for its trajectory are

$$x = (v \cos \alpha)t \qquad y = (v \sin \alpha)t - \tfrac{1}{2}gt^2$$

(See Example 5 in Section 10.4.) We know that the range (horizontal distance traveled) is maximized when $\alpha = 45°$. What value of α maximizes the total distance traveled by the projectile? (State your answer correct to the nearest degree.)

8. A cable has radius r and length L and is wound around a spool with radius R without overlapping. What is the shortest length along the spool that is covered by the cable?

9. Show that the curve with vector equation

$$\mathbf{r}(t) = \langle a_1 t^2 + b_1 t + c_1, a_2 t^2 + b_2 t + c_2, a_3 t^2 + b_3 t + c_3 \rangle$$

lies in a plane and find an equation of the plane.

Partial Derivatives

11

Physical quantities often depend on two or more variables. In this chapter we extend the basic ideas of differential calculus to such functions.

737

11.1 Functions of Several Variables

In Section 9.6 we discussed functions of two variables and their graphs. Here we study functions of two or more variables from four points of view:

- verbally   (by a description in words)
- numerically   (by a table of values)
- algebraically (by an explicit formula)
- visually   (by a graph or level curves)

Recall that a function f of two variables is a rule that assigns to each ordered pair (x, y) of real numbers in its domain a unique real number denoted by $f(x, y)$. In Example 3 in Section 9.6 we looked at the wave heights h in the open sea as a function of the wind speed v and the length of time t that the wind has been blowing at that speed. We presented a table of observed wave heights that represent the function $h = f(v, t)$ numerically. The function in the next example is also described verbally and numerically.

EXAMPLE 1   **Wind chill is a function of temperature and wind speed**   In regions with severe winter weather, the *wind-chill index* is often used to describe the apparent severity of the cold. This index W is a subjective temperature that depends on the actual temperature T and the wind speed v. So W is a function of T and v, and we can write $W = f(T, v)$. Table 1 records values of W compiled by the National Weather Service of the US and the Meteorological Service of Canada.

TABLE 1
Wind-chill index as a function of
air temperature and wind speed

Wind speed (km/h)

T＼v	5	10	15	20	25	30	40	50	60	70	80
5	4	3	2	1	1	0	−1	−1	−2	−2	−3
0	−2	−3	−4	−5	−6	−6	−7	−8	−9	−9	−10
−5	−7	−9	−11	−12	−12	−13	−14	−15	−16	−16	−17
−10	−13	−15	−17	−18	−19	−20	−21	−22	−23	−23	−24
−15	−19	−21	−23	−24	−25	−26	−27	−29	−30	−30	−31
−20	−24	−27	−29	−30	−32	−33	−34	−35	−36	−37	−38
−25	−30	−33	−35	−37	−38	−39	−41	−42	−43	−44	−45
−30	−36	−39	−41	−43	−44	−46	−48	−49	−50	−51	−52
−35	−41	−45	−48	−49	−51	−52	−54	−56	−57	−58	−60
−40	−47	−51	−54	−56	−57	−59	−61	−63	−64	−65	−67

Actual temperature (°C)

THE NEW WIND-CHILL INDEX

A new wind-chill index was introduced in November of 2001 and is more accurate than the old index for measuring how cold it feels when it's windy. The new index is based on a model of how fast a human face loses heat. It was developed through clinical trials in which volunteers were exposed to a variety of temperatures and wind speeds in a refrigerated wind tunnel.

For instance, the table shows that if the temperature is $-5°$C and the wind speed is 50 km/h, then subjectively it would feel as cold as a temperature of about $-15°$C with no wind. So

$$f(-5, 50) = -15$$

EXAMPLE 2   **The Cobb-Douglas production function**   In 1928 Charles Cobb and Paul Douglas published a study in which they modeled the growth of the American economy during the period 1899–1922. They considered a simplified view of the economy in

TABLE 2

Year	P	L	K
1899	100	100	100
1900	101	105	107
1901	112	110	114
1902	122	117	122
1903	124	122	131
1904	122	121	138
1905	143	125	149
1906	152	134	163
1907	151	140	176
1908	126	123	185
1909	155	143	198
1910	159	147	208
1911	153	148	216
1912	177	155	226
1913	184	156	236
1914	169	152	244
1915	189	156	266
1916	225	183	298
1917	227	198	335
1918	223	201	366
1919	218	196	387
1920	231	194	407
1921	179	146	417
1922	240	161	431

which production output is determined by the amount of labor involved and the amount of capital invested. While there are many other factors affecting economic performance, their model proved to be remarkably accurate. The function they used to model production was of the form

$$\boxed{1} \qquad P(L, K) = bL^{\alpha}K^{1-\alpha}$$

where P is the total production (the monetary value of all goods produced in a year), L is the amount of labor (the total number of person-hours worked in a year), and K is the amount of capital invested (the monetary worth of all machinery, equipment, and buildings). In Section 11.3 we will show how the form of Equation 1 follows from certain economic assumptions.

Cobb and Douglas used economic data published by the government to obtain Table 2. They took the year 1899 as a baseline and P, L, and K for 1899 were each assigned the value 100. The values for other years were expressed as percentages of the 1899 figures.

Cobb and Douglas used the method of least squares to fit the data of Table 2 to the function

$$\boxed{2} \qquad P(L, K) = 1.01L^{0.75}K^{0.25}$$

(See Exercise 49 for the details.)

If we use the model given by the function in Equation 2 to compute the production in the years 1910 and 1920, we get the values

$$P(147, 208) = 1.01(147)^{0.75}(208)^{0.25} \approx 161.9$$

$$P(194, 407) = 1.01(194)^{0.75}(407)^{0.25} \approx 235.8$$

which are quite close to the actual values, 159 and 231.

The production function (1) has subsequently been used in many settings, ranging from individual firms to global economics. It has become known as the **Cobb-Douglas production function**.

The domain of the production function in Example 2 is $\{(L, K) \mid L \geqslant 0, K \geqslant 0\}$ because L and K represent labor and capital and are therefore never negative. For a function f given by an algebraic formula, recall that the domain consists of all pairs (x, y) for which the expression for $f(x, y)$ is a well-defined real number.

EXAMPLE 3 Find the domain and range of $g(x, y) = \sqrt{9 - x^2 - y^2}$.

SOLUTION The domain of g is

$$D = \{(x, y) \mid 9 - x^2 - y^2 \geqslant 0\} = \{(x, y) \mid x^2 + y^2 \leqslant 9\}$$

which is the disk with center $(0, 0)$ and radius 3. (See Figure 1.) The range of g is

$$\left\{ z \mid z = \sqrt{9 - x^2 - y^2}, (x, y) \in D \right\}$$

Since z is a positive square root, $z \geqslant 0$. Also, because $9 - x^2 - y^2 \leqslant 9$, we have

$$\sqrt{9 - x^2 - y^2} \leqslant 3$$

So the range is

$$\{z \mid 0 \leqslant z \leqslant 3\} = [0, 3]$$

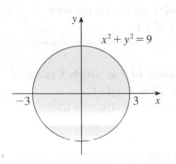

FIGURE 1
Domain of $g(x, y) = \sqrt{9 - x^2 - y^2}$

Visual Representations

One way to visualize a function of two variables is through its graph. Recall from Section 9.6 that the graph of f is the surface with equation $z = f(x, y)$.

V   EXAMPLE 4   Sketch the graph of $g(x, y) = \sqrt{9 - x^2 - y^2}$.

SOLUTION   The graph has equation $z = \sqrt{9 - x^2 - y^2}$. We square both sides of this equation to obtain $z^2 = 9 - x^2 - y^2$, or $x^2 + y^2 + z^2 = 9$, which we recognize as an equation of the sphere with center the origin and radius 3. But, since $z \geq 0$, the graph of g is just the top half of this sphere (see Figure 2).

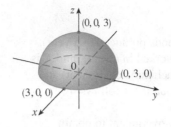

FIGURE 2

Graph of $g(x, y) = \sqrt{9 - x^2 - y^2}$

Note: An entire sphere can't be represented by a single function of x and y. As we saw in Example 4, the upper hemisphere of the sphere $x^2 + y^2 + z^2 = 9$ is represented by the function $g(x, y) = \sqrt{9 - x^2 - y^2}$. The lower hemisphere is represented by the function $h(x, y) = -\sqrt{9 - x^2 - y^2}$.

EXAMPLE 5   Use a computer to draw the graph of the Cobb-Douglas production function $P(L, K) = 1.01L^{0.75}K^{0.25}$.

SOLUTION   Figure 3 shows the graph of P for values of the labor L and capital K that lie between 0 and 300. The computer has drawn the surface by plotting vertical traces. We see from these traces that the value of the production P increases as either L or K increases, as is to be expected.

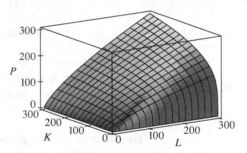

FIGURE 3

Another method for visualizing functions, borrowed from mapmakers, is a contour map on which points of constant elevation are joined to form *contour lines*, or *level curves*.

Definition   The **level curves** of a function f of two variables are the curves with equations $f(x, y) = k$, where k is a constant (in the range of f).

A level curve $f(x, y) = k$ is the set of all points in the domain of f at which f takes on a given value k. In other words, it shows where the graph of f has height k.

You can see from Figure 4 the relation between level curves and horizontal traces. The level curves $f(x, y) = k$ are just the traces of the graph of f in the horizontal plane $z = k$ projected down to the xy-plane. So if you draw the level curves of a function and visualize them being lifted up to the surface at the indicated height, then you can mentally piece together a picture of the graph. The surface is steep where the level curves are close together. It is somewhat flatter where they are farther apart.

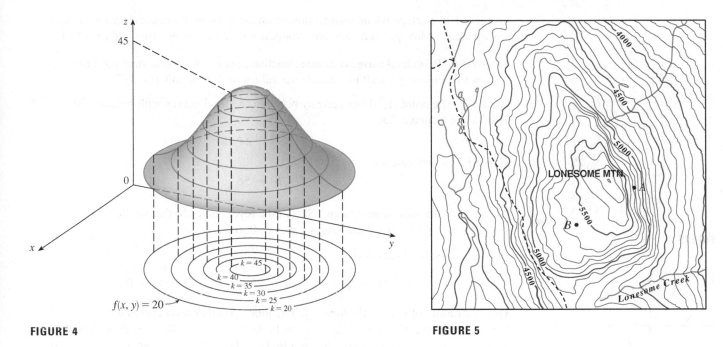

FIGURE 4

FIGURE 5

One common example of level curves occurs in topographic maps of mountainous regions, such as the map in Figure 5. The level curves are curves of constant elevation above sea level. If you walk along one of these contour lines, you neither ascend nor descend. Another common example is the temperature at locations (x, y) with longitude x and latitude y. Here the level curves are called **isothermals** and join locations with the same temperature. Figure 6 shows a weather map of the world indicating the average January temperatures. The isothermals are the curves that separate the colored bands.

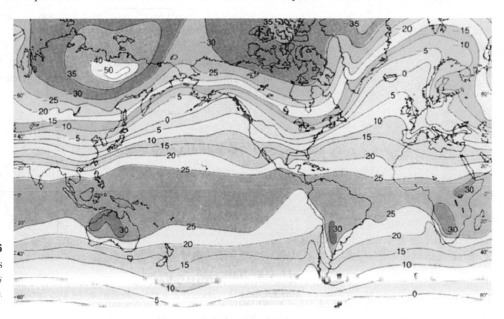

FIGURE 6
World mean sea-level temperatures
in January in degrees Celsius

From *Atmosphere: Introduction to Meteorology*, 4th Edition, 1989.
© 1989 Pearson Education, Inc.

In weather maps of atmospheric pressure at a given time as a function of longitude and latitude, the level curves are called **isobars**. They join locations with the same pressure (see

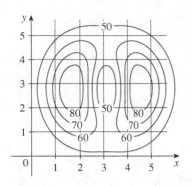

FIGURE 7

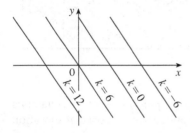

FIGURE 8
Contour map of
$f(x, y) = 6 - 3x - 2y$

Exercise 10). Surface winds tend to flow from areas of high pressure across the isobars toward areas of low pressure, and are strongest where the isobars are tightly packed.

EXAMPLE 6 **Using level curves to estimate function values** A contour map for a function f is shown in Figure 7. Use it to estimate the values of $f(1, 3)$ and $f(4, 5)$.

SOLUTION The point $(1, 3)$ lies partway between the level curves with z-values 70 and 80. We estimate that

$$f(1, 3) \approx 73$$

Similarly, we estimate that

$$f(4, 5) \approx 56$$

EXAMPLE 7 **Drawing a contour map** Sketch the level curves of the function $f(x, y) = 6 - 3x - 2y$ for the values $k = -6, 0, 6, 12$.

SOLUTION The level curves are

$$6 - 3x - 2y = k \qquad \text{or} \qquad 3x + 2y + (k - 6) = 0$$

This is a family of lines with slope $-\frac{3}{2}$. The four particular level curves with $k = -6, 0, 6$, and 12 are $3x + 2y - 12 = 0$, $3x + 2y - 6 = 0$, $3x + 2y = 0$, and $3x + 2y + 6 = 0$. They are sketched in Figure 8. The level curves are equally spaced parallel lines because the graph of f is a plane (see Figure 4 in Section 9.6).

V **EXAMPLE 8** Sketch the level curves of the function

$$g(x, y) = \sqrt{9 - x^2 - y^2} \qquad \text{for} \quad k = 0, 1, 2, 3$$

SOLUTION The level curves are

$$\sqrt{9 - x^2 - y^2} = k \qquad \text{or} \qquad x^2 + y^2 = 9 - k^2$$

This is a family of concentric circles with center $(0, 0)$ and radius $\sqrt{9 - k^2}$. The cases $k = 0, 1, 2, 3$ are shown in Figure 9. Try to visualize these level curves lifted up to form a surface and compare with the graph of g (a hemisphere) in Figure 2. (See TEC Visual 11.1A.)

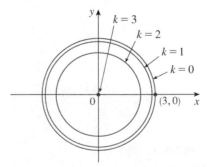

FIGURE 9
Contour map of $g(x, y) = \sqrt{9 - x^2 - y^2}$

EXAMPLE 9 Sketch some level curves of the function $h(x, y) = 4x^2 + y^2 + 1$.

SOLUTION The level curves are

$$4x^2 + y^2 + 1 = k \qquad \text{or} \qquad \frac{x^2}{\frac{1}{4}(k - 1)} + \frac{y^2}{k - 1} = 1$$

which, for $k > 1$, describes a family of ellipses with semiaxes $\frac{1}{2}\sqrt{k-1}$ and $\sqrt{k-1}$. Figure 10(a) shows a contour map of h drawn by a computer. Figure 10(b) shows these level curves lifted up to the graph of h (an elliptic paraboloid) where they become horizontal traces. We see from Figure 10 how the graph of h is put together from the level curves.

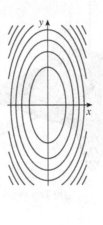

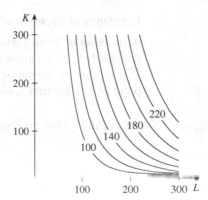

(a) Contour map   (b) Horizontal traces are raised level curves

FIGURE 10

The graph of $h(x, y) = 4x^2 + y^2 + 1$ is formed by lifting the level curves.

EXAMPLE 10 Plot level curves for the Cobb-Douglas production function of Example 2.

SOLUTION In Figure 11 we use a computer to draw a contour plot for the Cobb-Douglas production function

$$P(L, K) = 1.01L^{0.75}K^{0.25}$$

Level curves are labeled with the value of the production P. For instance, the level curve labeled 140 shows all values of the labor L and capital investment K that result in a production of $P = 140$. We see that, for a fixed value of P, as L increases K decreases, and vice versa.

FIGURE 11

For some purposes, a contour map is more useful than a graph. That is certainly true in Example 10. (Compare Figure 11 with Figure 3.) It is also true in estimating function values, as in Example 6.

Figure 12 shows some computer-generated level curves together with the corresponding computer-generated graphs. Notice that the level curves in part (c) crowd together near the origin. That corresponds to the fact that the graph in part (d) is very steep near the origin.

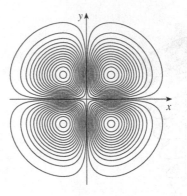

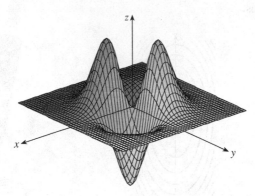

(a) Level curves of $f(x, y) = -xye^{-x^2-y^2}$

(b) Two views of $f(x, y) = -xye^{-x^2-y^2}$

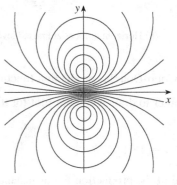

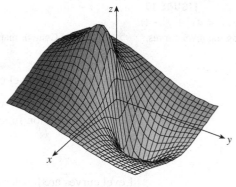

FIGURE 12

(c) Level curves of $f(x, y) = \dfrac{-3y}{x^2 + y^2 + 1}$

(d) $f(x, y) = \dfrac{-3y}{x^2 + y^2 + 1}$

Functions of Three or More Variables

A **function of three variables**, f, is a rule that assigns to each ordered triple (x, y, z) in a domain $D \subset \mathbb{R}^3$ a unique real number denoted by $f(x, y, z)$. For instance, the temperature T at a point on the surface of the earth depends on the longitude x and latitude y of the point and on the time t, so we could write $T = f(x, y, t)$.

EXAMPLE 11 Find the domain of f if

$$f(x, y, z) = \ln(z - y) + xy \sin z$$

SOLUTION The expression for $f(x, y, z)$ is defined as long as $z - y > 0$, so the domain of f is

$$D = \{(x, y, z) \in \mathbb{R}^3 \mid z > y\}$$

This is a **half-space** consisting of all points that lie above the plane $z = y$.

It's very difficult to visualize a function f of three variables by its graph, since that would lie in a four-dimensional space. However, we do gain some insight into f by examining its **level surfaces**, which are the surfaces with equations $f(x, y, z) = k$, where k is a constant. If the point (x, y, z) moves along a level surface, the value of $f(x, y, z)$ remains fixed.

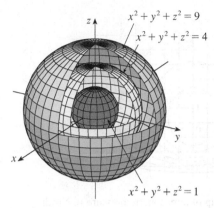

$x^2 + y^2 + z^2 = 9$

$x^2 + y^2 + z^2 = 4$

$x^2 + y^2 + z^2 = 1$

FIGURE 13

EXAMPLE 12 Find the level surfaces of the function

$$f(x, y, z) = x^2 + y^2 + z^2$$

SOLUTION The level surfaces are $x^2 + y^2 + z^2 = k$, where $k \geqslant 0$. These form a family of concentric spheres with radius $\sqrt{k}$. (See Figure 13.) Thus, as (x, y, z) varies over any sphere with center O, the value of $f(x, y, z)$ remains fixed. ▬

Functions of any number of variables can be considered. A **function of n variables** is a rule that assigns a number $z = f(x_1, x_2, \ldots, x_n)$ to an n-tuple $(x_1, x_2, \ldots, x_n)$ of real numbers. We denote by $\mathbb{R}^n$ the set of all such n-tuples. For example, if a company uses n different ingredients in making a food product, c_i is the cost per unit of the ith ingredient, and x_i units of the ith ingredient are used, then the total cost C of the ingredients is a function of the n variables $x_1, x_2, \ldots, x_n$:

$$\boxed{3} \qquad C - f(x_1, x_2, \ldots, x_n) = c_1 x_1 + c_2 x_2 + \cdots + c_n x_n$$

The function f is a real-valued function whose domain is a subset of $\mathbb{R}^n$. Sometimes we will use vector notation to write such functions more compactly: If $\mathbf{x} = \langle x_1, x_2, \ldots, x_n \rangle$, we often write $f(\mathbf{x})$ in place of $f(x_1, x_2, \ldots, x_n)$. With this notation we can rewrite the function defined in Equation 3 as

$$f(\mathbf{x}) = \mathbf{c} \cdot \mathbf{x}$$

where $\mathbf{c} = \langle c_1, c_2, \ldots, c_n \rangle$ and $\mathbf{c} \cdot \mathbf{x}$ denotes the dot product of the vectors $\mathbf{c}$ and $\mathbf{x}$ in V_n.

In view of the one-to-one correspondence between points $(x_1, x_2, \ldots, x_n)$ in $\mathbb{R}^n$ and their position vectors $\mathbf{x} = \langle x_1, x_2, \ldots, x_n \rangle$ in V_n, we have three ways of looking at a function f defined on a subset of $\mathbb{R}^n$:

1. As a function of n real variables $x_1, x_2, \ldots, x_n$
2. As a function of a single point variable $(x_1, x_2, \ldots, x_n)$
3. As a function of a single vector variable $\mathbf{x} = \langle x_1, x_2, \ldots, x_n \rangle$

We will see that all three points of view are useful.

11.1 Exercises

1. In Example 1 we considered the function $W = f(T, v)$, where W is the wind-chill index, T is the actual temperature, and v is the wind speed. A numerical representation is given in Table 1.
   (a) What is the value of $f(-15, 40)$? What is its meaning?
   (b) Describe in words the meaning of the question "For what value of v is $f(-20, v) = -30$?" Then answer the question.
   (c) Describe in words the meaning of the question "For what value of T is $f(T, 20) = -49$?" Then answer the question.
   (d) What is the meaning of the function $W - f(-5, v)$? Describe the behavior of this function.
   (e) What is the meaning of the function $W = f(T, 50)$? Describe the behavior of this function.

⊞ Graphing calculator or computer with graphing software required   **1.** Homework Hints available in TEC

2. The *temperature-humidity index I* (or humidex, for short) is the perceived air temperature when the actual temperature is T and the relative humidity is h, so we can write $I = f(T, h)$. The following table of values of I is an excerpt from a table compiled by the National Oceanic & Atmospheric Administration.

TABLE 3 Apparent temperature as a function of temperature and humidity

Relative humidity (%)

T \ h	20	30	40	50	60	70
80	77	78	79	81	82	83
85	82	84	86	88	90	93
90	87	90	93	96	100	106
95	93	96	101	107	114	124
100	99	104	110	120	132	144

Actual temperature (°F)

(a) What is the value of $f(95, 70)$? What is its meaning?
(b) For what value of h is $f(90, h) = 100$?
(c) For what value of T is $f(T, 50) = 88$?
(d) What are the meanings of the functions $I = f(80, h)$ and $I = f(100, h)$? Compare the behavior of these two functions of h.

3. Verify for the Cobb-Douglas production function

$$P(L, K) = 1.01L^{0.75}K^{0.25}$$

discussed in Example 2 that the production will be doubled if both the amount of labor and the amount of capital are doubled. Determine whether this is also true for the general production function

$$P(L, K) = bL^{\alpha}K^{1-\alpha}$$

4. The wind-chill index W discussed in Example 1 has been modeled by the following function:

$$W(T, v) = 13.12 + 0.6215T - 11.37v^{0.16} + 0.3965Tv^{0.16}$$

Check to see how closely this model agrees with the values in Table 1 for a few values of T and v.

5. Find and sketch the domain of the function $f(x, y) = \ln(9 - x^2 - 9y^2)$. What is the range of f?

6. Find and sketch the domain of the function $f(x, y) = \sqrt{y} + \sqrt{25 - x^2 - y^2}$.

7. Let $f(x, y, z) = \sqrt{x} + \sqrt{y} + \sqrt{z} + \ln(4 - x^2 - y^2 - z^2)$.
(a) Evaluate $f(1, 1, 1)$.
(b) Find and describe the domain of f.

8. Let $g(x, y, z) = x^3y^2z\sqrt{10 - x - y - z}$.
(a) Evaluate $g(1, 2, 3)$.
(b) Find and describe the domain of g.

9. A contour map for a function f is shown. Use it to estimate the values of $f(-3, 3)$ and $f(3, -2)$. What can you say about the shape of the graph?

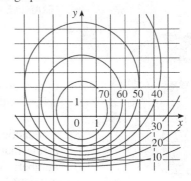

10. Shown is a contour map of atmospheric pressure in North America on August 12, 2008. On the level curves (called isobars) the pressure is indicated in millibars (mb).
(a) Estimate the pressure at C (Chicago), N (Nashville), S (San Francisco), and V (Vancouver).
(b) At which of these locations were the winds strongest?

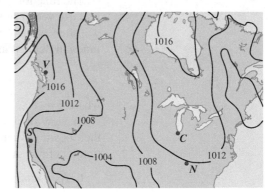

11. Level curves (isothermals) are shown for the water temperature (in °C) in Long Lake (Minnesota) in 1998 as a function of depth and time of year. Estimate the temperature in the lake on June 9 (day 160) at a depth of 10 m and on June 29 (day 180) at a depth of 5 m.

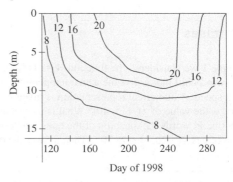

Day of 1998

12. Two contour maps are shown. One is for a function f whose graph is a cone. The other is for a function g whose graph is a paraboloid. Which is which, and why?

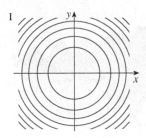

13. Locate the points A and B on the map of Lonesome Mountain (Figure 5). How would you describe the terrain near A? Near B?

14. Make a rough sketch of a contour map for the function whose graph is shown.

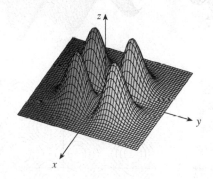

15–18 A contour map of a function is shown. Use it to make a rough sketch of the graph of f.

15.

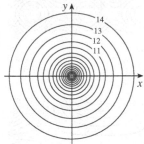

16.

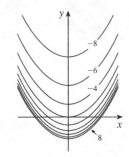

17.

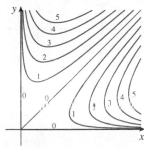

18.

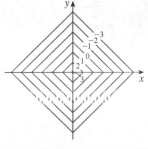

19–26 Draw a contour map of the function showing several level curves.

19. $f(x, y) = (y - 2x)^2$

20. $f(x, y) = x^3 - y$

21. $f(x, y) = \sqrt{x} + y$

22. $f(x, y) = \ln(x^2 + 4y^2)$

23. $f(x, y) = ye^x$

24. $f(x, y) = y \sec x$

25. $f(x, y) = \sqrt{y^2 - x^2}$

26. $f(x, y) = y/(x^2 + y^2)$

27–28 Sketch both a contour map and a graph of the function and compare them.

27. $f(x, y) = x^2 + 9y^2$

28. $f(x, y) = \sqrt{36 - 9x^2 - 4y^2}$

29. A thin metal plate, located in the xy-plane, has temperature $T(x, y)$ at the point (x, y). The level curves of T are called *isothermals* because at all points on such a curve the temperature is the same. Sketch some isothermals if the temperature function is given by

$$T(x, y) = \frac{100}{1 + x^2 + 2y^2}$$

30. If $V(x, y)$ is the electric potential at a point (x, y) in the xy-plane, then the level curves of V are called *equipotential curves* because at all points on such a curve the electric potential is the same. Sketch some equipotential curves if $V(x, y) = c/\sqrt{r^2 - x^2 - y^2}$, where c is a positive constant.

31–34 Use a computer to graph the function using various domains and viewpoints. Get a printout of one that, in your opinion, gives a good view. If your software also produces level curves, then plot some contour lines of the same function and compare with the graph.

31. $f(x, y) = xy^2 - x^3$ (monkey saddle)

32. $f(x, y) = xy^3 - yx^3$ (dog saddle)

33. $f(x, y) = e^{-(x^2+y^2)/3}(\sin(x^2) + \cos(y^2))$

34. $f(x, y) = \cos x \cos y$

Graphs and Contour Maps for Exercises 35–40

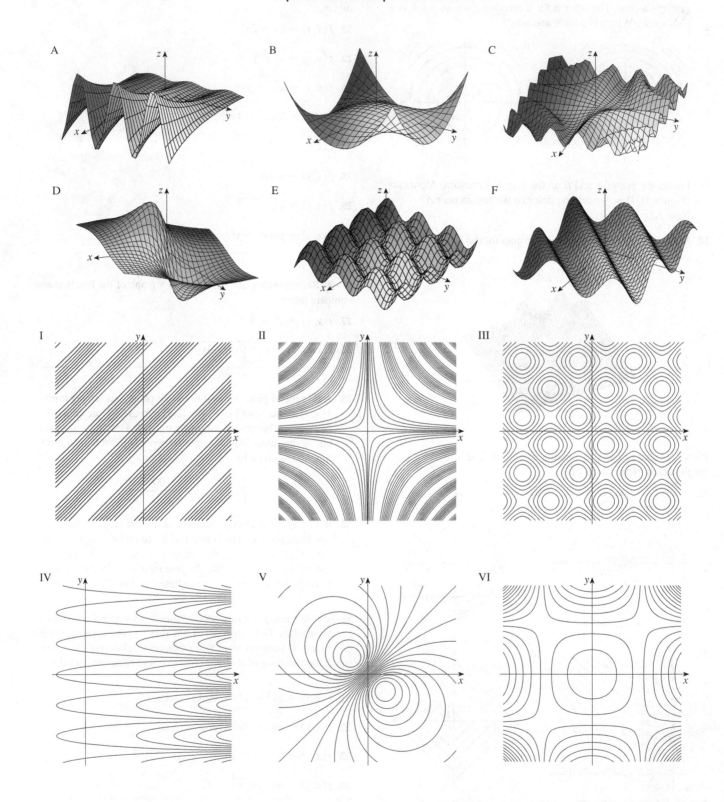

35–40 Match the function (a) with its graph (labeled A–F at the left) and (b) with its contour map (labeled I–VI). Give reasons for your choices.

35. $z = \sin(xy)$ **36.** $z = e^x \cos y$

37. $z = \sin(x - y)$ **38.** $z = \sin x - \sin y$

39. $z = (1 - x^2)(1 - y^2)$ **40.** $z = \dfrac{x - y}{1 + x^2 + y^2}$

41–44 Describe the level surfaces of the function.

41. $f(x, y, z) = x + 3y + 5z$

42. $f(x, y, z) = x^2 + 3y^2 + 5z^2$

43. $f(x, y, z) = y^2 + z^2$

44. $f(x, y, z) = x^2 - y^2 - z^2$

45–46 Describe how the graph of g is obtained from the graph of f.

45. (a) $g(x, y) = f(x, y) + 2$ (b) $g(x, y) = 2f(x, y)$
(c) $g(x, y) = -f(x, y)$ (d) $g(x, y) = 2 - f(x, y)$

46. (a) $g(x, y) = f(x - 2, y)$
(b) $g(x, y) = f(x, y + 2)$
(c) $g(x, y) = f(x + 3, y - 4)$

---

47. Use a computer to investigate the family of functions $f(x, y) = e^{cx^2 + y^2}$. How does the shape of the graph depend on c?

48. Graph the functions

$$f(x, y) = \sqrt{x^2 + y^2} \qquad f(x, y) = e^{\sqrt{x^2 + y^2}}$$

$$f(x, y) = \ln\sqrt{x^2 + y^2} \qquad f(x, y) = \sin\left(\sqrt{x^2 + y^2}\right)$$

and $$f(x, y) = \dfrac{1}{\sqrt{x^2 + y^2}}$$

In general, if g is a function of one variable, how is the graph of $f(x, y) = g\left(\sqrt{x^2 + y^2}\right)$ obtained from the graph of g?

49. (a) Show that, by taking logarithms, the general Cobb-Douglas function $P = bL^\alpha K^{1-\alpha}$ can be expressed as

$$\ln \frac{P}{K} = \ln b + \alpha \ln \frac{L}{K}$$

(b) If we let $x = \ln(L/K)$ and $y = \ln(P/K)$, the equation in part (a) becomes the linear equation $y = \alpha x + \ln b$. Use Table 2 (in Example 2) to make a table of values of $\ln(L/K)$ and $\ln(P/K)$ for the years 1899–1922. Then use a graphing calculator or computer to find the least squares regression line through the points $(\ln(L/K), \ln(P/K))$.
(c) Deduce that the Cobb-Douglas production function is $P = 1.01L^{0.75}K^{0.25}$.

11.2 Limits and Continuity

Let's compare the behavior of the functions

$$f(x, y) = \frac{\sin(x^2 + y^2)}{x^2 + y^2} \qquad \text{and} \qquad g(x, y) = \frac{x^2 - y^2}{x^2 + y^2}$$

as x and y both approach 0 [and therefore the point (x, y) approaches the origin]. Tables 1 and 2 show values of $f(x, y)$ and $g(x, y)$, correct to three decimal places, for points (x, y) near the origin. (Notice that neither function is defined at the origin.)

TABLE 1 Values of $f(x, y)$

x \ y	−1.0	−0.5	−0.2	0	0.2	0.5	1.0
−1.0	0.455	0.759	0.829	0.841	0.829	0.759	0.455
−0.5	0.759	0.959	0.986	0.990	0.986	0.959	0.759
−0.2	0.829	0.986	0.999	1.000	0.999	0.986	0.829
0	0.841	0.990	1.000		1.000	0.990	0.841
0.2	0.829	0.986	0.999	1.000	0.999	0.986	0.829
0.5	0.759	0.959	0.986	0.990	0.986	0.959	0.759
1.0	0.455	0.759	0.829	0.841	0.829	0.759	0.455

TABLE 2 Values of $g(x, y)$

x \ y	−1.0	−0.5	−0.2	0	0.2	0.5	1.0
−1.0	0.000	0.600	0.923	1.000	0.923	0.600	0.000
−0.5	−0.600	0.000	0.724	1.000	0.724	0.000	−0.600
−0.2	−0.923	−0.724	0.000	1.000	0.000	−0.724	−0.923
0	1.000	−1.000	−1.000		−1.000	−1.000	−1.000
0.2	−0.923	−0.724	0.000	1.000	0.000	−0.724	−0.923
0.5	−0.600	0.000	0.724	1.000	0.724	0.000	−0.600
1.0	0.000	0.600	0.923	1.000	0.923	0.600	0.000

It appears that as (x, y) approaches $(0, 0)$, the values of $f(x, y)$ are approaching 1 whereas the values of $g(x, y)$ aren't approaching any number. It turns out that these guesses based on numerical evidence are correct, and we write

$$\lim_{(x, y) \to (0, 0)} \frac{\sin(x^2 + y^2)}{x^2 + y^2} = 1 \quad \text{and} \quad \lim_{(x, y) \to (0, 0)} \frac{x^2 - y^2}{x^2 + y^2} \quad \text{does not exist}$$

In general, we use the notation

$$\lim_{(x, y) \to (a, b)} f(x, y) = L$$

to indicate that the values of $f(x, y)$ approach the number L as the point (x, y) approaches the point (a, b) along any path that stays within the domain of f.

A more precise definition of the limit of a function of two variables is given in Appendix D.

> **1** **Definition** We write
>
> $$\lim_{(x, y) \to (a, b)} f(x, y) = L$$
>
> and we say that the **limit of $f(x, y)$ as (x, y) approaches (a, b)** is L if we can make the values of $f(x, y)$ as close to L as we like by taking the point (x, y) sufficiently close to the point (a, b), but not equal to (a, b).

Other notations for the limit in Definition 1 are

$$\lim_{\substack{x \to a \\ y \to b}} f(x, y) = L \quad \text{and} \quad f(x, y) \to L \text{ as } (x, y) \to (a, b)$$

For functions of a single variable, when we let x approach a, there are only two possible directions of approach, from the left or from the right. We recall from Chapter 2 that if $\lim_{x \to a^-} f(x) \neq \lim_{x \to a^+} f(x)$, then $\lim_{x \to a} f(x)$ does not exist.

For functions of two variables the situation is not as simple because we can let (x, y) approach (a, b) from an infinite number of directions in any manner whatsoever (see Figure 1) as long as (x, y) stays within the domain of f.

Definition 1 says that the distance between $f(x, y)$ and L can be made arbitrarily small by making the distance from (x, y) to (a, b) sufficiently small (but not 0). The definition refers only to the *distance* between (x, y) and (a, b). It does not refer to the direction of approach. Therefore, if the limit exists, then $f(x, y)$ must approach the same limit no matter how (x, y) approaches (a, b). Thus, if we can find two different paths of approach along which the function $f(x, y)$ has different limits, then it follows that $\lim_{(x, y) \to (a, b)} f(x, y)$ does not exist.

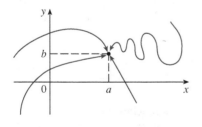

FIGURE 1

> If $f(x, y) \to L_1$ as $(x, y) \to (a, b)$ along a path C_1 and $f(x, y) \to L_2$ as $(x, y) \to (a, b)$ along a path C_2, where $L_1 \neq L_2$, then $\lim_{(x, y) \to (a, b)} f(x, y)$ does not exist.

V **EXAMPLE 1** Show that $\lim_{(x, y) \to (0, 0)} \dfrac{x^2 - y^2}{x^2 + y^2}$ does not exist.

SOLUTION Let $f(x, y) = (x^2 - y^2)/(x^2 + y^2)$. First let's approach $(0, 0)$ along the x-axis. Then $y = 0$ gives $f(x, 0) = x^2/x^2 = 1$ for all $x \neq 0$, so

$$f(x, y) \to 1 \quad \text{as} \quad (x, y) \to (0, 0) \text{ along the } x\text{-axis}$$

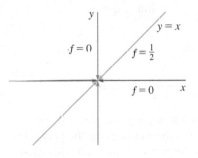

FIGURE 2

We now approach along the y-axis by putting $x = 0$. Then $f(0, y) = \dfrac{-y^2}{y^2} = -1$ for all $y \neq 0$, so

$$f(x, y) \to -1 \quad \text{as} \quad (x, y) \to (0, 0) \text{ along the } y\text{-axis}$$

(See Figure 2.) Since f has two different limits along two different lines, the given limit does not exist. (This confirms the conjecture we made on the basis of numerical evidence at the beginning of this section.)

EXAMPLE 2 **Deciding whether a limit exists**

If $f(x, y) = xy/(x^2 + y^2)$, does $\displaystyle\lim_{(x, y)\to(0, 0)} f(x, y)$ exist?

SOLUTION If $y = 0$, then $f(x, 0) = 0/x^2 = 0$. Therefore

$$f(x, y) \to 0 \quad \text{as} \quad (x, y) \to (0, 0) \text{ along the } x\text{-axis}$$

If $x = 0$, then $f(0, y) = 0/y^2 = 0$, so

$$f(x, y) \to 0 \quad \text{as} \quad (x, y) \to (0, 0) \text{ along the } y\text{-axis}$$

Although we have obtained identical limits along the axes, that does not show that the given limit is 0. Let's now approach $(0, 0)$ along another line, say $y = x$. For all $x \neq 0$,

$$f(x, x) = \frac{x^2}{x^2 + x^2} = \frac{1}{2}$$

FIGURE 3

Therefore $\quad f(x, y) \to \tfrac{1}{2} \quad \text{as} \quad (x, y) \to (0, 0) \text{ along } y = x$

(See Figure 3.) Since we have obtained different limits along different paths, the given limit does not exist.

Figure 4 sheds some light on Example 2. The ridge that occurs above the line $y = x$ corresponds to the fact that $f(x, y) = \tfrac{1}{2}$ for all points (x, y) on that line except the origin.

TEC In Visual 11.2 a rotating line on the surface in Figure 4 shows different limits at the origin from different directions.

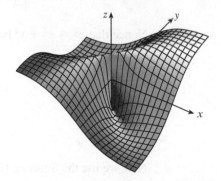

FIGURE 4

$$f(x, y) = \frac{xy}{x^2 + y^2}$$

V **EXAMPLE 3** If $f(x, y) = \dfrac{xy^2}{x^2 + y^4}$, does $\displaystyle\lim_{(x, y)\to(0, 0)} f(x, y)$ exist?

SOLUTION With the solution of Example 2 in mind, let's try to save time by letting $(x, y) \to (0, 0)$ along any nonvertical line through the origin. Then $y = mx$, where m is the slope, and

$$f(x, y) = f(x, mx) = \frac{x(mx)^2}{x^2 + (mx)^4} = \frac{m^2 x^3}{x^2 + m^4 x^4} = \frac{m^2 x}{1 + m^4 x^2}$$

So $\qquad\qquad f(x, y) \to 0 \quad \text{as} \quad (x, y) \to (0, 0) \text{ along } y = mx$

Figure 5 shows the graph of the function in Example 3. Notice the ridge above the parabola $x = y^2$.

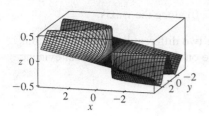

FIGURE 5

Thus f has the same limiting value along every nonvertical line through the origin. But that does not show that the given limit is 0, for if we now let $(x, y) \to (0, 0)$ along the parabola $x = y^2$, we have

$$f(x, y) = f(y^2, y) = \frac{y^2 \cdot y^2}{(y^2)^2 + y^4} = \frac{y^4}{2y^4} = \frac{1}{2}$$

so

$$f(x, y) \to \tfrac{1}{2} \quad \text{as} \quad (x, y) \to (0, 0) \text{ along } x = y^2$$

Since different paths lead to different limiting values, the given limit does not exist. ■

Now let's look at limits that *do* exist. Just as for functions of one variable, the calculation of limits for functions of two variables can be greatly simplified by the use of properties of limits. The Limit Laws listed in Section 2.3 can be extended to functions of two variables: The limit of a sum is the sum of the limits, the limit of a product is the product of the limits, and so on. In particular, the following equations are true.

$$\boxed{2} \qquad \lim_{(x, y) \to (a, b)} x = a \qquad \lim_{(x, y) \to (a, b)} y = b \qquad \lim_{(x, y) \to (a, b)} c = c$$

The Squeeze Theorem also holds.

EXAMPLE 4   **Guessing and proving a limit**   Find $\displaystyle\lim_{(x, y) \to (0, 0)} \frac{3x^2 y}{x^2 + y^2}$ if it exists.

SOLUTION   As in Example 3, we could show that the limit along any line through the origin is 0. This doesn't prove that the given limit is 0, but the limits along the parabolas $y = x^2$ and $x = y^2$ also turn out to be 0, so we begin to suspect that the limit does exist and is equal to 0. To prove it we look at the distance from $f(x, y)$ to 0:

$$\left| \frac{3x^2 y}{x^2 + y^2} - 0 \right| = \left| \frac{3x^2 y}{x^2 + y^2} \right| = \frac{3x^2 |y|}{x^2 + y^2}$$

Notice that $x^2 \leq x^2 + y^2$ because $y^2 \geq 0$. So

$$\frac{x^2}{x^2 + y^2} \leq 1$$

Thus

$$0 \leq \frac{3x^2 |y|}{x^2 + y^2} \leq 3|y|$$

Now we use the Squeeze Theorem. Since

$$\lim_{(x, y) \to (0, 0)} 0 = 0 \quad \text{and} \quad \lim_{(x, y) \to (0, 0)} 3|y| = 0 \qquad \text{[by (2)]}$$

we conclude that

$$\lim_{(x, y) \to (0, 0)} \frac{3x^2 y}{x^2 + y^2} = 0$$
■

Continuity

Recall that evaluating limits of *continuous* functions of a single variable is easy. It can be accomplished by direct substitution because the defining property of a continuous function is $\lim_{x \to a} f(x) = f(a)$. Continuous functions of two variables are also defined by the direct substitution property.

> **3** **Definition**   A function f of two variables is called **continuous at** (a, b) if
>
> $$\lim_{(x,\, y) \to (a,\, b)} f(x, y) = f(a, b)$$
>
> We say f is **continuous on** D if f is continuous at every point (a, b) in D.

The intuitive meaning of continuity is that if the point (x, y) changes by a small amount, then the value of $f(x, y)$ changes by a small amount. This means that a surface that is the graph of a continuous function has no hole or break.

Using the properties of limits, you can see that sums, differences, products, and quotients of continuous functions are continuous on their domains. Let's use this fact to give examples of continuous functions.

A **polynomial function of two variables** (or polynomial, for short) is a sum of terms of the form $cx^m y^n$, where c is a constant and m and n are nonnegative integers. A **rational function** is a ratio of polynomials. For instance,

$$f(x, y) = x^4 + 5x^3 y^2 + 6xy^4 - 7y + 6$$

is a polynomial, whereas

$$g(x, y) = \frac{2xy + 1}{x^2 + y^2}$$

is a rational function.

The limits in (2) show that the functions $f(x, y) = x$, $g(x, y) = y$, and $h(x, y) = c$ are continuous. Since any polynomial can be built up out of the simple functions f, g, and h by multiplication and addition, it follows that *all polynomials are continuous on* $\mathbb{R}^2$. Likewise, any rational function is continuous on its domain because it is a quotient of continuous functions.

▼ EXAMPLE 5   **Using continuity to find a limit**

Evaluate $\displaystyle\lim_{(x,\, y) \to (1,\, 2)} (x^2 y^3 - x^3 y^2 + 3x + 2y)$.

SOLUTION   Since $f(x, y) = x^2 y^3 - x^3 y^2 + 3x + 2y$ is a polynomial, it is continuous everywhere, so we can find the limit by direct substitution:

$$\lim_{(x,\, y) \to (1,\, 2)} (x^2 y^3 - x^3 y^2 + 3x + 2y) = 1^2 \cdot 2^3 - 1^3 \cdot 2^2 + 3 \cdot 1 + 2 \cdot 2 = 11 \qquad \blacksquare$$

EXAMPLE 6   Where is the function $f(x, y) = \dfrac{x^2 - y^2}{x^2 + y^2}$ continuous?

SOLUTION   The function f is discontinuous at $(0, 0)$ because it is not defined there. Since f is a rational function, it is continuous on its domain, which is the set $D = \{(x, y) \mid (x, y) \neq (0, 0)\}$. $\qquad \blacksquare$

EXAMPLE 7   **A function that is discontinuous at the origin**

Let

$$g(x, y) = \begin{cases} \dfrac{x^2 - y^2}{x^2 + y^2} & \text{if } (x, y) \neq (0, 0) \\ 0 & \text{if } (x, y) = (0, 0) \end{cases}$$

Here g is defined at $(0, 0)$ but g is still discontinuous there because $\lim_{(x,\, y) \to (0,\, 0)} g(x, y)$ does not exist (see Example 1). $\qquad \blacksquare$

Figure 6 shows the graph of the continuous function in Example 8.

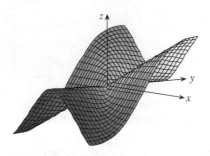

FIGURE 6

EXAMPLE 8   A function that is continuous everywhere

Let

$$f(x, y) = \begin{cases} \dfrac{3x^2 y}{x^2 + y^2} & \text{if } (x, y) \neq (0, 0) \\ 0 & \text{if } (x, y) = (0, 0) \end{cases}$$

We know f is continuous for $(x, y) \neq (0, 0)$ since it is equal to a rational function there. Also, from Example 4, we have

$$\lim_{(x, y) \to (0, 0)} f(x, y) = \lim_{(x, y) \to (0, 0)} \frac{3x^2 y}{x^2 + y^2} = 0 = f(0, 0)$$

Therefore f is continuous at $(0, 0)$, and so it is continuous on $\mathbb{R}^2$.

Just as for functions of one variable, composition is another way of combining two continuous functions to get a third. In fact, it can be shown that if f is a continuous function of two variables and g is a continuous function of a single variable that is defined on the range of f, then the composite function $h = g \circ f$ defined by $h(x, y) = g(f(x, y))$ is also a continuous function.

EXAMPLE 9   Where is the function $h(x, y) = \arctan(y/x)$ continuous?

SOLUTION   The function $f(x, y) = y/x$ is a rational function and therefore continuous except on the line $x = 0$. The function $g(t) = \arctan t$ is continuous everywhere. So the composite function

$$g(f(x, y)) = \arctan(y/x) = h(x, y)$$

is continuous except where $x = 0$. The graph in Figure 7 shows the break in the graph of h above the y-axis.

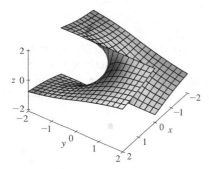

FIGURE 7

The function $h(x, y) = \arctan(y/x)$ is discontinuous where $x = 0$.

Everything that we have done in this section can be extended to functions of three or more variables. The notation

$$\lim_{(x, y, z) \to (a, b, c)} f(x, y, z) = L$$

means that the values of $f(x, y, z)$ approach the number L as the point (x, y, z) approaches the point (a, b, c) along any path in the domain of f. The function f is **continuous** at (a, b, c) if

$$\lim_{(x, y, z) \to (a, b, c)} f(x, y, z) = f(a, b, c)$$

For instance, the function

$$f(x, y, z) = \frac{1}{x^2 + y^2 + z^2 - 1}$$

is a rational function of three variables and so is continuous at every point in $\mathbb{R}^3$ except where $x^2 + y^2 + z^2 = 1$. In other words, it is discontinuous on the sphere with center the origin and radius 1.

11.2 Exercises

1. Suppose that $\lim_{(x,y) \to (3,1)} f(x, y) = 6$. What can you say about the value of $f(3, 1)$? What if f is continuous?

2. Explain why each function is continuous or discontinuous.
   (a) The outdoor temperature as a function of longitude, latitude, and time
   (b) Elevation (height above sea level) as a function of longitude, latitude, and time
   (c) The cost of a taxi ride as a function of distance traveled and time

3–4 Use a table of numerical values of $f(x, y)$ for (x, y) near the origin to make a conjecture about the value of the limit of $f(x, y)$ as $(x, y) \to (0, 0)$. Then explain why your guess is correct.

3. $f(x, y) = \dfrac{x^2y^3 + x^3y^2 - 5}{2 - xy}$ 4. $f(x, y) = \dfrac{2xy}{x^2 + 2y^2}$

5–20 Find the limit, if it exists, or show that the limit does not exist.

5. $\lim_{(x,y) \to (1,2)} (5x^3 - x^2y^2)$

6. $\lim_{(x,y) \to (1,-1)} e^{-xy} \cos(x + y)$

7. $\lim_{(x,y) \to (0,0)} \dfrac{y^4}{x^4 + 3y^4}$ 8. $\lim_{(x,y) \to (0,0)} \dfrac{x^2 + \sin^2 y}{2x^2 + y^2}$

9. $\lim_{(x,y) \to (0,0)} \dfrac{xy \cos y}{3x^2 + y^2}$ 10. $\lim_{(x,y) \to (0,0)} \dfrac{6x^3y}{2x^4 + y^4}$

11. $\lim_{(x,y) \to (0,0)} \dfrac{xy}{\sqrt{x^2 + y^2}}$ 12. $\lim_{(x,y) \to (0,0)} \dfrac{x^2 \sin^2 y}{x^2 + 2y^2}$

13. $\lim_{(x,y) \to (0,0)} \dfrac{x^2ye^y}{x^4 + 4y^2}$ 14. $\lim_{(x,y) \to (0,0)} \dfrac{xy^4}{x^2 + y^8}$

15. $\lim_{(x,y) \to (0,0)} \dfrac{x^2 + y^2}{\sqrt{x^2 + y^2 + 1} - 1}$ 16. $\lim_{(x,y) \to (0,0)} \dfrac{x^4 - y^4}{x^2 + y^2}$

17. $\lim_{(x,y,z) \to (3,0,1)} e^{-xy} \sin(\pi z/2)$

18. $\lim_{(x,y,z) \to (0,0,0)} \dfrac{x^2 + 2y^2 + 3z^2}{x^2 + y^2 + z^2}$

19. $\lim_{(x,y,z) \to (0,0,0)} \dfrac{xy + yz^2 + xz^2}{x^2 + y^2 + z^4}$

20. $\lim_{(x,y,z) \to (0,0,0)} \dfrac{yz}{x^2 + 4y^2 + 9z^2}$

21–22 Use a computer graph of the function to explain why the limit does not exist.

21. $\lim_{(x,y) \to (0,0)} \dfrac{2x^2 + 3xy + 4y^2}{3x^2 + 5y^2}$

22. $\lim_{(x,y) \to (0,0)} \dfrac{xy^3}{x^2 + y^6}$

23–24 Find $h(x, y) = g(f(x, y))$ and the set on which h is continuous.

23. $g(t) = t^2 + \sqrt{t}, \quad f(x, y) = 2x + 3y - 6$

24. $g(t) = t + \ln t, \quad f(x, y) = \dfrac{1 - xy}{1 + x^2y^2}$

25–26 Graph the function and observe where it is discontinuous. Then use the formula to explain what you have observed.

25. $f(x, y) = e^{1/(x-y)}$ 26. $f(x, y) = \dfrac{1}{1 - x^2 - y^2}$

27–34 Determine the set of points at which the function is continuous.

27. $F(x, y) = \arctan(x + \sqrt{y})$

28. $F(x, y) = \cos\sqrt{1 + x - y}$

29. $G(x, y) = \ln(x^2 + y^2 - 4)$

30. $H(x, y) = \dfrac{e^x + e^y}{e^{xy} - 1}$

31. $f(x, y, z) = \dfrac{\sqrt{y}}{x^2 - y^2 + z^2}$

32. $f(x, y, z) = \sqrt{x + y + z}$

33. $f(x, y) = \begin{cases} \dfrac{x^2y^3}{2x^2 + y^2} & \text{if } (x, y) \neq (0, 0) \\ 1 & \text{if } (x, y) = (0, 0) \end{cases}$

34. $f(x, y) = \begin{cases} \dfrac{xy}{x^2 + xy + y^2} & \text{if } (x, y) \neq (0, 0) \\ 0 & \text{if } (x, y) = (0, 0) \end{cases}$

35–36 Use polar coordinates to find the limit. [If (r, θ) are polar coordinates of the point (x, y) with $r \geq 0$, note that $r \to 0^+$ as $(x, y) \to (0, 0)$.]

35. $\lim_{(x,y) \to (0,0)} \dfrac{x^3 + y^3}{x^2 + y^2}$

36. $\displaystyle\lim_{(x,\,y)\to(0,\,0)} (x^2 + y^2)\ln(x^2 + y^2)$

37. Use spherical coordinates to find

$$\lim_{(x,\,y,\,z)\to(0,\,0,\,0)} \frac{xyz}{x^2 + y^2 + z^2}$$

38. At the beginning of this section we considered the function

$$f(x, y) = \frac{\sin(x^2 + y^2)}{x^2 + y^2}$$

and guessed that $f(x, y) \to 1$ as $(x, y) \to (0, 0)$ on the basis of numerical evidence. Use polar coordinates to confirm the value of the limit. Then graph the function.

39. Graph and discuss the continuity of the function

$$f(x, y) = \begin{cases} \dfrac{\sin xy}{xy} & \text{if } xy \neq 0 \\ 1 & \text{if } xy = 0 \end{cases}$$

40. Let

$$f(x, y) = \begin{cases} 0 & \text{if } y \leq 0 \text{ or } y \geq x^4 \\ 1 & \text{if } 0 < y < x^4 \end{cases}$$

(a) Show that $f(x, y) \to 0$ as $(x, y) \to (0, 0)$ along any path through $(0, 0)$ of the form $y = mx^a$ with $a < 4$.
(b) Despite part (a), show that f is discontinuous at $(0, 0)$.
(c) Show that f is discontinuous on two entire curves.

11.3 Partial Derivatives

On a hot day, extreme humidity makes us think the temperature is higher than it really is, whereas in very dry air we perceive the temperature to be lower than the thermometer indicates. The National Weather Service has devised the *heat index* (also called the temperature-humidity index, or humidex, in some countries) to describe the combined effects of temperature and humidity. The heat index I is the perceived air temperature when the actual temperature is T and the relative humidity is H. So I is a function of T and H and we can write $I = f(T, H)$. The following table of values of I is an excerpt from a table compiled by the National Weather Service.

TABLE 1

Heat index I as a function of temperature and humidity

T $\diagdown$ H	50	55	60	65	70	75	80	85	90
90	96	98	100	103	106	109	112	115	119
92	100	103	105	108	112	115	119	123	128
94	104	107	111	114	118	122	127	132	137
96	109	113	116	121	125	130	135	141	146
98	114	118	123	127	133	138	144	150	157
100	119	124	129	135	141	147	154	161	168

Relative humidity (%)

Actual temperature (°F)

If we concentrate on the highlighted column of the table, which corresponds to a relative humidity of $H = 70\%$, we are considering the heat index as a function of the single variable T for a fixed value of H. Let's write $g(T) = f(T, 70)$. Then $g(T)$ describes how the heat index I increases as the actual temperature T increases when the relative humidity is 70%. The derivative of g when $T = 96°F$ is the rate of change of I with respect to T when $T = 96°F$:

$$g'(96) = \lim_{h \to 0} \frac{g(96 + h) - g(96)}{h} = \lim_{h \to 0} \frac{f(96 + h, 70) - f(96, 70)}{h}$$

We can approximate $g'(96)$ using the values in Table 1 by taking $h = 2$ and -2:

$$g'(96) \approx \frac{g(98) - g(96)}{2} = \frac{f(98, 70) - f(96, 70)}{2} = \frac{133 - 125}{2} = 4$$

$$g'(96) \approx \frac{g(94) - g(96)}{-2} = \frac{f(94, 70) - f(96, 70)}{-2} = \frac{118 - 125}{-2} = 3.5$$

Averaging these values, we can say that the derivative $g'(96)$ is approximately 3.75. This means that, when the actual temperature is 96°F and the relative humidity is 70%, the apparent temperature (heat index) rises by about 3.75°F for every degree that the actual temperature rises!

Now let's look at the highlighted row in Table 1, which corresponds to a fixed temperature of $T = 96°F$. The numbers in this row are values of the function $G(H) = f(96, H)$, which describes how the heat index increases as the relative humidity H increases when the actual temperature is $T = 96°F$. The derivative of this function when $H = 70\%$ is the rate of change of I with respect to H when $H = 70\%$:

$$G'(70) = \lim_{h \to 0} \frac{G(70 + h) - G(70)}{h} = \lim_{h \to 0} \frac{f(96, 70 + h) - f(96, 70)}{h}$$

By taking $h = 5$ and -5, we approximate $G'(70)$ using the tabular values:

$$G'(70) \approx \frac{G(75) - G(70)}{5} = \frac{f(96, 75) - f(96, 70)}{5} = \frac{130 - 125}{5} = 1$$

$$G'(70) \approx \frac{G(65) - G(70)}{-5} = \frac{f(96, 65) - f(96, 70)}{-5} = \frac{121 - 125}{-5} = 0.8$$

By averaging these values we get the estimate $G'(70) \approx 0.9$. This says that, when the temperature is 96°F and the relative humidity is 70%, the heat index rises about 0.9°F for every percent that the relative humidity rises.

In general, suppose f is a function of two variables x and y and we let only x vary while keeping y fixed, say $y = b$, where b is a constant. Then we are really considering a function of a single variable x, namely, $g(x) = f(x, b)$. If g has a derivative at a, then we call it the **partial derivative of f with respect to x at (a, b)** and denote it by $f_x(a, b)$. Thus

$$\boxed{1 \qquad f_x(a, b) = g'(a) \qquad \text{where} \qquad g(x) = f(x, b)}$$

By the definition of a derivative, we have

$$g'(a) = \lim_{h \to 0} \frac{g(a + h) - g(a)}{h}$$

and so Equation 1 becomes

$$\boxed{2 \qquad f_x(a, b) = \lim_{h \to 0} \frac{f(a + h, b) - f(a, b)}{h}}$$

Similarly, the **partial derivative of f with respect to y at (a, b)**, denoted by $f_y(a, b)$, is obtained by keeping x fixed ($x = a$) and finding the ordinary derivative at b of the function $G(y) = f(a, y)$:

$$\boxed{3} \qquad f_y(a, b) = \lim_{h \to 0} \frac{f(a, b + h) - f(a, b)}{h}$$

With this notation for partial derivatives, we can write the rates of change of the heat index I with respect to the actual temperature T and relative humidity H when $T = 96°F$ and $H = 70\%$ as follows:

$$f_T(96, 70) \approx 3.75 \qquad f_H(96, 70) \approx 0.9$$

If we now let the point (a, b) vary in Equations 2 and 3, f_x and f_y become functions of two variables.

$\boxed{4}$ If f is a function of two variables, its **partial derivatives** are the functions f_x and f_y defined by

$$f_x(x, y) = \lim_{h \to 0} \frac{f(x + h, y) - f(x, y)}{h}$$

$$f_y(x, y) = \lim_{h \to 0} \frac{f(x, y + h) - f(x, y)}{h}$$

There are many alternative notations for partial derivatives. For instance, instead of f_x we can write f_1 or $D_1 f$ (to indicate differentiation with respect to the *first* variable) or $\partial f / \partial x$. But here $\partial f / \partial x$ can't be interpreted as a ratio of differentials.

Notations for Partial Derivatives   If $z = f(x, y)$, we write

$$f_x(x, y) = f_x = \frac{\partial f}{\partial x} = \frac{\partial}{\partial x} f(x, y) = \frac{\partial z}{\partial x} = f_1 = D_1 f = D_x f$$

$$f_y(x, y) = f_y = \frac{\partial f}{\partial y} = \frac{\partial}{\partial y} f(x, y) = \frac{\partial z}{\partial y} = f_2 = D_2 f = D_y f$$

To compute partial derivatives, all we have to do is remember from Equation 1 that the partial derivative with respect to x is just the *ordinary* derivative of the function g of a single variable that we get by keeping y fixed. Thus we have the following rule.

Rule for Finding Partial Derivatives of $z = f(x, y)$

1. To find f_x, regard y as a constant and differentiate $f(x, y)$ with respect to x.

2. To find f_y, regard x as a constant and differentiate $f(x, y)$ with respect to y.

EXAMPLE 1   Evaluating partial derivatives   If $f(x, y) = x^3 + x^2y^3 - 2y^2$, find $f_x(2, 1)$ and $f_y(2, 1)$.

SOLUTION   Holding y constant and differentiating with respect to x, we get

$$f_x(x, y) = 3x^2 + 2xy^3$$

and so

$$f_x(2, 1) = 3 \cdot 2^2 + 2 \cdot 2 \cdot 1^3 = 16$$

Holding x constant and differentiating with respect to y, we get

$$f_y(x, y) = 3x^2y^2 - 4y$$

$$f_y(2, 1) = 3 \cdot 2^2 \cdot 1^2 - 4 \cdot 1 = 8$$

Interpretations of Partial Derivatives

To give a geometric interpretation of partial derivatives, we recall that the equation $z = f(x, y)$ represents a surface S (the graph of f). If $f(a, b) = c$, then the point $P(a, b, c)$ lies on S. By fixing $y = b$, we are restricting our attention to the curve C_1 in which the vertical plane $y = b$ intersects S. (In other words, C_1 is the trace of S in the plane $y = b$.) Likewise, the vertical plane $x = a$ intersects S in a curve C_2. Both of the curves C_1 and C_2 pass through the point P. (See Figure 1.)

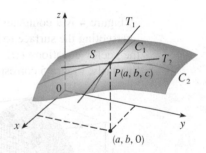

FIGURE 1

The partial derivatives of f at (a, b) are the slopes of the tangents to C_1 and C_2.

Notice that the curve C_1 is the graph of the function $g(x) = f(x, b)$, so the slope of its tangent T_1 at P is $g'(a) = f_x(a, b)$. The curve C_2 is the graph of the function $G(y) = f(a, y)$, so the slope of its tangent T_2 at P is $G'(b) = f_y(a, b)$.

Thus the partial derivatives $f_x(a, b)$ and $f_y(a, b)$ can be interpreted geometrically as the slopes of the tangent lines at $P(a, b, c)$ to the traces C_1 and C_2 of S in the planes $y = b$ and $x = a$.

As we have seen in the case of the heat index function, partial derivatives can also be interpreted as *rates of change*. If $z = f(x, y)$, then $\partial z/\partial x$ represents the rate of change of z with respect to x when y is fixed. Similarly, $\partial z/\partial y$ represents the rate of change of z with respect to y when x is fixed.

EXAMPLE 2   Partial derivatives as slopes of tangents   If $f(x, y) = 4 - x^2 - 2y^2$, find $f_x(1, 1)$ and $f_y(1, 1)$ and interpret these numbers as slopes.

SOLUTION   We have

$$f_x(x, y) = -2x \qquad f_y(x, y) = -4y$$

$$f_x(1, 1) = -2 \qquad f_y(1, 1) = -4$$

The graph of f is the paraboloid $z = 4 - x^2 - 2y^2$ and the vertical plane $y = 1$ intersects it in the parabola $z = 2 - x^2$, $y = 1$. (As in the preceding discussion, we label it C_1 in Figure 2.) The slope of the tangent line to this parabola at the point $(1, 1, 1)$ is $f_x(1, 1) = -2$. Similarly, the curve C_2 in which the plane $x = 1$ intersects the paraboloid is the parabola $z = 3 - 2y^2$, $x = 1$, and the slope of the tangent line at $(1, 1, 1)$ is $f_y(1, 1) = -4$. (See Figure 3.)

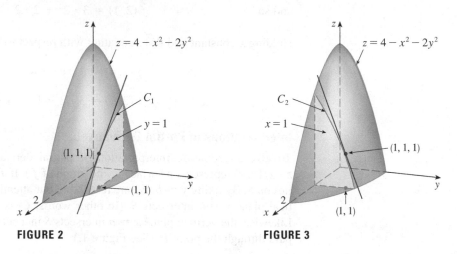

FIGURE 2   **FIGURE 3**

Figure 4 is a computer-drawn counterpart to Figure 2. Part (a) shows the plane $y = 1$ intersecting the surface to form the curve C_1 and part (b) shows C_1 and T_1. [We have used the vector equations $\mathbf{r}(t) = \langle t, 1, 2 - t^2 \rangle$ for C_1 and $\mathbf{r}(t) = \langle 1 + t, 1, 1 - 2t \rangle$ for T_1.] Similarly, Figure 5 corresponds to Figure 3.

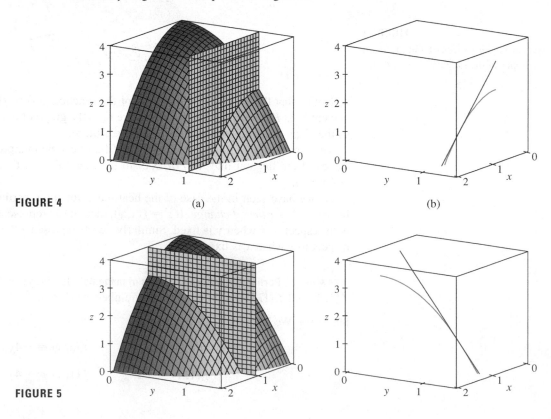

FIGURE 4   (a)   (b)

FIGURE 5

▼ **EXAMPLE 3** If $f(x, y) = \sin\left(\dfrac{x}{1 + y}\right)$, calculate $\dfrac{\partial f}{\partial x}$ and $\dfrac{\partial f}{\partial y}$.

SOLUTION Using the Chain Rule for functions of one variable, we have

$$\frac{\partial f}{\partial x} = \cos\left(\frac{x}{1 + y}\right) \cdot \frac{\partial}{\partial x}\left(\frac{x}{1 + y}\right) = \cos\left(\frac{x}{1 + y}\right) \cdot \frac{1}{1 + y}$$

$$\frac{\partial f}{\partial y} = \cos\left(\frac{x}{1 + y}\right) \cdot \frac{\partial}{\partial y}\left(\frac{x}{1 + y}\right) = -\cos\left(\frac{x}{1 + y}\right) \cdot \frac{x}{(1 + y)^2}$$

Some computer algebra systems can plot surfaces defined by implicit equations in three variables. Figure 6 shows such a plot of the surface defined by the equation in Example 4.

FIGURE 6

▼ **EXAMPLE 4** **Implicit partial differentiation** Find $\partial z / \partial x$ and $\partial z / \partial y$ if z is defined implicitly as a function of x and y by the equation

$$x^3 + y^3 + z^3 + 6xyz = 1$$

SOLUTION To find $\partial z / \partial x$, we differentiate implicitly with respect to x, being careful to treat y as a constant:

$$3x^2 + 3z^2 \frac{\partial z}{\partial x} + 6yz + 6xy \frac{\partial z}{\partial x} = 0$$

Solving this equation for $\partial z / \partial x$, we obtain

$$\frac{\partial z}{\partial x} = -\frac{x^2 + 2yz}{z^2 + 2xy}$$

Similarly, implicit differentiation with respect to y gives

$$\frac{\partial z}{\partial y} = -\frac{y^2 + 2xz}{z^2 + 2xy}$$

Functions of More Than Two Variables

Partial derivatives can also be defined for functions of three or more variables. For example, if f is a function of three variables x, y, and z, then its partial derivative with respect to x is defined as

$$f_x(x, y, z) = \lim_{h \to 0} \frac{f(x + h, y, z) - f(x, y, z)}{h}$$

and it is found by regarding y and z as constants and differentiating $f(x, y, z)$ with respect to x. If $w = f(x, y, z)$, then $f_x = \partial w / \partial x$ can be interpreted as the rate of change of w with respect to x when y and z are held fixed. But we can't interpret it geometrically because the graph of f lies in four-dimensional space.

In general, if u is a function of n variables, $u = f(x_1, x_2, \ldots, x_n)$, its partial derivative with respect to the ith variable x_i is

$$\frac{\partial u}{\partial x_i} = \lim_{h \to 0} \frac{f(x_1, \ldots, x_{i-1}, x_i + h, x_{i+1}, \ldots, x_n) - f(x_1, \ldots, x_i, \ldots, x_n)}{h}$$

and we also write

$$\frac{\partial u}{\partial x_i} = \frac{\partial f}{\partial x_i} = f_{x_i} = f_i = D_i f$$

EXAMPLE 5   **Partial derivatives of a function of three variables**
Find f_x, f_y, and f_z if $f(x, y, z) = e^{xy} \ln z$.

SOLUTION   Holding y and z constant and differentiating with respect to x, we have

$$f_x = ye^{xy} \ln z$$

Similarly, $f_y = xe^{xy} \ln z$ and $f_z = \dfrac{e^{xy}}{z}$

Higher Derivatives

If f is a function of two variables, then its partial derivatives f_x and f_y are also functions of two variables, so we can consider their partial derivatives $(f_x)_x$, $(f_x)_y$, $(f_y)_x$, and $(f_y)_y$, which are called the **second partial derivatives** of f. If $z = f(x, y)$, we use the following notation:

$$(f_x)_x = f_{xx} = f_{11} = \frac{\partial}{\partial x}\left(\frac{\partial f}{\partial x}\right) = \frac{\partial^2 f}{\partial x^2} = \frac{\partial^2 z}{\partial x^2}$$

$$(f_x)_y = f_{xy} = f_{12} = \frac{\partial}{\partial y}\left(\frac{\partial f}{\partial x}\right) = \frac{\partial^2 f}{\partial y\,\partial x} = \frac{\partial^2 z}{\partial y\,\partial x}$$

$$(f_y)_x = f_{yx} = f_{21} = \frac{\partial}{\partial x}\left(\frac{\partial f}{\partial y}\right) = \frac{\partial^2 f}{\partial x\,\partial y} = \frac{\partial^2 z}{\partial x\,\partial y}$$

$$(f_y)_y = f_{yy} = f_{22} = \frac{\partial}{\partial y}\left(\frac{\partial f}{\partial y}\right) = \frac{\partial^2 f}{\partial y^2} = \frac{\partial^2 z}{\partial y^2}$$

Thus the notation f_{xy} (or $\partial^2 f/\partial y\,\partial x$) means that we first differentiate with respect to x and then with respect to y, whereas in computing f_{yx} the order is reversed.

EXAMPLE 6   Find the second partial derivatives of

$$f(x, y) = x^3 + x^2 y^3 - 2y^2$$

SOLUTION   In Example 1 we found that

$$f_x(x, y) = 3x^2 + 2xy^3 \qquad f_y(x, y) = 3x^2 y^2 - 4y$$

Therefore

$$f_{xx} = \frac{\partial}{\partial x}(3x^2 + 2xy^3) = 6x + 2y^3 \qquad f_{xy} = \frac{\partial}{\partial y}(3x^2 + 2xy^3) = 6xy^2$$

$$f_{yx} = \frac{\partial}{\partial x}(3x^2 y^2 - 4y) = 6xy^2 \qquad f_{yy} = \frac{\partial}{\partial y}(3x^2 y^2 - 4y) = 6x^2 y - 4$$

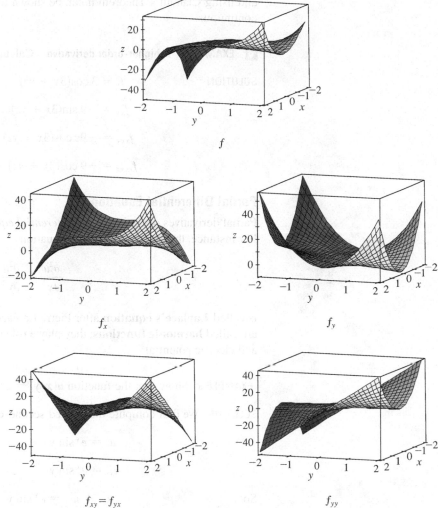

Figure 7 shows the graph of the function f in Example 6 and the graphs of its first- and second-order partial derivatives for $-2 \le x \le 2$, $-2 \le y \le 2$. Notice that these graphs are consistent with our interpretations of f_x and f_y as slopes of tangent lines to traces of the graph of f. For instance, the graph of f decreases if we start at $(0, -2)$ and move in the positive x-direction. This is reflected in the negative values of f_x. You should compare the graphs of f_{yx} and f_{yy} with the graph of f_y to see the relationships.

f

f_x

f_y

f_{xx}

$f_{xy} = f_{yx}$

f_{yy}

FIGURE 7

Notice that $f_{xy} = f_{yx}$ in Example 6. This is not just a coincidence. It turns out that the mixed partial derivatives f_{xy} and f_{yx} are equal for most functions that one meets in practice. The following theorem, which was discovered by the French mathematician Alexis Clairaut (1713–1765), gives conditions under which we can assert that $f_{xy} = f_{yx}$. The proof is given in Appendix E.

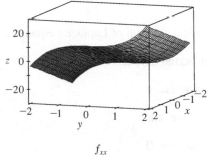

Clairaut

Alexis Clairaut was a child prodigy in mathematics: he read l'Hospital's textbook on calculus when he was ten and presented a paper on geometry to the French Academy of Sciences when he was 13. At the age of 18, Clairaut published *Recherches sur les courbes à double courbure*, which was the first systematic treatise on three-dimensional analytic geometry and included the calculus of space curves.

> **Clairaut's Theorem** Suppose f is defined on a disk D that contains the point (a, b). If the functions f_{xy} and f_{yx} are both continuous on D, then
> $$f_{xy}(a, b) = f_{yx}(a, b)$$

Partial derivatives of order 3 or higher can also be defined. For instance,

$$f_{xyy} = (f_{xy})_y = \frac{\partial}{\partial y}\left(\frac{\partial^2 f}{\partial y\, \partial x}\right) = \frac{\partial^3 f}{\partial y^2\, \partial x}$$

and using Clairaut's Theorem it can be shown that $f_{xyy} = f_{yxy} = f_{yyx}$ if these functions are continuous.

V **EXAMPLE 7** **A higher-order derivative**   Calculate f_{xxyz} if $f(x, y, z) = \sin(3x + yz)$.

SOLUTION
$$f_x = 3\cos(3x + yz)$$

$$f_{xx} = -9\sin(3x + yz)$$

$$f_{xxy} = -9z\cos(3x + yz)$$

$$f_{xxyz} = -9\cos(3x + yz) + 9yz\sin(3x + yz)$$

Partial Differential Equations

Partial derivatives occur in *partial differential equations* that express certain physical laws. For instance, the partial differential equation

$$\frac{\partial^2 u}{\partial x^2} + \frac{\partial^2 u}{\partial y^2} = 0$$

is called **Laplace's equation** after Pierre Laplace (1749–1827). Solutions of this equation are called **harmonic functions**; they play a role in problems of heat conduction, fluid flow, and electric potential.

EXAMPLE 8   Show that the function $u(x, y) = e^x \sin y$ is a solution of Laplace's equation.

SOLUTION   We first compute the needed second-order partial derivatives:

$$u_x = e^x \sin y \qquad\qquad u_y = e^x \cos y$$

$$u_{xx} = e^x \sin y \qquad\qquad u_{yy} = -e^x \sin y$$

So
$$u_{xx} + u_{yy} = e^x \sin y - e^x \sin y = 0$$

Therefore u satisfies Laplace's equation.

The **wave equation**

$$\frac{\partial^2 u}{\partial t^2} = a^2 \frac{\partial^2 u}{\partial x^2}$$

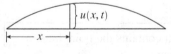

FIGURE 8

describes the motion of a waveform, which could be an ocean wave, a sound wave, a light wave, or a wave traveling along a vibrating string. For instance, if $u(x, t)$ represents the displacement of a vibrating violin string at time t and at a distance x from one end of the string (as in Figure 8), then $u(x, t)$ satisfies the wave equation. Here the constant a depends on the density of the string and on the tension in the string.

EXAMPLE 9   Verify that the function $u(x, t) = \sin(x - at)$ satisfies the wave equation.

SOLUTION
$$u_x = \cos(x - at) \qquad\qquad u_t = -a\cos(x - at)$$

$$u_{xx} = -\sin(x - at) \qquad\qquad u_{tt} = -a^2 \sin(x - at) = a^2 u_{xx}$$

So u satisfies the wave equation.

The Cobb-Douglas Production Function

In Example 2 in Section 11.1 we described the work of Cobb and Douglas in modeling the total production P of an economic system as a function of the amount of labor L and the capital investment K. Here we use partial derivatives to show how the particular form of their model follows from certain assumptions they made about the economy.

If the production function is denoted by $P = P(L, K)$, then the partial derivative $\partial P / \partial L$ is the rate at which production changes with respect to the amount of labor. Economists call it the marginal production with respect to labor or the *marginal productivity of labor*. Likewise, the partial derivative $\partial P / \partial K$ is the rate of change of production with respect to capital and is called the *marginal productivity of capital*. In these terms, the assumptions made by Cobb and Douglas can be stated as follows.

(i) If either labor or capital vanishes, then so will production.

(ii) The marginal productivity of labor is proportional to the amount of production per unit of labor.

(iii) The marginal productivity of capital is proportional to the amount of production per unit of capital.

Because the production per unit of labor is P/L, assumption (ii) says that

$$\frac{\partial P}{\partial L} = \alpha \frac{P}{L}$$

for some constant α. If we keep K constant ($K = K_0$), then this partial differential equation becomes an ordinary differential equation:

5
$$\frac{dP}{dL} = \alpha \frac{P}{L}$$

If we solve this separable differential equation by the methods of Section 7.3 (see also Exercise 77), we get

6
$$P(L, K_0) = C_1(K_0)L^{\alpha}$$

Notice that we have written the constant C_1 as a function of K_0 because it could depend on the value of K_0.

Similarly, assumption (iii) says that

$$\frac{\partial P}{\partial K} = \beta \frac{P}{K}$$

and we can solve this differential equation to get

7
$$P(L_0, K) = C_2(L_0)K^{\beta}$$

Comparing Equations 6 and 7, we have

8
$$P(L, K) = bL^{\alpha}K^{\beta}$$

where b is a constant that is independent of both L and K. Assumption (i) shows that $\alpha > 0$ and $\beta > 0$.

Notice from Equation 8 that if labor and capital are both increased by a factor m, then

$$P(mL, mK) = b(mL)^\alpha(mK)^\beta = m^{\alpha+\beta}bL^\alpha K^\beta = m^{\alpha+\beta}P(L, K)$$

If $\alpha + \beta = 1$, then $P(mL, mK) = mP(L, K)$, which means that production is also increased by a factor of m. That is why Cobb and Douglas assumed that $\alpha + \beta = 1$ and therefore

$$P(L, K) = bL^\alpha K^{1-\alpha}$$

This is the Cobb-Douglas production function that we discussed in Section 11.1.

11.3 Exercises

1. The temperature T at a location in the Northern Hemisphere depends on the longitude x, latitude y, and time t, so we can write $T = f(x, y, t)$. Let's measure time in hours from the beginning of January.
   (a) What are the meanings of the partial derivatives $\partial T/\partial x$, $\partial T/\partial y$, and $\partial T/\partial t$?
   (b) Honolulu has longitude 158° W and latitude 21° N. Suppose that at 9:00 AM on January 1 the wind is blowing hot air to the northeast, so the air to the west and south is warm and the air to the north and east is cooler. Would you expect $f_x(158, 21, 9)$, $f_y(158, 21, 9)$, and $f_t(158, 21, 9)$ to be positive or negative? Explain.

2. At the beginning of this section we discussed the function $I = f(T, H)$, where I is the heat index, T is the temperature, and H is the relative humidity. Use Table 1 to estimate $f_T(92, 60)$ and $f_H(92, 60)$. What are the practical interpretations of these values?

3. The wind-chill index W is the perceived temperature when the actual temperature is T and the wind speed is v, so we can write $W = f(T, v)$. The following table of values is an excerpt from Table 1 in Section 11.1.

Wind speed (km/h)

T \\ v	20	30	40	50	60	70
−10	−18	−20	−21	−22	−23	−23
−15	−24	−26	−27	−29	−30	−30
−20	−30	−33	−34	−35	−36	−37
−25	−37	−39	−41	−42	−43	−44

Actual temperature (°C)

(a) Estimate the values of $f_T(-15, 30)$ and $f_v(-15, 30)$. What are the practical interpretations of these values?

(b) In general, what can you say about the signs of $\partial W/\partial T$ and $\partial W/\partial v$?
(c) What appears to be the value of the following limit?

$$\lim_{v \to \infty} \frac{\partial W}{\partial v}$$

4. The wave heights h in the open sea depend on the speed v of the wind and the length of time t that the wind has been blowing at that speed. Values of the function $h = f(v, t)$ are recorded in feet in the following table.

Duration (hours)

v \\ t	5	10	15	20	30	40	50
10	2	2	2	2	2	2	2
15	4	4	5	5	5	5	5
20	5	7	8	8	9	9	9
30	9	13	16	17	18	19	19
40	14	21	25	28	31	33	33
50	19	29	36	40	45	48	50
60	24	37	47	54	62	67	69

Wind speed (knots)

(a) What are the meanings of the partial derivatives $\partial h/\partial v$ and $\partial h/\partial t$?
(b) Estimate the values of $f_v(40, 15)$ and $f_t(40, 15)$. What are the practical interpretations of these values?
(c) What appears to be the value of the following limit?

$$\lim_{t \to \infty} \frac{\partial h}{\partial t}$$

⌂ Graphing calculator or computer with graphing software required   CAS Computer algebra system required   **1.** Homework Hints available in TEC

5–8 Determine the signs of the partial derivatives for the function f whose graph is shown.

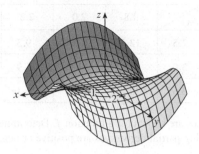

5. (a) $f_x(1, 2)$ (b) $f_y(1, 2)$

6. (a) $f_x(-1, 2)$ (b) $f_y(-1, 2)$

7. (a) $f_{xx}(-1, 2)$ (b) $f_{yy}(-1, 2)$

8. (a) $f_{xy}(1, 2)$ (b) $f_{xy}(-1, 2)$

9. The following surfaces, labeled a, b, and c, are graphs of a function f and its partial derivatives f_x and f_y. Identify each surface and give reasons for your choices.

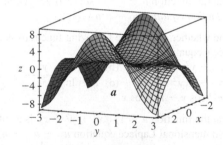

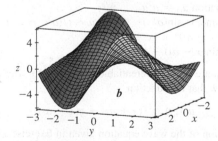

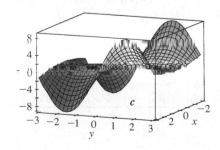

10. A contour map is given for a function f. Use it to estimate $f_x(2, 1)$ and $f_y(2, 1)$.

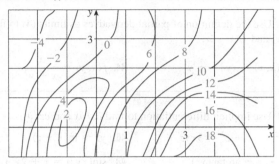

11. If $f(x, y) = 16 - 4x^2 - y^2$, find $f_x(1, 2)$ and $f_y(1, 2)$ and interpret these numbers as slopes. Illustrate with either hand-drawn sketches or computer plots.

12. If $f(x, y) = \sqrt{4 - x^2 - 4y^2}$, find $f_x(1, 0)$ and $f_y(1, 0)$ and interpret these numbers as slopes. Illustrate with either hand-drawn sketches or computer plots.

13–14 Find f_x and f_y and graph f, f_x, and f_y with domains and viewpoints that enable you to see the relationships between them.

13. $f(x, y) = x^2 + y^2 + x^2 y$ **14.** $f(x, y) = xe^{-x^2 - y^2}$

15–38 Find the first partial derivatives of the function.

15. $f(x, y) = y^5 - 3xy$ **16.** $f(x, y) = x^4 y^3 + 8x^2 y$

17. $f(x, t) = e^{-t} \cos \pi x$ **18.** $f(x, t) = \sqrt{x} \ln t$

19. $z = (2x + 3y)^{10}$ **20.** $z = \tan xy$

21. $f(x, y) = \dfrac{x - y}{x + y}$ **22.** $f(x, y) = x^y$

23. $w = \sin \alpha \cos \beta$ **24.** $w = e^v/(u + v^2)$

25. $f(r, s) = r \ln(r^2 + s^2)$ **26.** $f(x, t) = \arctan\left(x\sqrt{t}\,\right)$

27. $u = te^{w/t}$ **28.** $f(x, y) = \displaystyle\int_y^x \cos(t^2)\, dt$

29. $f(x, y, z) = xz - 5x^2 y^3 z^4$ **30.** $f(x, y, z) = x \sin(y - z)$

31. $w = \ln(x + 2y + 3z)$ **32.** $w = ze^{xyz}$

33. $u = xy \sin^{-1}(yz)$ **34.** $u = x^{y/z}$

35. $f(x, y, z, t) = xyz^2 \tan(yt)$ **36.** $f(x, y, z, t) = \dfrac{xy^2}{t + 2z}$

37. $u = \sqrt{x_1^2 + x_2^2 + \cdots + x_n^2}$

38. $u = \sin(x_1 + 2x_2 + \cdots + nx_n)$

39–42 Find the indicated partial derivatives.

39. $f(x, y) = \ln\left(x + \sqrt{x^2 + y^2}\,\right)$; $f_x(3, 4)$

40. $f(x, y) = \arctan(y/x)$; $f_x(2, 3)$

41. $f(x, y, z) = \dfrac{y}{x + y + z}$; $f_y(2, 1, -1)$

42. $f(x, y, z) = \sqrt{\sin^2 x + \sin^2 y + \sin^2 z}$; $f_z(0, 0, \pi/4)$

43–44 Use the definition of partial derivatives as limits (4) to find $f_x(x, y)$ and $f_y(x, y)$.

43. $f(x, y) = xy^2 - x^3 y$

44. $f(x, y) = \dfrac{x}{x + y^2}$

45–48 Use implicit differentiation to find $\partial z/\partial x$ and $\partial z/\partial y$.

45. $x^2 + y^2 + z^2 = 3xyz$

46. $yz = \ln(x + z)$

47. $x - z = \arctan(yz)$

48. $\sin(xyz) = x + 2y + 3z$

49–50 Find $\partial z/\partial x$ and $\partial z/\partial y$.

49. (a) $z = f(x) + g(y)$ (b) $z = f(x + y)$

50. (a) $z = f(x)g(y)$ (b) $z = f(xy)$
    (c) $z = f(x/y)$

51–56 Find all the second partial derivatives.

51. $f(x, y) = x^3 y^5 + 2x^4 y$

52. $f(x, y) = \sin^2(mx + ny)$

53. $w = \sqrt{u^2 + v^2}$

54. $v = \dfrac{xy}{x - y}$

55. $z = \arctan \dfrac{x + y}{1 - xy}$

56. $v = e^{xe^y}$

57–58 Verify that the conclusion of Clairaut's Theorem holds, that is, $u_{xy} = u_{yx}$.

57. $u = xe^{xy}$

58. $u = \tan(2x + 3y)$

59–64 Find the indicated partial derivative(s).

59. $f(x, y) = 3xy^4 + x^3 y^2$; f_{xxy}, f_{yyy}

60. $f(x, t) = x^2 e^{-ct}$; f_{ttt}, f_{txx}

61. $f(x, y, z) = \cos(4x + 3y + 2z)$; f_{xyz}, f_{yzz}

62. $f(r, s, t) = r \ln(rs^2 t^3)$; f_{rss}, f_{rst}

63. $u = e^{r\theta} \sin \theta$; $\dfrac{\partial^3 u}{\partial r^2 \, \partial \theta}$

64. $u = x^a y^b z^c$; $\dfrac{\partial^6 u}{\partial x \, \partial y^2 \, \partial z^3}$

65. If $f(x, y, z) = xy^2 z^3 + \arcsin(x\sqrt{z})$, find f_{xzy}. [*Hint:* Which order of differentiation is easiest?]

66. If $g(x, y, z) = \sqrt{1 + xz} + \sqrt{1 - xy}$, find g_{xyz}. [*Hint:* Use a different order of differentiation for each term.]

67. Use the table of values of $f(x, y)$ to estimate the values of $f_x(3, 2)$, $f_x(3, 2.2)$, and $f_{xy}(3, 2)$.

x \ y	1.8	2.0	2.2
2.5	12.5	10.2	9.3
3.0	18.1	17.5	15.9
3.5	20.0	22.4	26.1

68. Level curves are shown for a function f. Determine whether the following partial derivatives are positive or negative at the point P.
(a) f_x (b) f_y (c) f_{xx}
(d) f_{xy} (e) f_{yy}

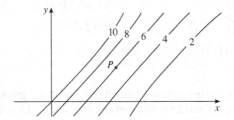

69. Verify that the function $u = e^{-\alpha^2 k^2 t} \sin kx$ is a solution of the *heat conduction equation* $u_t = \alpha^2 u_{xx}$.

70. Determine whether each of the following functions is a solution of Laplace's equation $u_{xx} + u_{yy} = 0$.
(a) $u = x^2 + y^2$ (b) $u = x^2 - y^2$
(c) $u = x^3 + 3xy^2$ (d) $u = \ln \sqrt{x^2 + y^2}$
(e) $u = e^{-x} \cos y - e^{-y} \cos x$

71. Verify that the function $u = 1/\sqrt{x^2 + y^2 + z^2}$ is a solution of the three-dimensional Laplace equation $u_{xx} + u_{yy} + u_{zz} = 0$.

72. Show that each of the following functions is a solution of the wave equation $u_{tt} = a^2 u_{xx}$.
(a) $u = \sin(kx) \sin(akt)$ (b) $u = t/(a^2 t^2 - x^2)$
(c) $u = (x - at)^6 + (x + at)^6$
(d) $u = \sin(x - at) + \ln(x + at)$

73. If f and g are twice differentiable functions of a single variable, show that the function

$$u(x, t) = f(x + at) + g(x - at)$$

is a solution of the wave equation given in Exercise 72.

74. If $u = e^{a_1 x_1 + a_2 x_2 + \cdots + a_n x_n}$, where $a_1^2 + a_2^2 + \cdots + a_n^2 = 1$, show that

$$\frac{\partial^2 u}{\partial x_1^2} + \frac{\partial^2 u}{\partial x_2^2} + \cdots + \frac{\partial^2 u}{\partial x_n^2} = u$$

75. If $u = xe^y + ye^x$, show that

$$\frac{\partial^3 u}{\partial x^3} + \frac{\partial^3 u}{\partial y^3} = x \frac{\partial^3 u}{\partial x \, \partial y^2} + y \frac{\partial^3 u}{\partial x^2 \, \partial y}$$

76. Show that the Cobb-Douglas production function $P = bL^{\alpha}K^{\beta}$ satisfies the equation

$$L\frac{\partial P}{\partial L} + K\frac{\partial P}{\partial K} = (\alpha + \beta)P$$

77. Show that the Cobb-Douglas production function satisfies $P(L, K_0) = C_1(K_0)L^{\alpha}$ by solving the differential equation

$$\frac{dP}{dL} = \alpha\frac{P}{L}$$

(See Equation 5.)

78. The temperature at a point (x, y) on a flat metal plate is given by $T(x, y) = 60/(1 + x^2 + y^2)$, where T is measured in °C and x, y in meters. Find the rate of change of temperature with respect to distance at the point $(2, 1)$ in (a) the x-direction and (b) the y-direction.

79. The total resistance R produced by three conductors with resistances R_1, R_2, R_3 connected in a parallel electrical circuit is given by the formula

$$\frac{1}{R} = \frac{1}{R_1} + \frac{1}{R_2} + \frac{1}{R_3}$$

Find $\partial R/\partial R_1$.

80. The *van der Waals equation* for n moles of a gas is

$$\left(P + \frac{n^2a}{V^2}\right)(V - nb) = nRT$$

where P is the pressure, V is the volume, and T is the temperature of the gas. The constant R is the universal gas constant and a and b are positive constants that are characteristic of a particular gas. Calculate $\partial T/\partial P$ and $\partial P/\partial V$.

81. (a) The gas law for a fixed mass m of an ideal gas at absolute temperature T, pressure P, and volume V is $PV = mRT$, where R is the gas constant. Show that

$$\frac{\partial P}{\partial V}\frac{\partial V}{\partial T}\frac{\partial T}{\partial P} = -1$$

(b) Show that, for an ideal gas,

$$T\frac{\partial P}{\partial T}\frac{\partial V}{\partial T} = mR$$

82. The wind-chill index is modeled by the function

$$W = 13.12 + 0.6215T - 11.37v^{0.16} + 0.3965Tv^{0.16}$$

where T is the temperature (°C) and v is the wind speed (km/h). When $T = -15$°C and $v = 30$ km/h, by how much would you expect the apparent temperature W to drop if the actual temperature decreases by 1°C? What if the wind speed increases by 1 km/h?

83. The kinetic energy of a body with mass m and velocity v is $K = \frac{1}{2}mv^2$. Show that

$$\frac{\partial K}{\partial m}\frac{\partial^2 K}{\partial v^2} = K$$

84. If a, b, c are the sides of a triangle and A, B, C are the opposite angles, find $\partial A/\partial a$, $\partial A/\partial b$, $\partial A/\partial c$ by implicit differentiation of the Law of Cosines.

85. You are told that there is a function f whose partial derivatives are $f_x(x, y) = x + 4y$ and $f_y(x, y) = 3x - y$. Should you believe it?

86. The paraboloid $z = 6 - x - x^2 - 2y^2$ intersects the plane $x = 1$ in a parabola. Find parametric equations for the tangent line to this parabola at the point $(1, 2, -4)$. Use a computer to graph the paraboloid, the parabola, and the tangent line on the same screen.

87. The ellipsoid $4x^2 + 2y^2 + z^2 = 16$ intersects the plane $y = 2$ in an ellipse. Find parametric equations for the tangent line to this ellipse at the point $(1, 2, 2)$.

88. In a study of frost penetration it was found that the temperature T at time t (measured in days) at a depth x (measured in feet) can be modeled by the function

$$T(x, t) = T_0 + T_1e^{-\lambda x}\sin(\omega t - \lambda x)$$

where $\omega = 2\pi/365$ and λ is a positive constant.
   (a) Find $\partial T/\partial x$. What is its physical significance?
   (b) Find $\partial T/\partial t$. What is its physical significance?
   (c) Show that T satisfies the heat equation $T_t = kT_{xx}$ for a certain constant k.
   (d) If $\lambda = 0.2$, $T_0 = 0$, and $T_1 = 10$, use a computer to graph $T(x, t)$.
   (e) What is the physical significance of the term $-\lambda x$ in the expression $\sin(\omega t - \lambda x)$?

89. If $f(x, y) = x(x^2 + y^2)^{-3/2}e^{\sin(x^2y)}$, find $f_x(1, 0)$. [*Hint:* Instead of finding $f_x(x, y)$ first, note that it's easier to use Equation 1 or Equation 2.]

90. If $f(x, y) = \sqrt[3]{x^3 + y^3}$, find $f_x(0, 0)$.

91. Let

$$f(x, y) = \begin{cases} \dfrac{x^3y - xy^3}{x^2 + y^2} & \text{if } (x, y) \neq (0, 0) \\ 0 & \text{if } (x, y) = (0, 0) \end{cases}$$

   (a) Use a computer to graph f.
   (b) Find $f_x(x, y)$ and $f_y(x, y)$ when $(x, y) \neq (0, 0)$.
   (c) Find $f_x(0, 0)$ and $f_y(0, 0)$ using Equations 2 and 3.
   (d) Show that $f_{xy}(0, 0) = -1$ and $f_{yx}(0, 0) = 1$.
   (e) Does the result of part (d) contradict Clairaut's Theorem? Use graphs of f_{xy} and f_{yx} to illustrate your answer.

11.4 Tangent Planes and Linear Approximations

One of the most important ideas in single-variable calculus is that as we zoom in toward a point on the graph of a differentiable function, the graph becomes indistinguishable from its tangent line and we can approximate the function by a linear function. (See Section 3.9.) Here we develop similar ideas in three dimensions. As we zoom in toward a point on a surface that is the graph of a differentiable function of two variables, the surface looks more and more like a plane (its tangent plane) and we can approximate the function by a linear function of two variables. We also extend the idea of a differential to functions of two or more variables.

Tangent Planes

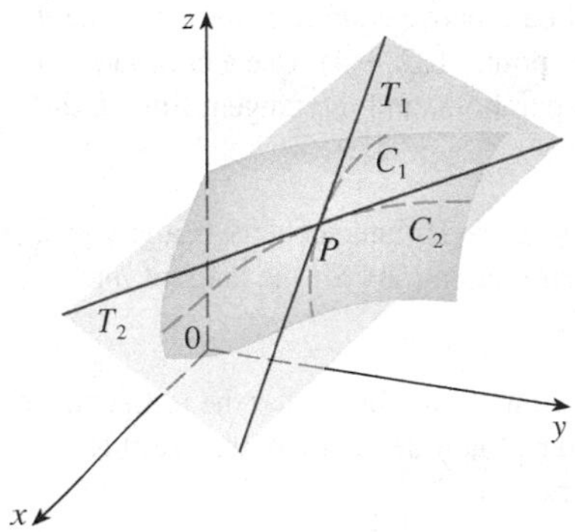

FIGURE 1
The tangent plane contains the tangent lines T_1 and T_2.

Suppose a surface S has equation $z = f(x, y)$, where f has continuous first partial derivatives, and let $P(x_0, y_0, z_0)$ be a point on S. As in the preceding section, let C_1 and C_2 be the curves obtained by intersecting the vertical planes $y = y_0$ and $x = x_0$ with the surface S. Then the point P lies on both C_1 and C_2. Let T_1 and T_2 be the tangent lines to the curves C_1 and C_2 at the point P. Then the **tangent plane** to the surface S at the point P is defined to be the plane that contains both tangent lines T_1 and T_2. (See Figure 1.)

We will see in Section 11.6 that if C is any other curve that lies on the surface S and passes through P, then its tangent line at P also lies in the tangent plane. Therefore you can think of the tangent plane to S at P as consisting of all possible tangent lines at P to curves that lie on S and pass through P. The tangent plane at P is the plane that most closely approximates the surface S near the point P.

We know from Equation 9.5.7 that any plane passing through the point $P(x_0, y_0, z_0)$ has an equation of the form

$$A(x - x_0) + B(y - y_0) + C(z - z_0) = 0$$

By dividing this equation by C and letting $a = -A/C$ and $b = -B/C$, we can write it in the form

> **1**
> $$z - z_0 = a(x - x_0) + b(y - y_0)$$

If Equation 1 represents the tangent plane at P, then its intersection with the plane $y = y_0$ must be the tangent line T_1. Setting $y = y_0$ in Equation 1 gives

$$z - z_0 = a(x - x_0) \qquad \text{where } y = y_0$$

and we recognize this as the equation (in point-slope form) of a line with slope a lying in the plane $y = y_0$. But from Section 11.3 we know that the slope of the tangent T_1 is $f_x(x_0, y_0)$. Therefore $a = f_x(x_0, y_0)$.

Similarly, putting $x = x_0$ in Equation 1, we get $z - z_0 = b(y - y_0)$, which must represent the tangent line T_2, so $b = f_y(x_0, y_0)$.

Note the similarity between the equation of a tangent plane and the equation of a tangent line:
$$y - y_0 = f'(x_0)(x - x_0)$$

> **2** Suppose f has continuous partial derivatives. An equation of the tangent plane to the surface $z = f(x, y)$ at the point $P(x_0, y_0, z_0)$ is
> $$z - z_0 = f_x(x_0, y_0)(x - x_0) + f_y(x_0, y_0)(y - y_0)$$

V EXAMPLE 1 Find the tangent plane to the elliptic paraboloid $z = 2x^2 + y^2$ at the point $(1, 1, 3)$.

SOLUTION Let $f(x, y) = 2x^2 + y^2$. Then

$$f_x(x, y) = 4x \qquad f_y(x, y) = 2y$$

$$f_x(1, 1) = 4 \qquad f_y(1, 1) = 2$$

Then (2) gives the equation of the tangent plane at $(1, 1, 3)$ as

$$z - 3 = 4(x - 1) + 2(y - 1)$$

or $\qquad z = 4x + 2y - 3$

Figure 2(a) shows the elliptic paraboloid and its tangent plane at $(1, 1, 3)$ that we found in Example 1. In parts (b) and (c) we zoom in toward the point $(1, 1, 3)$ by restricting the domain of the function $f(x, y) = 2x^2 + y^2$. Notice that the more we zoom in, the flatter the graph appears and the more it resembles its tangent plane.

TEC Visual 11.4 shows an animation of Figures 2 and 3.

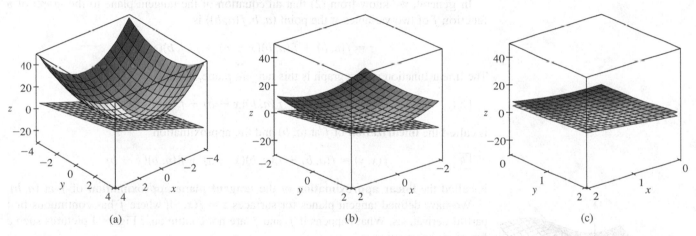

(a)   (b)   (c)

FIGURE 2 The elliptic paraboloid $z = 2x^2 + y^2$ appears to coincide with its tangent plane as we zoom in toward $(1, 1, 3)$.

In Figure 3 we corroborate this impression by zooming in toward the point $(1, 1)$ on a contour map of the function $f(x, y) = 2x^2 + y^2$. Notice that the more we zoom in, the more the level curves look like equally spaced parallel lines, which is characteristic of a plane.

FIGURE 3
Zooming in toward $(1, 1)$
on a contour map of
$f(x, y) = 2x^2 + y^2$

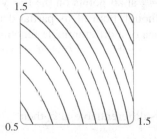
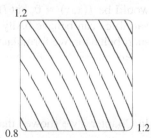
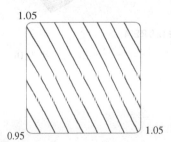

Linear Approximations

In Example 1 we found that an equation of the tangent plane to the graph of the function $f(x, y) = 2x^2 + y^2$ at the point $(1, 1, 3)$ is $z = 4x + 2y - 3$. Therefore, in view of the visual evidence in Figures 2 and 3, the linear function of two variables

$$L(x, y) = 4x + 2y - 3$$

is a good approximation to $f(x, y)$ when (x, y) is near $(1, 1)$. The function L is called the *linearization* of f at $(1, 1)$ and the approximation

$$f(x, y) \approx 4x + 2y - 3$$

is called the *linear approximation* or *tangent plane approximation* of f at $(1, 1)$.

For instance, at the point $(1.1, 0.95)$ the linear approximation gives

$$f(1.1, 0.95) \approx 4(1.1) + 2(0.95) - 3 = 3.3$$

which is quite close to the true value of $f(1.1, 0.95) = 2(1.1)^2 + (0.95)^2 = 3.3225$. But if we take a point farther away from $(1, 1)$, such as $(2, 3)$, we no longer get a good approximation. In fact, $L(2, 3) = 11$ whereas $f(2, 3) = 17$.

In general, we know from (2) that an equation of the tangent plane to the graph of a function f of two variables at the point $(a, b, f(a, b))$ is

$$z = f(a, b) + f_x(a, b)(x - a) + f_y(a, b)(y - b)$$

The linear function whose graph is this tangent plane, namely

$$\boxed{3} \qquad L(x, y) = f(a, b) + f_x(a, b)(x - a) + f_y(a, b)(y - b)$$

is called the **linearization** of f at (a, b) and the approximation

$$\boxed{4} \qquad f(x, y) \approx f(a, b) + f_x(a, b)(x - a) + f_y(a, b)(y - b)$$

is called the **linear approximation** or the **tangent plane approximation** of f at (a, b).

We have defined tangent planes for surfaces $z = f(x, y)$, where f has continuous first partial derivatives. What happens if f_x and f_y are not continuous? Figure 4 pictures such a function; its equation is

$$f(x, y) = \begin{cases} \dfrac{xy}{x^2 + y^2} & \text{if } (x, y) \neq (0, 0) \\ 0 & \text{if } (x, y) = (0, 0) \end{cases}$$

You can verify (see Exercise 48) that its partial derivatives exist at the origin and, in fact, $f_x(0, 0) = 0$ and $f_y(0, 0) = 0$, but f_x and f_y are not continuous. The linear approximation would be $f(x, y) \approx 0$, but $f(x, y) = \frac{1}{2}$ at all points on the line $y = x$. So a function of two variables can behave badly even though both of its partial derivatives exist. To rule out such behavior, we formulate the idea of a differentiable function of two variables.

Recall that for a function of one variable, $y = f(x)$, if x changes from a to $a + \Delta x$, we defined the increment of y as

$$\Delta y = f(a + \Delta x) - f(a)$$

In Chapter 3 we showed that if f is differentiable at a, then

$$\boxed{5} \qquad \Delta y = f'(a)\,\Delta x + \varepsilon\,\Delta x \qquad \text{where } \varepsilon \to 0 \text{ as } \Delta x \to 0$$

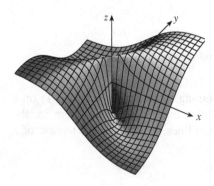

FIGURE 4

$f(x, y) = \dfrac{xy}{x^2 + y^2}$ if $(x, y) \neq (0, 0)$,

$f(0, 0) = 0$

This is Equation 3.4.8.

Now consider a function of two variables, $z = f(x, y)$, and suppose x changes from a to $a + \Delta x$ and y changes from b to $b + \Delta y$. Then the corresponding **increment** of z is

$$\boxed{6} \qquad \Delta z = f(a + \Delta x, b + \Delta y) - f(a, b)$$

Thus the increment Δz represents the change in the value of f when (x, y) changes from (a, b) to $(a + \Delta x, b + \Delta y)$. By analogy with (5) we define the differentiability of a function of two variables as follows.

$\boxed{7}$ **Definition**   If $z = f(x, y)$, then f is **differentiable** at (a, b) if Δz can be expressed in the form

$$\Delta z = f_x(a, b) \, \Delta x + f_y(a, b) \, \Delta y + \varepsilon_1 \, \Delta x + \varepsilon_2 \, \Delta y$$

where ε_1 and $\varepsilon_2 \to 0$ as $(\Delta x, \, \Delta y) \to (0, 0)$.

Definition 7 says that a differentiable function is one for which the linear approximation (4) is a good approximation when (x, y) is near (a, b). In other words, the tangent plane approximates the graph of f well near the point of tangency.

It's sometimes hard to use Definition 7 directly to check the differentiability of a function, but the next theorem provides a convenient sufficient condition for differentiability.

Theorem 8 is proved in Appendix E.

$\boxed{8}$ **Theorem**   If the partial derivatives f_x and f_y exist near (a, b) and are continuous at (a, b), then f is differentiable at (a, b).

$\boxed{V}$ **EXAMPLE 2**   **Using a linearization to estimate a function value**

Show that $f(x, y) = xe^{xy}$ is differentiable at $(1, 0)$ and find its linearization there. Then use it to approximate $f(1.1, -0.1)$.

SOLUTION   The partial derivatives are

$$f_x(x, y) = e^{xy} + xye^{xy} \qquad f_y(x, y) = x^2 e^{xy}$$

$$f_x(1, 0) = 1 \qquad\qquad f_y(1, 0) = 1$$

Figure 5 shows the graphs of the function f and its linearization L in Example 2.

Both f_x and f_y are continuous functions, so f is differentiable by Theorem 8. The linearization is

$$L(x, y) = f(1, 0) + f_x(1, 0)(x - 1) + f_y(1, 0)(y - 0)$$

$$= 1 + 1(x - 1) + 1 \cdot y = x + y$$

The corresponding linear approximation is

$$xe^{xy} \approx x + y$$

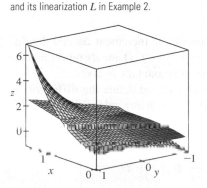

FIGURE 5

so

$$f(1.1, -0.1) \approx 1.1 - 0.1 = 1$$

Compare this with the actual value of $f(1.1, -0.1) = 1.1e^{-0.11} \approx 0.98542$.

EXAMPLE 3   **Estimating the heat index from tabular values**   At the beginning of Section 11.3 we discussed the heat index (perceived temperature) I as a function of the actual temperature T and the relative humidity H and gave the following table of values from the National Weather Service.

Relative humidity (%)

T \ H	50	55	60	65	70	75	80	85	90
90	96	98	100	103	106	109	112	115	119
92	100	103	105	108	112	115	119	123	128
94	104	107	111	114	118	122	127	132	137
96	109	113	116	121	125	130	135	141	146
98	114	118	123	127	133	138	144	150	157
100	119	124	129	135	141	147	154	161	168

Actual temperature (°F)

Find a linear approximation for the heat index $I = f(T, H)$ when T is near 96°F and H is near 70%. Use it to estimate the heat index when the temperature is 97°F and the relative humidity is 72%.

SOLUTION   We read from the table that $f(96, 70) = 125$. In Section 11.3 we used the tabular values to estimate that $f_T(96, 70) \approx 3.75$ and $f_H(96, 70) \approx 0.9$. (See page 757–58.) So the linear approximation is

$$f(T, H) \approx f(96, 70) + f_T(96, 70)(T - 96) + f_H(96, 70)(H - 70)$$

$$\approx 125 + 3.75(T - 96) + 0.9(H - 70)$$

In particular,

$$f(97, 72) \approx 125 + 3.75(1) + 0.9(2) = 130.55$$

Therefore, when $T = 97°F$ and $H = 72\%$, the heat index is

$$I \approx 131°F$$

Differentials

For a differentiable function of one variable, $y = f(x)$, we define the differential dx to be an independent variable; that is, dx can be given the value of any real number. The differential of y is then defined as

$$\boxed{9} \qquad\qquad dy = f'(x)\, dx$$

(See Section 3.9.) Figure 6 shows the relationship between the increment Δy and the differential dy: Δy represents the change in height of the curve $y = f(x)$ and dy represents the change in height of the tangent line when x changes by an amount $dx = \Delta x$.

For a differentiable function of two variables, $z = f(x, y)$, we define the **differentials** dx and dy to be independent variables; that is, they can be given any values. Then the **differential** dz, also called the **total differential**, is defined by

$$\boxed{10} \qquad dz = f_x(x, y)\, dx + f_y(x, y)\, dy = \frac{\partial z}{\partial x}\, dx + \frac{\partial z}{\partial y}\, dy$$

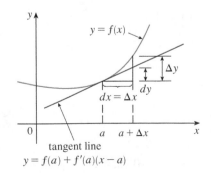

FIGURE 6

(Compare with Equation 9.) Sometimes the notation df is used in place of dz.

If we take $dx = \Delta x = x - a$ and $dy = \Delta y = y - b$ in Equation 10, then the differential of z is

$$dz = f_x(a, b)(x - a) + f_y(a, b)(y - b)$$

So, in the notation of differentials, the linear approximation (4) can be written as

$$f(x, y) \approx f(a, b) + dz$$

Figure 7 is the three-dimensional counterpart of Figure 6 and shows the geometric interpretation of the differential dz and the increment Δz: dz represents the change in height of the tangent plane, whereas Δz represents the change in height of the surface $z = f(x, y)$ when (x, y) changes from (a, b) to $(a + \Delta x, b + \Delta y)$.

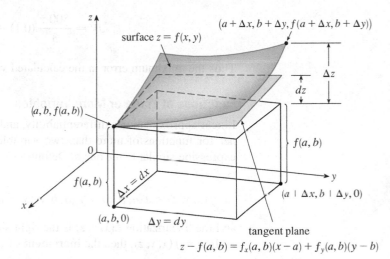

FIGURE 7

$z - f(a, b) = f_x(a, b)(x - a) + f_y(a, b)(y - b)$

▼ EXAMPLE 4 Differentials versus increments

(a) If $z = f(x, y) = x^2 + 3xy - y^2$, find the differential dz.

(b) If x changes from 2 to 2.05 and y changes from 3 to 2.96, compare the values of Δz and dz.

SOLUTION

(a) Definition 10 gives

$$dz = \frac{\partial z}{\partial x} dx + \frac{\partial z}{\partial y} dy = (2x + 3y) dx + (3x - 2y) dy$$

In Example 4, dz is close to Δz because the tangent plane is a good approximation to the surface $z = x^2 + 3xy - y^2$ near $(2, 3, 13)$. (See Figure 8.)

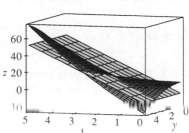

FIGURE 8

(b) Putting $x = 2$, $dx = \Delta x = 0.05$, $y = 3$, and $dy = \Delta y = -0.04$, we get

$$dz = [2(2) + 3(3)]0.05 + [3(2) - 2(3)](-0.04) = 0.65$$

The increment of z is

$$\Delta z = f(2.05, 2.96) - f(2, 3)$$
$$= [(2.05)^2 + 3(2.05)(2.96) - (2.96)^2] - [2^2 + 3(2)(3) - 3^2]$$
$$= 0.6449$$

Notice that $\Delta z \approx dz$ but dz is easier to compute.

EXAMPLE 5 Using differentials to estimate an error The base radius and height of a right circular cone are measured as 10 cm and 25 cm, respectively, with a possible error in measurement of as much as 0.1 cm in each. Use differentials to estimate the maximum error in the calculated volume of the cone.

SOLUTION The volume V of a cone with base radius r and height h is $V = \pi r^2 h/3$. So the differential of V is

$$dV = \frac{\partial V}{\partial r}\, dr + \frac{\partial V}{\partial h}\, dh = \frac{2\pi r h}{3}\, dr + \frac{\pi r^2}{3}\, dh$$

Since each error is at most 0.1 cm, we have $|\Delta r| \leq 0.1$, $|\Delta h| \leq 0.1$. To find the largest error in the volume we take the largest error in the measurement of r and of h. Therefore we take $dr = 0.1$ and $dh = 0.1$ along with $r = 10$, $h = 25$. This gives

$$dV = \frac{500\pi}{3}\,(0.1) + \frac{100\pi}{3}\,(0.1) = 20\pi$$

Thus the maximum error in the calculated volume is about 20π cm$^3 \approx 63$ cm^3.   ▬

Functions of Three or More Variables

Linear approximations, differentiability, and differentials can be defined in a similar manner for functions of more than two variables. A differentiable function is defined by an expression similar to the one in Definition 7. For such functions the **linear approximation** is

$$f(x, y, z) \approx f(a, b, c) + f_x(a, b, c)(x - a) + f_y(a, b, c)(y - b) + f_z(a, b, c)(z - c)$$

and the linearization $L(x, y, z)$ is the right side of this expression.

If $w = f(x, y, z)$, then the **increment** of w is

$$\Delta w = f(x + \Delta x, y + \Delta y, z + \Delta z) - f(x, y, z)$$

The **differential** dw is defined in terms of the differentials dx, dy, and dz of the independent variables by

$$dw = \frac{\partial w}{\partial x}\, dx + \frac{\partial w}{\partial y}\, dy + \frac{\partial w}{\partial z}\, dz$$

EXAMPLE 6 The dimensions of a rectangular box are measured to be 75 cm, 60 cm, and 40 cm, and each measurement is correct to within 0.2 cm. Use differentials to estimate the largest possible error when the volume of the box is calculated from these measurements.

SOLUTION If the dimensions of the box are x, y, and z, its volume is $V = xyz$ and so

$$dV = \frac{\partial V}{\partial x}\, dx + \frac{\partial V}{\partial y}\, dy + \frac{\partial V}{\partial z}\, dz = yz\, dx + xz\, dy + xy\, dz$$

We are given that $|\Delta x| \leq 0.2$, $|\Delta y| \leq 0.2$, and $|\Delta z| \leq 0.2$. To find the largest error in the volume, we therefore use $dx = 0.2$, $dy = 0.2$, and $dz = 0.2$ together with $x = 75$, $y = 60$, and $z = 40$:

$$\Delta V \approx dV = (60)(40)(0.2) + (75)(40)(0.2) + (75)(60)(0.2) = 1980$$

Thus an error of only 0.2 cm in measuring each dimension could lead to an error of as much as 1980 cm^3 in the calculated volume! This may seem like a large error, but it's only about 1% of the volume of the box.   ▬

Tangent Planes to Parametric Surfaces

Parametric surfaces were introduced in Section 10.5. We now find the tangent plane to a parametric surface S traced out by a vector function

$$\mathbf{r}(u, v) = x(u, v)\, \mathbf{i} + y(u, v)\, \mathbf{j} + z(u, v)\, \mathbf{k}$$

at a point P_0 with position vector $\mathbf{r}(u_0, v_0)$. If we keep u constant by putting $u = u_0$, then $\mathbf{r}(u_0, v)$ becomes a vector function of the single parameter v and defines a grid curve C_1 lying on S. (See Figure 9.) The tangent vector to C_1 at P_0 is obtained by taking the partial derivative of $\mathbf{r}$ with respect to v:

$$\mathbf{r}_v = \frac{\partial x}{\partial v}(u_0, v_0)\, \mathbf{i} + \frac{\partial y}{\partial v}(u_0, v_0)\, \mathbf{j} + \frac{\partial z}{\partial v}(u_0, v_0)\, \mathbf{k}$$

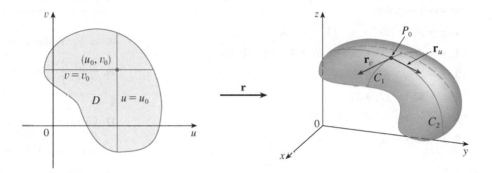

FIGURE 9

Similarly, if we keep v constant by putting $v = v_0$, we get a grid curve C_2 given by $\mathbf{r}(u, v_0)$ that lies on S, and its tangent vector at P_0 is

$$\mathbf{r}_u = \frac{\partial x}{\partial u}(u_0, v_0)\, \mathbf{i} + \frac{\partial y}{\partial u}(u_0, v_0)\, \mathbf{j} + \frac{\partial z}{\partial u}(u_0, v_0)\, \mathbf{k}$$

If $\mathbf{r}_u \times \mathbf{r}_v$ is not $\mathbf{0}$, then the surface S is called **smooth** (it has no "corners"). For a smooth surface, the **tangent plane** is the plane that contains the tangent vectors $\mathbf{r}_u$ and $\mathbf{r}_v$, and the vector $\mathbf{r}_u \times \mathbf{r}_v$ is a normal vector to the tangent plane.

☑ EXAMPLE 7 Find the tangent plane to the surface with parametric equations $x = u^2$, $y = v^2$, $z = u + 2v$ at the point $(1, 1, 3)$.

SOLUTION We first compute the tangent vectors:

$$\mathbf{r}_u = \frac{\partial x}{\partial u}\, \mathbf{i} + \frac{\partial y}{\partial u}\, \mathbf{j} + \frac{\partial z}{\partial u}\, \mathbf{k} = 2u\, \mathbf{i} + \mathbf{k}$$

$$\mathbf{r}_v = \frac{\partial x}{\partial v}\, \mathbf{i} + \frac{\partial y}{\partial v}\, \mathbf{j} + \frac{\partial z}{\partial v}\, \mathbf{k} = 2v\, \mathbf{j} + 2\, \mathbf{k}$$

Thus a normal vector to the tangent plane is

$$\mathbf{r}_u \times \mathbf{r}_v = \begin{vmatrix} \mathbf{i} & \mathbf{j} & \mathbf{k} \\ 2u & 0 & 1 \\ 0 & 2v & 2 \end{vmatrix} = -2v\, \mathbf{i} - 4u\, \mathbf{j} + 4uv\, \mathbf{k}$$

Figure 10 shows the self-intersecting surface in Example 7 and its tangent plane at $(1, 1, 3)$.

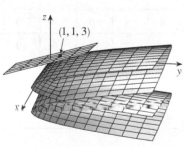

FIGURE 10

Notice that the point $(1, 1, 3)$ corresponds to the parameter values $u = 1$ and $v = 1$, so the normal vector there is

$$-2\,\mathbf{i} - 4\,\mathbf{j} + 4\,\mathbf{k}$$

Therefore an equation of the tangent plane at $(1, 1, 3)$ is

$$-2(x - 1) - 4(y - 1) + 4(z - 3) = 0$$

or
$$x + 2y - 2z + 3 = 0$$

11.4 Exercises

1–6 Find an equation of the tangent plane to the given surface at the specified point.

1. $z = 3y^2 - 2x^2 + x$, $(2, -1, -3)$

2. $z = 3(x - 1)^2 + 2(y + 3)^2 + 7$, $(2, -2, 12)$

3. $z = \sqrt{xy}$, $(1, 1, 1)$

4. $z = xe^{xy}$, $(2, 0, 2)$

5. $z = y \cos(x - y)$, $(2, 2, 2)$

6. $z = \ln(x - 2y)$, $(3, 1, 0)$

7–8 Graph the surface and the tangent plane at the given point. (Choose the domain and viewpoint so that you get a good view of both the surface and the tangent plane.) Then zoom in until the surface and the tangent plane become indistinguishable.

7. $z = x^2 + xy + 3y^2$, $(1, 1, 5)$

8. $z = \arctan(xy^2)$, $(1, 1, \pi/4)$

9–10 Draw the graph of f and its tangent plane at the given point. (Use your computer algebra system both to compute the partial derivatives and to graph the surface and its tangent plane.) Then zoom in until the surface and the tangent plane become indistinguishable.

9. $f(x, y) = \dfrac{xy \sin(x - y)}{1 + x^2 + y^2}$, $(1, 1, 0)$

10. $f(x, y) = e^{-xy/10}\left(\sqrt{x} + \sqrt{y} + \sqrt{xy}\right)$, $(1, 1, 3e^{-0.1})$

11–14 Explain why the function is differentiable at the given point. Then find the linearization $L(x, y)$ of the function at that point.

11. $f(x, y) = x\sqrt{y}$, $(1, 4)$

12. $f(x, y) = x^3 y^4$, $(1, 1)$

13. $f(x, y) = \dfrac{x}{x + y}$, $(2, 1)$

14. $f(x, y) = \sqrt{x + e^{4y}}$, $(3, 0)$

15–16 Verify the linear approximation at $(0, 0)$.

15. $\dfrac{2x + 3}{4y + 1} \approx 3 + 2x - 12y$ **16.** $\sqrt{y + \cos^2 x} \approx 1 + \tfrac{1}{2}y$

17. Given that f is a differentiable function with $f(2, 5) = 6$, $f_x(2, 5) = 1$, and $f_y(2, 5) = -1$, use a linear approximation to estimate $f(2.2, 4.9)$.

18. Find the linear approximation of the function $f(x, y) = \ln(x - 3y)$ at $(7, 2)$ and use it to approximate $f(6.9, 2.06)$. Illustrate by graphing f and the tangent plane.

19. Find the linear approximation of the function $f(x, y, z) = \sqrt{x^2 + y^2 + z^2}$ at $(3, 2, 6)$ and use it to approximate the number $\sqrt{(3.02)^2 + (1.97)^2 + (5.99)^2}$.

20. The wave heights h in the open sea depend on the speed v of the wind and the length of time t that the wind has been blowing at that speed. Values of the function $h = f(v, t)$ are recorded in feet in the following table. Use the table to find a linear approximation to the wave height function when v is near 40 knots and t is near 20 hours. Then estimate the wave heights when the wind has been blowing for 24 hours at 43 knots.

	Duration (hours)						
v \\ t	5	10	15	20	30	40	50
20	5	7	8	8	9	9	9
30	9	13	16	17	18	19	19
40	14	21	25	28	31	33	33
50	19	29	36	40	45	48	50
60	24	37	47	54	62	67	69

Wind speed (knots)

Graphing calculator or computer with graphing software required |CAS| Computer algebra system required   **1.** Homework Hints available in TEC

21. Use the table in Example 3 to find a linear approximation to the heat index function when the temperature is near 94°F and the relative humidity is near 80%. Then estimate the heat index when the temperature is 95°F and the relative humidity is 78%.

22. The wind-chill index W is the perceived temperature when the actual temperature is T and the wind speed is v, so we can write $W = f(T, v)$. The following table of values is an excerpt from Table 1 in Section 11.1. Use the table to find a linear approximation to the wind-chill index function when T is near $-15°C$ and v is near 50 km/h. Then estimate the wind-chill index when the temperature is $-17°C$ and the wind speed is 55 km/h.

Wind speed (km/h)

T $\diagdown$ v	20	30	40	50	60	70
−10	−18	−20	−21	−22	−23	−23
−15	−24	−26	−27	−29	−30	−30
−20	−30	−33	−34	−35	−36	−37
−25	−37	−39	−41	−42	−43	−44

Actual temperature (°C)

23–28 Find the differential of the function.

23. $z = x^3 \ln(y^2)$ **24.** $u = e^{-t}\sin(s + 2t)$

25. $m = p^5 q^3$ **26.** $T = \dfrac{v}{1 + uvw}$

27. $R = \alpha\beta^2 \cos \gamma$ **28.** $w = xye^{xz}$

29. If $z = 5x^2 + y^2$ and (x, y) changes from $(1, 2)$ to $(1.05, 2.1)$, compare the values of Δz and dz.

30. If $z = x^2 - xy + 3y^2$ and (x, y) changes from $(3, -1)$ to $(2.96, -0.95)$, compare the values of Δz and dz.

31. The length and width of a rectangle are measured as 30 cm and 24 cm, respectively, with an error in measurement of at most 0.1 cm in each. Use differentials to estimate the maximum error in the calculated area of the rectangle.

32. The dimensions of a closed rectangular box are measured as 80 cm, 60 cm, and 50 cm, respectively, with a possible error of 0.2 cm in each dimension. Use differentials to estimate the maximum error in calculating the surface area of the box.

33. Use differentials to estimate the amount of tin in a closed tin can with diameter 8 cm and height 12 cm if the tin is 0.04 cm thick.

34. The wind-chill index is modeled by the function

$$W = 13.12 + 0.6215T - 11.37v^{0.16} + 0.3965Tv^{0.16}$$

where T is the temperature (in °C) and v is the wind speed (in km/h). The wind speed is measured as 26 km/h, with a possible error of ± 2 km/h, and the temperature is measured as $-11°C$, with a possible error of $\pm 1°C$. Use differentials to estimate the maximum error in the calculated value of W due to the measurement errors in T and v.

35. A model for the surface area of a human body is given by $S = 0.1091w^{0.425}h^{0.725}$, where w is the weight (in pounds), h is the height (in inches), and S is measured in square feet. If the errors in measurement of w and h are at most 2%, use differentials to estimate the maximum percentage error in the calculated surface area.

36. The pressure, volume, and temperature of a mole of an ideal gas are related by the equation $PV = 8.31T$, where P is measured in kilopascals, V in liters, and T in kelvins. Use differentials to find the approximate change in the pressure if the volume increases from 12 L to 12.3 L and the temperature decreases from 310 K to 305 K.

37. If R is the total resistance of three resistors, connected in parallel, with resistances R_1, R_2, R_3, then

$$\frac{1}{R} = \frac{1}{R_1} + \frac{1}{R_2} + \frac{1}{R_3}$$

If the resistances are measured in ohms as $R_1 = 25\ \Omega$, $R_2 = 40\ \Omega$, and $R_3 = 50\ \Omega$, with a possible error of 0.5% in each case, estimate the maximum error in the calculated value of R.

38. Four positive numbers, each less than 50, are rounded to the first decimal place and then multiplied together. Use differentials to estimate the maximum possible error in the computed product that might result from the rounding.

39–43 Find an equation of the tangent plane to the parametric surface at the given point. If you have software that graphs parametric surfaces, use a computer to graph the surface and the tangent plane.

39. $x = u + v, \quad y = 3u^2, \quad z = u - v; \quad (2, 3, 0)$

40. $x = u^2, \quad y = v^2, \quad z = uv; \quad u = 1, v = 1$

41. $\mathbf{r}(u, v) = u^2\,\mathbf{i} + 2u \sin v\,\mathbf{j} + u \cos v\,\mathbf{k}; \quad u = 1, v = 0$

42. $\mathbf{r}(u, v) = uv\,\mathbf{i} + u \sin v\,\mathbf{j} + v \cos u\,\mathbf{k}; \quad u = 0, v = \pi$

43. $\mathbf{r}(u, v) = u\,\mathbf{i} + \ln(uv)\,\mathbf{j} + v\,\mathbf{k}; \quad u = 1, v = 1$

44. Suppose you need to know an equation of the tangent plane to a surface S at the point $P(2, 1, 3)$. You don't have an equation for S but you know that the curves

$$\mathbf{r}_1(t) = \langle 2 + 3t, 1 - t^2, 3 - 4t + t^2 \rangle$$

$$\mathbf{r}_2(u) = \langle 1 + u^2, 2u^3 - 1, 2u + 1 \rangle$$

both lie on S. Find an equation of the tangent plane at P.

45–46 Show that the function is differentiable by finding values of ε_1 and ε_2 that satisfy Definition 7.

45. $f(x, y) = x^2 + y^2$ **46.** $f(x, y) = xy - 5y^2$

47. Prove that if f is a function of two variables that is differentiable at (a, b), then f is continuous at (a, b).
  Hint: Show that

$$\lim_{(\Delta x, \Delta y) \to (0, 0)} f(a + \Delta x, b + \Delta y) = f(a, b)$$

48. (a) The function

$$f(x, y) = \begin{cases} \dfrac{xy}{x^2 + y^2} & \text{if } (x, y) \neq (0, 0) \\ 0 & \text{if } (x, y) = (0, 0) \end{cases}$$

was graphed in Figure 4. Show that $f_x(0, 0)$ and $f_y(0, 0)$ both exist but f is not differentiable at $(0, 0)$. [*Hint:* Use the result of Exercise 47.]
  (b) Explain why f_x and f_y are not continuous at $(0, 0)$.

11.5 The Chain Rule

Recall that the Chain Rule for functions of a single variable gives the rule for differentiating a composite function: If $y = f(x)$ and $x = g(t)$, where f and g are differentiable functions, then y is indirectly a differentiable function of t and

$$\boxed{1} \qquad \frac{dy}{dt} = \frac{dy}{dx}\frac{dx}{dt}$$

For functions of more than one variable, the Chain Rule has several versions, each of them giving a rule for differentiating a composite function. The first version (Theorem 2) deals with the case where $z = f(x, y)$ and each of the variables x and y is, in turn, a function of a variable t. This means that z is indirectly a function of t, $z = f(g(t), h(t))$, and the Chain Rule gives a formula for differentiating z as a function of t. We assume that f is differentiable (Definition 11.4.7). Recall that this is the case when f_x and f_y are continuous (Theorem 11.4.8).

> **2   The Chain Rule (Case 1)**   Suppose that $z = f(x, y)$ is a differentiable function of x and y, where $x = g(t)$ and $y = h(t)$ are both differentiable functions of t. Then z is a differentiable function of t and
>
> $$\frac{dz}{dt} = \frac{\partial f}{\partial x}\frac{dx}{dt} + \frac{\partial f}{\partial y}\frac{dy}{dt}$$

PROOF   A change of Δt in t produces changes of Δx in x and Δy in y. These, in turn, produce a change of Δz in z, and from Definition 11.4.7 we have

$$\Delta z = \frac{\partial f}{\partial x}\Delta x + \frac{\partial f}{\partial y}\Delta y + \varepsilon_1 \Delta x + \varepsilon_2 \Delta y$$

where $\varepsilon_1 \to 0$ and $\varepsilon_2 \to 0$ as $(\Delta x, \Delta y) \to (0, 0)$. [If the functions ε_1 and ε_2 are not defined at $(0, 0)$, we can define them to be 0 there.] Dividing both sides of this equation by Δt, we have

$$\frac{\Delta z}{\Delta t} = \frac{\partial f}{\partial x}\frac{\Delta x}{\Delta t} + \frac{\partial f}{\partial y}\frac{\Delta y}{\Delta t} + \varepsilon_1\frac{\Delta x}{\Delta t} + \varepsilon_2\frac{\Delta y}{\Delta t}$$

If we now let $\Delta t \to 0$, then $\Delta x = g(t + \Delta t) - g(t) \to 0$ because g is differentiable and therefore continuous. Similarly, $\Delta y \to 0$. This, in turn, means that $\varepsilon_1 \to 0$ and $\varepsilon_2 \to 0$, so

$$\frac{dz}{dt} = \lim_{\Delta t \to 0} \frac{\Delta z}{\Delta t}$$

$$= \frac{\partial f}{\partial x} \lim_{\Delta t \to 0} \frac{\Delta x}{\Delta t} + \frac{\partial f}{\partial y} \lim_{\Delta t \to 0} \frac{\Delta y}{\Delta t} + \left(\lim_{\Delta t \to 0} \varepsilon_1 \right) \lim_{\Delta t \to 0} \frac{\Delta x}{\Delta t} + \left(\lim_{\Delta t \to 0} \varepsilon_2 \right) \lim_{\Delta t \to 0} \frac{\Delta y}{\Delta t}$$

$$= \frac{\partial f}{\partial x} \frac{dx}{dt} + \frac{\partial f}{\partial y} \frac{dy}{dt} + 0 \cdot \frac{dx}{dt} + 0 \cdot \frac{dy}{dt}$$

$$= \frac{\partial f}{\partial x} \frac{dx}{dt} + \frac{\partial f}{\partial y} \frac{dy}{dt}$$

Since we often write $\partial z / \partial x$ in place of $\partial f / \partial x$, we can rewrite the Chain Rule in the form

$$\frac{dz}{dt} = \frac{\partial z}{\partial x} \frac{dx}{dt} + \frac{\partial z}{\partial y} \frac{dy}{dt}$$

Notice the similarity to the definition of the differential:

$$dz = \frac{\partial z}{\partial x} dx + \frac{\partial z}{\partial y} dy$$

EXAMPLE 1   Using the Chain Rule   If $z = x^2 y + 3xy^4$, where $x = \sin 2t$ and $y = \cos t$, find dz/dt when $t = 0$.

SOLUTION The Chain Rule gives

$$\frac{dz}{dt} = \frac{\partial z}{\partial x} \frac{dx}{dt} + \frac{\partial z}{\partial y} \frac{dy}{dt}$$

$$= (2xy + 3y^4)(2 \cos 2t) + (x^2 + 12xy^3)(-\sin t)$$

It's not necessary to substitute the expressions for x and y in terms of t. We simply observe that when $t = 0$, we have $x = \sin 0 = 0$ and $y = \cos 0 = 1$. Therefore

$$\left. \frac{dz}{dt} \right|_{t=0} = (0 + 3)(2 \cos 0) + (0 + 0)(-\sin 0) = 6$$

The derivative in Example 1 can be interpreted as the rate of change of z with respect to t as the point (x, y) moves along the curve C with parametric equations $x = \sin 2t$, $y = \cos t$. (See Figure 1.) In particular, when $t = 0$, the point (x, y) is $(0, 1)$ and $dz/dt = 6$ is the rate of increase as we move along the curve C through $(0, 1)$. If, for instance, $z = T(x, y) = x^2 y + 3xy^4$ represents the temperature at the point (x, y), then the composite function $z = T(\sin 2t, \cos t)$ represents the temperature at points on C and the derivative dz/dt represents the rate at which the temperature changes along C.

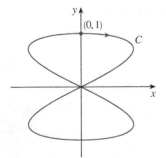

FIGURE 1

The curve $x = \sin 2t$, $y = \cos t$

▶ **EXAMPLE 2   The Chain Rule applied to chemistry**   The pressure P (in kilopascals), volume V (in liters), and temperature T (in kelvins) of a mole of an ideal gas are related by the equation $PV = 8.31T$. Find the rate at which the pressure is changing when the temperature is 300 K and increasing at a rate of 0.1 K/s and the volume is 100 L and increasing at a rate of 0.2 L/s.

SOLUTION If t represents the time elapsed in seconds, then at the given instant we have $T = 300$, $dT/dt = 0.1$, $V = 100$, $dV/dt = 0.2$. Since

$$P = 8.31 \frac{T}{V}$$

the Chain Rule gives

$$\frac{dP}{dt} = \frac{\partial P}{\partial T}\frac{dT}{dt} + \frac{\partial P}{\partial V}\frac{dV}{dt} = \frac{8.31}{V}\frac{dT}{dt} - \frac{8.31T}{V^2}\frac{dV}{dt}$$

$$= \frac{8.31}{100}(0.1) - \frac{8.31(300)}{100^2}(0.2) = -0.04155$$

The pressure is decreasing at a rate of about 0.042 kPa/s.

We now consider the situation where $z = f(x, y)$ but each of x and y is a function of two variables s and t: $x = g(s, t)$, $y = h(s, t)$. Then z is indirectly a function of s and t and we wish to find $\partial z/\partial s$ and $\partial z/\partial t$. Recall that in computing $\partial z/\partial t$ we hold s fixed and compute the ordinary derivative of z with respect to t. Therefore we can apply Theorem 2 to obtain

$$\frac{\partial z}{\partial t} = \frac{\partial z}{\partial x}\frac{\partial x}{\partial t} + \frac{\partial z}{\partial y}\frac{\partial y}{\partial t}$$

A similar argument holds for $\partial z/\partial s$ and so we have proved the following version of the Chain Rule.

---

3   The Chain Rule (Case 2)   Suppose that $z = f(x, y)$ is a differentiable function of x and y, where $x = g(s, t)$ and $y = h(s, t)$ are differentiable functions of s and t. Then

$$\frac{\partial z}{\partial s} = \frac{\partial z}{\partial x}\frac{\partial x}{\partial s} + \frac{\partial z}{\partial y}\frac{\partial y}{\partial s} \qquad \frac{\partial z}{\partial t} = \frac{\partial z}{\partial x}\frac{\partial x}{\partial t} + \frac{\partial z}{\partial y}\frac{\partial y}{\partial t}$$

EXAMPLE 3   The Chain Rule with two independent variables   If $z = e^x \sin y$, where $x = st^2$ and $y = s^2t$, find $\partial z/\partial s$ and $\partial z/\partial t$.

SOLUTION Applying Case 2 of the Chain Rule, we get

$$\frac{\partial z}{\partial s} = \frac{\partial z}{\partial x}\frac{\partial x}{\partial s} + \frac{\partial z}{\partial y}\frac{\partial y}{\partial s} = (e^x \sin y)(t^2) + (e^x \cos y)(2st)$$

$$= t^2 e^{st^2} \sin(s^2t) + 2ste^{st^2} \cos(s^2t)$$

$$\frac{\partial z}{\partial t} = \frac{\partial z}{\partial x}\frac{\partial x}{\partial t} + \frac{\partial z}{\partial y}\frac{\partial y}{\partial t} = (e^x \sin y)(2st) + (e^x \cos y)(s^2)$$

$$= 2ste^{st^2} \sin(s^2t) + s^2 e^{st^2} \cos(s^2t)$$

Case 2 of the Chain Rule contains three types of variables: s and t are **independent** variables, x and y are called **intermediate** variables, and z is the **dependent** variable. Notice that Theorem 3 has one term for each intermediate variable and each of these terms resembles the one-dimensional Chain Rule in Equation 1.

To remember the Chain Rule, it's helpful to draw the **tree diagram** in Figure 2. We draw branches from the dependent variable z to the intermediate variables x and y to indicate that z is a function of x and y. Then we draw branches from x and y to the independent variables s and t. On each branch we write the corresponding partial derivative. To find

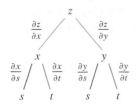

FIGURE 2

$\partial z/\partial s$, we find the product of the partial derivatives along each path from z to s and then add these products:

$$\frac{\partial z}{\partial s} = \frac{\partial z}{\partial x}\frac{\partial x}{\partial s} + \frac{\partial z}{\partial y}\frac{\partial y}{\partial s}$$

Similarly, we find $\partial z/\partial t$ by using the paths from z to t.

Now we consider the general situation in which a dependent variable u is a function of n intermediate variables $x_1, \ldots, x_n$, each of which is, in turn, a function of m independent variables $t_1, \ldots, t_m$. Notice that there are n terms, one for each intermediate variable. The proof is similar to that of Case 1.

---

4   **The Chain Rule (General Version)**   Suppose that u is a differentiable function of the n variables $x_1, x_2, \ldots, x_n$ and each x_j is a differentiable function of the m variables $t_1, t_2, \ldots, t_m$. Then u is a function of $t_1, t_2, \ldots, t_m$ and

$$\frac{\partial u}{\partial t_i} = \frac{\partial u}{\partial x_1}\frac{\partial x_1}{\partial t_i} + \frac{\partial u}{\partial x_2}\frac{\partial x_2}{\partial t_i} + \cdots + \frac{\partial u}{\partial x_n}\frac{\partial x_n}{\partial t_i}$$

for each $i = 1, 2, \ldots, m$.

▼ EXAMPLE 4   **The Chain Rule with two independent variables and four intermediate variables**
Write out the Chain Rule for the case where $w = f(x, y, z, t)$ and $x = x(u, v)$, $y = y(u, v)$, $z = z(u, v)$, and $t = t(u, v)$.

SOLUTION   We apply Theorem 4 with $n = 4$ and $m = 2$. Figure 3 shows the tree diagram. Although we haven't written the derivatives on the branches, it's understood that if a branch leads from y to u, then the partial derivative for that branch is $\partial y/\partial u$. With the aid of the tree diagram, we can now write the required expressions:

$$\frac{\partial w}{\partial u} = \frac{\partial w}{\partial x}\frac{\partial x}{\partial u} + \frac{\partial w}{\partial y}\frac{\partial y}{\partial u} + \frac{\partial w}{\partial z}\frac{\partial z}{\partial u} + \frac{\partial w}{\partial t}\frac{\partial t}{\partial u}$$

$$\frac{\partial w}{\partial v} = \frac{\partial w}{\partial x}\frac{\partial x}{\partial v} + \frac{\partial w}{\partial y}\frac{\partial y}{\partial v} + \frac{\partial w}{\partial z}\frac{\partial z}{\partial v} + \frac{\partial w}{\partial t}\frac{\partial t}{\partial v}$$

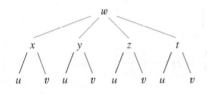

FIGURE 3

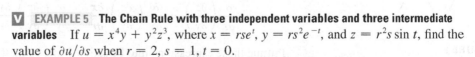

▼ EXAMPLE 5   **The Chain Rule with three independent variables and three intermediate variables**   If $u = x^4 y + y^2 z^3$, where $x = rse^t$, $y = rs^2 e^{-t}$, and $z = r^2 s \sin t$, find the value of $\partial u/\partial s$ when $r = 2$, $s = 1$, $t = 0$.

SOLUTION   With the help of the tree diagram in Figure 4, we have

$$\frac{\partial u}{\partial s} = \frac{\partial u}{\partial x}\frac{\partial x}{\partial s} + \frac{\partial u}{\partial y}\frac{\partial y}{\partial s} + \frac{\partial u}{\partial z}\frac{\partial z}{\partial s}$$

$$= (4x^3 y)(re^t) + (x^4 + 2yz^3)(2rse^{-t}) + (3y^2 z^2)(r^2 \sin t)$$

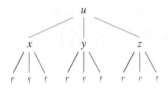

FIGURE 4

When $r = 2$, $s = 1$, and $t = 0$, we have $x = 2$, $y = 2$, and $z = 0$, so

$$\frac{\partial u}{\partial s} = (64)(2) + (16)(4) + (0)(0) = 192$$

EXAMPLE 6 If $g(s, t) = f(s^2 - t^2, t^2 - s^2)$ and f is differentiable, show that g satisfies the equation

$$t\,\frac{\partial g}{\partial s} + s\,\frac{\partial g}{\partial t} = 0$$

SOLUTION Let $x = s^2 - t^2$ and $y = t^2 - s^2$. Then $g(s, t) = f(x, y)$ and the Chain Rule gives

$$\frac{\partial g}{\partial s} = \frac{\partial f}{\partial x}\frac{\partial x}{\partial s} + \frac{\partial f}{\partial y}\frac{\partial y}{\partial s} = \frac{\partial f}{\partial x}\,(2s) + \frac{\partial f}{\partial y}\,(-2s)$$

$$\frac{\partial g}{\partial t} = \frac{\partial f}{\partial x}\frac{\partial x}{\partial t} + \frac{\partial f}{\partial y}\frac{\partial y}{\partial t} = \frac{\partial f}{\partial x}\,(-2t) + \frac{\partial f}{\partial y}\,(2t)$$

Therefore

$$t\,\frac{\partial g}{\partial s} + s\,\frac{\partial g}{\partial t} = \left(2st\,\frac{\partial f}{\partial x} - 2st\,\frac{\partial f}{\partial y}\right) + \left(-2st\,\frac{\partial f}{\partial x} + 2st\,\frac{\partial f}{\partial y}\right) = 0$$ ▪

EXAMPLE 7 If $z = f(x, y)$ has continuous second-order partial derivatives and $x = r^2 + s^2$ and $y = 2rs$, find (a) $\partial z/\partial r$ and (b) $\partial^2 z/\partial r^2$.

SOLUTION

(a) The Chain Rule gives

$$\frac{\partial z}{\partial r} = \frac{\partial z}{\partial x}\frac{\partial x}{\partial r} + \frac{\partial z}{\partial y}\frac{\partial y}{\partial r} = \frac{\partial z}{\partial x}\,(2r) + \frac{\partial z}{\partial y}\,(2s)$$

(b) Applying the Product Rule to the expression in part (a), we get

$$\boxed{5}\qquad \frac{\partial^2 z}{\partial r^2} = \frac{\partial}{\partial r}\left(2r\,\frac{\partial z}{\partial x} + 2s\,\frac{\partial z}{\partial y}\right)$$

$$= 2\,\frac{\partial z}{\partial x} + 2r\,\frac{\partial}{\partial r}\left(\frac{\partial z}{\partial x}\right) + 2s\,\frac{\partial}{\partial r}\left(\frac{\partial z}{\partial y}\right)$$

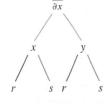

FIGURE 5

But, using the Chain Rule again (see Figure 5), we have

$$\frac{\partial}{\partial r}\left(\frac{\partial z}{\partial x}\right) = \frac{\partial}{\partial x}\left(\frac{\partial z}{\partial x}\right)\frac{\partial x}{\partial r} + \frac{\partial}{\partial y}\left(\frac{\partial z}{\partial x}\right)\frac{\partial y}{\partial r} = \frac{\partial^2 z}{\partial x^2}\,(2r) + \frac{\partial^2 z}{\partial y\,\partial x}\,(2s)$$

$$\frac{\partial}{\partial r}\left(\frac{\partial z}{\partial y}\right) = \frac{\partial}{\partial x}\left(\frac{\partial z}{\partial y}\right)\frac{\partial x}{\partial r} + \frac{\partial}{\partial y}\left(\frac{\partial z}{\partial y}\right)\frac{\partial y}{\partial r} = \frac{\partial^2 z}{\partial x\,\partial y}\,(2r) + \frac{\partial^2 z}{\partial y^2}\,(2s)$$

Putting these expressions into Equation 5 and using the equality of the mixed second-order derivatives, we obtain

$$\frac{\partial^2 z}{\partial r^2} = 2\,\frac{\partial z}{\partial x} + 2r\left(2r\,\frac{\partial^2 z}{\partial x^2} + 2s\,\frac{\partial^2 z}{\partial y\,\partial x}\right) + 2s\left(2r\,\frac{\partial^2 z}{\partial x\,\partial y} + 2s\,\frac{\partial^2 z}{\partial y^2}\right)$$

$$= 2\,\frac{\partial z}{\partial x} + 4r^2\,\frac{\partial^2 z}{\partial x^2} + 8rs\,\frac{\partial^2 z}{\partial x\,\partial y} + 4s^2\,\frac{\partial^2 z}{\partial y^2}$$ ▪

Implicit Differentiation

The Chain Rule can be used to give a more complete description of the process of implicit differentiation that was introduced in Sections 3.5 and 11.3. We suppose that an equation of the form $F(x, y) = 0$ defines y implicitly as a differentiable function of x, that is,

$y = f(x)$, where $F(x, f(x)) = 0$ for all x in the domain of f. If F is differentiable, we can apply Case 1 of the Chain Rule to differentiate both sides of the equation $F(x, y) = 0$ with respect to x. Since both x and y are functions of x, we obtain

$$\frac{\partial F}{\partial x} \frac{dx}{dx} + \frac{\partial F}{\partial y} \frac{dy}{dx} = 0$$

But $dx/dx = 1$, so if $\partial F/\partial y \neq 0$ we solve for dy/dx and obtain

$$\boxed{6} \qquad \frac{dy}{dx} = -\frac{\dfrac{\partial F}{\partial x}}{\dfrac{\partial F}{\partial y}} = -\frac{F_x}{F_y}$$

To derive this equation we assumed that $F(x, y) = 0$ defines y implicitly as a function of x. The **Implicit Function Theorem**, proved in advanced calculus, gives conditions under which this assumption is valid: It states that if F is defined on a disk containing (a, b), where $F(a, b) = 0$, $F_y(a, b) \neq 0$, and F_x and F_y are continuous on the disk, then the equation $F(x, y) = 0$ defines y as a function of x near the point (a, b) and the derivative of this function is given by Equation 6.

EXAMPLE 8   Implicit differentiation   Find y' if $x^3 + y^3 = 6xy$.

SOLUTION The given equation can be written as

$$F(x, y) = x^3 + y^3 - 6xy = 0$$

so Equation 6 gives

The solution to Example 8 should be compared to the one in Example 2 in Section 3.5.

$$\frac{dy}{dx} = -\frac{F_x}{F_y} = -\frac{3x^2 - 6y}{3y^2 - 6x} = -\frac{x^2 - 2y}{y^2 - 2x}$$

Now we suppose that z is given implicitly as a function $z = f(x, y)$ by an equation of the form $F(x, y, z) = 0$. This means that $F(x, y, f(x, y)) = 0$ for all (x, y) in the domain of f. If F and f are differentiable, then we can use the Chain Rule to differentiate the equation $F(x, y, z) = 0$ as follows:

$$\frac{\partial F}{\partial x} \frac{\partial x}{\partial x} + \frac{\partial F}{\partial y} \frac{\partial y}{\partial x} + \frac{\partial F}{\partial z} \frac{\partial z}{\partial x} = 0$$

But

$$\frac{\partial}{\partial x}(x) = 1 \qquad \text{and} \qquad \frac{\partial}{\partial x}(y) = 0$$

so this equation becomes

$$\frac{\partial F}{\partial x} + \frac{\partial F}{\partial z} \frac{\partial z}{\partial x} = 0$$

If $\partial F/\partial z \neq 0$, we solve for $\partial z/\partial x$ and obtain the first formula in Equations 7. The formula for $\partial z/\partial y$ is obtained in a similar manner.

$$\boxed{7} \qquad \frac{\partial z}{\partial x} = -\frac{\dfrac{\partial F}{\partial x}}{\dfrac{\partial F}{\partial z}} \qquad \frac{\partial z}{\partial y} = -\frac{\dfrac{\partial F}{\partial y}}{\dfrac{\partial F}{\partial z}}$$

Again, a version of the **Implicit Function Theorem** gives conditions under which our assumption is valid: If F is defined within a sphere containing (a, b, c), where $F(a, b, c) = 0$, $F_z(a, b, c) \neq 0$, and F_x, F_y, and F_z are continuous inside the sphere, then the equation $F(x, y, z) = 0$ defines z as a function of x and y near the point (a, b, c) and this function is differentiable, with partial derivatives given by (7).

EXAMPLE 9 Find $\dfrac{\partial z}{\partial x}$ and $\dfrac{\partial z}{\partial y}$ if $x^3 + y^3 + z^3 + 6xyz = 1$.

The solution to Example 9 should be compared to the one in Example 4 in Section 11.3.

SOLUTION Let $F(x, y, z) = x^3 + y^3 + z^3 + 6xyz - 1$. Then, from Equations 7, we have

$$\frac{\partial z}{\partial x} = -\frac{F_x}{F_z} = -\frac{3x^2 + 6yz}{3z^2 + 6xy} = -\frac{x^2 + 2yz}{z^2 + 2xy}$$

$$\frac{\partial z}{\partial y} = -\frac{F_y}{F_z} = -\frac{3y^2 + 6xz}{3z^2 + 6xy} = -\frac{y^2 + 2xz}{z^2 + 2xy}$$

11.5 Exercises

1–6 Use the Chain Rule to find dz/dt or dw/dt.

1. $z = x^2 + y^2 + xy$, $x = \sin t$, $y = e^t$

2. $z = \cos(x + 4y)$, $x = 5t^4$, $y = 1/t$

3. $z = \sqrt{1 + x^2 + y^2}$, $x = \ln t$, $y = \cos t$

4. $z = \tan^{-1}(y/x)$, $x = e^t$, $y = 1 - e^{-t}$

5. $w = xe^{y/z}$, $x = t^2$, $y = 1 - t$, $z = 1 + 2t$

6. $w = \ln\sqrt{x^2 + y^2 + z^2}$, $x = \sin t$, $y = \cos t$, $z = \tan t$

7–12 Use the Chain Rule to find $\partial z/\partial s$ and $\partial z/\partial t$.

7. $z = x^2 y^3$, $x = s \cos t$, $y = s \sin t$

8. $z = \arcsin(x - y)$, $x = s^2 + t^2$, $y = 1 - 2st$

9. $z = \sin\theta \cos\phi$, $\theta = st^2$, $\phi = s^2 t$

10. $z = e^{x+2y}$, $x = s/t$, $y = t/s$

11. $z = e^r \cos\theta$, $r = st$, $\theta = \sqrt{s^2 + t^2}$

12. $z = \tan(u/v)$, $u = 2s + 3t$, $v = 3s - 2t$

---

13. If $z = f(x, y)$, where f is differentiable, and

$$x = g(t) \qquad\qquad y = h(t)$$
$$g(3) = 2 \qquad\qquad h(3) = 7$$
$$g'(3) = 5 \qquad\qquad h'(3) = -4$$
$$f_x(2, 7) = 6 \qquad\qquad f_y(2, 7) = -8$$

find dz/dt when $t = 3$.

14. Let $W(s, t) = F(u(s, t), v(s, t))$, where F, u, and v are differentiable, and

$$u(1, 0) = 2 \qquad\qquad v(1, 0) = 3$$
$$u_s(1, 0) = -2 \qquad\qquad v_s(1, 0) = 5$$
$$u_t(1, 0) = 6 \qquad\qquad v_t(1, 0) = 4$$
$$F_u(2, 3) = -1 \qquad\qquad F_v(2, 3) = 10$$

Find $W_s(1, 0)$ and $W_t(1, 0)$.

---

1. Homework Hints available in TEC

15. Suppose f is a differentiable function of x and y, and $g(u, v) = f(e^u + \sin v, e^u + \cos v)$. Use the table of values to calculate $g_u(0, 0)$ and $g_v(0, 0)$.

	f	g	f_x	f_y
(0, 0)	3	6	4	8
(1, 2)	6	3	2	5

16. Suppose f is a differentiable function of x and y, and $g(r, s) = f(2r - s, s^2 - 4r)$. Use the table of values in Exercise 15 to calculate $g_r(1, 2)$ and $g_s(1, 2)$.

17–20 Use a tree diagram to write out the Chain Rule for the given case. Assume all functions are differentiable.

17. $u = f(x, y)$, where $x = x(r, s, t)$, $y = y(r, s, t)$

18. $R = f(x, y, z, t)$, where $x = x(u, v, w)$, $y = y(u, v, w)$, $z = z(u, v, w)$, $t = t(u, v, w)$

19. $w = f(r, s, t)$, where $r = r(x, y)$, $s = s(x, y)$, $t = t(x, y)$

20. $t = f(u, v, w)$, where $u = u(p, q, r, s)$, $v = v(p, q, r, s)$, $w = w(p, q, r, s)$

21–25 Use the Chain Rule to find the indicated partial derivatives.

21. $z = x^2 + xy^3$, $x = uv^2 + w^3$, $y = u + ve^w$;
$$\frac{\partial z}{\partial u}, \frac{\partial z}{\partial v}, \frac{\partial z}{\partial w} \quad \text{when } u = 2, v = 1, w = 0$$

22. $u = \sqrt{r^2 + s^2}$, $r = y + x \cos t$, $s = x + y \sin t$;
$$\frac{\partial u}{\partial x}, \frac{\partial u}{\partial y}, \frac{\partial u}{\partial t} \quad \text{when } x = 1, y = 2, t = 0$$

23. $R = \ln(u^2 + v^2 + w^2)$, $u = x + 2y$, $v = 2x - y$, $w = 2xy$;
$$\frac{\partial R}{\partial x}, \frac{\partial R}{\partial y} \quad \text{when } x = y = 1$$

24. $M = xe^{y-z^2}$, $x = 2uv$, $y = u - v$, $z = u + v$;
$$\frac{\partial M}{\partial u}, \frac{\partial M}{\partial v} \quad \text{when } u = 3, v = -1$$

25. $u = x^2 + yz$, $x = pr \cos \theta$, $y = pr \sin \theta$, $z = p + r$;
$$\frac{\partial u}{\partial p}, \frac{\partial u}{\partial r}, \frac{\partial u}{\partial \theta} \quad \text{when } p = 2, r = 3, \theta = 0$$

26–28 Use Equation 6 to find dy/dx.

26. $y^5 + x^2 y^3 = 1 + ye^{x^2}$

27. $\cos(x - y) = xe^y$

28. $\sin x + \cos y = \sin x \cos y$

29–32 Use Equations 7 to find $\partial z/\partial x$ and $\partial z/\partial y$.

29. $x^2 + y^2 + z^2 = 3xyz$
30. $xyz = \cos(x + y + z)$
31. $x - z = \arctan(yz)$
32. $yz = \ln(x + z)$

33. The temperature at a point (x, y) is $T(x, y)$, measured in degrees Celsius. A bug crawls so that its position after t seconds is given by $x = \sqrt{1 + t}$, $y = 2 + \frac{1}{3}t$, where x and y are measured in centimeters. The temperature function satisfies $T_x(2, 3) = 4$ and $T_y(2, 3) = 3$. How fast is the temperature rising on the bug's path after 3 seconds?

34. Wheat production W in a given year depends on the average temperature T and the annual rainfall R. Scientists estimate that the average temperature is rising at a rate of 0.15°C/year and rainfall is decreasing at a rate of 0.1 cm/year. They also estimate that, at current production levels, $\partial W/\partial T = -2$ and $\partial W/\partial R = 8$.
(a) What is the significance of the signs of these partial derivatives?
(b) Estimate the current rate of change of wheat production, dW/dt.

35. The speed of sound traveling through ocean water with salinity 35 parts per thousand has been modeled by the equation
$$C = 1449.2 + 4.6T - 0.055T^2 + 0.00029T^3 + 0.016D$$
where C is the speed of sound (in meters per second), T is the temperature (in degrees Celsius), and D is the depth below the ocean surface (in meters). A scuba diver began a leisurely dive into the ocean water; the diver's depth and the surrounding water temperature over time are recorded in the following graphs. Estimate the rate of change (with respect to time) of the speed of sound through the ocean water experienced by the diver 20 minutes into the dive. What are the units?

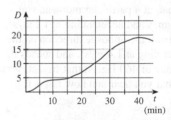
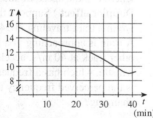

36. The radius of a right circular cone is increasing at a rate of 1.8 in/s while its height is decreasing at a rate of 2.5 in/s. At what rate is the volume of the cone changing when the radius is 120 in. and the height is 140 in.?

37. The length ℓ, width w, and height h of a box change with time. At a certain instant the dimensions are $\ell = 1$ m and $w = h = 2$ m, and ℓ and w are increasing at a rate of 2 m/s while h is decreasing at a rate of 3 m/s. At that instant find the rates at which the following quantities are changing.
(a) The volume
(b) The surface area
(c) The length of a diagonal

38. The voltage V in a simple electrical circuit is slowly decreasing as the battery wears out. The resistance R is slowly increasing as the resistor heats up. Use Ohm's Law, $V = IR$, to find how the current I is changing at the moment when $R = 400\ \Omega$, $I = 0.08$ A, $dV/dt = -0.01$ V/s, and $dR/dt = 0.03\ \Omega/$s.

39. The pressure of 1 mole of an ideal gas is increasing at a rate of 0.05 kPa/s and the temperature is increasing at a rate of 0.15 K/s. Use the equation in Example 2 to find the rate of change of the volume when the pressure is 20 kPa and the temperature is 320 K.

40. A manufacturer has modeled its yearly production function P (the value of its entire production in millions of dollars) as a Cobb-Douglas function

$$P(L, K) = 1.47L^{0.65}K^{0.35}$$

where L is the number of labor hours (in thousands) and K is the invested capital (in millions of dollars). Suppose that when $L = 30$ and $K = 8$, the labor force is decreasing at a rate of 2000 labor hours per year and capital is increasing at a rate of $500,000 per year. Find the rate of change of production.

41. One side of a triangle is increasing at a rate of 3 cm/s and a second side is decreasing at a rate of 2 cm/s. If the area of the triangle remains constant, at what rate does the angle between the sides change when the first side is 20 cm long, the second side is 30 cm, and the angle is $\pi/6$?

42. If a sound with frequency f_s is produced by a source traveling along a line with speed v_s and an observer is traveling with speed v_o along the same line from the opposite direction toward the source, then the frequency of the sound heard by the observer is

$$f_o = \left(\frac{c + v_o}{c - v_s}\right) f_s$$

where c is the speed of sound, about 332 m/s. (This is the **Doppler effect**.) Suppose that, at a particular moment, you are in a train traveling at 34 m/s and accelerating at 1.2 m/s^2. A train is approaching you from the opposite direction on the other track at 40 m/s, accelerating at 1.4 m/s^2, and sounds its whistle, which has a frequency of 460 Hz. At that instant, what is the perceived frequency that you hear and how fast is it changing?

43–46 Assume that all the given functions are differentiable.

43. If $z = f(x, y)$, where $x = r\cos\theta$ and $y = r\sin\theta$, (a) find $\partial z/\partial r$ and $\partial z/\partial\theta$ and (b) show that

$$\left(\frac{\partial z}{\partial x}\right)^2 + \left(\frac{\partial z}{\partial y}\right)^2 = \left(\frac{\partial z}{\partial r}\right)^2 + \frac{1}{r^2}\left(\frac{\partial z}{\partial\theta}\right)^2$$

44. If $u = f(x, y)$, where $x = e^s\cos t$ and $y = e^s\sin t$, show that

$$\left(\frac{\partial u}{\partial x}\right)^2 + \left(\frac{\partial u}{\partial y}\right)^2 = e^{-2s}\left[\left(\frac{\partial u}{\partial s}\right)^2 + \left(\frac{\partial u}{\partial t}\right)^2\right]$$

45. If $z = f(x - y)$, show that $\dfrac{\partial z}{\partial x} + \dfrac{\partial z}{\partial y} = 0$.

46. If $z = f(x, y)$, where $x = s + t$ and $y = s - t$, show that

$$\left(\frac{\partial z}{\partial x}\right)^2 - \left(\frac{\partial z}{\partial y}\right)^2 = \frac{\partial z}{\partial s}\frac{\partial z}{\partial t}$$

47–52 Assume that all the given functions have continuous second-order partial derivatives.

47. Show that any function of the form

$$z = f(x + at) + g(x - at)$$

is a solution of the wave equation

$$\frac{\partial^2 z}{\partial t^2} = a^2\frac{\partial^2 z}{\partial x^2}$$

[*Hint:* Let $u = x + at$, $v = x - at$.]

48. If $u = f(x, y)$, where $x = e^s\cos t$ and $y = e^s\sin t$, show that

$$\frac{\partial^2 u}{\partial x^2} + \frac{\partial^2 u}{\partial y^2} = e^{-2s}\left[\frac{\partial^2 u}{\partial s^2} + \frac{\partial^2 u}{\partial t^2}\right]$$

49. If $z = f(x, y)$, where $x = r^2 + s^2$ and $y = 2rs$, find $\partial^2 z/\partial r\,\partial s$. (Compare with Example 7.)

50. If $z = f(x, y)$, where $x = r\cos\theta$ and $y = r\sin\theta$, find (a) $\partial z/\partial r$, (b) $\partial z/\partial\theta$, and (c) $\partial^2 z/\partial r\,\partial\theta$.

51. If $z = f(x, y)$, where $x = r\cos\theta$ and $y = r\sin\theta$, show that

$$\frac{\partial^2 z}{\partial x^2} + \frac{\partial^2 z}{\partial y^2} = \frac{\partial^2 z}{\partial r^2} + \frac{1}{r^2}\frac{\partial^2 z}{\partial\theta^2} + \frac{1}{r}\frac{\partial z}{\partial r}$$

52. Suppose $z = f(x, y)$, where $x = g(s, t)$ and $y = h(s, t)$.
(a) Show that

$$\frac{\partial^2 z}{\partial t^2} = \frac{\partial^2 z}{\partial x^2}\left(\frac{\partial x}{\partial t}\right)^2 + 2\frac{\partial^2 z}{\partial x\,\partial y}\frac{\partial x}{\partial t}\frac{\partial y}{\partial t} + \frac{\partial^2 z}{\partial y^2}\left(\frac{\partial y}{\partial t}\right)^2$$
$$+ \frac{\partial z}{\partial x}\frac{\partial^2 x}{\partial t^2} + \frac{\partial z}{\partial y}\frac{\partial^2 y}{\partial t^2}$$

(b) Find a similar formula for $\partial^2 z/\partial s\,\partial t$.

53. Suppose that the equation $F(x, y, z) = 0$ implicitly defines each of the three variables x, y, and z as functions of the other two: $z = f(x, y)$, $y = g(x, z)$, $x = h(y, z)$. If F is differentiable and F_x, F_y, and F_z are all nonzero, show that

$$\frac{\partial z}{\partial x}\frac{\partial x}{\partial y}\frac{\partial y}{\partial z} = -1$$

54. Equation 6 is a formula for the derivative dy/dx of a function defined implicitly by an equation $F(x, y) = 0$, provided that F is differentiable and $F_y \neq 0$. Prove that if F has continuous second derivatives, then a formula for the second derivative of y is

$$\frac{d^2 y}{dx^2} = -\frac{F_{xx}F_y^2 - 2F_{xy}F_xF_y + F_{yy}F_x^2}{F_y^3}$$

11.6 Directional Derivatives and the Gradient Vector

0   50 100 150 200
(Distance in miles)

FIGURE 1

The weather map in Figure 1 shows a contour map of the temperature function $T(x, y)$ for the states of California and Nevada at 3:00 PM on a day in October. The level curves, or isothermals, join locations with the same temperature. The partial derivative T_x at a location such as Reno is the rate of change of temperature with respect to distance if we travel east from Reno; T_y is the rate of change of temperature if we travel north. But what if we want to know the rate of change of temperature when we travel southeast (toward Las Vegas), or in some other direction? In this section we introduce a type of derivative, called a *directional derivative,* that enables us to find the rate of change of a function of two or more variables in any direction.

Directional Derivatives

Recall that if $z = f(x, y)$, then the partial derivatives f_x and f_y are defined as

$$\boxed{1}$$

$$f_x(x_0, y_0) = \lim_{h \to 0} \frac{f(x_0 + h, y_0) - f(x_0, y_0)}{h}$$

$$f_y(x_0, y_0) = \lim_{h \to 0} \frac{f(x_0, y_0 + h) - f(x_0, y_0)}{h}$$

and represent the rates of change of z in the x- and y-directions, that is, in the directions of the unit vectors **i** and **j**.

Suppose that we now wish to find the rate of change of z at (x_0, y_0) in the direction of an arbitrary unit vector $\mathbf{u} = \langle a, b \rangle$. (See Figure 2.) To do this we consider the surface S with the equation $z = f(x, y)$ (the graph of f) and we let $z_0 = f(x_0, y_0)$. Then the point $P(x_0, y_0, z_0)$ lies on S. The vertical plane that passes through P in the direction of **u** intersects S in a curve C. (See Figure 3.) The slope of the tangent line T to C at the point P is the rate of change of z in the direction of **u**.

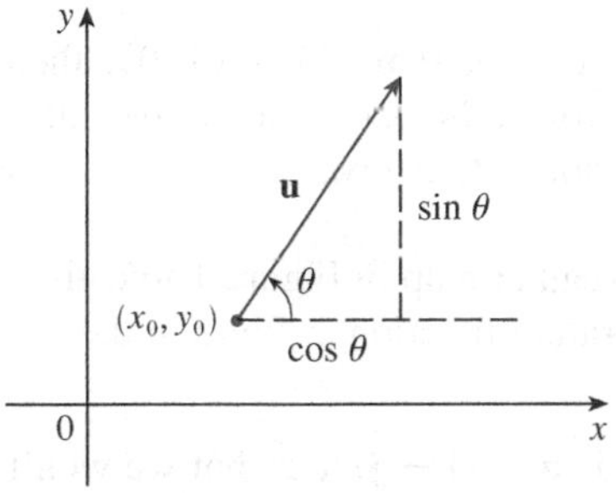

FIGURE 2
A unit vector $\mathbf{u} = \langle a, b \rangle = \langle \cos\theta, \sin\theta \rangle$

TEC Visual 11.6A animates Figure 3 by rotating **u** and therefore T.

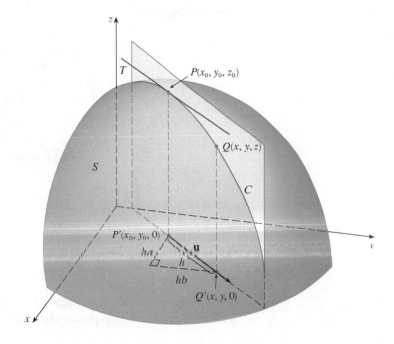

FIGURE 3

If $Q(x, y, z)$ is another point on C and P', Q' are the projections of P, Q onto the xy-plane, then the vector $\overrightarrow{P'Q'}$ is parallel to $\mathbf{u}$ and so

$$\overrightarrow{P'Q'} = h\mathbf{u} = \langle ha, hb \rangle$$

for some scalar h. Therefore $x - x_0 = ha$, $y - y_0 = hb$, so $x = x_0 + ha$, $y = y_0 + hb$, and

$$\frac{\Delta z}{h} = \frac{z - z_0}{h} = \frac{f(x_0 + ha, y_0 + hb) - f(x_0, y_0)}{h}$$

If we take the limit as $h \to 0$, we obtain the rate of change of z (with respect to distance) in the direction of $\mathbf{u}$, which is called the directional derivative of f in the direction of $\mathbf{u}$.

---

2 Definition   The **directional derivative** of f at (x_0, y_0) in the direction of a unit vector $\mathbf{u} = \langle a, b \rangle$ is

$$D_{\mathbf{u}} f(x_0, y_0) = \lim_{h \to 0} \frac{f(x_0 + ha, y_0 + hb) - f(x_0, y_0)}{h}$$

if this limit exists.

By comparing Definition 2 with Equations (1), we see that if $\mathbf{u} = \mathbf{i} = \langle 1, 0 \rangle$, then $D_{\mathbf{i}} f = f_x$ and if $\mathbf{u} = \mathbf{j} = \langle 0, 1 \rangle$, then $D_{\mathbf{j}} f = f_y$. In other words, the partial derivatives of f with respect to x and y are just special cases of the directional derivative.

EXAMPLE 1   **Estimating a directional derivative**   Use the weather map in Figure 1 to estimate the value of the directional derivative of the temperature function at Reno in the southeasterly direction.

SOLUTION   The unit vector directed toward the southeast is $\mathbf{u} = (\mathbf{i} - \mathbf{j})/\sqrt{2}$, but we won't need to use this expression. We start by drawing a line through Reno toward the southeast (see Figure 4).

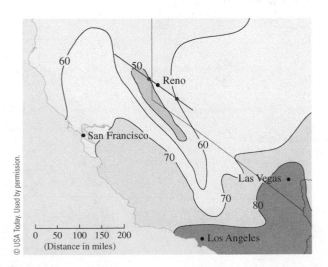

FIGURE 4

We approximate the directional derivative $D_{\mathbf{u}} T$ by the average rate of change of the temperature between the points where this line intersects the isothermals $T = 50$ and

$T = 60$. The temperature at the point southeast of Reno is $T = 60°F$ and the temperature at the point northwest of Reno is $T = 50°F$. The distance between these points looks to be about 75 miles. So the rate of change of the temperature in the southeasterly direction is

$$D_{\mathbf{u}} T \approx \frac{60 - 50}{75} = \frac{10}{75} \approx 0.13°F/mi$$

When we compute the directional derivative of a function defined by a formula, we generally use the following theorem.

---

3   **Theorem**   If f is a differentiable function of x and y, then f has a directional derivative in the direction of any unit vector $\mathbf{u} = \langle a, b \rangle$ and

$$D_{\mathbf{u}} f(x, y) = f_x(x, y)\, a + f_y(x, y)\, b$$

PROOF   If we define a function g of the single variable h by

$$g(h) = f(x_0 + ha, y_0 + hb)$$

then, by the definition of a derivative, we have

4
$$g'(0) = \lim_{h \to 0} \frac{g(h) - g(0)}{h} = \lim_{h \to 0} \frac{f(x_0 + ha, y_0 + hb) - f(x_0, y_0)}{h}$$

$$= D_{\mathbf{u}} f(x_0, y_0)$$

On the other hand, we can write $g(h) = f(x, y)$, where $x = x_0 + ha$, $y = y_0 + hb$, so the Chain Rule (Theorem 11.5.2) gives

$$g'(h) = \frac{\partial f}{\partial x} \frac{dx}{dh} + \frac{\partial f}{\partial y} \frac{dy}{dh} = f_x(x, y)\, a + f_y(x, y)\, b$$

If we now put $h = 0$, then $x = x_0$, $y = y_0$, and

5
$$g'(0) = f_x(x_0, y_0)\, a + f_y(x_0, y_0)\, b$$

Comparing Equations 4 and 5, we see that

$$D_{\mathbf{u}} f(x_0, y_0) = f_x(x_0, y_0)\, a + f_y(x_0, y_0)\, b$$

If the unit vector $\mathbf{u}$ makes an angle θ with the positive x-axis (as in Figure 2), then we can write $\mathbf{u} = \langle \cos\theta, \sin\theta \rangle$ and the formula in Theorem 3 becomes

6
$$D_{\mathbf{u}} f(x, y) = f_x(x, y) \cos\theta + f_y(x, y) \sin\theta$$

EXAMPLE 2   Find the directional derivative $D_{\mathbf{u}} f(x, y)$ if

$$f(x, y) = x^3 - 3xy + 4y^2$$

and $\mathbf{u}$ is the unit vector given by angle $\theta = \pi/6$. What is $D_{\mathbf{u}} f(1, 2)$?

The directional derivative $D_{\mathbf{u}} f(1, 2)$ in Example 2 represents the rate of change of z in the direction of $\mathbf{u}$. This is the slope of the tangent line to the curve of intersection of the surface $z = x^3 - 3xy + 4y^2$ and the vertical plane through $(1, 2, 0)$ in the direction of $\mathbf{u}$ shown in Figure 5.

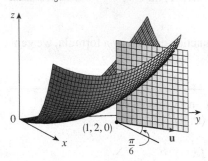

FIGURE 5

SOLUTION Formula 6 gives

$$D_{\mathbf{u}} f(x, y) = f_x(x, y) \cos \frac{\pi}{6} + f_y(x, y) \sin \frac{\pi}{6}$$

$$= (3x^2 - 3y) \frac{\sqrt{3}}{2} + (-3x + 8y)\tfrac{1}{2}$$

$$= \tfrac{1}{2}\left[3\sqrt{3}\, x^2 - 3x + (8 - 3\sqrt{3})y\right]$$

Therefore

$$D_{\mathbf{u}} f(1, 2) = \tfrac{1}{2}\left[3\sqrt{3}\,(1)^2 - 3(1) + (8 - 3\sqrt{3})(2)\right] = \frac{13 - 3\sqrt{3}}{2}$$

The Gradient Vector

Notice from Theorem 3 that the directional derivative of a differentiable function can be written as the dot product of two vectors:

$$\boxed{7} \qquad D_{\mathbf{u}} f(x, y) = f_x(x, y)\, a + f_y(x, y)\, b$$

$$= \langle f_x(x, y), f_y(x, y)\rangle \cdot \langle a, b\rangle$$

$$= \langle f_x(x, y), f_y(x, y)\rangle \cdot \mathbf{u}$$

The first vector in this dot product occurs not only in computing directional derivatives but in many other contexts as well. So we give it a special name (the *gradient* of f) and a special notation (**grad** f or ∇f, which is read "del f").

> $\boxed{8}$ **Definition** If f is a function of two variables x and y, then the **gradient** of f is the vector function ∇f defined by
>
> $$\nabla f(x, y) = \langle f_x(x, y), f_y(x, y)\rangle = \frac{\partial f}{\partial x}\, \mathbf{i} + \frac{\partial f}{\partial y}\, \mathbf{j}$$

EXAMPLE 3 **Evaluating a gradient vector** If $f(x, y) = \sin x + e^{xy}$, then

$$\nabla f(x, y) = \langle f_x, f_y\rangle = \langle \cos x + ye^{xy}, xe^{xy}\rangle$$

and

$$\nabla f(0, 1) = \langle 2, 0\rangle$$

With this notation for the gradient vector, we can rewrite the expression (7) for the directional derivative of a differentiable function as

$$\boxed{9} \qquad \boxed{D_{\mathbf{u}} f(x, y) = \nabla f(x, y) \cdot \mathbf{u}}$$

This expresses the directional derivative in the direction of $\mathbf{u}$ as the scalar projection of the gradient vector onto $\mathbf{u}$.

The gradient vector $\nabla f(2, -1)$ in Example 4 is shown in Figure 6 with initial point $(2, -1)$. Also shown is the vector **v** that gives the direction of the directional derivative. Both of these vectors are superimposed on a contour plot of the graph of f.

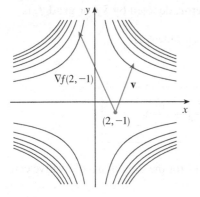

FIGURE 6

V **EXAMPLE 4**   **Using a gradient vector to find a directional derivative**   Find the directional derivative of the function $f(x, y) = x^2y^3 - 4y$ at the point $(2, -1)$ in the direction of the vector $\mathbf{v} = 2\mathbf{i} + 5\mathbf{j}$.

SOLUTION   We first compute the gradient vector at $(2, -1)$:

$$\nabla f(x, y) = 2xy^3\mathbf{i} + (3x^2y^2 - 4)\mathbf{j}$$

$$\nabla f(2, -1) = -4\mathbf{i} + 8\mathbf{j}$$

Note that **v** is not a unit vector, but since $|\mathbf{v}| = \sqrt{29}$, the unit vector in the direction of **v** is

$$\mathbf{u} = \frac{\mathbf{v}}{|\mathbf{v}|} = \frac{2}{\sqrt{29}}\mathbf{i} + \frac{5}{\sqrt{29}}\mathbf{j}$$

Therefore, by Equation 9, we have

$$D_{\mathbf{u}}f(2, -1) = \nabla f(2, -1) \cdot \mathbf{u} = (-4\mathbf{i} + 8\mathbf{j}) \cdot \left(\frac{2}{\sqrt{29}}\mathbf{i} + \frac{5}{\sqrt{29}}\mathbf{j}\right)$$

$$= \frac{-4 \cdot 2 + 8 \cdot 5}{\sqrt{29}} = \frac{32}{\sqrt{29}}$$

Functions of Three Variables

For functions of three variables we can define directional derivatives in a similar manner. Again $D_{\mathbf{u}}f(x, y, z)$ can be interpreted as the rate of change of the function in the direction of a unit vector **u**.

> **10**   **Definition**   The **directional derivative** of f at (x_0, y_0, z_0) in the direction of a unit vector $\mathbf{u} = \langle a, b, c \rangle$ is
>
> $$D_{\mathbf{u}}f(x_0, y_0, z_0) = \lim_{h \to 0} \frac{f(x_0 + ha, y_0 + hb, z_0 + hc) - f(x_0, y_0, z_0)}{h}$$
>
> if this limit exists.

If we use vector notation, then we can write both definitions (2 and 10) of the directional derivative in the compact form

> **11** $$D_{\mathbf{u}}f(\mathbf{x}_0) = \lim_{h \to 0} \frac{f(\mathbf{x}_0 + h\mathbf{u}) - f(\mathbf{x}_0)}{h}$$

where $\mathbf{x}_0 = \langle x_0, y_0 \rangle$ if $n = 2$ and $\mathbf{x}_0 = \langle x_0, y_0, z_0 \rangle$ if $n = 3$. This is reasonable because the vector equation of the line through $\mathbf{x}_0$ in the direction of the vector **u** is given by $\mathbf{x} = \mathbf{x}_0 + t\mathbf{u}$ (Equation 9.5.1) and so $f(\mathbf{x}_0 + h\mathbf{u})$ represents the value of f at a point on this line.

If $f(x, y, z)$ is differentiable and $\mathbf{u} = \langle a, b, c \rangle$, then the same method that was used to prove Theorem 3 can be used to show that

$$\boxed{12} \qquad D_\mathbf{u} f(x, y, z) = f_x(x, y, z)\, a + f_y(x, y, z)\, b + f_z(x, y, z)\, c$$

For a function f of three variables, the **gradient vector**, denoted by ∇f or **grad** f, is

$$\nabla f(x, y, z) = \langle f_x(x, y, z), f_y(x, y, z), f_z(x, y, z) \rangle$$

or, for short,

$$\boxed{13} \qquad \nabla f = \langle f_x, f_y, f_z \rangle = \frac{\partial f}{\partial x}\, \mathbf{i} + \frac{\partial f}{\partial y}\, \mathbf{j} + \frac{\partial f}{\partial z}\, \mathbf{k}$$

Then, just as with functions of two variables, Formula 12 for the directional derivative can be rewritten as

$$\boxed{14} \qquad D_\mathbf{u} f(x, y, z) = \nabla f(x, y, z) \cdot \mathbf{u}$$

⧸V⧹ EXAMPLE 5   If $f(x, y, z) = x \sin yz$, (a) find the gradient of f and (b) find the directional derivative of f at $(1, 3, 0)$ in the direction of $\mathbf{v} = \mathbf{i} + 2\mathbf{j} - \mathbf{k}$.

SOLUTION
(a) The gradient of f is

$$\nabla f(x, y, z) = \langle f_x(x, y, z), f_y(x, y, z), f_z(x, y, z) \rangle$$

$$= \langle \sin yz, xz \cos yz, xy \cos yz \rangle$$

(b) At $(1, 3, 0)$ we have $\nabla f(1, 3, 0) = \langle 0, 0, 3 \rangle$. The unit vector in the direction of $\mathbf{v} = \mathbf{i} + 2\mathbf{j} - \mathbf{k}$ is

$$\mathbf{u} = \frac{1}{\sqrt{6}}\, \mathbf{i} + \frac{2}{\sqrt{6}}\, \mathbf{j} - \frac{1}{\sqrt{6}}\, \mathbf{k}$$

Therefore Equation 14 gives

$$D_\mathbf{u} f(1, 3, 0) = \nabla f(1, 3, 0) \cdot \mathbf{u}$$

$$= 3\mathbf{k} \cdot \left(\frac{1}{\sqrt{6}}\, \mathbf{i} + \frac{2}{\sqrt{6}}\, \mathbf{j} - \frac{1}{\sqrt{6}}\, \mathbf{k} \right)$$

$$= 3\left(-\frac{1}{\sqrt{6}} \right) = -\sqrt{\frac{3}{2}}$$

Maximizing the Directional Derivative

Suppose we have a function f of two or three variables and we consider all possible directional derivatives of f at a given point. These give the rates of change of f in all possible directions. We can then ask the questions: In which of these directions does f change fastest and what is the maximum rate of change? The answers are provided by the following theorem.

15 Theorem Suppose f is a differentiable function of two or three variables. The maximum value of the directional derivative $D_{\mathbf{u}} f(\mathbf{x})$ is $|\nabla f(\mathbf{x})|$ and it occurs when $\mathbf{u}$ has the same direction as the gradient vector $\nabla f(\mathbf{x})$.

PROOF From Equation 9 or 14 we have

$$D_{\mathbf{u}} f = \nabla f \cdot \mathbf{u} = |\nabla f||\mathbf{u}| \cos \theta = |\nabla f| \cos \theta$$

where θ is the angle between ∇f and $\mathbf{u}$. The maximum value of $\cos \theta$ is 1 and this occurs when $\theta = 0$. Therefore the maximum value of $D_{\mathbf{u}} f$ is $|\nabla f|$ and it occurs when $\theta = 0$, that is, when $\mathbf{u}$ has the same direction as ∇f.

EXAMPLE 6 Determining a maximum rate of change

(a) If $f(x, y) = xe^y$, find the rate of change of f at the point $P(2, 0)$ in the direction from P to $Q(\frac{1}{2}, 2)$.

(b) In what direction does f have the maximum rate of change? What is this maximum rate of change?

SOLUTION

(a) We first compute the gradient vector:

$$\nabla f(x, y) = \langle f_x, f_y \rangle = \langle e^y, xe^y \rangle$$
$$\nabla f(2, 0) = \langle 1, 2 \rangle$$

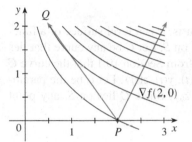

FIGURE 7

At (2, 0) the function in Example 6 increases fastest in the direction of the gradient vector $\nabla f(2, 0) = \langle 1, 2 \rangle$. Notice from Figure 7 that this vector appears to be perpendicular to the level curve through (2, 0). Figure 8 shows the graph of f and the gradient vector.

The unit vector in the direction of $\overrightarrow{PQ} = \langle -1.5, 2 \rangle$ is $\mathbf{u} = \langle -\frac{3}{5}, \frac{4}{5} \rangle$, so the rate of change of f in the direction from P to Q is

$$D_{\mathbf{u}} f(2, 0) = \nabla f(2, 0) \cdot \mathbf{u} = \langle 1, 2 \rangle \cdot \langle -\tfrac{3}{5}, \tfrac{4}{5} \rangle$$
$$= 1(-\tfrac{3}{5}) + 2(\tfrac{4}{5}) = 1$$

(b) According to Theorem 15, f increases fastest in the direction of the gradient vector $\nabla f(2, 0) = \langle 1, 2 \rangle$. The maximum rate of change is

$$|\nabla f(2, 0)| = |\langle 1, 2 \rangle| = \sqrt{5}$$

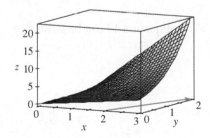

FIGURE 8

EXAMPLE 7 Suppose that the temperature at a point (x, y, z) in space is given by $T(x, y, z) = 80/(1 + x^2 + 2y^2 + 3z^2)$, where T is measured in degrees Celsius and x, y, z in meters. In which direction does the temperature increase fastest at the point $(1, 1, -2)$? What is the maximum rate of increase?

SOLUTION The gradient of T is

$$\nabla T = \frac{\partial T}{\partial x} \mathbf{i} + \frac{\partial T}{\partial y} \mathbf{j} + \frac{\partial T}{\partial z} \mathbf{k}$$

$$= -\frac{160x}{(1 + x^2 + 2y^2 + 3z^2)^2} \mathbf{i} - \frac{320y}{(1 + x^2 + 2y^2 + 3z^2)^2} \mathbf{j} - \frac{480z}{(1 + x^2 + 2y^2 + 3z^2)^2} \mathbf{k}$$

$$= \frac{160}{(1 + x^2 + 2y^2 + 3z^2)^2} (-x\mathbf{i} - 2y\mathbf{j} - 3z\mathbf{k})$$

At the point $(1, 1, -2)$ the gradient vector is

$$\nabla T(1, 1, -2) = \tfrac{160}{256}(-\mathbf{i} - 2\mathbf{j} + 6\mathbf{k}) = \tfrac{5}{8}(-\mathbf{i} - 2\mathbf{j} + 6\mathbf{k})$$

By Theorem 15 the temperature increases fastest in the direction of the gradient vector $\nabla T(1, 1, -2) = \tfrac{5}{8}(-\mathbf{i} - 2\mathbf{j} + 6\mathbf{k})$ or, equivalently, in the direction of $-\mathbf{i} - 2\mathbf{j} + 6\mathbf{k}$ or the unit vector $(-\mathbf{i} - 2\mathbf{j} + 6\mathbf{k})/\sqrt{41}$. The maximum rate of increase is the length of the gradient vector:

$$|\nabla T(1, 1, -2)| = \tfrac{5}{8}|-\mathbf{i} - 2\mathbf{j} + 6\mathbf{k}| = \tfrac{5}{8}\sqrt{41}$$

Therefore the maximum rate of increase of temperature is $\tfrac{5}{8}\sqrt{41} \approx 4°\text{C/m}$.

Tangent Planes to Level Surfaces

Suppose S is a surface with equation $F(x, y, z) = k$, that is, it is a level surface of a function F of three variables, and let $P(x_0, y_0, z_0)$ be a point on S. Let C be any curve that lies on the surface S and passes through the point P. Recall from Section 10.1 that the curve C is described by a continuous vector function $\mathbf{r}(t) = \langle x(t), y(t), z(t) \rangle$. Let t_0 be the parameter value corresponding to P; that is, $\mathbf{r}(t_0) = \langle x_0, y_0, z_0 \rangle$. Since C lies on S, any point $(x(t), y(t), z(t))$ must satisfy the equation of S, that is,

$$\boxed{16} \qquad F\big(x(t), y(t), z(t)\big) = k$$

If x, y, and z are differentiable functions of t and F is also differentiable, then we can use the Chain Rule to differentiate both sides of Equation 16 as follows:

$$\boxed{17} \qquad \frac{\partial F}{\partial x}\frac{dx}{dt} + \frac{\partial F}{\partial y}\frac{dy}{dt} + \frac{\partial F}{\partial z}\frac{dz}{dt} = 0$$

But, since $\nabla F = \langle F_x, F_y, F_z \rangle$ and $\mathbf{r}'(t) = \langle x'(t), y'(t), z'(t) \rangle$, Equation 17 can be written in terms of a dot product as

$$\nabla F \cdot \mathbf{r}'(t) = 0$$

In particular, when $t = t_0$ we have $\mathbf{r}(t_0) = \langle x_0, y_0, z_0 \rangle$, so

$$\boxed{18} \qquad \nabla F(x_0, y_0, z_0) \cdot \mathbf{r}'(t_0) = 0$$

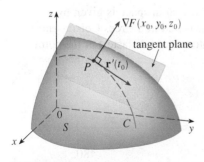

FIGURE 9

Equation 18 says that *the gradient vector at P, $\nabla F(x_0, y_0, z_0)$, is perpendicular to the tangent vector $\mathbf{r}'(t_0)$ to any curve C on S that passes through P.* (See Figure 9.) If $\nabla F(x_0, y_0, z_0) \neq \mathbf{0}$, it is therefore natural to define the **tangent plane to the level surface** $F(x, y, z) = k$ **at** $P(x_0, y_0, z_0)$ as the plane that passes through P and has normal vector $\nabla F(x_0, y_0, z_0)$. Using the standard equation of a plane (Equation 9.5.7), we can write the equation of this tangent plane as

$$\boxed{19} \qquad F_x(x_0, y_0, z_0)(x - x_0) + F_y(x_0, y_0, z_0)(y - y_0) + F_z(x_0, y_0, z_0)(z - z_0) = 0$$

The **normal line** to S at P is the line passing through P and perpendicular to the tangent plane. The direction of the normal line is therefore given by the gradient vector $\nabla F(x_0, y_0, z_0)$ and so, by Equation 9.5.3, its symmetric equations are

$$\boxed{20} \qquad \frac{x - x_0}{F_x(x_0, y_0, z_0)} = \frac{y - y_0}{F_y(x_0, y_0, z_0)} = \frac{z - z_0}{F_z(x_0, y_0, z_0)}$$

In the special case in which the equation of a surface S is of the form $z = f(x, y)$ (that is, S is the graph of a function f of two variables), we can rewrite the equation as

$$F(x, y, z) = f(x, y) - z = 0$$

and regard S as a level surface (with $k = 0$) of F. Then

$$F_x(x_0, y_0, z_0) = f_x(x_0, y_0)$$

$$F_y(x_0, y_0, z_0) = f_y(x_0, y_0)$$

$$F_z(x_0, y_0, z_0) = -1$$

so Equation 19 becomes

$$f_x(x_0, y_0)(x - x_0) + f_y(x_0, y_0)(y - y_0) - (z - z_0) = 0$$

which is equivalent to Equation 11.4.2. Thus our new, more general, definition of a tangent plane is consistent with the definition that was given for the special case of Section 11.4.

▶ **EXAMPLE 8**   Find the equations of the tangent plane and normal line at the point $(-2, 1, -3)$ to the ellipsoid

$$\frac{x^2}{4} + y^2 + \frac{z^2}{9} = 3$$

SOLUTION   The ellipsoid is the level surface (with $k = 3$) of the function

$$F(x, y, z) = \frac{x^2}{4} + y^2 + \frac{z^2}{9}$$

Figure 10 shows the ellipsoid, tangent plane, and normal line in Example 8.

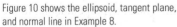

Therefore we have

$$F_x(x, y, z) = \frac{x}{2} \qquad\qquad F_y(x, y, z) = 2y \qquad\qquad F_z(x, y, z) = \frac{2z}{9}$$

$$F_x(-2, 1, -3) = -1 \qquad F_y(-2, 1, -3) = 2 \qquad F_z(-2, 1, -3) = -\tfrac{2}{3}$$

Then Equation 19 gives the equation of the tangent plane at $(-2, 1, -3)$ as

$$-1(x + 2) + 2(y - 1) - \tfrac{2}{3}(z + 3) = 0$$

which simplifies to $3x - 6y + 2z + 18 = 0$.
  By Equation 20, symmetric equations of the normal line are

$$\frac{x + 2}{-1} = \frac{y - 1}{2} = \frac{z + 3}{-\tfrac{2}{3}}$$

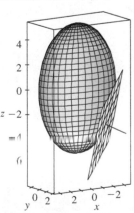

FIGURE 10

Significance of the Gradient Vector

We now summarize the ways in which the gradient vector is significant. We first consider a function f of three variables and a point $P(x_0, y_0, z_0)$ in its domain. On the one hand, we know from Theorem 15 that the gradient vector $\nabla f(x_0, y_0, z_0)$ gives the direction of fastest increase of f. On the other hand, we know that $\nabla f(x_0, y_0, z_0)$ is orthogonal to the level surface S of f through P. (Refer to Figure 9.) These two properties are quite compatible intuitively because as we move away from P on the level surface S, the value of f does not change at all. So it seems reasonable that if we move in the perpendicular direction, we get the maximum increase.

In like manner we consider a function f of two variables and a point $P(x_0, y_0)$ in its domain. Again the gradient vector $\nabla f(x_0, y_0)$ gives the direction of fastest increase of f. Also, by considerations similar to our discussion of tangent planes, it can be shown that $\nabla f(x_0, y_0)$ is perpendicular to the level curve $f(x, y) = k$ that passes through P. Again this is intuitively plausible because the values of f remain constant as we move along the curve. (See Figure 11.)

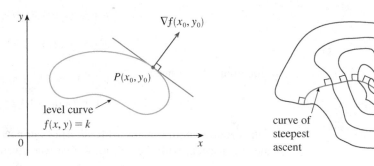

FIGURE 11   **FIGURE 12**

If we consider a topographical map of a hill and let $f(x, y)$ represent the height above sea level at a point with coordinates (x, y), then a curve of steepest ascent can be drawn as in Figure 12 by making it perpendicular to all of the contour lines. This phenomenon can also be noticed in Figure 5 in Section 11.1, where Lonesome Creek follows a curve of steepest descent.

Computer algebra systems have commands that plot sample gradient vectors. Each gradient vector $\nabla f(a, b)$ is plotted starting at the point (a, b). Figure 13 shows such a plot (called a *gradient vector field*) for the function $f(x, y) = x^2 - y^2$ superimposed on a contour map of f. As expected, the gradient vectors point "uphill" and are perpendicular to the level curves.

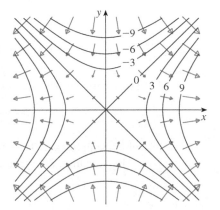

FIGURE 13

11.6 Exercises

1. Level curves for barometric pressure (in millibars) are shown for 6:00 AM on November 10, 1998. A deep low with pressure 972 mb is moving over northeast Iowa. The distance along the red line from K (Kearney, Nebraska) to S (Sioux City, Iowa) is 300 km. Estimate the value of the directional derivative of the pressure function at Kearney in the direction of Sioux City. What are the units of the directional derivative?

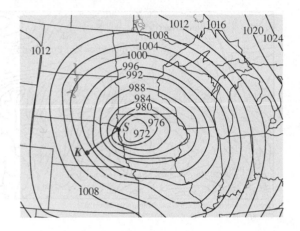

2. The contour map shows the average maximum temperature for November 2004 (in °C). Estimate the value of the directional derivative of this temperature function at Dubbo, New South Wales, in the direction of Sydney. What are the units?

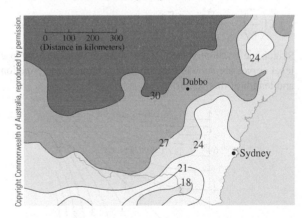

3. A table of values for the wind-chill index $W = f(T, v)$ is given in Exercise 3 on page 766. Use the table to estimate the value of $D_{\mathbf{u}} f(-20, 30)$, where $\mathbf{u} = (\mathbf{i} + \mathbf{j})/\sqrt{2}$.

4–6 Find the directional derivative of f at the given point in the direction indicated by the angle θ.

4. $f(x, y) = x^2 y^3 - y^4$, $(2, 1)$, $\theta = \pi/4$

5. $f(x, y) = ye^{-x}$, $(0, 4)$, $\theta = 2\pi/3$

6. $f(x, y) = x \sin(xy)$, $(2, 0)$, $\theta = \pi/3$

7–10

(a) Find the gradient of f.
(b) Evaluate the gradient at the point P.
(c) Find the rate of change of f at P in the direction of the vector $\mathbf{u}$.

7. $f(x, y) = \sin(2x + 3y)$, $P(-6, 4)$, $\mathbf{u} = \frac{1}{2}\left(\sqrt{3}\,\mathbf{i} - \mathbf{j}\right)$

8. $f(x, y) = y^2/x$, $P(1, 2)$, $\mathbf{u} = \frac{1}{3}\left(2\mathbf{i} + \sqrt{5}\,\mathbf{j}\right)$

9. $f(x, y, z) = xe^{2yz}$, $P(3, 0, 2)$, $\mathbf{u} = \left\langle \frac{2}{3}, -\frac{2}{3}, \frac{1}{3} \right\rangle$

10. $f(x, y, z) = \sqrt{x + yz}$, $P(1, 3, 1)$, $\mathbf{u} = \left\langle \frac{2}{7}, \frac{3}{7}, \frac{6}{7} \right\rangle$

11–17 Find the directional derivative of the function at the given point in the direction of the vector $\mathbf{v}$.

11. $f(x, y) = 1 + 2x\sqrt{y}$, $(3, 4)$, $\mathbf{v} = \langle 4, -3 \rangle$

12. $f(x, y) = \ln(x^2 + y^2)$, $(2, 1)$, $\mathbf{v} = \langle -1, 2 \rangle$

13. $g(p, q) = p^4 - p^2 q^3$, $(2, 1)$, $\mathbf{v} = \mathbf{i} + 3\mathbf{j}$

14. $g(r, s) = \tan^{-1}(rs)$, $(1, 2)$, $\mathbf{v} = 5\mathbf{i} + 10\mathbf{j}$

15. $f(x, y, z) = xe^y + ye^z + ze^x$, $(0, 0, 0)$, $\mathbf{v} = \langle 5, 1, -2 \rangle$

16. $f(x, y, z) = \sqrt{xyz}$, $(3, 2, 6)$, $\mathbf{v} = \langle -1, -2, 2 \rangle$

17. $g(x, y, z) = (x + 2y + 3z)^{3/2}$, $(1, 1, 2)$, $\mathbf{v} = 2\mathbf{j} - \mathbf{k}$

18. Use the figure to estimate $D_{\mathbf{u}} f(2, 2)$.

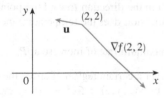

19. Find the directional derivative of $f(x, y) = \sqrt{xy}$ at $P(2, 8)$ in the direction of $Q(5, 4)$.

20. Find the directional derivative of $f(x, y, z) = xy + yz + zx$ at $P(1, -1, 3)$ in the direction of $Q(2, 4, 5)$.

21–24 Find the maximum rate of change of f at the given point and the direction in which it occurs.

21. $f(x, y) = \sin(xy)$, $(1, 0)$

22. $f(p, q) = qe^{-p} + pe^{-q}$, $(0, 0)$

23. $f(x, y, z) = \sqrt{x^2 + y^2 + z^2}$, $(3, 6, -2)$

24. $f(x, y, z) = (x + y)/z$, $(1, 1, -1)$

⊞ Graphing calculator or computer with graphing software required   **1.** Homework Hints available in TEC

25. (a) Show that a differentiable function f decreases most rapidly at $\mathbf{x}$ in the direction opposite to the gradient vector, that is, in the direction of $-\nabla f(\mathbf{x})$.

(b) Use the result of part (a) to find the direction in which the function $f(x, y) = x^4 y - x^2 y^3$ decreases fastest at the point $(2, -3)$.

26. Find the directions in which the directional derivative of $f(x, y) = ye^{-xy}$ at the point $(0, 2)$ has the value 1.

27. Find all points at which the direction of fastest change of the function $f(x, y) = x^2 + y^2 - 2x - 4y$ is $\mathbf{i} + \mathbf{j}$.

28. Near a buoy, the depth of a lake at the point with coordinates (x, y) is $z = 200 + 0.02x^2 - 0.001y^3$, where x, y, and z are measured in meters. A fisherman in a small boat starts at the point $(80, 60)$ and moves toward the buoy, which is located at $(0, 0)$. Is the water under the boat getting deeper or shallower when he departs? Explain.

29. The temperature T in a metal ball is inversely proportional to the distance from the center of the ball, which we take to be the origin. The temperature at the point $(1, 2, 2)$ is $120°$.

(a) Find the rate of change of T at $(1, 2, 2)$ in the direction toward the point $(2, 1, 3)$.

(b) Show that at any point in the ball the direction of greatest increase in temperature is given by a vector that points toward the origin.

30. The temperature at a point (x, y, z) is given by

$$T(x, y, z) = 200e^{-x^2-3y^2-9z^2}$$

where T is measured in °C and x, y, z in meters.

(a) Find the rate of change of temperature at the point $P(2, -1, 2)$ in the direction toward the point $(3, -3, 3)$.

(b) In which direction does the temperature increase fastest at P?

(c) Find the maximum rate of increase at P.

31. Suppose that over a certain region of space the electrical potential V is given by $V(x, y, z) = 5x^2 - 3xy + xyz$.

(a) Find the rate of change of the potential at $P(3, 4, 5)$ in the direction of the vector $\mathbf{v} = \mathbf{i} + \mathbf{j} - \mathbf{k}$.

(b) In which direction does V change most rapidly at P?

(c) What is the maximum rate of change at P?

32. Suppose you are climbing a hill whose shape is given by the equation $z = 1000 - 0.005x^2 - 0.01y^2$, where x, y, and z are measured in meters, and you are standing at a point with coordinates $(60, 40, 966)$. The positive x-axis points east and the positive y-axis points north.

(a) If you walk due south, will you start to ascend or descend? At what rate?

(b) If you walk northwest, will you start to ascend or descend? At what rate?

(c) In which direction is the slope largest? What is the rate of ascent in that direction? At what angle above the horizontal does the path in that direction begin?

33. Let f be a function of two variables that has continuous partial derivatives and consider the points $A(1, 3)$, $B(3, 3)$, $C(1, 7)$, and $D(6, 15)$. The directional derivative of f at A in the direction of the vector $\vec{AB}$ is 3 and the directional derivative at A in the direction of $\vec{AC}$ is 26. Find the directional derivative of f at A in the direction of the vector $\vec{AD}$.

34. Shown is a topographic map of Blue River Pine Provincial Park in British Columbia. Draw curves of steepest descent from Point A (descending to Mud Lake) and from point B.

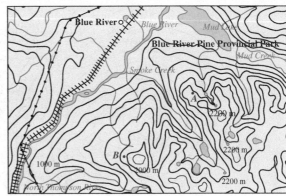

35. Show that the operation of taking the gradient of a function has the given property. Assume that u and v are differentiable functions of x and y and that a, b are constants.

(a) $\nabla(au + bv) = a\,\nabla u + b\,\nabla v$ (b) $\nabla(uv) = u\,\nabla v + v\,\nabla u$

(c) $\nabla\left(\dfrac{u}{v}\right) = \dfrac{v\,\nabla u - u\,\nabla v}{v^2}$ (d) $\nabla u^n = nu^{n-1}\,\nabla u$

36. Sketch the gradient vector $\nabla f(4, 6)$ for the function f whose level curves are shown. Explain how you chose the direction and length of this vector.

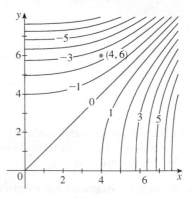

37. The **second directional derivative** of $f(x, y)$ is

$$D_{\mathbf{u}}^2 f(x, y) = D_{\mathbf{u}}[D_{\mathbf{u}} f(x, y)]$$

If $f(x, y) = x^3 + 5x^2 y + y^3$ and $\mathbf{u} = \left\langle \frac{3}{5}, \frac{4}{5} \right\rangle$, calculate $D_{\mathbf{u}}^2 f(2, 1)$.

38. (a) If $\mathbf{u} = \langle a, b \rangle$ is a unit vector and f has continuous second partial derivatives, show that

$$D_{\mathbf{u}}^2 f = f_{xx} a^2 + 2 f_{xy} ab + f_{yy} b^2$$

(b) Find the second directional derivative of $f(x, y) = xe^{2y}$ in the direction of $\mathbf{v} = \langle 4, 6 \rangle$.

39–44 Find equations of (a) the tangent plane and (b) the normal line to the given surface at the specified point.

39. $2(x - 2)^2 + (y - 1)^2 + (z - 3)^2 = 10$, $(3, 3, 5)$

40. $y = x^2 - z^2$, $(4, 7, 3)$

41. $x^2 - 2y^2 + z^2 + yz = 2$, $(2, 1, -1)$

42. $x - z = 4 \arctan(yz)$, $(1 + \pi, 1, 1)$

43. $z + 1 = xe^y \cos z$, $(1, 0, 0)$

44. $yz = \ln(x + z)$, $(0, 0, 1)$

45–46 Use a computer to graph the surface, the tangent plane, and the normal line on the same screen. Choose the domain carefully so that you avoid extraneous vertical planes. Choose the viewpoint so that you get a good view of all three objects.

45. $xy + yz + zx = 3$, $(1, 1, 1)$

46. $xyz = 6$, $(1, 2, 3)$

47. If $f(x, y) = xy$, find the gradient vector $\nabla f(3, 2)$ and use it to find the tangent line to the level curve $f(x, y) = 6$ at the point $(3, 2)$. Sketch the level curve, the tangent line, and the gradient vector.

48. If $g(x, y) = x^2 + y^2 - 4x$, find the gradient vector $\nabla g(1, 2)$ and use it to find the tangent line to the level curve $g(x, y) = 1$ at the point $(1, 2)$. Sketch the level curve, the tangent line, and the gradient vector.

49. Show that the equation of the tangent plane to the ellipsoid $x^2/a^2 + y^2/b^2 + z^2/c^2 = 1$ at the point (x_0, y_0, z_0) can be written as

$$\frac{xx_0}{a^2} + \frac{yy_0}{b^2} + \frac{zz_0}{c^2} = 1$$

50. At what point on the paraboloid $y = x^2 + z^2$ is the tangent plane parallel to the plane $x + 2y + 3z = 1$?

51. Are there any points on the hyperboloid $x^2 - y^2 - z^2 = 1$ where the tangent plane is parallel to the plane $z = x + y$?

52. Show that the ellipsoid $3x^2 + 2y^2 + z^2 = 9$ and the sphere $x^2 + y^2 + z^2 - 8x - 6y - 8z + 24 = 0$ are tangent to

each other at the point $(1, 1, 2)$. (This means that they have a common tangent plane at the point.)

53. Show that every plane that is tangent to the cone $x^2 + y^2 = z^2$ passes through the origin.

54. Show that every normal line to the sphere $x^2 + y^2 + z^2 = r^2$ passes through the center of the sphere.

55. Show that the sum of the x-, y-, and z-intercepts of any tangent plane to the surface $\sqrt{x} + \sqrt{y} + \sqrt{z} = \sqrt{c}$ is a constant.

56. Show that the pyramids cut off from the first octant by any tangent planes to the surface $xyz = 1$ at points in the first octant must all have the same volume.

57. Find parametric equations for the tangent line to the curve of intersection of the paraboloid $z = x^2 + y^2$ and the ellipsoid $4x^2 + y^2 + z^2 = 9$ at the point $(-1, 1, 2)$.

58. (a) The plane $y + z = 3$ intersects the cylinder $x^2 + y^2 = 5$ in an ellipse. Find parametric equations for the tangent line to this ellipse at the point $(1, 2, 1)$.

(b) Graph the cylinder, the plane, and the tangent line on the same screen.

59. (a) Two surfaces are called **orthogonal** at a point of intersection if their normal lines are perpendicular at that point. Show that surfaces with equations $F(x, y, z) = 0$ and $G(x, y, z) = 0$ are orthogonal at a point P where $\nabla F \neq \mathbf{0}$ and $\nabla G \neq \mathbf{0}$ if and only if

$$F_x G_x + F_y G_y + F_z G_z = 0 \quad \text{at } P$$

(b) Use part (a) to show that the surfaces $z^2 = x^2 + y^2$ and $x^2 + y^2 + z^2 = r^2$ are orthogonal at every point of intersection. Can you see why this is true without using calculus?

60. (a) Show that the function $f(x, y) = \sqrt[3]{xy}$ is continuous and the partial derivatives f_x and f_y exist at the origin but the directional derivatives in all other directions do not exist.

(b) Graph f near the origin and comment on how the graph confirms part (a).

61. Suppose that the directional derivatives of $f(x, y)$ are known at a given point in two nonparallel directions given by unit vectors $\mathbf{u}$ and $\mathbf{v}$. Is it possible to find ∇f at this point? If so, how would you do it?

62. Show that if $z = f(x, y)$ is differentiable at $\mathbf{x}_0 = \langle x_0, y_0 \rangle$, then

$$\lim_{\mathbf{x} \to \mathbf{x}_0} \frac{f(\mathbf{x}) - f(\mathbf{x}_0) - \nabla f(\mathbf{x}_0) \cdot (\mathbf{x} - \mathbf{x}_0)}{|\mathbf{x} - \mathbf{x}_0|} = 0$$

[*Hint:* Use Definition 11.4.7 directly.]

11.7 Maximum and Minimum Values

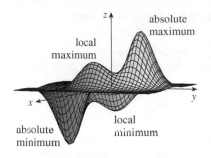

FIGURE 1

As we saw in Chapter 4, one of the main uses of ordinary derivatives is in finding maximum and minimum values (extreme values). In this section we see how to use partial derivatives to locate maxima and minima of functions of two variables. In particular, in Example 6 we will see how to maximize the volume of a box without a lid if we have a fixed amount of cardboard to work with.

Look at the hills and valleys in the graph of f shown in Figure 1. There are two points (a, b) where f has a *local maximum*, that is, where $f(a, b)$ is larger than nearby values of $f(x, y)$. The larger of these two values is the *absolute maximum*. Likewise, f has two *local minima*, where $f(a, b)$ is smaller than nearby values. The smaller of these two values is the *absolute minimum*.

> **1** **Definition** A function of two variables has a **local maximum** at (a, b) if $f(x, y) \leqslant f(a, b)$ when (x, y) is near (a, b). [This means that $f(x, y) \leqslant f(a, b)$ for all points (x, y) in some disk with center (a, b).] The number $f(a, b)$ is called a **local maximum value**. If $f(x, y) \geqslant f(a, b)$ when (x, y) is near (a, b), then f has a **local minimum** at (a, b) and $f(a, b)$ is a **local minimum value**.

If the inequalities in Definition 1 hold for *all* points (x, y) in the domain of f, then f has an **absolute maximum** (or **absolute minimum**) at (a, b).

Notice that the conclusion of Theorem 2 can be stated in the notation of gradient vectors as $\nabla f(a, b) = \mathbf{0}$.

> **2** **Fermat's Theorem for Functions of Two Variables** If f has a local maximum or minimum at (a, b) and the first-order partial derivatives of f exist there, then $f_x(a, b) = 0$ and $f_y(a, b) = 0$.

PROOF Let $g(x) = f(x, b)$. If f has a local maximum (or minimum) at (a, b), then g has a local maximum (or minimum) at a, so $g'(a) = 0$ by Fermat's Theorem for functions of one variable (see Theorem 4.2.4). But $g'(a) = f_x(a, b)$ (see Equation 11.3.1) and so $f_x(a, b) = 0$. Similarly, by applying Fermat's Theorem to the function $G(y) = f(a, y)$, we obtain $f_y(a, b) = 0$.   ⬚

If we put $f_x(a, b) = 0$ and $f_y(a, b) = 0$ in the equation of a tangent plane (Equation 11.4.2), we get $z = z_0$. Thus the geometric interpretation of Theorem 2 is that if the graph of f has a tangent plane at a local maximum or minimum, then the tangent plane must be horizontal.

A point (a, b) is called a **critical point** (or *stationary point*) of f if $f_x(a, b) = 0$ and $f_y(a, b) = 0$, or if one of these partial derivatives does not exist. Theorem 2 says that if f has a local maximum or minimum at (a, b), then (a, b) is a critical point of f. However, as in single-variable calculus, not all critical points give rise to maxima or minima. At a critical point, a function could have a local maximum or a local minimum or neither.

EXAMPLE 1 **A function with an absolute minimum**
Let $f(x, y) = x^2 + y^2 - 2x - 6y + 14$. Then

$$f_x(x, y) = 2x - 2 \qquad f_y(x, y) = 2y - 6$$

These partial derivatives are equal to 0 when $x = 1$ and $y = 3$, so the only critical point is $(1, 3)$. By completing the square, we find that

$$f(x, y) = 4 + (x - 1)^2 + (y - 3)^2$$

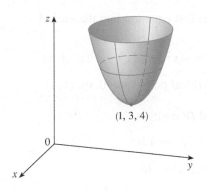

FIGURE 2
$z = x^2 + y^2 - 2x - 6y + 14$

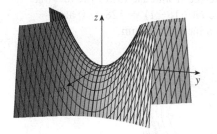

FIGURE 3
$z = y^2 - x^2$

Since $(x - 1)^2 \geqslant 0$ and $(y - 3)^2 \geqslant 0$, we have $f(x, y) \geqslant 4$ for all values of x and y. Therefore $f(1, 3) = 4$ is a local minimum, and in fact it is the absolute minimum of f. This can be confirmed geometrically from the graph of f, which is the elliptic paraboloid with vertex $(1, 3, 4)$ shown in Figure 2.

EXAMPLE 2   A function with no extreme values
Find the extreme values of $f(x, y) = y^2 - x^2$.

SOLUTION Since $f_x = -2x$ and $f_y = 2y$, the only critical point is $(0, 0)$. Notice that for points on the x-axis we have $y = 0$, so $f(x, y) = -x^2 < 0$ (if $x \neq 0$). However, for points on the y-axis we have $x = 0$, so $f(x, y) = y^2 > 0$ (if $y \neq 0$). Thus every disk with center $(0, 0)$ contains points where f takes positive values as well as points where f takes negative values. Therefore $f(0, 0) = 0$ can't be an extreme value for f, so f has no extreme value.

Example 2 illustrates the fact that a function need not have a maximum or minimum value at a critical point. Figure 3 shows how this is possible. The graph of f is the hyperbolic paraboloid $z = y^2 - x^2$, which has a horizontal tangent plane ($z = 0$) at the origin. You can see that $f(0, 0) = 0$ is a maximum in the direction of the x-axis but a minimum in the direction of the y-axis. Near the origin the graph has the shape of a saddle and so $(0, 0)$ is called a *saddle point* of f.

We need to be able to determine whether or not a function has an extreme value at a critical point. The following test, which is proved in Appendix E, is analogous to the Second Derivative Test for functions of one variable.

---

3   Second Derivatives Test   Suppose the second partial derivatives of f are continuous on a disk with center (a, b), and suppose that $f_x(a, b) = 0$ and $f_y(a, b) = 0$ [that is, (a, b) is a critical point of f]. Let

$$D = D(a, b) = f_{xx}(a, b)\,f_{yy}(a, b) - [f_{xy}(a, b)]^2$$

(a) If $D > 0$ and $f_{xx}(a, b) > 0$, then $f(a, b)$ is a local minimum.

(b) If $D > 0$ and $f_{xx}(a, b) < 0$, then $f(a, b)$ is a local maximum.

(c) If $D < 0$, then $f(a, b)$ is not a local maximum or minimum.

Note 1: In case (c) the point (a, b) is called a **saddle point** of f and the graph of f crosses its tangent plane at (a, b).

Note 2: If $D = 0$, the test gives no information: f could have a local maximum or local minimum at (a, b), or (a, b) could be a saddle point of f.

Note 3: To remember the formula for D, it's helpful to write it as a determinant:

$$D = \begin{vmatrix} f_{xx} & f_{xy} \\ f_{yx} & f_{yy} \end{vmatrix} = f_{xx}f_{yy} - (f_{xy})^2$$

V EXAMPLE 3   Classifying critical points   Find the local maximum and minimum values and saddle points of $f(x, y) = x^4 + y^4 - 4xy + 1$.

SOLUTION We first locate the critical points:

$$f_x = 4x^3 - 4y \qquad f_y = 4y^3 - 4x$$

Setting these partial derivatives equal to 0, we obtain the equations

$$x^3 - y = 0 \qquad \text{and} \qquad y^3 - x = 0$$

To solve these equations we substitute $y = x^3$ from the first equation into the second one. This gives

$$0 = x^9 - x = x(x^8 - 1) = x(x^4 - 1)(x^4 + 1) = x(x^2 - 1)(x^2 + 1)(x^4 + 1)$$

so there are three real roots: $x = 0, 1, -1$. The three critical points are $(0, 0)$, $(1, 1)$, and $(-1, -1)$.

Next we calculate the second partial derivatives and $D(x, y)$:

$$f_{xx} = 12x^2 \qquad f_{xy} = -4 \qquad f_{yy} = 12y^2$$

$$D(x, y) = f_{xx}f_{yy} - (f_{xy})^2 = 144x^2y^2 - 16$$

Since $D(0, 0) = -16 < 0$, it follows from case (c) of the Second Derivatives Test that the origin is a saddle point; that is, f has no local maximum or minimum at $(0, 0)$. Since $D(1, 1) = 128 > 0$ and $f_{xx}(1, 1) = 12 > 0$, we see from case (a) of the test that $f(1, 1) = -1$ is a local minimum. Similarly, we have $D(-1, -1) = 128 > 0$ and $f_{xx}(-1, -1) = 12 > 0$, so $f(-1, -1) = -1$ is also a local minimum.
The graph of f is shown in Figure 4.

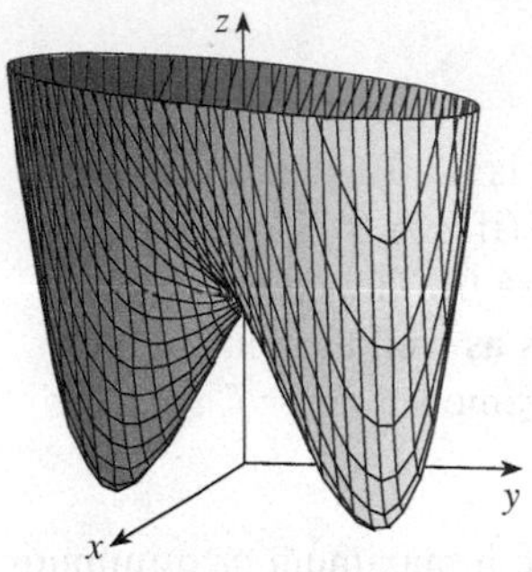

FIGURE 4

$z = x^4 + y^4 - 4xy + 1$

A contour map of the function f in Example 3 is shown in Figure 5. The level curves near $(1, 1)$ and $(-1, -1)$ are oval in shape and indicate that as we move away from $(1, 1)$ or $(-1, -1)$ in any direction the values of f are increasing. The level curves near $(0, 0)$, on the other hand, resemble hyperbolas. They reveal that as we move away from the origin (where the value of f is 1), the values of f decrease in some directions but increase in other directions. Thus the contour map suggests the presence of the minima and saddle point that we found in Example 3.

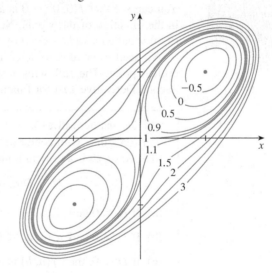

FIGURE 5

TEC In Module 11.7 you can use contour maps to estimate the locations of critical points.

EXAMPLE 4 Estimating critical points numerically Find and classify the critical points of the function

$$f(x, y) = 10x^2y - 5x^2 - 4y^2 - x^4 - 2y^4$$

Also find the highest point on the graph of f.

SOLUTION The first-order partial derivatives are

$$f_x = 20xy - 10x - 4x^3 \qquad f_y = 10x^2 - 8y - 8y^3$$

So to find the critical points we need to solve the equations

$$\boxed{4} \qquad\qquad\qquad 2x(10y - 5 - 2x^2) = 0$$

$$\boxed{5} \qquad\qquad\qquad 5x^2 - 4y - 4y^3 = 0$$

From Equation 4 we see that either

$$x = 0 \qquad \text{or} \qquad 10y - 5 - 2x^2 = 0$$

In the first case ($x = 0$), Equation 5 becomes $-4y(1 + y^2) = 0$, so $y = 0$ and we have the critical point $(0, 0)$.

In the second case ($10y - 5 - 2x^2 = 0$), we get

$$\boxed{6} \qquad\qquad x^2 = 5y - 2.5$$

and, putting this in Equation 5, we have $25y - 12.5 - 4y - 4y^3 = 0$. So we have to solve the cubic equation

$$\boxed{7} \qquad\qquad 4y^3 - 21y + 12.5 = 0$$

Using a graphing calculator or computer to graph the function

$$g(y) = 4y^3 - 21y + 12.5$$

as in Figure 6, we see that Equation 7 has three real roots. By zooming in, we can find the roots to four decimal places:

$$y \approx -2.5452 \qquad y \approx 0.6468 \qquad y \approx 1.8984$$

(Alternatively, we could have used Newton's method or a rootfinder to locate these roots.) From Equation 6, the corresponding x-values are given by

$$x = \pm\sqrt{5y - 2.5}$$

If $y \approx -2.5452$, then x has no corresponding real values. If $y \approx 0.6468$, then $x \approx \pm 0.8567$. If $y \approx 1.8984$, then $x \approx \pm 2.6442$. So we have a total of five critical points, which are analyzed in the following chart. All quantities are rounded to two decimal places.

Critical point	Value of f	f_{xx}	D	Conclusion
$(0, 0)$	0.00	-10.00	80.00	local maximum
$(\pm 2.64, 1.90)$	8.50	-55.93	2488.72	local maximum
$(\pm 0.86, 0.65)$	-1.48	-5.87	-187.64	saddle point

Figures 7 and 8 give two views of the graph of f and we see that the surface opens downward. [This can also be seen from the expression for $f(x, y)$: The dominant terms are $-x^4 - 2y^4$ when $|x|$ and $|y|$ are large.] Comparing the values of f at its local maximum points, we see that the absolute maximum value of f is $f(\pm 2.64, 1.90) \approx 8.50$. In other words, the highest points on the graph of f are $(\pm 2.64, 1.90, 8.50)$.

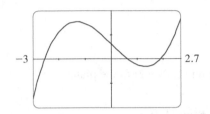

FIGURE 6

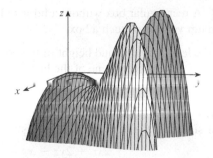

FIGURE 7

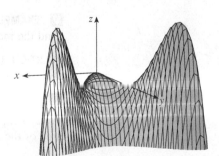

FIGURE 8

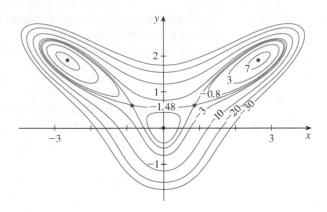

The five critical points of the function f in Example 4 are shown in red in the contour map of f in Figure 9.

FIGURE 9

▽ EXAMPLE 5   Find the shortest distance from the point $(1, 0, -2)$ to the plane $x + 2y + z = 4$.

SOLUTION   The distance from any point (x, y, z) to the point $(1, 0, -2)$ is

$$d = \sqrt{(x - 1)^2 + y^2 + (z + 2)^2}$$

but if (x, y, z) lies on the plane $x + 2y + z = 4$, then $z = 4 - x - 2y$ and so we have $d = \sqrt{(x - 1)^2 + y^2 + (6 - x - 2y)^2}$. We can minimize d by minimizing the simpler expression

$$d^2 = f(x, y) = (x - 1)^2 + y^2 + (6 - x - 2y)^2$$

By solving the equations

$$f_x = 2(x - 1) - 2(6 - x - 2y) = 4x + 4y - 14 = 0$$

$$f_y = 2y - 4(6 - x - 2y) = 4x + 10y - 24 = 0$$

we find that the only critical point is $\left(\frac{11}{6}, \frac{5}{3}\right)$. Since $f_{xx} = 4$, $f_{xy} = 4$, and $f_{yy} = 10$, we have $D(x, y) = f_{xx}f_{yy} - (f_{xy})^2 = 24 > 0$ and $f_{xx} > 0$, so by the Second Derivatives Test f has a local minimum at $\left(\frac{11}{6}, \frac{5}{3}\right)$. Intuitively, we can see that this local minimum is actually an absolute minimum because there must be a point on the given plane that is closest to $(1, 0, -2)$. If $x = \frac{11}{6}$ and $y = \frac{5}{3}$, then

$$d = \sqrt{(x - 1)^2 + y^2 + (6 - x - 2y)^2} = \sqrt{\left(\tfrac{5}{6}\right)^2 + \left(\tfrac{5}{3}\right)^2 + \left(\tfrac{5}{6}\right)^2} = \tfrac{5}{6}\sqrt{6}$$

Example 5 could also be solved using vectors. Compare with the methods of Section 9.5.

The shortest distance from $(1, 0, -2)$ to the plane $x + 2y + z = 4$ is $\frac{5}{6}\sqrt{6}$.   ▬

▽ EXAMPLE 6   A rectangular box without a lid is to be made from 12 m^2 of cardboard. Find the maximum volume of such a box.

SOLUTION   Let the length, width, and height of the box (in meters) be x, y, and z, as shown in Figure 10. Then the volume of the box is

$$V = xyz$$

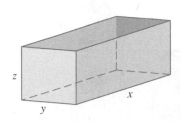

FIGURE 10

We can express V as a function of just two variables x and y by using the fact that the area of the four sides and the bottom of the box is

$$2xz + 2yz + xy = 12$$

Solving this equation for z, we get $z = (12 - xy)/[2(x + y)]$, so the expression for V becomes

$$V = xy \frac{12 - xy}{2(x + y)} = \frac{12xy - x^2y^2}{2(x + y)}$$

We compute the partial derivatives:

$$\frac{\partial V}{\partial x} = \frac{y^2(12 - 2xy - x^2)}{2(x + y)^2} \qquad \frac{\partial V}{\partial y} = \frac{x^2(12 - 2xy - y^2)}{2(x + y)^2}$$

If V is a maximum, then $\partial V/\partial x = \partial V/\partial y = 0$, but $x = 0$ or $y = 0$ gives $V = 0$, so we must solve the equations

$$12 - 2xy - x^2 = 0 \qquad 12 - 2xy - y^2 = 0$$

These imply that $x^2 = y^2$ and so $x = y$. (Note that x and y must both be positive in this problem.) If we put $x = y$ in either equation we get $12 - 3x^2 = 0$, which gives $x = 2$, $y = 2$, and $z = (12 - 2 \cdot 2)/[2(2 + 2)] = 1$.

We could use the Second Derivatives Test to show that this gives a local maximum of V, or we could simply argue from the physical nature of this problem that there must be an absolute maximum volume, which has to occur at a critical point of V, so it must occur when $x = 2$, $y = 2$, $z = 1$. Then $V = 2 \cdot 2 \cdot 1 = 4$, so the maximum volume of the box is 4 m³. ▬

Absolute Maximum and Minimum Values

For a function f of one variable, the Extreme Value Theorem says that if f is continuous on a closed interval $[a, b]$, then f has an absolute minimum value and an absolute maximum value. According to the Closed Interval Method in Section 4.2, we found these by evaluating f not only at the critical numbers but also at the endpoints a and b.

There is a similar situation for functions of two variables. Just as a closed interval contains its endpoints, a **closed set** in $\mathbb{R}^2$ is one that contains all its boundary points. [A boundary point of D is a point (a, b) such that every disk with center (a, b) contains points in D and also points not in D.] For instance, the disk

$$D = \{(x, y) \mid x^2 + y^2 \leqslant 1\}$$

which consists of all points on and inside the circle $x^2 + y^2 = 1$, is a closed set because it contains all of its boundary points (which are the points on the circle $x^2 + y^2 = 1$). But if even one point on the boundary curve were omitted, the set would not be closed. (See Figure 11.)

A **bounded set** in $\mathbb{R}^2$ is one that is contained within some disk. In other words, it is finite in extent. Then, in terms of closed and bounded sets, we can state the following counterpart of the Extreme Value Theorem in two dimensions.

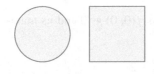

(a) Closed sets

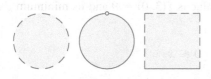

(b) Sets that are not closed

FIGURE 11

8 **Extreme Value Theorem for Functions of Two Variables** If f is continuous on a closed, bounded set D in $\mathbb{R}^2$, then f attains an absolute maximum value $f(x_1, y_1)$ and an absolute minimum value $f(x_2, y_2)$ at some points (x_1, y_1) and (x_2, y_2) in D.

To find the extreme values guaranteed by Theorem 8, we note that, by Theorem 2, if f has an extreme value at (x_1, y_1), then (x_1, y_1) is either a critical point of f or a boundary point of D. Thus we have the following extension of the Closed Interval Method.

---

9   To find the absolute maximum and minimum values of a continuous function f on a closed, bounded set D:

1. Find the values of f at the critical points of f in D.

2. Find the extreme values of f on the boundary of D.

3. The largest of the values from steps 1 and 2 is the absolute maximum value; the smallest of these values is the absolute minimum value.

EXAMPLE 7   **Testing for absolute extreme values on the boundary**   Find the absolute maximum and minimum values of the function $f(x, y) = x^2 - 2xy + 2y$ on the rectangle $D = \{(x, y) \mid 0 \le x \le 3, 0 \le y \le 2\}$.

SOLUTION Since f is a polynomial, it is continuous on the closed, bounded rectangle D, so Theorem 8 tells us there is both an absolute maximum and an absolute minimum. According to step 1 in (9), we first find the critical points. These occur when

$$f_x = 2x - 2y = 0 \qquad f_y = -2x + 2 = 0$$

so the only critical point is $(1, 1)$, and the value of f there is $f(1, 1) = 1$.

In step 2 we look at the values of f on the boundary of D, which consists of the four line segments L_1, L_2, L_3, L_4 shown in Figure 12. On L_1 we have $y = 0$ and

$$f(x, 0) = x^2 \qquad 0 \le x \le 3$$

This is an increasing function of x, so its minimum value is $f(0, 0) = 0$ and its maximum value is $f(3, 0) = 9$. On L_2 we have $x = 3$ and

$$f(3, y) = 9 - 4y \qquad 0 \le y \le 2$$

This is a decreasing function of y, so its maximum value is $f(3, 0) = 9$ and its minimum value is $f(3, 2) = 1$. On L_3 we have $y = 2$ and

$$f(x, 2) = x^2 - 4x + 4 \qquad 0 \le x \le 3$$

By the methods of Chapter 4, or simply by observing that $f(x, 2) = (x - 2)^2$, we see that the minimum value of this function is $f(2, 2) = 0$ and the maximum value is $f(0, 2) = 4$. Finally, on L_4 we have $x = 0$ and

$$f(0, y) = 2y \qquad 0 \le y \le 2$$

with maximum value $f(0, 2) = 4$ and minimum value $f(0, 0) = 0$. Thus, on the boundary, the minimum value of f is 0 and the maximum is 9.

In step 3 we compare these values with the value $f(1, 1) = 1$ at the critical point and conclude that the absolute maximum value of f on D is $f(3, 0) = 9$ and the absolute minimum value is $f(0, 0) = f(2, 2) = 0$. Figure 13 shows the graph of f.

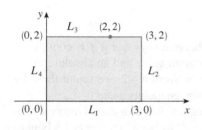

FIGURE 12

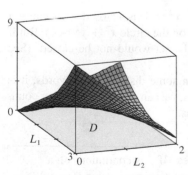

FIGURE 13

$f(x, y) = x^2 - 2xy + 2y$

11.7 Exercises

1. Suppose $(1, 1)$ is a critical point of a function f with continuous second derivatives. In each case, what can you say about f?

(a) $f_{xx}(1, 1) = 4$, $f_{xy}(1, 1) = 1$, $f_{yy}(1, 1) = 2$

(b) $f_{xx}(1, 1) = 4$, $f_{xy}(1, 1) = 3$, $f_{yy}(1, 1) = 2$

2. Suppose $(0, 2)$ is a critical point of a function g with continuous second derivatives. In each case, what can you say about g?

(a) $g_{xx}(0, 2) = -1$, $g_{xy}(0, 2) = 6$, $g_{yy}(0, 2) = 1$

(b) $g_{xx}(0, 2) = -1$, $g_{xy}(0, 2) = 2$, $g_{yy}(0, 2) = -8$

(c) $g_{xx}(0, 2) = 4$, $g_{xy}(0, 2) = 6$, $g_{yy}(0, 2) = 9$

3–4 Use the level curves in the figure to predict the location of the critical points of f and whether f has a saddle point or a local maximum or minimum at each critical point. Explain your reasoning. Then use the Second Derivatives Test to confirm your predictions.

3. $f(x, y) = 4 + x^3 + y^3 - 3xy$

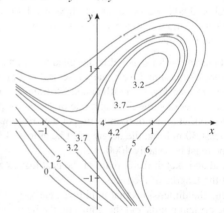

4. $f(x, y) = 3x - x^3 - 2y^2 + y^4$

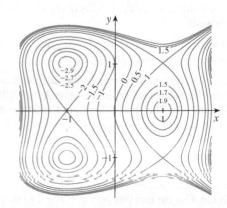

5–16 Find the local maximum and minimum values and saddle point(s) of the function. If you have three-dimensional graphing software, graph the function with a domain and viewpoint that reveal all the important aspects of the function.

5. $f(x, y) = x^2 + xy + y^2 + y$

6. $f(x, y) = x^3y + 12x^2 - 8y$

7. $f(x, y) = x^4 + y^4 - 4xy + 2$

8. $f(x, y) = xe^{-2x^2-2y^2}$

9. $f(x, y) = x^3 - 12xy + 8y^3$

10. $f(x, y) = xy + \dfrac{1}{x} + \dfrac{1}{y}$

11. $f(x, y) = e^x \cos y$

12. $f(x, y) = y \cos x$

13. $f(x, y) = (x^2 + y^2)e^{y^2 - x^2}$

14. $f(x, y) = e^y(y^2 - x^2)$

15. $f(x, y) = y^2 - 2y \cos x$, $-1 \le x \le 7$

16. $f(x, y) = \sin x \sin y$, $-\pi < x < \pi$, $-\pi < y < \pi$

17. Show that $f(x, y) = x^2 + 4y^2 - 4xy + 2$ has an infinite number of critical points and that $D = 0$ at each one. Then show that f has a local (and absolute) minimum at each critical point.

18. Show that $f(x, y) = x^2ye^{-x^2-y^2}$ has maximum values at $(\pm 1, 1/\sqrt{2})$ and minimum values at $(\pm 1, -1/\sqrt{2})$. Show also that f has infinitely many other critical points and $D = 0$ at each of them. Which of them give rise to maximum values? Minimum values? Saddle points?

⊞ **19–22** Use a graph or level curves or both to estimate the local maximum and minimum values and saddle point(s) of the function. Then use calculus to find these values precisely.

19. $f(x, y) = x^2 + y^2 + x^{-2}y^{-2}$

20. $f(x, y) = xye^{-x^2-y^2}$

21. $f(x, y) = \sin x + \sin y + \sin(x + y)$,
$0 \le x \le 2\pi$, $0 \le y \le 2\pi$

22. $f(x, y) = \sin x + \sin y + \cos(x + y)$,
$0 \le x \le \pi/4$, $0 \le y \le \pi/4$

⊞ **23–26** Use a graphing device as in Example 4 (or Newton's method or a rootfinder) to find the critical points of f correct to three decimal places. Then classify the critical points and find the highest or lowest points on the graph.

23. $f(x, y) = x^4 - 5x^2 + y^2 + 3x + 2$

⊞ Graphing calculator or computer with graphing software required   **1.** Homework Hints available in TEC

24. $f(x, y) = 5 - 10xy - 4x^2 + 3y - y^4$

25. $f(x, y) = 2x + 4x^2 - y^2 + 2xy^2 - x^4 - y^4$

26. $f(x, y) = e^x + y^4 - x^3 + 4\cos y$

27–32 Find the absolute maximum and minimum values of f on the set D.

27. $f(x, y) = 1 + 4x - 5y$, D is the closed triangular region with vertices $(0, 0)$, $(2, 0)$, and $(0, 3)$

28. $f(x, y) = 3 + xy - x - 2y$, D is the closed triangular region with vertices $(1, 0)$, $(5, 0)$, and $(1, 4)$

29. $f(x, y) = x^2 + y^2 + x^2y + 4$,
$D = \{(x, y) \mid |x| \le 1, \, |y| \le 1\}$

30. $f(x, y) = 4x + 6y - x^2 - y^2$,
$D = \{(x, y) \mid 0 \le x \le 4, 0 \le y \le 5\}$

31. $f(x, y) = 2x^3 + y^4$, $D = \{(x, y) \mid x^2 + y^2 \le 1\}$

32. $f(x, y) = x^3 - 3x - y^3 + 12y$, D is the quadrilateral whose vertices are $(-2, 3)$, $(2, 3)$, $(2, 2)$, and $(-2, -2)$.

---

33. For functions of one variable it is impossible for a continuous function to have two local maxima and no local minimum. But for functions of two variables such functions exist. Show that the function

$$f(x, y) = -(x^2 - 1)^2 - (x^2y - x - 1)^2$$

has only two critical points, but has local maxima at both of them. Then use a computer to produce a graph with a carefully chosen domain and viewpoint to see how this is possible.

34. If a function of one variable is continuous on an interval and has only one critical number, then a local maximum has to be an absolute maximum. But this is not true for functions of two variables. Show that the function

$$f(x, y) = 3xe^y - x^3 - e^{3y}$$

has exactly one critical point, and that f has a local maximum there that is not an absolute maximum. Then use a computer to produce a graph with a carefully chosen domain and viewpoint to see how this is possible.

35. Find the shortest distance from the point $(2, 1, -1)$ to the plane $x + y - z = 1$.

36. Find the point on the plane $x - y + z = 4$ that is closest to the point $(1, 2, 3)$.

37. Find the points on the cone $z^2 = x^2 + y^2$ that are closest to the point $(4, 2, 0)$.

38. Find the points on the surface $y^2 = 9 + xz$ that are closest to the origin.

39. Find three positive numbers whose sum is 100 and whose product is a maximum.

40. Find three positive numbers whose sum is 12 and the sum of whose squares is as small as possible.

41. Find the maximum volume of a rectangular box that is inscribed in a sphere of radius r.

42. Find the dimensions of the box with volume 1000 cm^3 that has minimal surface area.

43. Find the volume of the largest rectangular box in the first octant with three faces in the coordinate planes and one vertex in the plane $x + 2y + 3z = 6$.

44. Find the dimensions of the rectangular box with largest volume if the total surface area is given as 64 cm^2.

45. Find the dimensions of a rectangular box of maximum volume such that the sum of the lengths of its 12 edges is a constant c.

46. The base of an aquarium with given volume V is made of slate and the sides are made of glass. If slate costs five times as much (per unit area) as glass, find the dimensions of the aquarium that minimize the cost of the materials.

47. A cardboard box without a lid is to have a volume of 32,000 cm^3. Find the dimensions that minimize the amount of cardboard used.

48. A rectangular building is being designed to minimize heat loss. The east and west walls lose heat at a rate of 10 units/m^2 per day, the north and south walls at a rate of 8 units/m^2 per day, the floor at a rate of 1 unit/m^2 per day, and the roof at a rate of 5 units/m^2 per day. Each wall must be at least 30 m long, the height must be at least 4 m, and the volume must be exactly 4000 m^3.
(a) Find and sketch the domain of the heat loss as a function of the lengths of the sides.
(b) Find the dimensions that minimize heat loss. (Check both the critical points and the points on the boundary of the domain.)
(c) Could you design a building with even less heat loss if the restrictions on the lengths of the walls were removed?

49. If the length of the diagonal of a rectangular box must be L, what is the largest possible volume?

50. Three alleles (alternative versions of a gene) A, B, and O determine the four blood types A (AA or AO), B (BB or BO), O (OO), and AB. The Hardy-Weinberg Law states that the proportion of individuals in a population who carry two different alleles is

$$P = 2pq + 2pr + 2rq$$

where p, q, and r are the proportions of A, B, and O in the population. Use the fact that $p + q + r = 1$ to show that P is at most $\frac{2}{3}$.

51. Suppose that a scientist has reason to believe that two quantities x and y are related linearly, that is, $y = mx + b$, at least approximately, for some values of m and b. The scientist performs an experiment and collects data in the form of points $(x_1, y_1), (x_2, y_2), \ldots, (x_n, y_n)$, and then plots these points. The points don't lie exactly on a straight line, so the scientist wants to find constants m and b so that the line $y = mx + b$ "fits" the points as well as possible (see the figure).

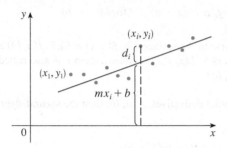

Let $d_i = y_i - (mx_i + b)$ be the vertical deviation of the point (x_i, y_i) from the line. The **method of least squares** determines m and b so as to minimize $\sum_{i=1}^{n} d_i^2$, the sum of the squares of these deviations. Show that, according to this method, the line of best fit is obtained when

$$m \sum_{i=1}^{n} x_i + bn = \sum_{i=1}^{n} y_i$$

$$m \sum_{i=1}^{n} x_i^2 + b \sum_{i=1}^{n} x_i = \sum_{i=1}^{n} x_i y_i$$

Thus the line is found by solving these two equations in the two unknowns m and b. (See Section 1.2 for a further discussion and applications of the method of least squares.)

52. Find an equation of the plane that passes through the point $(1, 2, 3)$ and cuts off the smallest volume in the first octant.

APPLIED PROJECT	**Designing a Dumpster**

For this project we locate a rectangular trash Dumpster in order to study its shape and construction. We then attempt to determine the dimensions of a container of similar design that minimize construction cost.

1. First locate a trash Dumpster in your area. Carefully study and describe all details of its construction, and determine its volume. Include a sketch of the container.

2. While maintaining the general shape and method of construction, determine the dimensions such a container of the same volume should have in order to minimize the cost of construction. Use the following assumptions in your analysis:

- The sides, back, and front are to be made from 12-gauge (0.1046 inch thick) steel sheets, which cost $0.70 per square foot (including any required cuts or bends).

- The base is to be made from a 10-gauge (0.1345 inch thick) steel sheet, which costs $0.90 per square foot.

- Lids cost approximately $50.00 each, regardless of dimensions.

- Welding costs approximately $0.18 per foot for material and labor combined.

Give justification of any further assumptions or simplifications made of the details of construction.

3. Describe how any of your assumptions or simplifications may affect the final result.

4. If you were hired as a consultant on this investigation, what would your conclusions be? Would you recommend altering the design of the Dumpster? If so, describe the savings that would result.

| DISCOVERY PROJECT | **Quadratic Approximations and Critical Points** |

The Taylor polynomial approximation to functions of one variable that we discussed in Chapter 8 can be extended to functions of two or more variables. Here we investigate quadratic approximations to functions of two variables and use them to give insight into the Second Derivatives Test for classifying critical points.

In Section 11.4 we discussed the linearization of a function f of two variables at a point (a, b):

$$L(x, y) = f(a, b) + f_x(a, b)(x - a) + f_y(a, b)(y - b)$$

Recall that the graph of L is the tangent plane to the surface $z = f(x, y)$ at $(a, b, f(a, b))$ and the corresponding linear approximation is $f(x, y) \approx L(x, y)$. The linearization L is also called the **first-degree Taylor polynomial** of f at (a, b).

1. If f has continuous second-order partial derivatives at (a, b), then the **second-degree Taylor polynomial** of f at (a, b) is

$$Q(x, y) = f(a, b) + f_x(a, b)(x - a) + f_y(a, b)(y - b)$$
$$+ \tfrac{1}{2} f_{xx}(a, b)(x - a)^2 + f_{xy}(a, b)(x - a)(y - b) + \tfrac{1}{2} f_{yy}(a, b)(y - b)^2$$

and the approximation $f(x, y) \approx Q(x, y)$ is called the **quadratic approximation** to f at (a, b). Verify that Q has the same first- and second-order partial derivatives as f at (a, b).

2. (a) Find the first- and second-degree Taylor polynomials L and Q of $f(x, y) = e^{-x^2 - y^2}$ at $(0, 0)$.
   (b) Graph f, L, and Q. Comment on how well L and Q approximate f.

3. (a) Find the first- and second-degree Taylor polynomials L and Q for $f(x, y) = xe^y$ at $(1, 0)$.
   (b) Compare the values of L, Q, and f at $(0.9, 0.1)$.
   (c) Graph f, L, and Q. Comment on how well L and Q approximate f.

4. In this problem we analyze the behavior of the polynomial $f(x, y) = ax^2 + bxy + cy^2$ (without using the Second Derivatives Test) by identifying the graph as a paraboloid.
   (a) By completing the square, show that if $a \neq 0$, then

$$f(x, y) = ax^2 + bxy + cy^2 = a\left[\left(x + \frac{b}{2a} y \right)^2 + \left(\frac{4ac - b^2}{4a^2} \right) y^2 \right]$$

   (b) Let $D = 4ac - b^2$. Show that if $D > 0$ and $a > 0$, then f has a local minimum at $(0, 0)$.
   (c) Show that if $D > 0$ and $a < 0$, then f has a local maximum at $(0, 0)$.
   (d) Show that if $D < 0$, then $(0, 0)$ is a saddle point.

5. (a) Suppose f is any function with continuous second-order partial derivatives such that $f(0, 0) = 0$ and $(0, 0)$ is a critical point of f. Write an expression for the second-degree Taylor polynomial, Q, of f at $(0, 0)$.
   (b) What can you conclude about Q from Problem 4?
   (c) In view of the quadratic approximation $f(x, y) \approx Q(x, y)$, what does part (b) suggest about f?

Graphing calculator or computer with graphing software required

11.8 Lagrange Multipliers

In Example 6 in Section 11.7 we maximized a volume function $V = xyz$ subject to the constraint $2xz + 2yz + xy = 12$, which expressed the side condition that the surface area was 12 m². In this section we present Lagrange's method for maximizing or minimizing a general function $f(x, y, z)$ subject to a constraint (or side condition) of the form $g(x, y, z) = k$.

It's easier to explain the geometric basis of Lagrange's method for functions of two variables. So we start by trying to find the extreme values of $f(x, y)$ subject to a constraint of the form $g(x, y) = k$. In other words, we seek the extreme values of $f(x, y)$ when the point (x, y) is restricted to lie on the level curve $g(x, y) = k$. Figure 1 shows this curve together with several level curves of f. These have the equations $f(x, y) = c$, where $c = 7$, 8, 9, 10, 11. To maximize $f(x, y)$ subject to $g(x, y) = k$ is to find the largest value of c such that the level curve $f(x, y) = c$ intersects $g(x, y) = k$. It appears from Figure 1 that this happens when these curves just touch each other, that is, when they have a common tangent line. (Otherwise, the value of c could be increased further.) This means that the normal lines at the point (x_0, y_0) where they touch are identical. So the gradient vectors are parallel; that is, $\nabla f(x_0, y_0) = \lambda \nabla g(x_0, y_0)$ for some scalar λ.

This kind of argument also applies to the problem of finding the extreme values of $f(x, y, z)$ subject to the constraint $g(x, y, z) = k$. Thus the point (x, y, z) is restricted to lie on the level surface S with equation $g(x, y, z) = k$. Instead of the level curves in Figure 1, we consider the level surfaces $f(x, y, z) = c$ and argue that if the maximum value of f is $f(x_0, y_0, z_0) = c$, then the level surface $f(x, y, z) = c$ is tangent to the level surface $g(x, y, z) = k$ and so the corresponding gradient vectors are parallel.

This intuitive argument can be made precise as follows. Suppose that a function f has an extreme value at a point $P(x_0, y_0, z_0)$ on the surface S and let C be a curve with vector equation $\mathbf{r}(t) = \langle x(t), y(t), z(t) \rangle$ that lies on S and passes through P. If t_0 is the parameter value corresponding to the point P, then $\mathbf{r}(t_0) = \langle x_0, y_0, z_0 \rangle$. The composite function $h(t) = f(x(t), y(t), z(t))$ represents the values that f takes on the curve C. Since f has an extreme value at (x_0, y_0, z_0), it follows that h has an extreme value at t_0, so $h'(t_0) = 0$. But if f is differentiable, we can use the Chain Rule to write

$$0 = h'(t_0)$$

$$= f_x(x_0, y_0, z_0)x'(t_0) + f_y(x_0, y_0, z_0)y'(t_0) + f_z(x_0, y_0, z_0)z'(t_0)$$

$$= \nabla f(x_0, y_0, z_0) \cdot \mathbf{r}'(t_0)$$

This shows that the gradient vector $\nabla f(x_0, y_0, z_0)$ is orthogonal to the tangent vector $\mathbf{r}'(t_0)$ to every such curve C. But we already know from Section 11.6 that the gradient vector of g, $\nabla g(x_0, y_0, z_0)$, is also orthogonal to $\mathbf{r}'(t_0)$ for every such curve. (See Equation 11.6.18.) This means that the gradient vectors $\nabla f(x_0, y_0, z_0)$ and $\nabla g(x_0, y_0, z_0)$ must be parallel. Therefore, if $\nabla g(x_0, y_0, z_0) \neq \mathbf{0}$, there is a number λ such that

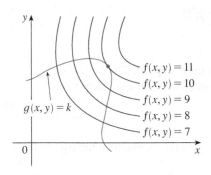

FIGURE 1

TEC Visual 11.8 animates Figure 1 for both level curves and level surfaces.

Lagrange multipliers are named after the French-Italian mathematician Joseph-Louis Lagrange (1736–1813). See page 272 for a biographical sketch of Lagrange.

$$\boxed{1} \qquad \nabla f(x_0, y_0, z_0) = \lambda \nabla g(x_0, y_0, z_0)$$

The number λ in Equation 1 is called a **Lagrange multiplier**. The procedure based on Equation 1 is as follows.

Method of Lagrange Multipliers To find the maximum and minimum values of $f(x, y, z)$ subject to the constraint $g(x, y, z) = k$ [assuming that these extreme values exist and $\nabla g \neq \mathbf{0}$ on the surface $g(x, y, z) = k$]:

(a) Find all values of x, y, z, and λ such that

$$\nabla f(x, y, z) = \lambda \nabla g(x, y, z)$$

and
$$g(x, y, z) = k$$

(b) Evaluate f at all the points (x, y, z) that result from step (a). The largest of these values is the maximum value of f; the smallest is the minimum value of f.

In deriving Lagrange's method we assumed that $\nabla g \neq \mathbf{0}$. In each of our examples you can check that $\nabla g \neq \mathbf{0}$ at all points where $g(x, y, z) = k$. See Exercise 21 for what can go wrong if $\nabla g = \mathbf{0}$.

If we write the vector equation $\nabla f = \lambda \nabla g$ in terms of components, then the equations in step (a) become

$$f_x = \lambda g_x \qquad f_y = \lambda g_y \qquad f_z = \lambda g_z \qquad g(x, y, z) = k$$

This is a system of four equations in the four unknowns x, y, z, and λ, but it is not necessary to find explicit values for λ.

For functions of two variables the method of Lagrange multipliers is similar to the method just described. To find the extreme values of $f(x, y)$ subject to the constraint $g(x, y) = k$, we look for values of x, y, and λ such that

$$\nabla f(x, y) = \lambda \nabla g(x, y) \qquad \text{and} \qquad g(x, y) = k$$

This amounts to solving three equations in three unknowns:

$$f_x = \lambda g_x \qquad f_y = \lambda g_y \qquad g(x, y) = k$$

Our first illustration of Lagrange's method is to reconsider the problem given in Example 6 in Section 11.7.

V **EXAMPLE 1** **Maximizing a volume using Lagrange multipliers** A rectangular box without a lid is to be made from 12 m² of cardboard. Find the maximum volume of such a box.

SOLUTION As in Example 6 in Section 11.7, we let x, y, and z be the length, width, and height, respectively, of the box in meters. Then we wish to maximize

$$V = xyz$$

subject to the constraint

$$g(x, y, z) = 2xz + 2yz + xy = 12$$

Using the method of Lagrange multipliers, we look for values of x, y, z, and λ such that $\nabla V = \lambda \nabla g$ and $g(x, y, z) = 12$. This gives the equations

$$V_x = \lambda g_x$$

$$V_y = \lambda g_y$$

$$V_z = \lambda g_z$$

$$2xz + 2yz + xy = 12$$

which become

$$\boxed{2} \qquad\qquad yz = \lambda(2z + y)$$

$$\boxed{3} \qquad\qquad xz = \lambda(2z + x)$$

$$\boxed{4} \qquad\qquad xy = \lambda(2x + 2y)$$

$$\boxed{5} \qquad\qquad 2xz + 2yz + xy = 12$$

There are no general rules for solving systems of equations. Sometimes some ingenuity is required. In the present example you might notice that if we multiply (2) by x, (3) by y, and (4) by z, then the left sides of these equations will be identical. Doing this, we have

Another method for solving the system of equations (2–5) is to solve each of Equations 2, 3, and 4 for λ and then to equate the resulting expressions.

$$\boxed{6} \qquad\qquad xyz = \lambda(2xz + xy)$$

$$\boxed{7} \qquad\qquad xyz = \lambda(2yz + xy)$$

$$\boxed{8} \qquad\qquad xyz = \lambda(2xz + 2yz)$$

We observe that $\lambda \neq 0$ because $\lambda = 0$ would imply $yz = xz = xy = 0$ from (2), (3), and (4) and this would contradict (5). Therefore, from (6) and (7), we have

$$2xz + xy = 2yz + xy$$

which gives $xz = yz$. But $z \neq 0$ (since $z = 0$ would give $V = 0$), so $x = y$. From (7) and (8) we have

$$2yz + xy = 2xz + 2yz$$

which gives $2xz = xy$ and so (since $x \neq 0$) $y = 2z$. If we now put $x = y = 2z$ in (5), we get

$$4z^2 + 4z^2 + 4z^2 = 12$$

Since x, y, and z are all positive, we therefore have $z = 1$ and so $x = 2$ and $y = 2$. This agrees with our answer in Section 11.7.　■

V **EXAMPLE 2**   Find the extreme values of the function $f(x, y) = x^2 + 2y^2$ on the circle $x^2 + y^2 = 1$.

SOLUTION   We are asked for the extreme values of f subject to the constraint $g(x, y) = x^2 + y^2 = 1$. Using Lagrange multipliers, we solve the equations $\nabla f = \lambda \nabla g$ and $g(x, y) = 1$, which can be written as

$$f_x = \lambda g_x \qquad f_y = \lambda g_y \qquad g(x, y) = 1$$

or as

$$\boxed{9} \qquad\qquad 2x = 2x\lambda$$

$$\boxed{10} \qquad\qquad 4y = 2y\lambda$$

$$\boxed{11} \qquad\qquad x^2 + y^2 = 1$$

From (9) we have $x = 0$ or $\lambda = 1$. If $x = 0$, then (11) gives $y = \pm 1$. If $\lambda = 1$, then $y = 0$ from (10), so then (11) gives $x = \pm 1$. Therefore f has possible extreme values at the points $(0, 1)$, $(0, -1)$, $(1, 0)$, and $(-1, 0)$. Evaluating f at these four points,

In geometric terms, Example 2 asks for the highest and lowest points on the curve C in Figure 2 that lies on the paraboloid $z = x^2 + 2y^2$ and directly above the constraint circle $x^2 + y^2 = 1$.

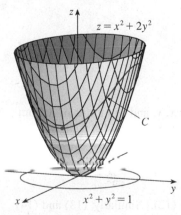

FIGURE 2

The geometry behind the use of Lagrange multipliers in Example 2 is shown in Figure 3. The extreme values of $f(x, y) = x^2 + 2y^2$ correspond to the level curves that touch the circle $x^2 + y^2 = 1$.

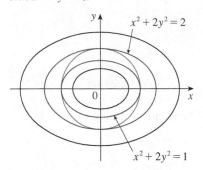

FIGURE 3

we find that

$$f(0, 1) = 2 \qquad f(0, -1) = 2 \qquad f(1, 0) = 1 \qquad f(-1, 0) = 1$$

Therefore the maximum value of f on the circle $x^2 + y^2 = 1$ is $f(0, \pm 1) = 2$ and the minimum value is $f(\pm 1, 0) = 1$. Checking with Figure 2, we see that these values look reasonable.   ▪

EXAMPLE 3 Find the extreme values of $f(x, y) = x^2 + 2y^2$ on the disk $x^2 + y^2 \le 1$.

SOLUTION According to the procedure in (11.7.9), we compare the values of f at the critical points with values at the points on the boundary. Since $f_x = 2x$ and $f_y = 4y$, the only critical point is $(0, 0)$. We compare the value of f at that point with the extreme values on the boundary from Example 2:

$$f(0, 0) = 0 \qquad f(\pm 1, 0) = 1 \qquad f(0, \pm 1) = 2$$

Therefore the maximum value of f on the disk $x^2 + y^2 \le 1$ is $f(0, \pm 1) = 2$ and the minimum value is $f(0, 0) = 0$.   ▪

EXAMPLE 4 Find the points on the sphere $x^2 + y^2 + z^2 = 4$ that are closest to and farthest from the point $(3, 1, -1)$.

SOLUTION The distance from a point (x, y, z) to the point $(3, 1, -1)$ is

$$d = \sqrt{(x - 3)^2 + (y - 1)^2 + (z + 1)^2}$$

but the algebra is simpler if we instead maximize and minimize the square of the distance:

$$d^2 = f(x, y, z) = (x - 3)^2 + (y - 1)^2 + (z + 1)^2$$

The constraint is that the point (x, y, z) lies on the sphere, that is,

$$g(x, y, z) = x^2 + y^2 + z^2 = 4$$

According to the method of Lagrange multipliers, we solve $\nabla f = \lambda \nabla g$, $g = 4$. This gives

$$\boxed{12} \qquad\qquad\qquad 2(x - 3) = 2x\lambda$$

$$\boxed{13} \qquad\qquad\qquad 2(y - 1) = 2y\lambda$$

$$\boxed{14} \qquad\qquad\qquad 2(z + 1) = 2z\lambda$$

$$\boxed{15} \qquad\qquad\qquad x^2 + y^2 + z^2 = 4$$

The simplest way to solve these equations is to solve for x, y, and z in terms of λ from (12), (13), and (14), and then substitute these values into (15). From (12) we have

$$x - 3 = x\lambda \quad \text{or} \quad x(1 - \lambda) = 3 \quad \text{or} \quad x = \frac{3}{1 - \lambda}$$

[Note that $1 - \lambda \ne 0$ because $\lambda = 1$ is impossible from (12).] Similarly, (13) and (14) give

$$y = \frac{1}{1 - \lambda} \qquad z = -\frac{1}{1 - \lambda}$$

Therefore, from (15), we have

$$\frac{3^2}{(1 - \lambda)^2} + \frac{1^2}{(1 - \lambda)^2} + \frac{(-1)^2}{(1 - \lambda)^2} = 4$$

which gives $(1 - \lambda)^2 = \frac{11}{4}$, $1 - \lambda = \pm\sqrt{11}/2$, so

$$\lambda = 1 \pm \frac{\sqrt{11}}{2}$$

These values of λ then give the corresponding points (x, y, z):

$$\left(\frac{6}{\sqrt{11}}, \frac{2}{\sqrt{11}}, -\frac{2}{\sqrt{11}}\right) \qquad \text{and} \qquad \left(-\frac{6}{\sqrt{11}}, -\frac{2}{\sqrt{11}}, \frac{2}{\sqrt{11}}\right)$$

It's easy to see that f has a smaller value at the first of these points, so the closest point is $(6/\sqrt{11}, 2/\sqrt{11}, -2/\sqrt{11})$ and the farthest is $(-6/\sqrt{11}, -2/\sqrt{11}, 2/\sqrt{11})$.

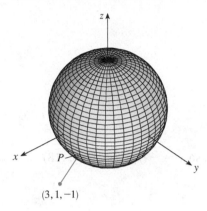

Figure 4 shows the sphere and the nearest point P in Example 4. Can you see how to find the coordinates of P without using calculus?

$(3, 1, -1)$

FIGURE 4

Two Constraints

Suppose now that we want to find the maximum and minimum values of a function $f(x, y, z)$ subject to two constraints (side conditions) of the form $g(x, y, z) = k$ and $h(x, y, z) = c$. Geometrically, this means that we are looking for the extreme values of f when (x, y, z) is restricted to lie on the curve of intersection C of the level surfaces $g(x, y, z) = k$ and $h(x, y, z) = c$. (See Figure 5.) Suppose f has such an extreme value at a point $P(x_0, y_0, z_0)$. We know from the beginning of this section that ∇f is orthogonal to C at P. But we also know that ∇g is orthogonal to $g(x, y, z) = k$ and ∇h is orthogonal to $h(x, y, z) = c$, so ∇g and ∇h are both orthogonal to C. This means that the gradient vector $\nabla f(x_0, y_0, z_0)$ is in the plane determined by $\nabla g(x_0, y_0, z_0)$ and $\nabla h(x_0, y_0, z_0)$. (We assume that these gradient vectors are not zero and not parallel.) So there are numbers λ and μ (called Lagrange multipliers) such that

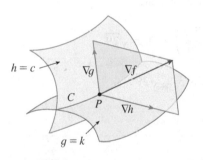

FIGURE 5

$$\boxed{16} \qquad \boxed{\nabla f(x_0, y_0, z_0) = \lambda\,\nabla g(x_0, y_0, z_0) + \mu\,\nabla h(x_0, y_0, z_0)}$$

In this case Lagrange's method is to look for extreme values by solving five equations in the five unknowns x, y, z, λ, and μ. These equations are obtained by writing Equation 16 in terms of its components and using the constraint equations:

$$f_x = \lambda g_x + \mu h_x$$

$$f_y = \lambda g_y + \mu h_y$$

$$f_z = \lambda g_z + \mu h_z$$

$$g(x, y, z) = k$$

$$h(x, y, z) = c$$

The cylinder $x^2 + y^2 = 1$ intersects the plane $x - y + z = 1$ in an ellipse (Figure 6). Example 5 asks for the maximum value of f when (x, y, z) is restricted to lie on the ellipse.

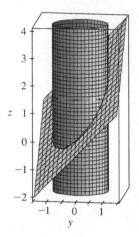

FIGURE 6

▽ EXAMPLE 5   A maximum problem with two constraints   Find the maximum value of the function $f(x, y, z) = x + 2y + 3z$ on the curve of intersection of the plane $x - y + z = 1$ and the cylinder $x^2 + y^2 = 1$.

SOLUTION   We maximize the function $f(x, y, z) = x + 2y + 3z$ subject to the constraints $g(x, y, z) = x - y + z = 1$ and $h(x, y, z) = x^2 + y^2 = 1$. The Lagrange condition is $\nabla f = \lambda \nabla g + \mu \nabla h$, so we solve the equations

$$\boxed{17} \qquad\qquad 1 = \lambda + 2x\mu$$

$$\boxed{18} \qquad\qquad 2 = -\lambda + 2y\mu$$

$$\boxed{19} \qquad\qquad 3 = \lambda$$

$$\boxed{20} \qquad\qquad x - y + z = 1$$

$$\boxed{21} \qquad\qquad x^2 + y^2 = 1$$

Putting $\lambda = 3$ [from (19)] in (17), we get $2x\mu = -2$, so $x = -1/\mu$. Similarly, (18) gives $y = 5/(2\mu)$. Substitution in (21) then gives

$$\frac{1}{\mu^2} + \frac{25}{4\mu^2} = 1$$

and so $\mu^2 = \frac{29}{4}$, $\mu = \pm\sqrt{29}/2$. Then $x = \mp 2/\sqrt{29}$, $y = \pm 5/\sqrt{29}$, and, from (20), $z = 1 - x + y = 1 \pm 7/\sqrt{29}$. The corresponding values of f are

$$\mp\frac{2}{\sqrt{29}} + 2\left(\pm\frac{5}{\sqrt{29}}\right) + 3\left(1 \pm \frac{7}{\sqrt{29}}\right) = 3 \pm \sqrt{29}$$

Therefore the maximum value of f on the given curve is $3 + \sqrt{29}$.

11.8 Exercises

1. Pictured are a contour map of f and a curve with equation $g(x, y) = 8$. Estimate the maximum and minimum values of f subject to the constraint that $g(x, y) = 8$. Explain your reasoning.

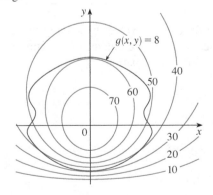

2. (a) Use a graphing calculator or computer to graph the circle $x^2 + y^2 = 1$. On the same screen, graph several curves of the form $x^2 + y = c$ until you find two that just touch the circle. What is the significance of the values of c for these two curves?

(b) Use Lagrange multipliers to find the extreme values of $f(x, y) = x^2 + y$ subject to the constraint $x^2 + y^2 = 1$. Compare your answers with those in part (a).

3–17 Use Lagrange multipliers to find the maximum and minimum values of the function subject to the given constraint(s).

3. $f(x, y) = x^2 + y^2$; $xy = 1$

4. $f(x, y) = 4x + 6y$; $x^2 + y^2 = 13$

5. $f(x, y) = x^2 y$; $x^2 + 2y^2 = 6$

⊞ Graphing calculator or computer with graphing software required   CAS Computer algebra system required   **1.** Homework Hints available in TEC

6. $f(x, y) = e^{xy};\quad x^3 + y^3 = 16$

7. $f(x, y, z) = 2x + 6y + 10z;\quad x^2 + y^2 + z^2 = 35$

8. $f(x, y, z) = 8x - 4z;\quad x^2 + 10y^2 + z^2 = 5$

9. $f(x, y, z) = xyz;\quad x^2 + 2y^2 + 3z^2 = 6$

10. $f(x, y, z) = x^2 y^2 z^2;\quad x^2 + y^2 + z^2 = 1$

11. $f(x, y, z) = x^2 + y^2 + z^2;\quad x^4 + y^4 + z^4 = 1$

12. $f(x, y, z) = x^4 + y^4 + z^4;\quad x^2 + y^2 + z^2 = 1$

13. $f(x, y, z, t) = x + y + z + t;\quad x^2 + y^2 + z^2 + t^2 = 1$

14. $f(x_1, x_2, \ldots, x_n) = x_1 + x_2 + \cdots + x_n;$

$x_1^2 + x_2^2 + \cdots + x_n^2 = 1$

15. $f(x, y, z) = x + 2y;\quad x + y + z = 1,\quad y^2 + z^2 = 4$

16. $f(x, y, z) = 3x - y - 3z;$
$x + y - z = 0,\quad x^2 + 2z^2 = 1$

17. $f(x, y, z) = yz + xy;\quad xy = 1,\quad y^2 + z^2 = 1$

18–19 Find the extreme values of f on the region described by the inequality.

18. $f(x, y) = 2x^2 + 3y^2 - 4x - 5,\quad x^2 + y^2 \leq 16$

19. $f(x, y) = e^{-xy},\quad x^2 + 4y^2 \leq 1$

---

20. Consider the problem of maximizing the function
$f(x, y) = 2x + 3y$ subject to the constraint $\sqrt{x} + \sqrt{y} = 5$.
(a) Try using Lagrange multipliers to solve the problem.
(b) Does $f(25, 0)$ give a larger value than the one in part (a)?
(c) Solve the problem by graphing the constraint equation and several level curves of f.
(d) Explain why the method of Lagrange multipliers fails to solve the problem.
(e) What is the significance of $f(9, 4)$?

21. Consider the problem of minimizing the function $f(x, y) = x$ on the curve $y^2 + x^4 - x^3 = 0$ (a piriform).
(a) Try using Lagrange multipliers to solve the problem.
(b) Show that the minimum value is $f(0, 0) = 0$ but the Lagrange condition $\nabla f(0, 0) = \lambda \nabla g(0, 0)$ is not satisfied for any value of λ.
(c) Explain why Lagrange multipliers fail to find the minimum value in this case.

22. (a) If your computer algebra system plots implicitly defined curves, use it to estimate the minimum and maximum values of $f(x, y) = x^3 + y^3 + 3xy$ subject to the constraint $(x - 3)^2 + (y - 3)^2 = 9$ by graphical methods.

(b) Solve the problem in part (a) with the aid of Lagrange multipliers. Use your CAS to solve the equations numerically. Compare your answers with those in part (a).

23. The total production P of a certain product depends on the amount L of labor used and the amount K of capital investment. In Sections 11.1 and 11.3 we discussed how the Cobb-Douglas model $P = bL^\alpha K^{1-\alpha}$ follows from certain economic assumptions, where b and α are positive constants and $\alpha < 1$. If the cost of a unit of labor is m and the cost of a unit of capital is n, and the company can spend only p dollars as its total budget, then maximizing the production P is subject to the constraint $mL + nK = p$. Show that the maximum production occurs when

$$L = \frac{\alpha p}{m} \quad \text{and} \quad K = \frac{(1 - \alpha)p}{n}$$

24. Referring to Exercise 23, we now suppose that the production is fixed at $bL^\alpha K^{1-\alpha} = Q$, where Q is a constant. What values of L and K minimize the cost function $C(L, K) = mL + nK$?

25. Use Lagrange multipliers to prove that the rectangle with maximum area that has a given perimeter p is a square.

26. Use Lagrange multipliers to prove that the triangle with maximum area that has a given perimeter p is equilateral.
Hint: Use Heron's formula for the area:

$$A = \sqrt{s(s - x)(s - y)(s - z)}$$

where $s = p/2$ and x, y, z are the lengths of the sides.

27–39 Use Lagrange multipliers to give an alternate solution to the indicated exercise in Section 11.7.

27. Exercise 35   **28.** Exercise 36

29. Exercise 37   **30.** Exercise 38

31. Exercise 39   **32.** Exercise 40

33. Exercise 41   **34.** Exercise 42

35. Exercise 43   **36.** Exercise 44

37. Exercise 45   **38.** Exercise 46

39. Exercise 49

---

40. Find the maximum and minimum volumes of a rectangular box whose surface area is 1500 cm² and whose total edge length is 200 cm.

41. The plane $x + y + 2z = 2$ intersects the paraboloid $z = x^2 + y^2$ in an ellipse. Find the points on this ellipse that are nearest to and farthest from the origin.

42. The plane $4x - 3y + 8z = 5$ intersects the cone $z^2 = x^2 + y^2$ in an ellipse.
  (a) Graph the cone, the plane, and the ellipse.
  (b) Use Lagrange multipliers to find the highest and lowest points on the ellipse.

CAS **43–44** Find the maximum and minimum values of f subject to the given constraints. Use a computer algebra system to solve the system of equations that arises in using Lagrange multipliers. (If your CAS finds only one solution, you may need to use additional commands.)

43. $f(x, y, z) = ye^{x-z}$; $9x^2 + 4y^2 + 36z^2 = 36$, $xy + yz = 1$

44. $f(x, y, z) = x + y + z$; $x^2 - y^2 = z$, $x^2 + z^2 = 4$

45. (a) Find the maximum value of
$$f(x_1, x_2, \ldots, x_n) = \sqrt[n]{x_1 x_2 \cdots x_n}$$
  given that $x_1, x_2, \ldots, x_n$ are positive numbers and $x_1 + x_2 + \cdots + x_n = c$, where c is a constant.

  (b) Deduce from part (a) that if $x_1, x_2, \ldots, x_n$ are positive numbers, then
$$\sqrt[n]{x_1 x_2 \cdots x_n} \leq \frac{x_1 + x_2 + \cdots + x_n}{n}$$
  This inequality says that the geometric mean of n numbers is no larger than the arithmetic mean of the numbers. Under what circumstances are these two means equal?

46. (a) Maximize $\sum_{i=1}^{n} x_i y_i$ subject to the constraints $\sum_{i=1}^{n} x_i^2 = 1$ and $\sum_{i=1}^{n} y_i^2 = 1$.
  (b) Put
$$x_i = \frac{a_i}{\sqrt{\sum a_j^2}} \quad \text{and} \quad y_i = \frac{b_i}{\sqrt{\sum b_j^2}}$$
  to show that
$$\sum a_i b_i \leq \sqrt{\sum a_j^2} \sqrt{\sum b_j^2}$$
  for any numbers $a_1, \ldots, a_n, b_1, \ldots, b_n$. This inequality is known as the Cauchy-Schwarz Inequality.

APPLIED PROJECT   Rocket Science

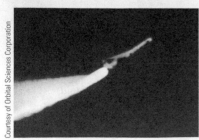

Courtesy of Orbital Sciences Corporation

Many rockets, such as the *Pegasus XL* currently used to launch satellites and the *Saturn V* that first put men on the moon, are designed to use three stages in their ascent into space. A large first stage initially propels the rocket until its fuel is consumed, at which point the stage is jettisoned to reduce the mass of the rocket. The smaller second and third stages function similarly in order to place the rocket's payload into orbit about the earth. (With this design, at least two stages are required in order to reach the necessary velocities, and using three stages has proven to be a good compromise between cost and performance.) Our goal here is to determine the individual masses of the three stages, which are to be designed in such a way as to minimize the total mass of the rocket while enabling it to reach a desired velocity.

For a single-stage rocket consuming fuel at a constant rate, the change in velocity resulting from the acceleration of the rocket vehicle has been modeled by

$$\Delta V = -c \ln\left(1 - \frac{(1 - S)M_r}{P + M_r}\right)$$

where M_r is the mass of the rocket engine including initial fuel, P is the mass of the payload, S is a *structural factor* determined by the design of the rocket (specifically, it is the ratio of the mass of the rocket vehicle without fuel to the total mass of the rocket with payload), and c is the (constant) speed of exhaust relative to the rocket.

Now consider a rocket with three stages and a payload of mass A. Assume that outside forces are negligible and that c and S remain constant for each stage. If M_i is the mass of the ith stage, we can initially consider the rocket engine to have mass M_1 and its payload to have mass $M_2 + M_3 + A$; the second and third stages can be handled similarly.

1. Show that the velocity attained after all three stages have been jettisoned is given by

$$v_f = c\left[\ln\left(\frac{M_1 + M_2 + M_3 + A}{SM_1 + M_2 + M_3 + A}\right) + \ln\left(\frac{M_2 + M_3 + A}{SM_2 + M_3 + A}\right) + \ln\left(\frac{M_3 + A}{SM_3 + A}\right)\right]$$

2. We wish to minimize the total mass $M = M_1 + M_2 + M_3$ of the rocket engine subject to the constraint that the desired velocity v_f from Problem 1 is attained. The method of

Lagrange multipliers is appropriate here, but difficult to implement using the current expressions. To simplify, we define variables N_i so that the constraint equation may be expressed as $v_f = c(\ln N_1 + \ln N_2 + \ln N_3)$. Since M is now difficult to express in terms of the N_i's, we wish to use a simpler function that will be minimized at the same place as M. Show that

$$\frac{M_1 + M_2 + M_3 + A}{M_2 + M_3 + A} = \frac{(1 - S)N_1}{1 - SN_1}$$

$$\frac{M_2 + M_3 + A}{M_3 + A} = \frac{(1 - S)N_2}{1 - SN_2}$$

$$\frac{M_3 + A}{A} = \frac{(1 - S)N_3}{1 - SN_3}$$

and conclude that

$$\frac{M + A}{A} = \frac{(1 - S)^3 N_1 N_2 N_3}{(1 - SN_1)(1 - SN_2)(1 - SN_3)}$$

3. Verify that $\ln((M + A)/A)$ is minimized at the same location as M; use Lagrange multipliers and the results of Problem 2 to find expressions for the values of N_i where the minimum occurs subject to the constraint $v_f = c(\ln N_1 + \ln N_2 + \ln N_3)$. [*Hint:* Use properties of logarithms to help simplify the expressions.]

4. Find an expression for the minimum value of M as a function of v_f.

5. If we want to put a three-stage rocket into orbit 100 miles above the earth's surface, a final velocity of approximately 17,500 mi/h is required. Suppose that each stage is built with a structural factor $S = 0.2$ and an exhaust speed of $c = 6000$ mi/h.
   (a) Find the minimum total mass M of the rocket engines as a function of A.
   (b) Find the mass of each individual stage as a function of A. (They are not equally sized!)

6. The same rocket would require a final velocity of approximately 24,700 mi/h in order to escape earth's gravity. Find the mass of each individual stage that would minimize the total mass of the rocket engines and allow the rocket to propel a 500-pound probe into deep space.

APPLIED PROJECT

Hydro-Turbine Optimization

The Katahdin Paper Company in Millinocket, Maine, operates a hydroelectric generating station on the Penobscot River. Water is piped from a dam to the power station. The rate at which the water flows through the pipe varies, depending on external conditions.

The power station has three different hydroelectric turbines, each with a known (and unique) power function that gives the amount of electric power generated as a function of the water flow arriving at the turbine. The incoming water can be apportioned in different volumes to each turbine, so the goal is to determine how to distribute water among the turbines to give the maximum total energy production for any rate of flow.

Using experimental evidence and *Bernoulli's equation*, the following quadratic models were determined for the power output of each turbine, along with the allowable flows of operation:

$$KW_1 = (-18.89 + 0.1277 Q_1 - 4.08 \cdot 10^{-5} Q_1^2)(170 - 1.6 \cdot 10^{-6} Q_T^2)$$

$$KW_2 = (-24.51 + 0.1358 Q_2 - 4.69 \cdot 10^{-5} Q_2^2)(170 - 1.6 \cdot 10^{-6} Q_T^2)$$

$$KW_3 = (-27.02 + 0.1380 Q_3 - 3.84 \cdot 10^{-5} Q_3^2)(170 - 1.6 \cdot 10^{-6} Q_T^2)$$

$$250 \leqslant Q_1 \leqslant 1110, \quad 250 \leqslant Q_2 \leqslant 1110, \quad 250 \leqslant Q_3 \leqslant 1225$$

where

$$Q_i = \text{flow through turbine } i \text{ in cubic feet per second}$$

$$KW_i = \text{power generated by turbine } i \text{ in kilowatts}$$

$$Q_T = \text{total flow through the station in cubic feet per second}$$

1. If all three turbines are being used, we wish to determine the flow Q_i to each turbine that will give the maximum total energy production. Our limitations are that the flows must sum to the total incoming flow and the given domain restrictions must be observed. Consequently, use Lagrange multipliers to find the values for the individual flows (as functions of Q_T) that maximize the total energy production $KW_1 + KW_2 + KW_3$ subject to the constraints $Q_1 + Q_2 + Q_3 = Q_T$ and the domain restrictions on each Q_i.

2. For which values of Q_T is your result valid?

3. For an incoming flow of 2500 ft³/s, determine the distribution to the turbines and verify (by trying some nearby distributions) that your result is indeed a maximum.

4. Until now we have assumed that all three turbines are operating; is it possible in some situations that more power could be produced by using only one turbine? Make a graph of the three power functions and use it to help decide if an incoming flow of 1000 ft³/s should be distributed to all three turbines or routed to just one. (If you determine that only one turbine should be used, which one would it be?) What if the flow is only 600 ft³/s?

5. Perhaps for some flow levels it would be advantageous to use two turbines. If the incoming flow is 1500 ft³/s, which two turbines would you recommend using? Use Lagrange multipliers to determine how the flow should be distributed between the two turbines to maximize the energy produced. For this flow, is using two turbines more efficient than using all three?

6. If the incoming flow is 3400 ft³/s, what would you recommend to the company?

11   Review

Concept Check

1. (a) What is a function of two variables?
   (b) Describe two methods for visualizing a function of two variables. What is the connection between them?

2. What is a function of three variables? How can you visualize such a function?

3. What does
   $$\lim_{(x,\,y) \to (a,\,b)} f(x, y) = L$$
   mean? How can you show that such a limit does not exist?

4. (a) What does it mean to say that f is continuous at (a, b)?
   (b) If f is continuous on $\mathbb{R}^2$, what can you say about its graph?

5. (a) Write expressions for the partial derivatives $f_x(a, b)$ and $f_y(a, b)$ as limits.

   (b) How do you interpret $f_x(a, b)$ and $f_y(a, b)$ geometrically? How do you interpret them as rates of change?
   (c) If $f(x, y)$ is given by a formula, how do you calculate f_x and f_y?

6. What does Clairaut's Theorem say?

7. How do you find a tangent plane to each of the following types of surfaces?
   (a) A graph of a function of two variables, $z = f(x, y)$
   (b) A level surface of a function of three variables, $F(x, y, z) = k$
   (c) A parametric surface given by a vector function $\mathbf{r}(u, v)$

8. Define the linearization of f at (a, b). What is the corresponding linear approximation? What is the geometric interpretation of the linear approximation?

9. (a) What does it mean to say that f is differentiable at (a, b)?
   (b) How do you usually verify that f is differentiable?

10. If $z = f(x, y)$, what are the differentials dx, dy, and dz?

11. State the Chain Rule for the case where $z = f(x, y)$ and x and y are functions of one variable. What if x and y are functions of two variables?

12. If z is defined implicitly as a function of x and y by an equation of the form $F(x, y, z) = 0$, how do you find $\partial z / \partial x$ and $\partial z / \partial y$?

13. (a) Write an expression as a limit for the directional derivative of f at (x_0, y_0) in the direction of a unit vector $\mathbf{u} = \langle a, b \rangle$. How do you interpret it as a rate? How do you interpret it geometrically?
   (b) If f is differentiable, write an expression for $D_{\mathbf{u}} f(x_0, y_0)$ in terms of f_x and f_y.

14. (a) Define the gradient vector ∇f for a function f of two or three variables.
   (b) Express $D_{\mathbf{u}} f$ in terms of ∇f.
   (c) Explain the geometric significance of the gradient.

15. What do the following statements mean?
   (a) f has a local maximum at (a, b).
   (b) f has an absolute maximum at (a, b).
   (c) f has a local minimum at (a, b).
   (d) f has an absolute minimum at (a, b).
   (e) f has a saddle point at (a, b).

16. (a) If f has a local maximum at (a, b), what can you say about its partial derivatives at (a, b)?
   (b) What is a critical point of f?

17. State the Second Derivatives Test.

18. (a) What is a closed set in $\mathbb{R}^2$? What is a bounded set?
   (b) State the Extreme Value Theorem for functions of two variables.
   (c) How do you find the values that the Extreme Value Theorem guarantees?

19. Explain how the method of Lagrange multipliers works in finding the extreme values of $f(x, y, z)$ subject to the constraint $g(x, y, z) = k$. What if there is a second constraint $h(x, y, z) = c$?

True-False Quiz

Determine whether the statement is true or false. If it is true, explain why. If it is false, explain why or give an example that disproves the statement.

1. $f_y(a, b) = \lim\limits_{y \to b} \dfrac{f(a, y) - f(a, b)}{y - b}$

2. There exists a function f with continuous second-order partial derivatives such that $f_x(x, y) = x + y^2$ and $f_y(x, y) = x - y^2$.

3. $f_{xy} = \dfrac{\partial^2 f}{\partial x \, \partial y}$

4. $D_{\mathbf{k}} f(x, y, z) = f_z(x, y, z)$

5. If $f(x, y) \to L$ as $(x, y) \to (a, b)$ along every straight line through (a, b), then $\lim_{(x, y) \to (a, b)} f(x, y) = L$.

6. If $f_x(a, b)$ and $f_y(a, b)$ both exist, then f is differentiable at (a, b).

7. If f has a local minimum at (a, b) and f is differentiable at (a, b), then $\nabla f(a, b) = \mathbf{0}$.

8. If f is a function, then
$$\lim_{(x, y) \to (2, 5)} f(x, y) = f(2, 5)$$

9. If $f(x, y) = \ln y$, then $\nabla f(x, y) = 1/y$.

10. If $(2, 1)$ is a critical point of f and
$$f_{xx}(2, 1) f_{yy}(2, 1) < [f_{xy}(2, 1)]^2$$
then f has a saddle point at $(2, 1)$.

11. If $f(x, y) = \sin x + \sin y$, then $-\sqrt{2} \leq D_{\mathbf{u}} f(x, y) \leq \sqrt{2}$.

12. If $f(x, y)$ has two local maxima, then f must have a local minimum.

Exercises

1–2 Find and sketch the domain of the function.

1. $f(x, y) = \ln(x + y + 1)$

2. $f(x, y) = \sqrt{4 - x^2 - y^2} + \sqrt{1 - x^2}$

3–4 Sketch the graph of the function.

3. $f(x, y) = 1 - y^2$

4. $f(x, y) = x^2 + (y - 2)^2$

⊞ Graphing calculator or computer with graphing software required

5–6 Sketch several level curves of the function.

5. $f(x, y) = \sqrt{4x^2 + y^2}$ **6.** $f(x, y) = e^x + y$

7. Make a rough sketch of a contour map for the function whose graph is shown.

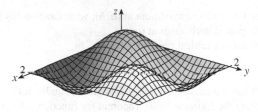

8. A contour map of a function f is shown. Use it to make a rough sketch of the graph of f.

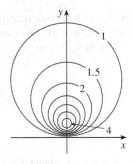

9–10 Evaluate the limit or show that it does not exist.

9. $\displaystyle\lim_{(x,y)\to(1,1)} \frac{2xy}{x^2 + 2y^2}$ **10.** $\displaystyle\lim_{(x,y)\to(0,0)} \frac{2xy}{x^2 + 2y^2}$

11. A metal plate is situated in the xy-plane and occupies the rectangle $0 \le x \le 10$, $0 \le y \le 8$, where x and y are measured in meters. The temperature at the point (x, y) in the plate is $T(x, y)$, where T is measured in degrees Celsius. Temperatures at equally spaced points were measured and recorded in the table.
(a) Estimate the values of the partial derivatives $T_x(6, 4)$ and $T_y(6, 4)$. What are the units?
(b) Estimate the value of $D_{\mathbf{u}} T(6, 4)$, where $\mathbf{u} = (\mathbf{i} + \mathbf{j})/\sqrt{2}$. Interpret your result.
(c) Estimate the value of $T_{xy}(6, 4)$.

x \ y	0	2	4	6	8
0	30	38	45	51	55
2	52	56	60	62	61
4	78	74	72	68	66
6	98	87	80	75	71
8	96	90	86	80	75
10	92	92	91	87	78

12. Find a linear approximation to the temperature function $T(x, y)$ in Exercise 11 near the point $(6, 4)$. Then use it to estimate the temperature at the point $(5, 3.8)$.

13–17 Find the first partial derivatives.

13. $f(x, y) = \sqrt{2x + y^2}$ **14.** $u = e^{-r} \sin 2\theta$

15. $g(u, v) = u \tan^{-1} v$ **16.** $w = \dfrac{x}{y - z}$

17. $T(p, q, r) = p \ln(q + e^r)$

18. The speed of sound traveling through ocean water is a function of temperature, salinity, and pressure. It has been modeled by the function

$$C = 1449.2 + 4.6T - 0.055T^2 + 0.00029T^3$$
$$+ (1.34 - 0.01T)(S - 35) + 0.016D$$

where C is the speed of sound (in meters per second), T is the temperature (in degrees Celsius), S is the salinity (the concentration of salts in parts per thousand, which means the number of grams of dissolved solids per 1000 g of water), and D is the depth below the ocean surface (in meters). Compute $\partial C/\partial T$, $\partial C/\partial S$, and $\partial C/\partial D$ when $T = 10°C$, $S = 35$ parts per thousand, and $D = 100$ m. Explain the physical significance of these partial derivatives.

19–22 Find all second partial derivatives of f.

19. $f(x, y) = 4x^3 - xy^2$ **20.** $z = xe^{-2y}$

21. $f(x, y, z) = x^k y^l z^m$ **22.** $v = r \cos(s + 2t)$

23. If $z = xy + xe^{y/x}$, show that $x\dfrac{\partial z}{\partial x} + y\dfrac{\partial z}{\partial y} = xy + z$.

24. If $z = \sin(x + \sin t)$, show that

$$\frac{\partial z}{\partial x} \frac{\partial^2 z}{\partial x \, \partial t} = \frac{\partial z}{\partial t} \frac{\partial^2 z}{\partial x^2}$$

25–29 Find equations of (a) the tangent plane and (b) the normal line to the given surface at the specified point.

25. $z = 3x^2 - y^2 + 2x$, $(1, -2, 1)$

26. $z = e^x \cos y$, $(0, 0, 1)$

27. $x^2 + 2y^2 - 3z^2 = 3$, $(2, -1, 1)$

28. $xy + yz + zx = 3$, $(1, 1, 1)$

29. $\mathbf{r}(u, v) = (u + v)\mathbf{i} + u^2\mathbf{j} + v^2\mathbf{k}$, $(3, 4, 1)$

30. Use a computer to graph the surface $z = x^2 + y^4$ and its tangent plane and normal line at $(1, 1, 2)$ on the same screen. Choose the domain and viewpoint so that you get a good view of all three objects.

31. Find the points on the hyperboloid $x^2 + 4y^2 - z^2 = 4$ where the tangent plane is parallel to the plane $2x + 2y + z = 5$.

32. Find du if $u = \ln(1 + se^{2t})$.

33. Find the linear approximation of the function $f(x, y, z) = x^3\sqrt{y^2 + z^2}$ at the point $(2, 3, 4)$ and use it to estimate the number $(1.98)^3\sqrt{(3.01)^2 + (3.97)^2}$.

34. The two legs of a right triangle are measured as 5 m and 12 m with a possible error in measurement of at most 0.2 cm in each. Use differentials to estimate the maximum error in the calculated value of (a) the area of the triangle and (b) the length of the hypotenuse.

35. If $u = x^2y^3 + z^4$, where $x = p + 3p^2$, $y = pe^p$, and $z = p\sin p$, use the Chain Rule to find du/dp.

36. If $v = x^2\sin y + ye^{xy}$, where $x = s + 2t$ and $y = st$, use the Chain Rule to find $\partial v/\partial s$ and $\partial v/\partial t$ when $s = 0$ and $t = 1$.

37. Suppose $z = f(x, y)$, where $x = g(s, t)$, $y = h(s, t)$, $g(1, 2) = 3$, $g_s(1, 2) = -1$, $g_t(1, 2) = 4$, $h(1, 2) = 6$, $h_s(1, 2) = -5$, $h_t(1, 2) = 10$, $f_x(3, 6) = 7$, and $f_y(3, 6) = 8$. Find $\partial z/\partial s$ and $\partial z/\partial t$ when $s = 1$ and $t = 2$.

38. Use a tree diagram to write out the Chain Rule for the case where $w = f(t, u, v)$, $t = t(p, q, r, s)$, $u = u(p, q, r, s)$, and $v = v(p, q, r, s)$ are all differentiable functions.

39. If $z = y + f(x^2 - y^2)$, where f is differentiable, show that

$$y\frac{\partial z}{\partial x} + x\frac{\partial z}{\partial y} = x$$

40. The length x of a side of a triangle is increasing at a rate of 3 in/s, the length y of another side is decreasing at a rate of 2 in/s, and the contained angle θ is increasing at a rate of 0.05 radian/s. How fast is the area of the triangle changing when $x = 40$ in, $y = 50$ in, and $\theta = \pi/6$?

41. If $z = f(u, v)$, where $u = xy$, $v = y/x$, and f has continuous second partial derivatives, show that

$$x^2\frac{\partial^2 z}{\partial x^2} - y^2\frac{\partial^2 z}{\partial y^2} = -4uv\frac{\partial^2 z}{\partial u\,\partial v} + 2v\frac{\partial z}{\partial v}$$

42. If $\cos(xyz) = 1 + x^2y^2 + z^2$, find $\dfrac{\partial z}{\partial x}$ and $\dfrac{\partial z}{\partial y}$.

43. Find the gradient of the function $f(x, y, z) = x^2e^{yz^2}$.

44. (a) When is the directional derivative of f a maximum?
(b) When is it a minimum?
(c) When is it 0?
(d) When is it half of its maximum value?

45–46 Find the directional derivative of f at the given point in the indicated direction.

45. $f(x, y) = x^2e^{-y}$, $(-2, 0)$,
in the direction toward the point $(2, -3)$

46. $f(x, y, z) = x^2y + x\sqrt{1 + z}$, $(1, 2, 3)$,
in the direction of $\mathbf{v} = 2\mathbf{i} + \mathbf{j} - 2\mathbf{k}$

47. Find the maximum rate of change of $f(x, y) = x^2y + \sqrt{y}$ at the point $(2, 1)$. In which direction does it occur?

48. Find the direction in which $f(x, y, z) = ze^{xy}$ increases most rapidly at the point $(0, 1, 2)$. What is the maximum rate of increase?

49. The contour map shows wind speed in knots during Hurricane Andrew on August 24, 1992. Use it to estimate the value of the directional derivative of the wind speed at Homestead, Florida, in the direction of the eye of the hurricane.

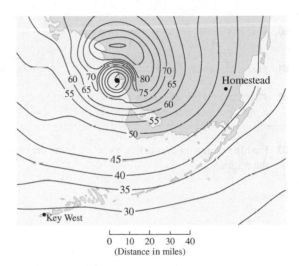

50. Find parametric equations of the tangent line at the point $(-2, 2, 4)$ to the curve of intersection of the surface $z = 2x^2 - y^2$ and the plane $z = 4$.

51–54 Find the local maximum and minimum values and saddle points of the function. If you have three-dimensional graphing software, graph the function with a domain and viewpoint that reveal all the important aspects of the function.

51. $f(x, y) = x^2 - xy + y^2 + 9x - 6y + 10$

52. $f(x, y) = x^3 - 6xy + 8y^3$

53. $f(x, y) = 3xy - x^2y - xy^2$

54. $f(x, y) = (x^2 + y)e^{y/2}$

55–56 Find the absolute maximum and minimum values of f on the set D.

55. $f(x, y) = 4xy^2 - x^2y^2 - xy^3$; D is the closed triangular region in the xy-plane with vertices $(0, 0)$, $(0, 6)$, and $(6, 0)$

56. $f(x, y) = e^{-x^2-y^2}(x^2 + 2y^2)$; D is the disk $x^2 + y^2 \leq 4$

57. Use a graph or level curves or both to estimate the local maximum and minimum values and saddle points of $f(x, y) = x^3 - 3x + y^4 - 2y^2$. Then use calculus to find these values precisely.

58. Use a graphing calculator or computer (or Newton's method or a computer algebra system) to find the critical points of $f(x, y) = 12 + 10y - 2x^2 - 8xy - y^4$ correct to three decimal places. Then classify the critical points and find the highest point on the graph.

59–62 Use Lagrange multipliers to find the maximum and minimum values of f subject to the given constraint(s).

59. $f(x, y) = x^2 y; \quad x^2 + y^2 = 1$

60. $f(x, y) = \dfrac{1}{x} + \dfrac{1}{y}; \quad \dfrac{1}{x^2} + \dfrac{1}{y^2} = 1$

61. $f(x, y, z) = xyz; \quad x^2 + y^2 + z^2 = 3$

62. $f(x, y, z) = x^2 + 2y^2 + 3z^2;$
$x + y + z = 1, \quad x - y + 2z = 2$

63. Find the points on the surface $xy^2 z^3 = 2$ that are closest to the origin.

64. A package in the shape of a rectangular box can be mailed by the US Postal Service if the sum of its length and girth (the perimeter of a cross-section perpendicular to the length) is at most 108 in. Find the dimensions of the package with largest volume that can be mailed.

65. A pentagon is formed by placing an isosceles triangle on a rectangle, as shown in the figure. If the pentagon has fixed perimeter P, find the lengths of the sides of the pentagon that maximize the area of the pentagon.

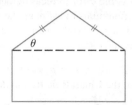

66. A particle of mass m moves on the surface $z = f(x, y)$. Let $x = x(t)$ and $y = y(t)$ be the x- and y-coordinates of the particle at time t.
(a) Find the velocity vector $\mathbf{v}$ and the kinetic energy $K = \frac{1}{2}m \lvert \mathbf{v} \rvert^2$ of the particle.
(b) Determine the acceleration vector $\mathbf{a}$.
(c) Let $z = x^2 + y^2$ and $x(t) = t \cos t$, $y(t) = t \sin t$. Find the velocity vector, the kinetic energy, and the acceleration vector.

Focus on Problem Solving

1. A rectangle with length L and width W is cut into four smaller rectangles by two lines parallel to the sides. Find the maximum and minimum values of the sum of the squares of the areas of the smaller rectangles.

2. Marine biologists have determined that when a shark detects the presence of blood in the water, it will swim in the direction in which the concentration of the blood increases most rapidly. Based on certain tests, the concentration of blood (in parts per million) at a point $P(x, y)$ on the surface of seawater is approximated by

$$C(x, y) = e^{-(x^2+2y^2)/10^4}$$

where x and y are measured in meters in a rectangular coordinate system with the blood source at the origin.
(a) Identify the level curves of the concentration function and sketch several members of this family together with a path that a shark will follow to the source.
(b) Suppose a shark is at the point (x_0, y_0) when it first detects the presence of blood in the water. Find an equation of the shark's path by setting up and solving a differential equation.

3. A long piece of galvanized sheet metal with width w is to be bent into a symmetric form with three straight sides to make a rain gutter. A cross-section is shown in the figure.
(a) Determine the dimensions that allow the maximum possible flow; that is, find the dimensions that give the maximum possible cross-sectional area.
(b) Would it be better to bend the metal into a gutter with a semicircular cross-section?

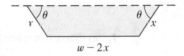

$$w - 2x$$

4. For what values of the number r is the function

$$f(x, y, z) = \begin{cases} \dfrac{(x + y + z)^r}{x^2 + y^2 + z^2} & \text{if } (x, y, z) \neq (0, 0, 0) \\ 0 & \text{if } (x, y, z) = (0, 0, 0) \end{cases}$$

continuous on $\mathbb{R}^3$?

5. Suppose f is a differentiable function of one variable. Show that all tangent planes to the surface $z = xf(y/x)$ intersect in a common point.

6. (a) Newton's method for approximating a root of an equation $f(x) = 0$ (see Section 4.7) can be adapted to approximating a solution of a system of equations $f(x, y) = 0$ and $g(x, y) = 0$. The surfaces $z = f(x, y)$ and $z = g(x, y)$ intersect in a curve that intersects the xy-plane at the point (r, s), which is the solution of the system. If an initial approximation (x_1, y_1) is close to this point, then the tangent planes to the surfaces at (x_1, y_1) intersect in a straight line that intersects the xy-plane in a point (x_2, y_2), which should be closer to (r, s). (Compare with Figure 2 in Section 4.7.) Show that

$$x_2 = x_1 - \frac{fg_y - f_y g}{f_x g_y - f_y g_x} \quad \text{and} \quad y_2 = y_1 - \frac{f_x g - f g_x}{f_x g_y - f_y g_x}$$

where f, g, and their partial derivatives are evaluated at (x_1, y_1). If we continue this procedure, we obtain successive approximations (x_n, y_n).

(b) It was Thomas Simpson (1710–1761) who formulated Newton's method as we know it today and who extended it to functions of two variables as in part (a). (See the biography of Simpson on page 408.) The example that he gave to illustrate the method was to solve the system of equations

$$x^x + y^y = 1000 \qquad x^y + y^x = 100$$

In other words, he found the points of intersection of the curves in the figure. Use the method of part (a) to find the coordinates of the points of intersection correct to six decimal places.

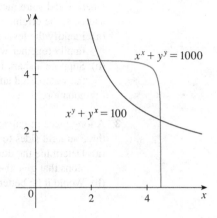

7. (a) Show that when Laplace's equation

$$\frac{\partial^2 u}{\partial x^2} + \frac{\partial^2 u}{\partial y^2} + \frac{\partial^2 u}{\partial z^2} = 0$$

is written in cylindrical coordinates, it becomes

$$\frac{\partial^2 u}{\partial r^2} + \frac{1}{r}\frac{\partial u}{\partial r} + \frac{1}{r^2}\frac{\partial^2 u}{\partial \theta^2} + \frac{\partial^2 u}{\partial z^2} = 0$$

(b) Show that when Laplace's equation is written in spherical coordinates, it becomes

$$\frac{\partial^2 u}{\partial \rho^2} + \frac{2}{\rho}\frac{\partial u}{\partial \rho} + \frac{\cot\phi}{\rho^2}\frac{\partial u}{\partial \phi} + \frac{1}{\rho^2}\frac{\partial^2 u}{\partial \phi^2} + \frac{1}{\rho^2\sin^2\phi}\frac{\partial^2 u}{\partial \theta^2} = 0$$

8. Among all planes that are tangent to the surface $xy^2z^2 = 1$, find the ones that are farthest from the origin.

9. If the ellipse $x^2/a^2 + y^2/b^2 = 1$ is to enclose the circle $x^2 + y^2 = 2y$, what values of a and b minimize the area of the ellipse?

Multiple Integrals

12

In this chapter we extend the idea of a definite integral to double and triple integrals of functions of two or three variables. These ideas are then used to compute volumes, surface areas, masses, and centroids of more general regions than we were able to consider in Chapter 6. We also use double integrals to calculate probabilities when two random variables are involved.

12.1 Double Integrals over Rectangles

In much the same way that our attempt to solve the area problem led to the definition of a definite integral, we now seek to find the volume of a solid and in the process we arrive at the definition of a double integral.

Review of the Definite Integral

First let's recall the basic facts concerning definite integrals of functions of a single variable. If $f(x)$ is defined for $a \leqslant x \leqslant b$, we start by dividing the interval $[a, b]$ into n subintervals $[x_{i-1}, x_i]$ of equal width $\Delta x = (b - a)/n$ and we choose sample points x_i^* in these subintervals. Then we form the Riemann sum

$$\boxed{1} \qquad \sum_{i=1}^{n} f(x_i^*)\, \Delta x$$

and take the limit of such sums as $n \to \infty$ to obtain the definite integral of f from a to b:

$$\boxed{2} \qquad \int_a^b f(x)\, dx = \lim_{n \to \infty} \sum_{i=1}^{n} f(x_i^*)\, \Delta x$$

In the special case where $f(x) \geqslant 0$, the Riemann sum can be interpreted as the sum of the areas of the approximating rectangles in Figure 1, and $\int_a^b f(x)\, dx$ represents the area under the curve $y = f(x)$ from a to b.

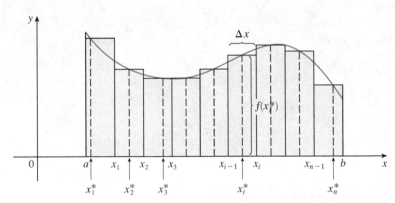

FIGURE 1

Volumes and Double Integrals

In a similar manner we consider a function f of two variables defined on a closed rectangle

$$R = [a, b] \times [c, d] = \left\{ (x, y) \in \mathbb{R}^2 \mid a \leqslant x \leqslant b,\ c \leqslant y \leqslant d \right\}$$

and we first suppose that $f(x, y) \geqslant 0$. The graph of f is a surface with equation $z = f(x, y)$. Let S be the solid that lies above R and under the graph of f, that is,

$$S = \left\{ (x, y, z) \in \mathbb{R}^3 \mid 0 \leqslant z \leqslant f(x, y),\ (x, y) \in R \right\}$$

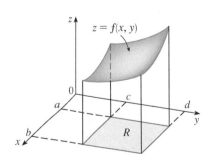

FIGURE 2

(See Figure 2.) Our goal is to find the volume of S.

The first step is to divide the rectangle R into subrectangles. We accomplish this by dividing the interval $[a, b]$ into m subintervals $[x_{i-1}, x_i]$ of equal width $\Delta x = (b - a)/m$ and dividing $[c, d]$ into n subintervals $[y_{j-1}, y_j]$ of equal width $\Delta y = (d - c)/n$. By drawing lines parallel to the coordinate axes through the endpoints of these subintervals, as in

Figure 3, we form the subrectangles

$$R_{ij} = [x_{i-1}, x_i] \times [y_{j-1}, y_j] = \{(x, y) \mid x_{i-1} \leqslant x \leqslant x_i,\ y_{j-1} \leqslant y \leqslant y_j\}$$

each with area $\Delta A = \Delta x\, \Delta y$.

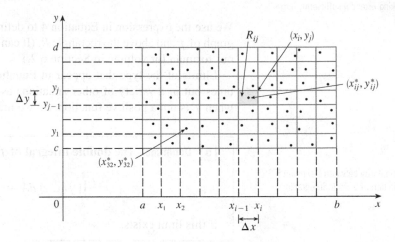

FIGURE 3

Dividing R into subrectangles

If we choose a **sample point** (x_{ij}^*, y_{ij}^*) in each R_{ij}, then we can approximate the part of S that lies above each R_{ij} by a thin rectangular box (or "column") with base R_{ij} and height $f(x_{ij}^*, y_{ij}^*)$ as shown in Figure 4. (Compare with Figure 1.) The volume of this box is the height of the box times the area of the base rectangle:

$$f(x_{ij}^*, y_{ij}^*)\, \Delta A$$

If we follow this procedure for all the rectangles and add the volumes of the corresponding boxes, we get an approximation to the total volume of S:

$$\boxed{3} \qquad\qquad V \approx \sum_{i=1}^{m} \sum_{j=1}^{n} f(x_{ij}^*, y_{ij}^*)\, \Delta A$$

(See Figure 5.) This double sum means that for each subrectangle we evaluate f at the chosen point and multiply by the area of the subrectangle, and then we add the results.

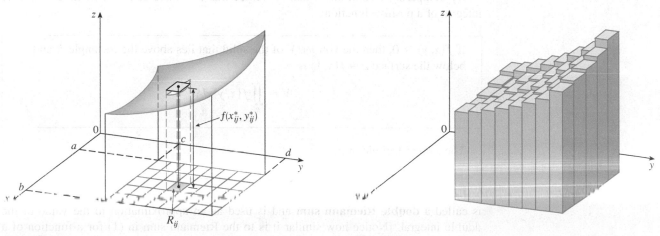

FIGURE 4   **FIGURE 5**

Our intuition tells us that the approximation given in (3) becomes better as m and n become larger and so we would expect that

The meaning of the double limit in Equation 4 is that we can make the double sum as close as we like to the number V [for any choice of (x_{ij}^*, y_{ij}^*) in R_{ij}] by taking m and n sufficiently large.

$$\boxed{4} \qquad V = \lim_{m, n \to \infty} \sum_{i=1}^{m} \sum_{j=1}^{n} f(x_{ij}^*, y_{ij}^*) \, \Delta A$$

We use the expression in Equation 4 to define the **volume** of the solid S that lies under the graph of f and above the rectangle R. (It can be shown that this definition is consistent with our formula for volume in Section 6.2.)

Limits of the type that appear in Equation 4 occur frequently, not just in finding volumes but in a variety of other situations as well   as we will see in Section 12.5—even when f is not a positive function. So we make the following definition.

Notice the similarity between Definition 5 and the definition of a single integral in Equation 2.

$\boxed{5}$ **Definition**   The **double integral** of f over the rectangle R is

$$\iint\limits_{R} f(x, y) \, dA = \lim_{m, n \to \infty} \sum_{i=1}^{m} \sum_{j=1}^{n} f(x_{ij}^*, y_{ij}^*) \, \Delta A$$

if this limit exists.

A function f is called **integrable** if the limit in Definition 5 exists. It is shown in courses on advanced calculus that all continuous functions are integrable. In fact, the double integral of f exists provided that f is "not too discontinuous." In particular, if f is bounded [that is, there is a constant M such that $|f(x, y)| \leq M$ for all (x, y) in R], and f is continuous there, except on a finite number of smooth curves, then f is integrable over R.

The sample point (x_{ij}^*, y_{ij}^*) can be chosen to be any point in the subrectangle R_{ij}, but if we choose it to be the upper right-hand corner of R_{ij} [namely (x_i, y_j), see Figure 3], then the expression for the double integral looks simpler:

$$\boxed{6} \qquad \iint\limits_{R} f(x, y) \, dA = \lim_{m, n \to \infty} \sum_{i=1}^{m} \sum_{j=1}^{n} f(x_i, y_j) \, \Delta A$$

By comparing Definitions 4 and 5, we see that a volume can be written as a double integral of a positive function:

If $f(x, y) \geq 0$, then the volume V of the solid that lies above the rectangle R and below the surface $z = f(x, y)$ is

$$V = \iint\limits_{R} f(x, y) \, dA$$

The sum in Definition 5,

$$\sum_{i=1}^{m} \sum_{j=1}^{n} f(x_{ij}^*, y_{ij}^*) \, \Delta A$$

is called a **double Riemann sum** and is used as an approximation to the value of the double integral. [Notice how similar it is to the Riemann sum in (1) for a function of a single variable.] If f happens to be a *positive* function, then the double Riemann sum represents the sum of volumes of columns, as in Figure 5, and is an approximation to the volume under the graph of f and above the rectangle R.

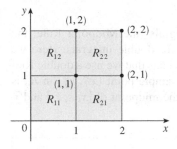

FIGURE 6

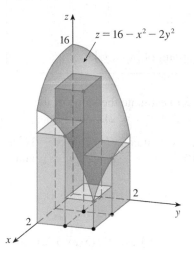

FIGURE 7

Ⅴ EXAMPLE 1 Using a double Riemann sum to estimate a volume Estimate the volume of the solid that lies above the square $R = [0, 2] \times [0, 2]$ and below the elliptic paraboloid $z = 16 - x^2 - 2y^2$. Divide R into four equal squares and choose the sample point to be the upper right corner of each square R_{ij}. Sketch the solid and the approximating rectangular boxes.

SOLUTION The squares are shown in Figure 6. The paraboloid is the graph of $f(x, y) = 16 - x^2 - 2y^2$ and the area of each square is $\Delta A = 1$. Approximating the volume by the Riemann sum with $m = n = 2$, we have

$$V \approx \sum_{i=1}^{2} \sum_{j=1}^{2} f(x_i, y_j)\, \Delta A$$

$$= f(1, 1)\, \Delta A + f(1, 2)\, \Delta A + f(2, 1)\, \Delta A + f(2, 2)\, \Delta A$$

$$= 13(1) + 7(1) + 10(1) + 4(1) = 34$$

This is the volume of the approximating rectangular boxes shown in Figure 7.   ▬

We get better approximations to the volume in Example 1 if we increase the number of squares. Figure 8 shows how the columns start to look more like the actual solid and the corresponding approximations become more accurate when we use 16, 64, and 256 squares. In the next section we will be able to show that the exact volume is 48.

FIGURE 8
The Riemann sum approximations to
the volume under $z = 16 - x^2 - 2y^2$
become more accurate as m and
n increase.

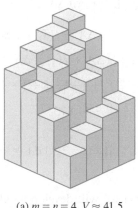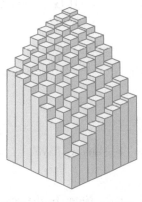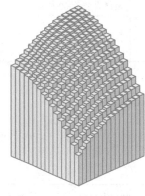

(a) $m = n = 4$, $V \approx 41.5$ (b) $m = n = 8$, $V \approx 44.875$ (c) $m = n = 16$, $V \approx 46.46875$

Ⅴ EXAMPLE 2 Evaluating a double integral by interpreting it geometrically
If $R = \{(x, y) \mid -1 \le x \le 1, -2 \le y \le 2\}$, evaluate the integral

$$\iint_R \sqrt{1 - x^2}\, dA$$

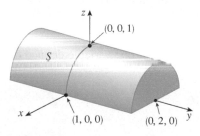

FIGURE 9

SOLUTION It would be very difficult to evaluate this integral directly from Definition 5 but, because $\sqrt{1 - x^2} \ge 0$, we can compute the integral by interpreting it as a volume. If $z = \sqrt{1 - x^2}$, then $x^2 + z^2 = 1$ and $z \ge 0$, so the given double integral represents the volume of the solid S that lies below the circular cylinder $x^2 + z^2 = 1$ and above the rectangle R. (See Figure 9.) The volume of S is the area of a semicircle with radius 1 times the length of the cylinder. Thus

$$\iint_R \sqrt{1 - x^2}\, dA = \tfrac{1}{2}\pi(1)^2 \times 4 = 2\pi$$ ▬

The Midpoint Rule

The methods that we used for approximating single integrals (the Midpoint Rule, the Trapezoidal Rule, Simpson's Rule) all have counterparts for double integrals. Here we consider only the Midpoint Rule for double integrals. This means that we use a double Riemann sum to approximate the double integral, where the sample point (x_{ij}^*, y_{ij}^*) in R_{ij} is chosen to be the center $(\bar{x}_i, \bar{y}_j)$ of R_{ij}. In other words, $\bar{x}_i$ is the midpoint of $[x_{i-1}, x_i]$ and $\bar{y}_j$ is the midpoint of $[y_{j-1}, y_j]$.

> **Midpoint Rule for Double Integrals**
>
> $$\iint\limits_{R} f(x, y)\, dA \approx \sum_{i=1}^{m} \sum_{j=1}^{n} f(\bar{x}_i, \bar{y}_j)\, \Delta A$$
>
> where $\bar{x}_i$ is the midpoint of $[x_{i-1}, x_i]$ and $\bar{y}_j$ is the midpoint of $[y_{j-1}, y_j]$.

⊻ EXAMPLE 3 Use the Midpoint Rule with $m = n = 2$ to estimate the value of the integral $\iint_R (x - 3y^2)\, dA$, where $R = \{(x, y) \mid 0 \leqslant x \leqslant 2, 1 \leqslant y \leqslant 2\}$.

SOLUTION In using the Midpoint Rule with $m = n = 2$, we evaluate $f(x, y) = x - 3y^2$ at the centers of the four subrectangles shown in Figure 10. So $\bar{x}_1 = \frac{1}{2}$, $\bar{x}_2 = \frac{3}{2}$, $\bar{y}_1 = \frac{5}{4}$, and $\bar{y}_2 = \frac{7}{4}$. The area of each subrectangle is $\Delta A = \frac{1}{2}$. Thus

$$\iint\limits_{R} (x - 3y^2)\, dA \approx \sum_{i=1}^{2} \sum_{j=1}^{2} f(\bar{x}_i, \bar{y}_j)\, \Delta A$$

$$= f(\bar{x}_1, \bar{y}_1)\, \Delta A + f(\bar{x}_1, \bar{y}_2)\, \Delta A + f(\bar{x}_2, \bar{y}_1)\, \Delta A + f(\bar{x}_2, \bar{y}_2)\, \Delta A$$

$$= f\left(\tfrac{1}{2}, \tfrac{5}{4}\right) \Delta A + f\left(\tfrac{1}{2}, \tfrac{7}{4}\right) \Delta A + f\left(\tfrac{3}{2}, \tfrac{5}{4}\right) \Delta A + f\left(\tfrac{3}{2}, \tfrac{7}{4}\right) \Delta A$$

$$= \left(-\tfrac{67}{16}\right)\tfrac{1}{2} + \left(-\tfrac{139}{16}\right)\tfrac{1}{2} + \left(-\tfrac{51}{16}\right)\tfrac{1}{2} + \left(-\tfrac{123}{16}\right)\tfrac{1}{2}$$

$$= -\tfrac{95}{8} = -11.875$$

Thus we have

$$\iint\limits_{R} (x - 3y^2)\, dA \approx -11.875$$

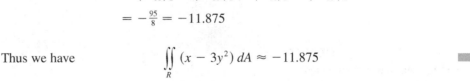

FIGURE 10

Number of subrectangles	Midpoint Rule approximation
1	-11.5000
4	-11.8750
16	-11.9687
64	-11.9922
256	-11.9980
1024	-11.9995

Note: In the next section we will develop an efficient method for computing double integrals and then we will see that the exact value of the double integral in Example 3 is -12. (Remember that the interpretation of a double integral as a volume is valid only when the integrand f is a *positive* function. The integrand in Example 3 is not a positive function, so its integral is not a volume. In Examples 2 and 3 in Section 12.2 we will discuss how to interpret integrals of functions that are not always positive in terms of volumes.) If we keep dividing each subrectangle in Figure 10 into four smaller ones with similar shape, we get the Midpoint Rule approximations displayed in the chart in the margin. Notice how these approximations approach the exact value of the double integral, -12.

Average Value

Recall from Section 6.5 that the average value of a function f of one variable defined on an interval $[a, b]$ is

$$f_{\text{ave}} = \frac{1}{b - a} \int_{a}^{b} f(x)\, dx$$

In a similar fashion we define the **average value** of a function f of two variables defined on a rectangle R to be

$$f_{ave} = \frac{1}{A(R)} \iint\limits_R f(x, y) \, dA$$

where $A(R)$ is the area of R.

If $f(x, y) \geqslant 0$, the equation

$$A(R) \times f_{ave} = \iint\limits_R f(x, y) \, dA$$

says that the box with base R and height f_{ave} has the same volume as the solid that lies under the graph of f. [If $z = f(x, y)$ describes a mountainous region and you chop off the tops of the mountains at height f_{ave}, then you can use them to fill in the valleys so that the region becomes completely flat. See Figure 11.]

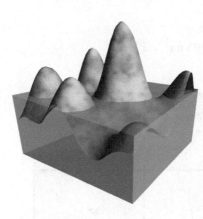

FIGURE 11

EXAMPLE 4   **Using the Midpoint Rule to estimate average snowfall**

The contour map in Figure 12 shows the snowfall, in inches, that fell on the state of Colorado on December 20 and 21, 2006. (The state is in the shape of a rectangle that measures 388 mi west to east and 276 mi south to north.) Use the contour map to estimate the average snowfall for the entire state of Colorado on those days.

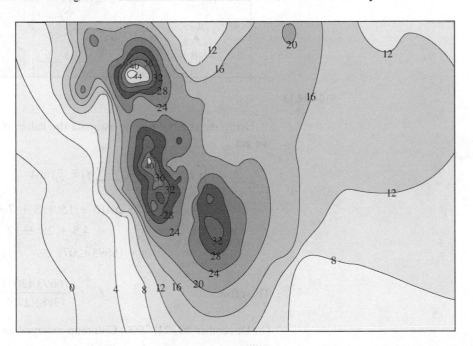

FIGURE 12

SOLUTION   Let's place the origin at the southwest corner of the state. Then $0 \leqslant x \leqslant 388$, $0 \leqslant y \leqslant 276$, and $f(x, y)$ is the snowfall, in inches, at a location x miles to the east and y miles to the north of the origin. If R is the rectangle that represents Colorado, then the average snowfall for the state on December 20–21 was

$$f_{ave} = \frac{1}{A(R)} \iint\limits_R f(x, y) \, dA$$

where $A(R) = 388 \cdot 276$. To estimate the value of this double integral, let's use the Midpoint Rule with $m = n = 4$. In other words, we divide R into 16 subrectangles of equal size, as in Figure 13. The area of each subrectangle is

$$\Delta A = \tfrac{1}{16}(388)(276) = 6693 \text{ mi}^2$$

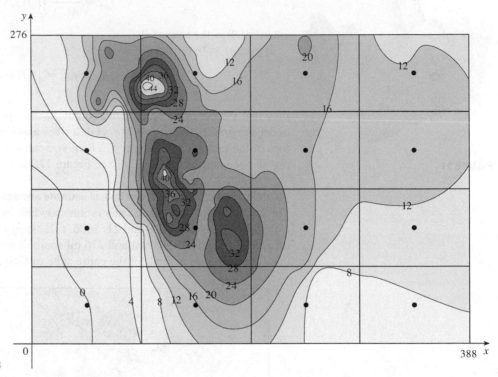

FIGURE 13

Using the contour map to estimate the value of f at the center of each subrectangle, we get

$$\iint\limits_{R} f(x, y) \, dA \approx \sum_{i=1}^{4} \sum_{j=1}^{4} f(\bar{x}_i, \bar{y}_j) \, \Delta A$$

$$\approx \Delta A[0 + 15 + 8 + 7 + 2 + 25 + 18.5 + 11$$
$$+ 4.5 + 28 + 17 + 13.5 + 12 + 15 + 17.5 + 13]$$

$$= (6693)(207)$$

Therefore
$$f_{\text{ave}} \approx \frac{(6693)(207)}{(388)(276)} \approx 12.9$$

On December 20–21, 2006, Colorado received an average of approximately 13 inches of snow.

Properties of Double Integrals

We list here three properties of double integrals that can be proved in the same manner as in Section 5.2. We assume that all of the integrals exist. Properties 7 and 8 are referred to as the *linearity* of the integral.

7
$$\iint\limits_{R} [f(x, y) + g(x, y)] \, dA = \iint\limits_{R} f(x, y) \, dA + \iint\limits_{R} g(x, y) \, dA$$

Double integrals behave this way because the double sums that define them behave this way.

8
$$\iint\limits_{R} c f(x, y) \, dA = c \iint\limits_{R} f(x, y) \, dA \qquad \text{where } c \text{ is a constant}$$

If $f(x, y) \geqslant g(x, y)$ for all (x, y) in R, then

$$\boxed{9} \qquad \iint\limits_R f(x, y)\, dA \geqslant \iint\limits_R g(x, y)\, dA$$

12.1 Exercises

1. (a) Estimate the volume of the solid that lies below the surface $z = xy$ and above the rectangle

   $$R = \{(x, y) \mid 0 \leqslant x \leqslant 6, 0 \leqslant y \leqslant 4\}$$

   Use a Riemann sum with $m = 3$, $n = 2$, and take the sample point to be the upper right corner of each square.
   (b) Use the Midpoint Rule to estimate the volume of the solid in part (a).

2. If $R = [0, 4] \times [-1, 2]$, use a Riemann sum with $m = 2$, $n = 3$ to estimate the value of $\iint_R (1 - xy^2)\, dA$. Take the sample points to be (a) the lower right corners and (b) the upper left corners of the rectangles.

3. (a) Use a Riemann sum with $m = n = 2$ to estimate the value of $\iint_R \sin(x + y)\, dA$, where $R = [0, \pi] \times [0, \pi]$. Take the sample points to be lower left corners.
   (b) Use the Midpoint Rule to estimate the integral in part (a).

4. (a) Estimate the volume of the solid that lies below the surface $z = x + 2y^2$ and above the rectangle $R = [0, 2] \times [0, 4]$. Use a Riemann sum with $m = n = 2$ and choose the sample points to be lower right corners.
   (b) Use the Midpoint Rule to estimate the volume in part (a).

5. A table of values is given for a function $f(x, y)$ defined on $R = [0, 4] \times [2, 4]$.
   (a) Estimate $\iint_R f(x, y)\, dA$ using the Midpoint Rule with $m = n = 2$.
   (b) Estimate the double integral with $m = n = 4$ by choosing the sample points to be the points closest to the origin.

x \ y	2.0	2.5	3.0	3.5	4.0
0	−3	−5	−6	−4	−1
1	−1	−2	−3	−1	1
2	1	0	1	1	1
3	2	2	1	3	7
4	3	4	2	5	9

6. A 20-ft-by-30-ft swimming pool is filled with water. The depth is measured at 5-ft intervals, starting at one corner of the pool, and the values are recorded in the table. Estimate the volume of water in the pool.

	0	5	10	15	20	25	30
0	2	3	4	6	7	8	8
5	2	3	4	7	8	10	8
10	2	4	6	8	10	12	10
15	2	3	4	5	6	8	7
20	2	2	2	2	3	4	4

7. Let V be the volume of the solid that lies under the graph of $f(x, y) = \sqrt{52 - x^2 - y^2}$ and above the rectangle given by $2 \leqslant x \leqslant 4, 2 \leqslant y \leqslant 6$. We use the lines $x = 3$ and $y = 4$ to divide R into subrectangles. Let L and U be the Riemann sums computed using lower left corners and upper right corners, respectively. Without calculating the numbers V, L, and U, arrange them in increasing order and explain your reasoning.

8. The figure shows level curves of a function f in the square $R = [0, 2] \times [0, 2]$. Use the Midpoint Rule with $m = n = 2$ to estimate $\iint_R f(x, y)\, dA$. How could you improve your estimate?

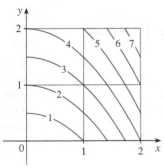

9. A contour map is shown (on page 838) for a function f on the square $R = [0, 4] \times [0, 4]$.
   (a) Use the Midpoint Rule with $m = n = 2$ to estimate the value of $\iint_R f(x, y)\, dA$.

(b) Estimate the average value of f.

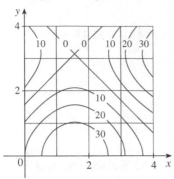

10. The contour map shows the temperature, in degrees Fahrenheit, at 4:00 PM on February 26, 2007, in Colorado. (The state measures 388 mi west to east and 276 mi south to north.) Use the Midpoint Rule with $m = n = 4$ to estimate the average temperature in Colorado at that time.

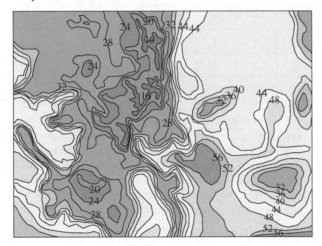

11–13 Evaluate the double integral by first identifying it as the volume of a solid.

11. $\iint_R 3\, dA$, $R = \{(x, y) \mid -2 \leqslant x \leqslant 2, 1 \leqslant y \leqslant 6\}$

12. $\iint_R (5 - x)\, dA$, $R = \{(x, y) \mid 0 \leqslant x \leqslant 5, 0 \leqslant y \leqslant 3\}$

13. $\iint_R (4 - 2y)\, dA$, $R = [0, 1] \times [0, 1]$

---

14. The integral $\iint_R \sqrt{9 - y^2}\, dA$, where $R = [0, 4] \times [0, 2]$, represents the volume of a solid. Sketch the solid.

15. Use a programmable calculator or computer (or the sum command on a CAS) to estimate

$$\iint_R \sqrt{1 + xe^{-y}}\, dA$$

where $R = [0, 1] \times [0, 1]$. Use the Midpoint Rule with the following numbers of squares of equal size: 1, 4, 16, 64, 256, and 1024.

16. Repeat Exercise 15 for the integral $\iint_R \sin\left(x + \sqrt{y}\,\right) dA$.

17. If f is a constant function, $f(x, y) = k$, and $R = [a, b] \times [c, d]$, show that

$$\iint_R k\, dA = k(b - a)(d - c)$$

18. Use the result of Exercise 17 to show that

$$0 \leqslant \iint_R \sin \pi x \cos \pi y\, dA \leqslant \frac{1}{32}$$

where $R = \left[0, \frac{1}{4}\right] \times \left[\frac{1}{4}, \frac{1}{2}\right]$.

12.2 Iterated Integrals

Recall that it is usually difficult to evaluate single integrals directly from the definition of an integral, but the Fundamental Theorem of Calculus provides a much easier method. The evaluation of double integrals from first principles is even more difficult, but in this section we see how to express a double integral as an iterated integral, which can then be evaluated by calculating two single integrals.

Suppose that f is a function of two variables that is integrable on the rectangle $R = [a, b] \times [c, d]$. We use the notation $\int_c^d f(x, y)\, dy$ to mean that x is held fixed and $f(x, y)$ is integrated with respect to y from $y = c$ to $y = d$. This procedure is called *partial integration with respect to* y. (Notice its similarity to partial differentiation.) Now $\int_c^d f(x, y)\, dy$ is a number that depends on the value of x, so it defines a function of x:

$$A(x) = \int_c^d f(x, y)\, dy$$

If we now integrate the function A with respect to x from $x = a$ to $x = b$, we get

$$\boxed{1} \qquad \int_a^b A(x)\, dx = \int_a^b \left[\int_c^d f(x, y)\, dy \right] dx$$

The integral on the right side of Equation 1 is called an **iterated integral**. Usually the brackets are omitted. Thus

$$\boxed{2} \qquad \int_a^b \int_c^d f(x, y)\, dy\, dx = \int_a^b \left[\int_c^d f(x, y)\, dy \right] dx$$

means that we first integrate with respect to y from c to d and then with respect to x from a to b.

Similarly, the iterated integral

$$\boxed{3} \qquad \int_c^d \int_a^b f(x, y)\, dx\, dy = \int_c^d \left[\int_a^b f(x, y)\, dx \right] dy$$

means that we first integrate with respect to x (holding y fixed) from $x = a$ to $x = b$ and then we integrate the resulting function of y with respect to y from $y = c$ to $y = d$. Notice that in both Equations 2 and 3 we work *from the inside out*.

EXAMPLE 1 Integrating in both orders Evaluate the iterated integrals.

(a) $\displaystyle \int_0^3 \int_1^2 x^2 y\, dy\, dx$
   (b) $\displaystyle \int_1^2 \int_0^3 x^2 y\, dx\, dy$

SOLUTION
(a) Regarding x as a constant, we obtain

$$\int_1^2 x^2 y\, dy = \left[x^2 \frac{y^2}{2} \right]_{y=1}^{y=2} = x^2 \left(\frac{2^2}{2} \right) - x^2 \left(\frac{1^2}{2} \right) = \tfrac{3}{2} x^2$$

Thus the function A in the preceding discussion is given by $A(x) = \frac{3}{2} x^2$ in this example. We now integrate this function of x from 0 to 3:

$$\int_0^3 \int_1^2 x^2 y\, dy\, dx = \int_0^3 \left[\int_1^2 x^2 y\, dy \right] dx$$

$$= \int_0^3 \tfrac{3}{2} x^2\, dx = \frac{x^3}{2} \bigg]_0^3 = \frac{27}{2}$$

(b) Here we first integrate with respect to x:

$$\int_1^2 \int_0^3 x^2 y\, dx\, dy = \int_1^2 \left[\int_0^3 x^2 y\, dx \right] dy = \int_1^2 \left[\frac{x^3}{3} y \right]_{x=0}^{x=3} dy$$

$$= \int_1^2 9y\, dy = 9 \frac{y^2}{2} \bigg|_1^2 = \frac{27}{2}$$

Notice that in Example 1 we obtained the same answer whether we integrated with respect to y or x first. In general, it turns out (see Theorem 4) that the two iterated integrals in Equations 2 and 3 are always equal; that is, the order of integration does not matter. (This is similar to Clairaut's Theorem on the equality of the mixed partial derivatives.)

The following theorem gives a practical method for evaluating a double integral by expressing it as an iterated integral (in either order).

Theorem 4 is named after the Italian mathematician Guido Fubini (1879–1943), who proved a very general version of this theorem in 1907. But the version for continuous functions was known to the French mathematician Augustin-Louis Cauchy almost a century earlier.

4   Fubini's Theorem   If f is continuous on the rectangle $R = \{(x, y) \mid a \le x \le b, c \le y \le d\}$, then

$$\iint\limits_{R} f(x, y)\, dA = \int_{a}^{b} \int_{c}^{d} f(x, y)\, dy\, dx = \int_{c}^{d} \int_{a}^{b} f(x, y)\, dx\, dy$$

More generally, this is true if we assume that f is bounded on R, f is discontinuous only on a finite number of smooth curves, and the iterated integrals exist.

The proof of Fubini's Theorem is too difficult to include in this book, but we can at least give an intuitive indication of why it is true for the case where $f(x, y) \ge 0$. Recall that if f is positive, then we can interpret the double integral $\iint_{R} f(x, y)\, dA$ as the volume V of the solid S that lies above R and under the surface $z = f(x, y)$. But we have another formula that we used for volume in Chapter 6, namely,

$$V = \int_{a}^{b} A(x)\, dx$$

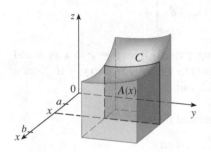

FIGURE 1

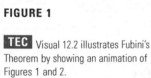

TEC Visual 12.2 illustrates Fubini's Theorem by showing an animation of Figures 1 and 2.

where $A(x)$ is the area of a cross-section of S in the plane through x perpendicular to the x-axis. From Figure 1 you can see that $A(x)$ is the area under the curve C whose equation is $z = f(x, y)$, where x is held constant and $c \le y \le d$. Therefore

$$A(x) = \int_{c}^{d} f(x, y)\, dy$$

and we have

$$\iint\limits_{R} f(x, y)\, dA = V = \int_{a}^{b} A(x)\, dx = \int_{a}^{b} \int_{c}^{d} f(x, y)\, dy\, dx$$

A similar argument, using cross-sections perpendicular to the y-axis as in Figure 2, shows that

$$\iint\limits_{R} f(x, y)\, dA = \int_{c}^{d} \int_{a}^{b} f(x, y)\, dx\, dy$$

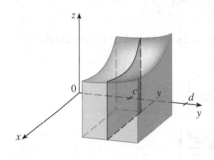

FIGURE 2

V   EXAMPLE 2   Using Fubini's Theorem to calculate a double integral   Evaluate the double integral $\iint_{R} (x - 3y^2)\, dA$, where $R = \{(x, y) \mid 0 \le x \le 2, 1 \le y \le 2\}$. (Compare with Example 3 in Section 12.1.)

SOLUTION 1   Fubini's Theorem gives

$$\iint\limits_{R} (x - 3y^2)\, dA = \int_{0}^{2} \int_{1}^{2} (x - 3y^2)\, dy\, dx = \int_{0}^{2} \left[xy - y^3 \right]_{y=1}^{y=2} dx$$

$$= \int_{0}^{2} (x - 7)\, dx = \frac{x^2}{2} - 7x \Big]_{0}^{2} = -12$$

Notice the negative answer in Example 2; nothing is wrong with that. The function f is not a positive function, so its integral doesn't represent a volume. From Figure 3 we see that f is always negative on R, so the value of the integral is the *negative* of the volume that lies *above* the graph of f and *below* R.

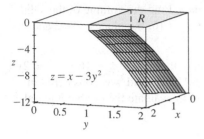

FIGURE 3

For a function f that takes on both positive and negative values, $\iint_R f(x, y)\, dA$ is a difference of volumes: $V_1 - V_2$, where V_1 is the volume above R and below the graph of f, and V_2 is the volume below R and above the graph. The fact that the integral in Example 3 is 0 means that these two volumes V_1 and V_2 are equal. (See Figure 4.)

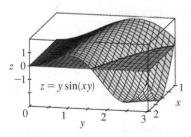

FIGURE 4

SOLUTION 2 Again applying Fubini's Theorem, but this time integrating with respect to x first, we have

$$\iint_R (x - 3y^2)\, dA = \int_1^2 \int_0^2 (x - 3y^2)\, dx\, dy$$

$$= \int_1^2 \left[\frac{x^2}{2} - 3xy^2\right]_{x=0}^{x=2} dy$$

$$= \int_1^2 (2 - 6y^2)\, dy = 2y - 2y^3 \big]_1^2 = -12$$

V EXAMPLE 3 Comparing the difficulty in different orders of integration
Evaluate $\iint_R y \sin(xy)\, dA$, where $R = [1, 2] \times [0, \pi]$.

SOLUTION 1 If we first integrate with respect to x, we get

$$\iint_R y \sin(xy)\, dA = \int_0^\pi \int_1^2 y \sin(xy)\, dx\, dy = \int_0^\pi \left[-\cos(xy)\right]_{x=1}^{x=2} dy$$

$$= \int_0^\pi (-\cos 2y + \cos y)\, dy$$

$$= -\tfrac{1}{2} \sin 2y + \sin y \big]_0^\pi = 0$$

SOLUTION 2 If we reverse the order of integration, we get

$$\iint_R y \sin(xy)\, dA = \int_1^2 \int_0^\pi y \sin(xy)\, dy\, dx$$

To evaluate the inner integral, we use integration by parts with

$$u = y \qquad\qquad dv = \sin(xy)\, dy$$

$$du = dy \qquad\qquad v = -\frac{\cos(xy)}{x}$$

and so

$$\int_0^\pi y \sin(xy)\, dy = -\frac{y \cos(xy)}{x}\bigg]_{y=0}^{y=\pi} + \frac{1}{x}\int_0^\pi \cos(xy)\, dy$$

$$= -\frac{\pi \cos \pi x}{x} + \frac{1}{x^2}\left[\sin(xy)\right]_{y=0}^{y=\pi}$$

$$= -\frac{\pi \cos \pi x}{x} + \frac{\sin \pi x}{x^2}$$

If we now integrate the first term by parts with $u = -1/x$ and $dv = \pi \cos \pi x\, dx$, we get $du = dx/x^2$, $v = \sin \pi x$, and

$$\int \left(\frac{\pi \cos \pi x}{x}\right) dx = -\frac{\sin \pi x}{x} - \int \frac{\sin \pi x}{x^2}\, dx$$

Therefore

$$\int \left(-\frac{\pi \cos \pi x}{x} + \frac{\sin \pi x}{x^2}\right) dx = -\frac{\sin \pi x}{x}$$

In Example 2, Solutions 1 and 2 are equally straightforward, but in Example 3 the first solution is much easier than the second one. Therefore, when we evaluate double integrals, it's wise to choose the order of integration that gives simpler integrals.

and so

$$\int_1^2 \int_0^\pi y \sin(xy) \, dy \, dx = \left[-\frac{\sin \pi x}{x} \right]_1^2$$

$$= -\frac{\sin 2\pi}{2} + \sin \pi = 0$$

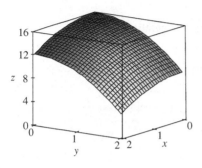

FIGURE 5

V EXAMPLE 4 **Using a double integral to compute a volume** Find the volume of the solid S that is bounded by the elliptic paraboloid $x^2 + 2y^2 + z = 16$, the planes $x = 2$ and $y = 2$, and the three coordinate planes.

SOLUTION We first observe that S is the solid that lies under the surface $z = 16 - x^2 - 2y^2$ and above the square $R = [0, 2] \times [0, 2]$. (See Figure 5.) This solid was considered in Example 1 in Section 12.1, but we are now in a position to evaluate the double integral using Fubini's Theorem. Therefore

$$V = \iint_R (16 - x^2 - 2y^2) \, dA = \int_0^2 \int_0^2 (16 - x^2 - 2y^2) \, dx \, dy$$

$$= \int_0^2 \left[16x - \tfrac{1}{3}x^3 - 2y^2x \right]_{x=0}^{x=2} dy$$

$$= \int_0^2 \left(\tfrac{88}{3} - 4y^2 \right) dy = \left[\tfrac{88}{3}y - \tfrac{4}{3}y^3 \right]_0^2 = 48$$

In the special case where $f(x, y)$ can be factored as the product of a function of x only and a function of y only, the double integral of f can be written in a particularly simple form. To be specific, suppose that $f(x, y) = g(x)h(y)$ and $R = [a, b] \times [c, d]$. Then Fubini's Theorem gives

$$\iint_R f(x, y) \, dA = \int_c^d \int_a^b g(x)h(y) \, dx \, dy = \int_c^d \left[\int_a^b g(x)h(y) \, dx \right] dy$$

In the inner integral, y is a constant, so $h(y)$ is a constant and we can write

$$\int_c^d \left[\int_a^b g(x)h(y) \, dx \right] dy = \int_c^d \left[h(y) \left(\int_a^b g(x) \, dx \right) \right] dy = \int_a^b g(x) \, dx \int_c^d h(y) \, dy$$

since $\int_a^b g(x) \, dx$ is a constant. Therefore, in this case, the double integral of f can be written as the product of two single integrals:

The function $f(x, y) = \sin x \cos y$ in Example 5 is positive on R, so the integral represents the volume of the solid that lies above R and below the graph of f shown in Figure 6.

$$\boxed{5} \quad \iint_R g(x)h(y) \, dA = \int_a^b g(x) \, dx \int_c^d h(y) \, dy \qquad \text{where } R = [a, b] \times [c, d]$$

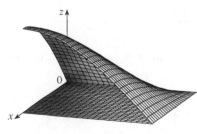

FIGURE 6

EXAMPLE 5 **Integrating a function of x times a function of y** If $R = [0, \pi/2] \times [0, \pi/2]$, then, by Equation 5,

$$\iint_R \sin x \cos y \, dA = \int_0^{\pi/2} \sin x \, dx \int_0^{\pi/2} \cos y \, dy$$

$$= \left[-\cos x \right]_0^{\pi/2} \left[\sin y \right]_0^{\pi/2} = 1 \cdot 1 = 1$$

12.2 Exercises

1–2 Find $\int_0^5 f(x, y)\, dx$ and $\int_0^1 f(x, y)\, dy$.

1. $f(x, y) = 12x^2y^3$

2. $f(x, y) = y + xe^y$

3–14 Calculate the iterated integral.

3. $\displaystyle\int_1^3 \int_0^1 (1 + 4xy)\, dx\, dy$

4. $\displaystyle\int_0^1 \int_1^2 (4x^3 - 9x^2y^2)\, dy\, dx$

5. $\displaystyle\int_0^2 \int_0^{\pi/2} x \sin y\, dy\, dx$

6. $\displaystyle\int_{\pi/6}^{\pi/2} \int_{-1}^5 \cos y\, dx\, dy$

7. $\displaystyle\int_0^2 \int_0^1 (2x + y)^8\, dx\, dy$

8. $\displaystyle\int_0^1 \int_1^2 \frac{xe^x}{y}\, dy\, dx$

9. $\displaystyle\int_1^4 \int_1^2 \left(\frac{x}{y} + \frac{y}{x}\right) dy\, dx$

10. $\displaystyle\int_0^1 \int_0^3 e^{x+3y}\, dx\, dy$

11. $\displaystyle\int_0^1 \int_0^1 (u - v)^5\, du\, dv$

12. $\displaystyle\int_0^1 \int_0^1 xy\sqrt{x^2 + y^2}\, dy\, dx$

13. $\displaystyle\int_0^2 \int_0^\pi r \sin^2\theta\, d\theta\, dr$

14. $\displaystyle\int_0^1 \int_0^1 \sqrt{s + t}\, ds\, dt$

15–22 Calculate the double integral.

15. $\displaystyle\iint_R (6x^2y^3 - 5y^4)\, dA, \quad R = \{(x, y) \mid 0 \le x \le 3,\ 0 \le y \le 1\}$

16. $\displaystyle\iint_R \cos(x + 2y)\, dA, \quad R = \{(x, y) \mid 0 \le x \le \pi,\ 0 \le y \le \pi/2\}$

17. $\displaystyle\iint_R \frac{xy^2}{x^2 + 1}\, dA, \quad R = \{(x, y) \mid 0 \le x \le 1,\ -3 \le y \le 3\}$

18. $\displaystyle\iint_R \frac{1 + x^2}{1 + y^2}\, dA, \quad R = \{(x, y) \mid 0 \le x \le 1,\ 0 \le y \le 1\}$

19. $\displaystyle\iint_R x \sin(x + y)\, dA, \quad R = [0, \pi/6] \times [0, \pi/3]$

20. $\displaystyle\iint_R \frac{x}{1 + xy}\, dA, \quad R = [0, 1] \times [0, 1]$

21. $\displaystyle\iint_R xye^{x^2y}\, dA, \quad R = [0, 1] \times [0, 2]$

22. $\displaystyle\iint_R \frac{x}{x^2 + y^2}\, dA, \quad R = [1, 2] \times [0, 1]$

23–24 Sketch the solid whose volume is given by the iterated integral.

23. $\displaystyle\int_0^1 \int_0^1 (4 - x - 2y)\, dx\, dy$

24. $\displaystyle\int_0^1 \int_0^1 (2 - x^2 - y^2)\, dy\, dx$

---

25. Find the volume of the solid that lies under the plane $3x + 2y + z = 12$ and above the rectangle $R = \{(x, y) \mid 0 \le x \le 1,\ -2 \le y \le 3\}$.

26. Find the volume of the solid that lies under the hyperbolic paraboloid $z = 4 + x^2 - y^2$ and above the square $R = [-1, 1] \times [0, 2]$.

27. Find the volume of the solid lying under the elliptic paraboloid $x^2/4 + y^2/9 + z = 1$ and above the rectangle $R = [-1, 1] \times [-2, 2]$.

28. Find the volume of the solid enclosed by the surface $z = 1 + e^x \sin y$ and the planes $x = \pm 1$, $y = 0$, $y = \pi$, and $z = 0$.

29. Find the volume of the solid enclosed by the surface $z = x \sec^2 y$ and the planes $z = 0$, $x = 0$, $x = 2$, $y = 0$, and $y = \pi/4$.

30. Find the volume of the solid in the first octant bounded by the cylinder $z = 16 - x^2$ and the plane $y = 5$.

31. Find the volume of the solid enclosed by the paraboloid $z = 2 + x^2 + (y - 2)^2$ and the planes $z = 1$, $x = 1$, $x = -1$, $y = 0$, and $y = 4$.

32. Graph the solid that lies between the surface $z = 2xy/(x^2 + 1)$ and the plane $z = x + 2y$ and is bounded by the planes $x = 0$, $x = 2$, $y = 0$, and $y = 4$. Then find its volume.

CAS **33.** Use a computer algebra system to find the exact value of the integral $\iint_R x^5y^3e^{xy}\, dA$, where $R = [0, 1] \times [0, 1]$. Then use the CAS to draw the solid whose volume is given by the integral.

CAS **34.** Graph the solid that lies between the surfaces $z = e^{-x^2}\cos(x^2 + y^2)$ and $z = 2 - x^2 - y^2$ for $|x| \le 1$, $|y| \le 1$. Use a computer algebra system to approximate the volume of this solid correct to four decimal places.

⌂ Graphing calculator or computer with graphing software required   **CAS** Computer algebra system required   **1.** Homework Hints available in TEC

35–36 Find the average value of f over the given rectangle.

35. $f(x, y) = x^2 y$, R has vertices $(-1, 0)$, $(-1, 5)$, $(1, 5)$, $(1, 0)$

36. $f(x, y) = e^y \sqrt{x + e^y}$, $R = [0, 4] \times [0, 1]$

37–38 Use symmetry to evaluate the double integral.

37. $\displaystyle\iint_R \frac{xy}{1 + x^4}\, dA$, $R = \{(x, y) \mid -1 \leqslant x \leqslant 1, 0 \leqslant y \leqslant 1\}$

38. $\displaystyle\iint_R (1 + x^2 \sin y + y^2 \sin x)\, dA$, $R = [-\pi, \pi] \times [-\mathrm{u}, \mathrm{u}]$

CAS **39.** Use your CAS to compute the iterated integrals

$$\int_0^1 \int_0^1 \frac{x - y}{(x + y)^3}\, dy\, dx \qquad \text{and} \qquad \int_0^1 \int_0^1 \frac{x - y}{(x + y)^3}\, dx\, dy$$

Do the answers contradict Fubini's Theorem? Explain what is happening.

40. (a) In what way are the theorems of Fubini and Clairaut similar?

(b) If $f(x, y)$ is continuous on $[a, b] \times [c, d]$ and

$$g(x, y) = \int_a^x \int_c^y f(s, t)\, dt\, ds$$

for $a < x < b$, $c < y < d$, show that $g_{xy} = g_{yx} = f(x, y)$.

12.3 Double Integrals over General Regions

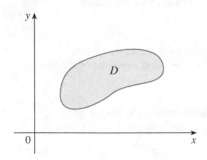

FIGURE 1

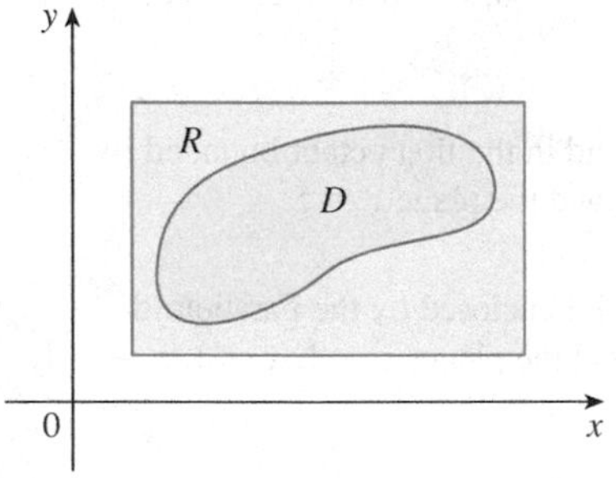

FIGURE 2

For single integrals, the region over which we integrate is always an interval. But for double integrals, we want to be able to integrate a function f not just over rectangles but also over regions D of more general shape, such as the one illustrated in Figure 1. We suppose that D is a bounded region, which means that D can be enclosed in a rectangular region R as in Figure 2. Then we define a new function F with domain R by

$$\boxed{1} \qquad F(x, y) = \begin{cases} f(x, y) & \text{if } (x, y) \text{ is in } D \\ 0 & \text{if } (x, y) \text{ is in } R \text{ but not in } D \end{cases}$$

If F is integrable over R, then we define the **double integral of f over D** by

$$\boxed{2} \qquad \iint_D f(x, y)\, dA = \iint_R F(x, y)\, dA \qquad \text{where } F \text{ is given by Equation 1}$$

Definition 2 makes sense because R is a rectangle and so $\iint_R F(x, y)\, dA$ has been previously defined in Section 12.1. The procedure that we have used is reasonable because the values of $F(x, y)$ are 0 when (x, y) lies outside D and so they contribute nothing to the integral. This means that it doesn't matter what rectangle R we use as long as it contains D.

In the case where $f(x, y) \geqslant 0$, we can still interpret $\iint_D f(x, y)\, dA$ as the volume of the solid that lies above D and under the surface $z = f(x, y)$ (the graph of f). You can see that this is reasonable by comparing the graphs of f and F in Figures 3 and 4 and remembering that $\iint_R F(x, y)\, dA$ is the volume under the graph of F.

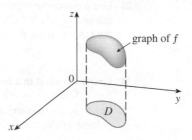

FIGURE 3

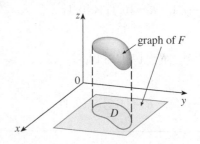

FIGURE 4

Figure 4 also shows that F is likely to have discontinuities at the boundary points of D. Nonetheless, if f is continuous on D and the boundary curve of D is "well behaved" (in a sense outside the scope of this book), then it can be shown that $\iint_R F(x, y)\, dA$ exists and therefore $\iint_D f(x, y)\, dA$ exists. In particular, this is the case for the following two types of regions.

A plane region D is said to be of **type I** if it lies between the graphs of two continuous functions of x, that is,

$$D = \{(x, y) \mid a \leq x \leq b,\ g_1(x) \leq y \leq g_2(x)\}$$

where g_1 and g_2 are continuous on $[a, b]$. Some examples of type I regions are shown in Figure 5.

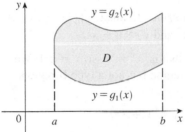
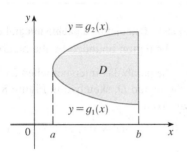
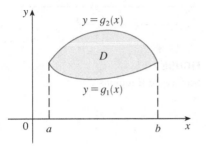

FIGURE 5   Some type I regions

FIGURE 6

In order to evaluate $\iint_D f(x, y)\, dA$ when D is a region of type I, we choose a rectangle $R = [a, b] \times [c, d]$ that contains D, as in Figure 6, and we let F be the function given by Equation 1; that is, F agrees with f on D and F is 0 outside D. Then, by Fubini's Theorem,

$$\iint_D f(x, y)\, dA = \iint_R F(x, y)\, dA = \int_a^b \int_c^d F(x, y)\, dy\, dx$$

Observe that $F(x, y) = 0$ if $y < g_1(x)$ or $y > g_2(x)$ because (x, y) then lies outside D. Therefore

$$\int_c^d F(x, y)\, dy = \int_{g_1(x)}^{g_2(x)} F(x, y)\, dy = \int_{g_1(x)}^{g_2(x)} f(x, y)\, dy$$

because $F(x, y) = f(x, y)$ when $g_1(x) \leq y \leq g_2(x)$. Thus we have the following formula that enables us to evaluate the double integral as an iterated integral.

---

3   If f is continuous on a type I region D such that

$$D = \{(x, y) \mid a \leq x \leq b,\ g_1(x) \leq y \leq g_2(x)\}$$

then

$$\iint_D f(x, y)\, dA = \int_a^b \int_{g_1(x)}^{g_2(x)} f(x, y)\, dy\, dx$$

The integral on the right side of (3) is an iterated integral that is similar to the ones we considered in the preceding section, except that in the inner integral we regard x as being constant not only in $f(x, y)$ but also in the limits of integration, $g_1(x)$ and $g_2(x)$.

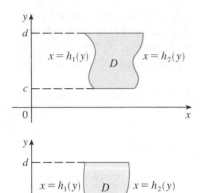

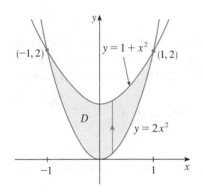

FIGURE 7
Some type II regions

We also consider plane regions of **type II**, which can be expressed as

$$\boxed{4} \qquad D = \left\{(x, y) \mid c \leq y \leq d, \; h_1(y) \leq x \leq h_2(y)\right\}$$

where h_1 and h_2 are continuous. Two such regions are illustrated in Figure 7.

Using the same methods that were used in establishing (3), we can show that

$$\boxed{5} \qquad \iint\limits_{D} f(x, y)\, dA = \int_{c}^{d} \int_{h_1(y)}^{h_2(y)} f(x, y)\, dx\, dy$$

where D is a type II region given by Equation 4.

▼ EXAMPLE 1   Calculating a double integral over a type I region   Evaluate $\iint_{D} (x + 2y)\, dA$, where D is the region bounded by the parabolas $y = 2x^2$ and $y = 1 + x^2$.

SOLUTION   The parabolas intersect when $2x^2 = 1 + x^2$, that is, $x^2 = 1$, so $x = \pm 1$. We note that the region D, sketched in Figure 8, is a type I region but not a type II region and we can write

$$D = \left\{(x, y) \mid -1 \leq x \leq 1, \; 2x^2 \leq y \leq 1 + x^2\right\}$$

Since the lower boundary is $y = 2x^2$ and the upper boundary is $y = 1 + x^2$, Equation 3 gives

$$
\begin{aligned}
\iint\limits_{D} (x + 2y)\, dA &= \int_{-1}^{1} \int_{2x^2}^{1+x^2} (x + 2y)\, dy\, dx = \int_{-1}^{1} \Big[xy + y^2 \Big]_{y=2x^2}^{y=1+x^2} dx \\[2mm]
&= \int_{-1}^{1} \big[x(1 + x^2) + (1 + x^2)^2 - x(2x^2) - (2x^2)^2 \big] dx \\[2mm]
&= \int_{-1}^{1} (-3x^4 - x^3 + 2x^2 + x + 1)\, dx \\[2mm]
&= -3\frac{x^5}{5} - \frac{x^4}{4} + 2\frac{x^3}{3} + \frac{x^2}{2} + x \Big]_{-1}^{1} = \frac{32}{15}
\end{aligned}
$$

FIGURE 8

Note: When we set up a double integral as in Example 1, it is essential to draw a diagram. Often it is helpful to draw a vertical arrow as in Figure 8. Then the limits of integration for the *inner* integral can be read from the diagram as follows: The arrow starts at the lower boundary $y = g_1(x)$, which gives the lower limit in the integral, and the arrow ends at the upper boundary $y = g_2(x)$, which gives the upper limit of integration. For a type II region the arrow is drawn horizontally from the left boundary to the right boundary.

EXAMPLE 2   A region that is both type I and type II   Find the volume of the solid that lies under the paraboloid $z = x^2 + y^2$ and above the region D in the xy-plane bounded by the line $y = 2x$ and the parabola $y = x^2$.

SOLUTION 1   From Figure 9 we see that D is a type I region and

$$D = \left\{(x, y) \mid 0 \leq x \leq 2, \; x^2 \leq y \leq 2x\right\}$$

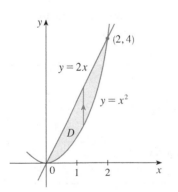

FIGURE 9
D as a type I region

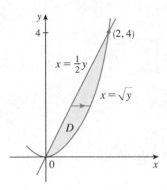

FIGURE 10
D as a type II region

Figure 11 shows the solid whose volume is calculated in Example 2. It lies above the xy-plane, below the paraboloid $z = x^2 + y^2$, and between the plane $y = 2x$ and the parabolic cylinder $y = x^2$.

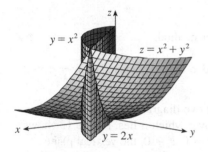

FIGURE 11

Therefore the volume under $z = x^2 + y^2$ and above D is

$$V = \iint_D (x^2 + y^2)\,dA = \int_0^2 \int_{x^2}^{2x} (x^2 + y^2)\,dy\,dx$$

$$= \int_0^2 \left[x^2 y + \frac{y^3}{3} \right]_{y=x^2}^{y=2x} dx = \int_0^2 \left[x^2(2x) + \frac{(2x)^3}{3} - x^2 x^2 - \frac{(x^2)^3}{3} \right] dx$$

$$= \int_0^2 \left(-\frac{x^6}{3} - x^4 + \frac{14x^3}{3} \right) dx = -\frac{x^7}{21} - \frac{x^5}{5} + \frac{7x^4}{6} \Big]_0^2 = \frac{216}{35}$$

SOLUTION 2 From Figure 10 we see that D can also be written as a type II region:

$$D = \left\{ (x, y) \mid 0 \leqslant y \leqslant 4, \ \tfrac{1}{2}y \leqslant x \leqslant \sqrt{y} \right\}$$

Therefore another expression for V is

$$V = \iint_D (x^2 + y^2)\,dA = \int_0^4 \int_{\frac{1}{2}y}^{\sqrt{y}} (x^2 + y^2)\,dx\,dy$$

$$= \int_0^4 \left[\frac{x^3}{3} + y^2 x \right]_{x=\frac{1}{2}y}^{x=\sqrt{y}} dy = \int_0^4 \left(\frac{y^{3/2}}{3} + y^{5/2} - \frac{y^3}{24} - \frac{y^3}{2} \right) dy$$

$$= \tfrac{2}{15}y^{5/2} + \tfrac{2}{7}y^{7/2} - \tfrac{13}{96}y^4 \Big]_0^4 = \tfrac{216}{35}$$

V EXAMPLE 3 Choosing the better description of a region   Evaluate $\iint_D xy\,dA$, where D is the region bounded by the line $y = x - 1$ and the parabola $y^2 = 2x + 6$.

SOLUTION The region D is shown in Figure 12. Again D is both type I and type II, but the description of D as a type I region is more complicated because the lower boundary consists of two parts. Therefore we prefer to express D as a type II region:

$$D = \left\{ (x, y) \mid -2 \leqslant y \leqslant 4, \ \tfrac{1}{2}y^2 - 3 \leqslant x \leqslant y + 1 \right\}$$

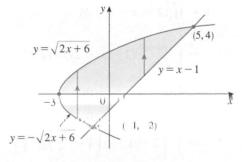

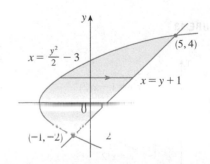

FIGURE 12

(a) D as a type I region

(b) D as a type II region

Then (5) gives

$$\iint\limits_{D} xy \, dA = \int_{-2}^{4} \int_{\frac{1}{2}y^2-3}^{y+1} xy \, dx \, dy = \int_{-2}^{4} \left[\frac{x^2}{2} y \right]_{x=\frac{1}{2}y^2-3}^{x=y+1} dy$$

$$= \frac{1}{2} \int_{-2}^{4} y \left[(y+1)^2 - \left(\frac{1}{2}y^2 - 3 \right)^2 \right] dy$$

$$= \frac{1}{2} \int_{-2}^{4} \left(-\frac{y^5}{4} + 4y^3 + 2y^2 - 8y \right) dy$$

$$= \frac{1}{2} \left[-\frac{y^6}{24} + y^4 + 2\frac{y^3}{3} - 4y^2 \right]_{-2}^{4} = 36$$

If we had expressed D as a type I region using Figure 12(a), then we would have obtained

$$\iint\limits_{D} xy \, dA = \int_{-3}^{-1} \int_{-\sqrt{2x+6}}^{\sqrt{2x+6}} xy \, dy \, dx + \int_{-1}^{5} \int_{x-1}^{\sqrt{2x+6}} xy \, dy \, dx$$

but this would have involved more work than the other method.

EXAMPLE 4   Find the volume of the tetrahedron bounded by the planes $x + 2y + z = 2$, $x = 2y$, $x = 0$, and $z = 0$.

SOLUTION   In a question such as this, it's wise to draw two diagrams: one of the three-dimensional solid and another of the plane region D over which it lies. Figure 13 shows the tetrahedron T bounded by the coordinate planes $x = 0$, $z = 0$, the vertical plane $x = 2y$, and the plane $x + 2y + z = 2$. Since the plane $x + 2y + z = 2$ intersects the xy-plane (whose equation is $z = 0$) in the line $x + 2y = 2$, we see that T lies above the triangular region D in the xy-plane bounded by the lines $x = 2y$, $x + 2y = 2$, and $x = 0$. (See Figure 14.)

The plane $x + 2y + z = 2$ can be written as $z = 2 - x - 2y$, so the required volume lies under the graph of the function $z = 2 - x - 2y$ and above

$$D = \left\{ (x, y) \mid 0 \le x \le 1, \ x/2 \le y \le 1 - x/2 \right\}$$

Therefore

$$V = \iint\limits_{D} (2 - x - 2y) \, dA$$

$$= \int_{0}^{1} \int_{x/2}^{1-x/2} (2 - x - 2y) \, dy \, dx$$

$$= \int_{0}^{1} \left[2y - xy - y^2 \right]_{y=x/2}^{y=1-x/2} dx$$

$$= \int_{0}^{1} \left[2 - x - x\left(1 - \frac{x}{2} \right) - \left(1 - \frac{x}{2} \right)^2 - x + \frac{x^2}{2} + \frac{x^2}{4} \right] dx$$

$$= \int_{0}^{1} (x^2 - 2x + 1) \, dx = \frac{x^3}{3} - x^2 + x \bigg]_{0}^{1} = \frac{1}{3}$$

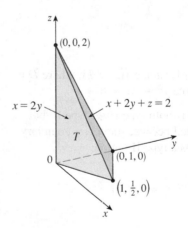

FIGURE 13

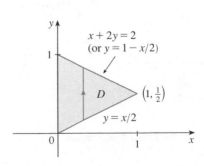

FIGURE 14

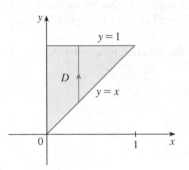

FIGURE 15
D as a type I region

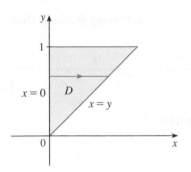

FIGURE 16
D as a type II region

V EXAMPLE 5 Reversing the order of integration

Evaluate the iterated integral $\int_0^1 \int_x^1 \sin(y^2)\, dy\, dx$.

SOLUTION If we try to evaluate the integral as it stands, we are faced with the task of first evaluating $\int \sin(y^2)\, dy$. But it's impossible to do so in finite terms since $\int \sin(y^2)\, dy$ is not an elementary function. (See the end of Section 5.8.) So we must change the order of integration. This is accomplished by first expressing the given iterated integral as a double integral. Using (3) backward, we have

$$\int_0^1 \int_x^1 \sin(y^2)\, dy\, dx = \iint_D \sin(y^2)\, dA$$

where
$$D = \{(x, y) \mid 0 \leqslant x \leqslant 1,\ x \leqslant y \leqslant 1\}$$

We sketch this region D in Figure 15. Then from Figure 16 we see that an alternative description of D is

$$D = \{(x, y) \mid 0 \leqslant y \leqslant 1,\ 0 \leqslant x \leqslant y\}$$

This enables us to use (5) to express the double integral as an iterated integral in the reverse order:

$$\int_0^1 \int_x^1 \sin(y^2)\, dy\, dx = \iint_D \sin(y^2)\, dA$$

$$= \int_0^1 \int_0^y \sin(y^2)\, dx\, dy = \int_0^1 \left[x \sin(y^2) \right]_{x=0}^{x=y}\, dy$$

$$= \int_0^1 y \sin(y^2)\, dy = -\tfrac{1}{2} \cos(y^2)\big]_0^1 = \tfrac{1}{2}(1 - \cos 1) \qquad \blacksquare$$

Properties of Double Integrals

We assume that all of the following integrals exist. The first three properties of double integrals over a region D follow immediately from Definition 2 in this section and Properties 7, 8, and 9 in Section 12.1.

$$\boxed{6} \qquad \iint_D [f(x, y) + g(x, y)]\, dA = \iint_D f(x, y)\, dA + \iint_D g(x, y)\, dA$$

$$\boxed{7} \qquad \iint_D cf(x, y)\, dA = c \iint_D f(x, y)\, dA$$

If $f(x, y) \geqslant g(x, y)$ for all (x, y) in D, then

$$\boxed{8} \qquad \iint_D f(x, y)\, dA \geqslant \iint_D g(x, y)\, dA$$

The next property of double integrals is similar to the property of single integrals given by the equation $\int_a^b f(x)\, dx = \int_a^c f(x)\, dx + \int_c^b f(x)\, dx$.

If $D = D_1 \cup D_2$, where D_1 and D_2 don't overlap except perhaps on their boundaries (see Figure 17), then

$$\boxed{9} \qquad \iint_D f(x, y)\, dA = \iint_{D_1} f(x, y)\, dA + \iint_{D_2} f(x, y)\, dA$$

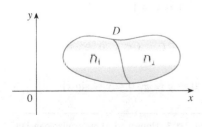

FIGURE 17

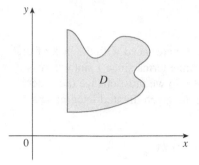

(a) D is neither type I nor type II.

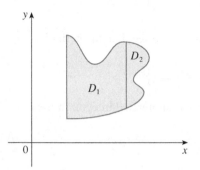

(b) $D = D_1 \cup D_2$; D_1 is type I, D_2 is type II.

FIGURE 18

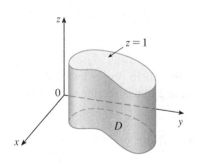

FIGURE 19
Cylinder with base D and height 1

Property 9 can be used to evaluate double integrals over regions D that are neither type I nor type II but can be expressed as a union of regions of type I or type II. Figure 18 illustrates this procedure. (See Exercises 53 and 54.)

The next property of integrals says that if we integrate the constant function $f(x, y) = 1$ over a region D, we get the area of D:

$$\boxed{10} \qquad \iint_D 1 \, dA = A(D)$$

Figure 19 illustrates why Equation 10 is true: A solid cylinder whose base is D and whose height is 1 has volume $A(D) \cdot 1 = A(D)$, but we know that we can also write its volume as $\iint_D 1 \, dA$.

Finally, we can combine Properties 7, 8, and 10 to prove the following property. (See Exercise 59.)

$$\boxed{11} \quad \text{If } m \leqslant f(x, y) \leqslant M \text{ for all } (x, y) \text{ in } D, \text{ then}$$

$$mA(D) \leqslant \iint_D f(x, y) \, dA \leqslant MA(D)$$

EXAMPLE 6 Use Property 11 to estimate the integral $\iint_D e^{\sin x \cos y} \, dA$, where D is the disk with center the origin and radius 2.

SOLUTION Since $-1 \leqslant \sin x \leqslant 1$ and $-1 \leqslant \cos y \leqslant 1$, we have $-1 \leqslant \sin x \cos y \leqslant 1$ and therefore

$$e^{-1} \leqslant e^{\sin x \cos y} \leqslant e^1 = e$$

Thus, using $m = e^{-1} = 1/e$, $M = e$, and $A(D) = \pi(2)^2$ in Property 11, we obtain

$$\frac{4\pi}{e} \leqslant \iint_D e^{\sin x \cos y} \, dA \leqslant 4\pi e$$

12.3 Exercises

1–6 Evaluate the iterated integral.

1. $\displaystyle\int_0^4 \int_0^{\sqrt{y}} xy^2 \, dx \, dy$

2. $\displaystyle\int_0^1 \int_{2x}^2 (x - y) \, dy \, dx$

3. $\displaystyle\int_0^1 \int_{x^2}^x (1 + 2y) \, dy \, dx$

4. $\displaystyle\int_0^2 \int_y^{2y} xy \, dx \, dy$

5. $\displaystyle\int_0^{\pi/2} \int_0^{\cos\theta} e^{\sin\theta} \, dr \, d\theta$

6. $\displaystyle\int_0^1 \int_0^v \sqrt{1 - v^2} \, du \, dv$

7–10 Evaluate the double integral.

7. $\displaystyle\iint_D y^2 \, dA, \quad D = \{(x, y) \mid -1 \leqslant y \leqslant 1, \ -y - 2 \leqslant x \leqslant y\}$

8. $\displaystyle\iint_D \frac{y}{x^5 + 1} \, dA, \quad D = \{(x, y) \mid 0 \leqslant x \leqslant 1, \ 0 \leqslant y \leqslant x^2\}$

9. $\displaystyle\iint_D x \, dA, \quad D = \{(x, y) \mid 0 \leqslant x \leqslant \pi, \ 0 \leqslant y \leqslant \sin x\}$

🖥 Graphing calculator or computer with graphing software required   CAS Computer algebra system required   **1.** Homework Hints available in TEC

10. $\iint\limits_D x^3 \, dA$, $D = \{(x, y) \mid 1 \leqslant x \leqslant e, \ 0 \leqslant y \leqslant \ln x\}$

---

11. Draw an example of a region that is
(a) type I but not type II
(b) type II but not type I

12. Draw an example of a region that is
(a) both type I and type II
(b) neither type I nor type II

13–14 Express D as a region of type I and also as a region of type II. Then evaluate the double integral in two ways.

13. $\iint\limits_D x \, dA$, D is enclosed by the lines $y = x, y = 0, x = 1$

14. $\iint\limits_D xy \, dA$, D is enclosed by the curves $y = x^2, y = 3x$

15–16 Set up iterated integrals for both orders of integration. Then evaluate the double integral using the easier order and explain why it's easier.

15. $\iint\limits_D y \, dA$, D is bounded by $y = x - 2, x = y^2$

16. $\iint\limits_D y^2 e^{xy} \, dA$, D is bounded by $y = x, y = 4, x = 0$

17–22 Evaluate the double integral.

17. $\iint\limits_D x \cos y \, dA$, D is bounded by $y = 0, \ y = x^2, \ x = 1$

18. $\iint\limits_D x\sqrt{y^2 - x^2} \, dA$, D is bounded by $x = 0, y = 1, y = x$

19. $\iint\limits_D y^3 \, dA$,

D is the triangular region with vertices $(0, 2), (1, 1), (3, 2)$

20. $\iint\limits_D xy^2 \, dA$, D is enclosed by $x = 0$ and $x = \sqrt{1 - y^2}$

21. $\iint\limits_D (2x - y) \, dA$,

D is bounded by the circle with center the origin and radius 2

22. $\iint\limits_D 2xy \, dA$, D is the triangular region with vertices $(0, 0)$, $(1, 2)$, and $(0, 3)$

23–32 Find the volume of the given solid.

23. Under the plane $x + 2y - z = 0$ and above the region bounded by $y = x$ and $y = x^4$

24. Under the surface $z = 2x + y^2$ and above the region bounded by $x = y^2$ and $x = y^3$

25. Under the surface $z = xy$ and above the triangle with vertices $(1, 1), (4, 1)$, and $(1, 2)$

26. Enclosed by the paraboloid $z = x^2 + 3y^2$ and the planes $x = 0, y = 1, y = x, z = 0$

27. Bounded by the coordinate planes and the plane $3x + 2y + z = 6$

28. Bounded by the planes $z = x, y = x, x + y = 2$, and $z = 0$

29. Enclosed by the cylinders $z = x^2, y = x^2$ and the planes $z = 0, y = 4$

30. Bounded by the cylinder $y^2 + z^2 = 4$ and the planes $x = 2y$, $x = 0, z = 0$ in the first octant

31. Bounded by the cylinder $x^2 + y^2 = 1$ and the planes $y = z$, $x = 0, z = 0$ in the first octant

32. Bounded by the cylinders $x^2 + y^2 = r^2$ and $y^2 + z^2 = r^2$

---

33. Use a graphing calculator or computer to estimate the x-coordinates of the points of intersection of the curves $y = x^4$ and $y = 3x - x^2$. If D is the region bounded by these curves, estimate $\iint_D x \, dA$.

34. Find the approximate volume of the solid in the first octant that is bounded by the planes $y = x, z = 0$, and $z = x$ and the cylinder $y = \cos x$. (Use a graphing device to estimate the points of intersection.)

35–36 Find the volume of the solid by subtracting two volumes.

35. The solid enclosed by the parabolic cylinders $y = 1 - x^2$, $y = x^2 - 1$ and the planes $x + y + z = 2$, $2x + 2y - z + 10 = 0$

36. The solid enclosed by the parabolic cylinder $y = x^2$ and the planes $z = 3y, z = 2 + y$

37–38 Sketch the solid whose volume is given by the iterated integral.

37. $\displaystyle\int_0^1 \int_0^{1-x} (1 - x - y) \, dy \, dx$ **38.** $\displaystyle\int_0^1 \int_0^{1-x^2} (1 - x) \, dy \, dx$

39–40 Use a computer algebra system to find the exact volume of the solid.

39. Under the surface $z = x^3 y^4 + xy^2$ and above the region bounded by the curves $y = x^3 - x$ and $y = x^2 + x$ for $x \geqslant 0$

40. Between the paraboloids $z = 2x^2 + y^2$ and $z = 8 - x^2 - 2y^2$ and inside the cylinder $x^2 + y^2 = 1$

41–46 Sketch the region of integration and change the order of integration.

41. $\displaystyle\int_0^4 \int_0^{\sqrt{x}} f(x, y)\, dy\, dx$ 　　　**42.** $\displaystyle\int_0^1 \int_{4x}^4 f(x, y)\, dy\, dx$

43. $\displaystyle\int_0^3 \int_{-\sqrt{9-y^2}}^{\sqrt{9-y^2}} f(x, y)\, dx\, dy$ 　　**44.** $\displaystyle\int_0^3 \int_0^{\sqrt{9-y}} f(x, y)\, dx\, dy$

45. $\displaystyle\int_1^2 \int_0^{\ln x} f(x, y)\, dy\, dx$ 　　**46.** $\displaystyle\int_0^1 \int_{\arctan x}^{\pi/4} f(x, y)\, dy\, dx$

47–52 Evaluate the integral by reversing the order of integration.

47. $\displaystyle\int_0^1 \int_{3y}^3 e^{x^2}\, dx\, dy$ 　　　**48.** $\displaystyle\int_0^{\sqrt{\pi}} \int_y^{\sqrt{\pi}} \cos(x^2)\, dx\, dy$

49. $\displaystyle\int_0^4 \int_{\sqrt{x}}^2 \frac{1}{y^3 + 1}\, dy\, dx$ 　**50.** $\displaystyle\int_0^1 \int_x^1 e^{x/y}\, dy\, dx$

51. $\displaystyle\int_0^1 \int_{\arcsin y}^{\pi/2} \cos x \sqrt{1 + \cos^2 x}\, dx\, dy$

52. $\displaystyle\int_0^8 \int_{\sqrt[3]{y}}^2 e^{x^4}\, dx\, dy$

53–54 Express D as a union of regions of type I or type II and evaluate the integral.

53. $\displaystyle\iint_D x^2\, dA$ 　　　　**54.** $\displaystyle\iint_D y\, dA$

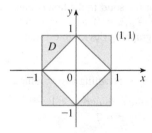　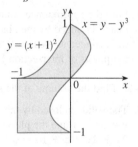

55–56 Use Property 11 to estimate the value of the integral.

55. $\displaystyle\iint_Q e^{-(x^2+y^2)^2}\, dA$, 　Q is the quarter-circle with center the origin and radius $\frac{1}{2}$ in the first quadrant

56. $\displaystyle\iint_T \sin^4(x + y)\, dA$, 　T is the triangle enclosed by the lines $y = 0$, $y = 2x$, and $x = 1$

57–58 Find the average value of f over the region D.

57. $f(x, y) = xy$, 　D is the triangle with vertices $(0, 0)$, $(1, 0)$, and $(1, 3)$

58. $f(x, y) = x \sin y$, 　D is enclosed by the curves $y = 0$, $y = x^2$, and $x = 1$

59. Prove Property 11.

60. In evaluating a double integral over a region D, a sum of iterated integrals was obtained as follows:

$$\iint_D f(x, y)\, dA = \int_0^1 \int_0^{2y} f(x, y)\, dx\, dy + \int_1^3 \int_0^{3-y} f(x, y)\, dx\, dy$$

Sketch the region D and express the double integral as an iterated integral with reversed order of integration.

61–65 Use geometry or symmetry, or both, to evaluate the double integral.

61. $\displaystyle\iint_D (x + 2)\, dA$, 　$D = \left\{(x, y) \mid 0 \leqslant y \leqslant \sqrt{9 - x^2}\right\}$

62. $\displaystyle\iint_D \sqrt{R^2 - x^2 - y^2}\, dA$,

D is the disk with center the origin and radius R

63. $\displaystyle\iint_D (2x + 3y)\, dA$, 　D is the rectangle $0 \leqslant x \leqslant a$, $0 \leqslant y \leqslant b$

64. $\displaystyle\iint_D (2 + x^2 y^3 - y^2 \sin x)\, dA$, 　$D = \left\{(x, y) \mid |x| + |y| \leqslant 1\right\}$

65. $\displaystyle\iint_D \left(ax^3 + by^3 + \sqrt{a^2 - x^2}\right) dA$, 　$D = [-a, a] \times [-b, b]$

CAS **66.** Graph the solid bounded by the plane $x + y + z = 1$ and the paraboloid $z = 4 - x^2 - y^2$ and find its exact volume. (Use your CAS to do the graphing, to find the equations of the boundary curves of the region of integration, and to evaluate the double integral.)

12.4 | Double Integrals in Polar Coordinates

See Appendix H for information about polar coordinates.

Suppose that we want to evaluate a double integral $\iint_R f(x, y)\, dA$, where R is one of the regions shown in Figure 1. In either case the description of R in terms of rectangular coordinates is rather complicated, but R is easily described using polar coordinates.

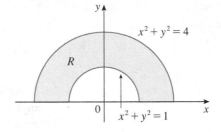

FIGURE 1

(a) $R = \{(r, \theta) \mid 0 \leqslant r \leqslant 1,\, 0 \leqslant \theta \leqslant 2\pi\}$ (b) $R = \{(r, \theta) \mid 1 \leqslant r \leqslant 2,\, 0 \leqslant \theta \leqslant \pi\}$

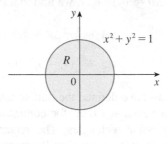

FIGURE 2

Recall from Figure 2 that the polar coordinates (r, θ) of a point are related to the rectangular coordinates (x, y) by the equations

$$r^2 = x^2 + y^2 \qquad x = r \cos \theta \qquad y = r \sin \theta$$

The regions in Figure 1 are special cases of a **polar rectangle**

$$R = \{(r, \theta) \mid a \leqslant r \leqslant b,\, \alpha \leqslant \theta \leqslant \beta\}$$

which is shown in Figure 3. In order to compute the double integral $\iint_R f(x, y)\, dA$, where R is a polar rectangle, we divide the interval $[a, b]$ into m subintervals $[r_{i-1}, r_i]$ of equal width $\Delta r = (b - a)/m$ and we divide the interval $[\alpha, \beta]$ into n subintervals $[\theta_{j-1}, \theta_j]$ of equal width $\Delta \theta = (\beta - \alpha)/n$. Then the circles $r = r_i$ and the rays $\theta = \theta_j$ divide the polar rectangle R into the small polar rectangles R_{ij} shown in Figure 4.

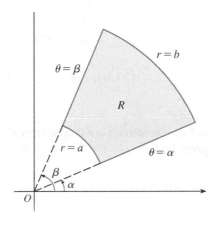

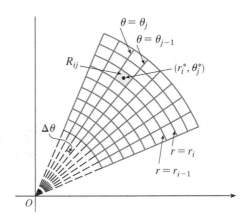

FIGURE 3 Polar rectangle   **FIGURE 4** Dividing R into polar subrectangles

The "center" of the polar subrectangle

$$R_{ij} = \{(r, \theta) \mid r_{i-1} \leqslant r \leqslant r_i,\, \theta_{j-1} \leqslant \theta \leqslant \theta_j\}$$

has polar coordinates

$$r_i^* = \tfrac{1}{2}(r_{i-1} + r_i) \qquad \theta_j^* = \tfrac{1}{2}(\theta_{j-1} + \theta_j)$$

We compute the area of R_{ij} using the fact that the area of a sector of a circle with radius r and central angle θ is $\frac{1}{2}r^2\theta$. Subtracting the areas of two such sectors, each of which has central angle $\Delta\theta = \theta_j - \theta_{j-1}$, we find that the area of R_{ij} is

$$\Delta A_i = \tfrac{1}{2}r_i^2\,\Delta\theta - \tfrac{1}{2}r_{i-1}^2\,\Delta\theta = \tfrac{1}{2}(r_i^2 - r_{i-1}^2)\,\Delta\theta$$

$$= \tfrac{1}{2}(r_i + r_{i-1})(r_i - r_{i-1})\,\Delta\theta = r_i^*\,\Delta r\,\Delta\theta$$

Although we have defined the double integral $\iint_R f(x, y)\,dA$ in terms of ordinary rectangles, it can be shown that, for continuous functions f, we always obtain the same answer using polar rectangles. The rectangular coordinates of the center of R_{ij} are $(r_i^* \cos\theta_j^*, r_i^* \sin\theta_j^*)$, so a typical Riemann sum is

$$\boxed{1} \quad \sum_{i=1}^{m}\sum_{j=1}^{n} f(r_i^* \cos\theta_j^*, r_i^* \sin\theta_j^*)\,\Delta A_i = \sum_{i=1}^{m}\sum_{j=1}^{n} f(r_i^* \cos\theta_j^*, r_i^* \sin\theta_j^*)\,r_i^*\,\Delta r\,\Delta\theta$$

If we write $g(r, \theta) = rf(r\cos\theta, r\sin\theta)$, then the Riemann sum in Equation 1 can be written as

$$\sum_{i=1}^{m}\sum_{j=1}^{n} g(r_i^*, \theta_j^*)\,\Delta r\,\Delta\theta$$

which is a Riemann sum for the double integral

$$\int_{\alpha}^{\beta}\int_{a}^{b} g(r, \theta)\,dr\,d\theta$$

Therefore we have

$$\iint\limits_R f(x, y)\,dA = \lim_{m,n\to\infty} \sum_{i=1}^{m}\sum_{j=1}^{n} f(r_i^* \cos\theta_j^*, r_i^* \sin\theta_j^*)\,\Delta A_i$$

$$= \lim_{m,n\to\infty} \sum_{i=1}^{m}\sum_{j=1}^{n} g(r_i^*, \theta_j^*)\,\Delta r\,\Delta\theta = \int_{\alpha}^{\beta}\int_{a}^{b} g(r, \theta)\,dr\,d\theta$$

$$= \int_{\alpha}^{\beta}\int_{a}^{b} f(r\cos\theta, r\sin\theta)\,r\,dr\,d\theta$$

$\boxed{2}$ **Change to Polar Coordinates in a Double Integral**   If f is continuous on a polar rectangle R given by $0 \le a \le r \le b$, $\alpha \le \theta \le \beta$, where $0 \le \beta - \alpha \le 2\pi$, then

$$\iint\limits_R f(x, y)\,dA = \int_{\alpha}^{\beta}\int_{a}^{b} f(r\cos\theta, r\sin\theta)\,r\,dr\,d\theta$$

The formula in (2) says that we convert from rectangular to polar coordinates in a double integral by writing $x = r\cos\theta$ and $y = r\sin\theta$, using the appropriate limits of integration for r and θ, and replacing dA by $r\,dr\,d\theta$. Be careful not to forget the additional factor r on the right side of Formula 2. A classical method for remembering this is shown

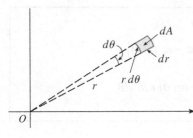

FIGURE 5

in Figure 5, where the "infinitesimal" polar rectangle can be thought of as an ordinary rectangle with dimensions $r\,d\theta$ and dr and therefore has "area" $dA = r\,dr\,d\theta$.

EXAMPLE 1 **Integrating over a region best described in polar coordinates**
Evaluate $\iint_R (3x + 4y^2)\,dA$, where R is the region in the upper half-plane bounded by the circles $x^2 + y^2 = 1$ and $x^2 + y^2 = 4$.

SOLUTION The region R can be described as

$$R = \{(x, y) \mid y \geq 0,\ 1 \leq x^2 + y^2 \leq 4\}$$

It is the half-ring shown in Figure 1(b), and in polar coordinates it is given by $1 \leq r \leq 2$, $0 \leq \theta \leq \pi$. Therefore, by Formula 2,

$$\iint_R (3x + 4y^2)\,dA = \int_0^\pi \int_1^2 (3r\cos\theta + 4r^2\sin^2\theta)\,r\,dr\,d\theta$$

$$= \int_0^\pi \int_1^2 (3r^2\cos\theta + 4r^3\sin^2\theta)\,dr\,d\theta$$

$$= \int_0^\pi \left[r^3\cos\theta + r^4\sin^2\theta \right]_{r=1}^{r=2} d\theta = \int_0^\pi (7\cos\theta + 15\sin^2\theta)\,d\theta$$

Here we use the trigonometric identity

$$\sin^2\theta = \tfrac{1}{2}(1 - \cos 2\theta)$$

as discussed in Section 5.7. Alternatively, we could have used Formula 63 in the Table of Integrals:

$$\int \sin^2 u\,du = \tfrac{1}{2}u - \tfrac{1}{4}\sin 2u + C$$

$$= \int_0^\pi \left[7\cos\theta + \tfrac{15}{2}(1 - \cos 2\theta) \right] d\theta$$

$$= 7\sin\theta + \frac{15\theta}{2} - \frac{15}{4}\sin 2\theta \Big]_0^\pi = \frac{15\pi}{2}$$

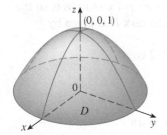

FIGURE 6

▶ EXAMPLE 2 **Finding a volume using polar coordinates** Find the volume of the solid bounded by the plane $z = 0$ and the paraboloid $z = 1 - x^2 - y^2$.

SOLUTION If we put $z = 0$ in the equation of the paraboloid, we get $x^2 + y^2 = 1$. This means that the plane intersects the paraboloid in the circle $x^2 + y^2 = 1$, so the solid lies under the paraboloid and above the circular disk D given by $x^2 + y^2 \leq 1$ [see Figures 6 and 1(a)]. In polar coordinates D is given by $0 \leq r \leq 1, 0 \leq \theta \leq 2\pi$. Since $1 - x^2 - y^2 = 1 - r^2$, the volume is

$$V = \iint_D (1 - x^2 - y^2)\,dA = \int_0^{2\pi} \int_0^1 (1 - r^2)\,r\,dr\,d\theta$$

$$= \int_0^{2\pi} d\theta \int_0^1 (r - r^3)\,dr = 2\pi \left[\frac{r^2}{2} - \frac{r^4}{4} \right]_0^1 = \frac{\pi}{2}$$

If we had used rectangular coordinates instead of polar coordinates, then we would have obtained

$$V = \iint_D (1 - x^2 - y^2)\,dA = \int_{-1}^1 \int_{-\sqrt{1-x^2}}^{\sqrt{1-x^2}} (1 - x^2 - y^2)\,dy\,dx$$

which is not easy to evaluate because it involves finding $\int (1 - x^2)^{3/2}\,dx$.

What we have done so far can be extended to the more complicated type of region shown in Figure 7. It's similar to the type II rectangular regions considered in Section 12.3. In fact, by combining Formula 2 in this section with Formula 12.3.5, we obtain the following formula.

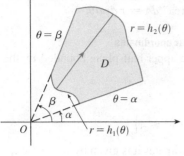

FIGURE 7
$D = \{(r, \theta) \mid \alpha \leqslant \theta \leqslant \beta, h_1(\theta) \leqslant r \leqslant h_2(\theta)\}$

3 If f is continuous on a polar region of the form

$$D = \{(r, \theta) \mid \alpha \leqslant \theta \leqslant \beta, h_1(\theta) \leqslant r \leqslant h_2(\theta)\}$$

then

$$\iint_D f(x, y)\, dA = \int_\alpha^\beta \int_{h_1(\theta)}^{h_2(\theta)} f(r\cos\theta, r\sin\theta)\, r\, dr\, d\theta$$

In particular, taking $f(x, y) = 1$, $h_1(\theta) = 0$, and $h_2(\theta) = h(\theta)$ in this formula, we see that the area of the region D bounded by $\theta = \alpha$, $\theta = \beta$, and $r = h(\theta)$ is

$$A(D) = \iint_D 1\, dA = \int_\alpha^\beta \int_0^{h(\theta)} r\, dr\, d\theta$$

$$= \int_\alpha^\beta \left[\frac{r^2}{2}\right]_0^{h(\theta)} d\theta = \int_\alpha^\beta \tfrac{1}{2}[h(\theta)]^2\, d\theta$$

and this agrees with Formula 3 in Appendix H.2.

V EXAMPLE 3 Find the volume of the solid that lies under the paraboloid $z = x^2 + y^2$, above the xy-plane, and inside the cylinder $x^2 + y^2 = 2x$.

SOLUTION The solid lies above the disk D whose boundary circle has equation $x^2 + y^2 = 2x$ or, after completing the square,

$$(x - 1)^2 + y^2 = 1$$

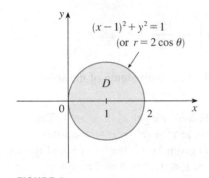

FIGURE 8

(See Figures 8 and 9.) In polar coordinates we have $x^2 + y^2 = r^2$ and $x = r\cos\theta$, so the boundary circle becomes $r^2 = 2r\cos\theta$, or $r = 2\cos\theta$. Thus the disk D is given by

$$D = \{(r, \theta) \mid -\pi/2 \leqslant \theta \leqslant \pi/2,\ 0 \leqslant r \leqslant 2\cos\theta\}$$

and, by Formula 3, we have

$$V = \iint_D (x^2 + y^2)\, dA = \int_{-\pi/2}^{\pi/2} \int_0^{2\cos\theta} r^2\, r\, dr\, d\theta$$

$$= \int_{-\pi/2}^{\pi/2} \left[\frac{r^4}{4}\right]_0^{2\cos\theta} d\theta = 4 \int_{-\pi/2}^{\pi/2} \cos^4\theta\, d\theta$$

$$= 8 \int_0^{\pi/2} \cos^4\theta\, d\theta$$

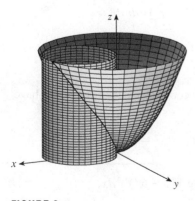

FIGURE 9

Using Formula 74 in the Table of Integrals with $n = 4$, we get

$$V = 8 \int_0^{\pi/2} \cos^4\theta\, d\theta = 8\left(\tfrac{1}{4}\cos^3\theta\,\sin\theta\Big]_0^{\pi/2} + \tfrac{3}{4} \int_0^{\pi/2} \cos^2\theta\, d\theta\right)$$

$$= 6 \int_0^{\pi/2} \cos^2\theta\, d\theta$$

Now we use Formula 64 in the Table of Integrals:

Instead of using tables, we could have used the identity $\cos^2\theta = \tfrac{1}{2}(1 + \cos 2\theta)$ twice.

$$V = 6 \int_0^{\pi/2} \cos^2\theta\, d\theta = 6\left[\tfrac{1}{2}\theta + \tfrac{1}{4}\sin 2\theta\right]_0^{\pi/2} = 6 \cdot \frac{1}{2} \cdot \frac{\pi}{2} = \frac{3\pi}{2}$$

12.4 Exercises

1–4 A region R is shown. Decide whether to use polar coordinates or rectangular coordinates and write $\iint_R f(x, y)\, dA$ as an iterated integral, where f is an arbitrary continuous function on R.

1.

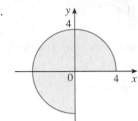

2.

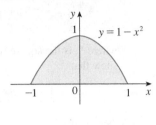

$y = 1 - x^2$

3.

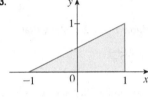

4.

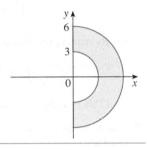

5–6 Sketch the region whose area is given by the integral and evaluate the integral.

5. $\displaystyle\int_{\pi}^{2\pi}\int_{4}^{7} r\, dr\, d\theta$

6. $\displaystyle\int_{0}^{\pi/2}\int_{0}^{4\cos\theta} r\, dr\, d\theta$

7–14 Evaluate the given integral by changing to polar coordinates.

7. $\iint_D xy\, dA$,
where D is the disk with center the origin and radius 3

8. $\iint_R (x + y)\, dA$, where R is the region that lies to the left of the y-axis between the circles $x^2 + y^2 = 1$ and $x^2 + y^2 = 4$

9. $\iint_R \cos(x^2 + y^2)\, dA$, where R is the region that lies above the x-axis within the circle $x^2 + y^2 = 9$

10. $\iint_R \sqrt{4 - x^2 - y^2}\, dA$,
where $R = \{(x, y) \mid x^2 + y^2 \leqslant 4,\ x \geqslant 0\}$

11. $\iint_D e^{-x^2-y^2}\, dA$, where D is the region bounded by the semicircle $x = \sqrt{4 - y^2}$ and the y-axis

12. $\iint_R ye^x\, dA$, where R is the region in the first quadrant enclosed by the circle $x^2 + y^2 = 25$

13. $\iint_R \arctan(y/x)\, dA$,
where $R = \{(x, y) \mid 1 \leqslant x^2 + y^2 \leqslant 4,\ 0 \leqslant y \leqslant x\}$

14. $\iint_D x\, dA$, where D is the region in the first quadrant that lies between the circles $x^2 + y^2 = 4$ and $x^2 + y^2 = 2x$

15–23 Use polar coordinates to find the volume of the given solid.

15. Under the cone $z = \sqrt{x^2 + y^2}$ and above the disk $x^2 + y^2 \leqslant 4$

16. Below the paraboloid $z = 18 - 2x^2 - 2y^2$ and above the xy-plane

17. Enclosed by the hyperboloid $-x^2 - y^2 + z^2 = 1$ and the plane $z = 2$

18. Inside the sphere $x^2 + y^2 + z^2 = 16$ and outside the cylinder $x^2 + y^2 = 4$

19. A sphere of radius a

20. Bounded by the paraboloid $z = 1 + 2x^2 + 2y^2$ and the plane $z = 7$ in the first octant

21. Above the cone $z = \sqrt{x^2 + y^2}$ and below the sphere $x^2 + y^2 + z^2 = 1$

22. Bounded by the paraboloids $z = 3x^2 + 3y^2$ and $z = 4 - x^2 - y^2$

23. Inside both the cylinder $x^2 + y^2 = 4$ and the ellipsoid $4x^2 + 4y^2 + z^2 = 64$

24. (a) A cylindrical drill with radius r_1 is used to bore a hole through the center of a sphere of radius r_2. Find the volume of the ring-shaped solid that remains.
(b) Express the volume in part (a) in terms of the height h of the ring. Notice that the volume depends only on h, not on r_1 or r_2.

25–26 Use a double integral to find the area of the region.

25. One loop of the rose $r = \cos 3\theta$

26. The region inside the cardioid $r = 1 + \cos\theta$ and outside the circle $r = 3\cos\theta$

27–30 Evaluate the iterated integral by converting to polar coordinates.

27. $\displaystyle\int_{-3}^{3}\int_{0}^{\sqrt{9-x^2}} \sin(x^2 + y^2)\, dy\, dx$

28. $\displaystyle\int_{0}^{a}\int_{-\sqrt{a^2-y^2}}^{0} x^2 y\, dx\, dy$

29. $\displaystyle\int_{0}^{1}\int_{y}^{\sqrt{2-y^2}} (x + y)\, dx\, dy$

30. $\displaystyle\int_{0}^{2}\int_{0}^{\sqrt{2x-x^2}} \sqrt{x^2 + y^2}\, dy\, dx$

31. A swimming pool is circular with a 40-ft diameter. The depth is constant along east-west lines and increases linearly from 2 ft at the south end to 7 ft at the north end. Find the volume of water in the pool.

1. Homework Hints available in TEC

32. An agricultural sprinkler distributes water in a circular pattern of radius 100 ft. It supplies water to a depth of e^{-r} feet per hour at a distance of r feet from the sprinkler.

(a) If $0 < R \leqslant 100$, what is the total amount of water supplied per hour to the region inside the circle of radius R centered at the sprinkler?

(b) Determine an expression for the average amount of water per hour per square foot supplied to the region inside the circle of radius R.

33. Find the average value of the function $f(x, y) = 1/\sqrt{x^2 + y^2}$ on the annular region $a^2 \leqslant x^2 + y^2 \leqslant b^2$, where $0 < a < b$.

34. Let D be the disk with center the origin and radius a. What is the average distance from points in D to the origin?

35. Use polar coordinates to combine the sum

$$\int_{1/\sqrt{2}}^{1} \int_{\sqrt{1-x^2}}^{x} xy \, dy \, dx + \int_{1}^{\sqrt{2}} \int_{0}^{x} xy \, dy \, dx + \int_{\sqrt{2}}^{2} \int_{0}^{\sqrt{4-x^2}} xy \, dy \, dx$$

into one double integral. Then evaluate the double integral.

36. (a) We define the improper integral (over the entire plane $\mathbb{R}^2$)

$$I = \iint_{\mathbb{R}^2} e^{-(x^2+y^2)} \, dA = \int_{-\infty}^{\infty} \int_{-\infty}^{\infty} e^{-(x^2+y^2)} \, dy \, dx$$

$$= \lim_{a \to \infty} \iint_{D_a} e^{-(x^2+y^2)} \, dA$$

where D_a is the disk with radius a and center the origin.

Show that

$$\int_{-\infty}^{\infty} \int_{-\infty}^{\infty} e^{-(x^2+y^2)} \, dA = \pi$$

(b) An equivalent definition of the improper integral in part (a) is

$$\iint_{\mathbb{R}^2} e^{-(x^2+y^2)} \, dA = \lim_{a \to \infty} \iint_{S_a} e^{-(x^2+y^2)} \, dA$$

where S_a is the square with vertices $(\pm a, \pm a)$. Use this to show that

$$\int_{-\infty}^{\infty} e^{-x^2} \, dx \int_{-\infty}^{\infty} e^{-y^2} \, dy = \pi$$

(c) Deduce that

$$\int_{-\infty}^{\infty} e^{-x^2} \, dx = \sqrt{\pi}$$

(d) By making the change of variable $t = \sqrt{2} \, x$, show that

$$\int_{-\infty}^{\infty} e^{-x^2/2} \, dx = \sqrt{2\pi}$$

(This is a fundamental result for probability and statistics.)

37. Use the result of Exercise 36 part (c) to evaluate the following integrals.

(a) $\int_0^{\infty} x^2 e^{-x^2} \, dx$ (b) $\int_0^{\infty} \sqrt{x} \, e^{-x} \, dx$

12.5 Applications of Double Integrals

We have already seen one application of double integrals: computing volumes. Another geometric application is finding areas of surfaces and this will be done in the next section. In this section we explore physical applications such as computing mass, electric charge, center of mass, and moment of inertia. We will see that these physical ideas are also important when applied to probability density functions of two random variables.

Density and Mass

In Chapter 6 we were able to use single integrals to compute moments and the center of mass of a thin plate or lamina with constant density. But now, equipped with the double integral, we can consider a lamina with variable density. Suppose the lamina occupies a region D of the xy-plane and its **density** (in units of mass per unit area) at a point (x, y) in D is given by $\rho(x, y)$, where ρ is a continuous function on D. This means that

$$\rho(x, y) = \lim \frac{\Delta m}{\Delta A}$$

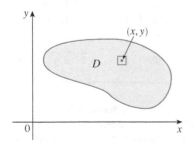

FIGURE 1

where Δm and ΔA are the mass and area of a small rectangle that contains (x, y) and the limit is taken as the dimensions of the rectangle approach 0. (See Figure 1.)

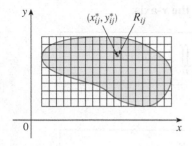

FIGURE 2

To find the total mass m of the lamina we divide a rectangle R containing D into subrectangles R_{ij} of the same size (as in Figure 2) and consider $\rho(x, y)$ to be 0 outside D. If we choose a point (x_{ij}^*, y_{ij}^*) in R_{ij}, then the mass of the part of the lamina that occupies R_{ij} is approximately $\rho(x_{ij}^*, y_{ij}^*)\,\Delta A$, where ΔA is the area of R_{ij}. If we add all such masses, we get an approximation to the total mass:

$$m \approx \sum_{i=1}^{k} \sum_{j=1}^{l} \rho(x_{ij}^*, y_{ij}^*)\,\Delta A$$

If we now increase the number of subrectangles, we obtain the total mass m of the lamina as the limiting value of the approximations:

$$\boxed{1} \qquad m = \lim_{k,l \to \infty} \sum_{i=1}^{k} \sum_{j=1}^{l} \rho(x_{ij}^*, y_{ij}^*)\,\Delta A = \iint_D \rho(x, y)\, dA$$

Physicists also consider other types of density that can be treated in the same manner. For example, if an electric charge is distributed over a region D and the charge density (in units of charge per unit area) is given by $\sigma(x, y)$ at a point (x, y) in D, then the total charge Q is given by

$$\boxed{2} \qquad Q = \iint_D \sigma(x, y)\, dA$$

EXAMPLE 1 **Finding charge by integrating charge density** Charge is distributed over the triangular region D in Figure 3 so that the charge density at (x, y) is $\sigma(x, y) = xy$, measured in coulombs per square meter (C/m^2). Find the total charge.

SOLUTION From Equation 2 and Figure 3 we have

$$Q = \iint_D \sigma(x, y)\, dA = \int_0^1 \int_{1-x}^1 xy \, dy \, dx$$

$$= \int_0^1 \left[x \frac{y^2}{2} \right]_{y=1-x}^{y=1} dx = \int_0^1 \frac{x}{2}[1^2 - (1 - x)^2]\, dx$$

$$= \tfrac{1}{2}\int_0^1 (2x^2 - x^3)\, dx = \frac{1}{2}\left[\frac{2x^3}{3} - \frac{x^4}{4} \right]_0^1 = \frac{5}{24}$$

Thus the total charge is $\frac{5}{24}$ C.

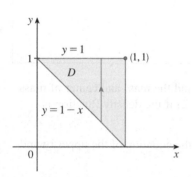

FIGURE 3

Moments and Centers of Mass

In Section 6.6 we found the center of mass of a lamina with constant density; here we consider a lamina with variable density. Suppose the lamina occupies a region D and has density function $\rho(x, y)$. Recall from Chapter 6 that we defined the moment of a particle about an axis as the product of its mass and its directed distance from the axis. We divide D into small rectangles as in Figure 2. Then the mass of R_{ij} is approximately $\rho(x_{ij}^*, y_{ij}^*)\,\Delta A$, so we can approximate the moment of R_{ij} with respect to the x-axis by

$$[\rho(x_{ij}^*, y_{ij}^*)\,\Delta A]\,y_{ij}^*$$

If we now add these quantities and take the limit as the number of subrectangles becomes large, we obtain the **moment** of the entire lamina **about the x-axis**:

$$\boxed{3} \qquad M_x = \lim_{m, n \to \infty} \sum_{i=1}^{m} \sum_{j=1}^{n} y_{ij}^* \, \rho(x_{ij}^*, y_{ij}^*) \, \Delta A = \iint\limits_{D} y \rho(x, y) \, dA$$

Similarly, the **moment about the y-axis** is

$$\boxed{4} \qquad M_y = \lim_{m, n \to \infty} \sum_{i=1}^{m} \sum_{j=1}^{n} x_{ij}^* \, \rho(x_{ij}^*, y_{ij}^*) \, \Delta A = \iint\limits_{D} x \rho(x, y) \, dA$$

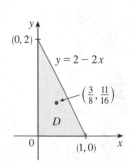

FIGURE 4

As before, we define the center of mass $(\bar{x}, \bar{y})$ so that $m\bar{x} = M_y$ and $m\bar{y} = M_x$. The physical significance is that the lamina behaves as if its entire mass is concentrated at its center of mass. Thus the lamina balances horizontally when supported at its center of mass (see Figure 4).

$\boxed{5}$ The coordinates $(\bar{x}, \bar{y})$ of the center of mass of a lamina occupying the region D and having density function $\rho(x, y)$ are

$$\bar{x} = \frac{M_y}{m} = \frac{1}{m} \iint\limits_{D} x \rho(x, y) \, dA \qquad \bar{y} = \frac{M_x}{m} = \frac{1}{m} \iint\limits_{D} y \rho(x, y) \, dA$$

where the mass m is given by

$$m = \iint\limits_{D} \rho(x, y) \, dA$$

▼ EXAMPLE 2   Center of mass of a nonuniform triangle   Find the mass and center of mass of a triangular lamina with vertices $(0, 0)$, $(1, 0)$, and $(0, 2)$ if the density function is $\rho(x, y) = 1 + 3x + y$.

SOLUTION   The triangle is shown in Figure 5. (Note that the equation of the upper boundary is $y = 2 - 2x$.) The mass of the lamina is

$$m = \iint\limits_{D} \rho(x, y) \, dA = \int_0^1 \int_0^{2-2x} (1 + 3x + y) \, dy \, dx$$

$$= \int_0^1 \left[y + 3xy + \frac{y^2}{2} \right]_{y=0}^{y=2-2x} dx$$

$$= 4 \int_0^1 (1 - x^2) \, dx = 4 \left[x - \frac{x^3}{3} \right]_0^1 = \frac{8}{3}$$

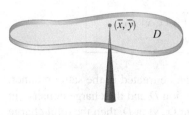

FIGURE 5

Then the formulas in (5) give

$$\bar{x} = \frac{1}{m} \iint\limits_{D} x \rho(x, y) \, dA = \frac{3}{8} \int_0^1 \int_0^{2-2x} (x + 3x^2 + xy) \, dy \, dx$$

$$= \frac{3}{8} \int_0^1 \left[xy + 3x^2 y + x\frac{y^2}{2} \right]_{y=0}^{y=2-2x} dx$$

$$= \frac{3}{2} \int_0^1 (x - x^3) \, dx = \frac{3}{2} \left[\frac{x^2}{2} - \frac{x^4}{4} \right]_0^1 = \frac{3}{8}$$

$$\bar{y} = \frac{1}{m} \iint\limits_{D} y\rho(x, y)\, dA = \frac{3}{8} \int_0^1 \int_0^{2-2x} (y + 3xy + y^2)\, dy\, dx$$

$$= \frac{3}{8} \int_0^1 \left[\frac{y^2}{2} + 3x\frac{y^2}{2} + \frac{y^3}{3} \right]_{y=0}^{y=2-2x} dx = \frac{1}{4} \int_0^1 (7 - 9x - 3x^2 + 5x^3)\, dx$$

$$= \frac{1}{4}\left[7x - 9\frac{x^2}{2} - x^3 + 5\frac{x^4}{4} \right]_0^1 = \frac{11}{16}$$

The center of mass is at the point $\left(\frac{3}{8}, \frac{11}{16}\right)$.

◨ **EXAMPLE 3** The density at any point on a semicircular lamina is proportional to the distance from the center of the circle. Find the center of mass of the lamina.

SOLUTION Let's place the lamina as the upper half of the circle $x^2 + y^2 = a^2$. (See Figure 6.) Then the distance from a point (x, y) to the center of the circle (the origin) is $\sqrt{x^2 + y^2}$. Therefore the density function is

$$\rho(x, y) = K\sqrt{x^2 + y^2}$$

where K is some constant. Both the density function and the shape of the lamina suggest that we convert to polar coordinates. Then $\sqrt{x^2 + y^2} = r$ and the region D is given by $0 \leqslant r \leqslant a$, $0 \leqslant \theta \leqslant \pi$. Thus the mass of the lamina is

$$m = \iint\limits_{D} \rho(x, y)\, dA = \iint\limits_{D} K\sqrt{x^2 + y^2}\, dA$$

$$= \int_0^\pi \int_0^a (Kr)\, r\, dr\, d\theta = K \int_0^\pi d\theta \int_0^a r^2\, dr$$

$$= K\pi \frac{r^3}{3}\bigg]_0^a = \frac{K\pi a^3}{3}$$

Both the lamina and the density function are symmetric with respect to the y-axis, so the center of mass must lie on the y-axis, that is, $\bar{x} = 0$. The y-coordinate is given by

$$\bar{y} = \frac{1}{m} \iint\limits_{D} y\rho(x, y)\, dA = \frac{3}{K\pi a^3} \int_0^\pi \int_0^a r \sin\theta\, (Kr)\, r\, dr\, d\theta$$

$$= \frac{3}{\pi a^3} \int_0^\pi \sin\theta\, d\theta \int_0^a r^3\, dr = \frac{3}{\pi a^3} \left[-\cos\theta \right]_0^\pi \left[\frac{r^4}{4} \right]_0^a$$

$$= \frac{3}{\pi a^3} \frac{2a^4}{4} = \frac{3a}{2\pi}$$

Therefore the center of mass is located at the point $(0, 3a/(2\pi))$.

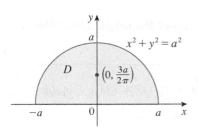

FIGURE 6

Compare the location of the center of mass in Example 3 with Example 7 in Section 6.6, where we found that the center of mass of a lamina with the same shape but uniform density is located at the point $(0, 4a/(3\pi))$.

Moment of Inertia

The **moment of inertia** (also called the **second moment**) of a particle of mass m about an axis is defined to be mr^2, where r is the distance from the particle to the axis. We extend this concept to a lamina with density function $\rho(x, y)$ and occupying a region D by proceeding as we did for ordinary moments. We divide D into small rectangles, approximate the moment of inertia of each subrectangle about the x-axis, and take the limit of the sum as the number of subrectangles becomes large. The result is the **moment of inertia** of the lamina **about the x-axis**:

$$
\boxed{6} \qquad I_x = \lim_{m,\,n \to \infty} \sum_{i=1}^{m} \sum_{j=1}^{n} (y_{ij}^{*})^2 \, \rho(x_{ij}^{*}, y_{ij}^{*}) \, \Delta A = \iint\limits_{D} y^2 \rho(x, y) \, dA
$$

Similarly, the **moment of inertia about the y-axis** is

$$
\boxed{7} \qquad I_y = \lim_{m,\,n \to \infty} \sum_{i=1}^{m} \sum_{j=1}^{n} (x_{ij}^{*})^2 \, \rho(x_{ij}^{*}, y_{ij}^{*}) \, \Delta A = \iint\limits_{D} x^2 \rho(x, y) \, dA
$$

It is also of interest to consider the **moment of inertia about the origin**, also called the **polar moment of inertia**:

$$
\boxed{8} \qquad I_0 = \lim_{m,\,n \to \infty} \sum_{i=1}^{m} \sum_{j=1}^{n} \left[(x_{ij}^{*})^2 + (y_{ij}^{*})^2 \right] \rho(x_{ij}^{*}, y_{ij}^{*}) \, \Delta A = \iint\limits_{D} (x^2 + y^2) \rho(x, y) \, dA
$$

Note that $I_0 = I_x + I_y$.

V EXAMPLE 4 Moments of inertia of a uniform disk   Find the moments of inertia I_x, I_y, and I_0 of a homogeneous disk D with density $\rho(x, y) = \rho$, center the origin, and radius a.

SOLUTION The boundary of D is the circle $x^2 + y^2 = a^2$ and in polar coordinates D is described by $0 \leqslant \theta \leqslant 2\pi$, $0 \leqslant r \leqslant a$. Let's compute I_0 first:

$$
I_0 = \iint\limits_{D} (x^2 + y^2)\rho \, dA = \rho \int_{0}^{2\pi} \int_{0}^{a} r^2 \, r \, dr \, d\theta
$$

$$
= \rho \int_{0}^{2\pi} d\theta \int_{0}^{a} r^3 \, dr = 2\pi\rho \left[\frac{r^4}{4} \right]_{0}^{a} = \frac{\pi\rho a^4}{2}
$$

Instead of computing I_x and I_y directly, we use the facts that $I_x + I_y = I_0$ and $I_x = I_y$ (from the symmetry of the problem). Thus

$$
I_x = I_y = \frac{I_0}{2} = \frac{\pi\rho a^4}{4}
$$

In Example 4 notice that the mass of the disk is

$$
m = \text{density} \times \text{area} = \rho(\pi a^2)
$$

so the moment of inertia of the disk about the origin (like a wheel about its axle) can be written as

$$
I_0 = \frac{\pi\rho a^4}{2} = \tfrac{1}{2}(\rho\pi a^2)a^2 = \tfrac{1}{2}ma^2
$$

Thus if we increase the mass or the radius of the disk, we thereby increase the moment of inertia. In general, the moment of inertia plays much the same role in rotational motion that mass plays in linear motion. The moment of inertia of a wheel is what makes it difficult to start or stop the rotation of the wheel, just as the mass of a car is what makes it difficult to start or stop the motion of the car.

Probability

In Section 6.8 we considered the *probability density function* f of a continuous random variable X. This means that $f(x) \ge 0$ for all x, $\int_{-\infty}^{\infty} f(x)\, dx = 1$, and the probability that X lies between a and b is found by integrating f from a to b:

$$P(a \le X \le b) = \int_a^b f(x)\, dx$$

Now we consider a pair of continuous random variables X and Y, such as the lifetimes of two components of a machine or the height and weight of an adult female chosen at random. The **joint density function** of X and Y is a function f of two variables such that the probability that (X, Y) lies in a region D is

$$P\big((X, Y) \in D\big) = \iint_D f(x, y)\, dA$$

In particular, if the region is a rectangle, the probability that X lies between a and b and Y lies between c and d is

$$P(a \le X \le b,\ c \le Y \le d) = \int_a^b \int_c^d f(x, y)\, dy\, dx$$

(See Figure 7.)

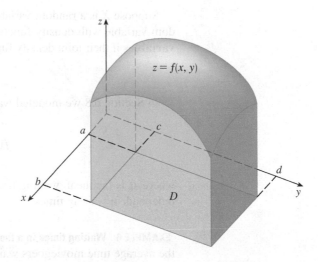

FIGURE 7

The probability that X lies between a and b and Y lies between c and d is the volume that lies above the rectangle $D = [a, b] \times [c, d]$ and below the graph of the joint density function.

Because probabilities aren't negative and are measured on a scale from 0 to 1, the joint density function has the following properties:

$$f(x, y) \ge 0 \qquad \iint_{\mathbb{R}^2} f(x, y)\, dA = 1$$

As in Exercise 36 in Section 12.4, the double integral over $\mathbb{R}^2$ is an improper integral defined as the limit of double integrals over expanding circles or squares, and we can write

$$\iint_{\mathbb{R}^2} f(x, y)\, dA = \int_{-\infty}^{\infty} \int_{-\infty}^{\infty} f(x, y)\, dx\, dy = 1$$

EXAMPLE 5 If the joint density function for X and Y is given by

$$f(x, y) = \begin{cases} C(x + 2y) & \text{if } 0 \leqslant x \leqslant 10,\ 0 \leqslant y \leqslant 10 \\ 0 & \text{otherwise} \end{cases}$$

find the value of the constant C. Then find $P(X \leqslant 7, Y \geqslant 2)$.

SOLUTION We find the value of C by ensuring that the double integral of f is equal to 1. Because $f(x, y) = 0$ outside the rectangle $[0, 10] \times [0, 10]$, we have

$$\int_{-\infty}^{\infty} \int_{-\infty}^{\infty} f(x, y)\, dy\, dx = \int_{0}^{10} \int_{0}^{10} C(x + 2y)\, dy\, dx = C \int_{0}^{10} \left[xy + y^2 \right]_{y=0}^{y=10} dx$$

$$= C \int_{0}^{10} (10x + 100)\, dx = 1500C$$

Therefore $1500C = 1$ and so $C = \frac{1}{1500}$.

Now we can compute the probability that X is at most 7 and Y is at least 2:

$$P(X \leqslant 7, Y \geqslant 2) = \int_{-\infty}^{7} \int_{2}^{\infty} f(x, y)\, dy\, dx = \int_{0}^{7} \int_{2}^{10} \tfrac{1}{1500}(x + 2y)\, dy\, dx$$

$$= \tfrac{1}{1500} \int_{0}^{7} \left[xy + y^2 \right]_{y=2}^{y=10} dx = \tfrac{1}{1500} \int_{0}^{7} (8x + 96)\, dx$$

$$= \tfrac{868}{1500} \approx 0.5787$$

Suppose X is a random variable with probability density function $f_1(x)$ and Y is a random variable with density function $f_2(y)$. Then X and Y are called **independent random variables** if their joint density function is the product of their individual density functions:

$$f(x, y) = f_1(x) f_2(y)$$

In Section 6.8 we modeled waiting times by using exponential density functions

$$f(t) = \begin{cases} 0 & \text{if } t < 0 \\ \mu^{-1} e^{-t/\mu} & \text{if } t \geqslant 0 \end{cases}$$

where μ is the mean waiting time. In the next example we consider a situation with two independent waiting times.

EXAMPLE 6   **Waiting times in a theater**   The manager of a movie theater determines that the average time moviegoers wait in line to buy a ticket for this week's film is 10 minutes and the average time they wait to buy popcorn is 5 minutes. Assuming that the waiting times are independent, find the probability that a moviegoer waits a total of less than 20 minutes before taking his or her seat.

SOLUTION Assuming that both the waiting time X for the ticket purchase and the waiting time Y in the refreshment line are modeled by exponential probability density functions, we can write the individual density functions as

$$f_1(x) = \begin{cases} 0 & \text{if } x < 0 \\ \tfrac{1}{10} e^{-x/10} & \text{if } x \geqslant 0 \end{cases} \qquad f_2(y) = \begin{cases} 0 & \text{if } y < 0 \\ \tfrac{1}{5} e^{-y/5} & \text{if } y \geqslant 0 \end{cases}$$

Since X and Y are independent, the joint density function is the product:

$$f(x, y) = f_1(x)f_2(y) = \begin{cases} \frac{1}{50}e^{-x/10}e^{-y/5} & \text{if } x \ge 0, \ y \ge 0 \\ 0 & \text{otherwise} \end{cases}$$

We are asked for the probability that $X + Y < 20$:

$$P(X + Y < 20) = P\big((X, Y) \in D\big)$$

where D is the triangular region shown in Figure 8. Thus

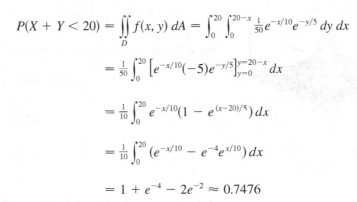

$$P(X + Y < 20) = \iint_D f(x, y) \, dA = \int_0^{20} \int_0^{20-x} \tfrac{1}{50}e^{-x/10}e^{-y/5} \, dy \, dx$$

$$= \tfrac{1}{50} \int_0^{20} \big[e^{-x/10}(-5)e^{-y/5}\big]_{y=0}^{y=20-x} \, dx$$

$$= \tfrac{1}{10} \int_0^{20} e^{-x/10}\big(1 - e^{(x-20)/5}\big) \, dx$$

$$= \tfrac{1}{10} \int_0^{20} \big(e^{-x/10} - e^{-4}e^{x/10}\big) \, dx$$

$$= 1 + e^{-4} - 2e^{-2} \approx 0.7476$$

This means that about 75% of the moviegoers wait less than 20 minutes before taking their seats.

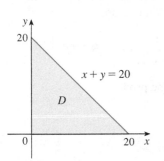

FIGURE 8

Expected Values

Recall from Section 6.8 that if X is a random variable with probability density function f, then its *mean* is

$$\mu = \int_{-\infty}^{\infty} xf(x) \, dx$$

Now if X and Y are random variables with joint density function f, we define the **X-mean** and **Y-mean**, also called the **expected values** of X and Y, to be

$$\boxed{9} \qquad \mu_1 = \iint_{\mathbb{R}^2} xf(x, y) \, dA \qquad \mu_2 = \iint_{\mathbb{R}^2} yf(x, y) \, dA$$

Notice how closely the expressions for μ_1 and μ_2 in (9) resemble the moments M_x and M_y of a lamina with density function ρ in Equations 3 and 4. In fact, we can think of probability as being like continuously distributed mass. We calculate probability the way we calculate mass—by integrating a density function. And because the total "probability mass" is 1, the expressions for $\bar{x}$ and $\bar{y}$ in (5) show that we can think of the expected values of X and Y, μ_1 and μ_2, as the coordinates of the "center of mass" of the probability distribution.

In the next example we deal with normal distributions. As in Section 6.8, a single random variable is *normally distributed* if its probability density function is of the form

$$f(x) = \frac{1}{\sigma\sqrt{2\pi}} \, e^{-(x-\mu)^2/(2\sigma^2)}$$

where μ is the mean and σ is the standard deviation.

EXAMPLE 7 A factory produces (cylindrically shaped) roller bearings that are sold as having diameter 4.0 cm and length 6.0 cm. In fact, the diameters X are normally distributed with mean 4.0 cm and standard deviation 0.01 cm while the lengths Y are normally distributed with mean 6.0 cm and standard deviation 0.01 cm. Assuming that X and Y are independent, write the joint density function and graph it. Find the probability that a bearing randomly chosen from the production line has either length or diameter that differs from the mean by more than 0.02 cm.

SOLUTION We are given that X and Y are normally distributed with $\mu_1 = 4.0$, $\mu_2 = 6.0$, and $\sigma_1 = \sigma_2 = 0.01$. So the individual density functions for X and Y are

$$f_1(x) = \frac{1}{0.01\sqrt{2\pi}}\, e^{-(x-4)^2/0.0002} \qquad f_2(y) = \frac{1}{0.01\sqrt{2\pi}}\, e^{-(y-6)^2/0.0002}$$

Since X and Y are independent, the joint density function is the product:

$$f(x, y) = f_1(x) f_2(y)$$

$$= \frac{1}{0.0002\pi}\, e^{-(x-4)^2/0.0002} e^{-(y-6)^2/0.0002}$$

$$= \frac{5000}{\pi}\, e^{-5000[(x-4)^2 + (y-6)^2]}$$

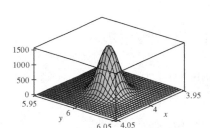

FIGURE 9
Graph of the bivariate normal joint density function in Example 7

A graph of this function is shown in Figure 9.

Let's first calculate the probability that both X and Y differ from their means by less than 0.02 cm. Using a calculator or computer to estimate the integral, we have

$$P(3.98 < X < 4.02, \ 5.98 < Y < 6.02) = \int_{3.98}^{4.02} \int_{5.98}^{6.02} f(x, y)\, dy\, dx$$

$$= \frac{5000}{\pi} \int_{3.98}^{4.02} \int_{5.98}^{6.02} e^{-5000[(x-4)^2 + (y-6)^2]}\, dy\, dx$$

$$\approx 0.91$$

Then the probability that either X or Y differs from its mean by more than 0.02 cm is approximately

$$1 - 0.91 = 0.09$$

12.5 Exercises

1. Electric charge is distributed over the rectangle $1 \leqslant x \leqslant 3$, $0 \leqslant y \leqslant 2$ so that the charge density at (x, y) is $\sigma(x, y) = 2xy + y^2$ (measured in coulombs per square meter). Find the total charge on the rectangle.

2. Electric charge is distributed over the disk $x^2 + y^2 \leqslant 4$ so that the charge density at (x, y) is $\sigma(x, y) = x + y + x^2 + y^2$ (measured in coulombs per square meter). Find the total charge on the disk.

3–10 Find the mass and center of mass of the lamina that occupies the region D and has the given density function ρ.

3. $D = \{(x, y) \mid 0 \leqslant x \leqslant 2, -1 \leqslant y \leqslant 1\}$; $\rho(x, y) = xy^2$

4. $D = \{(x, y) \mid 0 \leqslant x \leqslant a, 0 \leqslant y \leqslant b\}$; $\rho(x, y) = cxy$

5. D is the triangular region with vertices $(0, 0)$, $(2, 1)$, $(0, 3)$; $\rho(x, y) = x + y$

CAS Computer algebra system required   **1.** Homework Hints available in TEC

6. D is the triangular region enclosed by the lines $x = 0$, $y = x$, and $2x + y = 6$; $\rho(x, y) = x^2$

7. D is bounded by $y = e^x$, $y = 0$, $x = 0$, and $x = 1$; $\rho(x, y) = y$

8. D is bounded by $y = \sqrt{x}$, $y = 0$, and $x = 1$; $\rho(x, y) = x$

9. $D = \{(x, y) \mid 0 \leq y \leq \sin(\pi x/L), 0 \leq x \leq L\}$; $\rho(x, y) = y$

10. D is bounded by the parabolas $y = x^2$ and $x = y^2$; $\rho(x, y) = \sqrt{x}$

---

11. A lamina occupies the part of the disk $x^2 + y^2 \leq 1$ in the first quadrant. Find its center of mass if the density at any point is proportional to its distance from the x-axis.

12. Find the center of mass of the lamina in Exercise 11 if the density at any point is proportional to the square of its distance from the origin.

13. The boundary of a lamina consists of the semicircles $y = \sqrt{1 - x^2}$ and $y = \sqrt{4 - x^2}$ together with the portions of the x-axis that join them. Find the center of mass of the lamina if the density at any point is proportional to its distance from the origin.

14. Find the center of mass of the lamina in Exercise 13 if the density at any point is inversely proportional to its distance from the origin.

15. Find the center of mass of a lamina in the shape of an isosceles right triangle with equal sides of length a if the density at any point is proportional to the square of the distance from the vertex opposite the hypotenuse.

16. A lamina occupies the region inside the circle $x^2 + y^2 = 2y$ but outside the circle $x^2 + y^2 = 1$. Find the center of mass if the density at any point is inversely proportional to its distance from the origin.

17. Find the moments of inertia I_x, I_y, I_0 for the lamina of Exercise 7.

18. Find the moments of inertia I_x, I_y, I_0 for the lamina of Exercise 12.

19. Find the moments of inertia I_x, I_y, I_0 for the lamina of Exercise 15.

20. Consider a square fan blade with sides of length 2 and the lower left corner placed at the origin. If the density of the blade is $\rho(x, y) = 1 + 0.1x$, is it more difficult to rotate the blade about the x-axis or the y-axis?

21–22 Use a computer algebra system to find the mass, center of mass, and moments of inertia of the lamina that occupies the region D and has the given density function.

21. $D = \{(x, y) \mid 0 \leq y \leq \sin x, 0 \leq x \leq \pi\}$; $\rho(x, y) = xy$

22. D is enclosed by the cardioid $r = 1 + \cos\theta$; $\rho(x, y) = \sqrt{x^2 + y^2}$

---

23. The joint density function for a pair of random variables X and Y is
$$f(x, y) = \begin{cases} Cx(1 + y) & \text{if } 0 \leq x \leq 1, \ 0 \leq y \leq 2 \\ 0 & \text{otherwise} \end{cases}$$
    (a) Find the value of the constant C.
    (b) Find $P(X \leq 1, Y \leq 1)$.
    (c) Find $P(X + Y \leq 1)$.

24. (a) Verify that
$$f(x, y) = \begin{cases} 4xy & \text{if } 0 \leq x \leq 1, \ 0 \leq y \leq 1 \\ 0 & \text{otherwise} \end{cases}$$
    is a joint density function.
    (b) If X and Y are random variables whose joint density function is the function f in part (a), find
       (i) $P(X \geq \frac{1}{2})$ (ii) $P(X \geq \frac{1}{2}, Y \leq \frac{1}{2})$
    (c) Find the expected values of X and Y.

25. Suppose X and Y are random variables with joint density function
$$f(x, y) = \begin{cases} 0.1e^{-(0.5x + 0.2y)} & \text{if } x \geq 0, \ y \geq 0 \\ 0 & \text{otherwise} \end{cases}$$
    (a) Verify that f is indeed a joint density function.
    (b) Find the following probabilities.
       (i) $P(Y \geq 1)$ (ii) $P(X \leq 2, Y \leq 4)$
    (c) Find the expected values of X and Y.

26. (a) A lamp has two bulbs of a type with an average lifetime of 1000 hours. Assuming that we can model the probability of failure of these bulbs by an exponential density function with mean $\mu = 1000$, find the probability that both of the lamp's bulbs fail within 1000 hours.
    (b) Another lamp has just one bulb of the same type as in part (a). If one bulb burns out and is replaced by a bulb of the same type, find the probability that the two bulbs fail within a total of 1000 hours.

27. Suppose that X and Y are independent random variables, where X is normally distributed with mean 45 and standard deviation 0.5 and Y is normally distributed with mean 20 and standard deviation 0.1.
    (a) Find $P(40 \leq X \leq 50, 20 \leq Y \leq 25)$.
    (b) Find $P(4(X - 45)^2 + 100(Y - 20)^2 \leq 2)$.

28. Xavier and Yolanda both have classes that end at noon and they agree to meet every day after class. They arrive at the coffee shop independently. Xavier's arrival time is X and Yolanda's arrival time is Y, where X and Y are measured in minutes after noon. The individual density functions are
$$f_1(x) = \begin{cases} e^{-x} & \text{if } x \geq 0 \\ 0 & \text{if } x < 0 \end{cases} \qquad f_2(y) = \begin{cases} \frac{1}{50}y & \text{if } 0 \leq y \leq 10 \\ 0 & \text{otherwise} \end{cases}$$
    (Xavier arrives sometimes after noon and is more likely to arrive promptly than late. Yolanda always arrives by 12:10 PM and is more likely to arrive late than promptly.) After Yolanda arrives, she'll wait for up to half an hour for Xavier, but he won't wait for her. Find the probability that they meet.

29. When studying the spread of an epidemic, we assume that the probability that an infected individual will spread the disease to an uninfected individual is a function of the distance between them. Consider a circular city of radius 10 miles in which the population is uniformly distributed. For an uninfected individual at a fixed point $A(x_0, y_0)$, assume that the probability function is given by

$$f(P) = \tfrac{1}{20}[20 - d(P, A)]$$

where $d(P, A)$ denotes the distance between points P and A.

(a) Suppose the exposure of a person to the disease is the sum of the probabilities of catching the disease from all members of the population. Assume that the infected people are uniformly distributed throughout the city, with k infected individuals per square mile. Find a double integral that represents the exposure of a person residing at A.

(b) Evaluate the integral for the case in which A is the center of the city and for the case in which A is located on the edge of the city. Where would you prefer to live?

12.6   Surface Area

In this section we apply double integrals to the problem of computing the area of a surface. We start by finding a formula for the area of a parametric surface and then, as a special case, we deduce a formula for the surface area of the graph of a function of two variables.

We recall from Section 10.5 that a parametric surface S is defined by a vector-valued function of two parameters

$$\boxed{1} \qquad \mathbf{r}(u, v) = x(u, v)\,\mathbf{i} + y(u, v)\,\mathbf{j} + z(u, v)\,\mathbf{k}$$

or, equivalently, by parametric equations

$$x = x(u, v) \qquad y = y(u, v) \qquad z = z(u, v)$$

where (u, v) varies throughout a region D in the uv-plane.

We will find the area of S by dividing S into patches and approximating the area of each patch by the area of a piece of a tangent plane. So first let's recall from Section 11.4 how to find tangent planes to parametric surfaces.

Let P_0 be a point on S with position vector $\mathbf{r}(u_0, v_0)$. If we keep u constant by putting $u = u_0$, then $\mathbf{r}(u_0, v)$ becomes a vector function of the single parameter v and defines a grid curve C_1 lying on S. (See Figure 1.) The tangent vector to C_1 at P_0 is obtained by taking the partial derivative of $\mathbf{r}$ with respect to v:

$$\boxed{2} \qquad \mathbf{r}_v = \frac{\partial x}{\partial v}(u_0, v_0)\,\mathbf{i} + \frac{\partial y}{\partial v}(u_0, v_0)\,\mathbf{j} + \frac{\partial z}{\partial v}(u_0, v_0)\,\mathbf{k}$$

Similarly, if we keep v constant by putting $v = v_0$, we get a grid curve C_2 given by $\mathbf{r}(u, v_0)$ that lies on S, and its tangent vector at P_0 is

$$\boxed{3} \qquad \mathbf{r}_u = \frac{\partial x}{\partial u}(u_0, v_0)\,\mathbf{i} + \frac{\partial y}{\partial u}(u_0, v_0)\,\mathbf{j} + \frac{\partial z}{\partial u}(u_0, v_0)\,\mathbf{k}$$

If the **normal vector** $\mathbf{r}_u \times \mathbf{r}_v$ is not $\mathbf{0}$, then the surface S is called **smooth**. (It has no "corners".) In this case the tangent plane to S at P_0 exists and can be found using the normal vector.

Now we define the surface area of a general parametric surface given by Equation 1. For simplicity we start by considering a surface whose parameter domain D is a rectangle, and we divide it into subrectangles R_{ij}. Let's choose (u_i^*, v_j^*) to be the lower left corner of R_{ij}.

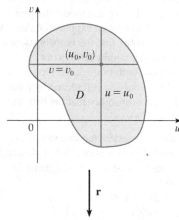

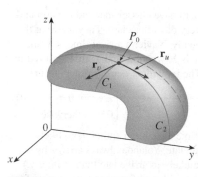

FIGURE 1

(See Figure 2.) The part S_{ij} of the surface S that corresponds to R_{ij} is called a *patch* and has the point P_{ij} with position vector $\mathbf{r}(u_i^*, v_j^*)$ as one of its corners. Let

$$\mathbf{r}_u^* = \mathbf{r}_u(u_i^*, v_j^*) \qquad \text{and} \qquad \mathbf{r}_v^* = \mathbf{r}_v(u_i^*, v_j^*)$$

be the tangent vectors at P_{ij} as given by Equations 3 and 2.

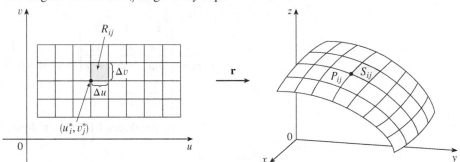

FIGURE 2

The image of the subrectangle R_{ij} is the patch S_{ij}.

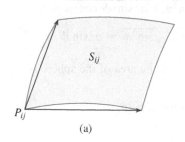

(a)

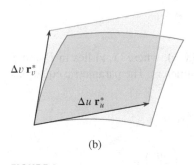

(b)

FIGURE 3

Approximating a patch by a parallelogram

Figure 3(a) shows how the two edges of the patch that meet at P_{ij} can be approximated by vectors. These vectors, in turn, can be approximated by the vectors $\Delta u\, \mathbf{r}_u^*$ and $\Delta v\, \mathbf{r}_v^*$ because partial derivatives can be approximated by difference quotients. So we approximate S_{ij} by the parallelogram determined by the vectors $\Delta u\, \mathbf{r}_u^*$ and $\Delta v\, \mathbf{r}_v^*$. As shown in Figure 3(b), this parallelogram lies in the tangent plane to S at P_{ij}. The area of this parallelogram is

$$|(\Delta u\, \mathbf{r}_u^*) \times (\Delta v\, \mathbf{r}_v^*)| = |\mathbf{r}_u^* \times \mathbf{r}_v^*|\, \Delta u\, \Delta v$$

and so an approximation to the area of S is

$$\sum_{i=1}^{m} \sum_{j=1}^{n} |\mathbf{r}_u^* \times \mathbf{r}_v^*|\, \Delta u\, \Delta v$$

Our intuition tells us that this approximation gets better as we increase the number of subrectangles, and we recognize the double sum as a Riemann sum for the double integral $\iint_D |\mathbf{r}_u \times \mathbf{r}_v|\, du\, dv$. This motivates the following definition.

---

4 **Definition** If a smooth parametric surface S is given by the equation

$$\mathbf{r}(u, v) = x(u, v)\, \mathbf{i} + y(u, v)\, \mathbf{j} + z(u, v)\, \mathbf{k} \qquad (u, v) \in D$$

and S is covered just once as (u, v) ranges throughout the parameter domain D, then the **surface area** of S is

$$A(S) = \iint_D |\mathbf{r}_u \times \mathbf{r}_v|\, dA$$

where $\quad \mathbf{r}_u = \dfrac{\partial x}{\partial u}\mathbf{i} + \dfrac{\partial y}{\partial u}\mathbf{j} + \dfrac{\partial z}{\partial u}\mathbf{k} \qquad \mathbf{r}_v = \dfrac{\partial x}{\partial v}\mathbf{i} + \dfrac{\partial y}{\partial v}\mathbf{j} + \dfrac{\partial z}{\partial v}\mathbf{k}$

EXAMPLE 1 **Area of a parametric surface** Find the surface area of a sphere of radius a.

SOLUTION In Example 4 in Section 10.5 we found the parametric representation

$$x = a \sin \phi \cos \theta \qquad y = a \sin \phi \sin \theta \qquad z = a \cos \phi$$

where the parameter domain is

$$D = \{(\phi, \theta) \mid 0 \leq \phi \leq \pi, \ 0 \leq \theta \leq 2\pi\}$$

We first compute the cross product of the tangent vectors:

$$\mathbf{r}_\phi \times \mathbf{r}_\theta = \begin{vmatrix} \mathbf{i} & \mathbf{j} & \mathbf{k} \\ \dfrac{\partial x}{\partial \phi} & \dfrac{\partial y}{\partial \phi} & \dfrac{\partial z}{\partial \phi} \\ \dfrac{\partial x}{\partial \theta} & \dfrac{\partial y}{\partial \theta} & \dfrac{\partial z}{\partial \theta} \end{vmatrix} = \begin{vmatrix} \mathbf{i} & \mathbf{j} & \mathbf{k} \\ a\cos\phi\cos\theta & a\cos\phi\sin\theta & -a\sin\phi \\ -a\sin\phi\sin\theta & a\sin\phi\cos\theta & 0 \end{vmatrix}$$

$$= a^2 \sin^2\phi \cos\theta \, \mathbf{i} + a^2 \sin^2\phi \sin\theta \, \mathbf{j} + a^2 \sin\phi \cos\phi \, \mathbf{k}$$

Thus

$$|\mathbf{r}_\phi \times \mathbf{r}_\theta| = \sqrt{a^4\sin^4\phi \, \cos^2\theta + a^4\sin^4\phi \, \sin^2\theta + a^4\sin^2\phi \, \cos^2\phi}$$

$$= \sqrt{a^4\sin^4\phi + a^4\sin^2\phi \, \cos^2\phi} = a^2\sqrt{\sin^2\phi} = a^2\sin\phi$$

since $\sin\phi \geq 0$ for $0 \leq \phi \leq \pi$. Therefore, by Definition 4, the area of the sphere is

$$A = \iint_D |\mathbf{r}_\phi \times \mathbf{r}_\theta| \, dA = \int_0^{2\pi} \int_0^{\pi} a^2 \sin\phi \, d\phi \, d\theta$$

$$= a^2 \int_0^{2\pi} d\theta \int_0^{\pi} \sin\phi \, d\phi = a^2(2\pi)2 = 4\pi a^2$$

Surface Area of a Graph

For the special case of a surface S with equation $z = f(x, y)$, where (x, y) lies in D and f has continuous partial derivatives, we take x and y as parameters. The parametric equations are

$$x = x \qquad y = y \qquad z = f(x, y)$$

so

$$\mathbf{r}_x = \mathbf{i} + \left(\frac{\partial f}{\partial x}\right)\mathbf{k} \qquad \mathbf{r}_y = \mathbf{j} + \left(\frac{\partial f}{\partial y}\right)\mathbf{k}$$

and

$$\boxed{5} \qquad \mathbf{r}_x \times \mathbf{r}_y = \begin{vmatrix} \mathbf{i} & \mathbf{j} & \mathbf{k} \\ 1 & 0 & \dfrac{\partial f}{\partial x} \\ 0 & 1 & \dfrac{\partial f}{\partial y} \end{vmatrix} = -\frac{\partial f}{\partial x}\mathbf{i} - \frac{\partial f}{\partial y}\mathbf{j} + \mathbf{k}$$

Thus the surface area formula in Definition 4 becomes

Notice the similarity between the surface area formula in Equation 6 and the arc length formula

$$L = \int_a^b \sqrt{1 + \left(\frac{dy}{dx}\right)^2} \, dx$$

from Section 6.4.

$$\boxed{6} \qquad A(S) = \iint_D \sqrt{1 + \left(\frac{\partial z}{\partial x}\right)^2 + \left(\frac{\partial z}{\partial y}\right)^2} \, dA$$

☑ **EXAMPLE 2** **Surface area of a graph** Find the area of the part of the paraboloid $z = x^2 + y^2$ that lies under the plane $z = 9$.

SOLUTION The plane intersects the paraboloid in the circle $x^2 + y^2 = 9$, $z = 9$. Therefore the given surface lies above the disk D with center the origin and radius 3. (See Figure 4.) Using Formula 6, we have

$$A = \iint_D \sqrt{1 + \left(\frac{\partial z}{\partial x}\right)^2 + \left(\frac{\partial z}{\partial y}\right)^2} \, dA = \iint_D \sqrt{1 + (2x)^2 + (2y)^2} \, dA$$

$$= \iint_D \sqrt{1 + 4(x^2 + y^2)} \, dA$$

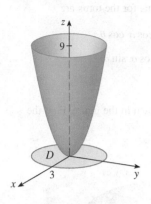

FIGURE 4

Converting to polar coordinates, we obtain

$$A = \int_0^{2\pi} \int_0^3 \sqrt{1 + 4r^2} \, r \, dr \, d\theta = \int_0^{2\pi} d\theta \int_0^3 r\sqrt{1 + 4r^2} \, dr$$

$$= 2\pi \left(\frac{1}{8}\right)\frac{2}{3}(1 + 4r^2)^{3/2}\Big]_0^3 = \frac{\pi}{6}\left(37\sqrt{37} - 1\right)$$

A common type of surface is a **surface of revolution** S obtained by rotating the curve $y = f(x)$, $a \le x \le b$, about the x-axis, where $f(x) \ge 0$ and f' is continuous. In Exercise 23 you are asked to use a parametric representation of S and Definition 4 to prove the following formula for the area of a surface of revolution:

$$\boxed{7} \qquad A = 2\pi \int_a^b f(x)\sqrt{1 + [f'(x)]^2} \, dx$$

12.6 Exercises

1–12 Find the area of the surface.

1. The part of the plane $x + 2y + 3z = 1$ that lies inside the cylinder $x^2 + y^2 = 3$

2. The part of the plane $2x - 5y + z = 10$ that lies above the triangle with vertices $(0, 0)$, $(0, 6)$, and $(4, 0)$

3. The part of the plane $3x + 2y + z = 6$ that lies in the first octant

4. The part of the plane with vector equation $\mathbf{r}(u, v) = \langle u + v, 2 - 3u, 1 + u - v \rangle$ that is given by $0 \le u \le 2, -1 \le v \le 1$

5. The part of the cone $z = \sqrt{x^2 + y^2}$ that lies between the plane $y = x$ and the cylinder $y = x^2$

6. The part of the surface $z = 1 + 3x + 2y^2$ that lies above the triangle with vertices $(0, 0)$, $(0, 1)$, and $(2, 1)$

7. The surface with parametric equations $x = u^2$, $y = uv$, $z = \frac{1}{2}v^2$, $0 \le u \le 1, 0 \le v \le 2$

8. The helicoid (or spiral ramp) with vector equation $\mathbf{r}(u, v) = u \cos v \, \mathbf{i} + u \sin v \, \mathbf{j} + v \, \mathbf{k}, 0 \le u \le 1, 0 \le v \le \pi$

9. The part of the surface $z = xy$ that lies within the cylinder $x^2 + y^2 = 1$

10. The part of the paraboloid $x = y^2 + z^2$ that lies inside the cylinder $y^2 + z^2 = 9$

11. The part of the sphere $x^2 + y^2 + z^2 = b^2$ that lies inside the cylinder $x^2 + y^2 = a^2$, where $0 < a < b$

12. The surface $z = \frac{2}{3}(x^{3/2} + y^{3/2})$, $0 \le x \le 1$, $0 \le y \le 1$

13–14 Find the area of the surface correct to four decimal places by expressing the area in terms of a single integral and using your calculator to estimate the integral.

13. The part of the surface $z = e^{-x^2-y^2}$ that lies above the disk $x^2 + y^2 \le 4$

---

14. The part of the surface $z = \cos(x^2 + y^2)$ that lies inside the cylinder $x^2 + y^2 = 1$

---

15. (a) Use the Midpoint Rule for double integrals (see Section 12.1) with six squares to estimate the area of the surface $z = 1/(1 + x^2 + y^2)$, $0 \leqslant x \leqslant 6, 0 \leqslant y \leqslant 4$.

CAS (b) Use a computer algebra system to approximate the surface area in part (a) to four decimal places. Compare with the answer to part (a).

16. (a) Use the Midpoint Rule for double integrals with $m = n = 2$ to estimate the area of the surface $z = xy + x^2 + y^2$, $0 \leqslant x \leqslant 2, 0 \leqslant y \leqslant 2$.

CAS (b) Use a computer algebra system to approximate the surface area in part (a) to four decimal places. Compare with the answer to part (a).

CAS **17.** Find the area of the surface with vector equation $\mathbf{r}(u, v) = \langle \cos^3 u \cos^3 v, \sin^3 u \cos^3 v, \sin^3 v \rangle$, $0 \leqslant u \leqslant \pi$, $0 \leqslant v \leqslant 2\pi$. State your answer correct to four decimal places.

CAS **18.** Find, to four decimal places, the area of the part of the surface $z = (1 + x^2)/(1 + y^2)$ that lies above the square $|x| + |y| \leqslant 1$. Illustrate by graphing this part of the surface.

CAS **19.** Find the exact area of the surface $z = 1 + 2x + 3y + 4y^2$, $1 \leqslant x \leqslant 4, 0 \leqslant y \leqslant 1$.

20. (a) Set up, but do not evaluate, a double integral for the area of the surface with parametric equations $x = au \cos v$, $y = bu \sin v$, $z = u^2$, $0 \leqslant u \leqslant 2, 0 \leqslant v \leqslant 2\pi$.
(b) Eliminate the parameters to show that the surface is an elliptic paraboloid and set up another double integral for the surface area.
(c) Use the parametric equations in part (a) with $a = 2$ and $b = 3$ to graph the surface.
CAS (d) For the case $a = 2, b = 3$, use a computer algebra system to find the surface area correct to four decimal places.

21. (a) Show that the parametric equations $x = a \sin u \cos v$, $y = b \sin u \sin v$, $z = c \cos u, 0 \leqslant u \leqslant \pi, 0 \leqslant v \leqslant 2\pi$, represent an ellipsoid.
(b) Use the parametric equations in part (a) to graph the ellipsoid for the case $a = 1, b = 2, c = 3$.
(c) Set up, but do not evaluate, a double integral for the surface area of the ellipsoid in part (b).

22. The figure shows the torus obtained by rotating about the z-axis the circle in the xz-plane with center $(b, 0, 0)$ and radius $a < b$. Parametric equations for the torus are

$$x = b \cos \theta + a \cos \alpha \cos \theta$$

$$y = b \sin \theta + a \cos \alpha \sin \theta$$

$$z = a \sin \alpha$$

where θ and α are the angles shown in the figure. Find the surface area of the torus.

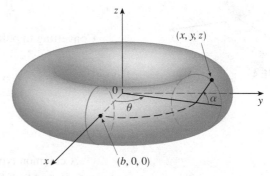

23. Use Definition 4 and the parametric equations for a surface of revolution (see Equations 10.5.3) to derive Formula 7.

24–25 Use Formula 7 to find the area of the surface obtained by rotating the given curve about the x-axis.

24. $y = x^3$, $0 \leqslant x \leqslant 2$

25. $y = \sqrt{1 + 4x}$, $1 \leqslant x \leqslant 5$

---

26. The figure shows the surface created when the cylinder $y^2 + z^2 = 1$ intersects the cylinder $x^2 + z^2 = 1$. Find the area of this surface.

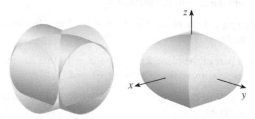

27. Find the area of the part of the sphere $x^2 + y^2 + z^2 = 4z$ that lies inside the paraboloid $z = x^2 + y^2$.

12.7 Triple Integrals

Just as we defined single integrals for functions of one variable and double integrals for functions of two variables, so we can define triple integrals for functions of three variables. Let's first deal with the simplest case where f is defined on a rectangular box:

$$\boxed{1} \qquad B = \{(x, y, z) \mid a \leqslant x \leqslant b,\ c \leqslant y \leqslant d,\ r \leqslant z \leqslant s\}$$

The first step is to divide B into sub-boxes. We do this by dividing the interval $[a, b]$ into l subintervals $[x_{i-1}, x_i]$ of equal width Δx, dividing $[c, d]$ into m subintervals of width Δy, and dividing $[r, s]$ into n subintervals of width Δz. The planes through the endpoints of these subintervals parallel to the coordinate planes divide the box B into lmn sub-boxes

$$B_{ijk} = [x_{i-1}, x_i] \times [y_{j-1}, y_j] \times [z_{k-1}, z_k]$$

which are shown in Figure 1. Each sub-box has volume $\Delta V = \Delta x\, \Delta y\, \Delta z$.

Then we form the **triple Riemann sum**

$$\boxed{2} \qquad \sum_{i=1}^{l} \sum_{j=1}^{m} \sum_{k=1}^{n} f(x_{ijk}^*, y_{ijk}^*, z_{ijk}^*)\, \Delta V$$

where the sample point $(x_{ijk}^*, y_{ijk}^*, z_{ijk}^*)$ is in B_{ijk}. By analogy with the definition of a double integral (12.1.5), we define the triple integral as the limit of the triple Riemann sums in (2).

$\boxed{3}$ **Definition** The **triple integral** of f over the box B is

$$\iiint_B f(x, y, z)\, dV = \lim_{l,\, m,\, n \to \infty} \sum_{i=1}^{l} \sum_{j=1}^{m} \sum_{k=1}^{n} f(x_{ijk}^*, y_{ijk}^*, z_{ijk}^*)\, \Delta V$$

if this limit exists.

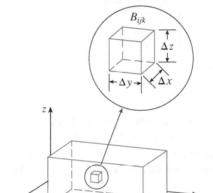

FIGURE 1

Again, the triple integral always exists if f is continuous. We can choose the sample point to be any point in the sub-box, but if we choose it to be the point (x_i, y_j, z_k) we get a simpler-looking expression for the triple integral:

$$\iiint_B f(x, y, z)\, dV = \lim_{l,\, m,\, n \to \infty} \sum_{i=1}^{l} \sum_{j=1}^{m} \sum_{k=1}^{n} f(x_i, y_j, z_k)\, \Delta V$$

Just as for double integrals, the practical method for evaluating triple integrals is to express them as iterated integrals as follows.

$\boxed{4}$ **Fubini's Theorem for Triple Integrals** If f is continuous on the rectangular box $B = [a, b] \times [c, d] \times [r, s]$, then

$$\iiint_B f(x, y, z)\, dV = \int_r^s \int_c^d \int_a^b f(x, y, z)\, dx\, dy\, dz$$

The iterated integral on the right side of Fubini's Theorem means that we integrate first with respect to x (keeping y and z fixed), then we integrate with respect to y (keeping z

fixed), and finally we integrate with respect to z. There are five other possible orders in which we can integrate, all of which give the same value. For instance, if we integrate with respect to y, then z, and then x, we have

$$\iiint_B f(x, y, z)\, dV = \int_a^b \int_r^s \int_c^d f(x, y, z)\, dy\, dz\, dx$$

V   EXAMPLE 1   Triple integral over a box   Evaluate the triple integral $\iiint_B xyz^2\, dV$, where B is the rectangular box given by

$$B = \{(x, y, z) \mid 0 \leqslant x \leqslant 1,\ -1 \leqslant y \leqslant 2,\ 0 \leqslant z \leqslant 3\}$$

SOLUTION   We could use any of the six possible orders of integration. If we choose to integrate with respect to x, then y, and then z, we obtain

$$\iiint_B xyz^2\, dV = \int_0^3 \int_{-1}^2 \int_0^1 xyz^2\, dx\, dy\, dz = \int_0^3 \int_{-1}^2 \left[\frac{x^2 yz^2}{2} \right]_{x=0}^{x=1} dy\, dz$$

$$= \int_0^3 \int_{-1}^2 \frac{yz^2}{2}\, dy\, dz = \int_0^3 \left[\frac{y^2 z^2}{4} \right]_{y=-1}^{y=2} dz$$

$$= \int_0^3 \frac{3z^2}{4}\, dz = \frac{z^3}{4} \bigg]_0^3 = \frac{27}{4}$$

Now we define the **triple integral over a general bounded region** E in three-dimensional space (a solid) by much the same procedure that we used for double integrals (12.3.2). We enclose E in a box B of the type given by Equation 1. Then we define a function F so that it agrees with f on E but is 0 for points in B that are outside E. By definition,

$$\iiint_E f(x, y, z)\, dV = \iiint_B F(x, y, z)\, dV$$

This integral exists if f is continuous and the boundary of E is "reasonably smooth." The triple integral has essentially the same properties as the double integral (Properties 6–9 in Section 12.3).

We restrict our attention to continuous functions f and to certain simple types of regions. A solid region E is said to be of **type 1** if it lies between the graphs of two continuous functions of x and y, that is,

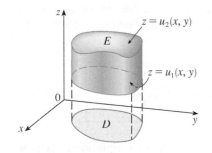

FIGURE 2
A type 1 solid region

$$\boxed{5} \qquad E = \{(x, y, z) \mid (x, y) \in D,\ u_1(x, y) \leqslant z \leqslant u_2(x, y)\}$$

where D is the projection of E onto the xy-plane as shown in Figure 2. Notice that the upper boundary of the solid E is the surface with equation $z = u_2(x, y)$, while the lower boundary is the surface $z = u_1(x, y)$.

By the same sort of argument that led to Formula 12.3.3, it can be shown that if E is a type 1 region given by Equation 5, then

$$\boxed{6} \qquad \iiint_E f(x, y, z)\, dV = \iint_D \left[\int_{u_1(x, y)}^{u_2(x, y)} f(x, y, z)\, dz \right] dA$$

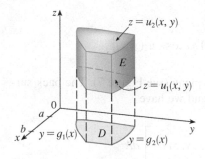

FIGURE 3
A type 1 solid region where the projection D is a type I plane region

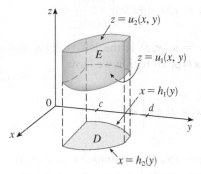

FIGURE 4
A type 1 solid region with a type II projection

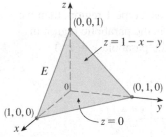

FIGURE 5

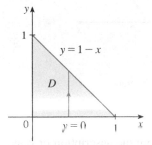

FIGURE 6

The meaning of the inner integral on the right side of Equation 6 is that x and y are held fixed, and therefore $u_1(x, y)$ and $u_2(x, y)$ are regarded as constants, while $f(x, y, z)$ is integrated with respect to z.

In particular, if the projection D of E onto the xy-plane is a type I plane region (as in Figure 3), then

$$E = \{(x, y, z) \mid a \leq x \leq b, \ g_1(x) \leq y \leq g_2(x), \ u_1(x, y) \leq z \leq u_2(x, y)\}$$

and Equation 6 becomes

7
$$\iiint\limits_{E} f(x, y, z) \, dV = \int_a^b \int_{g_1(x)}^{g_2(x)} \int_{u_1(x, y)}^{u_2(x, y)} f(x, y, z) \, dz \, dy \, dx$$

If, on the other hand, D is a type II plane region (as in Figure 4), then

$$E = \{(x, y, z) \mid c \leq y \leq d, \ h_1(y) \leq x \leq h_2(y), \ u_1(x, y) \leq z \leq u_2(x, y)\}$$

and Equation 6 becomes

8
$$\iiint\limits_{E} f(x, y, z) \, dV = \int_c^d \int_{h_1(y)}^{h_2(y)} \int_{u_1(x, y)}^{u_2(x, y)} f(x, y, z) \, dz \, dx \, dy$$

EXAMPLE 2 **Triple integral over a tetrahedron** Evaluate $\iiint_E z \, dV$, where E is the solid tetrahedron bounded by the four planes $x = 0$, $y = 0$, $z = 0$, and $x + y + z = 1$.

SOLUTION When we set up a triple integral it's wise to draw *two* diagrams: one of the solid region E (see Figure 5) and one of its projection D onto the xy-plane (see Figure 6). The lower boundary of the tetrahedron is the plane $z = 0$ and the upper boundary is the plane $x + y + z = 1$ (or $z = 1 - x - y$), so we use $u_1(x, y) = 0$ and $u_2(x, y) = 1 - x - y$ in Formula 7. Notice that the planes $x + y + z = 1$ and $z = 0$ intersect in the line $x + y = 1$ (or $y = 1 - x$) in the xy-plane. So the projection of E is the triangular region shown in Figure 6, and we have

9
$$E = \{(x, y, z) \mid 0 \leq x \leq 1, \ 0 \leq y \leq 1 - x, \ 0 \leq z \leq 1 - x - y\}$$

This description of E as a type 1 region enables us to evaluate the integral as follows:

$$\iiint\limits_{E} z \, dV = \int_0^1 \int_0^{1-x} \int_0^{1-x-y} z \, dz \, dy \, dx = \int_0^1 \int_0^{1-x} \left[\frac{z^2}{2} \right]_{z=0}^{z=1-x-y} dy \, dx$$

$$= \frac{1}{2} \int_0^1 \int_0^{1-x} (1 - x - y)^2 \, dy \, dx = \frac{1}{2} \int_0^1 \left[-\frac{(1 - x - y)^3}{3} \right]_{y=0}^{y=1-x} dx$$

$$= \frac{1}{6} \int_0^1 (1 - x)^3 \, dx = \frac{1}{6} \left[-\frac{(1 - x)^4}{4} \right]_0^1 = \frac{1}{24}$$

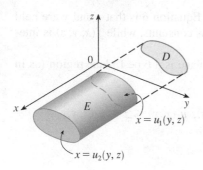

FIGURE 7
A type 2 region

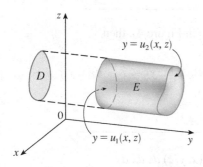

FIGURE 8
A type 3 region

A solid region E is of **type 2** if it is of the form

$$E = \{(x, y, z) \mid (y, z) \in D,\ u_1(y, z) \leqslant x \leqslant u_2(y, z)\}$$

where, this time, D is the projection of E onto the yz-plane (see Figure 7). The back surface is $x = u_1(y, z)$, the front surface is $x = u_2(y, z)$, and we have

$$\boxed{10} \qquad \iiint_E f(x, y, z)\, dV = \iint_D \left[\int_{u_1(y, z)}^{u_2(y, z)} f(x, y, z)\, dx \right] dA$$

Finally, a **type 3** region is of the form

$$E = \{(x, y, z) \mid (x, z) \in D,\ u_1(x, z) \leqslant y \leqslant u_2(x, z)\}$$

where D is the projection of E onto the xz-plane, $y = u_1(x, z)$ is the left surface, and $y = u_2(x, z)$ is the right surface (see Figure 8). For this type of region we have

$$\boxed{11} \qquad \iiint_E f(x, y, z)\, dV = \iint_D \left[\int_{u_1(x, z)}^{u_2(x, z)} f(x, y, z)\, dy \right] dA$$

In each of Equations 10 and 11 there may be two possible expressions for the integral depending on whether D is a type I or type II plane region (and corresponding to Equations 7 and 8).

▼ EXAMPLE 3   Choosing the best order of integration   Evaluate $\iiint_E \sqrt{x^2 + z^2}\, dV$, where E is the region bounded by the paraboloid $y = x^2 + z^2$ and the plane $y = 4$.

SOLUTION The solid E is shown in Figure 9. If we regard it as a type 1 region, then we need to consider its projection D_1 onto the xy-plane, which is the parabolic region in Figure 10. (The trace of $y = x^2 + z^2$ in the plane $z = 0$ is the parabola $y = x^2$.)

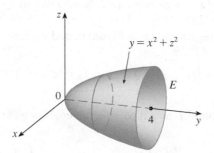

FIGURE 9
Region of integration

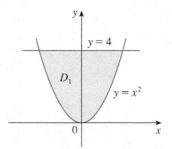

FIGURE 10
Projection onto xy-plane

From $y = x^2 + z^2$ we obtain $z = \pm\sqrt{y - x^2}$, so the lower boundary surface of E is $z = -\sqrt{y - x^2}$ and the upper surface is $z = \sqrt{y - x^2}$. Therefore the description of E as a type 1 region is

$$E = \{(x, y, z) \mid -2 \leqslant x \leqslant 2,\ x^2 \leqslant y \leqslant 4,\ -\sqrt{y - x^2} \leqslant z \leqslant \sqrt{y - x^2}\}$$

and so we obtain

$$\iiint\limits_E \sqrt{x^2 + z^2} \, dV = \int_{-2}^{2} \int_{x^2}^{4} \int_{-\sqrt{y-x^2}}^{\sqrt{y-x^2}} \sqrt{x^2 + z^2} \, dz \, dy \, dx$$

Although this expression is correct, it is extremely difficult to evaluate. So let's instead consider E as a type 3 region. As such, its projection D_3 onto the xz-plane is the disk $x^2 + z^2 \leqslant 4$ shown in Figure 11.

Then the left boundary of E is the paraboloid $y = x^2 + z^2$ and the right boundary is the plane $y = 4$, so taking $u_1(x, z) = x^2 + z^2$ and $u_2(x, z) = 4$ in Equation 11, we have

$$\iiint\limits_E \sqrt{x^2 + z^2} \, dV = \iint\limits_{D_3} \left[\int_{x^2+z^2}^{4} \sqrt{x^2 + z^2} \, dy \right] dA = \iint\limits_{D_3} (4 - x^2 - z^2)\sqrt{x^2 + z^2} \, dA$$

Although this integral could be written as

$$\int_{-2}^{2} \int_{-\sqrt{4-x^2}}^{\sqrt{4-x^2}} (4 - x^2 - z^2)\sqrt{x^2 + z^2} \, dz \, dx$$

it's easier to convert to polar coordinates in the xz-plane: $x = r\cos\theta, z = r\sin\theta$. This gives

$$\iiint\limits_E \sqrt{x^2 + z^2} \, dV = \iint\limits_{D_3} (4 - x^2 - z^2)\sqrt{x^2 + z^2} \, dA$$

$$= \int_0^{2\pi} \int_0^2 (4 - r^2) r \, r \, dr \, d\theta = \int_0^{2\pi} d\theta \int_0^2 (4r^2 - r^4) \, dr$$

$$= 2\pi \left[\frac{4r^3}{3} - \frac{r^5}{5} \right]_0^2 = \frac{128\pi}{15}$$

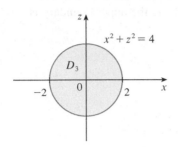

FIGURE 11
Projection onto xz-plane

⊘ The most difficult step in evaluating a triple integral is setting up an expression for the region of integration (such as Equation 9 in Example 2). Remember that the limits of integration in the inner integral contain at most two variables, the limits of integration in the middle integral contain at most one variable, and the limits of integration in the outer integral must be constants.

Applications of Triple Integrals

Recall that if $f(x) \geqslant 0$, then the single integral $\int_a^b f(x) \, dx$ represents the area under the curve $y = f(x)$ from a to b, and if $f(x, y) \geqslant 0$, then the double integral $\iint_D f(x, y) \, dA$ represents the volume under the surface $z = f(x, y)$ and above D. The corresponding interpretation of a triple integral $\iiint_E f(x, y, z) \, dV$, where $f(x, y, z) \geqslant 0$, is not very useful because it would be the "hypervolume" of a four-dimensional object and, of course, that is very difficult to visualize. (Remember that E is just the *domain* of the function f; the graph of f lies in four-dimensional space.) Nonetheless, the triple integral $\iiint_E f(x, y, z) \, dV$ can be interpreted in different ways in different physical situations, depending on the physical interpretations of x, y, z, and $f(x, y, z)$.

Let's begin with the special case where $f(x, y, z) = 1$ for all points in E. Then the triple integral does represent the volume of E:

12

$$V(E) = \iiint\limits_E dV$$

For example, you can see this in the case of a type 1 region by putting $f(x, y, z) = 1$ in Formula 6:

$$\iiint\limits_E 1 \, dV = \iint\limits_D \left[\int_{u_1(x, y)}^{u_2(x, y)} dz \right] dA = \iint\limits_D [u_2(x, y) - u_1(x, y)] \, dA$$

and from Section 12.3 we know this represents the volume that lies between the surfaces $z = u_1(x, y)$ and $z = u_2(x, y)$.

EXAMPLE 4   Use a triple integral to find the volume of the tetrahedron T bounded by the planes $x + 2y + z = 2$, $x = 2y$, $x = 0$, and $z = 0$.

SOLUTION   The tetrahedron T and its projection D onto the xy-plane are shown in Figures 12 and 13. The lower boundary of T is the plane $z = 0$ and the upper boundary is the plane $x + 2y + z = 2$, that is, $z = 2 - x - 2y$.

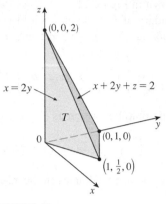

FIGURE 12   **FIGURE 13**

Therefore we have

$$V(T) = \iiint_T dV = \int_0^1 \int_{x/2}^{1-x/2} \int_0^{2-x-2y} dz\, dy\, dx$$

$$= \int_0^1 \int_{x/2}^{1-x/2} (2 - x - 2y)\, dy\, dx = \tfrac{1}{3}$$

by the same calculation as in Example 4 in Section 12.3.

(Notice that it is not necessary to use triple integrals to compute volumes. They simply give an alternative method for setting up the calculation.)

All the applications of double integrals in Section 12.5 can be immediately extended to triple integrals. For example, if the density function of a solid object that occupies the region E is $\rho(x, y, z)$, in units of mass per unit volume, at any given point (x, y, z), then its **mass** is

$$\boxed{13} \qquad\qquad m = \iiint_E \rho(x, y, z)\, dV$$

and its **moments** about the three coordinate planes are

$$\boxed{14} \qquad M_{yz} = \iiint_E x\rho(x, y, z)\, dV \qquad M_{xz} = \iiint_E y\rho(x, y, z)\, dV$$

$$M_{xy} = \iiint_E z\rho(x, y, z)\, dV$$

The **center of mass** is located at the point $(\bar{x}, \bar{y}, \bar{z})$, where

$$\boxed{15} \qquad\qquad \bar{x} = \frac{M_{yz}}{m} \qquad \bar{y} = \frac{M_{xz}}{m} \qquad \bar{z} = \frac{M_{xy}}{m}$$

If the density is constant, the center of mass of the solid is called the **centroid** of E. The **moments of inertia** about the three coordinate axes are

$$\boxed{16} \quad I_x = \iiint\limits_E (y^2 + z^2)\,\rho(x, y, z)\, dV \qquad I_y = \iiint\limits_E (x^2 + z^2)\,\rho(x, y, z)\, dV$$

$$I_z = \iiint\limits_E (x^2 + y^2)\,\rho(x, y, z)\, dV$$

As in Section 12.5, the total **electric charge** on a solid object occupying a region E and having charge density $\sigma(x, y, z)$ is

$$Q = \iiint\limits_E \sigma(x, y, z)\, dV$$

If we have three continuous random variables X, Y, and Z, their **joint density function** is a function of three variables such that the probability that (X, Y, Z) lies in E is

$$P((X, Y, Z) \in E) = \iiint\limits_E f(x, y, z)\, dV$$

In particular,

$$P(a \le X \le b, \ c \le Y \le d, \ r \le Z \le s) = \int_a^b \int_c^d \int_r^s f(x, y, z)\, dz\, dy\, dx$$

The joint density function satisfies

$$f(x, y, z) \ge 0 \qquad \int_{-\infty}^{\infty} \int_{-\infty}^{\infty} \int_{-\infty}^{\infty} f(x, y, z)\, dz\, dy\, dx = 1$$

▣ EXAMPLE 5 Find the center of mass of a solid of constant density that is bounded by the parabolic cylinder $x = y^2$ and the planes $x = z$, $z = 0$, and $x = 1$.

SOLUTION The solid E and its projection onto the xy-plane are shown in Figure 14. The lower and upper surfaces of E are the planes $z = 0$ and $z = x$, so we describe E as a type 1 region:

$$E = \{(x, y, z) \mid -1 \le y \le 1, \ y^2 \le x \le 1, \ 0 \le z \le x\}$$

Then, if the density is $\rho(x, y, z) = \rho$, the mass is

$$m = \iiint\limits_E \rho\, dV = \int_{-1}^{1} \int_{y^2}^{1} \int_0^x \rho\, dz\, dx\, dy$$

$$= \rho \int_{-1}^{1} \int_{y^2}^{1} x\, dx\, dy = \rho \int_{-1}^{1} \left[\frac{x^2}{2} \right]_{x=y^2}^{x=1} dy$$

$$= \frac{\rho}{2} \int_{-1}^{1} (1 - y^4)\, dy = \rho \int_0^1 (1 - y^4)\, dy$$

$$= \rho \left[y - \frac{y^5}{5} \right]_0^1 = \frac{4\rho}{5}$$

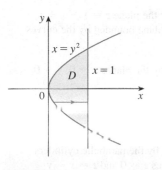

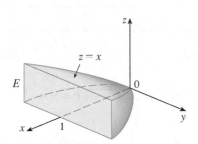

FIGURE 14

Because of the symmetry of E and ρ about the xz-plane, we can immediately say that $M_{xz} = 0$ and therefore $\bar{y} = 0$. The other moments are

$$M_{yz} = \iiint_E x\rho \, dV = \int_{-1}^{1} \int_{y^2}^{1} \int_{0}^{x} x\rho \, dz \, dx \, dy$$

$$= \rho \int_{-1}^{1} \int_{y^2}^{1} x^2 \, dx \, dy = \rho \int_{-1}^{1} \left[\frac{x^3}{3} \right]_{x=y^2}^{x=1} dy$$

$$= \frac{2\rho}{3} \int_{0}^{1} (1 - y^6) \, dy = \frac{2\rho}{3} \left[y - \frac{y^7}{7} \right]_{0}^{1} = \frac{4\rho}{7}$$

$$M_{xy} = \iiint_E z\rho \, dV = \int_{-1}^{1} \int_{y^2}^{1} \int_{0}^{x} z\rho \, dz \, dx \, dy$$

$$= \rho \int_{-1}^{1} \int_{y^2}^{1} \left[\frac{z^2}{2} \right]_{z=0}^{z=x} dx \, dy = \frac{\rho}{2} \int_{-1}^{1} \int_{y^2}^{1} x^2 \, dx \, dy$$

$$= \frac{\rho}{3} \int_{0}^{1} (1 - y^6) \, dy = \frac{2\rho}{7}$$

Therefore the center of mass is

$$(\bar{x}, \bar{y}, \bar{z}) = \left(\frac{M_{yz}}{m}, \frac{M_{xz}}{m}, \frac{M_{xy}}{m} \right) = \left(\tfrac{5}{7}, 0, \tfrac{5}{14} \right)$$

12.7 Exercises

1. Evaluate the integral in Example 1, integrating first with respect to y, then z, and then x.

2. Evaluate the integral $\iiint_E (xz - y^3) \, dV$, where

   $$E = \{(x, y, z) \mid -1 \le x \le 1, \, 0 \le y \le 2, \, 0 \le z \le 1\}$$

   using three different orders of integration.

3–8 Evaluate the iterated integral.

3. $\int_{0}^{1} \int_{0}^{z} \int_{0}^{x+z} 6xz \, dy \, dx \, dz$

4. $\int_{0}^{1} \int_{x}^{2x} \int_{0}^{y} 2xyz \, dz \, dy \, dx$

5. $\int_{0}^{3} \int_{0}^{1} \int_{0}^{\sqrt{1-z^2}} ze^{y} \, dx \, dz \, dy$

6. $\int_{0}^{1} \int_{0}^{z} \int_{0}^{y} ze^{-y^2} \, dx \, dy \, dz$

7. $\int_{0}^{\pi/2} \int_{0}^{y} \int_{0}^{x} \cos(x + y + z) \, dz \, dx \, dy$

8. $\int_{0}^{\sqrt{\pi}} \int_{0}^{x} \int_{0}^{xz} x^2 \sin y \, dy \, dz \, dx$

9–18 Evaluate the triple integral.

9. $\iiint_E 2x \, dV$, where

   $$E = \{(x, y, z) \mid 0 \le y \le 2, \, 0 \le x \le \sqrt{4 - y^2}, \, 0 \le z \le y\}$$

10. $\iiint_E yz \cos(x^5) \, dV$, where

    $$E = \{(x, y, z) \mid 0 \le x \le 1, \, 0 \le y \le x, \, x \le z \le 2x\}$$

11. $\iiint_E 6xy \, dV$, where E lies under the plane $z = 1 + x + y$ and above the region in the xy-plane bounded by the curves $y = \sqrt{x}$, $y = 0$, and $x = 1$

12. $\iiint_E y \, dV$, where E is bounded by the planes $x = 0$, $y = 0$, $z = 0$, and $2x + 2y + z = 4$

13. $\iiint_E x^2 e^{y} \, dV$, where E is bounded by the parabolic cylinder $z = 1 - y^2$ and the planes $z = 0$, $x = 1$, and $x = -1$

14. $\iiint_E xy \, dV$, where E is bounded by the parabolic cylinders $y = x^2$ and $x = y^2$ and the planes $z = 0$ and $z = x + y$

CAS Computer algebra system required   **1.** Homework Hints available in TEC

15. $\iiint_T x^2 \, dV$, where T is the solid tetrahedron with vertices $(0, 0, 0)$, $(1, 0, 0)$, $(0, 1, 0)$, and $(0, 0, 1)$

16. $\iiint_T xyz \, dV$, where T is the solid tetrahedron with vertices $(0, 0, 0)$, $(1, 0, 0)$, $(1, 1, 0)$, and $(1, 0, 1)$

17. $\iiint_E x \, dV$, where E is bounded by the paraboloid $x = 4y^2 + 4z^2$ and the plane $x = 4$

18. $\iiint_E z \, dV$, where E is bounded by the cylinder $y^2 + z^2 = 9$ and the planes $x = 0$, $y = 3x$, and $z = 0$ in the first octant

---

19–22 Use a triple integral to find the volume of the given solid.

19. The tetrahedron enclosed by the coordinate planes and the plane $2x + y + z = 4$

20. The solid bounded by the cylinder $y = x^2$ and the planes $z = 0$, $z = 4$, and $y = 9$

21. The solid enclosed by the cylinder $x^2 + y^2 = 9$ and the planes $y + z = 5$ and $z = 1$

22. The solid enclosed by the paraboloid $x = y^2 + z^2$ and the plane $x = 16$

---

23. (a) Express the volume of the wedge in the first octant that is cut from the cylinder $y^2 + z^2 = 1$ by the planes $y = x$ and $x = 1$ as a triple integral.

CAS (b) Use either the Table of Integrals (on Reference Pages 6–10) or a computer algebra system to find the exact value of the triple integral in part (a).

24. (a) In the **Midpoint Rule for triple integrals** we use a triple Riemann sum to approximate a triple integral over a box B, where $f(x, y, z)$ is evaluated at the center $(\bar{x}_i, \bar{y}_j, \bar{z}_k)$ of the box B_{ijk}. Use the Midpoint Rule to estimate $\iiint_B \sqrt{x^2 + y^2 + z^2} \, dV$, where B is the cube defined by $0 \le x \le 4$, $0 \le y \le 4$, $0 \le z \le 4$. Divide B into eight cubes of equal size.

CAS (b) Use a computer algebra system to approximate the integral in part (a) correct to the nearest integer. Compare with the answer to part (a).

25–26 Use the Midpoint Rule for triple integrals (Exercise 24) to estimate the value of the integral. Divide B into eight sub-boxes of equal size.

25. $\iiint_B \dfrac{1}{\ln(1 + x + y + z)} \, dV$, where
$B = \{(x, y, z) \mid 0 \le x \le 4,\ 0 \le y \le 8,\ 0 \le z \le 4\}$

26. $\iiint_B \sin(xy^2z^3) \, dV$, where
$B = \{(x, y, z) \mid 0 \le x \le 4,\ 0 \le y \le 2,\ 0 \le z \le 1\}$

27–28 Sketch the solid whose volume is given by the iterated integral.

27. $\displaystyle\int_0^1 \int_0^{1-x} \int_0^{2-2z} dy \, dz \, dx$

28. $\displaystyle\int_0^2 \int_0^{2-y} \int_0^{4-y^2} dx \, dz \, dy$

29–32 Express the integral $\iiint_E f(x, y, z) \, dV$ as an iterated integral in six different ways, where E is the solid bounded by the given surfaces.

29. $y = 4 - x^2 - 4z^2$, $y = 0$

30. $y^2 + z^2 = 9$, $x = -2$, $x = 2$

31. $y = x^2$, $z = 0$, $y + 2z = 4$

32. $x = 2$, $y = 2$, $z = 0$, $x + y - 2z = 2$

---

33. The figure shows the region of integration for the integral

$$\int_0^1 \int_{\sqrt{x}}^1 \int_0^{1-y} f(x, y, z) \, dz \, dy \, dx$$

Rewrite this integral as an equivalent iterated integral in the five other orders.

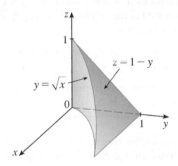

34. The figure shows the region of integration for the integral

$$\int_0^1 \int_0^{1-x^2} \int_0^{1-x} f(x, y, z) \, dy \, dz \, dx$$

Rewrite this integral as an equivalent iterated integral in the five other orders.

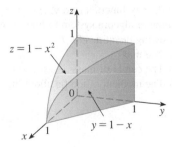

35–36 Write five other iterated integrals that are equal to the given iterated integral.

35. $\displaystyle\int_0^1 \int_y^1 \int_0^y f(x, y, z) \, dz \, dx \, dy$

36. $\displaystyle\int_0^1 \int_0^{x^2} \int_0^y f(x, y, z) \, dz \, dy \, dx$

37–40 Find the mass and center of mass of the solid E with the given density function ρ.

37. E is the solid of Exercise 11; $\rho(x, y, z) = 2$

38. E is bounded by the parabolic cylinder $z = 1 - y^2$ and the planes $x + z = 1$, $x = 0$, and $z = 0$; $\rho(x, y, z) = 4$

39. E is the cube given by $0 \leqslant x \leqslant a$, $0 \leqslant y \leqslant a$, $0 \leqslant z \leqslant a$; $\rho(x, y, z) = x^2 + y^2 + z^2$

40. E is the tetrahedron bounded by the planes $x = 0$, $y = 0$, $z = 0$, $x + y + z = 1$; $\rho(x, y, z) = y$

41–44 Assume that the solid has constant density k.

41. Find the moments of inertia for a cube with side length L if one vertex is located at the origin and three edges lie along the coordinate axes.

42. Find the moments of inertia for a rectangular brick with dimensions a, b, and c and mass M if the center of the brick is situated at the origin and the edges are parallel to the coordinate axes.

43. Find the moment of inertia about the z-axis of the solid cylinder $x^2 + y^2 \leqslant a^2$, $0 \leqslant z \leqslant h$.

44. Find the moment of inertia about the z-axis of the solid cone $\sqrt{x^2 + y^2} \leqslant z \leqslant h$.

45–46 Set up, but do not evaluate, integral expressions for (a) the mass, (b) the center of mass, and (c) the moment of inertia about the z-axis.

45. The solid of Exercise 21; $\rho(x, y, z) = \sqrt{x^2 + y^2}$

46. The hemisphere $x^2 + y^2 + z^2 \leqslant 1$, $z \geqslant 0$;
$\rho(x, y, z) = \sqrt{x^2 + y^2 + z^2}$

CAS **47.** Let E be the solid in the first octant bounded by the cylinder $x^2 + y^2 = 1$ and the planes $y = z$, $x = 0$, and $z = 0$ with the density function $\rho(x, y, z) = 1 + x + y + z$. Use a computer algebra system to find the exact values of the following quantities for E.
(a) The mass
(b) The center of mass
(c) The moment of inertia about the z-axis

CAS **48.** If E is the solid of Exercise 18 with density function $\rho(x, y, z) = x^2 + y^2$, find the following quantities, correct to three decimal places.
(a) The mass
(b) The center of mass
(c) The moment of inertia about the z-axis

49. The joint density function for random variables X, Y, and Z is $f(x, y, z) = Cxyz$ if $0 \leqslant x \leqslant 2$, $0 \leqslant y \leqslant 2$, $0 \leqslant z \leqslant 2$, and $f(x, y, z) = 0$ otherwise.
(a) Find the value of the constant C.
(b) Find $P(X \leqslant 1, Y \leqslant 1, Z \leqslant 1)$.
(c) Find $P(X + Y + Z \leqslant 1)$.

50. Suppose X, Y, and Z are random variables with joint density function $f(x, y, z) = Ce^{-(0.5x+0.2y+0.1z)}$ if $x \geqslant 0$, $y \geqslant 0$, $z \geqslant 0$, and $f(x, y, z) = 0$ otherwise.
(a) Find the value of the constant C.
(b) Find $P(X \leqslant 1, Y \leqslant 1)$.
(c) Find $P(X \leqslant 1, Y \leqslant 1, Z \leqslant 1)$.

51–52 The **average value** of a function $f(x, y, z)$ over a solid region E is defined to be

$$f_{\text{ave}} = \frac{1}{V(E)} \iiint\limits_{E} f(x, y, z) \, dV$$

where $V(E)$ is the volume of E. For instance, if ρ is a density function, then ρ_{ave} is the average density of E.

51. Find the average value of the function $f(x, y, z) = xyz$ over the cube with side length L that lies in the first octant with one vertex at the origin and edges parallel to the coordinate axes.

52. Find the average value of the function $f(x, y, z) = x^2z + y^2z$ over the region enclosed by the paraboloid $z = 1 - x^2 - y^2$ and the plane $z = 0$.

---

53. (a) Find the region E for which the triple integral

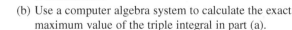
$$\iiint\limits_{E} (1 - x^2 - 2y^2 - 3z^2) \, dV$$

is a maximum.

CAS (b) Use a computer algebra system to calculate the exact maximum value of the triple integral in part (a).

DISCOVERY PROJECT	**Volumes of Hyperspheres**

In this project we find formulas for the volume enclosed by a hypersphere in n-dimensional space.

1. Use a double integral and the trigonometric substitution $y = r \sin \theta$, together with Formula 64 in the Table of Integrals, to find the area of a circle with radius r.

2. Use a triple integral and trigonometric substitution to find the volume of a sphere with radius r.

3. Use a quadruple integral to find the hypervolume enclosed by the hypersphere $x^2 + y^2 + z^2 + w^2 = r^2$ in $\mathbb{R}^4$. (Use only trigonometric substitution and the reduction formulas for $\int \sin^n x \, dx$ or $\int \cos^n x \, dx$.)

4. Use an n-tuple integral to find the volume enclosed by a hypersphere of radius r in n-dimensional space $\mathbb{R}^n$.   [*Hint:* The formulas are different for n even and n odd.]

12.8 Triple Integrals in Cylindrical and Spherical Coordinates

We saw in Section 12.4 that some double integrals are easier to evaluate using polar coordinates. In this section we see that some triple integrals are easier to evaluate using cylindrical or spherical coordinates.

Cylindrical Coordinates

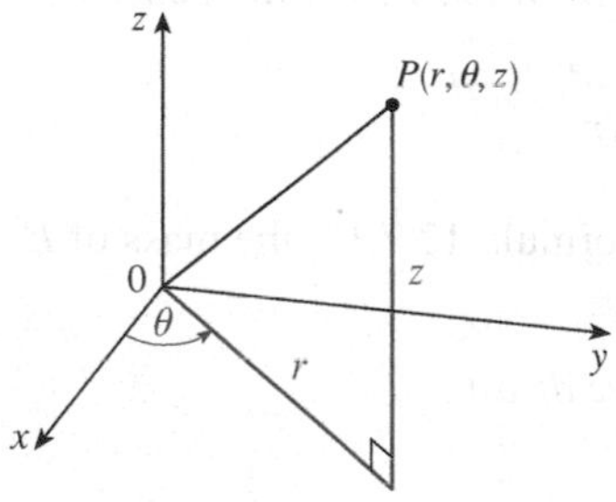

Recall from Section 9.7 that the cylindrical coordinates of a point P are (r, θ, z), where r, θ, and z are shown in Figure 1. Suppose that E is a type 1 region whose projection D onto the xy-plane is conveniently described in polar coordinates (see Figure 2). In particular, suppose that f is continuous and

$$E = \left\{ (x, y, z) \mid (x, y) \in D, \ u_1(x, y) \leqslant z \leqslant u_2(x, y) \right\}$$

where D is given in polar coordinates by

$$D = \left\{ (r, \theta) \mid \alpha \leqslant \theta \leqslant \beta, \ h_1(\theta) \leqslant r \leqslant h_2(\theta) \right\}$$

FIGURE 1

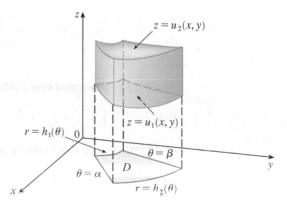

FIGURE 2

We know from Equation 12.7.6 that

$$\boxed{1} \qquad \iiint_E f(x, y, z) \, dV = \iint_D \left[\int_{u_1(x, y)}^{u_2(x, y)} f(x, y, z) \, dz \right] dA$$

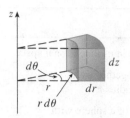

FIGURE 3
Volume element in cylindrical
coordinates: $dV = r\,dz\,dr\,d\theta$

But we also know how to evaluate double integrals in polar coordinates. In fact, combining Equation 1 with Equation 12.4.3, we obtain

$$\boxed{2} \quad \iiint\limits_E f(x, y, z)\,dV = \int_\alpha^\beta \int_{h_1(\theta)}^{h_2(\theta)} \int_{u_1(r\cos\theta,\, r\sin\theta)}^{u_2(r\cos\theta,\, r\sin\theta)} f(r\cos\theta, r\sin\theta, z)\, r\,dz\,dr\,d\theta$$

Formula 2 is the **formula for triple integration in cylindrical coordinates**. It says that we convert a triple integral from rectangular to cylindrical coordinates by writing $x = r\cos\theta$, $y = r\sin\theta$, leaving z as it is, using the appropriate limits of integration for z, r, and θ, and replacing dV by $r\,dz\,dr\,d\theta$. (Figure 3 shows how to remember this.) It is worthwhile to use this formula when E is a solid region easily described in cylindrical coordinates, and especially when the function $f(x, y, z)$ involves the expression $x^2 + y^2$.

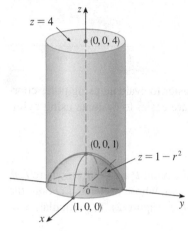

FIGURE 4

V EXAMPLE 1 **Finding mass with cylindrical coordinates**   A solid E lies within the cylinder $x^2 + y^2 = 1$, below the plane $z = 4$, and above the paraboloid $z = 1 - x^2 - y^2$. (See Figure 4.) The density at any point is proportional to its distance from the axis of the cylinder. Find the mass of E.

SOLUTION In cylindrical coordinates the cylinder is $r = 1$ and the paraboloid is $z = 1 - r^2$, so we can write

$$E = \left\{(r, \theta, z) \mid 0 \le \theta \le 2\pi,\ 0 \le r \le 1,\ 1 - r^2 \le z \le 4\right\}$$

Since the density at (x, y, z) is proportional to the distance from the z-axis, the density function is

$$f(x, y, z) = K\sqrt{x^2 + y^2} = Kr$$

where K is the proportionality constant. Therefore, from Formula 12.7.13, the mass of E is

$$m = \iiint\limits_E K\sqrt{x^2 + y^2}\,dV = \int_0^{2\pi} \int_0^1 \int_{1-r^2}^4 (Kr)\, r\,dz\,dr\,d\theta$$

$$= \int_0^{2\pi} \int_0^1 Kr^2[4 - (1 - r^2)]\,dr\,d\theta = K\int_0^{2\pi} d\theta \int_0^1 (3r^2 + r^4)\,dr$$

$$= 2\pi K \left[r^3 + \frac{r^5}{5} \right]_0^1 = \frac{12\pi K}{5}$$

EXAMPLE 2   **Integrating over a solid best described in cylindrical coordinates**

Evaluate $\displaystyle\int_{-2}^2 \int_{-\sqrt{4-x^2}}^{\sqrt{4-x^2}} \int_{\sqrt{x^2+y^2}}^2 (x^2 + y^2)\,dz\,dy\,dx$.

SOLUTION This iterated integral is a triple integral over the solid region

$$E = \left\{(x, y, z) \mid -2 \le x \le 2,\ -\sqrt{4 - x^2} \le y \le \sqrt{4 - x^2},\ \sqrt{x^2 + y^2} \le z \le 2\right\}$$

and the projection of E onto the xy-plane is the disk $x^2 + y^2 \le 4$. The lower surface of E is the cone $z = \sqrt{x^2 + y^2}$ and its upper surface is the plane $z = 2$. (See Figure 5.) This region has a much simpler description in cylindrical coordinates:

$$E = \left\{(r, \theta, z) \mid 0 \le \theta \le 2\pi,\ 0 \le r \le 2,\ r \le z \le 2\right\}$$

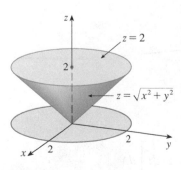

FIGURE 5

Therefore we have

$$\int_{-2}^{2}\int_{-\sqrt{4-x^2}}^{\sqrt{4-x^2}}\int_{\sqrt{x^2+y^2}}^{2}(x^2+y^2)\,dz\,dy\,dx=\iiint_{E}(x^2+y^2)\,dV$$

$$=\int_{0}^{2\pi}\int_{0}^{2}\int_{r}^{2}r^2\,r\,dz\,dr\,d\theta$$

$$=\int_{0}^{2\pi}d\theta\int_{0}^{2}r^3(2-r)\,dr$$

$$=2\pi\left[\tfrac{1}{2}r^4-\tfrac{1}{5}r^5\right]_{0}^{2}=\tfrac{16}{5}\pi$$

Spherical Coordinates

In Section 9.7 we defined the spherical coordinates (ρ,θ,ϕ) of a point (see Figure 6) and we demonstrated the following relationships between rectangular coordinates and spherical coordinates:

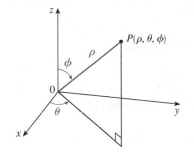

FIGURE 6
Spherical coordinates of P

$$\boxed{3}\qquad x=\rho\sin\phi\cos\theta\qquad y=\rho\sin\phi\sin\theta\qquad z=\rho\cos\phi$$

In this coordinate system the counterpart of a rectangular box is a **spherical wedge**

$$E=\left\{(\rho,\theta,\phi)\mid a\le\rho\le b,\ \alpha\le\theta\le\beta,\ c\le\phi\le d\right\}$$

where $a\ge0$ and $\beta-\alpha\le2\pi$, and $d-c\le\pi$. Although we defined triple integrals by dividing solids into small boxes, it can be shown that dividing a solid into small spherical wedges always gives the same result. So we divide E into smaller spherical wedges E_{ijk} by means of equally spaced spheres $\rho=\rho_i$, half-planes $\theta=\theta_j$, and half-cones $\phi=\phi_k$. Figure 7 shows that E_{ijk} is approximately a rectangular box with dimensions $\Delta\rho$, $\rho_i\,\Delta\phi$ (arc of a circle with radius ρ_i, angle $\Delta\phi$), and $\rho_i\sin\phi_k\,\Delta\theta$ (arc of a circle with radius $\rho_i\sin\phi_k$, angle $\Delta\theta$). So an approximation to the volume of E_{ijk} is given by

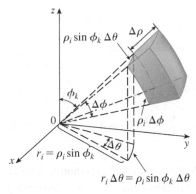

FIGURE 7

$$(\Delta\rho)\times(\rho_i\,\Delta\phi)\times(\rho_i\sin\phi_k\,\Delta\theta)=\rho_i^2\sin\phi_k\,\Delta\rho\,\Delta\theta\,\Delta\phi$$

Thus an approximation to a typical triple Riemann sum is

$$\sum_{i=1}^{l}\sum_{j=1}^{m}\sum_{k=1}^{n}f(\rho_i\sin\phi_k\cos\theta_j,\ \rho_i\sin\phi_k\sin\theta_j,\ \rho_i\cos\phi_k)\,\rho_i^2\sin\phi_k\,\Delta\rho\,\Delta\theta\,\Delta\phi$$

But this sum is a Riemann sum for the function

$$F(\rho,\theta,\phi)=f(\rho\sin\phi\cos\theta,\ \rho\sin\phi\sin\theta,\ \rho\cos\phi)\cdot\rho^2\sin\phi$$

Consequently, the following **formula for triple integration in spherical coordinates** is plausible.

$$\boxed{4}\quad\iiint_{E}f(x,y,z)\,dV$$

$$=\int_{c}^{d}\int_{\alpha}^{\beta}\int_{a}^{b}f(\rho\sin\phi\cos\theta,\ \rho\sin\phi\sin\theta,\ \rho\cos\phi)\,\rho^2\sin\phi\,d\rho\,d\theta\,d\phi$$

where E is a spherical wedge given by

$$E=\left\{(\rho,\theta,\phi)\mid a\le\rho\le b,\ \alpha\le\theta\le\beta,\ c\le\phi\le d\right\}$$

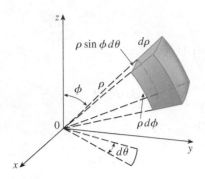

FIGURE 8

Volume element in spherical
coordinates: $dV = \rho^2 \sin \phi \, d\rho \, d\theta \, d\phi$

Formula 4 says that we convert a triple integral from rectangular coordinates to spherical coordinates by writing

$$x = \rho \sin \phi \cos \theta \qquad y = \rho \sin \phi \sin \theta \qquad z = \rho \cos \phi$$

using the appropriate limits of integration, and replacing dV by $\rho^2 \sin \phi \, d\rho \, d\theta \, d\phi$. This is illustrated in Figure 8.

This formula can be extended to include more general spherical regions such as

$$E = \left\{(\rho, \theta, \phi) \mid \alpha \leq \theta \leq \beta, \; c \leq \phi \leq d, \; g_1(\theta, \phi) \leq \rho \leq g_2(\theta, \phi)\right\}$$

In this case the formula is the same as in (4) except that the limits of integration for ρ are $g_1(\theta, \phi)$ and $g_2(\theta, \phi)$.

Usually, spherical coordinates are used in triple integrals when surfaces such as cones and spheres form the boundary of the region of integration.

▼ EXAMPLE 3 Evaluate $\iiint_B e^{(x^2+y^2+z^2)^{3/2}} \, dV$, where B is the unit ball:

$$B = \left\{(x, y, z) \mid x^2 + y^2 + z^2 \leq 1\right\}$$

SOLUTION Since the boundary of B is a sphere, we use spherical coordinates:

$$B = \left\{(\rho, \theta, \phi) \mid 0 \leq \rho \leq 1, \; 0 \leq \theta \leq 2\pi, \; 0 \leq \phi \leq \pi\right\}$$

In addition, spherical coordinates are appropriate because

$$x^2 + y^2 + z^2 = \rho^2$$

Thus (4) gives

$$\iiint_B e^{(x^2+y^2+z^2)^{3/2}} \, dV = \int_0^\pi \int_0^{2\pi} \int_0^1 e^{(\rho^2)^{3/2}} \rho^2 \sin \phi \, d\rho \, d\theta \, d\phi$$

$$= \int_0^\pi \sin \phi \, d\phi \int_0^{2\pi} d\theta \int_0^1 \rho^2 e^{\rho^3} \, d\rho$$

$$= \left[-\cos \phi\right]_0^\pi (2\pi) \left[\tfrac{1}{3}e^{\rho^3}\right]_0^1 = \tfrac{4}{3}\pi(e - 1)$$

Note: It would have been extremely awkward to evaluate the integral in Example 3 without spherical coordinates. In rectangular coordinates the iterated integral would have been

$$\int_{-1}^1 \int_{-\sqrt{1-x^2}}^{\sqrt{1-x^2}} \int_{-\sqrt{1-x^2-y^2}}^{\sqrt{1-x^2-y^2}} e^{(x^2+y^2+z^2)^{3/2}} \, dz \, dy \, dx$$

▼ EXAMPLE 4 A volume that is easier in spherical coordinates Use spherical coordinates to find the volume of the solid that lies above the cone $z = \sqrt{x^2 + y^2}$ and below the sphere $x^2 + y^2 + z^2 = z$. (See Figure 9.)

SOLUTION Notice that the sphere passes through the origin and has center $\left(0, 0, \tfrac{1}{2}\right)$. We write the equation of the sphere in spherical coordinates as

$$\rho^2 = \rho \cos \phi \qquad \text{or} \qquad \rho = \cos \phi$$

The equation of the cone can be written as

$$\rho \cos \phi = \sqrt{\rho^2 \sin^2\phi \, \cos^2\theta + \rho^2 \sin^2\phi \, \sin^2\theta} = \rho \sin \phi$$

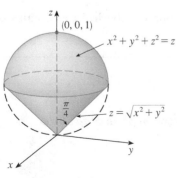

FIGURE 9

Figure 10 gives another look (this time drawn by Maple) at the solid of Example 4.

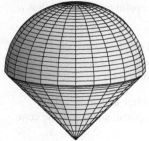

FIGURE 10

TEC Visual 12.8 shows an animation of Figure 11.

This gives $\sin \phi = \cos \phi$, or $\phi = \pi/4$. Therefore the description of the solid E in spherical coordinates is

$$E = \{(\rho, \theta, \phi) \mid 0 \le \theta \le 2\pi, \ 0 \le \phi \le \pi/4, \ 0 \le \rho \le \cos \phi\}$$

Figure 11 shows how E is swept out if we integrate first with respect to ρ, then ϕ, and then θ. The volume of E is

$$V(E) = \iiint\limits_{E} dV = \int_0^{2\pi} \int_0^{\pi/4} \int_0^{\cos \phi} \rho^2 \sin \phi \, d\rho \, d\phi \, d\theta$$

$$= \int_0^{2\pi} d\theta \int_0^{\pi/4} \sin \phi \left[\frac{\rho^3}{3}\right]_{\rho=0}^{\rho=\cos \phi} d\phi$$

$$= \frac{2\pi}{3} \int_0^{\pi/4} \sin \phi \cos^3 \phi \, d\phi = \frac{2\pi}{3} \left[-\frac{\cos^4 \phi}{4}\right]_0^{\pi/4} = \frac{\pi}{8}$$

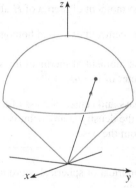

ρ varies from 0 to $\cos \phi$ while ϕ and θ are constant.

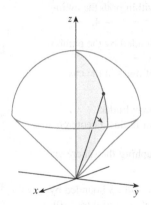

ϕ varies from 0 to $\pi/4$ while θ is constant.

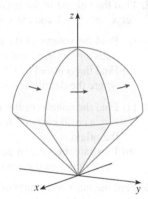

θ varies from 0 to 2π.

FIGURE 11

12.8 Exercises

1–4 Sketch the solid whose volume is given by the integral and evaluate the integral.

1. $\int_0^4 \int_0^{2\pi} \int_r^4 r \, dz \, d\theta \, dr$

2. $\int_0^{\pi/2} \int_0^2 \int_0^{9-r^2} r \, dz \, dr \, d\theta$

3. $\int_0^{\pi/6} \int_0^{\pi/2} \int_0^3 \rho^2 \sin \phi \, d\rho \, d\theta \, d\phi$

4. $\int_0^{2\pi} \int_{\pi/2}^{\pi} \int_1^2 \rho^2 \sin \phi \, d\rho \, d\phi \, d\theta$

5–6 Set up the triple integral of an arbitrary continuous function $f(x, y, z)$ in cylindrical or spherical coordinates over the solid shown.

5.

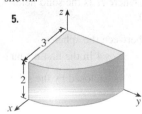

6.

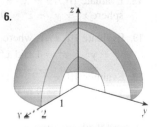

 Graphing calculator or computer with graphing software required [CAS] Computer algebra system required **1.** Homework Hints available in TEC

7–16 Use cylindrical coordinates.

7. Evaluate $\iiint_E \sqrt{x^2 + y^2}\, dV$, where E is the region that lies inside the cylinder $x^2 + y^2 = 16$ and between the planes $z = -5$ and $z = 4$.

8. Evaluate $\iiint_E (x^3 + xy^2)\, dV$, where E is the solid in the first octant that lies beneath the paraboloid $z = 1 - x^2 - y^2$.

9. Evaluate $\iiint_E e^z\, dV$, where E is enclosed by the paraboloid $z = 1 + x^2 + y^2$, the cylinder $x^2 + y^2 = 5$, and the xy-plane.

10. Evaluate $\iiint_E x\, dV$, where E is enclosed by the planes $z = 0$ and $z = x + y + 5$ and by the cylinders $x^2 + y^2 = 4$ and $x^2 + y^2 = 9$.

11. Evaluate $\iiint_E x^2\, dV$, where E is the solid that lies within the cylinder $x^2 + y^2 = 1$, above the plane $z = 0$, and below the cone $z^2 = 4x^2 + 4y^2$.

12. Find the volume of the solid that lies within both the cylinder $x^2 + y^2 = 1$ and the sphere $x^2 + y^2 + z^2 = 4$.

13. (a) Find the volume of the region E bounded by the paraboloids $z = x^2 + y^2$ and $z = 36 - 3x^2 - 3y^2$.
    (b) Find the centroid of E (the center of mass in the case where the density is constant).

14. (a) Find the volume of the solid that the cylinder $r = a \cos \theta$ cuts out of the sphere of radius a centered at the origin.
    (b) Illustrate the solid of part (a) by graphing the sphere and the cylinder on the same screen.

15. Find the mass and center of mass of the solid S bounded by the paraboloid $z = 4x^2 + 4y^2$ and the plane $z = a$ $(a > 0)$ if S has constant density K.

16. Find the mass of a ball B given by $x^2 + y^2 + z^2 \leq a^2$ if the density at any point is proportional to its distance from the z-axis.

17–30 Use spherical coordinates.

17. Evaluate $\iiint_B (x^2 + y^2 + z^2)^2\, dV$, where B is the ball with center the origin and radius 5.

18. Evaluate $\iiint_H (9 - x^2 - y^2)\, dV$, where H is the solid hemisphere $x^2 + y^2 + z^2 \leq 9$, $z \geq 0$.

19. Evaluate $\iiint_E z\, dV$, where E lies between the spheres $x^2 + y^2 + z^2 = 1$ and $x^2 + y^2 + z^2 = 4$ in the first octant.

20. Evaluate $\iiint_E e^{\sqrt{x^2+y^2+z^2}}\, dV$, where E is enclosed by the sphere $x^2 + y^2 + z^2 = 9$ in the first octant.

21. Evaluate $\iiint_E x^2\, dV$, where E is bounded by the xz-plane and the hemispheres $y = \sqrt{9 - x^2 - z^2}$ and $y = \sqrt{16 - x^2 - z^2}$.

22. Evaluate $\iiint_E xyz\, dV$, where E lies between the spheres $\rho = 2$ and $\rho = 4$ and above the cone $\phi = \pi/3$.

23. Find the volume of the part of the ball $\rho \leq a$ that lies between the cones $\phi = \pi/6$ and $\phi = \pi/3$.

24. Find the average distance from a point in a ball of radius a to its center.

25. (a) Find the volume of the solid that lies above the cone $\phi = \pi/3$ and below the sphere $\rho = 4 \cos \phi$.
    (b) Find the centroid of the solid in part (a).

26. Find the volume of the solid that lies within the sphere $x^2 + y^2 + z^2 = 4$, above the xy-plane, and below the cone $z = \sqrt{x^2 + y^2}$.

27. Find the centroid of the solid in Exercise 21.

28. Let H be a solid hemisphere of radius a whose density at any point is proportional to its distance from the center of the base.
    (a) Find the mass of H.
    (b) Find the center of mass of H.
    (c) Find the moment of inertia of H about its axis.

29. (a) Find the centroid of a solid homogeneous hemisphere of radius a.
    (b) Find the moment of inertia of the solid in part (a) about a diameter of its base.

30. Find the mass and center of mass of a solid hemisphere of radius a if the density at any point is proportional to its distance from the base.

31–34 Use cylindrical or spherical coordinates, whichever seems more appropriate.

31. Find the volume and centroid of the solid E that lies above the cone $z = \sqrt{x^2 + y^2}$ and below the sphere $x^2 + y^2 + z^2 = 1$.

32. Find the volume of the smaller wedge cut from a sphere of radius a by two planes that intersect along a diameter at an angle of $\pi/6$.

[CAS] **33.** Evaluate $\iiint_E z\, dV$, where E lies above the paraboloid $z = x^2 + y^2$ and below the plane $z = 2y$. Use either the Table of Integrals (on Reference Pages 6–10) or a computer algebra system to evaluate the integral.

34. (a) Find the volume enclosed by the torus $\rho = \sin \phi$.
    (b) Use a computer to draw the torus.

35–36 Evaluate the integral by changing to cylindrical coordinates.

35. $\displaystyle\int_{-2}^{2} \int_{-\sqrt{4-y^2}}^{\sqrt{4-y^2}} \int_{\sqrt{x^2+y^2}}^{2} xz\, dz\, dx\, dy$

36. $\displaystyle\int_{-3}^{3} \int_{0}^{\sqrt{9-x^2}} \int_{0}^{9-x^2-y^2} \sqrt{x^2 + y^2}\, dz\, dy\, dx$

37–38 Evaluate the integral by changing to spherical coordinates.

37. $\int_0^1 \int_0^{\sqrt{1-x^2}} \int_{\sqrt{x^2+y^2}}^{\sqrt{2-x^2-y^2}} xy \, dz \, dy \, dx$

38. $\int_{-a}^{a} \int_{-\sqrt{a^2-y^2}}^{\sqrt{a^2-y^2}} \int_{-\sqrt{a^2-x^2-y^2}}^{\sqrt{a^2-x^2-y^2}} (x^2z + y^2z + z^3) \, dz \, dx \, dy$

CAS **39.** In the Laboratory Project on page 687 we investigated the family of surfaces $\rho = 1 + \frac{1}{5} \sin m\theta \sin n\phi$ that have been used as models for tumors. The "bumpy sphere" with $m = 6$ and $n = 5$ is shown. Use a computer algebra system to find the volume it encloses.

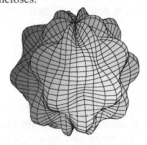

40. Show that

$$\int_{-\infty}^{\infty} \int_{-\infty}^{\infty} \int_{-\infty}^{\infty} \sqrt{x^2 + y^2 + z^2} \, e^{-(x^2+y^2+z^2)} \, dx \, dy \, dz = 2\pi$$

(The improper triple integral is defined as the limit of a triple integral over a solid sphere as the radius of the sphere increases indefinitely.)

41. When studying the formation of mountain ranges, geologists estimate the amount of work required to lift a mountain from sea level. Consider a mountain that is essentially in the shape of a right circular cone. Suppose that the weight density of the material in the vicinity of a point P is $g(P)$ and the height is $h(P)$.
(a) Find a definite integral that represents the total work done in forming the mountain.
(b) Assume that Mount Fuji in Japan is in the shape of a right circular cone with radius 62,000 ft, height 12,400 ft, and density a constant 200 lb/ft³. How much work was done in forming Mount Fuji if the land was initially at sea level?

APPLIED PROJECT

Roller Derby

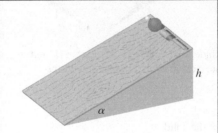

Suppose that a solid ball (a marble), a hollow ball (a squash ball), a solid cylinder (a steel bar), and a hollow cylinder (a lead pipe) roll down a slope. Which of these objects reaches the bottom first? (Make a guess before proceeding.)

To answer this question, we consider a ball or cylinder with mass m, radius r, and moment of inertia I (about the axis of rotation). If the vertical drop is h, then the potential energy at the top is mgh. Suppose the object reaches the bottom with velocity v and angular velocity ω, so $v = \omega r$. The kinetic energy at the bottom consists of two parts: $\frac{1}{2}mv^2$ from translation (moving down the slope) and $\frac{1}{2}I\omega^2$ from rotation. If we assume that energy loss from rolling friction is negligible, then conservation of energy gives

$$mgh = \tfrac{1}{2}mv^2 + \tfrac{1}{2}I\omega^2$$

1. Show that

$$v^2 = \frac{2gh}{1 + I^*} \qquad \text{where } I^* = \frac{I}{mr^2}$$

2. If $y(t)$ is the vertical distance traveled at time t, then the same reasoning as used in Problem 1 shows that $v^2 = 2gy/(1 + I^*)$ at any time t. Use this result to show that y satisfies the differential equation

$$\frac{dy}{dt} = \sqrt{\frac{2g}{1 + I^*}} \, (\sin \alpha) \sqrt{y}$$

where α is the angle of inclination of the plane.

3. By solving the differential equation in Problem 2, show that the total travel time is

$$T = \sqrt{\frac{2h(1 + I^*)}{g \sin^2\alpha}}$$

This shows that the object with the smallest value of I^* wins the race.

4. Show that $I^* = \frac{1}{2}$ for a solid cylinder and $I^* = 1$ for a hollow cylinder.

5. Calculate I^* for a partly hollow ball with inner radius a and outer radius r. Express your answer in terms of $b = a/r$. What happens as $a \to 0$ and as $a \to r$?

6. Show that $I^* = \frac{2}{5}$ for a solid ball and $I^* = \frac{2}{3}$ for a hollow ball. Thus the objects finish in the following order: solid ball, solid cylinder, hollow ball, hollow cylinder.

DISCOVERY PROJECT | **The Intersection of Three Cylinders**

The figure shows the solid enclosed by three circular cylinders with the same diameter that intersect at right angles. In this project we compute its volume and determine how its shape changes if the cylinders have different diameters.

1. Sketch carefully the solid enclosed by the three cylinders $x^2 + y^2 = 1$, $x^2 + z^2 = 1$, and $y^2 + z^2 = 1$. Indicate the positions of the coordinate axes and label the faces with the equations of the corresponding cylinders.

2. Find the volume of the solid in Problem 1.

CAS **3.** Use a computer algebra system to draw the edges of the solid.

4. What happens to the solid in Problem 1 if the radius of the first cylinder is different from 1? Illustrate with a hand-drawn sketch or a computer graph.

5. If the first cylinder is $x^2 + y^2 = a^2$, where $a < 1$, set up, but do not evaluate, a double integral for the volume of the solid. What if $a > 1$?

CAS Computer algebra system required

12.9 Change of Variables in Multiple Integrals

In one-dimensional calculus we often use a change of variable (a substitution) to simplify an integral. By reversing the roles of x and u, we can write the Substitution Rule (5.5.5) as

$$\boxed{1} \qquad \int_a^b f(x)\,dx = \int_c^d f(g(u))\,g'(u)\,du$$

where $x = g(u)$ and $a = g(c)$, $b = g(d)$. Another way of writing Formula 1 is as follows:

$$\boxed{2} \qquad \int_a^b f(x)\,dx = \int_c^d f(x(u))\,\frac{dx}{du}\,du$$

A change of variables can also be useful in double integrals. We have already seen one example of this: conversion to polar coordinates. The new variables r and θ are related to the old variables x and y by the equations

$$x = r\cos\theta \qquad y = r\sin\theta$$

and the change of variables formula (12.4.2) can be written as

$$\iint_R f(x, y)\,dA = \iint_S f(r\cos\theta, r\sin\theta)\,r\,dr\,d\theta$$

where S is the region in the $r\theta$-plane that corresponds to the region R in the xy-plane.

More generally, we consider a change of variables that is given by a **transformation** T from the uv-plane to the xy-plane:

$$T(u, v) = (x, y)$$

where x and y are related to u and v by the equations

$$\boxed{3} \qquad x = g(u, v) \qquad y = h(u, v)$$

or, as we sometimes write,

$$x = x(u, v) \qquad y = y(u, v)$$

We usually assume that T is a C^1 **transformation**, which means that g and h have continuous first-order partial derivatives.

A transformation T is really just a function whose domain and range are both subsets of $\mathbb{R}^2$. If $T(u_1, v_1) = (x_1, y_1)$, then the point (x_1, y_1) is called the **image** of the point (u_1, v_1). If no two points have the same image, T is called **one-to-one**. Figure 1 shows the effect of a transformation T on a region S in the uv-plane. T transforms S into a region R in the xy-plane called the **image of S**, consisting of the images of all points in S.

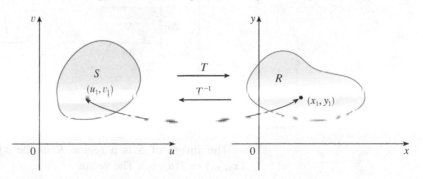

FIGURE 1

If T is a one-to-one transformation, then it has an **inverse transformation** T^{-1} from the xy-plane to the uv-plane and it may be possible to solve Equations 3 for u and v in terms of x and y:

$$u = G(x, y) \qquad v = H(x, y)$$

V **EXAMPLE 1** **Determining the image of a region under a transformation** A transformation is defined by the equations

$$x = u^2 - v^2 \qquad y = 2uv$$

Find the image of the square $S = \{(u, v) \mid 0 \le u \le 1, \ 0 \le v \le 1\}$.

SOLUTION The transformation maps the boundary of S into the boundary of the image. So we begin by finding the images of the sides of S. The first side, S_1, is given by $v = 0$ ($0 \le u \le 1$). (See Figure 2.) From the given equations we have $x = u^2$, $y = 0$, and so $0 \le x \le 1$. Thus S_1 is mapped into the line segment from $(0, 0)$ to $(1, 0)$ in the xy-plane. The second side, S_2, is $u = 1$ ($0 \le v \le 1$) and, putting $u = 1$ in the given equations, we get

$$x = 1 - v^2 \qquad y = 2v$$

Eliminating v, we obtain

$$\boxed{4} \qquad x = 1 - \frac{y^2}{4} \qquad 0 \le x \le 1$$

which is part of a parabola. Similarly, S_3 is given by $v = 1$ ($0 \le u \le 1$), whose image is the parabolic arc

$$\boxed{5} \qquad x = \frac{y^2}{4} - 1 \qquad -1 \le x \le 0$$

Finally, S_4 is given by $u = 0$ ($0 \le v \le 1$) whose image is $x = -v^2$, $y = 0$, that is, $-1 \le x \le 0$. (Notice that as we move around the square in the counterclockwise direction, we also move around the parabolic region in the counterclockwise direction.) The image of S is the region R (shown in Figure 2) bounded by the x-axis and the parabolas given by Equations 4 and 5. ▪

Now let's see how a change of variables affects a double integral. We start with a small rectangle S in the uv-plane whose lower left corner is the point (u_0, v_0) and whose dimensions are Δu and Δv. (See Figure 3.)

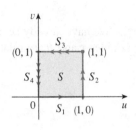

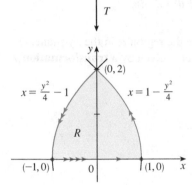

FIGURE 2

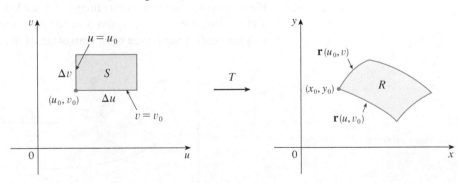

FIGURE 3

The image of S is a region R in the xy-plane, one of whose boundary points is $(x_0, y_0) = T(u_0, v_0)$. The vector

$$\mathbf{r}(u, v) = g(u, v)\,\mathbf{i} + h(u, v)\,\mathbf{j}$$

is the position vector of the image of the point (u, v). The equation of the lower side of S is $v = v_0$, whose image curve is given by the vector function $\mathbf{r}(u, v_0)$. The tangent vector at (x_0, y_0) to this image curve is

$$\mathbf{r}_u = g_u(u_0, v_0)\,\mathbf{i} + h_u(u_0, v_0)\,\mathbf{j} = \frac{\partial x}{\partial u}\,\mathbf{i} + \frac{\partial y}{\partial u}\,\mathbf{j}$$

Similarly, the tangent vector at (x_0, y_0) to the image curve of the left side of S (namely, $u = u_0$) is

$$\mathbf{r}_v = g_v(u_0, v_0)\,\mathbf{i} + h_v(u_0, v_0)\,\mathbf{j} = \frac{\partial x}{\partial v}\,\mathbf{i} + \frac{\partial y}{\partial v}\,\mathbf{j}$$

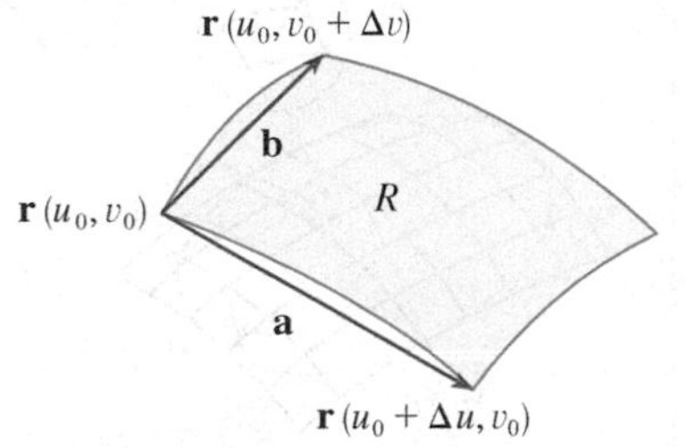

We can approximate the image region $R = T(S)$ by a parallelogram determined by the secant vectors

$$\mathbf{a} = \mathbf{r}(u_0 + \Delta u, v_0) - \mathbf{r}(u_0, v_0) \qquad \mathbf{b} = \mathbf{r}(u_0, v_0 + \Delta v) - \mathbf{r}(u_0, v_0)$$

shown in Figure 4. But

$$\mathbf{r}_u = \lim_{\Delta u \to 0} \frac{\mathbf{r}(u_0 + \Delta u, v_0) - \mathbf{r}(u_0, v_0)}{\Delta u}$$

and so $$\mathbf{r}(u_0 + \Delta u, v_0) - \mathbf{r}(u_0, v_0) \approx \Delta u\,\mathbf{r}_u$$

Similarly $$\mathbf{r}(u_0, v_0 + \Delta v) - \mathbf{r}(u_0, v_0) \approx \Delta v\,\mathbf{r}_v$$

This means that we can approximate R by a parallelogram determined by the vectors $\Delta u\,\mathbf{r}_u$ and $\Delta v\,\mathbf{r}_v$. (See Figure 5.) Therefore we can approximate the area of R by the area of this parallelogram, which, from Section 9.4, is

$$\boxed{6} \qquad \left| (\Delta u\,\mathbf{r}_u) \times (\Delta v\,\mathbf{r}_v) \right| = \left| \mathbf{r}_u \times \mathbf{r}_v \right| \Delta u\,\Delta v$$

Computing the cross product, we obtain

$$\mathbf{r}_u \times \mathbf{r}_v = \begin{vmatrix} \mathbf{i} & \mathbf{j} & \mathbf{k} \\ \dfrac{\partial x}{\partial u} & \dfrac{\partial y}{\partial u} & 0 \\ \dfrac{\partial x}{\partial v} & \dfrac{\partial y}{\partial v} & 0 \end{vmatrix} = \begin{vmatrix} \dfrac{\partial x}{\partial u} & \dfrac{\partial y}{\partial u} \\ \dfrac{\partial x}{\partial v} & \dfrac{\partial y}{\partial v} \end{vmatrix} \mathbf{k} = \begin{vmatrix} \dfrac{\partial x}{\partial u} & \dfrac{\partial x}{\partial v} \\ \dfrac{\partial y}{\partial u} & \dfrac{\partial y}{\partial v} \end{vmatrix} \mathbf{k}$$

The determinant that arises in this calculation is called the *Jacobian* of the transformation and is given a special notation.

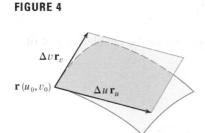

FIGURE 4

FIGURE 5

The Jacobian is named after the German mathematician Carl Gustav Jacob Jacobi (1804–1851). Although the French mathematician Cauchy first used these special determinants involving partial derivatives, Jacobi developed them into a method for evaluating multiple integrals.

$\boxed{7}$ **Definition** The **Jacobian** of the transformation T given by $x = g(u, v)$ and $y = h(u, v)$ is

$$\frac{\partial(x, y)}{\partial(u, v)} = \begin{vmatrix} \dfrac{\partial x}{\partial u} & \dfrac{\partial x}{\partial v} \\ \dfrac{\partial y}{\partial u} & \dfrac{\partial y}{\partial v} \end{vmatrix} = \frac{\partial x}{\partial u}\frac{\partial y}{\partial v} - \frac{\partial x}{\partial v}\frac{\partial y}{\partial u}$$

With this notation we can use Equation 6 to give an approximation to the area ΔA of R:

$$\boxed{8} \qquad \Delta A \approx \left| \frac{\partial(x, y)}{\partial(u, v)} \right| \Delta u \, \Delta v$$

where the Jacobian is evaluated at (u_0, v_0).

Next we divide a region S in the uv-plane into rectangles S_{ij} and call their images in the xy-plane R_{ij}. (See Figure 6.)

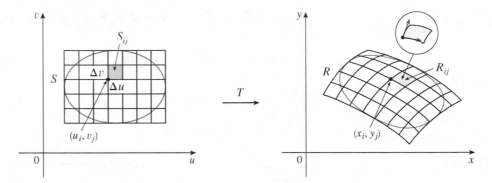

FIGURE 6

Applying the approximation (8) to each R_{ij}, we approximate the double integral of f over R as follows:

$$\iint\limits_R f(x, y) \, dA \approx \sum_{i=1}^{m} \sum_{j=1}^{n} f(x_i, y_j) \, \Delta A$$

$$\approx \sum_{i=1}^{m} \sum_{j=1}^{n} f\big(g(u_i, v_j), h(u_i, v_j)\big) \left| \frac{\partial(x, y)}{\partial(u, v)} \right| \Delta u \, \Delta v$$

where the Jacobian is evaluated at (u_i, v_j). Notice that this double sum is a Riemann sum for the integral

$$\iint\limits_S f\big(g(u, v), h(u, v)\big) \left| \frac{\partial(x, y)}{\partial(u, v)} \right| du \, dv$$

The foregoing argument suggests that the following theorem is true. (A full proof is given in books on advanced calculus.)

$\boxed{9}$ **Change of Variables in a Double Integral**   Suppose that T is a C^1 transformation whose Jacobian is nonzero and that maps a region S in the uv-plane onto a region R in the xy-plane. Suppose that f is continuous on R and that R and S are type I or type II plane regions. Suppose also that T is one-to-one, except perhaps on the boundary of S. Then

$$\iint\limits_R f(x, y) \, dA = \iint\limits_S f\big(x(u, v), y(u, v)\big) \left| \frac{\partial(x, y)}{\partial(u, v)} \right| du \, dv$$

Theorem 9 says that we change from an integral in x and y to an integral in u and v by expressing x and y in terms of u and v and writing

$$dA = \left| \frac{\partial(x, y)}{\partial(u, v)} \right| du \, dv$$

Notice the similarity between Theorem 9 and the one-dimensional formula in Equation 2. Instead of the derivative dx/du, we have the absolute value of the Jacobian, that is, $|\partial(x, y)/\partial(u, v)|$.

As a first illustration of Theorem 9, we show that the formula for integration in polar coordinates is just a special case. Here the transformation T from the $r\theta$-plane to the xy-plane is given by

$$x = g(r, \theta) = r\cos\theta \qquad y = h(r, \theta) = r\sin\theta$$

and the geometry of the transformation is shown in Figure 7: T maps an ordinary rectangle in the $r\theta$-plane to a polar rectangle in the xy-plane. The Jacobian of T is

$$\frac{\partial(x, y)}{\partial(r, \theta)} = \begin{vmatrix} \dfrac{\partial x}{\partial r} & \dfrac{\partial x}{\partial \theta} \\ \dfrac{\partial y}{\partial r} & \dfrac{\partial y}{\partial \theta} \end{vmatrix} = \begin{vmatrix} \cos\theta & -r\sin\theta \\ \sin\theta & r\cos\theta \end{vmatrix} = r\cos^2\theta + r\sin^2\theta = r > 0$$

Thus Theorem 9 gives

$$\iint_R f(x, y)\, dx\, dy = \iint_S f(r\cos\theta, r\sin\theta)\left|\frac{\partial(x, y)}{\partial(r, \theta)}\right| dr\, d\theta$$

$$= \int_\alpha^\beta \int_a^b f(r\cos\theta, r\sin\theta)\, r\, dr\, d\theta$$

which is the same as Formula 12.4.2.

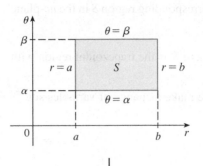
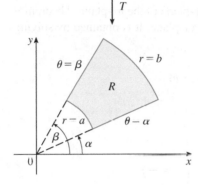

▼ EXAMPLE 2 **Evaluating a double integral with a change of variables**   Use the change of variables $x = u^2 - v^2$, $y = 2uv$ to evaluate the integral $\iint_R y\, dA$, where R is the region bounded by the x-axis and the parabolas $y^2 = 4 - 4x$ and $y^2 = 4 + 4x$, $y \ge 0$.

SOLUTION The region R is pictured in Figure 2 (on page 892). In Example 1 we discovered that $T(S) = R$, where S is the square $[0, 1] \times [0, 1]$. Indeed, the reason for making the change of variables to evaluate the integral is that S is a much simpler region than R. First we need to compute the Jacobian:

$$\frac{\partial(x, y)}{\partial(u, v)} = \begin{vmatrix} \dfrac{\partial x}{\partial u} & \dfrac{\partial x}{\partial v} \\ \dfrac{\partial y}{\partial u} & \dfrac{\partial y}{\partial v} \end{vmatrix} = \begin{vmatrix} 2u & -2v \\ 2v & 2u \end{vmatrix} = 4u^2 + 4v^2 > 0$$

Therefore, by Theorem 9,

$$\iint_R y\, dA = \iint_S 2uv \left|\frac{\partial(x, y)}{\partial(u, v)}\right| dA = \int_0^1 \int_0^1 (2uv)4(u^2 + v^2)\, du\, dv$$

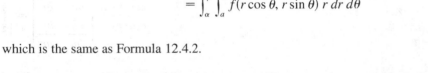

$$= 8\int_0^1 \int_0^1 (u^3v + uv^3)\, du\, dv = 8\int_0^1 \left[\tfrac{1}{4}u^4v + \tfrac{1}{2}u^2v^3\right]_{u=0}^{u=1} dv$$

$$= \int_0^1 (2v + 4v^3)\, dv = \left[v^2 + v^4\right]_0^1 = 2$$

Note: Example 2 was not a very difficult problem to solve because we were given a suitable change of variables. If we are not supplied with a transformation, then the first step is to think of an appropriate change of variables. If $f(x, y)$ is difficult to integrate, then the form of $f(x, y)$ may suggest a transformation. If the region of integration R is awkward, then the transformation should be chosen so that the corresponding region S in the uv-plane has a convenient description.

EXAMPLE 3   Evaluate the integral $\iint_R e^{(x+y)/(x-y)} \, dA$, where R is the trapezoidal region with vertices $(1, 0)$, $(2, 0)$, $(0, -2)$, and $(0, -1)$.

SOLUTION   Since it isn't easy to integrate $e^{(x+y)/(x-y)}$, we make a change of variables suggested by the form of this function:

$$\boxed{10} \qquad\qquad u = x + y \qquad v = x - y$$

These equations define a transformation T^{-1} from the xy-plane to the uv-plane. Theorem 9 talks about a transformation T from the uv-plane to the xy-plane. It is obtained by solving Equations 10 for x and y:

$$\boxed{11} \qquad\qquad x = \tfrac{1}{2}(u + v) \qquad y = \tfrac{1}{2}(u - v)$$

The Jacobian of T is

$$\frac{\partial(x, y)}{\partial(u, v)} = \begin{vmatrix} \dfrac{\partial x}{\partial u} & \dfrac{\partial x}{\partial v} \\[2mm] \dfrac{\partial y}{\partial u} & \dfrac{\partial y}{\partial v} \end{vmatrix} = \begin{vmatrix} \tfrac{1}{2} & \tfrac{1}{2} \\[1mm] \tfrac{1}{2} & -\tfrac{1}{2} \end{vmatrix} = -\tfrac{1}{2}$$

To find the region S in the uv-plane corresponding to R, we note that the sides of R lie on the lines

$$y = 0 \qquad x - y = 2 \qquad x = 0 \qquad x - y = 1$$

and, from either Equations 10 or Equations 11, the image lines in the uv-plane are

$$u = v \qquad v = 2 \qquad u = -v \qquad v = 1$$

Thus the region S is the trapezoidal region with vertices $(1, 1)$, $(2, 2)$, $(-2, 2)$, and $(-1, 1)$ shown in Figure 8. Since

$$S = \{(u, v) \mid 1 \leqslant v \leqslant 2, \ -v \leqslant u \leqslant v\}$$

Theorem 9 gives

$$\iint_R e^{(x+y)/(x-y)} \, dA = \iint_S e^{u/v} \left| \frac{\partial(x, y)}{\partial(u, v)} \right| du \, dv$$

$$= \int_1^2 \int_{-v}^{v} e^{u/v} \left(\tfrac{1}{2}\right) du \, dv = \tfrac{1}{2} \int_1^2 \left[v e^{u/v} \right]_{u=-v}^{u=v} dv$$

$$= \tfrac{1}{2} \int_1^2 (e - e^{-1}) v \, dv = \tfrac{3}{4}(e - e^{-1})$$

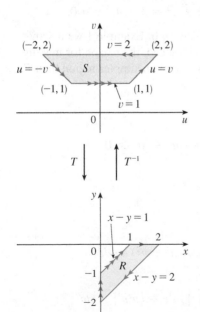

FIGURE 8

Triple Integrals

There is a similar change of variables formula for triple integrals. Let T be a transformation that maps a region S in uvw-space onto a region R in xyz-space by means of the equations

$$x = g(u, v, w) \qquad y = h(u, v, w) \qquad z = k(u, v, w)$$

The **Jacobian** of T is the following 3×3 determinant:

$$\boxed{12} \qquad \frac{\partial(x, y, z)}{\partial(u, v, w)} = \begin{vmatrix} \dfrac{\partial x}{\partial u} & \dfrac{\partial x}{\partial v} & \dfrac{\partial x}{\partial w} \\[2mm] \dfrac{\partial y}{\partial u} & \dfrac{\partial y}{\partial v} & \dfrac{\partial y}{\partial w} \\[2mm] \dfrac{\partial z}{\partial u} & \dfrac{\partial z}{\partial v} & \dfrac{\partial z}{\partial w} \end{vmatrix}$$

Under hypotheses similar to those in Theorem 9, we have the following formula for triple integrals:

$$\boxed{13} \quad \iiint\limits_{R} f(x, y, z) \, dV = \iiint\limits_{S} f\big(x(u, v, w), y(u, v, w), z(u, v, w)\big) \left| \frac{\partial(x, y, z)}{\partial(u, v, w)} \right| du \, dv \, dw$$

☑ EXAMPLE 4 **The spherical coordinate transformation** Use Formula 13 to derive the formula for triple integration in spherical coordinates.

SOLUTION Here the change of variables is given by

$$x = \rho \sin \phi \cos \theta \qquad y = \rho \sin \phi \sin \theta \qquad z = \rho \cos \phi$$

We compute the Jacobian as follows:

$$\frac{\partial(x, y, z)}{\partial(\rho, \theta, \phi)} = \begin{vmatrix} \sin \phi \cos \theta & -\rho \sin \phi \sin \theta & \rho \cos \phi \cos \theta \\ \sin \phi \sin \theta & \rho \sin \phi \cos \theta & \rho \cos \phi \sin \theta \\ \cos \phi & 0 & -\rho \sin \phi \end{vmatrix}$$

$$= \cos \phi \begin{vmatrix} -\rho \sin \phi \sin \theta & \rho \cos \phi \cos \theta \\ \rho \sin \phi \cos \theta & \rho \cos \phi \sin \theta \end{vmatrix} - \rho \sin \phi \begin{vmatrix} \sin \phi \cos \theta & -\rho \sin \phi \sin \theta \\ \sin \phi \sin \theta & \rho \sin \phi \cos \theta \end{vmatrix}$$

$$= \cos \phi \, (-\rho^2 \sin \phi \cos \phi \sin^2\theta - \rho^2 \sin \phi \cos \phi \cos^2\theta)$$

$$\qquad - \rho \sin \phi \, (\rho \sin^2\phi \cos^2\theta + \rho \sin^2\phi \sin^2\theta)$$

$$= -\rho^2 \sin \phi \cos^2\phi - \rho^2 \sin \phi \sin^2\phi = -\rho^2 \sin \phi$$

Since $0 \le \phi \le \pi$, we have $\sin \phi \ge 0$. Therefore

$$\left| \frac{\partial(x, y, z)}{\partial(\rho, \theta, \phi)} \right| = |-\rho^2 \sin \phi| = \rho^2 \sin \phi$$

and Formula 13 gives

$$\iiint\limits_{R} f(x, y, z) \, dV = \iiint\limits_{S} f(\rho \sin \phi \cos \theta, \rho \sin \phi \sin \theta, \rho \cos \phi) \, \rho^2 \sin \phi \, d\rho \, d\theta \, d\phi$$

which is equivalent to Formula 12.8.4.

12.9 Exercises

1–6 Find the Jacobian of the transformation.

1. $x = 5u - v, \quad y = u + 3v$

2. $x = uv, \quad y = u/v$

3. $x = e^{-r}\sin\theta, \quad y = e^r\cos\theta$

4. $x = e^{s+t}, \quad y = e^{s-t}$

5. $x = u/v, \quad y = v/w, \quad z = w/u$

6. $x = v + w^2, \quad y = w + u^2, \quad z = u + v^2$

7–10 Find the image of the set S under the given transformation.

7. $S = \{(u, v) \mid 0 \le u \le 3, \, 0 \le v \le 2\};$
$x = 2u + 3v, \; y = u - v$

8. S is the square bounded by the lines $u = 0, u = 1, v = 0,$
$v = 1; \quad x = v, \, y = u(1 + v^2)$

9. S is the triangular region with vertices $(0, 0), (1, 1), (0, 1);$
$x = u^2, \; y = v$

10. S is the disk given by $u^2 + v^2 \le 1; \quad x = au, \, y = bv$

11–14 A region R in the xy-plane is given. Find equations for a transformation T that maps a rectangular region S in the uv-plane onto R, where the sides of S are parallel to the u- and v- axes.

11. R is bounded by $y = 2x - 1, y = 2x + 1, y = 1 - x,$
$y = 3 - x$

12. R is the parallelogram with vertices $(0, 0), (4, 3), (2, 4), (-2, 1)$

13. R lies between the circles $x^2 + y^2 = 1$ and $x^2 + y^2 = 2$ in the first quadrant

14. R is bounded by the hyperbolas $y = 1/x, y = 4/x$ and the lines $y = x, y = 4x$ in the first quadrant

15–20 Use the given transformation to evaluate the integral.

15. $\iint_R (x - 3y)\, dA$, where R is the triangular region with vertices $(0, 0), (2, 1),$ and $(1, 2); \quad x = 2u + v, \, y = u + 2v$

16. $\iint_R (4x + 8y)\, dA$, where R is the parallelogram with vertices $(-1, 3), (1, -3), (3, -1),$ and $(1, 5);$
$x = \frac{1}{4}(u + v), \; y = \frac{1}{4}(v - 3u)$

17. $\iint_R x^2\, dA$, where R is the region bounded by the ellipse $9x^2 + 4y^2 = 36; \quad x = 2u, \, y = 3v$

18. $\iint_R (x^2 - xy + y^2)\, dA$, where R is the region bounded by the ellipse $x^2 - xy + y^2 = 2;$
$x = \sqrt{2}\, u - \sqrt{2/3}\, v, \; y = \sqrt{2}\, u + \sqrt{2/3}\, v$

19. $\iint_R xy\, dA$, where R is the region in the first quadrant bounded by the lines $y = x$ and $y = 3x$ and the hyperbolas $xy = 1, xy = 3; \quad x = u/v, \, y = v$

20. $\iint_R y^2\, dA$, where R is the region bounded by the curves $xy = 1, xy = 2, xy^2 = 1, xy^2 = 2; \quad u = xy, \, v = xy^2.$ Illustrate by using a graphing calculator or computer to draw R.

21. (a) Evaluate $\iiint_E dV$, where E is the solid enclosed by the ellipsoid $x^2/a^2 + y^2/b^2 + z^2/c^2 = 1$. Use the transformation $x = au, \, y = bv, \, z = cw$.
(b) The earth is not a perfect sphere; rotation has resulted in flattening at the poles. So the shape can be approximated by an ellipsoid with $a = b = 6378$ km and $c = 6356$ km. Use part (a) to estimate the volume of the earth.

22. If the solid of Exercise 21(a) has constant density k, find its moment of inertia about the z-axis.

23–27 Evaluate the integral by making an appropriate change of variables.

23. $\iint_R \dfrac{x - 2y}{3x - y}\, dA$, where R is the parallelogram enclosed by the lines $x - 2y = 0, x - 2y = 4, 3x - y = 1,$ and $3x - y = 8$

24. $\iint_R (x + y)e^{x^2-y^2}\, dA$, where R is the rectangle enclosed by the lines $x - y = 0, x - y = 2, x + y = 0,$ and $x + y = 3$

25. $\iint_R \cos\left(\dfrac{y - x}{y + x}\right) dA$, where R is the trapezoidal region with vertices $(1, 0), (2, 0), (0, 2),$ and $(0, 1)$

26. $\iint_R \sin(9x^2 + 4y^2)\, dA$, where R is the region in the first quadrant bounded by the ellipse $9x^2 + 4y^2 = 1$

27. $\iint_R e^{x+y}\, dA$, where R is given by the inequality $|x| + |y| \le 1$

28. Let f be continuous on $[0, 1]$ and let R be the triangular region with vertices $(0, 0), (1, 0),$ and $(0, 1)$. Show that
$$\iint_R f(x + y)\, dA = \int_0^1 uf(u)\, du$$

Graphing calculator or computer with graphing software required   **1.** Homework Hints available in TEC

12 Review

Concept Check

1. Suppose f is a continuous function defined on a rectangle $R = [a, b] \times [c, d]$.
  (a) Write an expression for a double Riemann sum of f. If $f(x, y) \geq 0$, what does the sum represent?
  (b) Write the definition of $\iint_R f(x, y)\, dA$ as a limit.
  (c) What is the geometric interpretation of $\iint_R f(x, y)\, dA$ if $f(x, y) \geq 0$? What if f takes on both positive and negative values?
  (d) How do you evaluate $\iint_R f(x, y)\, dA$?
  (e) What does the Midpoint Rule for double integrals say?
  (f) Write an expression for the average value of f.

2. (a) How do you define $\iint_D f(x, y)\, dA$ if D is a bounded region that is not a rectangle?
  (b) What is a type I region? How do you evaluate $\iint_D f(x, y)\, dA$ if D is a type I region?
  (c) What is a type II region? How do you evaluate $\iint_D f(x, y)\, dA$ if D is a type II region?
  (d) What properties do double integrals have?

3. How do you change from rectangular coordinates to polar coordinates in a double integral? Why would you want to make the change?

4. If a lamina occupies a plane region D and has density function $\rho(x, y)$, write expressions for each of the following in terms of double integrals.
  (a) The mass
  (b) The moments about the axes
  (c) The center of mass
  (d) The moments of inertia about the axes and the origin

5. Let f be a joint density function of a pair of continuous random variables X and Y.
  (a) Write a double integral for the probability that X lies between a and b and Y lies between c and d.
  (b) What properties does f possess?
  (c) What are the expected values of X and Y?

6. Write an expression for the area of a surface S for each of the following cases.
  (a) S is a parametric surface given by a vector function $\mathbf{r}(u, v)$, $(u, v) \in D$.
  (b) S has the equation $z = f(x, y)$, $(x, y) \in D$.
  (c) S is the surface of revolution obtained by rotating the curve $y = f(x)$, $a \leq x \leq b$, about the x-axis.

7. (a) Write the definition of the triple integral of f over a rectangular box B.
  (b) How do you evaluate $\iiint_B f(x, y, z)\, dV$?
  (c) How do you define $\iiint_E f(x, y, z)\, dV$ if E is a bounded solid region that is not a box?
  (d) What is a type 1 solid region? How do you evaluate $\iiint_E f(x, y, z)\, dV$ if E is such a region?
  (e) What is a type 2 solid region? How do you evaluate $\iiint_E f(x, y, z)\, dV$ if E is such a region?
  (f) What is a type 3 solid region? How do you evaluate $\iiint_E f(x, y, z)\, dV$ if E is such a region?

8. Suppose a solid object occupies the region E and has density function $\rho(x, y, z)$. Write expressions for each of the following.
  (a) The mass
  (b) The moments about the coordinate planes
  (c) The coordinates of the center of mass
  (d) The moments of inertia about the axes

9. (a) How do you change from rectangular coordinates to cylindrical coordinates in a triple integral?
  (b) How do you change from rectangular coordinates to spherical coordinates in a triple integral?
  (c) In what situations would you change to cylindrical or spherical coordinates?

10. (a) If a transformation T is given by $x = g(u, v)$, $y = h(u, v)$, what is the Jacobian of T?
  (b) How do you change variables in a double integral?
  (c) How do you change variables in a triple integral?

True-False Quiz

Determine whether the statement is true or false. If it is true, explain why. If it is false, explain why or give an example that disproves the statement.

1. $\displaystyle\int_{-1}^{2}\int_{0}^{6} x^2 \sin(x - y)\, dx\, dy = \int_{0}^{6}\int_{-1}^{2} x^2 \sin(x - y)\, dy\, dx$

2. $\displaystyle\int_{0}^{1}\int_{0}^{x} \sqrt{x + y^2}\, dy\, dx = \int_{0}^{x}\int_{0}^{1} \sqrt{x + y^2}\, dx\, dy$

3. $\displaystyle\int_{1}^{2}\int_{3}^{4} x^2 e^y\, dy\, dx = \int_{1}^{2} x^2\, dx \int_{3}^{4} e^y\, dy$

4. $\displaystyle\int_{-1}^{1}\int_{0}^{1} e^{x^2 + y^2} \sin y\, dx\, dy = 0$

5. If f is continuous on $[0, 1]$, then

$$\int_{0}^{1}\int_{0}^{1} f(x) f(y)\, dy\, dx = \left[\int_{0}^{1} f(x)\, dx \right]^2$$

6. $\displaystyle\int_{1}^{4}\int_{0}^{1} \left(x^2 + \sqrt{y}\, \right) \sin(x^2 y^2)\, dx\, dy \leq 9$

7. If D is the disk given by $x^2 + y^2 \le 4$, then

$$\iint_D \sqrt{4 - x^2 - y^2} \, dA = \tfrac{16}{3}\pi$$

8. The integral $\iiint_E kr^3 \, dz \, dr \, d\theta$ represents the moment of inertia about the z-axis of a solid E with constant density k.

9. The integral

$$\int_0^{2\pi} \int_0^2 \int_r^2 dz \, dr \, d\theta$$

represents the volume enclosed by the cone $z = \sqrt{x^2 + y^2}$ and the plane $z = 2$.

Exercises

1. A contour map is shown for a function f on the square $R = [0, 3] \times [0, 3]$. Use a Riemann sum with nine terms to estimate the value of $\iint_R f(x, y) \, dA$. Take the sample points to be the upper right corners of the squares.

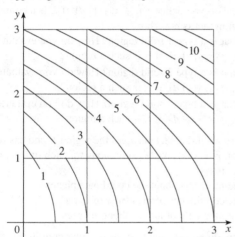

2. Use the Midpoint Rule to estimate the integral in Exercise 1.

3–8 Calculate the iterated integral.

3. $\displaystyle\int_1^2 \int_0^2 (y + 2xe^y) \, dx \, dy$

4. $\displaystyle\int_0^1 \int_0^1 ye^{xy} \, dx \, dy$

5. $\displaystyle\int_0^1 \int_0^x \cos(x^2) \, dy \, dx$

6. $\displaystyle\int_0^1 \int_x^{e^x} 3xy^2 \, dy \, dx$

7. $\displaystyle\int_0^\pi \int_0^1 \int_0^{\sqrt{1-y^2}} y \sin x \, dz \, dy \, dx$

8. $\displaystyle\int_0^1 \int_0^y \int_x^1 6xyz \, dz \, dx \, dy$

9–10 Write $\iint_R f(x, y) \, dA$ as an iterated integral, where R is the region shown and f is an arbitrary continuous function on R.

9.

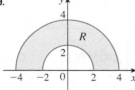

10.

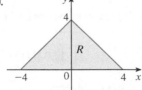

11. Describe the region whose area is given by the integral

$$\int_0^{\pi/2} \int_0^{\sin 2\theta} r \, dr \, d\theta$$

12. Describe the solid whose volume is given by the integral

$$\int_0^{\pi/2} \int_0^{\pi/2} \int_1^2 \rho^2 \sin \phi \, d\rho \, d\phi \, d\theta$$

and evaluate the integral.

13–14 Calculate the iterated integral by first reversing the order of integration.

13. $\displaystyle\int_0^1 \int_x^1 \cos(y^2) \, dy \, dx$

14. $\displaystyle\int_0^1 \int_{\sqrt{y}}^1 \frac{ye^{x^2}}{x^3} \, dx \, dy$

15–28 Calculate the value of the multiple integral.

15. $\iint_R ye^{xy} \, dA$, where $R = \{(x, y) \mid 0 \le x \le 2, \ 0 \le y \le 3\}$

16. $\iint_D xy \, dA$, where $D = \{(x, y) \mid 0 \le y \le 1, \ y^2 \le x \le y + 2\}$

17. $\displaystyle\iint_D \frac{y}{1 + x^2} \, dA$,
where D is bounded by $y = \sqrt{x}$, $y = 0$, $x = 1$

18. $\displaystyle\iint_D \frac{1}{1 + x^2} \, dA$, where D is the triangular region with vertices $(0, 0)$, $(1, 1)$, and $(0, 1)$

19. $\iint_D y \, dA$, where D is the region in the first quadrant bounded by the parabolas $x = y^2$ and $x = 8 - y^2$

20. $\iint_D y \, dA$, where D is the region in the first quadrant that lies above the hyperbola $xy = 1$ and the line $y = x$ and below the line $y = 2$

21. $\iint_D (x^2 + y^2)^{3/2} \, dA$, where D is the region in the first quadrant bounded by the lines $y = 0$ and $y = \sqrt{3}\, x$ and the circle $x^2 + y^2 = 9$

22. $\iint_D x \, dA$, where D is the region in the first quadrant that lies between the circles $x^2 + y^2 = 1$ and $x^2 + y^2 = 2$

 Graphing calculator or computer with graphing software required   CAS Computer algebra system required

23. $\iiint_E xy \, dV$, where
$E = \{(x, y, z) \mid 0 \le x \le 3, \, 0 \le y \le x, \, 0 \le z \le x + y\}$

24. $\iiint_T xy \, dV$, where T is the solid tetrahedron with vertices
$(0, 0, 0), \left(\frac{1}{3}, 0, 0\right), (0, 1, 0),$ and $(0, 0, 1)$

25. $\iiint_E y^2 z^2 \, dV$, where E is bounded by the paraboloid
$x = 1 - y^2 - z^2$ and the plane $x = 0$

26. $\iiint_E z \, dV$, where E is bounded by the planes $y = 0, z = 0,$
$x + y = 2$ and the cylinder $y^2 + z^2 = 1$ in the first octant

27. $\iiint_E yz \, dV$, where E lies above the plane $z = 0$, below the
plane $z = y$, and inside the cylinder $x^2 + y^2 = 4$

28. $\iiint_H z^3 \sqrt{x^2 + y^2 + z^2} \, dV$, where H is the solid hemisphere
that lies above the xy-plane and has center the origin and
radius 1

29–34 Find the volume of the given solid.

29. Under the paraboloid $z = x^2 + 4y^2$ and above the rectangle
$R = [0, 2] \times [1, 4]$

30. Under the surface $z = x^2 y$ and above the triangle in the
xy-plane with vertices $(1, 0), (2, 1),$ and $(4, 0)$

31. The solid tetrahedron with vertices $(0, 0, 0), (0, 0, 1),$
$(0, 2, 0),$ and $(2, 2, 0)$

32. Bounded by the cylinder $x^2 + y^2 = 4$ and the planes $z = 0$
and $y + z = 3$

33. One of the wedges cut from the cylinder $x^2 + 9y^2 = a^2$ by
the planes $z = 0$ and $z = mx$

34. Above the paraboloid $z = x^2 + y^2$ and below the half-cone
$z = \sqrt{x^2 + y^2}$

---

35. Consider a lamina that occupies the region D bounded by
the parabola $x = 1 - y^2$ and the coordinate axes in the first
quadrant with density function $\rho(x, y) = y$.
    (a) Find the mass of the lamina.
    (b) Find the center of mass.
    (c) Find the moments of inertia about the origin and about
the x- and y-axes.

36. A lamina occupies the part of the disk $x^2 + y^2 \le a^2$ that lies
in the first quadrant.
    (a) Find the centroid of the lamina.
    (b) Find the center of mass of the lamina if the density func-
tion is $\rho(x, y) = xy^2$.

37. (a) Find the centroid of a right circular cone with height h
and base radius a. (Place the cone so that its base is in
the xy-plane with center the origin and its axis along the
positive z-axis.)

(b) Find the moment of inertia of the cone about its axis
(the z-axis).

38. (a) Set up, but don't evaluate, an integral for the surface area
of the parametric surface given by the vector
function $\mathbf{r}(u, v) = v^2 \mathbf{i} - uv \mathbf{j} + u^2 \mathbf{k}, 0 \le u \le 3,$
$-3 \le v \le 3$.
    CAS (b) Use a computer algebra system to approximate the sur-
face area correct to four significant digits.

39. Find the area of the part of the surface $z = x^2 + y$ that lies
above the triangle with vertices $(0, 0), (1, 0),$ and $(0, 2)$.

CAS 40. Graph the surface $z = x \sin y, -3 \le x \le 3, -\pi \le y \le \pi,$
and find its surface area correct to four decimal places.

41. Use polar coordinates to evaluate
$$\int_0^3 \int_{-\sqrt{9-x^2}}^{\sqrt{9-x^2}} (x^3 + xy^2) \, dy \, dx$$

42. Use spherical coordinates to evaluate
$$\int_{-2}^2 \int_0^{\sqrt{4-y^2}} \int_{-\sqrt{4-x^2-y^2}}^{\sqrt{4-x^2-y^2}} y^2 \sqrt{x^2 + y^2 + z^2} \, dz \, dx \, dy$$

43. If D is the region bounded by the curves $y = 1 - x^2$ and
$y = e^x$, find the approximate value of the integral $\iint_D y^2 \, dA$.
(Use a graphing device to estimate the points of intersection
of the curves.)

CAS 44. Find the center of mass of the solid tetrahedron with vertices
$(0, 0, 0), (1, 0, 0), (0, 2, 0), (0, 0, 3)$ and density function
$\rho(x, y, z) = x^2 + y^2 + z^2$.

45. The joint density function for random variables X and Y is
$$f(x, y) = \begin{cases} C(x + y) & \text{if } 0 \le x \le 3, \, 0 \le y \le 2 \\ 0 & \text{otherwise} \end{cases}$$
    (a) Find the value of the constant C.
    (b) Find $P(X \le 2, Y \ge 1)$.
    (c) Find $P(X + Y \le 1)$.

46. A lamp has three bulbs, each of a type with average lifetime
800 hours. If we model the probability of failure of the
bulbs by an exponential density function with mean 800,
find the probability that all three bulbs fail within a total of
1000 hours.

47. Rewrite the integral
$$\int_{-1}^1 \int_{x^2}^1 \int_0^{1-y} f(x, y, z) \, dz \, dy \, dx$$
as an iterated integral in the order $dx \, dy \, dz$.

48. Give five other iterated integrals that are equal to
$$\int_0^2 \int_0^{y^3} \int_0^{y^2} f(x, y, z) \, dz \, dx \, dy$$

49. Use the transformation $u = x - y$, $v = x + y$ to evaluate

$$\iint\limits_{R} \frac{x - y}{x + y} \, dA$$

where R is the square with vertices $(0, 2)$, $(1, 1)$, $(2, 2)$, and $(1, 3)$.

50. Use the transformation $x = u^2$, $y = v^2$, $z = w^2$ to find the volume of the region bounded by the surface $\sqrt{x} + \sqrt{y} + \sqrt{z} = 1$ and the coordinate planes.

51. Use the change of variables formula and an appropriate transformation to evaluate $\iint_R xy \, dA$, where R is the square with vertices $(0, 0)$, $(1, 1)$, $(2, 0)$, and $(1, -1)$.

52. (a) Evaluate $\iint\limits_{D} \dfrac{1}{(x^2 + y^2)^{n/2}} \, dA$, where n is an integer and D is the region bounded by the circles with center the origin and radii r and R, $0 < r < R$.

(b) For what values of n does the integral in part (a) have a limit as $r \to 0^+$?

(c) Find $\iiint\limits_{E} \dfrac{1}{(x^2 + y^2 + z^2)^{n/2}} \, dV$, where E is the region bounded by the spheres with center the origin and radii r and R, $0 < r < R$.

(d) For what values of n does the integral in part (c) have a limit as $r \to 0^+$?

Focus on Problem Solving

1. If $[\![x]\!]$ denotes the greatest integer in x, evaluate the integral

$$\iint_R [\![x + y]\!] \, dA$$

where $R = \{(x, y) \mid 1 \leqslant x \leqslant 3, \ 2 \leqslant y \leqslant 5\}$.

2. Evaluate the integral

$$\int_0^1 \int_0^1 e^{\max\{x^2, y^2\}} \, dy \, dx$$

where $\max\{x^2, y^2\}$ means the larger of the numbers x^2 and y^2.

3. Find the average value of the function $f(x) = \int_x^1 \cos(t^2) \, dt$ on the interval $[0, 1]$.

4. If $\mathbf{a}$, $\mathbf{b}$, and $\mathbf{c}$ are constant vectors, $\mathbf{r}$ is the position vector $x\mathbf{i} + y\mathbf{j} + z\mathbf{k}$, and E is given by the inequalities $0 \leqslant \mathbf{a} \cdot \mathbf{r} \leqslant \alpha$, $0 \leqslant \mathbf{b} \cdot \mathbf{r} \leqslant \beta$, $0 \leqslant \mathbf{c} \cdot \mathbf{r} \leqslant \gamma$, show that

$$\iiint_E (\mathbf{a} \cdot \mathbf{r})(\mathbf{b} \cdot \mathbf{r})(\mathbf{c} \cdot \mathbf{r}) \, dV = \frac{(\alpha\beta\gamma)^2}{8 \, |\mathbf{a} \cdot (\mathbf{b} \times \mathbf{c})|}$$

5. The double integral $\displaystyle\int_0^1 \int_0^1 \frac{1}{1 - xy} \, dx \, dy$ is an improper integral and could be defined as the limit of double integrals over the rectangle $[0, t] \times [0, t]$ as $t \to 1^-$. But if we expand the integrand as a geometric series, we can express the integral as the sum of an infinite series. Show that

$$\int_0^1 \int_0^1 \frac{1}{1 - xy} \, dx \, dy = \sum_{n=1}^{\infty} \frac{1}{n^2}$$

6. Leonhard Euler was able to find the exact sum of the series in Problem 5. In 1736 he proved that

$$\sum_{n=1}^{\infty} \frac{1}{n^2} = \frac{\pi^2}{6}$$

In this problem we ask you to prove this fact by evaluating the double integral in Problem 5. Start by making the change of variables

$$x = \frac{u - v}{\sqrt{2}} \qquad y = \frac{u + v}{\sqrt{2}}$$

This gives a rotation about the origin through the angle $\pi/4$. You will need to sketch the corresponding region in the uv-plane.

    [*Hint:* If, in evaluating the integral, you encounter either of the expressions $(1 - \sin\theta)/\cos\theta$ or $(\cos\theta)/(1 + \sin\theta)$, you might like to use the identity $\cos\theta = \sin((\pi/2) - \theta)$ and the corresponding identity for $\sin\theta$.]

7. (a) Show that

$$\int_0^1 \int_0^1 \int_0^1 \frac{1}{1 - xyz} \, dx \, dy \, dz = \sum_{n=1}^{\infty} \frac{1}{n^3}$$

    (Nobody has ever been able to find the exact value of the sum of this series.)

  (b) Show that

$$\int_0^1 \int_0^1 \int_0^1 \frac{1}{1 + xyz} \, dx \, dy \, dz = \sum_{n=1}^{\infty} \frac{(-1)^{n-1}}{n^3}$$

Use this equation to evaluate the triple integral correct to two decimal places.

8. Show that

$$\int_0^\infty \frac{\arctan \pi x - \arctan x}{x}\, dx = \frac{\pi}{2} \ln \pi$$

by first expressing the integral as an iterated integral.

9. If f is continuous, show that

$$\int_0^x \int_0^y \int_0^z f(t)\, dt\, dz\, dy = \frac{1}{2} \int_0^x (x - t)^2 f(t)\, dt$$

10. (a) A lamina has constant density ρ and takes the shape of a disk with center the origin and radius R. Use Newton's Law of Gravitation (see page 722) to show that the magnitude of the force of attraction that the lamina exerts on a body with mass m located at the point $(0, 0, d)$ on the positive z-axis is

$$F = 2\pi G m \rho d\left(\frac{1}{d} - \frac{1}{\sqrt{R^2 + d^2}}\right)$$

[*Hint:* Divide the disk as in Figure 4 in Section 12.4 and first compute the vertical component of the force exerted by the polar subrectangle R_{ij}.]

(b) Show that the magnitude of the force of attraction of a lamina with density ρ that occupies an entire plane on an object with mass m located at a distance d from the plane is

$$F = 2\pi G m \rho$$

Notice that this expression does not depend on d.

11. The plane

$$\frac{x}{a} + \frac{y}{b} + \frac{z}{c} = 1 \qquad a > 0, \quad b > 0, \quad c > 0$$

cuts the solid ellipsoid

$$\frac{x^2}{a^2} + \frac{y^2}{b^2} + \frac{z^2}{c^2} \leqslant 1$$

into two pieces. Find the volume of the smaller piece.

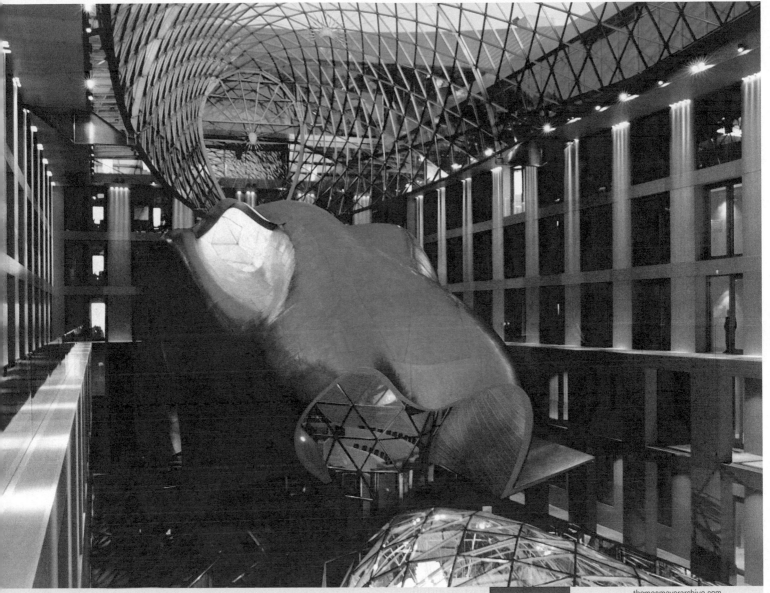

Vector Calculus

13

In this chapter we study the calculus of vector fields. (These are functions that assign vectors to points in space.) In particular we define line integrals (which can be used to find the work done by a force field in moving an object along a curve). Then we define surface integrals (which can be used to find the rate of fluid flow across a surface). The connections between these new types of integrals and the single, double, and triple integrals that we have already met are given by the higher-dimensional versions of the Fundamental Theorem of Calculus: Green's Theorem, Stokes' Theorem, and the Divergence Theorem.

13.1 | Vector Fields

The vectors in Figure 1 are air velocity vectors that indicate the wind speed and direction at points 10 m above the surface elevation in the San Francisco Bay area. (Notice that the wind patterns on consecutive days are quite different.) Associated with every point in the air we can imagine a wind velocity vector. This is an example of a *velocity vector field*.

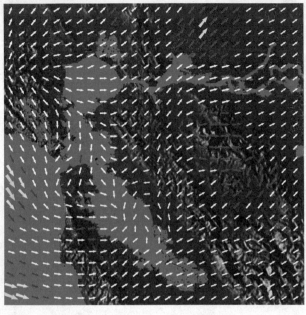

(a) 12:00 AM, February 20, 2007

(b) 2:00 PM, February 21, 2007

FIGURE 1 Velocity vector fields showing San Francisco Bay wind patterns

Other examples of velocity vector fields are illustrated in Figure 2: ocean currents and flow past an airfoil.

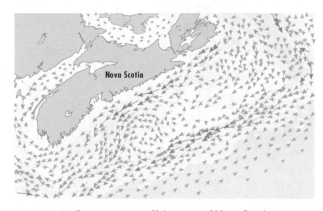

(a) Ocean currents off the coast of Nova Scotia

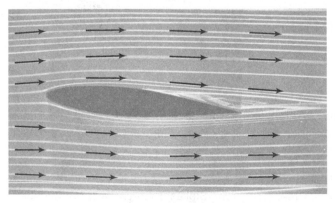

(b) Airflow past an inclined airfoil

FIGURE 2 Velocity vector fields

Another type of vector field, called a *force field*, associates a force vector with each point in a region. An example is the gravitational force field that we will look at in Example 4.

In general, a vector field is a function whose domain is a set of points in $\mathbb{R}^2$ (or $\mathbb{R}^3$) and whose range is a set of vectors in V_2 (or V_3).

> **1 Definition** Let D be a set in $\mathbb{R}^2$ (a plane region). A **vector field on** $\mathbb{R}^2$ is a function $\mathbf{F}$ that assigns to each point (x, y) in D a two-dimensional vector $\mathbf{F}(x, y)$.

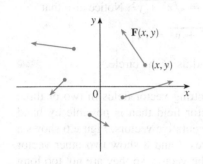

FIGURE 3
Vector field on $\mathbb{R}^2$

The best way to picture a vector field is to draw the arrow representing the vector $\mathbf{F}(x, y)$ starting at the point (x, y). Of course, it's impossible to do this for all points (x, y), but we can gain a reasonable impression of $\mathbf{F}$ by doing it for a few representative points in D as in Figure 3. Since $\mathbf{F}(x, y)$ is a two-dimensional vector, we can write it in terms of its **component functions** P and Q as follows:

$$\mathbf{F}(x, y) = P(x, y)\,\mathbf{i} + Q(x, y)\,\mathbf{j} = \langle P(x, y), Q(x, y) \rangle$$

or, for short,

$$\mathbf{F} = P\,\mathbf{i} + Q\,\mathbf{j}$$

Notice that P and Q are scalar functions of two variables and are sometimes called **scalar fields** to distinguish them from vector fields.

> **2 Definition** Let E be a subset of $\mathbb{R}^3$. A **vector field on** $\mathbb{R}^3$ is a function $\mathbf{F}$ that assigns to each point (x, y, z) in E a three-dimensional vector $\mathbf{F}(x, y, z)$.

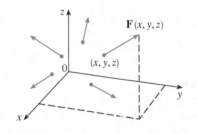

FIGURE 4
Vector field on $\mathbb{R}^3$

A vector field $\mathbf{F}$ on $\mathbb{R}^3$ is pictured in Figure 4. We can express it in terms of its component functions P, Q, and R as

$$\mathbf{F}(x, y, z) = P(x, y, z)\,\mathbf{i} + Q(x, y, z)\,\mathbf{j} + R(x, y, z)\,\mathbf{k}$$

As with the vector functions in Section 10.1, we can define continuity of vector fields and show that $\mathbf{F}$ is continuous if and only if its component functions P, Q, and R are continuous.

We sometimes identify a point (x, y, z) with its position vector $\mathbf{x} = \langle x, y, z \rangle$ and write $\mathbf{F}(\mathbf{x})$ instead of $\mathbf{F}(x, y, z)$. Then $\mathbf{F}$ becomes a function that assigns a vector $\mathbf{F}(\mathbf{x})$ to a vector $\mathbf{x}$.

▽ EXAMPLE 1 **Drawing a two-dimensional vector field** A vector field on $\mathbb{R}^2$ is defined by $\mathbf{F}(x, y) = -y\,\mathbf{i} + x\,\mathbf{j}$. Describe $\mathbf{F}$ by sketching some of the vectors $\mathbf{F}(x, y)$ as in Figure 3.

SOLUTION Since $\mathbf{F}(1, 0) = \mathbf{j}$, we draw the vector $\mathbf{j} = \langle 0, 1 \rangle$ starting at the point $(1, 0)$ in Figure 5. Since $\mathbf{F}(0, 1) = -\mathbf{i}$, we draw the vector $\langle -1, 0 \rangle$ with starting point $(0, 1)$. Continuing in this way, we calculate several other representative values of $\mathbf{F}(x, y)$ in the table and draw the corresponding vectors to represent the vector field in Figure 5.

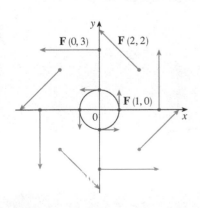

FIGURE 5
$\mathbf{F}(x, y) = -y\,\mathbf{i} + x\,\mathbf{j}$

(x, y)	$\mathbf{F}(x, y)$	(x, y)	$\mathbf{F}(x, y)$
$(1, 0)$	$\langle 0, 1 \rangle$	$(-1, 0)$	$\langle 0, -1 \rangle$
$(2, 2)$	$\langle -2, 2 \rangle$	$(-2, -2)$	$\langle 2, -2 \rangle$
$(3, 0)$	$\langle 0, 3 \rangle$	$(-3, 0)$	$\langle 0, -3 \rangle$
$(0, 1)$	$\langle -1, 0 \rangle$	$(0, -1)$	$\langle 1, 0 \rangle$
$(-2, 2)$	$\langle -2, -2 \rangle$	$(2, -2)$	$\langle 2, 2 \rangle$
$(0, 3)$	$\langle -3, 0 \rangle$	$(0, -3)$	$\langle 3, 0 \rangle$

It appears from Figure 5 that each arrow is tangent to a circle with center the origin. To confirm this, we take the dot product of the position vector $\mathbf{x} = x\,\mathbf{i} + y\,\mathbf{j}$ with the vector $\mathbf{F}(\mathbf{x}) = \mathbf{F}(x, y)$:

$$\mathbf{x} \cdot \mathbf{F}(\mathbf{x}) = (x\,\mathbf{i} + y\,\mathbf{j}) \cdot (-y\,\mathbf{i} + x\,\mathbf{j}) = -xy + yx = 0$$

This shows that $\mathbf{F}(x, y)$ is perpendicular to the position vector $\langle x, y \rangle$ and is therefore tangent to a circle with center the origin and radius $|\mathbf{x}| = \sqrt{x^2 + y^2}$. Notice also that

$$|\mathbf{F}(x, y)| = \sqrt{(-y)^2 + x^2} = \sqrt{x^2 + y^2} = |\mathbf{x}|$$

so the magnitude of the vector $\mathbf{F}(x, y)$ is equal to the radius of the circle.

Some computer algebra systems are capable of plotting vector fields in two or three dimensions. They give a better impression of the vector field than is possible by hand because the computer can plot a large number of representative vectors. Figure 6 shows a computer plot of the vector field in Example 1; Figures 7 and 8 show two other vector fields. Notice that the computer scales the lengths of the vectors so they are not too long and yet are proportional to their true lengths.

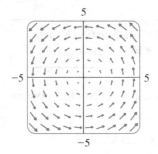

FIGURE 6
$\mathbf{F}(x, y) = \langle -y, x \rangle$

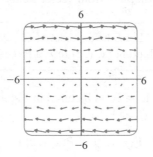

FIGURE 7
$\mathbf{F}(x, y) = \langle y, \sin x \rangle$

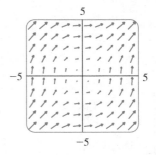

FIGURE 8
$\mathbf{F}(x, y) = \langle \ln(1 + y^2), \ln(1 + x^2) \rangle$

V   EXAMPLE 2   Drawing a three-dimensional vector field   Sketch the vector field on $\mathbb{R}^3$ given by $\mathbf{F}(x, y, z) = z\,\mathbf{k}$.

SOLUTION   The sketch is shown in Figure 9. Notice that all vectors are vertical and point upward above the xy-plane or downward below it. The magnitude increases with the distance from the xy-plane.

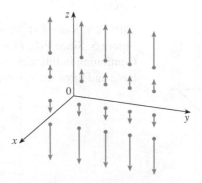

FIGURE 9
$\mathbf{F}(x, y, z) = z\,\mathbf{k}$

We were able to draw the vector field in Example 2 by hand because of its particularly simple formula. Most three-dimensional vector fields, however, are virtually impossible to sketch by hand and so we need to resort to a computer algebra system. Examples are shown in Figures 10, 11, and 12. Notice that the vector fields in Figures 10 and 11 have similar formulas, but all the vectors in Figure 11 point in the general direction of the negative y-axis because their y-components are all -2. If the vector field in Figure 12 represents a velocity field, then a particle would be swept upward and would spiral around the z-axis in the clockwise direction as viewed from above.

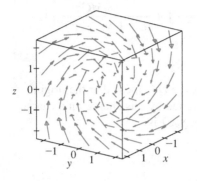

FIGURE 10
$\mathbf{F}(x, y, z) = y\,\mathbf{i} + z\,\mathbf{j} + x\,\mathbf{k}$

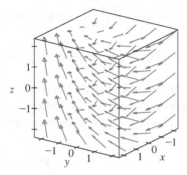

FIGURE 11
$\mathbf{F}(x, y, z) = y\,\mathbf{i} - 2\,\mathbf{j} + x\,\mathbf{k}$

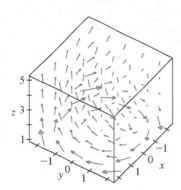

FIGURE 12
$\mathbf{F}(x, y, z) = \dfrac{y}{z}\,\mathbf{i} - \dfrac{x}{z}\,\mathbf{j} + \dfrac{z}{4}\,\mathbf{k}$

TEC In Visual 13.1 you can rotate the vector fields in Figures 10–12 as well as additional fields.

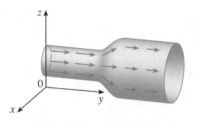

FIGURE 13
Velocity field in fluid flow

EXAMPLE 3 **Velocity fields** Imagine a fluid flowing steadily along a pipe and let $\mathbf{V}(x, y, z)$ be the velocity vector at a point (x, y, z). Then $\mathbf{V}$ assigns a vector to each point (x, y, z) in a certain domain E (the interior of the pipe) and so $\mathbf{V}$ is a vector field on $\mathbb{R}^3$ called a **velocity field**. A possible velocity field is illustrated in Figure 13. The speed at any given point is indicated by the length of the arrow.

Velocity fields also occur in other areas of physics. For instance, the vector field in Example 1 could be used as the velocity field describing the counterclockwise rotation of a wheel. We have seen other examples of velocity fields in Figures 1 and 2.

EXAMPLE 4 **The gravitational field** Newton's Law of Gravitation states that the magnitude of the gravitational force between two objects with masses m and M is

$$|\mathbf{F}| = \frac{mMG}{r^2}$$

where r is the distance between the objects and G is the gravitational constant. (This is an example of an inverse square law.) Let's assume that the object with mass M is located at the origin in $\mathbb{R}^3$. (For instance, M could be the mass of the earth and the origin would be at its center.) Let the position vector of the object with mass m be $\mathbf{x} = \langle x, y, z \rangle$. Then $r = |\mathbf{x}|$, so $r^2 = |\mathbf{x}|^2$. The gravitational force exerted on this second object acts toward the origin, and the unit vector in this direction is

$$-\frac{\mathbf{x}}{|\mathbf{x}|}$$

Therefore the gravitational force acting on the object at $\mathbf{x} = \langle x, y, z \rangle$ is

$$\boxed{3} \qquad \mathbf{F}(\mathbf{x}) = -\frac{mMG}{|\mathbf{x}|^3}\,\mathbf{x}$$

[Physicists often use the notation $\mathbf{r}$ instead of $\mathbf{x}$ for the position vector, so you may see

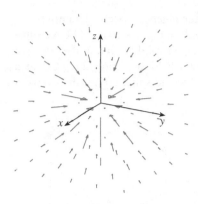

FIGURE 14
Gravitational force field

Formula 3 written in the form $\mathbf{F} = -(mMG/r^3)\mathbf{r}$.] The function given by Equation 3 is an example of a vector field, called the **gravitational field**, because it associates a vector [the force $\mathbf{F}(\mathbf{x})$] with every point $\mathbf{x}$ in space.

Formula 3 is a compact way of writing the gravitational field, but we can also write it in terms of its component functions by using the facts that $\mathbf{x} = x\,\mathbf{i} + y\,\mathbf{j} + z\,\mathbf{k}$ and $|\mathbf{x}| = \sqrt{x^2 + y^2 + z^2}$:

$$\mathbf{F}(x, y, z) = \frac{-mMGx}{(x^2 + y^2 + z^2)^{3/2}}\,\mathbf{i} + \frac{-mMGy}{(x^2 + y^2 + z^2)^{3/2}}\,\mathbf{j} + \frac{-mMGz}{(x^2 + y^2 + z^2)^{3/2}}\,\mathbf{k}$$

The gravitational field $\mathbf{F}$ is pictured in Figure 14.

EXAMPLE 5 **Electric force fields** Suppose an electric charge Q is located at the origin. According to Coulomb's Law, the electric force $\mathbf{F}(\mathbf{x})$ exerted by this charge on a charge q located at a point (x, y, z) with position vector $\mathbf{x} = \langle x, y, z \rangle$ is

$$\boxed{4} \qquad\qquad \mathbf{F}(\mathbf{x}) = \frac{\varepsilon q Q}{|\mathbf{x}|^3}\,\mathbf{x}$$

where ε is a constant (that depends on the units used). For like charges, we have $qQ > 0$ and the force is repulsive; for unlike charges, we have $qQ < 0$ and the force is attractive. Notice the similarity between Formulas 3 and 4. Both vector fields are examples of **force fields**.

Instead of considering the electric force $\mathbf{F}$, physicists often consider the force per unit charge:

$$\mathbf{E}(\mathbf{x}) = \frac{1}{q}\,\mathbf{F}(\mathbf{x}) = \frac{\varepsilon Q}{|\mathbf{x}|^3}\,\mathbf{x}$$

Then $\mathbf{E}$ is a vector field on $\mathbb{R}^3$ called the **electric field** of Q.

Gradient Fields

If f is a scalar function of two variables, recall from Section 11.6 that its gradient ∇f (or grad f) is defined by

$$\nabla f(x, y) = f_x(x, y)\,\mathbf{i} + f_y(x, y)\,\mathbf{j}$$

Therefore ∇f is really a vector field on $\mathbb{R}^2$ and is called a **gradient vector field**. Likewise, if f is a scalar function of three variables, its gradient is a vector field on $\mathbb{R}^3$ given by

$$\nabla f(x, y, z) = f_x(x, y, z)\,\mathbf{i} + f_y(x, y, z)\,\mathbf{j} + f_z(x, y, z)\,\mathbf{k}$$

EXAMPLE 6 Find the gradient vector field of $f(x, y) = x^2 y - y^3$. Plot the gradient vector field together with a contour map of f. How are they related?

SOLUTION The gradient vector field is given by

$$\nabla f(x, y) = \frac{\partial f}{\partial x}\,\mathbf{i} + \frac{\partial f}{\partial y}\,\mathbf{j} = 2xy\,\mathbf{i} + (x^2 - 3y^2)\,\mathbf{j}$$

Figure 15 shows a contour map of f with the gradient vector field. Notice that the gradient vectors are perpendicular to the level curves, as we would expect from Section 11.6.

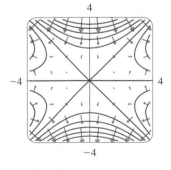

FIGURE 15

Notice also that the gradient vectors are long where the level curves are close to each other and short where the curves are farther apart. That's because the length of the gradient vector is the value of the directional derivative of f and closely spaced level curves indicate a steep graph.

A vector field $\mathbf{F}$ is called a **conservative vector field** if it is the gradient of some scalar function, that is, if there exists a function f such that $\mathbf{F} = \nabla f$. In this situation f is called a **potential function** for $\mathbf{F}$.

Not all vector fields are conservative, but such fields do arise frequently in physics. For example, the gravitational field $\mathbf{F}$ in Example 4 is conservative because if we define

$$f(x, y, z) = \frac{mMG}{\sqrt{x^2 + y^2 + z^2}}$$

then

$$\nabla f(x, y, z) = \frac{\partial f}{\partial x}\mathbf{i} + \frac{\partial f}{\partial y}\mathbf{j} + \frac{\partial f}{\partial z}\mathbf{k}$$

$$= \frac{-mMGx}{(x^2 + y^2 + z^2)^{3/2}}\mathbf{i} + \frac{-mMGy}{(x^2 + y^2 + z^2)^{3/2}}\mathbf{j} + \frac{-mMGz}{(x^2 + y^2 + z^2)^{3/2}}\mathbf{k}$$

$$= \mathbf{F}(x, y, z)$$

In Sections 13.3 and 13.5 we will learn how to tell whether or not a given vector field is conservative.

13.1 Exercises

1–10 Sketch the vector field $\mathbf{F}$ by drawing a diagram like Figure 5 or Figure 9.

1. $\mathbf{F}(x, y) = 0.3\,\mathbf{i} - 0.4\,\mathbf{j}$

2. $\mathbf{F}(x, y) = \frac{1}{2}x\,\mathbf{i} + y\,\mathbf{j}$

3. $\mathbf{F}(x, y) = y\,\mathbf{i} + \frac{1}{2}\,\mathbf{j}$

4. $\mathbf{F}(x, y) = (x - y)\,\mathbf{i} + x\,\mathbf{j}$

5. $\mathbf{F}(x, y) = \dfrac{y\,\mathbf{i} + x\,\mathbf{j}}{\sqrt{x^2 + y^2}}$

6. $\mathbf{F}(x, y) = \dfrac{y\,\mathbf{i} - x\,\mathbf{j}}{\sqrt{x^2 + y^2}}$

7. $\mathbf{F}(x, y, z) = \mathbf{k}$

8. $\mathbf{F}(x, y, z) = -y\,\mathbf{k}$

9. $\mathbf{F}(x, y, z) = x\,\mathbf{k}$

10. $\mathbf{F}(x, y, z) = \mathbf{j} - \mathbf{i}$

11–14 Match the vector fields $\mathbf{F}$ with the plots labeled I–IV. Give reasons for your choices.

11. $\mathbf{F}(x, y) = \langle y, x \rangle$

12. $\mathbf{F}(x, y) = \langle 1, \sin y \rangle$

13. $\mathbf{F}(x, y) = \langle x - 2, x + 1 \rangle$

14. $\mathbf{F}(x, y) = \langle y, 1/x \rangle$

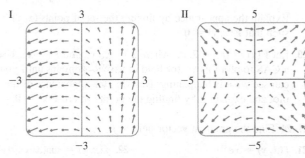

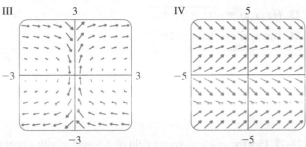

15–18 Match the vector fields **F** on $\mathbb{R}^3$ with the plots labeled I–IV. Give reasons for your choices.

15. $\mathbf{F}(x, y, z) = \mathbf{i} + 2\mathbf{j} + 3\mathbf{k}$ **16.** $\mathbf{F}(x, y, z) = \mathbf{i} + 2\mathbf{j} + z\mathbf{k}$

17. $\mathbf{F}(x, y, z) = x\mathbf{i} + y\mathbf{j} + 3\mathbf{k}$

18. $\mathbf{F}(x, y, z) = x\mathbf{i} + y\mathbf{j} + z\mathbf{k}$

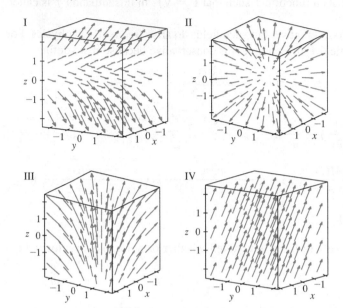

29–32 Match the functions f with the plots of their gradient vector fields labeled I–IV. Give reasons for your choices.

29. $f(x, y) = x^2 + y^2$ **30.** $f(x, y) = x(x + y)$

31. $f(x, y) = (x + y)^2$ **32.** $f(x, y) = \sin\sqrt{x^2 + y^2}$

I
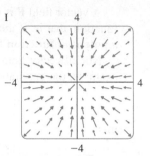

II
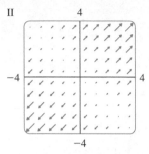

III
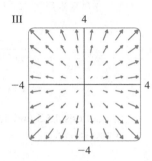

IV
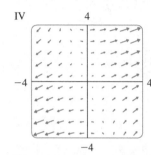

CAS **19.** If you have a CAS that plots vector fields (the command is `fieldplot` in Maple and `PlotVectorField` or `VectorPlot` in Mathematica), use it to plot

$$\mathbf{F}(x, y) = (y^2 - 2xy)\mathbf{i} + (3xy - 6x^2)\mathbf{j}$$

Explain the appearance by finding the set of points (x, y) such that $\mathbf{F}(x, y) = \mathbf{0}$.

CAS **20.** Let $\mathbf{F}(\mathbf{x}) = (r^2 - 2r)\mathbf{x}$, where $\mathbf{x} = \langle x, y \rangle$ and $r = |\mathbf{x}|$. Use a CAS to plot this vector field in various domains until you can see what is happening. Describe the appearance of the plot and explain it by finding the points where $\mathbf{F}(\mathbf{x}) = \mathbf{0}$.

21–24 Find the gradient vector field of f.

21. $f(x, y) = xe^{xy}$ **22.** $f(x, y) = \tan(3x - 4y)$

23. $f(x, y, z) = \sqrt{x^2 + y^2 + z^2}$

24. $f(x, y, z) = x\ln(y - 2z)$

25–26 Find the gradient vector field ∇f of f and sketch it.

25. $f(x, y) = x^2 - y$ **26.** $f(x, y) = \sqrt{x^2 + y^2}$

CAS **27–28** Plot the gradient vector field of f together with a contour map of f. Explain how they are related to each other.

27. $f(x, y) = \sin x + \sin y$ **28.** $f(x, y) = \sin(x + y)$

33. A particle moves in a velocity field $\mathbf{V}(x, y) = \langle x^2, x + y^2 \rangle$. If it is at position $(2, 1)$ at time $t = 3$, estimate its location at time $t = 3.01$.

34. At time $t = 1$, a particle is located at position $(1, 3)$. If it moves in a velocity field

$$\mathbf{F}(x, y) = \langle xy - 2, y^2 - 10 \rangle$$

find its approximate location at time $t = 1.05$.

35. The **flow lines** (or **streamlines**) of a vector field are the paths followed by a particle whose velocity field is the given vector field. Thus the vectors in a vector field are tangent to the flow lines.

(a) Use a sketch of the vector field $\mathbf{F}(x, y) = x\mathbf{i} - y\mathbf{j}$ to draw some flow lines. From your sketches, can you guess the equations of the flow lines?

(b) If parametric equations of a flow line are $x = x(t)$, $y = y(t)$, explain why these functions satisfy the differential equations $dx/dt = x$ and $dy/dt = -y$. Then solve the differential equations to find an equation of the flow line that passes through the point $(1, 1)$.

36. (a) Sketch the vector field $\mathbf{F}(x, y) = \mathbf{i} + x\mathbf{j}$ and then sketch some flow lines. What shape do these flow lines appear to have?

(b) If parametric equations of the flow lines are $x = x(t)$, $y = y(t)$, what differential equations do these functions satisfy? Deduce that $dy/dx = x$.

(c) If a particle starts at the origin in the velocity field given by $\mathbf{F}$, find an equation of the path it follows.

13.2 Line Integrals

In this section we define an integral that is similar to a single integral except that instead of integrating over an interval $[a, b]$, we integrate over a curve C. Such integrals are called *line integrals,* although "curve integrals" would be better terminology. They were invented in the early 19th century to solve problems involving fluid flow, forces, electricity, and magnetism.

We start with a plane curve C given by the parametric equations

$$\boxed{1} \qquad\qquad x = x(t) \qquad y = y(t) \qquad a \leqslant t \leqslant b$$

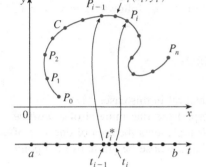

FIGURE 1

or, equivalently, by the vector equation $\mathbf{r}(t) = x(t)\,\mathbf{i} + y(t)\,\mathbf{j}$, and we assume that C is a smooth curve. [This means that $\mathbf{r}'$ is continuous and $\mathbf{r}'(t) \neq \mathbf{0}$. See Section 10.3.] If we divide the parameter interval $[a, b]$ into n subintervals $[t_{i-1}, t_i]$ of equal width and we let $x_i = x(t_i)$ and $y_i = y(t_i)$, then the corresponding points $P_i(x_i, y_i)$ divide C into n subarcs with lengths $\Delta s_1, \Delta s_2, \ldots, \Delta s_n$. (See Figure 1.) We choose any point $P_i^*(x_i^*, y_i^*)$ in the ith subarc. (This corresponds to a point t_i^* in $[t_{i-1}, t_i]$.) Now if f is any function of two variables whose domain includes the curve C, we evaluate f at the point (x_i^*, y_i^*), multiply by the length Δs_i of the subarc, and form the sum

$$\sum_{i=1}^{n} f(x_i^*, y_i^*)\, \Delta s_i$$

which is similar to a Riemann sum. Then we take the limit of these sums and make the following definition by analogy with a single integral.

$\boxed{2}$ **Definition** If f is defined on a smooth curve C given by Equations 1, then the **line integral of f along C** is

$$\int_C f(x, y)\, ds = \lim_{n \to \infty} \sum_{i=1}^{n} f(x_i^*, y_i^*)\, \Delta s_i$$

if this limit exists.

In Section 6.4 we found that the length of C is

$$L = \int_a^b \sqrt{\left(\frac{dx}{dt}\right)^2 + \left(\frac{dy}{dt}\right)^2}\; dt$$

A similar type of argument can be used to show that if f is a continuous function, then the limit in Definition 2 always exists and the following formula can be used to evaluate the line integral:

$$\boxed{3} \qquad \int_C f(x, y)\, ds = \int_a^b f(x(t), y(t)) \sqrt{\left(\frac{dx}{dt}\right)^2 + \left(\frac{dy}{dt}\right)^2}\; dt$$

The value of the line integral does not depend on the parametrization of the curve, provided that the curve is traversed exactly once as t increases from a to b.

The arc length function s is discussed in Section 10.3.

If $s(t)$ is the length of C between $\mathbf{r}(a)$ and $\mathbf{r}(t)$, then

$$\frac{ds}{dt} = \sqrt{\left(\frac{dx}{dt}\right)^2 + \left(\frac{dy}{dt}\right)^2}$$

So the way to remember Formula 3 is to express everything in terms of the parameter t: Use the parametric equations to express x and y in terms of t and write ds as

$$ds = \sqrt{\left(\frac{dx}{dt}\right)^2 + \left(\frac{dy}{dt}\right)^2}\, dt$$

In the special case where C is the line segment that joins $(a, 0)$ to $(b, 0)$, using x as the parameter, we can write the parametric equations of C as follows: $x = x$, $y = 0$, $a \leqslant x \leqslant b$. Formula 3 then becomes

$$\int_C f(x, y)\, ds = \int_a^b f(x, 0)\, dx$$

and so the line integral reduces to an ordinary single integral in this case.

Just as for an ordinary single integral, we can interpret the line integral of a *positive* function as an area. In fact, if $f(x, y) \geqslant 0$, $\int_C f(x, y)\, ds$ represents the area of one side of the "fence" or "curtain" in Figure 2, whose base is C and whose height above the point (x, y) is $f(x, y)$.

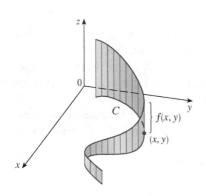

FIGURE 2

EXAMPLE 1 Integrating along a semicircle Evaluate $\int_C (2 + x^2 y)\, ds$, where C is the upper half of the unit circle $x^2 + y^2 = 1$.

SOLUTION In order to use Formula 3, we first need parametric equations to represent C. Recall that the unit circle can be parametrized by means of the equations

$$x = \cos t \qquad y = \sin t$$

and the upper half of the circle is described by the parameter interval $0 \leqslant t \leqslant \pi$. (See Figure 3.) Therefore Formula 3 gives

$$\int_C (2 + x^2 y)\, ds = \int_0^\pi (2 + \cos^2 t \sin t)\sqrt{\left(\frac{dx}{dt}\right)^2 + \left(\frac{dy}{dt}\right)^2}\, dt$$

$$= \int_0^\pi (2 + \cos^2 t \sin t)\sqrt{\sin^2 t + \cos^2 t}\, dt$$

$$= \int_0^\pi (2 + \cos^2 t \sin t)\, dt = \left[2t - \frac{\cos^3 t}{3}\right]_0^\pi$$

$$= 2\pi + \tfrac{2}{3}$$

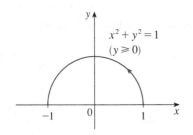

FIGURE 3

Suppose now that C is a **piecewise-smooth curve**; that is, C is a union of a finite number of smooth curves $C_1, C_2, \ldots, C_n$, where, as illustrated in Figure 4, the initial point of C_{i+1} is the terminal point of C_i. Then we define the integral of f along C as the sum of the integrals of f along each of the smooth pieces of C:

$$\int_C f(x, y)\, ds = \int_{C_1} f(x, y)\, ds + \int_{C_2} f(x, y)\, ds + \cdots + \int_{C_n} f(x, y)\, ds$$

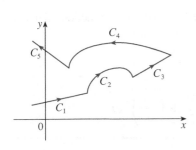

FIGURE 4
A piecewise-smooth curve

EXAMPLE 2   Integrating along a piecewise-smooth curve   Evaluate $\int_C 2x \, ds$, where C consists of the arc C_1 of the parabola $y = x^2$ from $(0, 0)$ to $(1, 1)$ followed by the vertical line segment C_2 from $(1, 1)$ to $(1, 2)$.

SOLUTION   The curve C is shown in Figure 5. C_1 is the graph of a function of x, so we can choose x as the parameter and the equations for C_1 become

$$x = x \qquad y = x^2 \qquad 0 \le x \le 1$$

Therefore

$$\int_{C_1} 2x \, ds = \int_0^1 2x \sqrt{\left(\frac{dx}{dx}\right)^2 + \left(\frac{dy}{dx}\right)^2} \, dx = \int_0^1 2x\sqrt{1 + 4x^2} \, dx$$

$$= \tfrac{1}{4} \cdot \tfrac{2}{3}(1 + 4x^2)^{3/2}\Big]_0^1 = \frac{5\sqrt{5} - 1}{6}$$

On C_2 we choose y as the parameter, so the equations of C_2 are

$$x = 1 \qquad y = y \qquad 1 \le y \le 2$$

and

$$\int_{C_2} 2x \, ds = \int_1^2 2(1) \sqrt{\left(\frac{dx}{dy}\right)^2 + \left(\frac{dy}{dy}\right)^2} \, dy = \int_1^2 2 \, dy = 2$$

Thus

$$\int_C 2x \, ds = \int_{C_1} 2x \, ds + \int_{C_2} 2x \, ds = \frac{5\sqrt{5} - 1}{6} + 2$$

Any physical interpretation of a line integral $\int_C f(x, y) \, ds$ depends on the physical interpretation of the function f. Suppose that $\rho(x, y)$ represents the linear density at a point (x, y) of a thin wire shaped like a curve C. Then the mass of the part of the wire from P_{i-1} to P_i in Figure 1 is approximately $\rho(x_i^*, y_i^*) \, \Delta s_i$ and so the total mass of the wire is approximately $\Sigma \, \rho(x_i^*, y_i^*) \, \Delta s_i$. By taking more and more points on the curve, we obtain the **mass** m of the wire as the limiting value of these approximations:

$$m = \lim_{n \to \infty} \sum_{i=1}^{n} \rho(x_i^*, y_i^*) \, \Delta s_i = \int_C \rho(x, y) \, ds$$

[For example, if $f(x, y) = 2 + x^2 y$ represents the density of a semicircular wire, then the integral in Example 1 would represent the mass of the wire.] The **center of mass** of the wire with density function ρ is located at the point $(\bar{x}, \bar{y})$, where

4
$$\bar{x} = \frac{1}{m} \int_C x \rho(x, y) \, ds \qquad \bar{y} = \frac{1}{m} \int_C y \rho(x, y) \, ds$$

Other physical interpretations of line integrals will be discussed later in this chapter.

V   EXAMPLE 3   Center of mass of a wire   A wire takes the shape of the semicircle $x^2 + y^2 = 1$, $y \ge 0$, and is thicker near its base than near the top. Find the center of mass of the wire if the linear density at any point is proportional to its distance from the line $y = 1$.

SOLUTION   As in Example 1 we use the parametrization $x = \cos t$, $y = \sin t$, $0 \le t \le \pi$, and find that $ds = dt$. The linear density is

$$\rho(x, y) = k(1 - y)$$

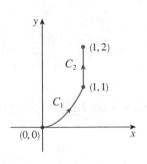

FIGURE 5
$C = C_1 \cup C_2$

where k is a constant, and so the mass of the wire is

$$m = \int_C k(1-y)\,ds = \int_0^\pi k(1-\sin t)\,dt = k\big[t + \cos t\big]_0^\pi = k(\pi - 2)$$

From Equations 4 we have

$$\bar{y} = \frac{1}{m}\int_C y\,\rho(x,y)\,ds = \frac{1}{k(\pi-2)}\int_C y\,k(1-y)\,ds$$

$$= \frac{1}{\pi-2}\int_0^\pi (\sin t - \sin^2 t)\,dt = \frac{1}{\pi-2}\Big[-\cos t - \tfrac{1}{2}t + \tfrac{1}{4}\sin 2t\Big]_0^\pi$$

$$= \frac{4-\pi}{2(\pi-2)}$$

By symmetry we see that $\bar{x} = 0$, so the center of mass is

$$\left(0,\ \frac{4-\pi}{2(\pi-2)}\right) \approx (0, 0.38)$$

See Figure 6.

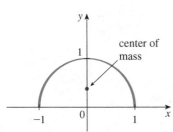

FIGURE 6

Two other line integrals are obtained by replacing Δs_i by either $\Delta x_i = x_i - x_{i-1}$ or $\Delta y_i = y_i - y_{i-1}$ in Definition 2. They are called the **line integrals of f along C with respect to x and y:**

$$\boxed{5} \qquad \int_C f(x,y)\,dx = \lim_{n\to\infty}\sum_{i=1}^n f(x_i^*, y_i^*)\,\Delta x_i$$

$$\boxed{6} \qquad \int_C f(x,y)\,dy = \lim_{n\to\infty}\sum_{i=1}^n f(x_i^*, y_i^*)\,\Delta y_i$$

When we want to distinguish the original line integral $\int_C f(x,y)\,ds$ from those in Equations 5 and 6, we call it the **line integral with respect to arc length.**

The following formulas say that line integrals with respect to x and y can also be evaluated by expressing everything in terms of t: $x = x(t)$, $y = y(t)$, $dx = x'(t)\,dt$, $dy = y'(t)\,dt$.

$$\boxed{7} \qquad \int_C f(x,y)\,dx = \int_a^b f\big(x(t), y(t)\big)\,x'(t)\,dt$$

$$\int_C f(x,y)\,dy = \int_a^b f\big(x(t), y(t)\big)\,y'(t)\,dt$$

It frequently happens that line integrals with respect to x and y occur together. When this happens, it's customary to abbreviate by writing

$$\int_C P(x,y)\,dx + \int_C Q(x,y)\,dy = \int_C P(x,y)\,dx + Q(x,y)\,dy$$

When we are setting up a line integral, sometimes the most difficult thing is to think of a parametric representation for a curve whose geometric description is given. In particular, we often need to parametrize a line segment, so it's useful to remember that a vector representation of the line segment that starts at $\mathbf{r}_0$ and ends at $\mathbf{r}_1$ is given by

$$\boxed{8} \qquad \boxed{\mathbf{r}(t) = (1 - t)\mathbf{r}_0 + t\mathbf{r}_1 \qquad 0 \leq t \leq 1}$$

(See Equation 9.5.4.)

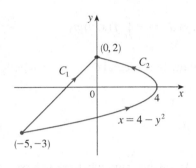

FIGURE 7

$\boxed{V}$ **EXAMPLE 4** **Integrating along two curves with the same endpoints**
Evaluate $\int_C y^2\,dx + x\,dy$, where (a) $C = C_1$ is the line segment from $(-5, -3)$ to $(0, 2)$ and (b) $C = C_2$ is the arc of the parabola $x = 4 - y^2$ from $(-5, -3)$ to $(0, 2)$. (See Figure 7.)

SOLUTION
(a) A parametric representation for the line segment is

$$x = 5t - 5 \qquad y = 5t - 3 \qquad 0 \leq t \leq 1$$

(Use Equation 8 with $\mathbf{r}_0 = \langle -5, -3 \rangle$ and $\mathbf{r}_1 = \langle 0, 2 \rangle$.) Then $dx = 5\,dt$, $dy = 5\,dt$, and Formulas 7 give

$$\int_{C_1} y^2\,dx + x\,dy = \int_0^1 (5t - 3)^2(5\,dt) + (5t - 5)(5\,dt)$$

$$= 5\int_0^1 (25t^2 - 25t + 4)\,dt$$

$$= 5\left[\frac{25t^3}{3} - \frac{25t^2}{2} + 4t\right]_0^1 = -\frac{5}{6}$$

(b) Since the parabola is given as a function of y, let's take y as the parameter and write C_2 as

$$x = 4 - y^2 \qquad y = y \qquad -3 \leq y \leq 2$$

Then $dx = -2y\,dy$ and by Formulas 7 we have

$$\int_{C_2} y^2\,dx + x\,dy = \int_{-3}^2 y^2(-2y)\,dy + (4 - y^2)\,dy$$

$$= \int_{-3}^2 (-2y^3 - y^2 + 4)\,dy$$

$$= \left[-\frac{y^4}{2} - \frac{y^3}{3} + 4y\right]_{-3}^2 = 40\tfrac{5}{6}$$

Notice that we got different answers in parts (a) and (b) of Example 4 even though the two curves had the same endpoints. Thus, in general, the value of a line integral depends not just on the endpoints of the curve but also on the path. (But see Section 13.3 for conditions under which the integral is independent of the path.)

Notice also that the answers in Example 4 depend on the direction, or orientation, of the curve. If $-C_1$ denotes the line segment from $(0, 2)$ to $(-5, -3)$, you can verify, using the parametrization

$$x = -5t \qquad y = 2 - 5t \qquad 0 \leq t \leq 1$$

that

$$\int_{-C_1} y^2\,dx + x\,dy = \tfrac{5}{6}$$

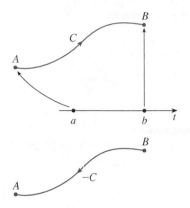

FIGURE 8

In general, a given parametrization $x = x(t)$, $y = y(t)$, $a \le t \le b$, determines an **orientation** of a curve C, with the positive direction corresponding to increasing values of the parameter t. (See Figure 8, where the initial point A corresponds to the parameter value a and the terminal point B corresponds to $t = b$.)

If $-C$ denotes the curve consisting of the same points as C but with the opposite orientation (from initial point B to terminal point A in Figure 8), then we have

$$\int_{-C} f(x, y)\, dx = -\int_C f(x, y)\, dx \qquad \int_{-C} f(x, y)\, dy = -\int_C f(x, y)\, dy$$

But if we integrate with respect to arc length, the value of the line integral does *not* change when we reverse the orientation of the curve:

$$\int_{-C} f(x, y)\, ds = \int_C f(x, y)\, ds$$

This is because Δs_i is always positive, whereas Δx_i and Δy_i change sign when we reverse the orientation of C.

Line Integrals in Space

We now suppose that C is a smooth space curve given by the parametric equations

$$x = x(t) \qquad y = y(t) \qquad z = z(t) \qquad a \le t \le b$$

or by a vector equation $\mathbf{r}(t) = x(t)\, \mathbf{i} + y(t)\, \mathbf{j} + z(t)\, \mathbf{k}$. If f is a function of three variables that is continuous on some region containing C, then we define the **line integral of f along C** (with respect to arc length) in a manner similar to that for plane curves:

$$\int_C f(x, y, z)\, ds = \lim_{n \to \infty} \sum_{i=1}^{n} f(x_i^*, y_i^*, z_i^*)\, \Delta s_i$$

We evaluate it using a formula similar to Formula 3:

$$\boxed{9} \qquad \int_C f(x, y, z)\, ds = \int_a^b f\big(x(t), y(t), z(t)\big) \sqrt{\left(\frac{dx}{dt}\right)^2 + \left(\frac{dy}{dt}\right)^2 + \left(\frac{dz}{dt}\right)^2}\; dt$$

Observe that the integrals in both Formulas 3 and 9 can be written in the more compact vector notation

$$\int_a^b f(\mathbf{r}(t)) \, |\mathbf{r}'(t)|\, dt$$

For the special case $f(x, y, z) = 1$, we get

$$\int_C ds = \int_a^b |\mathbf{r}'(t)|\, dt = L$$

where L is the length of the curve C (see Formula 10.3.3).

Line integrals along C with respect to x, y, and z can also be defined. For example,

$$\int_C f(x, y, z) \, dz = \lim_{n \to \infty} \sum_{i=1}^{n} f(x_i^*, y_i^*, z_i^*) \, \Delta z_i$$

$$= \int_a^b f\big(x(t), y(t), z(t)\big) \, z'(t) \, dt$$

Therefore, as with line integrals in the plane, we evaluate integrals of the form

10 $$\int_C P(x, y, z) \, dx + Q(x, y, z) \, dy + R(x, y, z) \, dz$$

by expressing everything (x, y, z, dx, dy, dz) in terms of the parameter t.

▼ EXAMPLE 5   A line integral in space   Evaluate $\int_C y \sin z \, ds$, where C is the circular helix given by the equations $x = \cos t$, $y = \sin t$, $z = t$, $0 \le t \le 2\pi$. (See Figure 9.)

SOLUTION Formula 9 gives

$$\int_C y \sin z \, ds = \int_0^{2\pi} (\sin t) \sin t \sqrt{\left(\frac{dx}{dt}\right)^2 + \left(\frac{dy}{dt}\right)^2 + \left(\frac{dz}{dt}\right)^2} \, dt$$

$$= \int_0^{2\pi} \sin^2 t \sqrt{\sin^2 t + \cos^2 t + 1} \, dt = \sqrt{2} \int_0^{2\pi} \tfrac{1}{2}(1 - \cos 2t) \, dt$$

$$= \frac{\sqrt{2}}{2} \Big[t - \tfrac{1}{2} \sin 2t \Big]_0^{2\pi} = \sqrt{2}\,\pi$$

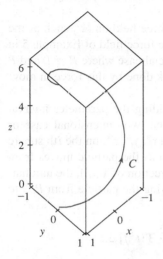

FIGURE 9

EXAMPLE 6   Evaluate $\int_C y \, dx + z \, dy + x \, dz$, where C consists of the line segment C_1 from $(2, 0, 0)$ to $(3, 4, 5)$, followed by the vertical line segment C_2 from $(3, 4, 5)$ to $(3, 4, 0)$.

SOLUTION The curve C is shown in Figure 10. Using Equation 8, we write C_1 as

$$\mathbf{r}(t) = (1 - t)\langle 2, 0, 0 \rangle + t \langle 3, 4, 5 \rangle = \langle 2 + t, 4t, 5t \rangle$$

or, in parametric form, as

$$x = 2 + t \qquad y = 4t \qquad z = 5t \qquad 0 \le t \le 1$$

Thus

$$\int_{C_1} y \, dx + z \, dy + x \, dz = \int_0^1 (4t) \, dt + (5t)4 \, dt + (2 + t)5 \, dt$$

$$= \int_0^1 (10 + 29t) \, dt = 10t + 29 \frac{t^2}{2} \bigg]_0^1 = 24.5$$

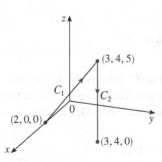

FIGURE 10

Likewise, C_2 can be written in the form

$$\mathbf{r}(t) = (1 - t)\langle 3, 4, 5 \rangle + t \langle 3, 4, 0 \rangle = \langle 3, 4, 5 - 5t \rangle$$

or $$x = 3 \qquad y = 4 \qquad z = 5 - 5t \qquad 0 \le t \le 1$$

Then $dx = 0 = dy$, so

$$\int_{C_2} y\,dx + z\,dy + x\,dz = \int_0^1 3(-5)\,dt = -15$$

Adding the values of these integrals, we obtain

$$\int_C y\,dx + z\,dy + x\,dz = 24.5 - 15 = 9.5$$

Line Integrals of Vector Fields

Recall from Section 6.6 that the work done by a variable force $f(x)$ in moving a particle from a to b along the x-axis is $W = \int_a^b f(x)\,dx$. Then in Section 9.3 we found that the work done by a constant force $\mathbf{F}$ in moving an object from a point P to another point Q in space is $W = \mathbf{F} \cdot \mathbf{D}$, where $\mathbf{D} = \overrightarrow{PQ}$ is the displacement vector.

Now suppose that $\mathbf{F} = P\,\mathbf{i} + Q\,\mathbf{j} + R\,\mathbf{k}$ is a continuous force field on $\mathbb{R}^3$, such as the gravitational field of Example 4 in Section 13.1 or the electric force field of Example 5 in Section 13.1. (A force field on $\mathbb{R}^2$ could be regarded as a special case where $R = 0$ and P and Q depend only on x and y.) We wish to compute the work done by this force in moving a particle along a smooth curve C.

We divide C into subarcs $P_{i-1}P_i$ with lengths Δs_i by dividing the parameter interval $[a, b]$ into subintervals of equal width. (See Figure 1 for the two-dimensional case or Figure 11 for the three-dimensional case.) Choose a point $P_i^*(x_i^*, y_i^*, z_i^*)$ on the ith subarc corresponding to the parameter value t_i^*. If Δs_i is small, then as the particle moves from P_{i-1} to P_i along the curve, it proceeds approximately in the direction of $\mathbf{T}(t_i^*)$, the unit tangent vector at P_i^*. Thus the work done by the force $\mathbf{F}$ in moving the particle from P_{i-1} to P_i is approximately

$$\mathbf{F}(x_i^*, y_i^*, z_i^*) \cdot [\Delta s_i\,\mathbf{T}(t_i^*)] = [\mathbf{F}(x_i^*, y_i^*, z_i^*) \cdot \mathbf{T}(t_i^*)]\,\Delta s_i$$

and the total work done in moving the particle along C is approximately

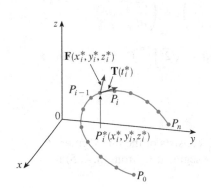

FIGURE 11

$$\boxed{11} \qquad \sum_{i=1}^n [\mathbf{F}(x_i^*, y_i^*, z_i^*) \cdot \mathbf{T}(x_i^*, y_i^*, z_i^*)]\,\Delta s_i$$

where $\mathbf{T}(x, y, z)$ is the unit tangent vector at the point (x, y, z) on C. Intuitively, we see that these approximations ought to become better as n becomes larger. Therefore we define the **work** W done by the force field $\mathbf{F}$ as the limit of the Riemann sums in (11), namely,

$$\boxed{12} \qquad W = \int_C \mathbf{F}(x, y, z) \cdot \mathbf{T}(x, y, z)\,ds = \int_C \mathbf{F} \cdot \mathbf{T}\,ds$$

Equation 12 says that *work is the line integral with respect to arc length of the tangential component of the force.*

If the curve C is given by the vector equation $\mathbf{r}(t) = x(t)\,\mathbf{i} + y(t)\,\mathbf{j} + z(t)\,\mathbf{k}$, then $\mathbf{T}(t) = \mathbf{r}'(t)/|\mathbf{r}'(t)|$, so using Equation 9 we can rewrite Equation 12 in the form

$$W = \int_a^b \left[\mathbf{F}(\mathbf{r}(t)) \cdot \frac{\mathbf{r}'(t)}{|\mathbf{r}'(t)|} \right] |\mathbf{r}'(t)|\,dt = \int_a^b \mathbf{F}(\mathbf{r}(t)) \cdot \mathbf{r}'(t)\,dt$$

This integral is often abbreviated as $\int_C \mathbf{F} \cdot d\mathbf{r}$ and occurs in other areas of physics as well. Therefore we make the following definition for the line integral of *any* continuous vector field.

> **13 Definition** Let $\mathbf{F}$ be a continuous vector field defined on a smooth curve C given by a vector function $\mathbf{r}(t)$, $a \leqslant t \leqslant b$. Then the **line integral of F along C** is
>
> $$\int_C \mathbf{F} \cdot d\mathbf{r} = \int_a^b \mathbf{F}(\mathbf{r}(t)) \cdot \mathbf{r}'(t)\, dt = \int_C \mathbf{F} \cdot \mathbf{T}\, ds$$

When using Definition 13, remember that $\mathbf{F}(\mathbf{r}(t))$ is just an abbreviation for $\mathbf{F}(x(t), y(t), z(t))$, so we evaluate $\mathbf{F}(\mathbf{r}(t))$ simply by putting $x = x(t)$, $y = y(t)$, and $z = z(t)$ in the expression for $\mathbf{F}(x, y, z)$. Notice also that we can formally write $d\mathbf{r} = \mathbf{r}'(t)\, dt$.

Figure 12 shows the force field and the curve in Example 7. The work done is negative because the field impedes movement along the curve.

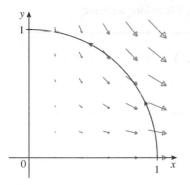

FIGURE 12

EXAMPLE 7 Find the work done by the force field $\mathbf{F}(x, y) = x^2\,\mathbf{i} - xy\,\mathbf{j}$ in moving a particle along the quarter-circle $\mathbf{r}(t) = \cos t\,\mathbf{i} + \sin t\,\mathbf{j}$, $0 \leqslant t \leqslant \pi/2$.

SOLUTION Since $x = \cos t$ and $y = \sin t$, we have

$$\mathbf{F}(\mathbf{r}(t)) = \cos^2 t\,\mathbf{i} - \cos t\,\sin t\,\mathbf{j}$$

and

$$\mathbf{r}'(t) = -\sin t\,\mathbf{i} + \cos t\,\mathbf{j}$$

Therefore the work done is

$$\int_C \mathbf{F} \cdot d\mathbf{r} = \int_0^{\pi/2} \mathbf{F}(\mathbf{r}(t)) \cdot \mathbf{r}'(t)\, dt = \int_0^{\pi/2} (-2\cos^2 t\,\sin t)\, dt$$

$$= 2\,\frac{\cos^3 t}{3}\Bigg]_0^{\pi/2} = -\frac{2}{3}$$

Note: Even though $\int_C \mathbf{F} \cdot d\mathbf{r} = \int_C \mathbf{F} \cdot \mathbf{T}\, ds$ and integrals with respect to arc length are unchanged when orientation is reversed, it is still true that

$$\int_{-C} \mathbf{F} \cdot d\mathbf{r} = -\int_C \mathbf{F} \cdot d\mathbf{r}$$

because the unit tangent vector $\mathbf{T}$ is replaced by its negative when C is replaced by $-C$.

Figure 13 shows the twisted cubic C in Example 8 and some typical vectors acting at three points on C.

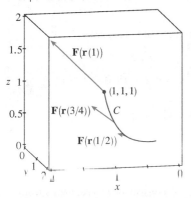

FIGURE 13

EXAMPLE 8 Line integral of a vector field Evaluate $\int_C \mathbf{F} \cdot d\mathbf{r}$, where $\mathbf{F}(x, y, z) = xy\,\mathbf{i} + yz\,\mathbf{j} + zx\,\mathbf{k}$ and C is the twisted cubic given by

$$x = t \qquad y = t^2 \qquad z = t^3 \qquad 0 \leqslant t \leqslant 1$$

SOLUTION We have

$$\mathbf{r}(t) = t\,\mathbf{i} + t^2\,\mathbf{j} + t^3\,\mathbf{k}$$

$$\mathbf{r}'(t) = \mathbf{i} + 2t\,\mathbf{j} + 3t^2\,\mathbf{k}$$

$$\mathbf{F}(\mathbf{r}(t)) = t^3\,\mathbf{i} + t^5\,\mathbf{j} + t^4\,\mathbf{k}$$

Thus
$$\int_C \mathbf{F} \cdot d\mathbf{r} = \int_0^1 \mathbf{F}(\mathbf{r}(t)) \cdot \mathbf{r}'(t)\, dt$$

$$= \int_0^1 (t^3 + 5t^6)\, dt = \frac{t^4}{4} + \frac{5t^7}{7} \bigg]_0^1 = \frac{27}{28}$$

Finally, we note the connection between line integrals of vector fields and line integrals of scalar fields. Suppose the vector field $\mathbf{F}$ on $\mathbb{R}^3$ is given in component form by the equation $\mathbf{F} = P\,\mathbf{i} + Q\,\mathbf{j} + R\,\mathbf{k}$. We use Definition 13 to compute its line integral along C:

$$\int_C \mathbf{F} \cdot d\mathbf{r} = \int_a^b \mathbf{F}(\mathbf{r}(t)) \cdot \mathbf{r}'(t)\, dt$$

$$= \int_a^b (P\,\mathbf{i} + Q\,\mathbf{j} + R\,\mathbf{k}) \cdot \left(x'(t)\,\mathbf{i} + y'(t)\,\mathbf{j} + z'(t)\,\mathbf{k}\right) dt$$

$$= \int_a^b \left[P(x(t), y(t), z(t)) x'(t) + Q(x(t), y(t), z(t)) y'(t) + R(x(t), y(t), z(t)) z'(t) \right] dt$$

But this last integral is precisely the line integral in (10). Therefore we have

$$\boxed{\int_C \mathbf{F} \cdot d\mathbf{r} = \int_C P\, dx + Q\, dy + R\, dz \qquad \text{where } \mathbf{F} = P\,\mathbf{i} + Q\,\mathbf{j} + R\,\mathbf{k}}$$

For example, the integral $\int_C y\, dx + z\, dy + x\, dz$ in Example 6 could be expressed as $\int_C \mathbf{F} \cdot d\mathbf{r}$ where

$$\mathbf{F}(x, y, z) = y\,\mathbf{i} + z\,\mathbf{j} + x\,\mathbf{k}$$

13.2 Exercises

1–16 Evaluate the line integral, where C is the given curve.

1. $\int_C y^3\, ds, \quad C: x = t^3, \ y = t, \ 0 \le t \le 2$

2. $\int_C xy\, ds, \quad C: x = t^2, \ y = 2t, \ 0 \le t \le 1$

3. $\int_C xy^4\, ds, \quad C$ is the right half of the circle $x^2 + y^2 = 16$

4. $\int_C x \sin y\, ds, \quad C$ is the line segment from $(0, 3)$ to $(4, 6)$

5. $\int_C \left(x^2 y^3 - \sqrt{x}\right) dy,$
C is the arc of the curve $y = \sqrt{x}$ from $(1, 1)$ to $(4, 2)$

6. $\int_C xe^y\, dx,$
C is the arc of the curve $x = e^y$ from $(1, 0)$ to $(e, 1)$

7. $\int_C xy\, dx + (x - y)\, dy, \quad C$ consists of line segments from $(0, 0)$ to $(2, 0)$ and from $(2, 0)$ to $(3, 2)$

8. $\int_C \sin x\, dx + \cos y\, dy, \quad C$ consists of the top half of the circle $x^2 + y^2 = 1$ from $(1, 0)$ to $(-1, 0)$ and the line segment from $(-1, 0)$ to $(-2, 3)$

9. $\int_C xyz\, ds,$
$C: x = 2 \sin t, \ y = t, \ z = -2 \cos t, \ 0 \le t \le \pi$

10. $\int_C xyz^2\, ds,$
C is the line segment from $(-1, 5, 0)$ to $(1, 6, 4)$

11. $\int_C xe^{yz}\, ds,$
C is the line segment from $(0, 0, 0)$ to $(1, 2, 3)$

12. $\int_C (2x + 9z)\, ds, \quad C: x = t, \ y = t^2, \ z = t^3, \ 0 \le t \le 1$

13. $\int_C x^2 y \sqrt{z}\, dz, \quad C: x = t^3, \ y = t, \ z = t^2, \ 0 \le t \le 1$

14. $\int_C z\, dx + x\, dy + y\, dz,$
$C: x = t^2, \ y = t^3, \ z = t^2, \ 0 \le t \le 1$

15. $\int_C (x + yz)\, dx + 2x\, dy + xyz\, dz, \quad C$ consists of line segments from $(1, 0, 1)$ to $(2, 3, 1)$ and from $(2, 3, 1)$ to $(2, 5, 2)$

16. $\int_C x^2\, dx + y^2\, dy + z^2\, dz, \quad C$ consists of line segments from $(0, 0, 0)$ to $(1, 2, -1)$ and from $(1, 2, -1)$ to $(3, 2, 0)$

⊞ Graphing calculator or computer with graphing software required   CAS Computer algebra system required   **1.** Homework Hints available in TEC

17. Let **F** be the vector field shown in the figure.
    (a) If C_1 is the vertical line segment from $(-3, -3)$ to $(-3, 3)$, determine whether $\int_{C_1} \mathbf{F} \cdot d\mathbf{r}$ is positive, negative, or zero.
    (b) If C_2 is the counterclockwise-oriented circle with radius 3 and center the origin, determine whether $\int_{C_2} \mathbf{F} \cdot d\mathbf{r}$ is positive, negative, or zero.

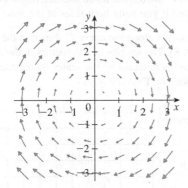

18. The figure shows a vector field **F** and two curves C_1 and C_2. Are the line integrals of **F** over C_1 and C_2 positive, negative, or zero? Explain.

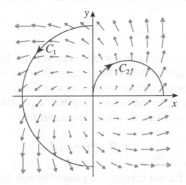

19–22 Evaluate the line integral $\int_C \mathbf{F} \cdot d\mathbf{r}$, where C is given by the vector function $\mathbf{r}(t)$.

19. $\mathbf{F}(x, y) = xy\,\mathbf{i} + 3y^2\,\mathbf{j}$,
    $\mathbf{r}(t) = 11t^4\,\mathbf{i} + t^3\,\mathbf{j}, \quad 0 \le t \le 1$

20. $\mathbf{F}(x, y, z) = (x + y)\,\mathbf{i} + (y - z)\,\mathbf{j} + z^2\,\mathbf{k}$,
    $\mathbf{r}(t) = t^2\,\mathbf{i} + t^3\,\mathbf{j} + t^2\,\mathbf{k}, \quad 0 \le t \le 1$

21. $\mathbf{F}(x, y, z) = \sin x\,\mathbf{i} + \cos y\,\mathbf{j} + xz\,\mathbf{k}$,
    $\mathbf{r}(t) = t^3\,\mathbf{i} - t^2\,\mathbf{j} + t\,\mathbf{k}, \quad 0 \le t \le 1$

22. $\mathbf{F}(x, y, z) = z\,\mathbf{i} + y\,\mathbf{j} - x\,\mathbf{k}$,
    $\mathbf{r}(t) = t\,\mathbf{i} + \sin t\,\mathbf{j} + \cos t\,\mathbf{k}, \quad 0 \le t \le \pi$

23–26 Use a calculator or CAS to evaluate the line integral correct to four decimal places.

23. $\int_C \mathbf{F} \cdot d\mathbf{r}$, where $\mathbf{F}(x, y) = xy\,\mathbf{i} + \sin y\,\mathbf{j}$ and
    $\mathbf{r}(t) = e^t\,\mathbf{i} + e^{-t^2}\,\mathbf{j}, \quad 1 \le t \le 2$

24. $\int_C \mathbf{F} \cdot d\mathbf{r}$, where $\mathbf{F}(x, y, z) = y \sin z\,\mathbf{i} + z \sin x\,\mathbf{j} + x \sin y\,\mathbf{k}$
    and $\mathbf{r}(t) = \cos t\,\mathbf{i} + \sin t\,\mathbf{j} + \sin 5t\,\mathbf{k}, \quad 0 \le t \le \pi$

25. $\int_C x \sin(y + z)\,ds$, where C has parametric equations $x = t^2$, $y = t^3$, $z = t^4$, $0 \le t \le 5$

26. $\int_C ze^{-xy}\,ds$, where C has parametric equations $x = t$, $y = t^2$, $z = e^{-t}$, $0 \le t \le 1$

CAS **27–28** Use a graph of the vector field **F** and the curve C to guess whether the line integral of **F** over C is positive, negative, or zero. Then evaluate the line integral.

27. $\mathbf{F}(x, y) = (x - y)\,\mathbf{i} + xy\,\mathbf{j}$,
    C is the arc of the circle $x^2 + y^2 = 4$ traversed counterclockwise from $(2, 0)$ to $(0, -2)$

28. $\mathbf{F}(x, y) = \dfrac{x}{\sqrt{x^2 + y^2}}\,\mathbf{i} + \dfrac{y}{\sqrt{x^2 + y^2}}\,\mathbf{j}$,
    C is the parabola $y = 1 + x^2$ from $(-1, 2)$ to $(1, 2)$

29. (a) Evaluate the line integral $\int_C \mathbf{F} \cdot d\mathbf{r}$, where $\mathbf{F}(x, y) = e^{x-1}\,\mathbf{i} + xy\,\mathbf{j}$ and C is given by $\mathbf{r}(t) = t^2\,\mathbf{i} + t^3\,\mathbf{j}, 0 \le t \le 1$.
    (b) Illustrate part (a) by using a graphing calculator or computer to graph C and the vectors from the vector field corresponding to $t = 0$, $1/\sqrt{2}$, and 1 (as in Figure 13).

30. (a) Evaluate the line integral $\int_C \mathbf{F} \cdot d\mathbf{r}$, where $\mathbf{F}(x, y, z) = x\,\mathbf{i} - z\,\mathbf{j} + y\,\mathbf{k}$ and C is given by $\mathbf{r}(t) = 2t\,\mathbf{i} + 3t\,\mathbf{j} - t^2\,\mathbf{k}, -1 \le t \le 1$.
    (b) Illustrate part (a) by using a computer to graph C and the vectors from the vector field corresponding to $t = \pm 1$ and $\pm \frac{1}{2}$ (as in Figure 13).

CAS 31. Find the exact value of $\int_C x^3y^2z\,ds$, where C is the curve with parametric equations $x = e^{-t}\cos 4t$, $y = e^{-t}\sin 4t$, $z = e^{-t}$, $0 \le t \le 2\pi$.

32. (a) Find the work done by the force field $\mathbf{F}(x, y) = x^2\,\mathbf{i} + xy\,\mathbf{j}$ on a particle that moves once around the circle $x^2 + y^2 = 4$ oriented in the counterclockwise direction.
    (b) Use a computer algebra system to graph the force field and circle on the same screen. Use the graph to explain your answer to part (a).

33. A thin wire is bent into the shape of a semicircle $x^2 + y^2 = 4$, $x \ge 0$. If the linear density is a constant k, find the mass and center of mass of the wire.

34. A thin wire has the shape of the first-quadrant part of the circle with center the origin and radius a. If the density function is $\rho(x, y) = kxy$, find the mass and center of mass of the wire.

35. (a) Write the formulas similar to Equations 4 for the center of mass $(\bar{x}, \bar{y}, \bar{z})$ of a thin wire in the shape of a space curve C if the wire has density function $\rho(x, y, z)$.

(b) Find the center of mass of a wire in the shape of the helix $x = 2 \sin t$, $y = 2 \cos t$, $z = 3t$, $0 \leqslant t \leqslant 2\pi$, if the density is a constant k.

36. Find the mass and center of mass of a wire in the shape of the helix $x = t$, $y = \cos t$, $z = \sin t$, $0 \leqslant t \leqslant 2\pi$, if the density at any point is equal to the square of the distance from the origin.

37. If a wire with linear density $\rho(x, y)$ lies along a plane curve C, its **moments of inertia** about the x- and y-axes are defined as

$$I_x = \int_C y^2 \rho(x, y) \, ds \qquad I_y = \int_C x^2 \rho(x, y) \, ds$$

Find the moments of inertia for the wire in Example 3.

38. If a wire with linear density $\rho(x, y, z)$ lies along a space curve C, its **moments of inertia** about the x-, y-, and z-axes are defined as

$$I_x = \int_C (y^2 + z^2) \rho(x, y, z) \, ds$$

$$I_y = \int_C (x^2 + z^2) \rho(x, y, z) \, ds$$

$$I_z = \int_C (x^2 + y^2) \rho(x, y, z) \, ds$$

Find the moments of inertia for the wire in Exercise 35.

39. Find the work done by the force field $\mathbf{F}(x, y) = x\mathbf{i} + (y + 2)\mathbf{j}$ in moving an object along an arch of the cycloid $\mathbf{r}(t) = (t - \sin t)\mathbf{i} + (1 - \cos t)\mathbf{j}$, $0 \leqslant t \leqslant 2\pi$.

40. Find the work done by the force field $\mathbf{F}(x, y) = x^2\mathbf{i} + ye^x\mathbf{j}$ on a particle that moves along the parabola $x = y^2 + 1$ from $(1, 0)$ to $(2, 1)$.

41. Find the work done by the force field $\mathbf{F}(x, y, z) = \langle y + z, x + z, x + y \rangle$ on a particle that moves along the line segment from $(1, 0, 0)$ to $(3, 4, 2)$.

42. The force exerted by an electric charge at the origin on a charged particle at a point (x, y, z) with position vector $\mathbf{r} = \langle x, y, z \rangle$ is $\mathbf{F}(\mathbf{r}) = K\mathbf{r}/|\mathbf{r}|^3$ where K is a constant. (See Example 5 in Section 13.1.) Find the work done as the particle moves along a straight line from $(2, 0, 0)$ to $(2, 1, 5)$.

43. A 160-lb man carries a 25-lb can of paint up a helical staircase that encircles a silo with a radius of 20 ft. If the silo is 90 ft high and the man makes exactly three complete revolutions climbing to the top, how much work is done by the man against gravity?

44. Suppose there is a hole in the can of paint in Exercise 43 and 9 lb of paint leaks steadily out of the can during the man's ascent. How much work is done?

45. (a) Show that a constant force field does zero work on a particle that moves once uniformly around the circle $x^2 + y^2 = 1$.

(b) Is this also true for a force field $\mathbf{F}(\mathbf{x}) = k\mathbf{x}$, where k is a constant and $\mathbf{x} = \langle x, y \rangle$?

46. The base of a circular fence with radius 10 m is given by $x = 10 \cos t$, $y = 10 \sin t$. The height of the fence at position (x, y) is given by the function $h(x, y) = 4 + 0.01(x^2 - y^2)$, so the height varies from 3 m to 5 m. Suppose that 1 L of paint covers 100 m^2. Sketch the fence and determine how much paint you will need if you paint both sides of the fence.

47. An object moves along the curve C shown in the figure from $(1, 2)$ to $(9, 8)$. The lengths of the vectors in the force field $\mathbf{F}$ are measured in newtons by the scales on the axes. Estimate the work done by $\mathbf{F}$ on the object.

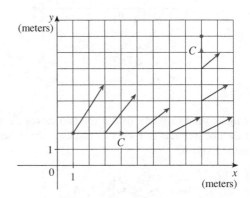

48. Experiments show that a steady current I in a long wire produces a magnetic field $\mathbf{B}$ that is tangent to any circle that lies in the plane perpendicular to the wire and whose center is the axis of the wire (as in the figure). *Ampère's Law* relates the electric current to its magnetic effects and states that

$$\int_C \mathbf{B} \cdot d\mathbf{r} = \mu_0 I$$

where I is the net current that passes through any surface bounded by a closed curve C, and μ_0 is a constant called the permeability of free space. By taking C to be a circle with radius r, show that the magnitude $B = |\mathbf{B}|$ of the magnetic field at a distance r from the center of the wire is

$$B = \frac{\mu_0 I}{2\pi r}$$

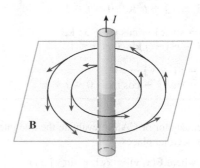

13.3 The Fundamental Theorem for Line Integrals

Recall from Section 5.4 that Part 2 of the Fundamental Theorem of Calculus can be written as

$$\boxed{1} \qquad \int_a^b F'(x)\,dx = F(b) - F(a)$$

where F' is continuous on $[a, b]$. We also called Equation 1 the Net Change Theorem: The integral of a rate of change is the net change.

If we think of the gradient vector ∇f of a function f of two or three variables as a sort of derivative of f, then the following theorem can be regarded as a version of the Fundamental Theorem for line integrals.

$\boxed{2}$ **Theorem**   Let C be a smooth curve given by the vector function $\mathbf{r}(t)$, $a \leqslant t \leqslant b$. Let f be a differentiable function of two or three variables whose gradient vector ∇f is continuous on C. Then

$$\int_C \nabla f \cdot d\mathbf{r} = f(\mathbf{r}(b)) - f(\mathbf{r}(a))$$

Note: Theorem 2 says that we can evaluate the line integral of a conservative vector field (the gradient vector field of the potential function f) simply by knowing the value of f at the endpoints of C. In fact, Theorem 2 says that the line integral of ∇f is the net change in f. If f is a function of two variables and C is a plane curve with initial point $A(x_1, y_1)$ and terminal point $B(x_2, y_2)$, as in Figure 1(a), then Theorem 2 becomes

$$\int_C \nabla f \cdot d\mathbf{r} = f(x_2, y_2) - f(x_1, y_1)$$

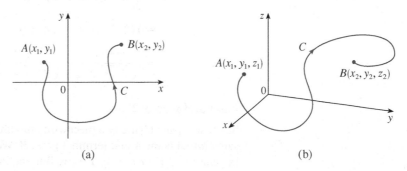

FIGURE 1   (a)   (b)

If f is a function of three variables and C is a space curve joining the point $A(x_1, y_1, z_1)$ to the point $B(x_2, y_2, z_2)$ as in Figure 1(b), then we have

$$\int_C \nabla f \cdot d\mathbf{r} = f(x_2, y_2, z_2) - f(x_1, y_1, z_1)$$

Let's prove Theorem 2 for this case.

PROOF OF THEOREM 2   Using Definition 13.2.13, we have

$$\int_C \nabla f \cdot d\mathbf{r} = \int_a^b \nabla f(\mathbf{r}(t)) \cdot \mathbf{r}'(t)\, dt$$

$$= \int_a^b \left(\frac{\partial f}{\partial x} \frac{dx}{dt} + \frac{\partial f}{\partial y} \frac{dy}{dt} + \frac{\partial f}{\partial z} \frac{dz}{dt} \right) dt$$

$$= \int_a^b \frac{d}{dt} f(\mathbf{r}(t))\, dt \qquad\qquad \text{(by the Chain Rule)}$$

$$= f(\mathbf{r}(b)) - f(\mathbf{r}(a))$$

The last step follows from the Fundamental Theorem of Calculus (Equation 1).   ▭

Although we have proved Theorem 2 for smooth curves, it is also true for piecewise-smooth curves. This can be seen by subdividing C into a finite number of smooth curves and adding the resulting integrals.

EXAMPLE 1   **Applying the Fundamental Theorem to the calculation of work**   Find the work done by the gravitational field

$$\mathbf{F}(\mathbf{x}) = -\frac{mMG}{|\mathbf{x}|^3} \mathbf{x}$$

in moving a particle with mass m from the point $(3, 4, 12)$ to the point $(2, 2, 0)$ along a piecewise-smooth curve C. (See Example 4 in Section 13.1.)

SOLUTION   From Section 13.1 we know that $\mathbf{F}$ is a conservative vector field and, in fact, $\mathbf{F} = \nabla f$, where

$$f(x, y, z) = \frac{mMG}{\sqrt{x^2 + y^2 + z^2}}$$

Therefore, by Theorem 2, the work done is

$$W = \int_C \mathbf{F} \cdot d\mathbf{r} = \int_C \nabla f \cdot d\mathbf{r}$$

$$= f(2, 2, 0) - f(3, 4, 12)$$

$$= \frac{mMG}{\sqrt{2^2 + 2^2}} - \frac{mMG}{\sqrt{3^2 + 4^2 + 12^2}} = mMG \left(\frac{1}{2\sqrt{2}} - \frac{1}{13} \right) \qquad ▬$$

Independence of Path

Suppose C_1 and C_2 are two piecewise-smooth curves (which are called **paths**) that have the same initial point A and terminal point B. We know from Example 4 in Section 13.2 that, in general, $\int_{C_1} \mathbf{F} \cdot d\mathbf{r} \neq \int_{C_2} \mathbf{F} \cdot d\mathbf{r}$. But one implication of Theorem 2 is that

$$\int_{C_1} \nabla f \cdot d\mathbf{r} = \int_{C_2} \nabla f \cdot d\mathbf{r}$$

whenever ∇f is continuous. In other words, the line integral of a *conservative* vector field depends only on the initial point and terminal point of a curve.

In general, if $\mathbf{F}$ is a continuous vector field with domain D, we say that the line integral $\int_C \mathbf{F} \cdot d\mathbf{r}$ is **independent of path** if $\int_{C_1} \mathbf{F} \cdot d\mathbf{r} = \int_{C_2} \mathbf{F} \cdot d\mathbf{r}$ for any two paths C_1 and C_2 in D that have the same initial and terminal points. With this terminology we can say that *line integrals of conservative vector fields are independent of path.*

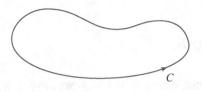

FIGURE 2
A closed curve

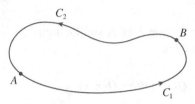

FIGURE 3

A curve is called **closed** if its terminal point coincides with its initial point, that is, $\mathbf{r}(b) = \mathbf{r}(a)$. (See Figure 2.) If $\int_C \mathbf{F} \cdot d\mathbf{r}$ is independent of path in D and C is any closed path in D, we can choose any two points A and B on C and regard C as being composed of the path C_1 from A to B followed by the path C_2 from B to A. (See Figure 3.) Then

$$\int_C \mathbf{F} \cdot d\mathbf{r} = \int_{C_1} \mathbf{F} \cdot d\mathbf{r} + \int_{C_2} \mathbf{F} \cdot d\mathbf{r} = \int_{C_1} \mathbf{F} \cdot d\mathbf{r} - \int_{-C_2} \mathbf{F} \cdot d\mathbf{r} = 0$$

since C_1 and $-C_2$ have the same initial and terminal points.

Conversely, if it is true that $\int_C \mathbf{F} \cdot d\mathbf{r} = 0$ whenever C is a closed path in D, then we demonstrate independence of path as follows. Take any two paths C_1 and C_2 from A to B in D and define C to be the curve consisting of C_1 followed by $-C_2$. Then

$$0 = \int_C \mathbf{F} \cdot d\mathbf{r} = \int_{C_1} \mathbf{F} \cdot d\mathbf{r} + \int_{-C_2} \mathbf{F} \cdot d\mathbf{r} = \int_{C_1} \mathbf{F} \cdot d\mathbf{r} - \int_{C_2} \mathbf{F} \cdot d\mathbf{r}$$

and so $\int_{C_1} \mathbf{F} \cdot d\mathbf{r} = \int_{C_2} \mathbf{F} \cdot d\mathbf{r}$. Thus we have proved the following theorem.

---

3 **Theorem** $\int_C \mathbf{F} \cdot d\mathbf{r}$ is independent of path in D if and only if $\int_C \mathbf{F} \cdot d\mathbf{r} = 0$ for every closed path C in D.

Since we know that the line integral of any conservative vector field $\mathbf{F}$ is independent of path, it follows that $\int_C \mathbf{F} \cdot d\mathbf{r} = 0$ for any closed path. The physical interpretation is that the work done by a conservative force field (such as the gravitational or electric field in Section 13.1) as it moves an object around a closed path is 0.

The following theorem says that the *only* vector fields that are independent of path are conservative. It is stated and proved for plane curves, but there is a similar version for space curves. We assume that D is **open**, which means that for every point P in D there is a disk with center P that lies entirely in D. (So D doesn't contain any of its boundary points.) In addition, we assume that D is **connected**: this means that any two points in D can be joined by a path that lies in D.

---

4 **Theorem** Suppose $\mathbf{F}$ is a vector field that is continuous on an open connected region D. If $\int_C \mathbf{F} \cdot d\mathbf{r}$ is independent of path in D, then $\mathbf{F}$ is a conservative vector field on D; that is, there exists a function f such that $\nabla f = \mathbf{F}$.

PROOF Let $A(a, b)$ be a fixed point in D. We construct the desired potential function f by defining

$$f(x, y) = \int_{(a, b)}^{(x, y)} \mathbf{F} \cdot d\mathbf{r}$$

for any point (x, y) in D. Since $\int_C \mathbf{F} \cdot d\mathbf{r}$ is independent of path, it does not matter which path C from (a, b) to (x, y) is used to evaluate $f(x, y)$. Since D is open, there exists a disk contained in D with center (x, y). Choose any point (x_1, y) in the disk with $x_1 < x$ and let C consist of any path C_1 from (a, b) to (x_1, y) followed by the horizontal line segment C_2 from (x_1, y) to (x, y). (See Figure 4.) Then

$$f(x, y) = \int_{C_1} \mathbf{F} \cdot d\mathbf{r} + \int_{C_2} \mathbf{F} \cdot d\mathbf{r} = \int_{(a, b)}^{(x_1, y)} \mathbf{F} \cdot d\mathbf{r} + \int_{C_2} \mathbf{F} \cdot d\mathbf{r}$$

Notice that the first of these integrals does not depend on x, so

$$\frac{\partial}{\partial x} f(x, y) = 0 + \frac{\partial}{\partial x} \int_{C_2} \mathbf{F} \cdot d\mathbf{r}$$

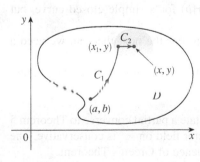

FIGURE 4

If we write $\mathbf{F} = P\,\mathbf{i} + Q\,\mathbf{j}$, then

$$\int_{C_2} \mathbf{F} \cdot d\mathbf{r} = \int_{C_2} P\,dx + Q\,dy$$

On C_2, y is constant, so $dy = 0$. Using t as the parameter, where $x_1 \leqslant t \leqslant x$, we have

$$\frac{\partial}{\partial x} f(x, y) = \frac{\partial}{\partial x} \int_{C_2} P\,dx + Q\,dy = \frac{\partial}{\partial x} \int_{x_1}^{x} P(t, y)\,dt = P(x, y)$$

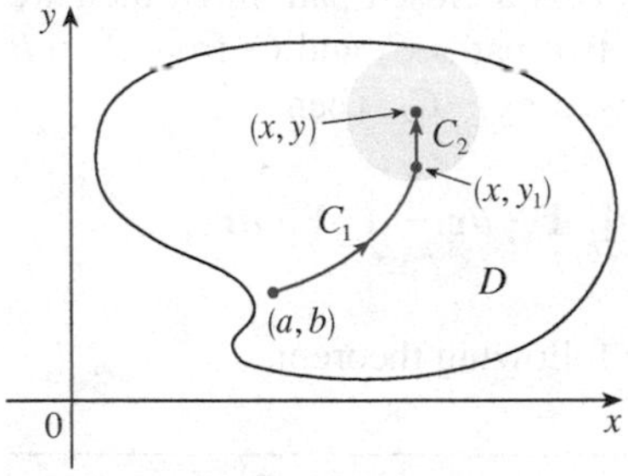

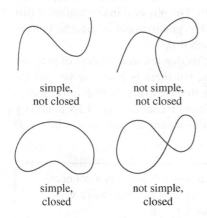

by Part 1 of the Fundamental Theorem of Calculus (see Section 5.4). A similar argument, using a vertical line segment (see Figure 5), shows that

$$\frac{\partial}{\partial y} f(x, y) = \frac{\partial}{\partial y} \int_{C_2} P\,dx + Q\,dy = \frac{\partial}{\partial y} \int_{y_1}^{y} Q(x, t)\,dt = Q(x, y)$$

Thus
$$\mathbf{F} = P\,\mathbf{i} + Q\,\mathbf{j} = \frac{\partial f}{\partial x}\,\mathbf{i} + \frac{\partial f}{\partial y}\,\mathbf{j} = \nabla f$$

which says that $\mathbf{F}$ is conservative.

FIGURE 5

The question remains: How is it possible to determine whether or not a vector field $\mathbf{F}$ is conservative? Suppose it is known that $\mathbf{F} = P\,\mathbf{i} + Q\,\mathbf{j}$ is conservative, where P and Q have continuous first-order partial derivatives. Then there is a function f such that $\mathbf{F} = \nabla f$, that is,

$$P = \frac{\partial f}{\partial x} \qquad \text{and} \qquad Q = \frac{\partial f}{\partial y}$$

Therefore, by Clairaut's Theorem,

$$\frac{\partial P}{\partial y} = \frac{\partial^2 f}{\partial y\,\partial x} = \frac{\partial^2 f}{\partial x\,\partial y} = \frac{\partial Q}{\partial x}$$

5 **Theorem** If $\mathbf{F}(x, y) = P(x, y)\,\mathbf{i} + Q(x, y)\,\mathbf{j}$ is a conservative vector field, where P and Q have continuous first-order partial derivatives on a domain D, then throughout D we have

$$\frac{\partial P}{\partial y} = \frac{\partial Q}{\partial x}$$

FIGURE 6

Types of curves

simple,
not closed

not simple,
not closed

simple,
closed

not simple,
closed

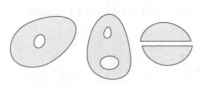

simply-connected region

regions that are not simply-connected

FIGURE 7

The converse of Theorem 5 is true only for a special type of region. To explain this, we first need the concept of a **simple curve**, which is a curve that doesn't intersect itself anywhere between its endpoints. [See Figure 6; $\mathbf{r}(a) = \mathbf{r}(b)$ for a simple closed curve, but $\mathbf{r}(t_1) \neq \mathbf{r}(t_2)$ when $a < t_1 < t_2 < b$.]

In Theorem 4 we needed an open connected region. For the next theorem we need a stronger condition. A **simply-connected region** in the plane is a connected region D such that every simple closed curve in D encloses only points that are in D. Notice from Figure 7 that, intuitively speaking, a simply-connected region contains no hole and can't consist of two separate pieces.

In terms of simply-connected regions, we can now state a partial converse to Theorem 5 that gives a convenient method for verifying that a vector field on $\mathbb{R}^2$ is conservative. The proof will be sketched in the next section as a consequence of Green's Theorem.

6 Theorem Let $\mathbf{F} = P\,\mathbf{i} + Q\,\mathbf{j}$ be a vector field on an open simply-connected region D. Suppose that P and Q have continuous first-order derivatives and

$$\frac{\partial P}{\partial y} = \frac{\partial Q}{\partial x} \qquad \text{throughout } D$$

Then $\mathbf{F}$ is conservative.

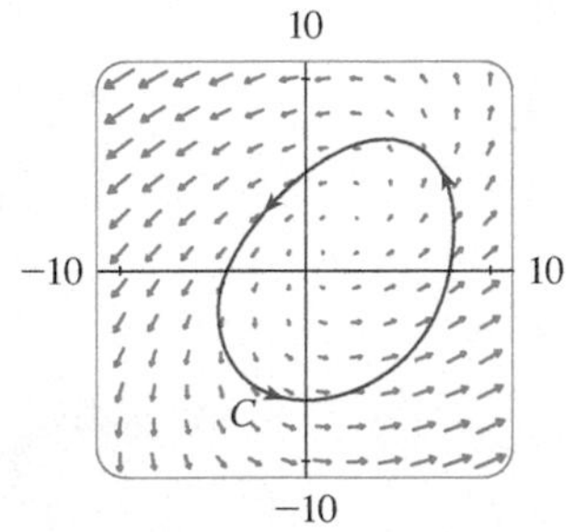

FIGURE 8

Figures 8 and 9 show the vector fields in Examples 2 and 3, respectively. The vectors in Figure 8 that start on the closed curve C all appear to point in roughly the same direction as C. So it looks as if $\int_C \mathbf{F} \cdot d\mathbf{r} > 0$ and therefore $\mathbf{F}$ is not conservative. The calculation in Example 2 confirms this impression. Some of the vectors near the curves C_1 and C_2 in Figure 9 point in approximately the same direction as the curves, whereas others point in the opposite direction. So it appears plausible that line integrals around all closed paths are 0. Example 3 shows that $\mathbf{F}$ is indeed conservative.

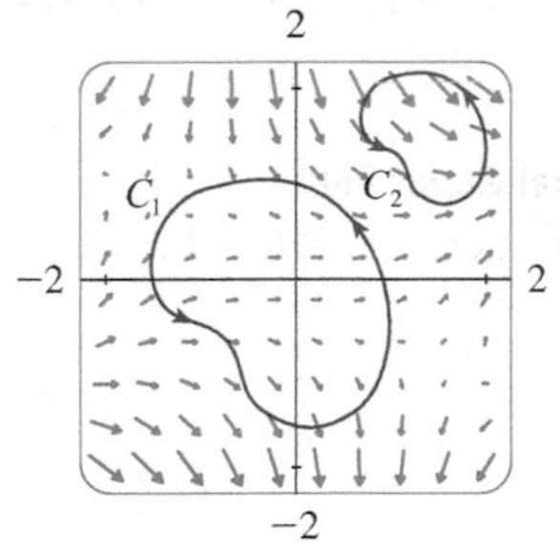

FIGURE 9

V EXAMPLE 2 Determine whether or not the vector field

$$\mathbf{F}(x, y) = (x - y)\,\mathbf{i} + (x - 2)\,\mathbf{j}$$

is conservative.

SOLUTION Let $P(x, y) = x - y$ and $Q(x, y) = x - 2$. Then

$$\frac{\partial P}{\partial y} = -1 \qquad \frac{\partial Q}{\partial x} = 1$$

Since $\partial P/\partial y \neq \partial Q/\partial x$, $\mathbf{F}$ is not conservative by Theorem 5.

V EXAMPLE 3 Determine whether or not the vector field

$$\mathbf{F}(x, y) = (3 + 2xy)\,\mathbf{i} + (x^2 - 3y^2)\,\mathbf{j}$$

is conservative.

SOLUTION Let $P(x, y) = 3 + 2xy$ and $Q(x, y) = x^2 - 3y^2$. Then

$$\frac{\partial P}{\partial y} = 2x = \frac{\partial Q}{\partial x}$$

Also, the domain of $\mathbf{F}$ is the entire plane ($D = \mathbb{R}^2$), which is open and simply-connected. Therefore we can apply Theorem 6 and conclude that $\mathbf{F}$ is conservative.

In Example 3, Theorem 6 told us that $\mathbf{F}$ is conservative, but it did not tell us how to find the (potential) function f such that $\mathbf{F} = \nabla f$. The proof of Theorem 4 gives us a clue as to how to find f. We use "partial integration" as in the following example.

EXAMPLE 4 Calculating the line integral of a conservative vector field

(a) If $\mathbf{F}(x, y) = (3 + 2xy)\,\mathbf{i} + (x^2 - 3y^2)\,\mathbf{j}$, find a function f such that $\mathbf{F} = \nabla f$.

(b) Evaluate the line integral $\int_C \mathbf{F} \cdot d\mathbf{r}$, where C is the curve given by

$$\mathbf{r}(t) = e^t \sin t\,\mathbf{i} + e^t \cos t\,\mathbf{j} \qquad 0 \leq t \leq \pi$$

SOLUTION

(a) From Example 3 we know that $\mathbf{F}$ is conservative and so there exists a function f with $\nabla f = \mathbf{F}$, that is,

$$\boxed{7} \qquad f_x(x, y) = 3 + 2xy$$

$$\boxed{8} \qquad f_y(x, y) = x^2 - 3y^2$$

Integrating (7) with respect to x, we obtain

$$\boxed{9} \qquad\qquad f(x, y) = 3x + x^2 y + g(y)$$

Notice that the constant of integration is a constant with respect to x, that is, a function of y, which we have called $g(y)$. Next we differentiate both sides of (9) with respect to y:

$$\boxed{10} \qquad\qquad f_y(x, y) = x^2 + g'(y)$$

Comparing (8) and (10), we see that

$$g'(y) = -3y^2$$

Integrating with respect to y, we have

$$g(y) = -y^3 + K$$

where K is a constant. Putting this in (9), we have

$$f(x, y) = 3x + x^2 y - y^3 + K$$

as the desired potential function.

(b) To use Theorem 2 all we have to know are the initial and terminal points of C, namely, $\mathbf{r}(0) = (0, 1)$ and $\mathbf{r}(\pi) = (0, -e^\pi)$. In the expression for $f(x, y)$ in part (a), any value of the constant K will do, so let's choose $K = 0$. Then we have

$$\int_C \mathbf{F} \cdot d\mathbf{r} = \int_C \nabla f \cdot d\mathbf{r} = f(0, -e^\pi) - f(0, 1) = e^{3\pi} - (-1) = e^{3\pi} + 1$$

This method is much shorter than the straightforward method for evaluating line integrals that we learned in Section 13.2.

A criterion for determining whether or not a vector field $\mathbf{F}$ on $\mathbb{R}^3$ is conservative is given in Section 13.5. Meanwhile, the next example shows that the technique for finding the potential function is much the same as for vector fields on $\mathbb{R}^2$.

V   EXAMPLE 5   Finding the potential function for a three-dimensional vector field
If $\mathbf{F}(x, y, z) = y^2 \mathbf{i} + (2xy + e^{3z})\mathbf{j} + 3ye^{3z}\mathbf{k}$, find a function f such that $\nabla f = \mathbf{F}$.

SOLUTION If there is such a function f, then

$$\boxed{11} \qquad\qquad f_x(x, y, z) = y^2$$

$$\boxed{12} \qquad\qquad f_y(x, y, z) = 2xy + e^{3z}$$

$$\boxed{13} \qquad\qquad f_z(x, y, z) = 3ye^{3z}$$

Integrating (11) with respect to x, we get

$$\boxed{14} \qquad\qquad f(x, y, z) = xy^2 + g(y, z)$$

where $g(y, z)$ is a constant with respect to x. Then differentiating (14) with respect to y, we have

$$f_y(x, y, z) = 2xy + g_y(y, z)$$

and comparison with (12) gives

$$g_y(y, z) = e^{3z}$$

Thus $g(y, z) = ye^{3z} + h(z)$ and we rewrite (14) as

$$f(x, y, z) = xy^2 + ye^{3z} + h(z)$$

Finally, differentiating with respect to z and comparing with (13), we obtain $h'(z) = 0$ and therefore $h(z) = K$, a constant. The desired function is

$$f(x, y, z) = xy^2 + ye^{3z} + K$$

It is easily verified that $\nabla f = \mathbf{F}$.

Conservation of Energy

Let's apply the ideas of this chapter to a continuous force field $\mathbf{F}$ that moves an object along a path C given by $\mathbf{r}(t)$, $a \leqslant t \leqslant b$, where $\mathbf{r}(a) = A$ is the initial point and $\mathbf{r}(b) = B$ is the terminal point of C. According to Newton's Second Law of Motion (see Section 10.4), the force $\mathbf{F}(\mathbf{r}(t))$ at a point on C is related to the acceleration $\mathbf{a}(t) = \mathbf{r}''(t)$ by the equation

$$\mathbf{F}(\mathbf{r}(t)) = m\mathbf{r}''(t)$$

So the work done by the force on the object is

$$W = \int_C \mathbf{F} \cdot d\mathbf{r} = \int_a^b \mathbf{F}(\mathbf{r}(t)) \cdot \mathbf{r}'(t)\, dt = \int_a^b m\mathbf{r}''(t) \cdot \mathbf{r}'(t)\, dt$$

$$= \frac{m}{2} \int_a^b \frac{d}{dt} [\mathbf{r}'(t) \cdot \mathbf{r}'(t)]\, dt \qquad \text{(Theorem 10.2.3, Formula 4)}$$

$$= \frac{m}{2} \int_a^b \frac{d}{dt} |\mathbf{r}'(t)|^2\, dt = \frac{m}{2} \Big[|\mathbf{r}'(t)|^2\Big]_a^b \qquad \text{(Fundamental Theorem of Calculus)}$$

$$= \frac{m}{2} \left(|\mathbf{r}'(b)|^2 - |\mathbf{r}'(a)|^2\right)$$

Therefore

$$\boxed{15} \qquad W = \tfrac{1}{2}m\,|\mathbf{v}(b)|^2 - \tfrac{1}{2}m\,|\mathbf{v}(a)|^2$$

where $\mathbf{v} = \mathbf{r}'$ is the velocity.

The quantity $\frac{1}{2}m\,|\mathbf{v}(t)|^2$, that is, half the mass times the square of the speed, is called the **kinetic energy** of the object. Therefore we can rewrite Equation 15 as

$$\boxed{16} \qquad W = K(B) - K(A)$$

which says that the work done by the force field along C is equal to the change in kinetic energy at the endpoints of C.

Now let's further assume that $\mathbf{F}$ is a conservative force field; that is, we can write $\mathbf{F} = \nabla f$. In physics, the **potential energy** of an object at the point (x, y, z) is defined as $P(x, y, z) = -f(x, y, z)$, so we have $\mathbf{F} = -\nabla P$. Then by Theorem 2 we have

$$W = \int_C \mathbf{F} \cdot d\mathbf{r} = -\int_C \nabla P \cdot d\mathbf{r} = -[P(\mathbf{r}(b)) - P(\mathbf{r}(a))] = P(A) - P(B)$$

Comparing this equation with Equation 16, we see that

$$P(A) + K(A) = P(B) + K(B)$$

which says that if an object moves from one point A to another point B under the influence of a conservative force field, then the sum of its potential energy and its kinetic energy remains constant. This is called the **Law of Conservation of Energy** and it is the reason the vector field is called *conservative*.

13.3 Exercises

1. The figure shows a curve C and a contour map of a function f whose gradient is continuous. Find $\int_C \nabla f \cdot d\mathbf{r}$.

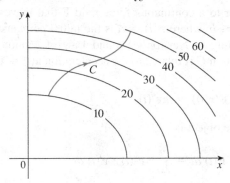

2. A table of values of a function f with continuous gradient is given. Find $\int_C \nabla f \cdot d\mathbf{r}$, where C has parametric equations

$$x = t^2 + 1 \qquad y = t^3 + t \qquad 0 \leqslant t \leqslant 1$$

x \ y	0	1	2
0	1	6	4
1	3	5	7
2	8	2	9

3–10 Determine whether or not $\mathbf{F}$ is a conservative vector field. If it is, find a function f such that $\mathbf{F} = \nabla f$.

3. $\mathbf{F}(x, y) = (2x - 3y)\,\mathbf{i} + (-3x + 4y - 8)\,\mathbf{j}$

4. $\mathbf{F}(x, y) = e^x \sin y\,\mathbf{i} + e^x \cos y\,\mathbf{j}$

5. $\mathbf{F}(x, y) = e^x \cos y\,\mathbf{i} + e^x \sin y\,\mathbf{j}$

6. $\mathbf{F}(x, y) = (2xy + y^{-2})\,\mathbf{i} + (x^2 - 2xy^{-3})\,\mathbf{j}, \quad y > 0$

7. $\mathbf{F}(x, y) = (ye^x + \sin y)\,\mathbf{i} + (e^x + x \cos y)\,\mathbf{j}$

8. $\mathbf{F}(x, y) = (3x^2 - 2y^2)\,\mathbf{i} + (4xy + 3)\,\mathbf{j}$

9. $\mathbf{F}(x, y) = (\ln y + 2xy^3)\,\mathbf{i} + (3x^2y^2 + x/y)\,\mathbf{j}$

10. $\mathbf{F}(x, y) = (xy \cos xy + \sin xy)\,\mathbf{i} + (x^2 \cos xy)\,\mathbf{j}$

11. The figure shows the vector field $\mathbf{F}(x, y) = \langle 2xy, x^2 \rangle$ and three curves that start at $(1, 2)$ and end at $(3, 2)$.
(a) Explain why $\int_C \mathbf{F} \cdot d\mathbf{r}$ has the same value for all three curves.
(b) What is this common value?

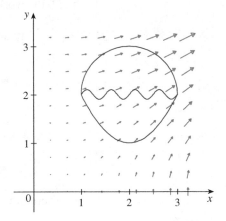

12–18 (a) Find a function f such that $\mathbf{F} = \nabla f$ and (b) use part (a) to evaluate $\int_C \mathbf{F} \cdot d\mathbf{r}$ along the given curve C.

12. $\mathbf{F}(x, y) = x^2\,\mathbf{i} + y^2\,\mathbf{j}$,
C is the arc of the parabola $y = 2x^2$ from $(-1, 2)$ to $(2, 8)$

13. $\mathbf{F}(x, y) = xy^2\,\mathbf{i} + x^2y\,\mathbf{j}$,
C: $\mathbf{r}(t) = \langle t + \sin \frac{1}{2}\pi t, t + \cos \frac{1}{2}\pi t \rangle, \quad 0 \leqslant t \leqslant 1$

14. $\mathbf{F}(x, y) = \dfrac{y^2}{1 + x^2}\,\mathbf{i} + 2y \arctan x\,\mathbf{j}$,
C: $\mathbf{r}(t) = t^2\,\mathbf{i} + 2t\,\mathbf{j}, \quad 0 \leqslant t \leqslant 1$

15. $\mathbf{F}(x, y, z) = yz\,\mathbf{i} + xz\,\mathbf{j} + (xy + 2z)\,\mathbf{k}$,
C is the line segment from $(1, 0, -2)$ to $(4, 6, 3)$

16. $F(x, y, z) = (2xz + y^2)\,i + 2xy\,j + (x^2 + 3z^2)\,k$,
   C: $x = t^2$, $y = t + 1$, $z = 2t - 1$, $0 \le t \le 1$

17. $F(x, y, z) = y^2 \cos z\,i + 2xy \cos z\,j - xy^2 \sin z\,k$,
   C: $r(t) = t^2\,i + \sin t\,j + t\,k$, $0 \le t \le \pi$

18. $F(x, y, z) = e^y\,i + xe^y\,j + (z + 1)e^z\,k$,
   C: $r(t) = t\,i + t^2\,j + t^3\,k$, $0 \le t \le 1$

19–20 Show that the line integral is independent of path and evaluate the integral.

19. $\int_C \tan y\,dx + x \sec^2 y\,dy$,
   C is any path from $(1, 0)$ to $(2, \pi/4)$

20. $\int_C (1 - ye^{-x})\,dx + e^{-x}\,dy$,
   C is any path from $(0, 1)$ to $(1, 2)$

---

21. Suppose you're asked to determine the curve that requires the least work for a force field F to move a particle from one point to another point. You decide to check first whether F is conservative, and indeed it turns out that it is. How would you reply to the request?

22. Suppose an experiment determines that the amount of work required for a force field F to move a particle from the point $(1, 2)$ to the point $(5, -3)$ along a curve C_1 is 1.2 J and the work done by F in moving the particle along another curve C_2 between the same two points is 1.4 J. What can you say about F? Why?

23–24 Find the work done by the force field F in moving an object from P to Q.

23. $F(x, y) = 2y^{3/2}\,i + 3x\sqrt{y}\,j$; $P(1, 1)$, $Q(2, 4)$

24. $F(x, y) = e^{-y}\,i - xe^{-y}\,j$; $P(0, 1)$, $Q(2, 0)$

25–26 Is the vector field shown in the figure conservative? Explain.

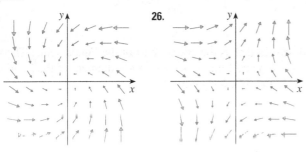

25.   **26.**

CAS **27.** If $F(x, y) = \sin y\,i + (1 + x \cos y)\,j$, use a plot to guess whether F is conservative. Then determine whether your guess is correct.

28. Let $F = \nabla f$, where $f(x, y) = \sin(x - 2y)$. Find curves C_1 and C_2 that are not closed and satisfy the equation.

(a) $\int_{C_1} F \cdot dr = 0$ (b) $\int_{C_2} F \cdot dr = 1$

29. Show that if the vector field $F = P\,i + Q\,j + R\,k$ is conservative and P, Q, R have continuous first-order partial derivatives, then

$$\frac{\partial P}{\partial y} = \frac{\partial Q}{\partial x} \qquad \frac{\partial P}{\partial z} = \frac{\partial R}{\partial x} \qquad \frac{\partial Q}{\partial z} = \frac{\partial R}{\partial y}$$

30. Use Exercise 29 to show that the line integral $\int_C y\,dx + x\,dy + xyz\,dz$ is not independent of path.

31–34 Determine whether or not the given set is (a) open, (b) connected, and (c) simply-connected.

31. $\{(x, y) \mid 0 < y < 3\}$ **32.** $\{(x, y) \mid 1 < |x| < 2\}$

33. $\{(x, y) \mid 1 \le x^2 + y^2 \le 4, y \ge 0\}$

34. $\{(x, y) \mid (x, y) \ne (2, 3)\}$

---

35. Let $F(x, y) = \dfrac{-y\,i + x\,j}{x^2 + y^2}$.

(a) Show that $\partial P/\partial y = \partial Q/\partial x$.

(b) Show that $\int_C F \cdot dr$ is not independent of path.
[*Hint:* Compute $\int_{C_1} F \cdot dr$ and $\int_{C_2} F \cdot dr$, where C_1 and C_2 are the upper and lower halves of the circle $x^2 + y^2 = 1$ from $(1, 0)$ to $(-1, 0)$.] Does this contradict Theorem 6?

36. (a) Suppose that F is an inverse square force field, that is,

$$F(r) = \frac{c\,r}{|r|^3}$$

for some constant c, where $r = x\,i + y\,j + z\,k$. Find the work done by F in moving an object from a point P_1 along a path to a point P_2 in terms of the distances d_1 and d_2 from these points to the origin.

(b) An example of an inverse square field is the gravitational field $F = -(mMG)r/|r|^3$ discussed in Example 4 in Section 13.1. Use part (a) to find the work done by the gravitational field when the earth moves from aphelion (at a maximum distance of 1.52×10^8 km from the sun) to perihelion (at a minimum distance of 1.47×10^8 km). (Use the values $m = 5.97 \times 10^{24}$ kg, $M = 1.99 \times 10^{30}$ kg, and $G = 6.67 \times 10^{-11}$ N·m²/kg².)

(c) Another example of an inverse square field is the electric force field $F = \varepsilon qQr/|r|^3$ discussed in Example 5 in Section 13.1. Suppose that an electron with a charge of -1.6×10^{-19} C is located at the origin. A positive unit charge is positioned a distance 10^{-12} m from the electron and moves to a position half that distance from the electron. Use part (a) to find the work done by the electric force field. (Use the value $\varepsilon = 8.985 \times 10^9$.)

13.4   Green's Theorem

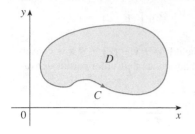

FIGURE 1

Green's Theorem gives the relationship between a line integral around a simple closed curve C and a double integral over the plane region D bounded by C. (See Figure 1. We assume that D consists of all points inside C as well as all points on C.) In stating Green's Theorem we use the convention that the **positive orientation** of a simple closed curve C refers to a single *counterclockwise* traversal of C. Thus, if C is given by the vector function $\mathbf{r}(t)$, $a \leqslant t \leqslant b$, then the region D is always on the left as the point $\mathbf{r}(t)$ traverses C. (See Figure 2.)

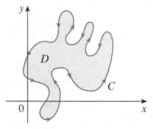

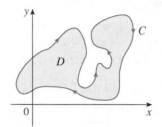

FIGURE 2   (a) Positive orientation   (b) Negative orientation

> **Green's Theorem**   Let C be a positively oriented, piecewise-smooth, simple closed curve in the plane and let D be the region bounded by C. If P and Q have continuous partial derivatives on an open region that contains D, then
>
> $$\int_C P\, dx + Q\, dy = \iint_D \left(\frac{\partial Q}{\partial x} - \frac{\partial P}{\partial y} \right) dA$$

Recall that the left side of this equation is another way of writing $\int_C \mathbf{F} \cdot d\mathbf{r}$, where $\mathbf{F} = P\,\mathbf{i} + Q\,\mathbf{j}$.

Note: The notation

$$\oint_C P\, dx + Q\, dy \qquad \text{or} \qquad \oint_C P\, dx + Q\, dy$$

is sometimes used to indicate that the line integral is calculated using the positive orientation of the closed curve C. Another notation for the positively oriented boundary curve of D is ∂D, so the equation in Green's Theorem can be written as

$$\boxed{1} \qquad \iint_D \left(\frac{\partial Q}{\partial x} - \frac{\partial P}{\partial y} \right) dA = \int_{\partial D} P\, dx + Q\, dy$$

Green's Theorem should be regarded as the counterpart of the Fundamental Theorem of Calculus for double integrals. Compare Equation 1 with the statement of the Fundamental Theorem of Calculus, Part 2, in the following equation:

$$\int_a^b F'(x)\, dx = F(b) - F(a)$$

In both cases there is an integral involving derivatives (F', $\partial Q/\partial x$, and $\partial P/\partial y$) on the left side of the equation. And in both cases the right side involves the values of the original functions (F, Q, and P) only on the *boundary* of the domain. (In the one-dimensional case, the domain is an interval $[a, b]$ whose boundary consists of just two points, a and b.)

Green's Theorem is not easy to prove in general, but we can give a proof for the special case where the region is both type I and type II (see Section 12.3). Let's call such regions **simple regions**.

PROOF OF GREEN'S THEOREM FOR THE CASE IN WHICH D IS A SIMPLE REGION Notice that Green's Theorem will be proved if we can show that

$$\boxed{2} \qquad \int_C P\,dx = -\iint_D \frac{\partial P}{\partial y}\,dA$$

and

$$\boxed{3} \qquad \int_C Q\,dy = \iint_D \frac{\partial Q}{\partial x}\,dA$$

We prove Equation 2 by expressing D as a type I region:

$$D = \left\{ (x, y) \mid a \leqslant x \leqslant b,\ g_1(x) \leqslant y \leqslant g_2(x) \right\}$$

where g_1 and g_2 are continuous functions. This enables us to compute the double integral on the right side of Equation 2 as follows:

$$\boxed{4} \qquad \iint_D \frac{\partial P}{\partial y}\,dA - \int_a^b \int_{g_1(x)}^{g_2(x)} \frac{\partial P}{\partial y}(x, y)\,dy\,dx = \int_a^b \left[P(x, g_2(x)) - P(x, g_1(x)) \right] dx$$

where the last step follows from the Fundamental Theorem of Calculus.

Now we compute the left side of Equation 2 by breaking up C as the union of the four curves C_1, C_2, C_3, and C_4 shown in Figure 3. On C_1 we take x as the parameter and write the parametric equations as $x = x$, $y = g_1(x)$, $a \leqslant x \leqslant b$. Thus

$$\int_{C_1} P(x, y)\,dx = \int_a^b P(x, g_1(x))\,dx$$

Observe that C_3 goes from right to left but $-C_3$ goes from left to right, so we can write the parametric equations of $-C_3$ as $x = x$, $y = g_2(x)$, $a \leqslant x \leqslant b$. Therefore

$$\int_{C_3} P(x, y)\,dx = -\int_{-C_3} P(x, y)\,dx = -\int_a^b P(x, g_2(x))\,dx$$

On C_2 or C_4 (either of which might reduce to just a single point), x is constant, so $dx = 0$ and

$$\int_{C_2} P(x, y)\,dx = 0 = \int_{C_4} P(x, y)\,dx$$

Hence

$$\int_C P(x, y)\,dx = \int_{C_1} P(x, y)\,dx + \int_{C_2} P(x, y)\,dx + \int_{C_3} P(x, y)\,dx + \int_{C_4} P(x, y)\,dx$$

$$= \int_a^b P(x, g_1(x))\,dx - \int_a^b P(x, g_2(x))\,dx$$

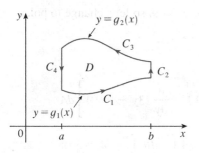

FIGURE 3

Comparing this expression with the one in Equation 4, we see that

$$\int_C P(x, y) \, dx = -\iint_D \frac{\partial P}{\partial y} \, dA$$

Equation 3 can be proved in much the same way by expressing D as a type II region (see Exercise 30). Then, by adding Equations 2 and 3, we obtain Green's Theorem. ▭

EXAMPLE 1 **Using Green's Theorem to calculate a line integral** Evaluate $\int_C x^4 \, dx + xy \, dy$, where C is the triangular curve consisting of the line segments from $(0, 0)$ to $(1, 0)$, from $(1, 0)$ to $(0, 1)$, and from $(0, 1)$ to $(0, 0)$.

SOLUTION Although the given line integral could be evaluated as usual by the methods of Section 13.2, that would involve setting up three separate integrals along the three sides of the triangle, so let's use Green's Theorem instead. Notice that the region D enclosed by C is simple and C has positive orientation (see Figure 4). If we let $P(x, y) = x^4$ and $Q(x, y) = xy$, then we have

$$\int_C x^4 \, dx + xy \, dy = \iint_D \left(\frac{\partial Q}{\partial x} - \frac{\partial P}{\partial y} \right) dA = \int_0^1 \int_0^{1-x} (y - 0) \, dy \, dx$$

$$= \int_0^1 \left[\tfrac{1}{2} y^2 \right]_{y=0}^{y=1-x} dx = \tfrac{1}{2} \int_0^1 (1 - x)^2 \, dx$$

$$= -\tfrac{1}{6}(1 - x)^3 \Big]_0^1 = \tfrac{1}{6}$$

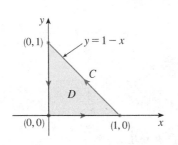

$y = 1 - x$

C

D

$(0, 1)$

$(0, 0)$

$(1, 0)$

FIGURE 4

▨ **EXAMPLE 2** **A line integral impossible to evaluate without Green's Theorem**
Evaluate $\oint_C (3y - e^{\sin x}) \, dx + \left(7x + \sqrt{y^4 + 1} \right) dy$, where C is the circle $x^2 + y^2 = 9$.

SOLUTION The region D bounded by C is the disk $x^2 + y^2 \le 9$, so let's change to polar coordinates after applying Green's Theorem:

$$\oint_C (3y - e^{\sin x}) \, dx + \left(7x + \sqrt{y^4 + 1} \right) dy$$

$$= \iint_D \left[\frac{\partial}{\partial x} \left(7x + \sqrt{y^4 + 1} \right) - \frac{\partial}{\partial y} \left(3y - e^{\sin x} \right) \right] dA$$

$$= \int_0^{2\pi} \int_0^3 (7 - 3) \, r \, dr \, d\theta = 4 \int_0^{2\pi} d\theta \int_0^3 r \, dr = 36\pi$$

Instead of using polar coordinates, we could simply use the fact that D is a disk of radius 3 and write

$$\iint_D 4 \, dA = 4 \cdot \pi(3)^2 = 36\pi$$

In Examples 1 and 2 we found that the double integral was easier to evaluate than the line integral. (Try setting up the line integral in Example 2 and you'll soon be convinced!) But sometimes it's easier to evaluate the line integral, and Green's Theorem is used in the reverse direction. For instance, if it is known that $P(x, y) = Q(x, y) = 0$ on the curve C, then Green's Theorem gives

$$\iint_D \left(\frac{\partial Q}{\partial x} - \frac{\partial P}{\partial y} \right) dA = \int_C P \, dx + Q \, dy = 0$$

no matter what values P and Q assume in the region D.

Another application of the reverse direction of Green's Theorem is in computing areas. Since the area of D is $\iint_D 1 \, dA$, we wish to choose P and Q so that

$$\frac{\partial Q}{\partial x} - \frac{\partial P}{\partial y} = 1$$

There are several possibilities:

$$P(x, y) = 0 \qquad P(x, y) = -y \qquad P(x, y) = -\tfrac{1}{2}y$$

$$Q(x, y) = x \qquad Q(x, y) = 0 \qquad Q(x, y) = \tfrac{1}{2}x$$

Then Green's Theorem gives the following formulas for the area of D:

5 $$A = \oint_C x \, dy = -\oint_C y \, dx = \tfrac{1}{2}\oint_C x \, dy - y \, dx$$

EXAMPLE 3 Find the area enclosed by the ellipse $\dfrac{x^2}{a^2} + \dfrac{y^2}{b^2} = 1$.

SOLUTION The ellipse has parametric equations $x = a \cos t$ and $y = b \sin t$, where $0 \leqslant t \leqslant 2\pi$. Using the third formula in Equation 5, we have

$$A = \tfrac{1}{2}\int_C x \, dy - y \, dx$$

$$= \tfrac{1}{2}\int_0^{2\pi} (a \cos t)(b \cos t) \, dt - (b \sin t)(\; a \sin t) \, dt$$

$$= \frac{ab}{2}\int_0^{2\pi} dt = \pi ab$$

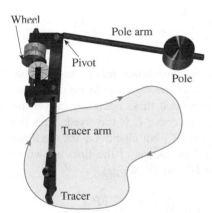

Wheel

Pole arm

Pivot

Pole

Tracer arm

Tracer

FIGURE 5
A Keuffel and Esser polar planimeter

Formula 5 can be used to explain how planimeters work. A **planimeter** is a mechanical instrument used for measuring the area of a region by tracing its boundary curve. These devices are useful in all the sciences: in biology for measuring the area of leaves or wings, in medicine for measuring the size of cross-sections of organs or tumors, in forestry for estimating the size of forested regions from photographs.

Figure 5 shows the operation of a polar planimeter: The pole is fixed and, as the tracer is moved along the boundary curve of the region, the wheel partly slides and partly rolls perpendicular to the tracer arm. The planimeter measures the distance that the wheel rolls and this is proportional to the area of the enclosed region. The explanation as a consequence of Formula 5 can be found in the following articles:

- R. W. Gatterman, "The planimeter as an example of Green's Theorem" *Amer. Math. Monthly,* Vol. 88 (1981), pp. 701–4.

- Tanya Leise, "As the planimeter wheel turns" *College Math. Journal,* Vol. 38 (2007), pp. 24–31.

Extended Versions of Green's Theorem

Although we have proved Green's Theorem only for the case where D is simple, we can now extend it to the case where D is a finite union of simple regions. For example, if D is the region shown in Figure 6, then we can write $D = D_1 \cup D_2$, where D_1 and D_2 are both simple. The boundary of D_1 is $C_1 \cup C_3$ and the boundary of D_2 is $C_2 \cup (-C_3)$ so, applying Green's Theorem to D_1 and D_2 separately, we get

$$\int_{C_1 \cup C_3} P \, dx + Q \, dy = \iint_{D_1} \left(\frac{\partial Q}{\partial x} - \frac{\partial P}{\partial y} \right) dA$$

$$\int_{C_2 \cup (-C_3)} P \, dx + Q \, dy = \iint_{D_2} \left(\frac{\partial Q}{\partial x} - \frac{\partial P}{\partial y} \right) dA$$

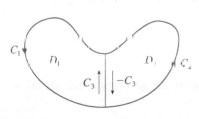

C_1

D_1

D_2

C_2

C_3 $-C_3$

FIGURE 6

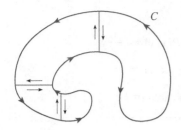

FIGURE 7

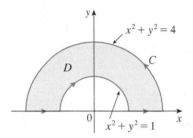

FIGURE 8

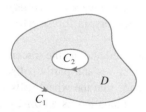

FIGURE 9

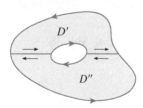

FIGURE 10

If we add these two equations, the line integrals along C_3 and $-C_3$ cancel, so we get

$$\int_{C_1 \cup C_2} P\,dx + Q\,dy = \iint_D \left(\frac{\partial Q}{\partial x} - \frac{\partial P}{\partial y} \right) dA$$

which is Green's Theorem for $D = D_1 \cup D_2$, since its boundary is $C = C_1 \cup C_2$.

The same sort of argument allows us to establish Green's Theorem for any finite union of nonoverlapping simple regions (see Figure 7).

V EXAMPLE 4 Evaluate $\oint_C y^2\,dx + 3xy\,dy$, where C is the boundary of the semiannular region D in the upper half-plane between the circles $x^2 + y^2 = 1$ and $x^2 + y^2 = 4$.

SOLUTION Notice that although D is not simple, the y-axis divides it into two simple regions (see Figure 8). In polar coordinates we can write

$$D = \{(r, \theta) \mid 1 \leqslant r \leqslant 2, \; 0 \leqslant \theta \leqslant \pi\}$$

Therefore Green's Theorem gives

$$\oint_C y^2\,dx + 3xy\,dy = \iint_D \left[\frac{\partial}{\partial x}(3xy) - \frac{\partial}{\partial y}(y^2) \right] dA$$

$$= \iint_D y\,dA = \int_0^\pi \int_1^2 (r\sin\theta)\,r\,dr\,d\theta$$

$$= \int_0^\pi \sin\theta\,d\theta \int_1^2 r^2\,dr = \left[-\cos\theta \right]_0^\pi \left[\tfrac{1}{3}r^3 \right]_1^2 = \frac{14}{3} \qquad \blacksquare$$

Green's Theorem can be extended to apply to regions with holes, that is, regions that are not simply-connected. Observe that the boundary C of the region D in Figure 9 consists of two simple closed curves C_1 and C_2. We assume that these boundary curves are oriented so that the region D is always on the left as the curve C is traversed. Thus the positive direction is counterclockwise for the outer curve C_1 but clockwise for the inner curve C_2. If we divide D into two regions D' and D'' by means of the lines shown in Figure 10 and then apply Green's Theorem to each of D' and D'', we get

$$\iint_D \left(\frac{\partial Q}{\partial x} - \frac{\partial P}{\partial y} \right) dA = \iint_{D'} \left(\frac{\partial Q}{\partial x} - \frac{\partial P}{\partial y} \right) dA + \iint_{D''} \left(\frac{\partial Q}{\partial x} - \frac{\partial P}{\partial y} \right) dA$$

$$= \int_{\partial D'} P\,dx + Q\,dy + \int_{\partial D''} P\,dx + Q\,dy$$

Since the line integrals along the common boundary lines are in opposite directions, they cancel and we get

$$\iint_D \left(\frac{\partial Q}{\partial x} - \frac{\partial P}{\partial y} \right) dA = \int_{C_1} P\,dx + Q\,dy + \int_{C_2} P\,dx + Q\,dy = \int_C P\,dx + Q\,dy$$

which is Green's Theorem for the region D.

V EXAMPLE 5 Using the general version of Green's Theorem
If $\mathbf{F}(x, y) = (-y\,\mathbf{i} + x\,\mathbf{j})/(x^2 + y^2)$, show that $\int_C \mathbf{F} \cdot d\mathbf{r} = 2\pi$ for every positively oriented simple closed path that encloses the origin.

SOLUTION Since C is an *arbitrary* closed path that encloses the origin, it's difficult to compute the given integral directly. So let's consider a counterclockwise-oriented circle

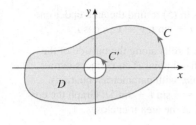

FIGURE 11

C' with center the origin and radius a, where a is chosen to be small enough that C' lies inside C. (See Figure 11.) Let D be the region bounded by C and C'. Then its positively oriented boundary is $C \cup (-C')$ and so the general version of Green's Theorem gives

$$\int_C P\,dx + Q\,dy + \int_{-C'} P\,dx + Q\,dy = \iint_D \left(\frac{\partial Q}{\partial x} - \frac{\partial P}{\partial y} \right) dA$$

$$= \iint_D \left[\frac{y^2 - x^2}{(x^2 + y^2)^2} - \frac{y^2 - x^2}{(x^2 + y^2)^2} \right] dA = 0$$

Therefore

$$\int_C P\,dx + Q\,dy = \int_{C'} P\,dx + Q\,dy$$

that is,

$$\int_C \mathbf{F} \cdot d\mathbf{r} = \int_{C'} \mathbf{F} \cdot d\mathbf{r}$$

We now easily compute this last integral using the parametrization given by $\mathbf{r}(t) = a \cos t\,\mathbf{i} + a \sin t\,\mathbf{j}$, $0 \le t \le 2\pi$. Thus

$$\int_C \mathbf{F} \cdot d\mathbf{r} = \int_{C'} \mathbf{F} \cdot d\mathbf{r} = \int_0^{2\pi} \mathbf{F}(\mathbf{r}(t)) \cdot \mathbf{r}'(t)\,dt$$

$$= \int_0^{2\pi} \frac{(-a \sin t)(-a \sin t) + (a \cos t)(a \cos t)}{a^2 \cos^2 t + a^2 \sin^2 t}\,dt = \int_0^{2\pi} dt = 2\pi \qquad \blacksquare$$

We end this section by using Green's Theorem to discuss a result that was stated in the preceding section.

SKETCH OF PROOF OF THEOREM 13.3.6 We're assuming that $\mathbf{F} = P\,\mathbf{i} + Q\,\mathbf{j}$ is a vector field on an open simply-connected region D, that P and Q have continuous first-order partial derivatives, and that

$$\frac{\partial P}{\partial y} = \frac{\partial Q}{\partial x} \qquad \text{throughout } D$$

If C is any simple closed path in D, and R is the region that C encloses, then Green's Theorem gives

$$\oint_C \mathbf{F} \cdot d\mathbf{r} = \oint_C P\,dx + Q\,dy = \iint_R \left(\frac{\partial Q}{\partial x} - \frac{\partial P}{\partial y} \right) dA = \iint_R 0\,dA = 0$$

A curve that is not simple crosses itself at one or more points and can be broken up into a number of simple curves. We have shown that the line integrals of $\mathbf{F}$ around these simple curves are all 0 and, adding these integrals, we see that $\int_C \mathbf{F} \cdot d\mathbf{r} = 0$ for any closed curve C. Therefore $\int_C \mathbf{F} \cdot d\mathbf{r}$ is independent of path in D by Theorem 13.3.3. It follows that $\mathbf{F}$ is a conservative vector field. $\qquad \square$

13.4 Exercises

1–4 Evaluate the line integral by two methods: (a) directly and (b) using Green's Theorem.

1. $\oint_C (x - y)\,dx + (x + y)\,dy$,
C is the circle with center the origin and radius 2

2. $\oint_C xy\,dx + x^2\,dy$,
C is the rectangle with vertices $(0, 0)$, $(3, 0)$, $(3, 1)$, and $(0, 1)$

3. $\oint_C xy\,dx + x^2 y^3\,dy$,
C is the triangle with vertices $(0, 0)$, $(1, 0)$, and $(1, 2)$

⊞ Graphing calculator or computer with graphing software required   [CAS] Computer algebra system required   **1.** Homework Hints available in TEC

4. $\oint_C x \, dx + y \, dy$, C consists of the line segments from $(0, 1)$ to $(0, 0)$ and from $(0, 0)$ to $(1, 0)$ and the parabola $y = 1 - x^2$ from $(1, 0)$ to $(0, 1)$

5–10 Use Green's Theorem to evaluate the line integral along the given positively oriented curve.

5. $\int_C xy^2 \, dx + 2x^2 y \, dy$,
C is the triangle with vertices $(0, 0)$, $(2, 2)$, and $(2, 4)$

6. $\int_C \cos y \, dx + x^2 \sin y \, dy$,
C is the rectangle with vertices $(0, 0)$, $(5, 0)$, $(5, 2)$, and $(0, 2)$

7. $\int_C \left(y + e^{\sqrt{x}}\right) dx + (2x + \cos y^2) \, dy$,
C is the boundary of the region enclosed by the parabolas $y = x^2$ and $x = y^2$

8. $\int_C xe^{-2x} \, dx + (x^4 + 2x^2 y^2) \, dy$,
C is the boundary of the region between the circles $x^2 + y^2 = 1$ and $x^2 + y^2 = 4$

9. $\int_C y^3 \, dx - x^3 \, dy$, C is the circle $x^2 + y^2 = 4$

10. $\int_C \sin y \, dx + x \cos y \, dy$, C is the ellipse $x^2 + xy + y^2 = 1$

11–14 Use Green's Theorem to evaluate $\int_C \mathbf{F} \cdot d\mathbf{r}$. (Check the orientation of the curve before applying the theorem.)

11. $\mathbf{F}(x, y) = \left\langle \sqrt{x} + y^3, \, x^2 + \sqrt{y} \right\rangle$,
C consists of the arc of the curve $y = \sin x$ from $(0, 0)$ to $(\pi, 0)$ and the line segment from $(\pi, 0)$ to $(0, 0)$

12. $\mathbf{F}(x, y) = \langle y^2 \cos x, \, x^2 + 2y \sin x \rangle$,
C is the triangle from $(0, 0)$ to $(2, 6)$ to $(2, 0)$ to $(0, 0)$

13. $\mathbf{F}(x, y) = \langle e^x + x^2 y, \, e^y - xy^2 \rangle$,
C is the circle $x^2 + y^2 = 25$ oriented clockwise

14. $\mathbf{F}(x, y) = \langle y - \ln(x^2 + y^2), \, 2 \tan^{-1}(y/x) \rangle$, C is the circle $(x - 2)^2 + (y - 3)^2 = 1$ oriented counterclockwise

---

CAS **15–16** Verify Green's Theorem by using a computer algebra system to evaluate both the line integral and the double integral.

15. $P(x, y) = y^2 e^x$, $Q(x, y) = x^2 e^y$,
C consists of the line segment from $(-1, 1)$ to $(1, 1)$ followed by the arc of the parabola $y = 2 - x^2$ from $(1, 1)$ to $(-1, 1)$

16. $P(x, y) = 2x - x^3 y^5$, $Q(x, y) = x^3 y^8$,
C is the ellipse $4x^2 + y^2 = 4$

---

17. Use Green's Theorem to find the work done by the force $\mathbf{F}(x, y) = x(x + y) \mathbf{i} + xy^2 \mathbf{j}$ in moving a particle from the origin along the x-axis to $(1, 0)$, then along the line segment to $(0, 1)$, and then back to the origin along the y-axis.

18. A particle starts at the point $(-2, 0)$, moves along the x-axis to $(2, 0)$, and then along the semicircle $y = \sqrt{4 - x^2}$ to the starting point. Use Green's Theorem to find the work done on this particle by the force field $\mathbf{F}(x, y) = \langle x, x^3 + 3xy^2 \rangle$.

19. Use one of the formulas in (5) to find the area under one arch of the cycloid $x = t - \sin t$, $y = 1 - \cos t$.

20. If a circle C with radius 1 rolls along the outside of the circle $x^2 + y^2 = 16$, a fixed point P on C traces out a curve called an *epicycloid*, with parametric equations $x = 5 \cos t - \cos 5t$, $y = 5 \sin t - \sin 5t$. Graph the epicycloid and use (5) to find the area it encloses.

21. (a) If C is the line segment connecting the point (x_1, y_1) to the point (x_2, y_2), show that
$$\int_C x \, dy - y \, dx = x_1 y_2 - x_2 y_1$$

(b) If the vertices of a polygon, in counterclockwise order, are (x_1, y_1), (x_2, y_2), ..., (x_n, y_n), show that the area of the polygon is
$$A = \tfrac{1}{2}[(x_1 y_2 - x_2 y_1) + (x_2 y_3 - x_3 y_2) + \cdots$$
$$+ (x_{n-1} y_n - x_n y_{n-1}) + (x_n y_1 - x_1 y_n)]$$

(c) Find the area of the pentagon with vertices $(0, 0)$, $(2, 1)$, $(1, 3)$, $(0, 2)$, and $(-1, 1)$.

22. Let D be a region bounded by a simple closed path C in the xy-plane. Use Green's Theorem to prove that the coordinates of the centroid $(\bar{x}, \bar{y})$ of D are
$$\bar{x} = \frac{1}{2A} \oint_C x^2 \, dy \qquad \bar{y} = -\frac{1}{2A} \oint_C y^2 \, dx$$
where A is the area of D.

23. Use Exercise 22 to find the centroid of a quarter-circular region of radius a.

24. Use Exercise 22 to find the centroid of the triangle with vertices $(0, 0)$, $(a, 0)$, and (a, b), where $a > 0$ and $b > 0$.

25. A plane lamina with constant density $\rho(x, y) = \rho$ occupies a region in the xy-plane bounded by a simple closed path C. Show that its moments of inertia about the axes are
$$I_x = -\frac{\rho}{3} \oint_C y^3 \, dx \qquad I_y = \frac{\rho}{3} \oint_C x^3 \, dy$$

26. Use Exercise 25 to find the moment of inertia of a circular disk of radius a with constant density ρ about a diameter. (Compare with Example 4 in Section 12.5.)

27. Use the method of Example 5 to calculate $\int_C \mathbf{F} \cdot d\mathbf{r}$, where
$$\mathbf{F}(x, y) = \frac{2xy \, \mathbf{i} + (y^2 - x^2) \, \mathbf{j}}{(x^2 + y^2)^2}$$
and C is any positively oriented simple closed curve that encloses the origin.

28. Calculate $\int_C \mathbf{F} \cdot d\mathbf{r}$, where $\mathbf{F}(x, y) = \langle x^2 + y, \, 3x - y^2 \rangle$ and C is the positively oriented boundary curve of a region D that has area 6.

29. If $\mathbf{F}$ is the vector field of Example 5, show that $\int_C \mathbf{F} \cdot d\mathbf{r} = 0$ for every simple closed path that does not pass through or enclose the origin.

30. Complete the proof of the special case of Green's Theorem by proving Equation 3.

31. Use Green's Theorem to prove the change of variables formula for a double integral (Formula 12.9.9) for the case where $f(x, y) = 1$:

$$\iint\limits_{R} dx \, dy = \iint\limits_{S} \left| \frac{\partial(x, y)}{\partial(u, v)} \right| du \, dv$$

Here R is the region in the xy-plane that corresponds to the region S in the uv-plane under the transformation given by $x = g(u, v)$, $y = h(u, v)$.
  [*Hint:* Note that the left side is $A(R)$ and apply the first part of Equation 5. Convert the line integral over ∂R to a line integral over ∂S and apply Green's Theorem in the uv-plane.]

13.5 Curl and Divergence

In this section we define two operations that can be performed on vector fields and that play a basic role in the applications of vector calculus to fluid flow and electricity and magnetism. Each operation resembles differentiation, but one produces a vector field whereas the other produces a scalar field.

Curl

If $\mathbf{F} = P\,\mathbf{i} + Q\,\mathbf{j} + R\,\mathbf{k}$ is a vector field on $\mathbb{R}^3$ and the partial derivatives of P, Q, and R all exist, then the **curl** of $\mathbf{F}$ is the vector field on $\mathbb{R}^3$ defined by

$$\boxed{1} \qquad \text{curl } \mathbf{F} = \left(\frac{\partial R}{\partial y} - \frac{\partial Q}{\partial z} \right) \mathbf{i} + \left(\frac{\partial P}{\partial z} - \frac{\partial R}{\partial x} \right) \mathbf{j} + \left(\frac{\partial Q}{\partial x} - \frac{\partial P}{\partial y} \right) \mathbf{k}$$

As an aid to our memory, let's rewrite Equation 1 using operator notation. We introduce the vector differential operator ∇ ("del") as

$$\nabla = \mathbf{i} \frac{\partial}{\partial x} + \mathbf{j} \frac{\partial}{\partial y} + \mathbf{k} \frac{\partial}{\partial z}$$

It has meaning when it operates on a scalar function to produce the gradient of f:

$$\nabla f = \mathbf{i} \frac{\partial f}{\partial x} + \mathbf{j} \frac{\partial f}{\partial y} + \mathbf{k} \frac{\partial f}{\partial z} = \frac{\partial f}{\partial x} \mathbf{i} + \frac{\partial f}{\partial y} \mathbf{j} + \frac{\partial f}{\partial z} \mathbf{k}$$

If we think of ∇ as a vector with components $\partial/\partial x$, $\partial/\partial y$, and $\partial/\partial z$, we can also consider the formal cross product of ∇ with the vector field $\mathbf{F}$ as follows:

$$\nabla \times \mathbf{F} = \begin{vmatrix} \mathbf{i} & \mathbf{j} & \mathbf{k} \\ \dfrac{\partial}{\partial x} & \dfrac{\partial}{\partial y} & \dfrac{\partial}{\partial z} \\ P & Q & R \end{vmatrix}$$

$$= \left(\frac{\partial R}{\partial y} - \frac{\partial Q}{\partial z} \right) \mathbf{i} + \left(\frac{\partial P}{\partial z} - \frac{\partial R}{\partial x} \right) \mathbf{j} + \left(\frac{\partial Q}{\partial x} - \frac{\partial P}{\partial y} \right) \mathbf{k}$$

$$= \text{curl } \mathbf{F}$$

So the easiest way to remember Definition 1 is by means of the symbolic expression

$$\boxed{2} \qquad \text{curl } \mathbf{F} = \nabla \times \mathbf{F}$$

EXAMPLE 1 **Computing curl** If $\mathbf{F}(x, y, z) = xz\,\mathbf{i} + xyz\,\mathbf{j} - y^2\,\mathbf{k}$, find curl $\mathbf{F}$.

SOLUTION Using Equation 2, we have

$$
\text{curl } \mathbf{F} = \nabla \times \mathbf{F} = \begin{vmatrix} \mathbf{i} & \mathbf{j} & \mathbf{k} \\ \dfrac{\partial}{\partial x} & \dfrac{\partial}{\partial y} & \dfrac{\partial}{\partial z} \\ xz & xyz & -y^2 \end{vmatrix}
$$

$$
= \left[\frac{\partial}{\partial y}(-y^2) - \frac{\partial}{\partial z}(xyz) \right] \mathbf{i} - \left[\frac{\partial}{\partial x}(-y^2) - \frac{\partial}{\partial z}(xz) \right] \mathbf{j}
$$

$$
+ \left[\frac{\partial}{\partial x}(xyz) - \frac{\partial}{\partial y}(xz) \right] \mathbf{k}
$$

$$
= (-2y - xy)\,\mathbf{i} - (0 - x)\,\mathbf{j} + (yz - 0)\,\mathbf{k}
$$

$$
= -y(2 + x)\,\mathbf{i} + x\,\mathbf{j} + yz\,\mathbf{k}
$$

CAS Most computer algebra systems have commands that compute the curl and divergence of vector fields. If you have access to a CAS, use these commands to check the answers to the examples and exercises in this section.

Recall that the gradient of a function f of three variables is a vector field on $\mathbb{R}^3$ and so we can compute its curl. The following theorem says that the curl of a gradient vector field is $\mathbf{0}$.

---

3 **Theorem** If f is a function of three variables that has continuous second-order partial derivatives, then

$$
\text{curl}(\nabla f) = \mathbf{0}
$$

PROOF We have

Notice the similarity to what we know from Section 9.4: $\mathbf{a} \times \mathbf{a} = \mathbf{0}$ for every three-dimensional vector $\mathbf{a}$.

$$
\text{curl}(\nabla f) = \nabla \times (\nabla f) = \begin{vmatrix} \mathbf{i} & \mathbf{j} & \mathbf{k} \\ \dfrac{\partial}{\partial x} & \dfrac{\partial}{\partial y} & \dfrac{\partial}{\partial z} \\ \dfrac{\partial f}{\partial x} & \dfrac{\partial f}{\partial y} & \dfrac{\partial f}{\partial z} \end{vmatrix}
$$

$$
= \left(\frac{\partial^2 f}{\partial y\,\partial z} - \frac{\partial^2 f}{\partial z\,\partial y} \right) \mathbf{i} + \left(\frac{\partial^2 f}{\partial z\,\partial x} - \frac{\partial^2 f}{\partial x\,\partial z} \right) \mathbf{j} + \left(\frac{\partial^2 f}{\partial x\,\partial y} - \frac{\partial^2 f}{\partial y\,\partial x} \right) \mathbf{k}
$$

$$
= 0\,\mathbf{i} + 0\,\mathbf{j} + 0\,\mathbf{k} = \mathbf{0}
$$

by Clairaut's Theorem.

Compare this with Exercise 29 in Section 13.3.

Since a conservative vector field is one for which $\mathbf{F} = \nabla f$, Theorem 3 can be rephrased as follows:

If $\mathbf{F}$ is conservative, then curl $\mathbf{F} = \mathbf{0}$.

This gives us a way of verifying that a vector field is not conservative.

⊽ **EXAMPLE 2** **Using curl F to show that F is not conservative**   Show that the vector field $\mathbf{F}(x, y, z) = xz\,\mathbf{i} + xyz\,\mathbf{j} - y^2\,\mathbf{k}$ is not conservative.

SOLUTION   In Example 1 we showed that

$$\operatorname{curl} \mathbf{F} = -y(2 + x)\,\mathbf{i} + x\,\mathbf{j} + yz\,\mathbf{k}$$

This shows that curl $\mathbf{F} \neq \mathbf{0}$ and so, by Theorem 3, $\mathbf{F}$ is not conservative. ▬

The converse of Theorem 3 is not true in general, but the following theorem says the converse is true if $\mathbf{F}$ is defined everywhere. (More generally it is true if the domain is simply-connected, that is, "has no hole.") Theorem 4 is the three-dimensional version of Theorem 13.3.6. Its proof requires Stokes' Theorem and is sketched at the end of Section 13.7.

---

4 **Theorem** If $\mathbf{F}$ is a vector field defined on all of $\mathbb{R}^3$ whose component functions have continuous partial derivatives and curl $\mathbf{F} = \mathbf{0}$, then $\mathbf{F}$ is a conservative vector field.

⊽ **EXAMPLE 3**   **Finding a potential function for a conservative vector field**
(a) Show that

$$\mathbf{F}(x, y, z) = y^2z^3\,\mathbf{i} + 2xyz^3\,\mathbf{j} + 3xy^2z^2\,\mathbf{k}$$

is a conservative vector field.
(b) Find a function f such that $\mathbf{F} = \nabla f$.

SOLUTION
(a) We compute the curl of $\mathbf{F}$:

$$\operatorname{curl} \mathbf{F} = \nabla \times \mathbf{F} = \begin{vmatrix} \mathbf{i} & \mathbf{j} & \mathbf{k} \\ \dfrac{\partial}{\partial x} & \dfrac{\partial}{\partial y} & \dfrac{\partial}{\partial z} \\ y^2z^3 & 2xyz^3 & 3xy^2z^2 \end{vmatrix}$$

$$= (6xyz^2 - 6xyz^2)\,\mathbf{i} - (3y^2z^2 - 3y^2z^2)\,\mathbf{j} + (2yz^3 - 2yz^3)\,\mathbf{k}$$

$$= \mathbf{0}$$

Since curl $\mathbf{F} = \mathbf{0}$ and the domain of $\mathbf{F}$ is $\mathbb{R}^3$, $\mathbf{F}$ is a conservative vector field by Theorem 4.

(b) The technique for finding f was given in Section 13.3. We have

5 $$f_x(x, y, z) = y^2z^3$$

6 $$f_y(x, y, z) = 2xyz^3$$

7 $$f_z(x, y, z) = 3xy^2z^2$$

Integrating (5) with respect to x, we obtain

8 $$f(x, y, z) = xy^2z^3 + g(y, z)$$

Differentiating (8) with respect to y, we get $f_y(x, y, z) = 2xyz^3 + g_y(y, z)$, so comparison with (6) gives $g_y(y, z) = 0$. Thus $g(y, z) = h(z)$ and

$$f_z(x, y, z) = 3xy^2z^2 + h'(z)$$

Then (7) gives $h'(z) = 0$. Therefore

$$f(x, y, z) = xy^2z^3 + K$$

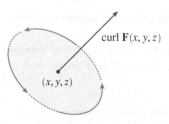

curl $\mathbf{F}(x, y, z)$

(x, y, z)

FIGURE 1

The reason for the name *curl* is that the curl vector is associated with rotations. One connection is explained in Exercise 37. Another occurs when $\mathbf{F}$ represents the velocity field in fluid flow (see Example 3 in Section 13.1). Particles near (x, y, z) in the fluid tend to rotate about the axis that points in the direction of curl $\mathbf{F}(x, y, z)$, and the length of this curl vector is a measure of how quickly the particles move around the axis (see Figure 1). If curl $\mathbf{F} = \mathbf{0}$ at a point P, then the fluid is free from rotations at P and $\mathbf{F}$ is called **irrotational** at P. In other words, there is no whirlpool or eddy at P. If curl $\mathbf{F} = \mathbf{0}$, then a tiny paddle wheel moves with the fluid but doesn't rotate about its axis. If curl $\mathbf{F} \neq \mathbf{0}$, the paddle wheel rotates about its axis. We give a more detailed explanation in Section 13.7 as a consequence of Stokes' Theorem.

Divergence

If $\mathbf{F} = P\mathbf{i} + Q\mathbf{j} + R\mathbf{k}$ is a vector field on $\mathbb{R}^3$ and $\partial P/\partial x$, $\partial Q/\partial y$, and $\partial R/\partial z$ exist, then the **divergence of F** is the function of three variables defined by

9
$$\text{div } \mathbf{F} = \frac{\partial P}{\partial x} + \frac{\partial Q}{\partial y} + \frac{\partial R}{\partial z}$$

Observe that curl $\mathbf{F}$ is a vector field but div $\mathbf{F}$ is a scalar field. In terms of the gradient operator $\nabla = (\partial/\partial x)\,\mathbf{i} + (\partial/\partial y)\,\mathbf{j} + (\partial/\partial z)\,\mathbf{k}$, the divergence of $\mathbf{F}$ can be written symbolically as the dot product of ∇ and $\mathbf{F}$:

10
$$\text{div } \mathbf{F} = \nabla \cdot \mathbf{F}$$

EXAMPLE 4 **Computing divergence** If $\mathbf{F}(x, y, z) = xz\,\mathbf{i} + xyz\,\mathbf{j} - y^2\,\mathbf{k}$, find div $\mathbf{F}$.

SOLUTION By the definition of divergence (Equation 9 or 10) we have

$$\text{div } \mathbf{F} = \nabla \cdot \mathbf{F} = \frac{\partial}{\partial x}(xz) + \frac{\partial}{\partial y}(xyz) + \frac{\partial}{\partial z}(-y^2) = z + xz$$

If $\mathbf{F}$ is a vector field on $\mathbb{R}^3$, then curl $\mathbf{F}$ is also a vector field on $\mathbb{R}^3$. As such, we can compute its divergence. The next theorem shows that the result is 0.

11 **Theorem** If $\mathbf{F} = P\mathbf{i} + Q\mathbf{j} + R\mathbf{k}$ is a vector field on $\mathbb{R}^3$ and P, Q, and R have continuous second-order partial derivatives, then

$$\text{div curl } \mathbf{F} = 0$$

Note the analogy with the scalar triple product: $\mathbf{a} \cdot (\mathbf{a} \times \mathbf{b}) = 0$.

PROOF Using the definitions of divergence and curl, we have

$$\text{div curl } \mathbf{F} = \nabla \cdot (\nabla \times \mathbf{F})$$

$$= \frac{\partial}{\partial x}\left(\frac{\partial R}{\partial y} - \frac{\partial Q}{\partial z}\right) + \frac{\partial}{\partial y}\left(\frac{\partial P}{\partial z} - \frac{\partial R}{\partial x}\right) + \frac{\partial}{\partial z}\left(\frac{\partial Q}{\partial x} - \frac{\partial P}{\partial y}\right)$$

$$= \frac{\partial^2 R}{\partial x\,\partial y} - \frac{\partial^2 Q}{\partial x\,\partial z} + \frac{\partial^2 P}{\partial y\,\partial z} - \frac{\partial^2 R}{\partial y\,\partial x} + \frac{\partial^2 Q}{\partial z\,\partial x} - \frac{\partial^2 P}{\partial z\,\partial y}$$

$$= 0$$

because the terms cancel in pairs by Clairaut's Theorem. ▢

V **EXAMPLE 5** Show that the vector field $\mathbf{F}(x, y, z) = xz\,\mathbf{i} + xyz\,\mathbf{j} - y^2\,\mathbf{k}$ can't be written as the curl of another vector field, that is, $\mathbf{F} \neq \text{curl } \mathbf{G}$.

SOLUTION In Example 4 we showed that

$$\text{div } \mathbf{F} = z + xz$$

and therefore div $\mathbf{F} \neq 0$. If it were true that $\mathbf{F} = \text{curl } \mathbf{G}$, then Theorem 11 would give

$$\text{div } \mathbf{F} = \text{div curl } \mathbf{G} = 0$$

which contradicts div $\mathbf{F} \neq 0$. Therefore $\mathbf{F}$ is not the curl of another vector field. ■

The reason for this interpretation of div $\mathbf{F}$ will be explained at the end of Section 13.8 as a consequence of the Divergence Theorem.

Again, the reason for the name *divergence* can be understood in the context of fluid flow. If $\mathbf{F}(x, y, z)$ is the velocity of a fluid (or gas), then div $\mathbf{F}(x, y, z)$ represents the net rate of change (with respect to time) of the mass of fluid (or gas) flowing from the point (x, y, z) per unit volume. In other words, div $\mathbf{F}(x, y, z)$ measures the tendency of the fluid to diverge from the point (x, y, z). If div $\mathbf{F} = 0$, then $\mathbf{F}$ is said to be **incompressible**.

Another differential operator occurs when we compute the divergence of a gradient vector field ∇f. If f is a function of three variables, we have

$$\text{div}(\nabla f) = \nabla \cdot (\nabla f) = \frac{\partial^2 f}{\partial x^2} + \frac{\partial^2 f}{\partial y^2} + \frac{\partial^2 f}{\partial z^2}$$

and this expression occurs so often that we abbreviate it as $\nabla^2 f$. The operator

$$\nabla^2 = \nabla \cdot \nabla$$

is called the **Laplace operator** because of its relation to **Laplace's equation**

$$\nabla^2 f = \frac{\partial^2 f}{\partial x^2} + \frac{\partial^2 f}{\partial y^2} + \frac{\partial^2 f}{\partial z^2} = 0$$

We can also apply the Laplace operator ∇^2 to a vector field

$$\mathbf{F} = P\,\mathbf{i} + Q\,\mathbf{j} + R\,\mathbf{k}$$

in terms of its components:

$$\nabla^2 \mathbf{F} = \nabla^2 P\,\mathbf{i} + \nabla^2 Q\,\mathbf{j} + \nabla^2 R\,\mathbf{k}$$

Vector Forms of Green's Theorem

The curl and divergence operators allow us to rewrite Green's Theorem in versions that will be useful in our later work. We suppose that the plane region D, its boundary curve C, and the functions P and Q satisfy the hypotheses of Green's Theorem. Then we consider the vector field $\mathbf{F} = P\,\mathbf{i} + Q\,\mathbf{j}$. Its line integral is

$$\oint_C \mathbf{F} \cdot d\mathbf{r} = \oint_C P\,dx + Q\,dy$$

and, regarding $\mathbf{F}$ as a vector field on $\mathbb{R}^3$ with third component 0, we have

$$\text{curl } \mathbf{F} = \begin{vmatrix} \mathbf{i} & \mathbf{j} & \mathbf{k} \\ \dfrac{\partial}{\partial x} & \dfrac{\partial}{\partial y} & \dfrac{\partial}{\partial z} \\ P(x,y) & Q(x,y) & 0 \end{vmatrix} = \left(\frac{\partial Q}{\partial x} - \frac{\partial P}{\partial y} \right) \mathbf{k}$$

Therefore

$$(\text{curl } \mathbf{F}) \cdot \mathbf{k} = \left(\frac{\partial Q}{\partial x} - \frac{\partial P}{\partial y} \right) \mathbf{k} \cdot \mathbf{k} = \frac{\partial Q}{\partial x} - \frac{\partial P}{\partial y}$$

and we can now rewrite the equation in Green's Theorem in the vector form

$$\boxed{12} \qquad \boxed{\;\oint_C \mathbf{F} \cdot d\mathbf{r} = \iint_D (\text{curl } \mathbf{F}) \cdot \mathbf{k}\, dA\;}$$

Equation 12 expresses the line integral of the tangential component of $\mathbf{F}$ along C as the double integral of the vertical component of curl $\mathbf{F}$ over the region D enclosed by C. We now derive a similar formula involving the *normal* component of $\mathbf{F}$.

If C is given by the vector equation

$$\mathbf{r}(t) = x(t)\,\mathbf{i} + y(t)\,\mathbf{j} \qquad a \leqslant t \leqslant b$$

then the unit tangent vector (see Section 10.2) is

$$\mathbf{T}(t) = \frac{x'(t)}{|\mathbf{r}'(t)|}\,\mathbf{i} + \frac{y'(t)}{|\mathbf{r}'(t)|}\,\mathbf{j}$$

You can verify that the outward unit normal vector to C is given by

$$\mathbf{n}(t) = \frac{y'(t)}{|\mathbf{r}'(t)|}\,\mathbf{i} - \frac{x'(t)}{|\mathbf{r}'(t)|}\,\mathbf{j}$$

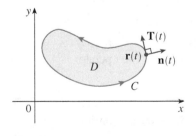

FIGURE 2

(See Figure 2.) Then, from Equation 13.2.3, we have

$$\oint_C \mathbf{F} \cdot \mathbf{n}\, ds = \int_a^b (\mathbf{F} \cdot \mathbf{n})(t)\,|\mathbf{r}'(t)|\, dt$$

$$= \int_a^b \left[\frac{P\big(x(t), y(t)\big)\,y'(t)}{|\mathbf{r}'(t)|} - \frac{Q\big(x(t), y(t)\big)\,x'(t)}{|\mathbf{r}'(t)|} \right] |\mathbf{r}'(t)|\, dt$$

$$= \int_a^b P\big(x(t), y(t)\big)\,y'(t)\, dt - Q\big(x(t), y(t)\big)\,x'(t)\, dt$$

$$= \int_C P\, dy - Q\, dx = \iint_D \left(\frac{\partial P}{\partial x} + \frac{\partial Q}{\partial y} \right) dA$$

by Green's Theorem. But the integrand in this double integral is just the divergence of **F**. So we have a second vector form of Green's Theorem.

$$\boxed{13} \qquad \oint_C \mathbf{F} \cdot \mathbf{n} \, ds = \iint_D \text{div } \mathbf{F}(x, y) \, dA$$

This version says that the line integral of the normal component of **F** along C is equal to the double integral of the divergence of **F** over the region D enclosed by C.

13.5 Exercises

1–8 Find (a) the curl and (b) the divergence of the vector field.

1. $\mathbf{F}(x, y, z) = xyz \, \mathbf{i} - x^2 y \, \mathbf{k}$

2. $\mathbf{F}(x, y, z) = x^2 yz \, \mathbf{i} + xy^2 z \, \mathbf{j} + xyz^2 \, \mathbf{k}$

3. $\mathbf{F}(x, y, z) = xye^z \, \mathbf{i} + yze^x \, \mathbf{k}$

4. $\mathbf{F}(x, y, z) = \sin yz \, \mathbf{i} + \sin zx \, \mathbf{j} + \sin xy \, \mathbf{k}$

5. $\mathbf{F}(x, y, z) = \dfrac{1}{\sqrt{x^2 + y^2 + z^2}}(x \, \mathbf{i} + y \, \mathbf{j} + z \, \mathbf{k})$

6. $\mathbf{F}(x, y, z) = e^{xy} \sin z \, \mathbf{j} + y \tan^{-1}(x/z) \, \mathbf{k}$

7. $\mathbf{F}(x, y, z) = \langle \ln x, \ln(xy), \ln(xyz) \rangle$

8. $\mathbf{F}(x, y, z) = \langle e^x, e^{xy}, e^{xyz} \rangle$

9–11 The vector field **F** is shown in the xy-plane and looks the same in all other horizontal planes. (In other words, **F** is independent of z and its z-component is 0.)
(a) Is div **F** positive, negative, or zero? Explain.
(b) Determine whether curl **F** = **0**. If not, in which direction does curl **F** point?

9.

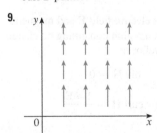

10.

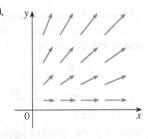

11.

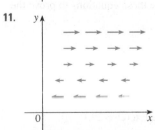

12. Let f be a scalar field and **F** a vector field. State whether each expression is meaningful. If not, explain why. If so, state whether it is a scalar field or a vector field.
(a) curl f (b) grad f
(c) div **F**   (d) curl(grad f)
(e) grad **F**   (f) grad(div **F**)
(g) div(grad f)   (h) grad(div f)
(i) curl(curl **F**)   (j) div(div **F**)
(k) (grad f) × (div **F**) (l) div(curl(grad f))

13–18 Determine whether or not the vector field is conservative. If it is conservative, find a function f such that $\mathbf{F} = \nabla f$.

13. $\mathbf{F}(x, y, z) = y^2 z^3 \, \mathbf{i} + 2xyz^3 \, \mathbf{j} + 3xy^2 z^2 \, \mathbf{k}$

14. $\mathbf{F}(x, y, z) = xyz^2 \, \mathbf{i} + x^2 yz^2 \, \mathbf{j} + x^2 y^2 z \, \mathbf{k}$

15. $\mathbf{F}(x, y, z) = 2xy \, \mathbf{i} + (x^2 + 2yz) \, \mathbf{j} + y^2 \, \mathbf{k}$

16. $\mathbf{F}(x, y, z) = e^z \, \mathbf{i} + \mathbf{j} + xe^z \, \mathbf{k}$

17. $\mathbf{F}(x, y, z) = ye^{-x} \, \mathbf{i} + e^{-x} \, \mathbf{j} + 2z \, \mathbf{k}$

18. $\mathbf{F}(x, y, z) = y \cos xy \, \mathbf{i} + x \cos xy \, \mathbf{j} - \sin z \, \mathbf{k}$

19. Is there a vector field **G** on $\mathbb{R}^3$ such that curl $\mathbf{G} = \langle x \sin y, \cos y, z - xy \rangle$? Explain.

20. Is there a vector field **G** on $\mathbb{R}^3$ such that curl $\mathbf{G} = \langle xyz, -y^2 z, yz^2 \rangle$? Explain.

21. Show that any vector field of the form

$$\mathbf{F}(x, y, z) = f(x) \, \mathbf{i} + g(y) \, \mathbf{j} + h(z) \, \mathbf{k}$$

where f, g, h are differentiable functions, is irrotational.

22. Show that any vector field of the form

$$\mathbf{F}(x, y, z) = f(y, z) \, \mathbf{i} + g(x, z) \, \mathbf{j} + h(x, y) \, \mathbf{k}$$

is incompressible.

23–29 Prove the identity, assuming that the appropriate partial derivatives exist and are continuous. If f is a scalar field and $\mathbf{F}$, $\mathbf{G}$ are vector fields, then $f\mathbf{F}$, $\mathbf{F} \cdot \mathbf{G}$, and $\mathbf{F} \times \mathbf{G}$ are defined by

$$(f\mathbf{F})(x, y, z) = f(x, y, z)\,\mathbf{F}(x, y, z)$$

$$(\mathbf{F} \cdot \mathbf{G})(x, y, z) = \mathbf{F}(x, y, z) \cdot \mathbf{G}(x, y, z)$$

$$(\mathbf{F} \times \mathbf{G})(x, y, z) = \mathbf{F}(x, y, z) \times \mathbf{G}(x, y, z)$$

23. $\operatorname{div}(\mathbf{F} + \mathbf{G}) = \operatorname{div} \mathbf{F} + \operatorname{div} \mathbf{G}$

24. $\operatorname{curl}(\mathbf{F} + \mathbf{G}) = \operatorname{curl} \mathbf{F} + \operatorname{curl} \mathbf{G}$

25. $\operatorname{div}(f\mathbf{F}) = f \operatorname{div} \mathbf{F} + \mathbf{F} \cdot \nabla f$

26. $\operatorname{curl}(f\mathbf{F}) = f \operatorname{curl} \mathbf{F} + (\nabla f) \times \mathbf{F}$

27. $\operatorname{div}(\mathbf{F} \times \mathbf{G}) = \mathbf{G} \cdot \operatorname{curl} \mathbf{F} - \mathbf{F} \cdot \operatorname{curl} \mathbf{G}$

28. $\operatorname{div}(\nabla f \times \nabla g) = 0$

29. $\operatorname{curl}(\operatorname{curl} \mathbf{F}) = \operatorname{grad}(\operatorname{div} \mathbf{F}) - \nabla^2 \mathbf{F}$

30–32 Let $\mathbf{r} = x\,\mathbf{i} + y\,\mathbf{j} + z\,\mathbf{k}$ and $r = |\mathbf{r}|$.

30. Verify each identity.
    (a) $\nabla \cdot \mathbf{r} = 3$ (b) $\nabla \cdot (r\mathbf{r}) = 4r$
    (c) $\nabla^2 r^3 = 12r$

31. Verify each identity.
    (a) $\nabla r = \mathbf{r}/r$ (b) $\nabla \times \mathbf{r} = \mathbf{0}$
    (c) $\nabla(1/r) = -\mathbf{r}/r^3$ (d) $\nabla \ln r = \mathbf{r}/r^2$

32. If $\mathbf{F} = \mathbf{r}/r^p$, find div $\mathbf{F}$. Is there a value of p for which div $\mathbf{F} = 0$?

---

33. Use Green's Theorem in the form of Equation 13 to prove **Green's first identity**:

$$\iint_D f\nabla^2 g\, dA = \oint_C f(\nabla g) \cdot \mathbf{n}\, ds - \iint_D \nabla f \cdot \nabla g\, dA$$

where D and C satisfy the hypotheses of Green's Theorem and the appropriate partial derivatives of f and g exist and are continuous. (The quantity $\nabla g \cdot \mathbf{n} = D_\mathbf{n} g$ occurs in the line integral. This is the directional derivative in the direction of the normal vector $\mathbf{n}$ and is called the **normal derivative** of g.)

34. Use Green's first identity (Exercise 33) to prove **Green's second identity**:

$$\iint_D (f\nabla^2 g - g\nabla^2 f)\, dA = \oint_C (f\nabla g - g\nabla f) \cdot \mathbf{n}\, ds$$

where D and C satisfy the hypotheses of Green's Theorem and the appropriate partial derivatives of f and g exist and are continuous.

35. Recall from Section 11.3 that a function g is called *harmonic* on D if it satisfies Laplace's equation, that is, $\nabla^2 g = 0$ on D. Use Green's first identity (with the same hypotheses as in

Exercise 33) to show that if g is harmonic on D, then $\oint_C D_\mathbf{n} g\, ds = 0$. Here $D_\mathbf{n} g$ is the normal derivative of g defined in Exercise 33.

36. Use Green's first identity to show that if f is harmonic on D, and if $f(x, y) = 0$ on the boundary curve C, then $\iint_D |\nabla f|^2\, dA = 0$. (Assume the same hypotheses as in Exercise 33.)

37. This exercise demonstrates a connection between the curl vector and rotations. Let B be a rigid body rotating about the z-axis. The rotation can be described by the vector $\mathbf{w} = \omega\mathbf{k}$, where ω is the angular speed of B, that is, the tangential speed of any point P in B divided by the distance d from the axis of rotation. Let $\mathbf{r} = \langle x, y, z \rangle$ be the position vector of P.
    (a) By considering the angle θ in the figure, show that the velocity field of B is given by $\mathbf{v} = \mathbf{w} \times \mathbf{r}$.
    (b) Show that $\mathbf{v} = -\omega y\,\mathbf{i} + \omega x\,\mathbf{j}$.
    (c) Show that curl $\mathbf{v} = 2\mathbf{w}$.

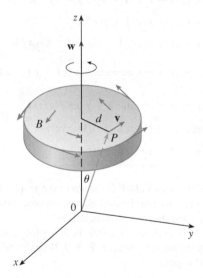

38. Maxwell's equations relating the electric field $\mathbf{E}$ and magnetic field $\mathbf{H}$ as they vary with time in a region containing no charge and no current can be stated as follows:

$$\operatorname{div} \mathbf{E} = 0 \qquad\qquad \operatorname{div} \mathbf{H} = 0$$

$$\operatorname{curl} \mathbf{E} = -\frac{1}{c}\frac{\partial \mathbf{H}}{\partial t} \qquad \operatorname{curl} \mathbf{H} = \frac{1}{c}\frac{\partial \mathbf{E}}{\partial t}$$

where c is the speed of light. Use these equations to prove the following:

(a) $\nabla \times (\nabla \times \mathbf{E}) = -\dfrac{1}{c^2}\dfrac{\partial^2 \mathbf{E}}{\partial t^2}$

(b) $\nabla \times (\nabla \times \mathbf{H}) = -\dfrac{1}{c^2}\dfrac{\partial^2 \mathbf{H}}{\partial t^2}$

(c) $\nabla^2 \mathbf{E} = \dfrac{1}{c^2}\dfrac{\partial^2 \mathbf{E}}{\partial t^2}$ [*Hint:* Use Exercise 29.]

(d) $\nabla^2 \mathbf{H} = \dfrac{1}{c^2}\dfrac{\partial^2 \mathbf{H}}{\partial t^2}$

39. We have seen that all vector fields of the form $\mathbf{F} = \nabla g$ satisfy the equation curl $\mathbf{F} = \mathbf{0}$ and that all vector fields of the form $\mathbf{F} = \text{curl } \mathbf{G}$ satisfy the equation div $\mathbf{F} = 0$ (assuming continuity of the appropriate partial derivatives). This suggests the question: Are there any equations that all functions of the form $f = \text{div } \mathbf{G}$ must satisfy? Show that the answer to this question is "No" by proving that *every* continuous function f on $\mathbb{R}^3$ is the divergence of some vector field.

[*Hint:* Let $\mathbf{G}(x, y, z) = \langle g(x, y, z), 0, 0 \rangle$, where $g(x, y, z) = \int_0^x f(t, y, z)\, dt$.]

13.6 Surface Integrals

The relationship between surface integrals and surface area is much the same as the relationship between line integrals and arc length. Suppose f is a function of three variables whose domain includes a surface S. We will define the surface integral of f over S in such a way that, in the case where $f(x, y, z) = 1$, the value of the surface integral is equal to the surface area of S. We start with parametric surfaces and then deal with the special case where S is the graph of a function of two variables.

Parametric Surfaces

Recall from Section 10.5 that a parametric surface S is defined by a vector function $\mathbf{r}(u, v)$ of two parameters u and v:

$$\mathbf{r}(u, v) = x(u, v)\, \mathbf{i} + y(u, v)\, \mathbf{j} + z(u, v)\, \mathbf{k} \qquad (u, v) \in D$$

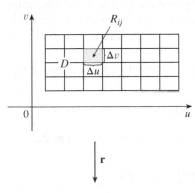

We first assume that the parameter domain D is a rectangle and we divide it into subrectangles R_{ij} with dimensions Δu and Δv. Then the surface S is divided into corresponding patches S_{ij} as in Figure 1. We evaluate f at a point P_{ij}^* in each patch, multiply by the area ΔS_{ij} of the patch, and form the Riemann sum

$$\sum_{i=1}^{m} \sum_{j=1}^{n} f(P_{ij}^*)\, \Delta S_{ij}$$

Then we take the limit as the number of patches increases and define the **surface integral of f over the surface S** as

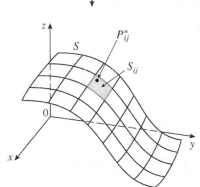

$$\boxed{1} \qquad \iint_S f(x, y, z)\, dS = \lim_{m,\, n \to \infty} \sum_{i=1}^{m} \sum_{j=1}^{n} f(P_{ij}^*)\, \Delta S_{ij}$$

FIGURE 1

Notice the analogy with the definition of a line integral (13.2.2) and also the analogy with the definition of a double integral (12.1.5).

To evaluate the surface integral in Equation 1 we approximate the patch area ΔS_{ij} by the area of an approximating parallelogram in the tangent plane. In our discussion of surface area in Section 12.6 we made the approximation

$$\Delta S_{ij} \approx |\mathbf{r}_u \times \mathbf{r}_v|\, \Delta u\, \Delta v$$

where
$$\mathbf{r}_u = \frac{\partial x}{\partial u}\, \mathbf{i} + \frac{\partial y}{\partial u}\, \mathbf{j} + \frac{\partial z}{\partial u}\, \mathbf{k} \qquad \mathbf{r}_v = \frac{\partial x}{\partial v}\, \mathbf{i} + \frac{\partial y}{\partial v}\, \mathbf{j} + \frac{\partial z}{\partial v}\, \mathbf{k}$$

are the tangent vectors at a corner of S_{ij}. If the components are continuous and $\mathbf{r}_u$ and $\mathbf{r}_v$ are nonzero and nonparallel in the interior of D, it can be shown from Definition 1, even when D is not a rectangle, that

We assume that the surface is covered only once as (u, v) ranges throughout D. The value of the surface integral does not depend on the parametrization that is used.

$$\boxed{2} \qquad \iint_S f(x, y, z)\, dS = \iint_D f(\mathbf{r}(u, v))\, |\mathbf{r}_u \times \mathbf{r}_v|\, dA$$

This should be compared with the formula for a line integral:

$$\int_C f(x, y, z)\, ds = \int_a^b f(\mathbf{r}(t))\, |\mathbf{r}'(t)|\, dt$$

Observe also that

$$\iint_S 1\, dS = \iint_D |\mathbf{r}_u \times \mathbf{r}_v|\, dA = A(S)$$

Formula 2 allows us to compute a surface integral by converting it into a double integral over the parameter domain D. When using this formula, remember that $f(\mathbf{r}(u, v))$ is evaluated by writing $x = x(u, v)$, $y = y(u, v)$, and $z = z(u, v)$ in the formula for $f(x, y, z)$.

EXAMPLE 1 **Integrating over a sphere**   Compute the surface integral $\iint_S x^2\, dS$, where S is the unit sphere $x^2 + y^2 + z^2 = 1$.

SOLUTION As in Example 4 in Section 10.5, we use the parametric representation

$$x = \sin\phi\cos\theta \quad y = \sin\phi\sin\theta \quad z = \cos\phi \quad 0 \le \phi \le \pi \quad 0 \le \theta \le 2\pi$$

that is, $\mathbf{r}(\phi, \theta) = \sin\phi\cos\theta\,\mathbf{i} + \sin\phi\sin\theta\,\mathbf{j} + \cos\phi\,\mathbf{k}$

As in Example 1 in Section 12.6, we can compute that

$$|\mathbf{r}_\phi \times \mathbf{r}_\theta| = \sin\phi$$

Therefore, by Formula 2,

Here we use the identities
$$\cos^2\theta = \tfrac{1}{2}(1 + \cos 2\theta)$$
$$\sin^2\phi = 1 - \cos^2\phi$$
Instead, we could use Formulas 64 and 67 in the Table of Integrals.

$$\iint_S x^2\, dS = \iint_D (\sin\phi\cos\theta)^2\, |\mathbf{r}_\phi \times \mathbf{r}_\theta|\, dA$$
$$= \int_0^{2\pi}\int_0^\pi \sin^2\phi\cos^2\theta\,\sin\phi\, d\phi\, d\theta = \int_0^{2\pi}\cos^2\theta\, d\theta \int_0^\pi \sin^3\phi\, d\phi$$
$$= \int_0^{2\pi}\tfrac{1}{2}(1 + \cos 2\theta)\, d\theta \int_0^\pi (\sin\phi - \sin\phi\cos^2\phi)\, d\phi$$
$$= \tfrac{1}{2}\left[\theta + \tfrac{1}{2}\sin 2\theta\right]_0^{2\pi}\left[-\cos\phi + \tfrac{1}{3}\cos^3\phi\right]_0^\pi = \frac{4\pi}{3}$$

Surface integrals have applications similar to those for the integrals we have previously considered. For example, if a thin sheet (say, of aluminum foil) has the shape of a surface S and the density (mass per unit area) at the point (x, y, z) is $\rho(x, y, z)$, then the total **mass** of the sheet is

$$m = \iint_S \rho(x, y, z)\, dS$$

and the **center of mass** is $(\bar{x}, \bar{y}, \bar{z})$, where

$$\bar{x} = \frac{1}{m} \iint_S x\,\rho(x, y, z)\, dS \qquad \bar{y} = \frac{1}{m} \iint_S y\,\rho(x, y, z)\, dS \qquad \bar{z} = \frac{1}{m} \iint_S z\,\rho(x, y, z)\, dS$$

Moments of inertia can also be defined as before (see Exercise 39).

Graphs

Any surface S with equation $z = g(x, y)$ can be regarded as a parametric surface with parametric equations

$$x = x \qquad y = y \qquad z = g(x, y)$$

and so we have
$$\mathbf{r}_x = \mathbf{i} + \left(\frac{\partial g}{\partial x} \right) \mathbf{k} \qquad \mathbf{r}_y = \mathbf{j} + \left(\frac{\partial g}{\partial y} \right) \mathbf{k}$$

Thus

$$\boxed{3} \qquad \mathbf{r}_x \times \mathbf{r}_y = -\frac{\partial g}{\partial x}\mathbf{i} - \frac{\partial g}{\partial y}\mathbf{j} + \mathbf{k}$$

and
$$|\mathbf{r}_x \times \mathbf{r}_y| = \sqrt{\left(\frac{\partial z}{\partial x} \right)^2 + \left(\frac{\partial z}{\partial y} \right)^2 + 1}$$

Therefore, in this case, Formula 2 becomes

$$\boxed{4} \qquad \iint_S f(x, y, z)\, dS = \iint_D f\big(x, y, g(x, y)\big) \sqrt{\left(\frac{\partial z}{\partial x} \right)^2 + \left(\frac{\partial z}{\partial y} \right)^2 + 1}\; dA$$

Similar formulas apply when it is more convenient to project S onto the yz-plane or xz-plane. For instance, if S is a surface with equation $y = h(x, z)$ and D is its projection onto the xz-plane, then

$$\iint_S f(x, y, z)\, dS = \iint_D f\big(x, h(x, z), z\big) \sqrt{\left(\frac{\partial y}{\partial x} \right)^2 + \left(\frac{\partial y}{\partial z} \right)^2 + 1}\; dA$$

EXAMPLE 2 **Integrating over the graph of a function** Evaluate $\iint_S y\, dS$, where S is the surface $z = x + y^2$, $0 \le x \le 1$, $0 \le y \le 2$. (See Figure 2.)

SOLUTION Since

$$\frac{\partial z}{\partial x} = 1 \qquad \text{and} \qquad \frac{\partial z}{\partial y} = 2y$$

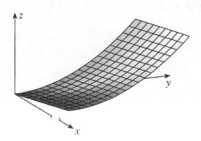

FIGURE 2

Formula 4 gives

$$\iint_S y \, dS = \iint_D y \sqrt{1 + \left(\frac{\partial z}{\partial x}\right)^2 + \left(\frac{\partial z}{\partial y}\right)^2} \, dA$$

$$= \int_0^1 \int_0^2 y\sqrt{1 + 1 + 4y^2} \, dy \, dx$$

$$= \int_0^1 dx \, \sqrt{2} \int_0^2 y\sqrt{1 + 2y^2} \, dy$$

$$= \sqrt{2} \left(\tfrac{1}{4}\right)\tfrac{2}{3}(1 + 2y^2)^{3/2}\big]_0^2 = \frac{13\sqrt{2}}{3}$$

If S is a piecewise-smooth surface, that is, a finite union of smooth surfaces $S_1, S_2, \dots,$ S_n that intersect only along their boundaries, then the surface integral of f over S is defined by

$$\iint_S f(x, y, z) \, dS = \iint_{S_1} f(x, y, z) \, dS + \cdots + \iint_{S_n} f(x, y, z) \, dS$$

V EXAMPLE 3 Integrating over a piecewise-smooth surface Evaluate $\iint_S z \, dS$, where S is the surface whose sides S_1 are given by the cylinder $x^2 + y^2 = 1$, whose bottom S_2 is the disk $x^2 + y^2 \leqslant 1$ in the plane $z = 0$, and whose top S_3 is the part of the plane $z = 1 + x$ that lies above S_2.

SOLUTION The surface S is shown in Figure 3. (We have changed the usual position of the axes to get a better look at S.) For S_1 we use θ and z as parameters (see Example 5 in Section 10.5) and write its parametric equations as

$$x = \cos\theta \qquad y = \sin\theta \qquad z = z$$

where

$$0 \leqslant \theta \leqslant 2\pi \qquad \text{and} \qquad 0 \leqslant z \leqslant 1 + x = 1 + \cos\theta$$

Therefore

$$\mathbf{r}_\theta \times \mathbf{r}_z = \begin{vmatrix} \mathbf{i} & \mathbf{j} & \mathbf{k} \\ -\sin\theta & \cos\theta & 0 \\ 0 & 0 & 1 \end{vmatrix} = \cos\theta\,\mathbf{i} + \sin\theta\,\mathbf{j}$$

and

$$|\mathbf{r}_\theta \times \mathbf{r}_z| = \sqrt{\cos^2\theta + \sin^2\theta} = 1$$

Thus the surface integral over S_1 is

$$\iint_{S_1} z \, dS = \iint_D z \,|\mathbf{r}_\theta \times \mathbf{r}_z|\, dA$$

$$= \int_0^{2\pi} \int_0^{1+\cos\theta} z \, dz \, d\theta = \int_0^{2\pi} \tfrac{1}{2}(1 + \cos\theta)^2 \, d\theta$$

$$= \tfrac{1}{2} \int_0^{2\pi} \left[1 + 2\cos\theta + \tfrac{1}{2}(1 + \cos 2\theta)\right] d\theta$$

$$= \tfrac{1}{2}\left[\tfrac{3}{2}\theta + 2\sin\theta + \tfrac{1}{4}\sin 2\theta\right]_0^{2\pi} = \frac{3\pi}{2}$$

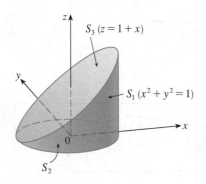

S_3 $(z = 1 + x)$

S_1 $(x^2 + y^2 = 1)$

S_2

FIGURE 3

Since S_2 lies in the plane $z = 0$, we have

$$\iint\limits_{S_2} z \, dS = \iint\limits_{S_2} 0 \, dS = 0$$

The top surface S_3 lies above the unit disk D and is part of the plane $z = 1 + x$. So, taking $g(x, y) = 1 + x$ in Formula 4 and converting to polar coordinates, we have

$$\iint\limits_{S_3} z \, dS = \iint\limits_{D} (1 + x) \sqrt{1 + \left(\frac{\partial z}{\partial x}\right)^2 + \left(\frac{\partial z}{\partial y}\right)^2} \, dA$$

$$= \int_0^{2\pi} \int_0^1 (1 + r \cos \theta) \sqrt{1 + 1 + 0} \, r \, dr \, d\theta$$

$$= \sqrt{2} \int_0^{2\pi} \int_0^1 (r + r^2 \cos \theta) \, dr \, d\theta$$

$$= \sqrt{2} \int_0^{2\pi} \left(\tfrac{1}{2} + \tfrac{1}{3} \cos \theta\right) d\theta$$

$$= \sqrt{2} \left[\frac{\theta}{2} + \frac{\sin \theta}{3}\right]_0^{2\pi} = \sqrt{2} \, \pi$$

Therefore

$$\iint\limits_{S} z \, dS = \iint\limits_{S_1} z \, dS + \iint\limits_{S_2} z \, dS + \iint\limits_{S_3} z \, dS$$

$$= \frac{3\pi}{2} + 0 + \sqrt{2} \, \pi = \left(\tfrac{3}{2} + \sqrt{2}\right)\pi$$

Oriented Surfaces

To define surface integrals of vector fields, we need to rule out nonorientable surfaces such as the Möbius strip shown in Figure 4. [It is named after the German geometer August Möbius (1790–1868).] You can construct one for yourself by taking a long rectangular strip of paper, giving it a half-twist, and taping the short edges together as in Figure 5. If an ant were to crawl along the Möbius strip starting at a point P, it would end up on the "other side" of the strip (that is, with its upper side pointing in the opposite direction). Then, if the ant continued to crawl in the same direction, it would end up back at the same point P without ever having crossed an edge. (If you have constructed a Möbius strip, try drawing a pencil line down the middle.) Therefore a Möbius strip really has only one side. You can graph the Möbius strip using the parametric equations in Exercise 32 in Section 10.5.

FIGURE 4
A Möbius strip

TEC Visual 13.6 shows a Möbius strip with a normal vector that can be moved along the surface.

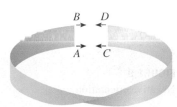

FIGURE 5
Constructing a Möbius strip

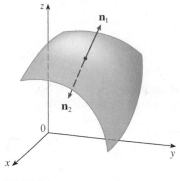

FIGURE 6

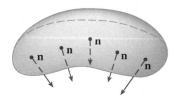

FIGURE 7
The two orientations
of an orientable surface

From now on we consider only orientable (two-sided) surfaces. We start with a surface S that has a tangent plane at every point (x, y, z) on S (except at any boundary point). There are two unit normal vectors $\mathbf{n}_1$ and $\mathbf{n}_2 = -\mathbf{n}_1$ at (x, y, z). (See Figure 6.)

If it is possible to choose a unit normal vector $\mathbf{n}$ at every such point (x, y, z) so that $\mathbf{n}$ varies continuously over S, then S is called an **oriented surface** and the given choice of $\mathbf{n}$ provides S with an **orientation**. There are two possible orientations for any orientable surface (see Figure 7).

For a surface $z = g(x, y)$ given as the graph of g, we use Equation 3 to associate with the surface a natural orientation given by the unit normal vector

$$\boxed{5} \qquad \mathbf{n} = \frac{-\dfrac{\partial g}{\partial x}\,\mathbf{i} - \dfrac{\partial g}{\partial y}\,\mathbf{j} + \mathbf{k}}{\sqrt{1 + \left(\dfrac{\partial g}{\partial x}\right)^2 + \left(\dfrac{\partial g}{\partial y}\right)^2}}$$

Since the $\mathbf{k}$-component is positive, this gives the *upward* orientation of the surface.

If S is a smooth orientable surface given in parametric form by a vector function $\mathbf{r}(u, v)$, then it is automatically supplied with the orientation of the unit normal vector

$$\boxed{6} \qquad \mathbf{n} = \frac{\mathbf{r}_u \times \mathbf{r}_v}{|\mathbf{r}_u \times \mathbf{r}_v|}$$

and the opposite orientation is given by $-\mathbf{n}$. For instance, in Example 4 in Section 10.5 we found the parametric representation

$$\mathbf{r}(\phi, \theta) = a \sin \phi \cos \theta \,\mathbf{i} + a \sin \phi \sin \theta \,\mathbf{j} + a \cos \phi \,\mathbf{k}$$

for the sphere $x^2 + y^2 + z^2 = a^2$. Then in Example 1 in Section 12.6 we found that

$$\mathbf{r}_\phi \times \mathbf{r}_\theta = a^2 \sin^2\phi \cos \theta \,\mathbf{i} + a^2 \sin^2\phi \sin \theta \,\mathbf{j} + a^2 \sin \phi \cos \phi \,\mathbf{k}$$

and

$$|\mathbf{r}_\phi \times \mathbf{r}_\theta| = a^2 \sin \phi$$

So the orientation induced by $\mathbf{r}(\phi, \theta)$ is defined by the unit normal vector

$$\mathbf{n} = \frac{\mathbf{r}_\phi \times \mathbf{r}_\theta}{|\mathbf{r}_\phi \times \mathbf{r}_\theta|} = \sin \phi \cos \theta \,\mathbf{i} + \sin \phi \sin \theta \,\mathbf{j} + \cos \phi \,\mathbf{k} = \frac{1}{a}\,\mathbf{r}(\phi, \theta)$$

Observe that $\mathbf{n}$ points in the same direction as the position vector, that is, outward from the sphere (see Figure 8). The opposite (inward) orientation would have been obtained (see Figure 9) if we had reversed the order of the parameters because $\mathbf{r}_\theta \times \mathbf{r}_\phi = -\mathbf{r}_\phi \times \mathbf{r}_\theta$.

For a **closed surface**, that is, a surface that is the boundary of a solid region E, the convention is that the **positive orientation** is the one for which the normal vectors point *outward* from E, and inward-pointing normals give the negative orientation (see Figures 8 and 9).

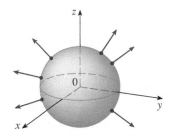

FIGURE 8
Positive orientation

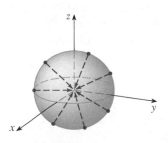

FIGURE 9
Negative orientation

Surface Integrals of Vector Fields

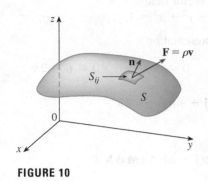

FIGURE 10

Suppose that S is an oriented surface with unit normal vector $\mathbf{n}$, and imagine a fluid with density $\rho(x, y, z)$ and velocity field $\mathbf{v}(x, y, z)$ flowing through S. (Think of S as an imaginary surface that doesn't impede the fluid flow, like a fishing net across a stream.) Then the rate of flow (mass per unit time) per unit area is $\rho\mathbf{v}$. If we divide S into small patches S_{ij}, as in Figure 10 (compare with Figure 1), then S_{ij} is nearly planar and so we can approximate the mass of fluid per unit time crossing S_{ij} in the direction of the normal $\mathbf{n}$ by the quantity

$$(\rho\mathbf{v} \cdot \mathbf{n})A(S_{ij})$$

where ρ, $\mathbf{v}$, and $\mathbf{n}$ are evaluated at some point on S_{ij}. (Recall that the component of the vector $\rho\mathbf{v}$ in the direction of the unit vector $\mathbf{n}$ is $\rho\mathbf{v} \cdot \mathbf{n}$.) By summing these quantities and taking the limit we get, according to Definition 1, the surface integral of the function $\rho\mathbf{v} \cdot \mathbf{n}$ over S:

$$\boxed{7} \qquad \iint_S \rho\mathbf{v} \cdot \mathbf{n} \, dS = \iint_S \rho(x, y, z) \, \mathbf{v}(x, y, z) \cdot \mathbf{n}(x, y, z) \, dS$$

and this is interpreted physically as the rate of flow through S.

If we write $\mathbf{F} = \rho\mathbf{v}$, then $\mathbf{F}$ is also a vector field on $\mathbb{R}^3$ and the integral in Equation 7 becomes

$$\iint_S \mathbf{F} \cdot \mathbf{n} \, dS$$

A surface integral of this form occurs frequently in physics, even when $\mathbf{F}$ is not $\rho\mathbf{v}$, and is called the *surface integral* (or *flux integral*) of $\mathbf{F}$ over S.

$\boxed{8}$ **Definition** If $\mathbf{F}$ is a continuous vector field defined on an oriented surface S with unit normal vector $\mathbf{n}$, then the **surface integral of F over S** is

$$\iint_S \mathbf{F} \cdot d\mathbf{S} = \iint_S \mathbf{F} \cdot \mathbf{n} \, dS$$

This integral is also called the **flux** of $\mathbf{F}$ across S.

In words, Definition 8 says that the surface integral of a vector field over S is equal to the surface integral of its normal component over S (as previously defined).

If S is given by a vector function $\mathbf{r}(u, v)$, then $\mathbf{n}$ is given by Equation 6, and from Definition 8 and Equation 2 we have

$$\iint_S \mathbf{F} \cdot d\mathbf{S} = \iint_S \mathbf{F} \cdot \frac{\mathbf{r}_u \times \mathbf{r}_v}{|\mathbf{r}_u \times \mathbf{r}_v|} \, dS$$

$$= \iint_D \left[\mathbf{F}(\mathbf{r}(u, v)) \cdot \frac{\mathbf{r}_u \times \mathbf{r}_v}{|\mathbf{r}_u \times \mathbf{r}_v|} \right] |\mathbf{r}_u \times \mathbf{r}_v| \, dA$$

where D is the parameter domain. Thus we have

Compare Equation 9 to the similar expression for evaluating line integrals of vector fields in Definition 13.2.13:

$$\int_C \mathbf{F} \cdot d\mathbf{r} = \int_a^b \mathbf{F}(\mathbf{r}(t)) \cdot \mathbf{r}'(t) \, dt$$

$$\boxed{9} \qquad \boxed{\iint_S \mathbf{F} \cdot d\mathbf{S} = \iint_D \mathbf{F} \cdot (\mathbf{r}_u \times \mathbf{r}_v) \, dA}$$

Figure 11 shows the vector field **F** in Example 4 at points on the unit sphere.

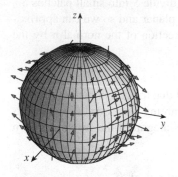

FIGURE 11

EXAMPLE 4   **Flux across a sphere**   Find the flux of the vector field $\mathbf{F}(x, y, z) = z\,\mathbf{i} + y\,\mathbf{j} + x\,\mathbf{k}$ across the unit sphere $x^2 + y^2 + z^2 = 1$.

SOLUTION   As in Example 1, we use the parametric representation

$$\mathbf{r}(\phi, \theta) = \sin\phi\,\cos\theta\,\mathbf{i} + \sin\phi\,\sin\theta\,\mathbf{j} + \cos\phi\,\mathbf{k} \qquad 0 \leqslant \phi \leqslant \pi \qquad 0 \leqslant \theta \leqslant 2\pi$$

Then
$$\mathbf{F}(\mathbf{r}(\phi, \theta)) = \cos\phi\,\mathbf{i} + \sin\phi\,\sin\theta\,\mathbf{j} + \sin\phi\,\cos\theta\,\mathbf{k}$$

and, from Example 1 in Section 12.6,

$$\mathbf{r}_\phi \times \mathbf{r}_\theta = \sin^2\phi\,\cos\theta\,\mathbf{i} + \sin^2\phi\,\sin\theta\,\mathbf{j} + \sin\phi\,\cos\phi\,\mathbf{k}$$

Therefore

$$\mathbf{F}(\mathbf{r}(\phi, \theta)) \cdot (\mathbf{r}_\phi \times \mathbf{r}_\theta) = \cos\phi\,\sin^2\phi\,\cos\theta + \sin^3\phi\,\sin^2\theta + \sin^2\phi\,\cos\phi\,\cos\theta$$

and, by Formula 9, the flux is

$$\iint_S \mathbf{F} \cdot d\mathbf{S} = \iint_D \mathbf{F} \cdot (\mathbf{r}_\phi \times \mathbf{r}_\theta)\,dA$$

$$= \int_0^{2\pi} \int_0^{\pi} (2\sin^2\phi\,\cos\phi\,\cos\theta + \sin^3\phi\,\sin^2\theta)\,d\phi\,d\theta$$

$$= 2\int_0^{\pi} \sin^2\phi\,\cos\phi\,d\phi \int_0^{2\pi} \cos\theta\,d\theta + \int_0^{\pi} \sin^3\phi\,d\phi \int_0^{2\pi} \sin^2\theta\,d\theta$$

$$= 0 + \int_0^{\pi} \sin^3\phi\,d\phi \int_0^{2\pi} \sin^2\theta\,d\theta \qquad \left(\text{since } \int_0^{2\pi} \cos\theta\,d\theta = 0\right)$$

$$= \frac{4\pi}{3}$$

by the same calculation as in Example 1.

If, for instance, the vector field in Example 4 is a velocity field describing the flow of a fluid with density 1, then the answer, $4\pi/3$, represents the rate of flow through the unit sphere in units of mass per unit time.

In the case of a surface S given by a graph $z = g(x, y)$, we can think of x and y as parameters and use Equation 3 to write

$$\mathbf{F} \cdot (\mathbf{r}_x \times \mathbf{r}_y) = (P\mathbf{i} + Q\mathbf{j} + R\mathbf{k}) \cdot \left(-\frac{\partial g}{\partial x}\mathbf{i} - \frac{\partial g}{\partial y}\mathbf{j} + \mathbf{k}\right)$$

Thus Formula 9 becomes

$$\boxed{10} \qquad \boxed{\iint_S \mathbf{F} \cdot d\mathbf{S} = \iint_D \left(-P\frac{\partial g}{\partial x} - Q\frac{\partial g}{\partial y} + R\right) dA}$$

This formula assumes the upward orientation of S; for a downward orientation we multiply by -1. Similar formulas can be worked out if S is given by $y = h(x, z)$ or $x = k(y, z)$. (See Exercises 35 and 36.)

V **EXAMPLE 5** **Surface integral of a vector field** Evaluate $\iint_S \mathbf{F} \cdot d\mathbf{S}$, where $\mathbf{F}(x, y, z) = y \mathbf{i} + x \mathbf{j} + z \mathbf{k}$ and S is the boundary of the solid region E enclosed by the paraboloid $z = 1 - x^2 - y^2$ and the plane $z = 0$.

SOLUTION S consists of a parabolic top surface S_1 and a circular bottom surface S_2. (See Figure 12.) Since S is a closed surface, we use the convention of positive (outward) orientation. This means that S_1 is oriented upward and we can use Equation 10 with D being the projection of S_1 on the xy-plane, namely, the disk $x^2 + y^2 \leq 1$. Since

$$P(x, y, z) = y \qquad Q(x, y, z) = x \qquad R(x, y, z) = z = 1 - x^2 - y^2$$

on S_1 and

$$\frac{\partial g}{\partial x} = -2x \qquad \frac{\partial g}{\partial y} = -2y$$

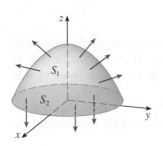

FIGURE 12

we have

$$\iint_{S_1} \mathbf{F} \cdot d\mathbf{S} = \iint_D \left(-P \frac{\partial g}{\partial x} - Q \frac{\partial g}{\partial y} + R \right) dA$$

$$= \iint_D [-y(-2x) - x(-2y) + 1 - x^2 - y^2] \, dA$$

$$= \iint_D (1 + 4xy - x^2 - y^2) \, dA$$

$$= \int_0^{2\pi} \int_0^1 (1 + 4r^2 \cos\theta \sin\theta - r^2) r \, dr \, d\theta$$

$$= \int_0^{2\pi} \int_0^1 (r - r^3 + 4r^3 \cos\theta \sin\theta) \, dr \, d\theta$$

$$= \int_0^{2\pi} \left(\tfrac{1}{4} + \cos\theta \sin\theta \right) d\theta = \tfrac{1}{4}(2\pi) + 0 = \frac{\pi}{2}$$

The disk S_2 is oriented downward, so its unit normal vector is $\mathbf{n} = -\mathbf{k}$ and we have

$$\iint_{S_2} \mathbf{F} \cdot d\mathbf{S} = \iint_{S_2} \mathbf{F} \cdot (-\mathbf{k}) \, dS = \iint_D (-z) \, dA = \iint_D 0 \, dA = 0$$

since $z = 0$ on S_2. Finally, we compute, by definition, $\iint_S \mathbf{F} \cdot d\mathbf{S}$ as the sum of the surface integrals of $\mathbf{F}$ over the pieces S_1 and S_2:

$$\iint_S \mathbf{F} \cdot d\mathbf{S} = \iint_{S_1} \mathbf{F} \cdot d\mathbf{S} + \iint_{S_2} \mathbf{F} \cdot d\mathbf{S} = \frac{\pi}{2} + 0 = \frac{\pi}{2}$$

Although we motivated the surface integral of a vector field using the example of fluid flow, this concept also arises in other physical situations. For instance, if $\mathbf{E}$ is an electric field (see Example 5 in Section 13.1), then the surface integral

$$\iint_S \mathbf{E} \cdot d\mathbf{S}$$

is called the **electric flux** of $\mathbf{E}$ through the surface S. One of the important laws of electrostatics is **Gauss's Law**, which says that the net charge enclosed by a closed surface S is

$$\boxed{11} \qquad Q = \varepsilon_0 \iint\limits_S \mathbf{E} \cdot d\mathbf{S}$$

where ε_0 is a constant (called the permittivity of free space) that depends on the units used. (In the SI system, $\varepsilon_0 \approx 8.8542 \times 10^{-12}$ C^2/N·m^2.) Therefore, if the vector field $\mathbf{F}$ in Example 4 represents an electric field, we can conclude that the charge enclosed by S is $Q = \frac{4}{3}\pi\varepsilon_0$.

Another application of surface integrals occurs in the study of heat flow. Suppose the temperature at a point (x, y, z) in a body is $u(x, y, z)$. Then the **heat flow** is defined as the vector field

$$\mathbf{F} = -K\,\nabla u$$

where K is an experimentally determined constant called the **conductivity** of the substance. The rate of heat flow across the surface S in the body is then given by the surface integral

$$\iint\limits_S \mathbf{F} \cdot d\mathbf{S} = -K \iint\limits_S \nabla u \cdot d\mathbf{S}$$

☑ **EXAMPLE 6** The temperature u in a metal ball is proportional to the square of the distance from the center of the ball. Find the rate of heat flow across a sphere S of radius a with center at the center of the ball.

SOLUTION Taking the center of the ball to be at the origin, we have

$$u(x, y, z) = C(x^2 + y^2 + z^2)$$

where C is the proportionality constant. Then the heat flow is

$$\mathbf{F}(x, y, z) = -K\,\nabla u = -KC(2x\,\mathbf{i} + 2y\,\mathbf{j} + 2z\,\mathbf{k})$$

where K is the conductivity of the metal. Instead of using the usual parametrization of the sphere as in Example 4, we observe that the outward unit normal to the sphere $x^2 + y^2 + z^2 = a^2$ at the point (x, y, z) is

$$\mathbf{n} = \frac{1}{a}(x\,\mathbf{i} + y\,\mathbf{j} + z\,\mathbf{k})$$

and so

$$\mathbf{F} \cdot \mathbf{n} = -\frac{2KC}{a}(x^2 + y^2 + z^2)$$

But on S we have $x^2 + y^2 + z^2 = a^2$, so $\mathbf{F} \cdot \mathbf{n} = -2aKC$. Therefore the rate of heat flow across S is

$$\iint\limits_S \mathbf{F} \cdot d\mathbf{S} = \iint\limits_S \mathbf{F} \cdot \mathbf{n}\, dS = -2aKC \iint\limits_S dS$$

$$= -2aKCA(S) = -2aKC(4\pi a^2) = -8KC\pi a^3 \qquad \blacksquare$$

13.6 Exercises

1. Let S be the boundary surface of the box enclosed by the planes $x = 0$, $x = 2$, $y = 0$, $y = 4$, $z = 0$, and $z = 6$. Approximate $\iint_S e^{-0.1(x+y+z)}\, dS$ by using a Riemann sum as in Definition 1, taking the patches S_{ij} to be the rectangles that are the faces of the box S and the points P_{ij}^* to be the centers of the rectangles.

2. A surface S consists of the cylinder $x^2 + y^2 = 1$, $-1 \leqslant z \leqslant 1$, together with its top and bottom disks. Suppose you know that f is a continuous function with

$$f(\pm 1, 0, 0) = 2 \qquad f(0, \pm 1, 0) = 3 \qquad f(0, 0, \pm 1) = 4$$

Estimate the value of $\iint_S f(x, y, z)\, dS$ by using a Riemann sum, taking the patches S_{ij} to be four quarter-cylinders and the top and bottom disks.

3. Let H be the hemisphere $x^2 + y^2 + z^2 = 50$, $z \geqslant 0$, and suppose f is a continuous function with $f(3, 4, 5) = 7$, $f(3, -4, 5) = 8$, $f(-3, 4, 5) = 9$, and $f(-3, -4, 5) = 12$. By dividing H into four patches, estimate the value of $\iint_H f(x, y, z)\, dS$.

4. Suppose that $f(x, y, z) = g\left(\sqrt{x^2 + y^2 + z^2}\right)$, where g is a function of one variable such that $g(2) = -5$. Evaluate $\iint_S f(x, y, z)\, dS$, where S is the sphere $x^2 + y^2 + z^2 = 4$.

5–20 Evaluate the surface integral.

5. $\iint_S (x + y + z)\, dS$,
S is the parallelogram with parametric equations $x = u + v$, $y = u - v$, $z = 1 + 2u + v$, $0 \leqslant u \leqslant 2$, $0 \leqslant v \leqslant 1$

6. $\iint_S xyz\, dS$,
S is the cone with parametric equations $x = u \cos v$, $y = u \sin v$, $z = u$, $0 \leqslant u \leqslant 1$, $0 \leqslant v \leqslant \pi/2$

7. $\iint_S y\, dS$, S is the helicoid with vector equation
$\mathbf{r}(u, v) = \langle u \cos v, u \sin v, v \rangle$, $0 \leqslant u \leqslant 1$, $0 \leqslant v \leqslant \pi$

8. $\iint_S (x^2 + y^2)\, dS$,
S is the surface with vector equation
$\mathbf{r}(u, v) = \langle 2uv, u^2 - v^2, u^2 + v^2 \rangle$, $u^2 + v^2 \leqslant 1$

9. $\iint_S x^2yz\, dS$,
S is the part of the plane $z = 1 + 2x + 3y$ that lies above the rectangle $[0, 3] \times [0, 2]$

10. $\iint_S xy\, dS$,
S is the triangular region with vertices $(1, 0, 0)$, $(0, 2, 0)$, and $(0, 0, 2)$

11. $\iint_S yz\, dS$,
S is the part of the plane $x + y + z = 1$ that lies in the first octant

12. $\iint_S y\, dS$,
S is the surface $z = \frac{2}{3}(x^{3/2} + y^{3/2})$, $0 \leqslant x \leqslant 1$, $0 \leqslant y \leqslant 1$

13. $\iint_S x^2z^2\, dS$,
S is the part of the cone $z^2 = x^2 + y^2$ that lies between the planes $z = 1$ and $z = 3$

14. $\iint_S z\, dS$,
S is the surface $x = y + 2z^2$, $0 \leqslant y \leqslant 1$, $0 \leqslant z \leqslant 1$

15. $\iint_S y\, dS$,
S is the part of the paraboloid $y = x^2 + z^2$ that lies inside the cylinder $x^2 + z^2 = 4$

16. $\iint_S y^2\, dS$,
S is the part of the sphere $x^2 + y^2 + z^2 = 4$ that lies inside the cylinder $x^2 + y^2 = 1$ and above the xy-plane

17. $\iint_S (x^2z + y^2z)\, dS$,
S is the hemisphere $x^2 + y^2 + z^2 = 4$, $z \geqslant 0$

18. $\iint_S xz\, dS$,
S is the boundary of the region enclosed by the cylinder $y^2 + z^2 = 9$ and the planes $x = 0$ and $x + y = 5$

19. $\iint_S (z + x^2y)\, dS$,
S is the part of the cylinder $y^2 + z^2 = 1$ that lies between the planes $x = 0$ and $x = 3$ in the first octant

20. $\iint_S (x^2 + y^2 + z^2)\, dS$,
S is the part of the cylinder $x^2 + y^2 = 9$ between the planes $z = 0$ and $z = 2$, together with its top and bottom disks

21–31 Evaluate the surface integral $\iint_S \mathbf{F} \cdot d\mathbf{S}$ for the given vector field $\mathbf{F}$ and the oriented surface S. In other words, find the flux of $\mathbf{F}$ across S. For closed surfaces, use the positive (outward) orientation.

21. $\mathbf{F}(x, y, z) = xy\,\mathbf{i} + yz\,\mathbf{j} + zx\,\mathbf{k}$, S is the part of the paraboloid $z = 4 - x^2 - y^2$ that lies above the square $0 \leqslant x \leqslant 1$, $0 \leqslant y \leqslant 1$, and has upward orientation

22. $\mathbf{F}(x, y, z) = z\,\mathbf{i} + y\,\mathbf{j} + x\,\mathbf{k}$,
S is the helicoid of Exercise 7 with upward orientation

23. $\mathbf{F}(x, y, z) = xze^y\,\mathbf{i} - xze^y\,\mathbf{j} + z\,\mathbf{k}$,
S is the part of the plane $x + y + z = 1$ in the first octant and has downward orientation

24. $\mathbf{F}(x, y, z) = x\,\mathbf{i} + y\,\mathbf{j} + z^4\,\mathbf{k}$,
S is the part of the cone $z = \sqrt{x^2 + y^2}$ beneath the plane $z = 1$ with downward orientation

25. $\mathbf{F}(x, y, z) = x\,\mathbf{i} - z\,\mathbf{j} + y\,\mathbf{k}$,
S is the part of the sphere $x^2 + y^2 + z^2 = 4$ in the first octant, with orientation toward the origin

26. $\mathbf{F}(x, y, z) = xz\,\mathbf{i} + x\,\mathbf{j} + y\,\mathbf{k}$,
S is the hemisphere $x^2 + y^2 + z^2 = 25$, $y \geqslant 0$, oriented in the direction of the positive y-axis

---

CAS Computer algebra system required   1. Homework Hints available in TEC

27. $\mathbf{F}(x, y, z) = y\,\mathbf{j} - z\,\mathbf{k}$,
S consists of the paraboloid $y = x^2 + z^2, 0 \leqslant y \leqslant 1$,
and the disk $x^2 + z^2 \leqslant 1, y = 1$

28. $\mathbf{F}(x, y, z) = x\,\mathbf{i} + y\,\mathbf{j} + 5\,\mathbf{k}$, S is the boundary of the
region enclosed by the cylinder $x^2 + z^2 = 1$ and the planes
$y = 0$ and $x + y = 2$

29. $\mathbf{F}(x, y, z) = x\,\mathbf{i} + 2y\,\mathbf{j} + 3z\,\mathbf{k}$,
S is the cube with vertices $(\pm 1, \pm 1, \pm 1)$

30. $\mathbf{F}(x, y, z) = y\,\mathbf{i} + (z - y)\,\mathbf{j} + x\,\mathbf{k}$,
S is the surface of the tetrahedron with vertices $(0, 0, 0)$,
$(1, 0, 0)$, $(0, 1, 0)$, and $(0, 0, 1)$

31. $\mathbf{F}(x, y, z) = x^2\,\mathbf{i} + y^2\,\mathbf{j} + z^2\,\mathbf{k}$, S is the boundary of the
solid half-cylinder $0 \leqslant z \leqslant \sqrt{1 - y^2}, 0 \leqslant x \leqslant 2$

CAS **32.** Let S be the surface $z = xy, 0 \leqslant x \leqslant 1, 0 \leqslant y \leqslant 1$.
(a) Evaluate $\iint_S xyz\,dS$ correct to four decimal places.
(b) Find the exact value of $\iint_S x^2 yz\,dS$

CAS **33.** Find the value of $\iint_S x^2 y^2 z^2\,dS$ correct to four decimal places,
where S is the part of the paraboloid $z = 3 - 2x^2 - y^2$ that
lies above the xy-plane.

CAS **34.** Find the flux of

$$\mathbf{F}(x, y, z) = \sin(xyz)\,\mathbf{i} + x^2 y\,\mathbf{j} + z^2 e^{x/5}\,\mathbf{k}$$

across the part of the cylinder $4y^2 + z^2 = 4$ that lies above
the xy-plane and between the planes $x = -2$ and $x = 2$ with
upward orientation. Illustrate by using a computer algebra
system to draw the cylinder and the vector field on the same
screen.

35. Find a formula for $\iint_S \mathbf{F} \cdot d\mathbf{S}$ similar to Formula 10 for the
case where S is given by $y = h(x, z)$ and $\mathbf{n}$ is the unit normal
that points toward the left.

36. Find a formula for $\iint_S \mathbf{F} \cdot d\mathbf{S}$ similar to Formula 10 for the
case where S is given by $x = k(y, z)$ and $\mathbf{n}$ is the unit normal
that points forward (that is, toward the viewer when the axes
are drawn in the usual way).

37. Find the center of mass of the hemisphere
$x^2 + y^2 + z^2 = a^2, z \geqslant 0$, if it has constant density.

38. Find the mass of a thin funnel in the shape of a cone
$z = \sqrt{x^2 + y^2}, 1 \leqslant z \leqslant 4$, if its density function is
$\rho(x, y, z) = 10 - z$.

39. (a) Give an integral expression for the moment of inertia I_z
about the z-axis of a thin sheet in the shape of a surface
S if the density function is ρ.
(b) Find the moment of inertia about the z-axis of the funnel
in Exercise 38.

40. Let S be the part of the sphere $x^2 + y^2 + z^2 = 25$ that lies
above the plane $z = 4$. If S has constant density k, find
(a) the center of mass and (b) the moment of inertia about
the z-axis.

41. A fluid has density $870 \text{ kg}/\text{m}^3$ and flows with velocity
$\mathbf{v} = z\,\mathbf{i} + y^2\,\mathbf{j} + x^2\,\mathbf{k}$, where x, y, and z are measured in
meters and the components of $\mathbf{v}$ in meters per second. Find
the rate of flow outward through the cylinder $x^2 + y^2 = 4$,
$0 \leqslant z \leqslant 1$.

42. Seawater has density $1025 \text{ kg}/\text{m}^3$ and flows in a velocity
field $\mathbf{v} = y\,\mathbf{i} + x\,\mathbf{j}$, where x, y, and z are measured in meters
and the components of $\mathbf{v}$ in meters per second. Find the rate
of flow outward through the hemisphere $x^2 + y^2 + z^2 = 9$,
$z \geqslant 0$.

43. Use Gauss's Law to find the charge contained in the solid
hemisphere $x^2 + y^2 + z^2 \leqslant a^2, z \geqslant 0$, if the electric field is

$$\mathbf{E}(x, y, z) = x\,\mathbf{i} + y\,\mathbf{j} + 2z\,\mathbf{k}$$

44. Use Gauss's Law to find the charge enclosed by the cube
with vertices $(\pm 1, \pm 1, \pm 1)$ if the electric field is

$$\mathbf{E}(x, y, z) = x\,\mathbf{i} + y\,\mathbf{j} + z\,\mathbf{k}$$

45. The temperature at the point (x, y, z) in a substance with
conductivity $K = 6.5$ is $u(x, y, z) = 2y^2 + 2z^2$. Find the rate
of heat flow inward across the cylindrical surface
$y^2 + z^2 = 6, 0 \leqslant x \leqslant 4$.

46. The temperature at a point in a ball with conductivity K is
inversely proportional to the distance from the center of the
ball. Find the rate of heat flow across a sphere S of radius a
with center at the center of the ball.

47. Let $\mathbf{F}$ be an inverse square field, that is, $\mathbf{F}(\mathbf{r}) = c\mathbf{r}/|\mathbf{r}|^3$ for
some constant c, where $\mathbf{r} = x\,\mathbf{i} + y\,\mathbf{j} + z\,\mathbf{k}$. Show that the
flux of $\mathbf{F}$ across a sphere S with center the origin is inde-
pendent of the radius of S.

13.7 Stokes' Theorem

Stokes' Theorem can be regarded as a higher-dimensional version of Green's Theorem.
Whereas Green's Theorem relates a double integral over a plane region D to a line integral
around its plane boundary curve, Stokes' Theorem relates a surface integral over a surface
S to a line integral around the boundary curve of S (which is a space curve). Figure 1 shows

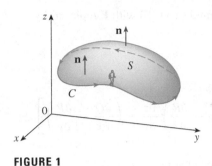

FIGURE 1

George Stokes

an oriented surface with unit normal vector **n**. The orientation of S induces the **positive orientation of the boundary curve C** shown in the figure. This means that if you walk in the positive direction around C with your head pointing in the direction of **n**, then the surface will always be on your left.

> **Stokes' Theorem** Let S be an oriented piecewise-smooth surface that is bounded by a simple, closed, piecewise-smooth boundary curve C with positive orientation. Let **F** be a vector field whose components have continuous partial derivatives on an open region in $\mathbb{R}^3$ that contains S. Then
>
> $$\int_C \mathbf{F} \cdot d\mathbf{r} = \iint_S \text{curl } \mathbf{F} \cdot d\mathbf{S}$$

Since

$$\int_C \mathbf{F} \cdot d\mathbf{r} = \int_C \mathbf{F} \cdot \mathbf{T}\, ds \quad \text{and} \quad \iint_S \text{curl } \mathbf{F} \cdot d\mathbf{S} = \iint_S \text{curl } \mathbf{F} \cdot \mathbf{n}\, dS$$

Stokes' Theorem says that the line integral around the boundary curve of S of the tangential component of **F** is equal to the surface integral of the normal component of the curl of **F**.

The positively oriented boundary curve of the oriented surface S is often written as ∂S, so Stokes' Theorem can be expressed as

$$\boxed{1} \qquad \iint_S \text{curl } \mathbf{F} \cdot d\mathbf{S} = \int_{\partial S} \mathbf{F} \cdot d\mathbf{r}$$

There is an analogy among Stokes' Theorem, Green's Theorem, and the Fundamental Theorem of Calculus. As before, there is an integral involving derivatives on the left side of Equation 1 (recall that curl **F** is a sort of derivative of **F**) and the right side involves the values of **F** only on the *boundary* of S.

In fact, in the special case where the surface S is flat and lies in the xy-plane with upward orientation, the unit normal is **k**, the surface integral becomes a double integral, and Stokes' Theorem becomes

$$\int_C \mathbf{F} \cdot d\mathbf{r} = \iint_S \text{curl } \mathbf{F} \cdot d\mathbf{S} = \iint_S (\text{curl } \mathbf{F}) \cdot \mathbf{k}\, dA$$

This is precisely the vector form of Green's Theorem given in Equation 13.5.12. Thus we see that Green's Theorem is really a special case of Stokes' Theorem.

Although Stokes' Theorem is too difficult for us to prove in its full generality, we can give a proof when S is a graph and **F**, S, and C are well behaved.

PROOF OF A SPECIAL CASE OF STOKES' THEOREM We assume that the equation of S is $z = g(x, y)$, $(x, y) \in D$, where g has continuous second-order partial derivatives and D is a simple plane region whose boundary curve C_1 corresponds to C. If the orientation of S is upward, then the positive orientation of C corresponds to the positive orientation of C_1. (See Figure 2.) We are also given that $\mathbf{F} = P\,\mathbf{i} + Q\,\mathbf{j} + R\,\mathbf{k}$, where the partial derivatives of P, Q, and R are continuous.

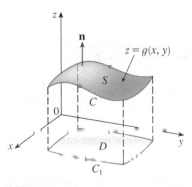

FIGURE 2

Since S is a graph of a function, we can apply Formula 13.6.10 with $\mathbf{F}$ replaced by curl $\mathbf{F}$. The result is

$$\boxed{2} \iint_S \text{curl }\mathbf{F} \cdot d\mathbf{S}$$

$$= \iint_D \left[-\left(\frac{\partial R}{\partial y} - \frac{\partial Q}{\partial z}\right)\frac{\partial z}{\partial x} - \left(\frac{\partial P}{\partial z} - \frac{\partial R}{\partial x}\right)\frac{\partial z}{\partial y} + \left(\frac{\partial Q}{\partial x} - \frac{\partial P}{\partial y}\right) \right] dA$$

where the partial derivatives of P, Q, and R are evaluated at $(x, y, g(x, y))$. If

$$x = x(t) \qquad y = y(t) \qquad a \leqslant t \leqslant b$$

is a parametric representation of C_1, then a parametric representation of C is

$$x = x(t) \qquad y = y(t) \qquad z = g(x(t), y(t)) \qquad a \leqslant t \leqslant b$$

This allows us, with the aid of the Chain Rule, to evaluate the line integral as follows:

$$\int_C \mathbf{F} \cdot d\mathbf{r} = \int_a^b \left(P\frac{dx}{dt} + Q\frac{dy}{dt} + R\frac{dz}{dt} \right) dt$$

$$= \int_a^b \left[P\frac{dx}{dt} + Q\frac{dy}{dt} + R\left(\frac{\partial z}{\partial x}\frac{dx}{dt} + \frac{\partial z}{\partial y}\frac{dy}{dt}\right) \right] dt$$

$$= \int_a^b \left[\left(P + R\frac{\partial z}{\partial x}\right)\frac{dx}{dt} + \left(Q + R\frac{\partial z}{\partial y}\right)\frac{dy}{dt} \right] dt$$

$$= \int_{C_1} \left(P + R\frac{\partial z}{\partial x}\right) dx + \left(Q + R\frac{\partial z}{\partial y}\right) dy$$

$$= \iint_D \left[\frac{\partial}{\partial x}\left(Q + R\frac{\partial z}{\partial y}\right) - \frac{\partial}{\partial y}\left(P + R\frac{\partial z}{\partial x}\right) \right] dA$$

where we have used Green's Theorem in the last step. Then, using the Chain Rule again and remembering that P, Q, and R are functions of x, y, and z and that z is itself a function of x and y, we get

$$\int_C \mathbf{F} \cdot d\mathbf{r} = \iint_D \left[\left(\frac{\partial Q}{\partial x} + \frac{\partial Q}{\partial z}\frac{\partial z}{\partial x} + \frac{\partial R}{\partial x}\frac{\partial z}{\partial y} + \frac{\partial R}{\partial z}\frac{\partial z}{\partial x}\frac{\partial z}{\partial y} + R\frac{\partial^2 z}{\partial x\,\partial y}\right) \right.$$

$$\left. - \left(\frac{\partial P}{\partial y} + \frac{\partial P}{\partial z}\frac{\partial z}{\partial y} + \frac{\partial R}{\partial y}\frac{\partial z}{\partial x} + \frac{\partial R}{\partial z}\frac{\partial z}{\partial y}\frac{\partial z}{\partial x} + R\frac{\partial^2 z}{\partial y\,\partial x}\right) \right] dA$$

Four of the terms in this double integral cancel and the remaining six terms can be arranged to coincide with the right side of Equation 2. Therefore

$$\int_C \mathbf{F} \cdot d\mathbf{r} = \iint_S \text{curl }\mathbf{F} \cdot d\mathbf{S} \qquad \square$$

▼ EXAMPLE 1 Using Stokes' Theorem to calculate a line integral   Evaluate $\int_C \mathbf{F} \cdot d\mathbf{r}$, where $\mathbf{F}(x, y, z) = -y^2\,\mathbf{i} + x\,\mathbf{j} + z^2\,\mathbf{k}$ and C is the curve of intersection of the plane $y + z = 2$ and the cylinder $x^2 + y^2 = 1$. (Orient C to be counterclockwise when viewed from above.)

SOLUTION The curve C (an ellipse) is shown in Figure 3. Although $\int_C \mathbf{F} \cdot d\mathbf{r}$ could be evaluated directly, it's easier to use Stokes' Theorem. We first compute

$$\text{curl } \mathbf{F} = \begin{vmatrix} \mathbf{i} & \mathbf{j} & \mathbf{k} \\ \dfrac{\partial}{\partial x} & \dfrac{\partial}{\partial y} & \dfrac{\partial}{\partial z} \\ -y^2 & x & z^2 \end{vmatrix} = (1 + 2y)\,\mathbf{k}$$

Although there are many surfaces with boundary C, the most convenient choice is the elliptical region S in the plane $y + z = 2$ that is bounded by C. If we orient S upward, then C has the induced positive orientation. The projection D of S onto the xy-plane is the disk $x^2 + y^2 \leqslant 1$ and so using Equation 13.6.10 with $z = g(x, y) = 2 - y$, we have

$$\int_C \mathbf{F} \cdot d\mathbf{r} = \iint_S \text{curl } \mathbf{F} \cdot d\mathbf{S} = \iint_D (1 + 2y)\,dA$$

$$= \int_0^{2\pi} \int_0^1 (1 + 2r\sin\theta)\,r\,dr\,d\theta$$

$$= \int_0^{2\pi} \left[\frac{r^2}{2} + 2\,\frac{r^3}{3}\sin\theta \right]_0^1 d\theta = \int_0^{2\pi} \left(\tfrac{1}{2} + \tfrac{2}{3}\sin\theta \right) d\theta$$

$$= \tfrac{1}{2}(2\pi) + 0 = \pi$$

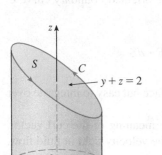

FIGURE 3

▼ EXAMPLE 2 Using Stokes' Theorem to calculate a surface integral   Use Stokes' Theorem to compute the integral $\iint_S \text{curl } \mathbf{F} \cdot d\mathbf{S}$, where $\mathbf{F}(x, y, z) = xz\,\mathbf{i} + yz\,\mathbf{j} + xy\,\mathbf{k}$ and S is the part of the sphere $x^2 + y^2 + z^2 = 4$ that lies inside the cylinder $x^2 + y^2 = 1$ and above the xy-plane. (See Figure 4.)

SOLUTION To find the boundary curve C we solve the equations $x^2 + y^2 + z^2 = 4$ and $x^2 + y^2 = 1$. Subtracting, we get $z^2 = 3$ and so $z = \sqrt{3}$ (since $z > 0$). Thus C is the circle given by the equations $x^2 + y^2 = 1$, $z = \sqrt{3}$. A vector equation of C is

$$\mathbf{r}(t) = \cos t\,\mathbf{i} + \sin t\,\mathbf{j} + \sqrt{3}\,\mathbf{k} \qquad 0 \leqslant t \leqslant 2\pi$$

so

$$\mathbf{r}'(t) = -\sin t\,\mathbf{i} + \cos t\,\mathbf{j}$$

Also, we have

$$\mathbf{F}(\mathbf{r}(t)) = \sqrt{3}\,\cos t\,\mathbf{i} + \sqrt{3}\,\sin t\,\mathbf{j} + \cos t\sin t\,\mathbf{k}$$

Therefore, by Stokes' Theorem,

$$\iint_S \text{curl } \mathbf{F} \cdot d\mathbf{S} = \int_C \mathbf{F} \cdot d\mathbf{r} = \int_0^{2\pi} \mathbf{F}(\mathbf{r}(t)) \cdot \mathbf{r}'(t)\,dt$$

$$= \int_0^{2\pi} (-\sqrt{3}\,\cos t\sin t + \sqrt{3}\,\sin t\cos t)\,dt$$

$$= \sqrt{3} \int_0^{2\pi} 0\,dt = 0$$

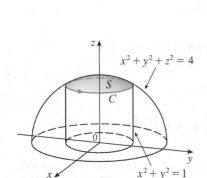

FIGURE 4

Note that in Example 2 we computed a surface integral simply by knowing the values of $\mathbf{F}$ on the boundary curve C. This means that if we have another oriented surface with the same boundary curve C, then we get exactly the same value for the surface integral!

In general, if S_1 and S_2 are oriented surfaces with the same oriented boundary curve C and both satisfy the hypotheses of Stokes' Theorem, then

$$\boxed{3} \qquad \iint\limits_{S_1} \text{curl } \mathbf{F} \cdot d\mathbf{S} = \int_C \mathbf{F} \cdot d\mathbf{r} = \iint\limits_{S_2} \text{curl } \mathbf{F} \cdot d\mathbf{S}$$

This fact is useful when it is difficult to integrate over one surface but easy to integrate over the other.

We now use Stokes' Theorem to throw some light on the meaning of the curl vector. Suppose that C is an oriented closed curve and $\mathbf{v}$ represents the velocity field in fluid flow. Consider the line integral

$$\int_C \mathbf{v} \cdot d\mathbf{r} = \int_C \mathbf{v} \cdot \mathbf{T} \, ds$$

and recall that $\mathbf{v} \cdot \mathbf{T}$ is the component of $\mathbf{v}$ in the direction of the unit tangent vector $\mathbf{T}$. This means that the closer the direction of $\mathbf{v}$ is to the direction of $\mathbf{T}$, the larger the value of $\mathbf{v} \cdot \mathbf{T}$. Thus $\int_C \mathbf{v} \cdot d\mathbf{r}$ is a measure of the tendency of the fluid to move around C and is called the **circulation** of $\mathbf{v}$ around C. (See Figure 5.)

Now let $P_0(x_0, y_0, z_0)$ be a point in the fluid and let S_a be a small disk with radius a and center P_0. Then $(\text{curl } \mathbf{F})(P) \approx (\text{curl } \mathbf{F})(P_0)$ for all points P on S_a because curl $\mathbf{F}$ is continuous. Thus, by Stokes' Theorem, we get the following approximation to the circulation around the boundary circle C_a:

$$\int_{C_a} \mathbf{v} \cdot d\mathbf{r} = \iint\limits_{S_a} \text{curl } \mathbf{v} \cdot d\mathbf{S} = \iint\limits_{S_a} \text{curl } \mathbf{v} \cdot \mathbf{n} \, dS$$

$$\approx \iint\limits_{S_a} \text{curl } \mathbf{v}(P_0) \cdot \mathbf{n}(P_0) \, dS = \text{curl } \mathbf{v}(P_0) \cdot \mathbf{n}(P_0) \pi a^2$$

This approximation becomes better as $a \to 0$ and we have

$$\boxed{4} \qquad \text{curl } \mathbf{v}(P_0) \cdot \mathbf{n}(P_0) = \lim_{a \to 0} \frac{1}{\pi a^2} \int_{C_a} \mathbf{v} \cdot d\mathbf{r}$$

Equation 4 gives the relationship between the curl and the circulation. It shows that curl $\mathbf{v} \cdot \mathbf{n}$ is a measure of the rotating effect of the fluid about the axis $\mathbf{n}$. The curling effect is greatest about the axis parallel to curl $\mathbf{v}$.

Finally, we mention that Stokes' Theorem can be used to prove Theorem 13.5.4 (which states that if curl $\mathbf{F} = \mathbf{0}$ on all of $\mathbb{R}^3$, then $\mathbf{F}$ is conservative). From our previous work (Theorems 13.3.3 and 13.3.4), we know that $\mathbf{F}$ is conservative if $\int_C \mathbf{F} \cdot d\mathbf{r} = 0$ for every closed path C. Given C, suppose we can find an orientable surface S whose boundary is C. (This can be done, but the proof requires advanced techniques.) Then Stokes' Theorem gives

$$\int_C \mathbf{F} \cdot d\mathbf{r} = \iint\limits_{S} \text{curl } \mathbf{F} \cdot d\mathbf{S} = \iint\limits_{S} \mathbf{0} \cdot d\mathbf{S} = 0$$

A curve that is not simple can be broken into a number of simple curves, and the integrals around these simple curves are all 0. Adding these integrals, we obtain $\int_C \mathbf{F} \cdot d\mathbf{r} = 0$ for any closed curve C.

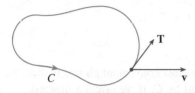

(a) $\int_C \mathbf{v} \cdot d\mathbf{r} > 0$, positive circulation

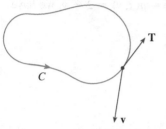

(b) $\int_C \mathbf{v} \cdot d\mathbf{r} < 0$, negative circulation

FIGURE 5

Imagine a tiny paddle wheel placed in the fluid at a point P, as in Figure 6; the paddle wheel rotates fastest when its axis is parallel to curl $\mathbf{v}$.

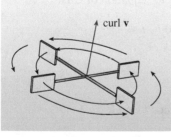

FIGURE 6

13.7 Exercises

1. A hemisphere H and a portion P of a paraboloid are shown. Suppose **F** is a vector field on $\mathbb{R}^3$ whose components have continuous partial derivatives. Explain why

$$\iint_H \text{curl } \mathbf{F} \cdot d\mathbf{S} = \iint_P \text{curl } \mathbf{F} \cdot d\mathbf{S}$$

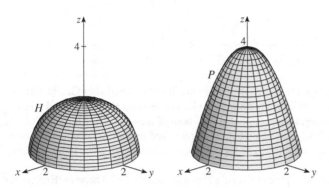

2–6 Use Stokes' Theorem to evaluate $\iint_S \text{curl } \mathbf{F} \cdot d\mathbf{S}$.

2. $\mathbf{F}(x, y, z) = 2y \cos z \, \mathbf{i} + e^x \sin z \, \mathbf{j} + xe^y \, \mathbf{k}$,
S is the hemisphere $x^2 + y^2 + z^2 = 9$, $z \geq 0$, oriented upward

3. $\mathbf{F}(x, y, z) = x^2z^2 \, \mathbf{i} + y^2z^2 \, \mathbf{j} + xyz \, \mathbf{k}$,
S is the part of the paraboloid $z = x^2 + y^2$ that lies inside the cylinder $x^2 + y^2 = 4$, oriented upward

4. $\mathbf{F}(x, y, z) = x^2y^3z \, \mathbf{i} + \sin(xyz) \, \mathbf{j} + xyz \, \mathbf{k}$,
S is the part of the cone $y^2 = x^2 + z^2$ that lies between the planes $y = 0$ and $y = 3$, oriented in the direction of the positive y-axis

5. $\mathbf{F}(x, y, z) = xyz \, \mathbf{i} + xy \, \mathbf{j} + x^2yz \, \mathbf{k}$,
S consists of the top and the four sides (but not the bottom) of the cube with vertices $(\pm 1, \pm 1, \pm 1)$, oriented outward [*Hint:* Use Equation 3.]

6. $\mathbf{F}(x, y, z) = e^{xy} \cos z \, \mathbf{i} + x^2z \, \mathbf{j} + xy \, \mathbf{k}$,
S is the hemisphere $x = \sqrt{1 - y^2 - z^2}$, oriented in the direction of the positive x-axis

7–10 Use Stokes' Theorem to evaluate $\int_C \mathbf{F} \cdot d\mathbf{r}$. In each case C is oriented counterclockwise as viewed from above.

7. $\mathbf{F}(x, y, z) = (x + y^2) \mathbf{i} + (y + z^2) \mathbf{j} + (z + x^2) \mathbf{k}$,
C is the triangle with vertices $(1, 0, 0)$, $(0, 1, 0)$, and $(0, 0, 1)$

8. $\mathbf{F}(x, y, z) = e^{-x} \mathbf{i} + e^x \mathbf{j} + e^z \mathbf{k}$,
C is the boundary of the part of the plane $2x + y + 2z = 2$ in the first octant

9. $\mathbf{F}(x, y, z) = yz \, \mathbf{i} + 2xz \, \mathbf{j} + e^{xy} \, \mathbf{k}$,
C is the circle $x^2 + y^2 = 16$, $z = 5$

10. $\mathbf{F}(x, y, z) = xy \, \mathbf{i} + 2z \, \mathbf{j} + 3y \, \mathbf{k}$, C is the curve of intersection of the plane $x + z = 5$ and the cylinder $x^2 + y^2 = 9$

11. (a) Use Stokes' Theorem to evaluate $\int_C \mathbf{F} \cdot d\mathbf{r}$, where

$$\mathbf{F}(x, y, z) = x^2z \, \mathbf{i} + xy^2 \, \mathbf{j} + z^2 \, \mathbf{k}$$

and C is the curve of intersection of the plane $x + y + z = 1$ and the cylinder $x^2 + y^2 = 9$ oriented counterclockwise as viewed from above.

(b) Graph both the plane and the cylinder with domains chosen so that you can see the curve C and the surface that you used in part (a).

(c) Find parametric equations for C and use them to graph C.

12. (a) Use Stokes' Theorem to evaluate $\int_C \mathbf{F} \cdot d\mathbf{r}$, where $\mathbf{F}(x, y, z) = x^2y \, \mathbf{i} + \frac{1}{3}x^3 \, \mathbf{j} + xy \, \mathbf{k}$ and C is the curve of intersection of the hyperbolic paraboloid $z = y^2 - x^2$ and the cylinder $x^2 + y^2 = 1$ oriented counterclockwise as viewed from above.

(b) Graph both the hyperbolic paraboloid and the cylinder with domains chosen so that you can see the curve C and the surface that you used in part (a).

(c) Find parametric equations for C and use them to graph C.

13–15 Verify that Stokes' Theorem is true for the given vector field **F** and surface S.

13. $\mathbf{F}(x, y, z) = -y \, \mathbf{i} + x \, \mathbf{j} - 2 \, \mathbf{k}$,
S is the cone $z^2 = x^2 + y^2$, $0 \leq z \leq 4$, oriented downward

14. $\mathbf{F}(x, y, z) = -2yz \, \mathbf{i} + y \, \mathbf{j} + 3x \, \mathbf{k}$,
S is the part of the paraboloid $z = 5 - x^2 - y^2$ that lies above the plane $z = 1$, oriented upward

15. $\mathbf{F}(x, y, z) = y \, \mathbf{i} + z \, \mathbf{j} + x \, \mathbf{k}$,
S is the hemisphere $x^2 + y^2 + z^2 = 1$, $y \geq 0$, oriented in the direction of the positive y-axis

16. Let C be a simple closed smooth curve that lies in the plane $x + y + z = 1$. Show that the line integral

$$\int_C z \, dx - 2x \, dy + 3y \, dz$$

depends only on the area of the region enclosed by C and not on the shape of C or its location in the plane.

17. A particle moves along line segments from the origin to the points $(1, 0, 0)$, $(1, 2, 1)$, $(0, 2, 1)$, and back to the origin under the influence of the force field

$$\mathbf{F}(x, y, z) = z^2 \, \mathbf{i} + 2xy \, \mathbf{j} + 4y^2 \, \mathbf{k}$$

Find the work done.

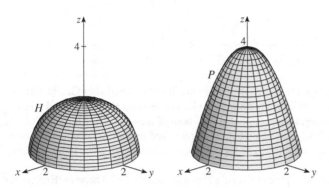 Graphing calculator or computer with graphing software required   **1.** Homework Hints available in TEC

18. Evaluate

$$\int_C (y + \sin x)\, dx + (z^2 + \cos y)\, dy + x^3\, dz$$

where C is the curve $\mathbf{r}(t) = \langle \sin t, \cos t, \sin 2t \rangle$, $0 \leqslant t \leqslant 2\pi$. [*Hint:* Observe that C lies on the surface $z = 2xy$.]

19. If S is a sphere and $\mathbf{F}$ satisfies the hypotheses of Stokes' Theorem, show that $\iint_S \text{curl } \mathbf{F} \cdot d\mathbf{S} = 0$.

20. Suppose S and C satisfy the hypotheses of Stokes' Theorem and f, g have continuous second-order partial derivatives. Use Exercises 24 and 26 in Section 13.5 to show the following.

(a) $\int_C (f \nabla g) \cdot d\mathbf{r} = \iint_S (\nabla f \times \nabla g) \cdot d\mathbf{S}$

(b) $\int_C (f \nabla f) \cdot d\mathbf{r} = 0$

(c) $\int_C (f \nabla g + g \nabla f) \cdot d\mathbf{r} = 0$

WRITING PROJECT   Three Men and Two Theorems

The photograph shows a stained-glass window at Cambridge University in honor of George Green.

Courtesy of the Masters and Fellows of Gonville and Caius College, University of Cambridge, England

www.stewartcalculus.com
The Internet is another source of information for this project. Click on *History of Mathematics*, then follow the links to the St. Andrew's site and that of the British Society for the History of Mathematics.

Although two of the most important theorems in vector calculus are named after George Green and George Stokes, a third man, William Thomson (also known as Lord Kelvin), played a large role in the formulation, dissemination, and application of both of these results. All three men were interested in how the two theorems could help to explain and predict physical phenomena in electricity and magnetism and fluid flow. The basic facts of the story are given in the margin notes on pages 935 and 961.

Write a report on the historical origins of Green's Theorem and Stokes' Theorem. Explain the similarities and relationship between the theorems. Discuss the roles that Green, Thomson, and Stokes played in discovering these theorems and making them widely known. Show how both theorems arose from the investigation of electricity and magnetism and were later used to study a variety of physical problems.

The dictionary edited by Gillispie [2] is a good source for both biographical and scientific information. The book by Hutchinson [5] gives an account of Stokes' life and the book by Thompson [8] is a biography of Lord Kelvin. The articles by Grattan-Guinness [3] and Gray [4] and the book by Cannell [1] give background on the extraordinary life and works of Green. Additional historical and mathematical information is found in the books by Katz [6] and Kline [7].

1. D. M. Cannell, *George Green, Mathematician and Physicist 1793–1841: The Background to His Life and Work* (Philadelphia: Society for Industrial and Applied Mathematics, 2001).

2. C. C. Gillispie, ed., *Dictionary of Scientific Biography* (New York: Scribner's, 1974). See the article on Green by P. J. Wallis in Volume XV and the articles on Thomson by Jed Buchwald and on Stokes by E. M. Parkinson in Volume XIII.

3. I. Grattan-Guinness, "Why did George Green write his essay of 1828 on electricity and magnetism?" *Amer. Math. Monthly*, Vol. 102 (1995), pp. 387–96.

4. J. Gray, "There was a jolly miller." *The New Scientist*, Vol. 139 (1993), pp. 24–27.

5. G. E. Hutchinson, *The Enchanted Voyage and Other Studies* (Westport, CT: Greenwood Press, 1978).

6. Victor Katz, *A History of Mathematics: An Introduction* (New York: HarperCollins, 1993), pp. 678–80.

7. Morris Kline, *Mathematical Thought from Ancient to Modern Times* (New York: Oxford University Press, 1972), pp. 683–85.

8. Sylvanus P. Thompson, *The Life of Lord Kelvin* (New York: Chelsea, 1976).

13.8 The Divergence Theorem

In Section 13.5 we rewrote Green's Theorem in a vector version as

$$\int_C \mathbf{F} \cdot \mathbf{n}\, ds = \iint_D \text{div } \mathbf{F}(x, y)\, dA$$

where C is the positively oriented boundary curve of the plane region D. If we were seeking to extend this theorem to vector fields on $\mathbb{R}^3$, we might make the guess that

$$\boxed{1} \qquad \iint_S \mathbf{F} \cdot \mathbf{n}\, dS = \iiint_E \text{div } \mathbf{F}(x, y, z)\, dV$$

where S is the boundary surface of the solid region E. It turns out that Equation 1 is true, under appropriate hypotheses, and is called the Divergence Theorem. Notice its similarity to Green's Theorem and Stokes' Theorem in that it relates the integral of a derivative of a function (div $\mathbf{F}$ in this case) over a region to the integral of the original function $\mathbf{F}$ over the boundary of the region.

At this stage you may wish to review the various types of regions over which we were able to evaluate triple integrals in Section 12.7. We state and prove the Divergence Theorem for regions E that are simultaneously of types 1, 2, and 3 and we call such regions **simple solid regions**. (For instance, regions bounded by ellipsoids or rectangular boxes are simple solid regions.) The boundary of E is a closed surface, and we use the convention, introduced in Section 13.6, that the positive orientation is outward; that is, the unit normal vector $\mathbf{n}$ is directed outward from E.

The Divergence Theorem is sometimes called Gauss's Theorem after the great German mathematician Karl Friedrich Gauss (1777–1855), who discovered this theorem during his investigation of electrostatics. In Eastern Europe the Divergence Theorem is known as Ostrogradsky's Theorem after the Russian mathematician Mikhail Ostrogradsky (1801–1862), who published this result in 1826.

> **The Divergence Theorem** Let E be a simple solid region and let S be the boundary surface of E, given with positive (outward) orientation. Let $\mathbf{F}$ be a vector field whose component functions have continuous partial derivatives on an open region that contains E. Then
>
> $$\iint_S \mathbf{F} \cdot d\mathbf{S} = \iiint_E \text{div } \mathbf{F}\, dV$$

Thus the Divergence Theorem states that, under the given conditions, the flux of $\mathbf{F}$ across the boundary surface of E is equal to the triple integral of the divergence of $\mathbf{F}$ over E.

PROOF Let $\mathbf{F} = P\,\mathbf{i} + Q\,\mathbf{j} + R\,\mathbf{k}$. Then

$$\text{div } \mathbf{F} = \frac{\partial P}{\partial x} + \frac{\partial Q}{\partial y} + \frac{\partial R}{\partial z}$$

so

$$\iiint_E \text{div } \mathbf{F}\, dV = \iiint_E \frac{\partial P}{\partial x}\, dV + \iiint_E \frac{\partial Q}{\partial y}\, dV + \iiint_E \frac{\partial R}{\partial z}\, dV$$

If $\mathbf{n}$ is the unit outward normal of S, then the surface integral on the left side of the

Divergence Theorem is

$$\iint\limits_{S} \mathbf{F} \cdot d\mathbf{S} = \iint\limits_{S} \mathbf{F} \cdot \mathbf{n}\, dS = \iint\limits_{S} (P\,\mathbf{i} + Q\,\mathbf{j} + R\,\mathbf{k}) \cdot \mathbf{n}\, dS$$

$$= \iint\limits_{S} P\,\mathbf{i} \cdot \mathbf{n}\, dS + \iint\limits_{S} Q\,\mathbf{j} \cdot \mathbf{n}\, dS + \iint\limits_{S} R\,\mathbf{k} \cdot \mathbf{n}\, dS$$

Therefore, to prove the Divergence Theorem, it suffices to prove the following three equations:

$$\boxed{2} \qquad \iint\limits_{S} P\,\mathbf{i} \cdot \mathbf{n}\, dS = \iiint\limits_{E} \frac{\partial P}{\partial x}\, dV$$

$$\boxed{3} \qquad \iint\limits_{S} Q\,\mathbf{j} \cdot \mathbf{n}\, dS = \iiint\limits_{E} \frac{\partial Q}{\partial y}\, dV$$

$$\boxed{4} \qquad \iint\limits_{S} R\,\mathbf{k} \cdot \mathbf{n}\, dS = \iiint\limits_{E} \frac{\partial R}{\partial z}\, dV$$

To prove Equation 4 we use the fact that E is a type 1 region:

$$E = \{(x, y, z) \mid (x, y) \in D, u_1(x, y) \leqslant z \leqslant u_2(x, y)\}$$

where D is the projection of E onto the xy-plane. By Equation 12.7.6, we have

$$\iiint\limits_{E} \frac{\partial R}{\partial z}\, dV = \iint\limits_{D} \left[\int_{u_1(x,y)}^{u_2(x,y)} \frac{\partial R}{\partial z}(x, y, z)\, dz \right] dA$$

and therefore, by the Fundamental Theorem of Calculus,

$$\boxed{5} \qquad \iiint\limits_{E} \frac{\partial R}{\partial z}\, dV = \iint\limits_{D} \left[R\big(x, y, u_2(x, y)\big) - R\big(x, y, u_1(x, y)\big) \right] dA$$

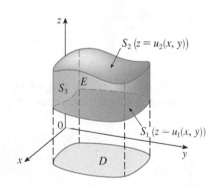

FIGURE 1

The boundary surface S consists of three pieces: the bottom surface S_1, the top surface S_2, and possibly a vertical surface S_3, which lies above the boundary curve of D. (See Figure 1. It might happen that S_3 doesn't appear, as in the case of a sphere.) Notice that on S_3 we have $\mathbf{k} \cdot \mathbf{n} = 0$, because $\mathbf{k}$ is vertical and $\mathbf{n}$ is horizontal, and so

$$\iint\limits_{S_3} R\,\mathbf{k} \cdot \mathbf{n}\, dS = \iint\limits_{S_3} 0\, dS = 0$$

Thus, regardless of whether there is a vertical surface, we can write

$$\boxed{6} \qquad \iint\limits_{S} R\,\mathbf{k} \cdot \mathbf{n}\, dS = \iint\limits_{S_1} R\,\mathbf{k} \cdot \mathbf{n}\, dS + \iint\limits_{S_2} R\,\mathbf{k} \cdot \mathbf{n}\, dS$$

The equation of S_2 is $z = u_2(x, y)$, $(x, y) \in D$, and the outward normal $\mathbf{n}$ points upward, so from Equation 13.6.10 (with $\mathbf{F}$ replaced by $R\,\mathbf{k}$) we have

$$\iint\limits_{S_2} R\,\mathbf{k} \cdot \mathbf{n}\, dS = \iint\limits_{D} R\big(x, y, u_2(x, y)\big)\, dA$$

On S_1 we have $z = u_1(x, y)$, but here the outward normal $\mathbf{n}$ points downward, so we multiply by -1:

$$\iint\limits_{S_1} R\,\mathbf{k}\cdot\mathbf{n}\,dS = -\iint\limits_{D} R\big(x, y, u_1(x, y)\big)\,dA$$

Therefore Equation 6 gives

$$\iint\limits_{S} R\,\mathbf{k}\cdot\mathbf{n}\,dS = \iint\limits_{D} \big[R\big(x, y, u_2(x, y)\big) - R\big(x, y, u_1(x, y)\big)\big]\,dA$$

Comparison with Equation 5 shows that

$$\iint\limits_{S} R\,\mathbf{k}\cdot\mathbf{n}\,dS = \iiint\limits_{E} \frac{\partial R}{\partial z}\,dV$$

Equations 2 and 3 are proved in a similar manner using the expressions for E as a type 2 or type 3 region, respectively.

> Notice that the method of proof of the Divergence Theorem is very similar to that of Green's Theorem.

▼ **EXAMPLE 1** **Using the Divergence Theorem to calculate flux**   Find the flux of the vector field $\mathbf{F}(x, y, z) = z\,\mathbf{i} + y\,\mathbf{j} + x\,\mathbf{k}$ over the unit sphere $x^2 + y^2 + z^2 = 1$.

SOLUTION First we compute the divergence of $\mathbf{F}$:

$$\operatorname{div} \mathbf{F} = \frac{\partial}{\partial x}(z) + \frac{\partial}{\partial y}(y) + \frac{\partial}{\partial z}(x) = 1$$

The unit sphere S is the boundary of the unit ball B given by $x^2 + y^2 + z^2 \le 1$. Thus the Divergence Theorem gives the flux as

> The solution in Example 1 should be compared with the solution in Example 4 in Section 13.6.

$$\iint\limits_{S} \mathbf{F}\cdot d\mathbf{S} = \iiint\limits_{B} \operatorname{div}\mathbf{F}\,dV = \iiint\limits_{B} 1\,dV = V(B) = \tfrac{4}{3}\pi(1)^3 = \frac{4\pi}{3}$$

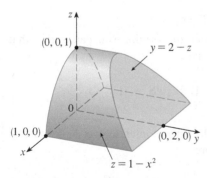

FIGURE 2

▼ **EXAMPLE 2**   **A surface integral that is much easier with the Divergence Theorem**
Evaluate $\iint_S \mathbf{F}\cdot d\mathbf{S}$, where

$$\mathbf{F}(x, y, z) = xy\,\mathbf{i} + \big(y^2 + e^{xz^2}\big)\mathbf{j} + \sin(xy)\,\mathbf{k}$$

and S is the surface of the region E bounded by the parabolic cylinder $z = 1 - x^2$ and the planes $z = 0$, $y = 0$, and $y + z = 2$. (See Figure 2.)

SOLUTION It would be extremely difficult to evaluate the given surface integral directly. (We would have to evaluate four surface integrals corresponding to the four pieces of S.) Furthermore, the divergence of $\mathbf{F}$ is much less complicated than $\mathbf{F}$ itself:

$$\operatorname{div} \mathbf{F} = \frac{\partial}{\partial x}(xy) + \frac{\partial}{\partial y}\big(y^2 + e^{xz^2}\big) + \frac{\partial}{\partial z}(\sin xy) = y + 2y = 3y$$

Therefore we use the Divergence Theorem to transform the given surface integral into a triple integral. The easiest way to evaluate the triple integral is to express E as a type 3 region:

$$E = \big\{(x, y, z) \mid -1 \le x \le 1,\ 0 \le z \le 1 - x^2,\ 0 \le y \le 2 - z\big\}$$

Then we have

$$\iint_S \mathbf{F} \cdot d\mathbf{S} = \iiint_E \operatorname{div} \mathbf{F} \, dV = \iiint_E 3y \, dV$$

$$= 3 \int_{-1}^{1} \int_0^{1-x^2} \int_0^{2-z} y \, dy \, dz \, dx = 3 \int_{-1}^{1} \int_0^{1-x^2} \frac{(2-z)^2}{2} \, dz \, dx$$

$$= \frac{3}{2} \int_{-1}^{1} \left[-\frac{(2-z)^3}{3} \right]_0^{1-x^2} dx = -\frac{1}{2} \int_{-1}^{1} [(x^2+1)^3 - 8] \, dx$$

$$= -\int_0^1 (x^6 + 3x^4 + 3x^2 - 7) \, dx = \frac{184}{35}$$

Although we have proved the Divergence Theorem only for simple solid regions, it can be proved for regions that are finite unions of simple solid regions. (The procedure is similar to the one we used in Section 13.4 to extend Green's Theorem.)

For example, let's consider the region E that lies between the closed surfaces S_1 and S_2, where S_1 lies inside S_2. Let $\mathbf{n}_1$ and $\mathbf{n}_2$ be outward normals of S_1 and S_2. Then the boundary surface of E is $S = S_1 \cup S_2$ and its normal $\mathbf{n}$ is given by $\mathbf{n} = -\mathbf{n}_1$ on S_1 and $\mathbf{n} = \mathbf{n}_2$ on S_2. (See Figure 3.) Applying the Divergence Theorem to S, we get

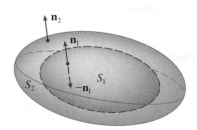

FIGURE 3

$$\boxed{7} \qquad \iiint_E \operatorname{div} \mathbf{F} \, dV = \iint_S \mathbf{F} \cdot d\mathbf{S} = \iint_S \mathbf{F} \cdot \mathbf{n} \, dS$$

$$= \iint_{S_1} \mathbf{F} \cdot (-\mathbf{n}_1) \, dS + \iint_{S_2} \mathbf{F} \cdot \mathbf{n}_2 \, dS$$

$$= -\iint_{S_1} \mathbf{F} \cdot d\mathbf{S} + \iint_{S_2} \mathbf{F} \cdot d\mathbf{S}$$

Let's apply this to the electric field (see Example 5 in Section 13.1):

$$\mathbf{E}(\mathbf{x}) = \frac{\varepsilon Q}{|\mathbf{x}|^3} \mathbf{x}$$

where S_1 is a small sphere with radius a and center the origin. You can verify that $\operatorname{div} \mathbf{E} = 0$. (See Exercise 23.) Therefore Equation 7 gives

$$\iint_{S_2} \mathbf{E} \cdot d\mathbf{S} = \iint_{S_1} \mathbf{E} \cdot d\mathbf{S} + \iiint_E \operatorname{div} \mathbf{E} \, dV = \iint_{S_1} \mathbf{E} \cdot d\mathbf{S} = \iint_{S_1} \mathbf{E} \cdot \mathbf{n} \, dS$$

The point of this calculation is that we can compute the surface integral over S_1 because S_1 is a sphere. The normal vector at $\mathbf{x}$ is $\mathbf{x}/|\mathbf{x}|$. Therefore

$$\mathbf{E} \cdot \mathbf{n} = \frac{\varepsilon Q}{|\mathbf{x}|^3} \mathbf{x} \cdot \left(\frac{\mathbf{x}}{|\mathbf{x}|} \right) = \frac{\varepsilon Q}{|\mathbf{x}|^4} \mathbf{x} \cdot \mathbf{x} = \frac{\varepsilon Q}{|\mathbf{x}|^2} = \frac{\varepsilon Q}{a^2}$$

since the equation of S_1 is $|\mathbf{x}| = a$. Thus we have

$$\iint_{S_2} \mathbf{E} \cdot d\mathbf{S} = \iint_{S_1} \mathbf{E} \cdot \mathbf{n} \, dS = \frac{\varepsilon Q}{a^2} \iint_{S_1} dS = \frac{\varepsilon Q}{a^2} A(S_1) = \frac{\varepsilon Q}{a^2} 4\pi a^2 = 4\pi \varepsilon Q$$

This shows that the electric flux of $\mathbf{E}$ is $4\pi\varepsilon Q$ through *any* closed surface S_2 that contains the origin. [This is a special case of Gauss's Law (Equation 13.6.11) for a single charge. The relationship between ε and ε_0 is $\varepsilon = 1/(4\pi\varepsilon_0)$.]

Another application of the Divergence Theorem occurs in fluid flow. Let $\mathbf{v}(x, y, z)$ be the velocity field of a fluid with constant density ρ. Then $\mathbf{F} = \rho\mathbf{v}$ is the rate of flow per unit area. If $P_0(x_0, y_0, z_0)$ is a point in the fluid and B_a is a ball with center P_0 and very small radius a, then div $\mathbf{F}(P) \approx$ div $\mathbf{F}(P_0)$ for all points in B_a since div $\mathbf{F}$ is continuous. We approximate the flux over the boundary sphere S_a as follows:

$$\iint_{S_a} \mathbf{F} \cdot d\mathbf{S} = \iiint_{B_a} \text{div } \mathbf{F} \, dV \approx \iiint_{B_a} \text{div } \mathbf{F}(P_0) \, dV = \text{div } \mathbf{F}(P_0)V(B_a)$$

This approximation becomes better as $a \to 0$ and suggests that

$$\boxed{8} \qquad \text{div } \mathbf{F}(P_0) = \lim_{a \to 0} \frac{1}{V(B_a)} \iint_{S_a} \mathbf{F} \cdot d\mathbf{S}$$

Equation 8 says that div $\mathbf{F}(P_0)$ is the net rate of outward flux per unit volume at P_0. (This is the reason for the name *divergence*.) If div $\mathbf{F}(P) > 0$, the net flow is outward near P and P is called a **source**. If div $\mathbf{F}(P) < 0$, the net flow is inward near P and P is called a **sink**.

For the vector field in Figure 4, it appears that the vectors that end near P_1 are shorter than the vectors that start near P_1. Thus the net flow is outward near P_1, so div $\mathbf{F}(P_1) > 0$ and P_1 is a source. Near P_2, on the other hand, the incoming arrows are longer than the outgoing arrows. Here the net flow is inward, so div $\mathbf{F}(P_2) < 0$ and P_2 is a sink. We can use the formula for $\mathbf{F}$ to confirm this impression. Since $\mathbf{F} = x^2\,\mathbf{i} + y^2\,\mathbf{j}$, we have div $\mathbf{F} = 2x + 2y$, which is positive when $y > -x$. So the points above the line $y = -x$ are sources and those below are sinks.

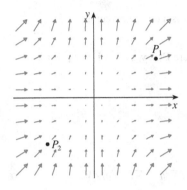

FIGURE 4

The vector field $\mathbf{F} = x^2\,\mathbf{i} + y^2\,\mathbf{j}$

13.8 Exercises

1–4 Verify that the Divergence Theorem is true for the vector field $\mathbf{F}$ on the region E.

1. $\mathbf{F}(x, y, z) = 3x\,\mathbf{i} + xy\,\mathbf{j} + 2xz\,\mathbf{k}$,
E is the cube bounded by the planes $x = 0$, $x = 1$, $y = 0$, $y = 1$, $z = 0$, and $z = 1$

2. $\mathbf{F}(x, y, z) = x^2\,\mathbf{i} + xy\,\mathbf{j} + z\,\mathbf{k}$,
E is the solid bounded by the paraboloid $z = 4 - x^2 - y^2$ and the xy-plane

3. $\mathbf{F}(x, y, z) = \langle z, y, x \rangle$,
E is the solid ball $x^2 + y^2 + z^2 \leqslant 16$

4. $\mathbf{F}(x, y, z) = \langle x^2, -y, z \rangle$,
E is the solid cylinder $y^2 + z^2 \leqslant 9, 0 \leqslant x \leqslant 2$

5–15 Use the Divergence Theorem to calculate the surface integral $\iint_S \mathbf{F} \cdot d\mathbf{S}$; that is, calculate the flux of $\mathbf{F}$ across S.

5. $\mathbf{F}(x, y, z) = xye^z\,\mathbf{i} + xy^2z^3\,\mathbf{j} - ye^z\,\mathbf{k}$,
S is the surface of the box bounded by the coordinate planes and the planes $x = 3$, $y = 2$, and $z = 1$

6. $\mathbf{F}(x, y, z) = x^3y\,\mathbf{i} + xy^2\,\mathbf{j} + xy\,\mathbf{k}$,
S is the surface of the box enclosed by the planes $x = 0$, $x = a$, $y = 0$, $y = b$, $z = 0$, and $z = c$, where a, b, and c are positive numbers

7. $\mathbf{F}(x, y, z) = 3xy^2\,\mathbf{i} + xe^z\,\mathbf{j} + z^3\,\mathbf{k}$,
S is the surface of the solid bounded by the cylinder $y^2 + z^2 = 1$ and the planes $x = -1$ and $x = 2$

8. $\mathbf{F}(x, y, z) = (x^3 + y^3)\,\mathbf{i} + (y^3 + z^3)\,\mathbf{j} + (z^3 + x^3)\,\mathbf{k}$,
S is the sphere with center the origin and radius 2

9. $\mathbf{F}(x, y, z) = x^2 \sin y\,\mathbf{i} + x \cos y\,\mathbf{j} - xz \sin y\,\mathbf{k}$,
S is the "fat sphere" $x^8 + y^8 + z^8 = 8$

10. $\mathbf{F}(x, y, z) = x^2y\,\mathbf{i} + xy^2\,\mathbf{j} + 2xyz\,\mathbf{k}$,
S is the surface of the tetrahedron bounded by the planes $x = 0$, $y = 0$, $z = 0$, and $x + 2y + z = 2$

11. $\mathbf{F}(x, y, z) = (\cos z + xy^2)\,\mathbf{i} + xe^{-z}\,\mathbf{j} + (\sin y + x^2z)\,\mathbf{k}$,
S is the surface of the solid bounded by the paraboloid $z = x^2 + y^2$ and the plane $z = 4$

12. $\mathbf{F}(x, y, z) = x^4\,\mathbf{i} - x^3z^2\,\mathbf{j} + 4xy^2z\,\mathbf{k}$,
S is the surface of the solid bounded by the cylinder $x^2 + y^2 = 1$ and the planes $z = x + 2$ and $z = 0$

13. $\mathbf{F}(x, y, z) = 4x^3z\,\mathbf{i} + 4y^3z\,\mathbf{j} + 3z^4\,\mathbf{k}$,
S is the sphere with radius R and center the origin

14. $\mathbf{F} = \mathbf{r}/|\mathbf{r}|$, where $\mathbf{r} = x\,\mathbf{i} + y\,\mathbf{j} + z\,\mathbf{k}$,
S consists of the hemisphere $z = \sqrt{1 - x^2 - y^2}$ and the disk $x^2 + y^2 \leqslant 1$ in the xy-plane

---

CAS Computer algebra system required   **1.** Homework Hints available in TEC

CAS **15.** $\mathbf{F}(x, y, z) = e^y \tan z\, \mathbf{i} + y\sqrt{3 - x^2}\, \mathbf{j} + x \sin y\, \mathbf{k}$,
S is the surface of the solid that lies above the xy-plane
and below the surface $z = 2 - x^4 - y^4$, $-1 \le x \le 1$,
$-1 \le y \le 1$

CAS **16.** Use a computer algebra system to plot the vector field
$\mathbf{F}(x, y, z) = \sin x \cos^2 y\, \mathbf{i} + \sin^3 y \cos^4 z\, \mathbf{j} + \sin^5 z \cos^6 x\, \mathbf{k}$
in the cube cut from the first octant by the planes $x = \pi/2$,
$y = \pi/2$, and $z = \pi/2$. Then compute the flux across the
surface of the cube.

17. Use the Divergence Theorem to evaluate $\iint_S \mathbf{F} \cdot d\mathbf{S}$, where
$\mathbf{F}(x, y, z) = z^2 x\, \mathbf{i} + \left(\frac{1}{3}y^3 + \tan z\right)\mathbf{j} + (x^2 z + y^2)\mathbf{k}$
and S is the top half of the sphere $x^2 + y^2 + z^2 = 1$.
[*Hint:* Note that S is not a closed surface. First compute
integrals over S_1 and S_2, where S_1 is the disk $x^2 + y^2 \le 1$,
oriented downward, and $S_2 = S \cup S_1$.]

18. Let $\mathbf{F}(x, y, z) = z \tan^{-1}(y^2)\mathbf{i} + z^3 \ln(x^2 + 1)\mathbf{j} + z\, \mathbf{k}$.
Find the flux of $\mathbf{F}$ across the part of the paraboloid
$x^2 + y^2 + z = 2$ that lies above the plane $z = 1$ and is
oriented upward.

19. A vector field $\mathbf{F}$ is shown. Use the interpretation of divergence derived in this section to determine whether div $\mathbf{F}$
is positive or negative at P_1 and at P_2.

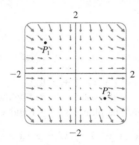

20. (a) Are the points P_1 and P_2 sources or sinks for the vector
field $\mathbf{F}$ shown in the figure? Give an explanation based
solely on the picture.
(b) Given that $\mathbf{F}(x, y) = \langle x, y^2 \rangle$, use the definition of divergence to verify your answer to part (a).

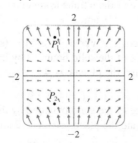

CAS **21–22** Plot the vector field and guess where div $\mathbf{F} > 0$ and
where div $\mathbf{F} < 0$. Then calculate div $\mathbf{F}$ to check your guess.

21. $\mathbf{F}(x, y) = \langle xy, x + y^2 \rangle$

22. $\mathbf{F}(x, y) = \langle x^2, y^2 \rangle$

23. Verify that div $\mathbf{E} = 0$ for the electric field $\mathbf{E}(\mathbf{x}) = \dfrac{\varepsilon Q}{|\mathbf{x}|^3} \mathbf{x}$.

24. Use the Divergence Theorem to evaluate
$\iint_S (2x + 2y + z^2)\, dS$ where S is the sphere
$x^2 + y^2 + z^2 = 1$.

25–30 Prove each identity, assuming that S and E satisfy the
conditions of the Divergence Theorem and the scalar functions
and components of the vector fields have continuous second-
order partial derivatives.

25. $\displaystyle\iint_S \mathbf{a} \cdot \mathbf{n}\, dS = 0$, where $\mathbf{a}$ is a constant vector

26. $\displaystyle V(E) = \frac{1}{3}\iint_S \mathbf{F} \cdot d\mathbf{S}$, where $\mathbf{F}(x, y, z) = x\, \mathbf{i} + y\, \mathbf{j} + z\, \mathbf{k}$

27. $\displaystyle\iint_S \operatorname{curl} \mathbf{F} \cdot d\mathbf{S} = 0$

28. $\displaystyle\iint_S D_{\mathbf{n}} f\, dS = \iiint_E \nabla^2 f\, dV$

29. $\displaystyle\iint_S (f \nabla g) \cdot \mathbf{n}\, dS = \iiint_E (f \nabla^2 g + \nabla f \cdot \nabla g)\, dV$

30. $\displaystyle\iint_S (f \nabla g - g \nabla f) \cdot \mathbf{n}\, dS = \iiint_E (f \nabla^2 g - g \nabla^2 f)\, dV$

31. Suppose S and E satisfy the conditions of the Divergence
Theorem and f is a scalar function with continuous partial
derivatives. Prove that

$$\iint_S f\mathbf{n}\, dS = \iiint_E \nabla f\, dV$$

These surface and triple integrals of vector functions are
vectors defined by integrating each component function.
[*Hint:* Start by applying the Divergence Theorem to $\mathbf{F} = f\mathbf{c}$,
where $\mathbf{c}$ is an arbitrary constant vector.]

32. A solid occupies a region E with surface S and is immersed
in a liquid with constant density ρ. We set up a coordinate
system so that the xy-plane coincides with the surface of the
liquid, and positive values of z are measured downward into
the liquid. Then the pressure at depth z is $p = \rho g z$, where g
is the acceleration due to gravity (see Section 6.6). The total
buoyant force on the solid due to the pressure distribution is
given by the surface integral

$$\mathbf{F} = -\iint_S p\mathbf{n}\, dS$$

where $\mathbf{n}$ is the outer unit normal. Use the result of Exercise 31 to show that $\mathbf{F} = -W\mathbf{k}$, where W is the weight of
the liquid displaced by the solid. (Note that $\mathbf{F}$ is directed
upward because z is directed downward.) The result is
Archimedes' principle: The buoyant force on an object
equals the weight of the displaced liquid.

13.9 Summary

The main results of this chapter are all higher-dimensional versions of the Fundamental Theorem of Calculus. To help you remember them, we collect them together here (without hypotheses) so that you can see more easily their essential similarity. Notice that in each case we have an integral of a "derivative" over a region on the left side, and the right side involves the values of the original function only on the *boundary* of the region.

Fundamental Theorem of Calculus

$$\int_a^b F'(x)\, dx = F(b) - F(a)$$

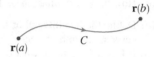

Fundamental Theorem for Line Integrals

$$\int_C \nabla f \cdot d\mathbf{r} = f(\mathbf{r}(b)) - f(\mathbf{r}(a))$$

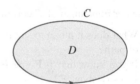

Green's Theorem

$$\iint_D \left(\frac{\partial Q}{\partial x} - \frac{\partial P}{\partial y} \right) dA = \int_C P\, dx + Q\, dy$$

Stokes' Theorem

$$\iint_S \operatorname{curl} \mathbf{F} \cdot d\mathbf{S} = \int_C \mathbf{F} \cdot d\mathbf{r}$$

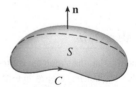

Divergence Theorem

$$\iiint_E \operatorname{div} \mathbf{F}\, dV = \iint_S \mathbf{F} \cdot d\mathbf{S}$$

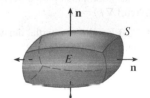

13 Review

Concept Check

1. What is a vector field? Give three examples that have physical meaning.

2. (a) What is a conservative vector field?
   (b) What is a potential function?

3. (a) Write the definition of the line integral of a scalar function f along a smooth curve C with respect to arc length.
   (b) How do you evaluate such a line integral?
   (c) Write expressions for the mass and center of mass of a thin wire shaped like a curve C if the wire has linear density function $\rho(x, y)$.
   (d) Write the definitions of the line integrals along C of a scalar function f with respect to x, y, and z.
   (e) How do you evaluate these line integrals?

4. (a) Define the line integral of a vector field $\mathbf{F}$ along a smooth curve C given by a vector function $\mathbf{r}(t)$.
   (b) If $\mathbf{F}$ is a force field, what does this line integral represent?
   (c) If $\mathbf{F} = \langle P, Q, R \rangle$, what is the connection between the line integral of $\mathbf{F}$ and the line integrals of the component functions P, Q, and R?

5. State the Fundamental Theorem for Line Integrals.

6. (a) What does it mean to say that $\int_C \mathbf{F} \cdot d\mathbf{r}$ is independent of path?
   (b) If you know that $\int_C \mathbf{F} \cdot d\mathbf{r}$ is independent of path, what can you say about $\mathbf{F}$?

7. State Green's Theorem.

8. Write expressions for the area enclosed by a curve C in terms of line integrals around C.

9. Suppose $\mathbf{F}$ is a vector field on $\mathbb{R}^3$.
   (a) Define curl $\mathbf{F}$.
   (b) Define div $\mathbf{F}$.
   (c) If $\mathbf{F}$ is a velocity field in fluid flow, what are the physical interpretations of curl $\mathbf{F}$ and div $\mathbf{F}$?

10. If $\mathbf{F} = P\,\mathbf{i} + Q\,\mathbf{j}$, how do you test to determine whether $\mathbf{F}$ is conservative? What if $\mathbf{F}$ is a vector field on $\mathbb{R}^3$?

11. (a) Write the definition of the surface integral of a scalar function f over a surface S.
    (b) How do you evaluate such an integral if S is a parametric surface given by a vector function $\mathbf{r}(u, v)$?
    (c) What if S is given by an equation $z = g(x, y)$?
    (d) If a thin sheet has the shape of a surface S, and the density at (x, y, z) is $\rho(x, y, z)$, write expressions for the mass and center of mass of the sheet.

12. (a) What is an oriented surface? Give an example of a non-orientable surface.
    (b) Define the surface integral (or flux) of a vector field $\mathbf{F}$ over an oriented surface S with unit normal vector $\mathbf{n}$.
    (c) How do you evaluate such an integral if S is a parametric surface given by a vector function $\mathbf{r}(u, v)$?
    (d) What if S is given by an equation $z = g(x, y)$?

13. State Stokes' Theorem.

14. State the Divergence Theorem.

15. In what ways are the Fundamental Theorem for Line Integrals, Green's Theorem, Stokes' Theorem, and the Divergence Theorem similar?

True-False Quiz

Determine whether the statement is true or false. If it is true, explain why. If it is false, explain why or give an example that disproves the statement.

1. If $\mathbf{F}$ is a vector field, then div $\mathbf{F}$ is a vector field.

2. If $\mathbf{F}$ is a vector field, then curl $\mathbf{F}$ is a vector field.

3. If f has continuous partial derivatives of all orders on $\mathbb{R}^3$, then $\text{div}(\text{curl } \nabla f) = 0$.

4. If f has continuous partial derivatives on $\mathbb{R}^3$ and C is any circle, then $\int_C \nabla f \cdot d\mathbf{r} = 0$.

5. If $\mathbf{F} = P\,\mathbf{i} + Q\,\mathbf{j}$ and $P_y = Q_x$ in an open region D, then $\mathbf{F}$ is conservative.

6. $\int_{-C} f(x, y)\, ds = -\int_C f(x, y)\, ds$

7. If S is a sphere and $\mathbf{F}$ is a constant vector field, then $\iint_S \mathbf{F} \cdot d\mathbf{S} = 0$.

8. There is a vector field $\mathbf{F}$ such that

$$\text{curl } \mathbf{F} = x\,\mathbf{i} + y\,\mathbf{j} + z\,\mathbf{k}$$

Exercises

1. A vector field **F**, a curve C, and a point P are shown.
   (a) Is $\int_C \mathbf{F} \cdot d\mathbf{r}$ positive, negative, or zero? Explain.
   (b) Is div **F**(P) positive, negative, or zero? Explain.

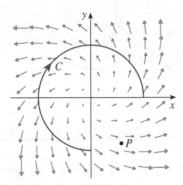

2-9 Evaluate the line integral.

2. $\int_C x \, ds$,
   C is the arc of the parabola $y = x^2$ from $(0, 0)$ to $(1, 1)$

3. $\int_C yz \cos x \, ds$,
   $C: x = t, \ y = 3 \cos t, \ z = 3 \sin t, \ 0 \leqslant t \leqslant \pi$

4. $\int_C y \, dx + (x + y^2) \, dy$, C is the ellipse $4x^2 + 9y^2 = 36$
   with counterclockwise orientation

5. $\int_C y^3 \, dx + x^2 \, dy$, C is the arc of the parabola $x = 1 - y^2$
   from $(0, -1)$ to $(0, 1)$

6. $\int_C \sqrt{xy} \, dx + e^y \, dy + xz \, dz$,
   C is given by $\mathbf{r}(t) = t^4 \mathbf{i} + t^2 \mathbf{j} + t^3 \mathbf{k}, 0 \leqslant t \leqslant 1$

7. $\int_C xy \, dx + y^2 \, dy + yz \, dz$,
   C is the line segment from $(1, 0, -1)$, to $(3, 4, 2)$

8. $\int_C \mathbf{F} \cdot d\mathbf{r}$, where $\mathbf{F}(x, y) = xy \mathbf{i} + x^2 \mathbf{j}$ and C is given by
   $\mathbf{r}(t) = \sin t \, \mathbf{i} + (1 + t) \mathbf{j}, 0 \leqslant t \leqslant \pi$

9. $\int_C \mathbf{F} \cdot d\mathbf{r}$, where $\mathbf{F}(x, y, z) = e^z \mathbf{i} + xz \mathbf{j} + (x + y) \mathbf{k}$ and
   C is given by $\mathbf{r}(t) = t^2 \mathbf{i} + t^3 \mathbf{j} - t \mathbf{k}, 0 \leqslant t \leqslant 1$

10. Find the work done by the force field
    $$\mathbf{F}(x, y, z) = z \mathbf{i} + x \mathbf{j} + y \mathbf{k}$$
    in moving a particle from the point $(3, 0, 0)$ to the point
    $(0, \pi/2, 3)$ along
    (a) a straight line
    (b) the helix $x = 3 \cos t, \ y = t, \ z = 3 \sin t$

11-12 Show that **F** is a conservative vector field. Then find a function f such that $\mathbf{F} = \nabla f$.

11. $\mathbf{F}(x, y) = (1 + xy)e^{xy} \mathbf{i} + (e^y + x^2 e^{xy}) \mathbf{j}$

12. $\mathbf{F}(x, y, z) = \sin y \, \mathbf{i} + x \cos y \, \mathbf{j} - \sin z \, \mathbf{k}$

13-14 Show that **F** is conservative and use this fact to evaluate $\int_C \mathbf{F} \cdot d\mathbf{r}$ along the given curve.

13. $\mathbf{F}(x, y) = (4x^3 y^2 - 2xy^3) \mathbf{i} + (2x^4 y - 3x^2 y^2 + 4y^3) \mathbf{j}$,
    $C: \mathbf{r}(t) = (t + \sin \pi t) \mathbf{i} + (2t + \cos \pi t) \mathbf{j}, \ 0 \leqslant t \leqslant 1$

14. $\mathbf{F}(x, y, z) = e^y \mathbf{i} + (xe^y + e^z) \mathbf{j} + ye^z \mathbf{k}$,
    C is the line segment from $(0, 2, 0)$ to $(4, 0, 3)$

15. Verify that Green's Theorem is true for the line integral
    $\int_C xy^2 \, dx - x^2 y \, dy$, where C consists of the parabola $y = x^2$
    from $(-1, 1)$ to $(1, 1)$ and the line segment from $(1, 1)$
    to $(-1, 1)$.

16. Use Green's Theorem to evaluate
    $$\int_C \sqrt{1 + x^3} \, dx + 2xy \, dy$$
    where C is the triangle with vertices $(0, 0)$, $(1, 0)$, and $(1, 3)$.

17. Use Green's Theorem to evaluate $\int_C x^2 y \, dx - xy^2 \, dy$,
    where C is the circle $x^2 + y^2 = 4$ with counterclockwise
    orientation.

18. Find curl **F** and div **F** if
    $$\mathbf{F}(x, y, z) = e^{-x} \sin y \, \mathbf{i} + e^{-y} \sin z \, \mathbf{j} + e^{-z} \sin x \, \mathbf{k}$$

19. Show that there is no vector field **G** such that
    $$\text{curl } \mathbf{G} = 2x \mathbf{i} + 3yz \mathbf{j} - xz^2 \mathbf{k}$$

20. Show that, under conditions to be stated on the vector fields
    F and **G**,
    $$\text{curl}(\mathbf{F} \times \mathbf{G}) = \mathbf{F} \, \text{div } \mathbf{G} - \mathbf{G} \, \text{div } \mathbf{F} + (\mathbf{G} \cdot \nabla)\mathbf{F} - (\mathbf{F} \cdot \nabla)\mathbf{G}$$

21. If C is any piecewise-smooth simple closed plane curve
    and f and g are differentiable functions, show that
    $\int_C f(x) \, dx + g(y) \, dy = 0$.

22. If f and g are twice differentiable functions, show that
    $$\nabla^2(fg) = f\nabla^2 g + g\nabla^2 f + 2\nabla f \cdot \nabla g$$

23. If f is a harmonic function, that is, $\nabla^2 f = 0$, show that the line
    integral $\int f_y \, dx - f_x \, dy$ is independent of path in any simple
    region D.

24. (a) Sketch the curve C with parametric equations
    $$x = \cos t \qquad y = \sin t \qquad z = \sin t \qquad 0 \leqslant t \leqslant 2\pi$$
    (b) Find $\int_C 2xe^{2y} \, dx + (2x^2 e^{2y} + 2y \cot z) \, dy - y^2 \csc^2 z \, dz$.

25–28 Evaluate the surface integral.

25. $\iint_S z \, dS$, where S is the part of the paraboloid $z = x^2 + y^2$ that lies under the plane $z = 4$

26. $\iint_S (x^2z + y^2z) \, dS$, where S is the part of the plane $z = 4 + x + y$ that lies inside the cylinder $x^2 + y^2 = 4$

27. $\iint_S \mathbf{F} \cdot d\mathbf{S}$, where $\mathbf{F}(x, y, z) = xz \, \mathbf{i} - 2y \, \mathbf{j} + 3x \, \mathbf{k}$ and S is the sphere $x^2 + y^2 + z^2 = 4$ with outward orientation

28. $\iint_S \mathbf{F} \cdot d\mathbf{S}$, where $\mathbf{F}(x, y, z) = x^2 \, \mathbf{i} + xy \, \mathbf{j} + z \, \mathbf{k}$ and S is the part of the paraboloid $z = x^2 + y^2$ below the plane $z = 1$ with upward orientation

---

29. Verify that Stokes' Theorem is true for the vector field $\mathbf{F}(x, y, z) = x^2 \, \mathbf{i} + y^2 \, \mathbf{j} + z^2 \, \mathbf{k}$, where S is the part of the paraboloid $z = 1 - x^2 - y^2$ that lies above the xy-plane and S has upward orientation.

30. Use Stokes' Theorem to evaluate $\iint_S \text{curl } \mathbf{F} \cdot d\mathbf{S}$, where $\mathbf{F}(x, y, z) = x^2yz \, \mathbf{i} + yz^2 \, \mathbf{j} + z^3 e^{xy} \, \mathbf{k}$, S is the part of the sphere $x^2 + y^2 + z^2 = 5$ that lies above the plane $z = 1$, and S is oriented upward.

31. Use Stokes' Theorem to evaluate $\int_C \mathbf{F} \cdot d\mathbf{r}$, where $\mathbf{F}(x, y, z) = xy \, \mathbf{i} + yz \, \mathbf{j} + zx \, \mathbf{k}$, and C is the triangle with vertices $(1, 0, 0)$, $(0, 1, 0)$, and $(0, 0, 1)$, oriented counterclockwise as viewed from above.

32. Use the Divergence Theorem to calculate the surface integral $\iint_S \mathbf{F} \cdot d\mathbf{S}$, where $\mathbf{F}(x, y, z) = x^3 \, \mathbf{i} + y^3 \, \mathbf{j} + z^3 \, \mathbf{k}$ and S is the surface of the solid bounded by the cylinder $x^2 + y^2 = 1$ and the planes $z = 0$ and $z = 2$.

33. Verify that the Divergence Theorem is true for the vector field $\mathbf{F}(x, y, z) = x \, \mathbf{i} + y \, \mathbf{j} + z \, \mathbf{k}$, where E is the unit ball $x^2 + y^2 + z^2 \leqslant 1$.

34. Compute the outward flux of

$$\mathbf{F}(x, y, z) = \frac{x \, \mathbf{i} + y \, \mathbf{j} + z \, \mathbf{k}}{(x^2 + y^2 + z^2)^{3/2}}$$

through the ellipsoid $4x^2 + 9y^2 + 6z^2 = 36$.

35. Let

$$\mathbf{F}(x, y, z) = (3x^2yz - 3y) \, \mathbf{i} + (x^3z - 3x) \, \mathbf{j} + (x^3y + 2z) \, \mathbf{k}$$

Evaluate $\int_C \mathbf{F} \cdot d\mathbf{r}$, where C is the curve with initial point $(0, 0, 2)$ and terminal point $(0, 3, 0)$ shown in the figure.

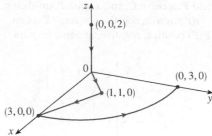

36. Let

$$\mathbf{F}(x, y) = \frac{(2x^3 + 2xy^2 - 2y) \, \mathbf{i} + (2y^3 + 2x^2y + 2x) \, \mathbf{j}}{x^2 + y^2}$$

Evaluate $\oint_C \mathbf{F} \cdot d\mathbf{r}$, where C is shown in the figure.

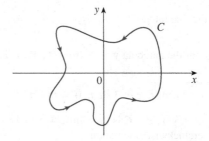

37. Find $\iint_S \mathbf{F} \cdot \mathbf{n} \, dS$, where $\mathbf{F}(x, y, z) = x \, \mathbf{i} + y \, \mathbf{j} + z \, \mathbf{k}$ and S is the outwardly oriented surface shown in the figure (the boundary surface of a cube with a unit corner cube removed).

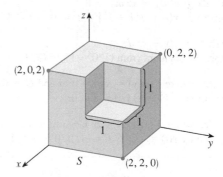

38. If the components of $\mathbf{F}$ have continuous second partial derivatives and S is the boundary surface of a simple solid region, show that $\iint_S \text{curl } \mathbf{F} \cdot d\mathbf{S} = 0$.

Focus on Problem Solving

1. Let S be a smooth parametric surface and let P be a point such that each line that starts at P intersects S at most once. The **solid angle** $\Omega(S)$ subtended by S at P is the set of lines starting at P and passing through S. Let $S(a)$ be the intersection of $\Omega(S)$ with the surface of the sphere with center P and radius a. Then the measure of the solid angle (in *steradians*) is defined to be

$$|\Omega(S)| = \frac{\text{area of } S(a)}{a^2}$$

   Apply the Divergence Theorem to the part of $\Omega(S)$ between $S(a)$ and S to show that

$$|\Omega(S)| = \iint_S \frac{\mathbf{r} \cdot \mathbf{n}}{r^3}\, dS$$

   where $\mathbf{r}$ is the radius vector from P to any point on S, $r = |\mathbf{r}|$, and the unit normal vector $\mathbf{n}$ is directed away from P.

   This shows that the definition of the measure of a solid angle is independent of the radius a of the sphere. Thus the measure of the solid angle is equal to the area subtended on a *unit* sphere. (Note the analogy with the definition of radian measure.) The total solid angle subtended by a sphere at its center is thus 4π steradians.

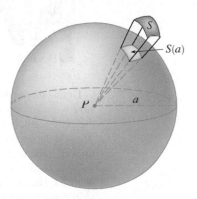

2. Prove the following identity:

$$\nabla(\mathbf{F} \cdot \mathbf{G}) = (\mathbf{F} \cdot \nabla)\mathbf{G} + (\mathbf{G} \cdot \nabla)\mathbf{F} + \mathbf{F} \times \operatorname{curl} \mathbf{G} + \mathbf{G} \times \operatorname{curl} \mathbf{F}$$

3. If $\mathbf{a}$ is a constant vector, $\mathbf{r} = x\,\mathbf{i} + y\,\mathbf{j} + z\,\mathbf{k}$, and S is an oriented, smooth surface with a simple, closed, smooth, positively oriented boundary curve C, show that

$$\iint_S 2\mathbf{a} \cdot d\mathbf{S} = \int_C (\mathbf{a} \times \mathbf{r}) \cdot d\mathbf{r}$$

4. Find the positively oriented simple closed curve C for which the value of the line integral

$$\int_C (y^3 - y)\, dx - 2x^3\, dy$$

   is a maximum.

5. Let C be a simple closed piecewise-smooth space curve that lies in a plane with unit normal vector $\mathbf{n} = \langle a, b, c \rangle$ and has positive orientation with respect to $\mathbf{n}$. Show that the plane area enclosed by C is

$$\tfrac{1}{2}\int_C (bz - cy)\, dx + (cx - az)\, dy + (ay - bx)\, dz$$

6. The figure depicts the sequence of events in each cylinder of a four-cylinder internal combustion engine. Each piston moves up and down and is connected by a pivoted arm to a rotating crankshaft. Let $P(t)$ and $V(t)$ be the pressure and volume within a cylinder at time t, where $a \leq t \leq b$ gives the time required for a complete cycle. The graph shows how P and V vary through one cycle of a four-stroke engine.

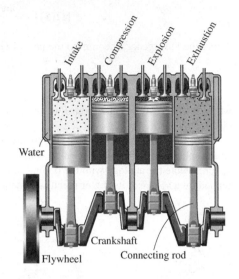

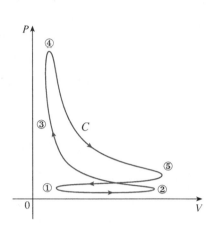

During the intake stroke (from ① to ②) a mixture of air and gasoline at atmospheric pressure is drawn into a cylinder through the intake valve as the piston moves downward. Then the piston rapidly compresses the mix with the valves closed in the compression stroke (from ② to ③) during which the pressure rises and the volume decreases. At ③ the sparkplug ignites the fuel, raising the temperature and pressure at almost constant volume to ④. Then, with valves closed, the rapid expansion forces the piston downward during the power stroke (from ④ to ⑤). The exhaust valve opens, temperature and pressure drop, and mechanical energy stored in a rotating flywheel pushes the piston upward, forcing the waste products out of the exhaust valve in the exhaust stroke. The exhaust valve closes and the intake valve opens. We're now back at ① and the cycle starts again.

(a) Show that the work done on the piston during one cycle of a four-stroke engine is
$W = \int_C P \, dV$, where C is the curve in the PV-plane shown in the figure.

[*Hint:* Let $x(t)$ be the distance from the piston to the top of the cylinder and note that the force on the piston is $\mathbf{F} = AP(t)\,\mathbf{i}$, where A is the area of the top of the piston. Then $W = \int_{C_1} \mathbf{F} \cdot d\mathbf{r}$, where C_1 is given by $\mathbf{r}(t) = x(t)\,\mathbf{i}$, $a \leq t \leq b$. An alternative approach is to work directly with Riemann sums.]

(b) Use Formula 13.4.5 to show that the work is the difference of the areas enclosed by the two loops of C.

Appendixes

A | Intervals, Inequalities, and Absolute Values

Certain sets of real numbers, called **intervals,** occur frequently in calculus and correspond geometrically to line segments. For example, if $a < b$, the **open interval** from a to b consists of all numbers between a and b and is denoted by the symbol (a, b). Using set-builder notation, we can write

$$(a, b) = \{x \mid a < x < b\}$$

FIGURE 1

Open interval (a, b)

Notice that the endpoints of the interval—namely, a and b—are excluded. This is indicated by the round brackets $(\ )$ and by the open dots in Figure 1. The **closed interval** from a to b is the set

$$[a, b] = \{x \mid a \leqslant x \leqslant b\}$$

FIGURE 2

Closed interval $[a, b]$

Here the endpoints of the interval are included. This is indicated by the square brackets $[\ ]$ and by the solid dots in Figure 2. It is also possible to include only one endpoint in an interval, as shown in Table 1.

1 | **Table of Intervals**

Table 1 lists the nine possible types of intervals. When these intervals are discussed, it is always assumed that $a < b$.

Notation	Set description	Picture
(a, b)	$\{x \mid a < x < b\}$	
$[a, b]$	$\{x \mid a \leqslant x \leqslant b\}$	
$[a, b)$	$\{x \mid a \leqslant x < b\}$	
$(a, b]$	$\{x \mid a < x \leqslant b\}$	
(a, ∞)	$\{x \mid x > a\}$	
$[a, \infty)$	$\{x \mid x \geqslant a\}$	
$(-\infty, b)$	$\{x \mid x < b\}$	
$(-\infty, b]$	$\{x \mid x \leqslant b\}$	
$(-\infty, \infty)$	$\mathbb{R}$ (set of all real numbers)	

We also need to consider infinite intervals such as

$$(a, \infty) = \{x \mid x > a\}$$

This does not mean that ∞ ("infinity") is a number. The notation (a, ∞) stands for the set of all numbers that are greater than a, so the symbol ∞ simply indicates that the interval extends indefinitely far in the positive direction.

Inequalities

When working with inequalities, note the following rules.

Rules for Inequalities

1. If $a < b$, then $a + c < b + c$.

2. If $a < b$ and $c < d$, then $a + c < b + d$.

3. If $a < b$ and $c > 0$, then $ac < bc$.

4. If $a < b$ and $c < 0$, then $ac > bc$.

5. If $0 < a < b$, then $1/a > 1/b$.

Rule 1 says that we can add any number to both sides of an inequality, and Rule 2 says that two inequalities can be added. However, we have to be careful with multiplication. Rule 3 says that we can multiply both sides of an inequality by a *positive* number, but Rule 4 says that if we multiply both sides of an inequality by a negative number, then we reverse the direction of the inequality. For example, if we take the inequality $3 < 5$ and multiply by 2, we get $6 < 10$, but if we multiply by -2, we get $-6 > -10$. Finally, Rule 5 says that if we take reciprocals, then we reverse the direction of an inequality (provided the numbers are positive).

EXAMPLE 1 Solve the inequality $1 + x < 7x + 5$.

SOLUTION The given inequality is satisfied by some values of x but not by others. To *solve* an inequality means to determine the set of numbers x for which the inequality is true. This is called the *solution set*.

First we subtract 1 from each side of the inequality (using Rule 1 with $c = -1$):

$$x < 7x + 4$$

Then we subtract $7x$ from both sides (Rule 1 with $c = -7x$):

$$6x < 4$$

Now we divide both sides by -6 $\left(\text{Rule 4 with } c = -\frac{1}{6} \right)$:

$$x > -\tfrac{4}{6} = -\tfrac{2}{3}$$

These steps can all be reversed, so the solution set consists of all numbers greater than $-\frac{2}{3}$. In other words, the solution of the inequality is the interval $\left(-\frac{2}{3}, \infty \right)$.

EXAMPLE 2 Solve the inequality $x^2 - 5x + 6 \le 0$.

SOLUTION First we factor the left side:

$$(x - 2)(x - 3) \le 0$$

We know that the corresponding equation $(x - 2)(x - 3) = 0$ has the solutions 2 and 3. The numbers 2 and 3 divide the real line into three intervals:

$$(-\infty, 2) \qquad (2, 3) \qquad (3, \infty)$$

On each of these intervals we determine the signs of the factors. For instance,

$$x \in (-\infty, 2) \quad \Rightarrow \quad x < 2 \quad \Rightarrow \quad x - 2 < 0$$

Then we record these signs in the following chart:

Interval	$x - 2$	$x - 3$	$(x - 2)(x - 3)$
$x < 2$	−	−	+
$2 < x < 3$	+	−	−
$x > 3$	+	+	+

Another method for obtaining the information in the chart is to use *test values*. For instance, if we use the test value $x = 1$ for the interval $(-\infty, 2)$, then substitution in $x^2 - 5x + 6$ gives

$$1^2 - 5(1) + 6 = 2$$

A visual method for solving Example 2 is to use a graphing device to graph the parabola $y = x^2 - 5x + 6$ (as in Figure 3) and observe that the curve lies on or below the x-axis when $2 \le x \le 3$.

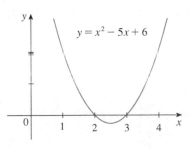

FIGURE 3

The polynomial $x^2 - 5x + 6$ doesn't change sign inside any of the three intervals, so we conclude that it is positive on $(-\infty, 2)$.

Then we read from the chart that $(x - 2)(x - 3)$ is negative when $2 < x < 3$. Thus the solution of the inequality $(x - 2)(x - 3) \le 0$ is

$$\{x \mid 2 \le x \le 3\} = [2, 3]$$

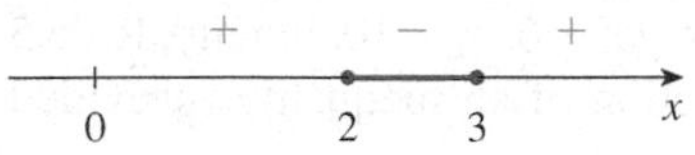

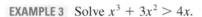

FIGURE 4

Notice that we have included the endpoints 2 and 3 because we are looking for values of x such that the product is either negative or zero. The solution is illustrated in Figure 4.

EXAMPLE 3 Solve $x^3 + 3x^2 > 4x$.

SOLUTION First we take all nonzero terms to one side of the inequality sign and factor the resulting expression:

$$x^3 + 3x^2 - 4x > 0 \qquad \text{or} \qquad x(x - 1)(x + 4) > 0$$

As in Example 2 we solve the corresponding equation $x(x - 1)(x + 4) = 0$ and use the solutions $x = -4$, $x = 0$, and $x = 1$ to divide the real line into four intervals $(-\infty, -4)$, $(-4, 0)$, $(0, 1)$, and $(1, \infty)$. On each interval the product keeps a constant sign as shown in the following chart:

Interval	x	$x - 1$	$x + 4$	$x(x - 1)(x + 4)$
$x < -4$	−	−	−	−
$-4 < x < 0$	−	−	+	+
$0 < x < 1$	+	−	+	−
$x > 1$	+	+	+	+

Then we read from the chart that the solution set is

$$\{x \mid -4 < x < 0 \ \text{ or } \ x > 1\} = (-4, 0) \cup (1, \infty)$$

FIGURE 5

The solution is illustrated in Figure 5.

Absolute Value

The **absolute value** of a number a, denoted by $|a|$, is the distance from a to 0 on the real number line. Distances are always positive or 0, so we have

$$|a| \ge 0 \qquad \text{for every number } a$$

For example,

$$|3| = 3 \qquad |-3| = 3 \qquad |0| = 0 \qquad |\sqrt{2} - 1| = \sqrt{2} - 1 \qquad |3 - \pi| = \pi - 3$$

In general, we have

Remember that if a is negative, then $-a$ is positive.

2

$$
\begin{aligned}
|a| &= a \qquad \text{if } a \ge 0 \\
|a| &= -a \qquad \text{if } a < 0
\end{aligned}
$$

EXAMPLE 4 Express $|3x - 2|$ without using the absolute-value symbol.

SOLUTION

$$|3x - 2| = \begin{cases} 3x - 2 & \text{if } 3x - 2 \geq 0 \\ -(3x - 2) & \text{if } 3x - 2 < 0 \end{cases}$$

$$= \begin{cases} 3x - 2 & \text{if } x \geq \frac{2}{3} \\ 2 - 3x & \text{if } x < \frac{2}{3} \end{cases}$$

Recall that the symbol $\sqrt{\ }$ means "the positive square root of." Thus $\sqrt{r} = s$ means $s^2 = r$ and $s \geq 0$. Therefore the equation $\sqrt{a^2} = a$ is not always true. It is true only when $a \geq 0$. If $a < 0$, then $-a > 0$, so we have $\sqrt{a^2} = -a$. In view of (2), we then have the equation

3
$$\sqrt{a^2} = |a|$$

which is true for all values of a.

Hints for the proofs of the following properties are given in the exercises.

Properties of Absolute Values Suppose a and b are any real numbers and n is an integer. Then

1. $|ab| = |a||b|$ **2.** $\left|\dfrac{a}{b}\right| = \dfrac{|a|}{|b|}$ $(b \neq 0)$ **3.** $|a^n| = |a|^n$

For solving equations or inequalities involving absolute values, it's often very helpful to use the following statements.

Suppose $a > 0$. Then

4. $|x| = a$ if and only if $x = \pm a$

5. $|x| < a$ if and only if $-a < x < a$

6. $|x| > a$ if and only if $x > a$ or $x < -a$

For instance, the inequality $|x| < a$ says that the distance from x to the origin is less than a, and you can see from Figure 6 that this is true if and only if x lies between $-a$ and a.

If a and b are any real numbers, then the distance between a and b is the absolute value of the difference, namely, $|a - b|$, which is also equal to $|b - a|$. (See Figure 7.)

EXAMPLE 5 Solve $|2x - 5| = 3$.

SOLUTION By Property 4 of absolute values, $|2x - 5| = 3$ is equivalent to

$$2x - 5 = 3 \quad \text{or} \quad 2x - 5 = -3$$

So $2x = 8$ or $2x = 2$. Thus $x = 4$ or $x = 1$.

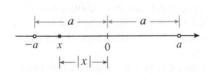

FIGURE 6

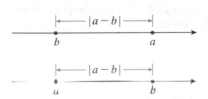

FIGURE 7
Length of a line segment $= |a - b|$

EXAMPLE 6 Solve $|x - 5| < 2$.

SOLUTION 1 By Property 5 of absolute values, $|x - 5| < 2$ is equivalent to

$$-2 < x - 5 < 2$$

Therefore, adding 5 to all sides, we have

$$3 < x < 7$$

and the solution set is the open interval $(3, 7)$.

SOLUTION 2 Geometrically, the solution set consists of all numbers x whose distance from 5 is less than 2. From Figure 8 we see that this is the interval $(3, 7)$.

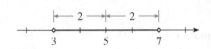

FIGURE 8

EXAMPLE 7 Solve $|3x + 2| \geq 4$.

SOLUTION By Properties 4 and 6 of absolute values, $|3x + 2| \geq 4$ is equivalent to

$$3x + 2 \geq 4 \quad \text{or} \quad 3x + 2 \leq -4$$

In the first case, $3x \geq 2$, which gives $x \geq \frac{2}{3}$. In the second case, $3x \leq -6$, which gives $x \leq -2$. So the solution set is

$$\left\{ x \mid x \leq -2 \text{ or } x \geq \frac{2}{3} \right\} = (-\infty, -2] \cup \left[\tfrac{2}{3}, \infty \right)$$

A Exercises

1–10 Rewrite the expression without using the absolute value symbol.

1. $|5 - 23|$

2. $|\pi - 2|$

3. $|\sqrt{5} - 5|$

4. $||-2| - |-3||$

5. $|x - 2|$ if $x < 2$

6. $|x - 2|$ if $x > 2$

7. $|x + 1|$

8. $|2x - 1|$

9. $|x^2 + 1|$

10. $|1 - 2x^2|$

11–26 Solve the inequality in terms of intervals and illustrate the solution set on the real number line.

11. $2x + 7 > 3$

12. $4 - 3x \geq 6$

13. $1 - x \leq 2$

14. $1 + 5x > 5 - 3x$

15. $0 \leq 1 - x < 1$

16. $1 < 3x + 4 \leq 16$

17. $(x - 1)(x - 2) > 0$

18. $x^2 < 2x + 8$

19. $x^2 < 3$

20. $x^2 \geq 5$

21. $x^3 - x^2 \leq 0$

22. $(x + 1)(x - 2)(x + 3) \geq 0$

23. $x^3 > x$

24. $x^3 + 3x < 4x^2$

25. $\dfrac{1}{x} < 4$

26. $-3 < \dfrac{1}{x} \leq 1$

27. The relationship between the Celsius and Fahrenheit temperature scales is given by $C = \frac{5}{9}(F - 32)$, where C is the temperature in degrees Celsius and F is the temperature in degrees Fahrenheit. What interval on the Celsius scale corresponds to the temperature range $50 \leq F \leq 95$?

28. Use the relationship between C and F given in Exercise 27 to find the interval on the Fahrenheit scale corresponding to the temperature range $20 \leq C \leq 30$.

29. As dry air moves upward, it expands and in so doing cools at a rate of about 1°C for each 100-m rise, up to about 12 km.
  (a) If the ground temperature is 20°C, write a formula for the temperature at height h.
  (b) What range of temperature can be expected if a plane takes off and reaches a maximum height of 5 km?

30. If a ball is thrown upward from the top of a building 128 ft high with an initial velocity of 16 ft/s, then the height h above the ground t seconds later will be

$$h = 128 + 16t - 16t^2$$

During what time interval will the ball be at least 32 ft above the ground?

31–32 Solve the equation for x.

31. $|x + 3| = |2x + 1|$

32. $|3x + 5| = 1$

33–40 Solve the inequality.

33. $|x| < 3$

34. $|x| \geqslant 3$

35. $|x - 4| < 1$

36. $|x - 6| < 0.1$

37. $|x + 5| \geqslant 2$

38. $|x + 1| \geqslant 3$

39. $|2x - 3| \leqslant 0.4$

40. $|5x - 2| < 6$

41. Solve the inequality $a(bx - c) \geqslant bc$ for x, assuming that a, b, and c are positive constants.

42. Solve the inequality $ax + b < c$ for x, assuming that a, b, and c are negative constants.

43. Prove that $|ab| = |a||b|$. [*Hint:* Use Equation 3.]

44. Show that if $0 < a < b$, then $a^2 < b^2$.

B   Coordinate Geometry

The points in a plane can be identified with ordered pairs of real numbers. We start by drawing two perpendicular coordinate lines that intersect at the origin O on each line. Usually one line is horizontal with positive direction to the right and is called the *x*-axis; the other line is vertical with positive direction upward and is called the *y*-axis.

Any point P in the plane can be located by a unique ordered pair of numbers as follows. Draw lines through P perpendicular to the *x*- and *y*-axes. These lines intersect the axes in points with coordinates a and b as shown in Figure 1. Then the point P is assigned the ordered pair (a, b). The first number a is called the **x-coordinate** of P; the second number b is called the **y-coordinate** of P. We say that P is the point with coordinates (a, b), and we denote the point by the symbol $P(a, b)$. Several points are labeled with their coordinates in Figure 2.

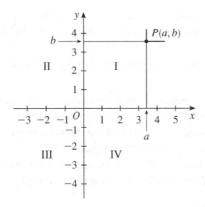

FIGURE 1

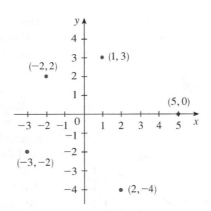

FIGURE 2

By reversing the preceding process we can start with an ordered pair (a, b) and arrive at the corresponding point P. Often we identify the point P with the ordered pair (a, b) and refer to "the point (a, b)." [Although the notation used for an open interval (a, b) is the same as the notation used for a point (a, b), you will be able to tell from the context which meaning is intended.]

This coordinate system is called the **rectangular coordinate system** or the **Cartesian coordinate system** in honor of the French mathematician René Descartes (1596–1650), even though another Frenchman, Pierre Fermat (1601–1665), invented the principles of analytic geometry at about the same time as Descartes. The plane supplied with this coordinate system is called the **coordinate plane** or the **Cartesian plane** and is denoted by $\mathbb{R}^2$.

The *x*- and *y*-axes are called the **coordinate axes** and divide the Cartesian plane into four quadrants, which are labeled I, II, III, and IV in Figure 1. Notice that the first quadrant consists of those points whose *x*- and *y*-coordinates are both positive.

EXAMPLE 1 Describe and sketch the regions given by the following sets.

(a) $\{(x, y) \mid x \geqslant 0\}$ (b) $\{(x, y) \mid y = 1\}$ (c) $\{(x, y) \mid |y| < 1\}$

SOLUTION

(a) The points whose x-coordinates are 0 or positive lie on the y-axis or to the right of it as indicated by the shaded region in Figure 3(a).

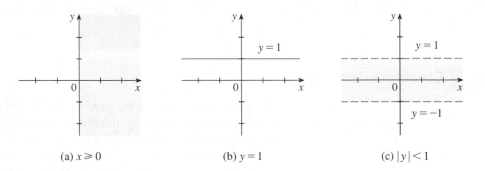

FIGURE 3   (a) $x \geqslant 0$ (b) $y = 1$ (c) $|y| < 1$

(b) The set of all points with y-coordinate 1 is a horizontal line one unit above the x-axis [see Figure 3(b)].

(c) Recall from Appendix A that

$$|y| < 1 \qquad \text{if and only if} \qquad -1 < y < 1$$

The given region consists of those points in the plane whose y-coordinates lie between -1 and 1. Thus the region consists of all points that lie between (but not on) the horizontal lines $y = 1$ and $y = -1$. [These lines are shown as dashed lines in Figure 3(c) to indicate that the points on these lines don't lie in the set.]

Recall from Appendix A that the distance between points a and b on a number line is $|a - b| = |b - a|$. Thus the distance between points $P_1(x_1, y_1)$ and $P_3(x_2, y_1)$ on a horizontal line must be $|x_2 - x_1|$ and the distance between $P_2(x_2, y_2)$ and $P_3(x_2, y_1)$ on a vertical line must be $|y_2 - y_1|$. (See Figure 4.)

To find the distance $|P_1P_2|$ between any two points $P_1(x_1, y_1)$ and $P_2(x_2, y_2)$, we note that triangle $P_1P_2P_3$ in Figure 4 is a right triangle, and so by the Pythagorean Theorem we have

$$|P_1P_2| = \sqrt{|P_1P_3|^2 + |P_2P_3|^2} = \sqrt{|x_2 - x_1|^2 + |y_2 - y_1|^2}$$

$$= \sqrt{(x_2 - x_1)^2 + (y_2 - y_1)^2}$$

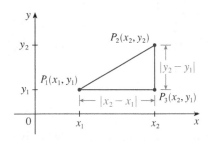

FIGURE 4

> **Distance Formula** The distance between the points $P_1(x_1, y_1)$ and $P_2(x_2, y_2)$ is
>
> $$|P_1P_2| = \sqrt{(x_2 - x_1)^2 + (y_2 - y_1)^2}$$

For instance, the distance between $(1, -2)$ and $(5, 3)$ is

$$\sqrt{(5 - 1)^2 + [3 - (-2)]^2} = \sqrt{4^2 + 5^2} = \sqrt{41}$$

Circles

An **equation of a curve** is an equation satisfied by the coordinates of the points on the curve and by no other points. Let's use the distance formula to find the equation of a circle with radius r and center (h, k). By definition, the circle is the set of all points $P(x, y)$ whose distance from the center $C(h, k)$ is r. (See Figure 5.) Thus P is on the circle if and only if $|PC| = r$. From the distance formula, we have

$$\sqrt{(x - h)^2 + (y - k)^2} = r$$

or equivalently, squaring both sides, we get

$$(x - h)^2 + (y - k)^2 = r^2$$

This is the desired equation.

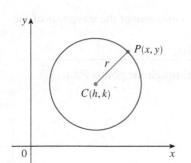

FIGURE 5

Equation of a Circle An equation of the circle with center (h, k) and radius r is

$$(x - h)^2 + (y - k)^2 = r^2$$

In particular, if the center is the origin $(0, 0)$, the equation is

$$x^2 + y^2 = r^2$$

For instance, an equation of the circle with radius 3 and center $(2, -5)$ is

$$(x - 2)^2 + (y + 5)^2 = 9$$

EXAMPLE 2 Sketch the graph of the equation $x^2 + y^2 + 2x - 6y + 7 = 0$ by first showing that it represents a circle and then finding its center and radius.

SOLUTION We first group the x-terms and y-terms as follows:

$$(x^2 + 2x) + (y^2 - 6y) = -7$$

Then we complete the square within each grouping, adding the appropriate constants (the squares of half the coefficients of x and y) to both sides of the equation:

$$(x^2 + 2x + 1) + (y^2 - 6y + 9) = -7 + 1 + 9$$

or $\qquad\qquad (x + 1)^2 + (y - 3)^2 = 3$

Comparing this equation with the standard equation of a circle, we see that $h = -1$, $k = 3$, and $r = \sqrt{3}$, so the given equation represents a circle with center $(-1, 3)$ and radius $\sqrt{3}$. It is sketched in Figure 6.

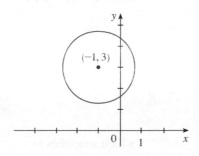

FIGURE 6
$x^2 + y^2 + 2x - 6y + 7 = 0$

Lines

To find the equation of a line L we use its *slope,* which is a measure of the steepness of the line.

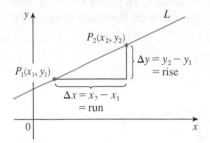

FIGURE 7

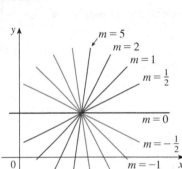

FIGURE 8

> **Definition** The **slope** of a nonvertical line that passes through the points $P_1(x_1, y_1)$ and $P_2(x_2, y_2)$ is
>
> $$m = \frac{\Delta y}{\Delta x} = \frac{y_2 - y_1}{x_2 - x_1}$$
>
> The slope of a vertical line is not defined.

Thus the slope of a line is the ratio of the change in y, Δy, to the change in x, Δx. (See Figure 7.) The slope is therefore the rate of change of y with respect to x. The fact that the line is straight means that the rate of change is constant.

Figure 8 shows several lines labeled with their slopes. Notice that lines with positive slope slant upward to the right, whereas lines with negative slope slant downward to the right. Notice also that the steepest lines are the ones for which the absolute value of the slope is largest, and a horizontal line has slope 0.

Now let's find an equation of the line that passes through a given point $P_1(x_1, y_1)$ and has slope m. A point $P(x, y)$ with $x \neq x_1$ lies on this line if and only if the slope of the line through P_1 and P is equal to m; that is,

$$\frac{y - y_1}{x - x_1} = m$$

This equation can be rewritten in the form

$$y - y_1 = m(x - x_1)$$

and we observe that this equation is also satisfied when $x = x_1$ and $y = y_1$. Therefore it is an equation of the given line.

> **Point-Slope Form of the Equation of a Line** An equation of the line passing through the point $P_1(x_1, y_1)$ and having slope m is
>
> $$y - y_1 = m(x - x_1)$$

EXAMPLE 3 Find an equation of the line through the points $(-1, 2)$ and $(3, -4)$.

SOLUTION The slope of the line is

$$m = \frac{-4 - 2}{3 - (-1)} = -\frac{3}{2}$$

Using the point-slope form with $x_1 = -1$ and $y_1 = 2$, we obtain

$$y - 2 = -\tfrac{3}{2}(x + 1)$$

which simplifies to $\qquad\qquad 3x + 2y = 1$

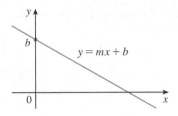

FIGURE 9

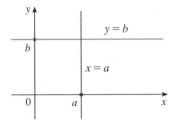

FIGURE 10

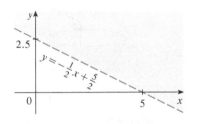

FIGURE 11

Suppose a nonvertical line has slope m and y-intercept b. (See Figure 9.) This means it intersects the y-axis at the point $(0, b)$, so the point-slope form of the equation of the line, with $x_1 = 0$ and $y_1 = b$, becomes

$$y - b = m(x - 0)$$

This simplifies as follows.

> **Slope-Intercept Form of the Equation of a Line**   An equation of the line with slope m and y-intercept b is
>
> $$y = mx + b$$

In particular, if a line is horizontal, its slope is $m = 0$, so its equation is $y = b$, where b is the y-intercept (see Figure 10). A vertical line does not have a slope, but we can write its equation as $x = a$, where a is the x-intercept, because the x-coordinate of every point on the line is a.

EXAMPLE 4   Graph the inequality $x + 2y > 5$.

SOLUTION   We are asked to sketch the graph of the set $\{(x, y) \mid x + 2y > 5\}$ and we begin by solving the inequality for y:

$$x + 2y > 5$$

$$2y > -x + 5$$

$$y > -\tfrac{1}{2}x + \tfrac{5}{2}$$

Compare this inequality with the equation $y = -\tfrac{1}{2}x + \tfrac{5}{2}$, which represents a line with slope $-\tfrac{1}{2}$ and y-intercept $\tfrac{5}{2}$. We see that the given graph consists of points whose y-coordinates are *larger* than those on the line $y = -\tfrac{1}{2}x + \tfrac{5}{2}$. Thus the graph is the region that lies *above* the line, as illustrated in Figure 11.

Parallel and Perpendicular Lines

Slopes can be used to show that lines are parallel or perpendicular. The following facts are proved, for instance, in *Precalculus: Mathematics for Calculus, Fifth Edition* by Stewart, Redlin, and Watson (Belmont, CA, 2006).

> **Parallel and Perpendicular Lines**
>
> **1.** Two nonvertical lines are parallel if and only if they have the same slope.
>
> **2.** Two lines with slopes m_1 and m_2 are perpendicular if and only if $m_1 m_2 = -1$; that is, their slopes are negative reciprocals:
>
> $$m_2 = -\frac{1}{m_1}$$

EXAMPLE 5   Find an equation of the line through the point $(5, 2)$ that is parallel to the line $4x + 6y + 5 = 0$.

SOLUTION   The given line can be written in the form

$$y = -\tfrac{2}{3}x - \tfrac{5}{6}$$

which is in slope-intercept form with $m = -\frac{2}{3}$. Parallel lines have the same slope, so the required line has slope $-\frac{2}{3}$ and its equation in point-slope form is

$$y - 2 = -\tfrac{2}{3}(x - 5)$$

We can write this equation as $2x + 3y = 16$. ▬

EXAMPLE 6 Show that the lines $2x + 3y = 1$ and $6x - 4y - 1 = 0$ are perpendicular.

SOLUTION The equations can be written as

$$y = -\tfrac{2}{3}x + \tfrac{1}{3} \qquad \text{and} \qquad y = \tfrac{3}{2}x - \tfrac{1}{4}$$

from which we see that the slopes are

$$m_1 = -\tfrac{2}{3} \qquad \text{and} \qquad m_2 = \tfrac{3}{2}$$

Since $m_1 m_2 = -1$, the lines are perpendicular. ▬

Conic Sections

Here we review the geometric definitions of parabolas, ellipses, and hyperbolas and their standard equations. They are called **conic sections**, or **conics**, because they result from intersecting a cone with a plane as shown in Figure 12.

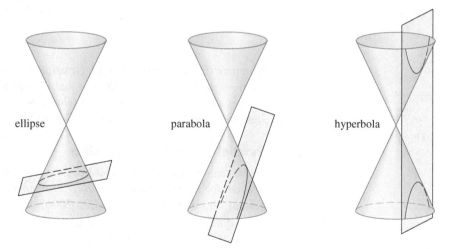

ellipse   parabola   hyperbola

FIGURE 12
Conics

Parabolas

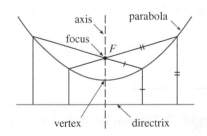

FIGURE 13

A **parabola** is the set of points in a plane that are equidistant from a fixed point F (called the **focus**) and a fixed line (called the **directrix**). This definition is illustrated by Figure 13. Notice that the point halfway between the focus and the directrix lies on the parabola; it is called the **vertex**. The line through the focus perpendicular to the directrix is called the **axis** of the parabola.

In the 16th century Galileo showed that the path of a projectile that is shot into the air at an angle to the ground is a parabola. Since then, parabolic shapes have been used in designing automobile headlights, reflecting telescopes, and suspension bridges. (See Problem 18 on page 254 for the reflection property of parabolas that makes them so useful.)

We obtain a particularly simple equation for a parabola if we place its vertex at the origin O and its directrix parallel to the x-axis as in Figure 14. If the focus is the point

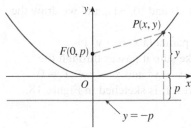

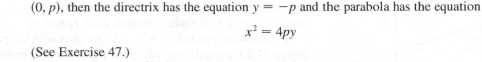

$(0, p)$, then the directrix has the equation $y = -p$ and the parabola has the equation

$$x^2 = 4py$$

(See Exercise 47.)

If we write $a = 1/(4p)$, then the equation of the parabola becomes

$$\boxed{y = ax^2}$$

FIGURE 14

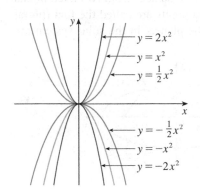

FIGURE 15

Figure 15 shows the graphs of several parabolas with equations of the form $y = ax^2$ for various values of the number a. We see that the parabola $y = ax^2$ opens upward if $a > 0$ and downward if $a < 0$ (as in Figure 16). The graph is symmetric with respect to the y-axis because its equation is unchanged when x is replaced by $-x$. This corresponds to the fact that the function $f(x) = ax^2$ is an even function.

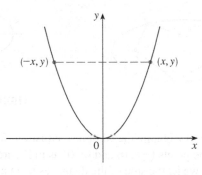

FIGURE 16

(a) $y = ax^2$, $a > 0$

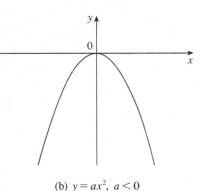

(b) $y = ax^2$, $a < 0$

If we interchange x and y in the equation $y = ax^2$, the result is $x = ay^2$, which also represents a parabola. (Interchanging x and y amounts to reflecting about the diagonal line $y = x$.) The parabola $x = ay^2$ opens to the right if $a > 0$ and to the left if $a < 0$. (See Figure 17.) This time the parabola is symmetric with respect to the x-axis because the equation is unchanged when y is replaced by $-y$.

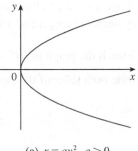

FIGURE 17

(a) $x = ay^2$, $a > 0$

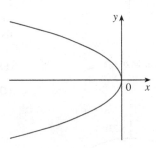

(b) $x = ay^2$, $a < 0$

EXAMPLE 7 Sketch the region bounded by the parabola $x = 1 - y^2$ and the line $x + y + 1 = 0$.

SOLUTION First we find the points of intersection by solving the two equations. Substituting $x = -y - 1$ into the equation $x = 1 - y^2$, we get $-y - 1 = 1 - y^2$, which gives

$$0 = y^2 - y - 2 = (y - 2)(y + 1)$$

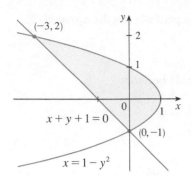

FIGURE 18

so $y = 2$ or -1. Thus the points of intersection are $(-3, 2)$ and $(0, -1)$, and we draw the line $x + y + 1 = 0$ passing through these points.

To sketch the parabola $x = 1 - y^2$ we start with the parabola $x = -y^2$ in Figure 17(b) and shift one unit to the right. We also make sure it passes through the points $(-3, 2)$ and $(0, -1)$. The region bounded by $x = 1 - y^2$ and $x + y + 1 = 0$ means the finite region whose boundaries are these curves. It is sketched in Figure 18.

Ellipses

An **ellipse** is the set of points in a plane the sum of whose distances from two fixed points F_1 and F_2 is a constant (see Figure 19). These two fixed points are called the **foci** (plural of **focus**). One of Kepler's laws is that the orbits of the planets in the solar system are ellipses with the sun at one focus.

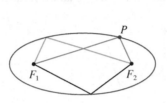

FIGURE 19

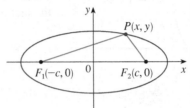

FIGURE 20

In order to obtain the simplest equation for an ellipse, we place the foci on the x-axis at the points $(-c, 0)$ and $(c, 0)$ as in Figure 20, so that the origin is halfway between the foci. If we let the sum of the distances from a point on the ellipse to the foci be $2a$, then we can write an equation of the ellipse as

$$\boxed{1}\qquad \boxed{\frac{x^2}{a^2} + \frac{y^2}{b^2} = 1}$$

where $c^2 = a^2 - b^2$. (See Exercise 49 and Figure 21.) Notice that the x-intercepts are $\pm a$, the y-intercepts are $\pm b$, the foci are $(\pm c, 0)$, and the ellipse is symmetric with respect to both axes. If the foci of an ellipse are located on the y-axis at $(0, \pm c)$, then we can find its equation by interchanging x and y in (1).

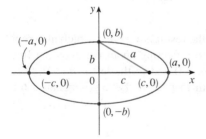

FIGURE 21
$$\frac{x^2}{a^2} + \frac{y^2}{b^2} = 1, \; a \geqslant b$$

EXAMPLE 8 Sketch the graph of $9x^2 + 16y^2 = 144$ and locate the foci.

SOLUTION Divide both sides of the equation by 144:

$$\frac{x^2}{16} + \frac{y^2}{9} = 1$$

The equation is now in the standard form for an ellipse, so we have $a^2 = 16$, $b^2 = 9$, $a = 4$, and $b = 3$. The x-intercepts are ± 4 and the y-intercepts are ± 3. Also, $c^2 = a^2 - b^2 = 7$, so $c = \sqrt{7}$ and the foci are $(\pm\sqrt{7}, 0)$. The graph is sketched in Figure 22.

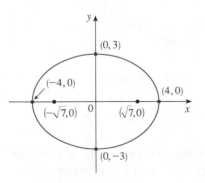

FIGURE 22
$9x^2 + 16y^2 = 144$

Like parabolas, ellipses have an interesting reflection property that has practical consequences. If a source of light or sound is placed at one focus of a surface with elliptical cross-sections, then all the light or sound is reflected off the surface to the other focus (see Exercise 55). This principle is used in *lithotripsy*, a treatment for kidney stones. A reflector with elliptical cross-section is placed in such a way that the kidney stone is at one focus. High-intensity sound waves generated at the other focus are reflected to the stone and destroy it without damaging surrounding tissue. The patient is spared the trauma of surgery and recovers within a few days.

Hyperbolas

A **hyperbola** is the set of all points in a plane the difference of whose distances from two fixed points F_1 and F_2 (the foci) is a constant. This definition is illustrated in Figure 23.

Notice that the definition of a hyperbola is similar to that of an ellipse; the only change is that the sum of distances has become a difference of distances. It is left as Exercise 51 to show that when the foci are on the x-axis at $(\pm c, 0)$ and the difference of distances is $|PF_1| - |PF_2| = \pm 2a$, then the equation of the hyperbola is

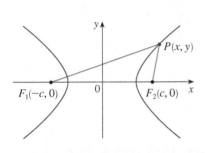

FIGURE 23

P is on the hyperbola when $|PF_1| - |PF_2| = \pm 2a.$

$$\boxed{2} \qquad \boxed{\dfrac{x^2}{a^2} - \dfrac{y^2}{b^2} = 1}$$

where $c^2 = a^2 + b^2$. Notice that the x-intercepts are again $\pm a$. But if we put $x = 0$ in Equation 2 we get $y^2 = -b^2$, which is impossible, so there is no y-intercept. The hyperbola is symmetric with respect to both axes.

To analyze the hyperbola further, we look at Equation 2 and obtain

$$\frac{x^2}{a^2} = 1 + \frac{y^2}{b^2} \geq 1$$

This shows that $x^2 \geq a^2$, so $|x| = \sqrt{x^2} \geq a$. Therefore we have $x \geq a$ or $x \leq -a$. This means that the hyperbola consists of two parts, called its *branches*.

When we draw a hyperbola it is useful to first draw its *asymptotes*, which are the lines $y = (b/a)x$ and $y = -(b/a)x$ shown in Figure 24. Both branches of the hyperbola approach the asymptotes; that is, they come arbitrarily close to the asymptotes. If the foci of a hyperbola are on the y-axis, we find its equation by reversing the roles of x and y.

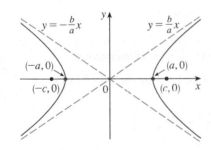

FIGURE 24

$\dfrac{x^2}{a^2} - \dfrac{y^2}{b^2} = 1$

EXAMPLE 9 Find the foci and asymptotes of the hyperbola $9x^2 - 16y^2 = 144$ and sketch its graph.

SOLUTION If we divide both sides of the equation by 144, it becomes

$$\frac{x^2}{16} - \frac{y^2}{9} = 1$$

which is of the form given in (2) with $a = 4$ and $b = 3$. Since $c^2 = 16 + 9 = 25$, the foci are $(\pm 5, 0)$. The asymptotes are the lines $y = \frac{3}{4}x$ and $y = -\frac{3}{4}x$. The graph is shown in Figure 25.

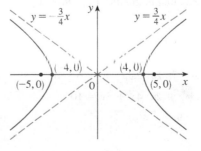

FIGURE 25

$9x^2 - 16y^2 = 144$

B   Exercises

1–2 Find the distance between the points.

1. $(1, 1)$, $(4, 5)$

2. $(1, -3)$, $(5, 7)$

3–4 Find the slope of the line through P and Q.

3. $P(-3, 3)$, $Q(-1, -6)$

4. $P(-1, -4)$, $Q(6, 0)$

---

5. Show that the points $(-2, 9)$, $(4, 6)$, $(1, 0)$, and $(-5, 3)$ are the vertices of a square.

6. (a) Show that the points $A(-1, 3)$, $B(3, 11)$, and $C(5, 15)$ are collinear (lie on the same line) by showing that $|AB| + |BC| = |AC|$.
(b) Use slopes to show that A, B, and C are collinear.

7–10 Sketch the graph of the equation.

7. $x = 3$

8. $y = -2$

9. $xy = 0$

10. $|y| = 1$

11–24 Find an equation of the line that satisfies the given conditions.

11. Through $(2, -3)$,   slope 6

12. Through $(-3, -5)$,   slope $-\frac{7}{2}$

13. Through $(2, 1)$ and $(1, 6)$

14. Through $(-1, -2)$ and $(4, 3)$

15. Slope 3, y-intercept -2

16. Slope $\frac{2}{5}$, y-intercept 4

17. x-intercept 1, y-intercept -3

18. x-intercept -8, y-intercept 6

19. Through $(4, 5)$,   parallel to the x-axis

20. Through $(4, 5)$,   parallel to the y-axis

21. Through $(1, -6)$,   parallel to the line $x + 2y = 6$

22. y-intercept 6,   parallel to the line $2x + 3y + 4 = 0$

23. Through $(-1, -2)$,   perpendicular to the line $2x + 5y + 8 = 0$

24. Through $\left(\frac{1}{2}, -\frac{2}{3}\right)$,   perpendicular to the line $4x - 8y = 1$

25–28 Find the slope and y-intercept of the line and draw its graph.

25. $x + 3y = 0$

26. $2x - 3y + 6 = 0$

27. $3x - 4y = 12$

28. $4x + 5y = 10$

29–36 Sketch the region in the xy-plane.

29. $\{(x, y) \mid x < 0\}$

30. $\{(x, y) \mid x \geq 1 \text{ and } y < 3\}$

31. $\{(x, y) \mid |x| \leq 2\}$

32. $\{(x, y) \mid |x| < 3 \text{ and } |y| < 2\}$

33. $\{(x, y) \mid 0 \leq y \leq 4 \text{ and } x \leq 2\}$

34. $\{(x, y) \mid y > 2x - 1\}$

35. $\{(x, y) \mid 1 + x \leq y \leq 1 - 2x\}$

36. $\left\{(x, y) \mid -x \leq y < \frac{1}{2}(x + 3)\right\}$

37–38 Find an equation of a circle that satisfies the given conditions.

37. Center $(3, -1)$, radius 5

38. Center $(-1, 5)$, passes through $(-4, -6)$

39–40 Show that the equation represents a circle and find the center and radius.

39. $x^2 + y^2 - 4x + 10y + 13 = 0$

40. $x^2 + y^2 + 6y + 2 = 0$

---

41. Show that the lines $2x - y = 4$ and $6x - 2y = 10$ are not parallel and find their point of intersection.

42. Show that the lines $3x - 5y + 19 = 0$ and $10x + 6y - 50 = 0$ are perpendicular and find their point of intersection.

43. Show that the midpoint of the line segment from $P_1(x_1, y_1)$ to $P_2(x_2, y_2)$ is
$$\left(\frac{x_1 + x_2}{2}, \frac{y_1 + y_2}{2} \right)$$

44. Find the midpoint of the line segment joining the points $(1, 3)$ and $(7, 15)$.

45. Find an equation of the perpendicular bisector of the line segment joining the points $A(1, 4)$ and $B(7, -2)$.

46. (a) Show that if the x- and y-intercepts of a line are nonzero numbers a and b, then the equation of the line can be put in the form
$$\frac{x}{a} + \frac{y}{b} = 1$$
This equation is called the **two-intercept form** of an equation of a line.
(b) Use part (a) to find an equation of the line whose x-intercept is 6 and whose y-intercept is -8.

47. Suppose that $P(x, y)$ is any point on the parabola with focus $(0, p)$ and directrix $y = -p$. (See Figure 14.) Use the definition of a parabola to show that $x^2 = 4py$.

48. Find the focus and directrix of the parabola $y = x^2$. Illustrate with a diagram.

49. Suppose an ellipse has foci $(\pm c, 0)$ and the sum of the distances from any point $P(x, y)$ on the ellipse to the foci is $2a$. Show that the coordinates of P satisfy Equation 1.

50. Find the foci of the ellipse $x^2 + 4y^2 = 4$ and sketch its graph.

51. Use the definition of a hyperbola to derive Equation 2 for a hyperbola with foci $(\pm c, 0)$.

52. (a) Find the foci and asymptotes of the hyperbola $x^2 - y^2 = 1$ and sketch its graph.
(b) Sketch the graph of $y^2 - x^2 = 1$.

53–54 Sketch the region bounded by the curves.

53. $x + 4y = 8$ and $x - 2y^2 = 8$

54. $y = 4 - x^2$ and $x - 2y = 2$

---

55. Let $P(x_1, y_1)$ be a point on the ellipse $x^2/a^2 + y^2/b^2 = 1$ with foci F_1 and F_2 and let α and β be the angles between the lines PF_1, PF_2 and the ellipse as shown in the figure. Prove that $\alpha = \beta$. This explains how whispering galleries and lithotripsy work. Sound coming from one focus is reflected and passes through the other focus. [*Hint:* Use the formula in Problem 17 on page 253 to show that $\tan \alpha = \tan \beta$.]

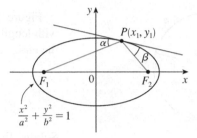

C   Trigonometry

Here we review the aspects of trigonometry that are used in calculus: radian measure, trigonometric functions, trigonometric identities, and inverse trigonometric functions.

Angles

Angles can be measured in degrees or in radians (abbreviated as rad). The angle given by a complete revolution contains $360°$, which is the same as 2π rad. Therefore

$$\boxed{1} \qquad \pi \text{ rad} = 180°$$

and

$$\boxed{2} \qquad 1 \text{ rad} = \left(\frac{180}{\pi}\right)^{\circ} \approx 57.3° \qquad 1° = \frac{\pi}{180} \text{ rad} \approx 0.017 \text{ rad}$$

EXAMPLE 1
(a) Find the radian measure of $60°$.   (b) Express $5\pi/4$ rad in degrees.

SOLUTION
(a) From Equation 1 or 2 we see that to convert from degrees to radians we multiply by $\pi/180$. Therefore

$$60° = 60\left(\frac{\pi}{180}\right) = \frac{\pi}{3} \text{ rad}$$

(b) To convert from radians to degrees we multiply by $180/\pi$. Thus

$$\frac{5\pi}{4} \text{ rad} = \frac{5\pi}{4}\left(\frac{180}{\pi}\right) = 225°$$

In calculus we use radians to measure angles except when otherwise indicated. The following table gives the correspondence between degree and radian measures of some common angles.

Degrees	0°	30°	45°	60°	90°	120°	135°	150°	180°	270°	360°
Radians	0	$\dfrac{\pi}{6}$	$\dfrac{\pi}{4}$	$\dfrac{\pi}{3}$	$\dfrac{\pi}{2}$	$\dfrac{2\pi}{3}$	$\dfrac{3\pi}{4}$	$\dfrac{5\pi}{6}$	π	$\dfrac{3\pi}{2}$	2π

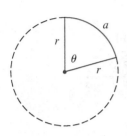

FIGURE 1

Figure 1 shows a sector of a circle with central angle θ and radius r subtending an arc with length a. Since the length of the arc is proportional to the size of the angle, and since the entire circle has circumference $2\pi r$ and central angle 2π, we have

$$\frac{\theta}{2\pi} = \frac{a}{2\pi r}$$

Solving this equation for θ and for a, we obtain

$$\boxed{3} \qquad \boxed{\; \theta = \frac{a}{r} \;} \qquad\qquad \boxed{\; a = r\theta \;}$$

Remember that Equations 3 are valid only when θ is measured in radians.

In particular, putting $a = r$ in Equation 3, we see that an angle of 1 rad is the angle subtended at the center of a circle by an arc equal in length to the radius of the circle (see Figure 2).

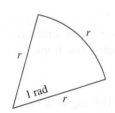

FIGURE 2

EXAMPLE 2
(a) If the radius of a circle is 5 cm, what angle is subtended by an arc of 6 cm?
(b) If a circle has radius 3 cm, what is the length of an arc subtended by a central angle of $3\pi/8$ rad?

SOLUTION
(a) Using Equation 3 with $a = 6$ and $r = 5$, we see that the angle is

$$\theta = \tfrac{6}{5} = 1.2 \text{ rad}$$

(b) With $r = 3$ cm and $\theta = 3\pi/8$ rad, the arc length is

$$a = r\theta = 3\left(\frac{3\pi}{8}\right) = \frac{9\pi}{8} \text{ cm}$$

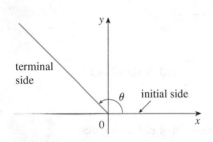

FIGURE 3 $\theta \geqslant 0$

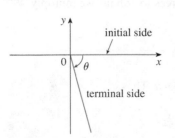

FIGURE 4 $\theta < 0$

The **standard position** of an angle occurs when we place its vertex at the origin of a coordinate system and its initial side on the positive x-axis as in Figure 3. A **positive** angle is obtained by rotating the initial side counterclockwise until it coincides with the terminal side. Likewise, **negative** angles are obtained by clockwise rotation as in Figure 4.

Figure 5 shows several examples of angles in standard position. Notice that different angles can have the same terminal side. For instance, the angles $3\pi/4$, $-5\pi/4$, and $11\pi/4$

have the same initial and terminal sides because

$$\frac{3\pi}{4} - 2\pi = -\frac{5\pi}{4} \qquad \frac{3\pi}{4} + 2\pi = \frac{11\pi}{4}$$

and 2π rad represents a complete revolution.

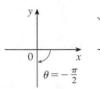

FIGURE 5
Angles in standard position

The Trigonometric Functions

For an acute angle θ the six trigonometric functions are defined as ratios of lengths of sides of a right triangle as follows (see Figure 6).

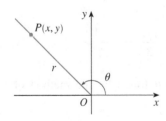

FIGURE 6

$$\boxed{4} \qquad \sin\theta = \frac{\text{opp}}{\text{hyp}} \qquad \csc\theta = \frac{\text{hyp}}{\text{opp}}$$

$$\cos\theta = \frac{\text{adj}}{\text{hyp}} \qquad \sec\theta = \frac{\text{hyp}}{\text{adj}}$$

$$\tan\theta = \frac{\text{opp}}{\text{adj}} \qquad \cot\theta = \frac{\text{adj}}{\text{opp}}$$

This definition doesn't apply to obtuse or negative angles, so for a general angle θ in standard position we let $P(x, y)$ be any point on the terminal side of θ and we let r be the distance $|OP|$ as in Figure 7. Then we define

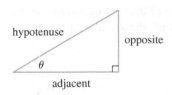

FIGURE 7

$$\boxed{5} \qquad \sin\theta = \frac{y}{r} \qquad \csc\theta = \frac{r}{y}$$

$$\cos\theta = \frac{x}{r} \qquad \sec\theta = \frac{r}{x}$$

$$\tan\theta = \frac{y}{x} \qquad \cot\theta = \frac{x}{y}$$

Since division by 0 is not defined, $\tan\theta$ and $\sec\theta$ are undefined when $x = 0$ and $\csc\theta$ and $\cot\theta$ are undefined when $y = 0$. Notice that the definitions in (4) and (5) are consistent when θ is an acute angle.

If θ is a number, the convention is that $\sin\theta$ means the sine of the angle whose *radian* measure is θ. For example, the expression $\sin 3$ implies that we are dealing with an angle of 3 rad. When finding a calculator approximation to this number, we must remember to set our calculator in radian mode, and then we obtain

$$\sin 3 \approx 0.14112$$

If we want to know the sine of the angle 3° we would write sin 3° and, with our calculator in degree mode, we find that

$$\sin 3° \approx 0.05234$$

The exact trigonometric ratios for certain angles can be read from the triangles in Figure 8. For instance,

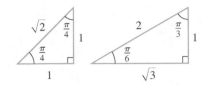
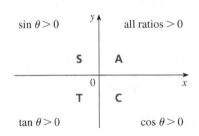

FIGURE 8

$$\sin \frac{\pi}{4} = \frac{1}{\sqrt{2}} \qquad \sin \frac{\pi}{6} = \frac{1}{2} \qquad \sin \frac{\pi}{3} = \frac{\sqrt{3}}{2}$$

$$\cos \frac{\pi}{4} = \frac{1}{\sqrt{2}} \qquad \cos \frac{\pi}{6} = \frac{\sqrt{3}}{2} \qquad \cos \frac{\pi}{3} = \frac{1}{2}$$

$$\tan \frac{\pi}{4} = 1 \qquad \tan \frac{\pi}{6} = \frac{1}{\sqrt{3}} \qquad \tan \frac{\pi}{3} = \sqrt{3}$$

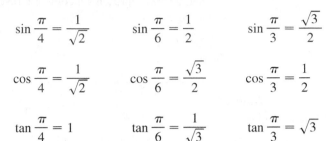

FIGURE 9

The signs of the trigonometric functions for angles in each of the four quadrants can be remembered by means of the rule "All Students Take Calculus" shown in Figure 9.

EXAMPLE 3 Find the exact trigonometric ratios for $\theta = 2\pi/3$.

SOLUTION From Figure 10 we see that a point on the terminal line for $\theta = 2\pi/3$ is $P(-1, \sqrt{3})$. Therefore, taking

$$x = -1 \qquad y = \sqrt{3} \qquad r = 2$$

in the definitions of the trigonometric ratios, we have

$$\sin \frac{2\pi}{3} = \frac{\sqrt{3}}{2} \qquad \cos \frac{2\pi}{3} = -\frac{1}{2} \qquad \tan \frac{2\pi}{3} = -\sqrt{3}$$

$$\csc \frac{2\pi}{3} = \frac{2}{\sqrt{3}} \qquad \sec \frac{2\pi}{3} = -2 \qquad \cot \frac{2\pi}{3} = -\frac{1}{\sqrt{3}}$$

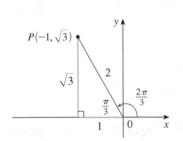

FIGURE 10

The following table gives some values of $\sin \theta$ and $\cos \theta$ found by the method of Example 3.

θ	0	$\frac{\pi}{6}$	$\frac{\pi}{4}$	$\frac{\pi}{3}$	$\frac{\pi}{2}$	$\frac{2\pi}{3}$	$\frac{3\pi}{4}$	$\frac{5\pi}{6}$	π	$\frac{3\pi}{2}$	2π
$\sin \theta$	0	$\frac{1}{2}$	$\frac{1}{\sqrt{2}}$	$\frac{\sqrt{3}}{2}$	1	$\frac{\sqrt{3}}{2}$	$\frac{1}{\sqrt{2}}$	$\frac{1}{2}$	0	-1	0
$\cos \theta$	1	$\frac{\sqrt{3}}{2}$	$\frac{1}{\sqrt{2}}$	$\frac{1}{2}$	0	$-\frac{1}{2}$	$-\frac{1}{\sqrt{2}}$	$-\frac{\sqrt{3}}{2}$	-1	0	1

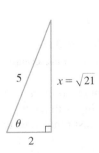

FIGURE 11

EXAMPLE 4 If $\cos \theta = \frac{2}{5}$ and $0 < \theta < \pi/2$, find the other five trigonometric functions of θ.

SOLUTION Since $\cos \theta = \frac{2}{5}$, we can label the hypotenuse as having length 5 and the adjacent side as having length 2 in Figure 11. If the opposite side has length x, then the

Pythagorean Theorem gives $x^2 + 4 = 25$ and so $x^2 = 21$, $x = \sqrt{21}$. We can now use the diagram to write the other five trigonometric functions:

$$\sin\theta = \frac{\sqrt{21}}{5} \qquad \tan\theta = \frac{\sqrt{21}}{2}$$

$$\csc\theta = \frac{5}{\sqrt{21}} \qquad \sec\theta = \frac{5}{2} \qquad \cot\theta = \frac{2}{\sqrt{21}}$$

EXAMPLE 5 Use a calculator to approximate the value of x in Figure 12.

SOLUTION From the diagram we see that

$$\tan 40° = \frac{16}{x}$$

Therefore
$$x = \frac{16}{\tan 40°} \approx 19.07$$

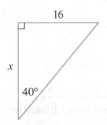

FIGURE 12

Trigonometric Identities

A trigonometric identity is a relationship among the trigonometric functions. The most elementary are the following, which are immediate consequences of the definitions of the trigonometric functions.

$$\boxed{6} \qquad \csc\theta = \frac{1}{\sin\theta} \qquad \sec\theta = \frac{1}{\cos\theta} \qquad \cot\theta = \frac{1}{\tan\theta}$$

$$\tan\theta = \frac{\sin\theta}{\cos\theta} \qquad \cot\theta = \frac{\cos\theta}{\sin\theta}$$

For the next identity we refer back to Figure 7. The distance formula (or, equivalently, the Pythagorean Theorem) tells us that $x^2 + y^2 = r^2$. Therefore

$$\sin^2\theta + \cos^2\theta = \frac{y^2}{r^2} + \frac{x^2}{r^2} = \frac{x^2 + y^2}{r^2} = \frac{r^2}{r^2} = 1$$

We have therefore proved one of the most useful of all trigonometric identities:

$$\boxed{7} \qquad \sin^2\theta + \cos^2\theta = 1$$

If we now divide both sides of Equation 7 by $\cos^2\theta$ and use Equations 6, we get

$$\boxed{8} \qquad \tan^2\theta + 1 = \sec^2\theta$$

Similarly, if we divide both sides of Equation 7 by $\sin^2\theta$, we get

$$\boxed{9} \qquad 1 + \cot^2\theta = \csc^2\theta$$

The identities

10a
$$\sin(-\theta) = -\sin\theta$$

10b
$$\cos(-\theta) = \cos\theta$$

Odd functions and even functions are discussed in Section 1.1.

show that sine is an odd function and cosine is an even function. They are easily proved by drawing a diagram showing θ and $-\theta$ in standard position (see Exercise 19).

Since the angles θ and $\theta + 2\pi$ have the same terminal side, we have

11
$$\sin(\theta + 2\pi) = \sin\theta \qquad \cos(\theta + 2\pi) = \cos\theta$$

These identities show that the sine and cosine functions are periodic with period 2π.

The remaining trigonometric identities are all consequences of two basic identities called the **addition formulas**:

12a
$$\sin(x + y) = \sin x \cos y + \cos x \sin y$$

12b
$$\cos(x + y) = \cos x \cos y - \sin x \sin y$$

The proofs of these addition formulas are outlined in Exercises 43, 44, and 45.

By substituting $-y$ for y in Equations 12a and 12b and using Equations 10a and 10b, we obtain the following **subtraction formulas**:

13a
$$\sin(x - y) = \sin x \cos y - \cos x \sin y$$

13b
$$\cos(x - y) = \cos x \cos y + \sin x \sin y$$

Then, by dividing the formulas in Equations 12 or Equations 13, we obtain the corresponding formulas for $\tan(x \pm y)$:

14a
$$\tan(x + y) = \frac{\tan x + \tan y}{1 - \tan x \tan y}$$

14b
$$\tan(x - y) = \frac{\tan x - \tan y}{1 + \tan x \tan y}$$

If we put $y = x$ in the addition formulas (12), we get the **double-angle formulas**:

15a
$$\sin 2x = 2 \sin x \cos x$$

15b
$$\cos 2x = \cos^2 x - \sin^2 x$$

Then, by using the identity $\sin^2 x + \cos^2 x = 1$, we obtain the following alternate forms of the double-angle formulas for $\cos 2x$:

16a
$$\cos 2x = 2\cos^2 x - 1$$

16b
$$\cos 2x = 1 - 2\sin^2 x$$

If we now solve these equations for $\cos^2 x$ and $\sin^2 x$, we get the following **half-angle formulas**, which are useful in integral calculus:

17a
$$\cos^2 x = \frac{1 + \cos 2x}{2}$$

17b
$$\sin^2 x = \frac{1 - \cos 2x}{2}$$

There are many other trigonometric identities, but those we have stated are the ones used most often in calculus. If you forget any of them, remember that they can all be deduced from Equations 12a and 12b.

EXAMPLE 6 Find all values of x in the interval $[0, 2\pi]$ such that $\sin x = \sin 2x$.

SOLUTION Using the double-angle formula (15a), we rewrite the given equation as

$$\sin x = 2\sin x \cos x \qquad \text{or} \qquad \sin x(1 - 2\cos x) = 0$$

Therefore there are two possibilities:

$$\sin x = 0 \qquad\qquad \text{or} \qquad 1 - 2\cos x = 0$$

$$x = 0, \pi, 2\pi \qquad\qquad \cos x = \tfrac{1}{2}$$

$$x = \frac{\pi}{3}, \frac{5\pi}{3}$$

The given equation has five solutions: 0, $\pi/3$, π, $5\pi/3$, and 2π. ▆

Graphs of the Trigonometric Functions

The graph of the function $f(x) = \sin x$, shown in Figure 13(a), is obtained by plotting points for $0 \leqslant x \leqslant 2\pi$ and then using the periodic nature of the function (from Equation 11) to complete the graph. Notice that the zeros of the sine function occur at the integer multiples of π, that is,

$$\sin x = 0 \qquad \text{whenever } x = n\pi, \quad n \text{ an integer}$$

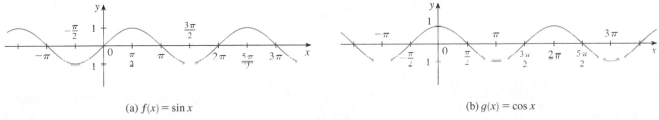

(a) $f(x) = \sin x$

(b) $g(x) = \cos x$

FIGURE 13

Because of the identity

$$\cos x = \sin\left(x + \frac{\pi}{2}\right)$$

(which can be verified using Equation 12a), the graph of cosine is obtained by shifting the graph of sine by an amount $\pi/2$ to the left [see Figure 13(b)]. Note that for both the sine and cosine functions the domain is $(-\infty, \infty)$ and the range is the closed interval $[-1, 1]$. Thus, for all values of x, we have

$$-1 \le \sin x \le 1 \qquad -1 \le \cos x \le 1$$

The graphs of the remaining four trigonometric functions are shown in Figure 14 and their domains are indicated there. Notice that tangent and cotangent have range $(-\infty, \infty)$, whereas cosecant and secant have range $(-\infty, -1] \cup [1, \infty)$. All four functions are periodic: tangent and cotangent have period π, whereas cosecant and secant have period 2π.

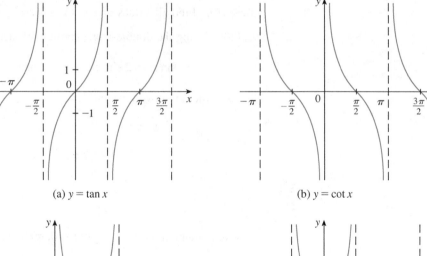

(a) $y = \tan x$ (b) $y = \cot x$

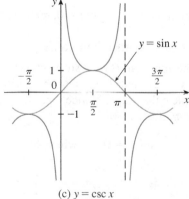

(c) $y = \csc x$

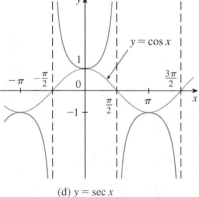

(d) $y = \sec x$

FIGURE 14

C | Exercises

1–2 Convert from degrees to radians.

1. (a) $210°$ (b) $9°$

2. (a) $-315°$ (b) $36°$

3–4 Convert from radians to degrees.

3. (a) 4π (b) $-\dfrac{3\pi}{8}$

4. (a) $-\dfrac{7\pi}{2}$ (b) $\dfrac{8\pi}{3}$

---

5. Find the length of a circular arc subtended by an angle of $\pi/12$ rad if the radius of the circle is 36 cm.

6. If a circle has radius 10 cm, find the length of the arc subtended by a central angle of $72°$.

7. A circle has radius 1.5 m. What angle is subtended at the center of the circle by an arc 1 m long?

8. Find the radius of a circular sector with angle $3\pi/4$ and arc length 6 cm.

9–10 Draw, in standard position, the angle whose measure is given.

9. (a) $315°$ (b) $-\dfrac{3\pi}{4}$ rad

10. (a) $\dfrac{7\pi}{3}$ rad   (b) -3 rad

11–12 Find the exact trigonometric ratios for the angle whose radian measure is given.

11. $\dfrac{3\pi}{4}$ **12.** $\dfrac{4\pi}{3}$

13–14 Find the remaining trigonometric ratios.

13. $\sin\theta = \dfrac{3}{5},\quad 0 < \theta < \dfrac{\pi}{2}$

14. $\tan\alpha = 2,\quad 0 < \alpha < \dfrac{\pi}{2}$

15–18 Find, correct to five decimal places, the length of the side labeled x.

15.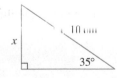

16.

17.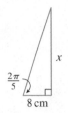

18.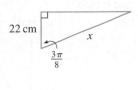

19–20 Prove each equation.

19. (a) Equation 10a   (b) Equation 10b

20. (a) Equation 14a   (b) Equation 14b

21–26 Prove the identity.

21. $\sin\left(\dfrac{\pi}{2} + x\right) = \cos x$ **22.** $\sin(\pi - x) = \sin x$

23. $\sin\theta \cot\theta = \cos\theta$ **24.** $(\sin x + \cos x)^2 = 1 + \sin 2x$

25. $\tan 2\theta = \dfrac{2\tan\theta}{1 - \tan^2\theta}$ **26.** $\cos 3\theta = 4\cos^3\theta - 3\cos\theta$

27–28 If $\sin x = \frac{1}{3}$ and $\sec y = \frac{5}{4}$, where x and y lie between 0 and $\pi/2$, evaluate the expression.

27. $\sin(x + y)$ **28.** $\cos 2y$

29–32 Find all values of x in the interval $[0, 2\pi]$ that satisfy the equation.

29. $2\cos x - 1 = 0$ **30.** $2\sin^2 x = 1$

31. $\sin 2x = \cos x$ **32.** $|\tan x| = 1$

33–36 Find all values of x in the interval $[0, 2\pi]$ that satisfy the inequality.

33. $\sin x \leqslant \frac{1}{2}$ **34.** $2\cos x + 1 > 0$

35. $-1 < \tan x < 1$ **36.** $\sin x > \cos x$

37–40 Graph the function by starting with the graphs in Figures 13 and 14 and applying the transformations of Section 1.3 where appropriate.

37. $y = \cos\left(x - \dfrac{\pi}{3}\right)$ **38.** $y = \tan 2x$

39. $y = \dfrac{1}{3}\tan\left(x - \dfrac{\pi}{2}\right)$ **40.** $y = |\sin x|$

41. Prove the **Law of Cosines**: If a triangle has sides with lengths a, b, and c, and θ is the angle between the sides with lengths a and b, then

$$c^2 = a^2 + b^2 - 2ab \cos \theta$$

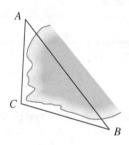

[*Hint:* Introduce a coordinate system so that θ is in standard position, as in the figure. Express x and y in terms of θ and then use the distance formula to compute c.]

42. In order to find the distance $|AB|$ across a small inlet, a point C was located as in the figure and the following measurements were recorded:

$$\angle C = 103° \qquad |AC| = 820 \text{ m} \qquad |BC| = 910 \text{ m}$$

Use the Law of Cosines from Exercise 41 to find the required distance.

43. Use the figure to prove the subtraction formula

$$\cos(\alpha - \beta) = \cos \alpha \, \cos \beta + \sin \alpha \, \sin \beta$$

[*Hint:* Compute c^2 in two ways (using the Law of Cosines from Exercise 41 and also using the distance formula) and compare the two expressions.]

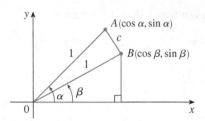

44. Use the formula in Exercise 43 to prove the addition formula for cosine (12b).

45. Use the addition formula for cosine and the identities

$$\cos\left(\frac{\pi}{2} - \theta\right) = \sin \theta \qquad \sin\left(\frac{\pi}{2} - \theta\right) = \cos \theta$$

to prove the subtraction formula (13a) for the sine function.

46. (a) Show that the area of a triangle with sides of lengths a and b and with included angle θ is

$$A = \tfrac{1}{2}ab \sin \theta$$

(b) Find the area of triangle ABC, correct to five decimal places, if

$$|AB| = 10 \text{ cm} \qquad |BC| = 3 \text{ cm} \qquad \angle ABC = 107°$$

D   Precise Definitions of Limits

The definitions of limits that have been given in this book are appropriate for intuitive understanding of the basic concepts of calculus. For the purposes of deeper understanding and rigorous proofs, however, the precise definitions of this appendix are necessary. In particular, the definition of a limit given here is used in Appendix E to prove that the limit of a sum is the sum of the limits.

When we say that $f(x)$ has a limit L as x approaches a, we mean, according to the intuitive definition in Section 2.2, that we can make $f(x)$ arbitrarily close to L by taking x close enough to a (but not equal to a). A more precise definition is based on the idea of specifying just how small we need to make the distance $|x - a|$ in order to make the distance $|f(x) - L|$ less than some given number. The following example illustrates the idea.

It is traditional to use the Greek letter δ (delta) in this situation.

EXAMPLE 1   Use a graph to find a number δ such that

$$\text{if} \qquad |x - 1| < \delta \qquad \text{then} \qquad |(x^3 - 5x + 6) - 2| < 0.2$$

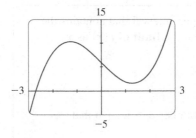

FIGURE 1

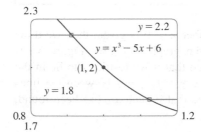

FIGURE 2

SOLUTION A graph of $f(x) = x^3 - 5x + 6$ is shown in Figure 1; we are interested in the region near the point $(1, 2)$. Notice that we can rewrite the inequality

$$|(x^3 - 5x + 6) - 2| < 0.2$$

as

$$1.8 < x^3 - 5x + 6 < 2.2$$

So we need to determine the values of x for which the curve $y = x^3 - 5x + 6$ lies between the horizontal lines $y = 1.8$ and $y = 2.2$. Therefore we graph the curves $y = x^3 - 5x + 6$, $y = 1.8$, and $y = 2.2$ near the point $(1, 2)$ in Figure 2. Then we use the cursor to estimate that the x-coordinate of the point of intersection of the line $y = 2.2$ and the curve $y = x^3 - 5x + 6$ is about 0.911. Similarly, $y = x^3 - 5x + 6$ intersects the line $y = 1.8$ when $x \approx 1.124$. So, rounding to be safe, we can say that

$$\text{if} \qquad 0.92 < x < 1.12 \qquad \text{then} \qquad 1.8 < x^3 - 5x + 6 < 2.2$$

This interval $(0.92, 1.12)$ is not symmetric about $x = 1$. The distance from $x = 1$ to the left endpoint is $1 - 0.92 = 0.08$ and the distance to the right endpoint is 0.12. We can choose δ to be the smaller of these numbers, that is, $\delta = 0.08$. Then we can rewrite our inequalities in terms of distances as follows:

$$\text{if} \qquad |x - 1| < 0.08 \qquad \text{then} \qquad |(x^3 - 5x + 6) - 2| < 0.2$$

This just says that by keeping x within 0.08 of 1, we are able to keep $f(x)$ within 0.2 of 2.

Although we chose $\delta = 0.08$, any smaller positive value of δ would also have worked.

Using the same graphical procedure as in Example 1, but replacing the number 0.2 by smaller numbers, we find that

$$\text{if} \qquad |x - 1| < 0.046 \qquad \text{then} \qquad |(x^3 - 5x + 6) - 2| < 0.1$$

$$\text{if} \qquad |x - 1| < 0.024 \qquad \text{then} \qquad |(x^3 - 5x + 6) - 2| < 0.05$$

$$\text{if} \qquad |x - 1| < 0.004 \qquad \text{then} \qquad |(x^3 - 5x + 6) - 2| < 0.01$$

In each case we have found a number δ such that the values of the function $f(x) = x^3 - 5x + 6$ lie in successively smaller intervals centered at 2 if the distance from x to 1 is less than δ. It turns out that it is always possible to find such a number δ, no matter how small the interval is. In other words, for *any* positive number ε, no matter how small, there exists a positive number δ such that

$$\text{if} \qquad |x - 1| < \delta \qquad \text{then} \qquad |(x^3 - 5x + 6) - 2| < \varepsilon$$

This indicates that

$$\lim_{x \to 1} (x^3 - 5x + 6) = 2$$

and suggests a more precise way of defining the limit of a general function.

The condition $0 < |x - a|$ is just another way of saying that $x \neq a$.

> **1**   **Definition**   Let f be a function defined on some open interval that contains the number a, except possibly at a itself. Then we say that the **limit of $f(x)$ as x approaches a is L**, and we write
>
> $$\lim_{x \to a} f(x) = L$$
>
> if for every number $\varepsilon > 0$ there is a corresponding number $\delta > 0$ such that
>
> $$\text{if} \quad 0 < |x - a| < \delta \quad \text{then} \quad |f(x) - L| < \varepsilon$$

Definition 1 is illustrated in Figures 3–5. If a number $\varepsilon > 0$ is given, then we draw the horizontal lines $y = L + \varepsilon$ and $y = L - \varepsilon$ and the graph of f. (See Figure 3.) If $\lim_{x \to a} f(x) = L$, then we can find a number $\delta > 0$ such that if we restrict x to lie in the interval $(a - \delta, a + \delta)$ and take $x \neq a$, then the curve $y = f(x)$ lies between the lines $y = L - \varepsilon$ and $y = L + \varepsilon$. (See Figure 4.) You can see that if such a δ has been found, then any smaller δ will also work.

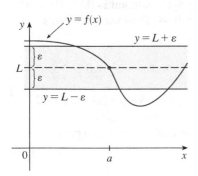

FIGURE 3

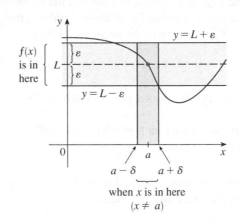

when x is in here
$(x \neq a)$

FIGURE 4

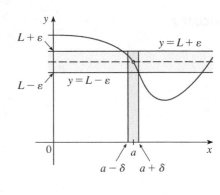

FIGURE 5

It's important to realize that the process illustrated in Figures 3 and 4 must work for *every* positive number ε no matter how small it is chosen. Figure 5 shows that if a smaller ε is chosen, then a smaller δ may be required.

EXAMPLE 2   Use the ε, δ definition to prove that $\lim_{x \to 0} x^2 = 0$.

SOLUTION   Let ε be a given positive number. According to Definition 1 with $a = 0$ and $L = 0$, we need to find a number δ such that

$$\text{if} \quad 0 < |x - 0| < \delta \quad \text{then} \quad |x^2 - 0| < \varepsilon$$

that is,

$$\text{if} \quad 0 < |x| < \delta \quad \text{then} \quad x^2 < \varepsilon$$

But, since the square root function is an increasing function, we know that

$$x^2 < \varepsilon \iff \sqrt{x^2} < \sqrt{\varepsilon} \iff |x| < \sqrt{\varepsilon}$$

So if we choose $\delta = \sqrt{\varepsilon}$, then $x^2 < \varepsilon \iff |x| < \delta$. (See Figure 6.) This shows that $\lim_{x \to 0} x^2 = 0$.

FIGURE 6

In proving limit statements it may be helpful to think of the definition of a limit as a challenge. First it challenges you with a number ε. Then you must be able to produce a suitable δ. You have to be able to do this for *every* $\varepsilon > 0$, not just a particular ε.

TEC In Module D you can explore the precise definition of a limit both graphically and numerically.

Imagine a contest between two people, A and B, and imagine yourself to be B. Person A stipulates that the fixed number L should be approximated by the values of $f(x)$ to within a degree of accuracy ε (say, 0.01). Person B then responds by finding a number δ such that $|f(x) - L| < \varepsilon$ whenever $0 < |x - a| < \delta$. Then A may become more exacting and challenge B with a smaller value of ε (say, 0.0001). Again B has to respond by finding a corresponding δ. Usually the smaller the value of ε, the smaller the corresponding value of δ must be. If B always wins, no matter how small A makes ε, then $\lim_{x \to a} f(x) = L$.

▼ **EXAMPLE 3** Prove that $\lim_{x \to 3} (4x - 5) = 7$.

SOLUTION

1. *Preliminary analysis of the problem (guessing a value for δ).* Let ε be a given positive number. We want to find a number δ such that

$$\text{if} \quad 0 < |x - 3| < \delta \quad \text{then} \quad |(4x - 5) - 7| < \varepsilon$$

But $|(4x - 5) - 7| = |4x - 12| = |4(x - 3)| = 4|x - 3|$. Therefore we want δ such that

$$\text{if} \quad 0 < |x - 3| < \delta \quad \text{then} \quad 4|x - 3| < \varepsilon$$

that is,

$$\text{if} \quad 0 < |x - 3| < \delta \quad \text{then} \quad |x - 3| < \frac{\varepsilon}{4}$$

This suggests that we should choose $\delta = \varepsilon/4$.

2. *Proof (showing that this δ works).* Given $\varepsilon > 0$, choose $\delta = \varepsilon/4$. If $0 < |x - 3| < \delta$, then

$$|(4x - 5) - 7| = |4x - 12| = 4|x - 3| < 4\delta = 4\left(\frac{\varepsilon}{4}\right) = \varepsilon$$

Thus

$$\text{if} \quad 0 < |x - 3| < \delta \quad \text{then} \quad |(4x - 5) - 7| < \varepsilon$$

Therefore, by the definition of a limit,

$$\lim_{x \to 3} (4x - 5) = 7$$

This example is illustrated by Figure 7.

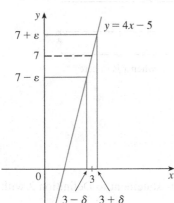

FIGURE 7

Note that in the solution of Example 3 there were two stages—guessing and proving. We made a preliminary analysis that enabled us to guess a value for δ. But then in the second stage we had to go back and prove in a careful, logical fashion that we had made a correct guess. This procedure is typical of much of mathematics. Sometimes it is necessary to first make an intelligent guess about the answer to a problem and then prove that the guess is correct.

It's not always easy to prove that limit statements are true using the ε, δ definition. For a more complicated function such as $f(x) = (6x^2 - 8x + 9)/(2x^2 - 1)$, a proof would require a great deal of ingenuity. Fortunately, this is not necessary because the Limit Laws stated in Section 2.3 can be proved using Definition 1, and then the limits of complicated functions can be found rigorously from the Limit Laws without resorting to the definition directly.

Limits at Infinity

Infinite limits and limits at infinity can also be defined in a precise way. The following is a precise version of Definition 4 in Section 2.5.

---

2 **Definition** Let f be a function defined on some interval (a, ∞). Then

$$\lim_{x \to \infty} f(x) = L$$

means that for every $\varepsilon > 0$ there is a corresponding number N such that

$$\text{if} \quad x > N \quad \text{then} \quad |f(x) - L| < \varepsilon$$

In words, this says that the values of $f(x)$ can be made arbitrarily close to L (within a distance ε, where ε is any positive number) by taking x sufficiently large (larger than N, where N depends on ε). Graphically it says that by choosing x large enough (larger than some number N) we can make the graph of f lie between the given horizontal lines $y = L - \varepsilon$ and $y = L + \varepsilon$ as in Figure 8. This must be true no matter how small we choose ε. If a smaller value of ε is chosen, then a larger value of N may be required.

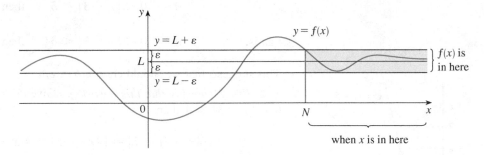

FIGURE 8
$\lim_{x \to \infty} f(x) = L$

In Example 5 in Section 2.5 we calculated that

$$\lim_{x \to \infty} \frac{3x^2 - x - 2}{5x^2 + 4x + 1} = \frac{3}{5}$$

In the next example we use a graphing device to relate this statement to Definition 2 with $L = \frac{3}{5}$ and $\varepsilon = 0.1$.

EXAMPLE 4 Use a graph to find a number N such that

$$\text{if} \quad x > N \quad \text{then} \quad \left| \frac{3x^2 - x - 2}{5x^2 + 4x + 1} - 0.6 \right| < 0.1$$

SOLUTION We rewrite the given inequality as

$$0.5 < \frac{3x^2 - x - 2}{5x^2 + 4x + 1} < 0.7$$

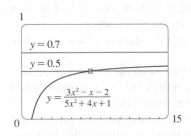

FIGURE 9

We need to determine the values of x for which the given curve lies between the horizontal lines $y = 0.5$ and $y = 0.7$. So we graph the curve and these lines in Figure 9. Then we use the cursor to estimate that the curve crosses the line $y = 0.5$ when $x \approx 6.7$. To the right of this number it seems that the curve stays between the lines $y = 0.5$ and $y = 0.7$. Rounding to be safe, we can say that

$$\text{if } \quad x > 7 \quad \text{then} \quad \left| \frac{3x^2 - x - 2}{5x^2 + 4x + 1} - 0.6 \right| < 0.1$$

In other words, for $\varepsilon = 0.1$ we can choose $N = 7$ (or any larger number) in Definition 2.

EXAMPLE 5 Use Definition 2 to prove that $\lim\limits_{x \to \infty} \dfrac{1}{x} = 0$.

SOLUTION Given $\varepsilon > 0$, we want to find N such that

$$\text{if } \quad x > N \quad \text{then} \quad \left| \frac{1}{x} - 0 \right| < \varepsilon$$

In computing the limit we may assume that $x > 0$. Then $1/x < \varepsilon \iff x > 1/\varepsilon$. Let's choose $N = 1/\varepsilon$. So

$$\text{if } \quad x > N = \frac{1}{\varepsilon} \quad \text{then} \quad \left| \frac{1}{x} - 0 \right| = \frac{1}{x} < \varepsilon$$

Therefore, by Definition 2,

$$\lim_{x \to \infty} \frac{1}{x} = 0$$

Figure 10 illustrates the proof by showing some values of ε and the corresponding values of N.

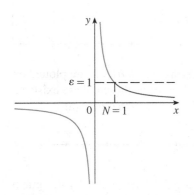

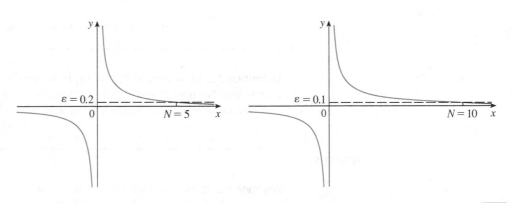

FIGURE 10

Infinite limits can also be formulated precisely. See Exercise 20.

Definite Integrals

In Section 5.2 we defined the definite integral of a function f on an interval $[a, b]$ as

$$\int_a^b f(x)\, dx = \lim_{n \to \infty} \sum_{i=1}^n f(x_i^*)\, \Delta x$$

where, at the nth stage, we have divided $[a, b]$ into n subintervals of equal width,

$\Delta x = (b - a)/n$, and x_i^* is any sample point in the ith subinterval. The precise meaning of this limit that defines the integral is as follows:

For every number $\varepsilon > 0$ there is an integer N such that

$$\left| \int_a^b f(x)\, dx - \sum_{i=1}^{n} f(x_i^*)\, \Delta x \right| < \varepsilon$$

for every integer $n > N$ and for every choice of x_i^* in the ith subinterval.

This means that a definite integral can be approximated to within any desired degree of accuracy by a Riemann sum.

Sequences

In Section 8.1 we used the notation

$$\lim_{n \to \infty} a_n = L$$

to mean that the terms of the sequence $\{a_n\}$ approach L as n becomes large. Notice that the following precise definition of the limit of a sequence is very similar to the definition of a limit of a function at infinity (Definition 2).

---

3 **Definition** A sequence $\{a_n\}$ has the **limit** L and we write

$$\lim_{n \to \infty} a_n = L \qquad \text{or} \qquad a_n \to L \text{ as } n \to \infty$$

if for every $\varepsilon > 0$ there is a corresponding integer N such that

$$\text{if} \quad n > N \quad \text{then} \quad |a_n - L| < \varepsilon$$

Definition 3 is illustrated by Figure 11, in which the terms $a_1, a_2, a_3, \ldots$ are plotted on a number line. No matter how small an interval $(L - \varepsilon, L + \varepsilon)$ is chosen, there exists an N such that all terms of the sequence from a_{N+1} onward must lie in that interval.

FIGURE 11

Another illustration of Definition 3 is given in Figure 12. The points on the graph of $\{a_n\}$ must lie between the horizontal lines $y = L + \varepsilon$ and $y = L - \varepsilon$ if $n > N$. This picture must be valid no matter how small ε is chosen, but usually a smaller ε requires a larger N.

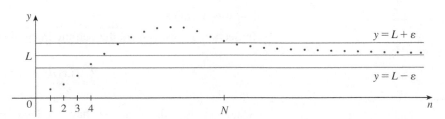

FIGURE 12

If you compare Definition 2 with Definition 3 you will see that the only difference between $\lim_{n \to \infty} a_n = L$ and $\lim_{x \to \infty} f(x) = L$ is that n is required to be an integer. The following definition shows how to make precise the idea that $\{a_n\}$ becomes infinite as n becomes infinite.

---

4 **Definition** The notation $\lim_{n \to \infty} a_n = \infty$ means that for every positive number M there is an integer N such that

$$\text{if} \quad n > N \quad \text{then} \quad a_n > M$$

EXAMPLE 6 Prove that $\lim_{n \to \infty} \sqrt{n} = \infty$.

SOLUTION Let M be any positive number. (Think of it as being very large.) Then

$$\sqrt{n} > M \quad \Longleftrightarrow \quad n > M^2$$

So if we take $N = M^2$, then Definition 4 shows that $\lim_{n \to \infty} \sqrt{n} = \infty$. ▬

Functions of Two Variables

Here is a precise version of Definition 1 in Section 11.2:

---

5 **Definition** Let f be a function of two variables whose domain D includes points arbitrarily close to (a, b). Then we say that the **limit of $f(x, y)$ as (x, y) approaches (a, b)** is L and we write

$$\lim_{(x, y) \to (a, b)} f(x, y) = L$$

if for every number $\varepsilon > 0$ there is a corresponding number $\delta > 0$ such that

$$\text{if} \quad (x, y) \in D \quad \text{and} \quad 0 < \sqrt{(x - a)^2 + (y - b)^2} < \delta \quad \text{then} \quad |f(x, y) - L| < \varepsilon$$

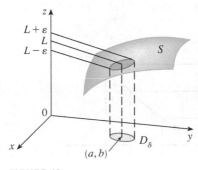

FIGURE 13

Notice that $|f(x, y) - L|$ is the distance between the numbers $f(x, y)$ and L, and $\sqrt{(x - a)^2 + (y - b)^2}$ is the distance between the point (x, y) and the point (a, b). Thus Definition 5 says that the distance between $f(x, y)$ and L can be made arbitrarily small by making the distance from (x, y) to (a, b) sufficiently small (but not 0). An illustration of Definition 5 is given in Figure 13 where the surface S is the graph of f. If $\varepsilon > 0$ is given, we can find $\delta > 0$ such that if (x, y) is restricted to lie in the disk D_δ with center (a, b) and radius δ, and if $(x, y) \neq (a, b)$, then the corresponding part of S lies between the horizontal planes $z = L - \varepsilon$ and $z = L + \varepsilon$.

EXAMPLE 7 Prove that $\lim_{(x, y) \to (0, 0)} \dfrac{3x^2 y}{x^2 + y^2} = 0$.

SOLUTION Let $\varepsilon > 0$. We want to find $\delta > 0$ such that

$$\text{if} \quad 0 < \sqrt{x^2 + y^2} < \delta \quad \text{then} \quad \left| \frac{3x^2 y}{x^2 + y^2} - 0 \right| < \varepsilon$$

that is,   if $0 < \sqrt{x^2 + y^2} < \delta$ then $\dfrac{3x^2|y|}{x^2 + y^2} < \varepsilon$

But $x^2 \leqslant x^2 + y^2$ since $y^2 \geqslant 0$, so $x^2/(x^2 + y^2) \leqslant 1$ and therefore

$$\frac{3x^2|y|}{x^2 + y^2} \leqslant 3|y| = 3\sqrt{y^2} \leqslant 3\sqrt{x^2 + y^2}$$

Thus if we choose $\delta = \varepsilon/3$ and let $0 < \sqrt{x^2 + y^2} < \delta$, then

$$\left| \frac{3x^2 y}{x^2 + y^2} - 0 \right| \leqslant 3\sqrt{x^2 + y^2} < 3\delta = 3\left(\frac{\varepsilon}{3}\right) = \varepsilon$$

Hence, by Definition 5,

$$\lim_{(x, y) \to (0, 0)} \frac{3x^2 y}{x^2 + y^2} = 0$$

D   Exercises

1. Use the given graph of $f(x) = 1/x$ to find a number δ such that

if $|x - 2| < \delta$ then $\left| \dfrac{1}{x} - 0.5 \right| < 0.2$

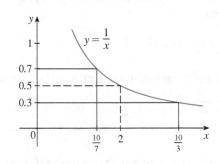

2. Use the given graph of f to find a number δ such that

if $0 < |x - 5| < \delta$ then $|f(x) - 3| < 0.6$

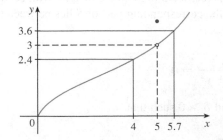

3. Use the given graph of $f(x) = \sqrt{x}$ to find a number δ such that

if $|x - 4| < \delta$ then $|\sqrt{x} - 2| < 0.4$

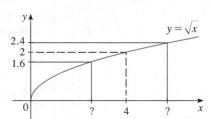

4. Use the given graph of $f(x) = x^2$ to find a number δ such that

if $|x - 1| < \delta$ then $|x^2 - 1| < \frac{1}{2}$

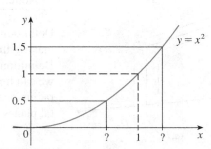

5. Use a graph to find a number δ such that

if $\left| x - \dfrac{\pi}{4} \right| < \delta$ then $|\tan x - 1| < 0.2$

Graphing calculator or computer with graphing software required   **1.** Homework Hints available in TEC

6. Use a graph to find a number δ such that

$$\text{if} \quad |x - 1| < \delta \quad \text{then} \quad \left| \frac{2x}{x^2 + 4} - 0.4 \right| < 0.1$$

7. For the limit

$$\lim_{x \to 1} (4 + x - 3x^3) = 2$$

illustrate Definition 1 by finding values of δ that correspond to $\varepsilon = 1$ and $\varepsilon = 0.1$.

8. For the limit

$$\lim_{x \to 0} \frac{e^x - 1}{x} = 1$$

illustrate Definition 1 by finding values of δ that correspond to $\varepsilon = 0.5$ and $\varepsilon = 0.1$.

9. Use Definition 1 to prove that $\lim_{x \to 0} x^3 = 0$.

10. (a) How would you formulate an ε, δ definition of the one-sided limit $\lim_{x \to a^-} f(x) = L$?
(b) Use your definition in part (a) to prove that $\lim_{x \to 0^+} \sqrt{x} = 0$.

11. A machinist is required to manufacture a circular metal disk with area 1000 cm^2.
(a) What radius produces such a disk?
(b) If the machinist is allowed an error tolerance of ± 5 cm^2 in the area of the disk, how close to the ideal radius in part (a) must the machinist control the radius?
(c) In terms of the ε, δ definition of $\lim_{x \to a} f(x) = L$, what is x? What is $f(x)$? What is a? What is L? What value of ε is given? What is the corresponding value of δ?

12. A crystal growth furnace is used in research to determine how best to manufacture crystals used in electronic components for the space shuttle. For proper growth of the crystal, the temperature must be controlled accurately by adjusting the input power. Suppose the relationship is given by

$$T(w) = 0.1w^2 + 2.155w + 20$$

where T is the temperature in degrees Celsius and w is the power input in watts.
(a) How much power is needed to maintain the temperature at 200°C?
(b) If the temperature is allowed to vary from 200°C by up to ± 1°C, what range of wattage is allowed for the input power?
(c) In terms of the ε, δ definition of $\lim_{x \to a} f(x) = L$, what is x? What is $f(x)$? What is a? What is L? What value of ε is given? What is the corresponding value of δ?

13. (a) Find a number δ such that if $|x - 2| < \delta$, then $|4x - 8| < \varepsilon$, where $\varepsilon = 0.1$.
(b) Repeat part (a) with $\varepsilon = 0.01$.

14. Given that $\lim_{x \to 2} (5x - 7) = 3$, illustrate Definition 1 by finding values of δ that correspond to $\varepsilon = 0.1$, $\varepsilon = 0.05$, and $\varepsilon = 0.01$.

15–16 Prove the statement using the ε, δ definition of a limit and illustrate with a diagram like Figure 7.

15. $\lim_{x \to -3} (1 - 4x) = 13$ **16.** $\lim_{x \to -2} \left(\tfrac{1}{2}x + 3\right) = 2$

17. Use a graph to find a number N such that

$$\text{if} \quad x > N \quad \text{then} \quad \left| \frac{6x^2 + 5x - 3}{2x^2 - 1} - 3 \right| < 0.2$$

18. For the limit

$$\lim_{x \to \infty} \frac{\sqrt{4x^2 + 1}}{x + 1} = 2$$

illustrate Definition 2 by finding values of N that correspond to $\varepsilon = 0.5$ and $\varepsilon = 0.1$.

19. (a) Determine how large we have to take x so that

$$1/x^2 < 0.0001$$

(b) Use Definition 2 to prove that

$$\lim_{x \to \infty} \frac{1}{x^2} = 0$$

20. (a) For what values of x is it true that

$$\frac{1}{x^2} > 1{,}000{,}000$$

(b) The precise definition of $\lim_{x \to a} f(x) = \infty$ states that for every positive number M (no matter how large) there is a corresponding positive number δ such that if $0 < |x - a| < \delta$, then $f(x) > M$. Use this definition to prove that $\lim_{x \to 0} (1/x^2) = \infty$.

21. (a) Use a graph to guess the value of the limit

$$\lim_{n \to \infty} \frac{n^5}{n!}$$

(b) Use a graph of the sequence in part (a) to find the smallest values of N that correspond to $\varepsilon = 0.1$ and $\varepsilon = 0.001$ in Definition 3.

22. Use Definition 3 to prove that $\lim_{n \to \infty} r^n = 0$ when $|r| < 1$.

23. Use Definition 3 to prove that if $\lim_{n \to \infty} |a_n| = 0$, then $\lim_{n \to \infty} a_n = 0$.

24. Use Definition 4 to prove that $\lim_{n \to \infty} n^3 = \infty$.

25. Use Definition 5 to prove that $\lim_{(x, y) \to (0, 0)} \frac{xy}{\sqrt{x^2 + y^2}} = 0$.

E | A Few Proofs

In this appendix we present proofs of some theorems that were stated in the main body of the text. We start by proving the Triangle Inequality, which is an important property of absolute value.

The Triangle Inequality If a and b are any real numbers, then

$$|a + b| \leq |a| + |b|$$

Observe that if the numbers a and b are both positive or both negative, then the two sides in the Triangle Inequality are actually equal. But if a and b have opposite signs, the left side involves a subtraction and the right side does not. This makes the Triangle Inequality seem reasonable, but we can prove it as follows.

Notice that

$$-|a| \leq a \leq |a|$$

is always true because a equals either $|a|$ or $-|a|$. The corresponding statement for b is

$$-|b| \leq b \leq |b|$$

Adding these inequalities, we get

$$-(|a| + |b|) \leq a + b \leq |a| + |b|$$

When combined, Properties 4 and 5 of absolute value (see Appendix A) say that

$$|x| \leq a \iff -a \leq x \leq a$$

If we now apply Properties 4 and 5 of absolute value from Appendix A (with x replaced by $a + b$ and a by $|a| + |b|$), we obtain

$$|a + b| \leq |a| + |b|$$

which is what we wanted to show.

Next we use the Triangle Inequality to prove the Sum Law for limits.

The Sum Law was first stated in Section 2.3.

Sum Law If $\lim_{x \to a} f(x) = L$ and $\lim_{x \to a} g(x) = M$ both exist, then

$$\lim_{x \to a} [f(x) + g(x)] = L + M$$

PROOF Let $\varepsilon > 0$ be given. According to Definition 1 in Appendix D, we must find $\delta > 0$ such that

$$\text{if} \quad 0 < |x - a| < \delta \quad \text{then} \quad |f(x) + g(x) - (L + M)| < \varepsilon$$

Using the Triangle Inequality we can write

$$\boxed{1} \qquad |f(x) + g(x) - (L + M)| = |(f(x) - L) + (g(x) - M)|$$
$$\leq |f(x) - L| + |g(x) - M|$$

We will make $|f(x) + g(x) - (L + M)|$ less than ε by making each of the terms $|f(x) - L|$ and $|g(x) - M|$ less than $\varepsilon/2$.

Since $\varepsilon/2 > 0$ and $\lim_{x \to a} f(x) = L$, there exists a number $\delta_1 > 0$ such that

$$\text{if} \quad 0 < |x - a| < \delta_1 \quad \text{then} \quad |f(x) - L| < \frac{\varepsilon}{2}$$

Similarly, since $\lim_{x \to a} g(x) = M$, there exists a number $\delta_2 > 0$ such that

$$\text{if} \quad 0 < |x - a| < \delta_2 \quad \text{then} \quad |g(x) - M| < \frac{\varepsilon}{2}$$

Let $\delta = \min\{\delta_1, \delta_2\}$, the smaller of the numbers δ_1 and δ_2. Notice that

$$\text{if} \quad 0 < |x - a| < \delta \quad \text{then} \quad 0 < |x - a| < \delta_1 \quad \text{and} \quad 0 < |x - a| < \delta_2$$

and so

$$|f(x) - L| < \frac{\varepsilon}{2} \quad \text{and} \quad |g(x) - M| < \frac{\varepsilon}{2}$$

Therefore, by (1),

$$|f(x) + g(x) - (L + M)| \leq |f(x) - L| + |g(x) - M|$$

$$< \frac{\varepsilon}{2} + \frac{\varepsilon}{2} = \varepsilon$$

To summarize,

$$\text{if} \quad 0 < |x - a| < \delta \quad \text{then} \quad |f(x) + g(x) - (L + M)| < \varepsilon$$

Thus, by the definition of a limit,

$$\lim_{x \to a} [f(x) + g(x)] = L + M$$

Fermat's Theorem was discussed in
Section 4.2.

Fermat's Theorem If f has a local maximum or minimum at c, and if $f'(c)$ exists, then $f'(c) = 0$.

PROOF Suppose, for the sake of definiteness, that f has a local maximum at c. Then, $f(c) \geq f(x)$ if x is sufficiently close to c. This implies that if h is sufficiently close to 0, with h being positive or negative, then

$$f(c) \geq f(c + h)$$

and therefore

$$f(c + h) - f(c) \leq 0$$

We can divide both sides of an inequality by a positive number. Thus, if $h > 0$ and h is sufficiently small, we have

$$\frac{f(c + h) - f(c)}{h} \leq 0$$

Taking the right-hand limit of both sides of this inequality (using Theorem 2.3.2), we get

$$\lim_{h \to 0^+} \frac{f(c + h) - f(c)}{h} \leq \lim_{h \to 0^+} 0 = 0$$

But since $f'(c)$ exists, we have

$$f'(c) = \lim_{h \to 0} \frac{f(c + h) - f(c)}{h} = \lim_{h \to 0^+} \frac{f(c + h) - f(c)}{h}$$

and so we have shown that $f'(c) \leq 0$.

If $h < 0$, then the direction of the inequality (2) is reversed when we divide by h:

$$\frac{f(c + h) - f(c)}{h} \geq 0 \qquad h < 0$$

So, taking the left-hand limit, we have

$$f'(c) = \lim_{h \to 0} \frac{f(c + h) - f(c)}{h} = \lim_{h \to 0^-} \frac{f(c + h) - f(c)}{h} \geq 0$$

We have shown that $f'(c) \geq 0$ and also that $f'(c) \leq 0$. Since both of these inequalities must be true, the only possibility is that $f'(c) = 0$.

We have proved Fermat's Theorem for the case of a local maximum. The case of a local minimum can be proved in a similar manner.

This theorem was stated and used in Section 8.1.

Theorem   If $\lim_{n \to \infty} a_n = L$ and the function f is continuous at L, then

$$\lim_{n \to \infty} f(a_n) = f(L)$$

PROOF   We must show that, given a number $\varepsilon > 0$, there is an integer N such that if $n > N$, then $|f(a_n) - f(L)| < \varepsilon$.

Suppose $\varepsilon > 0$. Since f is continuous at L, there is a number $\delta > 0$ such that if $|x - L| < \delta$, then $|f(x) - f(L)| < \varepsilon$. Because $\lim_{n \to \infty} a_n = L$, there is an integer N such that if $n > N$, then $|a_n - L| < \delta$. Suppose $n > N$. Then $|a_n - L| < \delta$ and so $|f(a_n) - f(L)| < \varepsilon$.

This shows that $\lim_{n \to \infty} f(a_n) = f(L)$.

Clairaut's Theorem was discussed in Section 11.3.

Clairaut's Theorem   Suppose f is defined on a disk D that contains the point (a, b). If the functions f_{xy} and f_{yx} are both continuous on D, then $f_{xy}(a, b) = f_{yx}(a, b)$.

PROOF   For small values of h, $h \neq 0$, consider the difference

$$\Delta(h) = [f(a + h, b + h) - f(a + h, b)] - [f(a, b + h) - f(a, b)]$$

Notice that if we let $g(x) = f(x, b + h) - f(x, b)$, then

$$\Delta(h) = g(a + h) - g(a)$$

By the Mean Value Theorem, there is a number c between a and $a + h$ such that

$$g(a + h) - g(a) = g'(c)h = h[f_x(c, b + h) - f_x(c, b)]$$

Applying the Mean Value Theorem again, this time to f_x, we get a number d between b and $b + h$ such that

$$f_x(c, b + h) - f_x(c, b) = f_{xy}(c, d)h$$

Combining these equations, we obtain

$$\Delta(h) = h^2 f_{xy}(c, d)$$

If $h \to 0$, then $(c, d) \to (a, b)$, so the continuity of f_{xy} at (a, b) gives

$$\lim_{h \to 0} \frac{\Delta(h)}{h^2} = \lim_{(c, d) \to (a, b)} f_{xy}(c, d) = f_{xy}(a, b)$$

Similarly, by writing

$$\Delta(h) = [f(a + h, b + h) - f(a, b + h)] - [f(a + h, b) - f(a, b)]$$

and using the Mean Value Theorem twice and the continuity of f_{yx} at (a, b), we obtain

$$\lim_{h \to 0} \frac{\Delta(h)}{h^2} = f_{yx}(a, b)$$

It follows that $f_{xy}(a, b) = f_{yx}(a, b)$. ▯

This was stated as Theorem 8 in Section 11.4.

> **Theorem** If the partial derivatives f_x and f_y exist near (a, b) and are continuous at (a, b), then f is differentiable at (a, b).

PROOF Let

$$\Delta z = f(a + \Delta x, b + \Delta y) - f(a, b)$$

According to (11.4.7), to prove that f is differentiable at (a, b) we have to show that we can write Δz in the form

$$\Delta z = f_x(a, b)\,\Delta x + f_y(a, b)\,\Delta y + \varepsilon_1\,\Delta x + \varepsilon_2\,\Delta y$$

where ε_1 and $\varepsilon_2 \to 0$ as $(\Delta x, \Delta y) \to (0, 0)$.

Referring to Figure 1, we write

$$\boxed{3} \quad \Delta z = [f(a + \Delta x, b + \Delta y) - f(a, b + \Delta y)] + [f(a, b + \Delta y) - f(a, b)]$$

Observe that the function of a single variable

$$g(x) = f(x, b + \Delta y)$$

is defined on the interval $[a, a + \Delta x]$ and $g'(x) = f_x(x, b + \Delta y)$. If we apply the Mean Value Theorem to g, we get

$$g(a + \Delta x) - g(a) = g'(u)\,\Delta x$$

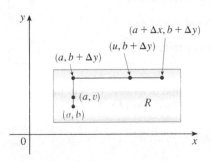

FIGURE 1

where u is some number between a and $a + \Delta x$. In terms of f, this equation becomes

$$f(a + \Delta x, b + \Delta y) - f(a, b + \Delta y) = f_x(u, b + \Delta y)\,\Delta x$$

This gives us an expression for the first part of the right side of Equation 3. For the second part we let $h(y) = f(a, y)$. Then h is a function of a single variable defined on the interval $[b, b + \Delta y]$ and $h'(y) = f_y(a, y)$. A second application of the Mean Value Theorem then gives

$$h(b + \Delta y) - h(b) = h'(v)\,\Delta y$$

where v is some number between b and $b + \Delta y$. In terms of f, this becomes

$$f(a, b + \Delta y) - f(a, b) = f_y(a, v)\,\Delta y$$

We now substitute these expressions into Equation 3 and obtain

$$\Delta z = f_x(u, b + \Delta y)\,\Delta x + f_y(a, v)\,\Delta y$$
$$= f_x(a, b)\,\Delta x + [f_x(u, b + \Delta y) - f_x(a, b)]\,\Delta x + f_y(a, b)\,\Delta y$$
$$+ [f_y(a, v) - f_y(a, b)]\,\Delta y$$
$$= f_x(a, b)\,\Delta x + f_y(a, b)\,\Delta y + \varepsilon_1\,\Delta x + \varepsilon_2\,\Delta y$$

where
$$\varepsilon_1 = f_x(u, b + \Delta y) - f_x(a, b)$$
$$\varepsilon_2 = f_y(a, v) - f_y(a, b)$$

Since $(u, b + \Delta y) \to (a, b)$ and $(a, v) \to (a, b)$ as $(\Delta x, \Delta y) \to (0, 0)$ and since f_x and f_y are continuous at (a, b), we see that $\varepsilon_1 \to 0$ and $\varepsilon_2 \to 0$ as $(\Delta x, \Delta y) \to (0, 0)$.

Therefore f is differentiable at (a, b).

The Second Derivatives Test was discussed in Section 11.7. Parts (b) and (c) have similar proofs.

Second Derivatives Test Suppose the second partial derivatives of f are continuous on a disk with center (a, b), and suppose that $f_x(a, b) = 0$ and $f_y(a, b) = 0$ [that is, (a, b) is a critical point of f]. Let

$$D = D(a, b) = f_{xx}(a, b)f_{yy}(a, b) - [f_{xy}(a, b)]^2$$

(a) If $D > 0$ and $f_{xx}(a, b) > 0$, then $f(a, b)$ is a local minimum.

(b) If $D > 0$ and $f_{xx}(a, b) < 0$, then $f(a, b)$ is a local maximum.

(c) If $D < 0$, then $f(a, b)$ is not a local maximum or minimum.

PROOF OF PART (A) We compute the second-order directional derivative of f in the direction of $\mathbf{u} = \langle h, k \rangle$. The first-order derivative is given by Theorem 11.6.3:

$$D_{\mathbf{u}}f = f_x h + f_y k$$

Applying this theorem a second time, we have

$$D_{\mathbf{u}}^2 f = D_{\mathbf{u}}(D_{\mathbf{u}} f) = \frac{\partial}{\partial x}(D_{\mathbf{u}} f)h + \frac{\partial}{\partial y}(D_{\mathbf{u}} f)k$$

$$= (f_{xx}h + f_{yx}k)h + (f_{xy}h + f_{yy}k)k$$

$$= f_{xx}h^2 + 2f_{xy}hk + f_{yy}k^2 \qquad \text{(by Clairaut's Theorem)}$$

If we complete the square in this expression, we obtain

$$\boxed{4} \qquad D_{\mathbf{u}}^2 f = f_{xx}\left(h + \frac{f_{xy}}{f_{xx}}k\right)^2 + \frac{k^2}{f_{xx}}(f_{xx}f_{yy} - f_{xy}^2)$$

We are given that $f_{xx}(a, b) > 0$ and $D(a, b) > 0$. But f_{xx} and $D = f_{xx}f_{yy} - f_{xy}^2$ are continuous functions, so there is a disk B with center (a, b) and radius $\delta > 0$ such that $f_{xx}(x, y) > 0$ and $D(x, y) > 0$ whenever (x, y) is in B. Therefore, by looking at Equation 4, we see that $D_{\mathbf{u}}^2 f(x, y) > 0$ whenever (x, y) is in B. This means that if C is the curve obtained by intersecting the graph of f with the vertical plane through $P(a, b, f(a, b))$ in the direction of $\mathbf{u}$, then C is concave upward on an interval of length 2δ. This is true in the direction of every vector $\mathbf{u}$, so if we restrict (x, y) to lie in B, the graph of f lies above its horizontal tangent plane at P. Thus $f(x, y) \geq f(a, b)$ whenever (x, y) is in B. This shows that $f(a, b)$ is a local minimum.

F | Sigma Notation

A convenient way of writing sums uses the Greek letter Σ (capital sigma, corresponding to our letter S) and is called **sigma notation**.

This tells us to end with $i = n$.

This tells us to add. $\longrightarrow \displaystyle\sum_{i=m}^{n} a_i$

This tells us to start with $i = m$.

$\boxed{1}$ **Definition** If $a_m, a_{m+1}, \ldots, a_n$ are real numbers and m and n are integers such that $m \leq n$, then

$$\sum_{i=m}^{n} a_i = a_m + a_{m+1} + a_{m+2} + \cdots + a_{n-1} + a_n$$

With function notation, Definition 1 can be written as

$$\sum_{i=m}^{n} f(i) = f(m) + f(m + 1) + f(m + 2) + \cdots + f(n - 1) + f(n)$$

Thus the symbol $\sum_{i=m}^{n}$ indicates a summation in which the letter i (called the **index of summation**) takes on consecutive integer values beginning with m and ending with n, that is, $m, m + 1, \ldots, n$. Other letters can also be used as the index of summation.

EXAMPLE 1

(a) $\displaystyle\sum_{i=1}^{4} i^2 = 1^2 + 2^2 + 3^2 + 4^2 = 30$

(b) $\displaystyle\sum_{i=3}^{n} i = 3 + 4 + 5 + \cdots + (n-1) + n$

(c) $\displaystyle\sum_{j=0}^{5} 2^j = 2^0 + 2^1 + 2^2 + 2^3 + 2^4 + 2^5 = 63$

(d) $\displaystyle\sum_{k=1}^{n} \frac{1}{k} = 1 + \frac{1}{2} + \frac{1}{3} + \cdots + \frac{1}{n}$

(e) $\displaystyle\sum_{i=1}^{3} \frac{i-1}{i^2+3} = \frac{1-1}{1^2+3} + \frac{2-1}{2^2+3} + \frac{3-1}{3^2+3} = 0 + \frac{1}{7} + \frac{1}{6} = \frac{13}{42}$

(f) $\displaystyle\sum_{i=1}^{4} 2 = 2 + 2 + 2 + 2 = 8$

EXAMPLE 2 Write the sum $2^3 + 3^3 + \cdots + n^3$ in sigma notation.

SOLUTION There is no unique way of writing a sum in sigma notation. We could write

$$2^3 + 3^3 + \cdots + n^3 = \sum_{i=2}^{n} i^3$$

or

$$2^3 + 3^3 + \cdots + n^3 = \sum_{j=1}^{n-1} (j+1)^3$$

or

$$2^3 + 3^3 + \cdots + n^3 = \sum_{k=0}^{n-2} (k+2)^3$$

The following theorem gives three simple rules for working with sigma notation.

---

2 Theorem If c is any constant (that is, it does not depend on i), then

(a) $\displaystyle\sum_{i=m}^{n} ca_i = c \sum_{i=m}^{n} a_i$ (b) $\displaystyle\sum_{i=m}^{n} (a_i + b_i) = \sum_{i=m}^{n} a_i + \sum_{i=m}^{n} b_i$

(c) $\displaystyle\sum_{i=m}^{n} (a_i - b_i) = \sum_{i=m}^{n} a_i - \sum_{i=m}^{n} b_i$

PROOF To see why these rules are true, all we have to do is write both sides in expanded form. Rule (a) is just the distributive property of real numbers:

$$ca_m + ca_{m+1} + \cdots + ca_n = c(a_m + a_{m+1} + \cdots + a_n)$$

Rule (b) follows from the associative and commutative properties:

$$(a_m + b_m) + (a_{m+1} + b_{m+1}) + \cdots + (a_n + b_n)$$

$$= (a_m + a_{m+1} + \cdots + a_n) + (b_m + b_{m+1} + \cdots + b_n)$$

Rule (c) is proved similarly.

EXAMPLE 3 Find $\displaystyle\sum_{i=1}^{n} 1$.

SOLUTION
$$\sum_{i=1}^{n} 1 = \underbrace{1 + 1 + \cdots + 1}_{n \text{ terms}} = n$$

EXAMPLE 4 Prove the formula for the sum of the first n positive integers:

$$\sum_{i=1}^{n} i = 1 + 2 + 3 + \cdots + n = \frac{n(n+1)}{2}$$

SOLUTION This formula can be proved by mathematical induction (see page 84) or by the following method used by the German mathematician Karl Friedrich Gauss (1777–1855) when he was ten years old.

Write the sum S twice, once in the usual order and once in reverse order:

$$S = 1 + \quad 2 \quad + \quad 3 \quad + \cdots + (n-1) + n$$

$$S = n + (n-1) + (n-2) + \cdots + \quad 2 \quad + 1$$

Adding all columns vertically, we get

$$2S = (n+1) + (n+1) + (n+1) + \cdots + (n+1) + (n+1)$$

On the right side there are n terms, each of which is $n+1$, so

$$2S = n(n+1) \qquad \text{or} \qquad S = \frac{n(n+1)}{2}$$

EXAMPLE 5 Prove the formula for the sum of the squares of the first n positive integers:

$$\sum_{i=1}^{n} i^2 = 1^2 + 2^2 + 3^2 + \cdots + n^2 = \frac{n(n+1)(2n+1)}{6}$$

SOLUTION 1 Let S be the desired sum. We start with the *telescoping sum* (or collapsing sum):

Most terms cancel in pairs.

$$\sum_{i=1}^{n} [(1+i)^3 - i^3] = (2^3 - 1^3) + (3^3 - 2^3) + (4^3 - 3^3) + \cdots + [(n+1)^3 - n^3]$$

$$= (n+1)^3 - 1^3 = n^3 + 3n^2 + 3n$$

On the other hand, using Theorem 2 and Examples 3 and 4, we have

$$\sum_{i=1}^{n} [(1+i)^3 - i^3] = \sum_{i=1}^{n} [3i^2 + 3i + 1] = 3\sum_{i=1}^{n} i^2 + 3\sum_{i=1}^{n} i + \sum_{i=1}^{n} 1$$

$$= 3S + 3 \frac{n(n+1)}{2} + n = 3S + \tfrac{3}{2}n^2 + \tfrac{5}{2}n$$

Thus we have

$$n^3 + 3n^2 + 3n = 3S + \tfrac{3}{2}n^2 + \tfrac{5}{2}n$$

Solving this equation for S, we obtain

$$3S = n^3 + \tfrac{3}{2}n^2 + \tfrac{1}{2}n$$

or

$$S = \frac{2n^3 + 3n^2 + n}{6} = \frac{n(n + 1)(2n + 1)}{6}$$

Principle of Mathematical Induction

Let S_n be a statement involving the positive integer n. Suppose that

1. S_1 is true.

2. If S_k is true, then S_{k+1} is true.

Then S_n is true for all positive integers n.

See pages 84 and 87 for a more thorough discussion of mathematical induction.

SOLUTION 2 Let S_n be the given formula.

1. S_1 is true because

$$1^2 = \frac{1(1 + 1)(2 \cdot 1 + 1)}{6}$$

2. Assume that S_k is true; that is,

$$1^2 + 2^2 + 3^2 + \cdots + k^2 = \frac{k(k + 1)(2k + 1)}{6}$$

Then

$$
\begin{aligned}
1^2 + 2^2 + 3^2 + \cdots + (k + 1)^2 &= (1^2 + 2^2 + 3^2 + \cdots + k^2) + (k + 1)^2 \\
&= \frac{k(k + 1)(2k + 1)}{6} + (k + 1)^2 \\
&= (k + 1)\frac{k(2k + 1) + 6(k + 1)}{6} \\
&= (k + 1)\frac{2k^2 + 7k + 6}{6} \\
&= \frac{(k + 1)(k + 2)(2k + 3)}{6} \\
&= \frac{(k + 1)[(k + 1) + 1][2(k + 1) + 1]}{6}
\end{aligned}
$$

So S_{k+1} is true.

By the Principle of Mathematical Induction, S_n is true for all n.

We list the results of Examples 3, 4, and 5 together with a similar result for cubes (see Exercises 37–40) as Theorem 3. These formulas are needed for finding areas and evaluating integrals in Chapter 5.

---

3 **Theorem** Let c be a constant and n a positive integer. Then

(a) $\displaystyle\sum_{i=1}^{n} 1 = n$

(b) $\displaystyle\sum_{i=1}^{n} c = nc$

(c) $\displaystyle\sum_{i=1}^{n} i = \frac{n(n + 1)}{2}$

(d) $\displaystyle\sum_{i=1}^{n} i^2 = \frac{n(n + 1)(2n + 1)}{6}$

(e) $\displaystyle\sum_{i=1}^{n} i^3 = \left[\frac{n(n + 1)}{2}\right]^2$

EXAMPLE 6 Evaluate $\displaystyle\sum_{i=1}^{n} i(4i^2 - 3)$.

SOLUTION Using Theorems 2 and 3, we have

$$\sum_{i=1}^{n} i(4i^2 - 3) = \sum_{i=1}^{n} (4i^3 - 3i) = 4\sum_{i=1}^{n} i^3 - 3\sum_{i=1}^{n} i$$

$$= 4\left[\frac{n(n+1)}{2}\right]^2 - 3\,\frac{n(n+1)}{2}$$

$$= \frac{n(n+1)[2n(n+1) - 3]}{2}$$

$$= \frac{n(n+1)(2n^2 + 2n - 3)}{2}$$

The type of calculation in Example 7 arises in Chapter 5 when we compute areas.

EXAMPLE 7 Find $\displaystyle\lim_{n\to\infty} \sum_{i=1}^{n} \frac{3}{n}\left[\left(\frac{i}{n}\right)^2 + 1\right]$.

SOLUTION

$$\lim_{n\to\infty} \sum_{i=1}^{n} \frac{3}{n}\left[\left(\frac{i}{n}\right)^2 + 1\right] = \lim_{n\to\infty} \sum_{i=1}^{n} \left[\frac{3}{n^3} i^2 + \frac{3}{n}\right]$$

$$= \lim_{n\to\infty} \left[\frac{3}{n^3} \sum_{i=1}^{n} i^2 + \frac{3}{n} \sum_{i=1}^{n} 1\right]$$

$$= \lim_{n\to\infty} \left[\frac{3}{n^3}\,\frac{n(n+1)(2n+1)}{6} + \frac{3}{n}\cdot n\right]$$

$$= \lim_{n\to\infty} \left[\frac{1}{2}\cdot\frac{n}{n}\cdot\left(\frac{n+1}{n}\right)\left(\frac{2n+1}{n}\right) + 3\right]$$

$$= \lim_{n\to\infty} \left[\frac{1}{2}\cdot 1\left(1 + \frac{1}{n}\right)\left(2 + \frac{1}{n}\right) + 3\right]$$

$$= \tfrac{1}{2}\cdot 1\cdot 1\cdot 2 + 3 = 4$$

F Exercises

1–10 Write the sum in expanded form.

1. $\displaystyle\sum_{i=1}^{5} \sqrt{i}$

2. $\displaystyle\sum_{i=1}^{6} \frac{1}{i+1}$

3. $\displaystyle\sum_{i=4}^{6} 3^i$

4. $\displaystyle\sum_{i=4}^{6} i^3$

5. $\displaystyle\sum_{k=0}^{4} \frac{2k-1}{2k+1}$

6. $\displaystyle\sum_{k=5}^{8} x^k$

7. $\displaystyle\sum_{i=1}^{n} i^{10}$

8. $\displaystyle\sum_{j=n}^{n+3} j^2$

9. $\displaystyle\sum_{j=0}^{n-1} (-1)^j$

10. $\displaystyle\sum_{i=1}^{n} f(x_i)\,\Delta x_i$

11–20 Write the sum in sigma notation.

11. $1 + 2 + 3 + 4 + \cdots + 10$

12. $\sqrt{3} + \sqrt{4} + \sqrt{5} + \sqrt{6} + \sqrt{7}$

13. $\frac{1}{2} + \frac{2}{3} + \frac{3}{4} + \frac{4}{5} + \cdots + \frac{19}{20}$

14. $\frac{3}{7} + \frac{4}{8} + \frac{5}{9} + \frac{6}{10} + \cdots + \frac{23}{27}$

15. $2 + 4 + 6 + 8 + \cdots + 2n$

16. $1 + 3 + 5 + 7 + \cdots + (2n - 1)$

17. $1 + 2 + 4 + 8 + 16 + 32$

18. $\frac{1}{1} + \frac{1}{4} + \frac{1}{9} + \frac{1}{16} + \frac{1}{25} + \frac{1}{36}$

19. $x + x^2 + x^3 + \cdots + x^n$

20. $1 - x + x^2 - x^3 + \cdots + (-1)^n x^n$

21–35 Find the value of the sum.

21. $\displaystyle\sum_{i=4}^{8} (3i - 2)$

22. $\displaystyle\sum_{i=3}^{6} i(i + 2)$

23. $\displaystyle\sum_{j=1}^{6} 3^{j+1}$

24. $\displaystyle\sum_{k=0}^{8} \cos k\pi$

25. $\displaystyle\sum_{n=1}^{20} (-1)^n$

26. $\displaystyle\sum_{i=1}^{100} 4$

27. $\displaystyle\sum_{i=0}^{4} (2^i + i^2)$

28. $\displaystyle\sum_{i=-2}^{4} 2^{3-i}$

29. $\displaystyle\sum_{i=1}^{n} 2i$

30. $\displaystyle\sum_{i=1}^{n} (2 - 5i)$

31. $\displaystyle\sum_{i=1}^{n} (i^2 + 3i + 4)$

32. $\displaystyle\sum_{i=1}^{n} (3 + 2i)^2$

33. $\displaystyle\sum_{i=1}^{n} (i + 1)(i + 2)$

34. $\displaystyle\sum_{i=1}^{n} i(i + 1)(i + 2)$

35. $\displaystyle\sum_{i=1}^{n} (i^3 - i - 2)$

---

36. Find the number n such that $\displaystyle\sum_{i=1}^{n} i = 78$.

37. Prove formula (b) of Theorem 3.

38. Prove formula (e) of Theorem 3 using mathematical induction.

39. Prove formula (e) of Theorem 3 using a method similar to that of Example 5, Solution 1 [start with $(1 + i)^4 - i^4$].

40. Prove formula (e) of Theorem 3 using the following method published by Abu Bekr Mohammed ibn Alhusain Alkarchi in about AD 1010. The figure shows a square $ABCD$ in which sides AB and AD have been divided into segments of lengths 1, 2, 3, ..., n. Thus the side of the square has length $n(n + 1)/2$ so the area is $[n(n + 1)/2]^2$. But the area is also the sum of the

areas of the n "gnomons" $G_1, G_2, \ldots, G_n$ shown in the figure. Show that the area of G_i is i^3 and conclude that formula (e) is true.

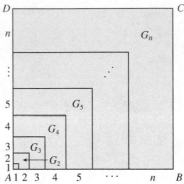

41. Evaluate each telescoping sum.

(a) $\displaystyle\sum_{i=1}^{n} [i^4 - (i - 1)^4]$

(b) $\displaystyle\sum_{i=1}^{100} (5^i - 5^{i-1})$

(c) $\displaystyle\sum_{i=3}^{99} \left(\frac{1}{i} - \frac{1}{i + 1} \right)$

(d) $\displaystyle\sum_{i=1}^{n} (a_i - a_{i-1})$

42. Prove the generalized triangle inequality:

$$\left| \sum_{i=1}^{n} a_i \right| \le \sum_{i=1}^{n} |a_i|$$

43–46 Find the limit.

43. $\displaystyle\lim_{n \to \infty} \sum_{i=1}^{n} \frac{1}{n} \left(\frac{i}{n} \right)^2$

44. $\displaystyle\lim_{n \to \infty} \sum_{i=1}^{n} \frac{1}{n} \left[\left(\frac{i}{n} \right)^3 + 1 \right]$

45. $\displaystyle\lim_{n \to \infty} \sum_{i=1}^{n} \frac{2}{n} \left[\left(\frac{2i}{n} \right)^3 + 5 \left(\frac{2i}{n} \right) \right]$

46. $\displaystyle\lim_{n \to \infty} \sum_{i=1}^{n} \frac{3}{n} \left[\left(1 + \frac{3i}{n} \right)^3 - 2 \left(1 + \frac{3i}{n} \right) \right]$

---

47. Prove the formula for the sum of a finite geometric series with first term a and common ratio $r \ne 1$:

$$\sum_{i=1}^{n} ar^{i-1} = a + ar + ar^2 + \cdots + ar^{n-1} = \frac{a(r^n - 1)}{r - 1}$$

48. Evaluate $\displaystyle\sum_{i=1}^{n} \frac{3}{2^{i-1}}$.

49. Evaluate $\displaystyle\sum_{i=1}^{n} (2i + 2^i)$.

50. Evaluate $\displaystyle\sum_{i=1}^{m} \left[\sum_{j=1}^{n} (i + j) \right]$.

G | Integration of Rational Functions by Partial Fractions

In this appendix we show how to integrate any rational function (a ratio of polynomials) by expressing it as a sum of simpler fractions, called *partial fractions,* that we already know how to integrate. To illustrate the method, observe that by taking the fractions $2/(x - 1)$ and $1/(x + 2)$ to a common denominator we obtain

$$\frac{2}{x - 1} - \frac{1}{x + 2} = \frac{2(x + 2) - (x - 1)}{(x - 1)(x + 2)} = \frac{x + 5}{x^2 + x - 2}$$

If we now reverse the procedure, we see how to integrate the function on the right side of this equation:

$$\int \frac{x + 5}{x^2 + x - 2}\, dx = \int \left(\frac{2}{x - 1} - \frac{1}{x + 2}\right) dx$$

$$= 2 \ln|x - 1| - \ln|x + 2| + C$$

To see how the method of partial fractions works in general, let's consider a rational function

$$f(x) = \frac{P(x)}{Q(x)}$$

where P and Q are polynomials. It's possible to express f as a sum of simpler fractions provided that the degree of P is less than the degree of Q. Such a rational function is called *proper.* Recall that if

$$P(x) = a_n x^n + a_{n-1} x^{n-1} + \cdots + a_1 x + a_0$$

where $a_n \neq 0$, then the degree of P is n and we write $\deg(P) = n$.

If f is improper, that is, $\deg(P) \geqslant \deg(Q)$, then we must take the preliminary step of dividing Q into P (by long division) until a remainder $R(x)$ is obtained such that $\deg(R) < \deg(Q)$. The division statement is

$$\boxed{1} \qquad\qquad f(x) = \frac{P(x)}{Q(x)} = S(x) + \frac{R(x)}{Q(x)}$$

where S and R are also polynomials.

As the following example illustrates, sometimes this preliminary step is all that is required.

$\boxed{\text{V}}$ **EXAMPLE 1** Find $\displaystyle\int \frac{x^3 + x}{x - 1}\, dx$.

SOLUTION Since the degree of the numerator is greater than the degree of the denominator, we first perform the long division. This enables us to write

$$\int \frac{x^3 + x}{x - 1}\, dx = \int \left(x^2 + x + 2 + \frac{2}{x - 1}\right) dx$$

$$= \frac{x^3}{3} + \frac{x^2}{2} + 2x + 2 \ln|x - 1| + C$$

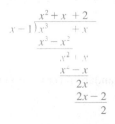

$$
\begin{array}{r}
x^2 + x + 2 \\
x - 1 \overline{\smash{)}\; x^3 \qquad\;\; + x} \\
\underline{x^3 - x^2} \\
x^2 + x \\
\underline{x^2 - x} \\
2x \\
\underline{2x - 2} \\
2
\end{array}
$$

The next step is to factor the denominator $Q(x)$ as far as possible. It can be shown that any polynomial Q can be factored as a product of linear factors (of the form $ax + b$) and irreducible quadratic factors (of the form $ax^2 + bx + c$, where $b^2 - 4ac < 0$). For instance, if $Q(x) = x^4 - 16$, we could factor it as

$$Q(x) = (x^2 - 4)(x^2 + 4) = (x - 2)(x + 2)(x^2 + 4)$$

The third step is to express the proper rational function $R(x)/Q(x)$ (from Equation 1) as a sum of **partial fractions** of the form

$$\frac{A}{(ax + b)^i} \qquad \text{or} \qquad \frac{Ax + B}{(ax^2 + bx + c)^j}$$

A theorem in algebra guarantees that it is always possible to do this. We explain the details for the four cases that occur.

Case I   **The denominator $Q(x)$ is a product of distinct linear factors.**
This means that we can write

$$Q(x) = (a_1x + b_1)(a_2x + b_2) \cdots (a_kx + b_k)$$

where no factor is repeated (and no factor is a constant multiple of another). In this case the partial fraction theorem states that there exist constants $A_1, A_2, \ldots, A_k$ such that

$$\boxed{2} \qquad \frac{R(x)}{Q(x)} = \frac{A_1}{a_1x + b_1} + \frac{A_2}{a_2x + b_2} + \cdots + \frac{A_k}{a_kx + b_k}$$

These constants can be determined as in the following example.

$\boxed{\text{V}}$ **EXAMPLE 2**   Evaluate $\displaystyle\int \frac{x^2 + 2x - 1}{2x^3 + 3x^2 - 2x}\, dx$.

SOLUTION   Since the degree of the numerator is less than the degree of the denominator, we don't need to divide. We factor the denominator as

$$2x^3 + 3x^2 - 2x = x(2x^2 + 3x - 2) = x(2x - 1)(x + 2)$$

Since the denominator has three distinct linear factors, the partial fraction decomposition of the integrand (2) has the form

$$\boxed{3} \qquad \frac{x^2 + 2x - 1}{x(2x - 1)(x + 2)} = \frac{A}{x} + \frac{B}{2x - 1} + \frac{C}{x + 2}$$

Another method for finding A, B, and C is given in the note after this example.

To determine the values of A, B, and C, we multiply both sides of this equation by the product of the denominators, $x(2x - 1)(x + 2)$, obtaining

$$\boxed{4} \qquad x^2 + 2x - 1 = A(2x - 1)(x + 2) + Bx(x + 2) + Cx(2x - 1)$$

Expanding the right side of Equation 4 and writing it in the standard form for polynomials, we get

$$\boxed{5} \qquad x^2 + 2x - 1 = (2A + B + 2C)x^2 + (3A + 2B - C)x - 2A$$

The polynomials in Equation 5 are identical, so their coefficients must be equal. The coefficient of x^2 on the right side, $2A + B + 2C$, must equal the coefficient of x^2 on the left side—namely, 1. Likewise, the coefficients of x are equal and the constant terms are equal. This gives the following system of equations for A, B, and C:

$$2A +\ B + 2C = 1$$
$$3A + 2B -\ C = 2$$
$$-2A \qquad\qquad = -1$$

Solving, we get $A = \frac{1}{2}$, $B = \frac{1}{5}$, and $C = -\frac{1}{10}$, and so

We could check our work by taking the terms to a common denominator and adding them.

$$\int \frac{x^2 + 2x - 1}{2x^3 + 3x^2 - 2x}\, dx = \int \left[\frac{1}{2}\frac{1}{x} + \frac{1}{5}\frac{1}{2x - 1} - \frac{1}{10}\frac{1}{x + 2}\right] dx$$

$$= \tfrac{1}{2}\ln|x| + \tfrac{1}{10}\ln|2x - 1| - \tfrac{1}{10}\ln|x + 2| + K$$

Figure 1 shows the graphs of the integrand in Example 2 and its indefinite integral (with $K = 0$). Which is which?

In integrating the middle term we have made the mental substitution $u = 2x - 1$, which gives $du = 2\,dx$ and $dx = du/2$.

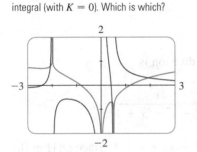

FIGURE 1

Note: We can use an alternative method to find the coefficients A, B, and C in Example 2. Equation 4 is an identity; it is true for every value of x. Let's choose values of x that simplify the equation. If we put $x = 0$ in Equation 4, then the second and third terms on the right side vanish and the equation then becomes $-2A = -1$, or $A = \frac{1}{2}$. Likewise, $x = \frac{1}{2}$ gives $5B/4 = \frac{1}{4}$ and $x = -2$ gives $10C = -1$, so $B = \frac{1}{5}$ and $C = -\frac{1}{10}$. (You may object that Equation 3 is not valid for $x = 0, \frac{1}{2}$, or -2, so why should Equation 4 be valid for those values? In fact, Equation 4 is true for all values of x, even $x = 0, \frac{1}{2}$, and -2. See Exercise 45 for the reason.)

EXAMPLE 3 Find $\int \dfrac{dx}{x^2 - a^2}$, where $a \neq 0$.

SOLUTION The method of partial fractions gives

$$\frac{1}{x^2 - a^2} = \frac{1}{(x - a)(x + a)} = \frac{A}{x - a} + \frac{B}{x + a}$$

and therefore

$$A(x + a) + B(x - a) = 1$$

Using the method of the preceding note, we put $x = a$ in this equation and get $A(2a) = 1$, so $A = 1/(2a)$. If we put $x = -a$, we get $B(-2a) = 1$, so $B = -1/(2a)$. Thus

$$\int \frac{dx}{x^2 - a^2} = \frac{1}{2a} \int \left(\frac{1}{x - a} - \frac{1}{x + a}\right) dx$$

$$= \frac{1}{2a}\Big[\ln|x - a| - \ln|x + a|\Big] + C$$

Since $\ln x - \ln y = \ln(x/y)$, we can write the integral as

$$\int \frac{dx}{x^2 - a^2} = \frac{1}{2a} \ln \left| \frac{x-a}{x+a} \right| + C$$

Case II $Q(x)$ **is a product of linear factors, some of which are repeated.**
Suppose the first linear factor $(a_1x + b_1)$ is repeated r times; that is, $(a_1x + b_1)^r$ occurs in the factorization of $Q(x)$. Then instead of the single term $A_1/(a_1x + b_1)$ in Equation 2, we would use

$$\boxed{6} \qquad \frac{A_1}{a_1x + b_1} + \frac{A_2}{(a_1x + b_1)^2} + \cdots + \frac{A_r}{(a_1x + b_1)^r}$$

By way of illustration, we could write

$$\frac{x^3 - x + 1}{x^2(x-1)^3} = \frac{A}{x} + \frac{B}{x^2} + \frac{C}{x-1} + \frac{D}{(x-1)^2} + \frac{E}{(x-1)^3}$$

but we prefer to work out in detail a simpler example.

EXAMPLE 4 Find $\int \dfrac{x^4 - 2x^2 + 4x + 1}{x^3 - x^2 - x + 1} dx$.

SOLUTION The first step is to divide. The result of long division is

$$\frac{x^4 - 2x^2 + 4x + 1}{x^3 - x^2 - x + 1} = x + 1 + \frac{4x}{x^3 - x^2 - x + 1}$$

The second step is to factor the denominator $Q(x) = x^3 - x^2 - x + 1$. Since $Q(1) = 0$, we know that $x - 1$ is a factor and we obtain

$$x^3 - x^2 - x + 1 = (x-1)(x^2 - 1) = (x-1)(x-1)(x+1)$$
$$= (x-1)^2(x+1)$$

Since the linear factor $x - 1$ occurs twice, the partial fraction decomposition is

$$\frac{4x}{(x-1)^2(x+1)} = \frac{A}{x-1} + \frac{B}{(x-1)^2} + \frac{C}{x+1}$$

Multiplying by the least common denominator, $(x-1)^2(x+1)$, we get

$$\boxed{7} \qquad 4x = A(x-1)(x+1) + B(x+1) + C(x-1)^2$$
$$= (A + C)x^2 + (B - 2C)x + (-A + B + C)$$

Now we equate coefficients:

$$A \qquad + C = 0$$
$$B - 2C = 4$$
$$-A + B + C = 0$$

Another method for finding the coefficients:
Put $x = 1$ in (7): $B = 2$.
Put $x = -1$: $C = -1$.
Put $x = 0$: $A = B + C = 1$.

Solving, we obtain $A = 1$, $B = 2$, and $C = -1$, so

$$\int \frac{x^4 - 2x^2 + 4x + 1}{x^3 - x^2 - x + 1}\, dx = \int \left[x + 1 + \frac{1}{x - 1} + \frac{2}{(x - 1)^2} - \frac{1}{x + 1} \right] dx$$

$$= \frac{x^2}{2} + x + \ln|x - 1| - \frac{2}{x - 1} - \ln|x + 1| + K$$

$$= \frac{x^2}{2} + x - \frac{2}{x - 1} + \ln\left|\frac{x - 1}{x + 1}\right| + K$$

Case III $Q(x)$ **contains irreducible quadratic factors, none of which is repeated.**
If $Q(x)$ has the factor $ax^2 + bx + c$, where $b^2 - 4ac < 0$, then, in addition to the partial fractions in Equations 2 and 6, the expression for $R(x)/Q(x)$ will have a term of the form

$$\boxed{8} \qquad \frac{Ax + B}{ax^2 + bx + c}$$

where A and B are constants to be determined. For instance, the function given by $f(x) = x/[(x - 2)(x^2 + 1)(x^2 + 4)]$ has a partial fraction decomposition of the form

$$\frac{x}{(x - 2)(x^2 + 1)(x^2 + 4)} = \frac{A}{x - 2} + \frac{Bx + C}{x^2 + 1} + \frac{Dx + E}{x^2 + 4}$$

When integrating the term given in (8), it will often be necessary to use the formula

$$\boxed{9} \qquad \int \frac{dx}{x^2 + a^2} = \frac{1}{a} \tan^{-1}\left(\frac{x}{a}\right) + C$$

V EXAMPLE 5 Evaluate $\displaystyle\int \frac{2x^2 - x + 4}{x^3 + 4x}\, dx$.

SOLUTION Since $x^3 + 4x = x(x^2 + 4)$ can't be factored further, we write

$$\frac{2x^2 - x + 4}{x(x^2 + 4)} = \frac{A}{x} + \frac{Bx + C}{x^2 + 4}$$

Multiplying by $x(x^2 + 4)$, we have

$$2x^2 - x + 4 = A(x^2 + 4) + (Bx + C)x$$

$$= (A + B)x^2 + Cx + 4A$$

Equating coefficients, we obtain

$$A + B = 2 \qquad C = -1 \qquad 4A = 4$$

Thus $A = 1$, $B = 1$, and $C = -1$ and so

$$\int \frac{2x^2 - x + 4}{x^3 + 4x}\, dx = \int \left(\frac{1}{x} + \frac{x - 1}{x^2 + 4}\right) dx$$

In order to integrate the second term we split it into two parts:

$$\int \frac{x-1}{x^2+4}\,dx = \int \frac{x}{x^2+4}\,dx - \int \frac{1}{x^2+4}\,dx$$

We make the substitution $u = x^2 + 4$ in the first of these integrals so that $du = 2x\,dx$. We evaluate the second integral by means of Formula 9 with $a = 2$:

$$\int \frac{2x^2 - x + 4}{x(x^2+4)}\,dx = \int \frac{1}{x}\,dx + \int \frac{x}{x^2+4}\,dx - \int \frac{1}{x^2+4}\,dx$$

$$= \ln|x| + \tfrac{1}{2}\ln(x^2+4) - \tfrac{1}{2}\tan^{-1}(x/2) + K$$

EXAMPLE 6 Evaluate $\displaystyle\int \frac{4x^2 - 3x + 2}{4x^2 - 4x + 3}\,dx$.

SOLUTION Since the degree of the numerator is *not less than* the degree of the denominator, we first divide and obtain

$$\frac{4x^2 - 3x + 2}{4x^2 - 4x + 3} = 1 + \frac{x-1}{4x^2 - 4x + 3}$$

Notice that the quadratic $4x^2 - 4x + 3$ is irreducible because its discriminant is $b^2 - 4ac = -32 < 0$. This means it can't be factored, so we don't need to use the partial fraction technique.

To integrate the given function we complete the square in the denominator:

$$4x^2 - 4x + 3 = (2x - 1)^2 + 2$$

This suggests that we make the substitution $u = 2x - 1$. Then, $du = 2\,dx$ and $x = \tfrac{1}{2}(u + 1)$, so

$$\int \frac{4x^2 - 3x + 2}{4x^2 - 4x + 3}\,dx = \int \left(1 + \frac{x-1}{4x^2 - 4x + 3}\right) dx$$

$$= x + \tfrac{1}{2}\int \frac{\tfrac{1}{2}(u+1) - 1}{u^2 + 2}\,du = x + \tfrac{1}{4}\int \frac{u-1}{u^2+2}\,du$$

$$= x + \tfrac{1}{4}\int \frac{u}{u^2+2}\,du - \tfrac{1}{4}\int \frac{1}{u^2+2}\,du$$

$$= x + \tfrac{1}{8}\ln(u^2+2) - \frac{1}{4}\cdot\frac{1}{\sqrt{2}}\tan^{-1}\left(\frac{u}{\sqrt{2}}\right) + C$$

$$= x + \tfrac{1}{8}\ln(4x^2 - 4x + 3) - \frac{1}{4\sqrt{2}}\tan^{-1}\left(\frac{2x-1}{\sqrt{2}}\right) + C$$

Note: Example 6 illustrates the general procedure for integrating a partial fraction of the form

$$\frac{Ax + B}{ax^2 + bx + c} \qquad \text{where } b^2 - 4ac < 0$$

We complete the square in the denominator and then make a substitution that brings the integral into the form

$$\int \frac{Cu + D}{u^2 + a^2}\, du = C \int \frac{u}{u^2 + a^2}\, du + D \int \frac{1}{u^2 + a^2}\, du$$

Then the first integral is a logarithm and the second is expressed in terms of $\tan^{-1}$.

Case IV $Q(x)$ **contains a repeated irreducible quadratic factor.**
If $Q(x)$ has the factor $(ax^2 + bx + c)^r$, where $b^2 - 4ac < 0$, then instead of the single partial fraction (8), the sum

$$\boxed{10} \qquad \frac{A_1 x + B_1}{ax^2 + bx + c} + \frac{A_2 x + B_2}{(ax^2 + bx + c)^2} + \cdots + \frac{A_r x + B_r}{(ax^2 + bx + c)^r}$$

occurs in the partial fraction decomposition of $R(x)/Q(x)$. Each of the terms in (10) can be integrated by using a substitution or by first completing the square.

EXAMPLE 7 Write out the form of the partial fraction decomposition of the function

$$\frac{x^3 + x^2 + 1}{x(x - 1)(x^2 + x + 1)(x^2 + 1)^3}$$

SOLUTION

$$\frac{x^3 + x^2 + 1}{x(x - 1)(x^2 + x + 1)(x^2 + 1)^3}$$

$$= \frac{A}{x} + \frac{B}{x - 1} + \frac{Cx + D}{x^2 + x + 1} + \frac{Ex + F}{x^2 + 1} + \frac{Gx + H}{(x^2 + 1)^2} + \frac{Ix + J}{(x^2 + 1)^3}$$

It would be extremely tedious to work out by hand the numerical values of the coefficients in Example 7. Most computer algebra systems, however, can find the numerical values very quickly. For instance, the Maple command

    convert(f, parfrac, x)

or the Mathematica command

        Apart[f]

gives the following values:

$A = -1$, $\quad B = \frac{1}{8}$, $\quad C = D = -1$,

$E = \frac{15}{8}$, $\quad F = -\frac{1}{8}$, $\quad G = H = \frac{3}{4}$,

$\quad I = -\frac{1}{2}$, $\quad J = \frac{1}{2}$

EXAMPLE 8 Evaluate $\displaystyle \int \frac{1 - x + 2x^2 - x^3}{x(x^2 + 1)^2}\, dx$.

SOLUTION The form of the partial fraction decomposition is

$$\frac{1 - x + 2x^2 - x^3}{x(x^2 + 1)^2} = \frac{A}{x} + \frac{Bx + C}{x^2 + 1} + \frac{Dx + E}{(x^2 + 1)^2}$$

Multiplying by $x(x^2 + 1)^2$, we have

$$-x^3 + 2x^2 - x + 1 = A(x^2 + 1)^2 + (Bx + C)x(x^2 + 1) + (Dx + E)x$$

$$= A(x^4 + 2x^2 + 1) + B(x^4 + x^2) + C(x^3 + x) + Dx^2 + Ex$$

$$= (A + B)x^4 + Cx^3 + (2A + B + D)x^2 + (C + E)x + A$$

If we equate coefficients, we get the system

$$A + B = 0 \qquad C = -1 \qquad 2A + B + D = 2 \qquad C + E = -1 \qquad A = 1$$

which has the solution $A = 1$, $B = -1$, $C = -1$, $D = 1$, and $E = 0$.

Thus

$$\int \frac{1 - x + 2x^2 - x^3}{x(x^2 + 1)^2} \, dx = \int \left(\frac{1}{x} - \frac{x+1}{x^2+1} + \frac{x}{(x^2+1)^2} \right) dx$$

$$= \int \frac{dx}{x} - \int \frac{x}{x^2+1} \, dx - \int \frac{dx}{x^2+1} + \int \frac{x \, dx}{(x^2+1)^2}$$

In the second and fourth terms we made the mental substitution $u = x^2 + 1$.

$$= \ln|x| - \tfrac{1}{2} \ln(x^2 + 1) - \tan^{-1}x - \frac{1}{2(x^2+1)} + K$$

G   Exercises

1–6 Write out the form of the partial fraction decomposition of the function (as in Example 7). Do not determine the numerical values of the coefficients.

1. (a) $\dfrac{2x}{(x+3)(3x+1)}$ (b) $\dfrac{1}{x^3 + 2x^2 + x}$

2. (a) $\dfrac{x}{x^2 + x - 2}$ (b) $\dfrac{x^2}{x^2 + x + 2}$

3. (a) $\dfrac{x^4 + 1}{x^5 + 4x^3}$ (b) $\dfrac{1}{(x^2 - 9)^2}$

4. (a) $\dfrac{x^3}{x^2 + 4x + 3}$ (b) $\dfrac{2x+1}{(x+1)^3(x^2+4)^2}$

5. (a) $\dfrac{x^4}{x^4 - 1}$ (b) $\dfrac{t^4 + t^2 + 1}{(t^2+1)(t^2+4)^2}$

6. (a) $\dfrac{x^4}{(x^3 + x)(x^2 - x + 3)}$ (b) $\dfrac{1}{x^6 - x^3}$

7–34 Evaluate the integral.

7. $\displaystyle\int \frac{x}{x-6} \, dx$ **8.** $\displaystyle\int \frac{r^2}{r+4} \, dr$

9. $\displaystyle\int \frac{x-9}{(x+5)(x-2)} \, dx$ **10.** $\displaystyle\int \frac{1}{(t+4)(t-1)} \, dt$

11. $\displaystyle\int_2^3 \frac{1}{x^2 - 1} \, dx$ **12.** $\displaystyle\int_0^1 \frac{x-1}{x^2 + 3x + 2} \, dx$

13. $\displaystyle\int \frac{ax}{x^2 - bx} \, dx$ **14.** $\displaystyle\int \frac{1}{(x+a)(x+b)} \, dx$

15. $\displaystyle\int_3^4 \frac{x^3 - 2x^2 - 4}{x^3 - 2x^2} \, dx$ **16.** $\displaystyle\int_0^1 \frac{x^3 - 4x - 10}{x^2 - x - 6} \, dx$

17. $\displaystyle\int_1^2 \frac{4y^2 - 7y - 12}{y(y+2)(y-3)} \, dy$ **18.** $\displaystyle\int \frac{x^2 + 2x - 1}{x^3 - x} \, dx$

19. $\displaystyle\int \frac{1}{(x+5)^2(x-1)} \, dx$ **20.** $\displaystyle\int \frac{x^2 - 5x + 16}{(2x+1)(x-2)^2} \, dx$

21. $\displaystyle\int \frac{5x^2 + 3x - 2}{x^3 + 2x^2} \, dx$ **22.** $\displaystyle\int \frac{x^2 - x + 6}{x^3 + 3x} \, dx$

23. $\displaystyle\int \frac{10}{(x-1)(x^2+9)} \, dx$ **24.** $\displaystyle\int \frac{x^2 - 2x - 1}{(x-1)^2(x^2+1)} \, dx$

25. $\displaystyle\int \frac{x^3 + x^2 + 2x + 1}{(x^2+1)(x^2+2)} \, dx$ **26.** $\displaystyle\int \frac{x^2 + x + 1}{(x^2+1)^2} \, dx$

27. $\displaystyle\int \frac{x+4}{x^2 + 2x + 5} \, dx$ **28.** $\displaystyle\int_0^1 \frac{x}{x^2 + 4x + 13} \, dx$

29. $\displaystyle\int \frac{1}{x^3 - 1} \, dx$ **30.** $\displaystyle\int \frac{x^3}{x^3 + 1} \, dx$

31. $\displaystyle\int \frac{dx}{x(x^2+4)^2}$ **32.** $\displaystyle\int \frac{x^4 + 3x^2 + 1}{x^5 + 5x^3 + 5x} \, dx$

33. $\displaystyle\int \frac{x-3}{(x^2 + 2x + 4)^2} \, dx$ **34.** $\displaystyle\int \frac{3x^2 + x + 4}{x^4 + 3x^2 + 2} \, dx$

35–38 Make a substitution to express the integrand as a rational function and then evaluate the integral.

35. $\displaystyle\int_9^{16} \frac{\sqrt{x}}{x-4} \, dx$ **36.** $\displaystyle\int \frac{dx}{2\sqrt{x+3} + x}$

37. $\displaystyle\int \frac{e^{2x}}{e^{2x} + 3e^x + 2} \, dx$ **38.** $\displaystyle\int \frac{\cos x}{\sin^2 x + \sin x} \, dx$

39. Use a graph of $f(x) = 1/(x^2 - 2x - 3)$ to decide whether $\int_0^2 f(x) \, dx$ is positive or negative. Use the graph to give a rough estimate of the value of the integral and then use partial fractions to find the exact value.

40. Graph both $y = 1/(x^3 - 2x^2)$ and an antiderivative on the same screen.

⊞ Graphing calculator or computer with graphing software required |CAS| Computer algebra system required   **1.** Homework Hints available in TEC

41. One method of slowing the growth of an insect population without using pesticides is to introduce into the population a number of sterile males that mate with fertile females but produce no offspring. If P represents the number of female insects in a population, S the number of sterile males introduced each generation, and r the population's natural growth rate, then the female population is related to time t by

$$t = \int \frac{P + S}{P[(r - 1)P - S]} \, dP$$

Suppose an insect population with 10,000 females grows at a rate of $r = 0.10$ and 900 sterile males are added. Evaluate the integral to give an equation relating the female population to time. (Note that the resulting equation can't be solved explicitly for P.)

42. The region under the curve

$$y = \frac{1}{x^2 + 3x + 2}$$

from $x = 0$ to $x = 1$ is rotated about the x-axis. Find the volume of the resulting solid.

CAS **43.** (a) Use a computer algebra system to find the partial fraction decomposition of the function

$$f(x) = \frac{4x^3 - 27x^2 + 5x - 32}{30x^5 - 13x^4 + 50x^3 - 286x^2 - 299x - 70}$$

(b) Use part (a) to find $\int f(x) \, dx$ (by hand) and compare with the result of using the CAS to integrate f directly. Comment on any discrepancy.

CAS **44.** (a) Find the partial fraction decomposition of the function

$$f(x) = \frac{12x^5 - 7x^3 - 13x^2 + 8}{100x^6 - 80x^5 + 116x^4 - 80x^3 + 41x^2 - 20x + 4}$$

(b) Use part (a) to find $\int f(x) \, dx$ and graph f and its indefinite integral on the same screen.

(c) Use the graph of f to discover the main features of the graph of $\int f(x) \, dx$.

45. Suppose that F, G, and Q are polynomials and

$$\frac{F(x)}{Q(x)} = \frac{G(x)}{Q(x)}$$

for all x except when $Q(x) = 0$. Prove that $F(x) = G(x)$ for all x. [*Hint:* Use continuity.]

46. If f is a quadratic function such that $f(0) = 1$ and

$$\int \frac{f(x)}{x^2(x + 1)^3} \, dx$$

is a rational function, find the value of $f'(0)$.

H | Polar Coordinates

Polar coordinates offer an alternative way of locating points in a plane. They are useful because, for certain types of regions and curves, polar coordinates provide very simple descriptions and equations. The principal applications of this idea occur in multivariable calculus: the evaluation of double integrals and the derivation of Kepler's laws of planetary motion.

H.1 | Curves in Polar Coordinates

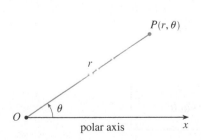

FIGURE 1

A coordinate system represents a point in the plane by an ordered pair of numbers called coordinates. Usually we use Cartesian coordinates, which are directed distances from two perpendicular axes. Here we describe a coordinate system introduced by Newton, called the **polar coordinate system**, which is more convenient for many purposes.

We choose a point in the plane that is called the **pole** (or origin) and is labeled O. Then we draw a ray (half-line) starting at O called the **polar axis**. This axis is usually drawn horizontally to the right and corresponds to the positive x-axis in Cartesian coordinates.

If P is any other point in the plane, let r be the distance from O to P and let θ be the angle (usually measured in radians) between the polar axis and the line OP as in Figure 1. Then the point P is represented by the ordered pair (r, θ) and r, θ are called **polar coordinates** of P. We use the convention that an angle is positive if measured in the counterclock-

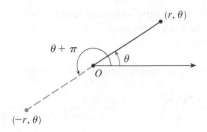

FIGURE 2

wise direction from the polar axis and negative in the clockwise direction. If $P = O$, then $r = 0$ and we agree that $(0, \theta)$ represents the pole for any value of θ.

We extend the meaning of polar coordinates (r, θ) to the case in which r is negative by agreeing that, as in Figure 2, the points $(-r, \theta)$ and (r, θ) lie on the same line through O and at the same distance $|r|$ from O, but on opposite sides of O. If $r > 0$, the point (r, θ) lies in the same quadrant as θ; if $r < 0$, it lies in the quadrant on the opposite side of the pole. Notice that $(-r, \theta)$ represents the same point as $(r, \theta + \pi)$.

EXAMPLE 1 Plot the points whose polar coordinates are given.

(a) $(1, 5\pi/4)$ (b) $(2, 3\pi)$ (c) $(2, -2\pi/3)$ (d) $(-3, 3\pi/4)$

SOLUTION The points are plotted in Figure 3. In part (d) the point $(-3, 3\pi/4)$ is located three units from the pole in the fourth quadrant because the angle $3\pi/4$ is in the second quadrant and $r = -3$ is negative.

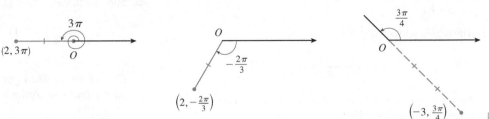

FIGURE 3

In the Cartesian coordinate system every point has only one representation, but in the polar coordinate system each point has many representations. For instance, the point $(1, 5\pi/4)$ in Example 1(a) could be written as $(1, -3\pi/4)$ or $(1, 13\pi/4)$ or $(-1, \pi/4)$. (See Figure 4.)

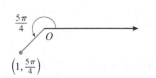  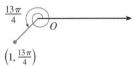 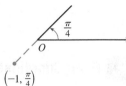

FIGURE 4

In fact, since a complete counterclockwise rotation is given by an angle 2π, the point represented by polar coordinates (r, θ) is also represented by

$$(r, \theta + 2n\pi) \qquad \text{and} \qquad (-r, \theta + (2n + 1)\pi)$$

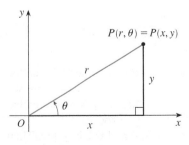

FIGURE 5

where n is any integer.

The connection between polar and Cartesian coordinates can be seen from Figure 5, in which the pole corresponds to the origin and the polar axis coincides with the positive x-axis. If the point P has Cartesian coordinates (x, y) and polar coordinates (r, θ), then, from the figure, we have

$$\cos \theta = \frac{x}{r} \qquad \sin \theta = \frac{y}{r}$$

and so

$$\boxed{1} \qquad \boxed{\quad x = r \cos \theta \qquad y = r \sin \theta \quad}$$

Although Equations 1 were deduced from Figure 5, which illustrates the case where $r > 0$ and $0 < \theta < \pi/2$, these equations are valid for all values of r and θ. (See the general definition of $\sin \theta$ and $\cos \theta$ in Appendix C.)

Equations 1 allow us to find the Cartesian coordinates of a point when the polar coordinates are known. To find r and θ when x and y are known, we use the equations

$$\boxed{2} \qquad \boxed{r^2 = x^2 + y^2 \qquad \tan \theta = \frac{y}{x}}$$

which can be deduced from Equations 1 or simply read from Figure 5.

EXAMPLE 2 Convert the point $(2, \pi/3)$ from polar to Cartesian coordinates.

SOLUTION Since $r = 2$ and $\theta = \pi/3$, Equations 1 give

$$x = r \cos \theta = 2 \cos \frac{\pi}{3} = 2 \cdot \frac{1}{2} = 1$$

$$y = r \sin \theta = 2 \sin \frac{\pi}{3} = 2 \cdot \frac{\sqrt{3}}{2} = \sqrt{3}$$

Therefore the point is $\left(1, \sqrt{3}\right)$ in Cartesian coordinates.

EXAMPLE 3 Represent the point with Cartesian coordinates $(1, -1)$ in terms of polar coordinates.

SOLUTION If we choose r to be positive, then Equations 2 give

$$r = \sqrt{x^2 + y^2} = \sqrt{1^2 + (-1)^2} = \sqrt{2}$$

$$\tan \theta = \frac{y}{x} = -1$$

Since the point $(1, -1)$ lies in the fourth quadrant, we can choose $\theta = -\pi/4$ or $\theta = 7\pi/4$. Thus one possible answer is $\left(\sqrt{2}, -\pi/4\right)$; another is $\left(\sqrt{2}, 7\pi/4\right)$.

Note: Equations 2 do not uniquely determine θ when x and y are given because, as θ increases through the interval $0 \le \theta < 2\pi$, each value of $\tan \theta$ occurs twice. Therefore, in converting from Cartesian to polar coordinates, it's not good enough just to find r and θ that satisfy Equations 2. As in Example 3, we must choose θ so that the point (r, θ) lies in the correct quadrant.

The **graph of a polar equation** $r = f(\theta)$, or more generally $F(r, \theta) = 0$, consists of all points P that have at least one polar representation (r, θ) whose coordinates satisfy the equation.

⊽ EXAMPLE 4 What curve is represented by the polar equation $r = 2$?

SOLUTION The curve consists of all points (r, θ) with $r = 2$. Since r represents the distance from the point to the pole, the curve $r = 2$ represents the circle with center O and radius 2. In general, the equation $r = a$ represents a circle with center O and radius $|a|$. (See Figure 6.)

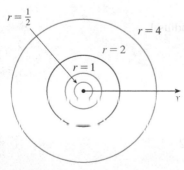

FIGURE 6

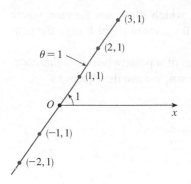

FIGURE 7

EXAMPLE 5 Sketch the polar curve $\theta = 1$.

SOLUTION This curve consists of all points (r, θ) such that the polar angle θ is 1 radian. It is the straight line that passes through O and makes an angle of 1 radian with the polar axis (see Figure 7). Notice that the points $(r, 1)$ on the line with $r > 0$ are in the first quadrant, whereas those with $r < 0$ are in the third quadrant.

EXAMPLE 6

(a) Sketch the curve with polar equation $r = 2 \cos \theta$.

(b) Find a Cartesian equation for this curve.

SOLUTION

(a) In Figure 8 we find the values of r for some convenient values of θ and plot the corresponding points (r, θ). Then we join these points to sketch the curve, which appears to be a circle. We have used only values of θ between 0 and π, since if we let θ increase beyond π, we obtain the same points again.

FIGURE 8

Table of values and graph of $r = 2 \cos \theta$

θ	$r = 2 \cos \theta$
0	2
$\pi/6$	$\sqrt{3}$
$\pi/4$	$\sqrt{2}$
$\pi/3$	1
$\pi/2$	0
$2\pi/3$	-1
$3\pi/4$	$-\sqrt{2}$
$5\pi/6$	$-\sqrt{3}$
π	-2

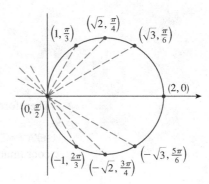

(b) To convert the given equation into a Cartesian equation we use Equations 1 and 2. From $x = r \cos \theta$ we have $\cos \theta = x/r$, so the equation $r = 2 \cos \theta$ becomes $r = 2x/r$, which gives

$$2x = r^2 = x^2 + y^2 \qquad \text{or} \qquad x^2 + y^2 - 2x = 0$$

Completing the square, we obtain

$$(x - 1)^2 + y^2 = 1$$

which is an equation of a circle with center $(1, 0)$ and radius 1.

Figure 9 shows a geometrical illustration that the circle in Example 6 has the equation $r = 2 \cos \theta$. The angle OPQ is a right angle (Why?) and so $r/2 = \cos \theta$.

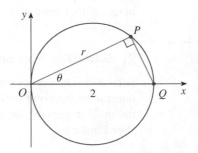

FIGURE 9

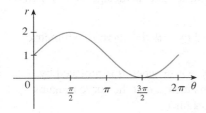

FIGURE 10
$r = 1 + \sin\theta$ in Cartesian coordinates,
$0 \leqslant \theta \leqslant 2\pi$

V EXAMPLE 7 Sketch the curve $r = 1 + \sin\theta$.

SOLUTION Instead of plotting points as in Example 6, we first sketch the graph of $r = 1 + \sin\theta$ in *Cartesian* coordinates in Figure 10 by shifting the sine curve up one unit. This enables us to read at a glance the values of r that correspond to increasing values of θ. For instance, we see that as θ increases from 0 to $\pi/2$, r (the distance from O) increases from 1 to 2, so we sketch the corresponding part of the polar curve in Figure 11(a). As θ increases from $\pi/2$ to π, Figure 10 shows that r decreases from 2 to 1, so we sketch the next part of the curve as in Figure 11(b). As θ increases from π to $3\pi/2$, r decreases from 1 to 0 as shown in part (c). Finally, as θ increases from $3\pi/2$ to 2π, r increases from 0 to 1 as shown in part (d). If we let θ increase beyond 2π or decrease beyond 0, we would simply retrace our path. Putting together the parts of the curve from Figure 11(a)–(d), we sketch the complete curve in part (e). It is called a **cardioid** because it's shaped like a heart.

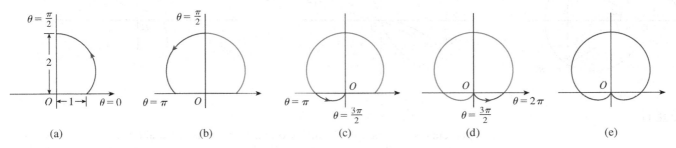

(a)   (b)   (c)   (d)   (e)

FIGURE 11 Stages in sketching the cardioid $r = 1 + \sin\theta$

EXAMPLE 8 Sketch the curve $r = \cos 2\theta$.

SOLUTION As in Example 7, we first sketch $r = \cos 2\theta$, $0 \leqslant \theta \leqslant 2\pi$, in Cartesian coordinates in Figure 12. As θ increases from 0 to $\pi/4$, Figure 12 shows that r decreases from 1 to 0 and so we draw the corresponding portion of the polar curve in Figure 13 (indicated by ①). As θ increases from $\pi/4$ to $\pi/2$, r goes from 0 to -1. This means that the distance from O increases from 0 to 1, but instead of being in the first quadrant this portion of the polar curve (indicated by ②) lies on the opposite side of the pole in the third quadrant. The remainder of the curve is drawn in a similar fashion, with the arrows and numbers indicating the order in which the portions are traced out. The resulting curve has four loops and is called a **four-leaved rose**.

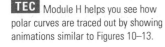 **TEC** Module H helps you see how polar curves are traced out by showing animations similar to Figures 10–13.

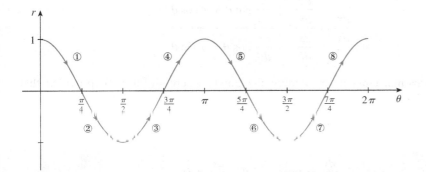

FIGURE 12
$r = \cos 2\theta$ in Cartesian coordinates

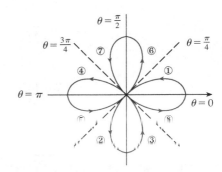

FIGURE 13
Four-leaved rose $r = \cos 2\theta$

When we sketch polar curves it is sometimes helpful to take advantage of symmetry. The following three rules are explained by Figure 14.

(a) If a polar equation is unchanged when θ is replaced by $-\theta$, the curve is symmetric about the polar axis.

(b) If the equation is unchanged when r is replaced by $-r$, or when θ is replaced by $\theta + \pi$, the curve is symmetric about the pole. (This means that the curve remains unchanged if we rotate it through $180°$ about the origin.)

(c) If the equation is unchanged when θ is replaced by $\pi - \theta$, the curve is symmetric about the vertical line $\theta = \pi/2$.

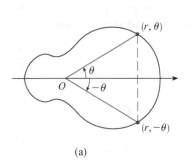   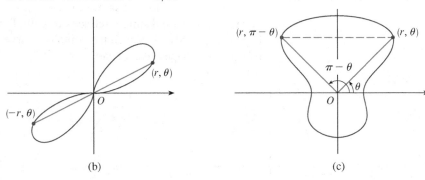

(a)   (b)   (c)

FIGURE 14

The curves sketched in Examples 6 and 8 are symmetric about the polar axis, since $\cos(-\theta) = \cos\theta$. The curves in Examples 7 and 8 are symmetric about $\theta = \pi/2$ because $\sin(\pi - \theta) = \sin\theta$ and $\cos 2(\pi - \theta) = \cos 2\theta$. The four-leaved rose is also symmetric about the pole. These symmetry properties could have been used in sketching the curves. For instance, in Example 6 we need only have plotted points for $0 \leq \theta \leq \pi/2$ and then reflected about the polar axis to obtain the complete circle.

Tangents to Polar Curves

To find a tangent line to a polar curve $r = f(\theta)$ we regard θ as a parameter and write its parametric equations as

$$x = r\cos\theta = f(\theta)\cos\theta \qquad y = r\sin\theta = f(\theta)\sin\theta$$

Then, using the method for finding slopes of parametric curves (Equation 3.4.7) and the Product Rule, we have

$$\boxed{3} \qquad \frac{dy}{dx} = \frac{\dfrac{dy}{d\theta}}{\dfrac{dx}{d\theta}} = \frac{\dfrac{dr}{d\theta}\sin\theta + r\cos\theta}{\dfrac{dr}{d\theta}\cos\theta - r\sin\theta}$$

We locate horizontal tangents by finding the points where $dy/d\theta = 0$ (provided that $dx/d\theta \neq 0$). Likewise, we locate vertical tangents at the points where $dx/d\theta = 0$ (provided that $dy/d\theta \neq 0$).

Notice that if we are looking for tangent lines at the pole, then $r = 0$ and Equation 3 simplifies to

$$\frac{dy}{dx} = \tan\theta \qquad \text{if} \quad \frac{dr}{d\theta} \neq 0$$

For instance, in Example 8 we found that $r = \cos 2\theta = 0$ when $\theta = \pi/4$ or $3\pi/4$. This means that the lines $\theta = \pi/4$ and $\theta = 3\pi/4$ (or $y = x$ and $y = -x$) are tangent lines to $r = \cos 2\theta$ at the origin.

EXAMPLE 9

(a) For the cardioid $r = 1 + \sin \theta$ of Example 7, find the slope of the tangent line when $\theta = \pi/3$.

(b) Find the points on the cardioid where the tangent line is horizontal or vertical.

SOLUTION Using Equation 3 with $r = 1 + \sin \theta$, we have

$$\frac{dy}{dx} = \frac{\dfrac{dr}{d\theta}\sin\theta + r\cos\theta}{\dfrac{dr}{d\theta}\cos\theta - r\sin\theta} = \frac{\cos\theta\sin\theta + (1 + \sin\theta)\cos\theta}{\cos\theta\cos\theta - (1 + \sin\theta)\sin\theta}$$

$$= \frac{\cos\theta(1 + 2\sin\theta)}{1 - 2\sin^2\theta - \sin\theta} = \frac{\cos\theta(1 + 2\sin\theta)}{(1 + \sin\theta)(1 - 2\sin\theta)}$$

(a) The slope of the tangent at the point where $\theta = \pi/3$ is

$$\left.\frac{dy}{dx}\right|_{\theta=\pi/3} = \frac{\cos(\pi/3)(1 + 2\sin(\pi/3))}{(1 + \sin(\pi/3))(1 - 2\sin(\pi/3))} = \frac{\frac{1}{2}\left(1 + \sqrt{3}\right)}{\left(1 + \sqrt{3}/2\right)\left(1 - \sqrt{3}\right)}$$

$$= \frac{1 + \sqrt{3}}{\left(2 + \sqrt{3}\right)\left(1 - \sqrt{3}\right)} = \frac{1 + \sqrt{3}}{-1 - \sqrt{3}} = -1$$

(b) Observe that

$$\frac{dy}{d\theta} = \cos\theta(1 + 2\sin\theta) = 0 \qquad \text{when } \theta = \frac{\pi}{2}, \frac{3\pi}{2}, \frac{7\pi}{6}, \frac{11\pi}{6}$$

$$\frac{dx}{d\theta} = (1 + \sin\theta)(1 - 2\sin\theta) = 0 \qquad \text{when } \theta = \frac{3\pi}{2}, \frac{\pi}{6}, \frac{5\pi}{6}$$

Therefore there are horizontal tangents at the points $(2, \pi/2)$, $(\frac{1}{2}, 7\pi/6)$, $(\frac{1}{2}, 11\pi/6)$ and vertical tangents at $(\frac{3}{2}, \pi/6)$ and $(\frac{3}{2}, 5\pi/6)$. When $\theta = 3\pi/2$, both $dy/d\theta$ and $dx/d\theta$ are 0, so we must be careful. Using l'Hospital's Rule, we have

$$\lim_{\theta \to (3\pi/2)^-} \frac{dy}{dx} = \left(\lim_{\theta \to (3\pi/2)^-} \frac{1 + 2\sin\theta}{1 - 2\sin\theta}\right)\left(\lim_{\theta \to (3\pi/2)^-} \frac{\cos\theta}{1 + \sin\theta}\right)$$

$$= -\frac{1}{3} \lim_{\theta \to (3\pi/2)^-} \frac{\cos\theta}{1 + \sin\theta} = -\frac{1}{3} \lim_{\theta \to (3\pi/2)^-} \frac{-\sin\theta}{\cos\theta} = \infty$$

By symmetry,

$$\lim_{\theta \to (3\pi/2)^+} \frac{dy}{dx} = -\infty$$

Thus there is a vertical tangent line at the pole (see Figure 15).

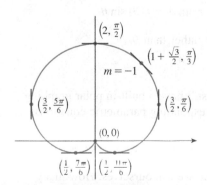

FIGURE 15

Tangent lines for $r = 1 + \sin \theta$

Note: Instead of having to remember Equation 3, we could employ the method used to derive it. For instance, in Example 9 we could have written

$$x = r \cos \theta = (1 + \sin \theta) \cos \theta = \cos \theta + \tfrac{1}{2} \sin 2\theta$$

$$y = r \sin \theta = (1 + \sin \theta) \sin \theta = \sin \theta + \sin^2 \theta$$

Then we have

$$\frac{dy}{dx} = \frac{dy/d\theta}{dx/d\theta} = \frac{\cos \theta + 2 \sin \theta \cos \theta}{-\sin \theta + \cos 2\theta} = \frac{\cos \theta + \sin 2\theta}{-\sin \theta + \cos 2\theta}$$

which is equivalent to our previous expression.

Graphing Polar Curves with Graphing Devices

Although it's useful to be able to sketch simple polar curves by hand, we need to use a graphing calculator or computer when we are faced with a curve as complicated as the ones shown in Figures 16 and 17.

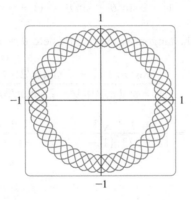

FIGURE 16
$r = \sin^2(2.4\theta) + \cos^4(2.4\theta)$

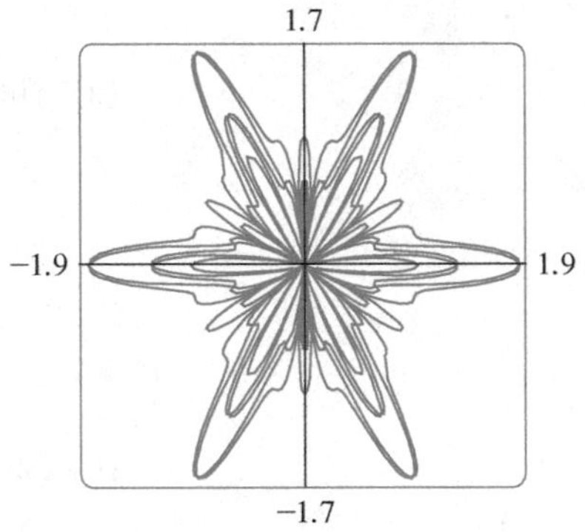

FIGURE 17
$r = \sin^2(1.2\theta) + \cos^3(6\theta)$

Some graphing devices have commands that enable us to graph polar curves directly. With other machines we need to convert to parametric equations first. In this case we take the polar equation $r = f(\theta)$ and write its parametric equations as

$$x = r \cos \theta = f(\theta) \cos \theta \qquad y = r \sin \theta = f(\theta) \sin \theta$$

Some machines require that the parameter be called t rather than θ.

EXAMPLE 10   Graph the curve $r = \sin(8\theta/5)$.

SOLUTION   Let's assume that our graphing device doesn't have a built-in polar graphing command. In this case we need to work with the corresponding parametric equations, which are

$$x = r \cos \theta = \sin(8\theta/5) \cos \theta \qquad y = r \sin \theta = \sin(8\theta/5) \sin \theta$$

In any case we need to determine the domain for θ. So we ask ourselves: How many complete rotations are required until the curve starts to repeat itself? If the answer is n, then

$$\sin \frac{8(\theta + 2n\pi)}{5} = \sin\left(\frac{8\theta}{5} + \frac{16n\pi}{5} \right) = \sin \frac{8\theta}{5}$$

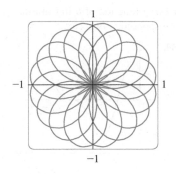

FIGURE 18
$r = \sin(8\theta/5)$

In Exercise 47 you are asked to prove analytically what we have discovered from the graphs in Figure 19.

and so we require that $16n\pi/5$ be an even multiple of π. This will first occur when $n = 5$. Therefore we will graph the entire curve if we specify that $0 \leq \theta \leq 10\pi$. Switching from θ to t, we have the equations

$$x = \sin(8t/5)\cos t \qquad y = \sin(8t/5)\sin t \qquad 0 \leq t \leq 10\pi$$

and Figure 18 shows the resulting curve. Notice that this rose has 16 loops.

V EXAMPLE 11 Investigate the family of polar curves given by $r = 1 + c\sin\theta$. How does the shape change as c changes? (These curves are called **limaçons**, after a French word for snail, because of the shape of the curves for certain values of c.)

SOLUTION Figure 19 shows computer-drawn graphs for various values of c. For $c > 1$ there is a loop that decreases in size as c decreases. When $c = 1$ the loop disappears and the curve becomes the cardioid that we sketched in Example 7. For c between 1 and $\frac{1}{2}$ the cardioid's cusp is smoothed out and becomes a "dimple." When c decreases from $\frac{1}{2}$ to 0, the limaçon is shaped like an oval. This oval becomes more circular as $c \to 0$, and when $c = 0$ the curve is just the circle $r = 1$.

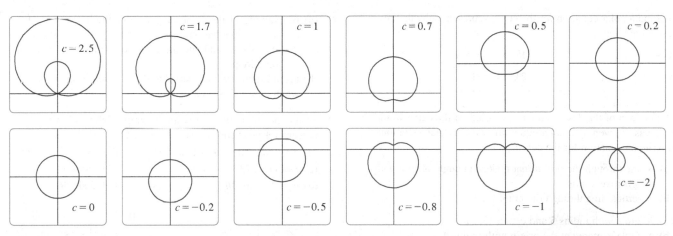

FIGURE 19
Members of the family of
limaçons $r = 1 + c\sin\theta$

The remaining parts of Figure 19 show that as c becomes negative, the shapes change in reverse order. In fact, these curves are reflections about the horizontal axis of the corresponding curves with positive c.

H.1 Exercises

1–2 Plot the point whose polar coordinates are given. Then find two other pairs of polar coordinates of this point, one with $r > 0$ and one with $r < 0$.

1. (a) $(2, \pi/3)$ (b) $(1, -3\pi/4)$ (c) $(-1, \pi/2)$

2. (a) $(1, 7\pi/4)$ (b) $(-3, \pi/6)$ (c) $(1, -1)$

3–4 Plot the point whose polar coordinates are given. Then find the Cartesian coordinates of the point.

3. (a) $(1, \pi)$ (b) $(2, -2\pi/3)$ (c) $(-2, 3\pi/4)$

4. (a) $\left(-\sqrt{2}, 5\pi/4\right)$ (b) $(1, 5\pi/2)$ (c) $(2, -7\pi/6)$

5–6 The Cartesian coordinates of a point are given.
(i) Find polar coordinates (r, θ) of the point, where $r > 0$ and $0 \leq \theta < 2\pi$.
(ii) Find polar coordinates (r, θ) of the point, where $r < 0$ and $0 \leq \theta < 2\pi$.

5. (a) $(2, -2)$ (b) $\left(-1, \sqrt{3}\,\right)$

6. (a) $\left(3\sqrt{3}, 3\right)$ (b) $(1, -2)$

7–12 Sketch the region in the plane consisting of points whose polar coordinates satisfy the given conditions.

7. $1 \le r \le 2$

8. $r \ge 0, \quad \pi/3 \le \theta \le 2\pi/3$

9. $0 \le r < 4, \quad -\pi/2 \le \theta < \pi/6$

10. $2 < r \le 5, \quad 3\pi/4 < \theta < 5\pi/4$

11. $2 < r < 3, \quad 5\pi/3 \le \theta \le 7\pi/3$

12. $r \ge 1, \quad \pi \le \theta \le 2\pi$

13–16 Identify the curve by finding a Cartesian equation for the curve.

13. $r = 3 \sin \theta$

14. $r = 2 \sin \theta + 2 \cos \theta$

15. $r = \csc \theta$

16. $r = \tan \theta \sec \theta$

17–20 Find a polar equation for the curve represented by the given Cartesian equation.

17. $x = -y^2$

18. $x + y = 9$

19. $x^2 + y^2 = 2cx$

20. $xy = 4$

21–22 For each of the described curves, decide if the curve would be more easily given by a polar equation or a Cartesian equation. Then write an equation for the curve.

21. (a) A line through the origin that makes an angle of $\pi/6$ with the positive x-axis
(b) A vertical line through the point $(3, 3)$

22. (a) A circle with radius 5 and center $(2, 3)$
(b) A circle centered at the origin with radius 4

23–42 Sketch the curve with the given polar equation.

23. $\theta = -\pi/6$

24. $r^2 - 3r + 2 = 0$

25. $r = \sin \theta$

26. $r = -3 \cos \theta$

27. $r = 2(1 - \sin \theta), \; \theta \ge 0$

28. $r = 1 - 3 \cos \theta$

29. $r = \theta, \; \theta \ge 0$

30. $r = \ln \theta, \; \theta \ge 1$

31. $r = 4 \sin 3\theta$

32. $r = \cos 5\theta$

33. $r = 2 \cos 4\theta$

34. $r = 3 \cos 6\theta$

35. $r = 1 - 2 \sin \theta$

36. $r = 2 + \sin \theta$

37. $r^2 = 9 \sin 2\theta$

38. $r^2 = \cos 4\theta$

39. $r = 2 \cos(3\theta/2)$

40. $r^2\theta = 1$

41. $r = 1 + 2 \cos 2\theta$

42. $r = 1 + 2 \cos(\theta/2)$

43–44 The figure shows a graph of r as a function of θ in Cartesian coordinates. Use it to sketch the corresponding polar curve.

43. 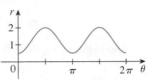   **44.**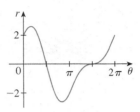

---

45. Show that the polar curve $r = 4 + 2 \sec \theta$ (called a **conchoid**) has the line $x = 2$ as a vertical asymptote by showing that $\lim_{r \to \pm\infty} x = 2$. Use this fact to help sketch the conchoid.

46. Show that the curve $r = \sin \theta \tan \theta$ (called a **cissoid of Diocles**) has the line $x = 1$ as a vertical asymptote. Show also that the curve lies entirely within the vertical strip $0 \le x < 1$. Use these facts to help sketch the cissoid.

47. (a) In Example 11 the graphs suggest that the limaçon $r = 1 + c \sin \theta$ has an inner loop when $|c| > 1$. Prove that this is true, and find the values of θ that correspond to the inner loop.
(b) From Figure 19 it appears that the limaçon loses its dimple when $c = \frac{1}{2}$. Prove this.

48. Match the polar equations with the graphs labeled I–VI. Give reasons for your choices. (Don't use a graphing device.)
(a) $r = \sqrt{\theta}, \quad 0 \le \theta \le 16\pi$ (b) $r = \theta^2, \quad 0 \le \theta \le 16\pi$
(c) $r = \cos(\theta/3)$ (d) $r = 1 + 2 \cos \theta$
(e) $r = 2 + \sin 3\theta$ (f) $r = 1 + 2 \sin 3\theta$

I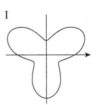

II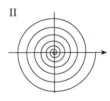

III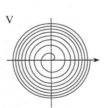

IV

V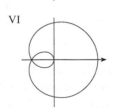

VI

49–52 Find the slope of the tangent line to the given polar curve at the point specified by the value of θ.

49. $r = 1/\theta$, $\theta = \pi$

50. $r = 2 - \sin\theta$, $\theta = \pi/3$

51. $r = \cos 2\theta$, $\theta = \pi/4$

52. $r = \cos(\theta/3)$, $\theta = \pi$

53–56 Find the points on the given curve where the tangent line is horizontal or vertical.

53. $r = 3\cos\theta$

54. $r = e^\theta$

55. $r = 1 + \cos\theta$

56. $r = 1 - \sin\theta$

---

57. Show that the polar equation $r = a\sin\theta + b\cos\theta$, where $ab \neq 0$, represents a circle, and find its center and radius.

58. Show that the curves $r = a\sin\theta$ and $r = a\cos\theta$ intersect at right angles.

59–62 Use a graphing device to graph the polar curve. Choose the parameter interval carefully to make sure that you produce an appropriate curve.

59 $r = e^{\sin\theta} - 2\cos(4\theta)$ (butterfly curve)

60. $r = |\tan\theta|^{|\cot\theta|}$ (valentine curve)

61. $r = 2 - 5\sin(\theta/6)$

62. $r = \cos(\theta/2) + \cos(\theta/3)$

---

63. How are the graphs of $r = 1 + \sin(\theta - \pi/6)$ and $r = 1 + \sin(\theta - \pi/3)$ related to the graph of $r = 1 + \sin\theta$? In general, how is the graph of $r = f(\theta - \alpha)$ related to the graph of $r = f(\theta)$?

64. Use a graph to estimate the y-coordinate of the highest points on the curve $r = \sin 2\theta$. Then use calculus to find the exact value.

65. (a) Investigate the family of curves defined by the polar equations $r = \sin n\theta$, where n is a positive integer. How is the number of loops related to n?
(b) What happens if the equation in part (a) is replaced by $r = |\sin n\theta|$?

66. A family of curves is given by the equations $r = 1 + c\sin n\theta$, where c is a real number and n is a positive integer. How

does the graph change as n increases? How does it change as c changes? Illustrate by graphing enough members of the family to support your conclusions.

67. A family of curves has polar equations

$$r = \frac{1 - a\cos\theta}{1 + a\cos\theta}$$

Investigate how the graph changes as the number a changes. In particular, you should identify the transitional values of a for which the basic shape of the curve changes.

68. The astronomer Giovanni Cassini (1625–1712) studied the family of curves with polar equations

$$r^4 - 2c^2r^2\cos 2\theta + c^4 - a^4 = 0$$

where a and c are positive real numbers. These curves are called the **ovals of Cassini** even though they are oval shaped only for certain values of a and c. (Cassini thought that these curves might represent planetary orbits better than Kepler's ellipses.) Investigate the variety of shapes that these curves may have. In particular, how are a and c related to each other when the curve splits into two parts?

69. Let P be any point (except the origin) on the curve $r = f(\theta)$. If ψ is the angle between the tangent line at P and the radial line OP, show that

$$\tan\psi = \frac{r}{dr/d\theta}$$

[*Hint:* Observe that $\psi = \phi - \theta$ in the figure.]

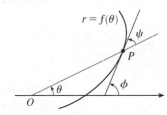

70. (a) Use Exercise 69 to show that the angle between the tangent line and the radial line is $\psi = \pi/4$ at every point on the curve $r = e^\theta$.
(b) Illustrate part (a) by graphing the curve and the tangent lines at the points where $\theta = 0$ and $\pi/2$.
(c) Prove that any polar curve $r = f(\theta)$ with the property that the angle ψ between the radial line and the tangent line is a constant must be of the form $r = Ce^{k\theta}$, where C and k are constants.

H.2 | Areas and Lengths in Polar Coordinates

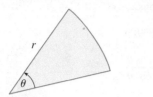

FIGURE 1

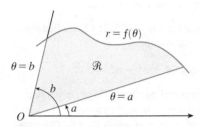

FIGURE 2

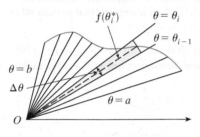

FIGURE 3

In this section we develop the formula for the area of a region whose boundary is given by a polar equation. We need to use the formula for the area of a sector of a circle

$$\boxed{1} \qquad A = \tfrac{1}{2}r^2\theta$$

where, as in Figure 1, r is the radius and θ is the radian measure of the central angle. Formula 1 follows from the fact that the area of a sector is proportional to its central angle: $A = (\theta/2\pi)\pi r^2 = \tfrac{1}{2}r^2\theta$.

Let $\mathcal{R}$ be the region, illustrated in Figure 2, bounded by the polar curve $r = f(\theta)$ and by the rays $\theta = a$ and $\theta = b$, where f is a positive continuous function and where $0 < b - a \leq 2\pi$. We divide the interval $[a, b]$ into subintervals with endpoints θ_0, $\theta_1, \theta_2, \ldots, \theta_n$ and equal width $\Delta\theta$. The rays $\theta = \theta_i$ then divide $\mathcal{R}$ into n smaller regions with central angle $\Delta\theta = \theta_i - \theta_{i-1}$. If we choose θ_i^* in the ith subinterval $[\theta_{i-1}, \theta_i]$, then the area ΔA_i of the ith region is approximated by the area of the sector of a circle with central angle $\Delta\theta$ and radius $f(\theta_i^*)$. (See Figure 3.)

Thus from Formula 1 we have

$$\Delta A_i \approx \tfrac{1}{2}[f(\theta_i^*)]^2\,\Delta\theta$$

and so an approximation to the total area A of $\mathcal{R}$ is

$$\boxed{2} \qquad A \approx \sum_{i=1}^{n} \tfrac{1}{2}[f(\theta_i^*)]^2\,\Delta\theta$$

It appears from Figure 3 that the approximation in (2) improves as $n \to \infty$. But the sums in (2) are Riemann sums for the function $g(\theta) = \tfrac{1}{2}[f(\theta)]^2$, so

$$\lim_{n\to\infty} \sum_{i=1}^{n} \tfrac{1}{2}[f(\theta_i^*)]^2\,\Delta\theta = \int_a^b \tfrac{1}{2}[f(\theta)]^2\,d\theta$$

It therefore appears plausible (and can in fact be proved) that the formula for the area A of the polar region $\mathcal{R}$ is

$$\boxed{3} \qquad A = \int_a^b \tfrac{1}{2}[f(\theta)]^2\,d\theta$$

Formula 3 is often written as

$$\boxed{4} \qquad A = \int_a^b \tfrac{1}{2}r^2\,d\theta$$

with the understanding that $r = f(\theta)$. Note the similarity between Formulas 1 and 4.

When we apply Formula 3 or 4 it is helpful to think of the area as being swept out by a rotating ray through O that starts with angle a and ends with angle b.

V EXAMPLE 1 Find the area enclosed by one loop of the four-leaved rose $r = \cos 2\theta$.

SOLUTION The curve $r = \cos 2\theta$ was sketched in Example 8 in Section H.1. Notice from Figure 4 that the region enclosed by the right loop is swept out by a ray that rotates from $\theta = -\pi/4$ to $\theta = \pi/4$. Therefore Formula 4 gives

$$A = \int_{-\pi/4}^{\pi/4} \tfrac{1}{2} r^2 \, d\theta = \tfrac{1}{2} \int_{-\pi/4}^{\pi/4} \cos^2 2\theta \, d\theta = \int_0^{\pi/4} \cos^2 2\theta \, d\theta$$

We could evaluate the integral using Formula 64 in the Table of Integrals. Or, as in Section 5.7, we could use the identity $\cos^2 x = \tfrac{1}{2}(1 + \cos 2x)$ to write

$$A = \int_0^{\pi/4} \tfrac{1}{2}(1 + \cos 4\theta) \, d\theta = \tfrac{1}{2}\left[\theta + \tfrac{1}{4}\sin 4\theta\right]_0^{\pi/4} = \frac{\pi}{8}$$

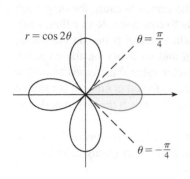

FIGURE 4

V EXAMPLE 2 Find the area of the region that lies inside the circle $r = 3 \sin \theta$ and outside the cardioid $r = 1 + \sin \theta$.

SOLUTION The cardioid (see Example 7 in Section H.1) and the circle are sketched in Figure 5 and the desired region is shaded. The values of a and b in Formula 4 are determined by finding the points of intersection of the two curves. They intersect when $3 \sin \theta = 1 + \sin \theta$, which gives $\sin \theta = \tfrac{1}{2}$, so $\theta = \pi/6, 5\pi/6$. The desired area can be found by subtracting the area inside the cardioid between $\theta = \pi/6$ and $\theta = 5\pi/6$ from the area inside the circle from $\pi/6$ to $5\pi/6$. Thus

$$A = \tfrac{1}{2}\int_{\pi/6}^{5\pi/6} (3 \sin \theta)^2 \, d\theta - \tfrac{1}{2}\int_{\pi/6}^{5\pi/6} (1 + \sin \theta)^2 \, d\theta$$

Since the region is symmetric about the vertical axis $\theta = \pi/2$, we can write

$$A = 2\left[\tfrac{1}{2}\int_{\pi/6}^{\pi/2} 9 \sin^2\theta \, d\theta - \tfrac{1}{2}\int_{\pi/6}^{\pi/2} (1 + 2 \sin \theta + \sin^2\theta) \, d\theta\right]$$

$$= \int_{\pi/6}^{\pi/2} (8 \sin^2\theta - 1 - 2 \sin \theta) \, d\theta$$

$$= \int_{\pi/6}^{\pi/2} (3 - 4 \cos 2\theta - 2 \sin \theta) \, d\theta \qquad \text{[because } \sin^2\theta = \tfrac{1}{2}(1 - \cos 2\theta)\text{]}$$

$$= 3\theta - 2 \sin 2\theta + 2 \cos \theta \Big]_{\pi/6}^{\pi/2} = \pi$$

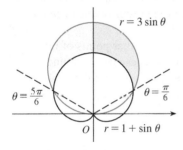

FIGURE 5

Example 2 illustrates the procedure for finding the area of the region bounded by two polar curves. In general, let $\mathcal{R}$ be a region, as illustrated in Figure 6, that is bounded by curves with polar equations $r = f(\theta)$, $r = g(\theta)$, $\theta = a$, and $\theta = b$, where $f(\theta) \geq g(\theta) \geq 0$ and $0 < b - a \leq 2\pi$. The area A of $\mathcal{R}$ is found by subtracting the area inside $r = g(\theta)$ from the area inside $r = f(\theta)$, so using Formula 3 we have

$$A = \int_a^b \tfrac{1}{2}[f(\theta)]^2 \, d\theta - \int_a^b \tfrac{1}{2}[g(\theta)]^2 \, d\theta$$

$$= \tfrac{1}{2}\int_a^b \left([f(\theta)]^2 - [g(\theta)]^2\right) d\theta$$

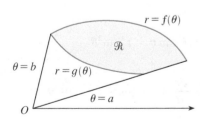

FIGURE 6

⊘ **CAUTION** The fact that a single point has many representations in polar coordinates sometimes makes it difficult to find all the points of intersection of two polar curves. For instance, it is obvious from Figure 5 that the circle and the cardioid have three points of intersection; however, in Example 2 we solved the equations $r = 3 \sin \theta$ and $r = 1 + \sin \theta$

and found only two such points, $\left(\frac{3}{2}, \pi/6\right)$ and $\left(\frac{3}{2}, 5\pi/6\right)$. The origin is also a point of intersection, but we can't find it by solving the equations of the curves because the origin has no single representation in polar coordinates that satisfies both equations. Notice that, when represented as $(0, 0)$ or $(0, \pi)$, the origin satisfies $r = 3 \sin\theta$ and so it lies on the circle; when represented as $(0, 3\pi/2)$, it satisfies $r = 1 + \sin\theta$ and so it lies on the cardioid. Think of two points moving along the curves as the parameter value θ increases from 0 to 2π. On one curve the origin is reached at $\theta = 0$ and $\theta = \pi$; on the other curve it is reached at $\theta = 3\pi/2$. The points don't collide at the origin because they reach the origin at different times, but the curves intersect there nonetheless.

Thus, to find *all* points of intersection of two polar curves, it is recommended that you draw the graphs of both curves. It is especially convenient to use a graphing calculator or computer to help with this task.

EXAMPLE 3   Find all points of intersection of the curves $r = \cos 2\theta$ and $r = \frac{1}{2}$.

SOLUTION If we solve the equations $r = \cos 2\theta$ and $r = \frac{1}{2}$, we get $\cos 2\theta = \frac{1}{2}$ and therefore $2\theta = \pi/3, 5\pi/3, 7\pi/3, 11\pi/3$. Thus the values of θ between 0 and 2π that satisfy both equations are $\theta = \pi/6, 5\pi/6, 7\pi/6, 11\pi/6$. We have found four points of intersection: $\left(\frac{1}{2}, \pi/6\right)$, $\left(\frac{1}{2}, 5\pi/6\right)$, $\left(\frac{1}{2}, 7\pi/6\right)$, and $\left(\frac{1}{2}, 11\pi/6\right)$.

However, you can see from Figure 7 that the curves have four other points of intersection—namely, $\left(\frac{1}{2}, \pi/3\right)$, $\left(\frac{1}{2}, 2\pi/3\right)$, $\left(\frac{1}{2}, 4\pi/3\right)$, and $\left(\frac{1}{2}, 5\pi/3\right)$. These can be found using symmetry or by noticing that another equation of the circle is $r = -\frac{1}{2}$ and then solving the equations $r = \cos 2\theta$ and $r = -\frac{1}{2}$.

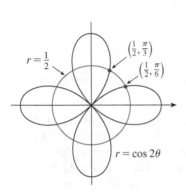

FIGURE 7

Arc Length

To find the length of a polar curve $r = f(\theta)$, $a \leq \theta \leq b$, we regard θ as a parameter and write the parametric equations of the curve as

$$x = r \cos\theta = f(\theta) \cos\theta \qquad y = r \sin\theta = f(\theta) \sin\theta$$

Using the Product Rule and differentiating with respect to θ, we obtain

$$\frac{dx}{d\theta} = \frac{dr}{d\theta} \cos\theta - r \sin\theta \qquad \frac{dy}{d\theta} = \frac{dr}{d\theta} \sin\theta + r \cos\theta$$

so, using $\cos^2\theta + \sin^2\theta = 1$, we have

$$\left(\frac{dx}{d\theta}\right)^2 + \left(\frac{dy}{d\theta}\right)^2 = \left(\frac{dr}{d\theta}\right)^2 \cos^2\theta - 2r \frac{dr}{d\theta} \cos\theta \sin\theta + r^2 \sin^2\theta$$

$$+ \left(\frac{dr}{d\theta}\right)^2 \sin^2\theta + 2r \frac{dr}{d\theta} \sin\theta \cos\theta + r^2 \cos^2\theta$$

$$= \left(\frac{dr}{d\theta}\right)^2 + r^2$$

Assuming that f' is continuous, we can use Formula 6.4.1 to write the arc length as

$$L = \int_a^b \sqrt{\left(\frac{dx}{d\theta}\right)^2 + \left(\frac{dy}{d\theta}\right)^2}\, d\theta$$

Therefore the length of a curve with polar equation $r = f(\theta)$, $a \leqslant \theta \leqslant b$, is

$$\boxed{5} \qquad L = \int_a^b \sqrt{r^2 + \left(\frac{dr}{d\theta}\right)^2} \, d\theta$$

V EXAMPLE 4   Find the length of the cardioid $r = 1 + \sin\theta$.

SOLUTION   The cardioid is shown in Figure 8. (We sketched it in Example 7 in Section H.1.) Its full length is given by the parameter interval $0 \leqslant \theta \leqslant 2\pi$, so Formula 5 gives

$$L = \int_0^{2\pi} \sqrt{r^2 + \left(\frac{dr}{d\theta}\right)^2} \, d\theta = \int_0^{2\pi} \sqrt{(1 + \sin\theta)^2 + \cos^2\theta} \, d\theta$$

$$= \int_0^{2\pi} \sqrt{2 + 2\sin\theta} \, d\theta$$

We could evaluate this integral by multiplying and dividing the integrand by $\sqrt{2 - 2\sin\theta}$, or we could use a computer algebra system. In any event, we find that the length of the cardioid is $L = 8$.

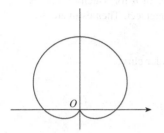

FIGURE 8
$r = 1 + \sin\theta$

H.2 Exercises

1–4 Find the area of the region that is bounded by the given curve and lies in the specified sector.

1. $r = \theta^2$, $0 \leqslant \theta \leqslant \pi/4$ **2.** $r = e^{\theta/2}$, $\pi \leqslant \theta \leqslant 2\pi$

3. $r = \sin\theta$, $\pi/3 \leqslant \theta \leqslant 2\pi/3$ **4.** $r = \sqrt{\sin\theta}$, $0 \leqslant \theta \leqslant \pi$

5–8 Find the area of the shaded region.

5.

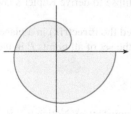
$r = \sqrt{\theta}$

6.
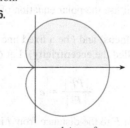
$r = 1 + \cos\theta$

7.
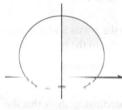
$r = 4 + 3\sin\theta$

8.
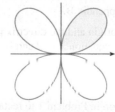
$r = \sin 2\theta$

9–12 Sketch the curve and find the area that it encloses.

9. $r^2 = 4\cos 2\theta$ **10.** $r = 2 - \sin\theta$

11. $r = 2\cos 3\theta$ **12.** $r = 2 + \cos 2\theta$

13–14 Graph the curve and find the area that it encloses.

13. $r = 1 + 2\sin 6\theta$ **14.** $r = 2\sin\theta + 3\sin 9\theta$

15–18 Find the area of the region enclosed by one loop of the curve.

15. $r = \sin 2\theta$ **16.** $r = 4\sin 3\theta$

17. $r = 1 + 2\sin\theta$ (inner loop)

18. $r = 2\cos\theta - \sec\theta$

19–22 Find the area of the region that lies inside the first curve and outside the second curve.

19. $r = 2\cos\theta$, $r = 1$ **20.** $r = 1 - \sin\theta$, $r = 1$

21. $r = 3\cos\theta$, $r = 1 + \cos\theta$

22. $r = 3\sin\theta$, $r = 2 - \sin\theta$

Graphing calculator or computer with graphing software required   **1.** Homework Hints available in TEC

23–26 Find the area of the region that lies inside both curves.

23. $r = \sqrt{3}\cos\theta, \quad r = \sin\theta$

24. $r = 1 + \cos\theta, \quad r = 1 - \cos\theta$

25. $r = \sin 2\theta, \quad r = \cos 2\theta$

26. $r = 3 + 2\cos\theta, \quad r = 3 + 2\sin\theta$

27. Find the area inside the larger loop and outside the smaller loop of the limaçon $r = \frac{1}{2} + \cos\theta$.

28. When recording live performances, sound engineers often use a microphone with a cardioid pickup pattern because it suppresses noise from the audience. Suppose the microphone is placed 4 m from the front of the stage (as in the figure) and the boundary of the optimal pickup region is given by the cardioid $r = 8 + 8\sin\theta$, where r is measured in meters and the microphone is at the pole. The musicians want to know the area they will have on stage within the optimal pickup range of the microphone. Answer their question.

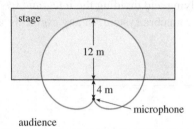

29–32 Find all points of intersection of the given curves.

29. $r = 2\sin 2\theta, \quad r = 1$

30. $r = \cos 3\theta, \quad r = \sin 3\theta$

31. $r = \sin\theta, \quad r = \sin 2\theta$

32. $r^2 = \sin 2\theta, \quad r^2 = \cos 2\theta$

 33. The points of intersection of the cardioid $r = 1 + \sin\theta$ and the spiral loop $r = 2\theta$, $-\pi/2 \leqslant \theta \leqslant \pi/2$, can't be found exactly. Use a graphing device to find the approximate values of θ at which they intersect. Then use these values to estimate the area that lies inside both curves.

 34. Use a graph to estimate the values of θ for which the curves $r = 3 + \sin 5\theta$ and $r = 6\sin\theta$ intersect. Then estimate the area that lies inside both curves.

35–38 Find the exact length of the polar curve.

35. $r = 3\sin\theta, \quad 0 \leqslant \theta \leqslant \pi/3$

36. $r = e^{2\theta}, \quad 0 \leqslant \theta \leqslant 2\pi$

37. $r = \theta^2, \quad 0 \leqslant \theta \leqslant 2\pi$

38. $r = \theta, \quad 0 \leqslant \theta \leqslant 2\pi$

39–40 Use a calculator to find the length of the curve correct to four decimal places.

39. $r = 3\sin 2\theta$ **40.** $r = 4\sin 3\theta$

DISCOVERY PROJECT   Conic Sections in Polar Coordinates

In this project we give a unified treatment of all three types of conic sections in terms of a focus and directrix. We will see that if we place the focus at the origin, then a conic section has a simple polar equation. In Chapter 10 we will use the polar equation of an ellipse to derive Kepler's laws of planetary motion.

Let F be a fixed point (called the **focus**) and l be a fixed line (called the **directrix**) in a plane. Let e be a fixed positive number (called the **eccentricity**). Let C be the set of all points P in the plane such that

$$\frac{|PF|}{|Pl|} = e$$

(that is, the ratio of the distance from F to the distance from l is the constant e). Notice that if the eccentricity is $e = 1$, then $|PF| = |Pl|$ and so the given condition simply becomes the definition of a parabola as given in Appendix B.

1. If we place the focus F at the origin and the directrix parallel to the y-axis and d units to the right, then the directrix has equation $x = d$ and is perpendicular to the polar axis. If the point P has polar coordinates (r, θ), use Figure 1 to show that

$$r = e(d - r\cos\theta)$$

2. By converting the polar equation in Problem 1 to rectangular coordinates, show that the curve C is an ellipse if $e < 1$. (See Appendix B for a discussion of ellipses.)

FIGURE 1

 Graphing calculator or computer with graphing software required

3. Show that C is a hyperbola if $e > 1$.

4. Show that the polar equation

$$r = \frac{ed}{1 + e \cos \theta}$$

represents an ellipse if $e < 1$, a parabola if $e = 1$, or a hyperbola if $e > 1$.

5. For each of the following conics, find the eccentricity and directrix. Then identify and sketch the conic.

(a) $r = \dfrac{4}{1 + 3 \cos \theta}$ (b) $r = \dfrac{8}{3 + 3 \cos \theta}$ (c) $r = \dfrac{2}{2 + \cos \theta}$

6. Graph the conics $r = e/(1 - e \cos \theta)$ with $e = 0.4, 0.6, 0.8$, and 1.0 on a common screen. How does the value of e affect the shape of the curve?

7. (a) Show that the polar equation of an ellipse with directrix $x = d$ can be written in the form

$$r = \frac{a(1 - e^2)}{1 - e \cos \theta}$$

(b) Find an approximate polar equation for the elliptical orbit of the planet Earth around the sun (at one focus) given that the eccentricity is about 0.017 and the length of the major axis is about 2.99×10^8 km.

8. (a) The planets move around the sun in elliptical orbits with the sun at one focus. The positions of a planet that are closest to and farthest from the sun are called its *perihelion* and *aphelion*, respectively. (See Figure 2.) Use Problem 7(a) to show that the perihelion distance from a planet to the sun is $a(1 - e)$ and the aphelion distance is $a(1 + e)$.

(b) Use the data of Problem 7(b) to find the distances from the planet Earth to the sun at perihelion and at aphelion.

9. (a) The planet Mercury travels in an elliptical orbit with eccentricity 0.206. Its minimum distance from the sun is 4.6×10^7 km. Use the results of Problem 8(a) to find its maximum distance from the sun.

(b) Find the distance traveled by the planet Mercury during one complete orbit around the sun. (Use your calculator or computer algebra system to evaluate the definite integral.)

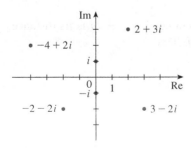

FIGURE 2

I │ Complex Numbers

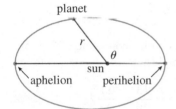

FIGURE 1

Complex numbers as points in the Argand plane

A **complex number** can be represented by an expression of the form $a + bi$, where a and b are real numbers and i is a symbol with the property that $i^2 = -1$. The complex number $a + bi$ can also be represented by the ordered pair (a, b) and plotted as a point in a plane (called the Argand plane) as in Figure 1. Thus the complex number $i = 0 + 1 \cdot i$ is identified with the point $(0, 1)$.

The **real part** of the complex number $a + bi$ is the real number a and the **imaginary part** is the real number b. Thus the real part of $4 - 3i$ is 4 and the imaginary part is -3. Two complex numbers $a + bi$ and $c + di$ are **equal** if $a = c$ and $b = d$, that is, their real parts are equal and their imaginary parts are equal. In the Argand plane the horizontal axis is called the real axis and the vertical axis is called the imaginary axis.

The sum and difference of two complex numbers are defined by adding or subtracting their real parts and their imaginary parts:

$$(a + bi) + (c + di) = (a + c) + (b + d)i$$

$$(a + bi) - (c + di) = (a - c) + (b - d)i$$

For instance,

$$(1 - i) + (4 + 7i) = (1 + 4) + (-1 + 7)i = 5 + 6i$$

The product of complex numbers is defined so that the usual commutative and distributive laws hold:

$$(a + bi)(c + di) = a(c + di) + (bi)(c + di)$$

$$= ac + adi + bci + bdi^2$$

Since $i^2 = -1$, this becomes

$$(a + bi)(c + di) = (ac - bd) + (ad + bc)i$$

EXAMPLE 1

$$(-1 + 3i)(2 - 5i) = (-1)(2 - 5i) + 3i(2 - 5i)$$

$$= -2 + 5i + 6i - 15(-1) = 13 + 11i$$

Division of complex numbers is much like rationalizing the denominator of a rational expression. For the complex number $z = a + bi$, we define its **complex conjugate** to be $\bar{z} = a - bi$. To find the quotient of two complex numbers we multiply numerator and denominator by the complex conjugate of the denominator.

EXAMPLE 2 Express the number $\dfrac{-1 + 3i}{2 + 5i}$ in the form $a + bi$.

SOLUTION We multiply numerator and denominator by the complex conjugate of $2 + 5i$, namely $2 - 5i$, and we take advantage of the result of Example 1:

$$\frac{-1 + 3i}{2 + 5i} = \frac{-1 + 3i}{2 + 5i} \cdot \frac{2 - 5i}{2 - 5i} = \frac{13 + 11i}{2^2 + 5^2} = \frac{13}{29} + \frac{11}{29}i$$

The geometric interpretation of the complex conjugate is shown in Figure 2: $\bar{z}$ is the reflection of z in the real axis. We list some of the properties of the complex conjugate in the following box. The proofs follow from the definition and are requested in Exercise 18.

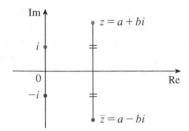

FIGURE 2

Properties of Conjugates

$$\overline{z + w} = \bar{z} + \bar{w} \qquad \overline{zw} = \bar{z}\,\bar{w} \qquad \overline{z^n} = \bar{z}^n$$

The **modulus**, or **absolute value**, $|z|$ of a complex number $z = a + bi$ is its distance from the origin. From Figure 3 we see that if $z = a + bi$, then

$$\boxed{|z| = \sqrt{a^2 + b^2}}$$

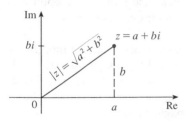

FIGURE 3

Notice that

$$z\bar{z} = (a + bi)(a - bi) = a^2 + abi - abi - b^2i^2 = a^2 + b^2$$

and so

$$\boxed{z\bar{z} = |z|^2}$$

This explains why the division procedure in Example 2 works in general:

$$\frac{z}{w} = \frac{z\overline{w}}{w\overline{w}} = \frac{z\overline{w}}{|w|^2}$$

Since $i^2 = -1$, we can think of i as a square root of -1. But notice that we also have $(-i)^2 = i^2 = -1$ and so $-i$ is also a square root of -1. We say that i is the **principal square root** of -1 and write $\sqrt{-1} = i$. In general, if c is any positive number, we write

$$\sqrt{-c} = \sqrt{c}\; i$$

With this convention, the usual derivation and formula for the roots of the quadratic equation $ax^2 + bx + c = 0$ are valid even when $b^2 - 4ac < 0$:

$$x = \frac{-b \pm \sqrt{b^2 - 4ac}}{2a}$$

EXAMPLE 3 Find the roots of the equation $x^2 + x + 1 = 0$.

SOLUTION Using the quadratic formula, we have

$$x = \frac{-1 \pm \sqrt{1^2 - 4 \cdot 1}}{2} = \frac{-1 \pm \sqrt{-3}}{2} = \frac{-1 \pm \sqrt{3}\; i}{2}$$ ▬

We observe that the solutions of the equation in Example 3 are complex conjugates of each other. In general, the solutions of any quadratic equation $ax^2 + bx + c = 0$ with real coefficients a, b, and c are always complex conjugates. (If z is real, $\overline{z} = z$, so z is its own conjugate.)

We have seen that if we allow complex numbers as solutions, then every quadratic equation has a solution. More generally, it is true that every polynomial equation

$$a_n x^n + a_{n-1} x^{n-1} + \cdots + a_1 x + a_0 = 0$$

of degree at least one has a solution among the complex numbers. This fact is known as the Fundamental Theorem of Algebra and was proved by Gauss.

Polar Form

We know that any complex number $z = a + bi$ can be considered as a point (a, b) and that any such point can be represented by polar coordinates (r, θ) with $r \geqslant 0$. In fact,

$$a = r \cos \theta \qquad b = r \sin \theta$$

as in Figure 4. Therefore we have

$$z = a + bi = (r \cos \theta) + (r \sin \theta)i$$

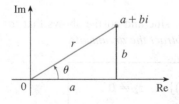

FIGURE 4

Thus we can write any complex number z in the form

$$z = r(\cos\theta + i\sin\theta)$$

where

$$r = |z| = \sqrt{a^2 + b^2} \qquad \text{and} \qquad \tan\theta = \frac{b}{a}$$

The angle θ is called the **argument** of z and we write $\theta = \arg(z)$. Note that $\arg(z)$ is not unique; any two arguments of z differ by an integer multiple of 2π.

EXAMPLE 4 Write the following numbers in polar form.

(a) $z = 1 + i$ 　　　　　　　　　　　(b) $w = \sqrt{3} - i$

SOLUTION

(a) We have $r = |z| = \sqrt{1^2 + 1^2} = \sqrt{2}$ and $\tan \theta = 1$, so we can take $\theta = \pi/4$. Therefore the polar form is

$$z = \sqrt{2}\left(\cos\frac{\pi}{4} + i \sin\frac{\pi}{4}\right)$$

(b) Here we have $r = |w| = \sqrt{3 + 1} = 2$ and $\tan \theta = -1/\sqrt{3}$. Since w lies in the fourth quadrant, we take $\theta = -\pi/6$ and

$$w = 2\left[\cos\left(-\frac{\pi}{6}\right) + i \sin\left(-\frac{\pi}{6}\right)\right]$$

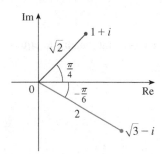

FIGURE 5

The numbers z and w are shown in Figure 5.

The polar form of complex numbers gives insight into multiplication and division. Let

$$z_1 = r_1(\cos\theta_1 + i \sin\theta_1) \qquad z_2 = r_2(\cos\theta_2 + i \sin\theta_2)$$

be two complex numbers written in polar form. Then

$$z_1 z_2 = r_1 r_2(\cos\theta_1 + i \sin\theta_1)(\cos\theta_2 + i \sin\theta_2)$$

$$= r_1 r_2[(\cos\theta_1 \cos\theta_2 - \sin\theta_1 \sin\theta_2) + i(\sin\theta_1 \cos\theta_2 + \cos\theta_1 \sin\theta_2)]$$

Therefore, using the addition formulas for cosine and sine, we have

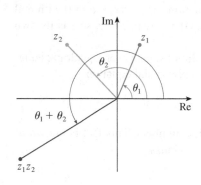

$\boxed{1}$ 　　　　$$z_1 z_2 = r_1 r_2[\cos(\theta_1 + \theta_2) + i \sin(\theta_1 + \theta_2)]$$

This formula says that *to multiply two complex numbers we multiply the moduli and add the arguments*. (See Figure 6.)

FIGURE 6

A similar argument using the subtraction formulas for sine and cosine shows that *to divide two complex numbers we divide the moduli and subtract the arguments*.

$$\frac{z_1}{z_2} = \frac{r_1}{r_2}[\cos(\theta_1 - \theta_2) + i \sin(\theta_1 - \theta_2)] \qquad z_2 \neq 0$$

In particular, taking $z_1 = 1$ and $z_2 = z$ (and therefore $\theta_1 = 0$ and $\theta_2 = \theta$), we have the following, which is illustrated in Figure 7.

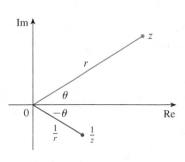

FIGURE 7

If　$z = r(\cos\theta + i \sin\theta)$, 　then　$\dfrac{1}{z} = \dfrac{1}{r}(\cos\theta - i \sin\theta)$.

EXAMPLE 5 Find the product of the complex numbers $1 + i$ and $\sqrt{3} - i$ in polar form.

SOLUTION From Example 4 we have

$$1 + i = \sqrt{2}\left(\cos\frac{\pi}{4} + i\sin\frac{\pi}{4}\right)$$

and

$$\sqrt{3} - i = 2\left[\cos\left(-\frac{\pi}{6}\right) + i\sin\left(-\frac{\pi}{6}\right)\right]$$

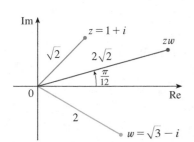

So, by Equation 1,

$$(1 + i)(\sqrt{3} - i) = 2\sqrt{2}\left[\cos\left(\frac{\pi}{4} - \frac{\pi}{6}\right) + i\sin\left(\frac{\pi}{4} - \frac{\pi}{6}\right)\right]$$

$$= 2\sqrt{2}\left(\cos\frac{\pi}{12} + i\sin\frac{\pi}{12}\right)$$

FIGURE 8

This is illustrated in Figure 8.

Repeated use of Formula 1 shows how to compute powers of a complex number. If

$$z = r(\cos\theta + i\sin\theta)$$

then

$$z^2 = r^2(\cos 2\theta + i\sin 2\theta)$$

and

$$z^3 = zz^2 = r^3(\cos 3\theta + i\sin 3\theta)$$

In general, we obtain the following result, which is named after the French mathematician Abraham De Moivre (1667–1754).

> **2** **De Moivre's Theorem** If $z = r(\cos\theta + i\sin\theta)$ and n is a positive integer, then
> $$z^n = [r(\cos\theta + i\sin\theta)]^n = r^n(\cos n\theta + i\sin n\theta)$$

This says that *to take the nth power of a complex number we take the nth power of the modulus and multiply the argument by n.*

EXAMPLE 6 Find $\left(\frac{1}{2} + \frac{1}{2}i\right)^{10}$.

SOLUTION Since $\frac{1}{2} + \frac{1}{2}i = \frac{1}{2}(1 + i)$, it follows from Example 4(a) that $\frac{1}{2} + \frac{1}{2}i$ has the polar form

$$\frac{1}{2} + \frac{1}{2}i = \frac{\sqrt{2}}{2}\left(\cos\frac{\pi}{4} + i\sin\frac{\pi}{4}\right)$$

So by De Moivre's Theorem,

$$\left(\frac{1}{2} + \frac{1}{2}i\right)^{10} = \left(\frac{\sqrt{2}}{2}\right)^{10}\left(\cos\frac{10\pi}{4} + i\sin\frac{10\pi}{4}\right)$$

$$= \frac{2^5}{2^{10}}\left(\cos\frac{5\pi}{2} + i\sin\frac{5\pi}{2}\right) = \frac{1}{32}i$$

De Moivre's Theorem can also be used to find the nth roots of complex numbers. An nth root of the complex number z is a complex number w such that

$$w^n = z$$

Writing these two numbers in trigonometric form as

$$w = s(\cos \phi + i \sin \phi) \quad \text{and} \quad z = r(\cos \theta + i \sin \theta)$$

and using De Moivre's Theorem, we get

$$s^n(\cos n\phi + i \sin n\phi) = r(\cos \theta + i \sin \theta)$$

The equality of these two complex numbers shows that

$$s^n = r \quad \text{or} \quad s = r^{1/n}$$

and

$$\cos n\phi = \cos \theta \quad \text{and} \quad \sin n\phi = \sin \theta$$

From the fact that sine and cosine have period 2π it follows that

$$n\phi = \theta + 2k\pi \quad \text{or} \quad \phi = \frac{\theta + 2k\pi}{n}$$

Thus

$$w = r^{1/n}\left[\cos\left(\frac{\theta + 2k\pi}{n}\right) + i \sin\left(\frac{\theta + 2k\pi}{n}\right)\right]$$

Since this expression gives a different value of w for $k = 0, 1, 2, \ldots, n - 1$, we have the following.

---

3   **Roots of a Complex Number**   Let $z = r(\cos \theta + i \sin \theta)$ and let n be a positive integer. Then z has the n distinct nth roots

$$w_k = r^{1/n}\left[\cos\left(\frac{\theta + 2k\pi}{n}\right) + i \sin\left(\frac{\theta + 2k\pi}{n}\right)\right]$$

where $k = 0, 1, 2, \ldots, n - 1$.

Notice that each of the nth roots of z has modulus $|w_k| = r^{1/n}$. Thus all the nth roots of z lie on the circle of radius $r^{1/n}$ in the complex plane. Also, since the argument of each successive nth root exceeds the argument of the previous root by $2\pi/n$, we see that the nth roots of z are equally spaced on this circle.

EXAMPLE 7   Find the six sixth roots of $z = -8$ and graph these roots in the complex plane.

SOLUTION   In trigonometric form, $z = 8(\cos \pi + i \sin \pi)$. Applying Equation 3 with $n = 6$, we get

$$w_k = 8^{1/6}\left(\cos \frac{\pi + 2k\pi}{6} + i \sin \frac{\pi + 2k\pi}{6}\right)$$

We get the six sixth roots of -8 by taking $k = 0, 1, 2, 3, 4, 5$ in this formula:

$$w_0 = 8^{1/6}\left(\cos\frac{\pi}{6} + i\sin\frac{\pi}{6}\right) = \sqrt{2}\left(\frac{\sqrt{3}}{2} + \frac{1}{2}i\right)$$

$$w_1 = 8^{1/6}\left(\cos\frac{\pi}{2} + i\sin\frac{\pi}{2}\right) = \sqrt{2}\,i$$

$$w_2 = 8^{1/6}\left(\cos\frac{5\pi}{6} + i\sin\frac{5\pi}{6}\right) = \sqrt{2}\left(-\frac{\sqrt{3}}{2} + \frac{1}{2}i\right)$$

$$w_3 = 8^{1/6}\left(\cos\frac{7\pi}{6} + i\sin\frac{7\pi}{6}\right) = \sqrt{2}\left(-\frac{\sqrt{3}}{2} - \frac{1}{2}i\right)$$

$$w_4 = 8^{1/6}\left(\cos\frac{3\pi}{2} + i\sin\frac{3\pi}{2}\right) = -\sqrt{2}\,i$$

$$w_5 = 8^{1/6}\left(\cos\frac{11\pi}{6} + i\sin\frac{11\pi}{6}\right) = \sqrt{2}\left(\frac{\sqrt{3}}{2} - \frac{1}{2}i\right)$$

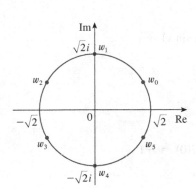

FIGURE 9
The six sixth roots of $z = -8$

All these points lie on the circle of radius $\sqrt{2}$ as shown in Figure 9.

Complex Exponentials

We also need to give a meaning to the expression e^z when $z = x + iy$ is a complex number. The theory of infinite series as developed in Chapter 8 can be extended to the case where the terms are complex numbers. Using the Taylor series for e^x (8.7.11) as our guide, we define

$$\boxed{4} \qquad e^z = \sum_{n=0}^{\infty} \frac{z^n}{n!} = 1 + z + \frac{z^2}{2!} + \frac{z^3}{3!} + \cdots$$

and it turns out that this complex exponential function has the same properties as the real exponential function. In particular, it is true that

$$\boxed{5} \qquad e^{z_1+z_2} = e^{z_1}e^{z_2}$$

If we put $z = iy$, where y is a real number, in Equation 4, and use the facts that

$$i^2 = -1, \quad i^3 = i^2 i = -i, \quad i^4 = 1, \quad i^5 = i, \quad \ldots$$

we get

$$e^{iy} = 1 + iy + \frac{(iy)^2}{2!} + \frac{(iy)^3}{3!} + \frac{(iy)^4}{4!} + \frac{(iy)^5}{5!} + \cdots$$

$$= 1 + iy - \frac{y^2}{2!} - i\frac{y^3}{3!} + \frac{y^4}{4!} + i\frac{y^5}{5!} + \cdots$$

$$= \left(1 - \frac{y^2}{2!} + \frac{y^4}{4!} - \frac{y^6}{6!} + \cdots\right) + i\left(y - \frac{y^3}{3!} + \frac{y^5}{5!} - \cdots\right)$$

$$= \cos y + i\sin y$$

Here we have used the Taylor series for cos y and sin y (Equations 8.7.16 and 8.7.15). The result is a famous formula called **Euler's formula**:

$$\boxed{6} \qquad\qquad \boxed{e^{iy} = \cos y + i \sin y}$$

Combining Euler's formula with Equation 5, we get

$$\boxed{7} \qquad\qquad e^{x+iy} = e^x e^{iy} = e^x(\cos y + i \sin y)$$

EXAMPLE 8 Evaluate: (a) $e^{i\pi}$ (b) $e^{-1+i\pi/2}$

We could write the result of Example 8(a) as
$$e^{i\pi} + 1 = 0$$
This equation relates the five most famous numbers in all of mathematics: 0, 1, e, i, and π.

SOLUTION

(a) From Euler's equation (6) we have

$$e^{i\pi} = \cos \pi + i \sin \pi = -1 + i(0) = -1$$

(b) Using Equation 7 we get

$$e^{-1+i\pi/2} = e^{-1}\left(\cos \frac{\pi}{2} + i \sin \frac{\pi}{2}\right) = \frac{1}{e}[0 + i(1)] = \frac{i}{e}$$

Finally, we note that Euler's equation provides us with an easier method of proving De Moivre's Theorem:

$$[r(\cos \theta + i \sin \theta)]^n = (re^{i\theta})^n = r^n e^{in\theta} = r^n(\cos n\theta + i \sin n\theta)$$

▮ Exercises

1–14 Evaluate the expression and write your answer in the form $a + bi$.

1. $(5 - 6i) + (3 + 2i)$

2. $\left(4 - \frac{1}{2}i\right) - \left(9 + \frac{5}{2}i\right)$

3. $(2 + 5i)(4 - i)$

4. $(1 - 2i)(8 - 3i)$

5. $\overline{12 + 7i}$

6. $\overline{2i\left(\frac{1}{2} - i\right)}$

7. $\dfrac{1 + 4i}{3 + 2i}$

8. $\dfrac{3 + 2i}{1 - 4i}$

9. $\dfrac{1}{1 + i}$

10. $\dfrac{3}{4 - 3i}$

11. i^3

12. i^{100}

13. $\sqrt{-25}$

14. $\sqrt{-3}\,\sqrt{-12}$

15–17 Find the complex conjugate and the modulus of the number.

15. $12 - 5i$

16. $-1 + 2\sqrt{2}\,i$

17. $-4i$

18. Prove the following properties of complex numbers.
 (a) $\overline{z + w} = \bar{z} + \bar{w}$ (b) $\overline{zw} = \bar{z}\,\bar{w}$
 (c) $\overline{z^n} = \bar{z}^n$, where n is a positive integer
   [*Hint:* Write $z = a + bi$, $w = c + di$.]

19–24 Find all solutions of the equation.

19. $4x^2 + 9 = 0$

20. $x^4 = 1$

21. $x^2 + 2x + 5 = 0$

22. $2x^2 - 2x + 1 = 0$

23. $z^2 + z + 2 = 0$

24. $z^2 + \frac{1}{2}z + \frac{1}{4} = 0$

25–28 Write the number in polar form with argument between 0 and 2π.

25. $-3 + 3i$

26. $1 - \sqrt{3}\,i$

27. $3 + 4i$

28. $8i$

29–32 Find polar forms for zw, z/w, and $1/z$ by first putting z and w into polar form.

29. $z = \sqrt{3} + i$, $w = 1 + \sqrt{3}\,i$

30. $z = 4\sqrt{3} - 4i$, $w = 8i$

31. $z = 2\sqrt{3} - 2i, \quad w = -1 + i$

32. $z = 4(\sqrt{3} + i), \quad w = -3 - 3i$

33–36 Find the indicated power using De Moivre's Theorem.

33. $(1 + i)^{20}$

34. $(1 - \sqrt{3}\,i)^5$

35. $(2\sqrt{3} + 2i)^5$

36. $(1 - i)^8$

37–40 Find the indicated roots. Sketch the roots in the complex plane.

37. The eighth roots of 1

38. The fifth roots of 32

39. The cube roots of i

40. The cube roots of $1 + i$

41–46 Write the number in the form $a + bi$.

41. $e^{i\pi/2}$

42. $e^{2\pi i}$

43. $e^{i\pi/3}$

44. $e^{-i\pi}$

45. $e^{2+i\pi}$

46. $e^{\pi+i}$

47. Use De Moivre's Theorem with $n = 3$ to express $\cos 3\theta$ and $\sin 3\theta$ in terms of $\cos \theta$ and $\sin \theta$.

48. Use Euler's formula to prove the following formulas for $\cos x$ and $\sin x$:

$$\cos x = \frac{e^{ix} + e^{-ix}}{2} \qquad \sin x = \frac{e^{ix} - e^{-ix}}{2i}$$

49. If $u(x) = f(x) + ig(x)$ is a complex-valued function of a real variable x and the real and imaginary parts $f(x)$ and $g(x)$ are differentiable functions of x, then the derivative of u is defined to be $u'(x) = f'(x) + ig'(x)$. Use this together with Equation 7 to prove that if $F(x) = e^{rx}$, then $F'(x) = re^{rx}$ when $r = a + bi$ is a complex number.

50. (a) If u is a complex-valued function of a real variable, its indefinite integral $\int u(x)\, dx$ is an antiderivative of u. Evaluate

$$\int e^{(1+i)x}\, dx$$

(b) By considering the real and imaginary parts of the integral in part (a), evaluate the real integrals

$$\int e^x \cos x\, dx \qquad \text{and} \qquad \int e^x \sin x\, dx$$

(c) Compare with the method used in Example 4 in Section 5.6.

J Answers to Odd-Numbered Exercises

CHAPTER 1

EXERCISES 1.1 ▪ PAGE 21

1. (a) 3   (b) -0.2 (c) 0, 3   (d) -0.8
(e) $[-2, 4], [-1, 3]$ (f) $[-2, 1]$
3. $[-85, 115]$ **5.** No
7. Yes, $[-3, 2], [-3, -2] \cup [-1, 3]$
9. Diet, exercise, or illness
11.

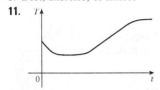

13. (a) 500 MW; 730 MW   (b) 4 AM; noon
15.

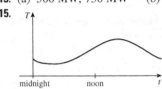

17.

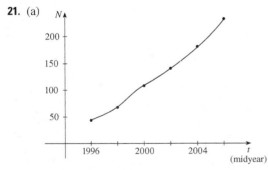

19.

21. (a)

(b) 126 million; 207 million
23. 12, 16, $3a^2 - a + 2$, $3a^2 + a + 2$, $3a^2 + 5a + 4$,
$6a^2 - 2a + 4$, $12a^2 - 2a + 2$, $3a^4 - a^2 + 2$,
$9a^4 - 6a^3 + 13a^2 - 4a + 4$, $3a^2 + 6ah + 3h^2 - a - h + 2$
25. $-3 - h$ **27.** $-1/(ax)$
29. $(-\infty, -3) \cup (-3, 3) \cup (3, \infty)$
31. $(-\infty, \infty)$
33. $(-\infty, 0) \cup (5, \infty)$

35. $(-\infty, \infty)$

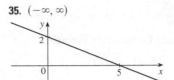

37. $(-\infty, \infty)$

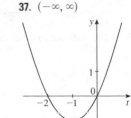

39. $[5, \infty)$

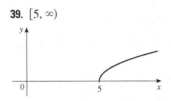

41. $(-\infty, 0) \cup (0, \infty)$

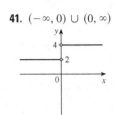

43. $(-\infty, \infty)$

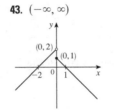

45. $(-\infty, \infty)$

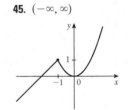

47. $f(x) = \frac{5}{2}x - \frac{11}{2}, 1 \le x \le 5$ **49.** $f(x) = 1 - \sqrt{-x}$
51. $f(x) = \begin{cases} -x + 3 & \text{if } 0 \le x \le 3 \\ 2x - 6 & \text{if } 3 < x \le 5 \end{cases}$
53. $A(L) = 10L - L^2, 0 < L < 10$
55. $A(x) = \sqrt{3}x^2/4, x > 0$ **57.** $S(x) = x^2 + (8/x), x > 0$
59. $V(x) = 4x^3 - 64x^2 + 240x, 0 < x < 6$
61. (a)   (b) $400, $1900

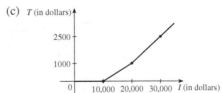

(c)

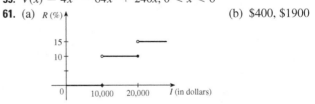

63. f is odd, g is even   **65.** (a) $(-5, 3)$ (b) $(-5, -3)$
67. Odd   **69.** Neither   **71.** Even
73. Even; odd; neither (unless $f = 0$ or $g = 0$)

EXERCISES 1.2 ▪ PAGE 35

1. (a) Logarithmic   (b) Root   (c) Rational
(d) Polynomial, degree 2   (e) Exponential   (f) Trigonometric
3. (a) h (b) f (c) g

5. (a) $y = 2x + b$,
where b is the y-intercept.

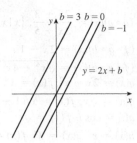

(b) $y = mx + 1 - 2m$,
where m is the slope.
See graph at right.
(c) $y = 2x - 3$

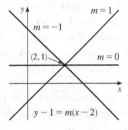

7. Their graphs have slope -1.

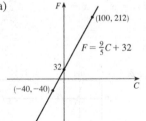

9. $f(x) = -3x(x + 1)(x - 2)$
11. (a) 8.34, change in mg for every 1 year change   (b) 8.34 mg
13. (a)

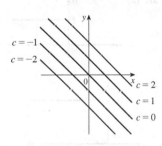

(b) $\frac{9}{5}$, change in °F for every
1°C change; 32, Fahrenheit
temperature corresponding
to 0°C

15. (a) $T = \frac{1}{6}N + \frac{307}{6}$ (b) $\frac{1}{6}$, change in °F for every chirp per
minute change   (c) 76°F
17. (a) $P = 0.434d + 15$ (b) 196 ft
19. (a) Cosine   (b) Linear
21. (a)

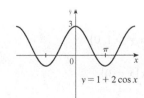

Linear model is
appropriate.

(b) $y = -0.000105x + 14.521$

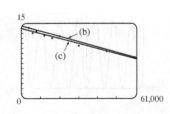

(c) $y = -0.00009979x + 13.951$ [See graph in (b).]
(d) About 11.5 per 100 population   (e) About 6%   (f) No
23. (a)

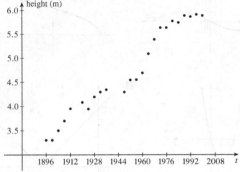

Linear model is appropriate.
(b) $y = -0.027t - 47.758$
(c) 6.35 m; higher than actual value
(d) No
25. $y \approx 0.0012937x^3 - 7.06142x^2 + 12,823x - 7,743,770$;
1914 million

EXERCISES 1.3 ■ PAGE 43

1. (a) $y = f(x) + 3$ (b) $y = f(x) - 3$ (c) $y = f(x - 3)$
(d) $y = f(x + 3)$ (e) $y = -f(x)$ (f) $y = f(-x)$
(g) $y = 3f(x)$ (h) $y = \frac{1}{3}f(x)$
3. (a) 3   (b) 1   (c) 4   (d) 5   (e) 2
5. (a)

(b)

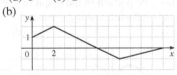

(c)

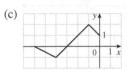

(d)

7. $y = -\sqrt{-x^2 - 5x - 4} - 1$
9.

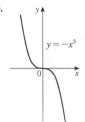

11.

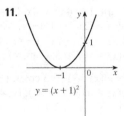

13.

15.

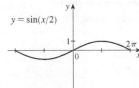

$y = \sin(x/2)$

17.

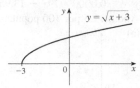

$y = \sqrt{x + 3}$

19.

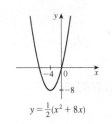

$y = \frac{1}{2}(x^2 + 8x)$

21.

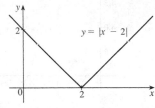

$y = |x - 2|$

23.

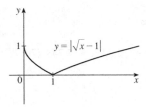

$y = |\sqrt{x} - 1|$

25. $L(t) = 12 + 2 \sin\left[\dfrac{2\pi}{365}(t - 80)\right]$

27. (a) The portion of the graph of $y = f(x)$ to the right of the y-axis is reflected about the y-axis.
(b)

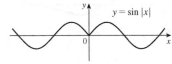

$y = \sin|x|$

(c)

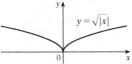

$y = \sqrt{|x|}$

29. (a) $(f + g)(x) = x^3 + 5x^2 - 1, (-\infty, \infty)$
(b) $(f - g)(x) = x^3 - x^2 + 1, (-\infty, \infty)$
(c) $(fg)(x) = 3x^5 + 6x^4 - x^3 - 2x^2, (-\infty, \infty)$
(d) $(f/g)(x) = \dfrac{x^3 + 2x^2}{3x^2 - 1}, \{x \mid x \neq \pm 1/\sqrt{3}\}$

31. (a) $(f \circ g)(x) = 4x^2 + 4x, (-\infty, \infty)$
(b) $(g \circ f)(x) = 2x^2 - 1, (-\infty, \infty)$
(c) $(f \circ f)(x) = x^4 - 2x^2, (-\infty, \infty)$
(d) $(g \circ g)(x) = 4x + 3, (-\infty, \infty)$

33. (a) $(f \circ g)(x) = 1 - 3 \cos x, (-\infty, \infty)$
(b) $(g \circ f)(x) = \cos(1 - 3x), (-\infty, \infty)$
(c) $(f \circ f)(x) = 9x - 2, (-\infty, \infty)$
(d) $(g \circ g)(x) = \cos(\cos x), (-\infty, \infty)$

35. (a) $(f \circ g)(x) = \dfrac{2x^2 + 6x + 5}{(x + 2)(x + 1)}, \{x \mid x \neq -2, -1\}$

(b) $(g \circ f)(x) = \dfrac{x^2 + x + 1}{(x + 1)^2}, \{x \mid x \neq -1, 0\}$

(c) $(f \circ f)(x) = \dfrac{x^4 + 3x^2 + 1}{x(x^2 + 1)}, \{x \mid x \neq 0\}$

(d) $(g \circ g)(x) = \dfrac{2x + 3}{3x + 5}, \{x \mid x \neq -2, -\frac{5}{3}\}$

37. $(f \circ g \circ h)(x) = 2x - 1$
39. $(f \circ g \circ h)(x) = \sqrt{x^6 + 4x^3 + 1}$
41. $g(x) = 2x + x^2, f(x) = x^4$
43. $g(x) = \sqrt[3]{x}, f(x) = x/(1 + x)$
45. $g(t) = \cos t, f(t) = \sqrt{t}$
47. $h(x) = x^2, g(x) = 3^x, f(x) = 1 - x$
49. $h(x) = \sqrt{x}, g(x) = \sec x, f(x) = x^4$
51. (a) 4   (b) 3   (c) 0   (d) Does not exist; $f(6) = 6$ is not in the domain of g.   (e) 4   (f) -2
53. (a) $r(t) = 60t$ (b) $(A \circ r)(t) = 3600\pi t^2$; the area of the circle as a function of time
55. (a) $s = \sqrt{d^2 + 36}$ (b) $d = 30t$
(c) $(f \circ g)(t) = \sqrt{900t^2 + 36}$; the distance between the lighthouse and the ship as a function of the time elapsed since noon
57. (a)

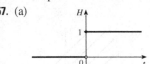

(b)

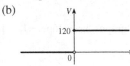

$V(t) = 120H(t)$

(c)

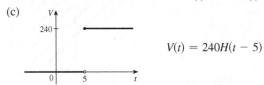

$V(t) = 240H(t - 5)$

59. Yes; $m_1 m_2$
61. (a) $f(x) = x^2 + 6$ (b) $g(x) = x^2 + x - 1$
63. Yes

EXERCISES 1.4 ▪ PAGE 51

1. (c)   **3.**

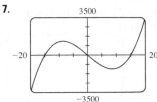

5.

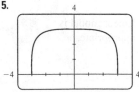

7.

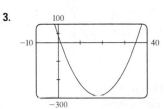

9.

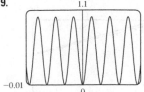

11.

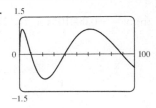

13.

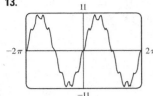

15. (b) Yes; two are needed

17.

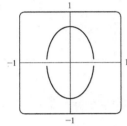

19. No   **21.** $-0.72, 1.22$ **23.** 0.65
25. g **27.** $-0.85 < x < 0.85$
29. (a)

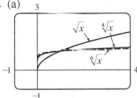

(b)

(c)

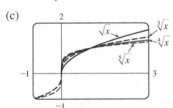

(d) Graphs of even roots are similar to $\sqrt{x}$, graphs of odd roots are similar to $\sqrt[3]{x}$. As n increases, the graph of $y = \sqrt[n]{x}$ becomes steeper near 0 and flatter for $x > 1$.

31.

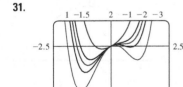

If $c < -1.5$, the graph has three humps: two minimum points and a maximum point. These humps get flatter as c increases until at $c = -1.5$ two of the humps disappear and there is only one minimum point. This single hump then moves to the right and approaches the origin as c increases.
33. The hump gets larger and moves to the right.
35. If $c < 0$, the loop is to the right of the origin, if $c > 0$, the loop is to the left. The closer c is to 0, the larger the loop.

EXERCISES 1.5 ■ PAGE 59

1. (a) 4   (b) $x^{-4/3}$
3. (a) $16b^{12}$ (b) $648y^7$
5. (a) $f(x) = a^x, a > 0$ (b) $\mathbb{R}$ (c) $(0, \infty)$

(d) See Figures 4(c), 4(b), and 4(a), respectively.
7.

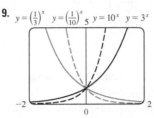

All approach 0 as $x \to -\infty$, all pass through (0, 1), and all are increasing. The larger the base, the faster the rate of increase.

9.

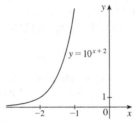

The functions with base greater than 1 are increasing and those with base less than 1 are decreasing. The latter are reflections of the former about the y-axis.

11.

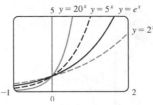

13.

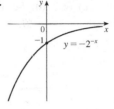

15.

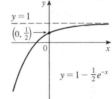

17. (a) $y = e^x - 2$ (b) $y = e^{x-2}$ (c) $y = -e^x$
(d) $y = e^{-x}$ (e) $y = -e^{-x}$
19. (a) $(-\infty, -1) \cup (-1, 1) \cup (1, \infty)$ (b) $(-\infty, \infty)$
21. $f(x) = 3 \cdot 2^x$ **27.** At $x \approx 35.8$
29. (a) 3200   (b) $100 \cdot 2^{t/3}$ (c) 10,159
(d)

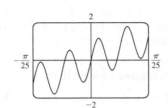

$t \approx 26.9$ h

31. (a) 25 mg   (b) $200 \cdot 2^{-t/5}$ (c) 10.9 mg   (d) 38.2 days
33. $y = ab^t$, where $a \approx 3.154832569 \times 10^{-12}$ and $b \approx 1.017764706$; 5498 million; 7417 million

EXERCISES 1.6 ■ PAGE 69

1. (a) See Definition 1.
(b) It must pass the Horizontal Line Test.
3. No   **5.** No   **7.** Yes   **9.** No
11. Yes   **13.** No   **15.** 2   **17.** 0
19. $F = \frac{9}{5}C + 32$; the Fahrenheit temperature as a function of the Celsius temperature; $[-273.15, \infty)$

21. $y = \frac{1}{3}(x - 1)^2 - \frac{2}{3}, x \geqslant 1$

23. $y = \frac{1}{2}(1 + \ln x)$ **25.** $y = e^x - 3$

27. $f^{-1}(x) = \sqrt[4]{x - 1}$ **29.**

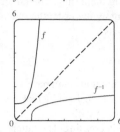
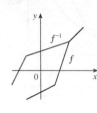

31. (a) $f^{-1}(x) = \sqrt{1 - x^2}, 0 \leqslant x \leqslant 1; f^{-1}$ and f are the same function.   (b) Quarter-circle in the first quadrant

33. (a) It's defined as the inverse of the exponential function with base a, that is, $\log_a x = y \iff a^y = x$.

(b) $(0, \infty)$ (c) $\mathbb{R}$ (d) See Figure 11.

35. (a) 3   (b) -3 **37.** (a) 3   (b) -2 **39.** $\ln 1215$

41. $\ln \dfrac{(1 + x^2)\sqrt{x}}{\sin x}$

43.

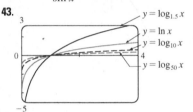

All graphs approach $-\infty$ as $x \to 0^+$, all pass through $(1, 0)$, and all are increasing. The larger the base, the slower the rate of increase.

45. About 1,084,588 mi

47. (a)

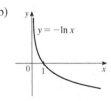

(b)

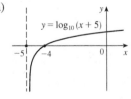

49. (a) $\frac{1}{4}(7 - \ln 6)$ (b) $\frac{1}{3}(e^2 + 10)$

51. (a) $5 + \log_2 3$ or $5 + (\ln 3)/\ln 2$ (b) $\frac{1}{2}(1 + \sqrt{1 + 4e})$

53. (a) $x < \ln 10$ (b) $x > 1/e$

55. (a) $\left(-\infty, \frac{1}{2}\ln 3\right]$ (b) $f^{-1}(x) = \frac{1}{2}\ln(3 - x^2), [0, \sqrt{3})$

57.

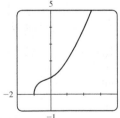

The graph passes the Horizontal Line Test.

$f^{-1}(x) = -\frac{1}{6}\sqrt[3]{4}\left(\sqrt[3]{D - 27x^2 + 20} - \sqrt[3]{D + 27x^2 - 20} + \sqrt[3]{2}\right),$ where $D = 3\sqrt{3}\sqrt{27x^4 - 40x^2 + 16}$; two of the expressions are complex.

59. (a) $f^{-1}(n) = (3/\ln 2)\ln(n/100)$; the time elapsed when there are n bacteria   (b) After about 26.9 hours

61. (a) $y = \ln x + 3$ (b) $y = \ln(x + 3)$ (c) $y = -\ln x$

(d) $y = \ln(-x)$ (e) $y = e^x$ (f) $y = e^{-x}$ (g) $y = -e^x$

(h) $y = e^x - 3$

EXERCISES 1.7 ■ PAGE 76

1.

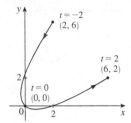

3.

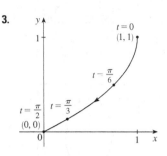

5. (a)

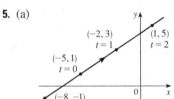

(b) $y = \frac{2}{3}x + \frac{13}{3}$

7. (a)

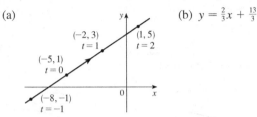

(b) $y = 1 - x^2, x \geqslant 0$

9. (a) $x^2 + y^2 = 1, y \geqslant 0$ (b)

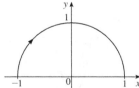

11. (a) $y = 1/x, y > 1$ (b)

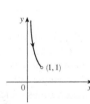

13. (a) $y = \frac{1}{2}\ln x + 1$ (b)

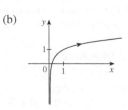

15. (a) $y = 1 - 2x^2, -1 \leqslant x \leqslant 1$ (b)

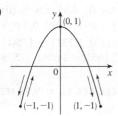

17. Moves counterclockwise along the circle $(x - 3)^2 + (y - 1)^2 = 4$ from $(3, 3)$ to $(3, -1)$
19. Moves 3 times clockwise around the ellipse $(x^2/25) + (y^2/4) = 1$, starting and ending at $(0, -2)$
21. It is contained in the rectangle described by $1 \leqslant x \leqslant 4$ and $2 \leqslant y \leqslant 3$.
23.

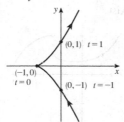

25.

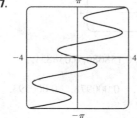

27.

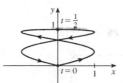

29. (b) $x = -2 + 5t, y = 7 - 8t, 0 \leqslant t \leqslant 1$
31. (a) $x = 2 \cos t, y = 1 - 2 \sin t, 0 \leqslant t \leqslant 2\pi$
(b) $x = 2 \cos t, y = 1 + 2 \sin t, 0 \leqslant t \leqslant 6\pi$
(c) $x = 2 \cos t, y = 1 + 2 \sin t, \pi/2 \leqslant t \leqslant 3\pi/2$
35. The curve $y = x^{2/3}$ is generated in (a). In (b), only the portion with $x \geqslant 0$ is generated, and in (c) we get only the portion with $x > 0$.
39. $x = a \cos \theta, y = b \sin \theta; (x^2/a^2) + (y^2/b^2) = 1$, ellipse
41. (a) Two points of intersection

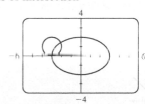

(b) One collision point at $(-3, 0)$ when $t = 3\pi/2$
(c) There are still two intersection points, but no collision point.

43. For $c = 0$, there is a cusp; for $c > 0$, there is a loop whose size increases as c increases.

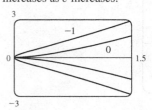 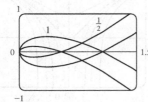

45. As n increases, the number of oscillations increases; a and b determine the width and height.

CHAPTER 1 REVIEW ■ PAGE 80

True-False Quiz

1 False   **3.** False   **5.** True   **7.** False   **9.** True
11. False

Exercises
1. (a) 2.7   (b) 2.3, 5.6   (c) $[-6, 6]$ (d) $[-4, 4]$
(e) $[-4, 4]$ (f) No; it fails the Horizontal Line Test.
(g) Odd; its graph is symmetric about the origin.
3. $2a + h - 2$ **5.** $\left(-\infty, \frac{1}{3}\right) \cup \left(\frac{1}{3}, \infty\right), (-\infty, 0) \cup (0, \infty)$
7. $(-6, \infty), \mathbb{R}$
9. (a) Shift the graph 8 units upward.
(b) Shift the graph 8 units to the left.
(c) Stretch the graph vertically by a factor of 2, then shift it 1 unit upward.
(d) Shift the graph 2 units to the right and 2 units downward.
(e) Reflect the graph about the x-axis.
(f) Reflect the graph about the line $y = x$ (assuming f is one-to-one).

11. 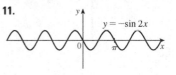   **13.**

15.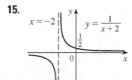

17. (a) Neither   (b) Odd   (c) Even   (d) Neither
19. (a) $(f \circ g)(x) = \ln(x^2 - 9), (-\infty, -3) \cup (3, \infty)$
(b) $(g \circ f)(x) = (\ln x)^2 - 9, (0, \infty)$
(c) $(f \circ f)(x) = \ln \ln x, (1, \infty)$
(d) $(g \circ g)(x) = (x^2 - 9)^2 - 9, (-\infty, \infty)$
21. $y = 0.2493x - 423.4818$; about 77.6 years
23. 1   **25.** (a) 9   (b) 2
27. (a) $\frac{1}{16}$ g   (b) $m(t) = 2^{-t/4}$
(c) $t(m) = -4 \log_2 m$; the time elapsed when there are m grams of ^{100}Pd   (d) About 26.6 days

29.

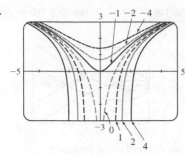

For $c < 0$, f is defined everywhere. As c increases, the dip at $x = 0$ becomes deeper. For $c \geqslant 0$, the graph has asymptotes at $x = \pm\sqrt{c}$.

31. (a)

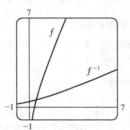

(b) $y = \sqrt{\ln x}$

33.

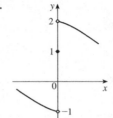

PRINCIPLES OF PROBLEM SOLVING ■ **PAGE 88**

1. $a = 4\sqrt{h^2 - 16}/h$, where a is the length of the altitude and h is the length of the hypotenuse

3. $-\frac{7}{3}, 9$

5.

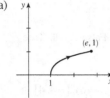

7.

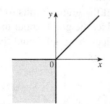

9.

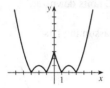

11. 5   **13.** $x \in \left[-1, 1 - \sqrt{3}\right) \cup \left(1 + \sqrt{3}, 3\right]$

15. 40 mi/h   **19.** $f_n(x) = x^{2^{n+1}}$

CHAPTER 2

EXERCISES 2.1 ■ **PAGE 94**

1. (a) $-44.4, -38.8, -27.8, -22.2, -16.\overline{6}$
(b) -33.3 (c) $-33\frac{1}{3}$

3. (a) (i) 0.333333   (ii) 0.263158   (iii) 0.251256
(iv) 0.250125   (v) 0.2   (vi) 0.238095   (vii) 0.248756
(viii) 0.249875   (b) $\frac{1}{4}$ (c) $y = \frac{1}{4}x + \frac{1}{4}$

5. (a) (i) -32 ft/s   (ii) -25.6 ft/s   (iii) -24.8 ft/s
(iv) -24.16 ft/s   (b) -24 ft/s

7. (a) (i) 4.65 m/s   (ii) 5.6 m/s   (iii) 7.55 m/s
(iv) 7 m/s   (b) 6.3 m/s

9. (a) 0, 1.7321, -1.0847, -2.7433, 4.3301, -2.8173, 0,
-2.1651, -2.6061, -5, 3.4202; no   (c) -31.4

EXERCISES 2.2 ■ **PAGE 102**

1. Yes
3. (a) 2   (b) 3   (c) Does not exist   (d) 4
(e) Does not exist
5. (a) -1 (b) -2 (c) Does not exist   (d) 2   (e) 0
(f) Does not exist   (g) 1   (h) 3
7. $\lim\limits_{x \to a} f(x)$ exists for all a except $a = -1$.
9. (a) 1   (b) 0   (c) Does not exist
11. (a) -2 (b) 2   (c) Does not exist
13.

15.

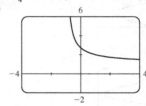

17. $\frac{2}{3}$ **19.** 5   **21.** $\frac{1}{4}$ **23.** $\frac{3}{5}$ **25.** (a) -1.5
27. (a) 2.71828   (b)

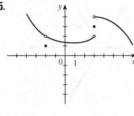

29. (a) 0.998000, 0.638259, 0.358484, 0.158680, 0.038851, 0.008928, 0.001465; 0
(b) 0.000572, -0.000614, -0.000907, -0.000978, -0.000993, -0.001000; -0.001
31. Within 0.021; within 0.011

EXERCISES 2.3 ■ **PAGE 111**

1. (a) -6 (b) -8 (c) 2   (d) -6
(e) Does not exist   (f) 0
3. 59   **5.** 390   **7.** $\frac{3}{2}$ **9.** 4   **11.** Does not exist
13. $\frac{6}{5}$ **15.** 8   **17.** $\frac{1}{12}$
19. $-\frac{1}{16}$ **21.** $\frac{1}{128}$ **23.** $-\frac{1}{2}$ **25.** (a), (b) $\frac{2}{3}$
29. 7   **33.** 6
35. Does not exist
37. (a) (i) 1   (ii) 1   (iii) 3   (iv) -2 (v) -1
(vi) Does not exist
(b)

39. (a) (i) -2 (ii) Does not exist (iii) -3
(b) (i) $n - 1$ (ii) n (c) a is not an integer.
45. 8   **49.** $15; -1$

EXERCISES 2.4 ▪ PAGE 121

1. $\lim_{x \to 4} f(x) = f(4)$
3. (a) $f(-4)$ is not defined and $\lim_{x \to a} f(x)$ [for $a = -2, 2,$ and 4] does not exist
(b) -4, neither; -2, left; 2, right; 4, right

5.
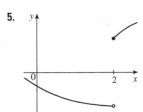
7.
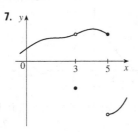

9. (a)
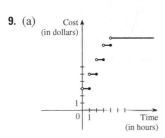

(b) Discontinuous at $t = 1, 2, 3, 4$
11. 6
15. $\lim_{x \to 0} f(x)$ does not exist.   **17.** $\lim_{x \to 0} f(x) \neq f(0)$

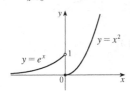

19. $[\frac{1}{2}, \infty)$ **21.** $(-\infty, \infty)$ **23.** $(-\infty, -1) \cup (1, \infty)$
25. $x = 0$

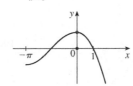

27. $\frac{7}{3}$ **29.** 1
33. 0, right; 1, left

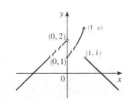

35. $\frac{2}{3}$ **37.** (a) $g(x) = x^3 + x^2 + x + 1$ (b) $g(x) = x^2 + x$
45. (b) $(0.86, 0.87)$ **47.** (b) 70.347
51. Yes

EXERCISES 2.5 ▪ PAGE 132

1. (a) As x approaches 2, $f(x)$ becomes large.   (b) As x approaches 1 from the right, $f(x)$ becomes large negative.
(c) As x becomes large, $f(x)$ approaches 5.   (d) As x becomes large negative, $f(x)$ approaches 3.
3. (a) ∞ (b) ∞ (c) $-\infty$ (d) 1 (e) 2
(f) $x = -1, x = 2, y = 1, y = 2$
5.
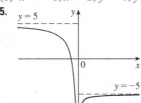
7.
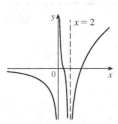

9.
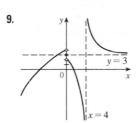

11. 0   **13.** $x \approx -1.62, x \approx 0.62, x = 1; y = 1$
15. ∞ **17.** 0   **19.** $-\infty$ **21.** $-\infty$ **23.** $\frac{1}{2}$ **25.** 2
27. $\frac{1}{6}$ **29.** 0   **31.** Does not exist   **33.** 0   **35.** $-\infty$
37. ∞ **39.** $y = 2; x = -2, x = 1$ **41.** $x = 5$
43. (a), (b) $-\frac{1}{2}$ **45.** $y = 3$ **47.** $f(x) = \dfrac{2 - x}{x^2(x - 3)}$
49. (a) $\frac{5}{4}$ (b) 5   **51.** (a) 0   (b) $\pm\infty$ **53.** 5
55. (b) It approaches the concentration of the brine being pumped into the tank.
57. (b) $x > 23.03$ (c) Yes, $x > 10 \ln 10$

EXERCISES 2.6 ▪ PAGE 142

1. (a) $\dfrac{f(x) - f(3)}{x - 3}$ (b) $\lim_{x \to 3} \dfrac{f(x) - f(3)}{x - 3}$
3. (a) 2   (b) $y = 2x + 1$ (c)
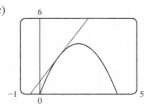

5. $y = -8x + 12$ **7.** $y = \frac{1}{2}x + \frac{1}{2}$
9. (a) $8a - 6a^2$ (b) $y = 2x + 3, y = -8x + 19$
(c)
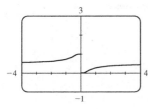

11. (a) Right: $0 < t < 1$ and $4 < t < 6$; left: $2 < t < 3$;
standing still: $1 < t < 2$ and $3 < t < 4$

(b)
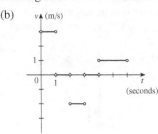

13. -24 ft/s
15. $-2/a^3$ m/s; -2 m/s; $-\frac{1}{4}$ m/s; $-\frac{2}{27}$ m/s
17. $g'(0), 0, g'(4), g'(2), g'(-2)$
19. $f(2) = 3; f'(2) = 4$
21.
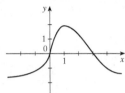

23. $y = 3x - 1$
25. (a) $-\frac{3}{5}; y = -\frac{3}{5}x + \frac{16}{5}$ (b)
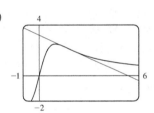

27. $6a - 4$ **29.** $\dfrac{5}{(a + 3)^2}$ **31.** $-\dfrac{1}{\sqrt{1 - 2a}}$

33. $f(x) = x^{10}, a = 1$ or $f(x) = (1 + x)^{10}, a = 0$
35. $f(x) = 2^x, a = 5$
37. $f(x) = \cos x, a = \pi$ or $f(x) = \cos(\pi + x), a = 0$
39. 1 m/s; 1 m/s
41.
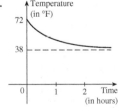
Greater (in magnitude)

43. (a) (i) 23 million/year   (ii) 20.5 million/year
(iii) 16 million/year
(b) 18.25 million/year   (c) 17 million/year
45. (a) (i) \$20.25/unit   (ii) \$20.05/unit   (b) \$20/unit
47. (a) The rate at which the cost is changing per ounce of gold
produced; dollars per ounce
(b) When the 800th ounce of gold is produced, the cost of
production is \$17/oz.
(c) Decrease in the short term; increase in the long term
49. $5°$F/h

51. (a) The rate at which the oxygen solubility changes with
respect to the water temperature; $(mg/L)/°C$
(b) $S'(16) \approx -0.25$; as the temperature increases past $16°C$,
the oxygen solubility is decreasing at a rate of 0.25 $(mg/L)/°C$.
53. Does not exist

EXERCISES 2.7 ■ PAGE 155
1. (a) -0.2 (b) 0 (c) 1 (d) 2
(e) 1 (f) 0 (g) -0.2
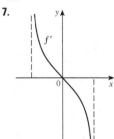

3. (a) II   (b) IV   (c) I   (d) III
5.
7.
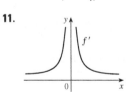

9.
11.

13.
1963 to 1971

15.
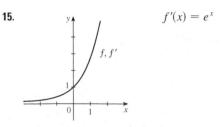
$f'(x) = e^x$

17. (a) $0, 1, 2, 4$ (b) $-1, -2, -4$ (c) $f'(x) = 2x$
19. $f'(x) = \frac{1}{2}, \mathbb{R}, \mathbb{R}$ **21.** $f'(t) = 5 - 18t, \mathbb{R}, \mathbb{R}$
23. $f'(x) = 2x - 6x^2, \mathbb{R}, \mathbb{R}$
25. $g'(x) = 1/\sqrt{1 + 2x}, \left[-\frac{1}{2}, \infty\right), \left(-\frac{1}{2}, \infty\right)$
27. $G'(t) = \dfrac{4}{(t + 1)^2}, (-\infty, -1) \cup (-1, \infty), (-\infty, -1) \cup (-1, \infty)$
29. $f'(x) = 4x^3, \mathbb{R}, \mathbb{R}$ **31.** (a) $f'(x) = 4x^3 + 2$

33. (a) The rate at which the unemployment rate is changing, in percent unemployed per year

(b)

t	$U'(t)$	t	$U'(t)$
1998	−0.30	2003	−0.15
1999	−0.25	2004	−0.45
2000	0.25	2005	−0.45
2001	0.90	2006	−0.25
2002	0.65	2007	0.00

35. −4 (corner); 0 (discontinuity)
37. −1 (vertical tangent); 4 (corner)
39.

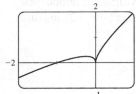

Differentiable at −1; not differentiable at 0

41. $a = f, b = f', c = f''$
43. a = acceleration, b = velocity, c = position
45. $6x + 2$; 6

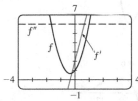

47.

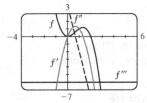

$f'(x) = 4x - 3x^2$,
$f''(x) = 4 - 6x$,
$f'''(x) = -6$,
$f^{(4)}(x) = 0$

49. (a) $\frac{1}{3}a^{-2/3}$

51. $f'(x) = \begin{cases} -1 & \text{if } x < 6 \\ 1 & \text{if } x > 6 \end{cases}$

or $f'(x) = \dfrac{x - 6}{|x - 6|}$

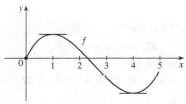

55. 63°

EXERCISES 2.8 ■ PAGE 162

Abbreviations: inc, increasing; dec, decreasing; loc, local; max, maximum; min, minimum

1. (a) Inc on (0, 1), (4, 5), dec on (1, 4)
(b) Loc max at $x = 1$; loc min at $x = 4$
(c)

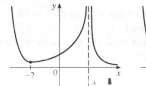

3. (a) Inc on $(-2, -1)$, $(0, 1)$, $(2, 3)$; dec on $(-1, 0)$, $(1, 2)$
(b) Loc max at $x = -1, 1$; loc min at $x = 0, 2$
(c)

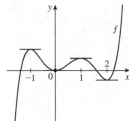

5. Inc on $(2, 5)$; dec on $(-\infty, 2)$ and $(5, \infty)$ **7.** $f''(1)$
9. If $D(t)$ is the size of the deficit as a function of time, then at the time of the speech $D'(t) > 0$, but $D''(t) < 0$.
11. (a) The rate starts small, grows rapidly, levels off, then decreases and becomes negative.
(b) $(1932, 2.5)$ and $(1937, 4.3)$; the rate of change of population density starts to decrease in 1932 and starts to increase in 1937.
13. $K(3) - K(2)$; CD
15. (a) Inc on $(0, 2)$, $(4, 6)$, $(8, \infty)$; dec on $(2, 4)$, $(6, 8)$
(b) Loc max at $x = 2, 6$; loc min at $x = 4, 8$
(c) CU on $(3, 6)$, $(6, \infty)$; CD on $(0, 3)$
(d) 3
(e) See graph at right.

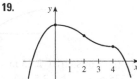

17.

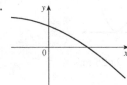

19.

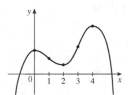

21.

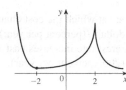

23.

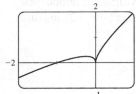

25. (a) Inc on $(0, \infty)$; dec on $(-\infty, 0)$
(b) Min at $x = 0$
27. (a) Inc on $\left(-\infty, -\sqrt{\frac{1}{3}}\right)$, $\left(\sqrt{\frac{1}{3}}, \infty\right)$; dec on $\left(-\sqrt{\frac{1}{3}}, \sqrt{\frac{1}{3}}\right)$
(b) CU on $(0, \infty)$; CD on $(-\infty, 0)$
(c) IP at $(0, 0)$
29. b

31.

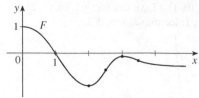

33.

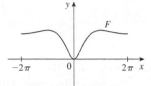

CHAPTER 2 REVIEW ▪ PAGE 165

True-False Quiz

1. False   **3.** True   **5.** False   **7.** True   **9.** True
11. False   **13.** True   **15.** False   **17.** False

Exercises

1. (a) (i) 3   (ii) 0   (iii) Does not exist   (iv) 2
(v) ∞   (vi) −∞   (vii) 4   (viii) −1
(b) $y = 4, y = -1$ (c) $x = 0, x = 2$ (d) −3, 0, 2, 4
3. 1   **5.** $\frac{3}{2}$ **7.** 3   **9.** ∞   **11.** $\frac{4}{7}$ **13.** −∞   **15.** $\frac{1}{2}$
17. 2   **19.** $x = 0, y = 0$ **21.** 1
23. (a) (i) 3   (ii) 0   (iii) Does not exist   (iv) 0   (v) 0   (vi) 0
(b) At 0 and 3   (c)

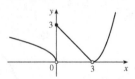

27. (a) (i) 3 m/s   (ii) 2.75 m/s   (iii) 2.625 m/s
(iv) 2.525 m/s   (b) 2.5 m/s
29. $f''(5), 0, f'(5), f'(2), 1, f'(3)$
31. (a) −0.736   (b) $y \approx -0.736x + 1.104$
(c)

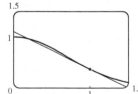

33. (a) The rate at which the cost changes with respect to the interest rate; dollars/(percent per year)
(b) As the interest rate increases past 10%, the cost is increasing at a rate of $1200/(percent per year).
(c) Always positive
35.

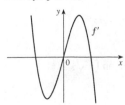

37. (a) $f'(x) = -\frac{5}{2}(3 - 5x)^{-1/2}$ (b) $\left(-\infty, \frac{3}{5}\right], \left(-\infty, \frac{3}{5}\right)$
(c)

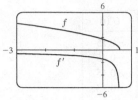

39. −4 (discontinuity), −1 (corner), 2 (discontinuity),
5 (vertical tangent)
41. The rate at which the total value of US currency in circulation is changing in billions of dollars per year; $22.2 billion/year
43. (a) Inc on $(-2, 0)$ and $(2, \infty)$; dec on $(-\infty, -2)$ and $(0, 2)$
(b) Max at 0; min at −2 and 2
(c) CU on $(-\infty, -1)$ and $(1, \infty)$; CD on $(-1, 1)$
(d)

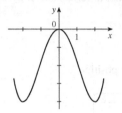

45.

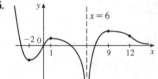

47. (a) About 35 ft/s   (b) About (8, 180)
(c) The point at which the car's velocity is maximized

FOCUS ON PROBLEM SOLVING ▪ PAGE 170

1. $\frac{2}{3}$ **3.** −4   **5.** 1   **7.** $a = \frac{1}{2} \pm \frac{1}{2}\sqrt{5}$
9. (b) Yes   (c) Yes; no   **11.** $\left(\pm\sqrt{3}/2, \frac{1}{4}\right)$
13. (a) 0   (b) 1   (c) $f'(x) = x^2 + 1$ **15.** $\frac{3}{4}$

CHAPTER 3

EXERCISES 3.1 ▪ PAGE 181

1. (a) See Definition of the Number e (page 180).
(b) 0.99, 1.03; $2.7 < e < 2.8$
3. $f'(x) = 0$ **5.** $f'(t) = -\frac{2}{3}$ **7.** $f'(x) = 3x^2 - 4$
9. $f'(t) = t^3$ **11.** $A'(s) = 60/s^6$ **13.** $g'(t) = -\frac{3}{2}t^{-7/4}$
15. $y' = 3e^x - \frac{4}{3}x^{-4/3}$ **17.** $F'(x) = \frac{5}{32}x^4$
19. $y' = \frac{3}{2}\sqrt{x} + \dfrac{2}{\sqrt{x}} - \dfrac{3}{2x\sqrt{x}}$
21. $y' = 0$ **23.** $u' = \frac{1}{5}t^{-4/5} + 10t^{3/2}$
25. $z' = -10A/y^{11} + Be^y$ **27.** $y = \frac{1}{4}x + \frac{3}{4}$
29. Tangent: $y = 2x + 2$; normal: $y = -\frac{1}{2}x + 2$
31. $y = 3x - 1$ **33.** $e^x - 5$ **35.** $45x^{14} - 15x^2$ **37.** 3

39. (a)

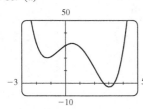

(c) $4x^3 - 9x^2 - 12x + 7$

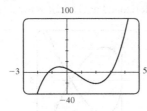

41. $f'(x) = 100x^9 + 25x^4 - 1; f''(x) = 900x^8 + 100x^3$

43. $f'(x) = 2 - \frac{15}{4}x^{-1/4}, f''(x) = \frac{15}{16}x^{-5/4}$

45. (a) $v(t) = 3t^2 - 3, a(t) = 6t$ (b) 12 m/s^2
(c) $a(1) = 6 \text{ m/s}^2$

47. $(-\infty, \ln 5)$ **49.** $(-2, 21), (1, -6)$

53. $y = 12x - 15, y = 12x + 17$

55. $y = \frac{1}{3}x - \frac{1}{3}$ **57.** $(\pm 2, 4)$ **61.** $P(x) = x^2 - x + 3$

63. (a) $F(x) = \frac{1}{3}x^3 + C, C$ any real number; infinitely many
(b) $F(x) = \frac{1}{4}x^4 + C, \frac{1}{5}x^5 + C, C$ any real number
(c) $F(x) = x^{n+1}/(n + 1) + C, C$ any real number

65. $y = 2x^2 - x$ **67.** $y = \frac{3}{16}x^3 - \frac{9}{4}x + 3$

69. $a = -\frac{1}{2}, b = 2$ **71.** 1000   **73.** 3; 1

EXERCISES 3.2 ■ PAGE 188

1. $1 - 2x + 6x^2 - 8x^3$ **3.** $f'(x) = e^x(x^3 + 3x^2 + 2x + 2)$

5. $y' = (x - 2)e^x/x^3$ **7.** $g'(x) = 5/(2x + 1)^2$

9. $F'(y) = 5 + 14/y^2 + 9/y^4$

11. $y' = \dfrac{x^2(3 - x^2)}{(1 - x^2)^2}$ **13.** $y' = \dfrac{2t(-t^4 - 4t^2 + 7)}{(t^4 - 3t^2 + 1)^2}$

15. $y' = (r^2 - 2)e^r$ **17.** $y' = 2v - 1/\sqrt{v}$

19. $f'(t) = \dfrac{4 + t^{1/2}}{(2 + \sqrt{t})^2}$ **21.** $f'(x) = -ACe^x/(B + Ce^x)^2$

23. $f'(x) = 2cx/(x^2 + c)^2$

25. $(x^4 + 4x^3)e^x; (x^4 + 8x^3 + 12x^2)e^x$

27. $\dfrac{2x^2 + 2x}{(1 + 2x)^2}; \dfrac{2}{(1 + 2x)^3}$

29. $y = \frac{1}{2}x + \frac{1}{2}$ **31.** $y = 2x; y = -\frac{1}{2}x$

33. (a) $y = \frac{1}{2}x + 1$ (b)

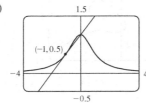

35. (a) $e^x(x^3 + 3x^2 - x - 1)$ (b)

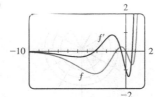

37. (a) $f'(x) = \dfrac{4x}{(x^2 + 1)^2}; f''(x) = \dfrac{4(1 - 3x^2)}{(x^2 + 1)^3}$

(b)

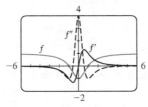

39. $\frac{1}{4}$ **41.** (a) -16 (b) $-\frac{20}{9}$ (c) 20

43. 7   **45.** (a) 0   (b) $-\frac{2}{3}$

47. (a) $y' = xg'(x) + g(x)$

(b) $y' = \dfrac{g(x) - xg'(x)}{[g(x)]^2}$ (c) $y' = \dfrac{xg'(x) - g(x)}{x^2}$

49. \$1.627 billion/year   **51.** $(-3, \infty)$

53. Two, $\left(-2 \pm \sqrt{3}, \frac{1}{2}(1 \mp \sqrt{3})\right)$ **55.** 1   **57.** (c) $3e^{3x}$

59. $f'(x) = (x^2 + 2x)e^x, f''(x) = (x^2 + 4x + 2)e^x,$
$f'''(x) = (x^2 + 6x + 6)e^x, f^{(4)}(x) = (x^2 + 8x + 12)e^x,$
$f^{(5)}(x) = (x^2 + 10x + 20)e^x; f^{(n)}(x) = [x^2 + 2nx + n(n - 1)]e^x$

EXERCISES 3.3 ■ PAGE 195

1. $f'(x) - 6x + 2 \sin x$ **3.** $f'(x) = \cos x - \frac{1}{7}\csc^2 x$

5. $y' = \sec \theta (\sec^2\theta + \tan^2\theta)$

7. $y' = -c \sin t + t(t \cos t + 2 \sin t)$

9. $y' = \dfrac{2 - \tan x + x \sec^2 x}{(2 - \tan x)^2}$ **11.** $f'(\theta) = \dfrac{\sec \theta \tan \theta}{(1 + \sec \theta)^2}$

13. $f'(x) = e^x \csc x (-x \cot x + x + 1)$

19. $y = 2\sqrt{3}x - \frac{2}{3}\sqrt{3}\pi + 2$ **21.** $y = x + 1$

23. (a) $y = 2x$ (b)

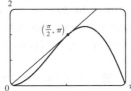

25. (a) $\sec x \tan x - 1$

27. $\theta \cos \theta + \sin \theta; 2 \cos \theta - \theta \sin \theta$

29. (a) $f'(x) = (1 + \tan x)/\sec x$ (b) $f'(x) = \cos x + \sin x$

31. $(2n + 1)\pi \pm \frac{1}{3}\pi, n$ an integer   **33.** $(\pi/3, 5\pi/3)$

35. (a) $v(t) = 8 \cos t, a(t) = -8 \sin t$
(b) $4\sqrt{3}, -4, -4\sqrt{3}$; to the left

37. 5 ft/rad   **39.** $-\cos x$

41. $A = -\frac{3}{10}, B = -\frac{1}{10}$

43. 3   **45.** $\frac{1}{7}$

47. (a) $\sec^2 x = \dfrac{1}{\cos^2 x}$ (b) $\sec x \tan x = \dfrac{\sin x}{\cos^2 x}$

(c) $\cos x - \sin x = \dfrac{\cot x - 1}{\csc x}$

49. 1

EXERCISES 3.4 ▪ PAGE 205

1. $\dfrac{4}{3\sqrt[3]{(1 + 4x)^2}}$ **3.** $\pi \sec^2 \pi x$ **5.** $e^{\sqrt{x}}/(2\sqrt{x})$

7. $F'(x) = 10x(x^4 + 3x^2 - 2)^4(2x^2 + 3)$

9. $F'(x) = -\dfrac{1}{\sqrt{1 - 2x}}$ **11.** $f'(z) = -\dfrac{2z}{(z^2 + 1)^2}$

13. $y' = -3x^2 \sin(a^3 + x^3)$ **15.** $h'(t) = 3t^2 - 3^t \ln 3$

17. $y' = e^{-kx}(-kx + 1)$

19. $y' = 8(2x - 5)^3(8x^2 - 5)^{-4}(-4x^2 + 30x - 5)$

21. $y' = (\cos x - x \sin x)e^{x \cos x}$ **23.** $y' = \dfrac{-12x(x^2 + 1)^2}{(x^2 - 1)^4}$

25. $y' = 4 \sec^2 x \tan x$ **27.** $y' = (r^2 + 1)^{-3/2}$

29. $y' = 2 \cos(\tan 2x) \sec^2(2x)$ **31.** $y' = 2^{\sin \pi x}(\pi \ln 2) \cos \pi x$

33. $y' = -2 \cos \theta \cot(\sin \theta) \csc^2(\sin \theta)$

35. $y' = \dfrac{-\pi \cos(\tan \pi x) \sec^2(\pi x) \sin\sqrt{\sin(\tan \pi x)}}{2\sqrt{\sin(\tan \pi x)}}$

37. $y' = -2x \sin(x^2);\ y'' = -4x^2\cos(x^2) - 2 \sin(x^2)$

39. $e^{\alpha x}(\beta \cos \beta x + \alpha \sin \beta x);$
$e^{\alpha x}[(\alpha^2 - \beta^2) \sin \beta x + 2\alpha\beta \cos \beta x]$

41. $y = 20x + 1$ **43.** $y = -x + \pi$

45. (a) $y = \frac{1}{2}x + 1$ (b)

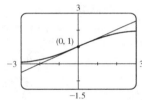

47. (a) $f'(x) = \dfrac{2 - 2x^2}{\sqrt{2 - x^2}}$

49. $((\pi/2) + 2n\pi, 3), ((3\pi/2) + 2n\pi, -1),\ n$ an integer

51. 24   **53.** (a) 30   (b) 36

55. (a) $\frac{3}{4}$ (b) Does not exist   (c) -2 **57.** -17.4

59. (a) $F'(x) = e^x f'(e^x)$ (b) $G'(x) = e^{f(x)}f'(x)$

61. 120   **63.** 96

67. $-2^{50} \cos 2x$ **69.** $v(t) = \frac{5}{2}\pi \cos(10\pi t)$ cm/s

71. (a) $\dfrac{dB}{dt} = \dfrac{7\pi}{54} \cos\dfrac{2\pi t}{5.4}$ (b) 0.16

73. $v(t) = 2e^{-1.5t}(2\pi \cos 2\pi t - 1.5 \sin 2\pi t)$

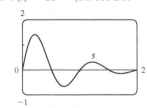 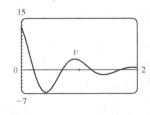

75. dv/dt is the rate of change of velocity with respect to time; dv/ds is the rate of change of velocity with respect to displacement

77. (a) $Q = ab^t$, where $a \approx 100.012437$, $b \approx 0.0000451459$
(b) -670.63 μA

79. $y = -x$ **81.** $y = -(2/e)x + 3$

83. Horizontal at $(6, \pm16)$, vertical at $(10, 0)$

85. (a) $y = \sqrt{3}x - 3\sqrt{3}, y = -\sqrt{3}x + 3\sqrt{3}$
(b) Horizontal at $(1, \pm2)$; vertical at $(0, 0)$
(c)

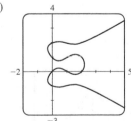

87. (b) The factored form   **89.** (b) $-n \cos^{n-1}x \sin[(n + 1)x]$

EXERCISES 3.5 ▪ PAGE 214

1. (a) $y' = -(y + 2 + 6x)/x$
(b) $y = (4/x) - 2 - 3x, y' = -(4/x^2) - 3$

3. $y' = -x^2/y^2$ **5.** $y' = \dfrac{2x + y}{2y - x}$

7. $y' = \dfrac{3y^2 - 5x^4 - 4x^3y}{x^4 + 3y^2 - 6xy}$ **9.** $y' = \dfrac{-2xy^2 - \sin y}{2x^2y + x \cos y}$

11. $y' = \tan x \tan y$ **13.** $y' = \dfrac{y(y - e^{x/y})}{y^2 - xe^{x/y}}$

15. $y' = \dfrac{e^y \sin x + y \cos(xy)}{e^y \cos x - x \cos(xy)}$ **17.** $-\frac{16}{13}$

19. $x' = \dfrac{-2x^4y + x^3 - 6xy^2}{4x^3y^2 - 3x^2y + 2y^3}$ **21.** $y = \frac{1}{2}x$

23. $y = -x + 2$ **25.** $y = x + \frac{1}{2}$ **27.** $y = -\frac{9}{13}x + \frac{40}{13}$

29. (a) $y = \frac{9}{2}x - \frac{5}{2}$ (b)

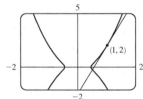

31. $-81/y^3$ **33.** $-2x/y^5$ **35.** $1/e^2$

37. (a)   Eight; $x \approx 0.42, 1.58$

(b) $y = -x + 1, y = \frac{1}{3}x + 2$ (c) $1 \mp \frac{1}{3}\sqrt{3}$

39. $\left(\pm\frac{5}{4}\sqrt{3}, \pm\frac{5}{4}\right)$

41.   **43.**

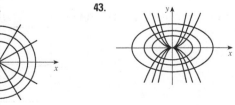

47. (a) $\dfrac{V^3(nb - V)}{PV^3 - n^2aV + 2n^3ab}$ (b) -4.04 L/atm
51. $(\pm\sqrt{3}, 0)$ **53.** $(-1, -1), (1, 1)$ **55.** (a) 0   (b) $-\frac{1}{2}$

EXERCISES 3.6 ■ PAGE 220

1. (a) $\pi/3$ (b) π **3.** (a) $\pi/4$ (b) $\pi/4$
5. $2/\sqrt{5}$ **7.** $\frac{2}{3}\sqrt{2}$ **11.** $x/\sqrt{1 + x^2}$
13.

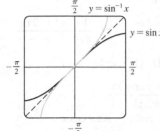

The second graph is the reflection of the first graph about the line $y = x$.

17. $y' = \dfrac{2\tan^{-1}x}{1 + x^2}$ **19.** $y' = \dfrac{1}{\sqrt{-x^2 - x}}$
21. $G'(x) = -1 - \dfrac{x\arccos x}{\sqrt{1 - x^2}}$
23. $y' = -\dfrac{2e^{2x}}{\sqrt{1 - e^{4x}}}$ **25.** $y' = -\dfrac{\sin\theta}{1 + \cos^2\theta}$
27. $y' = \sin^{-1}x$ **29.** $y' = \dfrac{\sqrt{a^2 - b^2}}{a + b\cos x}$
31. $g'(x) = \dfrac{2}{\sqrt{1 - (3 - 2x)^2}}$; $[1, 2], (1, 2)$ **33.** $\pi/6$
35. $1 - \dfrac{x\arcsin x}{\sqrt{1 - x^2}}$ **37.** $-\pi/2$ **39.** $\pi/2$ **41.** (b) $\frac{3}{2}$

EXERCISES 3.7 ■ PAGE 226

1. The differentiation formula is simplest.
3. $f'(x) = \dfrac{\cos(\ln x)}{x}$ **5.** $f'(x) = \dfrac{3}{(3x - 1)\ln 2}$
7. $f'(x) = \dfrac{1}{5x\sqrt[5]{(\ln x)^4}}$ **9.** $f'(x) = \dfrac{\sin x}{x} + \cos x\ln(5x)$
11. $F'(t) = \dfrac{6}{2t + 1} - \dfrac{12}{3t - 1}$ **13.** $g'(x) = \dfrac{2x^2 - 1}{x(x^2 - 1)}$
15. $y' = \dfrac{10x + 1}{5x^2 + x - 2}$ **17.** $y' = \dfrac{-x}{1 + x}$
19. $y' = \dfrac{1}{\ln 10} + \log_{10}x$
21. $y' = x + 2x\ln(2x)$; $y'' = 3 + 2\ln(2x)$
23. $f'(x) = \dfrac{2x - 1 - (x - 1)\ln(x - 1)}{(x - 1)[1 - \ln(x - 1)]^2}$;
$(1, 1 + e) \cup (1 + e, \infty)$
25. $y = 3x - 9$ **27.** $y = 3x - 2$
29. (a) $(0, 1/e)$ (b) $(0, \infty)$ **31.** 7
33. $y' = (2x + 1)^5(x^4 - 3)^6\left(\dfrac{10}{2x + 1} + \dfrac{24x^3}{x^4 - 3}\right)$

35. $y' = \dfrac{\sin^2x\tan^4x}{(x^2 + 1)^2}\left(2\cot x + \dfrac{4\sec^2x}{\tan x} - \dfrac{4x}{x^2 + 1}\right)$
37. $y' = x^x(1 + \ln x)$
39. $y' = (\cos x)^x(-x\tan x + \ln\cos x)$
41. $y' = (\tan x)^{1/x}\left(\dfrac{\sec^2x}{x\tan x} - \dfrac{\ln\tan x}{x^2}\right)$
43. $y' = \dfrac{2x}{x^2 + y^2 - 2y}$ **45.** $f^{(n)}(x) = \dfrac{(-1)^{n-1}(n - 1)!}{(x - 1)^n}$

EXERCISES 3.8 ■ PAGE 237

1. (a) $3t^2 - 24t + 36$ (b) -9 ft/s   (c) $t = 2, 6$
(d) $0 \le t < 2, t > 6$ (e) 96 ft
(f)
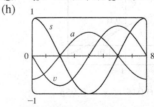
(g) $6t - 24$; -6 ft/s²
(h)

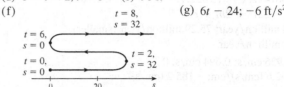

(i) Speeding up when $2 < t < 4$ or $t > 6$; slowing down when $0 \le t < 2$ or $4 < t < 6$

3. (a) $-\dfrac{\pi}{4}\sin\left(\dfrac{\pi t}{4}\right)$ (b) $-\frac{1}{8}\pi\sqrt{2}$ ft/s   (c) $t = 0, 4, 8$
(d) $4 < t < 8$ (e) 4 ft
(f)

(g) $-\frac{1}{16}\pi^2\cos(\pi t/4)$; $\frac{1}{32}\pi^2\sqrt{2}$ ft/s²
(h)

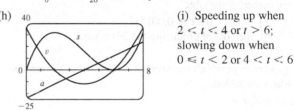

(i) Speeding up when $0 < t < 2, 4 < t < 6, 8 < t < 10$; slowing down when $2 < t < 4, 6 < t < 8$
5. (a) Speeding up when $0 < t < 1$ or $2 < t < 3$; slowing down when $1 < t < 2$
(b) Speeding up when $1 < t < 2$ or $3 < t < 4$; slowing down when $0 < t < 1$ or $2 < t < 3$
7. (a) $t = 4$ s
(b) $t = 1.5$ s; the velocity has an absolute minimum.
9. (a) 5.02 m/s   (b) $\sqrt{17}$ m/s
11. (a) 30 mm²/mm; the rate at which the area is increasing with respect to side length as x reaches 15 mm
(b) $\Delta A \approx 2x\,\Delta x$

13. (a) (i) 5π (ii) 4.5π (iii) 4.1π
(b) 4π (c) $\Delta A \approx 2\pi r\,\Delta r$
15. (a) $8\pi\,\text{ft}^2/\text{ft}$ (b) $16\pi\,\text{ft}^2/\text{ft}$ (c) $24\pi\,\text{ft}^2/\text{ft}$
The rate increases as the radius increases.
17. (a) $6\,\text{kg/m}$ (b) $12\,\text{kg/m}$ (c) $18\,\text{kg/m}$
At the right end; at the left end
19. (a) $4.75\,\text{A}$ (b) $5\,\text{A}; t = \tfrac{2}{3}\,\text{s}$
21. (a) $dV/dP = -C/P^2$ (b) At the beginning
23. $400(3^t)\ln 3; \approx 6850\,\text{bacteria/h}$
25. (a) 16 million/year; 78.5 million/year
(b) $P(t) = at^3 + bt^2 + ct + d$, where $a \approx 0.00129371$,
$b \approx -7.061422, c \approx 12{,}822.979, d \approx -7{,}743{,}770$
(c) $P'(t) = 3at^2 + 2bt + c$
(d) 14.48 million/year; 75.29 million/year (smaller)
(e) 81.62 million/year
27. (a) $0.926\,\text{cm/s}; 0.694\,\text{cm/s}; 0$
(b) $0; -92.6\,(\text{cm/s})/\text{cm}; -185.2\,(\text{cm/s})/\text{cm}$
(c) At the center; at the edge
29. (a) $C'(x) = 12 - 0.2x + 0.0015x^2$
(b) \$32/yard; the cost of producing the 201st yard
(c) \$32.20
31. (a) $[xp'(x) - p(x)]/x^2$; the average productivity increases as new workers are added.
33. $-0.2436\,\text{K/min}$
35. (a) 0 and 0 (b) $C = 0$
(c) $(0, 0), (500, 50)$; it is possible for the species to coexist.

EXERCISES 3.9 ■ PAGE 245

1. $148°\text{F}$; underestimate
3. $22.6\%, 24.2\%$; too high; tangent lines lie above the curve
5. $L(x) = -10x - 6$ **7.** $L(x) = -x + \pi/2$
9. $\sqrt{1 - x} \approx 1 - \tfrac{1}{2}x$;
$\sqrt{0.9} \approx 0.95$,
$\sqrt{0.99} \approx 0.995$

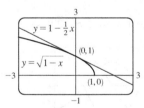

11. $-1.204 < x < 0.706$ **13.** $-0.045 < x < 0.055$
15. 32.08 **17.** 4.02
23. (a) $dy = -\dfrac{2}{(u - 1)^2}\,du$ (b) $dy = -\dfrac{6r^2}{(1 + r^3)^3}\,dr$
25. (a) $dy = \tfrac{1}{10}e^{x/10}\,dx$ (b) $0.01; 0.0101$
27. (a) $270\,\text{cm}^3, 0.01, 1\%$ (b) $36\,\text{cm}^2, 0.00\overline{6}, 0.\overline{6}\%$
29. (a) $84/\pi \approx 27\,\text{cm}^2; \tfrac{1}{84} \approx 0.012 = 1.2\%$
(b) $1764/\pi^2 \approx 179\,\text{cm}^3; \tfrac{1}{56} \approx 0.018 = 1.8\%$
31. (a) $2\pi rh\,\Delta r$ (b) $\pi(\Delta r)^2 h$
33. A 5% increase in the radius corresponds to a 20% increase in blood flow.
35. (a) $4.8, 5.2$ (b) Too large

CHAPTER 3 REVIEW ■ PAGE 248

True-False Quiz
1. True   **3.** True   **5.** False   **7.** False   **9.** True
11. True

Exercises
1. $6x(x^4 - 3x^2 + 5)^2(2x^2 - 3)$ **3.** $\dfrac{1}{2\sqrt{x}} - \dfrac{4}{3\sqrt[3]{x^7}}$
5. $\dfrac{2(2x^2 + 1)}{\sqrt{x^2 + 1}}$ **7.** $2\cos 2\theta\,e^{\sin 2\theta}$
9. $\dfrac{t^2 + 1}{(1 - t^2)^2}$ **11.** $-\dfrac{e^{1/x}(1 + 2x)}{x^4}$ **13.** $\dfrac{1 - y^4}{4xy^3} + \dfrac{2xy}{x^2 - 3}$
15. $\dfrac{2\sec 2\theta\,(\tan 2\theta - 1)}{(1 + \tan 2\theta)^2}$ **17.** $(1 + c^2)e^{cx}\sin x$
19. $\dfrac{2}{(1 + 2x)\ln 5}$ **21.** $\dfrac{2x - y\cos(xy)}{x\cos(xy) + 1}$
23. $3^{x\ln x}(\ln 3)(1 + \ln x)$ **25.** $\cot x - \sin x\cos x$
27. $\dfrac{4x}{1 + 16x^2} + \tan^{-1}(4x)$ **29.** $5\sec 5x$
31. $2\cos\theta\,\tan(\sin\theta)\,\sec^2(\sin\theta)$
33. $\cos(\tan\sqrt{1 + x^3})(\sec^2\sqrt{1 + x^3})\dfrac{3x^2}{2\sqrt{1 + x^3}}$
35. $\dfrac{-3\sin(e^{\sqrt{\tan 3x}})e^{\sqrt{\tan 3x}}\sec^2(3x)}{2\sqrt{\tan 3x}}$ **37.** $-\tfrac{4}{27}$
39. $2^x(\ln 2)^n$ **41.** $y = 2\sqrt{3}x + 1 - \pi\sqrt{3}/3$
43. $y = 2x + 2$ **45.** $y = -x + 2; y = x + 2$
47. (a) $\dfrac{10 - 3x}{2\sqrt{5 - x}}$ (b) $y = \tfrac{7}{4}x + \tfrac{1}{4}, y = -x + 8$
(c)

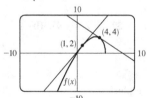

49. $e^{\sin x}(x\cos x + 1)$

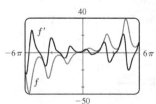

The sizes of the oscillations of f and f' are linked.

51. (a) 2 (b) 44 **53.** $2xg(x) + x^2g'(x)$ **55.** $2g(x)g'(x)$
57. $g'(e^x)e^x$ **59.** $g'(x)/g(x)$ **61.** $\dfrac{f'(x)[g(x)]^2 + g'(x)\,[f(x)]^2}{[f(x) + g(x)]^2}$
63. $(-3, 0)$ **65.** $\left(\pm 2/\sqrt{6}, \mp 1/\sqrt{6}\right)$ **67.** $y = -\tfrac{2}{3}x^2 + \tfrac{14}{3}x$
69. $v(t) = -Ae^{-ct}[c\cos(\omega t + \delta) + \omega\sin(\omega t + \delta)]$,
$a(t) = Ae^{-ct}[(c^2 - \omega^2)\cos(\omega t + \delta) + 2c\omega\sin(\omega t + \delta)]$
71. $4\,\text{kg/m}$
73. (a) $C'(x) = 2 - 0.04x + 0.00021x^2$
(b) \$0.10/unit; the approximate cost of producing the 101st unit
(c) $C(101) - C(100) = 0.10107$
(d) About 95.24; at this value of x the marginal cost is minimized.

75. (a) $L(x) = 1 + x$; $\sqrt[3]{1 + 3x} \approx 1 + x$; $\sqrt[3]{1.03} \approx 1.01$
(b) $-0.23 < x < 0.40$
77. $(\cos \theta)'|_{\theta=\pi/3} = -\sqrt{3}/2$ **79.** $\frac{1}{4}$

FOCUS ON PROBLEM SOLVING ■ PAGE 252

1. $\left(0, \frac{5}{4}\right)$ **5.** $3\sqrt{2}$
7. (a) $4\pi\sqrt{3}/\sqrt{11}$ rad/s   (b) $40\left(\cos\theta + \sqrt{8 + \cos^2\theta}\right)$ cm
(c) $-480\pi \sin\theta \left(1 + \cos\theta/\sqrt{8 + \cos^2\theta}\right)$ cm/s
11. $x_T \in (3, \infty)$, $y_T \in (2, \infty)$, $x_N \in \left(0, \frac{5}{3}\right)$, $y_N \in \left(-\frac{5}{2}, 0\right)$
15. $2\sqrt{e}$ **17.** (b) (i) 53° (or 127°)   (ii) 63° (or 117°)
19. R approaches the midpoint of the radius AO.
21. $(1, -2), (-1, 0)$ **23.** $\sqrt{29}/58$

CHAPTER 4

EXERCISES 4.1 ■ PAGE 260

1. $dV/dt = 3x^2\,dx/dt$ **3.** 48 cm²/s   **5.** $3/(25\pi)$ m/min
7. (a) 1   (b) 25   **9.** $\pm\frac{46}{13}$
11. (a) The rate of decrease of the surface area is 1 cm²/min.
(b) The rate of decrease of the diameter when the diameter is 10 cm
(c) 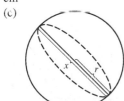   (d) $S = \pi x^2$
(e) $1/(20\pi)$ cm/min

13. (a) The plane's altitude is 1 mi and its speed is 500 mi/h.
(b) The rate at which the distance from the plane to the station is increasing when the plane is 2 mi from the station
(c) 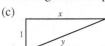   (d) $y^2 = x^2 + 1$
(e) $250\sqrt{3}$ mi/h

15. 65 mi/h   **17.** $837/\sqrt{8674} \approx 8.99$ ft/s
19. -1.6 cm/min   **21.** $\frac{720}{13} \approx 55.4$ km/h
23. 5 m   **25.** $10/\sqrt{133} \approx 0.87$ ft/s   **27.** $\frac{4}{5}$ ft/min
29. $6/(5\pi) \approx 0.38$ ft/min   **31.** 0.3 m²/s   **33.** 80 cm³/min
35. $\frac{107}{810} \approx 0.132\ \Omega$/s   **37.** (a) 360 ft/s   (b) 0.096 rad/s
39. $\frac{10}{9}\pi$ km/min   **41.** $1650/\sqrt{31} \approx 296$ km/h
43. $\frac{7}{4}\sqrt{15} \approx 6.78$ m/s

EXERCISES 4.2 ■ PAGE 268

Abbreviations: abs, absolute; loc, local; max, maximum; min, minimum

1. Abs min: smallest function value on the entire domain of the function; loc min at c: smallest function value when x is near c
3. Abs max at s, abs min at r, loc max at c, loc min at b and r
5. Abs max $f(4) = 5$, loc max $f(4) = 5$ and $f(6) = 4$,
loc min $f(2) = 2$ and $f(1) = f(5) = 3$

7. 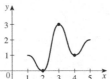   **9.**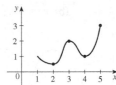

11. (a) 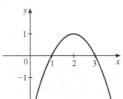   (b)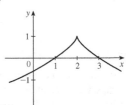

(c)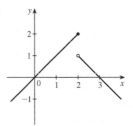

13. (a) 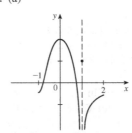   (b)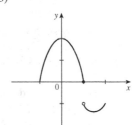

15. Abs max $f(3) = 4$
17. None   **19.** Abs max $f(2) = \ln 2$
21. Abs max $f(0) = 1$ **23.** $\frac{1}{3}$
25. $-4, 2$ **27.** $0, \frac{1}{2}\left(-1 \pm \sqrt{5}\right)$ **29.** $0, 2$
31. $0, \frac{4}{9}$ **33.** $0, \frac{8}{7}, 4$ **35.** $n\pi$ (n an integer)
37. $0, \frac{2}{3}$ **39.** 10   **41.** $f(2) = 16, f(5) = 7$
43. $f(-1) = 8, f(2) = -19$ **45.** $f(3) = 66, f(\pm 1) = 2$
47. $f(\sqrt{2}) = 2, f(-1) = -\sqrt{3}$
49. $f(2) = 2/\sqrt{e}, f(-1) = -1/\sqrt[8]{e}$
51. $f(1) = \ln 3, f\left(-\frac{1}{2}\right) = \ln\frac{3}{4}$
53. $f(\pi/6) = \frac{3}{2}\sqrt{3}, f(\pi/2) = 0$
55. $f\left(\dfrac{a}{a+b}\right) = \dfrac{a^a b^b}{(a+b)^{a+b}}$
57. (a) 2.19, 1.81   (b) $\frac{6}{25}\sqrt{\frac{3}{5}} + 2, -\frac{6}{25}\sqrt{\frac{3}{5}} + 2$
59. (a) 0.32, 0.00   (b) $\frac{3}{16}\sqrt{3}, 0$ **61.** ≈ 3.9665°C
63. Cheapest, $t \approx 0.855$ (June 1994);
most expensive, $t \approx 4.618$ (March 1998)

65. (a) $r = \frac{2}{3}r_0$ (b) $v = \frac{4}{27}kr_0^3$
(c)

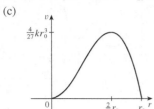

EXERCISES 4.3 ■ PAGE 279

Abbreviations: inc, increasing; dec, decreasing; CD, concave downward; CU, concave upward; HA, horizontal asymptote; VA, vertical asymptote; IP, inflection point(s)

1. 0.8, 3.2, 4.4, 6.1

3. (a) I/D Test (b) Concavity Test
(c) Find points at which the concavity changes.

5. (a) 3, 5 (b) 2, 4, 6 (c) 1, 7

7. (a) Inc on $(-\infty, -3)$, $(2, \infty)$; dec on $(-3, 2)$
(b) Loc max $f(-3) = 81$; loc min $f(2) = -44$
(c) CU on $\left(-\frac{1}{2}, \infty\right)$; CD on $\left(-\infty, -\frac{1}{2}\right)$; IP $\left(-\frac{1}{2}, \frac{37}{2}\right)$

9. (a) Inc on $(-1, 0)$, $(1, \infty)$; dec on $(-\infty, -1)$, $(0, 1)$
(b) Loc max $f(0) = 3$; loc min $f(\pm 1) = 2$
(c) CU on $\left(-\infty, -\sqrt{3}/3\right)$, $\left(\sqrt{3}/3, \infty\right)$;
CD on $\left(-\sqrt{3}/3, \sqrt{3}/3\right)$; IP $\left(\pm\sqrt{3}/3, \frac{22}{9}\right)$

11. (a) Inc on $(0, \pi/4)$, $(5\pi/4, 2\pi)$; dec on $(\pi/4, 5\pi/4)$
(b) Loc max $f(\pi/4) = \sqrt{2}$; loc min $f(5\pi/4) = -\sqrt{2}$
(c) CU on $(3\pi/4, 7\pi/4)$; CD on $(0, 3\pi/4)$, $(7\pi/4, 2\pi)$;
IP $(3\pi/4, 0)$, $(7\pi/4, 0)$

13. (a) Inc on $\left(-\frac{1}{3}\ln 2, \infty\right)$; dec on $\left(-\infty, -\frac{1}{3}\ln 2\right)$
(b) Loc min $f\left(-\frac{1}{3}\ln 2\right) = 2^{-2/3} + 2^{1/3}$ (c) CU on $(-\infty, \infty)$

15. (a) Inc on $(0, e^2)$; dec on (e^2, ∞)
(b) Loc max $f(e^2) = 2/e$
(c) CU on $(e^{8/3}, \infty)$; CD on $(0, e^{8/3})$; IP $\left(e^{8/3}, \frac{8}{3}e^{-4/3}\right)$

17. Loc max $f\left(\frac{3}{4}\right) = \frac{5}{4}$

19. (a) f has a local maximum at 2.
(b) f has a horizontal tangent at 6.

21. (a) Inc on $(-\infty, -1)$, $(2, \infty)$;
dec on $(-1, 2)$
(b) Loc max $f(-1) = 7$;
loc min $f(2) = -20$
(c) CU on $\left(\frac{1}{2}, \infty\right)$; CD on $\left(-\infty, \frac{1}{2}\right)$;
IP $\left(\frac{1}{2}, -\frac{13}{2}\right)$
(d) See graph at right.

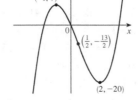

23. (a) Inc on $(-\infty, -1)$, $(0, 1)$;
dec on $(-1, 0)$, $(1, \infty)$
(b) Loc max $f(-1) = 3, f(1) = 3$;
loc min $f(0) = 2$
(c) CU on $\left(-1/\sqrt{3}, 1/\sqrt{3}\right)$;
CD on $\left(-\infty, -1/\sqrt{3}\right)$, $\left(1/\sqrt{3}, \infty\right)$;
IP $\left(\pm 1/\sqrt{3}, \frac{23}{9}\right)$
(d) See graph at right.

25. (a) Inc on $(-\infty, -2)$, $(0, \infty)$;
dec on $(-2, 0)$
(b) Loc max $h(-2) = 7$;
loc min $h(0) = -1$
(c) CU on $(-1, \infty)$;
CD on $(-\infty, -1)$; IP $(-1, 3)$
(d) See graph at right.

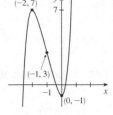

27. (a) Inc on $(-2, \infty)$;
dec on $(-3, -2)$
(b) Loc min $A(-2) = -2$
(c) CU on $(-3, \infty)$
(d) See graph at right.

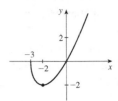

29. (a) Inc on $(-1, \infty)$;
dec on $(-\infty, -1)$
(b) Loc min $C(-1) = -3$
(c) CU on $(-\infty, 0)$, $(2, \infty)$;
CD on $(0, 2)$;
IP $(0, 0)$, $\left(2, 6\sqrt[3]{2}\right)$
(d) See graph at right

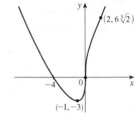

31. (a) Inc on $(\pi, 2\pi)$;
dec on $(0, \pi)$
(b) Loc min $f(\pi) = -1$
(c) CU on $(\pi/3, 5\pi/3)$;
CD on $(0, \pi/3)$, $(5\pi/3, 2\pi)$;
IP $\left(\pi/3, \frac{5}{4}\right)$, $\left(5\pi/3, \frac{5}{4}\right)$
(d) See graph at right.

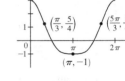

33. (a) HA $y = 1$, VA $x = -1$, $x = 1$
(b) Inc on $(-\infty, -1)$, $(-1, 0)$;
dec on $(0, 1)$, $(1, \infty)$
(c) Loc max $f(0) = 0$
(d) CU on $(-\infty, -1)$, $(1, \infty)$;
CD on $(-1, 1)$
(e) See graph at right.

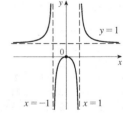

35. (a) HA $y = 0$
(b) Dec on $(-\infty, \infty)$
(c) None
(d) CU on $(-\infty, \infty)$
(e) See graph at right.

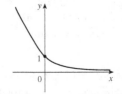

37. (a) VA $x = 0$, $x = e$
(b) Dec on $(0, e)$
(c) None
(d) CU on $(0, 1)$; CD on $(1, e)$;
IP $(1, 0)$
(e) See graph at right.

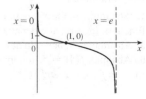

39. (a) HA $y = 1$, VA $x = -1$
(b) Inc on $(-\infty, -1)$, $(-1, \infty)$
(c) None
(d) CU on $(-\infty, -1)$, $\left(-1, -\frac{1}{2}\right)$;
CD on $\left(-\frac{1}{2}, \infty\right)$; IP $\left(-\frac{1}{2}, 1/e^2\right)$
(e) See graph at right.

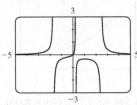

41. $(3, \infty)$
43. (a) Loc and abs max $f(1) = \sqrt{2}$, no min
(b) $\frac{1}{4}\left(3 - \sqrt{17}\right)$
45. (b) CU on $(0.94, 2.57)$, $(3.71, 5.35)$;
CD on $(0, 0.94)$, $(2.57, 3.71)$, $(5.35, 2\pi)$;
IP $(0.94, 0.44)$, $(2.57, -0.63)$, $(3.71, -0.63)$, $(5.35, 0.44)$
47. CU on $(-\infty, -0.6)$, $(0.0, \infty)$; CD on $(-0.6, 0.0)$
49. (a) Very unhappy (b) Unhappy (c) Happy
(d) Very happy

51. $\dfrac{2t}{3t^2 - 12}$, $\dfrac{-2(t^2 + 4)}{9(t^2 - 4)^3}$, $-2 < t < 2$

53.

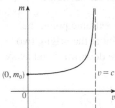

55.

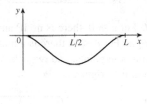

57. 28.57 min, when the rate of increase of drug level in the bloodstream is greatest; 85.71 min, when rate of decrease is greatest
59. $f(x) = \frac{1}{9}(2x^3 + 3x^2 - 12x + 7)$ **63.** 17
71. (a) $a = 0$, $b = -1$ (b) $y = -x$ at $(0, 0)$

EXERCISES 4.4 ■ PAGE 288

1. Inc on $(0.92, 2.5)$, $(2.58, \infty)$; dec on $(-\infty, 0.92)$, $(2.5, 2.58)$;
loc max $f(2.5) = 4$; loc min $f(0.92) \approx -5.12$, $f(2.58) \approx 3.998$;
CU on $(-\infty, 1.46)$, $(2.54, \infty)$;
CD on $(1.46, 2.54)$; IP $(1.46, -1.40)$, $(2.54, 3.999)$

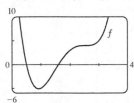

3. Inc on $(-15, 4.40)$, $(18.93, \infty)$;
dec on $(-\infty, -15)$, $(4.40, 18.93)$;
loc max $f(4.40) \approx 53,800$; loc min $f(-15) \approx -9,700,000$,
$f(18.93) \approx -12,700,000$; CU on $(-\infty, -11.34)$, $(0, 2.92)$,
$(15.08, \infty)$; CD on $(-11.34, 0)$, $(2.92, 15.08)$;
IP $(0, 0)$, $\approx (-11.34, -6,250,000)$, $(2.92, 31,800)$,
$(15.08, -8,150,000)$

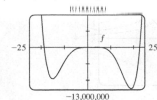

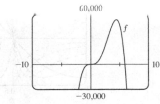

5. Inc on $(-\infty, -1.7)$, $(-1.7, 0.24)$, $(0.24, 1)$;
dec on $(1, 2.46)$, $(2.46, \infty)$; loc max $f(1) = -\frac{1}{3}$;
CU on $(-\infty, -1.7)$, $(-0.506, 0.24)$, $(2.46, \infty)$;
CD on $(-1.7, -0.506)$, $(0.24, 2.46)$; IP $(-0.506, -0.192)$

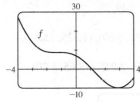

7. Inc on $(-1.49, -1.07)$, $(2.89, 4)$; dec on $(-4, -1.49)$,
$(-1.07, 2.89)$; loc max $f(-1.07) \approx 8.79$;
loc min $f(-1.49) \approx 8.75$, $f(2.89) \approx -9.99$; CU on $(-4, -1.28)$,
$(1.28, 4)$; CD on $(-1.28, 1.28)$; IP $(-1.28, 8.77)$, $(1.28, -1.48)$

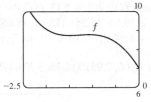

9. Inc on $\left(-8 - \sqrt{61}, -8 + \sqrt{61}\right)$; dec on $\left(-\infty, -8 - \sqrt{61}\right)$,
$\left(-8 + \sqrt{61}, 0\right)$, $(0, \infty)$; CU on $\left(-12 - \sqrt{138}, -12 + \sqrt{138}\right)$,
$(0, \infty)$, CD on $\left(-\infty, -12 - \sqrt{138}\right)$, $\left(-12 + \sqrt{138}, 0\right)$

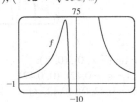

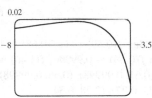

11. Loc max $f(-5.6) \approx 0.018$, $f(0.82) \approx -281.5$,
$f(5.2) \approx 0.0145$; loc min $f(3) = 0$

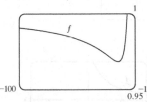

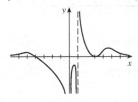

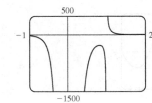

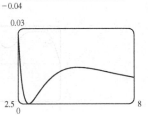

13. $f'(x) = -\dfrac{x(x + 1)^2(x^3 + 10x^2 - 14x - 16)}{(x - 2)^3(x - 4)^5}$

$f''(x) = 2\dfrac{(x + 1)(x^8 + 36x^6 + 6x^5 - 628x^4 + 684x^3 - 672x + 64)}{(x - 2)^4(x - 4)^6}$

CU on $(-35.3, -5.0)$, $(-1, -0.5)$, $(-0.1, 2)$, $(2, 4)$, $(4, \infty)$;
CD on $(-\infty, -35.3)$, $(-5.0, -1)$, $(-0.5, -0.1)$;
IP $(-35.3, -0.015)$, $(-5.0, -0.005)$, $(-1, 0)$, $(-0.5, 0.00001)$,
$(-0.1, 0.0000066)$

15. Inc on $(0, 0.43)$; dec on $(0.43, \infty)$; loc max $f(0.43) \approx 0.41$;
CU on $(0.94, \infty)$; CD on $(0, 0.94)$; IP $(0.94, 0.34)$

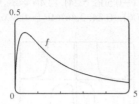

17. Inc on $(-4.91, -4.51)$, $(0, 1.77)$, $(4.91, 8.06)$, $(10.79, 14.34)$,
$(17.08, 20)$;
dec on $(-4.51, -4.10)$, $(1.77, 4.10)$, $(8.06, 10.79)$, $(14.34, 17.08)$;
loc max $f(-4.51) \approx 0.62$, $f(1.77) \approx 2.58$, $f(8.06) \approx 3.60$,
$f(14.34) \approx 4.39$;
loc min $f(10.79) \approx 2.43$, $f(17.08) \approx 3.49$;
CU on $(9.60, 12.25)$, $(15.81, 18.65)$;
CD on $(-4.91, -4.10)$, $(0, 4.10)$, $(4.91, 9.60)$, $(12.25, 15.81)$,
$(18.65, 20)$;
IP at $(9.60, 2.95)$, $(12.25, 3.27)$, $(15.81, 3.91)$, $(18.65, 4.20)$

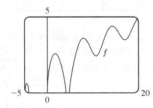

19. Inc on $(-\infty, 0)$, $(0, \infty)$;
CU on $(-\infty, -0.42)$, $(0, 0.42)$;
CD on $(-0.42, 0)$, $(0.42, \infty)$;
IP $(\mp 0.42, \pm 0.83)$

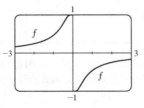

21. Max $f(0.59) \approx 1$, $f(0.68) \approx 1$, $f(1.96) \approx 1$;
min $f(0.64) \approx 0.99996$, $f(1.46) \approx 0.49$, $f(2.73) \approx -0.51$;
IP $(0.61, 0.99998)$, $(0.66, 0.99998)$, $(1.17, 0.72)$,
$(1.75, 0.77)$, $(2.28, 0.34)$

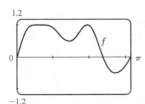

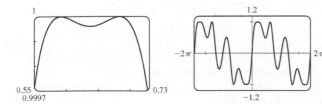

23.

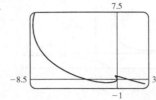

Vertical tangents at $(0, 0)$, $\left(-\frac{3}{16}, \frac{3}{8}\right)$, $(-8, 6)$; horizontal tangents at
$\left(-(2\sqrt{3} + 5)/9, -2\sqrt{3}/9\right)$, $\left((2\sqrt{3} - 5)/9, 2\sqrt{3}/9\right)$

25. For $c = 0$, there is a cusp; for $c > 0$, there is a loop whose size
increases as c increases and the curve intersects itself at $(0, c)$; leftmost point $\left(-2c\sqrt{3c}/9, c/3\right)$, rightmost point $\left(2c\sqrt{3c}/9, c/3\right)$

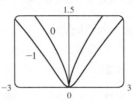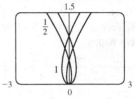

27. For $c \geqslant 0$, there is no IP and only one extreme point, the
origin. For $c < 0$, there is a maximum point at the origin, two
minimum points, and two IPs, which move downward and away
from the origin as $c \to -\infty$.

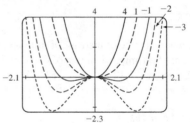

29. For $c < 0$, there is no extreme point and one IP, which
decreases along the x-axis. For $c > 0$, there is no IP, and one
minimum point.

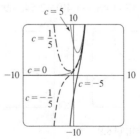

31. For $c > 0$, the maximum and minimum values are always
$\pm\frac{1}{2}$, but the extreme points and IPs move closer to the y-axis as c
increases. $c = 0$ is a transitional value: when c is replaced by $-c$,
the curve is reflected in the x-axis.

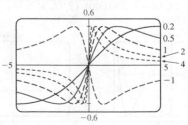

33. For $|c| < 1$, the graph has loc max and min values; for $|c| \geq 1$ it does not. The function increases for $c \geq 1$ and decreases for $c \leq -1$. As c changes, the IPs move vertically but not horizontally.

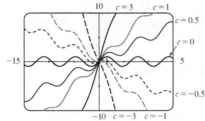

35. (a) Positive   (b)

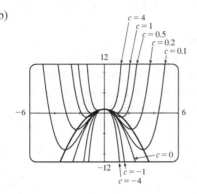

EXERCISES 4.5 ▪ PAGE 296

1. (a) Indeterminate   (b) 0   (c) 0
(d) ∞, $-\infty$, or does not exist   (e) Indeterminate
3. (a) $-\infty$ (b) Indeterminate   (c) ∞
5. 2   **7.** $-\infty$ **9.** ∞ **11.** 0   **13.** $-\infty$
15. 3   **17.** $\ln \frac{5}{3}$ **19.** $\frac{1}{2}$ **21.** $-1/\pi^2$ **23.** $\frac{1}{2}a(a-1)$
25. $\frac{1}{24}$ **27.** π **29.** 3   **31.** 0   **33.** $\frac{1}{2}$ **35.** $\frac{1}{2}$ **37.** ∞
39. 1   **41.** e^{-2} **43.** 1   **45.** e^4 **47.** e^2 **49.** $\frac{1}{4}$
51. HA $y = 0$

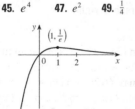

53. HA $y = 0$, VA $x = 0$

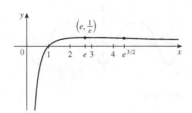

55. (a)

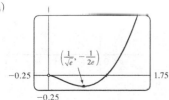

(b) $\lim_{x \to 0^+} f(x) = 0$
(c) Loc min $f(1/\sqrt{e}) = -1/(2e)$; CD on $(0, e^{-3/2})$; CU on $(e^{-3/2}, \infty)$
57. (a)

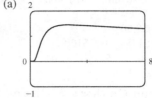

(b) $\lim_{x \to 0^+} x^{1/x} = 0$, $\lim_{x \to \infty} x^{1/x} = 1$
(c) Loc max $f(e) = e^{1/e}$ (d) IP at $x \approx 0.58, 4.37$
59.

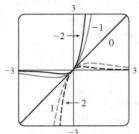

For $c > 0$, $\lim_{x \to \infty} f(x) = 0$ and $\lim_{x \to -\infty} f(x) = -\infty$.
For $c < 0$, $\lim_{x \to \infty} f(x) = \infty$ and $\lim_{x \to -\infty} f(x) = 0$.
As $|c|$ increases, the max and min points and the IPs get closer to the origin.
61. 1   **69.** $\frac{16}{9}a$ **71.** $\frac{1}{2}$ **73.** 56

EXERCISES 4.6 ▪ PAGE 305

1. (a) 11, 12   (b) 11.5, 11.5   **3.** 10, 10
5. 25 m by 25 m   **7.** $N = 1$
9. (a)

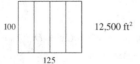
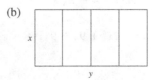

(b)

(c) $A = xy$ (d) $5x + 2y = 750$ (e) $A(x) = 375x - \frac{5}{2}x^2$
(f) 14,062.5 ft²
11. 1000 cm³   **15.** $\left(\frac{1}{3}, \pm\frac{4}{3}\sqrt{2}\right)$ **17.** $1/2, \sqrt{3}/4$
19. $4\pi r^3/(3\sqrt{3})$ **21.** Base $\sqrt{3}r$, height $3r/2$
23. Width $60/(4 + \pi)$ ft; rectangle height $30/(4 + \pi)$ ft
25. (a) Use all of the wire for the square
(b) $40\sqrt{3}/(9 + 4\sqrt{3})$ m for the square
27. $V = 2\pi R^3/(9\sqrt{3})$ **31.** $E^2/(4r)$
33. (a) $\frac{3}{2}s^2 \csc \theta (\csc \theta - \sqrt{3} \cot \theta)$ (b) $\cos^{-1}(1/\sqrt{3}) \approx 55°$
(c) $6s[h + s/(2\sqrt{2})]$

35. ≈ 4.85 km east of the refinery

37. $10\sqrt[3]{3}/\left(1 + \sqrt[3]{3}\right)$ ft from the stronger source

39. $y = -\frac{5}{3}x + 10$ **41.** $2\sqrt{6}$

43. (b) (i) \$342,491; \$342/unit; \$390/unit   (ii) 400
(iii) \$320/unit

45. (a) $p(x) = 19 - \frac{1}{3000}x$ (b) \$9.50

47. (a) $p(x) = 550 - \frac{1}{10}x$ (b) \$175   (c) \$100

49. $(a^{2/3} + b^{2/3})^{3/2}$ **53.** $x = 6$ in.   **55.** $\frac{1}{2}(L + W)^2$

57. At a distance $5 - 2\sqrt{5}$ from A

59. (a) About 5.1 km from B (b) C is close to B; C is close to
D; $W/L = \sqrt{25 + x^2}/x$, where $x = |BC|$ (c) ~ 1.07, no such
value   (d) $\sqrt{41}/4 \approx 1.6$

61. (a) $T_1 = D/c_1$, $T_2 = (2h \sec \theta)/c_1 + (D - 2h \tan \theta)/c_2$,
$T_3 = \sqrt{4h^2 + D^2}/c_1$
(c) $c_1 \approx 3.85$ km/s, $c_2 \approx 7.66$ km/s, $h \approx 0.42$ km

EXERCISES 4.7 ■ PAGE 315

1. (a) $x_2 \approx 2.3$, $x_3 \approx 3$ (b) No   **3.** $\frac{4}{5}$ **5.** 1.1797

7. 1.1785   **9.** -1.25 **11.** 1.82056420

13. -0.724492, 1.220744   **15.** 1.412391, 3.057104

17. -1.93822883, -1.21997997, 1.13929375, 2.98984102

19. -1.97806681, -0.82646233

21. 0.21916368, 1.08422462   **23.** (b) 31.622777

29. $(0.904557, 1.855277)$ **31.** $(0.410245, 0.347810)$

33. 0.76286%

EXERCISES 4.8 ■ PAGE 321

1. $F(x) = \frac{1}{2}x + \frac{1}{4}x^3 - \frac{1}{5}x^4 + C$

3. $F(x) = \frac{2}{3}x^3 + \frac{1}{2}x^2 - x + C$ **5.** $F(x) = 4x^{5/4} - 4x^{7/4} + C$

7. $F(x) = 4x^{3/2} - \frac{6}{7}x^{7/6} + C$

9. $F(x) = \begin{cases} -5/(4x^8) + C_1 & \text{if } x < 0 \\ -5/(4x^8) + C_2 & \text{if } x > 0 \end{cases}$

11. $F(u) = \frac{1}{3}u^3 - 6u^{-1/2} + C$

13. $G(\theta) = \sin \theta + 5 \cos \theta + C$

15. $F(x) = \frac{1}{2}x^2 - \ln |x| - 1/x^2 + C$

17. $F(x) = x^5 - \frac{1}{3}x^6 + 4$ **19.** $x^3 + x^4 + Cx + D$

21. $\frac{3}{20}x^{8/3} + Cx + D$ **23.** $x - 3x^2 + 8$

25. $4x^{3/2} + 2x^{5/2} + 4$ **27.** $2 \sin t + \tan t + 4 - 2\sqrt{3}$

29. $-x^2 + 2x^3 - x^4 + 12x + 4$

31. $-\sin \theta - \cos \theta + 5\theta + 4$ **33.** $x^2 - 2x^3 + 9x + 9$

35. $x^2 - \cos x - \frac{1}{2}\pi x$ **37.** 10

39.

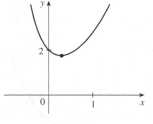

41. $s(t) = 1 - \cos t - \sin t$

43. (a) $s(t) = 450 - 4.9t^2$ (b) $\sqrt{450/4.9} \approx 9.58$ s
(c) $-9.8\sqrt{450/4.9} \approx -93.9$ m/s   (d) About 9.09 s

47. \$742.08   **49.** 225 ft   **51.** $\frac{88}{15} \approx 5.87$ ft/s^2

53. 62,500 km/h^2 ≈ 4.82 m/s^2

57. (a) 22.9125 mi   (b) 21.675 mi   (c) 30 min 33 s
(d) 55.425 mi

CHAPTER 4 REVIEW ■ PAGE 323

True-False Quiz

1. False   **3.** False   **5.** True   **7.** False   **9.** True

11. True   **13.** False   **15.** True   **17.** True   **19.** True

Exercises

1. Abs max $f(4) = 5$, abs and loc min $f(3) = 1$

3. Abs max $f(2) = \frac{2}{5}$, abs and loc min $f\left(-\frac{1}{3}\right) = -\frac{9}{2}$

5. Abs max $f(\pi) = \pi$; abs min $f(0) = 0$;
loc max $f(\pi/3) = (\pi/3) + \frac{1}{2}\sqrt{3}$;
loc min $f(2\pi/3) = (2\pi/3) - \frac{1}{2}\sqrt{3}$

7. (a) None
(b) Dec on $(-\infty, \infty)$
(c) None
(d) CU on $(-\infty, 0)$; CD on $(0, \infty)$;
IP $(0, 2)$
(e) See graph at right.

9. (a) None
(b) Inc on $\left(-\infty, \frac{3}{4}\right)$, dec on $\left(\frac{3}{4}, 1\right)$
(c) Loc max $f\left(\frac{3}{4}\right) = \frac{5}{4}$
(d) CD on $(-\infty, 1)$
(e) See graph at right.

11. (a) None
(b) Inc on $(2n\pi, (2n + 1)\pi)$, n an integer;
dec on $((2n + 1)\pi, (2n + 2)\pi)$
(c) Loc max $f((2n + 1)\pi) = 2$; loc min $f(2n\pi) = -2$
(d) CU on $(2n\pi - (\pi/3), 2n\pi + (\pi/3))$;
CD on $(2n\pi + (\pi/3), 2n\pi + (5\pi/3))$; IPs $\left(2n\pi \pm (\pi/3), -\frac{1}{4}\right)$
(e)

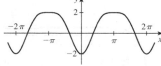

13. (a) None
(b) Inc on $\left(\frac{1}{4} \ln 3, \infty\right)$,
dec on $\left(-\infty, \frac{1}{4} \ln 3\right)$
(c) Loc min
$f\left(\frac{1}{4} \ln 3\right) = 3^{1/4} + 3^{-3/4}$
(d) CU on $(-\infty, \infty)$
(e) See graph at right.

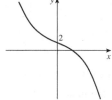

15. Inc on $\left(-\sqrt{3}, 0\right), \left(0, \sqrt{3}\right)$;
dec on $\left(-\infty, -\sqrt{3}\right), \left(\sqrt{3}, \infty\right)$;
loc max $f\left(\sqrt{3}\right) = \frac{2}{9}\sqrt{3}$,
loc min $f\left(-\sqrt{3}\right) = -\frac{2}{9}\sqrt{3}$;
CU on $\left(-\sqrt{6}, 0\right), \left(\sqrt{6}, \infty\right)$;
CD on $\left(-\infty, -\sqrt{6}\right), \left(0, \sqrt{6}\right)$;
IP $\left(\sqrt{6}, \frac{5}{36}\sqrt{6}\right), \left(-\sqrt{6}, -\frac{5}{36}\sqrt{6}\right)$

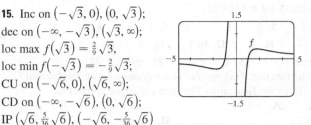

17. Inc on $(-0.23, 0), (1.62, \infty)$; dec on $(-\infty, -0.23), (0, 1.62)$;
loc max $f(0) = 2$; loc min $f(-0.23) \approx 1.96$, $f(1.62) \approx -19.2$;
CU on $(-\infty, -0.12), (1.24, \infty)$;
CD on $(-0.12, 1.24)$; IP $(-0.12, 1.98), (1.24, -12.1)$

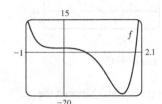   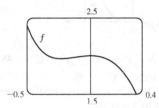

19.

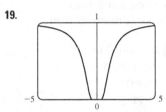 $\left(\pm 0.82, 0.22\right); \left(\pm\sqrt{2/3}, e^{-3/2}\right)$

21. $-2.96, -0.18, 3.01; -1.57, 1.57; -2.16, -0.75, 0.46, 2.21$
23. For $C > -1$, f is periodic with period 2π and has local maxima at $2n\pi + \pi/2$, n an integer. For $C \leq -1$, f has no graph. For $-1 < C \leq 1$, f has vertical asymptotes. For $C > 1$, f is continuous on $\mathbb{R}$. As C increases, f moves upward and its oscillations become less pronounced.
25. $a = -3, b = 7$ **27.** π **29.** 8   **31.** 0   **33.** $\frac{1}{2}$
35. 400 ft/h   **37.** 13 ft/s   **39.** 500 and 125
41. $3\sqrt{3}\,r^2$ **43.** $4/\sqrt{3}$ cm from D; at C
45. $L = C$ **47.** \$11.50   **49.** 1.16718557
51. $F(x) = e^x - 4\sqrt{x} + C$ **53.** $f(t) = t^2 + 3\cos t + 2$
55. $f(x) = \frac{1}{2}x^2 - x^3 + 4x^4 + 2x + 1$
57. $s(t) = t^2 - \tan^{-1}t + 1$
59. (b) $0.1e^x - \cos x + 0.9$ (c)

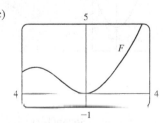

61. No
63. (b) About 8.5 in. by 2 in.   (c) $20/\sqrt{3}$ in., $20\sqrt{2/3}$ in.

65. (a) $20\sqrt{2} \approx 28$ ft
(b) $\dfrac{dI}{dt} = \dfrac{-480k(h-4)}{[(h-4)^2 + 1600]^{5/2}}$, where k is the constant of proportionality

FOCUS ON PROBLEM SOLVING ▪ PAGE 328

5. Abs max $f(-5) = e^{45}$, no abs min
7. $(-2, 4), (2, -4)$ **9.** 24   **11.** $-3.5 < a < -2.5$
13. $c > 0$ (one IP) and $c < -e/6$ (two IP)   **17.** $(m/2, m^2/4)$
23. $2 + \frac{375}{128}\pi \approx 11.204$ cm³/min

CHAPTER 5

EXERCISES 5.1 ▪ PAGE 341

1. (a) $L_4 = 33$, $R_4 = 41$

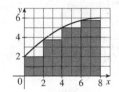   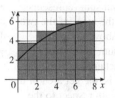

(b) $L_8 \approx 35.1$, $R_8 \approx 39.1$

3. (a) 0.7908, underestimate   (b) 1.1835, overestimate

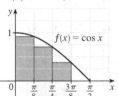   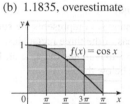

5. (a) 8, 6.875   (b) 5, 5.375

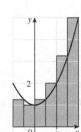 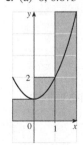 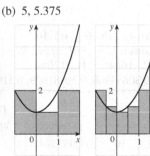

(c) 5.75, 5.9375

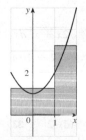 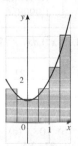

(d) M_6

7. 0.2533, 0.2170, 0.2101, 0.2050; 0.2
9. (a) Left: 0.8100, 0.7937, 0.7904;
right: 0.7600, 0.7770, 0.7804
11. 34.7 ft, 44.8 ft   **13.** 63.2 L, 70 L   **15.** 155 ft

17. $\lim\limits_{n\to\infty} \sum\limits_{i=1}^{n} \dfrac{2(1+2i/n)}{(1+2i/n)^2+1} \cdot \dfrac{2}{n}$ **19.** $\lim\limits_{n\to\infty} \sum\limits_{i=1}^{n} \left(\dfrac{i\pi}{2n}\cos\dfrac{i\pi}{2n}\right)\dfrac{\pi}{2n}$

21. The region under the graph of $y=\tan x$ from 0 to $\pi/4$
23. (a) $L_n < A < R_n$

25. (a) $\lim\limits_{n\to\infty} \dfrac{64}{n^6}\sum\limits_{i=1}^{n} i^5$ (b) $\dfrac{n^2(n+1)^2(2n^2+2n-1)}{12}$ (c) $\dfrac{32}{3}$

27. $\sin b$, 1

EXERCISES 5.2 ■ PAGE 353

1. −6
The Riemann sum represents
the sum of the areas of the two
rectangles above the x-axis
minus the sum of the areas of
the three rectangles below the
x-axis; that is, the net area of the
rectangles with respect to the
x-axis.

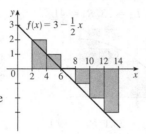

3. 2.322986
The Riemann sum represents the sum
of the areas of the three rectangles
above the x-axis minus the area of the
rectangle below the x-axis.

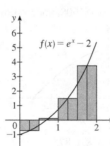

5. (a) 4   (b) 6   (c) 10
7. Lower, $L_5 = -64$; upper, $R_5 = 16$
9. 124.1644   **11.** 0.3084
13. 0.30843908, 0.30981629, 0.31015563
15.

n	R_n
5	1.933766
10	1.983524
50	1.999342
100	1.999836

The values of R_n appear to be approaching 2.

17. $\int_2^6 x\ln(1+x^2)\,dx$ **19.** $\int_1^8 \sqrt{2x+x^2}\,dx$ **21.** 42

23. $\frac{4}{3}$ **25.** 3.75   **27.** $\lim\limits_{n\to\infty} \sum\limits_{i=1}^{n} \dfrac{2+4i/n}{1+(2+4i/n)^5}\cdot\dfrac{4}{n}$

29. $\lim\limits_{n\to\infty} \sum\limits_{i=1}^{n} \left(\sin\dfrac{5\pi i}{n}\right)\dfrac{\pi}{n} = \dfrac{2}{5}$

31. (a) 4   (b) 10   (c) −3   (d) 2   **33.** $-\frac{3}{4}$
35. $3+\frac{9}{4}\pi$ **37.** 2.5   **39.** 0
41. $\int_{-1}^5 f(x)\,dx$ **43.** 122   **45.** $e^5 - e^3$
47. B < E < A < D < C   **49.** 15   **53.** $\int_0^1 x^4\,dx$

EXERCISES 5.3 ■ PAGE 363

1. $-\frac{10}{3}$ **3.** $\frac{56}{15}$ **5.** $\frac{5}{9}$ **7.** $-2+1/e$ **9.** $\frac{49}{3}$ **11.** $\frac{40}{3}$
13. $\frac{55}{63}$ **15.** 1   **17.** $\ln 3$ **19.** π **21.** $e^2 - 1$
23. $\ln 2 + 7$ **25.** $1+\pi/4$ **27.** $\pi/6$ **29.** −3.5
31. The function $f(x) = 1/x^2$ is not continuous on the interval $[-1,3]$, so the Evaluation Theorem cannot be applied.
33. 2   **35.** ≈ 1.36
37. 3.75   **41.** $\sin x + \frac{1}{4}x^2 + C$

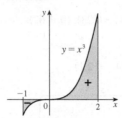

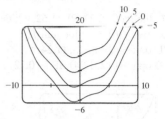

43. $2t - t^2 + \frac{1}{3}t^3 - \frac{1}{4}t^4 + C$ **45.** $\tan\alpha + C$
47. $\sec x + C$ **49.** $\frac{4}{3}$
51. The increase in the child's weight (in pounds) between the ages of 5 and 10
53. Number of gallons of oil leaked in the first 2 hours
55. Increase in revenue when production is increased from 1000 to 5000 units
57. Newton-meters   **59.** (a) $-\frac{3}{2}$ m   (b) $\frac{41}{6}$ m
61. (a) $v(t) = \frac{1}{2}t^2 + 4t + 5$ m/s   (b) $416\frac{2}{3}$ m
63. $46\frac{2}{3}$ kg   **65.** 1.4 mi   **67.** $58,000
69. (b) At most 40%; $\frac{5}{36}$ **73.** 3   **75.** $\frac{1}{4}$

EXERCISES 5.4 ■ PAGE 372

1. One process undoes what the other one does. See the Fundamental Theorem of Calculus, page 371.
3. (a) 0, 2, 5, 7, 3   (d)
(b) (0, 3)
(c) $x = 3$

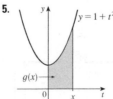

5. $g'(x) = 1 + x^2$

7. $g'(x) = 1/(x^3+1)$
9. $g'(y) = y^2\sin y$ **11.** $F'(x) = -\sqrt{1+\sec x}$
13. $h'(x) = -\dfrac{\arctan(1/x)}{x^2}$ **15.** $y' = \sqrt{\tan x + \sqrt{\tan x}}\,\sec^2 x$
17. $g'(x) = \dfrac{-2(4x^2-1)}{4x^2+1} + \dfrac{3(9x^2-1)}{9x^2+1}$

19. (a) Loc max at 1 and 5; loc min at 3 and 7
(b) $x = 9$
(c) $\left(\frac{1}{2}, 2\right), (4, 6), (8, 9)$
(d) See graph at right.

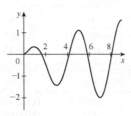

21. $(-1, 1)$ **23.** $(-4, 0)$ **25.** 29
27. (a) $-2\sqrt{n}$, $\sqrt{4n-2}$, n an integer > 0
(b) $(0, 1), \left(-\sqrt{4n-1}, -\sqrt{4n-3}\right)$, and $\left(\sqrt{4n-1}, \sqrt{4n+1}\right)$,
n an integer > 0 (c) 0.74
29. $f(x) = \int_1^x (2^t/t)\, dt$ **31.** $f(x) = x^{3/2}$, $a = 9$
33. (b) Average expenditure over $[0, t]$; minimize average expenditure

EXERCISES 5.5 ■ PAGE 381

1. $-e^{-x} + C$ **3.** $\frac{2}{9}(x^3 + 1)^{3/2} + C$ **5.** $-\frac{1}{4}\cos^4\theta + C$
7. $-\frac{1}{2}\cos(x^2) + C$ **9.** $\frac{1}{63}(3x-2)^{21} + C$
11. $-(1/\pi)\cos \pi t + C$ **13.** $\frac{1}{3}(\ln x)^3 + C$
15. $-\frac{1}{3}\ln|5 - 3x| + C$ **17.** $\frac{2}{3}\sqrt{3ax + bx^3} + C$
19. $\frac{2}{3}(1 + e^x)^{3/2} + C$ **21.** $-1/(\sin x) + C$
23. $\frac{1}{15}(x^3 + 3x)^5 + C$ **25.** $-\frac{2}{3}(\cot x)^{3/2} + C$
27. $\ln|\sin^{-1}x| + C$ **29.** $\frac{1}{3}\sec^3 x + C$
31. $\frac{1}{40}(2x + 5)^{10} - \frac{5}{36}(2x + 5)^9 + C$
33. $-\ln(1 + \cos^2 x) + C$ **35.** $\tan^{-1}x + \frac{1}{2}\ln(1 + x^2) + C$
37. $\frac{1}{8}(x^2 - 1)^4 + C$ **39.** $-e^{\cos x} + C$

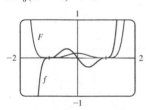 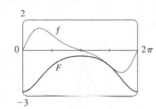

41. $2/\pi$ **43.** $\frac{45}{28}$ **45.** $\frac{182}{9}$ **47.** $2(e^2 - e)$
49. 0   **51.** $\frac{16}{15}$ **53.** $\ln(e + 1)$ **55.** 2   **57.** $\frac{1}{6}$
59. 6π **61.** All three areas are equal.   **63.** ≈ 4512 L
65. $\dfrac{5}{4\pi}\left(1 - \cos\dfrac{2\pi t}{5}\right)$ L   **67.** 5

EXERCISES 5.6 ■ PAGE 387

1. $\frac{1}{3}x^3 \ln x - \frac{1}{9}x^3 + C$ **3.** $\frac{1}{5}x \sin 5x + \frac{1}{25}\cos 5x + C$
5. $2(r - 2)e^{r/2} + C$
7. $-\dfrac{1}{\pi}x^2 \cos \pi x + \dfrac{2}{\pi^2}x \sin \pi x + \dfrac{2}{\pi^3}\cos \pi x + C$
9. $x \ln \sqrt[3]{x} - \frac{1}{3}x + C$ **11.** $t \arctan 4t - \frac{1}{8}\ln(1 + 16t^2) + C$
13. $\frac{1}{13}e^{2\theta}(2 \sin 3\theta - 3 \cos 3\theta) + C$ **15.** $\pi/3$ **17.** $\frac{1}{2} - \frac{1}{2}\ln 2$
19. $\frac{1}{4} - \frac{3}{4}e^{-2}$ **21.** $\frac{1}{6}(\pi + 6 - 3\sqrt{3})$
23. $2(\ln 2)^2 - 4 \ln 2 + 2$
25. $2\sqrt{x} \sin \sqrt{x} + 2 \cos \sqrt{x} + C$ **27.** $-\frac{1}{2} - \pi/4$
29. $\frac{1}{2}(x^2 - 1) \ln(1 + x) - \frac{1}{4}x^2 + \frac{1}{2}x + \frac{3}{4} + C$

31. $-\frac{1}{2}xe^{-2x} - \frac{1}{4}e^{-2x} + C$

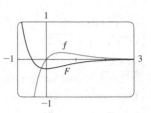

33. $\frac{1}{3}x^2(1 + x^2)^{3/2} - \frac{2}{15}(1 + x^2)^{5/2} + C$

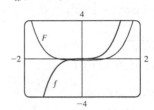

35. (b) $-\frac{1}{4}\cos x \sin^3 x + \frac{3}{8}x - \frac{3}{16}\sin 2x + C$
37. (b) $\frac{2}{3}, \frac{8}{15}$
41. $x[(\ln x)^3 - 3(\ln x)^2 + 6 \ln x - 6] + C$
43. $2 - e^{-t}(t^2 + 2t + 2)$ m   **45.** 2

EXERCISES 5.7 ■ PAGE 393

1. $\frac{1}{5}\cos^5 x - \frac{1}{3}\cos^3 x + C$ **3.** $-\frac{11}{384}$ **5.** π
7. $\frac{1}{3}\sec^3 x - \sec x + C$ **9.** $\frac{8}{15}$
11. $-\dfrac{\sqrt{9 - x^2}}{x} - \sin^{-1}\left(\dfrac{x}{3}\right) + C$
13. $-\dfrac{\sqrt{x^2 + 4}}{4x} + C$ **15.** $\dfrac{\pi}{24} + \dfrac{\sqrt{3}}{8} - \dfrac{1}{4}$
17. $-\dfrac{\sqrt{4 - x^2}}{4x} + C$
19. (a) $\dfrac{A}{x + 3} + \dfrac{B}{3x + 1}$ (b) $\dfrac{A}{x} + \dfrac{B}{x + 1} + \dfrac{C}{(x + 1)^2}$
21. $\frac{1}{2}\ln|2x + 1| + 2 \ln|x - 1| + C$
23. $\frac{1}{2}\ln\frac{3}{2}$ **25.** $\ln|x - 1| - \frac{1}{2}\ln(x^2 + 9) - \frac{1}{3}\tan^{-1}(x/3) + C$
27. $\frac{1}{2}\ln(x^2 + 1) + (1/\sqrt{2})\tan^{-1}(x/\sqrt{2}) + C$
29. $x + 6 \ln|x - 6| + C$
31. $\frac{1}{2}x^2 - 2 \ln(x^2 + 4) + 2 \tan^{-1}(x/2) + C$
33. $2 + \ln\frac{25}{9}$ **35.** $\dfrac{2}{\sqrt{3}}\tan^{-1}\left(\dfrac{2x + 1}{\sqrt{3}}\right) + C$

EXERCISES 5.8 ■ PAGE 399

1. $\dfrac{1}{2\pi}\tan^2(\pi x) + \dfrac{1}{\pi}\ln|\cos(\pi x)| + C$
3. $-\sqrt{4x^2 + 9}/(9x) + C$ **5.** $\frac{1}{2}(e^{2x} + 1)\arctan(e^x) - \frac{1}{2}e^x + C$
7. $\pi^3 - 6\pi$ **9.** $-\frac{1}{2}\tan^2(1/z) - \ln|\cos(1/z)| + C$
11. $\dfrac{2y - 1}{8}\sqrt{6 + 4y - 4y^2} + \dfrac{7}{8}\sin^{-1}\left(\dfrac{2y - 1}{\sqrt{7}}\right)$
$\quad - \frac{1}{12}(6 + 4y - 4y^2)^{3/2} + C$

13. $\frac{1}{9}\sin^3 x\,[3\ln(\sin x) - 1] + C$ **15.** $\frac{1}{2\sqrt{3}}\ln\left|\dfrac{e^x + \sqrt{3}}{e^x - \sqrt{3}}\right| + C$

17. $\frac{1}{5}\ln\left|x^5 + \sqrt{x^{10} - 2}\,\right| + C$

19. $\frac{1}{2}(\ln x)\sqrt{4 + (\ln x)^2} + 2\ln\!\left[\ln x + \sqrt{4 + (\ln x)^2}\,\right] + C$

21. $\sqrt{e^{2x} - 1} - \cos^{-1}(e^{-x}) + C$

25. $\frac{1}{3}\tan x \sec^2 x + \frac{2}{3}\tan x + C$

27. $\frac{1}{4}x(x^2 + 2)\sqrt{x^2 + 4} - 2\ln\!\left(\sqrt{x^2 + 4} + x\right) + C$

29. $\frac{1}{10}(1 + 2x)^{5/2} - \frac{1}{6}(1 + 2x)^{3/2} + C$

31. $-\ln|\cos x| - \frac{1}{2}\tan^2 x + \frac{1}{4}\tan^4 x + C$

33. (a) $-\ln\left|\dfrac{1 + \sqrt{1 - x^2}}{x}\right| + C$;

both have domain $(-1, 0) \cup (0, 1)$

EXERCISES 5.9 ■ PAGE 411

1. (a) $L_2 = 6, R_2 = 12, M_2 \approx 9.6$
(b) L_2 is an underestimate, R_2 and M_2 are overestimates.
(c) $T_2 = 9 < I$ (d) $L_n < T_n < I < M_n < R_n$

3. (a) $T_4 \approx 0.895759$ (underestimate)
(b) $M_4 \approx 0.908907$ (overestimate)
$T_4 < I < M_4$

5. (a) $M_{10} \approx 0.806598, E_M \approx -0.001879$
(b) $S_{10} \approx 0.804779, E_S \approx -0.000060$

7. (a) 2.413790   (b) 2.411453   (c) 2.412232

9. (a) 0.146879   (b) 0.147391   (c) 0.147219

11. (a) 0.451948   (b) 0.451991   (c) 0.451976

13. (a) 4.513618   (b) 4.748256   (c) 4.675111

15. (a) -0.495333 (b) -0.543321 (c) -0.526123

17. (a) $T_8 \approx 0.902333, M_8 \approx 0.905620$
(b) $|E_T| \le 0.0078, |E_M| \le 0.0039$
(c) $n = 71$ for T_n, $n = 50$ for M_n

19. (a) $T_{10} \approx 1.983524, E_T \approx 0.016476$;
$M_{10} \approx 2.008248, E_M \approx -0.008248$;
$S_{10} \approx 2.000110, E_S \approx -0.000110$
(b) $|E_T| \le 0.025839, |E_M| \le 0.012919, |E_S| \le 0.000170$
(c) $n = 509$ for T_n, $n = 360$ for M_n, $n = 22$ for S_n

21. (a) 2.8   (b) 7.954926518   (c) 0.2894
(d) 7.954926521   (e) The actual error is much smaller.
(f) 10.9   (g) 7.953789422   (h) 0.0593
(i) The actual error is smaller.   (j) $n \ge 50$

23.

n	L_n	R_n	T_n	M_n
5	0.742943	1.286599	1.014771	0.992621
10	0.867782	1.139610	1.003696	0.998152
20	0.932967	1.068881	1.000924	0.999538

n	E_L	E_R	E_T	E_M
5	0.257057	-0.286599	-0.014771	0.007379
10	0.132218	-0.139610	-0.003696	0.001848
20	0.067033	-0.068881	-0.000924	0.000462

Observations are the same as after Example 1.

25.

n	T_n	M_n	S_n
6	6.695473	6.252572	6.403292
12	6.474023	6.363008	6.400206

n	E_T	E_M	E_S
6	-0.295473	0.147428	-0.003292
12	-0.074023	0.036992	-0.000206

Observations are the same as after Example 1.

27. (a) 19.8 (b) 20.6 (c) $20.5\overline{3}$
29. $37.7\overline{3}$ ft/s   **31.** 10,177 megawatt-hours
33. (a) 23.44 (b) $0.341\overline{3}$ **35.** 59.4
37.

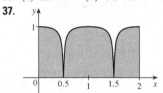

EXERCISES 5.10 ■ PAGE 421

Abbreviations: C, convergent; D, divergent

1. (a) Infinite interval   (b) Infinite discontinuity
(c) Infinite discontinuity   (d) Infinite interval
3. $\frac{1}{2} - 1/(2t^2)$; 0.495, 0.49995, 0.4999995; 0.5
5. 2   **7.** D   **9.** $2e^{-2}$ **11.** D   **13.** 0   **15.** D
17. $\frac{1}{25}$ **19.** D   **21.** $\pi/9$ **23.** $\frac{1}{2}$ **25.** D
27. $\frac{32}{3}$ **29.** $\frac{75}{4}$ **31.** D   **33.** $\frac{8}{3}\ln 2 - \frac{8}{9}$
35. e **37.** $2\pi/3$

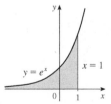 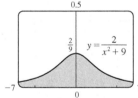

39. Infinite area

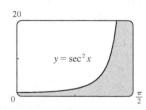

41. (a)

t	$\displaystyle\int_1^t [(\sin^2 x)/x^2]\,dx$
2	0.447453
5	0.577101
10	0.621306
100	0.668479
1,000	0.672957
10,000	0.673407

It appears that the integral is convergent.

(c)

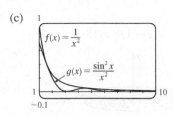

43. C   **45.** D   **47.** D   **49.** π **51.** $p < 1, 1/(1 - p)$
55. (a)

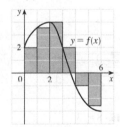

(b) The rate at which the fraction $F(t)$ increases as t increases
(c) 1; all bulbs burn out eventually
57. 8264.5 years   **59.** 1000   **63.** $C = 1; \ln 2$ **65.** No

CHAPTER 5 REVIEW ▪ PAGE 424

True-False Quiz

1. True   **3.** True   **5.** False   **7.** True   **9.** True
11. False   **13.** False   **15.** False   **17.** False   **19.** False
21. False   **23.** False

Exercises

1. (a) 8   (b) 5.7

    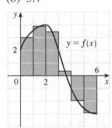

3. $\frac{1}{2} + \pi/4$ **5.** 3   **7.** f is c, f' is b, $\int_0^x f(t)\, dt$ is a
9. 37   **11.** $\frac{9}{10}$ **13.** $-(1/x) - 2 \ln|x| + x + C$
15. $\frac{1}{2} \ln 2$ **17.** $\frac{1}{3} \sin 1$ **19.** $(1/\pi)(e^\pi - 1)$
21. $\sqrt{x^2 + 4x} + C$ **23.** $5 + 10 \ln \frac{2}{3}$ **25.** 0
27. $\frac{64}{5} \ln 4 - \frac{124}{25}$ **29.** $\frac{1}{2} \ln \left| \frac{t + 2}{t + 4} \right| + C$
31. $3e^{\sqrt[3]{x}}(x^{2/3} - 2x^{1/3} + 2) + C$ **33.** $\ln|1 + \sec \theta| + C$
35. $2\sqrt{1 + \sin x} + C$ **37.** $\frac{64}{5}$ **39.** $F'(x) = x^2/(1 + x^3)$
41. $y' = (2e^x - e^{\sqrt{x}})/(2x)$ **43.** $\frac{1}{2}[e^x\sqrt{1 - e^{2x}} + \sin^{-1}(e^x)] + C$
45. $\frac{1}{4}(2x + 1)\sqrt{x^2 + x + 1} + \frac{1}{8} \ln(x + \frac{1}{2} + \sqrt{x^2 + x + 1}) + C$
47 (a) 1.090608 (overestimate)
(b) 1.088840 (underestimate)   (c) 1.089429 (unknown)
49. (a) $0.00\overline{6}$, $n \geq 259$ (b) $0.00\overline{3}$, $n \geq 183$
51. (a) 3.8   (b) 1.7867, 0.000646   (c) $n \geq 30$
53. $4 \leq \int_1^3 \sqrt{x^2 + 3}\, dx \leq 4\sqrt{3}$ **55.** $\frac{1}{36}$ **57.** D   **59.** 2
61. C   **63.** (a) $29.1\overline{6}$ m   (b) 29.5 m

65. Number of barrels of oil consumed from Jan. 1, 2000, through Jan. 1, 2008
67. $Ce^{-x^2/(4kt)}/\sqrt{4\pi kt}$ **69.** $e^{2x}(1 + 2x)/(1 - e^{-x})$

FOCUS ON PROBLEM SOLVING ▪ PAGE 429

1. About 1.85 inches from the center   **3.** $\pi/2$ **5.** $f(x) = \frac{1}{2}x$
7. e^{-2} **9.** $2k$ **11.** Does not exist   **13.** $[-1, 2]$
15. $\sqrt{1 + \sin^4 x} \cos x$ **17.** $\frac{1}{8}\pi - \frac{1}{12}$ **19.** 0

23. (b) $y = -\sqrt{L^2 - x^2} - L \ln\left(\dfrac{L - \sqrt{L^2 - x^2}}{x} \right)$

CHAPTER 6

EXERCISES 6.1 ▪ PAGE 436

1. $\frac{32}{3}$ **3.** $e - (1/e) + \frac{10}{3}$ **5.** $e - (1/e) + \frac{4}{3}$ **7.** $\frac{1}{3}$
9. $\frac{8}{3}$ **11.** $\frac{32}{3}$ **13.** 72   **15.** $e - 2$ **17.** $\ln 2$
19. 0, 0.90; 0.04   **21.** 1, 1.38; 0.05
23. $\frac{1}{2}$

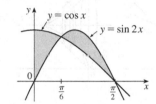

25. 118 ft   **27.** 84 m^2 **29.** 8868; increase in population over a 10-year period   **31.** $r\sqrt{R^2 - r^2} + \pi r^2/2 - R^2 \arcsin(r/R)$
33. πab **35.** $3 - e$ **37.** $24\sqrt{3}/5$ **39.** ± 6
41. $4^{2/3}$ **43.** $f(t) = 3t^2$ **45.** $0 < m < 1; m - \ln m - 1$

EXERCISES 6.2 ▪ PAGE 446

1. $19\pi/12$

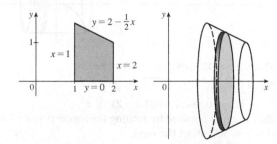

3. 162π

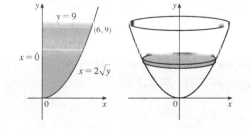

5. $4\pi/21$

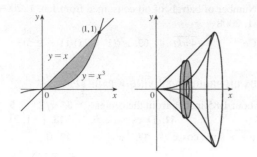

7. $64\pi/15$

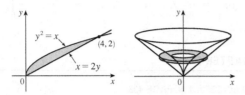

9. $\pi/6$

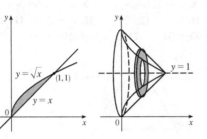

11. $2\pi\left(\frac{4}{3}\pi - \sqrt{3}\right)$

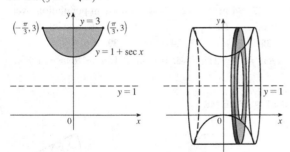

13. $\pi/2$ **15.** $108\pi/5$ **17.** $13\pi/30$

19. $\pi \int_{-2\sqrt{2}}^{2\sqrt{2}} \left[5^2 - \left(\sqrt{1+y^2} + 2\right)^2\right] dy$

21. $-1.288, 0.884; 23.780$ **23.** $\frac{11}{8}\pi^2$

25. (a) Solid obtained by rotating the region $0 \le y \le \cos x$,
$0 \le x \le \pi/2$ about the x-axis
(b) Solid obtained by rotating the region above the x-axis bounded
by $x = y^2$ and $x = y^4$ about the y-axis

27. 1110 cm^3 **29.** (a) 190 (b) 823

31. $\frac{1}{3}\pi r^2 h$ **33.** $\pi h^2\left(r - \frac{1}{3}h\right)$ **35.** $\frac{2}{3}b^2 h$ **37.** 10 cm^3

39. 24 **41.** $\frac{1}{3}$ **43.** $\frac{8}{15}$ **45.** (a) $8\pi R \int_0^r \sqrt{r^2 - y^2}\, dy$

(b) $2\pi^2 r^2 R$ **47.** (b) $\pi r^2 h$ **49.** $\frac{5}{12}\pi r^3$

51. $8 \int_0^r \sqrt{R^2 - y^2} \sqrt{r^2 - y^2}\, dy$

EXERCISES 6.3 ■ PAGE 453

1. Circumference $= 2\pi x$, height $= x(x-1)^2$; $\pi/15$

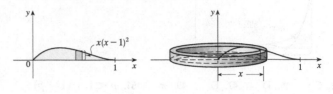

3. 2π

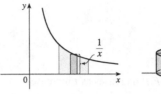
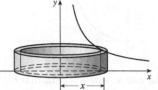

5. $\pi(1 - 1/e)$

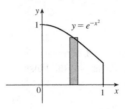
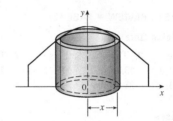

7. 16π

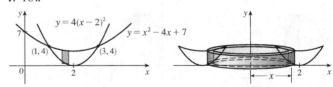

9. $21\pi/2$ **11.** $16\pi/3$ **13.** $7\pi/15$ **15.** $8\pi/3$

17. $5\pi/14$ **19.** $\int_0^\pi 2\pi(4 - y)\sqrt{\sin y}\, dy$ **21.** 3.70

23. (a) Solid obtained by rotating the region $0 \le y \le x^4$,
$0 \le x \le 3$ about the y-axis
(b) Solid obtained by rotating the region bounded by
(i) $x = 1 - y^2$, $x = 0$, and $y = 0$, or (ii) $x = y^2$, $x = 1$, and $y = 0$
about the line $y = 3$

25. 0.13 **27.** $\frac{1}{32}\pi^3$ **29.** 8π **31.** $\frac{4}{3}\pi$

33. $2\pi(12 - 4\ln 4)$ **35.** $\frac{4}{3}\pi r^3$ **37.** $\frac{1}{3}\pi r^2 h$

EXERCISES 6.4 ■ PAGE 458

1. $4\sqrt{5}$ **3.** 3.8202

5. $\int_0^{2\pi} \sqrt{3 - 2\sin t - 2\cos t}\, dt \approx 10.0367$ **7.** $4\sqrt{2} - 2$

9. $\left(13\sqrt{13} - 8\right)/27$ **11.** $\frac{3}{4} + \frac{1}{2}\ln 2$

13. $e^3 + 11 - e^{-8}$

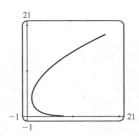

15. $\sqrt{2}\,(e^\pi - 1)$

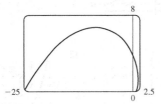

17. 5.115840   **19.** 40.056222

21. (a), (b)

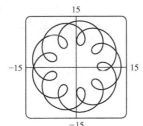

$L_1 = 4$,
$L_2 \approx 6.43$,
$L_4 \approx 7.50$

(c) $\int_0^4 \sqrt{1 + [4(3-x)/(3(4-x)^{2/3})]^2}\,dx$ (d) 7.7988

23. $\frac{205}{128} - \frac{81}{512}\ln 3$ **25.** $\ln(\sqrt{2}+1)$ **27.** 209.1 m

29. 29.36 in.

33. (a)

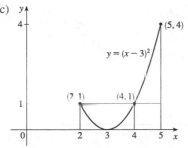

$t \in [0, 4\pi]$

(b) 294

EXERCISES 6.5 ▪ PAGE 463

1. $\frac{8}{3}$ **3.** $\frac{45}{28}$ **5.** $2/(5\pi)$

7. (a) 1   (b) 2, 4   (c)

9. (a) $4/\pi$ (b) $\approx 1.24, 2.81$

(c)

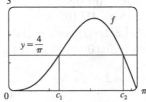

13. 38.6   **15.** $(50 + 28/\pi)°F \approx 59°F$
17. 6 kg/m   **19.** $5/(4\pi) \approx 0.4$ L

EXERCISES 6.6 ▪ PAGE 472

1. 9 ft-lb   **3.** 180 J   **5.** $\frac{15}{4}$ ft-lb

7. (a) $\frac{25}{24} \approx 1.04$ J   (b) 10.8 cm   **9.** $W_2 = 3W_1$

11. (a) 625 ft-lb   (b) $\frac{1875}{4}$ ft-lb   **13.** 650,000 ft-lb

15. 3857 J   **17.** 2450 J   **19.** $\approx 1.06 \times 10^6$ J

21. $\approx 1.04 \times 10^5$ ft-lb   **23.** 2.0 m

27. (a) $Gm_1m_2\left(\dfrac{1}{a} - \dfrac{1}{b}\right)$ (b) $\approx 8.50 \times 10^9$ J

29. (a) 187.5 lb/ft^2 (b) 1875 lb   (c) 562.5 lb

31. 6.7×10^4 N   **33.** 9.8×10^3 N   **35.** 1.2×10^4 lb

37. 5.27×10^5 N

39. (a) 5.63×10^3 lb   (b) 5.06×10^4 lb

(c) 4.88×10^4 lb   (d) 3.03×10^5 lb

41. 2.5×10^5 N   **43.** $10; 1; \left(\frac{1}{21}, \frac{10}{21}\right)$

45. $(0, 1.6)$ **47.** $\left(\dfrac{1}{e-1}, \dfrac{e+1}{4}\right)$ **49.** $60; 160; \left(\frac{8}{3}, 1\right)$

51. (b) $\left(\frac{1}{2}, \frac{2}{5}\right)$

EXERCISES 6.7 ▪ PAGE 479

1. $38,000   **3.** $43,866,933.33   **5.** $407.25

7. $12,000   **9.** 3727; $37,753

11. $\frac{2}{3}(16\sqrt{2} - 8) \approx 9.75 million   **13.** $\dfrac{(1-k)(b^{2-k} - a^{2-k})}{(2-k)(b^{1-k} - a^{1-k})}$

15. 1.19×10^{-4} cm^3/s   **17.** 6.60 L/min   **19.** 5.77 L/min

EXERCISES 6.8 ▪ PAGE 486

1. (a) The probability that a randomly chosen tire will have a lifetime between 30,000 and 40,000 miles
(b) The probability that a randomly chosen tire will have a lifetime of at least 25,000 miles

3. (b) $1 - \frac{3}{8}\sqrt{3} \approx 0.35$

5. (a) $1/\pi$ (b) $\frac{1}{2}$

7. (a) $f(x) \geq 0$ for all x and $\int_{-\infty}^{\infty} f(x)\,dx = 1$ (b) 5

11. (a) $e^{-4/2.5} \approx 0.20$ (b) $1 - e^{-4/2.5} \approx 0.55$ (c) If you aren't served within 10 minutes, you get a free hamburger.

13. $\approx 44\%$

15. (a) 0.0668   (b) $\approx 5.21\%$

17. ≈ 0.9545

CHAPTER 6 REVIEW ▪ PAGE 488

1. $\frac{8}{3}$ **3.** $\frac{7}{12}$ **5.** 9π **7.** (a) 0.38   (b) 0.87

9. (a) $2\pi/15$ (b) $\pi/6$ (c) $8\pi/15$ **11.** $1656\pi/5$

13. $\frac{4}{3}\pi(2ah + h^2)^{3/2}$ **15.** $\int_{-\pi/3}^{\pi/3} 2\pi(\pi/2 - x)(\cos^2 x - \frac{1}{4})\,dx$

17. (a) Solid obtained by rotating the region $0 \leqslant y \leqslant \sqrt{2}\cos x$, $0 \leqslant x \leqslant \pi/2$ about the x-axis

(b) Solid obtained by rotating the region $2 - \sqrt{x} \leqslant y \leqslant 2 - x^2$, $0 \leqslant x \leqslant 1$ about the x-axis

19. 36   **21.** $\frac{125}{3}\sqrt{3}$ m³   **23.** $2(5\sqrt{5} - 1)$ **25.** $\frac{15}{2}$

27. 3.2 J   **29.** (a) $8000\pi/3 \approx 8378$ ft-lb   (b) 2.1 ft

31. ≈ 458 lb   **33.** $\$7166.67$ **35.** $f(x)$

37. (a) $f(x) \geqslant 0$ for all x and $\int_{-\infty}^{\infty} f(x)\,dx = 1$
(b) ≈ 0.3455 (c) 5, yes

39. (a) $1 - e^{-3/8} \approx 0.31$ (b) $e^{-5/4} \approx 0.29$
(c) $8 \ln 2 \approx 5.55$ min

FOCUS ON PROBLEM SOLVING ▪ PAGE 491

1. $f(x) = \sqrt{2x/\pi}$ **3.** (b) 0.2261   (c) 0.6736 m
(d) (i) $1/(105\pi) \approx 0.003$ in/s   (ii) $370\pi/3$ s ≈ 6.5 min
7. Height $\sqrt{2}\,b$, volume $\left(\frac{28}{27}\sqrt{6} - 2\right)\pi b^3$ **9.** $\ln(\pi/2)$
13. 0.14 m   **15.** $b = 2a$

CHAPTER 7

EXERCISES 7.1 ▪ PAGE 498

3. (a) $\frac{1}{2}, -1$ **5.** (d)

7. (a) It must be either 0 or decreasing
(c) $y = 0$ (d) $y = 1/(x + 2)$
9. (a) $0 < P < 4200$ (b) $P > 4200$
(c) $P = 0, P = 4200$
13. (a) III   (b) I   (c) IV   (d) II
15. (a) At the beginning; stays positive, but decreases

(c)
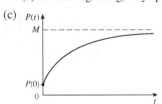

EXERCISES 7.2 ▪ PAGE 506

1. (a)
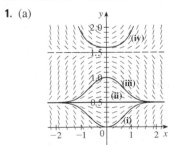

(b) $y = 0.5, y = 1.5$

3. III   **5.** IV

7.
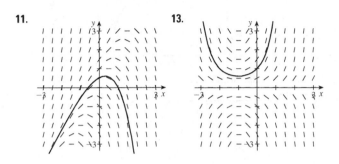

9.

11.

13.
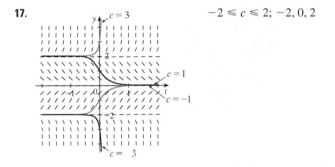

15.
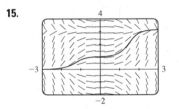

17.
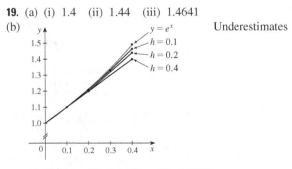

$-2 \leqslant c \leqslant 2; -2, 0, 2$

19. (a) (i) 1.4   (ii) 1.44   (iii) 1.4641
(b)

Underestimates

(c) (i) 0.0918   (ii) 0.0518   (iii) 0.0277
It appears that the error is also halved (approximately).

21. $-1, -3, -6.5, -12.25$ **23.** 1.7616
25. (a) (i) 3   (ii) 2.3928   (iii) 2.3701   (iv) 2.3681
(c) (i) -0.6321 (ii) -0.0249 (iii) -0.0022 (iv) -0.0002
It appears that the error is also divided by 10 (approximately).
27. (a), (d)   (b) 3
                            (c) Yes; $Q = 3$
                            (e) 2.77 C

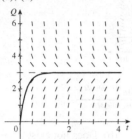

EXERCISES 7.3 ■ PAGE 514

1. $y = \dfrac{2}{K - x^2}, y = 0$ **3.** $y = K\sqrt{x^2 + 1}$
5. $\frac{1}{2}y^2 - \cos y = \frac{1}{2}x^2 + \frac{1}{4}x^4 + C$
7. $y = \pm\sqrt{[3(te^t - e^t + C)]^{2/3} - 1}$ **9.** $u = Ae^{2t+t^2/2} - 1$
11. $y = -\sqrt{x^2 + 9}$ **13.** $u = -\sqrt{t^2 + \tan t + 25}$
15. $\frac{1}{2}y^2 + \frac{1}{3}(3 + y^2)^{3/2} = \frac{1}{2}x^2 \ln x - \frac{1}{4}x^2 + \frac{41}{12}$
17. $y = \dfrac{4a}{\sqrt{3}} \sin x - a$
19. $y = e^{x^2/2}$ **21.** $y = Ke^x - x - 1$
23. (a) $\sin^{-1}y = x^2 + C$
(b) $y = \sin(x^2), -\sqrt{\pi/2} \le x \le \sqrt{\pi/2}$ (c) No

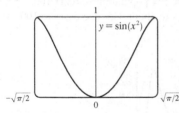

25. $\cos y = \cos x - 1$

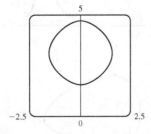

27. (a)   (b) $y = \dfrac{1}{K - x}$

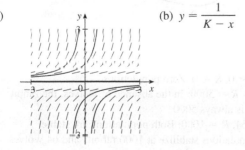

29. $y = Cx^2$

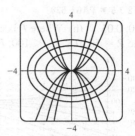

31. $x^2 - y^2 = C$

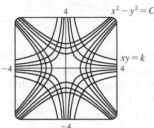

33. $y = 1 + e^{2-x^2/2}$ **35.** $y = \left(\frac{1}{2}x^2 + 2\right)^2$
37. $Q(t) = 3 - 3e^{-4t}$; 3   **39.** $P(t) = M - Me^{-kt}$; M
41. (a) $x = a - \dfrac{4}{(kt + 2/\sqrt{a})^2}$

(b) $t = \dfrac{2}{k\sqrt{a - b}}\left(\tan^{-1}\sqrt{\dfrac{b}{a - b}} - \tan^{-1}\sqrt{\dfrac{b - x}{a - b}}\right)$
43. (a) $C(t) = (C_0 - r/k)e^{-kt} + r/k$
(b) r/k; the concentration approaches r/k regardless of the value of C_0
45. (a) $15e^{-t/100}$ kg   (b) $15e^{-0.2} \approx 12.3$ kg
47. About 4.9%   **49.** g/k
51. (a) $L_1 = KL_2^k$ (b) $B = KV^{0.0794}$

53. (a) $dA/dt = k\sqrt{A}\,(M - A)$ (b) $A(t) = M\left(\dfrac{Ce^{\sqrt{M}kt} - 1}{Ce^{\sqrt{M}kt} + 1}\right)^2$,

where $C = \dfrac{\sqrt{M} + \sqrt{A_0}}{\sqrt{M} - \sqrt{A_0}}$ and $A_0 = A(0)$

EXERCISES 7.4 ■ PAGE 527

1. About 235
3. (a) $100(4.2)^t$ (b) ≈ 7409 (c) $\approx 10,632$ bacteria/h
(d) $(\ln 100)/(\ln 4.2) \approx 3.2$ h
5. (a) 1508 million, 1871 million   (b) 2161 million
(c) 3972 million; wars in the first half of century, increased life
expectancy in second half
7. (a) $Ce^{-0.0005t}$ (b) $-2000 \ln 0.9 \approx 211$ s
9. (a) $100 \times 2^{-t/30}$ mg   (b) ≈ 9.92 mg   (c) ≈ 199.3 years
11. ≈ 2500 years   **13.** (a) $\approx 137°F$ (b) ≈ 116 min
15. (a) $13.3°C$ (b) ≈ 67.74 min
17. (a) ≈ 64.5 kPa   (b) ≈ 39.9 kPa
19. (a) (i) $\$3828.84$ (ii) $\$3840.25$ (iii) $\$3850.08$
(iv) $\$3851.61$ (v) $\$3852.01$ (vi) $\$3852.08$
(b) $dA/dt = 0.05A$, $A(0) = 3000$

21. (a) $P(t) = \dfrac{m}{k} + \left(P_0 - \dfrac{m}{k}\right)e^{kt}$ (b) $m < kP_0$
(c) $m = kP_0, m > kP_0$ (d) Declining

EXERCISES 7.5 ▪ PAGE 538

1. (a) 100; 0.05   (b) Where P is close to 0 or 100; on the line $P = 50$; $0 < P_0 < 100$; $P_0 > 100$

(c)

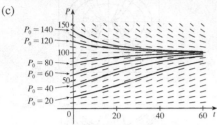

Solutions approach 100; some increase and some decrease, some have an inflection point but others don't; solutions with $P_0 = 20$ and $P_0 = 40$ have inflection points at $P = 50$

(d) $P = 0$, $P = 100$; other solutions move away from $P = 0$ and toward $P = 100$

3. (a) $3.23 \times 10^7 \, \text{kg}$ (b) ≈ 1.55 years

5. 9000

7. (a) $dP/dt = \frac{1}{265}P(1 - P/100)$, P in billions
(b) 5.49 billion   (c) In billions: 7.81, 27.72
(d) In billions: 5.48, 7.61, 22.41

9. (a) $dy/dt = ky(1 - y)$ (b) $y = \dfrac{y_0}{y_0 + (1 - y_0)e^{-kt}}$

(c) 3:36 PM

13. $P_E(t) = 1578.3(1.0933)^t + 94{,}000$;

$$P_L(t) = \frac{32{,}658.5}{1 + 12.75e^{-0.1706t}} + 94{,}000$$

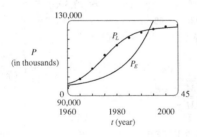

15. (a) Fish are caught at a rate of 15 per week.
(b) See part (d).   (c) $P = 250$, $P = 750$

(d)

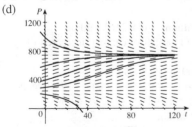

$0 < P_0 < 250: P \to 0$;
$P_0 = 250: P \to 250$;
$P_0 > 250: P \to 750$

(e) $P(t) = \dfrac{250 - 750ke^{t/25}}{1 - ke^{t/25}}$

where $k = \frac{1}{11}, -\frac{1}{9}$

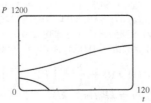

17. (b)

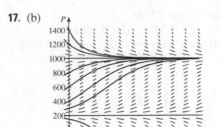

$0 < P_0 < 200: P \to 0$;
$P_0 = 200: P \to 200$;
$P_0 > 200: P \to 1000$

(c) $P(t) = \dfrac{m(M - P_0) + M(P_0 - m)e^{(M-m)(k/M)t}}{M - P_0 + (P_0 - m)e^{(M-m)(k/M)t}}$

19. (a) $P(t) = P_0 e^{(k/r)[\sin(rt - \phi) + \sin \phi]}$ (b) Does not exist

EXERCISES 7.6 ▪ PAGE 545

1. (a) $x = $ predators, $y = $ prey; growth is restricted only by predators, which feed only on prey.
(b) $x = $ prey, $y = $ predators; growth is restricted by carrying capacity and by predators, which feed only on prey.

3. (a) Competition
(b) (i) $x = 0$, $y = 0$: zero populations
(ii) $x = 0$, $y = 400$: In the absence of an x-population, the y-population stabilizes at 400.
(iii) $x = 125$, $y = 0$: In the absence of a y-population, the x-population stabilizes at 125.
(iv) $x = 50$, $y = 300$: Both populations are stable.

5. (a) The rabbit population starts at about 300, increases to 2400, then decreases back to 300. The fox population starts at 100, decreases to about 20, increases to about 315, decreases to 100, and the cycle starts again.

(b)

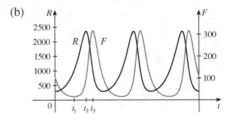

7.

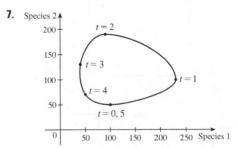

11. (a) Population stabilizes at 5000.
(b) (i) $W = 0$, $R = 0$: Zero populations
(ii) $W = 0$, $R = 5000$: In the absence of wolves, the rabbit population is always 5000.
(iii) $W = 64$, $R = 1000$: Both populations are stable.
(c) The populations stabilize at 1000 rabbits and 64 wolves.

(d)

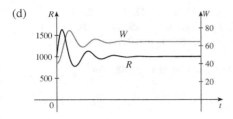

(d)

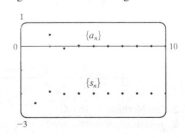

CHAPTER 7 REVIEW ■ PAGE 547

True-False Quiz

1. True **3.** False **5.** True

Exercises

1. (a)

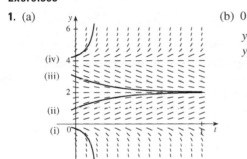

(b) $0 \leqslant c \leqslant 4$;
$y = 0$, $y = 2$,
$y - 4$

3. (a)

$y(0.3) \approx 0.8$

(b) 0.75676
(c) $y = x$ and $y = -x$; there is a loc max or loc min

5. $y = \pm\sqrt{\ln(x^2 + 2x^{3/2} + C)}$ **7.** $r(t) = 5e^{t-t^2}$

9. $x = C - \frac{1}{2}y^2$

11. (a) $200(3.24)^t$ (b) $\approx 22{,}040$
(c) $\approx 25{,}910$ bacteria/h (d) $(\ln 50)/(\ln 3.24) \approx 3.33$ h

13. (a) $C_0 e^{-kt}$ (b) ≈ 100 h

15. (a) $P(t) = \dfrac{2000}{1 + 19e^{-0.1t}}$; ≈ 560 (b) $t = -10 \ln \frac{2}{57} \approx 33.5$

17. (a) $L(t) = L_\infty - [L_\infty - L(0)]e^{-kt}$ (b) $L(t) = 53 - 43e^{-0.2t}$

19. 15 days **21.** $k \ln h + h = (-R/V)t + C$

23. (a) Stabilizes at 200,000
(b) (i) $x = 0$, $y = 0$: Zero populations
(ii) $x = 200{,}000$, $y = 0$: In the absence of birds, the insect population is always 200,000.
(iii) $x = 25{,}000$, $y = 175$: Both populations are stable.
(c) The populations stabilize at 25,000 insects and 175 birds.

FOCUS ON PROBLEM SOLVING ■ PAGE 551

1. $f(x) = \pm 10e^x$ **5.** $y = x^{1/n}$ **7.** $20°C$

9. (b) $f(x) = \dfrac{x^2 - L^2}{4L} - \frac{1}{2}L \ln\left(\dfrac{x}{L}\right)$ (c) No

11. (a) 9.8 h (b) $31{,}900\pi$ ft^2; 2000π ft^2/h
(c) 5.1 h

13. $x^2 + (y - 6)^2 = 25$

CHAPTER 8

EXERCISES 8.1 ■ PAGE 562

Abbreviations: C, convergent; D, divergent

1. (a) A sequence is an ordered list of numbers. It can also be defined as a function whose domain is the set of positive integers.
(b) The terms a_n approach 8 as n becomes large.
(c) The terms a_n become large as n becomes large.

3. $\frac{1}{3}, \frac{2}{5}, \frac{3}{7}, \frac{4}{9}, \frac{5}{11}, \frac{6}{13}$; yes; $\frac{1}{2}$ **5.** $a_n = 1/(2n - 1)$

7. $a_n = 5n - 3$ **9.** $a_n = \left(-\frac{2}{3}\right)^{n-1}$ **11.** 5
13. 1 **15.** 1 **17.** 1 **19.** 0 **21.** 0 **23.** 0
25. 0 **27.** e^2 **29.** 0 **31.** D **33.** $\ln 2$ **35.** 1
37. $\frac{1}{2}$ **39.** D
41. (a) 1060, 1123.60, 1191.02, 1262.48, 1338.23 (b) D
43. (a) $P_n = 1.08P_{n-1} - 300$ (b) 5734
45. (a) D (b) C **47.** (b) $\frac{1}{2}(1 + \sqrt{5})$
49. Decreasing; yes **51.** Not monotonic; no
53. Convergent by the Monotonic Sequence Theorem; $5 \leqslant L < 8$
55. $\frac{1}{2}(3 + \sqrt{5})$ **57.** 62

EXERCISES 8.2 ■ PAGE 572

1. (a) A sequence is an ordered list of numbers whereas a series is the *sum* of a list of numbers.
(b) A series is convergent if the sequence of partial sums is a convergent sequence. A series is divergent if it is not convergent.

3. -2.40000, -1.92000,
-2.01600, -1.99680,
-2.00064, -1.99987,
-2.00003, -1.99999,
-2.00000, -2.00000;
convergent, sum $= -2$

5. 0.44721, 1.15432,
1.98637, 2.88080,
3.80927, 4.75796,
5.71948, 6.68962,
7.66581, 8.64639;
divergent

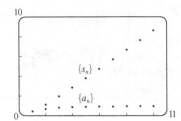

7. 0.29289, 0.42265,
0.50000, 0.55279,
0.59175, 0.62204,
0.64645, 0.66667,
0.68377, 0.69849;
convergent, sum $= 1$

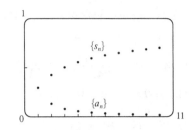

9. (a) C   (b) D   **11.** D   **13.** $\frac{25}{3}$ **15.** 60   **17.** D
19. D   **21.** D   **23.** $\frac{5}{2}$ **25.** D   **27.** D   **29.** $e/(e-1)$
31. $\frac{3}{2}$ **33.** $\frac{11}{6}$
35. (b) 1   (c) 2   (d) All rational numbers with a terminating
decimal representation, except 0.
37. $\frac{2}{9}$ **39.** 5063/3300   **41.** $-3 < x < 3$; $\dfrac{x}{3-x}$
43. All x; $\dfrac{2}{2-\cos x}$ **45.** 1
47. $a_1 = 0, a_n = \dfrac{2}{n(n+1)}$ for $n > 1$, sum $= 1$
49. (a) 105.25 mg   (b) $\dfrac{100(1 - 0.05^n)}{1 - 0.05}$ mg
(c) The quantity of the drug approaches $\dfrac{100}{0.95} \approx 105.26$ mg
51. (a) $S_n = \dfrac{D(1 - c^n)}{1 - c}$ (b) 5   **53.** $\frac{1}{2}(\sqrt{3} - 1)$
57. $\dfrac{1}{n(n+1)}$ **59.** The series is divergent.
63. $\{s_n\}$ is bounded and increasing.
65. (a) $0, \frac{1}{9}, \frac{2}{9}, \frac{1}{3}, \frac{2}{3}, \frac{7}{9}, \frac{8}{9}, 1$
67. (a) $\frac{1}{2}, \frac{5}{6}, \frac{23}{24}, \frac{119}{120}; \dfrac{(n+1)! - 1}{(n+1)!}$ (c) 1

EXERCISES 8.3 ■ PAGE 583

1. C

3. (a) Nothing   (b) C
5. p-series; geometric series; $b < -1$; $-1 < b < 1$ **7.** D

9. C   **11.** D   **13.** C   **15.** C   **17.** D   **19.** C
21. C   **23.** D   **25.** D   **27.** C   **29.** D   **31.** $p > 1$
33. (a) 1.54977, error $\leqslant 0.1$ (b) 1.64522, error $\leqslant 0.005$
(c) $n > 1000$
35. 0.00145   **37.** 1.249, error < 0.1 **43.** Yes

EXERCISES 8.4 ■ PAGE 591

1. (a) A series whose terms are alternately positive and
negative   (b) $0 < b_{n+1} \leqslant b_n$ and $\lim_{n\to\infty} b_n = 0$,
where $b_n = |a_n|$ (c) $|R_n| \leqslant b_{n+1}$
3. C   **5.** C   **7.** D   **9.** C
11. An underestimate   **13.** $p > 0$ **15.** 5   **17.** -0.5507
19. 0.0676   **21.** No   **23.** Yes   **25.** Yes   **27.** No
29. Yes   **31.** Yes   **33.** Yes   **35.** D   **37.** (a) and (d)
39. AC

EXERCISES 8.5 ■ PAGE 597

1. A series of the form $\sum_{n=0}^{\infty} c_n(x - a)^n$, where x is a variable
and a and the c_n's are constants
3. 1, $[-1, 1)$ **5.** 1, $[-1, 1]$ **7.** ∞, $(-\infty, \infty)$
9. 2, $(-2, 2)$ **11.** $\frac{1}{2}, \left(-\frac{1}{2}, \frac{1}{2}\right]$ **13.** 1, $[1, 3]$
15. $\frac{1}{3}, \left[-\frac{13}{3}, -\frac{11}{3}\right)$ **17.** $\frac{1}{4}, \left[-\frac{1}{2}, 0\right]$ **19.** 0, $\left\{\frac{1}{2}\right\}$
21. $b, (a - b, a + b)$ **23.** ∞, $(-\infty, \infty)$
25. (a) Yes   (b) No   **27.** k^k
29. (a) $(-\infty, \infty)$
(b), (c)

31. $(-1, 1), f(x) = (1 + 2x)/(1 - x^2)$ **33.** 2   **35.** No

EXERCISES 8.6 ■ PAGE 603

1. 10   **3.** $\displaystyle\sum_{n=0}^{\infty} (-1)^n x^n, (-1, 1)$ **5.** $2 \displaystyle\sum_{n=0}^{\infty} \dfrac{1}{3^{n+1}} x^n, (-3, 3)$
7. $\displaystyle\sum_{n=0}^{\infty} (-1)^n \dfrac{1}{9^{n+1}} x^{2n+1}, (-3, 3)$ **9.** $1 + 2\displaystyle\sum_{n=1}^{\infty} x^n, (-1, 1)$
11. (a) $\displaystyle\sum_{n=0}^{\infty} (-1)^n (n+1) x^n, R = 1$
(b) $\dfrac{1}{2} \displaystyle\sum_{n=0}^{\infty} (-1)^n (n+2)(n+1) x^n, R = 1$
(c) $\dfrac{1}{2} \displaystyle\sum_{n=2}^{\infty} (-1)^n n(n-1) x^n, R = 1$
13. $\ln 5 - \displaystyle\sum_{n=1}^{\infty} \dfrac{x^n}{n5^n}, R = 5$

15. $\sum_{n=0}^{\infty} (-1)^n 4^n (n+1) x^{n+1}, R = \frac{1}{4}$

17. $\sum_{n=0}^{\infty} (2n+1) x^n, R = 1$

19. $\sum_{n=0}^{\infty} (-1)^n \frac{1}{16^{n+1}} x^{2n+1}, R = 4$

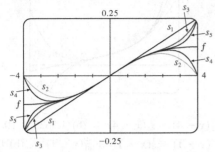

21. $\sum_{n=0}^{\infty} \frac{2x^{2n+1}}{2n+1}, R = 1$

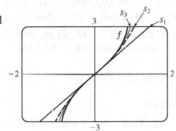

23. $C + \sum_{n=0}^{\infty} \frac{t^{8n+2}}{8n+2}, R = 1$

25. $C + \sum_{n=1}^{\infty} (-1)^{n+1} \frac{x^{2n-1}}{4n^2-1}, R = 1$

27. 0.199989   **29.** 0.000983   **31.** 0.19740

33. (b) 0.920   **37.** $[-1, 1], [-1, 1), (-1, 1)$

EXERCISES 8.7 ▪ PAGE 616

1. $b_8 = f^{(8)}(5)/8!$ **3.** $\sum_{n=0}^{\infty} (n+1) x^n, R = 1$

5. $\sum_{n=0}^{\infty} (n+1) x^n, R = 1$

7. $\sum_{n=0}^{\infty} (-1)^n \frac{\pi^{2n+1}}{(2n+1)!} x^{2n+1}, R = \infty$

9. $\sum_{n=0}^{\infty} \frac{5^n}{n!} x^n, R = \infty$

11. $-1 - 2(x-1) + 3(x-1)^2 + 4(x-1)^3 + (x-1)^4, R = \infty$

13. $\sum_{n=0}^{\infty} \frac{e^3}{n!} (x-3)^n, R = \infty$

15. $\sum_{n=0}^{\infty} (-1)^{n+1} \frac{1}{(2n)!} (x-\pi)^{2n}, R = \infty$

17. $\frac{1}{3} + \sum_{n=1}^{\infty} (-1)^n \frac{1 \cdot 3 \cdot 5 \cdots (2n-1)}{2^n \cdot 3^{2n+1} \cdot n!} (x-9)^n, R = 9$

21. $1 + \frac{x}{2} + \sum_{n=2}^{\infty} (-1)^{n-1} \frac{1 \cdot 3 \cdot 5 \cdots (2n-3)}{2^n n!} x^n, R = 1$

23. $\sum_{n=0}^{\infty} (-1)^n \frac{(n+1)(n+2)}{2^{n+4}} x^n, R = 2$

25. $\sum_{n=0}^{\infty} (-1)^n \frac{\pi^{2n+1}}{(2n+1)!} x^{2n+1}, R = \infty$

27. $\sum_{n=0}^{\infty} \frac{2^n + 1}{n!} x^n, R = \infty$

29. $\sum_{n=0}^{\infty} (-1)^n \frac{1}{2^{2n}(2n)!} x^{4n+1}, R = \infty$

31. $\frac{1}{2}x + \sum_{n=1}^{\infty} (-1)^n \frac{1 \cdot 3 \cdot 5 \cdots (2n-1)}{n! 2^{3n+1}} x^{2n+1}, R = 2$

33. $\sum_{n=1}^{\infty} (-1)^{n+1} \frac{2^{2n-1}}{(2n)!} x^{2n}, R = \infty$

35. $\sum_{n=0}^{\infty} (-1)^n \frac{1}{(2n)!} x^{4n}, R = \infty$

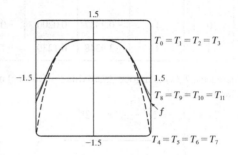

37. $\sum_{n=1}^{\infty} \frac{(-1)^{n-1}}{(n-1)!} x^n, R = \infty$

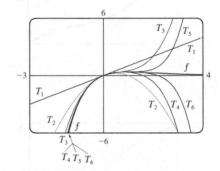

39. 0.81873

41. (a) $1 + \sum_{n=1}^{\infty} \frac{1 \cdot 3 \cdot 5 \cdots (2n-1)}{2^n n!} x^{2n}$

(b) $x + \sum_{n=1}^{\infty} \frac{1 \cdot 3 \cdot 5 \cdots (2n-1)}{(2n+1)2^n n!} x^{2n+1}$

43. $C + \sum_{n=0}^{\infty} (-1)^n \frac{x^{6n+2}}{(6n+2)(2n)!}, R = \infty$

45. $C + \sum_{n=1}^{\infty} (-1)^n \frac{1}{2n (2n)!} x^{2n}, R = \infty$

47. 0.440   **49.** 0.40102   **51.** $\frac{1}{2}$ **53.** $\frac{1}{120}$

55. $1 - \frac{3}{2}x^2 + \frac{25}{24}x^4$ **57.** $1 + \frac{1}{6}x^2 + \frac{7}{360}x^4$ **59.** e^{-x^4}

61. $\ln \frac{8}{5}$ **63.** $1/\sqrt{2}$ **65.** $e^3 - 1$

EXERCISES 8.8 ■ PAGE 625

1. (a) $T_0(x) = 1 = T_1(x)$, $T_2(x) = 1 - \frac{1}{2}x^2 = T_3(x)$,
$T_4(x) = 1 - \frac{1}{2}x^2 + \frac{1}{24}x^4 = T_5(x)$,
$T_6(x) = 1 - \frac{1}{2}x^2 + \frac{1}{24}x^4 - \frac{1}{720}x^6$

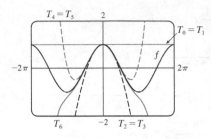

(b)

x	f	$T_0 = T_1$	$T_2 = T_3$	$T_4 = T_5$	T_6
$\frac{\pi}{4}$	0.7071	1	0.6916	0.7074	0.7071
$\frac{\pi}{2}$	0	1	-0.2337	0.0200	-0.0009
π	-1	1	-3.9348	0.1239	-1.2114

(c) As n increases, $T_n(x)$ is a good approximation to $f(x)$ on a larger and larger interval.

3. $\frac{1}{2} - \frac{1}{4}(x - 2) + \frac{1}{8}(x - 2)^2 - \frac{1}{16}(x - 2)^3$

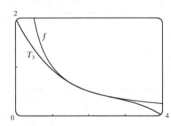

5. $-\left(x - \frac{\pi}{2}\right) + \frac{1}{6}\left(x - \frac{\pi}{2}\right)^3$

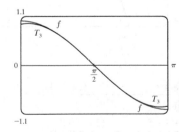

7. $x - 2x^2 + 2x^3$

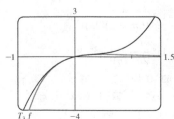

9. $T_5(x) = 1 - 2\left(x - \frac{\pi}{4}\right) + 2\left(x - \frac{\pi}{4}\right)^2 - \frac{8}{3}\left(x - \frac{\pi}{4}\right)^3$
$+ \frac{10}{3}\left(x - \frac{\pi}{4}\right)^4 - \frac{64}{15}\left(x - \frac{\pi}{4}\right)^5$

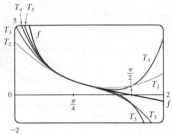

11. (a) $2 + \frac{1}{4}(x - 4) - \frac{1}{64}(x - 4)^2$ (b) 1.5625×10^{-5}
13. (a) $1 + \frac{2}{3}(x - 1) - \frac{1}{9}(x - 1)^2 + \frac{4}{81}(x - 1)^3$ (b) 0.000097
15. (a) $1 + x^2$ (b) 0.00006   **17.** (a) $x^2 - \frac{1}{6}x^4$ (b) 0.042
19. 0.17365   **21.** Four   **23.** $-1.037 < x < 1.037$
25. $-0.86 < x < 0.86$ **27.** 21 m, no
31. (c) They differ by about 8×10^{-9} km.

CHAPTER 8 REVIEW ■ PAGE 629

True-False Quiz

1. False   **3.** True   **5.** False   **7.** False   **9.** False
11. True   **13.** True   **15.** False   **17.** True   **19.** True

Exercises

1. $\frac{1}{2}$ **3.** D   **5.** 0   **7.** e^{12} **9.** C   **11.** C   **13.** D
15. C   **17.** C   **19.** $\frac{1}{11}$ **21.** $\pi/4$ **23.** $\frac{4111}{3330}$
25. 0.9721   **27.** 0.18976224, error $< 6.4 \times 10^{-7}$
31. 4, $[-6, 2)$ **33.** 0.5, [2.5, 3.5)

35. $\frac{1}{2} \sum_{n=0}^{\infty} (-1)^n \left[\frac{1}{(2n)!} \left(x - \frac{\pi}{6}\right)^{2n} + \frac{\sqrt{3}}{(2n + 1)!} \left(x - \frac{\pi}{6}\right)^{2n+1} \right]$

37. $\sum_{n=0}^{\infty} (-1)^n x^{n+2}, R = 1$ **39.** $\ln 4 - \sum_{n=1}^{\infty} \frac{x^n}{n 4^n}, R = 4$

41. $\sum_{n=0}^{\infty} (-1)^n \frac{x^{8n+4}}{(2n + 1)!}, R = \infty$

43. $\frac{1}{2} + \sum_{n=1}^{\infty} \frac{1 \cdot 5 \cdot 9 \cdot \cdots \cdot (4n - 3)}{n! 2^{6n+1}} x^n, R = 16$

45. $C + \ln |x| + \sum_{n=1}^{\infty} \frac{x^n}{n \cdot n!}$

47. (a) $1 + \frac{1}{2}(x - 1) - \frac{1}{8}(x - 1)^2 + \frac{1}{16}(x - 1)^3$
(b)   (c) 0.000006

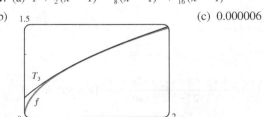

49. $-\frac{1}{6}$

PRINCIPLES OF PROBLEM SOLVING ■ **PAGE 631**

1. $15!/5! = 10{,}897{,}286{,}400$
3. (a) $s_n = 3 \cdot 4^n$, $l_n = 1/3^n$, $p_n = 4^n/3^{n-1}$ (c) $\frac{2}{5}\sqrt{3}$

5. $\ln\frac{1}{2}$ **11.** $\dfrac{\pi}{2\sqrt{3}} - 1$

13. $-\left(\dfrac{\pi}{2} - \pi k\right)^2$ where k is a positive integer

CHAPTER 9

EXERCISES 9.1 ■ PAGE 638

1. $(4, 0, -3)$ **3.** $Q; R$

5. A vertical plane that intersects the xy-plane in the line $y = 2 - x$, $z = 0$ (see graph at right)

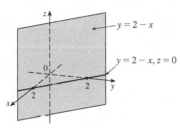

7. (a) $|PQ| = 6$, $|QR| = 2\sqrt{10}$, $|RP| = 6$; isosceles triangle
(b) $|PQ| = 3$, $|QR| = 3\sqrt{5}$, $|RP| = 6$; right triangle
9. (a) No   (b) Yes
11. $(x - 3)^2 + (y - 8)^2 + (z - 1)^2 = 30$
13. $(3, -2, 1)$, 5 **15.** $(2, 0, -6)$, $9/\sqrt{2}$
17. (b) $\frac{5}{2}, \frac{1}{2}\sqrt{94}, \frac{1}{2}\sqrt{85}$
19. (a) $(x - 2)^2 + (y + 3)^2 + (z - 6)^2 = 36$
(b) $(x - 2)^2 + (y + 3)^2 + (z - 6)^2 = 4$
(c) $(x - 2)^2 + (y + 3)^2 + (z - 6)^2 = 9$
21. A plane parallel to the yz-plane and 5 units in front of it
23. A half-space consisting of all points to the left of the plane $y = 8$
25. All points on or between the horizontal planes $z = 0$ and $z = 6$
27. All points on a circle with radius 2 and center on the z-axis that is contained in the plane $z = -1$
29. All points on or inside a sphere with radius $\sqrt{3}$ and center O
31. All points on or inside a circular cylinder of radius 3 with axis the y-axis
33. $0 < x < 5$ **35.** $r^2 < x^2 + y^2 + z^2 < R^2$
37. (a) $(2, 1, 4)$ (b)

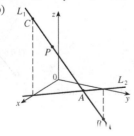

39. $14x - 6y - 10z = 9$, a plane perpendicular to AB
41. $2\sqrt{3} - 3$

EXERCISES 9.2 ■ PAGE 646

1. (a) Scalar   (b) Vector   (c) Vector   (d) Scalar
3. $\overrightarrow{AB} = \overrightarrow{DC}, \overrightarrow{DA} = \overrightarrow{CB}, \overrightarrow{DE} = \overrightarrow{EB}, \overrightarrow{EA} = \overrightarrow{CE}$

5. (a)      (b)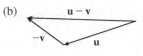

(c)   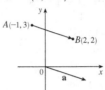   (d)

7. $\mathbf{a} = \langle 3, -1 \rangle$ **9.** $\mathbf{a} = \langle 2, 0, -2 \rangle$

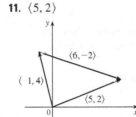

11. $\langle 5, 2 \rangle$ **13.** $\langle 0, 1, -1 \rangle$

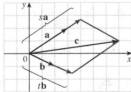

15. $\langle 2, -18 \rangle$, $\langle 1, -42 \rangle$, 13, 10
17. $-\mathbf{i} + \mathbf{j} + 2\mathbf{k}$, $-4\mathbf{i} + \mathbf{j} + 9\mathbf{k}$, $\sqrt{14}$, $\sqrt{82}$
19. $-\dfrac{3}{\sqrt{58}}\mathbf{i} + \dfrac{7}{\sqrt{58}}\mathbf{j}$ **21.** $\frac{8}{9}\mathbf{i} - \frac{1}{9}\mathbf{j} + \frac{4}{9}\mathbf{k}$
23. $\langle 2, 2\sqrt{3} \rangle$ **25.** ≈ 45.96 ft/s, ≈ 38.57 ft/s
27. $100\sqrt{7} \approx 264.6$ N, $\approx 139.1°$
29. $\sqrt{493} \approx 22.2$ mi/h, N8°W
31. $\mathbf{T}_1 = -196\mathbf{i} + 3.92\mathbf{j}$, $\mathbf{T}_2 = 196\mathbf{i} + 3.92\mathbf{j}$
33. $\pm(\mathbf{i} + 4\mathbf{j})/\sqrt{17}$
35. (a), (b)   (d) $s = \frac{9}{7}, t = \frac{11}{7}$

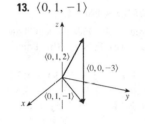

37. $\mathbf{a} \approx \langle 0.50, 0.31, 0.81 \rangle$
39. A sphere with radius 1, centered at (x_0, y_0, z_0)

EXERCISES 9.3 ■ PAGE 653

1. (b), (c), (d) are meaningful   **3.** -15
5. 14 **7.** 19 **9.** 1 **11.** $\mathbf{u} \cdot \mathbf{v} = \frac{1}{2}$, $\mathbf{u} \cdot \mathbf{w} = -\frac{1}{2}$
15. $\cos^{-1}\left(\dfrac{9 + 4\sqrt{7}}{20}\right) \approx 95°$ **17.** $\cos^{-1}\left(\dfrac{-1}{2\sqrt{7}}\right) \approx 101°$
19. $45°, 45°, 90°$
21. (a) Neither   (b) Orthogonal
(c) Orthogonal   (d) Parallel
23. Yes   **25.** $(\mathbf{i} - \mathbf{j} - \mathbf{k})/\sqrt{3}$ [or $(-\mathbf{i} + \mathbf{j} + \mathbf{k})/\sqrt{3}$]
27. $45°$ **29.** $3, \langle \frac{9}{5}, -\frac{12}{5} \rangle$ **31.** $1/\sqrt{21}, \frac{2}{21}\mathbf{i} - \frac{1}{21}\mathbf{j} + \frac{4}{21}\mathbf{k}$

35. $\langle 0, 0, -2\sqrt{10} \rangle$ or any vector of the form
$\langle s, t, 3s - 2\sqrt{10} \rangle, s, t \in \mathbb{R}$
37. 144 J   **39.** $2400 \cos(40°) \approx 1839$ ft-lb
41. $\frac{13}{5}$ **43.** $\cos^{-1}(1/\sqrt{3}) \approx 55°$

EXERCISES 9.4 ■ PAGE 661

1. (a) Scalar   (b) Meaningless   (c) Vector
(d) Meaningless   (e) Meaningless   (f) Scalar
3. $96\sqrt{3}$; into the page   **5.** $10.8 \sin 80° \approx 10.6$ N·m
7. $16\mathbf{i} + 48\mathbf{k}$ **9.** $15\mathbf{i} - 3\mathbf{j} + 3\mathbf{k}$ **11.** $\frac{1}{2}\mathbf{i} - \mathbf{j} + \frac{3}{2}\mathbf{k}$
13. $t^4\mathbf{i} - 2t^3\mathbf{j} + t^2\mathbf{k}$ **15.** $\mathbf{0}$ **17.** $\mathbf{i} + \mathbf{j} + \mathbf{k}$
19. $\langle -2/\sqrt{6}, -1/\sqrt{6}, 1/\sqrt{6} \rangle, \langle 2/\sqrt{6}, 1/\sqrt{6}, -1/\sqrt{6} \rangle$
21. 16   **23.** (a) $\langle 13, -14, 5 \rangle$ (b) $\frac{1}{2}\sqrt{390}$
25. ≈ 417 N   **27.** 82   **29.** 3
33. (b) $\sqrt{97/3}$ **39.** (a) No   (b) No   (c) Yes

EXERCISES 9.5 ■ PAGE 670

1. (a) True   (b) False   (c) True   (d) False   (e) False
(f) True   (g) False   (h) True   (i) True   (j) False
(k) True
3. $\mathbf{r} = (2\mathbf{i} + 2.4\mathbf{j} + 3.5\mathbf{k}) + t(3\mathbf{i} + 2\mathbf{j} - \mathbf{k})$;
$x = 2 + 3t, y = 2.4 + 2t, z = 3.5 - t$
5. $\mathbf{r} = (\mathbf{i} + 6\mathbf{k}) + t(\mathbf{i} + 3\mathbf{j} + \mathbf{k})$;
$x = 1 + t, y = 3t, z = 6 + t$
7. $x = 2 + 2t, y = 1 + \frac{1}{2}t$,
$z = -3 - 4t$;
$(x - 2)/2 = 2y - 2 = (z + 3)/(-4)$
9. $x = 1 + t, y = -1 + 2t, z = 1 + t$;
$x - 1 = (y + 1)/2 = z - 1$
11. Yes
13. (a) $(x - 1)/(-1) = (y + 5)/2 = (z - 6)/(-3)$
(b) $(-1, -1, 0), (-\frac{3}{2}, 0, -\frac{3}{2}), (0, -3, 3)$
15. $\mathbf{r}(t) = (2\mathbf{i} - \mathbf{j} + 4\mathbf{k}) + t(2\mathbf{i} + 7\mathbf{j} - 3\mathbf{k}), 0 \le t \le 1$
17. Parallel   **19.** Skew   **21.** $-2x + y + 5z = 1$
23. $3x - 7z = -9$ **25.** $x + y + z = 2$
27. $33x + 10y + 4z = 190$ **29.** $x - 2y + 4z = -1$
31. $3x - 8y - z = -38$

33.
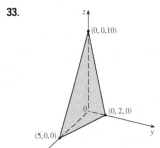
35.
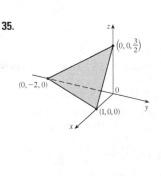

37. $(2, 3, 5)$ **39.** Perpendicular
41. Neither, $\cos^{-1}(\frac{1}{3}) \approx 70.5°$

43. (a) $x = 1, y = -t, z = t$ (b) $\cos^{-1}\left(\dfrac{5}{3\sqrt{3}}\right) \approx 15.8°$

45. $x = 1, y - 2 = -z$ **47.** $(x/a) + (y/b) + (z/c) = 1$
49. $x = 3t, y = 1 - t, z = 2 - 2t$
51. P_2 and P_3 are parallel, P_1 and P_4 are identical
53. $\sqrt{61/14}$ **55.** $\frac{18}{7}$ **57.** $5/(2\sqrt{14})$ **61.** $1/\sqrt{6}$

EXERCISES 9.6 ■ PAGE 680

1. (a) 25; a 40-knot wind blowing in the open sea for 15 h will create waves about 25 ft high.
(b) $f(30, t)$ is a function of t giving the wave heights produced by 30-knot winds blowing for t hours.
(c) $f(v, 30)$ is a function of v giving the wave heights produced by winds of speed v blowing for 30 hours.
3. (a) 1   (b) $\mathbb{R}^2$ (c) $[-1, 1]$
5. $\{(x, y) \mid y \ge x^2, x \ne \pm 1\}$

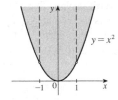

7. $\{(x, y) \mid -1 \le x \le 1, -1 \le y \le 1\}$

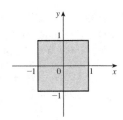

9. $z = 3$, horizontal plane

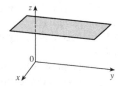

11. $3x + 2y + z = 6$, plane

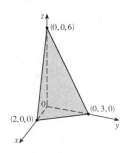

13. $z = y^2 + 1$, parabolic cylinder

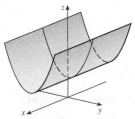

15. (a) VI   (b) V   (c) I   (d) IV   (e) II   (f) III

17. $z = \sqrt{4x^2 + y^2}$

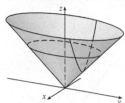

19.

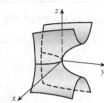

21. $x^2 + \dfrac{(y-2)^2}{4} + (z-3)^2 = 1$

Ellipsoid with center $(0, 2, 3)$

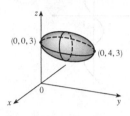

23. (a) A circle of radius 1 centered at the origin
(b) A circular cylinder of radius 1 with axis the z-axis
(c) A circular cylinder of radius 1 with axis the y-axis
25. (a) $x = k$, $y^2 - z^2 = 1 - k^2$, hyperbola $(k \neq \pm 1)$;
$y = k$, $x^2 - z^2 = 1 - k^2$, hyperbola $(k \neq \pm 1)$;
$z = k$, $x^2 + y^2 = 1 + k^2$, circle
(b) The hyperboloid is rotated so that it has axis the y-axis
(c) The hyperboloid is shifted one unit in the negative y-direction
27. III
29.

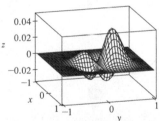

f appears to have a maximum value of about 0.044. There are two local maximum points and two local minimum points.
31.

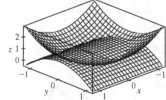

EXERCISES 9.7 ▪ PAGE 686

1. See pages 682–83.
3. (a)

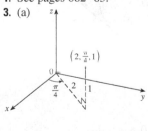

$(\sqrt{2}, \sqrt{2}, 1)$

(b)

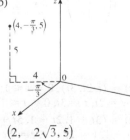

$(2, \ 2\sqrt{3}, 5)$

5. (a) $\left(\sqrt{2}, 7\pi/4, 4\right)$ (b) $\left(2, 4\pi/3, 2\right)$
7. (a)

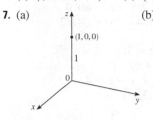

$(0, 0, 1)$ $\left(\sqrt{2}/2, \sqrt{6}/2, \sqrt{2}\right)$

9. (a) $\left(4, \pi/3, \pi/6\right)$ (b) $\left(\sqrt{2}, 3\pi/2, 3\pi/4\right)$
11. Vertical half-plane through the z-axis   **13.** Half-cone
15. Circular paraboloid
17. Circular cylinder, radius 1, axis parallel to the z-axis
19. Sphere, radius $\frac{1}{2}$, center $\left(0, \frac{1}{2}, 0\right)$
21. (a) $r = 2 \sin \theta$ (b) $\rho \sin \phi = 2 \sin \theta$
23. (a) $z = 6 - r(3 \cos \theta + 2 \sin \theta)$
(b) $\rho(3 \sin \phi \cos \theta + 2 \sin \phi \sin \theta + \cos \phi) = 6$
25.

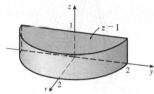

27.

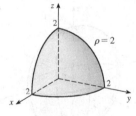

29.

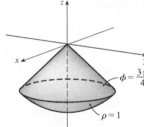

31. Cylindrical coordinates: $6 \leqslant r \leqslant 7$, $0 \leqslant \theta \leqslant 2\pi$, $0 \leqslant z \leqslant 20$
33. $0 \leqslant \phi \leqslant \pi/4$, $0 \leqslant \rho \leqslant \cos \phi$
35.

CHAPTER 9 REVIEW ▪ PAGE 688

True-False Quiz

1. True   **3.** True   **5.** True   **7.** True   **9.** True
11. False   **13.** False   **15.** False   **17.** True

Exercises
1. (a) $(x + 1)^2 + (y - 2)^2 + (z - 1)^2 = 69$
(b) $(y - 2)^2 + (z - 1)^2 = 68$, $x = 0$
(c) Center $(4, -1, -3)$, radius 5

3. $\mathbf{u} \cdot \mathbf{v} = 3\sqrt{2}$; $|\mathbf{u} \times \mathbf{v}| = 3\sqrt{2}$; out of the page
5. $-2, -4$ **7.** (a) 2 (b) -2 (c) -2 (d) 0
9. $\cos^{-1}(\frac{1}{3}) \approx 71°$ **11.** (a) $\langle 4, -3, 4 \rangle$ (b) $\sqrt{41}/2$
13. 166 N, 114 N
15. $x = 4 - 3t, y = -1 + 2t, z = 2 + 3t$
17. $x = -2 + 2t, y = 2 - t, z = 4 + 5t$
19. $-4x + 3y + z = -14$ **21.** $x + y + z = 4$
23. Skew   **25.** (a) $22/\sqrt{26}$ (b) $3/\sqrt{2}$
27. $\{(x, y) \mid x > y^2\}$

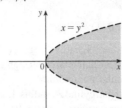

29. 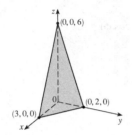   **31.**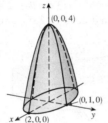

33. Ellipsoid

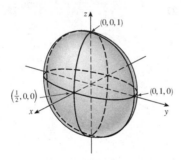

35. Circular cylinder

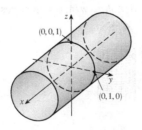

37. $(\sqrt{3}, 3, 2), (4, \pi/3, \pi/3)$
39. $(2\sqrt{2}, 2\sqrt{2}, 4\sqrt{3}), (4, \pi/4, 4\sqrt{3})$
41. $r^2 + z^2 = 4, \rho = 2$ **43.** $z = 4r^2$

FOCUS ON PROBLEM SOLVING ▪ PAGE 691
1. $(\sqrt{3} - \frac{3}{2})$ m
3. (a) $(x + 1)/(-2c) = (y - c)/(c^2 - 1) = (z - c)/(c^2 + 1)$
(b) $x^2 + y^2 = t^2 + 1, z = t$ (c) $4\pi/3$
5. 20

CHAPTER 10

EXERCISES 10.1 ▪ PAGE 699
1. $(-1, 2]$ **3.** $\langle -1, \pi/2, 0 \rangle$
5. 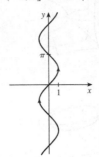   **7.**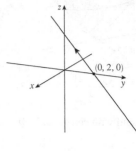

9. 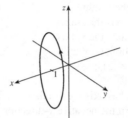   **11.**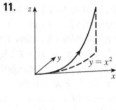

13.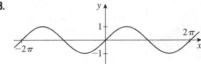

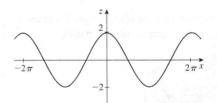

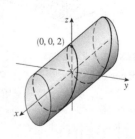
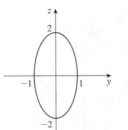

15. $\mathbf{r}(t) = \langle t, 2t, 3t \rangle, 0 \leq t \leq 1$;
$x = t, y = 2t, z = 3t, 0 \leq t \leq 1$
17. $\mathbf{r}(t) = \langle 3t + 1, 2t - 1, 5t + 2 \rangle, 0 \leq t \leq 1$;
$x = 3t + 1, y = 2t - 1, z = 5t + 2, 0 \leq t \leq 1$
19. II   **21.** V   **23.** IV

25.

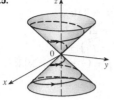

27. $(0, 0, 0), (1, 0, 1)$

3. (a), (c)

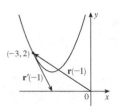

(b) $\mathbf{r}'(t) = \langle 1, 2t \rangle$

29.

31.

5. (a), (c)

7. (a), (c)

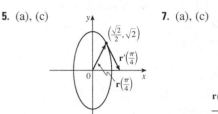

(b) $\mathbf{r}'(t) = \cos t\,\mathbf{i} - 2\sin t\,\mathbf{j}$ (b) $\mathbf{r}'(t) = e^t\,\mathbf{i} + 3e^{3t}\,\mathbf{j}$

9. $\mathbf{r}'(t) = \langle t\cos t + \sin t, 2t, \cos 2t - 2t\sin 2t \rangle$

11. $\mathbf{r}'(t) = 2te^{t^2}\,\mathbf{i} + [3/(1 + 3t)]\,\mathbf{k}$ **13.** $\mathbf{r}'(t) = \mathbf{b} + 2t\mathbf{c}$

15. $\langle \frac{1}{3}, \frac{2}{3}, \frac{2}{3} \rangle$ **17.** $\frac{3}{5}\mathbf{j} + \frac{4}{5}\mathbf{k}$

33.

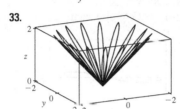

19. $\langle 1, e^t, (t + 1)e^t \rangle, \langle 1/\sqrt{3}, 1/\sqrt{3}, 1/\sqrt{3} \rangle$,

$\langle 0, e^t, (t + 2)e^t \rangle, (t^2 + 3t + 3)e^{2t}$

21. $x = 3 + t, y = 2t, z = 2 + 4t$

23. $x = 1 - t, y = t, z = 1 - t$

25. $\mathbf{r}(t) = (3 - 4t)\,\mathbf{i} + (4 + 3t)\,\mathbf{j} + (2 - 6t)\,\mathbf{k}$

37. $\mathbf{r}(t) = t\,\mathbf{i} + \frac{1}{2}(t^2 - 1)\,\mathbf{j} + \frac{1}{2}(t^2 + 1)\,\mathbf{k}$

27. $x = t, y = 1 - t, z = 2t$

39. $\mathbf{r}(t) = \cos t\,\mathbf{i} + \sin t\,\mathbf{j} + \cos 2t\,\mathbf{k}, 0 \le t \le 2\pi$

29. $x = -\pi - t, y = \pi + t, z = -\pi t$

41. $x = 2\cos t, y = 2\sin t, z = 4\cos^2 t$ **43.** Yes

31. $66°$ **33.** $4\mathbf{i} - 3\mathbf{j} + 5\mathbf{k}$ **35.** $\mathbf{i} + \mathbf{j} + \mathbf{k}$

37. $\tan t\,\mathbf{i} + \frac{1}{8}(t^2 + 1)^4\,\mathbf{j} + (\frac{1}{3}t^3\ln t - \frac{1}{9}t^3)\,\mathbf{k} + \mathbf{C}$

EXERCISES 10.2 ▪ PAGE 706

39. $t^2\,\mathbf{i} + t^3\,\mathbf{j} + (\frac{2}{3}t^{3/2} - \frac{2}{3})\,\mathbf{k}$

1. (a)

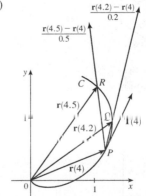

45. $2t\cos t + 2\sin t - 2\cos t\sin t$ **47.** 35

EXERCISES 10.3 ▪ PAGE 714

1. $20\sqrt{29}$ **3.** $e - e^{-1}$ **5.** $\frac{1}{27}(13^{3/2} - 8)$ **7.** 15.3841

9. 1.2780   **11.** 42

13. $\mathbf{r}(t(s)) = \dfrac{2}{\sqrt{29}}s\,\mathbf{i} + \left(1 - \dfrac{3}{\sqrt{29}}s\right)\mathbf{j} + \left(5 + \dfrac{4}{\sqrt{29}}s\right)\mathbf{k}$

15. $(3\sin 1, 4, 3\cos 1)$

17. (a) $\langle (2/\sqrt{29})\cos t, 5/\sqrt{29}, (-2/\sqrt{29})\sin t \rangle$,

$\langle -\sin t, 0, -\cos t \rangle$ (b) $\frac{2}{29}$

(b), (d)

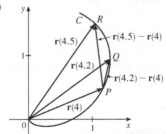

19. (a) $\dfrac{1}{e^{2t} + 1}\langle \sqrt{2}e^t, e^{2t}, -1 \rangle, \dfrac{1}{e^{2t} + 1}\langle 1 - e^{2t}, \sqrt{2}e^t, \sqrt{2}e^t \rangle$

(b) $\sqrt{2}e^{2t}/(e^{2t} + 1)^2$

21. $6t^2/(9t^4 + 4t^2)^{3/2}$ **23.** $\frac{4}{25}$ **25.** $\frac{1}{7}\sqrt{\frac{19}{14}}$

27. $12x^2/(1 + 16x^6)^{3/2}$

29. $e^x|x + 2|/[1 + (xe^x + e^x)^2]^{3/2}$

31. $(-\frac{1}{2}\ln 2, 1/\sqrt{2})$; approaches 0

33. (a) P (b) 1.3, 0.7

35.

(c) $\mathbf{r}'(4) = \lim\limits_{h \to 0} \dfrac{\mathbf{r}(4 + h) - \mathbf{r}(4)}{h}$; $\mathbf{T}(4) = \dfrac{\mathbf{r}'(4)}{|\mathbf{r}'(4)|}$

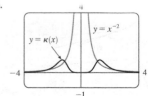

37. a is $y = f(x)$, b is $y = \kappa(x)$

39. $\kappa(t) = \dfrac{6\sqrt{4\cos^2 t - 12\cos t + 13}}{(17 - 12\cos t)^{3/2}}$

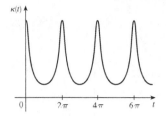

integer multiples of 2π

41. $6t^2/(4t^2 + 9t^4)^{3/2}$

43. $1/(\sqrt{2}e^t)$ **45.** $\left\langle \frac{2}{3}, \frac{2}{3}, \frac{1}{3}\right\rangle, \left\langle -\frac{1}{3}, \frac{2}{3}, -\frac{2}{3}\right\rangle, \left\langle -\frac{2}{3}, \frac{1}{3}, \frac{2}{3}\right\rangle$

47. $y = 6x + \pi$, $x + 6y = 6\pi$

49. $\left(x + \frac{5}{2}\right)^2 + y^2 = \frac{81}{4}$, $x^2 + \left(y - \frac{5}{3}\right)^2 = \frac{16}{9}$

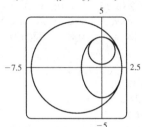

51. $(-1, -3, 1)$

53. $2x + y + 4z = 7$, $6x - 8y - z = -3$

61. 2.07×10^{10} Å ≈ 2 m

EXERCISES 10.4 ■ PAGE 724

1. (a) $1.8\mathbf{i} - 3.8\mathbf{j} - 0.7\mathbf{k}$, $2.0\mathbf{i} - 2.4\mathbf{j} - 0.6\mathbf{k}$,
$2.8\mathbf{i} + 1.8\mathbf{j} - 0.3\mathbf{k}$, $2.8\mathbf{i} + 0.8\mathbf{j} - 0.4\mathbf{k}$
(b) $2.4\mathbf{i} - 0.8\mathbf{j} - 0.5\mathbf{k}$, 2.58

3. $\mathbf{v}(t) = \langle -t, 1\rangle$
$\mathbf{a}(t) = \langle -1, 0\rangle$
$|\mathbf{v}(t)| = \sqrt{t^2 + 1}$

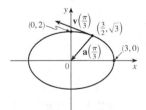

5. $\mathbf{v}(t) = -3\sin t\,\mathbf{i} + 2\cos t\,\mathbf{j}$
$\mathbf{a}(t) = -3\cos t\,\mathbf{i} - 2\sin t\,\mathbf{j}$
$|\mathbf{v}(t)| = \sqrt{5\sin^2 t + 4}$

7. $\mathbf{v}(t) = \mathbf{i} + 2t\,\mathbf{j}$
$\mathbf{a}(t) = 2\,\mathbf{j}$
$|\mathbf{v}(t)| = \sqrt{1 + 4t^2}$

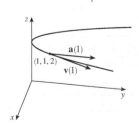

9. $\sqrt{2}\,\mathbf{i} + e^t\,\mathbf{j} - e^{-t}\,\mathbf{k}$, $e^t\,\mathbf{j} + e^{-t}\,\mathbf{k}$, $e^t + e^{-t}$

11. $e^t[(\cos t - \sin t)\mathbf{i} + (\sin t + \cos t)\mathbf{j} + (t + 1)\mathbf{k}]$,
$e^t[-2\sin t\,\mathbf{i} + 2\cos t\,\mathbf{j} + (t + 2)\mathbf{k}]$, $e^t\sqrt{t^2 + 2t + 3}$

13. $\mathbf{v}(t) = t\,\mathbf{i} + 2t\,\mathbf{j} + \mathbf{k}$, $\mathbf{r}(t) = \left(\frac{1}{2}t^2 + 1\right)\mathbf{i} + t^2\,\mathbf{j} + t\,\mathbf{k}$

15. (a) $\mathbf{r}(t) = \left(\frac{1}{3}t^3 + t\right)\mathbf{i} + (t - \sin t + 1)\mathbf{j} + \left(\frac{1}{4} - \frac{1}{4}\cos 2t\right)\mathbf{k}$
(b)

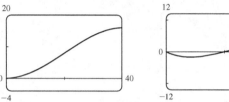

17. $t = 4$

19. $\mathbf{r}(t) = t\,\mathbf{i} - t\,\mathbf{j} + \frac{5}{2}t^2\,\mathbf{k}$, $|\mathbf{v}(t)| = \sqrt{25t^2 + 2}$

21. (a) ≈ 3535 m   (b) ≈ 1531 m   (c) 200 m/s

23. 30 m/s   **25.** $\approx 10.2°$, $\approx 79.8°$

27. $13.0° < \theta < 36.0°$, $55.4° < \theta < 85.5°$

29. (a) 16 m   (b) $\approx 23.6°$ upstream

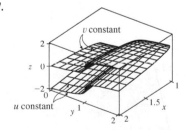

31. The path is contained in a circle that lies in a plane perpendicular to $\mathbf{c}$ with center on a line through the origin in the direction of $\mathbf{c}$.

33. $(18t^3 + 4t)/\sqrt{9t^4 + 4t^2}$, $6t^2/\sqrt{9t^4 + 4t^2}$

35. $0, 1$ **37.** 4.5 cm/s², 9.0 cm/s²   **39.** $t = 1$

EXERCISES 10.5 ■ PAGE 731

1. P: no; Q: yes

3. Plane through $(0, 3, 1)$ containing vectors $\langle 1, 0, 4\rangle$, $\langle 1, -1, 5\rangle$

5. Hyperbolic paraboloid

7.

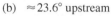

9.

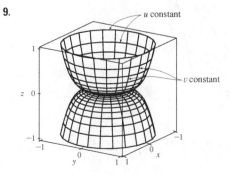

11.

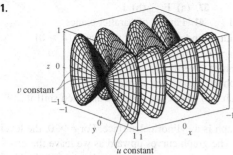

v constant

u constant

13. IV   **15.** II   **17.** III
19. $x = 1 + u + v, y = 2 + u - v, z = -3 - u + v$
21. $x = x, z = z, y = \sqrt{1 - x^2 + z^2}$
23. $x = 2 \sin \phi \cos \theta, y = 2 \sin \phi \sin \theta,$
$z = 2 \cos \phi, 0 \le \phi \le \pi/4, 0 \le \theta \le 2\pi$
$\left[\text{or } x = x, y = y, z = \sqrt{4 - x^2 - y^2}, x^2 + y^2 \le 2 \right]$
25. $x = x, y = 4 \cos \theta, z = 4 \sin \theta, 0 \le x \le 5, 0 \le \theta \le 2\pi$
29. $x = x, y = e^{-x} \cos \theta,$
$z = e^{-x} \sin \theta, 0 \le x \le 3,$
$0 \le \theta \le 2\pi$

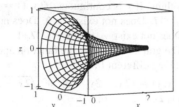

31. (b)

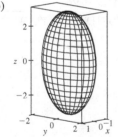

33. (a) Direction reverses   (b) Number of coils doubles

CHAPTER 10 REVIEW ■ PAGE 733

True-False Quiz

1. True   **3.** False   **5.** False   **7.** True   **9.** False
11. True

Exercises

1. (a)

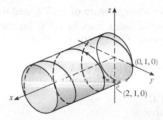

(0, 1, 0)

(2, 1, 0)

(b) $\mathbf{r}'(t) = \mathbf{i} - \pi \sin \pi t \, \mathbf{j} + \pi \cos \pi t \, \mathbf{k},$
$\mathbf{r}''(t) = -\pi^2 \cos \pi t \, \mathbf{j} - \pi^2 \sin \pi t \, \mathbf{k}$
3. $\mathbf{r}(t) = 4 \cos t \, \mathbf{i} + 4 \sin t \, \mathbf{j} + (5 - 4 \cos t) \mathbf{k}, 0 \le t \le 2\pi$
5. $\frac{1}{3}\mathbf{i} - (2/\pi^2)\mathbf{j} + (2/\pi)\mathbf{k}$ **7.** 86.631   **9.** $\pi/2$

11. (a) $\langle t^2, t, 1 \rangle / \sqrt{t^4 + t^2 + 1}$
(b) $\langle t^3 + 2t, 1 - t^4, -2t^3 - t \rangle / \sqrt{t^8 + 5t^6 + 6t^4 + 5t^2 + 1}$
(c) $\sqrt{t^8 + 5t^6 + 6t^4 + 5t^2 + 1}/(t^4 + t^2 + 1)^2$
13. $12/17^{3/2}$ **15.** $x - 2y + 2\pi = 0$
17. $\mathbf{v}(t) = (1 + \ln t)\mathbf{i} + \mathbf{j} - e^{-t}\mathbf{k},$
$|\mathbf{v}(t)| = \sqrt{2 + 2\ln t + (\ln t)^2 + e^{-2t}}, \mathbf{a}(t) = (1/t)\mathbf{i} + e^{-t}\mathbf{k}$
19. (a) About 3.8 ft above the ground, 60.8 ft from the athlete
(b) ≈ 21.4 ft   (c) ≈ 64.2 ft from the athlete
21. $x = 2 \sin \phi \cos \theta, y = 2 \sin \phi \sin \theta, z = 2 \cos \phi,$
$0 \le \theta \le 2\pi, \pi/3 \le \phi \le 2\pi/3$
23. $\pi |t|$

FOCUS ON PROBLEM SOLVING ■ PAGE 735

1. (a) $\mathbf{v} = \omega R(-\sin \omega t \, \mathbf{i} + \cos \omega t \, \mathbf{j})$ (c) $\mathbf{a} = -\omega^2 \mathbf{r}$
3. (a) $90°, v_0^2/(2g)$
5. (a) ≈ 0.94 ft to the right of the table's edge, ≈ 15 ft/s
(b) $\approx 7.6°$ (c) ≈ 2.13 ft to the right of the table's edge
7. $56°$
9. $\mathbf{r}(u, v) = \mathbf{c} + u\mathbf{a} + v\mathbf{b}$ where $\mathbf{a} = \langle a_1, a_2, a_3 \rangle,$
$\mathbf{b} = \langle b_1, b_2, b_3 \rangle, \mathbf{c} = \langle c_1, c_2, c_3 \rangle$

CHAPTER 11

EXERCISES 11.1 ■ PAGE 745

1. (a) -27; a temperature of $-15°C$ with wind blowing at
40 km/h feels equivalent to about $-27°C$ without wind.
(b) When the temperature is $-20°C$, what wind speed gives a wind
chill of $-30°C$?   20 km/h
(c) With a wind speed of 20 km/h, what temperature gives a wind
chill of $-49°C$? $35°C$
(d) A function of wind speed that gives wind-chill values when the
temperature is $-5°C$
(e) A function of temperature that gives wind-chill values when
the wind speed is 50 km/h
3. Yes
5. $\{(x, y) \mid \frac{1}{9}x^2 + y^2 < 1\}, (-\infty, \ln 9]$

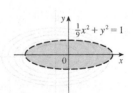

$\frac{1}{9}x^2 + y^2 = 1$

7. (a) 3   (b) $\{(x, y, z) \mid x^2 + y^2 + z^2 < 4, x \ge 0, y \ge 0, z \ge 0\}$,
interior of a sphere of radius 2, center the origin, in the first octant
9. $\approx 56, \approx 35$ **11.** $11°C, 19.5°C$ **13.** Steep; nearly flat
15.   **17.**

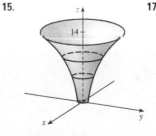

14

5

19. $(y - 2x)^2 = k$

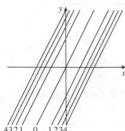

21. $y = -\sqrt{x} + k$

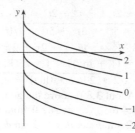

23. $y = ke^{-x}$

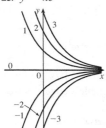

25. $y^2 - x^2 = k^2$

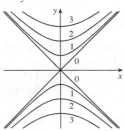

27. $x^2 + 9y^2 = k$

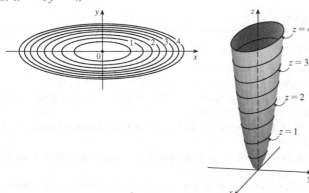

29.

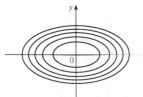

31.

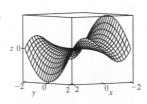

33.

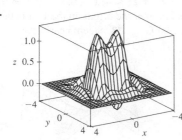

35. (a) C   (b) II   **37.** (a) F   (b) I
39. (a) B   (b) VI   **41.** Family of parallel planes
43. Family of circular cylinders with axis the x-axis ($k > 0$)
45. (a) Shift the graph of f upward 2 units
(b) Stretch the graph of f vertically by a factor of 2
(c) Reflect the graph of f about the xy-plane
(d) Reflect the graph of f about the xy-plane and then shift it upward 2 units
47. If $c = 0$, the graph is a cylindrical surface. For $c > 0$, the level curves are ellipses. The graph curves upward as we leave the origin, and the steepness increases as c increases. For $c < 0$, the level curves are hyperbolas. The graph curves upward in the y-direction and downward, approaching the xy-plane, in the x-direction giving a saddle-shaped appearance near $(0, 0, 1)$.
49. (b) $y = 0.75x + 0.01$

EXERCISES 11.2 ■ **PAGE 755**

1. Nothing; if f is continuous, $f(3, 1) = 6$ **3.** $-\frac{5}{2}$
5. 1   **7.** Does not exist   **9.** Does not exist   **11.** 0
13. Does not exist   **15.** 2   **17.** 1   **19.** Does not exist
21. The graph shows that the function approaches different numbers along different lines.
23. $h(x, y) = (2x + 3y - 6)^2 + \sqrt{2x + 3y - 6}$;
$\{(x, y) \mid 2x + 3y \geq 6\}$
25. Along the line $y = x$ **27.** $\{(x, y) \mid y \geq 0\}$
29. $\{(x, y) \mid x^2 + y^2 > 4\}$ **31.** $\{(x, y, z) \mid y \geq 0, y \neq \sqrt{x^2 + z^2}\}$
33. $\{(x, y) \mid (x, y) \neq (0, 0)\}$ **35.** 0
37. 0
39.

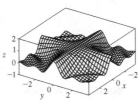

f is continuous on $\mathbb{R}^2$

EXERCISES 11.3 ■ **PAGE 766**

1. (a) The rate of change of temperature as longitude varies, with latitude and time fixed; the rate of change as only latitude varies; the rate of change as only time varies.
(b) Positive, negative, positive
3. (a) $f_T(-15, 30) \approx 1.3$; for a temperature of $-15°C$ and wind speed of 30 km/h, the wind-chill index rises by $1.3°C$ for each degree the temperature increases. $f_v(-15, 30) \approx -0.15$; for a temperature of $-15°C$ and wind speed of 30 km/h, the wind-chill index decreases by $0.15°C$ for each km/h the wind speed increases.
(b) Positive, negative   (c) 0
5. (a) Positive   (b) Negative
7. (a) Positive   (b) Negative
9. $c = f, b = f_x, a = f_y$

11. $f_x(1, 2) = -8 = $ slope of C_1, $f_y(1, 2) = -4 = $ slope of C_2

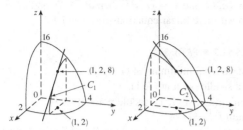

13. $f_x = 2x + 2xy$, $f_y = 2y + x^2$

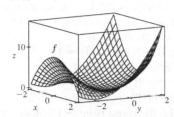

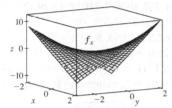

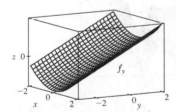

15. $f_x(x, y) = -3y, f_y(x, y) = 5y^4 - 3x$

17. $f_x(x, t) = -\pi e^{-t} \sin \pi x, f_t(x, t) = -e^{-t} \cos \pi x$

19. $\partial z/\partial x = 20(2x + 3y)^9, \partial z/\partial y = 30(2x + 3y)^9$

21. $f_x(x, y) = 2y/(x + y)^2, f_y(x, y) = -2x/(x + y)^2$

23. $\partial w/\partial \alpha = \cos \alpha \cos \beta, \partial w/\partial \beta = -\sin \alpha \sin \beta$

25. $f_r(r, s) = \dfrac{2r^2}{r^2 + s^2} + \ln(r^2 + s^2), f_s(r, s) = \dfrac{2rs}{r^2 + s^2}$

27. $\partial u/\partial t = e^{w/t}(1 - w/t), \partial u/\partial w = e^{w/t}$

29. $f_x = z - 10xy^3z^4, f_y = -15x^2y^2z^4, f_z = x - 20x^2y^3z^3$

31. $\partial w/\partial x = 1/(x + 2y + 3z), \partial w/\partial y = 2/(x + 2y + 3z), \partial w/\partial z = 3/(x + 2y + 3z)$

33. $\partial u/\partial x = y \sin^{-1}(yz), \partial u/\partial y = x \sin^{-1}(yz) + xyz/\sqrt{1 - y^2z^2}, \partial u/\partial z = xy^2/\sqrt{1 - y^2z^2}$

35. $f_x = y^2 \tan(yt), f_y = xyz^4t \sec^2(yt) + xz^2 \tan(yt), f_z = 2xyz \tan(yt), f_t = xy^2z^2 \sec^2(yt)$

37. $\partial u/\partial x_i = x_i/\sqrt{x_1^2 + x_2^2 + \cdots + x_n^2}$

39. $\frac{1}{5}$ **41.** $\frac{1}{4}$

43. $f_x(x, y) = y^2 - 3x^2y, f_y(x, y) = 2xy - x^3$

45. $\dfrac{\partial z}{\partial x} = \dfrac{3yz - 2x}{2z - 3xy}, \dfrac{\partial z}{\partial y} = \dfrac{3xz - 2y}{2z - 3xy}$

47. $\dfrac{\partial z}{\partial x} = \dfrac{1 + y^2z^2}{1 + y + y^2z^2}, \dfrac{\partial z}{\partial y} = \dfrac{-z}{1 + y + y^2z^2}$

49. (a) $f'(x), g'(y)$ (b) $f'(x + y), f'(x + y)$

51. $f_{xx} = 6xy^5 + 24x^2y, f_{xy} = 15x^2y^4 + 8x^3 = f_{yx}, f_{yy} = 20x^3y^3$

53. $w_{uu} = v^2/(u^2 + v^2)^{3/2}, w_{uv} = -uv/(u^2 + v^2)^{3/2} = w_{vu}, w_{vv} = u^2/(u^2 + v^2)^{3/2}$

55. $z_{xx} = -2x/(1 + x^2)^2, z_{xy} = 0 = z_{yx}, z_{yy} = -2y/(1 + y^2)^2$

59. $12xy, 72xy$

61. $24 \sin(4x + 3y + 2z), 12 \sin(4x + 3y + 2z)$

63. $\theta e^{r\theta}(2 \sin \theta + \theta \cos \theta + r\theta \sin \theta)$ **65.** $6yz^2$

67. $\approx 12.2, \approx 16.8, \approx 23.25$ **79.** R^2/R_1^2

85. No **87.** $x = 1 + t, y = 2, z = 2 - 2t$ **89.** -2

91. (a)

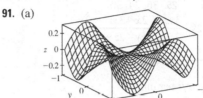

(b) $f_x(x, y) = \dfrac{x^4y + 4x^2y^3 - y^5}{(x^2 + y^2)^2}, f_y(x, y) = \dfrac{x^5 - 4x^3y^2 - xy^4}{(x^2 + y^2)^2}$

(c) $0, 0$ (e) No, since f_{xy} and f_{yx} are not continuous.

EXERCISES 11.4 ■ PAGE 778

1. $z = -7x - 6y + 5$ **3.** $x + y - 2z = 0$ **5.** $z = y$

7. **9.**

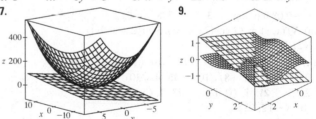

11. $2x + \frac{1}{4}y - 1$ **13.** $\frac{1}{9}x - \frac{2}{9}y + \frac{2}{3}$ **17.** 6.3

19. $\frac{3}{7}x + \frac{2}{7}y + \frac{6}{7}z$; 6.9914 **21.** $4T + H - 329$; 129°F

23. $dz = 3x^2 \ln(y^2) \, dx + (2x^3/y) \, dy$

25. $dm = 5p^4q^3 \, dp + 3p^5q^2 \, dq$

27. $dR = \beta^2 \cos \gamma \, d\alpha + 2\alpha\beta \cos \gamma \, d\beta - \alpha\beta^2 \sin \gamma \, d\gamma$

29. $\Delta z = 0.9225, dz = 0.9$ **31.** 5.4 cm² **33.** 16 cm³

35. 2.3% **37.** $\frac{1}{17} \approx 0.059 \, \Omega$ **39.** $3x - y + 3z = 3$

41. $-x + 2z = 1$ **43.** $x - y + z = 2$

45. $\varepsilon_1 = \Delta x, \varepsilon_2 = \Delta y$

EXERCISES 11.5 ■ PAGE 786

1. $(2x + y) \cos t + (2y + x)e^t$

3. $[(x/t) - y \sin t]/\sqrt{1 + x^2 + y^2}$

5. $e^{y/t}[2t - (x/t) - (2xy/t^2)]$

7. $\partial z/\partial s = 2xy^3 \cos t + 3x^2y^2 \sin t, \partial z/\partial t = -2sxy^3 \sin t + 3sx^2y^2 \cos t$

9. $\partial z/\partial s = t^2 \cos \theta \cos \phi - 2st \sin \theta \sin \phi, \partial z/\partial t = 2st \cos \theta \cos \phi - s^2 \sin \theta \sin \phi$

11. $\dfrac{\partial z}{\partial s} = e^r\left(t\cos\theta - \dfrac{s}{\sqrt{s^2 + t^2}}\sin\theta\right),$

$\dfrac{\partial z}{\partial t} = e^r\left(s\cos\theta - \dfrac{t}{\sqrt{s^2 + t^2}}\sin\theta\right)$

13. 62   **15.** 7, 2

17. $\dfrac{\partial u}{\partial r} = \dfrac{\partial u}{\partial x}\dfrac{\partial x}{\partial r} + \dfrac{\partial u}{\partial y}\dfrac{\partial y}{\partial r}, \dfrac{\partial u}{\partial s} = \dfrac{\partial u}{\partial x}\dfrac{\partial x}{\partial s} + \dfrac{\partial u}{\partial y}\dfrac{\partial y}{\partial s},$

$\dfrac{\partial u}{\partial t} = \dfrac{\partial u}{\partial x}\dfrac{\partial x}{\partial t} + \dfrac{\partial u}{\partial y}\dfrac{\partial y}{\partial t}$

19. $\dfrac{\partial w}{\partial x} = \dfrac{\partial w}{\partial r}\dfrac{\partial r}{\partial x} + \dfrac{\partial w}{\partial s}\dfrac{\partial s}{\partial x} + \dfrac{\partial w}{\partial t}\dfrac{\partial t}{\partial x},$

$\dfrac{\partial w}{\partial y} = \dfrac{\partial w}{\partial r}\dfrac{\partial r}{\partial y} + \dfrac{\partial w}{\partial s}\dfrac{\partial s}{\partial y} + \dfrac{\partial w}{\partial t}\dfrac{\partial t}{\partial y}$

21. 85, 178, 54   **23.** $\frac{9}{7}, \frac{9}{7}$ **25.** 36, 24, 30

27. $\dfrac{\sin(x - y) + e^y}{\sin(x - y) - xe^y}$ **29.** $\dfrac{3yz - 2x}{2z - 3xy}, \dfrac{3xz - 2y}{2z - 3xy}$

31. $\dfrac{1 + y^2z^2}{1 + y + y^2z^2}, -\dfrac{z}{1 + y + y^2z^2}$

33. 2°C/s   **35.** ≈ -0.33 m/s per minute

37. (a) 6 m³/s   (b) 10 m²/s   (c) 0 m/s

39. ≈ -0.27 L/s   **41.** $-1/(12\sqrt{3})$ rad/s

43. (a) $\partial z/\partial r = (\partial z/\partial x)\cos\theta + (\partial z/\partial y)\sin\theta,$
$\partial z/\partial\theta = -(\partial z/\partial x)r\sin\theta + (\partial z/\partial y)r\cos\theta$

49. $4rs\,\partial^2 z/\partial x^2 + (4r^2 + 4s^2)\partial^2 z/\partial x\,\partial y + 4rs\,\partial^2 z/\partial y^2 + 2\,\partial z/\partial y$

EXERCISES 11.6 ■ PAGE 799

1. ≈ -0.08 mb/km   **3.** ≈ 0.778 **5.** $2 + \sqrt{3}/2$

7. (a) $\nabla f(x, y) = \langle 2\cos(2x + 3y), 3\cos(2x + 3y)\rangle$
(b) $\langle 2, 3\rangle$ (c) $\sqrt{3} - \frac{3}{2}$

9. (a) $\langle e^{2yz}, 2xze^{2yz}, 2xye^{2yz}\rangle$ (b) $\langle 1, 12, 0\rangle$ (c) $-\frac{22}{3}$

11. 23/10   **13.** $-8/\sqrt{10}$ **15.** $4/\sqrt{30}$ **17.** $9/(2\sqrt{5})$

19. 2/5   **21.** 1, $\langle 0, 1\rangle$ **23.** 1, $\langle 3, 6, -2\rangle$

25. (b) $\langle -12, 92\rangle$

27. All points on the line $y = x + 1$

29. (a) $-40/(3\sqrt{3})$

31. (a) $32/\sqrt{3}$ (b) $\langle 38, 6, 12\rangle$ (c) $2\sqrt{406}$

33. $\frac{327}{13}$ **37.** $\frac{774}{25}$

39. (a) $x + y + z = 11$ (b) $x - 3 = y - 3 = z - 5$

41. (a) $4x - 5y - z = 4$ (b) $\dfrac{x - 2}{4} = \dfrac{y - 1}{-5} = \dfrac{z + 1}{-1}$

43. (a) $x + y - z = 1$ (b) $x - 1 = y = -z$

45.   **47.** $\langle 2, 3\rangle$, $2x + 3y = 12$

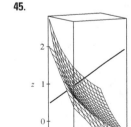

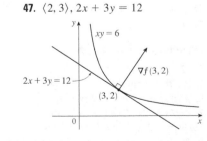

51. No   **57.** $x = -1 - 10t, y = 1 - 16t, z = 2 - 12t$

61. If $\mathbf{u} = \langle a, b\rangle$ and $\mathbf{v} = \langle c, d\rangle$, then $af_x + bf_y$ and $cf_x + df_y$ are known, so we solve linear equations for f_x and f_y.

EXERCISES 11.7 ■ PAGE 809

1. (a) f has a local minimum at $(1, 1)$.
(b) f has a saddle point at $(1, 1)$.

3. Local minimum at $(1, 1)$, saddle point at $(0, 0)$

5. Minimum $f\left(\frac{1}{3}, -\frac{2}{3}\right) = -\frac{1}{3}$

7. Minima $f(1, 1) = 0$, $f(-1, -1) = 0$, saddle point at $(0, 0)$

9. Minimum $f(2, 1) = -8$, saddle point at $(0, 0)$

11. None   **13.** Minimum $f(0, 0) = 0$, saddle points at $(\pm 1, 0)$

15. Minima $f(0, 1) = f(\pi, -1) = f(2\pi, 1) = -1$,
saddle points at $(\pi/2, 0)$, $(3\pi/2, 0)$

19. Minima $f(1, \pm 1) = 3, f(-1, \pm 1) = 3$

21. Maximum $f(\pi/3, \pi/3) = 3\sqrt{3}/2$,
minimum $f(5\pi/3, 5\pi/3) = -3\sqrt{3}/2$, saddle point at (π, π)

23. Minima $f(-1.714, 0) \approx -9.200$, $f(1.402, 0) \approx 0.242$,
saddle point $(0.312, 0)$, lowest point $(-1.714, 0, -9.200)$

25. Maxima $f(-1.267, 0) \approx 1.310$, $f(1.629, \pm 1.063) \approx 8.105$,
saddle points $(-0.259, 0)$, $(1.526, 0)$,
highest points $(1.629, \pm 1.063, 8.105)$

27. Maximum $f(2, 0) = 9$, minimum $f(0, 3) = -14$

29. Maximum $f(\pm 1, 1) = 7$, minimum $f(0, 0) = 4$

31. Maximum $f(1, 0) = 2$, minimum $f(-1, 0) = -2$

33.

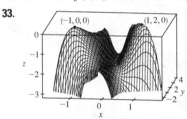

35. $\sqrt{3}$ **37.** $(2, 1, \sqrt{5}), (2, 1, -\sqrt{5})$ **39.** $\frac{100}{3}, \frac{100}{3}, \frac{100}{3}$

41. $8r^3/(3\sqrt{3})$ **43.** $\frac{4}{3}$ **45.** Cube, edge length $c/12$

47. Square base of side 40 cm, height 20 cm   **49.** $L^3/(3\sqrt{3})$

EXERCISES 11.8 ■ PAGE 818

1. $\approx 59, 30$

3. No maximum, minimum $f(1, 1) = f(-1, -1) = 2$

5. Maximum $f(\pm 2, 1) = 4$, minimum $f(\pm 2, -1) = -4$

7. Maximum $f(1, 3, 5) = 70$, minimum $f(-1, -3, -5) = -70$

9. Maximum $2/\sqrt{3}$, minimum $-2/\sqrt{3}$

11. Maximum $\sqrt{3}$, minimum 1

13. Maximum $f\left(\frac{1}{2}, \frac{1}{2}, \frac{1}{2}, \frac{1}{2}\right) = 2$,
minimum $f\left(-\frac{1}{2}, -\frac{1}{2}, -\frac{1}{2}, -\frac{1}{2}\right) = -2$

15. Maximum $f\left(1, \sqrt{2}, -\sqrt{2}\right) = 1 + 2\sqrt{2}$,
minimum $f\left(1, -\sqrt{2}, \sqrt{2}\right) = 1 - 2\sqrt{2}$

17. Maximum $\frac{3}{2}$, minimum $\frac{1}{2}$

19. Maxima $f\left(\pm 1/\sqrt{2}, \mp 1/(2\sqrt{2})\right) = e^{1/4}$,
minima $f\left(\pm 1/\sqrt{2}, \pm 1/(2\sqrt{2})\right) = e^{-1/4}$

27–37. See Exercises 35–49 in Section 11.7.

39. $L^3/(3\sqrt{3})$

41. Nearest $\left(\frac{1}{2}, \frac{1}{2}, \frac{1}{2}\right)$, farthest $(-1, -1, 2)$
43. Maximum ≈ 9.7938, minimum ≈ -5.3506
45. (a) c/n (b) When $x_1 = x_2 = \cdots = x_n$

CHAPTER 11 REVIEW ▪ PAGE 823

True-False Quiz

1. True   **3.** False   **5.** False   **7.** True   **9.** False
11. True

Exercises

1. $\{(x, y) \mid y > -x - 1\}$ **3.**

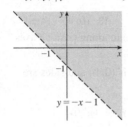

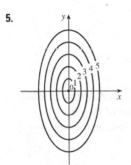

$y = -x - 1$

5.

7.

9. $\frac{2}{3}$
11. (a) $\approx 3.5°C/m$, $-3.0°C/m$ (b) $\approx 0.35°C/m$ by
Equation 11.6.9 (Definition 11.6.2 gives $\approx 1.1°C/m$.)
(c) -0.25
13. $f_x = 1/\sqrt{2x + y^2}$, $f_y = y/\sqrt{2x + y^2}$
15. $g_u = \tan^{-1} v$, $g_v = u/(1 + v^2)$
17. $T_p = \ln(q + e^r)$, $T_q = p/(q + e^r)$, $T_r = pe^r/(q + e^r)$
19. $f_{xx} = 24x$, $f_{xy} = -2y = f_{yx}$, $f_{yy} = -2x$
21. $f_{xx} = k(k - 1)x^{k-2}y^l z^m$, $f_{xy} = klx^{k-1}y^{l-1}z^m = f_{yx}$,
$f_{xz} = kmx^{k-1}y^l z^{m-1} = f_{zx}$, $f_{yy} = l(l - 1)x^k y^{l-2}z^m$,
$f_{yz} = lmx^k y^{l-1}z^{m-1} = f_{zy}$, $f_{zz} = m(m - 1)x^k y^l z^{m-2}$
25. (a) $z = 8x + 4y + 1$ (b) $\dfrac{x - 1}{8} = \dfrac{y + 2}{4} = \dfrac{z - 1}{-1}$
27. (a) $2x - 2y - 3z = 3$ (b) $\dfrac{x - 2}{4} = \dfrac{y + 1}{-4} = \dfrac{z - 1}{-6}$
29. (a) $4x - y - 2z = 6$
(b) $x = 3 + 8t$, $y = 4 - 2t$, $z = 1 - 4t$
31. $\left(2, \frac{1}{2}, 1\right), \left(-2, -\frac{1}{2}, 1\right)$
33. $60x + \frac{24}{5}y + \frac{32}{5}z - 120$; 38.656
35. $2xy^3(1 + 6p) + 3x^2 y^2(pe^p + e^p) + 4z^3(p\cos p + \sin p)$
37. $-47, 108$
43. $\langle 2xe^{yz^2}, x^2 z^2 e^{yz^2}, 2x^2 yz e^{yz^2} \rangle$ **45.** $-\frac{4}{5}$
47. $\sqrt{145}/2, \langle 4, \frac{9}{2} \rangle$ **49.** $\approx \frac{5}{8}$ knot/mi

51. Minimum $f(-4, 1) = -11$
53. Maximum $f(1, 1) = 1$; saddle points $(0, 0), (0, 3), (3, 0)$
55. Maximum $f(1, 2) = 4$, minimum $f(2, 4) = -64$
57. Maximum $f(-1, 0) = 2$, minima $f(1, \pm 1) = -3$,
saddle points $(-1, \pm 1), (1, 0)$
59. Maximum $f(\pm\sqrt{2/3}, 1/\sqrt{3}) = 2/(3\sqrt{3})$,
minimum $f(\pm\sqrt{2/3}, -1/\sqrt{3}) = -2/(3\sqrt{3})$
61. Maximum 1, minimum -1
63. $\left(\pm 3^{-1/4}, 3^{-1/4}\sqrt{2}, \pm 3^{1/4}\right), \left(\pm 3^{-1/4}, -3^{-1/4}\sqrt{2}, \pm 3^{1/4}\right)$
65. $P(2 - \sqrt{3}), P(3 - \sqrt{3})/6, P(2\sqrt{3} - 3)/3$

FOCUS ON PROBLEM SOLVING ▪ PAGE 827

1. $L^2 W^2, \frac{1}{4}L^2 W^2$ **3.** (a) $x = w/3$, base $= w/3$ (b) Yes
9. $\sqrt{3/2}, 3/\sqrt{2}$

CHAPTER 12

EXERCISES 12.1 ▪ PAGE 837

1. (a) 288   (b) 144   **3.** (a) $\pi^2/2 \approx 4.935$ (b) 0
5. (a) 4   (b) -8 **7.** $U < V < L$
9. (a) ≈ 248 (b) ≈ 15.5 **11.** 60   **13.** 3
15. 1.141606, 1.143191, 1.143535, 1.143617, 1.143637, 1.143642

EXERCISES 12.2 ▪ PAGE 843

1. $500y^3, 3x^2$ **3.** 10   **5.** 2   **7.** 261,632/45   **9.** $\frac{21}{2}\ln 2$
11. 0   **13.** π **15.** $\frac{21}{2}$ **17.** 9 ln 2
19. $\frac{1}{2}(\sqrt{3} - 1) - \frac{1}{12}\pi$ **21.** $\frac{1}{2}(e^2 - 3)$
23.

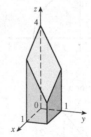

25. $\frac{95}{2}$ **27.** $\frac{166}{27}$ **29.** 2   **31.** $\frac{64}{3}$
33. $21e - 57$

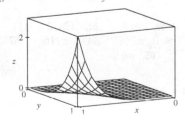

35. $\frac{5}{6}$ **37.** 0
39. Fubini's Theorem does not apply. The integrand has an infinite
discontinuity at the origin.

EXERCISES 12.3 ▪ PAGE 850

1. 32   **3.** $\frac{3}{10}$ **5.** $e - 1$ **7.** $\frac{4}{3}$ **9.** π

11. (a)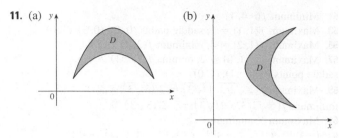
(b)

13. Type I: $D = \{(x, y) \mid 0 \le x \le 1, 0 \le y \le x\}$,
type II: $D = \{(x, y) \mid 0 \le y \le 1, y \le x \le 1\}$; $\frac{1}{3}$

15. $\int_0^1 \int_{-\sqrt{x}}^{\sqrt{x}} y \, dy \, dx + \int_1^4 \int_{x-2}^{\sqrt{x}} y \, dy \, dx = \int_{-1}^2 \int_{y^2}^{y+2} y \, dx \, dy = \frac{9}{4}$

17. $\frac{1}{2}(1 - \cos 1)$ **19.** $\frac{147}{20}$ **21.** 0 **23.** $\frac{7}{18}$ **25.** $\frac{31}{8}$

27. 6 **29.** $\frac{128}{15}$ **31.** $\frac{1}{3}$ **33.** 0, 1.213; 0.713 **35.** $\frac{64}{3}$

37.

39. 13,984,735,616/14,549,535

41. $\int_0^2 \int_{y^2}^4 f(x, y) \, dx \, dy$ **43.** $\int_{-3}^3 \int_0^{\sqrt{9-x^2}} f(x, y) \, dy \, dx$

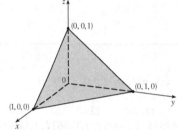

45. $\int_0^{\ln 2} \int_{e^y}^2 f(x, y) \, dx \, dy$

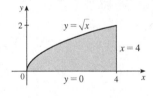

47. $\frac{1}{6}(e^9 - 1)$ **49.** $\frac{1}{3} \ln 9$ **51.** $\frac{1}{3}(2\sqrt{2} - 1)$ **53.** 1

55. $(\pi/16)e^{-1/16} \le \iint_Q e^{-(x^2+y^2)^2} dA \le \pi/16$ **57.** $\frac{3}{4}$ **61.** 9π

63. $a^2b + \frac{3}{2}ab^2$ **65.** $\pi a^2 b$

EXERCISES 12.4 ■ PAGE 857

1. $\int_0^{3\pi/2} \int_0^4 f(r \cos\theta, r \sin\theta) r \, dr \, d\theta$ **3.** $\int_{-1}^1 \int_0^{(x+1)/2} f(x, y) \, dy \, dx$

5.

$33\pi/2$

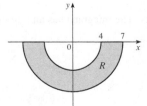

7. 0 **9.** $\frac{1}{2}\pi \sin 9$ **11.** $(\pi/2)(1 - e^{-4})$ **13.** $\frac{3}{64}\pi^2$

15. $\frac{16}{3}\pi$ **17.** $\frac{4}{3}\pi$ **19.** $\frac{4}{3}\pi a^3$ **21.** $(2\pi/3)\left[1 - (1/\sqrt{2})\right]$

23. $(8\pi/3)(64 - 24\sqrt{3})$ **25.** $\pi/12$ **27.** $\frac{1}{2}\pi(1 - \cos 9)$

29. $2\sqrt{2}/3$ **31.** $1800\pi \, \text{ft}^3$ **33.** $2/(a + b)$

35. $\frac{15}{16}$ **37.** (a) $\sqrt{\pi}/4$ (b) $\sqrt{\pi}/2$

EXERCISES 12.5 ■ PAGE 866

1. $\frac{64}{3}$ C **3.** $\frac{4}{3}$, $\left(\frac{4}{3}, 0\right)$ **5.** 6, $\left(\frac{3}{4}, \frac{3}{2}\right)$

7. $\frac{1}{4}(e^2 - 1)$, $\left(\dfrac{e^2 + 1}{2(e^2 - 1)}, \dfrac{4(e^3 - 1)}{9(e^2 - 1)}\right)$

9. $L/4$, $(L/2, 16/(9\pi))$ **11.** $\left(\frac{3}{8}, 3\pi/16\right)$ **13.** $(0, 45/(14\pi))$

15. $(2a/5, 2a/5)$ if vertex is $(0, 0)$ and sides are along positive axes

17. $\frac{1}{16}(e^4 - 1), \frac{1}{8}(e^2 - 1), \frac{1}{16}(e^4 + 2e^2 - 3)$

19. $7ka^6/180, 7ka^6/180, 7ka^6/90$ if vertex is $(0, 0)$ and sides are
along positive axes

21. $m = \pi^2/8$, $(\bar{x}, \bar{y}) = \left(\dfrac{2\pi}{3} - \dfrac{1}{\pi}, \dfrac{16}{9\pi}\right)$, $I_x = 3\pi^2/64$,
$I_y = \frac{1}{16}(\pi^4 - 3\pi^2)$, $I_0 = \pi^4/16 - 9\pi^2/64$

23. (a) $\frac{1}{2}$ (b) 0.375 (c) $\frac{5}{48} \approx 0.1042$

25. (b) (i) $e^{-0.2} \approx 0.8187$

(ii) $1 + e^{-1.8} - e^{-0.8} - e^{-1} \approx 0.3481$ (c) 2, 5

27. (a) ≈ 0.500 (b) ≈ 0.632

29. (a) $\iint_D k\left[1 - \frac{1}{20}\sqrt{(x - x_0)^2 + (y - y_0)^2}\right] dA$, where D is the
disk with radius 10 mi centered at the center of the city
(b) $200\pi k/3 \approx 209k$, $200\left(\pi/2 - \frac{8}{9}\right)k \approx 136k$, on the edge

EXERCISES 12.6 ■ PAGE 871

1. $\sqrt{14}\pi$ **3.** $3\sqrt{14}$ **5.** $\sqrt{2}/6$ **7.** 4

9. $(2\pi/3)(2\sqrt{2} - 1)$ **11.** $4\pi b\left(b - \sqrt{b^2 - a^2}\right)$ **13.** 13.9783

15. (a) 24.2055 (b) 24.2476 **17.** 4.4506

19. $\frac{45}{8}\sqrt{14} + \frac{15}{16} \ln\left[(11\sqrt{5} + 3\sqrt{70})/(3\sqrt{5} + \sqrt{70})\right]$

21. (b)

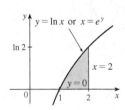

(c) $\int_0^{2\pi} \int_0^\pi \sqrt{36 \sin^4 u \cos^2 v + 9 \sin^4 u \sin^2 v + 4 \cos^2 u \sin^2 u} \, du \, dv$

25. $\frac{98}{3}\pi$ **27.** 4π.

EXERCISES 12.7 ■ PAGE 880

1. $\frac{27}{4}$ **3.** 1 **5.** $\frac{1}{3}(e^3 - 1)$ **7.** $-\frac{1}{3}$ **9.** 4 **11.** $\frac{65}{28}$

13. $8/(3e)$ **15.** $\frac{1}{60}$ **17.** $16\pi/3$ **19.** $\frac{16}{3}$ **21.** 36π

23. (a) $\int_0^1 \int_0^x \int_0^{\sqrt{1-y^2}} dz \, dy \, dx$ (b) $\frac{1}{4}\pi - \frac{1}{3}$ **25.** 60.533

27.

29. $\int_{-2}^{2} \int_{0}^{4-x^2} \int_{-\sqrt{4-x^2-y}/2}^{\sqrt{4-x^2-y}/2} f(x, y, z)\, dz\, dy\, dx$

$= \int_{0}^{4} \int_{-\sqrt{4-y}}^{\sqrt{4-y}} \int_{-\sqrt{4-x^2-y}/2}^{\sqrt{4-x^2-y}/2} f(x, y, z)\, dz\, dx\, dy$

$= \int_{-1}^{1} \int_{0}^{4-4z^2} \int_{-\sqrt{4-y-4z^2}}^{\sqrt{4-y-4z^2}} f(x, y, z)\, dx\, dy\, dz$

$= \int_{0}^{4} \int_{-\sqrt{4-y}/2}^{\sqrt{4-y}/2} \int_{-\sqrt{4-y-4z^2}}^{\sqrt{4-y-4z^2}} f(x, y, z)\, dx\, dz\, dy$

$= \int_{-2}^{2} \int_{-\sqrt{4-x^2}/2}^{\sqrt{4-x^2}/2} \int_{0}^{4-x^2-4z^2} f(x, y, z)\, dy\, dz\, dx$

$= \int_{-1}^{1} \int_{-\sqrt{4-4z^2}}^{\sqrt{4-4z^2}} \int_{0}^{4-x^2-4z^2} f(x, y, z)\, dy\, dx\, dz$

31. $\int_{-2}^{2} \int_{x^2}^{4} \int_{0}^{2-y/2} f(x, y, z)\, dz\, dy\, dx$

$= \int_{0}^{4} \int_{-\sqrt{y}}^{\sqrt{y}} \int_{0}^{2-y/2} f(x, y, z)\, dz\, dx\, dy$

$= \int_{0}^{2} \int_{0}^{4-2z} \int_{-\sqrt{y}}^{\sqrt{y}} f(x, y, z)\, dx\, dy\, dz$

$= \int_{0}^{4} \int_{0}^{2-y/2} \int_{-\sqrt{y}}^{\sqrt{y}} f(x, y, z)\, dx\, dz\, dy$

$= \int_{-2}^{2} \int_{0}^{2-x^2/2} \int_{x^2}^{4-2z} f(x, y, z)\, dy\, dz\, dx$

$= \int_{0}^{2} \int_{-\sqrt{4-2z}}^{\sqrt{4-2z}} \int_{r^2}^{4-2z} f(x, y, z)\, dy\, dx\, dz$

33. $\int_{0}^{1} \int_{\sqrt{x}}^{1} \int_{0}^{1-y} f(x, y, z)\, dz\, dy\, dx$

$= \int_{0}^{1} \int_{0}^{y^2} \int_{0}^{1-y} f(x, y, z)\, dz\, dx\, dy$

$= \int_{0}^{1} \int_{0}^{1-z} \int_{0}^{y^2} f(x, y, z)\, dx\, dy\, dz$

$= \int_{0}^{1} \int_{0}^{1-y} \int_{0}^{y^2} f(x, y, z)\, dx\, dz\, dy$

$= \int_{0}^{1} \int_{0}^{1-\sqrt{x}} \int_{\sqrt{x}}^{1-z} f(x, y, z)\, dy\, dz\, dx$

$= \int_{0}^{1} \int_{0}^{(1-z)^2} \int_{\sqrt{x}}^{1-z} f(x, y, z)\, dy\, dx\, dz$

35. $\int_{0}^{1} \int_{y}^{1} \int_{0}^{y} f(x, y, z)\, dz\, dx\, dy = \int_{0}^{1} \int_{0}^{x} \int_{0}^{y} f(x, y, z)\, dz\, dy\, dx$

$= \int_{0}^{1} \int_{z}^{1} \int_{y}^{1} f(x, y, z)\, dx\, dy\, dz = \int_{0}^{1} \int_{0}^{y} \int_{y}^{1} f(x, y, z)\, dx\, dz\, dy$

$= \int_{0}^{1} \int_{0}^{x} \int_{z}^{x} f(x, y, z)\, dy\, dz\, dx = \int_{0}^{1} \int_{z}^{1} \int_{z}^{x} f(x, y, z)\, dy\, dx\, dz$

37. $\frac{79}{30}, \left(\frac{358}{553}, \frac{33}{79}, \frac{571}{553}\right)$ **39.** $a^5, (7a/12, 7a/12, 7a/12)$

41. $I_x = I_y = I_z = \frac{2}{3}kL^5$ **43.** $\frac{1}{2}\pi kha^4$

45. (a) $m = \int_{-3}^{3} \int_{-\sqrt{9-x^2}}^{\sqrt{9-x^2}} \int_{1}^{5-y} \sqrt{x^2 + y^2}\, dz\, dy\, dx$

(b) $(\bar{x}, \bar{y}, \bar{z})$, where

$\bar{x} = (1/m) \int_{-3}^{3} \int_{-\sqrt{9-x^2}}^{\sqrt{9-x^2}} \int_{1}^{5-y} x\sqrt{x^2 + y^2}\, dz\, dy\, dx$

$\bar{y} = (1/m) \int_{-3}^{3} \int_{-\sqrt{9-x^2}}^{\sqrt{9-x^2}} \int_{1}^{5-y} y\sqrt{x^2 + y^2}\, dz\, dy\, dx$

$\bar{z} = (1/m) \int_{-3}^{3} \int_{-\sqrt{9-x^2}}^{\sqrt{9-x^2}} \int_{1}^{5-y} z\sqrt{x^2 + y^2}\, dz\, dy\, dx$

(c) $\int_{-3}^{3} \int_{-\sqrt{9-x^2}}^{\sqrt{9-x^2}} \int_{1}^{5-y} (x^2 + y^2)^{3/2}\, dz\, dy\, dx$

47. (a) $\frac{3}{32}\pi + \frac{11}{24}$

(b) $\left(\dfrac{28}{9\pi + 44}, \dfrac{30\pi + 128}{45\pi + 220}, \dfrac{45\pi + 208}{135\pi + 660}\right)$

(c) $\frac{1}{240}(68 + 15\pi)$

49. (a) $\frac{1}{8}$ (b) $\frac{1}{64}$ (c) $\frac{1}{5760}$ **51.** $L^3/8$

53. (a) The region bounded by the ellipsoid $x^2 + 2y^2 + 3z^2 = 1$

(b) $4\sqrt{6}\pi/45$

EXERCISES 12.8 ■ PAGE 887

1.

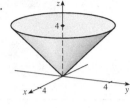

3.

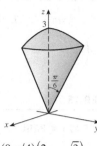

$64\pi/3$ $(9\pi/4)(2 - \sqrt{3})$

5. $\int_{0}^{\pi/2} \int_{0}^{3} \int_{0}^{2} f(r\cos\theta, r\sin\theta, z)\, r\, dz\, dr\, d\theta$

7. 384π **9.** $\pi(e^6 - e - 5)$ **11.** $2\pi/5$

13. (a) 162π (b) $(0, 0, 15)$ **15.** $\pi Ka^2/8, (0, 0, 2a/3)$

17. $312{,}500\pi/7$ **19.** $15\pi/16$ **21.** $1562\pi/15$

23. $(\sqrt{3} - 1)\pi a^3/3$ **25.** (a) 10π (b) $(0, 0, 2.1)$

27. $\left(0, \frac{525}{296}, 0\right)$ **29.** (a) $\left(0, 0, \frac{3}{8}a\right)$ (b) $4K\pi a^5/15$

31. $\frac{1}{3}\pi(2 - \sqrt{2}), \left(0, 0, 3/[8(2 - \sqrt{2})]\right)$

33. $5\pi/6$ **35.** 0 **37.** $(4\sqrt{2} - 5)/15$ **39.** $136\pi/99$

41. (a) $\iiint_C h(P)g(P)\, dV$, where C is the cone

(b) $\approx 3.1 \times 10^{19}$ ft-lb

EXERCISES 12.9 ■ PAGE 898

1. 16 **3.** $\sin^2\theta - \cos^2\theta$ **5.** 0

7. The parallelogram with vertices $(0, 0), (6, 3), (12, 1), (6, -2)$

9. The region bounded by the line $y = 1$, the y-axis, and $y = \sqrt{x}$

11. $x = \frac{1}{3}(v - u), y = \frac{1}{3}(u + 2v)$ is one possible transformation, where $S = \{(u, v) \mid -1 \leqslant u \leqslant 1, 1 \leqslant v \leqslant 3\}$

13. $x = u\cos v, y = u\sin v$ is one possible transformation, where $S = \left\{(u, v) \mid 1 \leqslant u \leqslant \sqrt{2}, 0 \leqslant v \leqslant \pi/2\right\}$

15. -3 **17.** 6π **19.** $2\ln 3$

21. (a) $\frac{4}{3}\pi abc$ (b) 1.083×10^{12} km^3

23. $\frac{8}{5}\ln 8$ **25.** $\frac{3}{2}\sin 1$ **27.** $e - e^{-1}$

CHAPTER 12 REVIEW ■ PAGE 899

True-False Quiz

1. True   **3.** True   **5.** True   **7.** True   **9.** False

Exercises

1. ≈ 64.0 **3.** $4e^2 - 4e + 3$ **5.** $\frac{1}{2}\sin 1$ **7.** $\frac{2}{3}$

9. $\int_{0}^{\pi} \int_{2}^{4} f(r\cos\theta, r\sin\theta)\, r\, dr\, d\theta$

11. The region inside the loop of the four-leaved rose $r = \sin 2\theta$ in the first quadrant

13. $\frac{1}{2}\sin 1$ **15.** $\frac{1}{2}e^6 - \frac{7}{2}$ **17.** $\frac{1}{4}\ln 2$ **19.** 8

21. $81\pi/5$ **23.** $\frac{81}{2}$ **25.** $\pi/96$ **27.** $\frac{64}{15}$

29. 176 **31.** $\frac{2}{3}$ **33.** $2ma^3/9$

35. (a) $\frac{1}{4}$ (b) $\left(\frac{1}{3}, \frac{8}{15}\right)$ (c) $I_0 = \frac{1}{8}, I_x = \frac{1}{12}, I_y = \frac{1}{24}$

37. (a) $(0, 0, h/4)$ (b) $\pi a^4 h/10$

39. $\ln(\sqrt{2} + \sqrt{3}) + \sqrt{2}/3$ **41.** $\frac{486}{5}$ **43.** 0.0512

45. (a) $\frac{1}{15}$ (b) $\frac{1}{3}$ (c) $\frac{1}{45}$

47. $\int_{0}^{1} \int_{0}^{1-z} \int_{-\sqrt{y}}^{\sqrt{y}} f(x, y, z)\, dx\, dy\, dz$ **49.** $-\ln 2$ **51.** 0

FOCUS ON PROBLEM SOLVING ▪ PAGE 903

1. 30   **3.** $\frac{1}{2}\sin 1$ **7.** (b) 0.90

11. $abc\pi\left(\dfrac{2}{3} - \dfrac{8}{9\sqrt{3}}\right)$

CHAPTER 13

EXERCISES 13.1 ▪ PAGE 911

1.

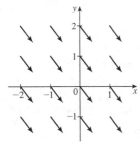

3.

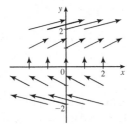

5.

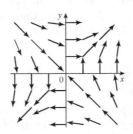

7.

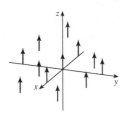

9.

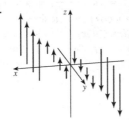

11. II   **13.** I   **15.** IV   **17.** III
19.   The line $y - 2x$

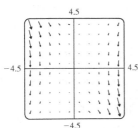

21. $\nabla f(x, y) = (xy + 1)e^{xy}\,\mathbf{i} + x^2e^{xy}\,\mathbf{j}$

23. $\nabla f(x, y, z) = \dfrac{x}{\sqrt{x^2 + y^2 + z^2}}\,\mathbf{i}$
$+ \dfrac{y}{\sqrt{x^2 + y^2 + z^2}}\,\mathbf{j} + \dfrac{z}{\sqrt{x^2 + y^2 + z^2}}\,\mathbf{k}$

25. $\nabla f(x, y) = 2x\,\mathbf{i} - \mathbf{j}$

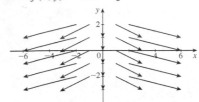

27.

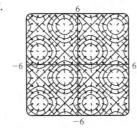

29. III   **31.** II   **33.** (2.04, 1.03)
35. (a)   (b) $y = 1/x, x > 0$

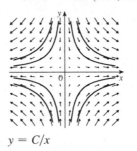

$y = C/x$

EXERCISES 13.2 ▪ PAGE 922

1. $\frac{1}{54}(145^{3/2} - 1)$ **3.** 1638.4   **5.** $\frac{243}{8}$ **7.** $\frac{17}{3}$ **9.** $\sqrt{5}\,\pi$
11. $\frac{1}{12}\sqrt{14}(e^6 - 1)$ **13.** $\frac{1}{5}$ **15.** $\frac{97}{3}$
17. (a) Positive   (b) Negative
19. 45   **21.** $\frac{6}{5} - \cos 1 - \sin 1$ **23.** 1.9633   **25.** 15.0074
27. $3\pi + \frac{2}{3}$

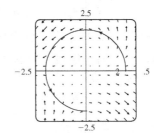

29. (a) $\frac{11}{8} - 1/e$ (b) 2.1

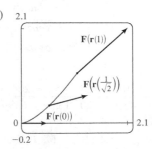

31. $\frac{172,704}{5,632,705}\sqrt{2}(1 - e^{-14\pi})$ **33.** $2\pi k, (4/\pi, 0)$

35. (a) $\bar{x} = (1/m)\int_C x\rho(x, y, z)\, ds$,

$\bar{y} = (1/m)\int_C y\rho(x, y, z)\, ds$,

$\bar{z} = (1/m)\int_C z\rho(x, y, z)\, ds$, where $m = \int_C \rho(x, y, z)\, ds$

(b) $(0, 0, 3\pi)$

37. $I_x = k\left(\frac{1}{2}\pi - \frac{4}{3}\right)$, $I_y = k\left(\frac{1}{2}\pi - \frac{2}{3}\right)$

39. $2\pi^2$ **41.** 26 **43.** $\approx 1.67 \times 10^4$ ft-lb **45.** (b) Yes

47. ≈ 22 J

EXERCISES 13.3 ▪ PAGE 932

1. 40 **3.** $f(x, y) = x^2 - 3xy + 2y^2 - 8y + K$

5. Not conservative **7.** $f(x, y) = ye^x + x \sin y + K$

9. $f(x, y) = x \ln y + x^2 y^3 + K$

11. (b) 16 **13.** (a) $f(x, y) = \frac{1}{2}x^2 y^2$ (b) 2

15. (a) $f(x, y, z) = xyz + z^2$ (b) 77

17. (a) $f(x, y, z) = xy^2 \cos z$ (b) 0 **19.** 2

21. It doesn't matter which curve is chosen.

23. 30 **25.** No **27.** Conservative

31. (a) Yes (b) Yes (c) Yes

33. (a) No (b) Yes (c) Yes

EXERCISES 13.4 ▪ PAGE 939

1. 8π **3.** $\frac{2}{3}$ **5.** 12 **7.** $\frac{1}{3}$ **9.** -24π **11.** $\frac{4}{3} - 2\pi$

13. $\frac{625}{2}\pi$ **15.** $-8e + 48e^{-1}$ **17.** $-\frac{1}{12}$ **19.** 3π **21.** (c) $\frac{9}{2}$

23. $(4a/3\pi, 4a/3\pi)$ if the region is the portion of the disk $x^2 + y^2 = a^2$ in the first quadrant

27. 0

EXERCISES 13.5 ▪ PAGE 947

1. (a) $-x^2 \mathbf{i} + 3xy\,\mathbf{j} - xz\,\mathbf{k}$ (b) yz

3. (a) $ze^x \mathbf{i} + (xye^z - yze^x)\,\mathbf{j} - xe^z\,\mathbf{k}$ (b) $y(e^z + e^x)$

5. (a) $\mathbf{0}$ (b) $2/\sqrt{x^2 + y^2 + z^2}$

7. (a) $\langle 1/y, -1/x, 1/x \rangle$ (b) $1/x + 1/y + 1/z$

9. (a) Negative (b) curl $\mathbf{F} = \mathbf{0}$

11. (a) Zero (b) curl $\mathbf{F}$ points in the negative z-direction

13. $f(x, y, z) = xy^2 z^3 + K$ **15.** $f(x, y, z) = x^2 y + y^2 z + K$

17. Not conservative **19.** No

EXERCISES 13.6 ▪ PAGE 959

1. 49.09 **3.** 900π **5.** $11\sqrt{14}$ **7.** $\frac{2}{3}(2\sqrt{2} - 1)$

9. $171\sqrt{14}$ **11.** $\sqrt{3}/24$ **13.** $364\sqrt{2}\,\pi/3$

15. $(\pi/60)(391\sqrt{17} + 1)$ **17.** 16π **19.** 12 **21.** $\frac{713}{180}$

23. $-\frac{1}{6}$ **25.** $-\frac{4}{3}\pi$ **27.** 0 **29.** 48 **31.** $2\pi + \frac{8}{3}$

33. 3.4895

35. $\iint_S \mathbf{F} \cdot d\mathbf{S} = \iint_D [P(\partial h/\partial x) - Q + R(\partial h/\partial z)]\, dA$, where D = projection of S on xz-plane

37. $(0, 0, a/2)$

39. (a) $I_z = \iint_S (x^2 + y^2)\rho(x, y, z)\, dS$ (b) $4329\sqrt{2}\,\pi/5$

41. 0 kg/s **43.** $\frac{8}{3}\pi a^3 \varepsilon_0$ **45.** 1248π

EXERCISES 13.7 ▪ PAGE 965

3. 0 **5.** 0 **7.** -1 **9.** 80π

11. (a) $81\pi/2$ (b)

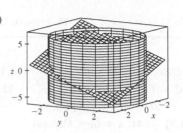

(c) $x = 3\cos t$, $y = 3 \sin t$,

$z = 1 - 3(\cos t + \sin t)$,

$0 \le t \le 2\pi$

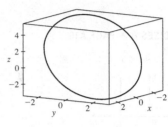

17. 3

EXERCISES 13.8 ▪ PAGE 971

5. $\frac{9}{2}$ **7.** $9\pi/2$ **9.** 0 **11.** $32\pi/3$ **13.** 0

15. $341\sqrt{2}/60 + \frac{81}{20}\arcsin(\sqrt{3}/3)$

17. $13\pi/20$ **19.** Negative at P_1, positive at P_2

21. div $\mathbf{F} > 0$ in quadrants I, II; div $\mathbf{F} < 0$ in quadrants III, IV

CHAPTER 13 REVIEW ▪ PAGE 974

True-False Quiz

1. False **3.** True **5.** False **7.** True

Exercises

1. (a) Negative (b) Positive **3.** $6\sqrt{10}$ **5.** $\frac{4}{15}$

7. $\frac{110}{3}$ **9.** $\frac{11}{12} - 4/e$ **11.** $f(x, y) = e^y + xe^{xy}$ **13.** 0

17. -8π **25.** $(\pi/60)(391\sqrt{17} + 1)$ **27.** $-64\pi/3$

31. $-\frac{1}{2}$ **35.** -4 **37.** 21

APPENDIXES

EXERCISES A ▪ PAGE A6

1. 18 **3.** $5 - \sqrt{5}$ **5.** $2 - x$

7. $|x + 1| = \begin{cases} x + 1 & \text{for } x \ge -1 \\ -x - 1 & \text{for } x < -1 \end{cases}$ **9.** $x^2 + 1$

11. $(-2, \infty)$ **13.** $[-1, \infty)$

15. $(0, 1]$ **17.** $(-\infty, 1) \cup (2, \infty)$

19. $(-\sqrt{3}, \sqrt{3})$ **21.** $(-\infty, 1]$

23. $(-1, 0) \cup (1, \infty)$ **25.** $(-\infty, 0) \cup (\frac{1}{4}, \infty)$

27. $10 \le C \le 35$ **29.** (a) $T = 20 - 10h, 0 \le h \le 12$
(b) $-30°C \le T \le 20°C$ **31.** $2, -\frac{4}{3}$ **33.** $(-3, 3)$
35. $(3, 5)$ **37.** $(-\infty, -7] \cup [-3, \infty)$
39. $[1.3, 1.7]$ **41.** $x \ge (a + b)c/(ab)$

EXERCISES B ■ PAGE A16

1. 5 **3.** $-\frac{9}{2}$

7.

9.

11. $y = 6x - 15$ **13.** $5x + y = 11$ **15.** $y = 3x - 2$
17. $y = 3x - 3$ **19.** $y = 5$ **21.** $x + 2y + 11 = 0$
23. $5x - 2y + 1 = 0$
25. $m = -\frac{1}{3},$ **27.** $m = \frac{3}{4},$
$\quad b = 0$ $\quad b = -3$

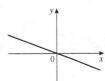

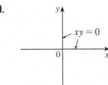

29.

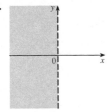

31.

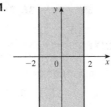

33.

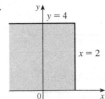

35.

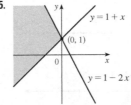

37. $(x - 3)^2 + (y + 1)^2 = 25$ **39.** $(2, -5), 4$ **41.** $(1, -2)$
45. $y = x - 3$

53.

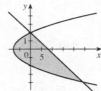

EXERCISES C ■ PAGE A25

1. (a) $7\pi/6$ (b) $\pi/20$ **3.** (a) $720°$ (b) $-67.5°$
5. 3π cm   **7.** $\frac{2}{3}$ rad $= (120/\pi)°$
9. (a)   (b)

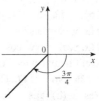

11. $\sin(3\pi/4) = 1/\sqrt{2}, \cos(3\pi/4) = -1/\sqrt{2}, \tan(3\pi/4) = -1,$
$\csc(3\pi/4) = \sqrt{2}, \sec(3\pi/4) = -\sqrt{2}, \cot(3\pi/4) = -1$
13. $\cos \theta = \frac{4}{5}, \tan \theta = \frac{3}{4}, \csc \theta = \frac{5}{3}, \sec \theta = \frac{5}{4}, \cot \theta = \frac{4}{3}$
15. 5.73576 cm   **17.** 24.62147 cm   **27.** $\frac{1}{15}(4 + 6\sqrt{2})$
29. $\pi/3, 5\pi/3$ **31.** $\pi/6, \pi/2, 5\pi/6, 3\pi/2$
33. $0 \le x \le \pi/6$ and $5\pi/6 \le x \le 2\pi$
35. $0 \le x < \pi/4, 3\pi/4 < x < 5\pi/4, 7\pi/4 < x \le 2\pi$

37.

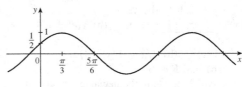

39.

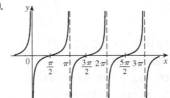

EXERCISES D ■ PAGE A34

1. $\frac{4}{7}$ (or any smaller positive number)
3. 1.44 (or any smaller positive number)
5. 0.0906 (or any smaller positive number)
7. $0.11, 0.012$ (or smaller positive numbers)
11. (a) $\sqrt{1000/\pi}$ cm   (b) Within approximately 0.0445 cm
(c) Radius; area; $\sqrt{1000/\pi}$; 1000; 5; ≈ 0.0445

13. (a) 0.025   (b) 0.0025   **17.** $N \geqslant 13$

19. (a) $x > 100$ **21.** (a) 0   (b) 9, 11

EXERCISES F ■ PAGE A45

1. $\sqrt{1} + \sqrt{2} + \sqrt{3} + \sqrt{4} + \sqrt{5}$ **3.** $3^4 + 3^5 + 3^6$

5. $-1 + \frac{1}{3} + \frac{3}{5} + \frac{5}{7} + \frac{7}{9}$ **7.** $1^{10} + 2^{10} + 3^{10} + \cdots + n^{10}$

9. $1 - 1 + 1 - 1 + \cdots + (-1)^{n-1}$ **11.** $\sum_{i=1}^{10} i$

13. $\sum_{i=1}^{19} \dfrac{i}{i+1}$ **15.** $\sum_{i=1}^{n} 2i$ **17.** $\sum_{i=0}^{5} 2^i$ **19.** $\sum_{i=1}^{n} x^i$

21. 80   **23.** 3276   **25.** 0   **27.** 61   **29.** $n(n+1)$

31. $n(n^2 + 6n + 17)/3$ **33.** $n(n^2 + 6n + 11)/3$

35. $n(n^3 + 2n^2 - n - 10)/4$

41. (a) n^4 (b) $5^{100} - 1$ (c) $\frac{97}{300}$ (d) $a_n - a_0$

43. $\frac{1}{3}$ **45.** 14   **49.** $2^{n+1} + n^2 + n - 2$

EXERCISES G ■ PAGE A54

1. (a) $\dfrac{A}{x+3} + \dfrac{B}{3x+1}$ (b) $\dfrac{A}{x} + \dfrac{B}{x+1} + \dfrac{C}{(x+1)^2}$

3. (a) $\dfrac{A}{x} + \dfrac{B}{x^2} + \dfrac{C}{x^3} + \dfrac{Dx+E}{x^2+4}$

(b) $\dfrac{A}{x+3} + \dfrac{B}{(x+3)^2} + \dfrac{C}{x-3} + \dfrac{D}{(x-3)^2}$

5. (a) $1 + \dfrac{A}{x-1} + \dfrac{B}{x+1} + \dfrac{Cx+D}{x^2+1}$

(b) $\dfrac{At+B}{t^2+1} + \dfrac{Ct+D}{t^2+4} + \dfrac{Et+F}{(t^2+4)^2}$

7. $x + 6\ln|x-6| + C$

9. $2\ln|x+5| - \ln|x-2| + C$ **11.** $\frac{1}{2}\ln\frac{3}{2}$

13. $a\ln|x-b| + C$ **15.** $\frac{7}{6} + \ln\frac{2}{3}$

17. $\frac{27}{5}\ln 2 - \frac{9}{5}\ln 3 \left(\text{or } \frac{9}{5}\ln\frac{8}{3}\right)$

19. $-\dfrac{1}{36}\ln|x+5| + \dfrac{1}{6}\dfrac{1}{x+5} + \dfrac{1}{36}\ln|x-1| + C$

21. $2\ln|x| + (1/x) + 3\ln|x+2| + C$

23. $\ln|x-1| - \frac{1}{2}\ln(x^2+9) - \frac{1}{3}\tan^{-1}(x/3) + C$

25. $\frac{1}{2}\ln(x^2+1) + \left(1/\sqrt{2}\right)\tan^{-1}(x/\sqrt{2}) + C$

27. $\frac{1}{2}\ln(x^2+2x+5) + \frac{3}{2}\tan^{-1}\left(\dfrac{x+1}{2}\right) + C$

29. $\frac{1}{3}\ln|x-1| - \frac{1}{6}\ln(x^2+x+1) - \dfrac{1}{\sqrt{3}}\tan^{-1}\dfrac{2x+1}{\sqrt{3}} + C$

31. $\frac{1}{16}\ln|x| - \frac{1}{32}\ln(x^2+4) + \dfrac{1}{8(x^2+4)} + C$

33. $\dfrac{-1}{2(x^2+2x+4)} - \dfrac{2\sqrt{3}}{9}\tan^{-1}\left(\dfrac{x+1}{\sqrt{3}}\right) - \dfrac{2(x+1)}{3(x^2+2x+4)} + C$

35. $2 + \ln\frac{25}{9}$ **37.** $\ln\left[\dfrac{(e^x+2)^2}{e^x+1}\right] + C$

39. $-\frac{1}{2}\ln 3 \approx -0.55$

41. $t = -\ln P - \frac{1}{9}\ln(0.9P + 900) + C$, where $C \approx 10.23$

43. (a)
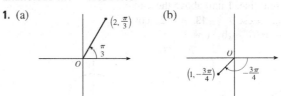

(b) $\dfrac{4822}{4879}\ln|5x+2| - \dfrac{334}{323}\ln|2x+1| - \dfrac{3146}{80,155}\ln|3x-7| + \dfrac{11,049}{260,015}\ln(x^2+x+5) + \dfrac{75,772}{260,015\sqrt{19}}\tan^{-1}\dfrac{2x+1}{\sqrt{19}} + C$

The CAS omits the absolute value signs and the constant of integration.

EXERCISES H.1 ■ PAGE A63

1. (a)   (b)
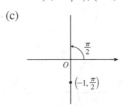

$(2, 7\pi/3), (-2, 4\pi/3)$ $(1, 5\pi/4), (-1, \pi/4)$

(c)

$(1, 3\pi/2), (-1, 5\pi/2)$

3. (a)   (b)
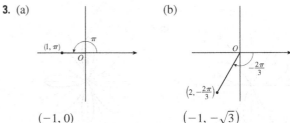

$(-1, 0)$ $(-1, -\sqrt{3})$

(c)

$(\sqrt{2}, -\sqrt{2})$

5. (a) (i) $\left(2\sqrt{2}, 7\pi/4\right)$ (ii) $\left(-2\sqrt{2}, 3\pi/4\right)$
(b) (i) $(2, 2\pi/3)$ (ii) $(-2, 5\pi/3)$

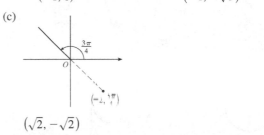

7.
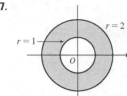

9.
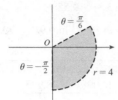

11.
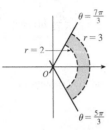

13. Circle, center $\left(0, \frac{3}{2}\right)$, radius $\frac{3}{2}$

15. Horizontal line, 1 unit above the x-axis

17. $r = -\cot\theta\,\csc\theta$ **19.** $r = 2c\cos\theta$

21. (a) $\theta = \pi/6$ (b) $x = 3$

23.
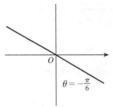

25.
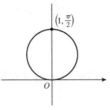

27.
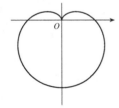

29.

31.
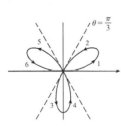

33.
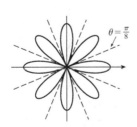

35.
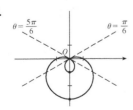

37.
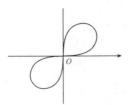

39.

41.
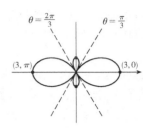

43.
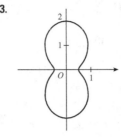

45.
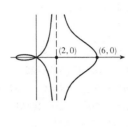

47. (a) For $c < -1$, the inner loop begins at $\theta = \sin^{-1}(-1/c)$ and ends at $\theta = \pi - \sin^{-1}(-1/c)$; for $c > 1$, it begins at $\theta = \pi + \sin^{-1}(1/c)$ and ends at $\theta = 2\pi - \sin^{-1}(1/c)$.

49. $-\pi$ **51.** 1

53. Horizontal at $\left(3/\sqrt{2}, \pi/4\right), \left(-3/\sqrt{2}, 3\pi/4\right)$; vertical at $(3, 0), (0, \pi/2)$

55. Horizontal at $\left(\frac{3}{2}, \pi/3\right), (0, \pi)$ [the pole], and $\left(\frac{3}{2}, 5\pi/3\right)$; vertical at $(2, 0), \left(\frac{1}{2}, 2\pi/3\right), \left(\frac{1}{2}, 4\pi/3\right)$

57. Center $(b/2, a/2)$, radius $\sqrt{a^2 + b^2}/2$

59.
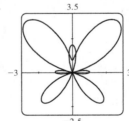

61.
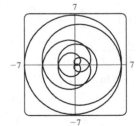

63. By counterclockwise rotation through angle $\pi/6$, $\pi/3$, or α about the origin

65. (a) A rose with n loops if n is odd and $2n$ loops if n is even (b) Number of loops is always $2n$

67. For $0 < a < 1$, the curve is an oval, which develops a dimple as $a \to 1^-$. When $a > 1$, the curve splits into two parts, one of which has a loop.

EXERCISES H.2 ■ PAGE A69

1. $\pi^5/10{,}240$ **3.** $\pi/12 + \frac{1}{8}\sqrt{3}$ **5.** π^2 **7.** $\frac{41}{4}\pi$

9. 4

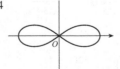

11. π

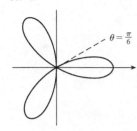

$\theta = \frac{\pi}{6}$

13. 3π

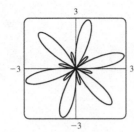

15. $\frac{1}{8}\pi$ **17.** $\pi - \frac{3}{2}\sqrt{3}$ **19.** $\frac{1}{3}\pi + \frac{1}{2}\sqrt{3}$ **21.** π

23. $\frac{5}{24}\pi - \frac{1}{4}\sqrt{3}$ **25.** $\frac{1}{2}\pi - 1$ **27.** $\frac{1}{4}(\pi + 3\sqrt{3})$

29. $(1, \theta)$ where $\theta = \pi/12, 5\pi/12, 13\pi/12, 17\pi/12$
and $(-1, \theta)$ where $\theta = 7\pi/12, 11\pi/12, 19\pi/12, 23\pi/12$

31. $(\frac{1}{2}\sqrt{3}, \pi/3), (\frac{1}{2}\sqrt{3}, 2\pi/3)$, and the pole

33. Intersection at $\theta \approx 0.89, 2.25$; area ≈ 3.46 **35.** π

37. $\frac{8}{3}[(\pi^2 + 1)^{3/2} - 1]$ **39.** 29.0653

EXERCISES I ■ PAGE A78

1. $8 - 4i$ **3.** $13 + 18i$ **5.** $12 - 7i$ **7.** $\frac{11}{13} + \frac{10}{13}i$

9. $\frac{1}{2} - \frac{1}{2}i$ **11.** $-i$ **13.** $5i$ **15.** $12 + 5i, 13$

17. $4i, 4$ **19.** $\pm\frac{3}{2}i$ **21.** $-1 \pm 2i$

23. $-\frac{1}{2} \pm (\sqrt{7}/2)i$ **25.** $3\sqrt{2}[\cos(3\pi/4) + i\sin(3\pi/4)]$

27. $5\{\cos[\tan^{-1}(\frac{4}{3})] + i\sin[\tan^{-1}(\frac{4}{3})]\}$

29. $4[\cos(\pi/2) + i\sin(\pi/2)], \cos(-\pi/6) + i\sin(-\pi/6),$
$\frac{1}{2}[\cos(-\pi/6) + i\sin(-\pi/6)]$

31. $4\sqrt{2}[\cos(7\pi/12) + i\sin(7\pi/12)],$
$(2\sqrt{2})[\cos(13\pi/12) + i\sin(13\pi/12)], \frac{1}{4}[\cos(\pi/6) + i\sin(\pi/6)]$

33. -1024 **35.** $-512\sqrt{3} + 512i$

37. $\pm 1, \pm i, (1/\sqrt{2})(\pm 1 \pm i)$ **39.** $\pm(\sqrt{3}/2) + \frac{1}{2}i, -i$

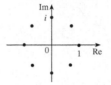 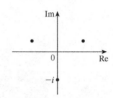

41. i **43.** $\frac{1}{2} + (\sqrt{3}/2)i$ **45.** $-e^2$

47. $\cos 3\theta = \cos^3\theta - 3\cos\theta\sin^2\theta,$
$\sin 3\theta = 3\cos^2\theta\sin\theta - \sin^3\theta$

Index

ALGEBRA

Arithmetic Operations

$$a(b + c) = ab + ac$$

$$\frac{a}{b} + \frac{c}{d} = \frac{ad + bc}{bd}$$

$$\frac{a + c}{b} = \frac{a}{b} + \frac{c}{b}$$

$$\frac{\frac{a}{b}}{\frac{c}{d}} = \frac{a}{b} \times \frac{d}{c} = \frac{ad}{bc}$$

Exponents and Radicals

$$x^m x^n = x^{m+n}$$

$$\frac{x^m}{x^n} = x^{m-n}$$

$$(x^m)^n = x^{mn}$$

$$x^{-n} = \frac{1}{x^n}$$

$$(xy)^n = x^n y^n$$

$$\left(\frac{x}{y}\right)^n = \frac{x^n}{y^n}$$

$$x^{1/n} = \sqrt[n]{x}$$

$$x^{m/n} = \sqrt[n]{x^m} = \left(\sqrt[n]{x}\right)^m$$

$$\sqrt[n]{xy} = \sqrt[n]{x}\sqrt[n]{y}$$

$$\sqrt[n]{\frac{x}{y}} = \frac{\sqrt[n]{x}}{\sqrt[n]{y}}$$

Factoring Special Polynomials

$$x^2 - y^2 = (x + y)(x - y)$$

$$x^3 + y^3 = (x + y)(x^2 - xy + y^2)$$

$$x^3 - y^3 = (x - y)(x^2 + xy + y^2)$$

Binomial Theorem

$$(x + y)^2 = x^2 + 2xy + y^2 \qquad (x - y)^2 = x^2 - 2xy + y^2$$

$$(x + y)^3 = x^3 + 3x^2y + 3xy^2 + y^3$$

$$(x - y)^3 = x^3 - 3x^2y + 3xy^2 - y^3$$

$$(x + y)^n = x^n + nx^{n-1}y + \frac{n(n - 1)}{2}x^{n-2}y^2$$

$$+ \cdots + \binom{n}{k}x^{n-k}y^k + \cdots + nxy^{n-1} + y^n$$

where $\binom{n}{k} = \dfrac{n(n - 1) \cdots (n - k + 1)}{1 \cdot 2 \cdot 3 \cdot \cdots \cdot k}$

Quadratic Formula

If $ax^2 + bx + c = 0$, then $x = \dfrac{-b \pm \sqrt{b^2 - 4ac}}{2a}$.

Inequalities and Absolute Value

If $a < b$ and $b < c$, then $a < c$.

If $a < b$, then $a + c < b + c$.

If $a < b$ and $c > 0$, then $ca < cb$.

If $a < b$ and $c < 0$, then $ca > cb$.

If $a > 0$, then

$|x| = a$ means $x = a$ or $x = -a$

$|x| < a$ means $-a < x < a$

$|x| > a$ means $x > a$ or $x < -a$

GEOMETRY

Geometric Formulas

Formulas for area A, circumference C, and volume V:

Triangle	Circle	Sector of Circle
$A = \frac{1}{2}bh$	$A = \pi r^2$	$A = \frac{1}{2}r^2\theta$
$= \frac{1}{2}ab \sin\theta$	$C = 2\pi r$	$s = r\theta$ (θ in radians)

 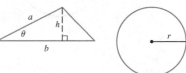

Sphere	Cylinder	Cone
$V = \frac{4}{3}\pi r^3$	$V = \pi r^2 h$	$V = \frac{1}{3}\pi r^2 h$
$A = 4\pi r^2$		$A = \pi r\sqrt{r^2 + h^2}$

Distance and Midpoint Formulas

Distance between $P_1(x_1, y_1)$ and $P_2(x_2, y_2)$:

$$d = \sqrt{(x_2 - x_1)^2 + (y_2 - y_1)^2}$$

Midpoint of $\overline{P_1 P_2}$: $\left(\dfrac{x_1 + x_2}{2}, \dfrac{y_1 + y_2}{2}\right)$

Lines

Slope of line through $P_1(x_1, y_1)$ and $P_2(x_2, y_2)$:

$$m = \frac{y_2 - y_1}{x_2 - x_1}$$

Point-slope equation of line through $P_1(x_1, y_1)$ with slope m:

$$y - y_1 = m(x - x_1)$$

Slope-intercept equation of line with slope m and y-intercept b:

$$y = mx + b$$

Circles

Equation of the circle with center (h, k) and radius r:

$$(x - h)^2 + (y - k)^2 = r^2$$

1

TRIGONOMETRY

Angle Measurement

π radians $= 180°$

$1° = \dfrac{\pi}{180}$ rad $\qquad$ 1 rad $= \dfrac{180°}{\pi}$

$s = r\theta$

(θ in radians)

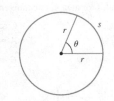

Right Angle Trigonometry

$\sin\theta = \dfrac{\text{opp}}{\text{hyp}} \qquad \csc\theta = \dfrac{\text{hyp}}{\text{opp}}$

$\cos\theta = \dfrac{\text{adj}}{\text{hyp}} \qquad \sec\theta = \dfrac{\text{hyp}}{\text{adj}}$

$\tan\theta = \dfrac{\text{opp}}{\text{adj}} \qquad \cot\theta = \dfrac{\text{adj}}{\text{opp}}$

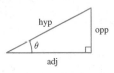

Trigonometric Functions

$\sin\theta = \dfrac{y}{r} \qquad \csc\theta = \dfrac{r}{y}$

$\cos\theta = \dfrac{x}{r} \qquad \sec\theta = \dfrac{r}{x}$

$\tan\theta = \dfrac{y}{x} \qquad \cot\theta = \dfrac{x}{y}$

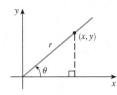

Graphs of Trigonometric Functions

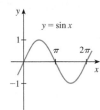
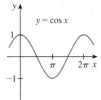

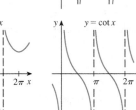

Trigonometric Functions of Important Angles

θ	radians	$\sin\theta$	$\cos\theta$	$\tan\theta$
$0°$	0	0	1	0
$30°$	$\pi/6$	$1/2$	$\sqrt{3}/2$	$\sqrt{3}/3$
$45°$	$\pi/4$	$\sqrt{2}/2$	$\sqrt{2}/2$	1
$60°$	$\pi/3$	$\sqrt{3}/2$	$1/2$	$\sqrt{3}$
$90°$	$\pi/2$	1	0	—

Fundamental Identities

$\csc\theta = \dfrac{1}{\sin\theta} \qquad\qquad \sec\theta = \dfrac{1}{\cos\theta}$

$\tan\theta = \dfrac{\sin\theta}{\cos\theta} \qquad\qquad \cot\theta = \dfrac{\cos\theta}{\sin\theta}$

$\cot\theta = \dfrac{1}{\tan\theta} \qquad\qquad \sin^2\theta + \cos^2\theta = 1$

$1 + \tan^2\theta = \sec^2\theta \qquad 1 + \cot^2\theta = \csc^2\theta$

$\sin(-\theta) = -\sin\theta \qquad \cos(-\theta) = \cos\theta$

$\tan(-\theta) = -\tan\theta \qquad \sin\left(\dfrac{\pi}{2} - \theta\right) = \cos\theta$

$\cos\left(\dfrac{\pi}{2} - \theta\right) = \sin\theta \qquad \tan\left(\dfrac{\pi}{2} - \theta\right) = \cot\theta$

The Law of Sines

$\dfrac{\sin A}{a} = \dfrac{\sin B}{b} = \dfrac{\sin C}{c}$

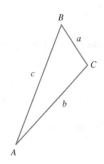

The Law of Cosines

$a^2 = b^2 + c^2 - 2bc\cos A$

$b^2 = a^2 + c^2 - 2ac\cos B$

$c^2 = a^2 + b^2 - 2ab\cos C$

Addition and Subtraction Formulas

$\sin(x + y) = \sin x \cos y + \cos x \sin y$

$\sin(x - y) = \sin x \cos y - \cos x \sin y$

$\cos(x + y) = \cos x \cos y - \sin x \sin y$

$\cos(x - y) = \cos x \cos y + \sin x \sin y$

$\tan(x + y) = \dfrac{\tan x + \tan y}{1 - \tan x \tan y}$

$\tan(x - y) = \dfrac{\tan x - \tan y}{1 + \tan x \tan y}$

Double-Angle Formulas

$\sin 2x = 2\sin x \cos x$

$\cos 2x = \cos^2 x - \sin^2 x = 2\cos^2 x - 1 = 1 - 2\sin^2 x$

$\tan 2x = \dfrac{2\tan x}{1 - \tan^2 x}$

Half-Angle Formulas

$\sin^2 x = \dfrac{1 - \cos 2x}{2} \qquad \cos^2 x = \dfrac{1 + \cos 2x}{2}$

SPECIAL FUNCTIONS

Power Functions $f(x) = x^a$

(i) $f(x) = x^n$, n a positive integer

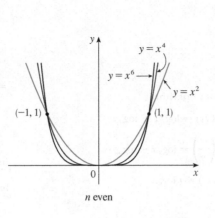

$y = x^4$
$y = x^6$
$y = x^2$
$(-1, 1)$ $(1, 1)$

n even

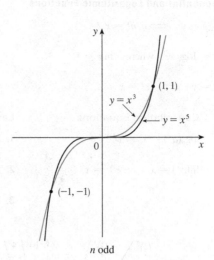

$(1, 1)$
$y = x^3$
$y = x^5$
$(-1, -1)$

n odd

(ii) $f(x) = x^{1/n} = \sqrt[n]{x}$, n a positive integer

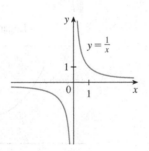

$(1, 1)$

$f(x) = \sqrt{x}$

$(1, 1)$

$f(x) = \sqrt[3]{x}$

(iii) $f(x) = x^{-1} = \dfrac{1}{x}$

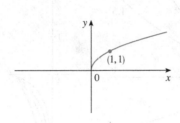

$y = \dfrac{1}{x}$

1

0 1

Inverse Trigonometric Functions

$\arcsin x = \sin^{-1} x = y \iff \sin y = x$ and $-\dfrac{\pi}{2} \leq y \leq \dfrac{\pi}{2}$

$\arccos x = \cos^{-1} x = y \iff \cos y = x$ and $0 \leq y \leq \pi$

$\arctan x = \tan^{-1} x = y \iff \tan y = x$ and $-\dfrac{\pi}{2} < y < \dfrac{\pi}{2}$

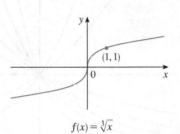

$\dfrac{\pi}{2}$

0

$-\dfrac{\pi}{2}$

$\displaystyle \lim_{x \to -\infty} \tan^{-1} x = -\dfrac{\pi}{2}$

$\displaystyle \lim_{x \to \infty} \tan^{-1} x = \dfrac{\pi}{2}$

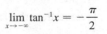

$y = \tan^{-1} x = \arctan x$

SPECIAL FUNCTIONS

Exponential and Logarithmic Functions

$\log_a x = y \iff a^y = x$

$\ln x = \log_e x, \quad \text{where} \quad \ln e = 1$

$\ln x = y \iff e^y = x$

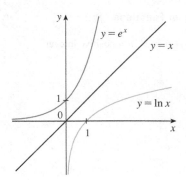

Cancellation Equations

$\log_a(a^x) = x \qquad a^{\log_a x} = x$

$\ln(e^x) = x \qquad e^{\ln x} = x$

Laws of Logarithms

1. $\log_a(xy) = \log_a x + \log_a y$

2. $\log_a\left(\dfrac{x}{y}\right) = \log_a x - \log_a y$

3. $\log_a(x^r) = r \log_a x$

$\displaystyle\lim_{x \to -\infty} e^x = 0 \qquad \lim_{x \to \infty} e^x = \infty$

$\displaystyle\lim_{x \to 0^+} \ln x = -\infty \qquad \lim_{x \to \infty} \ln x = \infty$

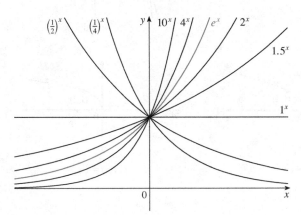

Exponential functions

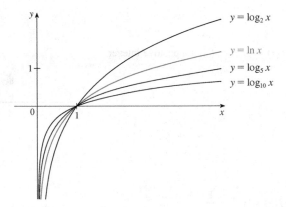

Logarithmic functions

Hyperbolic Functions

$\sinh x = \dfrac{e^x - e^{-x}}{2} \qquad\qquad \operatorname{csch} x = \dfrac{1}{\sinh x}$

$\cosh x = \dfrac{e^x + e^{-x}}{2} \qquad\qquad \operatorname{sech} x = \dfrac{1}{\cosh x}$

$\tanh x = \dfrac{\sinh x}{\cosh x} \qquad\qquad \coth x = \dfrac{\cosh x}{\sinh x}$

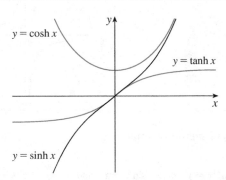

Inverse Hyperbolic Functions

$y = \sinh^{-1}x \iff \sinh y = x$

$y = \cosh^{-1}x \iff \cosh y = x \quad \text{and} \quad y \geq 0$

$y = \tanh^{-1}x \iff \tanh y = x$

$\sinh^{-1}x = \ln\left(x + \sqrt{x^2 + 1}\right)$

$\cosh^{-1}x = \ln\left(x + \sqrt{x^2 - 1}\right)$

$\tanh^{-1}x = \tfrac{1}{2}\ln\left(\dfrac{1 + x}{1 - x}\right)$

DIFFERENTIATION RULES

General Formulas

1. $\dfrac{d}{dx}(c) = 0$

2. $\dfrac{d}{dx}[cf(x)] = cf'(x)$

3. $\dfrac{d}{dx}[f(x) + g(x)] = f'(x) + g'(x)$

4. $\dfrac{d}{dx}[f(x) - g(x)] = f'(x) - g'(x)$

5. $\dfrac{d}{dx}[f(x)g(x)] = f(x)g'(x) + g(x)f'(x)$ (Product Rule)

6. $\dfrac{d}{dx}\left[\dfrac{f(x)}{g(x)}\right] = \dfrac{g(x)f'(x) - f(x)g'(x)}{[g(x)]^2}$ (Quotient Rule)

7. $\dfrac{d}{dx}f(g(x)) = f'(g(x))g'(x)$ (Chain Rule)

8. $\dfrac{d}{dx}(x^n) = nx^{n-1}$ (Power Rule)

Exponential and Logarithmic Functions

9. $\dfrac{d}{dx}(e^x) = e^x$

10. $\dfrac{d}{dx}(a^x) = a^x \ln a$

11. $\dfrac{d}{dx}\ln|x| = \dfrac{1}{x}$

12. $\dfrac{d}{dx}(\log_a x) = \dfrac{1}{x \ln a}$

Trigonometric Functions

13. $\dfrac{d}{dx}(\sin x) = \cos x$

14. $\dfrac{d}{dx}(\cos x) = -\sin x$

15. $\dfrac{d}{dx}(\tan x) = \sec^2 x$

16. $\dfrac{d}{dx}(\csc x) = -\csc x \cot x$

17. $\dfrac{d}{dx}(\sec x) = \sec x \tan x$

18. $\dfrac{d}{dx}(\cot x) = -\csc^2 x$

Inverse Trigonometric Functions

19. $\dfrac{d}{dx}(\sin^{-1}x) = \dfrac{1}{\sqrt{1-x^2}}$

20. $\dfrac{d}{dx}(\cos^{-1}x) = -\dfrac{1}{\sqrt{1-x^2}}$

21. $\dfrac{d}{dx}(\tan^{-1}x) = \dfrac{1}{1+x^2}$

22. $\dfrac{d}{dx}(\csc^{-1}x) = -\dfrac{1}{x\sqrt{x^2-1}}$

23. $\dfrac{d}{dx}(\sec^{-1}x) = \dfrac{1}{x\sqrt{x^2-1}}$

24. $\dfrac{d}{dx}(\cot^{-1}x) = -\dfrac{1}{1+x^2}$

Hyperbolic Functions

25. $\dfrac{d}{dx}(\sinh x) = \cosh x$

26. $\dfrac{d}{dx}(\cosh x) = \sinh x$

27. $\dfrac{d}{dx}(\tanh x) = \text{sech}^2 x$

28. $\dfrac{d}{dx}(\text{csch } x) = -\text{csch } x \coth x$

29. $\dfrac{d}{dx}(\text{sech } x) = -\text{sech } x \tanh x$

30. $\dfrac{d}{dx}(\coth x) = -\text{csch}^2 x$

Inverse Hyperbolic Functions

31. $\dfrac{d}{dx}(\sinh^{-1}x) = \dfrac{1}{\sqrt{1+x^2}}$

32. $\dfrac{d}{dx}(\cosh^{-1}x) = \dfrac{1}{\sqrt{x^2-1}}$

33. $\dfrac{d}{dx}(\tanh^{-1}x) = \dfrac{1}{1-x^2}$

34. $\dfrac{d}{dx}(\text{csch}^{-1}x) = -\dfrac{1}{|x|\sqrt{x^2+1}}$

35. $\dfrac{d}{dx}(\text{sech}^{-1}x) = -\dfrac{1}{x\sqrt{1-x^2}}$

36. $\dfrac{d}{dx}(\coth^{-1}x) = \dfrac{1}{1-x^2}$

TABLE OF INTEGRALS

Basic Forms

1. $\displaystyle\int u\,dv = uv - \int v\,du$

2. $\displaystyle\int u^n\,du = \frac{u^{n+1}}{n+1} + C, \quad n \neq -1$

3. $\displaystyle\int \frac{du}{u} = \ln|u| + C$

4. $\displaystyle\int e^u\,du = e^u + C$

5. $\displaystyle\int a^u\,du = \frac{a^u}{\ln a} + C$

6. $\displaystyle\int \sin u\,du = -\cos u + C$

7. $\displaystyle\int \cos u\,du = \sin u + C$

8. $\displaystyle\int \sec^2 u\,du = \tan u + C$

9. $\displaystyle\int \csc^2 u\,du = -\cot u + C$

10. $\displaystyle\int \sec u \tan u\,du = \sec u + C$

11. $\displaystyle\int \csc u \cot u\,du = -\csc u + C$

12. $\displaystyle\int \tan u\,du = \ln|\sec u| + C$

13. $\displaystyle\int \cot u\,du = \ln|\sin u| + C$

14. $\displaystyle\int \sec u\,du = \ln|\sec u + \tan u| + C$

15. $\displaystyle\int \csc u\,du = \ln|\csc u - \cot u| + C$

16. $\displaystyle\int \frac{du}{\sqrt{a^2 - u^2}} = \sin^{-1}\frac{u}{a} + C, \quad a > 0$

17. $\displaystyle\int \frac{du}{a^2 + u^2} = \frac{1}{a}\tan^{-1}\frac{u}{a} + C$

18. $\displaystyle\int \frac{du}{u\sqrt{u^2 - a^2}} = \frac{1}{a}\sec^{-1}\frac{u}{a} + C$

19. $\displaystyle\int \frac{du}{a^2 - u^2} = \frac{1}{2a}\ln\left|\frac{u+a}{u-a}\right| + C$

20. $\displaystyle\int \frac{du}{u^2 - a^2} = \frac{1}{2a}\ln\left|\frac{u-a}{u+a}\right| + C$

Forms Involving $\sqrt{a^2 + u^2}$, $a > 0$

21. $\displaystyle\int \sqrt{a^2 + u^2}\,du = \frac{u}{2}\sqrt{a^2 + u^2} + \frac{a^2}{2}\ln\left(u + \sqrt{a^2 + u^2}\right) + C$

22. $\displaystyle\int u^2\sqrt{a^2 + u^2}\,du = \frac{u}{8}(a^2 + 2u^2)\sqrt{a^2 + u^2} - \frac{a^4}{8}\ln\left(u + \sqrt{a^2 + u^2}\right) + C$

23. $\displaystyle\int \frac{\sqrt{a^2 + u^2}}{u}\,du = \sqrt{a^2 + u^2} - a\ln\left|\frac{a + \sqrt{a^2 + u^2}}{u}\right| + C$

24. $\displaystyle\int \frac{\sqrt{a^2 + u^2}}{u^2}\,du = -\frac{\sqrt{a^2 + u^2}}{u} + \ln\left(u + \sqrt{a^2 + u^2}\right) + C$

25. $\displaystyle\int \frac{du}{\sqrt{a^2 + u^2}} = \ln\left(u + \sqrt{a^2 + u^2}\right) + C$

26. $\displaystyle\int \frac{u^2\,du}{\sqrt{a^2 + u^2}} = \frac{u}{2}\sqrt{a^2 + u^2} - \frac{a^2}{2}\ln\left(u + \sqrt{a^2 + u^2}\right) + C$

27. $\displaystyle\int \frac{du}{u\sqrt{a^2 + u^2}} = -\frac{1}{a}\ln\left|\frac{\sqrt{a^2 + u^2} + a}{u}\right| + C$

28. $\displaystyle\int \frac{du}{u^2\sqrt{a^2 + u^2}} = -\frac{\sqrt{a^2 + u^2}}{a^2 u} + C$

29. $\displaystyle\int \frac{du}{(a^2 + u^2)^{3/2}} = \frac{u}{a^2\sqrt{a^2 + u^2}} + C$

TABLE OF INTEGRALS

Forms Involving $\sqrt{a^2 - u^2}$, $a > 0$

30. $\displaystyle\int \sqrt{a^2 - u^2}\,du = \frac{u}{2}\sqrt{a^2 - u^2} + \frac{a^2}{2}\sin^{-1}\frac{u}{a} + C$

31. $\displaystyle\int u^2\sqrt{a^2 - u^2}\,du = \frac{u}{8}(2u^2 - a^2)\sqrt{a^2 - u^2} + \frac{a^4}{8}\sin^{-1}\frac{u}{a} + C$

32. $\displaystyle\int \frac{\sqrt{a^2 - u^2}}{u}\,du = \sqrt{a^2 - u^2} - a\ln\left|\frac{a + \sqrt{a^2 - u^2}}{u}\right| + C$

33. $\displaystyle\int \frac{\sqrt{a^2 - u^2}}{u^2}\,du = -\frac{1}{u}\sqrt{a^2 - u^2} - \sin^{-1}\frac{u}{a} + C$

34. $\displaystyle\int \frac{u^2\,du}{\sqrt{a^2 - u^2}} = -\frac{u}{2}\sqrt{a^2 - u^2} + \frac{a^2}{2}\sin^{-1}\frac{u}{a} + C$

35. $\displaystyle\int \frac{du}{u\sqrt{a^2 - u^2}} = -\frac{1}{a}\ln\left|\frac{a + \sqrt{a^2 - u^2}}{u}\right| + C$

36. $\displaystyle\int \frac{du}{u^2\sqrt{a^2 - u^2}} = -\frac{1}{a^2 u}\sqrt{a^2 - u^2} + C$

37. $\displaystyle\int (a^2 - u^2)^{3/2}\,du = -\frac{u}{8}(2u^2 - 5a^2)\sqrt{a^2 - u^2} + \frac{3a^4}{8}\sin^{-1}\frac{u}{a} + C$

38. $\displaystyle\int \frac{du}{(a^2 - u^2)^{3/2}} = \frac{u}{a^2\sqrt{a^2 - u^2}} + C$

Forms Involving $\sqrt{u^2 - a^2}$, $a > 0$

39. $\displaystyle\int \sqrt{u^2 - a^2}\,du = \frac{u}{2}\sqrt{u^2 - a^2} - \frac{a^2}{2}\ln\left|u + \sqrt{u^2 - a^2}\right| + C$

40. $\displaystyle\int u^2\sqrt{u^2 - a^2}\,du = \frac{u}{8}(2u^2 - a^2)\sqrt{u^2 - a^2} - \frac{a^4}{8}\ln\left|u + \sqrt{u^2 - a^2}\right| + C$

41. $\displaystyle\int \frac{\sqrt{u^2 - a^2}}{u}\,du = \sqrt{u^2 - a^2} - a\cos^{-1}\frac{a}{|u|} + C$

42. $\displaystyle\int \frac{\sqrt{u^2 - a^2}}{u^2}\,du = -\frac{\sqrt{u^2 - a^2}}{u} + \ln\left|u + \sqrt{u^2 - a^2}\right| + C$

43. $\displaystyle\int \frac{du}{\sqrt{u^2 - a^2}} = \ln\left|u + \sqrt{u^2 - a^2}\right| + C$

44. $\displaystyle\int \frac{u^2\,du}{\sqrt{u^2 - a^2}} = \frac{u}{2}\sqrt{u^2 - a^2} + \frac{a^2}{2}\ln\left|u + \sqrt{u^2 - a^2}\right| + C$

45. $\displaystyle\int \frac{du}{u^2\sqrt{u^2 - a^2}} = \frac{\sqrt{u^2 - a^2}}{a^2 u} + C$

46. $\displaystyle\int \frac{du}{(u^2 - a^2)^{3/2}} = -\frac{u}{a^2\sqrt{u^2 - a^2}} + C$

TABLE OF INTEGRALS

Forms Involving $a + bu$

47. $\displaystyle \int \frac{u\,du}{a + bu} = \frac{1}{b^2}\left(a + bu - a \ln|a + bu|\right) + C$

48. $\displaystyle \int \frac{u^2\,du}{a + bu} = \frac{1}{2b^3}\left[(a + bu)^2 - 4a(a + bu) + 2a^2 \ln|a + bu|\right] + C$

49. $\displaystyle \int \frac{du}{u(a + bu)} = \frac{1}{a}\ln\left|\frac{u}{a + bu}\right| + C$

50. $\displaystyle \int \frac{du}{u^2(a + bu)} = -\frac{1}{au} + \frac{b}{a^2}\ln\left|\frac{a + bu}{u}\right| + C$

51. $\displaystyle \int \frac{u\,du}{(a + bu)^2} = \frac{a}{b^2(a + bu)} + \frac{1}{b^2}\ln|a + bu| + C$

52. $\displaystyle \int \frac{du}{u(a + bu)^2} = \frac{1}{a(a + bu)} - \frac{1}{a^2}\ln\left|\frac{a + bu}{u}\right| + C$

53. $\displaystyle \int \frac{u^2\,du}{(a + bu)^2} = \frac{1}{b^3}\left(a + bu - \frac{a^2}{a + bu} - 2a\ln|a + bu|\right) + C$

54. $\displaystyle \int u\sqrt{a + bu}\,du = \frac{2}{15b^2}(3bu - 2a)(a + bu)^{3/2} + C$

55. $\displaystyle \int \frac{u\,du}{\sqrt{a + bu}} = \frac{2}{3b^2}(bu - 2a)\sqrt{a + bu} + C$

56. $\displaystyle \int \frac{u^2\,du}{\sqrt{a + bu}} = \frac{2}{15b^3}(8a^2 + 3b^2u^2 - 4abu)\sqrt{a + bu} + C$

57. $\displaystyle \int \frac{du}{u\sqrt{a + bu}} = \frac{1}{\sqrt{a}}\ln\left|\frac{\sqrt{a + bu} - \sqrt{a}}{\sqrt{a + bu} + \sqrt{a}}\right| + C, \quad \text{if } a > 0$

$\displaystyle \qquad\qquad\quad = \frac{2}{\sqrt{-a}}\tan^{-1}\sqrt{\frac{a + bu}{-a}} + C, \qquad \text{if } a < 0$

58. $\displaystyle \int \frac{\sqrt{a + bu}}{u}\,du = 2\sqrt{a + bu} + a\int \frac{du}{u\sqrt{a + bu}}$

59. $\displaystyle \int \frac{\sqrt{a + bu}}{u^2}\,du = -\frac{\sqrt{a + bu}}{u} + \frac{b}{2}\int \frac{du}{u\sqrt{a + bu}}$

60. $\displaystyle \int u^n\sqrt{a + bu}\,du = \frac{2}{b(2n + 3)}\left[u^n(a + bu)^{3/2} - na\int u^{n-1}\sqrt{a + bu}\,du\right]$

61. $\displaystyle \int \frac{u^n\,du}{\sqrt{a + bu}} = \frac{2u^n\sqrt{a + bu}}{b(2n + 1)} - \frac{2na}{b(2n + 1)}\int \frac{u^{n-1}\,du}{\sqrt{a + bu}}$

62. $\displaystyle \int \frac{du}{u^n\sqrt{a + bu}} = -\frac{\sqrt{a + bu}}{a(n - 1)u^{n-1}} - \frac{b(2n - 3)}{2a(n - 1)}\int \frac{du}{u^{n-1}\sqrt{a + bu}}$

TABLE OF INTEGRALS

Trigonometric Forms

63. $\displaystyle\int \sin^2 u\, du = \frac{1}{2}u - \frac{1}{4}\sin 2u + C$

64. $\displaystyle\int \cos^2 u\, du = \frac{1}{2}u + \frac{1}{4}\sin 2u + C$

65. $\displaystyle\int \tan^2 u\, du = \tan u - u + C$

66. $\displaystyle\int \cot^2 u\, du = -\cot u - u + C$

67. $\displaystyle\int \sin^3 u\, du = -\frac{1}{3}(2 + \sin^2 u)\cos u + C$

68. $\displaystyle\int \cos^3 u\, du = \frac{1}{3}(2 + \cos^2 u)\sin u + C$

69. $\displaystyle\int \tan^3 u\, du = \frac{1}{2}\tan^2 u + \ln|\cos u| + C$

70. $\displaystyle\int \cot^3 u\, du = -\frac{1}{2}\cot^2 u - \ln|\sin u| + C$

71. $\displaystyle\int \sec^3 u\, du = \frac{1}{2}\sec u \tan u + \frac{1}{2}\ln|\sec u + \tan u| + C$

72. $\displaystyle\int \csc^3 u\, du = -\frac{1}{2}\csc u \cot u + \frac{1}{2}\ln|\csc u - \cot u| + C$

73. $\displaystyle\int \sin^n u\, du = -\frac{1}{n}\sin^{n-1}u\cos u + \frac{n-1}{n}\int \sin^{n-2}u\, du$

74. $\displaystyle\int \cos^n u\, du = \frac{1}{n}\cos^{n-1}u\sin u + \frac{n-1}{n}\int \cos^{n-2}u\, du$

75. $\displaystyle\int \tan^n u\, du = \frac{1}{n-1}\tan^{n-1}u - \int \tan^{n-2}u\, du$

76. $\displaystyle\int \cot^n u\, du = \frac{-1}{n-1}\cot^{n-1}u - \int \cot^{n-2}u\, du$

77. $\displaystyle\int \sec^n u\, du = \frac{1}{n-1}\tan u \sec^{n-2}u + \frac{n-2}{n-1}\int \sec^{n-2}u\, du$

78. $\displaystyle\int \csc^n u\, du = \frac{-1}{n-1}\cot u \csc^{n-2}u + \frac{n-2}{n-1}\int \csc^{n-2}u\, du$

79. $\displaystyle\int \sin au \sin bu\, du = \frac{\sin(a-b)u}{2(a-b)} - \frac{\sin(a+b)u}{2(a+b)} + C$

80. $\displaystyle\int \cos au \cos bu\, du = \frac{\sin(a-b)u}{2(a-b)} + \frac{\sin(a+b)u}{2(a+b)} + C$

81. $\displaystyle\int \sin au \cos bu\, du = -\frac{\cos(a-b)u}{2(a-b)} - \frac{\cos(a+b)u}{2(a+b)} + C$

82. $\displaystyle\int u \sin u\, du = \sin u - u \cos u + C$

83. $\displaystyle\int u \cos u\, du = \cos u + u \sin u + C$

84. $\displaystyle\int u^n \sin u\, du = -u^n \cos u + n\int u^{n-1}\cos u\, du$

85. $\displaystyle\int u^n \cos u\, du = u^n \sin u - n\int u^{n-1}\sin u\, du$

86. $\displaystyle\int \sin^n u \cos^m u\, du = -\frac{\sin^{n-1}u\cos^{m+1}u}{n+m} + \frac{n-1}{n+m}\int \sin^{n-2}u\cos^m u\, du$

$\displaystyle\qquad\qquad = \frac{\sin^{n+1}u\cos^{m-1}u}{n+m} + \frac{m-1}{n+m}\int \sin^n u\cos^{m-2}u\, du$

Inverse Trigonometric Forms

87. $\displaystyle\int \sin^{-1}u\, du = u\sin^{-1}u + \sqrt{1-u^2} + C$

88. $\displaystyle\int \cos^{-1}u\, du = u\cos^{-1}u - \sqrt{1-u^2} + C$

89. $\displaystyle\int \tan^{-1}u\, du = u\tan^{-1}u - \frac{1}{2}\ln(1+u^2) + C$

90. $\displaystyle\int u\sin^{-1}u\, du = \frac{2u^2-1}{4}\sin^{-1}u + \frac{u\sqrt{1-u^2}}{4} + C$

91. $\displaystyle\int u\cos^{-1}u\, du = \frac{2u^2-1}{4}\cos^{-1}u - \frac{u\sqrt{1-u^2}}{4} + C$

92. $\displaystyle\int u\tan^{-1}u\, du = \frac{u^2+1}{2}\tan^{-1}u - \frac{u}{2} + C$

93. $\displaystyle\int u^n \sin^{-1}u\, du = \frac{1}{n+1}\left[u^{n+1}\sin^{-1}u - \int \frac{u^{n+1}\, du}{\sqrt{1-u^2}}\right], \quad n \neq -1$

94. $\displaystyle\int u^n \cos^{-1}u\, du = \frac{1}{n+1}\left[u^{n+1}\cos^{-1}u + \int \frac{u^{n+1}\, du}{\sqrt{1-u^2}}\right], \quad n \neq -1$

95. $\displaystyle\int u^n \tan^{-1}u\, du = \frac{1}{n+1}\left[u^{n+1}\tan^{-1}u - \int \frac{u^{n+1}\, du}{1+u^2}\right], \quad n \neq -1$

TABLE OF INTEGRALS

Exponential and Logarithmic Forms

96. $\int u e^{au} \, du = \dfrac{1}{a^2}(au - 1)e^{au} + C$

97. $\int u^n e^{au} \, du = \dfrac{1}{a} u^n e^{au} - \dfrac{n}{a} \int u^{n-1} e^{au} \, du$

98. $\int e^{au} \sin bu \, du = \dfrac{e^{au}}{a^2 + b^2}(a \sin bu - b \cos bu) + C$

99. $\int e^{au} \cos bu \, du = \dfrac{e^{au}}{a^2 + b^2}(a \cos bu + b \sin bu) + C$

100. $\int \ln u \, du = u \ln u - u + C$

101. $\int u^n \ln u \, du = \dfrac{u^{n+1}}{(n+1)^2}[(n+1)\ln u - 1] + C$

102. $\int \dfrac{1}{u \ln u} \, du = \ln |\ln u| + C$

Hyperbolic Forms

103. $\int \sinh u \, du = \cosh u + C$

104. $\int \cosh u \, du = \sinh u + C$

105. $\int \tanh u \, du = \ln \cosh u + C$

106. $\int \coth u \, du = \ln |\sinh u| + C$

107. $\int \operatorname{sech} u \, du = \tan^{-1}|\sinh u| + C$

108. $\int \operatorname{csch} u \, du = \ln \left| \tanh \tfrac{1}{2} u \right| + C$

109. $\int \operatorname{sech}^2 u \, du = \tanh u + C$

110. $\int \operatorname{csch}^2 u \, du = -\coth u + C$

111. $\int \operatorname{sech} u \tanh u \, du = -\operatorname{sech} u + C$

112. $\int \operatorname{csch} u \coth u \, du = -\operatorname{csch} u + C$

Forms Involving $\sqrt{2au - u^2}$, $a > 0$

113. $\int \sqrt{2au - u^2} \, du = \dfrac{u - a}{2} \sqrt{2au - u^2} + \dfrac{a^2}{2} \cos^{-1}\left(\dfrac{a - u}{a}\right) + C$

114. $\int u \sqrt{2au - u^2} \, du = \dfrac{2u^2 - au - 3a^2}{6} \sqrt{2au - u^2} + \dfrac{a^3}{2} \cos^{-1}\left(\dfrac{a - u}{a}\right) + C$

115. $\int \dfrac{\sqrt{2au - u^2}}{u} \, du = \sqrt{2au - u^2} + a \cos^{-1}\left(\dfrac{a - u}{a}\right) + C$

116. $\int \dfrac{\sqrt{2au - u^2}}{u^2} \, du = -\dfrac{2\sqrt{2au - u^2}}{u} - \cos^{-1}\left(\dfrac{a - u}{a}\right) + C$

117. $\int \dfrac{du}{\sqrt{2au - u^2}} = \cos^{-1}\left(\dfrac{a - u}{a}\right) + C$

118. $\int \dfrac{u \, du}{\sqrt{2au - u^2}} = -\sqrt{2au - u^2} + a \cos^{-1}\left(\dfrac{a - u}{a}\right) + C$

119. $\int \dfrac{u^2 \, du}{\sqrt{2au - u^2}} = -\dfrac{(u + 3a)}{2} \sqrt{2au - u^2} + \dfrac{3a^2}{2} \cos^{-1}\left(\dfrac{a - u}{a}\right) + C$

120. $\int \dfrac{du}{u\sqrt{2au - u^2}} = -\dfrac{\sqrt{2au - u^2}}{au} + C$

7 □ DIFFERENTIAL EQUATIONS

7.1 Modeling with Differential Equations

1. $y = \frac{2}{3}e^x + e^{-2x}$ $\Rightarrow$ $y' = \frac{2}{3}e^x - 2e^{-2x}$. To show that y is a solution of the differential equation, we will substitute the

expressions for y and y' in the left-hand side of the equation and show that the left-hand side is equal to the right hand side.

$$\text{LHS} = y' + 2y = \frac{2}{3}e^x - 2e^{-2x} + 2\left(\frac{2}{3}e^x + e^{-2x}\right) = \frac{2}{3}e^x - 2e^{-2x} + \frac{4}{3}e^x + 2e^{-2x}$$

$$= \frac{6}{3}e^x = 2e^x = \text{RHS}$$

3. (a) $y = e^{rx}$ $\Rightarrow$ $y' = re^{rx}$ $\Rightarrow$ $y'' = r^2 e^{rx}$. Substituting these expressions into the differential equation

$2y'' + y' - y = 0$, we get $2r^2 e^{rx} + re^{rx} - e^{rx} = 0$ $\Rightarrow$ $(2r^2 + r - 1)e^{rx} = 0$ $\Rightarrow$

$(2r - 1)(r + 1) = 0$ [since e^{rx} is never zero] $\Rightarrow$ $r = \frac{1}{2}$ or -1.

(b) Let $r_1 = \frac{1}{2}$ and $r_2 = -1$, so we need to show that every member of the family of functions $y = ae^{x/2} + be^{-x}$ is a

solution of the differential equation $2y'' + y' - y = 0$.

$y = ae^{x/2} + be^{-x}$ $\Rightarrow$ $y' = \frac{1}{2}ae^{x/2} - be^{-x}$ $\Rightarrow$ $y'' = \frac{1}{4}ae^{x/2} + be^{-x}$.

$$\text{LHS} = 2y'' + y' - y = 2\left(\frac{1}{4}ae^{x/2} + be^{-x}\right) + \left(\frac{1}{2}ae^{x/2} - be^{-x}\right) - \left(ae^{x/2} + be^{-x}\right)$$

$$= \frac{1}{2}ae^{x/2} + 2be^{-x} + \frac{1}{2}ae^{x/2} - be^{-x} - ae^{x/2} - be^{-x}$$

$$= \left(\frac{1}{2}a + \frac{1}{2}a - a\right)e^{x/2} + (2b - b - b)e^{-x}$$

$$= 0 = \text{RHS}$$

5. (a) $y = \sin x$ $\Rightarrow$ $y' = \cos x$ $\Rightarrow$ $y'' = -\sin x$.

$\text{LHS} = y'' + y = -\sin x + \sin x = 0 \neq \sin x$, so $y = \sin x$ **is not** a solution of the differential equation.

(b) $y = \cos x$ $\Rightarrow$ $y' = -\sin x$ $\Rightarrow$ $y'' = -\cos x$.

$\text{LHS} = y'' + y = -\cos x + \cos x = 0 \neq \sin x$, so $y = \cos x$ **is not** a solution of the differential equation.

(c) $y = \frac{1}{2}x \sin x$ $\Rightarrow$ $y' = \frac{1}{2}(x \cos x + \sin x)$ $\Rightarrow$ $y'' = \frac{1}{2}(-x \sin x + \cos x + \cos x)$.

$\text{LHS} = y'' + y = \frac{1}{2}(-x \sin x + 2 \cos x) + \frac{1}{2}x \sin x = \cos x \neq \sin x$, so $y = \frac{1}{2}x \sin x$ **is not** a solution of the

differential equation.

(d) $y = -\frac{1}{2}x \cos x$ $\Rightarrow$ $y' = -\frac{1}{2}(-x \sin x + \cos x)$ $\Rightarrow$ $y'' = -\frac{1}{2}(-x \cos x - \sin x - \sin x)$.

$\text{LHS} = y'' + y = -\frac{1}{2}(-x \cos x - 2 \sin x) + \left(-\frac{1}{2}x \cos x\right) = \sin x = \text{RHS}$, so $y = -\frac{1}{2}x \cos x$ **is a** solution of the

differential equation.

7. (a) Since the derivative $y' = -y^2$ is always negative (or 0 if $y = 0$), the function y must be decreasing (or equal to 0) on any

interval on which it is defined.

(b) $y = \dfrac{1}{x+C} \implies y' = -\dfrac{1}{(x+C)^2}$. LHS $= y' = -\dfrac{1}{(x+C)^2} = -\left(\dfrac{1}{x+C}\right)^2 = -y^2 =$ RHS

(c) $y = 0$ is a solution of $y' = -y^2$ that is not a member of the family in part (b).

(d) If $y(x) = \dfrac{1}{x+C}$, then $y(0) = \dfrac{1}{0+C} = \dfrac{1}{C}$. Since $y(0) = 0.5$, $\dfrac{1}{C} = \dfrac{1}{2} \implies C = 2$, so $y = \dfrac{1}{x+2}$.

9. (a) $\dfrac{dP}{dt} = 1.2P\left(1 - \dfrac{P}{4200}\right)$. Now $\dfrac{dP}{dt} > 0 \implies 1 - \dfrac{P}{4200} > 0$ [assuming that $P > 0$] $\implies \dfrac{P}{4200} < 1 \implies$

$P < 4200 \implies$ the population is increasing for $0 < P < 4200$.

(b) $\dfrac{dP}{dt} < 0 \implies P > 4200$

(c) $\dfrac{dP}{dt} = 0 \implies P = 4200$ or $P = 0$

11. (a) This function is increasing *and* also decreasing. But $dy/dt = e^t(y-1)^2 \geq 0$ for all t, implying that the graph of the

solution of the differential equation cannot be decreasing on any interval.

(b) When $y = 1$, $dy/dt = 0$, but the graph does not have a horizontal tangent line.

13. (a) $y' = 1 + x^2 + y^2 \geq 1$ and $y' \to \infty$ as $x \to \infty$. The only curve satisfying these conditions is labeled III.

(b) $y' = xe^{-x^2-y^2} > 0$ if $x > 0$ and $y' < 0$ if $x < 0$. The only curve with negative tangent slopes when $x < 0$ and positive

tangent slopes when $x > 0$ is labeled I.

(c) $y' = \dfrac{1}{1 + e^{x^2+y^2}} > 0$ and $y' \to 0$ as $x \to \infty$. The only curve satisfying these conditions is labeled IV.

(d) $y' = \sin(xy)\cos(xy) = 0$ if $y = 0$, which is the solution graph labeled II.

15. (a) P increases most rapidly at the beginning, since there are usually many simple, easily-learned sub-skills associated with

learning a skill. As t increases, we would expect dP/dt to remain positive, but decrease. This is because as time

progresses, the only points left to learn are the more difficult ones.

(b) $\dfrac{dP}{dt} = k(M - P)$ is always positive, so the level of performance P (c)

is increasing. As P gets close to M, dP/dt gets close to 0; that is,

the performance levels off, as explained in part (a).

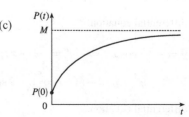

7.2   Direction Fields and Euler's Method

1. (a)

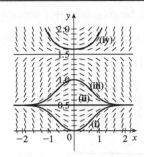

(b) It appears that the constant functions $y = 0.5$ and $y = 1.5$ are equilibrium solutions. Note that these two values of y satisfy the given differential equation $y' = x \cos \pi y$.

3. $y' = 2 - y$. The slopes at each point are independent of x, so the slopes are the same along each line parallel to the x-axis. Thus, III is the direction field for this equation. Note that for $y = 2$, $y' = 0$.

5. $y' = x + y - 1 = 0$ on the line $y = -x + 1$. Direction field IV satisfies this condition. Notice also that on the line $y = -x$ we have $y' = -1$, which is true in IV.

7. (a) $y(0) = 1$

(b) $y(0) = 2$

(c) $y(0) = -1$

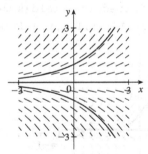

9.

x	y	$y' = \frac{1}{2}y$
0	0	0
0	1	0.5
0	2	1
0	-3	-1.5
0	-2	-1

Note that for $y = 0$, $y' = 0$. The three solution curves sketched go through $(0, 0)$, $(0, 1)$, and $(0, -1)$.

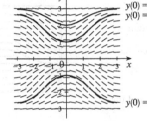

11.

x	y	$y' = y - 2x$
-2	-2	2
-2	2	6
2	2	-2
2	-2	-6

Note that $y' = 0$ for any point on the line $y = 2x$. The slopes are positive to the left of the line and negative to the right of the line. The solution curve in the graph passes through $(1, 0)$.

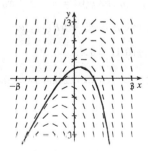

13.

x	y	$y' = y + xy$
0	± 2	± 2
1	± 2	± 4
-3	± 2	∓ 4

Note that $y' = y(x+1) = 0$ for any point on $y = 0$ or on $x = -1$. The slopes are positive when the factors y and $x + 1$ have the same sign and negative when they have opposite signs. The solution curve in the graph passes through $(0, 1)$.

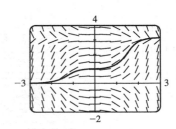

15. In Maple, we can use either `directionfield` (in Maple's share library) or `DEtools[DEplot]` to plot the direction field. To plot the solution, we can either use the initial-value option in `directionfield`, or actually solve the equation.

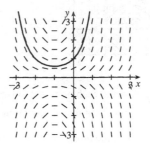

In Mathematica, we use `PlotVectorField` for the direction field, and the `Plot[Evaluate[...]]` construction to plot the solution, which is

$$y = 2\arctan\left(e^{x^3/3} \cdot \tan\tfrac{1}{2}\right).$$

In Derive, use `Direction_Field` (in utility file ODE_APPR) to plot the direction field. Then use `DSOLVE1(-x^2*SIN(y),1,x,y,0,1)` (in utility file ODE1) to solve the equation. Simplify each result.

17.

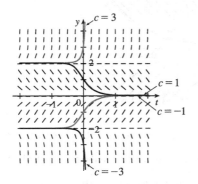

The direction field is for the differential equation $y' = y^3 - 4y$.

$L = \lim\limits_{t \to \infty} y(t)$ exists for $-2 \le c \le 2$;

$L = \pm 2$ for $c = \pm 2$ and $L = 0$ for $-2 < c < 2$.

For other values of c, L does not exist.

19. (a) $y' = F(x, y) = y$ and $y(0) = 1 \quad \Rightarrow \quad x_0 = 0, y_0 = 1.$

(i) $h = 0.4$ and $y_1 = y_0 + hF(x_0, y_0) \quad \Rightarrow \quad y_1 = 1 + 0.4 \cdot 1 = 1.4.$ $x_1 = x_0 + h = 0 + 0.4 = 0.4,$ so $y_1 = y(0.4) = 1.4.$

(ii) $h = 0.2 \quad \Rightarrow \quad x_1 = 0.2$ and $x_2 = 0.4,$ so we need to find $y_2.$

$y_1 = y_0 + hF(x_0, y_0) = 1 + 0.2y_0 = 1 + 0.2 \cdot 1 = 1.2,$

$y_2 = y_1 + hF(x_1, y_1) = 1.2 + 0.2y_1 = 1.2 + 0.2 \cdot 1.2 = 1.44.$

(iii) $h = 0.1 \Rightarrow x_4 = 0.4$, so we need to find y_4. $y_1 = y_0 + hF(x_0, y_0) = 1 + 0.1y_0 = 1 + 0.1 \cdot 1 = 1.1$,

$y_2 = y_1 + hF(x_1, y_1) = 1.1 + 0.1y_1 = 1.1 + 0.1 \cdot 1.1 = 1.21$,

$y_3 = y_2 + hF(x_2, y_2) = 1.21 + 0.1y_2 = 1.21 + 0.1 \cdot 1.21 = 1.331$,

$y_4 = y_3 + hF(x_3, y_3) = 1.331 + 0.1y_3 = 1.331 + 0.1 \cdot 1.331 = 1.4641$.

(b)

We see that the estimates are underestimates since they are all below the graph of $y = e^x$.

(c) (i) For $h = 0.4$: (exact value) − (approximate value) $= e^{0.4} - 1.4 \approx 0.0918$

(ii) For $h = 0.2$: (exact value) − (approximate value) $= e^{0.4} - 1.44 \approx 0.0518$

(iii) For $h = 0.1$: (exact value) − (approximate value) $= e^{0.4} - 1.4641 \approx 0.0277$

Each time the step size is halved, the error estimate also appears to be halved (approximately).

21. $h = 0.5$, $x_0 = 1$, $y_0 = 0$, and $F(x, y) = y - 2x$.

Note that $x_1 = x_0 + h = 1 + 0.5 = 1.5$, $x_2 = 2$, and $x_3 = 2.5$.

$y_1 = y_0 + hF(x_0, y_0) = 0 + 0.5F(1, 0) = 0.5[0 - 2(1)] = -1$.

$y_2 = y_1 + hF(x_1, y_1) = -1 + 0.5F(1.5, -1) = -1 + 0.5[-1 - 2(1.5)] = -3$.

$y_3 = y_2 + hF(x_2, y_2) = -3 + 0.5F(2, -3) = -3 + 0.5[-3 - 2(2)] = -6.5$.

$y_4 = y_3 + hF(x_3, y_3) = -6.5 + 0.5F(2.5, -6.5) = -6.5 + 0.5[-6.5 - 2(2.5)] = -12.25$.

23. $h = 0.1$, $x_0 = 0$, $y_0 = 1$, and $F(x, y) = y + xy$.

Note that $x_1 = x_0 + h = 0 + 0.1 = 0.1$, $x_2 = 0.2$, $x_3 = 0.3$, and $x_4 = 0.4$.

$y_1 = y_0 + hF(x_0, y_0) = 1 + 0.1F(0, 1) = 1 + 0.1[1 + (0)(1)] = 1.1$.

$y_2 = y_1 + hF(x_1, y_1) = 1.1 + 0.1F(0.1, 1.1) = 1.1 + 0.1[1.1 + (0.1)(1.1)] = 1.221$.

$y_3 = y_2 + hF(x_2, y_2) = 1.221 + 0.1F(0.2, 1.221) = 1.221 + 0.1[1.221 + (0.2)(1.221)] = 1.36752$.

$y_4 = y_3 + hF(x_3, y_3) = 1.36752 + 0.1F(0.3, 1.36752) = 1.36752 + 0.1[1.36752 + (0.3)(1.36752)]$
$= 1.5452976$.

$y_5 = y_4 + hF(x_4, y_4) = 1.5452976 + 0.1F(0.4, 1.5452976)$
$= 1.5452976 + 0.1[1.5452976 + (0.4)(1.5452976)] = 1.761639264$.

Thus, $y(0.5) \approx 1.7616$.

25. (a) $dy/dx + 3x^2 y = 6x^2$ ⟹ $y' = 6x^2 - 3x^2 y$. Store this expression in Y_1 and use the following simple program to evaluate $y(1)$ for each part, using $H = h = 1$ and $N = 1$ for part (i), $H = 0.1$ and $N = 10$ for part (ii), and so forth.

$$h \to H: 0 \to X: 3 \to Y:$$

$$\text{For}(I, 1, N): Y + H \times Y_1 \to Y: X + H \to X:$$

$$\text{End(loop)}:$$

Display Y.   [To see all iterations, include this statement in the loop.]

(i) $H = 1, N = 1$ ⟹ $y(1) = 3$

(ii) $H = 0.1, N = 10$ ⟹ $y(1) \approx 2.3928$

(iii) $H = 0.01, N = 100$ ⟹ $y(1) \approx 2.3701$

(iv) $H = 0.001, N = 1000$ ⟹ $y(1) \approx 2.3681$

(b) $y = 2 + e^{-x^3}$ ⟹ $y' = -3x^2 e^{-x^3}$

$$\text{LHS} = y' + 3x^2 y = -3x^2 e^{-x^3} + 3x^2\left(2 + e^{-x^3}\right) = -3x^2 e^{-x^3} + 6x^2 + 3x^2 e^{-x^3} = 6x^2 = \text{RHS}$$

$$y(0) = 2 + e^{-0} = 2 + 1 = 3$$

(c) The exact value of $y(1)$ is $2 + e^{-1^3} = 2 + e^{-1}$.

(i) For $h = 1$: (exact value) − (approximate value) $= 2 + e^{-1} - 3 \approx -0.6321$

(ii) For $h = 0.1$: (exact value) − (approximate value) $= 2 + e^{-1} - 2.3928 \approx -0.0249$

(iii) For $h = 0.01$: (exact value) − (approximate value) $= 2 + e^{-1} - 2.3701 \approx -0.0022$

(iv) For $h = 0.001$: (exact value) − (approximate value) $= 2 + e^{-1} - 2.3681 \approx -0.0002$

In (ii)–(iv), it seems that when the step size is divided by 10, the error estimate is also divided by 10 (approximately).

27. (a) $R\dfrac{dQ}{dt} + \dfrac{1}{C}Q = E(t)$ becomes $5Q' + \dfrac{1}{0.05}Q = 60$

or $Q' + 4Q = 12$.

(b) From the graph, it appears that the limiting value of the charge Q is about 3.

(c) If $Q' = 0$, then $4Q = 12$ ⟹ $Q = 3$ is an equilibrium solution.

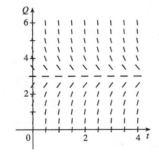

(d)

(e) $Q' + 4Q = 12$ ⟹ $Q' = 12 - 4Q$. Now $Q(0) = 0$, so $t_0 = 0$ and $Q_0 = 0$.

$$Q_1 = Q_0 + hF(t_0, Q_0) = 0 + 0.1(12 - 4 \cdot 0) = 1.2$$

$$Q_2 = Q_1 + hF(t_1, Q_1) = 1.2 + 0.1(12 - 4 \cdot 1.2) = 1.92$$

$$Q_3 = Q_2 + hF(t_2, Q_2) = 1.92 + 0.1(12 - 4 \cdot 1.92) = 2.352$$

$$Q_4 = Q_3 + hF(t_3, Q_3) = 2.352 + 0.1(12 - 4 \cdot 2.352) = 2.6112$$

$$Q_5 = Q_4 + hF(t_4, Q_4) = 2.6112 + 0.1(12 - 4 \cdot 2.6112) = 2.76672$$

Thus, $Q_5 = Q(0.5) \approx 2.77$ C.

7.3   Separable Equations

1. $\dfrac{dy}{dx} = xy^2 \;\Rightarrow\; \dfrac{dy}{y^2} = x\,dx \;[y \neq 0] \;\Rightarrow\; \displaystyle\int y^{-2}\,dy = \int x\,dx \;\Rightarrow\; -y^{-1} = \tfrac{1}{2}x^2 + C \;\Rightarrow$

$\dfrac{1}{y} = -\tfrac{1}{2}x^2 - C \;\Rightarrow\; y = \dfrac{1}{-\frac{1}{2}x^2 - C} = \dfrac{2}{K - x^2}$, where $K = -2C$. $y = 0$ is also a solution.

3. $(x^2 + 1)y' = xy \;\Rightarrow\; \dfrac{dy}{dx} = \dfrac{xy}{x^2 + 1} \;\Rightarrow\; \dfrac{dy}{y} = \dfrac{x\,dx}{x^2 + 1} \quad [y \neq 0] \;\Rightarrow\; \displaystyle\int \dfrac{dy}{y} = \int \dfrac{x\,dx}{x^2 + 1} \;\Rightarrow$

$\ln|y| = \tfrac{1}{2}\ln(x^2 + 1) + C \quad [u = x^2 + 1,\, du = 2x\,dx] \;= \ln(x^2 + 1)^{1/2} + \ln e^C = \ln\!\left(e^C \sqrt{x^2 + 1}\right) \;\Rightarrow$

$|y| = e^C \sqrt{x^2 + 1} \;\Rightarrow\; y = K\sqrt{x^2 + 1}$, where $K = \pm e^C$ is a constant. (In our derivation, K was nonzero, but we can restore the excluded case $y = 0$ by allowing K to be zero.)

5. $(y + \sin y)\,y' = x + x^3 \;\Rightarrow\; (y + \sin y)\dfrac{dy}{dx} = x + x^3 \;\Rightarrow\; \displaystyle\int (y + \sin y)\,dy = \int (x + x^3)\,dx \;\Rightarrow$

$\tfrac{1}{2}y^2 - \cos y = \tfrac{1}{2}x^2 + \tfrac{1}{4}x^4 + C$. We cannot solve explicitly for y.

7. $\dfrac{dy}{dt} = \dfrac{te^t}{y\sqrt{1 + y^2}} \;\Rightarrow\; y\sqrt{1 + y^2}\,dy = te^t\,dt \;\Rightarrow\; \int y\sqrt{1 + y^2}\,dy = \int te^t\,dt \;\Rightarrow\; \tfrac{1}{3}(1 + y^2)^{3/2} = te^t - e^t + C$

[where the first integral is evaluated by substitution and the second by parts] $\;\Rightarrow\; 1 + y^2 = [3(te^t - e^t + C)]^{2/3} \;\Rightarrow$

$y = \pm\sqrt{[3(te^t - e^t + C)]^{2/3} - 1}$

9. $\dfrac{du}{dt} = 2 + 2u + t + tu \;\Rightarrow\; \dfrac{du}{dt} = (1 + u)(2 + t) \;\Rightarrow\; \displaystyle\int \dfrac{du}{1 + u} = \int (2 + t)dt \quad [u \neq -1] \;\Rightarrow$

$\ln|1 + u| = \tfrac{1}{2}t^2 + 2t + C \;\Rightarrow\; |1 + u| = e^{t^2/2 + 2t + C} = Ke^{t^2/2 + 2t}$, where $K = e^C \;\Rightarrow\; 1 + u = \pm Ke^{t^2/2 + 2t} \;\Rightarrow$

$u = -1 \pm Ke^{t^2/2 + 2t}$ where $K > 0$. $u = -1$ is also a solution, so $u = -1 + Ae^{t^2/2 + 2t}$, where A is an arbitrary constant.

11. $\dfrac{dy}{dx} = \dfrac{x}{y} \;\Rightarrow\; y\,dy = x\,dx \;\Rightarrow\; \int y\,dy = \int x\,dx \;\Rightarrow\; \tfrac{1}{2}y^2 = \tfrac{1}{2}x^2 + C$. $y(0) = -3 \;\Rightarrow$

$\tfrac{1}{2}(-3)^2 = \tfrac{1}{2}(0)^2 + C \;\Rightarrow\; C = \tfrac{9}{2}$, so $\tfrac{1}{2}y^2 = \tfrac{1}{2}x^2 + \tfrac{9}{2} \;\Rightarrow\; y^2 = x^2 + 9 \;\Rightarrow\; y = -\sqrt{x^2 + 9}$ since $y(0) = -3 < 0$.

13. $\dfrac{du}{dt} = \dfrac{2t + \sec^2 t}{2u}$, $u(0) = -5$. $\int 2u\,du = \int (2t + \sec^2 t)\,dt \;\Rightarrow\; u^2 = t^2 + \tan t + C$,

where $[u(0)]^2 = 0^2 + \tan 0 + C \;\Rightarrow\; C = (-5)^2 = 25$. Therefore, $u^2 = t^2 + \tan t + 25$, so $u = \pm\sqrt{t^2 + \tan t + 25}$.

Since $u(0) = -5$, we must have $u = -\sqrt{t^2 + \tan t + 25}$.

15. $x\ln x = y\left(1 + \sqrt{3 + y^2}\right)y'$, $y(1) = 1$. $\int x\ln x\,dx = \int\left(y + y\sqrt{3 + y^2}\right)dy \;\Rightarrow\; \tfrac{1}{2}x^2\ln x - \int \tfrac{1}{2}x\,dx$

[use parts with $u = \ln x$, $dv = x\,dx$] $= \tfrac{1}{2}y^2 + \tfrac{1}{3}(3 + y^2)^{3/2} \;\Rightarrow\; \tfrac{1}{2}x^2\ln x - \tfrac{1}{4}x^2 + C = \tfrac{1}{2}y^2 + \tfrac{1}{3}(3 + y^2)^{3/2}$.

Now $y(1) = 1 \;\Rightarrow\; 0 - \tfrac{1}{4} + C = \tfrac{1}{2} + \tfrac{1}{3}(4)^{3/2} \;\Rightarrow\; C = \tfrac{1}{2} + \tfrac{8}{3} + \tfrac{1}{4} = \tfrac{41}{12}$, so

$\tfrac{1}{2}x^2\ln x - \tfrac{1}{4}x^2 + \tfrac{41}{12} = \tfrac{1}{2}y^2 + \tfrac{1}{3}(3 + y^2)^{3/2}$. We do not solve explicitly for y.

17. $y' \tan x = a + y$, $0 < x < \pi/2$ $\Rightarrow$ $\dfrac{dy}{dx} = \dfrac{a + y}{\tan x}$ $\Rightarrow$ $\dfrac{dy}{a + y} = \cot x \, dx$ $\quad [a + y \neq 0]$ $\Rightarrow$

$\displaystyle\int \dfrac{dy}{a + y} = \int \dfrac{\cos x}{\sin x} \, dx$ $\Rightarrow$ $\ln|a + y| = \ln|\sin x| + C$ $\Rightarrow$ $|a + y| = e^{\ln|\sin x| + C} = e^{\ln|\sin x|} \cdot e^C = e^C |\sin x|$ $\Rightarrow$

$a + y = K \sin x$, where $K = \pm e^C$. (In our derivation, K was nonzero, but we can restore the excluded case

$y = -a$ by allowing K to be zero.) $\quad y(\pi/3) = a$ $\Rightarrow$ $a + a = K \sin\left(\dfrac{\pi}{3}\right)$ $\Rightarrow$ $2a = K\dfrac{\sqrt{3}}{2}$ $\Rightarrow$ $K = \dfrac{4a}{\sqrt{3}}$.

Thus, $a + y = \dfrac{4a}{\sqrt{3}} \sin x$ and so $y = \dfrac{4a}{\sqrt{3}} \sin x - a$.

19. If the slope at the point (x, y) is xy, then we have $\dfrac{dy}{dx} = xy$ $\Rightarrow$ $\dfrac{dy}{y} = x \, dx$ $\quad [y \neq 0]$ $\Rightarrow$ $\displaystyle\int \dfrac{dy}{y} = \int x \, dx$ $\Rightarrow$

$\ln|y| = \tfrac{1}{2}x^2 + C$. $\quad y(0) = 1$ $\Rightarrow$ $\ln 1 = 0 + C$ $\Rightarrow$ $C = 0$. Thus, $|y| = e^{x^2/2}$ $\Rightarrow$ $y = \pm e^{x^2/2}$, so $y = e^{x^2/2}$

since $y(0) = 1 > 0$. Note that $y = 0$ is not a solution because it doesn't satisfy the initial condition $y(0) = 1$.

21. $u = x + y$ $\Rightarrow$ $\dfrac{d}{dx}(u) = \dfrac{d}{dx}(x + y)$ $\Rightarrow$ $\dfrac{du}{dx} = 1 + \dfrac{dy}{dx}$, but $\dfrac{dy}{dx} = x + y = u$, so $\dfrac{du}{dx} = 1 + u$ $\Rightarrow$

$\dfrac{du}{1 + u} = dx$ $\quad [u \neq -1]$ $\Rightarrow$ $\displaystyle\int \dfrac{du}{1 + u} = \int dx$ $\Rightarrow$ $\ln|1 + u| = x + C$ $\Rightarrow$ $|1 + u| = e^{x + C}$ $\Rightarrow$

$1 + u = \pm e^C e^x$ $\Rightarrow$ $u = \pm e^C e^x - 1$ $\Rightarrow$ $x + y = \pm e^C e^x - 1$ $\Rightarrow$ $y = Ke^x - x - 1$, where $K = \pm e^C \neq 0$.

If $u = -1$, then $-1 = x + y$ $\Rightarrow$ $y = -x - 1$, which is just $y = Ke^x - x - 1$ with $K = 0$. Thus, the general solution

is $y = Ke^x - x - 1$, where $K \in \mathbb{R}$.

23. (a) $y' = 2x\sqrt{1 - y^2}$ $\Rightarrow$ $\dfrac{dy}{dx} = 2x\sqrt{1 - y^2}$ $\Rightarrow$ $\dfrac{dy}{\sqrt{1 - y^2}} = 2x \, dx$ $\Rightarrow$ $\displaystyle\int \dfrac{dy}{\sqrt{1 - y^2}} = \int 2x \, dx$ $\Rightarrow$

$\sin^{-1} y = x^2 + C$ for $-\tfrac{\pi}{2} \leq x^2 + C \leq \tfrac{\pi}{2}$.

(b) $y(0) = 0$ $\Rightarrow$ $\sin^{-1} 0 = 0^2 + C$ $\Rightarrow$ $C = 0$,

so $\sin^{-1} y = x^2$ and $y = \sin(x^2)$ for $-\sqrt{\pi/2} \leq x \leq \sqrt{\pi/2}$.

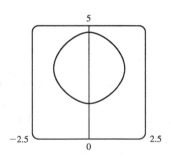

(c) For $\sqrt{1 - y^2}$ to be a real number, we must have $-1 \leq y \leq 1$; that is, $-1 \leq y(0) \leq 1$. Thus, the initial-value problem

$y' = 2x\sqrt{1 - y^2}$, $y(0) = 2$ does *not* have a solution.

25. $\dfrac{dy}{dx} = \dfrac{\sin x}{\sin y}$, $y(0) = \dfrac{\pi}{2}$. So $\int \sin y \, dy = \int \sin x \, dx$ $\Leftrightarrow$

$-\cos y = -\cos x + C$ $\Leftrightarrow$ $\cos y = \cos x - C$. From the initial condition,

we need $\cos \tfrac{\pi}{2} = \cos 0 - C$ $\Rightarrow$ $0 = 1 - C$ $\Rightarrow$ $C = 1$, so the solution is

$\cos y = \cos x - 1$. Note that we cannot take $\cos^{-1}$ of both sides, since that would

unnecessarily restrict the solution to the case where $-1 \leq \cos x - 1$ $\Leftrightarrow$ $0 \leq \cos x$,

as $\cos^{-1}$ is defined only on $[-1, 1]$. Instead we plot the graph using Maple's

plots[implicitplot] or Mathematica's Plot[Evaluate[···]].

27. (a) , (c)

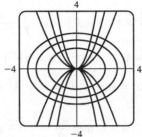

(b) $y' = y^2$ $\Rightarrow$ $\dfrac{dy}{dx} = y^2$ $\Rightarrow$ $\displaystyle\int y^{-2}\, dy = \int dx$ $\Rightarrow$

$-y^{-1} = x + C$ $\Rightarrow$ $\dfrac{1}{y} = -x - C$ $\Rightarrow$

$y = \dfrac{1}{K - x}$, where $K = -C$. $y = 0$ is also a solution.

29. The curves $x^2 + 2y^2 = k^2$ form a family of ellipses with major axis on the x-axis. Differentiating gives

$\dfrac{d}{dx}(x^2 + 2y^2) = \dfrac{d}{dx}(k^2)$ $\Rightarrow$ $2x + 4yy' = 0$ $\Rightarrow$ $4yy' = -2x$ $\Rightarrow$ $y' = \dfrac{-x}{2y}$. Thus, the slope of the tangent line

at any point (x, y) on one of the ellipses is $y' = \dfrac{-x}{2y}$, so the orthogonal trajectories

must satisfy $y' = \dfrac{2y}{x}$ $\Leftrightarrow$ $\dfrac{dy}{dx} = \dfrac{2y}{x}$ $\Leftrightarrow$ $\dfrac{dy}{y} = 2 = \dfrac{dx}{x}$ $\Leftrightarrow$

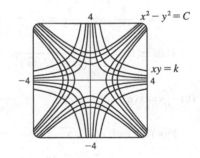

$\displaystyle\int \dfrac{dy}{y} = 2\int \dfrac{dx}{x}$ $\Leftrightarrow$ $\ln|y| = 2\ln|x| + C_1$ $\Leftrightarrow$ $\ln|y| = \ln|x|^2 + C_1$ $\Leftrightarrow$

$|y| = e^{\ln x^2 + C_1}$ $\Leftrightarrow$ $y = \pm x^2 \cdot e^{C_1} = Cx^2$. This is a family of parabolas.

31. The curves $y = k/x$ form a family of hyperbolas with asymptotes $x = 0$ and $y = 0$. Differentiating gives

$\dfrac{d}{dx}(y) = \dfrac{d}{dx}\left(\dfrac{k}{x}\right)$ $\Rightarrow$ $y' = -\dfrac{k}{x^2}$ $\Rightarrow$ $y' = -\dfrac{xy}{x^2}$ [since $y = k/x$ $\Rightarrow$ $xy = k$] $\rightarrow$ $y' - -\dfrac{y}{x}$. Thus, the slope

of the tangent line at any point (x, y) on one of the hyperbolas is $y' = -y/x$,

so the orthogonal trajectories must satisfy $y' = x/y$ $\Leftrightarrow$ $\dfrac{dy}{dx} = \dfrac{x}{y}$ $\Leftrightarrow$

$y\, dy = x\, dx$ $\Leftrightarrow$ $\int y\, dy = \int x\, dx$ $\Leftrightarrow$ $\tfrac{1}{2}y^2 = \tfrac{1}{2}x^2 + C_1$ $\Leftrightarrow$

$y^2 = x^2 + C_2$ $\Leftrightarrow$ $x^2 - y^2 = C$. This is a family of hyperbolas with

asymptotes $y = \pm x$.

33. $y(x) = 2 + \displaystyle\int_2^x [t - ty(t)]\, dt$ $\Rightarrow$ $y'(x) = x - xy(x)$ [by FTC 1] $\Rightarrow$ $\dfrac{dy}{dx} = x(1 - y)$ $\Rightarrow$

$\displaystyle\int \dfrac{dy}{1 - y} = \int x\, dx$ $\Rightarrow$ $-\ln|1 - y| = \tfrac{1}{2}x^2 + C$. Letting $x = 2$ in the original integral equation

gives us $y(2) = 2 + 0 = 2$. Thus, $-\ln|1 - 2| = \tfrac{1}{2}(2)^2 + C$ $\Rightarrow$ $0 = 2 + C$ $\Rightarrow$ $C = -2$.

Thus, $-\ln|1 - y| = \tfrac{1}{2}x^2 - 2$ $\Rightarrow$ $\ln|1 - y| = 2 - \tfrac{1}{2}x^2$ $\Rightarrow$ $|1 - y| = e^{2 - x^2/2}$ $\Rightarrow$

$1 - y = \pm e^{2 - x^2/2}$ $\Rightarrow$ $y = 1 + e^{2 - x^2/2}$ [$y(2) = 2$].

35. $y(x) = 4 + \displaystyle\int_0^x 2t\sqrt{y(t)}\,dt \;\Rightarrow\; y'(x) = 2x\sqrt{y(x)} \;\Rightarrow\; \dfrac{dy}{dx} = 2x\sqrt{y} \;\Rightarrow\; \displaystyle\int \dfrac{dy}{\sqrt{y}} = \int 2x\,dx \;\Rightarrow$

$2\sqrt{y} = x^2 + C$. Letting $x = 0$ in the original integral equation gives us $y(0) = 4 + 0 = 4$.

Thus, $2\sqrt{4} = 0^2 + C \;\Rightarrow\; C = 4$. $2\sqrt{y} = x^2 + 4 \;\Rightarrow\; \sqrt{y} = \tfrac{1}{2}x^2 + 2 \;\Rightarrow\; y = \left(\tfrac{1}{2}x^2 + 2\right)^2$.

37. From Exercise 7.2.27, $\dfrac{dQ}{dt} = 12 - 4Q \;\Leftrightarrow\; \displaystyle\int \dfrac{dQ}{12 - 4Q} = \int dt \;\Leftrightarrow\; -\tfrac{1}{4}\ln|12 - 4Q| = t + C \;\Leftrightarrow$

$\ln|12 - 4Q| = -4t - 4C \;\Leftrightarrow\; |12 - 4Q| = e^{-4t - 4C} \;\Leftrightarrow\; 12 - 4Q = Ke^{-4t} \;\;[K = \pm e^{-4C}] \;\Leftrightarrow$

$4Q = 12 - Ke^{-4t} \;\Leftrightarrow\; Q = 3 - Ae^{-4t} \;\;[A = K/4]$. $Q(0) = 0 \;\Leftrightarrow\; 0 = 3 - A \;\Leftrightarrow\; A = 3 \;\Leftrightarrow$

$Q(t) = 3 - 3e^{-4t}$. As $t \to \infty$, $Q(t) \to 3 - 0 = 3$ (the limiting value).

39. $\dfrac{dP}{dt} = k(M - P) \;\Leftrightarrow\; \displaystyle\int \dfrac{dP}{P - M} = \int (-k)\,dt \;\Leftrightarrow\; \ln|P - M| = -kt + C \;\Leftrightarrow\; |P - M| = e^{-kt + C} \;\Leftrightarrow$

$P - M = Ae^{-kt} \;\;[A = \pm e^C] \;\Leftrightarrow\; P = M + Ae^{-kt}$. If we assume that performance is at level 0 when $t = 0$, then

$P(0) = 0 \;\Leftrightarrow\; 0 = M + A \;\Leftrightarrow\; A = -M \;\Leftrightarrow\; P(t) = M - Me^{-kt}$. $\displaystyle\lim_{t\to\infty} P(t) = M - M \cdot 0 = M$.

41. (a) If $a = b$, then $\dfrac{dx}{dt} = k(a - x)(b - x)^{1/2}$ becomes $\dfrac{dx}{dt} = k(a - x)^{3/2} \;\Rightarrow\; (a - x)^{-3/2}\,dx = k\,dt \;\Rightarrow$

$\displaystyle\int (a - x)^{-3/2}\,dx = \int k\,dt \;\Rightarrow\; 2(a - x)^{-1/2} = kt + C$ [by substitution] $\;\Rightarrow\; \dfrac{2}{kt + C} = \sqrt{a - x} \;\Rightarrow$

$\left(\dfrac{2}{kt + C}\right)^2 = a - x \;\Rightarrow\; x(t) = a - \dfrac{4}{(kt + C)^2}$. The initial concentration of HBr is 0, so $x(0) = 0 \;\Rightarrow$

$0 = a - \dfrac{4}{C^2} \;\Rightarrow\; \dfrac{4}{C^2} = a \;\Rightarrow\; C^2 = \dfrac{4}{a} \;\Rightarrow\; C = 2/\sqrt{a}$ [C is positive since $kt + C = 2(a - x)^{-1/2} > 0$].

Thus, $x(t) = a - \dfrac{4}{\left(kt + 2/\sqrt{a}\right)^2}$.

(b) $\dfrac{dx}{dt} = k(a - x)(b - x)^{1/2} \;\Rightarrow\; \dfrac{dx}{(a - x)\sqrt{b - x}} = k\,dt \;\Rightarrow\; \displaystyle\int \dfrac{dx}{(a - x)\sqrt{b - x}} = \int k\,dt$ $(\star)$.

From the hint, $u = \sqrt{b - x} \;\Rightarrow\; u^2 = b - x \;\Rightarrow\; 2u\,du = -dx$, so

$$\int \dfrac{dx}{(a - x)\sqrt{b - x}} = \int \dfrac{-2u\,du}{[a - (b - u^2)]u} = -2\int \dfrac{du}{a - b + u^2} = -2\int \dfrac{du}{\left(\sqrt{a - b}\right)^2 + u^2}$$

$$\overset{17}{=} -2\left(\dfrac{1}{\sqrt{a - b}}\tan^{-1}\dfrac{u}{\sqrt{a - b}}\right)$$

So $(\star)$ becomes $\dfrac{-2}{\sqrt{a - b}}\tan^{-1}\dfrac{\sqrt{b - x}}{\sqrt{a - b}} = kt + C$. Now $x(0) = 0 \;\Rightarrow\; C = \dfrac{-2}{\sqrt{a - b}}\tan^{-1}\dfrac{\sqrt{b}}{\sqrt{a - b}}$ and we have

$\dfrac{-2}{\sqrt{a - b}}\tan^{-1}\dfrac{\sqrt{b - x}}{\sqrt{a - b}} = kt - \dfrac{2}{\sqrt{a - b}}\tan^{-1}\dfrac{\sqrt{b}}{\sqrt{a - b}} \;\Rightarrow\; \dfrac{2}{\sqrt{a - b}}\left(\tan^{-1}\sqrt{\dfrac{b}{a - b}} - \tan^{-1}\sqrt{\dfrac{b - x}{a - b}}\right) = kt \;\Rightarrow$

$t(x) = \dfrac{2}{k\sqrt{a - b}}\left(\tan^{-1}\sqrt{\dfrac{b}{a - b}} - \tan^{-1}\sqrt{\dfrac{b - x}{a - b}}\right)$.

43. (a) $\dfrac{dC}{dt} = r - kC \;\Rightarrow\; \dfrac{dC}{dt} = -(kC - r) \;\Rightarrow\; \displaystyle\int \dfrac{dC}{kC - r} = \int -dt \;\Rightarrow\; (1/k)\ln|kC - r| = -t + M_1 \;\Rightarrow$

$\ln|kC - r| = -kt + M_2 \;\Rightarrow\; |kC - r| = e^{-kt + M_2} \;\Rightarrow\; kC - r = M_3 e^{-kt} \;\Rightarrow\; kC = M_3 e^{-kt} + r \;\Rightarrow$

$C(t) = M_4 e^{-kt} + r/k. \;\; C(0) = C_0 \;\Rightarrow\; C_0 = M_4 + r/k \;\Rightarrow\; M_4 = C_0 - r/k \;\Rightarrow$

$C(t) = (C_0 - r/k)e^{-kt} + r/k.$

(b) If $C_0 < r/k$, then $C_0 - r/k < 0$ and the formula for $C(t)$ shows that $C(t)$ increases and $\lim\limits_{t \to \infty} C(t) = r/k$.

As t increases, the formula for $C(t)$ shows how the role of C_0 steadily diminishes as that of r/k increases.

45. (a) Let $y(t)$ be the amount of salt (in kg) after t minutes. Then $y(0) = 15$. The amount of liquid in the tank is 1000 L at all

times, so the concentration at time t (in minutes) is $y(t)/1000$ kg/L and $\dfrac{dy}{dt} = -\left[\dfrac{y(t)}{1000}\,\dfrac{\text{kg}}{\text{L}}\right]\left(10\,\dfrac{\text{L}}{\text{min}}\right) = -\dfrac{y(t)}{100}\,\dfrac{\text{kg}}{\text{min}}.$

$\displaystyle\int \dfrac{dy}{y} = -\dfrac{1}{100}\int dt \;\Rightarrow\; \ln y = -\dfrac{t}{100} + C$, and $y(0) = 15 \;\Rightarrow\; \ln 15 = C$, so $\ln y = \ln 15 - \dfrac{t}{100}.$

It follows that $\ln\left(\dfrac{y}{15}\right) = -\dfrac{t}{100}$ and $\dfrac{y}{15} = e^{-t/100}$, so $y = 15e^{-t/100}$ kg.

(b) After 20 minutes, $y = 15e^{-20/100} = 15e^{-0.2} \approx 12.3$ kg.

47. Let $y(t)$ be the amount of alcohol in the vat after t minutes. Then $y(0) = 0.04(500) = 20$ gal. The amount of beer in the vat

is 500 gallons at all times, so the percentage at time t (in minutes) is $y(t)/500 \times 100$, and the change in the amount of alcohol

with respect to time t is $\dfrac{dy}{dt} = $ rate in $-$ rate out $= 0.06\left(5\,\dfrac{\text{gal}}{\text{min}}\right) - \dfrac{y(t)}{500}\left(5\,\dfrac{\text{gal}}{\text{min}}\right) = 0.3 - \dfrac{y}{100} = \dfrac{30 - y}{100}\,\dfrac{\text{gal}}{\text{min}}.$

Hence, $\displaystyle\int \dfrac{dy}{30 - y} = \int \dfrac{dt}{100}$ and $-\ln|30 - y| = \frac{1}{100}t + C$. Because $y(0) = 20$, we have $-\ln 10 = C$, so

$-\ln|30 - y| = \frac{1}{100}t - \ln 10 \;\Rightarrow\; \ln|30 - y| = -t/100 + \ln 10 \;\Rightarrow\; \ln|30 - y| = \ln e^{-t/100} + \ln 10 \;\Rightarrow$

$\ln|30 - y| = \ln(10e^{-t/100}) \;\Rightarrow\; |30 - y| = 10e^{-t/100}$. Since y is continuous, $y(0) = 20$, and the right-hand side is

never zero, we deduce that $30 - y$ is always positive. Thus, $30 - y = 10e^{-t/100} \;\Rightarrow\; y = 30 - 10e^{-t/100}$. The

percentage of alcohol is $p(t) = y(t)/500 \times 100 = y(t)/5 = 6 - 2e^{-t/100}$. The percentage of alcohol after one hour is

$p(60) = 6 - 2e^{-60/100} \approx 4.9.$

49. Assume that the raindrop begins at rest, so that $v(0) = 0$. $dm/dt = km$ and $(mv)' = gm \;\Rightarrow\; mv' + vm' = gm \;\Rightarrow$

$mv' + v(km) = gm \;\Rightarrow\; v' + vk = g \;\Rightarrow\; \dfrac{dv}{dt} = g - kv \;\Rightarrow\; \displaystyle\int \dfrac{dv}{g - kv} = \int dt \;\Rightarrow$

$-(1/k)\ln|g - kv| = t + C \;\Rightarrow\; \ln|g - kv| = -kt - kC \;\Rightarrow\; g - kv = Ae^{-kt}. \;\; v(0) = 0 \;\Rightarrow\; A = g.$

So $kv = g - ge^{-kt} \;\Rightarrow\; v = (g/k)(1 - e^{-kt})$. Since $k > 0$, as $t \to \infty$, $e^{-kt} \to 0$ and therefore, $\lim\limits_{t \to \infty} v(t) = g/k.$

51. (a) $\dfrac{1}{L_1}\dfrac{dL_1}{dt} = k\dfrac{1}{L_2}\dfrac{dL_2}{dt} \;\Rightarrow\; \dfrac{d}{dt}(\ln L_1) = \dfrac{d}{dt}(k\ln L_2) \;\Rightarrow\; \displaystyle\int \dfrac{d}{dt}(\ln L_1)\,dt = \int \dfrac{d}{dt}(\ln L_2^k)\,dt \;\Rightarrow$

$\ln L_1 = \ln L_2^k + C \;\Rightarrow\; L_1 = e^{\ln L_2^k + C} = e^{\ln L_2^k}e^C \;\Rightarrow\; L_1 = KL_2^k$ where $K = e^C.$

(b) From part (a) with $L_1 = B$, $L_2 = V$, and $k = 0.0794$, we have $B = KV^{0.0794}.$

53. (a) The rate of growth of the area is jointly proportional to $\sqrt{A(t)}$ and $M - A(t)$; that is, the rate is proportional to the product of those two quantities. So for some constant k, $dA/dt = k\sqrt{A}\,(M - A)$. We are interested in the maximum of the function dA/dt (when the tissue grows the fastest), so we differentiate, using the Chain Rule and then substituting for dA/dt from the differential equation:

$$\frac{d}{dt}\left(\frac{dA}{dt}\right) = k\left[\sqrt{A}\,(-1)\frac{dA}{dt} + (M - A)\cdot \tfrac{1}{2}A^{-1/2}\frac{dA}{dt}\right] = \tfrac{1}{2}kA^{-1/2}\frac{dA}{dt}[-2A + (M - A)]$$

$$= \tfrac{1}{2}kA^{-1/2}\left[k\sqrt{A}(M - A)\right][M - 3A] = \tfrac{1}{2}k^2(M - A)(M - 3A)$$

This is 0 when $M - A = 0$ [this situation never actually occurs, since the graph of $A(t)$ is asymptotic to the line $y = M$ as in the logistic model] and when $M - 3A = 0 \;\Leftrightarrow\; A(t) = M/3$. This represents a maximum by the First Derivative Test, since $\dfrac{d}{dt}\left(\dfrac{dA}{dt}\right)$ goes from positive to negative when $A(t) = M/3$.

(b) From the CAS, we get $A(t) = M\left(\dfrac{Ce^{\sqrt{M}kt} - 1}{Ce^{\sqrt{M}kt} + 1}\right)^2$. To get C in terms of the initial area A_0 and the maximum area M, we substitute $t = 0$ and $A = A_0 = A(0)$: $A_0 = M\left(\dfrac{C - 1}{C + 1}\right)^2 \;\Leftrightarrow\; (C + 1)\sqrt{A_0} = (C - 1)\sqrt{M} \;\Leftrightarrow\;$

$$C\sqrt{A_0} + \sqrt{A_0} = C\sqrt{M} - \sqrt{M} \;\Leftrightarrow\; \sqrt{M} + \sqrt{A_0} = C\sqrt{M} - C\sqrt{A_0} \;\Leftrightarrow\;$$

$$\sqrt{M} + \sqrt{A_0} = C\left(\sqrt{M} - \sqrt{A_0}\right) \;\Leftrightarrow\; C = \frac{\sqrt{M} + \sqrt{A_0}}{\sqrt{M} - \sqrt{A_0}}. \quad \text{[Notice that if } A_0 = 0, \text{ then } C = 1.]$$

7.4 Exponential Growth and Decay

1. The relative growth rate is $\dfrac{1}{P}\dfrac{dP}{dt} = 0.7944$, so $\dfrac{dP}{dt} = 0.7944P$ and, by Theorem 2, $P(t) = P(0)e^{0.7944t} = 2e^{0.7944t}$.

Thus, $P(6) = 2e^{0.7944(6)} \approx 234.99$ or about 235 members.

3. (a) By Theorem 2, $P(t) = P(0)e^{kt} = 100e^{kt}$. Now $P(1) = 100e^{k(1)} = 420 \;\Rightarrow\; e^k = \frac{420}{100} \;\Rightarrow\; k = \ln 4.2$.

So $P(t) = 100e^{(\ln 4.2)t} = 100(4.2)^t$.

(b) $P(3) = 100(4.2)^3 = 7408.8 \approx 7409$ bacteria

(c) $dP/dt = kP \;\Rightarrow\; P'(3) = k \cdot P(3) = (\ln 4.2)\left(100(4.2)^3\right)$ [from part (a)] $\approx 10{,}632$ bacteria/h

(d) $P(t) = 100(4.2)^t = 10{,}000 \;\Rightarrow\; (4.2)^t = 100 \;\Rightarrow\; t = (\ln 100)/(\ln 4.2) \approx 3.2$ hours

5. (a) Let the population (in millions) in the year t be $P(t)$. Since the initial time is the year 1750, we substitute $t - 1750$ for t in

Theorem 2, so the exponential model gives $P(t) = P(1750)e^{k(t-1750)}$. Then $P(1800) = 980 = 790e^{k(1800-1750)}$ $\Rightarrow$

$\frac{980}{790} = e^{k(50)}$ $\Rightarrow$ $\ln\frac{980}{790} = 50k$ $\Rightarrow$ $k = \frac{1}{50}\ln\frac{980}{790} \approx 0.0043104$. So with this model, we have

$P(1900) = 790e^{k(1900-1750)} \approx 1508$ million, and $P(1950) = 790e^{k(1950-1750)} \approx 1871$ million. Both of these

estimates are much too low.

(b) In this case, the exponential model gives $P(t) = P(1850)e^{k(t-1850)}$ $\Rightarrow$ $P(1900) = 1650 = 1260e^{k(1900-1850)}$ $\Rightarrow$

$\ln\frac{1650}{1260} = k(50)$ $\Rightarrow$ $k = \frac{1}{50}\ln\frac{1650}{1260} \approx 0.005393$. So with this model, we estimate

$P(1950) = 1260e^{k(1950-1850)} \approx 2161$ million. This is still too low, but closer than the estimate of $P(1950)$ in part (a).

(c) The exponential model gives $P(t) = P(1900)e^{k(t-1900)}$ $\Rightarrow$ $P(1950) = 2560 = 1650e^{k(1950-1900)}$ $\Rightarrow$

$\ln\frac{2560}{1650} = k(50)$ $\Rightarrow$ $k = \frac{1}{50}\ln\frac{2560}{1650} \approx 0.008785$. With this model, we estimate

$P(2000) = 1650e^{k(2000-1900)} \approx 3972$ million. This is much too low. The discrepancy is explained by the fact that the

world birth rate (average yearly number of births per person) is about the same as always, whereas the mortality rate

(especially the infant mortality rate) is much lower, owing mostly to advances in medical science and to the wars in the first

part of the twentieth century. The exponential model assumes, among other things, that the birth and mortality rates will

remain constant.

7. (a) If $y = [N_2O_5]$ then by Theorem 2, $\dfrac{dy}{dt} = -0.0005y$ $\Rightarrow$ $y(t) = y(0)e^{-0.0005t} = Ce^{-0.0005t}$.

(b) $y(t) = Ce^{-0.0005t} = 0.9C$ $\Rightarrow$ $e^{-0.0005t} = 0.9$ $\Rightarrow$ $-0.0005t = \ln 0.9$ $\Rightarrow$ $t = -2000\ln 0.9 \approx 211$ s

9. (a) If $y(t)$ is the mass (in mg) remaining after t years, then $y(t) = y(0)e^{kt} = 100e^{kt}$.

$y(30) = 100e^{30k} = \frac{1}{2}(100)$ $\Rightarrow$ $e^{30k} = \frac{1}{2}$ $\Rightarrow$ $k = -(\ln 2)/30$ $\Rightarrow$ $y(t) = 100e^{-(\ln 2)t/30} = 100 \cdot 2^{-t/30}$

(b) $y(100) = 100 \cdot 2^{-100/30} \approx 9.92$ mg

(c) $100e^{-(\ln 2)t/30} = 1$ $\Rightarrow$ $-(\ln 2)t/30 = \ln\frac{1}{100}$ $\Rightarrow$ $t = -30\frac{\ln 0.01}{\ln 2} \approx 199.3$ years

11. Let $y(t)$ be the level of radioactivity. Thus, $y(t) = y(0)e^{-kt}$ and k is determined by using the half-life:

$y(5730) = \frac{1}{2}y(0)$ $\Rightarrow$ $y(0)e^{-k(5730)} = \frac{1}{2}y(0)$ $\Rightarrow$ $e^{-5730k} = \frac{1}{2}$ $\Rightarrow$ $-5730k = \ln\frac{1}{2}$ $\Rightarrow$ $k = -\dfrac{\ln\frac{1}{2}}{5730} = \dfrac{\ln 2}{5730}$.

If 74% of the ^{14}C remains, then we know that $y(t) = 0.74y(0)$ $\Rightarrow$ $0.74 = e^{-t(\ln 2)/5730}$ $\Rightarrow$ $\ln 0.74 = -\dfrac{t\ln 2}{5730}$ $\Rightarrow$

$t = -\dfrac{5730(\ln 0.74)}{\ln 2} \approx 2489 \approx 2500$ years.

13. (a) Using Newton's Law of Cooling, $\dfrac{dT}{dt} = k(T - T_s)$, we have $\dfrac{dT}{dt} = k(T - 75)$. Now let $y = T - 75$, so

$y(0) = T(0) - 75 = 185 - 75 = 110$, so y is a solution of the initial-value problem $dy/dt = ky$ with $y(0) = 110$ and by

Theorem 2 we have $y(t) = y(0)e^{kt} = 110e^{kt}$.

$y(30) = 110e^{30k} = 150 - 75 \;\Rightarrow\; e^{30k} = \frac{75}{110} = \frac{15}{22} \;\Rightarrow\; k = \frac{1}{30}\ln\frac{15}{22}$, so $y(t) = 110e^{\frac{1}{30}t\ln\left(\frac{15}{22}\right)}$ and

$y(45) = 110e^{\frac{45}{30}\ln\left(\frac{15}{22}\right)} \approx 62°\mathrm{F}$. Thus, $T(45) \approx 62 + 75 = 137°\mathrm{F}$.

(b) $T(t) = 100 \;\Rightarrow\; y(t) = 25.$ $\;\; y(t) = 110e^{\frac{1}{30}t\ln\left(\frac{15}{22}\right)} = 25 \;\Rightarrow\; e^{\frac{1}{30}t\ln\left(\frac{15}{22}\right)} = \frac{25}{110} \;\Rightarrow\; \frac{1}{30}t\ln\frac{15}{22} = \ln\frac{25}{110} \;\Rightarrow\;$

$t = \dfrac{30\ln\frac{25}{110}}{\ln\frac{15}{22}} \approx 116$ min.

15. $\dfrac{dT}{dt} = k(T - 20)$. Letting $y = T - 20$, we get $\dfrac{dy}{dt} = ky$, so $y(t) = y(0)e^{kt}$. $\;\; y(0) = T(0) - 20 = 5 - 20 = -15$, so

$y(25) = y(0)e^{25k} = -15e^{25k}$, and $y(25) = T(25) - 20 = 10 - 20 = -10$, so $-15e^{25k} = -10 \;\Rightarrow\; e^{25k} = \frac{2}{3}$. Thus,

$25k = \ln\left(\frac{2}{3}\right)$ and $k = \frac{1}{25}\ln\left(\frac{2}{3}\right)$, so $y(t) = y(0)e^{kt} = -15e^{(1/25)\ln(2/3)t}$. More simply, $e^{25k} = \frac{2}{3} \;\Rightarrow\; e^k = \left(\frac{2}{3}\right)^{1/25} \;\Rightarrow\;$

$e^{kt} = \left(\frac{2}{3}\right)^{t/25} \;\Rightarrow\; y(t) = -15 \cdot \left(\frac{2}{3}\right)^{t/25}$.

(a) $T(50) = 20 + y(50) = 20 - 15 \cdot \left(\frac{2}{3}\right)^{50/25} = 20 - 15 \cdot \left(\frac{2}{3}\right)^2 = 20 - \frac{20}{3} = 13.\overline{3}°\mathrm{C}$

(b) $15 = T(t) = 20 + y(t) = 20 - 15 \cdot \left(\frac{2}{3}\right)^{t/25} \;\Rightarrow\; 15 \cdot \left(\frac{2}{3}\right)^{t/25} = 5 \;\Rightarrow\; \left(\frac{2}{3}\right)^{t/25} = \frac{1}{3} \;\Rightarrow\;$

$(t/25)\ln\left(\frac{2}{3}\right) = \ln\left(\frac{1}{3}\right) \;\Rightarrow\; t = 25\ln\left(\frac{1}{3}\right)/\ln\left(\frac{2}{3}\right) \approx 67.74$ min.

17. (a) Let $P(h)$ be the pressure at altitude h. Then $dP/dh = kP \;\Rightarrow\; P(h) = P(0)e^{kh} = 101.3e^{kh}$.

$P(1000) = 101.3e^{1000k} = 87.14 \;\Rightarrow\; 1000k = \ln\left(\frac{87.14}{101.3}\right) \;\Rightarrow\; k = \frac{1}{1000}\ln\left(\frac{87.14}{101.3}\right) \;\Rightarrow\;$

$P(h) = 101.3\,e^{\frac{1}{1000}h\ln\left(\frac{87.14}{101.3}\right)}$, so $P(3000) = 101.3e^{3\ln\left(\frac{87.14}{101.3}\right)} \approx 64.5$ kPa.

(b) $P(6187) = 101.3\,e^{\frac{6187}{1000}\ln\left(\frac{87.14}{101.3}\right)} \approx 39.9$ kPa

19. (a) Using $A = A_0\left(1 + \dfrac{r}{n}\right)^{nt}$ with $A_0 = 3000$, $r = 0.05$, and $t = 5$, we have:

(i) Annually: $n = 1$; $A = 3000\left(1 + \frac{0.05}{1}\right)^{1.5} = \$3828.84$

(ii) Semiannually: $n = 2$; $A = 3000\left(1 + \frac{0.05}{2}\right)^{2.5} = \$3840.25$

(iii) Monthly: $n = 12$; $A = 3000\left(1 + \frac{0.05}{12}\right)^{12.5} = \$3850.08$

(iv) Weekly: $n = 52$; $A = 3000\left(1 + \frac{0.05}{52}\right)^{52.5} = \$3851.61$

(v) Daily: $n = 365$; $A = 3000\left(1 + \frac{0.05}{365}\right)^{365.5} = \$3852.01$

(vi) Continuously: $A = 3000e^{(0.05)5} = \$3852.08$

(b) $dA/dt = 0.05A$ and $A(0) = 3000$.

21. (a) $\dfrac{dP}{dt} = kP - m = k\left(P - \dfrac{m}{k}\right)$. Let $y = P - \dfrac{m}{k}$, so $\dfrac{dy}{dt} = \dfrac{dP}{dt}$ and the differential equation becomes $\dfrac{dy}{dt} = ky$.

The solution is $y = y_0 e^{kt}$ $\Rightarrow$ $P - \dfrac{m}{k} = \left(P_0 - \dfrac{m}{k}\right)e^{kt}$ $\Rightarrow$ $P(t) = \dfrac{m}{k} + \left(P_0 - \dfrac{m}{k}\right)e^{kt}$.

(b) Since $k > 0$, there will be an exponential expansion $\Leftrightarrow$ $P_0 - \dfrac{m}{k} > 0$ $\Leftrightarrow$ $m < kP_0$.

(c) The population will be constant if $P_0 - \dfrac{m}{k} = 0$ $\Leftrightarrow$ $m = kP_0$. It will decline if $P_0 - \dfrac{m}{k} < 0$ $\Leftrightarrow$ $m > kP_0$.

(d) $P_0 = 8,000,000$, $k = \alpha - \beta = 0.016$, $m = 210,000$ $\Rightarrow$ $m > kP_0 \,(= 128,000)$, so by part (c), the population was declining.

7.5 The Logistic Equation

1. (a) $dP/dt = 0.05P - 0.0005P^2 = 0.05P(1 - 0.01P) = 0.05P(1 - P/100)$. Comparing to Equation 4,

$dP/dt = kP(1 - P/M)$, we see that the carrying capacity is $M = 100$ and the value of k is 0.05.

(b) The slopes close to 0 occur where P is near 0 or 100. The largest slopes appear to be on the line $P = 50$. The solutions are increasing for $0 < P_0 < 100$ and decreasing for $P_0 > 100$.

(c)

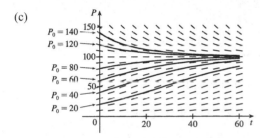

All of the solutions approach $P - 100$ as t increases. As in part (b), the solutions differ since for $0 < P_0 < 100$ they are increasing, and for $P_0 > 100$ they are decreasing. Also, some have an IP and some don't. It appears that the solutions which have $P_0 = 20$ and $P_0 = 40$ have inflection points at $P = 50$.

(d) The equilibrium solutions are $P = 0$ (trivial solution) and $P = 100$. The increasing solutions move away from $P = 0$ and all nonzero solutions approach $P = 100$ as $t \to \infty$.

3. (a) $\dfrac{dy}{dt} = ky\left(1 - \dfrac{y}{M}\right)$ $\Rightarrow$ $y(t) = \dfrac{M}{1 + Ae^{-kt}}$ with $A = \dfrac{M - y(0)}{y(0)}$. With $M = 8 \times 10^7$, $k = 0.71$, and

$y(0) = 2 \times 10^7$, we get the model $y(t) = \dfrac{8 \times 10^7}{1 + 3e^{-0.71t}}$, so $y(1) = \dfrac{8 \times 10^7}{1 + 3e^{-0.71}} \approx 3.23 \times 10^7$ kg.

(b) $y(t) = 4 \times 10^7$ $\Rightarrow$ $\dfrac{8 \times 10^7}{1 + 3e^{-0.71t}} = 4 \times 10^7$ $\Rightarrow$ $2 = 1 + 3e^{-0.71t}$ $\Rightarrow$ $e^{-0.71t} = \dfrac{1}{3}$ $\Rightarrow$

$-0.71t = \ln\dfrac{1}{3}$ $\Rightarrow$ $t = \dfrac{\ln 3}{0.71} \approx 1.55$ years

5. Using (4), $A = \dfrac{M - P_0}{P_0} = \dfrac{10,000 - 1000}{1000} = 9$, so $P(t) = \dfrac{10,000}{1 + 9e^{-kt}}$. $P(1) = 2500$ $\Rightarrow$ $2500 = \dfrac{10,000}{1 + 9e^{-k(1)}}$ $\Rightarrow$

$1 + 9e^{-k} = 4$ $\Rightarrow$ $9e^{-k} = 3$ $\Rightarrow$ $e^{-k} = \dfrac{1}{3}$ $\Rightarrow$ $-k = \ln\dfrac{1}{3}$ $\Rightarrow$ $k = \ln 3$. After another three years, $t = 4$,

and $P(4) = \dfrac{10,000}{1 + 9e^{-(\ln 3)4}} = \dfrac{10,000}{1 + 9\left(e^{\ln 3}\right)^{-4}} = \dfrac{10,000}{1 + 9(3)^{-4}} = \dfrac{10,000}{1 + \frac{1}{9}} = \dfrac{10,000}{\frac{10}{9}} = 9000$.

7. (a) We will assume that the difference in the birth and death rates is 20 million/year. Let $t = 0$ correspond to the year 1990

and use a unit of 1 billion for all calculations. $k \approx \dfrac{1}{P}\dfrac{dP}{dt} = \dfrac{1}{5.3}(0.02) = \dfrac{1}{265}$, so

$$\frac{dP}{dt} = kP\left(1 - \frac{P}{M}\right) = \frac{1}{265}P\left(1 - \frac{P}{100}\right), \qquad P \text{ in billions}$$

(b) $A = \dfrac{M - P_0}{P_0} = \dfrac{100 - 5.3}{5.3} = \dfrac{947}{53} \approx 17.8679$. $P(t) = \dfrac{M}{1 + Ae^{-kt}} = \dfrac{100}{1 + \frac{947}{53}e^{-(1/265)t}}$, so $P(10) \approx 5.49$ billion.

(c) $P(110) \approx 7.81$, and $P(510) \approx 27.72$. The predictions are 7.81 billion in the year 2100 and 27.72 billion in 2500.

(d) If $M = 50$, then $P(t) = \dfrac{50}{1 + \frac{447}{53}e^{-(1/265)t}}$. So $P(10) \approx 5.48$, $P(110) \approx 7.61$, and $P(510) \approx 22.41$. The predictions

become 5.48 billion in the year 2000, 7.61 billion in 2100, and 22.41 billion in the year 2500.

9. (a) Our assumption is that $\dfrac{dy}{dt} = ky(1 - y)$, where y is the fraction of the population that has heard the rumor.

(b) Using the logistic equation (1), $\dfrac{dP}{dt} = kP\left(1 - \dfrac{P}{M}\right)$, we substitute $y = \dfrac{P}{M}$, $P = My$, and $\dfrac{dP}{dt} = M\dfrac{dy}{dt}$,

to obtain $M\dfrac{dy}{dt} = k(My)(1 - y) \quad\Leftrightarrow\quad \dfrac{dy}{dt} = ky(1 - y)$, our equation in part (a).

Now the solution to (1) is $P(t) = \dfrac{M}{1 + Ae^{-kt}}$, where $A = \dfrac{M - P_0}{P_0}$.

We use the same substitution to obtain $My = \dfrac{M}{1 + \dfrac{M - My_0}{My_0}e^{-kt}} \quad\Rightarrow\quad y = \dfrac{y_0}{y_0 + (1 - y_0)e^{-kt}}$.

Alternatively, we could use the same steps as outlined in the solution of Equation 1.

(c) Let t be the number of hours since 8 AM. Then $y_0 = y(0) = \dfrac{80}{1000} = 0.08$ and $y(4) = \dfrac{1}{2}$, so

$\dfrac{1}{2} = y(4) = \dfrac{0.08}{0.08 + 0.92e^{-4k}}$. Thus, $0.08 + 0.92e^{-4k} = 0.16$, $e^{-4k} = \dfrac{0.08}{0.92} = \dfrac{2}{23}$, and $e^{-k} = \left(\dfrac{2}{23}\right)^{1/4}$,

so $y = \dfrac{0.08}{0.08 + 0.92(2/23)^{t/4}} = \dfrac{2}{2 + 23(2/23)^{t/4}}$. Solving this equation for t, we get

$$2y + 23y\left(\frac{2}{23}\right)^{t/4} = 2 \;\Rightarrow\; \left(\frac{2}{23}\right)^{t/4} = \frac{2 - 2y}{23y} \;\Rightarrow\; \left(\frac{2}{23}\right)^{t/4} = \frac{2}{23}\cdot\frac{1 - y}{y} \;\Rightarrow\; \left(\frac{2}{23}\right)^{t/4 - 1} = \frac{1 - y}{y}.$$

It follows that $\dfrac{t}{4} - 1 = \dfrac{\ln[(1 - y)/y]}{\ln\frac{2}{23}}$, so $t = 4\left[1 + \dfrac{\ln((1 - y)/y)}{\ln\frac{2}{23}}\right]$.

When $y = 0.9$, $\dfrac{1 - y}{y} = \dfrac{1}{9}$, so $t = 4\left(1 - \dfrac{\ln 9}{\ln\frac{2}{23}}\right) \approx 7.6$ h or 7 h 36 min. Thus, 90% of the population will have heard

the rumor by 3:36 PM.

11. (a) $\dfrac{dP}{dt} = kP\left(1 - \dfrac{P}{M}\right) \;\Rightarrow\; \dfrac{d^2P}{dt^2} = k\left[P\left(-\dfrac{1}{M}\dfrac{dP}{dt}\right) + \left(1 - \dfrac{P}{M}\right)\dfrac{dP}{dt}\right] = k\dfrac{dP}{dt}\left(-\dfrac{P}{M} + 1 - \dfrac{P}{M}\right)$

$$= k\left[kP\left(1 - \frac{P}{M}\right)\right]\left(1 - \frac{2P}{M}\right) = k^2P\left(1 - \frac{P}{M}\right)\left(1 - \frac{2P}{M}\right)$$

(b) P grows fastest when P' has a maximum, that is, when $P'' = 0$. From part (a), $P'' = 0 \;\Leftrightarrow\; P = 0$, $P = M$,

or $P = M/2$. Since $0 < P < M$, we see that $P'' = 0 \;\Leftrightarrow\; P = M/2$.

13. Following the hint, we choose $t = 0$ to correspond to 1960 and subtract

94,000 from each of the population figures. We then use a calculator to

obtain the models and add 94,000 to get the exponential function

$P_E(t) = 1578.3(1.0933)^t + 94,000$ and the logistic function

$P_L(t) = \dfrac{32,658.5}{1 + 12.75e^{-0.1706t}} + 94,000.$ P_L is a reasonably accurate

model, while P_E is not, since an exponential model would only be used

for the first few data points.

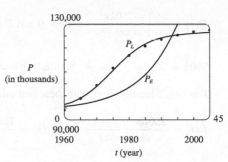

15. (a) The term -15 represents a harvesting of fish at a constant rate—in this case, 15 fish/week. This is the rate at which fish

are caught.

(b)

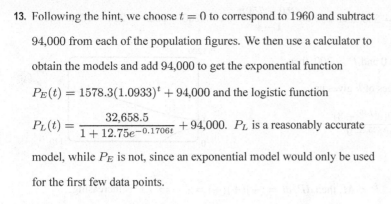

(c) From the graph in part (b), it appears that $P(t) = 250$ and $P(t) = 750$

are the equilibrium solutions. We confirm this analytically by solving the

equation $dP/dt = 0$ as follows: $0.08P(1 - P/1000) - 15 = 0$ $\Rightarrow$

$0.08P - 0.00008P^2 - 15 = 0$ $\Rightarrow$

$-0.00008(P^2 - 1000P + 187,500) = 0$ $\Rightarrow$

$(P - 250)(P - 750) = 0$ $\Rightarrow$ $P = 250$ or 750.

(d)

For $0 < P_0 < 250$, $P(t)$ decreases to 0. For $P_0 = 250$, $P(t)$ remains

constant. For $250 < P_0 < 750$, $P(t)$ increases and approaches 750.

For $P_0 = 750$, $P(t)$ remains constant. For $P_0 > 750$, $P(t)$ decreases

and approaches 750.

(e) $\dfrac{dP}{dt} = 0.08P\left(1 - \dfrac{P}{1000}\right) - 15$ $\Leftrightarrow$ $-\dfrac{100,000}{8} \cdot \dfrac{dP}{dt} = (0.08P - 0.00008P^2 - 15) \cdot \left(-\dfrac{100,000}{8}\right)$ $\Leftrightarrow$

$-12,500\dfrac{dP}{dt} = P^2 - 1000P + 187,500$ $\Leftrightarrow$ $\dfrac{dP}{(P - 250)(P - 750)} = -\dfrac{1}{12,500}\,dt$ $\Leftrightarrow$

$\displaystyle\int\left(\dfrac{-1/500}{P - 250} + \dfrac{1/500}{P - 750}\right)dP = -\dfrac{1}{12,500}\,dt$ $\Leftrightarrow$ $\displaystyle\int\left(\dfrac{1}{P - 250} - \dfrac{1}{P - 750}\right)dP = \dfrac{1}{25}\,dt$ $\Leftrightarrow$

$\ln|P - 250| - \ln|P - 750| = \tfrac{1}{25}t + C$ $\Leftrightarrow$ $\ln\left|\dfrac{P - 250}{P - 750}\right| = \tfrac{1}{25}t + C$ $\Leftrightarrow$ $\left|\dfrac{P - 250}{P - 750}\right| = e^{t/25+C} = ke^{t/25}$ $\Leftrightarrow$

$\dfrac{P - 250}{P - 750} = ke^{t/25}$ $\Leftrightarrow$ $P - 250 = Pke^{t/25} - 750ke^{t/25}$ $\Leftrightarrow$ $P - Pke^{t/25} = 250 - 750ke^{t/25}$ $\Leftrightarrow$

$P(t) = \dfrac{250 - 750ke^{t/25}}{1 - ke^{t/25}}$. If $t = 0$ and $P = 200$, then $200 = \dfrac{250 - 750k}{1 - k}$ ⇔ $200 - 200k = 250 - 750k$ ⇔

$550k = 50$ ⇔ $k = \frac{1}{11}$. Similarly, if $t = 0$ and $P = 300$, then

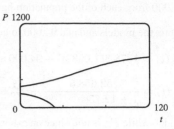

$k = -\frac{1}{9}$. Simplifying P with these two values of k gives us

$P(t) = \dfrac{250(3e^{t/25} - 11)}{e^{t/25} - 11}$ and $P(t) = \dfrac{750(e^{t/25} + 3)}{e^{t/25} + 9}$.

17. (a) $\dfrac{dP}{dt} = (kP)\left(1 - \dfrac{P}{M}\right)\left(1 - \dfrac{m}{P}\right)$. If $m < P < M$, then $dP/dt = (+)(+)(+) = +$ ⇒ P is increasing.

If $0 < P < m$, then $dP/dt = (+)(+)(-) = -$ ⇒ P is decreasing.

(b)

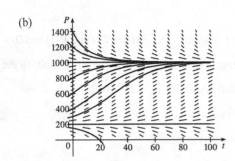

$k = 0.08$, $M = 1000$, and $m = 200$ ⇒

$$\frac{dP}{dt} = 0.08P\left(1 - \frac{P}{1000}\right)\left(1 - \frac{200}{P}\right)$$

For $0 < P_0 < 200$, the population dies out. For $P_0 = 200$, the population
is steady. For $200 < P_0 < 1000$, the population increases and approaches
1000. For $P_0 > 1000$, the population decreases and approaches 1000.

The equilibrium solutions are $P(t) = 200$ and $P(t) = 1000$.

(c) $\dfrac{dP}{dt} = kP\left(1 - \dfrac{P}{M}\right)\left(1 - \dfrac{m}{P}\right) = kP\left(\dfrac{M - P}{M}\right)\left(\dfrac{P - m}{P}\right) = \dfrac{k}{M}(M - P)(P - m)$ ⇔

$\displaystyle\int \dfrac{dP}{(M - P)(P - m)} = \int \dfrac{k}{M}\,dt$. By partial fractions, $\dfrac{1}{(M - P)(P - m)} = \dfrac{A}{M - P} + \dfrac{B}{P - m}$, so

$A(P - m) + B(M - P) = 1$.

If $P = m$, $B = \dfrac{1}{M - m}$; if $P = M$, $A = \dfrac{1}{M - m}$, so $\dfrac{1}{M - m}\displaystyle\int\left(\dfrac{1}{M - P} + \dfrac{1}{P - m}\right)dP = \int \dfrac{k}{M}\,dt$ ⇒

$\dfrac{1}{M - m}\left(-\ln|M - P| + \ln|P - m|\right) = \dfrac{k}{M}t + C$ ⇒ $\dfrac{1}{M - m}\ln\left|\dfrac{P - m}{M - P}\right| = \dfrac{k}{M}t + C$ ⇒

$\ln\left|\dfrac{P - m}{M - P}\right| = (M - m)\dfrac{k}{M}t + C_1$ ⇔ $\dfrac{P - m}{M - P} = De^{(M - m)(k/M)t}$ $[D = \pm e^{C_1}]$.

Let $t = 0$: $\dfrac{P_0 - m}{M - P_0} = D$. So $\dfrac{P - m}{M - P} = \dfrac{P_0 - m}{M - P_0}e^{(M - m)(k/M)t}$.

Solving for P, we get $P(t) = \dfrac{m(M - P_0) + M(P_0 - m)e^{(M - m)(k/M)t}}{M - P_0 + (P_0 - m)e^{(M - m)(k/M)t}}$.

(d) If $P_0 < m$, then $P_0 - m < 0$. Let $N(t)$ be the numerator of the expression for $P(t)$ in part (c). Then

$N(0) = P_0(M - m) > 0$, and $P_0 - m < 0$ ⇔ $\displaystyle\lim_{t \to \infty} M(P_0 - m)e^{(M - m)(k/M)t} = -\infty$ ⇒ $\displaystyle\lim_{t \to \infty} N(t) = -\infty$.

Since N is continuous, there is a number t such that $N(t) = 0$ and thus $P(t) = 0$. So the species will become extinct.

19. (a) $dP/dt = kP\cos(rt - \phi)$ $\Rightarrow$ $(dP)/P = k\cos(rt - \phi)\,dt$ $\Rightarrow$ $\int(dP)/P = k\int\cos(rt - \phi)\,dt$ $\Rightarrow$

$\ln P = (k/r)\sin(rt - \phi) + C$. (Since this is a growth model, $P > 0$ and we can write $\ln P$ instead of $\ln|P|$.) Since

$P(0) = P_0$, we obtain $\ln P_0 = (k/r)\sin(-\phi) + C = -(k/r)\sin\phi + C$ $\Rightarrow$ $C = \ln P_0 + (k/r)\sin\phi$. Thus,

$\ln P = (k/r)\sin(rt - \phi) + \ln P_0 + (k/r)\sin\phi$, which we can rewrite as $\ln(P/P_0) = (k/r)[\sin(rt - \phi) + \sin\phi]$ or,

after exponentiation, $P(t) = P_0 e^{(k/r)[\sin(rt-\phi)+\sin\phi]}$.

(b)   As k increases, the amplitude
increases, but the minimum value
stays the same.

As r increases, the amplitude and
the period decrease.

A change in ϕ produces slight
adjustments in the phase shift and
amplitude.

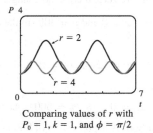

Comparing values of k with
$P_0 = 1, r = 2$, and $\phi = \pi/2$

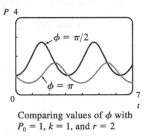

Comparing values of r with
$P_0 = 1, k = 1$, and $\phi = \pi/2$

Comparing values of ϕ with
$P_0 = 1, k = 1$, and $r = 2$

$P(t)$ oscillates between $P_0 e^{(k/r)(1+\sin\phi)}$ and $P_0 e^{(k/r)(-1+\sin\phi)}$ (the extreme values are attained when $rt - \phi$ is an odd

multiple of $\frac{\pi}{2}$), so $\lim\limits_{t\to\infty} P(t)$ does not exist.

7.6   Predator-Prey Systems

1. (a) $dx/dt = -0.05x + 0.0001xy$. If $y = 0$, we have $dx/dt = -0.05x$, which indicates that in the absence of y, x declines at

a rate proportional to itself. So x represents the predator population and y represents the prey population. The growth of

the prey population, $0.1y$ (from $dy/dt = 0.1y - 0.005xy$), is restricted only by encounters with predators (the term

$-0.005xy$). The predator population increases only through the term $0.0001xy$; that is, by encounters with the prey and

not through additional food sources.

(b) $dy/dt = -0.015y + 0.00008xy$. If $x = 0$, we have $dy/dt = -0.015y$, which indicates that in the absence of x, y would

decline at a rate proportional to itself. So y represents the predator population and x represents the prey population. The

growth of the prey population, $0.2x$ (from $dx/dt = 0.2x - 0.0002x^2 - 0.006xy = 0.2x(1 - 0.001x) - 0.006xy$), is

restricted by a carrying capacity of 1000 [from the term $1 - 0.001x = 1 - x/1000$] and by encounters with predators (the

term $-0.006xy$). The predator population increases only through the term $0.00008xy$; that is, by encounters with the prey

and not through additional food sources.

3. (a) $dx/dt = 0.5x - 0.004x^2 - 0.001xy = 0.5x(1 - x/125) - 0.001xy$.

$dy/dt = 0.4y - 0.001y^2 - 0.002xy = 0.4y(1 - y/400) - 0.002xy$.

The system shows that x and y have carrying capacities of 125 and 400. An increase in x reduces the growth rate of y due to the negative term $-0.002xy$. An increase in y reduces the growth rate of x due to the negative term $-0.001xy$. Hence the system describes a competition model.

(b) $dx/dt = 0 \Rightarrow x(0.5 - 0.004x - 0.001y) = 0 \Rightarrow x(500 - 4x - y) = 0$ **(1)** and $dy/dt = 0 \Rightarrow$

$y(0.4 - 0.001y - 0.002x) = 0 \Rightarrow y(400 - y - 2x) = 0$ **(2)**.

From **(1)** and **(2)**, we get four equilibrium solutions.

(i) $x = 0$ and $y = 0$: If the populations are zero, there is no change.

(ii) $x = 0$ and $400 - y - 2x = 0 \Rightarrow x = 0$ and $y = 400$: In the absence of an x-population, the y-population stabilizes at 400.

(iii) $500 - 4x - y = 0$ and $y = 0 \Rightarrow x = 125$ and $y = 0$: In the absence of y-population, the x-population stabilizes at 125.

(iv) $500 - 4x - y = 0$ and $400 - y - 2x = 0 \Rightarrow y = 500 - 4x$ and $y = 400 - 2x \Rightarrow 500 - 4x = 400 - 2x \Rightarrow 100 = 2x \Rightarrow x = 50$ and $y = 300$: A y-population of 300 is just enough to support a constant x-population of 50.

5. (a) At $t = 0$, there are about 300 rabbits and 100 foxes. At $t = t_1$, the number of foxes reaches a minimum of about 20 while the number of rabbits is about 1000. At $t = t_2$, the number of rabbits reaches a maximum of about 2400, while the number of foxes rebounds to 100. At $t = t_3$, the number of rabbits decreases to about 1000 and the number of foxes reaches a maximum of about 315. As t increases, the number of foxes decreases greatly to 100, and the number of rabbits decreases to 300 (the initial populations), and the cycle starts again.

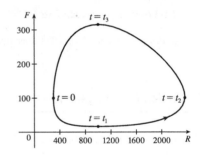

(b)

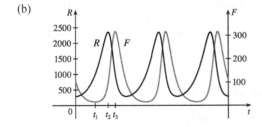

7.

9. $\dfrac{dW}{dR} = \dfrac{-0.02W + 0.00002RW}{0.08R - 0.001RW}$ $\Leftrightarrow$ $(0.08 - 0.001W)R\,dW = (-0.02 + 0.00002R)W\,dR$ $\Leftrightarrow$

$\dfrac{0.08 - 0.001W}{W}\,dW = \dfrac{-0.02 + 0.00002R}{R}\,dR$ $\Leftrightarrow$ $\displaystyle\int\left(\dfrac{0.08}{W} - 0.001\right)dW = \int\left(-\dfrac{0.02}{R} + 0.00002\right)dR$ $\Leftrightarrow$

$0.08\ln|W| - 0.001W = -0.02\ln|R| + 0.00002R + K$ $\Leftrightarrow$ $0.08\ln W + 0.02\ln R = 0.001W + 0.00002R + K$ $\Leftrightarrow$

$\ln\left(W^{0.08}R^{0.02}\right) = 0.00002R + 0.001W + K$ $\Leftrightarrow$ $W^{0.08}R^{0.02} = e^{0.00002R + 0.001W + K}$ $\Leftrightarrow$

$R^{0.02}W^{0.08} = Ce^{0.00002R}e^{0.001W}$ $\Leftrightarrow$ $\dfrac{R^{0.02}W^{0.08}}{e^{0.00002R}e^{0.001W}} = C$. In general, if $\dfrac{dy}{dx} = \dfrac{-ry + bxy}{kx - axy}$, then $C = \dfrac{x^r y^k}{e^{bx}e^{ay}}$.

11. (a) Letting $W = 0$ gives us $dR/dt = 0.08R(1 - 0.0002R)$. $dR/dt = 0$ $\Leftrightarrow$ $R = 0$ or 5000. Since $dR/dt > 0$ for

$0 < R < 5000$, we would expect the rabbit population to *increase* to 5000 for these values of R. Since $dR/dt < 0$ for

$R > 5000$, we would expect the rabbit population to *decrease* to 5000 for these values of R. Hence, in the absence of

wolves, we would expect the rabbit population to stabilize at 5000.

(b) R and W are constant $\Rightarrow$ $R' = 0$ and $W' = 0$ $\Rightarrow$

$$\begin{cases} 0 = 0.08R(1 - 0.0002R) - 0.001RW \\ 0 = -0.02W + 0.00002RW \end{cases} \Rightarrow \begin{cases} 0 = R[0.08(1 - 0.0002R) - 0.001W] \\ 0 - W(-0.02 + 0.00002R) \end{cases}$$

The second equation is true if $W = 0$ or $R = \dfrac{0.02}{0.00002} = 1000$. If $W = 0$ in the first equation, then either $R = 0$ or

$R = \dfrac{1}{0.0002} = 5000$ [as in part (a)]. If $R - 1000$, then $0 - 1000[0.08(1 - 0.0002 \cdot 1000) - 0.001W]$ $\Leftrightarrow$

$0 = 80(1 - 0.2) - W$ $\Leftrightarrow$ $W = 64$.

Case (i): $W = 0, R = 0$: both populations are zero

Case (ii): $W = 0, R = 5000$: see part (a)

Case (iii): $R = 1000, W = 64$: the predator/prey interaction balances and the populations are stable.

(c) The populations of wolves and rabbits fluctuate around 64 and 1000, respectively, and eventually stabilize at those values.

(d)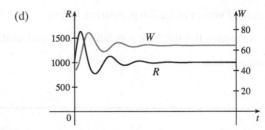

7 Review

CONCEPT CHECK

---

1. (a) A differential equation is an equation that contains an unknown function and one or more of its derivatives.

(b) The order of a differential equation is the order of the highest derivative that occurs in the equation.

(c) An initial condition is a condition of the form $y(t_0) = y_0$.

2. $y' = x^2 + y^2 \geq 0$ for all x and y. $y' = 0$ only at the origin, so there is a horizontal tangent at $(0, 0)$, but nowhere else. The graph of the solution is increasing on every interval.

3. See the paragraph preceding Example 1 in Section 7.2.

4. See the paragraph following Figure 14 in Section 7.2.

5. A separable equation is a first-order differential equation in which the expression for dy/dx can be factored as a function of x times a function of y, that is, $dy/dx = g(x)f(y)$. We can solve the equation by integrating both sides of the equation $dy/f(y) = g(x)dx$ and solving for y.

6. (a) $\dfrac{dy}{dt} = ky$; the relative growth rate, $\dfrac{1}{y}\dfrac{dy}{dt}$, is constant.

(b) The equation in part (a) is an appropriate model for population growth, assuming that there is enough room and nutrition to support the growth.

(c) If $y(0) = y_0$, then the solution is $y(t) = y_0 e^{kt}$.

7. (a) $dP/dt = kP(1 - P/M)$, where M is the carrying capacity.

(b) The equation in part (a) is an appropriate model for population growth, assuming that the population grows at a rate proportional to the size of the population in the beginning, but eventually levels off and approaches its carrying capacity because of limited resources.

8. (a) $dF/dt = kF - aFS$ and $dS/dt = -rS + bFS$.

(b) In the absence of sharks, an ample food supply would support exponential growth of the fish population, that is, $dF/dt = kF$, where k is a positive constant. In the absence of fish, we assume that the shark population would decline at a rate proportional to itself, that is, $dS/dt = -rS$, where r is a positive constant.

TRUE-FALSE QUIZ

---

1. True.   Since $y^4 \geq 0$, $y' = -1 - y^4 < 0$ and the solutions are decreasing functions.

3. False. $x + y$ cannot be written in the form $g(x)f(y)$.

5. True.   By comparing $\dfrac{dy}{dt} = 2y\left(1 - \dfrac{y}{5}\right)$ with the logistic differential equation (7.5.1), we see that the carrying capacity is 5; that is, $\lim\limits_{t \to \infty} y = 5$.

EXERCISES

1. (a)

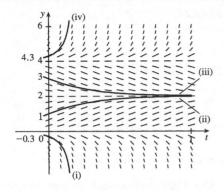

(b) $\lim\limits_{t\to\infty} y(t)$ appears to be finite for $0 \le c \le 4$. In fact

$\lim\limits_{t\to\infty} y(t) = 4$ for $c = 4$, $\lim\limits_{t\to\infty} y(t) = 2$ for $0 < c < 4$, and

$\lim\limits_{t\to\infty} y(t) = 0$ for $c = 0$. The equilibrium solutions are

$y(t) = 0$, $y(t) = 2$, and $y(t) = 4$.

3. (a)

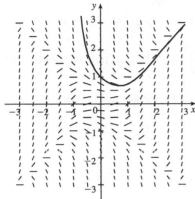

We estimate that when $x = 0.3$, $y = 0.8$, so $y(0.3) \approx 0.8$.

(b) $h = 0.1$, $x_0 = 0$, $y_0 = 1$ and $F(x,y) = x^2 - y^2$. So $y_n = y_{n-1} + 0.1\left(x_{n-1}^2 - y_{n-1}^2\right)$. Thus,

$$y_1 = 1 + 0.1\left(0^2 - 1^2\right) = 0.9,\ y_2 = 0.9 + 0.1\left(0.1^2 - 0.9^2\right) = 0.82,\ y_3 = 0.82 + 0.1\left(0.2^2 - 0.82^2\right) = 0.75676.$$

This is close to our graphical estimate of $y(0.3) \approx 0.8$.

(c) The centers of the horizontal line segments of the direction field are located on the lines $y = x$ and $y = -x$.

When a solution curve crosses one of these lines, it has a local maximum or minimum.

5. $2ye^{y^2}y' = 2x + 3\sqrt{x} \ \Rightarrow \ 2ye^{y^2}\dfrac{dy}{dx} = 2x + 3\sqrt{x} \ \Rightarrow \ 2ye^{y^2}\,dy = \left(2x + 3\sqrt{x}\right)dx \ \Rightarrow$

$\int 2ye^{y^2}\,dy = \int \left(2x + 3\sqrt{x}\right)dx \ \Rightarrow \ e^{y^2} = x^2 + 2x^{3/2} + C \ \Rightarrow \ y^2 = \ln(x^2 + 2x^{3/2} + C) \ \Rightarrow$

$y = \pm\sqrt{\ln(x^2 + 2x^{3/2} + C)}$

7. $\dfrac{dr}{dt} + 2tr = r \ \Rightarrow \ \dfrac{dr}{dt} = r - 2tr = r(1 - 2t) \ \Rightarrow \ \int \dfrac{dr}{r} = \int (1 - 2t)\,dt \ \Rightarrow \ \ln|r| = t - t^2 + C \ \Rightarrow$

$|r| = e^{t-t^2+C} = ke^{t-t^2}$. Since $r(0) = 5$, $5 = ke^0 = k$. Thus, $r(t) = 5e^{t-t^2}$.

9. $\dfrac{d}{dx}(y) = \dfrac{d}{dx}(ke^x) \ \Rightarrow \ y' = ke^x = y$, so the orthogonal trajectories must have $y' = -\dfrac{1}{y} \ \Rightarrow \ \dfrac{dy}{dx} = -\dfrac{1}{y} \ \Rightarrow$

$y\,dy = -dx \ \rightarrow \ \int y\,dy = -\int dx \ \rightarrow \ \tfrac{1}{2}y^2 = -x + C \ \rightarrow \ x = C - \tfrac{1}{2}y^2$, which are parabolas with a horizontal axis.

11. (a) $y(t) = y(0)e^{kt} = 200e^{kt}$ $\Rightarrow$ $y(0.5) = 200e^{0.5k} = 360$ $\Rightarrow$ $e^{0.5k} = 1.8$ $\Rightarrow$ $0.5k = \ln 1.8$ $\Rightarrow$

$k = 2\ln 1.8 = \ln(1.8)^2 = \ln 3.24$ $\Rightarrow$ $y(t) = 200e^{(\ln 3.24)t} = 200(3.24)^t$

(b) $y(4) = 200(3.24)^4 \approx 22{,}040$ bacteria

(c) $y'(t) = 200(3.24)^t \cdot \ln 3.24$, so $y'(4) = 200(3.24)^4 \cdot \ln 3.24 \approx 25{,}910$ bacteria per hour

(d) $200(3.24)^t = 10{,}000$ $\Rightarrow$ $(3.24)^t = 50$ $\Rightarrow$ $t \ln 3.24 = \ln 50$ $\Rightarrow$ $t = \ln 50 / \ln 3.24 \approx 3.33$ hours

13. (a) $C'(t) = -kC(t)$ $\Rightarrow$ $C(t) = C(0)e^{-kt}$ by Theorem 7.4.2. But $C(0) = C_0$, so $C(t) = C_0 e^{-kt}$.

(b) $C(30) = \frac{1}{2}C_0$ since the concentration is reduced by half. Thus, $\frac{1}{2}C_0 = C_0 e^{-30k}$ $\Rightarrow$ $\ln\frac{1}{2} = -30k$ $\Rightarrow$

$k = -\frac{1}{30}\ln\frac{1}{2} = \frac{1}{30}\ln 2$. Since 10% of the original concentration remains if 90% is eliminated, we want the value of t

such that $C(t) = \frac{1}{10}C_0$. Therefore, $\frac{1}{10}C_0 = C_0 e^{-t(\ln 2)/30}$ $\Rightarrow$ $\ln 0.1 = -t(\ln 2)/30$ $\Rightarrow$ $t = -\frac{30}{\ln 2}\ln 0.1 \approx 100$ h.

15. (a) Using (1) and (4) in Section 7.5, we see that for $\dfrac{dP}{dt} = 0.1P\left(1 - \dfrac{P}{2000}\right)$ with $P(0) = 100$, we have $k = 0.1$,

$M = 2000$, $P_0 = 100$, and $A = \dfrac{2000 - 100}{100} = 19$. Thus, the solution of the initial-value problem is

$P(t) = \dfrac{2000}{1 + 19e^{-0.1t}}$ and $P(20) = \dfrac{2000}{1 + 19e^{-2}} \approx 560$.

(b) $P = 1200$ $\Leftrightarrow$ $1200 = \dfrac{2000}{1 + 19e^{-0.1t}}$ $\Leftrightarrow$ $1 + 19e^{-0.1t} = \dfrac{2000}{1200}$ $\Leftrightarrow$ $19e^{-0.1t} = \dfrac{5}{3} - 1$ $\Leftrightarrow$

$e^{-0.1t} = \left(\frac{2}{3}\right)/19$ $\Leftrightarrow$ $-0.1t = \ln\frac{2}{57}$ $\Leftrightarrow$ $t = -10\ln\frac{2}{57} \approx 33.5$.

17. (a) $\dfrac{dL}{dt} \propto L_\infty - L$ $\Rightarrow$ $\dfrac{dL}{dt} = k(L_\infty - L)$ $\Rightarrow$ $\displaystyle\int \dfrac{dL}{L_\infty - L} = \int k\,dt$ $\Rightarrow$ $-\ln|L_\infty - L| = kt + C$ $\Rightarrow$

$\ln|L_\infty - L| = -kt - C$ $\Rightarrow$ $|L_\infty - L| = e^{-kt - C}$ $\Rightarrow$ $L_\infty - L = Ae^{-kt}$ $\Rightarrow$ $L = L_\infty - Ae^{-kt}$.

At $t = 0$, $L = L(0) = L_\infty - A$ $\Rightarrow$ $A = L_\infty - L(0)$ $\Rightarrow$ $L(t) = L_\infty - [L_\infty - L(0)]e^{-kt}$.

(b) $L_\infty = 53$ cm, $L(0) = 10$ cm, and $k = 0.2$ $\Rightarrow$ $L(t) = 53 - (53 - 10)e^{-0.2t} = 53 - 43e^{-0.2t}$.

19. Let P represent the population and I the number of infected people. The rate of spread dI/dt is jointly proportional to I and

to $P - I$, so for some constant k, $\dfrac{dI}{dt} = kI(P - I)$ $\Rightarrow$ $I(t) = \dfrac{I_0 P}{I_0 + (P - I_0)e^{-kPt}}$ [from the discussion of logistic

growth in Section 7.5].

Now, measuring t in days, we substitute $t = 7$, $P = 5000$, $I_0 = 160$ and $I(7) = 1200$ to find k:

$1200 = \dfrac{160 \cdot 5000}{160 + (5000 - 160)e^{-5000 \cdot 7 \cdot k}}$ $\Leftrightarrow$ $3 = \dfrac{2000}{160 + 4840e^{-35{,}000k}}$ $\Leftrightarrow$ $480 + 14{,}520e^{-35{,}000k} = 2000$ $\Leftrightarrow$

$e^{-35{,}000k} = \dfrac{2000 - 480}{14{,}520}$ $\Leftrightarrow$ $-35{,}000k = \ln\dfrac{38}{363}$ $\Leftrightarrow$ $k = \dfrac{-1}{35{,}000}\ln\dfrac{38}{363} \approx 0.00006448$. Next, let

$I = 5000 \times 80\% = 4000$, and solve for t: $4000 = \dfrac{160 \cdot 5000}{160 + (5000 - 160)e^{-k \cdot 5000 \cdot t}}$ $\Leftrightarrow$ $1 = \dfrac{200}{160 + 4840e^{-5000kt}}$ $\Leftrightarrow$

$$160 + 4840e^{-5000kt} = 200 \quad \Leftrightarrow \quad e^{-5000kt} = \frac{200 - 160}{4840} \quad \Leftrightarrow \quad -5000kt = \ln\frac{1}{121} \quad \Leftrightarrow$$

$$t = \frac{-1}{5000k}\ln\frac{1}{121} = \frac{1}{\frac{1}{7}\ln\frac{38}{363}} \cdot \ln\frac{1}{121} = 7 \cdot \frac{\ln 121}{\ln\frac{363}{38}} \approx 14.875. \text{ So it takes about 15 days for 80\% of the population}$$

to be infected.

21. $\dfrac{dh}{dt} = -\dfrac{R}{V}\left(\dfrac{h}{k+h}\right) \;\;\Rightarrow\;\; \displaystyle\int \dfrac{k+h}{h}\,dh = \int\left(-\dfrac{R}{V}\right)dt \;\;\Rightarrow\;\; \int\left(1+\dfrac{k}{h}\right)dh = -\dfrac{R}{V}\int 1\,dt \;\;\Rightarrow$

$h + k\ln h = -\dfrac{R}{V}t + C$. This equation gives a relationship between h and t, but it is not possible to isolate h and express it in

terms of t.

23. (a) $dx/dt = 0.4x(1 - 0.000005x) - 0.002xy$, $dy/dt = -0.2y + 0.000008xy$. If $y = 0$, then

$dx/dt = 0.4x(1 - 0.000005x)$, so $dx/dt = 0 \quad \Leftrightarrow \quad x = 0$ or $x = 200{,}000$, which shows that the insect population

increases logistically with a carrying capacity of 200,000. Since $dx/dt > 0$ for $0 < x < 200{,}000$ and $dx/dt < 0$ for

$x > 200{,}000$, we expect the insect population to stabilize at 200,000.

(b) x and y are constant $\;\Rightarrow\; x' = 0$ and $y' = 0 \;\Rightarrow$

$$\begin{cases} 0 = 0.4x(1 - 0.000005x) - 0.002xy \\ 0 = -0.2y + 0.000008xy \end{cases} \Rightarrow \begin{cases} 0 = 0.4x[(1 - 0.000005x) - 0.005y] \\ 0 = y(-0.2 + 0.000008x) \end{cases}$$

The second equation is true if $y = 0$ or $x = \frac{0.2}{0.000008} = 25{,}000$. If $y = 0$ in the first equation, then either $x = 0$

or $x = \frac{1}{0.000005} = 200{,}000$. If $x = 25{,}000$, then $0 = 0.4(25{,}000)[(1 - 0.000005 \cdot 25{,}000) - 0.005y] \;\;\Rightarrow$

$0 = 10{,}000[(1 - 0.125) - 0.005y] \;\;\Rightarrow\;\; 0 = 8750 - 50y \;\;\Rightarrow\;\; y = 175.$

Case (i): $y = 0$, $x = 0$: Zero populations

Case (ii): $y = 0$, $x = 200{,}000$: In the absence of birds, the insect population is always 200,000.

Case (iii): $x = 25{,}000$, $y = 175$: The predator/prey interaction balances and the populations are stable.

(c) The populations of the birds and insects fluctuate

around 175 and 25,000, respectively, and

eventually stabilize at those values.

(d)

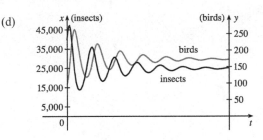

1. We use the Fundamental Theorem of Calculus to differentiate the given equation:

$$[f(x)]^2 = 100 + \int_0^x \left\{ [f(t)]^2 + [f'(t)]^2 \right\} dt \quad \Rightarrow \quad 2f(x)f'(x) = [f(x)]^2 + [f'(x)]^2 \quad \Rightarrow$$

$$[f(x)]^2 + [f'(x)]^2 - 2f(x)f'(x) = 0 \quad \Rightarrow \quad [f(x) - f'(x)]^2 = 0 \quad \Leftrightarrow \quad f(x) = f'(x).$$ We can solve this as a separable

equation, or else use Theorem 7.4.2 with $k = 1$, which says that the solutions are $f(x) = Ce^x$. Now $[f(0)]^2 = 100$, so

$f(0) = C = \pm 10$, and hence $f(x) = \pm 10e^x$ are the only functions satisfying the given equation.

3. $f'(x) = \lim\limits_{h \to 0} \dfrac{f(x+h) - f(x)}{h} = \lim\limits_{h \to 0} \dfrac{f(x)\,[f(h) - 1]}{h}$ [since $f(x + h) = f(x)f(h)$]

$\qquad = f(x) \lim\limits_{h \to 0} \dfrac{f(h) - 1}{h} = f(x) \lim\limits_{h \to 0} \dfrac{f(h) - f(0)}{h - 0} = f(x)f'(0) = f(x)$

Therefore, $f'(x) = f(x)$ for all x and from Theorem 7.4.2 we get $f(x) = Ae^x$.

Now $f(0) = 1 \quad \Rightarrow \quad A = 1 \quad \Rightarrow \quad f(x) = e^x$.

5. "The area under the graph of f from 0 to x is proportional to the $(n + 1)$st power of $f(x)$" translates to

$$\int_0^x f(t)\, dt = k[f(x)]^{n+1} \text{ for some constant } k. \text{ By FTC1, } \frac{d}{dx} \int_0^x f(t)\, dt = \frac{d}{dx} \left\{ k[f(x)]^{n+1} \right\} \quad \Rightarrow$$

$$f(x) = k(n+1)[f(x)]^n f'(x) \quad \Rightarrow \quad 1 = k(n+1)[f(x)]^{n-1} f'(x) \quad \Rightarrow \quad 1 = k(n+1)y^{n-1} \frac{dy}{dx} \quad \Rightarrow$$

$$k(n+1)y^{n-1}\, dy = dx \quad \Rightarrow \quad \int k(n+1)y^{n-1}\, dy = \int dx \quad \Rightarrow \quad k(n+1)\frac{1}{n}y^n = x + C.$$

Now $f(0) = 0 \quad \Rightarrow \quad 0 = 0 + C \quad \Rightarrow \quad C = 0$ and then $f(1) = 1 \quad \Rightarrow \quad k(n+1)\dfrac{1}{n} = 1 \quad \Rightarrow \quad k = \dfrac{n}{n+1},$

so $y^n = x$ and $y = f(x) = x^{1/n}$.

7. Let $y(t)$ denote the temperature of the peach pie t minutes after 5:00 PM and R the temperature of the room. Newton's Law of

Cooling gives us $dy/dt = k(y - R)$. Solving for y we get $\dfrac{dy}{y - R} = k\, dt \quad \Rightarrow \quad \ln|y - R| = kt + C \quad \Rightarrow$

$|y - R| = e^{kt + C} \quad \Rightarrow \quad y - R = \pm e^{kt} \cdot e^C \quad \Rightarrow \quad y = Me^{kt} + R,$ where M is a nonzero constant. We are given

temperatures at three times.

$$y(0) = 100 \quad \Rightarrow \quad 100 = M + R \quad \Rightarrow \quad R = 100 - M$$

$$y(10) = 80 \quad \Rightarrow \quad 80 = Me^{10k} + R \qquad \qquad \textbf{(1)}$$

$$y(20) = 65 \quad \Rightarrow \quad 65 = Me^{20k} + R \qquad \qquad \textbf{(2)}$$

Substituting $100 - M$ for R in **(1)** and **(2)** gives us

$$-20 = Me^{10k} - M \ \textbf{(3)} \quad \text{and} \quad -35 = Me^{20k} - M \ \textbf{(4)}$$

Dividing **(3)** by **(4)** gives us $\dfrac{-20}{-35} = \dfrac{M\left(e^{10k} - 1\right)}{M\left(e^{20k} - 1\right)} \quad \Rightarrow \quad \dfrac{4}{7} = \dfrac{e^{10k} - 1}{e^{20k} - 1} \quad \Rightarrow \quad 4e^{20k} - 4 = 7e^{10k} - 7 \quad \Rightarrow$

$4e^{20k} - 7e^{10k} + 3 = 0$. This is a quadratic equation in e^{10k}. $(4e^{10k} - 3)(e^{10k} - 1) = 0 \Rightarrow e^{10k} = \frac{3}{4}$ or $1 \Rightarrow$

$10k = \ln\frac{3}{4}$ or $\ln 1 \Rightarrow k = \frac{1}{10}\ln\frac{3}{4}$ since k is a nonzero constant of proportionality. Substituting $\frac{3}{4}$ for e^{10k} in (3) gives us

$-20 = M \cdot \frac{3}{4} - M \Rightarrow -20 = -\frac{1}{4}M \Rightarrow M = 80$. Now $R = 100 - M$ so $R = 20°C$.

9. (a) While running from $(L, 0)$ to (x, y), the dog travels a distance

$s = \int_x^L \sqrt{1 + (dy/dx)^2}\, dx = -\int_L^x \sqrt{1 + (dy/dx)^2}\, dx$, so

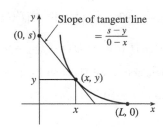

$\dfrac{ds}{dx} = -\sqrt{1 + (dy/dx)^2}$. The dog and rabbit run at the same speed, so the

rabbit's position when the dog has traveled a distance s is $(0, s)$. Since the

dog runs straight for the rabbit, $\dfrac{dy}{dx} = \dfrac{s - y}{0 - x}$ (see the figure).

Thus, $s = y - x\dfrac{dy}{dx} \Rightarrow \dfrac{ds}{dx} = \dfrac{dy}{dx} - \left(x\dfrac{d^2y}{dx^2} + 1 \cdot \dfrac{dy}{dx}\right) = -x\dfrac{d^2y}{dx^2}$. Equating the two expressions for $\dfrac{ds}{dx}$

gives us $x\dfrac{d^2y}{dx^2} = \sqrt{1 + \left(\dfrac{dy}{dx}\right)^2}$, as claimed.

(b) Letting $z = \dfrac{dy}{dx}$, we obtain the differential equation $x\dfrac{dz}{dx} = \sqrt{1 + z^2}$, or $\dfrac{dz}{\sqrt{1 + z^2}} = \dfrac{dx}{x}$. Integrating:

$\ln x = \displaystyle\int \dfrac{dz}{\sqrt{1 + z^2}} \overset{25}{=} \ln(z + \sqrt{1 + z^2}) + C$. When $x = L$, $z = dy/dx = 0$, so $\ln L = \ln 1 + C$. Therefore, $C = \ln L$,

so $\ln x = \ln(\sqrt{1 + z^2} + z) + \ln L = \ln[L(\sqrt{1 + z^2} + z)] \Rightarrow x = L(\sqrt{1 + z^2} + z) \Rightarrow \sqrt{1 + z^2} = \dfrac{x}{L} - z \Rightarrow$

$1 + z^2 = \left(\dfrac{x}{L}\right)^2 - \dfrac{2xz}{L} + z^2 \Rightarrow \left(\dfrac{x}{L}\right)^2 - 2z\left(\dfrac{x}{L}\right) - 1 = 0 \Rightarrow z = \dfrac{(x/L)^2 - 1}{2(x/L)} = \dfrac{x^2 - L^2}{2Lx} = \dfrac{x}{2L} - \dfrac{L}{2}\dfrac{1}{x}$

[for $x > 0$]. Since $z = \dfrac{dy}{dx}$, $y = \dfrac{x^2}{4L} - \dfrac{L}{2}\ln x + C_1$. Since $y = 0$ when $x = L$, $0 = \dfrac{L}{4} - \dfrac{L}{2}\ln L + C_1 \Rightarrow$

$C_1 = \dfrac{L}{2}\ln L - \dfrac{L}{4}$. Thus, $y = \dfrac{x^2}{4L} - \dfrac{L}{2}\ln x + \dfrac{L}{2}\ln L - \dfrac{L}{4} = \dfrac{x^2 - L^2}{4L} - \dfrac{L}{2}\ln\left(\dfrac{x}{L}\right)$.

(c) As $x \to 0^+$, $y \to \infty$, so the dog never catches the rabbit.

11. (a) We are given that $V = \frac{1}{3}\pi r^2 h$, $dV/dt = 60{,}000\pi$ ft^3/h, and $r = 1.5h = \frac{3}{2}h$. So $V = \frac{1}{3}\pi\left(\frac{3}{2}h\right)^2 h = \frac{3}{4}\pi h^3 \Rightarrow$

$\dfrac{dV}{dt} = \frac{3}{4}\pi \cdot 3h^2\dfrac{dh}{dt} = \frac{9}{4}\pi h^2\dfrac{dh}{dt}$. Therefore, $\dfrac{dh}{dt} = \dfrac{4(dV/dt)}{9\pi h^2} = \dfrac{240{,}000\pi}{9\pi h^2} = \dfrac{80{,}000}{3h^2}$ (⋆) $\Rightarrow$

$\int 3h^2\, dh = \int 80{,}000\, dt \Rightarrow h^3 = 80{,}000t + C$. When $t = 0$, $h = 60$. Thus, $C = 60^3 = 216{,}000$, so

$h^3 = 80{,}000t + 216{,}000$. Let $h = 100$. Then $100^3 = 1{,}000{,}000 = 80{,}000t + 216{,}000 \Rightarrow$

$80{,}000t = 784{,}000 \Rightarrow t = 9.8$, so the time required is 9.8 hours.

(b) The floor area of the silo is $F = \pi \cdot 200^2 = 40{,}000\pi$ ft^2, and the area of the base of the pile is

$A = \pi r^2 = \pi \left(\frac{3}{2}h\right)^2 = \frac{9\pi}{4}h^2$. So the area of the floor which is not covered when $h = 60$ is

$F - A = 40{,}000\pi - 8100\pi = 31{,}900\pi \approx 100{,}217$ ft^2. Now $A = \frac{9\pi}{4}h^2 \;\Rightarrow\; dA/dt = \frac{9\pi}{4} \cdot 2h\,(dh/dt)$,

and from $(\star)$ in part (a) we know that when $h = 60$, $dh/dt = \frac{80{,}000}{3(60)^2} = \frac{200}{27}$ ft/h. Therefore,

$dA/dt = \frac{9\pi}{4}(2)(60)\left(\frac{200}{27}\right) = 2000\pi \approx 6283$ ft^2/h.

(c) At $h = 90$ ft, $dV/dt = 60{,}000\pi - 20{,}000\pi = 40{,}000\pi$ ft^3/h. From $(\star)$ in part (a),

$\dfrac{dh}{dt} = \dfrac{4(dV/dt)}{9\pi h^2} = \dfrac{4(40{,}000\pi)}{9\pi h^2} = \dfrac{160{,}000}{9h^2} \;\Rightarrow\; \int 9h^2\,dh = \int 160{,}000\,dt \;\Rightarrow\; 3h^3 = 160{,}000t + C$. When $t = 0$,

$h = 90$; therefore, $C = 3 \cdot 729{,}000 = 2{,}187{,}000$. So $3h^3 = 160{,}000t + 2{,}187{,}000$. At the top, $h = 100 \;\Rightarrow\;$

$3(100)^3 = 160{,}000t + 2{,}187{,}000 \;\Rightarrow\; t = \frac{813{,}000}{160{,}000} \approx 5.1$. The pile reaches the top after about 5.1 h.

13. Let $P(a, b)$ be any point on the curve. If m is the slope of the tangent line at P, then $m = y'(a)$, and an equation of the

normal line at P is $y - b = -\dfrac{1}{m}(x - a)$, or equivalently, $y = -\dfrac{1}{m}x + b + \dfrac{a}{m}$. The y-intercept is always 6, so

$b + \dfrac{a}{m} = 6 \;\Rightarrow\; \dfrac{a}{m} = 6 - b \;\Rightarrow\; m = \dfrac{a}{6 - b}$. We will solve the equivalent differential equation $\dfrac{dy}{dx} = \dfrac{x}{6 - y} \;\Rightarrow\;$

$(6 - y)\,dy = x\,dx \;\Rightarrow\; \displaystyle\int (6 - y)\,dy = \int x\,dx \;\Rightarrow\; 6y - \tfrac{1}{2}y^2 = \tfrac{1}{2}x^2 + C \;\Rightarrow\; 12y - y^2 = x^2 + K$.

Since $(3, 2)$ is on the curve, $12(2) - 2^2 = 3^2 + K \;\Rightarrow\; K = 11$. So the curve is given by $12y - y^2 = x^2 + 11 \;\Rightarrow\;$

$x^2 + y^2 - 12y + 36 = -11 + 36 \;\Rightarrow\; x^2 + (y - 6)^2 = 25$, a circle with center $(0, 6)$ and radius 5.

8 ☐ INFINITE SEQUENCES AND SERIES

8.1 Sequences

1. (a) A sequence is an ordered list of numbers. It can also be defined as a function whose domain is the set of positive integers.

   (b) The terms a_n approach 8 as n becomes large. In fact, we can make a_n as close to 8 as we like by taking n sufficiently large.

   (c) The terms a_n become large as n becomes large. In fact, we can make a_n as large as we like by taking n sufficiently large.

3. The first six terms of $a_n = \dfrac{n}{2n+1}$ are $\dfrac{1}{3}, \dfrac{2}{5}, \dfrac{3}{7}, \dfrac{4}{9}, \dfrac{5}{11}, \dfrac{6}{13}$. It appears that the sequence is approaching $\dfrac{1}{2}$.

$$\lim_{n\to\infty} \frac{n}{2n+1} = \lim_{n\to\infty} \frac{1}{2+1/n} = \frac{1}{2}$$

5. $\left\{1, \frac{1}{3}, \frac{1}{5}, \frac{1}{7}, \frac{1}{9}, \ldots\right\}$. The denominator of the nth term is the nth positive odd integer, so $a_n = \dfrac{1}{2n-1}$.

7. $\{2, 7, 12, 17, \ldots\}$. Each term is larger than the preceding one by 5, so $a_n = a_1 + d(n-1) = 2 + 5(n-1) = 5n - 3$.

9. $\left\{1, -\frac{2}{3}, \frac{4}{9}, -\frac{8}{27}, \ldots\right\}$. Each term is $-\frac{2}{3}$ times the preceding one, so $a_n = \left(-\frac{2}{3}\right)^{n-1}$.

11. $a_n = \dfrac{3+5n^2}{n+n^2} = \dfrac{(3+5n^2)/n^2}{(n+n^2)/n^2} = \dfrac{5+3/n^2}{1+1/n}$, so $a_n \to \dfrac{5+0}{1+0} = 5$ as $n \to \infty$. Converges

13. $a_n = 1 - (0.2)^n$, so $\lim\limits_{n\to\infty} a_n = 1 - 0 = 1$ by (7). Converges

15. Because the natural exponential function is continuous at 0, Theorem 5 enables us to write

$$\lim_{n\to\infty} a_n = \lim_{n\to\infty} e^{1/n} = e^{\lim_{n\to\infty}(1/n)} = e^0 = 1.$$ Converges

17. If $b_n = \dfrac{2n\pi}{1+8n}$, then $\lim\limits_{n\to\infty} b_n = \lim\limits_{n\to\infty} \dfrac{(2n\pi)/n}{(1+8n)/n} = \lim\limits_{n\to\infty} \dfrac{2\pi}{1/n + 8} = \dfrac{2\pi}{8} = \dfrac{\pi}{4}$. Since $\tan$ is continuous at $\frac{\pi}{4}$, by

Theorem 5, $\lim\limits_{n\to\infty} \tan\left(\dfrac{2n\pi}{1+8n}\right) = \tan\left(\lim\limits_{n\to\infty} \dfrac{2n\pi}{1+8n}\right) = \tan\dfrac{\pi}{4} = 1.$ Converges

19. $a_n = \dfrac{(-1)^{n-1}n}{n^2+1} = \dfrac{(-1)^{n-1}}{n+1/n}$, so $0 \le |a_n| = \dfrac{1}{n+1/n} \le \dfrac{1}{n} \to 0$ as $n \to \infty$, so $a_n \to 0$ by the Squeeze Theorem and

Theorem 4. Converges

21. $a_n = \dfrac{e^n + e^{-n}}{e^{2n} - 1} \cdot \dfrac{e^{-n}}{e^{-n}} = \dfrac{1 + e^{-2n}}{e^n - e^{-n}} \to 0$ as $n \to \infty$ because $1 + e^{-2n} \to 1$ and $e^n - e^{-n} \to \infty$. Converges

23. $a_n = n^2 e^{-n} = \dfrac{n^2}{e^n}$. Since $\lim\limits_{x\to\infty} \dfrac{x^2}{e^x} \overset{\text{H}}{=} \lim\limits_{x\to\infty} \dfrac{2x}{e^x} \overset{\text{H}}{=} \lim\limits_{x\to\infty} \dfrac{2}{e^x} = 0$, it follows from Theorem 2 that $\lim\limits_{n\to\infty} a_n = 0$. Converges

25. $0 \le \dfrac{\cos^2 n}{2^n} \le \dfrac{1}{2^n}$ [since $0 \le \cos^2 n \le 1$],   so since $\lim\limits_{n\to\infty} \dfrac{1}{2^n} = 0$, $\left\{\dfrac{\cos^2 n}{2^n}\right\}$ converges to 0 by the Squeeze Theorem.

1

27. $y = \left(1 + \dfrac{2}{x}\right)^x \;\Rightarrow\; \ln y = x \ln\left(1 + \dfrac{2}{x}\right)$, so

$$\lim_{x\to\infty} \ln y = \lim_{x\to\infty} \frac{\ln(1 + 2/x)}{1/x} \stackrel{\text{H}}{=} \lim_{x\to\infty} \frac{\left(\dfrac{1}{1+2/x}\right)\left(-\dfrac{2}{x^2}\right)}{-1/x^2} = \lim_{x\to\infty} \frac{2}{1 + 2/x} = 2 \;\Rightarrow$$

$$\lim_{x\to\infty}\left(1 + \frac{2}{x}\right)^x = \lim_{x\to\infty} e^{\ln y} = e^2, \text{ so by Theorem 2, } \lim_{n\to\infty}\left(1 + \frac{2}{n}\right)^n = e^2. \quad \text{Convergent}$$

29. $a_n = \dfrac{(2n-1)!}{(2n+1)!} = \dfrac{(2n-1)!}{(2n+1)(2n)(2n-1)!} = \dfrac{1}{(2n+1)(2n)} \to 0$ as $n \to \infty$. Converges

31. $\{0, 1, 0, 0, 1, 0, 0, 0, 1, \dots\}$ diverges since the sequence takes on only two values, 0 and 1, and never stays arbitrarily close to either one (or any other value) for n sufficiently large.

33. $a_n = \ln(2n^2 + 1) - \ln(n^2 + 1) = \ln\left(\dfrac{2n^2 + 1}{n^2 + 1}\right) = \ln\left(\dfrac{2 + 1/n^2}{1 + 1/n^2}\right) \to \ln 2$ as $n \to \infty$. Convergent

35.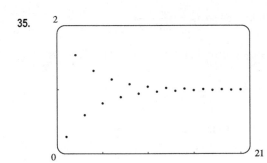

From the graph, it appears that the sequence converges to 1.

$\{(-2/e)^n\}$ converges to 0 by (7), and hence $\{1 + (-2/e)^n\}$ converges to $1 + 0 = 1$.

37.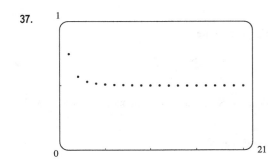

From the graph, it appears that the sequence converges to $\frac{1}{2}$.

As $n \to \infty$,

$$a_n = \sqrt{\frac{3 + 2n^2}{8n^2 + n}} = \sqrt{\frac{3/n^2 + 2}{8 + 1/n}} \;\Rightarrow\; \sqrt{\frac{0 + 2}{8 + 0}} = \sqrt{\frac{1}{4}} = \frac{1}{2},$$

so $\displaystyle\lim_{n\to\infty} a_n = \frac{1}{2}$.

39.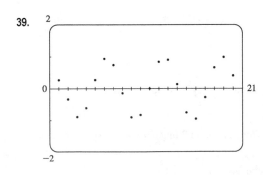

From the graph, it appears that the sequence $\{a_n\} = \left\{\dfrac{n^2 \cos n}{1 + n^2}\right\}$ is divergent, since it oscillates between 1 and -1 (approximately). To prove this, suppose that $\{a_n\}$ converges to L. If $b_n = \dfrac{n^2}{1 + n^2}$, then

$\{b_n\}$ converges to 1, and $\displaystyle\lim_{n\to\infty} \frac{a_n}{b_n} = \frac{L}{1} = L$. But $\dfrac{a_n}{b_n} = \cos n$, so

$\displaystyle\lim_{n\to\infty} \frac{a_n}{b_n}$ does not exist. This contradiction shows that $\{a_n\}$ diverges.

41. (a) $a_n = 1000(1.06)^n \Rightarrow a_1 = 1060$, $a_2 = 1123.60$, $a_3 = 1191.02$, $a_4 = 1262.48$, and $a_5 = 1338.23$.

(b) $\lim_{n \to \infty} a_n = 1000 \lim_{n \to \infty} (1.06)^n$, so the sequence diverges by (7) with $r = 1.06 > 1$.

43. (a) We are given that the initial population is 5000, so $P_0 = 5000$. The number of catfish increases by 8% per month and is

decreased by 300 per month, so $P_1 = P_0 + 8\%P_0 - 300 = 1.08P_0 - 300$, $P_2 = 1.08P_1 - 300$, and so on. Thus,

$P_n = 1.08P_{n-1} - 300$.

(b) Using the recursive formula with $P_0 = 5000$, we get $P_1 = 5100$, $P_2 = 5208$, $P_3 = 5325$ (rounding any portion of a

catfish), $P_4 = 5451$, $P_5 = 5587$, and $P_6 = 5734$, which is the number of catfish in the pond after six months.

45. (a) $a_1 = 1$, $a_{n+1} = 4 - a_n$ for $n \geq 1$. $a_1 = 1$, $a_2 = 4 - a_1 = 4 - 1 = 3$, $a_3 = 4 - a_2 = 4 - 3 = 1$,

$a_4 = 4 - a_3 = 4 - 1 = 3$, $a_5 = 4 - a_4 = 4 - 3 = 1$. Since the terms of the sequence alternate between 1 and 3,

the sequence is divergent.

(b) $a_1 = 2$, $a_2 = 4 - a_1 = 4 - 2 = 2$, $a_3 = 4 - a_2 = 4 - 2 = 2$. Since all of the terms are 2, $\lim_{n \to \infty} a_n = 2$ and hence, the

sequence is convergent.

47. (a) Let a_n be the number of rabbit pairs in the nth month. Clearly $a_1 = 1 = a_2$. In the nth month, each pair that is

2 or more months old (that is, a_{n-2} pairs) will produce a new pair to add to the a_{n-1} pairs already present. Thus,

$a_n = a_{n-1} + a_{n-2}$, so that $\{a_n\} = \{f_n\}$, the Fibonacci sequence.

(b) $a_n = \dfrac{f_{n+1}}{f_n} \Rightarrow a_{n-1} = \dfrac{f_n}{f_{n-1}} = \dfrac{f_{n-1} + f_{n-2}}{f_{n-1}} = 1 + \dfrac{f_{n-2}}{f_{n-1}} = 1 + \dfrac{1}{f_{n-1}/f_{n-2}} = 1 + \dfrac{1}{a_{n-2}}$. If $L = \lim_{n \to \infty} a_n$,

then $L = \lim_{n \to \infty} a_{n-1}$ and $L = \lim_{n \to \infty} a_{n-2}$, so L must satisfy $L = 1 + \dfrac{1}{L} \Rightarrow L^2 - L - 1 = 0 \Rightarrow L = \frac{1+\sqrt{5}}{2}$

[since L must be positive].

49. $a_n = \dfrac{1}{2n+3}$ is decreasing since $a_{n+1} = \dfrac{1}{2(n+1)+3} = \dfrac{1}{2n+5} < \dfrac{1}{2n+3} = a_n$ for each $n \geq 1$. The sequence is

bounded since $0 < a_n \leq \frac{1}{5}$ for all $n \geq 1$. Note that $a_1 = \frac{1}{5}$.

51. The terms of $a_n = n(-1)^n$ alternate in sign, so the sequence is not monotonic. The first five terms are $-1, 2, -3, 4$, and -5.

Since $\lim_{n \to \infty} |a_n| = \lim_{n \to \infty} n = \infty$, the sequence is not bounded.

53. Since $\{a_n\}$ is a decreasing sequence, $a_n > a_{n+1}$ for all $n \geq 1$. Because all of its terms lie between 5 and 8, $\{a_n\}$ is a

bounded sequence. By the Monotonic Sequence Theorem, $\{a_n\}$ is convergent; that is, $\{a_n\}$ has a limit L. L must be less than

8 since $\{a_n\}$ is decreasing, so $5 \leq L < 8$.

55. $a_1 = 1$, $a_{n+1} = 3 - \dfrac{1}{a_n}$.   We show by induction that $\{a_n\}$ is increasing and bounded above by 3. Let P_n be the proposition

that $a_{n+1} > a_n$ and $0 < a_n < 3$. Clearly P_1 is true. Assume that P_n is true. Then $a_{n+1} > a_n \Rightarrow \dfrac{1}{a_{n+1}} < \dfrac{1}{a_n} \Rightarrow$

$-\dfrac{1}{a_{n+1}} > -\dfrac{1}{a_n}$. Now $a_{n+2} = 3 - \dfrac{1}{a_{n+1}} > 3 - \dfrac{1}{a_n} = a_{n+1}$ $\Leftrightarrow$ P_{n+1}. This proves that $\{a_n\}$ is increasing and bounded

above by 3, so $1 = a_1 < a_n < 3$, that is, $\{a_n\}$ is bounded, and hence convergent by the Monotonic Sequence Theorem.

If $L = \lim\limits_{n\to\infty} a_n$, then $\lim\limits_{n\to\infty} a_{n+1} = L$ also, so L must satisfy $L = 3 - 1/L$ $\Rightarrow$ $L^2 - 3L + 1 = 0$ $\Rightarrow$ $L = \frac{3\pm\sqrt{5}}{2}$.

But $L > 1$, so $L = \frac{3+\sqrt{5}}{2}$.

57. $(0.8)^n < 0.000001$ $\Rightarrow$ $\ln(0.8)^n < \ln(0.000001)$ $\Rightarrow$ $n\ln(0.8) < \ln(0.000001)$ $\Rightarrow$ $n > \dfrac{\ln(0.000001)}{\ln(0.8)}$ $\Rightarrow$

$n > 61.9$, so n must be at least 62 to satisfy the given inequality.

59. (a) Suppose $\{p_n\}$ converges to p. Then $p_{n+1} = \dfrac{bp_n}{a+p_n}$ $\Rightarrow$ $\lim\limits_{n\to\infty} p_{n+1} = \dfrac{b\,\lim\limits_{n\to\infty} p_n}{a + \lim\limits_{n\to\infty} p_n}$ $\Rightarrow$ $p = \dfrac{bp}{a+p}$ $\Rightarrow$

$p^2 + ap = bp$ $\Rightarrow$ $p(p+a-b) = 0$ $\Rightarrow$ $p = 0$ or $p = b - a$.

(b) $p_{n+1} = \dfrac{bp_n}{a+p_n} = \dfrac{\left(\dfrac{b}{a}\right)p_n}{1 + \dfrac{p_n}{a}} < \left(\dfrac{b}{a}\right)p_n$ since $1 + \dfrac{p_n}{a} > 1$.

(c) By part (b), $p_1 < \left(\dfrac{b}{a}\right)p_0$, $p_2 < \left(\dfrac{b}{a}\right)p_1 < \left(\dfrac{b}{a}\right)^2 p_0$, $p_3 < \left(\dfrac{b}{a}\right)p_2 < \left(\dfrac{b}{a}\right)^3 p_0$, etc. In general, $p_n < \left(\dfrac{b}{a}\right)^n p_0$,

so $\lim\limits_{n\to\infty} p_n \le \lim\limits_{n\to\infty} \left(\dfrac{b}{a}\right)^n \cdot p_0 = 0$ since $b < a$. $\left[\text{By (7), } \lim\limits_{n\to\infty} r^n = 0 \text{ if } -1 < r < 1. \text{ Here } r = \dfrac{b}{a} \in (0, 1).\right]$

(d) Let $a < b$. We first show, by induction, that if $p_0 < b - a$, then $p_n < b - a$ and $p_{n+1} > p_n$.

For $n = 0$, we have $p_1 - p_0 = \dfrac{bp_0}{a+p_0} - p_0 = \dfrac{p_0(b-a-p_0)}{a+p_0} > 0$ since $p_0 < b - a$. So $p_1 > p_0$.

Now we suppose the assertion is true for $n = k$, that is, $p_k < b - a$ and $p_{k+1} > p_k$. Then

$b - a - p_{k+1} = b - a - \dfrac{bp_k}{a+p_k} = \dfrac{a(b-a) + bp_k - ap_k - bp_k}{a+p_k} = \dfrac{a(b-a-p_k)}{a+p_k} > 0$ because $p_k < b - a$. So

$p_{k+1} < b - a$. And $p_{k+2} - p_{k+1} = \dfrac{bp_{k+1}}{a+p_{k+1}} - p_{k+1} = \dfrac{p_{k+1}(b-a-p_{k+1})}{a+p_{k+1}} > 0$ since $p_{k+1} < b - a$. Therefore,

$p_{k+2} > p_{k+1}$. Thus, the assertion is true for $n = k + 1$. It is therefore true for all n by mathematical induction.

A similar proof by induction shows that if $p_0 > b - a$, then $p_n > b - a$ and $\{p_n\}$ is decreasing.

In either case the sequence $\{p_n\}$ is bounded and monotonic, so it is convergent by the Monotonic Sequence Theorem.

It then follows from part (a) that $\lim\limits_{n\to\infty} p_n = b - a$.

8.2   Series

1. (a) A sequence is an ordered list of numbers whereas a series is the *sum* of a list of numbers.

(b) A series is convergent if the sequence of partial sums is a convergent sequence. A series is divergent if it is not convergent.

3.

n	s_n
1	−2.40000
2	−1.92000
3	−2.01600
4	−1.99680
5	−2.00064
6	−1.99987
7	−2.00003
8	−1.99999
9	−2.00000
10	−2.00000

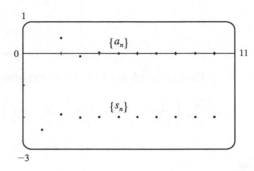

From the graph and the table, it seems that the series converges to -2. In fact, it is a geometric series with $a = -2.4$ and $r = -\frac{1}{5}$, so its sum is $\displaystyle\sum_{n=1}^{\infty} \frac{12}{(-5)^n} = \frac{-2.4}{1 - \left(-\frac{1}{5}\right)} = \frac{-2.4}{1.2} = -2$.

Note that the dot corresponding to $n = 1$ is part of both $\{a_n\}$ and $\{s_n\}$.

TI-86 Note: To graph $\{a_n\}$ and $\{s_n\}$, set your calculator to Param mode and DrawDot mode. (DrawDot is under GRAPH, MORE, FORMT (F3).) Now under E(t) = make the assignments: `xt1=t, yt1=12/(-5)^t, xt2=t, yt2=sum seq(yt1,t,1,t,1)`. (sum and seq are under LIST, OPS (F5), MORE.) Under WIND use `1,10,1,0,10,1,-3,1,1` to obtain a graph similar to the one above. Then use TRACE (F4) to see the values.

5.

n	s_n
1	0.44721
2	1.15432
3	1.98637
4	2.88080
5	3.80927
6	4.75796
7	5.71948
8	6.68962
9	7.66581
10	8.64639

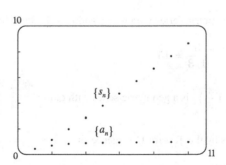

The series $\displaystyle\sum_{n=1}^{\infty} \frac{n}{\sqrt{n^2 + 4}}$ diverges, since its terms do not approach 0.

7.

n	s_n
1	0.29289
2	0.42265
3	0.50000
4	0.55279
5	0.59175
6	0.62204
7	0.64645
8	0.66667
9	0.68377
10	0.69849

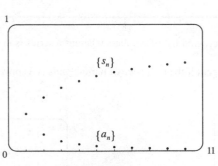

From the graph and the table, it seems that the series converges.

$$\sum_{n=1}^{k}\left(\frac{1}{\sqrt{n}}-\frac{1}{\sqrt{n+1}}\right)=\left(\frac{1}{\sqrt{1}}-\frac{1}{\sqrt{2}}\right)+\left(\frac{1}{\sqrt{2}}-\frac{1}{\sqrt{3}}\right)+\cdots+\left(\frac{1}{\sqrt{k}}-\frac{1}{\sqrt{k+1}}\right)$$
$$=1-\frac{1}{\sqrt{k+1}},$$

so $\displaystyle\sum_{n=1}^{\infty}\left(\frac{1}{\sqrt{n}}-\frac{1}{\sqrt{n+1}}\right)=\lim_{k\to\infty}\left(1-\frac{1}{\sqrt{k+1}}\right)=1.$

9. (a) $\displaystyle\lim_{n\to\infty}a_n=\lim_{n\to\infty}\frac{2n}{3n+1}=\frac{2}{3}$, so the *sequence* $\{a_n\}$ is convergent by (8.1.1).

(b) Since $\displaystyle\lim_{n\to\infty}a_n=\frac{2}{3}\neq0$, the *series* $\displaystyle\sum_{n=1}^{\infty}a_n$ is divergent by the Test for Divergence.

11. $3-4+\frac{16}{3}-\frac{64}{9}+\cdots$ is a geometric series with ratio $r=-\frac{4}{3}$. Since $|r|=\frac{4}{3}>1$, the series diverges.

13. $10-2+0.4-0.08+\cdots$ is a geometric series with ratio $-\frac{2}{10}=-\frac{1}{5}$. Since $|r|=\frac{1}{5}<1$, the series converges to
$$\frac{a}{1-r}=\frac{10}{1-(-1/5)}=\frac{10}{6/5}=\frac{50}{6}=\frac{25}{3}.$$

15. $\displaystyle\sum_{n=1}^{\infty}5\left(\frac{2}{3}\right)^{n-1}$ is a geometric series with $a=5$ and $r=\frac{2}{3}$. Since $|r|=\frac{2}{3}<1$, the series converges to
$$\frac{a}{1-r}=\frac{5}{1-2/3}=\frac{5}{1/3}=15.$$

17. $\displaystyle\sum_{n=0}^{\infty}\frac{\pi^n}{3^{n+1}}=\frac{1}{3}\sum_{n=0}^{\infty}\left(\frac{\pi}{3}\right)^n$ is a geometric series with ratio $r=\frac{\pi}{3}$. Since $|r|>1$, the series diverges.

19. $\displaystyle\sum_{n=1}^{\infty}\frac{n-1}{3n-1}$ diverges by the Test for Divergence since $\displaystyle\lim_{n\to\infty}a_n=\lim_{n\to\infty}\frac{n-1}{3n-1}=\frac{1}{3}\neq0.$

21. $\displaystyle\sum_{k=2}^{\infty}\frac{k^2}{k^2-1}$ diverges by the Test for Divergence since $\displaystyle\lim_{k\to\infty}a_k=\lim_{k\to\infty}\frac{k^2}{k^2-1}=1\neq0.$

23. Converges.
$$\sum_{n=1}^{\infty}\frac{1+2^n}{3^n}=\sum_{n=1}^{\infty}\left(\frac{1}{3^n}+\frac{2^n}{3^n}\right)=\sum_{n=1}^{\infty}\left[\left(\frac{1}{3}\right)^n+\left(\frac{2}{3}\right)^n\right]\qquad\text{[sum of two convergent geometric series]}$$
$$=\frac{1/3}{1-1/3}+\frac{2/3}{1-2/3}=\frac{1}{2}+2=\frac{5}{2}$$

25. $\displaystyle\sum_{n=1}^{\infty}\sqrt[n]{2}=2+\sqrt{2}+\sqrt[3]{2}+\sqrt[4]{2}+\cdots$ diverges by the Test for Divergence since
$$\lim_{n\to\infty}a_n=\lim_{n\to\infty}\sqrt[n]{2}=\lim_{n\to\infty}2^{1/n}=2^0=1\neq0.$$

27. $\sum\limits_{n=1}^{\infty} \arctan n$ diverges by the Test for Divergence since $\lim\limits_{n\to\infty} a_n = \lim\limits_{n\to\infty} \arctan n = \frac{\pi}{2} \neq 0$.

29. $\sum\limits_{n=1}^{\infty} \dfrac{1}{e^n} = \sum\limits_{n=1}^{\infty} \left(\dfrac{1}{e}\right)^n$ is a geometric series with first term $a = \dfrac{1}{e}$ and ratio $r = \dfrac{1}{e}$. Since $|r| = \dfrac{1}{e} < 1$, the series converges

to $\dfrac{1/e}{1 - 1/e} = \dfrac{1/e}{1 - 1/e} \cdot \dfrac{e}{e} = \dfrac{1}{e - 1}$. By Example 6, $\sum\limits_{n=1}^{\infty} \dfrac{1}{n(n+1)} = 1$. Thus, by Theorem 8(ii),

$$\sum\limits_{n=1}^{\infty} \left(\dfrac{1}{e^n} + \dfrac{1}{n(n+1)}\right) = \sum\limits_{n=1}^{\infty} \dfrac{1}{e^n} + \sum\limits_{n=1}^{\infty} \dfrac{1}{n(n+1)} = \dfrac{1}{e-1} + 1 = \dfrac{1}{e-1} + \dfrac{e-1}{e-1} = \dfrac{e}{e-1}.$$

31. Using partial fractions, the partial sums of the series $\sum\limits_{n=2}^{\infty} \dfrac{2}{n^2 - 1}$ are

$$s_n = \sum\limits_{i=2}^{n} \dfrac{2}{(i-1)(i+1)} = \sum\limits_{i=2}^{n} \left(\dfrac{1}{i-1} - \dfrac{1}{i+1}\right)$$

$$= \left(1 - \dfrac{1}{3}\right) + \left(\dfrac{1}{2} - \dfrac{1}{4}\right) + \left(\dfrac{1}{3} - \dfrac{1}{5}\right) + \cdots + \left(\dfrac{1}{n-3} - \dfrac{1}{n-1}\right) + \left(\dfrac{1}{n-2} - \dfrac{1}{n}\right)$$

This sum is a telescoping series and $s_n = 1 + \dfrac{1}{2} - \dfrac{1}{n-1} - \dfrac{1}{n}$.

Thus, $\sum\limits_{n=2}^{\infty} \dfrac{2}{n^2 - 1} = \lim\limits_{n\to\infty} s_n = \lim\limits_{n\to\infty} \left(1 + \dfrac{1}{2} - \dfrac{1}{n-1} - \dfrac{1}{n}\right) = \dfrac{3}{2}$.

33. For the series $\sum\limits_{n=1}^{\infty} \dfrac{3}{n(n+3)}$, $s_n = \sum\limits_{i=1}^{n} \dfrac{3}{i(i+3)} = \sum\limits_{i=1}^{n} \left(\dfrac{1}{i} - \dfrac{1}{i+3}\right)$ [using partial fractions]. The latter sum is

$$\left(1 - \tfrac{1}{4}\right) + \left(\tfrac{1}{2} - \tfrac{1}{5}\right) + \left(\tfrac{1}{3} - \tfrac{1}{6}\right) + \left(\tfrac{1}{4} - \tfrac{1}{7}\right) + \cdots + \left(\tfrac{1}{n-3} - \tfrac{1}{n}\right) + \left(\tfrac{1}{n-2} - \tfrac{1}{n+1}\right) + \left(\tfrac{1}{n-1} - \tfrac{1}{n+2}\right) + \left(\tfrac{1}{n} - \tfrac{1}{n+3}\right)$$

$$= 1 + \tfrac{1}{2} + \tfrac{1}{3} - \tfrac{1}{n+1} - \tfrac{1}{n+2} - \tfrac{1}{n+3} \quad \text{[telescoping series]}$$

Thus, $\sum\limits_{n=1}^{\infty} \dfrac{3}{n(n+3)} = \lim\limits_{n\to\infty} s_n = \lim\limits_{n\to\infty} \left(1 + \tfrac{1}{2} + \tfrac{1}{3} - \tfrac{1}{n+1} - \tfrac{1}{n+2} - \tfrac{1}{n+3}\right) = 1 + \tfrac{1}{2} + \tfrac{1}{3} = \tfrac{11}{6}$. Converges

35. (a) Many people would guess that $x < 1$, but note that x consists of an infinite number of 9s.

(b) $x = 0.99999\ldots = \dfrac{9}{10} + \dfrac{9}{100} + \dfrac{9}{1000} + \dfrac{9}{10,000} + \cdots = \sum\limits_{n=1}^{\infty} \dfrac{9}{10^n}$, which is a geometric series with $a_1 = 0.9$ and

$r = 0.1$. Its sum is $\dfrac{0.9}{1 - 0.1} = \dfrac{0.9}{0.9} = 1$, that is, $x = 1$.

(c) The number 1 has two decimal representations, $1.00000\ldots$ and $0.99999\ldots$.

(d) Except for 0, all rational numbers that have a terminating decimal representation can be written in more than one way. For example, 0.5 can be written as $0.49999\ldots$ as well as $0.50000\ldots$.

37. $0.\overline{2} = \dfrac{2}{10} + \dfrac{2}{10^2} + \cdots$ is a geometric series with $a = \dfrac{2}{10}$ and $r = \dfrac{1}{10}$. It converges to $\dfrac{a}{1-r} = \dfrac{2/10}{1 - 1/10} = \dfrac{2}{9}$.

39. $1.5\overline{42} = 1.53 + \dfrac{42}{10^4} + \dfrac{42}{10^6} + \cdots$. Now $\dfrac{42}{10^4} + \dfrac{42}{10^6} + \cdots$ is a geometric series with $a = \dfrac{42}{10^4}$ and $r = \dfrac{1}{10^2}$.

It converges to $\dfrac{a}{1-r} = \dfrac{42/10^4}{1 - 1/10^2} = \dfrac{42/10^4}{99/10^2} = \dfrac{42}{9900}$.

Thus, $1.5\overline{42} = 1.53 + \dfrac{42}{9900} = \dfrac{153}{100} + \dfrac{42}{9900} = \dfrac{15{,}147}{9900} + \dfrac{42}{9900} = \dfrac{15{,}189}{9900}$ or $\dfrac{5063}{3300}$.

41. $\sum_{n=1}^{\infty} \dfrac{x^n}{3^n} = \sum_{n=1}^{\infty} \left(\dfrac{x}{3}\right)^n$ is a geometric series with $r = \dfrac{x}{3}$, so the series converges $\Leftrightarrow |r| < 1 \Leftrightarrow \dfrac{|x|}{3} < 1 \Leftrightarrow |x| < 3$;

that is, $-3 < x < 3$. In that case, the sum of the series is $\dfrac{a}{1-r} = \dfrac{x/3}{1-x/3} = \dfrac{x/3}{1-x/3} \cdot \dfrac{3}{3} = \dfrac{x}{3-x}$.

43. $\sum_{n=0}^{\infty} \dfrac{\cos^n x}{2^n}$ is a geometric series with first term 1 and ratio $r = \dfrac{\cos x}{2}$, so it converges $\Leftrightarrow |r| < 1$. But $|r| = \dfrac{|\cos x|}{2} \le \dfrac{1}{2}$

for all x. Thus, the series converges for all real values of x and the sum of the series is $\dfrac{1}{1-(\cos x)/2} = \dfrac{2}{2-\cos x}$.

45. After defining f, We use `convert(f,parfrac);` in Maple, `Apart` in Mathematica, or `Expand Rational` and

`Simplify` in Derive to find that the general term is $\dfrac{3n^2+3n+1}{(n^2+n)^3} = \dfrac{1}{n^3} - \dfrac{1}{(n+1)^3}$. So the nth partial sum is

$$s_n = \sum_{k=1}^{n} \left(\dfrac{1}{k^3} - \dfrac{1}{(k+1)^3}\right) = \left(1 - \dfrac{1}{2^3}\right) + \left(\dfrac{1}{2^3} - \dfrac{1}{3^3}\right) + \cdots + \left(\dfrac{1}{n^3} - \dfrac{1}{(n+1)^3}\right) = 1 - \dfrac{1}{(n+1)^3}$$

The series converges to $\lim_{n\to\infty} s_n = 1$. This can be confirmed by directly computing the sum using `sum(f,1..infinity);`

(in Maple), `Sum[f,{n,1,Infinity}]` (in Mathematica), or `Calculus Sum` (from 1 to ∞) and `Simplify` (in Derive).

47. For $n = 1$, $a_1 = 0$ since $s_1 = 0$. For $n > 1$,

$$a_n = s_n - s_{n-1} = \dfrac{n-1}{n+1} - \dfrac{(n-1)-1}{(n-1)+1} = \dfrac{(n-1)n - (n+1)(n-2)}{(n+1)n} = \dfrac{2}{n(n+1)}$$

Also, $\sum_{n=1}^{\infty} a_n = \lim_{n\to\infty} s_n = \lim_{n\to\infty} \dfrac{1-1/n}{1+1/n} = 1$.

49. (a) After the first pill is taken, 100 mg of the drug is in the body. After the second pill is taken, 100 mg plus 100(5%) mg remains in the body. After the third pill is taken 100 mg plus 100(5%) mg plus [100(5%)](5%) mg remains in the body. This gives us $100 + 100(0.05) + 100(0.05)^2 = 105.25$ mg of the drug remaining in the body after the patient takes three pills.

(b) Continuing the pattern established in part (a), we get $100 + 100(0.05) + 100(0.05)^2 + \cdots + 100(0.05)^{n-1}$ mg after n pills are taken. By (3), this sum is $\dfrac{100(1 - 0.05^n)}{1 - 0.05}$.

(c) The amount of the drug remaining in the body in the long run can be approximated by summing the infinite series with $a_1 = 100$ and $r = 0.05$. This sum is $\dfrac{100}{1 - 0.05} = \dfrac{100}{0.95} \approx 105.26$ mg.

51. (a) The first step in the chain occurs when the local government spends D dollars. The people who receive it spend a fraction c of those D dollars, that is, Dc dollars. Those who receive the Dc dollars spend a fraction c of it, that is, Dc^2 dollars. Continuing in this way, we see that the total spending after n transactions is

$$S_n = D + Dc + Dc^2 + \cdots + Dc^{n-1} = \dfrac{D(1-c^n)}{1-c} \text{ by (3)}.$$

(b) $\lim_{n\to\infty} S_n = \lim_{n\to\infty} \dfrac{D(1-c^n)}{1-c} = \dfrac{D}{1-c} \lim_{n\to\infty}(1-c^n) = \dfrac{D}{1-c} \left[\text{since } 0 < c < 1 \Rightarrow \lim_{n\to\infty} c^n = 0\right]$

$\qquad = \dfrac{D}{s}$ [since $c + s = 1$] $= kD$ [since $k = 1/s$]

If $c = 0.8$, then $s = 1 - c = 0.2$ and the multiplier is $k = 1/s = 5$.

53. $\sum_{n=2}^{\infty}(1+c)^{-n}$ is a geometric series with $a=(1+c)^{-2}$ and $r=(1+c)^{-1}$, so the series converges when

$\left|(1+c)^{-1}\right|<1 \quad\Leftrightarrow\quad |1+c|>1 \quad\Leftrightarrow\quad 1+c>1 \text{ or } 1+c<-1 \quad\Leftrightarrow\quad c>0 \text{ or } c<-2.$ We calculate the sum of the

series and set it equal to 2: $\dfrac{(1+c)^{-2}}{1-(1+c)^{-1}}=2 \quad\Leftrightarrow\quad \left(\dfrac{1}{1+c}\right)^2=2-2\left(\dfrac{1}{1+c}\right) \quad\Leftrightarrow\quad 1=2(1+c)^2-2(1+c) \quad\Leftrightarrow$

$2c^2+2c-1=0 \quad\Leftrightarrow\quad c=\dfrac{-2\pm\sqrt{12}}{4}=\dfrac{\pm\sqrt{3}-1}{2}.$ However, the negative root is inadmissible because $-2<\dfrac{-\sqrt{3}-1}{2}<0.$

So $c=\dfrac{\sqrt{3}-1}{2}.$

55. $e^{s_n}=e^{1+\frac{1}{2}+\frac{1}{3}+\cdots+\frac{1}{n}}=e^1 e^{1/2}e^{1/3}\cdots e^{1/n}>(1+1)\left(1+\tfrac{1}{2}\right)\left(1+\tfrac{1}{3}\right)\cdots\left(1+\tfrac{1}{n}\right) \qquad [e^x>1+x]$

$\qquad =\dfrac{2}{1}\dfrac{3}{2}\dfrac{4}{3}\cdots\dfrac{n+1}{n}=n+1$

Thus, $e^{s_n}>n+1$ and $\lim\limits_{n\to\infty}e^{s_n}=\infty.$ Since $\{s_n\}$ is increasing, $\lim\limits_{n\to\infty}s_n=\infty,$ implying that the harmonic series is

divergent.

57. Let d_n be the diameter of $C_n.$ We draw lines from the centers of the C_i to

the center of D (or C), and using the Pythagorean Theorem, we can write

$1^2+\left(1-\tfrac{1}{2}d_1\right)^2=\left(1+\tfrac{1}{2}d_1\right)^2 \quad\Leftrightarrow$

$1=\left(1+\tfrac{1}{2}d_1\right)^2-\left(1-\tfrac{1}{2}d_1\right)^2=2d_1 \text{ [difference of squares]} \quad\Rightarrow\quad d_1=\tfrac{1}{2}.$

Similarly,

$1=\left(1+\tfrac{1}{2}d_2\right)^2-\left(1-d_1-\tfrac{1}{2}d_2\right)^2=2d_2+2d_1-d_1^2-d_1 d_2$

$\qquad =(2-d_1)(d_1+d_2) \quad\Leftrightarrow$

$d_2=\dfrac{1}{2-d_1}-d_1=\dfrac{(1-d_1)^2}{2-d_1},\ 1=\left(1+\tfrac{1}{2}d_3\right)^2-\left(1-d_1-d_2-\tfrac{1}{2}d_3\right)^2 \quad\Leftrightarrow\quad d_3=\dfrac{\left[1-(d_1+d_2)\right]^2}{2-(d_1+d_2)},$ and in general,

$d_{n+1}=\dfrac{\left(1-\sum_{i=1}^{n}d_i\right)^2}{2-\sum_{i=1}^{n}d_i}.$ If we actually calculate d_2 and d_3 from the formulas above, we find that they are $\dfrac{1}{6}=\dfrac{1}{2\cdot 3}$ and

$\dfrac{1}{12}=\dfrac{1}{3\cdot 4}$ respectively, so we suspect that in general, $d_n=\dfrac{1}{n(n+1)}.$ To prove this, we use induction: Assume that for all

$k\le n,\ d_k=\dfrac{1}{k(k+1)}=\dfrac{1}{k}-\dfrac{1}{k+1}.$ Then $\sum\limits_{i=1}^{n}d_i=1-\dfrac{1}{n+1}=\dfrac{n}{n+1}$ [telescoping sum]. Substituting this into our

formula for $d_{n+1},$ we get $d_{n+1}=\dfrac{\left[1-\dfrac{n}{n+1}\right]^2}{2-\left(\dfrac{n}{n+1}\right)}=\dfrac{\dfrac{1}{(n+1)^2}}{\dfrac{n+2}{n+1}}=\dfrac{1}{(n+1)(n+2)},$ and the induction is complete.

Now, we observe that the partial sums $\sum_{i=1}^{n}d_i$ of the diameters of the circles approach 1 as $n\to\infty;$ that is,

$\sum\limits_{n=1}^{\infty}a_n=\sum\limits_{n=1}^{\infty}\dfrac{1}{n(n+1)}=1,$ which is what we wanted to prove.

59. The series $1-1+1-1+1-1+\cdots$ diverges (geometric series with $r=-1$) so we cannot say that

$0=1-1+1-1+1-1+\cdots.$

61. Suppose on the contrary that $\sum(a_n + b_n)$ converges. Then $\sum(a_n + b_n)$ and $\sum a_n$ are convergent series. So by

Theorem 8(iii), $\sum[(a_n + b_n) - a_n]$ would also be convergent. But $\sum[(a_n + b_n) - a_n] = \sum b_n$, a contradiction, since

$\sum b_n$ is given to be divergent.

63. The partial sums $\{s_n\}$ form an increasing sequence, since $s_n - s_{n-1} = a_n > 0$ for all n. Also, the sequence $\{s_n\}$ is bounded

since $s_n \le 1000$ for all n. So by the Monotonic Sequence Theorem, the sequence of partial sums converges, that is, the series

$\sum a_n$ is convergent.

65. (a) At the first step, only the interval $\left(\frac{1}{3}, \frac{2}{3}\right)$ (length $\frac{1}{3}$) is removed. At the second step, we remove the intervals $\left(\frac{1}{9}, \frac{2}{9}\right)$ and

$\left(\frac{7}{9}, \frac{8}{9}\right)$, which have a total length of $2 \cdot \left(\frac{1}{3}\right)^2$. At the third step, we remove 2^2 intervals, each of length $\left(\frac{1}{3}\right)^3$. In general,

at the nth step we remove 2^{n-1} intervals, each of length $\left(\frac{1}{3}\right)^n$, for a length of $2^{n-1} \cdot \left(\frac{1}{3}\right)^n = \frac{1}{3}\left(\frac{2}{3}\right)^{n-1}$. Thus, the total

length of all removed intervals is $\sum_{n=1}^{\infty} \frac{1}{3}\left(\frac{2}{3}\right)^{n-1} = \frac{1/3}{1-2/3} = 1$ [geometric series with $a = \frac{1}{3}$ and $r = \frac{2}{3}$]. Notice that at

the nth step, the leftmost interval that is removed is $\left(\left(\frac{1}{3}\right)^n, \left(\frac{2}{3}\right)^n\right)$, so we never remove 0, and 0 is in the Cantor set. Also,

the rightmost interval removed is $\left(1 - \left(\frac{2}{3}\right)^n, 1 - \left(\frac{1}{3}\right)^n\right)$, so 1 is never removed. Some other numbers in the Cantor set

are $\frac{1}{3}, \frac{2}{3}, \frac{1}{9}, \frac{2}{9}, \frac{7}{9}$, and $\frac{8}{9}$.

(b) The area removed at the first step is $\frac{1}{9}$; at the second step, $8 \cdot \left(\frac{1}{9}\right)^2$; at the third step, $(8)^2 \cdot \left(\frac{1}{9}\right)^3$. In general, the area

removed at the nth step is $(8)^{n-1}\left(\frac{1}{9}\right)^n = \frac{1}{9}\left(\frac{8}{9}\right)^{n-1}$, so the total area of all removed squares is

$$\sum_{n=1}^{\infty} \frac{1}{9}\left(\frac{8}{9}\right)^{n-1} = \frac{1/9}{1 - 8/9} = 1.$$

67. (a) For $\sum_{n=1}^{\infty} \frac{n}{(n+1)!}$, $s_1 = \frac{1}{1\cdot 2} = \frac{1}{2}$, $s_2 = \frac{1}{2} + \frac{2}{1\cdot 2\cdot 3} = \frac{5}{6}$, $s_3 = \frac{5}{6} + \frac{3}{1\cdot 2\cdot 3\cdot 4} = \frac{23}{24}$,

$s_4 = \frac{23}{24} + \frac{4}{1\cdot 2\cdot 3\cdot 4\cdot 5} = \frac{119}{120}$. The denominators are $(n+1)!$, so a guess would be $s_n = \frac{(n+1)! - 1}{(n+1)!}$.

(b) For $n = 1$, $s_1 = \frac{1}{2} = \frac{2! - 1}{2!}$, so the formula holds for $n = 1$. Assume $s_k = \frac{(k+1)! - 1}{(k+1)!}$. Then

$$s_{k+1} = \frac{(k+1)! - 1}{(k+1)!} + \frac{k+1}{(k+2)!} = \frac{(k+1)! - 1}{(k+1)!} + \frac{k+1}{(k+1)!(k+2)} = \frac{(k+2)! - (k+2) + k + 1}{(k+2)!}$$
$$= \frac{(k+2)! - 1}{(k+2)!}$$

Thus, the formula is true for $n = k + 1$. So by induction, the guess is correct.

(c) $\lim_{n\to\infty} s_n = \lim_{n\to\infty} \frac{(n+1)! - 1}{(n+1)!} = \lim_{n\to\infty}\left[1 - \frac{1}{(n+1)!}\right] = 1$ and so $\sum_{n=1}^{\infty} \frac{n}{(n+1)!} = 1$.

8.3   The Integral and Comparison Tests; Estimating Sums

1. The picture shows that $a_2 = \dfrac{1}{2^{1.3}} < \displaystyle\int_1^2 \dfrac{1}{x^{1.3}}\,dx$,

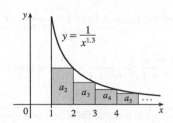

$a_3 = \dfrac{1}{3^{1.3}} < \displaystyle\int_2^3 \dfrac{1}{x^{1.3}}\,dx$, and so on, so $\displaystyle\sum_{n=2}^{\infty} \dfrac{1}{n^{1.3}} < \int_1^{\infty} \dfrac{1}{x^{1.3}}\,dx$. The

integral converges by (5.10.2) with $p = 1.3 > 1$, so the series converges.

3. (a) We cannot say anything about $\sum a_n$. If $a_n > b_n$ for all n and $\sum b_n$ is convergent, then $\sum a_n$ could be convergent or

divergent. (See the note after Example 2.)

(b) If $a_n < b_n$ for all n, then $\sum a_n$ is convergent. [This is part (i) of the Comparison Test.]

5. $\displaystyle\sum_{n=1}^{\infty} n^b$ is a p-series with $p = -b$. $\displaystyle\sum_{n=1}^{\infty} b^n$ is a geometric series. By (1), the p-series is convergent if $p > 1$. In this case,

$\displaystyle\sum_{n=1}^{\infty} n^b = \sum_{n=1}^{\infty} \left(1/n^{-b}\right)$, so $-b > 1 \;\Leftrightarrow\; b < -1$ are the values for which the series converge. A geometric series

$\displaystyle\sum_{n=1}^{\infty} ar^{n-1}$ converges if $|r| < 1$, so $\displaystyle\sum_{n=1}^{\infty} b^n$ converges if $|b| < 1 \;\Leftrightarrow\; -1 < b < 1$.

7. The function $f(x) = 1/\sqrt[5]{x} = x^{-1/5}$ is continuous, positive, and decreasing on $[1, \infty)$, so the Integral Test applies.

$\displaystyle\int_1^{\infty} x^{-1/5}\,dx = \lim_{t \to \infty} \int_1^t x^{-1/5}\,dx = \lim_{t \to \infty} \left[\tfrac{5}{4} x^{4/5}\right]_1^t = \lim_{t \to \infty} \left(\tfrac{5}{4} t^{4/5} - \tfrac{5}{4}\right) - \infty$, so $\displaystyle\sum_{n=1}^{\infty} 1/\sqrt[5]{n}$ diverges.

9. $\dfrac{n}{2n^3 + 1} < \dfrac{n}{2n^3} = \dfrac{1}{2n^2} < \dfrac{1}{n^2}$ for all $n \geq 1$, so $\displaystyle\sum_{n=1}^{\infty} \dfrac{n}{2n^3 + 1}$ converges by comparison with $\displaystyle\sum_{n=1}^{\infty} \dfrac{1}{n^2}$, which converges

because it is a p-series with $p = 2 > 1$.

11. The series $\displaystyle\sum_{n=1}^{\infty} \dfrac{1}{n^{0.85}}$ is a p-series with $p = 0.85 \leq 1$, so it diverges by (1). Therefore, the series $\displaystyle\sum_{n=1}^{\infty} \dfrac{2}{n^{0.85}}$ must also diverge,

for if it converged, then $\displaystyle\sum_{n=1}^{\infty} \dfrac{1}{n^{0.85}}$ would have to converge [by Theorem 8(i) in Section 8.2].

13. $1 + \dfrac{1}{8} + \dfrac{1}{27} + \dfrac{1}{64} + \dfrac{1}{125} + \cdots = \displaystyle\sum_{n=1}^{\infty} \dfrac{1}{n^3}$. This is a p-series with $p = 3 > 1$, so it converges by (1).

15. $f(x) = xe^{-x}$ is continuous and positive on $[1, \infty)$. $f'(x) = -xe^{-x} + e^{-x} = e^{-x}(1 - x) < 0$ for $x > 1$, so f is decreasing

on $[1, \infty)$. Thus, the Integral Test applies.

$\displaystyle\int_1^{\infty} xe^{-x}\,dx = \lim_{b \to \infty} \int_1^b xe^{-x}\,dx = \lim_{b \to \infty} \left[-xe^{-x} - e^{-x}\right]_1^b$ [by parts] $= \lim_{b \to \infty} \left[-be^{-b} - e^{-b} + e^{-1} + e^{-1}\right] = 2/e$

since $\displaystyle\lim_{b \to \infty} be^{-b} = \lim_{b \to \infty} (b/e^b) \overset{\text{H}}{=} \lim_{b \to \infty} (1/e^b) = 0$ and $\displaystyle\lim_{b \to \infty} e^{-b} = 0$. Thus, $\sum_{n=1}^{\infty} ne^{-n}$ converges.

17. $f(x) = \dfrac{1}{x \ln x}$ is continuous and positive on $[2, \infty)$, and also decreasing since $f'(x) = -\dfrac{1 + \ln x}{x^2 (\ln x)^2} < 0$ for $x > 2$, so we can

use the Integral Test. $\displaystyle\int_2^\infty \dfrac{1}{x \ln x}\, dx = \lim_{t\to\infty} \left[\ln(\ln x)\right]_2^t = \lim_{t\to\infty} \left[\ln(\ln t) - \ln(\ln 2)\right] = \infty$, so the series $\displaystyle\sum_{n=2}^\infty \dfrac{1}{n \ln n}$ diverges.

19. $\dfrac{\cos^2 n}{n^2 + 1} \le \dfrac{1}{n^2 + 1} < \dfrac{1}{n^2}$, so the series $\displaystyle\sum_{n=1}^\infty \dfrac{\cos^2 n}{n^2 + 1}$ converges by comparison with the p-series $\displaystyle\sum_{n=1}^\infty \dfrac{1}{n^2}$ $[p = 2 > 1]$.

21. $\dfrac{n-1}{n\, 4^n}$ is positive for $n > 1$ and $\dfrac{n-1}{n\, 4^n} < \dfrac{n}{n\, 4^n} = \dfrac{1}{4^n} = \left(\dfrac{1}{4}\right)^n$, so $\displaystyle\sum_{n=1}^\infty \dfrac{n-1}{n\, 4^n}$ converges by comparison with the convergent

geometric series $\displaystyle\sum_{n=1}^\infty \left(\dfrac{1}{4}\right)^n$.

23. $1 + \dfrac{1}{3} + \dfrac{1}{5} + \dfrac{1}{7} + \dfrac{1}{9} + \cdots = \displaystyle\sum_{n=1}^\infty \dfrac{1}{2n-1}$.   The function $f(x) = \dfrac{1}{2x - 1}$ is

continuous, positive, and decreasing on $[1, \infty)$, so the Integral Test applies.

$\displaystyle\int_1^\infty \dfrac{1}{2x - 1}\, dx = \lim_{t\to\infty} \int_1^t \dfrac{1}{2x - 1}\, dx = \lim_{t\to\infty} \left[\tfrac{1}{2} \ln |2x - 1|\right]_1^t = \tfrac{1}{2} \lim_{t\to\infty} \left(\ln(2t - 1) - 0\right) = \infty$, so the series $\displaystyle\sum_{n=1}^\infty \dfrac{1}{2n-1}$

diverges.

25. Use the Limit Comparison Test with $a_n = \dfrac{1 + 4^n}{1 + 3^n}$ and $b_n = \dfrac{4^n}{3^n}$:

$$\lim_{n\to\infty} \dfrac{a_n}{b_n} = \lim_{n\to\infty} \dfrac{\dfrac{1 + 4^n}{1 + 3^n}}{\dfrac{4^n}{3^n}} = \lim_{n\to\infty} \dfrac{1 + 4^n}{1 + 3^n} \cdot \dfrac{3^n}{4^n} = \lim_{n\to\infty} \dfrac{1 + 4^n}{4^n} \cdot \dfrac{3^n}{1 + 3^n} = \lim_{n\to\infty} \left(\dfrac{1}{4^n} + 1\right) \cdot \dfrac{1}{\dfrac{1}{3^n} + 1} = 1 > 0$$

Since the geometric series $\sum b_n = \sum \left(\tfrac{4}{3}\right)^n$ diverges, so does $\displaystyle\sum_{n=1}^\infty \dfrac{1 + 4^n}{1 + 3^n}$. Alternatively, use the Comparison Test with

$\dfrac{1 + 4^n}{1 + 3^n} > \dfrac{1 + 4^n}{3^n + 3^n} > \dfrac{4^n}{2(3^n)} = \dfrac{1}{2}\left(\dfrac{4}{3}\right)^n$ or use the Test for Divergence.

27. $\dfrac{2 + (-1)^n}{n \sqrt{n}} \le \dfrac{3}{n \sqrt{n}}$, and $\displaystyle\sum_{n=1}^\infty \dfrac{3}{n \sqrt{n}}$ converges because it is a constant multiple of the convergent p-series $\displaystyle\sum_{n=1}^\infty \dfrac{1}{n \sqrt{n}}$

$\left[p = \tfrac{3}{2} > 1\right]$, so the given series converges by the Comparison Test.

29. Use the Limit Comparison Test with $a_n = \sin\left(\dfrac{1}{n}\right)$ and $b_n = \dfrac{1}{n}$. Then $\sum a_n$ and $\sum b_n$ are series with positive terms and

$\displaystyle\lim_{n\to\infty} \dfrac{a_n}{b_n} = \lim_{n\to\infty} \dfrac{\sin(1/n)}{1/n} = \lim_{\theta\to 0} \dfrac{\sin\theta}{\theta} = 1 > 0$. Since $\displaystyle\sum_{n=1}^\infty b_n$ is the divergent harmonic series,

$\displaystyle\sum_{n=1}^\infty \sin(1/n)$ also diverges.   [Note that we could also use l'Hospital's Rule to evaluate the limit:

$\displaystyle\lim_{x\to\infty} \dfrac{\sin(1/x)}{1/x} \overset{\text{H}}{=} \lim_{x\to\infty} \dfrac{\cos(1/x) \cdot \left(-1/x^2\right)}{-1/x^2} = \lim_{x\to\infty} \cos\dfrac{1}{x} = \cos 0 = 1.]$

31. We have already shown (in Exercise 17) that when $p = 1$ the series $\sum\limits_{n=2}^{\infty} \dfrac{1}{n(\ln n)^p}$ diverges, so assume that $p \neq 1$.

$f(x) = \dfrac{1}{x(\ln x)^p}$ is continuous and positive on $[2, \infty)$, and $f'(x) = -\dfrac{p + \ln x}{x^2(\ln x)^{p+1}} < 0$ if $x > e^{-p}$, so that f is eventually

decreasing and we can use the Integral Test.

$$\int_2^{\infty} \frac{1}{x(\ln x)^p}\, dx = \lim_{t \to \infty} \left[\frac{(\ln x)^{1-p}}{1-p} \right]_2^t \quad [\text{for } p \neq 1] = \lim_{t \to \infty} \left[\frac{(\ln t)^{1-p}}{1-p} - \frac{(\ln 2)^{1-p}}{1-p} \right]$$

This limit exists whenever $1 - p < 0 \iff p > 1$, so the series converges for $p > 1$.

33. (a) $f(x) = \dfrac{1}{x^2}$ is positive and continuous and $f'(x) = -\dfrac{2}{x^3}$ is negative for $x > 0$, and so the Integral Test applies.

$$\sum_{n=1}^{\infty} \frac{1}{n^2} \approx s_{10} = \frac{1}{1^2} + \frac{1}{2^2} + \frac{1}{3^2} + \cdots + \frac{1}{10^2} \approx 1.549768.$$

$R_{10} \leq \displaystyle\int_{10}^{\infty} \frac{1}{x^2}\, dx = \lim_{t \to \infty} \left[\frac{-1}{x} \right]_{10}^t = \lim_{t \to \infty} \left(-\frac{1}{t} + \frac{1}{10} \right) = \frac{1}{10}$, so the error is at most 0.1.

(b) $s_{10} + \displaystyle\int_{11}^{\infty} \frac{1}{x^2}\, dx \leq s \leq s_{10} + \int_{10}^{\infty} \frac{1}{x^2}\, dx \quad \Rightarrow \quad s_{10} + \frac{1}{11} \leq s \leq s_{10} + \frac{1}{10} \quad \Rightarrow$

$1.549768 + 0.090909 = 1.640677 \leq s \leq 1.549768 + 0.1 = 1.649768$, so we get $s \approx 1.64522$ (the average of 1.640677

and 1.649768) with error ≤ 0.005 (the maximum of $1.649768 - 1.64522$ and $1.64522 - 1.640677$, rounded up).

(c) $R_n \leq \displaystyle\int_n^{\infty} \frac{1}{x^2}\, dx = \frac{1}{n}$. So $R_n < 0.001$ if $\dfrac{1}{n} < \dfrac{1}{1000} \iff n > 1000$.

35. $f(x) = 1/(2x + 1)^6$ is continuous, positive, and decreasing on $[1, \infty)$, so the Integral Test applies. Using (3),

$R_n \leq \displaystyle\int_n^{\infty} (2x + 1)^{-6}\, dx = \lim_{t \to \infty} \left[\frac{-1}{10(2x+1)^5} \right]_n^t = \frac{1}{10(2n+1)^5}$. To be correct to five decimal places, we want

$\dfrac{1}{10(2n+1)^5} \leq \dfrac{5}{10^6} \iff (2n+1)^5 \geq 20{,}000 \iff n \geq \frac{1}{2}\left(\sqrt[5]{20{,}000} - 1 \right) \approx 3.12$, so use $n = 4$.

$s_4 = \displaystyle\sum_{n=1}^{4} \frac{1}{(2n+1)^6} = \frac{1}{3^6} + \frac{1}{5^6} + \frac{1}{7^6} + \frac{1}{9^6} \approx 0.001\,446 \approx 0.00145$.

37. $\displaystyle\sum_{n=1}^{10} \frac{1}{\sqrt{n^4 + 1}} = \frac{1}{\sqrt{2}} + \frac{1}{\sqrt{17}} + \frac{1}{\sqrt{82}} + \cdots + \frac{1}{\sqrt{10{,}001}} \approx 1.24856$. Now $\dfrac{1}{\sqrt{n^4 + 1}} < \dfrac{1}{\sqrt{n^4}} = \dfrac{1}{n^2}$, so the error is

$R_{10} \leq T_{10} \leq \displaystyle\int_{10}^{\infty} \frac{1}{x^2}\, dx = \lim_{t \to \infty} \left[-\frac{1}{x} \right]_{10}^t = \lim_{t \to \infty} \left(-\frac{1}{t} + \frac{1}{10} \right) = \frac{1}{10} = 0.1$.

39. (a) From the figure, $a_2 + a_3 + \cdots + a_n \leq \int_1^n f(x)\, dx$, so with

$f(x) = \dfrac{1}{x}, \ \dfrac{1}{2} + \dfrac{1}{3} + \dfrac{1}{4} + \cdots + \dfrac{1}{n} \leq \displaystyle\int_1^n \frac{1}{x}\, dx = \ln n$.

Thus, $s_n = 1 + \dfrac{1}{2} + \dfrac{1}{3} + \dfrac{1}{4} + \cdots + \dfrac{1}{n} \leq 1 + \ln n$.

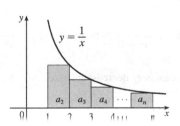

(b) By part (a), $s_{10^6} \leq 1 + \ln 10^6 \approx 14.82 < 15$ and

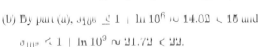

$s_{10^9} \leq 1 + \ln 10^9 \approx 21.72 < 22$.

41. Since $\dfrac{d_n}{10^n} \le \dfrac{9}{10^n}$ for each n, and since $\displaystyle\sum_{n=1}^{\infty} \dfrac{9}{10^n}$ is a convergent geometric series ($|r| = \frac{1}{10} < 1$), $0.d_1 d_2 d_3 \ldots = \displaystyle\sum_{n=1}^{\infty} \dfrac{d_n}{10^n}$ will always converge by the Comparison Test.

43. Yes. Since $\sum a_n$ is a convergent series with positive terms, $\displaystyle\lim_{n\to\infty} a_n = 0$ by Theorem 8.2.6, and $\sum b_n = \sum \sin(a_n)$ is a series with positive terms (for large enough n). We have $\displaystyle\lim_{n\to\infty} \dfrac{b_n}{a_n} = \lim_{n\to\infty} \dfrac{\sin(a_n)}{a_n} = 1 > 0$ by Theorem 3.3.2. Thus, $\sum b_n$ is also convergent by the Limit Comparison Test.

45. $\displaystyle\lim_{n\to\infty} n a_n = \lim_{n\to\infty} \dfrac{a_n}{1/n}$, so we apply the Limit Comparison Test with $b_n = \dfrac{1}{n}$. Since $\displaystyle\lim_{n\to\infty} n a_n > 0$ we know that either both series converge or both series diverge, and we also know that $\displaystyle\sum_{n=1}^{\infty} \dfrac{1}{n}$ diverges [p-series with $p = 1$]. Therefore, $\sum a_n$ must be divergent.

8.4 Other Convergence Tests

1. (a) An alternating series is a series whose terms are alternately positive and negative.

(b) An alternating series $\displaystyle\sum_{n=1}^{\infty} a_n = \sum_{n=1}^{\infty} (-1)^{n-1} b_n$, where $b_n = |a_n|$, converges if $0 < b_{n+1} \le b_n$ for all n and $\displaystyle\lim_{n\to\infty} b_n = 0$. (This is the Alternating Series Test.)

(c) The error involved in using the partial sum s_n as an approximation to the total sum s is the remainder $R_n = s - s_n$ and the size of the error is smaller than b_{n+1}; that is, $|R_n| \le b_{n+1}$. (This is the Alternating Series Estimation Theorem.)

3. $\dfrac{4}{7} - \dfrac{4}{8} + \dfrac{4}{9} - \dfrac{4}{10} + \dfrac{4}{11} - \cdots = \displaystyle\sum_{n=1}^{\infty} (-1)^{n-1} \dfrac{4}{n+6}$. Now $b_n = \dfrac{4}{n+6} > 0$, $\{b_n\}$ is decreasing, and $\displaystyle\lim_{n\to\infty} b_n = 0$, so the series converges by the Alternating Series Test.

5. $\displaystyle\sum_{n=1}^{\infty} a_n = \sum_{n=1}^{\infty} (-1)^{n-1} \dfrac{1}{2n+1} = \sum_{n=1}^{\infty} (-1)^{n-1} b_n$. Now $b_n = \dfrac{1}{2n+1} > 0$, $\{b_n\}$ is decreasing, and $\displaystyle\lim_{n\to\infty} b_n = 0$, so the series converges by the Alternating Series Test.

7. $\displaystyle\sum_{n=1}^{\infty} a_n = \sum_{n=1}^{\infty} (-1)^n \dfrac{3n-1}{2n+1} = \sum_{n=1}^{\infty} (-1)^n b_n$. Now $\displaystyle\lim_{n\to\infty} b_n = \lim_{n\to\infty} \dfrac{3 - 1/n}{2 + 1/n} = \dfrac{3}{2} \ne 0$. Since $\displaystyle\lim_{n\to\infty} a_n \ne 0$ (in fact the limit does not exist), the series diverges by the Test for Divergence.

9. $b_n = \dfrac{n}{n^2+9} > 0$, and if $f(x) = \dfrac{x}{x^2+9}$, then $f'(x) = \dfrac{(x^2+9)(1) - x(2x)}{(x^2+9)^2} = \dfrac{9 - x^2}{(x^2+9)^2} < 0$ for $x > 3$, so $\{b_n\}$ is eventually decreasing. Also, $\displaystyle\lim_{n\to\infty} b_n = \lim_{n\to\infty} \dfrac{n}{n^2+9} = \lim_{n\to\infty} \dfrac{1}{n+9/n} = 0$, so the series $\displaystyle\sum_{n=1}^{\infty} (-1)^{n+1} \dfrac{n}{n^2+9}$ converges by the Alternating Series Test.

11. $\sum\limits_{n=1}^{\infty} \dfrac{(-1)^{n-1}}{n} = 1 - \dfrac{1}{2} + \dfrac{1}{3} - \dfrac{1}{4} + \cdots + \dfrac{1}{49} - \dfrac{1}{50} + \dfrac{1}{51} - \dfrac{1}{52} + \cdots$. The 50th partial sum of this series is an

underestimate, since $\sum\limits_{n=1}^{\infty} \dfrac{(-1)^{n-1}}{n} = s_{50} + \left(\dfrac{1}{51} - \dfrac{1}{52}\right) + \left(\dfrac{1}{53} - \dfrac{1}{54}\right) + \cdots$, and the terms in parentheses are all positive.

The result can be seen geometrically in Figure 1.

13. If $p > 0$, $\dfrac{1}{(n+1)^p} \le \dfrac{1}{n^p}$ ($\{1/n^p\}$ is decreasing) and $\lim\limits_{n \to \infty} \dfrac{1}{n^p} = 0$, so the series converges by the Alternating Series Test.

If $p \le 0$, $\lim\limits_{n \to \infty} \dfrac{(-1)^{n-1}}{n^p}$ does not exist, so the series diverges by the Test for Divergence. Thus, $\sum\limits_{n=1}^{\infty} \dfrac{(-1)^{n-1}}{n^p}$

converges $\Leftrightarrow$ $p > 0$.

15. The series $\sum\limits_{n=1}^{\infty} \dfrac{(-1)^{n+1}}{n^6}$ satisfies (i) of the Alternating Series Test because $\dfrac{1}{(n+1)^6} < \dfrac{1}{n^6}$ and (ii) $\lim\limits_{n \to \infty} \dfrac{1}{n^6} = 0$, so the

series is convergent. Now $b_5 = \dfrac{1}{5^6} = 0.000064 > 0.00005$ and $b_6 = \dfrac{1}{6^6} \approx 0.00002 < 0.00005$, so by the Alternating Series

Estimation Theorem, $n = 5$. (That is, since the 6th term is less than the desired error, we need to add the first 5 terms to get the

sum to the desired accuracy.)

17.

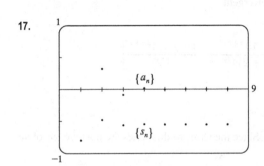

The graph gives us an estimate for the sum of the series

$\sum\limits_{n=1}^{\infty} \dfrac{(-0.8)^n}{n!}$ of -0.55.

$b_8 = \dfrac{(0.8)^n}{8!} \approx 0.000\,004$, so

$$\sum_{n=1}^{\infty} \dfrac{(-0.8)^n}{n!} \approx s_7 = \sum_{n=1}^{7} \dfrac{(-0.8)^n}{n!}$$

$$\approx -0.8 + 0.32 - 0.085\overline{3} + 0.0170\overline{6} - 0.002\,731 + 0.000\,364 - 0.000\,042 \approx -0.5507$$

Adding b_8 to s_7 does not change the fourth decimal place of s_7, so the sum of the series, correct to four decimal places,

is -0.5507.

19. $b_7 = \dfrac{7^2}{10^7} = 0.000\,004\,9$, so

$$\sum_{n=1}^{\infty} \dfrac{(-1)^{n-1} n^2}{10^n} \approx s_6 = \sum_{n=1}^{6} \dfrac{(-1)^{n-1} n^2}{10^n} = \dfrac{1}{10} - \dfrac{4}{100} + \dfrac{9}{1000} - \dfrac{16}{10,000} + \dfrac{25}{100,000} - \dfrac{36}{1,000,000} = 0.067\,614$$

Adding b_7 to s_6 does not change the fourth decimal place of s_6, so the sum of the series, correct to four decimal places, is

0.0676.

21. Using the Ratio Test, $\displaystyle\lim_{n\to\infty}\left|\frac{a_{n+1}}{a_n}\right| = \lim_{n\to\infty}\left|\frac{(-3)^{n+1}/(n+1)^3}{(-3)^n/n^3}\right| = \lim_{n\to\infty}\left|\frac{(-3)n^3}{(n+1)^3}\right| = 3\lim_{n\to\infty}\left(\frac{n}{n+1}\right)^3 = 3 > 1$,

so the series $\displaystyle\sum_{n=1}^{\infty}\frac{(-3)^n}{n^3}$ diverges.

23. Using the Ratio Test, $\displaystyle\lim_{n\to\infty}\left|\frac{a_{n+1}}{a_n}\right| = \lim_{n\to\infty}\left|\frac{(-10)^{n+1}}{(n+1)!}\cdot\frac{n!}{(-10)^n}\right| = \lim_{n\to\infty}\left|\frac{-10}{n+1}\right| = 0 < 1$, so the series $\displaystyle\sum_{n=0}^{\infty}\frac{(-10)^n}{n!}$ is

absolutely convergent.

25. $\displaystyle\lim_{k\to\infty}\left|\frac{a_{k+1}}{a_k}\right| = \lim_{k\to\infty}\left[\frac{(k+1)\left(\frac{2}{3}\right)^{k+1}}{k\left(\frac{2}{3}\right)^k}\right] = \lim_{k\to\infty}\frac{k+1}{k}\left(\frac{2}{3}\right)^1 = \frac{2}{3}\lim_{k\to\infty}\left(1+\frac{1}{k}\right) = \frac{2}{3}(1) = \frac{2}{3} < 1$, so the series

$\displaystyle\sum_{n=1}^{\infty}k\left(\frac{2}{3}\right)^k$ is absolutely convergent by the Ratio Test. Since the terms of this series are positive, absolute convergence is the

same as convergence.

27. Consider the series whose terms are the absolute values of the terms of the given series. $\displaystyle\sum_{n=1}^{\infty}\left|\frac{(-1)^{n-1}}{\sqrt{n}}\right| = \sum_{n=1}^{\infty}\frac{1}{n^{1/2}}$, which is

a divergent p-series $(p = \frac{1}{2} \le 1)$. Thus, $\displaystyle\sum_{n=1}^{\infty}\frac{(-1)^{n-1}}{\sqrt{n}}$ is *not* absolutely convergent.

29. $\displaystyle\lim_{n\to\infty}\left|\frac{a_{n+1}}{a_n}\right| = \lim_{n\to\infty}\left[\frac{10^{n+1}}{(n+2)4^{2(n+1)+1}}\cdot\frac{(n+1)4^{2n+1}}{10^n}\right] = \lim_{n\to\infty}\left[\frac{10^{n+1}}{(n+2)4^{2n+3}}\cdot\frac{(n+1)4^{2n+1}}{10^n}\right]$

$\displaystyle = \lim_{n\to\infty}\left(\frac{10}{4^2}\cdot\frac{n+1}{n+2}\right) = \frac{5}{8} < 1$,

so the series $\displaystyle\sum_{n=1}^{\infty}\frac{10^n}{(n+1)4^{2n+1}}$ is absolutely convergent by the Ratio Test. Since the terms of this series are positive, absolute

convergence is the same as convergence.

31. $\displaystyle\left|\frac{(-1)^n\arctan n}{n^2}\right| < \frac{\pi/2}{n^2}$, so since $\displaystyle\sum_{n=1}^{\infty}\frac{\pi/2}{n^2} = \frac{\pi}{2}\sum_{n=1}^{\infty}\frac{1}{n^2}$ converges $(p = 2 > 1)$, the given series $\displaystyle\sum_{n=1}^{\infty}\frac{(-1)^n\arctan n}{n^2}$

converges absolutely by the Comparison Test.

33. Use the Ratio Test with the series

$$1 - \frac{1\cdot 3}{3!} + \frac{1\cdot 3\cdot 5}{5!} - \frac{1\cdot 3\cdot 5\cdot 7}{7!} + \cdots + (-1)^{n-1}\frac{1\cdot 3\cdot 5\cdot\cdots\cdot(2n-1)}{(2n-1)!} + \cdots = \sum_{n=1}^{\infty}(-1)^{n-1}\frac{1\cdot 3\cdot 5\cdot\cdots\cdot(2n-1)}{(2n-1)!}.$$

$$\lim_{n\to\infty}\left|\frac{a_{n+1}}{a_n}\right| = \lim_{n\to\infty}\left|\frac{(-1)^n\cdot 1\cdot 3\cdot 5\cdot\cdots\cdot(2n-1)[2(n+1)-1]}{[2(n+1)-1]!}\cdot\frac{(2n-1)!}{(-1)^{n-1}\cdot 1\cdot 3\cdot 5\cdot\cdots\cdot(2n-1)}\right|$$

$$= \lim_{n\to\infty}\left|\frac{(-1)(2n+1)(2n-1)!}{(2n+1)(2n)(2n-1)!}\right| = \lim_{n\to\infty}\frac{1}{2n} = 0 < 1,$$

so the given series is absolutely convergent and therefore convergent.

35. By the recursive definition, $\displaystyle\lim_{n\to\infty}\left|\frac{a_{n+1}}{a_n}\right| = \lim_{n\to\infty}\left|\frac{5n+1}{4n+3}\right| = \frac{5}{4} > 1$, so the series diverges by the Ratio Test.

37. (a) $\displaystyle\lim_{n\to\infty}\left|\frac{1/(n+1)^3}{1/n^3}\right| = \lim_{n\to\infty}\frac{n^3}{(n+1)^3} = \lim_{n\to\infty}\frac{1}{(1+1/n)^3} = 1$. Inconclusive

(b) $\displaystyle\lim_{n\to\infty}\left|\frac{(n+1)}{2^{n+1}}\cdot\frac{2^n}{n}\right| = \lim_{n\to\infty}\frac{n+1}{2n} = \lim_{n\to\infty}\left(\frac{1}{2}+\frac{1}{2n}\right) = \frac{1}{2}$. Conclusive (convergent)

(c) $\displaystyle\lim_{n\to\infty}\left|\frac{(-3)^n}{\sqrt{n+1}}\cdot\frac{\sqrt{n}}{(-3)^{n-1}}\right| = 3\lim_{n\to\infty}\sqrt{\frac{n}{n+1}} = 3\lim_{n\to\infty}\sqrt{\frac{1}{1+1/n}} = 3$. Conclusive (divergent)

(d) $\displaystyle\lim_{n\to\infty}\left|\frac{\sqrt{n+1}}{1+(n+1)^2}\cdot\frac{1+n^2}{\sqrt{n}}\right| = \lim_{n\to\infty}\left[\sqrt{1+\frac{1}{n}}\cdot\frac{1/n^2+1}{1/n^2+(1+1/n)^2}\right] = 1$. Inconclusive

39. $\displaystyle\lim_{n\to\infty}\sqrt[n]{|a_n|} = \lim_{n\to\infty}\frac{n^2+1}{2n^2+1} = \lim_{n\to\infty}\frac{1+1/n^2}{2+1/n^2} = \frac{1}{2} < 1$, so the series $\displaystyle\sum_{n=1}^{\infty}\left(\frac{n^2+1}{2n^2+1}\right)^n$ is absolutely convergent by the

Root Test.

41. (a) $\displaystyle\lim_{n\to\infty}\left|\frac{a_{n+1}}{a_n}\right| = \lim_{n\to\infty}\left|\frac{x^{n+1}}{(n+1)!}\cdot\frac{n!}{x^n}\right| = \lim_{n\to\infty}\left|\frac{x}{n+1}\right| = |x|\lim_{n\to\infty}\frac{1}{n+1} = |x|\cdot 0 = 0 < 1$, so by the Ratio Test the

series $\displaystyle\sum_{n=0}^{\infty}\frac{x^n}{n!}$ converges for all x.

(b) Since the series of part (a) always converges, we must have $\displaystyle\lim_{n\to\infty}\frac{x^n}{n!} = 0$ by Theorem 8.2.6.

8.5 Power Series

1. A power series is a series of the form $\sum_{n=0}^{\infty}c_n x^n = c_0 + c_1 x + c_2 x^2 + c_3 x^3 + \cdots$, where x is a variable and the c_n's are

constants called the coefficients of the series.

More generally, a series of the form $\sum_{n=0}^{\infty}c_n(x-a)^n = c_0 + c_1(x-a) + c_2(x-a)^2 + \cdots$ is called a power series in

$(x-a)$ or a power series centered at a or a power series about a, where a is a constant.

3. If $a_n = \dfrac{x^n}{\sqrt{n}}$, then $\displaystyle\lim_{n\to\infty}\left|\frac{a_{n+1}}{a_n}\right| = \lim_{n\to\infty}\left|\frac{x^{n+1}}{\sqrt{n+1}}\cdot\frac{\sqrt{n}}{x^n}\right| = \lim_{n\to\infty}\left|\frac{x}{\sqrt{n+1}/\sqrt{n}}\right| = \lim_{n\to\infty}\frac{|x|}{\sqrt{1+1/n}} = |x|$.

By the Ratio Test, the series $\displaystyle\sum_{n=1}^{\infty}\frac{x^n}{\sqrt{n}}$ converges when $|x| < 1$, so the radius of convergence $R = 1$. Now we'll check the

endpoints, that is, $x = \pm 1$. When $x = 1$, the series $\displaystyle\sum_{n=1}^{\infty}\frac{1}{\sqrt{n}}$ diverges because it is a p-series with $p = \frac{1}{2} \leq 1$. When $x = -1$,

the series $\displaystyle\sum_{n=1}^{\infty}\frac{(-1)^n}{\sqrt{n}}$ converges by the Alternating Series Test. Thus, the interval of convergence is $I = [-1, 1)$.

5. If $a_n = \dfrac{(-1)^{n-1}x^n}{n^3}$, then

$$\lim_{n\to\infty}\left|\frac{a_{n+1}}{a_n}\right| = \lim_{n\to\infty}\left|\frac{(-1)^n x^{n+1}}{(n+1)^3}\cdot\frac{n^3}{(-1)^{n-1}x^n}\right| = \lim_{n\to\infty}\left|\frac{(-1)xn^3}{(n+1)^3}\right| = \lim_{n\to\infty}\left[\left(\frac{n}{n+1}\right)^3|x|\right] = 1^3\cdot|x| = |x|.\ \text{By the}$$

Ratio Test, the series $\displaystyle\sum_{n=1}^{\infty}\frac{(-1)^{n-1}x^n}{n^3}$ converges when $|x| < 1$, so the radius of convergence $R = 1$. Now we'll check the

endpoints, that is, $x = \pm 1$. When $x = 1$, the series $\displaystyle\sum_{n=1}^{\infty}\frac{(-1)^{n-1}}{n^3}$ converges by the Alternating Series Test. When $x = -1$,

the series $\displaystyle\sum_{n=1}^{\infty}\frac{(-1)^{n-1}(-1)^n}{n^3} = -\sum_{n=1}^{\infty}\frac{1}{n^3}$ converges because it is a constant multiple of a convergent p-series $[p = 3 > 1]$.

Thus, the interval of convergence is $I = [-1, 1]$.

7. If $a_n = \dfrac{x^n}{n!}$, then $\displaystyle\lim_{n\to\infty}\left|\frac{a_{n+1}}{a_n}\right| = \lim_{n\to\infty}\left|\frac{x^{n+1}}{(n+1)!}\cdot\frac{n!}{x^n}\right| = \lim_{n\to\infty}\left|\frac{x}{n+1}\right| = |x|\lim_{n\to\infty}\frac{1}{n+1} = |x|\cdot 0 = 0 < 1$ for *all* real x.

So, by the Ratio Test, $R = \infty$ and $I = (-\infty, \infty)$.

9. If $a_n = (-1)^n\dfrac{n^2 x^n}{2^n}$, then

$$\lim_{n\to\infty}\left|\frac{a_{n+1}}{a_n}\right| = \lim_{n\to\infty}\left|\frac{(n+1)^2 x^{n+1}}{2^{n+1}}\cdot\frac{2^n}{n^2 x^n}\right| = \lim_{n\to\infty}\left|\frac{x(n+1)^2}{2n^2}\right| = \lim_{n\to\infty}\left[\frac{|x|}{2}\left(1+\frac{1}{n}\right)^2\right] = \frac{|x|}{2}(1)^2 = \tfrac{1}{2}|x|.\ \text{By the}$$

Ratio Test, the series $\displaystyle\sum_{n=1}^{\infty}(-1)^n\frac{n^2 x^n}{2^n}$ converges when $\tfrac{1}{2}|x| < 1 \iff |x| < 2$, so the radius of convergence is $R = 2$.

When $x = \pm 2$, both series $\displaystyle\sum_{n=1}^{\infty}(-1)^n\frac{n^2(\pm 2)^n}{2^n} = \sum_{n=1}^{\infty}(\mp 1)^n n^2$ diverge by the Test for Divergence since

$\displaystyle\lim_{n\to\infty}\left|(\mp 1)^n n^2\right| = \infty$. Thus, the interval of convergence is $I = (-2, 2)$.

11. $a_n = \dfrac{(-2)^n x^n}{\sqrt[4]{n}}$, so $\displaystyle\lim_{n\to\infty}\left|\frac{a_{n+1}}{a_n}\right| = \lim_{n\to\infty}\frac{2^{n+1}|x|^{n+1}}{\sqrt[4]{n+1}}\cdot\frac{\sqrt[4]{n}}{2^n|x|^n} = \lim_{n\to\infty}2|x|\sqrt[4]{\frac{n}{n+1}} = 2|x|$, so by the Ratio Test, the

series converges when $2|x| < 1 \iff |x| < \tfrac{1}{2}$, so $R = \tfrac{1}{2}$. When $x = -\tfrac{1}{2}$, we get the divergent p-series $\displaystyle\sum_{n=1}^{\infty}\frac{1}{\sqrt[4]{n}}$

$[p = \tfrac{1}{4} \le 1]$. When $x = \tfrac{1}{2}$, we get the series $\displaystyle\sum_{n=1}^{\infty}\frac{(-1)^n}{\sqrt[4]{n}}$, which converges by the Alternating Series Test.

Thus, $I = \left(-\tfrac{1}{2}, \tfrac{1}{2}\right]$.

13. If $a_n = \dfrac{(x-2)^n}{n^2+1}$, then $\displaystyle\lim_{n\to\infty}\left|\frac{a_{n+1}}{a_n}\right| = \lim_{n\to\infty}\left|\frac{(x-2)^{n+1}}{(n+1)^2+1}\cdot\frac{n^2+1}{(x-2)^n}\right| = |x-2|\lim_{n\to\infty}\frac{n^2+1}{(n+1)^2+1} = |x-2|.\ \text{By the}$

Ratio Test, the series $\displaystyle\sum_{n=0}^{\infty}\frac{(x-2)^n}{n^2+1}$ converges when $|x-2| < 1\ [R = 1] \iff -1 < x-2 < 1 \iff 1 < x < 3$. When

$x = 1$, the series $\displaystyle\sum_{n=0}^{\infty}(-1)^n\frac{1}{n^2+1}$ converges by the Alternating Series Test; when $x = 3$, the series $\displaystyle\sum_{n=0}^{\infty}\frac{1}{n^2+1}$ converges by

comparison with the p-series $\displaystyle\sum_{n=1}^{\infty}\frac{1}{n^2}\ [p = 2 > 1]$. Thus, the interval of convergence is $I = [1, 3]$.

15. If $a_n = \dfrac{3^n (x+4)^n}{\sqrt{n}}$, then $\displaystyle\lim_{n\to\infty} \left| \dfrac{a_{n+1}}{a_n} \right| = \lim_{n\to\infty} \left| \dfrac{3^{n+1}(x+4)^{n+1}}{\sqrt{n+1}} \cdot \dfrac{\sqrt{n}}{3^n(x+4)^n} \right| = 3\,|x+4| \lim_{n\to\infty} \dfrac{\sqrt{n}}{\sqrt{n+1}} = 3\,|x+4|.$

By the Ratio Test, the series $\displaystyle\sum_{n=1}^{\infty} \dfrac{3^n(x+4)^n}{\sqrt{n}}$ converges when $3\,|x+4| < 1 \iff |x+4| < \frac{1}{3} \quad \left[R = \frac{1}{3}\right] \iff$

$-\frac{1}{3} < x + 4 < \frac{1}{3} \iff -\frac{13}{3} < x < -\frac{11}{3}$. When $x = -\frac{13}{3}$, the series $\displaystyle\sum_{n=1}^{\infty} (-1)^n \dfrac{1}{\sqrt{n}}$ converges by the Alternating Series

Test; when $x = -\frac{11}{3}$, the series $\displaystyle\sum_{n=1}^{\infty} \dfrac{1}{\sqrt{n}}$ diverges $\left[p = \frac{1}{2} \le 1\right]$. Thus, the interval of convergence is $I = \left[-\frac{13}{3}, -\frac{11}{3}\right)$.

17. $\displaystyle\lim_{n\to\infty} \left| \dfrac{a_{n+1}}{a_n} \right| = \lim_{n\to\infty} \left[\dfrac{|4x+1|^{n+1}}{(n+1)^2} \cdot \dfrac{n^2}{|4x+1|^n} \right] = \lim_{n\to\infty} \dfrac{|4x+1|}{(1+1/n)^2} = |4x+1|$, so by the Ratio Test, the series

converges when $|4x+1| < 1 \iff -1 < 4x+1 < 1 \iff -2 < 4x < 0 \iff -\frac{1}{2} < x < 0$, so $R = \frac{1}{4}$. When $x = -\frac{1}{2}$,

the series becomes $\displaystyle\sum_{n=1}^{\infty} \dfrac{(-1)^n}{n^2}$, which converges by the Alternating Series Test. When $x = 0$, the series becomes $\displaystyle\sum_{n=1}^{\infty} \dfrac{1}{n^2}$,

a convergent p-series $[p = 2 > 1]$. $I = \left[-\frac{1}{2}, 0\right]$.

19. If $a_n = n!\,(2x-1)^n$, then $\displaystyle\lim_{n\to\infty} \left| \dfrac{a_{n+1}}{a_n} \right| = \lim_{n\to\infty} \left| \dfrac{(n+1)!\,(2x-1)^{n+1}}{n!(2x-1)^n} \right| = \lim_{n\to\infty} (n+1)\,|2x-1| \to \infty$ as $n \to \infty$

for all $x \ne \frac{1}{2}$. Since the series diverges for all $x \ne \frac{1}{2}$, $R = 0$ and $I = \left\{\frac{1}{2}\right\}$.

21. $a_n = \dfrac{n}{b^n}(x-a)^n$, where $b > 0$.

$\displaystyle\lim_{n\to\infty} \left| \dfrac{a_{n+1}}{a_n} \right| = \lim_{n\to\infty} \dfrac{(n+1)\,|x-a|^{n+1}}{b^{n+1}} \cdot \dfrac{b^n}{n\,|x-a|^n} = \lim_{n\to\infty} \left(1 + \dfrac{1}{n}\right) \dfrac{|x-a|}{b} = \dfrac{|x-a|}{b}.$

By the Ratio Test, the series converges when $\dfrac{|x-a|}{b} < 1 \iff |x-a| < b \quad [\text{so } R = b] \iff -b < x-a < b \iff$

$a - b < x < a + b$. When $|x-a| = b$, $\displaystyle\lim_{n\to\infty} |a_n| = \lim_{n\to\infty} n = \infty$, so the series diverges. Thus, $I = (a-b, a+b)$.

23. If $a_n = \dfrac{x^n}{1 \cdot 3 \cdot 5 \cdot \cdots \cdot (2n-1)}$, then

$\displaystyle\lim_{n\to\infty} \left| \dfrac{a_{n+1}}{a_n} \right| = \lim_{n\to\infty} \left| \dfrac{x^{n+1}}{1 \cdot 3 \cdot 5 \cdot \cdots \cdot (2n-1)(2n+1)} \cdot \dfrac{1 \cdot 3 \cdot 5 \cdot \cdots \cdot (2n-1)}{x^n} \right| = \lim_{n\to\infty} \dfrac{|x|}{2n+1} = 0 < 1$. Thus, by

the Ratio Test, the series $\displaystyle\sum_{n=1}^{\infty} \dfrac{x^n}{1 \cdot 3 \cdot 5 \cdot \cdots \cdot (2n-1)}$ converges for *all* real x and we have $R = \infty$ and $I = (-\infty, \infty)$.

25. (a) We are given that the power series $\sum_{n=0}^{\infty} c_n x^n$ is convergent for $x = 4$. So by Theorem 3, it must converge for at least

$-4 < x \le 4$. In particular, it converges when $x = -2$; that is, $\sum_{n=0}^{\infty} c_n(-2)^n$ is convergent.

(b) It does not follow that $\sum_{n=0}^{\infty} c_n(-4)^n$ is necessarily convergent. [See the comments after Theorem 3 about convergence at

the endpoint of an interval. An example is $c_n = (-1)^n/(n4^n)$.]

27. If $a_n = \dfrac{(n!)^k}{(kn)!} x^n$, then

$$\lim_{n \to \infty} \left| \frac{a_{n+1}}{a_n} \right| = \lim_{n \to \infty} \frac{[(n+1)!]^k \,(kn)!}{(n!)^k \,[k(n+1)]!} |x| = \lim_{n \to \infty} \frac{(n+1)^k}{(kn+k)(kn+k-1) \cdots (kn+2)(kn+1)} |x|$$

$$= \lim_{n \to \infty} \left[\frac{(n+1)}{(kn+1)} \frac{(n+1)}{(kn+2)} \cdots \frac{(n+1)}{(kn+k)} \right] |x|$$

$$= \lim_{n \to \infty} \left[\frac{n+1}{kn+1} \right] \lim_{n \to \infty} \left[\frac{n+1}{kn+2} \right] \cdots \lim_{n \to \infty} \left[\frac{n+1}{kn+k} \right] |x|$$

$$= \left(\frac{1}{k} \right)^k |x| < 1 \quad \Leftrightarrow \quad |x| < k^k \text{ for convergence, and the radius of convergence is } R = k^k.$$

29. (a) If $a_n = \dfrac{(-1)^n \, x^{2n+1}}{n!(n+1)! \, 2^{2n+1}}$, then

$$\lim_{n \to \infty} \left| \frac{a_{n+1}}{a_n} \right| = \lim_{n \to \infty} \left| \frac{x^{2n+3}}{(n+1)!(n+2)! \, 2^{2n+3}} \cdot \frac{n!(n+1)! \, 2^{2n+1}}{x^{2n+1}} \right| = \left(\frac{x}{2} \right)^2 \lim_{n \to \infty} \frac{1}{(n+1)(n+2)} = 0 \text{ for all } x.$$

So $J_1(x)$ converges for all x and its domain is $(-\infty, \infty)$.

(b), (c) The initial terms of $J_1(x)$ up to $n = 5$ are $a_0 = \dfrac{x}{2}$,

$a_1 = -\dfrac{x^3}{16}$, $a_2 = \dfrac{x^5}{384}$, $a_3 = -\dfrac{x^7}{18{,}432}$, $a_4 = \dfrac{x^9}{1{,}474{,}560}$,

and $a_5 = -\dfrac{x^{11}}{176{,}947{,}200}$. The partial sums

seem to approximate $J_1(x)$ well near the origin, but as $|x|$ increases,

we need to take a large number of terms to get a good

approximation.

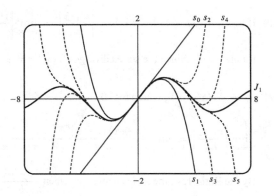

31. $s_{2n-1} = 1 + 2x + x^2 + 2x^3 + x^4 + 2x^5 + \cdots + x^{2n-2} + 2x^{2n-1}$

$$= 1(1+2x) + x^2(1+2x) + x^4(1+2x) + \cdots + x^{2n-2}(1+2x) = (1+2x)(1 + x^2 + x^4 + \cdots + x^{2n-2})$$

$$= (1+2x)\frac{1 - x^{2n}}{1 - x^2} \text{ [by (8.2.3) with } r = x^2] \quad \to \quad \frac{1+2x}{1-x^2} \text{ as } n \to \infty \text{ by (8.2.4)], when } |x| < 1.$$

Also $s_{2n} = s_{2n-1} + x^{2n} \to \dfrac{1+2x}{1-x^2}$ since $x^{2n} \to 0$ for $|x| < 1$. Therefore, $s_n \to \dfrac{1+2x}{1-x^2}$ since s_{2n} and s_{2n-1} both

approach $\dfrac{1+2x}{1-x^2}$ as $n \to \infty$. Thus, the interval of convergence is $(-1, 1)$ and $f(x) = \dfrac{1+2x}{1-x^2}$.

33. For $2 < x < 3$, $\sum c_n x^n$ diverges and $\sum d_n x^n$ converges. By Exercise 8.2.61, $\sum (c_n + d_n) x^n$ diverges. Since both series

converge for $|x| < 2$, the radius of convergence of $\sum (c_n + d_n) x^n$ is 2.

35. No. If a power series is centered at a, its interval of convergence is symmetric about a. If a power series has an infinite radius

of convergence, then its interval of convergence must be $(-\infty, \infty)$, not $[0, \infty)$.

8.6   Representations of Functions as Power Series

1. If $f(x) = \sum\limits_{n=0}^{\infty} c_n x^n$ has radius of convergence 10, then $f'(x) = \sum\limits_{n=1}^{\infty} n c_n x^{n-1}$ also has radius of convergence 10 by

Theorem 2.

3. Our goal is to write the function in the form $\dfrac{1}{1-r}$, and then use Equation (1) to represent the function as a sum of a power

series. $f(x) = \dfrac{1}{1+x} = \dfrac{1}{1-(-x)} = \sum\limits_{n=0}^{\infty}(-x)^n = \sum\limits_{n=0}^{\infty}(-1)^n x^n$ with $|-x| < 1 \iff |x| < 1$, so $R = 1$ and $I = (-1,1)$.

5. $f(x) = \dfrac{2}{3-x} = \dfrac{2}{3}\left(\dfrac{1}{1-x/3}\right) = \dfrac{2}{3}\sum\limits_{n=0}^{\infty}\left(\dfrac{x}{3}\right)^n$ or, equivalently, $2\sum\limits_{n=0}^{\infty}\dfrac{1}{3^{n+1}}x^n$. The series converges when $\left|\dfrac{x}{3}\right| < 1$,

that is, when $|x| < 3$, so $R = 3$ and $I = (-3,3)$.

7. $f(x) = \dfrac{x}{9+x^2} = \dfrac{x}{9}\left[\dfrac{1}{1+(x/3)^2}\right] = \dfrac{x}{9}\left[\dfrac{1}{1-\{-(x/3)^2\}}\right] = \dfrac{x}{9}\sum\limits_{n=0}^{\infty}\left[-\left(\dfrac{x}{3}\right)^2\right]^n = \dfrac{x}{9}\sum\limits_{n=0}^{\infty}(-1)^n\dfrac{x^{2n}}{9^n} = \sum\limits_{n=0}^{\infty}(-1)^n\dfrac{x^{2n+1}}{9^{n+1}}$

The geometric series $\sum\limits_{n=0}^{\infty}\left[-\left(\dfrac{x}{3}\right)^2\right]^n$ converges when $\left|-\left(\dfrac{x}{3}\right)^2\right| < 1 \iff \dfrac{|x^2|}{9} < 1 \iff |x|^2 < 9 \iff |x| < 3$, so

$R = 3$ and $I = (-3,3)$.

9. $f(x) = \dfrac{1+x}{1-x} = (1+x)\left(\dfrac{1}{1-x}\right) = (1+x)\sum\limits_{n=0}^{\infty}x^n = \sum\limits_{n=0}^{\infty}x^n + \sum\limits_{n=0}^{\infty}x^{n+1} = 1 + \sum\limits_{n=1}^{\infty}x^n + \sum\limits_{n=1}^{\infty}x^n = 1 + 2\sum\limits_{n=1}^{\infty}x^n.$

The series converges when $|x| < 1$, so $R = 1$ and $I = (-1,1)$.

A second approach: $f(x) = \dfrac{1+x}{1-x} = \dfrac{-(1-x)+2}{1-x} = -1 + 2\left(\dfrac{1}{1-x}\right) = -1 + 2\sum\limits_{n=0}^{\infty}x^n = 1 + 2\sum\limits_{n=1}^{\infty}x^n.$

A third approach:

$f(x) = \dfrac{1+x}{1-x} = (1+x)\left(\dfrac{1}{1-x}\right) = (1+x)(1+x+x^2+x^3+\cdots)$

$= (1+x+x^2+x^3+\cdots) + (x+x^2+x^3+x^4+\cdots) = 1 + 2x + 2x^2 + 2x^3 + \cdots = 1 + 2\sum\limits_{n=1}^{\infty}x^n.$

11. (a) $f(x) = \dfrac{1}{(1+x)^2} = \dfrac{d}{dx}\left(\dfrac{-1}{1+x}\right) = -\dfrac{d}{dx}\left[\sum\limits_{n=0}^{\infty}(-1)^n x^n\right]$ [from Exercise 3]

$= \sum\limits_{n=1}^{\infty}(-1)^{n+1}nx^{n-1}$ [from Theorem 2(i)] $= \sum\limits_{n=0}^{\infty}(-1)^n(n+1)x^n$ with $R = 1$.

In the last step, note that we *decreased* the initial value of the summation variable n by 1, and then *increased* each

occurrence of n in the term by 1 [also note that $(-1)^{n+2} = (-1)^n$].

(b) $f(x) = \dfrac{1}{(1+x)^3} = -\dfrac{1}{2}\dfrac{d}{dx}\left[\dfrac{1}{(1+x)^2}\right] = -\dfrac{1}{2}\dfrac{d}{dx}\left[\sum\limits_{n=0}^{\infty}(-1)^n(n+1)x^n\right]$ [from part (a)]

$= -\dfrac{1}{2}\sum\limits_{n=1}^{\infty}(-1)^n(n+1)nx^{n-1} = \dfrac{1}{2}\sum\limits_{n=0}^{\infty}(-1)^n(n+2)(n+1)x^n$ with $R = 1$.

(c) $f(x) = \dfrac{x^2}{(1+x)^3} = x^2\cdot\dfrac{1}{(1+x)^3} = x^2\cdot\dfrac{1}{2}\sum\limits_{n=0}^{\infty}(-1)^n(n+2)(n+1)x^n$ [from part (b)]

$= \dfrac{1}{2}\sum\limits_{n=0}^{\infty}(-1)^n(n+2)(n+1)x^{n+2}$

To write the power series with x^n rather than x^{n+2}, we will *decrease* each occurrence of n in the term by 2 and *increase*

the initial value of the summation variable by 2. This gives us $\dfrac{1}{2}\sum\limits_{n=2}^{\infty}(-1)^n(n)(n-1)x^n$ with $R = 1$.

13. $f(x) = \ln(5-x) = -\int \dfrac{dx}{5-x} = -\dfrac{1}{5}\int \dfrac{dx}{1-x/5} = -\dfrac{1}{5}\int\left[\sum\limits_{n=0}^{\infty}\left(\dfrac{x}{5}\right)^{n}\right]dx = C - \dfrac{1}{5}\sum\limits_{n=0}^{\infty}\dfrac{x^{n+1}}{5^{n}(n+1)} = C - \sum\limits_{n=1}^{\infty}\dfrac{x^{n}}{n\,5^{n}}$

Putting $x=0$, we get $C = \ln 5$. The series converges for $|x/5| < 1 \;\Leftrightarrow\; |x| < 5$, so $R = 5$.

15. We know that $\dfrac{1}{1+4x} = \dfrac{1}{1-(-4x)} = \sum\limits_{n=0}^{\infty}(-4x)^{n}$. Differentiating, we get

$\dfrac{-4}{(1+4x)^{2}} = \sum\limits_{n=1}^{\infty}(-4)^{n}nx^{n-1} = \sum\limits_{n=0}^{\infty}(-4)^{n+1}(n+1)x^{n}$, so

$f(x) = \dfrac{x}{(1+4x)^{2}} = \dfrac{-x}{4}\cdot\dfrac{-4}{(1+4x)^{2}} = \dfrac{-x}{4}\sum\limits_{n=0}^{\infty}(-4)^{n+1}(n+1)x^{n} = \sum\limits_{n=0}^{\infty}(-1)^{n}4^{n}(n+1)x^{n+1}$

for $|-4x| < 1 \;\Leftrightarrow\; |x| < \frac{1}{4}$, so $R = \frac{1}{4}$.

17. By Example 5, $\dfrac{1}{(1-x)^{2}} = \sum\limits_{n=0}^{\infty}(n+1)x^{n}$. Thus,

$$f(x) = \dfrac{1+x}{(1-x)^{2}} = \dfrac{1}{(1-x)^{2}} + \dfrac{x}{(1-x)^{2}} = \sum\limits_{n=0}^{\infty}(n+1)x^{n} + \sum\limits_{n=0}^{\infty}(n+1)x^{n+1}$$

$$= \sum\limits_{n=0}^{\infty}(n+1)x^{n} + \sum\limits_{n=1}^{\infty}nx^{n} \qquad \text{[make the starting values equal]}$$

$$= 1 + \sum\limits_{n=1}^{\infty}[(n+1)+n]x^{n} = 1 + \sum\limits_{n=1}^{\infty}(2n+1)x^{n} = \sum\limits_{n=0}^{\infty}(2n+1)x^{n} \text{ with } R = 1.$$

19. $f(x) = \dfrac{x}{x^{2}+16} = \dfrac{x}{16}\left(\dfrac{1}{1-(-x^{2}/16)}\right) = \dfrac{x}{16}\sum\limits_{n=0}^{\infty}\left(-\dfrac{x^{2}}{16}\right)^{n} = \dfrac{x}{16}\sum\limits_{n=0}^{\infty}(-1)^{n}\dfrac{1}{16^{n}}x^{2n} = \sum\limits_{n=0}^{\infty}(-1)^{n}\dfrac{1}{16^{n+1}}x^{2n+1}$.

The series converges when $\left|-x^{2}/16\right| < 1 \;\Leftrightarrow\; x^{2} < 16 \;\Leftrightarrow\; |x| < 4$, so $R = 4$. The partial sums are $s_{1} = \dfrac{x}{16}$,

$s_{2} = s_{1} - \dfrac{x^{3}}{16^{2}}$, $s_{3} = s_{2} + \dfrac{x^{5}}{16^{3}}$, $s_{4} = s_{3} - \dfrac{x^{7}}{16^{4}}$, $s_{5} = s_{4} + \dfrac{x^{9}}{16^{5}}$, ... Note that s_{1} corresponds to the first term of the infinite

sum, regardless of the value of the summation variable and the value of the exponent.

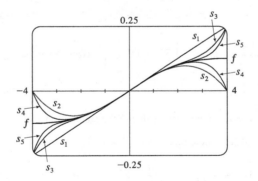

As n increases, $s_{n}(x)$ approximates f better on the interval of convergence, which is $(-4, 4)$.

21. $f(x) = \ln\left(\dfrac{1+x}{1-x}\right) = \ln(1+x) - \ln(1-x) = \int \dfrac{dx}{1+x} + \int \dfrac{dx}{1-x} = \int \dfrac{dx}{1-(-x)} + \int \dfrac{dx}{1-x}$

$= \int\left[\sum\limits_{n=0}^{\infty}(-1)^{n}x^{n} + \sum\limits_{n=0}^{\infty}x^{n}\right]dx = \int\left[(1-x+x^{2}-x^{3}+x^{4}-\cdots) + (1+x+x^{2}+x^{3}+x^{4}+\cdots)\right]dx$

$= \int(2+2x^{2}+2x^{4}+\cdots)\,dx = \int\sum\limits_{n=0}^{\infty}2x^{2n}\,dx = C + \sum\limits_{n=0}^{\infty}\dfrac{2x^{2n+1}}{2n+1}$

But $f(0) = \ln\frac{1}{1} = 0$, so $C = 0$ and we have $f(x) = \sum\limits_{n=0}^{\infty}\dfrac{2x^{2n+1}}{2n+1}$ with $R = 1$. If $x = \pm 1$, then $f(x) = \pm 2\sum\limits_{n=0}^{\infty}\dfrac{1}{2n+1}$,

which both diverge by the Limit Comparison Test with $b_n = \dfrac{1}{n}$. The partial sums are $s_1 = \dfrac{2x}{1}$, $s_2 = s_1 + \dfrac{2x^3}{3}$,

$s_3 = s_2 + \dfrac{2x^5}{5}, \ldots$.

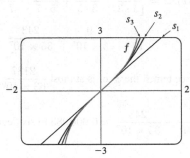

As n increases, $s_n(x)$ approximates f better on the interval of convergence, which is $(-1, 1)$.

23. $\dfrac{t}{1-t^8} = t\cdot\dfrac{1}{1-t^8} = t\sum\limits_{n=0}^{\infty}(t^8)^n = \sum\limits_{n=0}^{\infty}t^{8n+1} \quad\Rightarrow\quad \displaystyle\int\dfrac{t}{1-t^8}\,dt = C + \sum\limits_{n=0}^{\infty}\dfrac{t^{8n+2}}{8n+2}$. The series for $\dfrac{1}{1-t^8}$ converges

when $\left|t^8\right| < 1 \quad\Leftrightarrow\quad |t| < 1$, so $R = 1$ for that series and also the series for $t/(1-t^8)$. By Theorem 2, the series for

$\displaystyle\int\dfrac{t}{1-t^8}\,dt$ also has $R = 1$.

25. By Example 7, $\tan^{-1}x = \sum\limits_{n=0}^{\infty}(-1)^n\dfrac{x^{2n+1}}{2n+1}$ with $R = 1$, so

$x - \tan^{-1}x = x - \left(x - \dfrac{x^3}{3} + \dfrac{x^5}{5} - \dfrac{x^7}{7} + \cdots\right) = \dfrac{x^3}{3} - \dfrac{x^5}{5} + \dfrac{x^7}{7} - \cdots = \sum\limits_{n=1}^{\infty}(-1)^{n+1}\dfrac{x^{2n+1}}{2n+1}$ and

$\dfrac{x - \tan^{-1}x}{x^3} = \sum\limits_{n=1}^{\infty}(-1)^{n+1}\dfrac{x^{2n-2}}{2n+1}$, so

$\displaystyle\int\dfrac{x - \tan^{-1}x}{x^3}\,dx = C + \sum\limits_{n=1}^{\infty}(-1)^{n+1}\dfrac{x^{2n-1}}{(2n+1)(2n-1)} = C + \sum\limits_{n=1}^{\infty}(-1)^{n+1}\dfrac{x^{2n-1}}{4n^2-1}$. By Theorem 2, $R = 1$.

27. $\dfrac{1}{1+x^5} = \dfrac{1}{1-(-x^5)} = \sum\limits_{n=0}^{\infty}(-x^5)^n = \sum\limits_{n=0}^{\infty}(-1)^n x^{5n} \quad\Rightarrow$

$\displaystyle\int\dfrac{1}{1+x^5}\,dx = \int\sum\limits_{n=0}^{\infty}(-1)^n x^{5n}\,dx = C + \sum\limits_{n=0}^{\infty}(-1)^n\dfrac{x^{5n+1}}{5n+1}$. Thus,

$I = \displaystyle\int_0^{0.2}\dfrac{1}{1+x^5}\,dx = \left[x - \dfrac{x^6}{6} + \dfrac{x^{11}}{11} - \cdots\right]_0^{0.2} = 0.2 - \dfrac{(0.2)^6}{6} + \dfrac{(0.2)^{11}}{11} - \cdots$. The series is alternating, so if we use

the first two terms, the error is at most $(0.2)^{11}/11 \approx 1.9\times 10^{-9}$. So $I \approx 0.2 - (0.2)^6/6 \approx 0.199\,989$ to six decimal places.

29. We substitute $3x$ for x in Example 7, and find that

$$\int x \arctan(3x)\,dx = \int x \sum_{n=0}^{\infty} (-1)^n \frac{(3x)^{2n+1}}{2n+1}\,dx = \int \sum_{n=0}^{\infty} (-1)^n \frac{3^{2n+1}\,x^{2n+2}}{2n+1}\,dx = C + \sum_{n=0}^{\infty} (-1)^n \frac{3^{2n+1}\,x^{2n+3}}{(2n+1)(2n+3)}$$

So

$$\int_0^{0.1} x \arctan(3x)\,dx = \left[\frac{3x^3}{1\cdot3} - \frac{3^3 x^5}{3\cdot5} + \frac{3^5 x^7}{5\cdot7} - \frac{3^7 x^9}{7\cdot9} + \cdots \right]_0^{0.1}$$

$$= \frac{1}{10^3} - \frac{9}{5\times10^5} + \frac{243}{35\times10^7} - \frac{2187}{63\times10^9} + \cdots.$$

The series is alternating, so if we use three terms, the error is at most $\dfrac{2187}{63\times10^9} \approx 3.5\times10^{-8}$. So

$$\int_0^{0.1} x \arctan(3x)\,dx \approx \frac{1}{10^3} - \frac{9}{5\times10^5} + \frac{243}{35\times10^7} \approx 0.000\,983 \text{ to six decimal places.}$$

31. By Example 7, $\arctan x = x - \dfrac{x^3}{3} + \dfrac{x^5}{5} - \dfrac{x^7}{7} + \cdots$, so $\arctan 0.2 = 0.2 - \dfrac{(0.2)^3}{3} + \dfrac{(0.2)^5}{5} - \dfrac{(0.2)^7}{7} + \cdots$.

The series is alternating, so if we use three terms, the error is at most $\dfrac{(0.2)^7}{7} \approx 0.000\,002$.

Thus, to five decimal places, $\arctan 0.2 \approx 0.2 - \dfrac{(0.2)^3}{3} + \dfrac{(0.2)^5}{5} \approx 0.197\,40$.

33. (a) $J_0(x) = \displaystyle\sum_{n=0}^{\infty} \frac{(-1)^n x^{2n}}{2^{2n}(n!)^2}$, $J_0'(x) = \displaystyle\sum_{n=1}^{\infty} \frac{(-1)^n 2n x^{2n-1}}{2^{2n}(n!)^2}$, and $J_0''(x) = \displaystyle\sum_{n=1}^{\infty} \frac{(-1)^n 2n(2n-1)x^{2n-2}}{2^{2n}(n!)^2}$, so

$$x^2 J_0''(x) + x J_0'(x) + x^2 J_0(x) = \sum_{n=1}^{\infty} \frac{(-1)^n 2n(2n-1)x^{2n}}{2^{2n}(n!)^2} + \sum_{n=1}^{\infty} \frac{(-1)^n 2n x^{2n}}{2^{2n}(n!)^2} + \sum_{n=0}^{\infty} \frac{(-1)^n x^{2n+2}}{2^{2n}(n!)^2}$$

$$= \sum_{n=1}^{\infty} \frac{(-1)^n 2n(2n-1)x^{2n}}{2^{2n}(n!)^2} + \sum_{n=1}^{\infty} \frac{(-1)^n 2n x^{2n}}{2^{2n}(n!)^2} + \sum_{n=1}^{\infty} \frac{(-1)^{n-1} x^{2n}}{2^{2n-2}\,[(n-1)!]^2}$$

$$= \sum_{n=1}^{\infty} \frac{(-1)^n 2n(2n-1)x^{2n}}{2^{2n}(n!)^2} + \sum_{n=1}^{\infty} \frac{(-1)^n 2n x^{2n}}{2^{2n}(n!)^2} + \sum_{n=1}^{\infty} \frac{(-1)^n (-1)^{-1} 2^2 n^2 x^{2n}}{2^{2n}(n!)^2}$$

$$= \sum_{n=1}^{\infty} (-1)^n \left[\frac{2n(2n-1) + 2n - 2^2 n^2}{2^{2n}(n!)^2} \right] x^{2n}$$

$$= \sum_{n=1}^{\infty} (-1)^n \left[\frac{4n^2 - 2n + 2n - 4n^2}{2^{2n}(n!)^2} \right] x^{2n} = 0$$

(b) $\displaystyle\int_0^1 J_0(x)\,dx = \int_0^1 \left[\sum_{n=0}^{\infty} \frac{(-1)^n x^{2n}}{2^{2n}(n!)^2} \right] dx = \int_0^1 \left(1 - \frac{x^2}{4} + \frac{x^4}{64} - \frac{x^6}{2304} + \cdots \right) dx$

$$= \left[x - \frac{x^3}{3\cdot4} + \frac{x^5}{5\cdot64} - \frac{x^7}{7\cdot2304} + \cdots \right]_0^1 = 1 - \frac{1}{12} + \frac{1}{320} - \frac{1}{16,128} + \cdots$$

Since $\frac{1}{16,128} \approx 0.000062$, it follows from The Alternating Series Estimation Theorem that, correct to three decimal places,

$\int_0^1 J_0(x)\,dx \approx 1 - \frac{1}{12} + \frac{1}{320} \approx 0.920$.

35. (a) $f(x) = \sum\limits_{n=0}^{\infty} \dfrac{x^n}{n!} \Rightarrow f'(x) = \sum\limits_{n=1}^{\infty} \dfrac{nx^{n-1}}{n!} = \sum\limits_{n=1}^{\infty} \dfrac{x^{n-1}}{(n-1)!} = \sum\limits_{n=0}^{\infty} \dfrac{x^n}{n!} = f(x)$

(b) By Theorem 7.4.2, the only solution to the differential equation $df(x)/dx = f(x)$ is $f(x) = Ke^x$, but $f(0) = 1$, so

$K = 1$ and $f(x) = e^x$.

Or: We could solve the equation $df(x)/dx = f(x)$ as a separable differential equation.

37. If $a_n = \dfrac{x^n}{n^2}$, then by the Ratio Test, $\lim\limits_{n\to\infty}\left|\dfrac{a_{n+1}}{a_n}\right| = \lim\limits_{n\to\infty}\left|\dfrac{x^{n+1}}{(n+1)^2}\cdot\dfrac{n^2}{x^n}\right| = |x| \lim\limits_{n\to\infty}\left(\dfrac{n}{n+1}\right)^2 = |x| < 1$ for

convergence, so $R = 1$. When $x = \pm 1$, $\sum\limits_{n=1}^{\infty}\left|\dfrac{x^n}{n^2}\right| = \sum\limits_{n=1}^{\infty}\dfrac{1}{n^2}$ which is a convergent p-series ($p = 2 > 1$), so the interval of

convergence for f is $[-1, 1]$. By Theorem 2, the radii of convergence of f' and f'' are both 1, so we need only check the

endpoints. $f(x) = \sum\limits_{n=1}^{\infty}\dfrac{x^n}{n^2} \Rightarrow f'(x) = \sum\limits_{n=1}^{\infty}\dfrac{nx^{n-1}}{n^2} = \sum\limits_{n=0}^{\infty}\dfrac{x^n}{n+1}$, and this series diverges for $x = 1$ (harmonic series)

and converges for $x = -1$ (Alternating Series Test), so the interval of convergence is $[-1, 1)$. $f''(x) = \sum\limits_{n=1}^{\infty}\dfrac{nx^{n-1}}{n+1}$ diverges

at both 1 and -1 (Test for Divergence) since $\lim\limits_{n\to\infty}\dfrac{n}{n+1} = 1 \neq 0$, so its interval of convergence is $(-1, 1)$.

39. By Example 7, $\tan^{-1}x = \sum\limits_{n=0}^{\infty}(-1)^n\dfrac{x^{2n+1}}{2n+1}$ for $|x| < 1$. In particular, for $x = \dfrac{1}{\sqrt{3}}$, we

have $\dfrac{\pi}{6} = \tan^{-1}\left(\dfrac{1}{\sqrt{3}}\right) = \sum\limits_{n=0}^{\infty}(-1)^n\dfrac{(1/\sqrt{3})^{2n+1}}{2n+1} = \sum\limits_{n=0}^{\infty}(-1)^n\left(\dfrac{1}{3}\right)^n\dfrac{1}{\sqrt{3}}\dfrac{1}{2n+1}$, so

$\pi = \dfrac{6}{\sqrt{3}}\sum\limits_{n=0}^{\infty}\dfrac{(-1)^n}{(2n+1)3^n} = 2\sqrt{3}\sum\limits_{n=0}^{\infty}\dfrac{(-1)^n}{(2n+1)3^n}$.

8.7 Taylor and Maclaurin Series

1. Using Theorem 5 with $\sum\limits_{n=0}^{\infty}b_n(x-5)^n$, $b_n = \dfrac{f^{(n)}(a)}{n!}$, so $b_8 = \dfrac{f^{(8)}(5)}{8!}$.

3. Since $f^{(n)}(0) = (n+1)!$, Equation 7 gives the Maclaurin series

$\sum\limits_{n=0}^{\infty}\dfrac{f^{(n)}(0)}{n!}x^n = \sum\limits_{n=0}^{\infty}\dfrac{(n+1)!}{n!}x^n = \sum\limits_{n=0}^{\infty}(n+1)x^n$. Applying the Ratio Test with $a_n = (n+1)x^n$ gives us

$\lim\limits_{n\to\infty}\left|\dfrac{a_{n+1}}{a_n}\right| = \lim\limits_{n\to\infty}\left|\dfrac{(n+2)x^{n+1}}{(n+1)x^n}\right| = |x|\lim\limits_{n\to\infty}\dfrac{n+2}{n+1} = |x|\cdot 1 = |x|$. For convergence, we must have $|x| < 1$, so the

radius of convergence $R = 1$.

5.

n	$f^{(n)}(x)$	$f^{(n)}(0)$
0	$(1-x)^{-2}$	1
1	$2(1-x)^{-3}$	2
2	$6(1-x)^{-4}$	6
3	$24(1-x)^{-5}$	24
4	$120(1-x)^{-6}$	120
$\vdots$	$\vdots$	$\vdots$

$$(1-x)^{-2} = f(0) + f'(0)x + \frac{f''(0)}{2!}x^2 + \frac{f'''(0)}{3!}x^3 + \frac{f^{(4)}(0)}{4!}x^4 + \cdots$$

$$= 1 + 2x + \frac{6}{2}x^2 + \frac{24}{6}x^3 + \frac{120}{24}x^4 + \cdots$$

$$= 1 + 2x + 3x^2 + 4x^3 + 5x^4 + \cdots = \sum_{n=0}^{\infty}(n+1)x^n$$

$$\lim_{n\to\infty}\left|\frac{a_{n+1}}{a_n}\right| = \lim_{n\to\infty}\left|\frac{(n+2)x^{n+1}}{(n+1)x^n}\right| = |x|\lim_{n\to\infty}\frac{n+2}{n+1} = |x|\,(1) = |x| < 1$$

for convergence, so $R = 1$.

7.

n	$f^{(n)}(x)$	$f^{(n)}(0)$
0	$\sin\pi x$	0
1	$\pi\cos\pi x$	π
2	$-\pi^2\sin\pi x$	0
3	$-\pi^3\cos\pi x$	$-\pi^3$
4	$\pi^4\sin\pi x$	0
5	$\pi^5\cos\pi x$	π^5
$\vdots$	$\vdots$	$\vdots$

$$\sin\pi x = f(0) + f'(0)x + \frac{f''(0)}{2!}x^2 + \frac{f'''(0)}{3!}x^3$$

$$+ \frac{f^{(4)}(0)}{4!}x^4 + \frac{f^{(5)}(0)}{5!}x^5 + \cdots$$

$$= 0 + \pi x + 0 - \frac{\pi^3}{3!}x^3 + 0 + \frac{\pi^5}{5!}x^5 + \cdots$$

$$= \pi x - \frac{\pi^3}{3!}x^3 + \frac{\pi^5}{5!}x^5 - \frac{\pi^7}{7!}x^7 + \cdots$$

$$= \sum_{n=0}^{\infty}(-1)^n\frac{\pi^{2n+1}}{(2n+1)!}x^{2n+1}$$

$$\lim_{n\to\infty}\left|\frac{a_{n+1}}{a_n}\right| = \lim_{n\to\infty}\left|\frac{\pi^{2n+3}\,x^{2n+3}}{(2n+3)!}\cdot\frac{(2n+1)!}{\pi^{2n+1}\,x^{2n+1}}\right| = \lim_{n\to\infty}\frac{\pi^2\,x^2}{(2n+3)(2n+2)}$$

$$= 0 < 1 \quad \text{for all } x, \text{ so } R = \infty.$$

9.

n	$f^{(n)}(x)$	$f^{(n)}(0)$
0	e^{5x}	1
1	$5e^{5x}$	5
2	5^2e^{5x}	25
3	5^3e^{5x}	125
4	5^4e^{5x}	625
$\vdots$	$\vdots$	$\vdots$

$$e^{5x} = \sum_{n=0}^{\infty}\frac{f^{(n)}(0)}{n!}x^n = \sum_{n=0}^{\infty}\frac{5^n}{n!}x^n.$$

$$\lim_{n\to\infty}\left|\frac{a_{n+1}}{a_n}\right| = \lim_{n\to\infty}\left[\frac{5^{n+1}\,|x|^{n+1}}{(n+1)!}\cdot\frac{n!}{5^n\,|x|^n}\right]$$

$$= \lim_{n\to\infty}\frac{5\,|x|}{n+1} = 0 < 1 \quad \text{for all } x, \text{ so } R = \infty.$$

11.

n	$f^{(n)}(x)$	$f^{(n)}(1)$
0	$x^4 - 3x^2 + 1$	-1
1	$4x^3 - 6x$	-2
2	$12x^2 - 6$	6
3	$24x$	24
4	24	24
5	0	0
6	0	0
$\vdots$	$\vdots$	$\vdots$

$f^{(n)}(x) = 0$ for $n \geq 5$, so f has a finite series expansion about $a = 1$.

$$f(x) = x^4 - 3x^2 + 1 = \sum_{n=0}^{4}\frac{f^{(n)}(1)}{n!}(x-1)^n$$

$$= \frac{-1}{0!}(x-1)^0 + \frac{-2}{1!}(x-1)^1 + \frac{6}{2!}(x-1)^2 + \frac{24}{3!}(x-1)^3 + \frac{24}{4!}(x-1)^4$$

$$= -1 - 2(x-1) + 3(x-1)^2 + 4(x-1)^3 + (x-1)^4$$

A finite series converges for all x, so $R = \infty$.

13. $f(x) = e^x \;\Rightarrow\; f^{(n)}(x) = e^x$, so $f^{(n)}(3) = e^3$ and $e^x = \sum\limits_{n=0}^{\infty} \dfrac{e^3}{n!}(x-3)^n$. If $a_n = \dfrac{e^3}{n!}(x-3)^n$, then

$$\lim_{n\to\infty}\left|\frac{a_{n+1}}{a_n}\right| = \lim_{n\to\infty}\left|\frac{e^3(x-3)^{n+1}}{(n+1)!}\cdot\frac{n!}{e^3(x-3)^n}\right| = \lim_{n\to\infty}\frac{|x-3|}{n+1} = 0 < 1 \text{ for all } x, \text{ so } R = \infty.$$

15.

n	$f^{(n)}(x)$	$f^{(n)}(\pi)$
0	$\cos x$	-1
1	$-\sin x$	0
2	$-\cos x$	1
3	$\sin x$	0
4	$\cos x$	-1
⋮	⋮	⋮

$$\cos x = \sum_{k=0}^{\infty}\frac{f^{(k)}(\pi)}{k!}(x-\pi)^k = -1 + \frac{(x-\pi)^2}{2!} - \frac{(x-\pi)^4}{4!} + \frac{(x-\pi)^6}{6!} - \cdots$$

$$= \sum_{n=0}^{\infty}(-1)^{n+1}\frac{(x-\pi)^{2n}}{(2n)!}$$

$$\lim_{n\to\infty}\left|\frac{a_{n+1}}{a_n}\right| = \lim_{n\to\infty}\left[\frac{|x-\pi|^{2n+2}}{(2n+2)!}\cdot\frac{(2n)!}{|x-\pi|^{2n}}\right]$$

$$= \lim_{n\to\infty}\frac{|x-\pi|^2}{(2n+2)(2n+1)} = 0 < 1 \quad \text{for all } x, \text{ so } R = \infty.$$

17.

n	$f^{(n)}(x)$	$f^{(n)}(9)$
0	$x^{-1/2}$	$\frac{1}{3}$
1	$-\frac{1}{2}x^{-3/2}$	$-\frac{1}{2}\cdot\frac{1}{3^3}$
2	$\frac{3}{4}x^{-5/2}$	$-\frac{1}{2}\cdot\left(-\frac{3}{2}\right)\cdot\frac{1}{3^5}$
3	$-\frac{15}{8}x^{-7/2}$	$-\frac{1}{2}\cdot\left(-\frac{3}{2}\right)\cdot\left(-\frac{5}{2}\right)\cdot\frac{1}{3^7}$
⋮	⋮	⋮

$$\frac{1}{\sqrt{x}} = \frac{1}{3} - \frac{1}{2\cdot 3^3}(x-9) + \frac{3}{2^2\cdot 3^5}\frac{(x-9)^2}{2!}$$

$$- \frac{3\cdot 5}{2^3\cdot 3^7}\frac{(x-9)^3}{3!} + \cdots$$

$$= \frac{1}{3} + \sum_{n=1}^{\infty}(-1)^n\frac{1\cdot 3\cdot 5\cdot\,\cdots\,\cdot(2n-1)}{2^n\cdot 3^{2n+1}\cdot n!}(x-9)^n.$$

$$\lim_{n\to\infty}\left|\frac{a_{n+1}}{a_n}\right| = \lim_{n\to\infty}\left[\frac{1\cdot 3\cdot 5\cdot\,\cdots\,\cdot(2n-1)[2(n+1)-1]\,|x-9|^{n+1}}{2^{n+1}\cdot 3^{[2(n+1)+1]}\cdot(n+1)!}\cdot\frac{2^n\cdot 3^{2n+1}\cdot n!}{1\cdot 3\cdot 5\cdot\,\cdots\,\cdot(2n-1)\,|x-9|^n}\right]$$

$$= \lim_{n\to\infty}\left[\frac{(2n+1)\,|x-9|}{2\cdot 3^2(n+1)}\right] = \frac{1}{9}|x-9| < 1 \quad \text{for convergence, so } |x-9| < 9 \text{ and } R = 9.$$

19. If $f(x) = \sin \pi x$, then $f^{(n+1)}(x) = \pm\pi^{n+1}\sin\pi x$ or $\pm\pi^{n+1}\cos\pi x$. In each case, $\left|f^{(n+1)}(x)\right| \leq \pi^{n+1}$, so by Formula 9

with $a = 0$ and $M = \pi^{n+1}$, $|R_n(x)| \leq \dfrac{\pi^{n+1}}{(n+1)!}|x|^{n+1} = \dfrac{|\pi x|^{n+1}}{(n+1)!}$. Thus, $|R_n(x)| \to 0$ as $n \to \infty$ by Equation 10.

So $\lim\limits_{n\to\infty} R_n(x) = 0$ and, by Theorem 8, the series in Exercise 7 represents $\sin \pi x$ for all x.

21. The general binomial series in (17) is

$$(1+x)^k = \sum_{n=0}^{\infty}\binom{k}{n}x^n = 1 + kx + \frac{k(k-1)}{2!}x^2 + \frac{k(k-1)(k-2)}{3!}x^3 + \cdots.$$

$$(1+x)^{1/2} = \sum_{n=0}^{\infty}\binom{\frac{1}{2}}{n}x^n = 1 + \left(\tfrac{1}{2}\right)x + \frac{\left(\frac{1}{2}\right)\left(-\frac{1}{2}\right)}{2!}x^2 + \frac{\left(\frac{1}{2}\right)\left(-\frac{1}{2}\right)\left(-\frac{3}{2}\right)}{3!}x^3 + \cdots$$

$$= 1 + \frac{x}{2} - \frac{x^2}{2^2\cdot 2!} + \frac{1\cdot 3\cdot x^3}{2^3\cdot 3!} - \frac{1\cdot 3\cdot 5\cdot x^4}{2^4\cdot 4!} + \cdots$$

$$= 1 + \frac{x}{2} + \sum_{n=2}^{\infty}\frac{(-1)^{n-1}1\cdot 3\cdot 5\cdot\,\cdots\,\cdot(2n-3)x^n}{2^n\; n!} \quad \text{for } |x| < 1, \text{ so } R = 1$$

23. $\dfrac{1}{(2+x)^3} = \dfrac{1}{[2(1+x/2)]^3} = \dfrac{1}{8}\left(1+\dfrac{x}{2}\right)^{-3} = \dfrac{1}{8}\sum\limits_{n=0}^{\infty}\binom{-3}{n}\left(\dfrac{x}{2}\right)^n$. The binomial coefficient is

$$\binom{-3}{n} = \dfrac{(-3)(-4)(-5)\cdots\cdots(-3-n+1)}{n!} = \dfrac{(-3)(-4)(-5)\cdots\cdots[-(n+2)]}{n!}$$

$$= \dfrac{(-1)^n \cdot 2\cdot3\cdot4\cdot5\cdots\cdots(n+1)(n+2)}{2\cdot n!} = \dfrac{(-1)^n(n+1)(n+2)}{2}$$

Thus, $\dfrac{1}{(2+x)^3} = \dfrac{1}{8}\sum\limits_{n=0}^{\infty}\dfrac{(-1)^n(n+1)(n+2)}{2}\dfrac{x^n}{2^n} = \sum\limits_{n=0}^{\infty}\dfrac{(-1)^n(n+1)(n+2)x^n}{2^{n+4}}$ for $\left|\dfrac{x}{2}\right| < 1 \iff |x| < 2$, so $R=2$.

25. $\sin x = \sum\limits_{n=0}^{\infty}(-1)^n\dfrac{x^{2n+1}}{(2n+1)!} \Rightarrow f(x) = \sin(\pi x) = \sum\limits_{n=0}^{\infty}(-1)^n\dfrac{(\pi x)^{2n+1}}{(2n+1)!} = \sum\limits_{n=0}^{\infty}(-1)^n\dfrac{\pi^{2n+1}}{(2n+1)!}x^{2n+1}$, $R=\infty$.

27. $e^x = \sum\limits_{n=0}^{\infty}\dfrac{x^n}{n!} \Rightarrow e^{2x} = \sum\limits_{n=0}^{\infty}\dfrac{(2x)^n}{n!} = \sum\limits_{n=0}^{\infty}\dfrac{2^n x^n}{n!}$, so $f(x) = e^x + e^{2x} = \sum\limits_{n=0}^{\infty}\dfrac{1}{n!}x^n + \sum\limits_{n=0}^{\infty}\dfrac{2^n}{n!}x^n = \sum\limits_{n=0}^{\infty}\dfrac{2^n+1}{n!}x^n$,

$R=\infty$.

29. $\cos x = \sum\limits_{n=0}^{\infty}(-1)^n\dfrac{x^{2n}}{(2n)!} \Rightarrow \cos\left(\tfrac{1}{2}x^2\right) = \sum\limits_{n=0}^{\infty}(-1)^n\dfrac{\left(\tfrac{1}{2}x^2\right)^{2n}}{(2n)!} = \sum\limits_{n=0}^{\infty}(-1)^n\dfrac{x^{4n}}{2^{2n}(2n)!}$, so

$$f(x) = x\cos\left(\tfrac{1}{2}x^2\right) = \sum\limits_{n=0}^{\infty}(-1)^n\dfrac{1}{2^{2n}(2n)!}x^{4n+1}, R=\infty.$$

31. We must write the binomial in the form $(1+$ expression$)$, so we'll factor out a 4.

$$\dfrac{x}{\sqrt{4+x^2}} = \dfrac{x}{\sqrt{4(1+x^2/4)}} = \dfrac{x}{2\sqrt{1+x^2/4}} = \dfrac{x}{2}\left(1+\dfrac{x^2}{4}\right)^{-1/2} = \dfrac{x}{2}\sum\limits_{n=0}^{\infty}\binom{-\tfrac{1}{2}}{n}\left(\dfrac{x^2}{4}\right)^n$$

$$= \dfrac{x}{2}\left[1+\left(-\tfrac{1}{2}\right)\dfrac{x^2}{4} + \dfrac{\left(-\tfrac{1}{2}\right)\left(-\tfrac{3}{2}\right)}{2!}\left(\dfrac{x^2}{4}\right)^2 + \dfrac{\left(-\tfrac{1}{2}\right)\left(-\tfrac{3}{2}\right)\left(-\tfrac{5}{2}\right)}{3!}\left(\dfrac{x^2}{4}\right)^3 + \cdots\right]$$

$$= \dfrac{x}{2} + \dfrac{x}{2}\sum\limits_{n=1}^{\infty}(-1)^n\dfrac{1\cdot3\cdot5\cdots\cdots(2n-1)}{2^n\cdot4^n\cdot n!}x^{2n}$$

$$= \dfrac{x}{2} + \sum\limits_{n=1}^{\infty}(-1)^n\dfrac{1\cdot3\cdot5\cdots\cdots(2n-1)}{n!\,2^{3n+1}}x^{2n+1} \text{ and } \dfrac{x^2}{4} < 1 \iff \dfrac{|x|}{2} < 1 \iff |x| < 2, \text{ so } R=2.$$

33. $\sin^2 x = \dfrac{1}{2}(1-\cos 2x) = \dfrac{1}{2}\left[1 - \sum\limits_{n=0}^{\infty}\dfrac{(-1)^n(2x)^{2n}}{(2n)!}\right] = \dfrac{1}{2}\left[1 - 1 - \sum\limits_{n=1}^{\infty}\dfrac{(-1)^n(2x)^{2n}}{(2n)!}\right] = \sum\limits_{n=1}^{\infty}\dfrac{(-1)^{n+1}2^{2n-1}x^{2n}}{(2n)!}$,

$R=\infty$

35. $\cos x = \sum\limits_{n=0}^{\infty}(-1)^n\dfrac{x^{2n}}{(2n)!} \Rightarrow f(x) = \cos\left(x^2\right) = \sum\limits_{n=0}^{\infty}\dfrac{(-1)^n\left(x^2\right)^{2n}}{(2n)!} = \sum\limits_{n=0}^{\infty}\dfrac{(-1)^n x^{4n}}{(2n)!}, R=\infty$

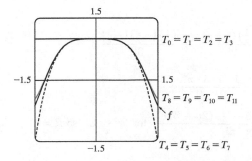

Notice that, as n increases, $T_n(x)$

becomes a better approximation to $f(x)$.

37. $e^x \overset{(11)}{=} \sum\limits_{n=0}^{\infty} \dfrac{x^n}{n!}$, so $e^{-x} = \sum\limits_{n=0}^{\infty} \dfrac{(-x)^n}{n!} = \sum\limits_{n=0}^{\infty} (-1)^n \dfrac{x^n}{n!}$, so

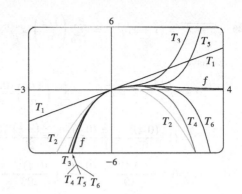

$$f(x) = xe^{-x} = \sum_{n=0}^{\infty} (-1)^n \frac{1}{n!} x^{n+1}$$

$$= x - x^2 + \tfrac{1}{2}x^3 - \tfrac{1}{6}x^4 + \tfrac{1}{24}x^5 - \tfrac{1}{120}x^6 + \cdots$$

$$= \sum_{n=1}^{\infty} (-1)^{n-1} \frac{x^n}{(n-1)!}$$

The series for e^x converges for all x, so the same is true of the series for $f(x)$; that is, $R = \infty$. From the graphs of f and the first few Taylor polynomials, we see that $T_n(x)$ provides a closer fit to $f(x)$ near 0 as n increases.

39. $e^x = \sum\limits_{n=0}^{\infty} \dfrac{x^n}{n!}$, so $e^{-0.2} = \sum\limits_{n=0}^{\infty} \dfrac{(-0.2)^n}{n!} = 1 - 0.2 + \dfrac{1}{2!}(0.2)^2 - \dfrac{1}{3!}(0.2)^3 + \dfrac{1}{4!}(0.2)^4 - \dfrac{1}{5!}(0.2)^5 + \dfrac{1}{6!}(0.2)^6 - \cdots$.

But $\dfrac{1}{6!}(0.2)^6 = 8.\overline{8} \times 10^{-8}$, so by the Alternating Series Estimation Theorem, $e^{-0.2} \approx \sum\limits_{n=0}^{5} \dfrac{(-0.2)^n}{n!} \approx 0.81873$, correct to five decimal places.

41. (a) $1/\sqrt{1-x^2} = \left[1 + (-x^2)\right]^{-1/2} = 1 + \left(-\tfrac{1}{2}\right)(-x^2) + \dfrac{\left(-\tfrac{1}{2}\right)\left(-\tfrac{3}{2}\right)}{2!}(-x^2)^2 + \dfrac{\left(-\tfrac{1}{2}\right)\left(-\tfrac{3}{2}\right)\left(-\tfrac{5}{2}\right)}{3!}(-x^2)^3 + \cdots$

$$= 1 + \sum_{n=1}^{\infty} \frac{1 \cdot 3 \cdot 5 \cdots (2n-1)}{2^n \cdot n!} x^{2n}$$

(b) $\sin^{-1} x = \displaystyle\int \dfrac{1}{\sqrt{1-x^2}}\, dx = C + x + \sum_{n=1}^{\infty} \dfrac{1 \cdot 3 \cdot 5 \cdots (2n-1)}{(2n+1)2^n \cdot n!} x^{2n+1}$

$$= x + \sum_{n=1}^{\infty} \frac{1 \cdot 3 \cdot 5 \cdots (2n-1)}{(2n+1)2^n \cdot n!} x^{2n+1} \quad \text{since } 0 = \sin^{-1} 0 = C.$$

43. $\cos x \overset{(16)}{=} \sum\limits_{n=0}^{\infty} (-1)^n \dfrac{x^{2n}}{(2n)!} \quad\Rightarrow\quad \cos(x^3) = \sum\limits_{n=0}^{\infty} (-1)^n \dfrac{(x^3)^{2n}}{(2n)!} = \sum\limits_{n=0}^{\infty} (-1)^n \dfrac{x^{6n}}{(2n)!} \quad\Rightarrow$

$x\cos(x^3) = \sum\limits_{n=0}^{\infty} (-1)^n \dfrac{x^{6n+1}}{(2n)!} \quad\Rightarrow\quad \displaystyle\int x\cos(x^3)\, dx = C + \sum\limits_{n=0}^{\infty} (-1)^n \dfrac{x^{6n+2}}{(6n+2)(2n)!}$, with $R = \infty$.

45. $\cos x \overset{(16)}{=} \sum\limits_{n=0}^{\infty} (-1)^n \dfrac{x^{2n}}{(2n)!} \quad\Rightarrow\quad \cos x - 1 = \sum\limits_{n=1}^{\infty} (-1)^n \dfrac{x^{2n}}{(2n)!} \quad\Rightarrow\quad \dfrac{\cos x - 1}{x} = \sum\limits_{n=1}^{\infty} (-1)^n \dfrac{x^{2n-1}}{(2n)!} \quad\Rightarrow$

$\displaystyle\int \dfrac{\cos x - 1}{x}\, dx = C + \sum\limits_{n=1}^{\infty} (-1)^n \dfrac{x^{2n}}{2n \cdot (2n)!}$, with $R = \infty$.

47. By Exercise 43, $\displaystyle\int x\cos(x^3)\, dx = C + \sum\limits_{n=0}^{\infty} (-1)^n \dfrac{x^{6n+2}}{(6n+2)(2n)!}$, so

$\displaystyle\int_0^1 x\cos(x^3)\, dx = \left[\sum\limits_{n=0}^{\infty} (-1)^n \dfrac{x^{6n+2}}{(6n+2)(2n)!}\right]_0^1 = \sum\limits_{n=0}^{\infty} \dfrac{(-1)^n}{(6n+2)(2n)!} = \dfrac{1}{2} - \dfrac{1}{8 \cdot 2!} + \dfrac{1}{14 \cdot 4!} - \dfrac{1}{20 \cdot 6!} + \cdots$, but

$\dfrac{1}{20 \cdot 6!} = \dfrac{1}{14\,400} \approx 0.000\,069$, so $\displaystyle\int_0^1 x\cos(x^3)\, dx \approx \dfrac{1}{2} - \dfrac{1}{16} + \dfrac{1}{336} \approx 0.440$ (correct to three decimal places) by the Alternating Series Estimation Theorem.

49. $\sqrt{1+x^4} = (1+x^4)^{1/2} = \sum_{n=0}^{\infty} \binom{1/2}{n}(x^4)^n$, so $\int \sqrt{1+x^4}\,dx = C + \sum_{n=0}^{\infty} \binom{1/2}{n}\frac{x^{4n+1}}{4n+1}$ and hence, since $0.4 < 1$,

we have

$$I = \int_0^{0.4} \sqrt{1+x^4}\,dx = \sum_{n=0}^{\infty} \binom{1/2}{n}\frac{(0.4)^{4n+1}}{4n+1}$$

$$= (1)\frac{(0.4)^1}{0!} + \frac{\frac{1}{2}}{1!}\frac{(0.4)^5}{5} + \frac{\frac{1}{2}(-\frac{1}{2})}{2!}\frac{(0.4)^9}{9} + \frac{\frac{1}{2}(-\frac{1}{2})(-\frac{3}{2})}{3!}\frac{(0.4)^{13}}{13} + \frac{\frac{1}{2}(-\frac{1}{2})(-\frac{3}{2})(-\frac{5}{2})}{4!}\frac{(0.4)^{17}}{17} + \cdots$$

$$= 0.4 + \frac{(0.4)^5}{10} - \frac{(0.4)^9}{72} + \frac{(0.4)^{13}}{208} - \frac{5(0.4)^{17}}{2176} + \cdots$$

Now $\frac{(0.4)^9}{72} \approx 3.6 \times 10^{-6} < 5 \times 10^{-6}$, so by the Alternating Series Estimation Theorem, $I \approx 0.4 + \frac{(0.4)^5}{10} \approx 0.40102$

(correct to five decimal places).

51. $\lim_{x\to 0}\frac{x - \ln(1+x)}{x^2} = \lim_{x\to 0}\frac{x - (x - \frac{1}{2}x^2 + \frac{1}{3}x^3 - \frac{1}{4}x^4 + \frac{1}{5}x^5 - \cdots)}{x^2} = \lim_{x\to 0}\frac{\frac{1}{2}x^2 - \frac{1}{3}x^3 + \frac{1}{4}x^4 - \frac{1}{5}x^5 + \cdots}{x^2}$

$$= \lim_{x\to 0}\left(\frac{1}{2} - \frac{1}{3}x + \frac{1}{4}x^2 - \frac{1}{5}x^3 + \cdots\right) = \frac{1}{2}$$

since power series are continuous functions.

53. $\lim_{x\to 0}\frac{\sin x - x + \frac{1}{6}x^3}{x^5} = \lim_{x\to 0}\frac{\left(x - \frac{1}{3!}x^3 + \frac{1}{5!}x^5 - \frac{1}{7!}x^7 + \cdots\right) - x + \frac{1}{6}x^3}{x^5}$

$$= \lim_{x\to 0}\frac{\frac{1}{5!}x^5 - \frac{1}{7!}x^7 + \cdots}{x^5} = \lim_{x\to 0}\left(\frac{1}{5!} - \frac{x^2}{7!} + \frac{x^4}{9!} - \cdots\right) = \frac{1}{5!} = \frac{1}{120}$$

since power series are continuous functions.

55. From Equation 11, we have $e^{-x^2} = 1 - \frac{x^2}{1!} + \frac{x^4}{2!} - \frac{x^6}{3!} + \cdots$ and we know that $\cos x = 1 - \frac{x^2}{2!} + \frac{x^4}{4!} - \cdots$ from

Equation 16. Therefore, $e^{-x^2}\cos x = \left(1 - x^2 + \frac{1}{2}x^4 - \cdots\right)\left(1 - \frac{1}{2}x^2 + \frac{1}{24}x^4 - \cdots\right)$. Writing only the terms with

degree ≤ 4, we get $e^{-x^2}\cos x = 1 - \frac{1}{2}x^2 + \frac{1}{24}x^4 - x^2 + \frac{1}{2}x^4 + \frac{1}{2}x^4 + \cdots = 1 - \frac{3}{2}x^2 + \frac{25}{24}x^4 + \cdots$.

57. $\frac{x}{\sin x} \overset{(15)}{=} \frac{x}{x - \frac{1}{6}x^3 + \frac{1}{120}x^5 - \cdots}$.

$$
\begin{array}{r}
1 + \frac{1}{6}x^2 + \frac{7}{360}x^4 + \cdots \\
x - \frac{1}{6}x^3 + \frac{1}{120}x^5 - \cdots \overline{\smash{\big)}\, x } \\
\underline{x - \frac{1}{6}x^3 + \frac{1}{120}x^5 - \cdots} \\
\frac{1}{6}x^3 - \frac{1}{120}x^5 + \cdots \\
\underline{\frac{1}{6}x^3 - \frac{1}{36}x^5 + \cdots} \\
\frac{7}{360}x^5 + \cdots \\
\underline{\frac{7}{360}x^5 + \cdots} \\
\cdots
\end{array}
$$

From the long division above, $\frac{x}{\sin x} = 1 + \frac{1}{6}x^2 + \frac{7}{360}x^4 + \cdots$.

59. $\sum_{n=0}^{\infty}(-1)^n\frac{x^{4n}}{n!} = \sum_{n=0}^{\infty}\frac{(-x^4)^n}{n!} = e^{-x^4}$, by (11).

61. $\displaystyle\sum_{n=1}^{\infty} (-1)^{n-1} \frac{3^n}{n5^n} = \sum_{n=1}^{\infty} (-1)^{n-1} \frac{(3/5)^n}{n} = \ln\left(1 + \frac{3}{5}\right)$ [from Table 1] $= \ln\dfrac{8}{5}$

63. $\displaystyle\sum_{n=0}^{\infty} \frac{(-1)^n \, \pi^{2n+1}}{4^{2n+1}(2n+1)!} = \sum_{n=0}^{\infty} \frac{(-1)^n \left(\frac{\pi}{4}\right)^{2n+1}}{(2n+1)!} = \sin\frac{\pi}{4} = \frac{1}{\sqrt{2}}$, by (15).

65. $3 + \dfrac{9}{2!} + \dfrac{27}{3!} + \dfrac{81}{4!} + \cdots = \dfrac{3^1}{1!} + \dfrac{3^2}{2!} + \dfrac{3^3}{3!} + \dfrac{3^4}{4!} + \cdots = \displaystyle\sum_{n=1}^{\infty} \frac{3^n}{n!} = \sum_{n=0}^{\infty} \frac{3^n}{n!} - 1 = e^3 - 1$, by (11).

67. Assume that $|f'''(x)| \leq M$, so $f'''(x) \leq M$ for $a \leq x \leq a+d$. Now $\int_a^x f'''(t)\,dt \leq \int_a^x M\,dt \ \Rightarrow$

$f''(x) - f''(a) \leq M(x-a) \ \Rightarrow\ f''(x) \leq f''(a) + M(x-a)$. Thus, $\int_a^x f''(t)\,dt \leq \int_a^x [f''(a) + M(t-a)]\,dt \ \Rightarrow$

$f'(x) - f'(a) \leq f''(a)(x-a) + \frac{1}{2}M(x-a)^2 \ \Rightarrow\ f'(x) \leq f'(a) + f''(a)(x-a) + \frac{1}{2}M(x-a)^2 \ \Rightarrow$

$\int_a^x f'(t)\,dt \leq \int_a^x \left[f'(a) + f''(a)(t-a) + \frac{1}{2}M(t-a)^2\right] dt \ \Rightarrow$

$f(x) - f(a) \leq f'(a)(x-a) + \frac{1}{2}f''(a)(x-a)^2 + \frac{1}{6}M(x-a)^3$. So

$f(x) - f(a) - f'(a)(x-a) - \frac{1}{2}f''(a)(x-a)^2 \leq \frac{1}{6}M(x-a)^3$. But

$R_2(x) = f(x) - T_2(x) = f(x) - f(a) - f'(a)(x-a) - \frac{1}{2}f''(a)(x-a)^2$, so $R_2(x) \leq \frac{1}{6}M(x-a)^3$.

A similar argument using $f'''(x) \geq -M$ shows that $R_2(x) \geq -\frac{1}{6}M(x-a)^3$. So $|R_2(x_2)| \leq \frac{1}{6}M\,|x-a|^3$.

Although we have assumed that $x > a$, a similar calculation shows that this inequality is also true if $x < a$.

69. (a) $g(x) = \displaystyle\sum_{n=0}^{\infty} \binom{k}{n} x^n \ \Rightarrow\ g'(x) = \sum_{n=1}^{\infty} \binom{k}{n} n x^{n-1}$, so

$(1+x)g'(x) = (1+x)\displaystyle\sum_{n=1}^{\infty} \binom{k}{n} n x^{n-1} = \sum_{n=1}^{\infty} \binom{k}{n} n x^{n-1} + \sum_{n=1}^{\infty} \binom{k}{n} n x^n$

$= \displaystyle\sum_{n=0}^{\infty} \binom{k}{n+1}(n+1)x^n + \sum_{n=0}^{\infty} \binom{k}{n} n x^n$ $\qquad \left[\begin{array}{c}\text{Replace } n \text{ with } n+1 \\ \text{in the first series}\end{array}\right]$

$= \displaystyle\sum_{n=0}^{\infty} (n+1)\frac{k(k-1)(k-2)\cdots(k-n+1)(k-n)}{(n+1)!}x^n + \sum_{n=0}^{\infty} \left[(n)\frac{k(k-1)(k-2)\cdots(k-n+1)}{n!}\right]x^n$

$= \displaystyle\sum_{n=0}^{\infty} \frac{(n+1)k(k-1)(k-2)\cdots(k-n+1)}{(n+1)!}\left[(k-n)+n\right]x^n$

$= k\displaystyle\sum_{n=0}^{\infty} \frac{k(k-1)(k-2)\cdots(k-n+1)}{n!}x^n = k\sum_{n=0}^{\infty} \binom{k}{n}x^n = kg(x)$

Thus, $g'(x) = \dfrac{kg(x)}{1+x}$.

(b) $h(x) = (1+x)^{-k}g(x) \ \Rightarrow$

$\begin{aligned} h'(x) &= -k(1+x)^{-k-1}g(x) + (1+x)^{-k}g'(x) &&\text{[Product Rule]}\\ &= -k(1+x)^{-k-1}g(x) + (1+x)^{-k}\frac{kg(x)}{1+x} &&\text{[from part (a)]}\\ &= -k(1+x)^{-k-1}g(x) + k(1+x)^{-k-1}g(x) = 0 \end{aligned}$

(c) From part (b) we see that $h(x)$ must be constant for $x \in (-1,1)$, so $h(x) = h(0) = 1$ for $x \in (-1,1)$.

Thus, $h(x) = 1 = (1+x)^{-k}g(x) \ \Leftrightarrow\ g(x) = (1+x)^k$ for $x \in (-1,1)$.

8.8 Applications of Taylor Polynomials

1. (a)

n	$f^{(n)}(x)$	$f^{(n)}(0)$	$T_n(x)$
0	$\cos x$	1	1
1	$-\sin x$	0	1
2	$-\cos x$	-1	$1 - \frac{1}{2}x^2$
3	$\sin x$	0	$1 - \frac{1}{2}x^2$
4	$\cos x$	1	$1 - \frac{1}{2}x^2 + \frac{1}{24}x^4$
5	$-\sin x$	0	$1 - \frac{1}{2}x^2 + \frac{1}{24}x^4$
6	$-\cos x$	-1	$1 - \frac{1}{2}x^2 + \frac{1}{24}x^4 - \frac{1}{720}x^6$

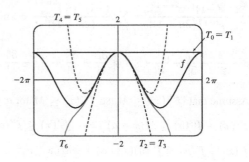

(b)

x	f	$T_0 = T_1$	$T_2 = T_3$	$T_4 = T_5$	T_6
$\frac{\pi}{4}$	0.7071	1	0.6916	0.7074	0.7071
$\frac{\pi}{2}$	0	1	-0.2337	0.0200	-0.0009
π	-1	1	-3.9348	0.1239	-1.2114

(c) As n increases, $T_n(x)$ is a good approximation to $f(x)$ on a larger and larger interval.

3.

n	$f^{(n)}(x)$	$f^{(n)}(2)$
0	$1/x$	$\frac{1}{2}$
1	$-1/x^2$	$-\frac{1}{4}$
2	$2/x^3$	$\frac{1}{4}$
3	$-6/x^4$	$-\frac{3}{8}$

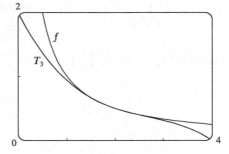

$$T_3(x) = \sum_{n=0}^{3} \frac{f^{(n)}(2)}{n!}(x-2)^n$$

$$= \frac{\frac{1}{2}}{0!} - \frac{\frac{1}{4}}{1!}(x-2) + \frac{\frac{1}{4}}{2!}(x-2)^2 - \frac{\frac{3}{8}}{3!}(x-2)^3$$

$$= \frac{1}{2} - \frac{1}{4}(x-2) + \frac{1}{8}(x-2)^2 - \frac{1}{16}(x-2)^3$$

5.

n	$f^{(n)}(x)$	$f^{(n)}(\pi/2)$
0	$\cos x$	0
1	$-\sin x$	-1
2	$-\cos x$	0
3	$\sin x$	1

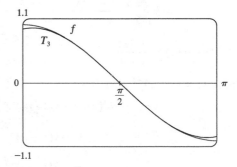

$$T_3(x) = \sum_{n=0}^{3} \frac{f^{(n)}(\pi/2)}{n!}\left(x - \frac{\pi}{2}\right)^n$$

$$= -\left(x - \frac{\pi}{2}\right) + \frac{1}{6}\left(x - \frac{\pi}{2}\right)^3$$

7.

n	$f^{(n)}(x)$	$f^{(n)}(0)$
0	xe^{-2x}	0
1	$(1-2x)e^{-2x}$	1
2	$4(x-1)e^{-2x}$	-4
3	$4(3-2x)e^{-2x}$	12

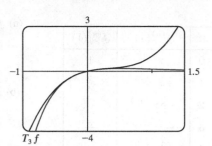

$$T_3(x) = \sum_{n=0}^{3} \frac{f^{(n)}(0)}{n!}x^n = \frac{0}{1}\cdot 1 + \frac{1}{1}x^1 + \frac{-4}{2}x^2 + \frac{12}{6}x^3 = x - 2x^2 + 2x^3$$

9. You may be able to simply find the Taylor polynomials for

$f(x) = \cot x$ using your CAS. We will list the values of $f^{(n)}(\pi/4)$

for $n = 0$ to $n = 5$.

n	0	1	2	3	4	5
$f^{(n)}(\pi/4)$	1	-2	4	-16	80	-512

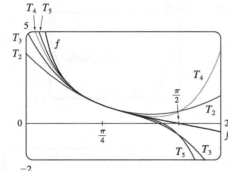

$$T_5(x) = \sum_{n=0}^{5} \frac{f^{(n)}(\pi/4)}{n!}\left(x - \tfrac{\pi}{4}\right)^n$$

$$= 1 - 2\left(x - \tfrac{\pi}{4}\right) + 2\left(x - \tfrac{\pi}{4}\right)^2 - \tfrac{8}{3}\left(x - \tfrac{\pi}{4}\right)^3 + \tfrac{10}{3}\left(x - \tfrac{\pi}{4}\right)^4 - \tfrac{64}{15}\left(x - \tfrac{\pi}{4}\right)^5$$

For $n = 2$ to $n = 5$, $T_n(x)$ is the polynomial consisting of all the terms up to and including the $\left(x - \tfrac{\pi}{4}\right)^n$ term.

11.

n	$f^{(n)}(x)$	$f^{(n)}(4)$
0	$\sqrt{x}$	2
1	$\frac{1}{2}x^{-1/2}$	$\frac{1}{4}$
2	$-\frac{1}{4}x^{-3/2}$	$-\frac{1}{32}$
3	$\frac{3}{8}x^{-5/2}$	

(a) $f(x) = \sqrt{x} \approx T_2(x) = 2 + \frac{1}{4}(x-4) - \frac{1/32}{2!}(x-4)^2$

$$= 2 + \tfrac{1}{4}(x-4) - \tfrac{1}{64}(x-4)^2$$

(b) $|R_2(x)| \le \dfrac{M}{3!}|x-4|^3$, where $|f'''(x)| \le M$. Now $4 \le x \le 4.2 \Rightarrow$

$|x-4| \le 0.2 \Rightarrow |x-4|^3 \le 0.008$. Since $f'''(x)$ is decreasing

on $[4, 4.2]$, we can take $M = |f'''(4)| = \tfrac{3}{8}4^{-5/2} = \tfrac{3}{256}$, so

$$|R_2(x)| \le \frac{3/256}{6}(0.008) = \frac{0.008}{512} = 0.000\,015\,625.$$

(c) 0.00002

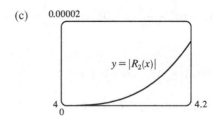

$y = |R_2(x)|$

From the graph of $|R_2(x)| = |\sqrt{x} - T_2(x)|$, it seems that the

error is less than 1.52×10^{-5} on $[4, 4.2]$.

13.

n	$f^{(n)}(x)$	$f^{(n)}(1)$
0	$x^{2/3}$	1
1	$\frac{2}{3}x^{-1/3}$	$\frac{2}{3}$
2	$-\frac{2}{9}x^{-4/3}$	$-\frac{2}{9}$
3	$\frac{8}{27}x^{-7/3}$	$\frac{8}{27}$
4	$-\frac{56}{81}x^{-10/3}$	

(a) $f(x) = x^{2/3} \approx T_3(x) = 1 + \frac{2}{3}(x-1) - \frac{2/9}{2!}(x-1)^2 + \frac{8/27}{3!}(x-1)^3$

$$= 1 + \frac{2}{3}(x-1) - \frac{1}{9}(x-1)^2 + \frac{4}{81}(x-1)^3$$

(b) $|R_3(x)| \le \dfrac{M}{4!}|x-1|^4$, where $\left|f^{(4)}(x)\right| \le M$. Now $0.8 \le x \le 1.2 \;\Rightarrow$

$|x-1| \le 0.2 \;\Rightarrow\; |x-1|^4 \le 0.0016$. Since $\left|f^{(4)}(x)\right|$ is decreasing

on $[0.8, 1.2]$, we can take $M = \left|f^{(4)}(0.8)\right| = \frac{56}{81}(0.8)^{-10/3}$, so

$$|R_3(x)| \le \frac{\frac{56}{81}(0.8)^{-10/3}}{24}(0.0016) \approx 0.000\,096\,97.$$

(c)

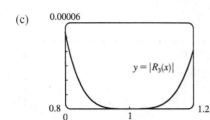

0.00006

$y = |R_3(x)|$

0.8   1   1.2
0

From the graph of $|R_3(x)| = \left|x^{2/3} - T_3(x)\right|$, it seems that the

error is less than $0.000\,053\,3$ on $[0.8, 1.2]$.

15.

n	$f^{(n)}(x)$	$f^{(n)}(0)$
0	e^{x^2}	1
1	$e^{x^2}(2x)$	0
2	$e^{x^2}(2+4x^2)$	2
3	$e^{x^2}(12x+8x^3)$	0
4	$e^{x^2}(12+48x^2+16x^4)$	

(a) $f(x) = e^{x^2} \approx T_3(x) = 1 + \dfrac{2}{2!}x^2 = 1 + x^2$

(b) $|R_3(x)| \le \dfrac{M}{4!}|x|^4$, where $\left|f^{(4)}(x)\right| \le M$. Now $0 \le x \le 0.1 \;\Rightarrow$

$x^4 \le (0.1)^4$, and letting $x = 0.1$ gives

$$|R_3(x)| \le \frac{e^{0.01}(12+0.48+0.0016)}{24}(0.1)^4 \approx 0.00006.$$

(c)

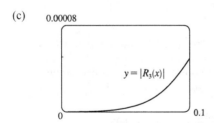

0.00008

$y = |R_3(x)|$

0   0.1

From the graph of $|R_3(x)| = \left|e^{x^2} - T_3(x)\right|$, it appears that the

error is less than $0.000\,051$ on $[0, 0.1]$.

17.

n	$f^{(n)}(x)$	$f^{(n)}(0)$
0	$x \sin x$	0
1	$\sin x + x \cos x$	0
2	$2\cos x - x \sin x$	2
3	$-3\sin x - x \cos x$	0
4	$-4\cos x + x \sin x$	-4
5	$5\sin x + x \cos x$	

(a) $f(x) = x \sin x \approx T_4(x) = \dfrac{2}{2!}(x-0)^2 + \dfrac{-4}{4!}(x-0)^4 = x^2 - \dfrac{1}{6}x^4$

(b) $|R_4(x)| \le \dfrac{M}{5!}|x|^5$, where $\left|f^{(5)}(x)\right| \le M$. Now $-1 \le x \le 1 \;\Rightarrow$

$|x| \le 1$, and a graph of $f^{(5)}(x)$ shows that $\left|f^{(5)}(x)\right| \le 5$ for $-1 \le x \le 1$.

Thus, we can take $M = 5$ and get $|R_4(x)| \le \dfrac{5}{5!} \cdot 1^5 = \dfrac{1}{24} = 0.041\overline{6}$.

(c)

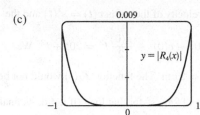

From the graph of $|R_4(x)| = |x \sin x - T_4(x)|$, it seems that the error is less than 0.0082 on $[-1, 1]$.

19. From Exercise 5, $\cos x = -\left(x - \frac{\pi}{2}\right) + \frac{1}{6}\left(x - \frac{\pi}{2}\right)^3 + R_3(x)$, where $|R_3(x)| \le \dfrac{M}{4!}\left|x - \frac{\pi}{2}\right|^4$ with

$\left|f^{(4)}(x)\right| = |\cos x| \le M = 1$. Now $x = 80° = (90° - 10°) = \left(\frac{\pi}{2} - \frac{\pi}{18}\right) = \frac{4\pi}{9}$ radians, so the error is

$\left|R_3\left(\frac{4\pi}{9}\right)\right| \le \frac{1}{24}\left(\frac{\pi}{18}\right)^4 \approx 0.000\,039$, which means our estimate would *not* be accurate to five decimal places. However,

$T_3 = T_4$, so we can use $\left|R_4\left(\frac{4\pi}{9}\right)\right| \le \frac{1}{120}\left(\frac{\pi}{18}\right)^5 \approx 0.000\,001$. Therefore, to five decimal places,

$\cos 80° \approx -\left(-\frac{\pi}{18}\right) + \frac{1}{6}\left(-\frac{\pi}{18}\right)^3 \approx 0.17365$.

21. All derivatives of e^x are e^x, so $|R_n(x)| \le \dfrac{e^x}{(n+1)!}|x|^{n+1}$, where $0 < x < 0.1$. Letting $x = 0.1$,

$R_n(0.1) \le \dfrac{e^{0.1}}{(n+1)!}(0.1)^{n+1} < 0.00001$, and by trial and error we find that $n = 3$ satisfies this inequality since

$R_3(0.1) < 0.0000046$. Thus, by adding the four terms of the Maclaurin series for e^x corresponding to $n = 0, 1, 2$, and 3,

we can estimate $e^{0.1}$ to within 0.00001. (In fact, this sum is $1.105\overline{16}$ and $e^{0.1} \approx 1.10517$.)

23. $\sin x = x - \frac{1}{3!}x^3 + \frac{1}{5!}x^5 - \cdots$. By the Alternating Series

Estimation Theorem, the error in the approximation

$\sin x = x - \frac{1}{3!}x^3$ is less than $\left|\frac{1}{5!}x^5\right| < 0.01 \quad \Leftrightarrow$

$\left|x^5\right| < 120(0.01) \quad \Leftrightarrow \quad |x| < (1.2)^{1/5} \approx 1.037$. The curves

$y = x - \frac{1}{6}x^3$ and $y = \sin x - 0.01$ intersect at $x \approx 1.043$, so

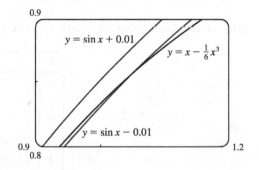

the graph confirms our estimate. Since both the sine function

and the given approximation are odd functions, we need to check the estimate only for $x > 0$. Thus, the desired range of

values for x is $-1.037 < x < 1.037$.

25. $\arctan x = x - \dfrac{x^3}{3} + \dfrac{x^5}{5} - \dfrac{x^7}{7} + \cdots$. By the Alternating Series

Estimation Theorem, the error is less than $\left|-\frac{1}{7}x^7\right| < 0.05 \quad \Leftrightarrow$

$\left|x^7\right| < 0.35 \quad \Leftrightarrow \quad |x| < (0.35)^{1/7} \approx 0.8607$. The curves

$y = x - \frac{1}{3}x^3 + \frac{1}{5}x^5$ and $y = \arctan x + 0.05$ intersect at

$x \approx 0.9245$, so the graph confirms our estimate. Since both the

arctangent function and the given approximation are odd functions,

we need to check the estimate only for $x > 0$. Thus, the desired

range of values for x is $-0.86 < x < 0.86$.

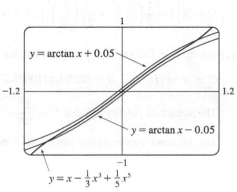

27. Let $s(t)$ be the position function of the car, and for convenience set $s(0) = 0$. The velocity of the car is $v(t) = s'(t)$ and the acceleration is $a(t) = s''(t)$, so the second degree Taylor polynomial is $T_2(t) = s(0) + v(0)t + \dfrac{a(0)}{2}t^2 = 20t + t^2$. We estimate the distance traveled during the next second to be $s(1) \approx T_2(1) = 20 + 1 = 21$ m. The function $T_2(t)$ would not be accurate over a full minute, since the car could not possibly maintain an acceleration of 2 m/s^2 for that long (if it did, its final speed would be 140 m/s ≈ 313 mi/h!).

29. $E = \dfrac{q}{D^2} - \dfrac{q}{(D+d)^2} = \dfrac{q}{D^2} - \dfrac{q}{D^2(1+d/D)^2} = \dfrac{q}{D^2}\left[1 - \left(1 + \dfrac{d}{D}\right)^{-2}\right].$

We use the Binomial Series to expand $(1 + d/D)^{-2}$:

$$E = \dfrac{q}{D^2}\left[1 - \left(1 - 2\left(\dfrac{d}{D}\right) + \dfrac{2\cdot 3}{2!}\left(\dfrac{d}{D}\right)^2 - \dfrac{2\cdot 3\cdot 4}{3!}\left(\dfrac{d}{D}\right)^3 + \cdots\right)\right] = \dfrac{q}{D^2}\left[2\left(\dfrac{d}{D}\right) - 3\left(\dfrac{d}{D}\right)^2 + 4\left(\dfrac{d}{D}\right)^3 - \cdots\right]$$

$$\approx \dfrac{q}{D^2}\cdot 2\left(\dfrac{d}{D}\right) = 2qd\cdot\dfrac{1}{D^3}$$

when D is much larger than d; that is, when P is far away from the dipole.

31. (a) L is the length of the arc subtended by the angle θ, so $L = R\theta$ $\Rightarrow$

$\theta = L/R$. Now $\sec\theta = (R+C)/R$ $\Rightarrow$ $R\sec\theta = R+C$ $\Rightarrow$

$C = R\sec\theta - R = R\sec(L/R) - R.$

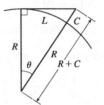

(b) First we'll find a Taylor polynomial $T_4(x)$ for $f(x) = \sec x$ at $x = 0$.

n	$f^{(n)}(x)$	$f^{(n)}(0)$
0	$\sec x$	1
1	$\sec x \tan x$	0
2	$\sec x(2\tan^2 x + 1)$	1
3	$\sec x \tan x(6\tan^2 x + 5)$	0
4	$\sec x(24\tan^4 x + 28\tan^2 x + 5)$	5

Thus, $f(x) = \sec x \approx T_4(x) = 1 + \frac{1}{2!}(x-0)^2 + \frac{5}{4!}(x-0)^4 = 1 + \frac{1}{2}x^2 + \frac{5}{24}x^4$. By part (a),

$$C \approx R\left[1 + \dfrac{1}{2}\left(\dfrac{L}{R}\right)^2 + \dfrac{5}{24}\left(\dfrac{L}{R}\right)^4\right] - R = R + \dfrac{1}{2}R\cdot\dfrac{L^2}{R^2} + \dfrac{5}{24}R\cdot\dfrac{L^4}{R^4} - R = \dfrac{L^2}{2R} + \dfrac{5L^4}{24R^3}.$$

(c) Taking $L = 100$ km and $R = 6370$ km, the formula in part (a) says that

$C = R\sec(L/R) - R = 6370\sec(100/6370) - 6370 \approx 0.785\,009\,965\,44$ km.

The formula in part (b) says that $C \approx \dfrac{L^2}{2R} + \dfrac{5L^4}{24R^3} = \dfrac{100^2}{2\cdot 6370} + \dfrac{5\cdot 100^4}{24\cdot 6370^3} \approx 0.785\,009\,957\,36$ km.

The difference between these two results is only $0.000\,000\,008\,08$ km, or $0.000\,008\,08$ m!

33. Using $f(x) = T_n(x) + R_n(x)$ with $n = 1$ and $x = r$, we have $f(r) = T_1(r) + R_1(r)$, where T_1 is the first-degree Taylor polynomial of f at a. Because $a = x_n$, $f(r) = f(x_n) + f'(x_n)(r - x_n) + R_1(r)$. But r is a root of f, so $f(r) = 0$

and we have $0 = f(x_n) + f'(x_n)(r - x_n) + R_1(r)$. Taking the first two terms to the left side gives us

$f'(x_n)(x_n - r) - f(x_n) = R_1(r)$. Dividing by $f'(x_n)$, we get $x_n - r - \dfrac{f(x_n)}{f'(x_n)} = \dfrac{R_1(r)}{f'(x_n)}$. By the formula for Newton's

method, the left side of the preceding equation is $x_{n+1} - r$, so $|x_{n+1} - r| = \left| \dfrac{R_1(r)}{f'(x_n)} \right|$. Taylor's Inequality gives us

$|R_1(r)| \leq \dfrac{|f''(r)|}{2!} |r - x_n|^2$. Combining this inequality with the facts $|f''(x)| \leq M$ and $|f'(x)| \geq K$ gives us

$|x_{n+1} - r| \leq \dfrac{M}{2K} |x_n - r|^2$.

8   Review

CONCEPT CHECK

---

1. (a) See Definition 8.1.1.

   (b) See Definition 8.2.2.

   (c) The terms of the sequence $\{a_n\}$ approach 3 as n becomes large.

   (d) By adding sufficiently many terms of the series, we can make the partial sums as close to 3 as we like.

2. (a) See the definition on page 561.

   (b) A sequence is monotonic if it is either increasing or decreasing.

   (c) By Theorem 8.1.8, every bounded, monotonic sequence is convergent.

3. (a) See (4) in Section 8.2.

   (b) The p-series $\displaystyle\sum_{n=1}^{\infty} \dfrac{1}{n^p}$ is convergent if $p > 1$.

4. If $\sum a_n = 3$, then $\displaystyle\lim_{n \to \infty} a_n = 0$ and $\displaystyle\lim_{n \to \infty} s_n = 3$.

5. (a) *Test for Divergence:* If $\displaystyle\lim_{n \to \infty} a_n$ does not exist or if $\displaystyle\lim_{n \to \infty} a_n \neq 0$, then the series $\sum_{n=1}^{\infty} a_n$ is divergent.

   (b) *Integral Test:* Suppose f is a continuous, positive, decreasing function on $[1, \infty)$ and let $a_n = f(n)$. Then the series

   $\sum_{n=1}^{\infty} a_n$ is convergent if and only if the improper integral $\int_1^{\infty} f(x)\, dx$ is convergent. In other words:

   (i) If $\int_1^{\infty} f(x)\, dx$ is convergent, then $\sum_{n=1}^{\infty} a_n$ is convergent.

   (ii) If $\int_1^{\infty} f(x)\, dx$ is divergent, then $\sum_{n=1}^{\infty} a_n$ is divergent.

   (c) *Comparison Test:* Suppose that $\sum a_n$ and $\sum b_n$ are series with positive terms.

   (i) If $\sum b_n$ is convergent and $a_n \leq b_n$ for all n, then $\sum a_n$ is also convergent.

   (ii) If $\sum b_n$ is divergent and $a_n \geq b_n$ for all n, then $\sum a_n$ is also divergent.

   (d) *Limit Comparison Test:* Suppose that $\sum a_n$ and $\sum b_n$ are series with positive terms. If $\displaystyle\lim_{n \to \infty} (a_n / b_n) = c$, where c is a

   finite number and $c > 0$, then either both series converge or both diverge.

(e) *Alternating Series Test:* If the alternating series $\sum_{n=1}^{\infty}(-1)^{n-1}b_n = b_1 - b_2 + b_3 - b_4 + b_5 - b_6 + \cdots$ $[b_n > 0]$

satisfies (i) $b_{n+1} \le b_n$ for all n and (ii) $\lim_{n \to \infty} b_n = 0$, then the series is convergent.

(f) *Ratio Test:*

(i) If $\lim_{n \to \infty} \left| \dfrac{a_{n+1}}{a_n} \right| = L < 1$, then the series $\sum_{n=1}^{\infty} a_n$ is absolutely convergent (and therefore convergent).

(ii) If $\lim_{n \to \infty} \left| \dfrac{a_{n+1}}{a_n} \right| = L > 1$ or $\lim_{n \to \infty} \left| \dfrac{a_{n+1}}{a_n} \right| = \infty$, then the series $\sum_{n=1}^{\infty} a_n$ is divergent.

(iii) If $\lim_{n \to \infty} \left| \dfrac{a_{n+1}}{a_n} \right| = 1$, the Ratio Test is inconclusive; that is, no conclusion can be drawn about the convergence or

divergence of $\sum a_n$.

6. (a) A series $\sum a_n$ is called *absolutely convergent* if the series of absolute values $\sum |a_n|$ is convergent.

(b) If a series $\sum a_n$ is absolutely convergent, then it is convergent.

7. (a) Use (4) in Section 8.3.

(b) See Example 8 in Section 8.3.

(c) By adding terms until you reach the desired accuracy given by the Alternating Series Estimation Theorem.

8. (a) $\sum_{n=0}^{\infty} c_n (x - a)^n$

(b) Given the power series $\sum_{n=0}^{\infty} c_n (x - a)^n$, the radius of convergence is:

(i) 0 if the series converges only when $x = a$

(ii) ∞ if the series converges for all x, or

(iii) a positive number R such that the series converges if $|x - a| < R$ and diverges if $|x - a| > R$.

(c) The interval of convergence of a power series is the interval that consists of all values of x for which the series converges. Corresponding to the cases in part (b), the interval of convergence is: (i) the single point $\{a\}$, (ii) all real numbers, that is, the real number line $(-\infty, \infty)$, or (iii) an interval with endpoints $a - R$ and $a + R$ which can contain neither, either, or both of the endpoints. In this case, we must test the series for convergence at each endpoint to determine the interval of convergence.

9. (a), (b) See Theorem 8.6.2.

10. (a) $T_n(x) = \sum_{i=0}^{n} \dfrac{f^{(i)}(a)}{i!} (x - a)^i$

(b) $\sum_{n=0}^{\infty} \dfrac{f^{(n)}(a)}{n!} (x - a)^n$

(c) $\sum_{n=0}^{\infty} \dfrac{f^{(n)}(0)}{n!} x^n$ [$a = 0$ in part (b)]

(d) See Theorem 8.7.8.

(e) See Taylor's Inequality (8.7.9).

11. (a)–(f) See the table on page 613.

12. See the binomial series (8.7.17) for the expansion. The radius of convergence for the binomial series is 1.

TRUE-FALSE QUIZ

1. False.   See Note 2 after Theorem 8.2.6.

3. True.   If $\lim\limits_{n \to \infty} a_n = L$, then as $n \to \infty$, $2n + 1 \to \infty$, so $a_{2n+1} \to L$.

5. False.   For example, take $c_n = (-1)^n/(n6^n)$.

7. False, since $\lim\limits_{n\to\infty} \left| \dfrac{a_{n+1}}{a_n} \right| = \lim\limits_{n\to\infty} \left| \dfrac{1}{(n+1)^3} \cdot \dfrac{n^3}{1} \right| = \lim\limits_{n\to\infty} \left| \dfrac{n^3}{(n+1)^3} \cdot \dfrac{1/n^3}{1/n^3} \right| = \lim\limits_{n\to\infty} \dfrac{1}{(1+1/n)^3} = 1$.

9. False.   See the note after Example 4 in Section 8.3.

11. True.   See (7) in Section 8.1.

13. True.   By Theorem 8.7.5 the coefficient of x^3 is $\dfrac{f'''(0)}{3!} = \dfrac{1}{3} \Rightarrow f'''(0) = 2$.

           Or: Use Theorem 8.6.2 to differentiate f three times.

15. False.   For example, let $a_n = b_n = (-1)^n$. Then $\{a_n\}$ and $\{b_n\}$ are divergent, but $a_n b_n = 1$, so $\{a_n b_n\}$ is convergent.

17. True by Theorem 8.4.1.   [$\sum (-1)^n a_n$ is absolutely convergent and hence convergent.]

19. True. $0.99999\ldots = 0.9 + 0.9(0.1)^1 + 0.9(0.1)^2 + 0.9(0.1)^3 + \cdots = \sum\limits_{n=1}^{\infty} (0.9)(0.1)^{n-1} = \dfrac{0.9}{1 - 0.1} = 1$ by the formula

           for the sum of a geometric series [$S = a_1/(1 - r)$] with ratio r satisfying $|r| < 1$.

EXERCISES

1. $\left\{ \dfrac{2 + n^3}{1 + 2n^3} \right\}$ converges since $\lim\limits_{n\to\infty} \dfrac{2 + n^3}{1 + 2n^3} = \lim\limits_{n\to\infty} \dfrac{2/n^3 + 1}{1/n^3 + 2} = \dfrac{1}{2}$.

3. $\lim\limits_{n\to\infty} a_n = \lim\limits_{n\to\infty} \dfrac{n^3}{1 + n^2} = \lim\limits_{n\to\infty} \dfrac{n}{1/n^2 + 1} = \infty$, so the sequence diverges.

5. $|a_n| = \left| \dfrac{n \sin n}{n^2 + 1} \right| \le \dfrac{n}{n^2 + 1} < \dfrac{1}{n}$, so $|a_n| \to 0$ as $n \to \infty$. Thus, $\lim\limits_{n\to\infty} a_n = 0$. The sequence $\{a_n\}$ is convergent.

7. $\left\{\left(1+\dfrac{3}{n}\right)^{4n}\right\}$ is convergent. Let $y=\left(1+\dfrac{3}{x}\right)^{4x}$. Then

$$\lim_{x\to\infty}\ln y=\lim_{x\to\infty}4x\ln(1+3/x)=\lim_{x\to\infty}\frac{\ln(1+3/x)}{1/(4x)}\overset{\text{H}}{=}\lim_{x\to\infty}\frac{\dfrac{1}{1+3/x}\left(-\dfrac{3}{x^2}\right)}{-1/(4x^2)}=\lim_{x\to\infty}\frac{12}{1+3/x}=12,\text{ so}$$

$$\lim_{x\to\infty}y=\lim_{n\to\infty}\left(1+\frac{3}{n}\right)^{4n}=e^{12}.$$

9. $\dfrac{n}{n^3+1}<\dfrac{n}{n^3}=\dfrac{1}{n^2}$, so $\displaystyle\sum_{n=1}^{\infty}\frac{n}{n^3+1}$ converges by the Comparison Test with the convergent p-series $\displaystyle\sum_{n=1}^{\infty}\frac{1}{n^2}$ $[p=2>1]$.

11. $\displaystyle\lim_{n\to\infty}\left|\frac{a_{n+1}}{a_n}\right|=\lim_{n\to\infty}\left[\frac{(n+1)^3}{5^{n+1}}\cdot\frac{5^n}{n^3}\right]=\lim_{n\to\infty}\left(1+\frac{1}{n}\right)^3\cdot\frac{1}{5}=\frac{1}{5}<1$, so $\displaystyle\sum_{n=1}^{\infty}\frac{n^3}{5^n}$ converges by the Ratio Test.

13. Let $f(x)=\dfrac{1}{x\sqrt{\ln x}}$. Then f is continuous, positive, and decreasing on $[2,\infty)$, so the Integral Test applies.

$$\int_2^{\infty}f(x)\,dx=\lim_{t\to\infty}\int_2^t\frac{1}{x\sqrt{\ln x}}\,dx\quad\left[u=\ln x,\,du=\frac{1}{x}\,dx\right]=\lim_{t\to\infty}\int_{\ln 2}^{\ln t}u^{-1/2}\,du=\lim_{t\to\infty}\left[2\sqrt{u}\right]_{\ln 2}^{\ln t}$$

$$=\lim_{t\to\infty}\left(2\sqrt{\ln t}-2\sqrt{\ln 2}\right)=\infty,$$

so the series $\displaystyle\sum_{n=2}^{\infty}\frac{1}{n\sqrt{\ln n}}$ diverges.

15. $b_n=\dfrac{\sqrt{n}}{n+1}>0$, $\{b_n\}$ is decreasing, and $\displaystyle\lim_{n\to\infty}b_n=0$, so the series $\displaystyle\sum_{n=1}^{\infty}(-1)^{n-1}\frac{\sqrt{n}}{n+1}$ converges by the Alternating

Series Test.

17. $\displaystyle\lim_{n\to\infty}\left|\frac{a_{n+1}}{a_n}\right|=\lim_{n\to\infty}\frac{1\cdot 3\cdot 5\cdots\cdots(2n-1)(2n+1)}{5^{n+1}\,(n+1)!}\cdot\frac{5^n\,n!}{1\cdot 3\cdot 5\cdots\cdots(2n-1)}=\lim_{n\to\infty}\frac{2n+1}{5(n+1)}=\frac{2}{5}<1$, so the series

converges by the Ratio Test.

19. $\displaystyle\sum_{n=1}^{\infty}\frac{(-3)^{n-1}}{2^{3n}}=\sum_{n=1}^{\infty}\frac{(-3)^{n-1}}{(2^3)^n}=\sum_{n=1}^{\infty}\frac{(-3)^{n-1}}{8^n}=\frac{1}{8}\sum_{n=1}^{\infty}\frac{(-3)^{n-1}}{8^{n-1}}=\frac{1}{8}\sum_{n=1}^{\infty}\left(-\frac{3}{8}\right)^{n-1}=\frac{1}{8}\left(\frac{1}{1-(-3/8)}\right)$

$$=\frac{1}{8}\cdot\frac{8}{11}=\frac{1}{11}$$

21. $\displaystyle\sum_{n=1}^{\infty}[\tan^{-1}(n+1)-\tan^{-1}n]=\lim_{n\to\infty}s_n$

$$=\lim_{n\to\infty}[(\tan^{-1}2-\tan^{-1}1)+(\tan^{-1}3-\tan^{-1}2)+\cdots+(\tan^{-1}(n+1)-\tan^{-1}n)]$$

$$=\lim_{n\to\infty}[\tan^{-1}(n+1)-\tan^{-1}1]=\frac{\pi}{2}-\frac{\pi}{4}=\frac{\pi}{4}$$

23. $1.2345345345\ldots = 1.2 + 0.0\overline{345} = \dfrac{12}{10} + \dfrac{345/10{,}000}{1 - 1/1000} = \dfrac{12}{10} + \dfrac{345}{9990} = \dfrac{4111}{3330}$

25. $\displaystyle\sum_{n=1}^{\infty} \dfrac{(-1)^{n+1}}{n^5} = 1 - \dfrac{1}{32} + \dfrac{1}{243} - \dfrac{1}{1024} + \dfrac{1}{3125} - \dfrac{1}{7776} + \dfrac{1}{16{,}807} - \dfrac{1}{32{,}768} + \cdots.$

Since $b_8 = \dfrac{1}{8^5} = \dfrac{1}{32{,}768} < 0.000031$, $\displaystyle\sum_{n=1}^{\infty} \dfrac{(-1)^{n+1}}{n^5} \approx \sum_{n=1}^{7} \dfrac{(-1)^{n+1}}{n^5} \approx 0.9721.$

27. $\displaystyle\sum_{n=1}^{\infty} \dfrac{1}{2 + 5^n} \approx \sum_{n=1}^{8} \dfrac{1}{2 + 5^n} \approx 0.18976224.$ To estimate the error, note that $\dfrac{1}{2 + 5^n} < \dfrac{1}{5^n}$, so the remainder term is

$R_8 = \displaystyle\sum_{n=9}^{\infty} \dfrac{1}{2 + 5^n} < \sum_{n=9}^{\infty} \dfrac{1}{5^n} = \dfrac{1/5^9}{1 - 1/5} = 6.4 \times 10^{-7}$ $\left[\text{geometric series with } a = \tfrac{1}{5^9} \text{ and } r = \tfrac{1}{5}\right].$

29. Use the Limit Comparison Test. $\displaystyle\lim_{n\to\infty} \left| \dfrac{\left(\frac{n+1}{n}\right)a_n}{a_n} \right| = \lim_{n\to\infty} \dfrac{n+1}{n} = \lim_{n\to\infty}\left(1 + \dfrac{1}{n}\right) = 1 > 0.$

Since $\sum |a_n|$ is convergent, so is $\displaystyle\sum \left| \left(\dfrac{n+1}{n}\right) a_n \right|$, by the Limit Comparison Test.

31. $\displaystyle\lim_{n\to\infty} \left| \dfrac{a_{n+1}}{a_n} \right| = \lim_{n\to\infty} \left[\dfrac{|x+2|^{n+1}}{(n+1)\,4^{n+1}} \cdot \dfrac{n\,4^n}{|x+2|^n} \right] = \lim_{n\to\infty}\left[\dfrac{n}{n+1} \dfrac{|x+2|}{4} \right] = \dfrac{|x+2|}{4} < 1 \;\Leftrightarrow\; |x+2| < 4,$ so $R = 4.$

$|x+2| < 4 \;\Leftrightarrow\; -4 < x + 2 < 4 \;\Leftrightarrow\; -6 < x < 2.$ If $x = -6$, then the series $\displaystyle\sum_{n-1}^{\infty} \dfrac{(x+2)^n}{n\,4^n}$ becomes

$\displaystyle\sum_{n=1}^{\infty} \dfrac{(-4)^n}{n4^n} = \sum_{n=1}^{\infty} \dfrac{(-1)^n}{n}$, the alternating harmonic series, which converges by the Alternating Series Test. When $x = 2$, the

series becomes the harmonic series $\displaystyle\sum_{n=1}^{\infty} \dfrac{1}{n}$, which diverges. Thus, $I = [-6, 2).$

33. $\displaystyle\lim_{n\to\infty}\left|\dfrac{a_{n+1}}{a_n}\right| = \lim_{n\to\infty}\left| \dfrac{2^{n+1}(x-3)^{n+1}}{\sqrt{n+4}} \cdot \dfrac{\sqrt{n+3}}{2^n(x-3)^n} \right| = 2\,|x-3| \lim_{n\to\infty}\sqrt{\dfrac{n+3}{n+4}} = 2\,|x-3| < 1 \;\Leftrightarrow\; |x-3| < \tfrac{1}{2},$

so $R = \tfrac{1}{2}.$ $|x - 3| < \tfrac{1}{2} \;\Leftrightarrow\; -\tfrac{1}{2} < x - 3 < \tfrac{1}{2} \;\Leftrightarrow\; \tfrac{5}{2} < x < \tfrac{7}{2}.$ For $x = \tfrac{7}{2}$, the series $\displaystyle\sum_{n=1}^{\infty} \dfrac{2^n(x-3)^n}{\sqrt{n+3}}$ becomes

$\displaystyle\sum_{n=0}^{\infty} \dfrac{1}{\sqrt{n+3}} = \sum_{n=3}^{\infty} \dfrac{1}{n^{1/2}}$, which diverges $\left[p = \tfrac{1}{2} \leq 1\right]$, but for $x = \tfrac{5}{2}$, we get $\displaystyle\sum_{n=0}^{\infty} \dfrac{(-1)^n}{\sqrt{n+3}}$, which is a convergent

alternating series, so $I = \left[\tfrac{5}{2}, \tfrac{7}{2}\right).$

35.

n	$f^{(n)}(x)$	$f^{(n)}\left(\frac{\pi}{6}\right)$
0	$\sin x$	$\frac{1}{2}$
1	$\cos x$	$\frac{\sqrt{3}}{2}$
2	$-\sin x$	$-\frac{1}{2}$
3	$-\cos x$	$-\frac{\sqrt{3}}{2}$
4	$\sin x$	$\frac{1}{2}$
⋮	⋮	⋮

$$\sin x = f\left(\frac{\pi}{6}\right) + f'\left(\frac{\pi}{6}\right)\left(x - \frac{\pi}{6}\right) + \frac{f''\left(\frac{\pi}{6}\right)}{2!}\left(x - \frac{\pi}{6}\right)^2 + \frac{f^{(3)}\left(\frac{\pi}{6}\right)}{3!}\left(x - \frac{\pi}{6}\right)^3 + \frac{f^{(4)}\left(\frac{\pi}{6}\right)}{4!}\left(x - \frac{\pi}{6}\right)^4 + \cdots$$

$$= \frac{1}{2}\left[1 - \frac{1}{2!}\left(x - \frac{\pi}{6}\right)^2 + \frac{1}{4!}\left(x - \frac{\pi}{6}\right)^4 - \cdots\right] + \frac{\sqrt{3}}{2}\left[\left(x - \frac{\pi}{6}\right) - \frac{1}{3!}\left(x - \frac{\pi}{6}\right)^3 + \cdots\right]$$

$$= \frac{1}{2}\sum_{n=0}^{\infty}(-1)^n\frac{1}{(2n)!}\left(x - \frac{\pi}{6}\right)^{2n} + \frac{\sqrt{3}}{2}\sum_{n=0}^{\infty}(-1)^n\frac{1}{(2n+1)!}\left(x - \frac{\pi}{6}\right)^{2n+1}$$

37. $\dfrac{1}{1+x} = \dfrac{1}{1-(-x)} = \sum_{n=0}^{\infty}(-x)^n = \sum_{n=0}^{\infty}(-1)^n x^n$ for $|x| < 1$ $\Rightarrow$ $\dfrac{x^2}{1+x} = \sum_{n=0}^{\infty}(-1)^n x^{n+2}$ with $R = 1$.

39. $\displaystyle\int \frac{1}{4-x}\,dx = -\ln(4-x) + C$ and

$$\int \frac{1}{4-x}\,dx = \frac{1}{4}\int\frac{1}{1-x/4}\,dx = \frac{1}{4}\int\sum_{n=0}^{\infty}\left(\frac{x}{4}\right)^n dx = \frac{1}{4}\int\sum_{n=0}^{\infty}\frac{x^n}{4^n}\,dx = \frac{1}{4}\sum_{n=0}^{\infty}\frac{x^{n+1}}{4^n(n+1)} + C. \text{ So}$$

$$\ln(4-x) = -\frac{1}{4}\sum_{n=0}^{\infty}\frac{x^{n+1}}{4^n(n+1)} + C = -\sum_{n=0}^{\infty}\frac{x^{n+1}}{4^{n+1}(n+1)} + C = -\sum_{n=1}^{\infty}\frac{x^n}{n4^n} + C. \text{ Putting } x = 0, \text{ we get } C = \ln 4.$$

Thus, $f(x) = \ln(4-x) = \ln 4 - \displaystyle\sum_{n=1}^{\infty}\frac{x^n}{n4^n}$. The series converges for $|x/4| < 1$ $\Leftrightarrow$ $|x| < 4$, so $R = 4$.

Another solution:

$$\ln(4-x) = \ln[4(1-x/4)] = \ln 4 + \ln(1-x/4) = \ln 4 + \ln[1 + (-x/4)]$$

$$= \ln 4 + \sum_{n=1}^{\infty}(-1)^{n+1}\frac{(-x/4)^n}{n} \text{ [from Table 1]} = \ln 4 + \sum_{n=1}^{\infty}(-1)^{2n+1}\frac{x^n}{n4^n} = \ln 4 - \sum_{n=1}^{\infty}\frac{x^n}{n4^n}.$$

41. $\sin x = \displaystyle\sum_{n=0}^{\infty}\frac{(-1)^n x^{2n+1}}{(2n+1)!}$ $\Rightarrow$ $\sin(x^4) = \displaystyle\sum_{n=0}^{\infty}\frac{(-1)^n (x^4)^{2n+1}}{(2n+1)!} = \sum_{n=0}^{\infty}\frac{(-1)^n x^{8n+4}}{(2n+1)!}$ for all x, so the radius of

convergence is ∞.

43. $f(x) = \dfrac{1}{\sqrt[4]{16-x}} = \dfrac{1}{\sqrt[4]{16(1-x/16)}} = \dfrac{1}{\sqrt[4]{16}\left(1-\frac{1}{16}x\right)^{1/4}} = \frac{1}{2}\left(1-\frac{1}{16}x\right)^{-1/4}$

$= \dfrac{1}{2}\left[1 + \left(-\dfrac{1}{4}\right)\left(-\dfrac{x}{16}\right) + \dfrac{\left(-\frac{1}{4}\right)\left(-\frac{5}{4}\right)}{2!}\left(-\dfrac{x}{16}\right)^2 + \dfrac{\left(-\frac{1}{4}\right)\left(-\frac{5}{4}\right)\left(-\frac{9}{4}\right)}{3!}\left(-\dfrac{x}{16}\right)^3 + \cdots\right]$

$= \dfrac{1}{2} + \sum_{n=1}^{\infty} \dfrac{1\cdot 5\cdot 9\cdot \cdots\cdot (4n-3)}{2\cdot 4^n\cdot n!\cdot 16^n}\, x^n = \dfrac{1}{2} + \sum_{n=1}^{\infty} \dfrac{1\cdot 5\cdot 9\cdot \cdots\cdot (4n-3)}{2^{6n+1}\, n!}\, x^n$

for $\left|-\dfrac{x}{16}\right| < 1 \quad\Leftrightarrow\quad |x| < 16$, so $R = 16$.

45. $e^x = \sum_{n=0}^{\infty} \dfrac{x^n}{n!}$, so $\dfrac{e^x}{x} = \dfrac{1}{x}\sum_{n=0}^{\infty}\dfrac{x^n}{n!} = \sum_{n=0}^{\infty}\dfrac{x^{n-1}}{n!} = x^{-1} + \sum_{n=1}^{\infty}\dfrac{x^{n-1}}{n!} = \dfrac{1}{x} + \sum_{n=1}^{\infty}\dfrac{x^{n-1}}{n!}$ and

$\displaystyle\int \dfrac{e^x}{x}\, dx = C + \ln|x| + \sum_{n=1}^{\infty}\dfrac{x^n}{n\cdot n!}.$

47. (a)

n	$f^{(n)}(x)$	$f^{(n)}(1)$
0	$x^{1/2}$	1
1	$\frac{1}{2}x^{-1/2}$	$\frac{1}{2}$
2	$-\frac{1}{4}x^{-3/2}$	$-\frac{1}{4}$
3	$\frac{3}{8}x^{-5/2}$	$\frac{3}{8}$
4	$-\frac{15}{16}x^{-7/2}$	$-\frac{15}{16}$
$\vdots$	$\vdots$	$\vdots$

$\sqrt{x} \approx T_3(x) = 1 + \dfrac{1/2}{1!}(x-1) - \dfrac{1/4}{2!}(x-1)^2 + \dfrac{3/8}{3!}(x-1)^3$

$= 1 + \frac{1}{2}(x-1) - \frac{1}{8}(x-1)^2 + \frac{1}{16}(x-1)^3$

(b)

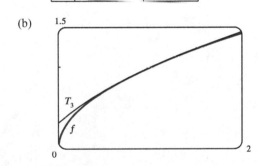

(c) $|R_3(x)| \le \dfrac{M}{4!}|x-1|^4$, where $\left|f^{(4)}(x)\right| \le M$ with

$f^{(4)}(x) = -\frac{15}{16}x^{-7/2}$. Now $0.9 \le x \le 1.1 \quad\Rightarrow$

$-0.1 \le x - 1 \le 0.1 \quad\Rightarrow\quad (x-1)^4 \le (0.1)^4,$

and letting $x = 0.9$ gives $M = \dfrac{15}{16(0.9)^{7/2}}$, so

$|R_3(x)| \le \dfrac{15}{16(0.9)^{7/2}\, 4!}(0.1)^4 \approx 0.000\,005\,648$

$\approx 0.000\,006 = 6 \times 10^{-6}$

(d)

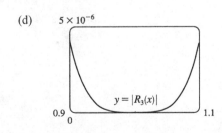

$y = |R_3(x)|$

From the graph of $|R_3(x)| = |\sqrt{x} - T_3(x)|$, it appears that

the error is less than 5×10^{-6} on $[0.9, 1.1]$.

49. $\sin x = \sum_{n=0}^{\infty}(-1)^n \dfrac{x^{2n+1}}{(2n+1)!} = x - \dfrac{x^3}{3!} + \dfrac{x^5}{5!} - \dfrac{x^7}{7!} + \cdots$, so $\sin x - x = -\dfrac{x^3}{3!} + \dfrac{x^5}{5!} - \dfrac{x^7}{7!} + \cdots$ and

$\dfrac{\sin x - x}{x^3} = -\dfrac{1}{3!} + \dfrac{x^2}{5!} - \dfrac{x^4}{7!} + \cdots$. Thus, $\lim_{x\to 0}\dfrac{\sin x - x}{x^3} = \lim_{x\to 0}\left(-\dfrac{1}{6} + \dfrac{x^2}{120} - \dfrac{x^4}{5040} + \cdots\right) = -\dfrac{1}{6}.$

☐ FOCUS ON PROBLEM SOLVING

1. It would be far too much work to compute 15 derivatives of f. The key idea is to remember that $f^{(n)}(0)$ occurs in the

   coefficient of x^n in the Maclaurin series of f. We start with the Maclaurin series for sin: $\sin x = x - \dfrac{x^3}{3!} + \dfrac{x^5}{5!} - \cdots$.

   Then $\sin(x^3) = x^3 - \dfrac{x^9}{3!} + \dfrac{x^{15}}{5!} - \cdots$, and so the coefficient of x^{15} is $\dfrac{f^{(15)}(0)}{15!} = \dfrac{1}{5!}$. Therefore,

   $f^{(15)}(0) = \dfrac{15!}{5!} = 6 \cdot 7 \cdot 8 \cdot 9 \cdot 10 \cdot 11 \cdot 12 \cdot 13 \cdot 14 \cdot 15 = 10{,}897{,}286{,}400.$

3. (a) At each stage, each side is replaced by four shorter sides, each of length

   $\frac{1}{3}$ of the side length at the preceding stage. Writing s_0 and ℓ_0 for the

   number of sides and the length of the side of the initial triangle, we

   generate the table at right. In general, we have $s_n = 3 \cdot 4^n$ and

   $\ell_n = \left(\frac{1}{3}\right)^n$, so the length of the perimeter at the nth stage of construction

   is $p_n = s_n \ell_n = 3 \cdot 4^n \cdot \left(\frac{1}{3}\right)^n = 3 \cdot \left(\frac{4}{3}\right)^n.$

$s_0 = 3$	$\ell_0 = 1$
$s_1 = 3 \cdot 4$	$\ell_1 = 1/3$
$s_2 = 3 \cdot 4^2$	$\ell_2 = 1/3^2$
$s_3 = 3 \cdot 4^3$	$\ell_3 = 1/3^3$
$\vdots$	$\vdots$

   (b) $p_n = \dfrac{4^n}{3^{n-1}} = 4\left(\dfrac{4}{3}\right)^{n-1}$. Since $\frac{4}{3} > 1$, $p_n \to \infty$ as $n \to \infty$.

   (c) The area of each of the small triangles added at a given stage is one-ninth of the area of the triangle added at the preceding

   stage. Let a be the area of the original triangle. Then the area a_n of each of the small triangles added at stage n is

   $a_n = a \cdot \dfrac{1}{9^n} = \dfrac{a}{9^n}$. Since a small triangle is added to each side at every stage, it follows that the total area A_n added to the

   figure at the nth stage is $A_n = s_{n-1} \cdot a_n = 3 \cdot 4^{n-1} \cdot \dfrac{a}{9^n} = a \cdot \dfrac{4^{n-1}}{3^{2n-1}}$. Then the total area enclosed by the snowflake

   curve is $A = a + A_1 + A_2 + A_3 + \cdots = a + a \cdot \dfrac{1}{3} + a \cdot \dfrac{4}{3^3} + a \cdot \dfrac{4^2}{3^5} + a \cdot \dfrac{4^3}{3^7} + \cdots$. After the first term, this is a

   geometric series with common ratio $\dfrac{4}{9}$, so $A = a + \dfrac{a/3}{1 - \frac{4}{9}} = a + \dfrac{a}{3} \cdot \dfrac{9}{5} = \dfrac{8a}{5}$. But the area of the original equilateral

   triangle with side 1 is $a = \dfrac{1}{2} \cdot 1 \cdot \sin\dfrac{\pi}{3} = \dfrac{\sqrt{3}}{4}$. So the area enclosed by the snowflake curve is $\dfrac{8}{5} \cdot \dfrac{\sqrt{3}}{4} = \dfrac{2\sqrt{3}}{5}$.

5. $\ln\left(1 - \dfrac{1}{n^2}\right) = \ln\left(\dfrac{n^2 - 1}{n^2}\right) = \ln\dfrac{(n+1)(n-1)}{n^2} = \ln[(n+1)(n-1)] - \ln n^2$

   $\qquad = \ln(n+1) + \ln(n-1) - 2\ln n = \ln(n-1) - \ln n - \ln n + \ln(n+1)$

   $\qquad = \ln\dfrac{n-1}{n} - [\ln n - \ln(n+1)] = \ln\dfrac{n-1}{n} - \ln\dfrac{n}{n+1}.$

   Let $s_k = \displaystyle\sum_{n=2}^{k} \ln\left(1 - \dfrac{1}{n^2}\right) = \sum_{n=2}^{k}\left(\ln\dfrac{n-1}{n} - \ln\dfrac{n}{n+1}\right)$ for $k \geq 2$. Then

   $s_k = \left(\ln\dfrac{1}{2} - \ln\dfrac{2}{3}\right) + \left(\ln\dfrac{2}{3} - \ln\dfrac{3}{4}\right) + \cdots + \left(\ln\dfrac{k-1}{k} - \ln\dfrac{k}{k+1}\right) = \ln\dfrac{1}{2} - \ln\dfrac{k}{k+1}$, so

   $\displaystyle\sum_{n=2}^{\infty} \ln\left(1 - \dfrac{1}{n^2}\right) = \lim_{k \to \infty} s_k = \lim_{k \to \infty}\left(\ln\dfrac{1}{2} - \ln\dfrac{k}{k+1}\right) = \ln\dfrac{1}{2} - \ln 1 = \ln 1 - \ln 2 - \ln 1 = -\ln 2.$

45

7. $u = 1 + \dfrac{x^3}{3!} + \dfrac{x^6}{6!} + \dfrac{x^9}{9!} + \cdots,\ v = x + \dfrac{x^4}{4!} + \dfrac{x^7}{7!} + \dfrac{x^{10}}{10!} + \cdots,\ w = \dfrac{x^2}{2!} + \dfrac{x^5}{5!} + \dfrac{x^8}{8!} + \cdots.$

Use the Ratio Test to show that the series for u, v, and w have positive radii of convergence (∞ in each case), so

Theorem 8.6.2 applies, and hence, we may differentiate each of these series:

$$\frac{du}{dx} = \frac{3x^2}{3!} + \frac{6x^5}{6!} + \frac{9x^8}{9!} + \cdots = \frac{x^2}{2!} + \frac{x^5}{5!} + \frac{x^8}{8!} + \cdots = w$$

Similarly, $\dfrac{dv}{dx} = 1 + \dfrac{x^3}{3!} + \dfrac{x^6}{6!} + \dfrac{x^9}{9!} + \cdots = u$, and $\dfrac{dw}{dx} = x + \dfrac{x^4}{4!} + \dfrac{x^7}{7!} + \dfrac{x^{10}}{10!} + \cdots = v.$

So $u' = w$, $v' = u$, and $w' = v$. Now differentiate the left hand side of the desired equation:

$$\frac{d}{dx}(u^3 + v^3 + w^3 - 3uvw) = 3u^2u' + 3v^2v' + 3w^2w' - 3(u'vw + uv'w + uvw')$$

$$= 3u^2w + 3v^2u + 3w^2v - 3(vw^2 + u^2w + uv^2) = 0 \quad \Rightarrow$$

$u^3 + v^3 + w^3 - 3uvw = C$. To find the value of the constant C, we put $x = 0$ in the last equation and get

$1^3 + 0^3 + 0^3 - 3(1 \cdot 0 \cdot 0) = C \quad \Rightarrow \quad C = 1$, so $u^3 + v^3 + w^3 - 3uvw = 1.$

9. If L is the length of a side of the equilateral triangle, then the area is $A = \frac{1}{2}L \cdot \frac{\sqrt{3}}{2}L = \frac{\sqrt{3}}{4}L^2$ and so $L^2 = \frac{4}{\sqrt{3}}A$.

Let r be the radius of one of the circles. When there are n rows of circles, the figure shows that

$$L = \sqrt{3}\,r + r + (n-2)(2r) + r + \sqrt{3}\,r = r\left(2n - 2 + 2\sqrt{3}\right), \text{ so } r = \frac{L}{2\left(n + \sqrt{3} - 1\right)}.$$

The number of circles is $1 + 2 + \cdots + n = \dfrac{n(n+1)}{2}$, and so the total area of the circles is

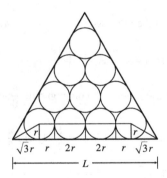

$$A_n = \frac{n(n+1)}{2}\pi r^2 = \frac{n(n+1)}{2}\,\pi\,\frac{L^2}{4\left(n + \sqrt{3} - 1\right)^2}$$

$$= \frac{n(n+1)}{2}\,\pi\,\frac{4A/\sqrt{3}}{4\left(n + \sqrt{3} - 1\right)^2} = \frac{n(n+1)}{\left(n + \sqrt{3} - 1\right)^2}\,\frac{\pi A}{2\sqrt{3}} \quad \Rightarrow$$

$$\frac{A_n}{A} = \frac{n(n+1)}{\left(n + \sqrt{3} - 1\right)^2}\,\frac{\pi}{2\sqrt{3}}$$

$$= \frac{1 + 1/n}{\left[1 + (\sqrt{3} - 1)/n\right]^2}\,\frac{\pi}{2\sqrt{3}} \to \frac{\pi}{2\sqrt{3}} \text{ as } n \to \infty$$

11. By Table 1 in Section 8.7, $\tan^{-1}x = \displaystyle\sum_{n=0}^{\infty}(-1)^n \frac{x^{2n+1}}{2n+1}$ for $|x| < 1$. In particular, for $x = \dfrac{1}{\sqrt{3}}$, we

have $\dfrac{\pi}{6} = \tan^{-1}\left(\dfrac{1}{\sqrt{3}}\right) = \displaystyle\sum_{n=0}^{\infty}(-1)^n \frac{(1/\sqrt{3})^{2n+1}}{2n+1} = \displaystyle\sum_{n=0}^{\infty}(-1)^n\left(\dfrac{1}{3}\right)^n \frac{1}{\sqrt{3}}\frac{1}{2n+1}$, so

$$\pi = \frac{6}{\sqrt{3}}\sum_{n=0}^{\infty}\frac{(-1)^n}{(2n+1)3^n} = 2\sqrt{3}\sum_{n=0}^{\infty}\frac{(-1)^n}{(2n+1)3^n} = 2\sqrt{3}\left(1 + \sum_{n=1}^{\infty}\frac{(-1)^n}{(2n+1)3^n}\right) \Rightarrow \sum_{n=1}^{\infty}\frac{(-1)^n}{(2n+1)3^n} = \frac{\pi}{2\sqrt{3}} - 1.$$

13. Let $f(x)$ denote the left-hand side of the equation $1 + \dfrac{x}{2!} + \dfrac{x^2}{4!} + \dfrac{x^3}{6!} + \dfrac{x^4}{8!} + \cdots = 0$. If $x \geq 0$, then $f(x) \geq 1$ and there are

no solutions of the equation. Note that $f(-x^2) = 1 - \dfrac{x^2}{2!} + \dfrac{x^4}{4!} - \dfrac{x^6}{6!} + \dfrac{x^8}{8!} - \cdots = \cos x$. The solutions of $\cos x = 0$ for

$x < 0$ are given by $x = \dfrac{\pi}{2} - \pi k$, where k is a positive integer. Thus, the solutions of $f(x) = 0$ are $x = -\left(\dfrac{\pi}{2} - \pi k\right)^2$, where

k is a positive integer.

15. Call the series S. We group the terms according to the number of digits in their denominators:

$$S = \underbrace{\left(\tfrac{1}{1} + \tfrac{1}{2} + \cdots + \tfrac{1}{8} + \tfrac{1}{9}\right)}_{g_1} + \underbrace{\left(\tfrac{1}{11} + \cdots + \tfrac{1}{99}\right)}_{g_2} + \underbrace{\left(\tfrac{1}{111} + \cdots + \tfrac{1}{999}\right)}_{g_3} + \cdots$$

Now in the group g_n, since we have 9 choices for each of the n digits in the denominator, there are 9^n terms.

Furthermore, each term in g_n is less than $\frac{1}{10^{n-1}}$ [except for the first term in g_1]. So $g_n < 9^n \cdot \frac{1}{10^{n-1}} = 9\left(\frac{9}{10}\right)^{n-1}$.

Now $\sum\limits_{n=1}^{\infty} 9\left(\frac{9}{10}\right)^{n-1}$ is a geometric series with $a = 9$ and $r = \frac{9}{10} < 1$. Therefore, by the Comparison Test,

$$S = \sum_{n=1}^{\infty} g_n < \sum_{n=1}^{\infty} 9\left(\tfrac{9}{10}\right)^{n-1} = \frac{9}{1 - 9/10} = 90.$$

9 ☐ VECTORS AND THE GEOMETRY OF SPACE

9.1 Three-Dimensional Coordinate Systems

1. We start at the origin, which has coordinates $(0,0,0)$. First we move 4 units along the positive x-axis, affecting only the x-coordinate, bringing us to the point $(4,0,0)$. We then move 3 units straight downward, in the negative z-direction. Thus only the z-coordinate is affected, and we arrive at $(4,0,-3)$.

3. The distance from a point to the xz-plane is the absolute value of the y-coordinate of the point. $Q(-5,-1,4)$ has the y-coordinate with the smallest absolute value, so Q is the point closest to the xz-plane. $R(0,3,8)$ must lie in the yz-plane since the distance from R to the yz-plane, given by the x-coordinate of R, is 0.

5. The equation $x+y=2$ represents the set of all points in $\mathbb{R}^3$ whose x- and y-coordinates have a sum of 2, or equivalently where $y=2-x$. This is the set $\{(x, 2-x, z) \mid x \in \mathbb{R}, z \in \mathbb{R}\}$ which is a vertical plane that intersects the xy-plane in the line $y=2-x$, $z=0$.

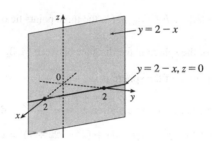

7. (a) We can find the lengths of the sides of the triangle by using the distance formula between pairs of vertices:

$$|PQ| = \sqrt{(7-3)^2 + [0-(-2)]^2 + [1-(-3)]^2} = \sqrt{16+4+16} = 6$$

$$|QR| = \sqrt{(1-7)^2 + (2-0)^2 + (1-1)^2} = \sqrt{36+4+0} = \sqrt{40} = 2\sqrt{10}$$

$$|RP| = \sqrt{(3-1)^2 + (-2-2)^2 + (-3-1)^2} = \sqrt{4+16+16} = 6$$

The longest side is QR, but the Pythagorean Theorem is not satisfied: $|PQ|^2 + |RP|^2 \neq |QR|^2$. Thus PQR is not a right triangle. PQR is isosceles, as two sides have the same length.

(b) Compute the lengths of the sides of the triangle by using the distance formula between pairs of vertices:

$$|PQ| = \sqrt{(4-2)^2 + [1-(-1)]^2 + (1-0)^2} = \sqrt{4+4+1} = 3$$

$$|QR| = \sqrt{(4-4)^2 + (-5-1)^2 + (4-1)^2} = \sqrt{0+36+9} = \sqrt{45} = 3\sqrt{5}$$

$$|RP| = \sqrt{(2-4)^2 + [-1-(-5)]^2 + (0-4)^2} = \sqrt{4+16+16} = 6$$

Since the Pythagorean Theorem is satisfied by $|PQ|^2 + |RP|^2 = |QR|^2$, PQR is a right triangle. PQR is not isosceles, as no two sides have the same length.

9. (a) First we find the distances between points:

$$|AB| = \sqrt{(3-2)^2 + (7-4)^2 + (-2-2)^2} = \sqrt{26}$$

$$|BC| = \sqrt{(1-3)^2 + (3-7)^2 + [3-(-2)]^2} = \sqrt{45} = 3\sqrt{5}$$

$$|AC| = \sqrt{(1-2)^2 + (3-4)^2 + (3-2)^2} = \sqrt{3}$$

In order for the points to lie on a straight line, the sum of the two shortest distances must be equal to the longest distance.

Since $\sqrt{26} + \sqrt{3} \neq 3\sqrt{5}$, the three points do not lie on a straight line.

(b) First we find the distances between points:

$$|DE| = \sqrt{(1-0)^2 + [-2-(-5)]^2 + (4-5)^2} = \sqrt{11}$$

$$|EF| = \sqrt{(3-1)^2 + [4-(-2)]^2 + (2-4)^2} = \sqrt{44} = 2\sqrt{11}$$

$$|DF| = \sqrt{(3-0)^2 + [4-(-5)]^2 + (2-5)^2} = \sqrt{99} = 3\sqrt{11}$$

Since $|DE| + |EF| = |DF|$, the three points lie on a straight line.

11. The radius of the sphere is the distance between $(4,3,-1)$ and $(3,8,1)$: $r = \sqrt{(3-4)^2 + (8-3)^2 + [1-(-1)]^2} = \sqrt{30}$.

Thus, an equation of the sphere is $(x-3)^2 + (y-8)^2 + (z-1)^2 = 30$.

13. Completing squares in the equation $x^2 + y^2 + z^2 - 6x + 4y - 2z = 11$ gives

$(x^2 - 6x + 9) + (y^2 + 4y + 4) + (z^2 - 2z + 1) = 11 + 9 + 4 + 1 \quad \Rightarrow \quad (x-3)^2 + (y+2)^2 + (z-1)^2 = 25$, which we

recognize as an equation of a sphere with center $(3, -2, 1)$ and radius 5.

15. Completing squares in the equation $2x^2 - 8x + 2y^2 + 2z^2 + 24z = 1$ gives

$2(x^2 - 4x + 4) + 2y^2 + 2(z^2 + 12z + 36) = 1 + 8 + 72 \quad \Rightarrow \quad 2(x-2)^2 + 2y^2 + 2(z+6)^2 = 81 \quad \Rightarrow$

$(x-2)^2 + y^2 + (z+6)^2 = \frac{81}{2}$, which we recognize as an equation of a sphere with center $(2, 0, -6)$ and

radius $\sqrt{\frac{81}{2}} = 9/\sqrt{2}$.

17. (a) If the midpoint of the line segment from $P_1(x_1, y_1, z_1)$ to $P_2(x_2, y_2, z_2)$ is $Q = \left(\frac{x_1 + x_2}{2}, \frac{y_1 + y_2}{2}, \frac{z_1 + z_2}{2}\right)$,

then the distances $|P_1Q|$ and $|QP_2|$ are equal, and each is half of $|P_1P_2|$. We verify that this is the case:

$$|P_1P_2| = \sqrt{(x_2 - x_1)^2 + (y_2 - y_1)^2 + (z_2 - z_1)^2}$$

$$|P_1Q| = \sqrt{\left[\tfrac{1}{2}(x_1 + x_2) - x_1\right]^2 + \left[\tfrac{1}{2}(y_1 + y_2) - y_1\right]^2 + \left[\tfrac{1}{2}(z_1 + z_2) - z_1\right]^2}$$

$$= \sqrt{\left(\tfrac{1}{2}x_2 - \tfrac{1}{2}x_1\right)^2 + \left(\tfrac{1}{2}y_2 - \tfrac{1}{2}y_1\right)^2 + \left(\tfrac{1}{2}z_2 - \tfrac{1}{2}z_1\right)^2}$$

$$= \sqrt{\left(\tfrac{1}{2}\right)^2 \left[(x_2 - x_1)^2 + (y_2 - y_1)^2 + (z_2 - z_1)^2\right]} = \tfrac{1}{2}\sqrt{(x_2 - x_1)^2 + (y_2 - y_1)^2 + (z_2 - z_1)^2}$$

$$= \tfrac{1}{2}|P_1P_2|$$

$$|QP_2| = \sqrt{\left[x_2 - \tfrac{1}{2}(x_1 + x_2)\right]^2 + \left[y_2 - \tfrac{1}{2}(y_1 + y_2)\right]^2 + \left[z_2 - \tfrac{1}{2}(z_1 + z_2)\right]^2}$$

$$= \sqrt{\left(\tfrac{1}{2}x_2 - \tfrac{1}{2}x_1\right)^2 + \left(\tfrac{1}{2}y_2 - \tfrac{1}{2}y_1\right)^2 + \left(\tfrac{1}{2}z_2 - \tfrac{1}{2}z_1\right)^2} = \sqrt{\left(\tfrac{1}{2}\right)^2 \left[(x_2 - x_1)^2 + (y_2 - y_1)^2 + (z_2 - z_1)^2\right]}$$

$$= \tfrac{1}{2}\sqrt{(x_2 - x_1)^2 + (y_2 - y_1)^2 + (z_2 - z_1)^2} = \tfrac{1}{2}|P_1 P_2|$$

So Q is indeed the midpoint of $P_1 P_2$.

(b) By part (a), the midpoints of sides AB, BC and CA are $P_1\left(-\tfrac{1}{2}, 1, 4\right)$, $P_2\left(1, \tfrac{1}{2}, 5\right)$ and $P_3\left(\tfrac{5}{2}, \tfrac{3}{2}, 4\right)$. (Recall that a median of a triangle is a line segment from a vertex to the midpoint of the opposite side.) Then the lengths of the medians are:

$$|AP_2| = \sqrt{0^2 + \left(\tfrac{1}{2} - 2\right)^2 + (5 - 3)^2} = \sqrt{\tfrac{9}{4} + 4} = \sqrt{\tfrac{25}{4}} = \tfrac{5}{2}$$

$$|BP_3| = \sqrt{\left(\tfrac{5}{2} + 2\right)^2 + \left(\tfrac{3}{2}\right)^2 + (4 - 5)^2} = \sqrt{\tfrac{81}{4} + \tfrac{9}{4} + 1} = \sqrt{\tfrac{94}{4}} = \tfrac{1}{2}\sqrt{94}$$

$$|CP_1| = \sqrt{\left(-\tfrac{1}{2} - 4\right)^2 + (1 - 1)^2 + (4 - 5)^2} = \sqrt{\tfrac{81}{4} + 1} = \tfrac{1}{2}\sqrt{85}$$

19. (a) Since the sphere touches the xy-plane, its radius is the distance from its center, $(2, -3, 6)$, to the xy-plane, namely 6. Therefore $r = 6$ and an equation of the sphere is $(x - 2)^2 + (y + 3)^2 + (z - 6)^2 = 6^2 = 36$.

(b) The radius of this sphere is the distance from its center $(2, -3, 6)$ to the yz-plane, which is 2. Therefore, an equation is $(x - 2)^2 + (y + 3)^2 + (z - 6)^2 = 4$.

(c) Here the radius is the distance from the center $(2, -3, 6)$ to the xz-plane, which is 3. Therefore, an equation is $(x - 2)^2 + (y + 3)^2 + (z - 6)^2 = 9$.

21. The equation $x = 5$ represents a plane parallel to the yz-plane and 5 units in front of it.

23. The inequality $y < 8$ represents a half-space consisting of all points to the left of the plane $y = 8$.

25. The inequality $0 \le z \le 6$ represents all points on or between the horizontal planes $z = 0$ (the xy-plane) and $z = 6$.

27. Because $z = -1$, all points in the region must lie in the horizontal plane $z = -1$. In addition, $x^2 + y^2 = 4$, so the region consists of all points that lie on a circle with radius 2 and center on the z-axis that is contained in the plane $z = -1$.

29. The inequality $x^2 + y^2 + z^2 \le 3$ is equivalent to $\sqrt{x^2 + y^2 + z^2} \le \sqrt{3}$, so the region consists of those points whose distance from the origin is at most $\sqrt{3}$. This is the set of all points on or inside the sphere with radius $\sqrt{3}$ and center $(0, 0, 0)$.

31. Here $x^2 + z^2 \le 9$ or equivalently $\sqrt{x^2 + z^2} \le 3$ which describes the set of all points in $\mathbb{R}^3$ whose distance from the y-axis is at most 3. Thus, the inequality represents the region consisting of all points on or inside a circular cylinder of radius 3 with axis the y-axis.

33. This describes all points whose x-coordinate is between 0 and 5, that is, $0 < x < 5$.

35. This describes a region all of whose points have a distance to the origin which is greater than r, but smaller than R. So inequalities describing the region are $r < \sqrt{x^2 + y^2 + z^2} < R$, or $r^2 < x^2 + y^2 + z^2 < R^2$.

37. (a) To find the x- and y-coordinates of the point P, we project it onto L_2 and

project the resulting point Q onto the x- and y-axes. To find the

z-coordinate, we project P onto either the xz-plane or the yz-plane

(using our knowledge of its x- or y-coordinate) and then project the

resulting point onto the z-axis. (Or, we could draw a line parallel to QO

from P to the z-axis.) The coordinates of P are $(2, 1, 4)$.

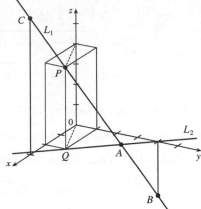

(b) A is the intersection of L_1 and L_2, B is directly below the

y-intercept of L_2, and C is directly above the x-intercept of L_2.

39. We need to find a set of points $\{P(x, y, z) \mid |AP| = |BP|\}$.

$$\sqrt{(x+1)^2 + (y-5)^2 + (z-3)^2} = \sqrt{(x-6)^2 + (y-2)^2 + (z+2)^2} \quad \Rightarrow$$

$$(x+1)^2 + (y-5) + (z-3)^2 = (x-6)^2 + (y-2)^2 + (z+2)^2 \quad \Rightarrow$$

$$x^2 + 2x + 1 + y^2 - 10y + 25 + z^2 - 6z + 9 = x^2 - 12x + 36 + y^2 - 4y + 4 + z^2 + 4z + 4 \quad \Rightarrow \quad 14x - 6y - 10z = 9.$$

Thus the set of points is a plane perpendicular to the line segment joining A and B (since this plane must contain the

perpendicular bisector of the line segment AB).

41. The sphere $x^2 + y^2 + z^2 = 4$ has center $(0, 0, 0)$ and radius 2. Completing squares in $x^2 - 4x + y^2 - 4y + z^2 - 4z = -11$

gives $(x^2 - 4x + 4) + (y^2 - 4y + 4) + (z^2 - 4z + 4) = -11 + 4 + 4 + 4 \quad \Rightarrow \quad (x-2)^2 + (y-2)^2 + (z-2)^2 = 1$,

so this is the sphere with center $(2, 2, 2)$ and radius 1. The (shortest) distance between the spheres is measured along

the line segment connecting their centers. The distance between $(0, 0, 0)$ and $(2, 2, 2)$ is

$$\sqrt{(2-0)^2 + (2-0)^2 + (2-0)^2} = \sqrt{12} = 2\sqrt{3}, \text{ and subtracting the radius of each circle, the distance between the}$$

spheres is $2\sqrt{3} - 2 - 1 = 2\sqrt{3} - 3$.

9.2 Vectors

1. (a) The cost of a theater ticket is a scalar, because it has only magnitude.

(b) The current in a river is a vector, because it has both magnitude (the speed of the current) and direction at any given
location.

(c) If we assume that the initial path is linear, the initial flight path from Houston to Dallas is a vector, because it has both
magnitude (distance) and direction.

(d) The population of the world is a scalar, because it has only magnitude.

3. Vectors are equal when they share the same length and direction (but not necessarily location). Using the symmetry of the

parallelogram as a guide, we see that $\overrightarrow{AB} = \overrightarrow{DC}$, $\overrightarrow{DA} = \overrightarrow{CB}$, $\overrightarrow{DE} = \overrightarrow{EB}$, and $\overrightarrow{EA} = \overrightarrow{CE}$.

5. (a)   (b) 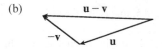 (c) (d)

7. $\mathbf{a} = \langle 2 - (-1), 2 - 3 \rangle = \langle 3, -1 \rangle$

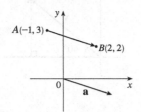

9. $\mathbf{a} = \langle 2 - 0, 3 - 3, -1 - 1 \rangle = \langle 2, 0, -2 \rangle$

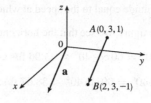

11. $\langle -1, 4 \rangle + \langle 6, -2 \rangle = \langle -1 + 6, 4 + (-2) \rangle = \langle 5, 2 \rangle$

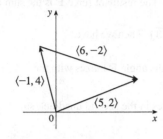

13. $\langle 0, 1, 2 \rangle + \langle 0, 0, -3 \rangle = \langle 0 + 0, 1 + 0, 2 + (-3) \rangle$
$$= \langle 0, 1, -1 \rangle$$

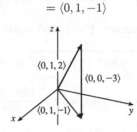

15. $\mathbf{a} + \mathbf{b} = \langle 5 + (-3), -12 + (-6) \rangle = \langle 2, -18 \rangle$

$2\mathbf{a} + 3\mathbf{b} = \langle 10, -24 \rangle + \langle -9, -18 \rangle = \langle 1, -42 \rangle$

$|\mathbf{a}| = \sqrt{5^2 + (-12)^2} = \sqrt{169} = 13$

$|\mathbf{a} - \mathbf{b}| = |\langle 5 - (-3), -12 - (-6) \rangle| = |\langle 8, -6 \rangle| = \sqrt{8^2 + (-6)^2} = \sqrt{100} = 10$

17. $\mathbf{a} + \mathbf{b} = (\mathbf{i} + 2\mathbf{j} - 3\mathbf{k}) + (-2\mathbf{i} - \mathbf{j} + 5\mathbf{k}) = -\mathbf{i} + \mathbf{j} + 2\mathbf{k}$

$2\mathbf{a} + 3\mathbf{b} = 2(\mathbf{i} + 2\mathbf{j} - 3\mathbf{k}) + 3(-2\mathbf{i} - \mathbf{j} + 5\mathbf{k}) = 2\mathbf{i} + 4\mathbf{j} - 6\mathbf{k} - 6\mathbf{i} - 3\mathbf{j} + 15\mathbf{k} = -4\mathbf{i} + \mathbf{j} + 9\mathbf{k}$

$|\mathbf{a}| = \sqrt{1^2 + 2^2 + (-3)^2} = \sqrt{14}$

$|\mathbf{a} - \mathbf{b}| = |(\mathbf{i} + 2\mathbf{j} - 3\mathbf{k}) - (-2\mathbf{i} - \mathbf{j} + 5\mathbf{k})| = |3\mathbf{i} + 3\mathbf{j} - 8\mathbf{k}| = \sqrt{3^2 + 3^2 + (-8)^2} = \sqrt{82}$

19. The vector $-3\mathbf{i} + 7\mathbf{j}$ has length $|-3\mathbf{i} + 7\mathbf{j}| = \sqrt{(-3)^2 + 7^2} = \sqrt{58}$, so by Equation 4 the unit vector with the same

direction is $\dfrac{1}{\sqrt{58}}(-3\mathbf{i} + 7\mathbf{j}) = -\dfrac{3}{\sqrt{58}}\mathbf{i} + \dfrac{7}{\sqrt{58}}\mathbf{j}$.

21. The vector $8\mathbf{i} - \mathbf{j} + 4\mathbf{k}$ has length $|8\mathbf{i} - \mathbf{j} + 4\mathbf{k}| = \sqrt{8^2 + (-1)^2 + 4^2} = \sqrt{81} = 9$, so by Equation 4 the unit vector with

the same direction is $\frac{1}{9}(8\mathbf{i} - \mathbf{j} + 4\mathbf{k}) = \frac{8}{9}\mathbf{i} - \frac{1}{9}\mathbf{j} + \frac{4}{9}\mathbf{k}$.

23. From the figure, we see that the x-component of $\mathbf{v}$ is

$v_1 = |\mathbf{v}|\cos(\pi/3) = 4 \cdot \frac{1}{2} = 2$ and the y-component is

$v_2 = |\mathbf{v}|\sin(\pi/3) = 4 \cdot \frac{\sqrt{3}}{2} = 2\sqrt{3}$. Thus

$\mathbf{v} = \langle v_1, v_2 \rangle = \langle 2, 2\sqrt{3} \rangle$.

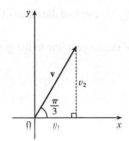

25. The velocity vector **v** makes an angle of $40°$ with the horizontal and has magnitude equal to the speed at which the football was thrown. From the figure, we see that the horizontal component of **v** is $|\mathbf{v}|\cos 40° = 60\cos 40° \approx 45.96$ ft/s and the vertical component is $|\mathbf{v}|\sin 40° = 60\sin 40° \approx 38.57$ ft/s.

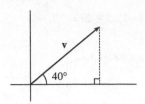

27. The given force vectors can be expressed in terms of their horizontal and vertical components as $-300\,\mathbf{i}$ and $200\cos 60°\,\mathbf{i} + 200\sin 60°\,\mathbf{j} = 200\left(\frac{1}{2}\right)\mathbf{i} + 200\left(\frac{\sqrt{3}}{2}\right)\mathbf{j} = 100\,\mathbf{i} + 100\sqrt{3}\,\mathbf{j}$. The resultant force **F** is the sum of these two vectors: $\mathbf{F} = (-300 + 100)\,\mathbf{i} + (0 + 100\sqrt{3})\,\mathbf{j} = -200\,\mathbf{i} + 100\sqrt{3}\,\mathbf{j}$. Then we have

$|\mathbf{F}| \approx \sqrt{(-200)^2 + (100\sqrt{3})^2} = \sqrt{70{,}000} = 100\sqrt{7} \approx 264.6$ N. Let θ be the angle **F** makes with the

positive x-axis. Then $\tan\theta = \dfrac{100\sqrt{3}}{-200} = -\dfrac{\sqrt{3}}{2}$ and the terminal point of **F** lies in the second quadrant, so

$\theta = \tan^{-1}\left(-\dfrac{\sqrt{3}}{2}\right) + 180° \approx -40.9° + 180° = 139.1°.$

29. With respect to the water's surface, the woman's velocity is the vector sum of the velocity of the ship with respect to the water, and the woman's velocity with respect to the ship. If we let north be the positive y-direction, then

$\mathbf{v} = \langle 0, 22 \rangle + \langle -3, 0 \rangle = \langle -3, 22 \rangle$. The woman's speed is $|\mathbf{v}| = \sqrt{9 + 484} \approx 22.2$ mi/h. The vector **v** makes an angle θ

with the east, where $\theta = \tan^{-1}\left(\frac{22}{-3}\right) \approx 98°$. Therefore, the woman's direction is about $\mathrm{N}(98 - 90)°\mathrm{W} = \mathrm{N}8°\mathrm{W}$.

31. Let $\mathbf{T}_1$ and $\mathbf{T}_2$ represent the tension vectors in each side of the clothesline as shown in the figure. $\mathbf{T}_1$ and $\mathbf{T}_2$ have equal vertical components and opposite horizontal components, so we can write

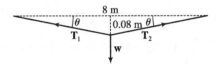

$\mathbf{T}_1 = -a\,\mathbf{i} + b\,\mathbf{j}$ and $\mathbf{T}_2 = a\,\mathbf{i} + b\,\mathbf{j}$ $[a, b > 0]$. By similar triangles, $\dfrac{b}{a} = \dfrac{0.08}{4} \;\Rightarrow\; a = 50b$. The force due to gravity

acting on the shirt has magnitude $0.8g \approx (0.8)(9.8) = 7.84$ N, hence we have $\mathbf{w} = -7.84\,\mathbf{j}$. The resultant $\mathbf{T}_1 + \mathbf{T}_2$

of the tensile forces counterbalances $\mathbf{w}$, so $\mathbf{T}_1 + \mathbf{T}_2 = -\mathbf{w} \;\Rightarrow\; (-a\,\mathbf{i} + b\,\mathbf{j}) + (a\,\mathbf{i} + b\,\mathbf{j}) = 7.84\,\mathbf{j} \;\Rightarrow\;$

$(-50b\,\mathbf{i} + b\,\mathbf{j}) + (50b\,\mathbf{i} + b\,\mathbf{j}) = 2b\,\mathbf{j} = 7.84\,\mathbf{j} \;\Rightarrow\; b = \frac{7.84}{2} = 3.92$ and $a = 50b = 196$. Thus the tensions are

$\mathbf{T}_1 = -a\,\mathbf{i} + b\,\mathbf{j} = -196\,\mathbf{i} + 3.92\,\mathbf{j}$ and $\mathbf{T}_2 = a\,\mathbf{i} + b\,\mathbf{j} = 196\,\mathbf{i} + 3.92\,\mathbf{j}$.

Alternatively, we can find the value of θ and proceed as in Example 7.

33. The slope of the tangent line to the graph of $y = x^2$ at the point $(2, 4)$ is

$$\left.\frac{dy}{dx}\right|_{x=2} = 2x\Big|_{x=2} = 4$$

and a parallel vector is $\mathbf{i} + 4\,\mathbf{j}$ which has length $|\mathbf{i} + 4\,\mathbf{j}| = \sqrt{1^2 + 4^2} = \sqrt{17}$, so unit vectors parallel to the tangent line are

$\pm\frac{1}{\sqrt{17}}\,(\mathbf{i} + 4\,\mathbf{j}).$

35. (a), (b)

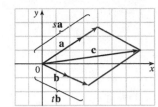

(c) From the sketch, we estimate that $s \approx 1.3$ and $t \approx 1.6$.

(d) $\mathbf{c} = s\,\mathbf{a} + t\,\mathbf{b} \quad \Leftrightarrow \quad 7 = 3s + 2t$ and $1 = 2s - t$.

Solving these equations gives $s = \frac{9}{7}$ and $t = \frac{11}{7}$.

37.

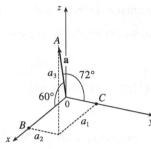

Let $\mathbf{a} = \langle a_1, a_2, a_3 \rangle$, as shown in the figure. Since $|\mathbf{a}| = 1$ and triangle ABO is a right

triangle, we have $\cos 60^\circ = \dfrac{a_1}{1} \quad \Rightarrow \quad a_1 = \cos 60^\circ$. Similarly, triangle ACO is a

right triangle, so $a_2 = \cos 72^\circ$. Finally, since $|\mathbf{a}| = 1$ we have

$$\sqrt{(\cos 60^\circ)^2 + (\cos 72^\circ)^2 + a_3^2} = 1 \quad \Rightarrow \quad a_3^2 = 1 - (\cos 60^\circ)^2 - (\cos 72^\circ)^2 \quad \Rightarrow$$

$a_3 = \sqrt{1 - (\cos 60^\circ)^2 - (\cos 72^\circ)^2}$. Thus

$$\mathbf{a} = \left\langle \cos 60^\circ, \cos 72^\circ, \sqrt{1 - (\cos 60^\circ)^2 - (\cos 72^\circ)^2} \right\rangle \approx \langle 0.50, 0.31, 0.81 \rangle.$$

39. $|\mathbf{r} - \mathbf{r}_0|$ is the distance between the points (x, y, z) and (x_0, y_0, z_0), so the set of points is a sphere with radius 1 and

center (x_0, y_0, z_0).

Alternate method: $|\mathbf{r} - \mathbf{r}_0| = 1 \quad \Leftrightarrow \quad \sqrt{(x - x_0)^2 + (y - y_0)^2 + (z - z_0)^2} = 1 \quad \Leftrightarrow$

$(x - x_0)^2 + (y - y_0)^2 + (z - z_0)^2 = 1$, which is the equation of a sphere with radius 1 and center (x_0, y_0, z_0).

41. $\mathbf{a} + (\mathbf{b} + \mathbf{c}) = \langle a_1, a_2 \rangle + (\langle b_1, b_2 \rangle + \langle c_1, c_2 \rangle) = \langle a_1, a_2 \rangle + \langle b_1 + c_1, b_2 + c_2 \rangle$

$\qquad = \langle a_1 + b_1 + c_1, a_2 + b_2 + c_2 \rangle = \langle (a_1 + b_1) + c_1, (a_2 + b_2) + c_2 \rangle$

$\qquad = \langle a_1 + b_1, a_2 + b_2 \rangle + \langle c_1, c_2 \rangle = (\langle a_1, a_2 \rangle + \langle b_1, b_2 \rangle) + \langle c_1, c_2 \rangle$

$\qquad = (\mathbf{a} + \mathbf{b}) + \mathbf{c}$

43. Consider triangle ABC, where D and E are the midpoints of AB and BC. We know that $\overrightarrow{AB} + \overrightarrow{BC} = \overrightarrow{AC}$ **(1)** and

$\overrightarrow{DB} + \overrightarrow{BE} = \overrightarrow{DE}$ **(2)**. However, $\overrightarrow{DB} = \frac{1}{2}\overrightarrow{AB}$, and $\overrightarrow{BE} = \frac{1}{2}\overrightarrow{BC}$. Substituting these expressions for $\overrightarrow{DB}$ and $\overrightarrow{BE}$ into

(2) gives $\frac{1}{2}\overrightarrow{AB} + \frac{1}{2}\overrightarrow{BC} = \overrightarrow{DE}$. Comparing this with **(1)** gives $\overrightarrow{DE} = \frac{1}{2}\overrightarrow{AC}$. Therefore $\overrightarrow{AC}$ and $\overrightarrow{DE}$ are parallel and

$\left|\overrightarrow{DE}\right| = \frac{1}{2}\left|\overrightarrow{AC}\right|$.

9.3   The Dot Product

1. (a) $\mathbf{a} \cdot \mathbf{b}$ is a scalar, and the dot product is defined only for vectors, so $(\mathbf{a} \cdot \mathbf{b}) \cdot \mathbf{c}$ has no meaning.

(b) $(\mathbf{a} \cdot \mathbf{b})\,\mathbf{c}$ is a scalar multiple of a vector, so it does have meaning.

(c) Both $|\mathbf{a}|$ and $\mathbf{b} \cdot \mathbf{c}$ are scalars, so $|\mathbf{a}|\,(\mathbf{b} \cdot \mathbf{c})$ is an ordinary product of real numbers, and has meaning.

(d) Both $\mathbf{a}$ and $\mathbf{b} + \mathbf{c}$ are vectors, so the dot product $\mathbf{a} \cdot (\mathbf{b} + \mathbf{c})$ has meaning.

(e) $\mathbf{a} \cdot \mathbf{b}$ is a scalar, but $\mathbf{c}$ is a vector, and so the two quantities cannot be added and $\mathbf{a} \cdot \mathbf{b} + \mathbf{c}$ has no meaning.

(f) $|\mathbf{a}|$ is a scalar, and the dot product is defined only for vectors, so $|\mathbf{a}| \cdot (\mathbf{b} + \mathbf{c})$ has no meaning.

3. By the definition of the dot product, $\mathbf{a} \cdot \mathbf{b} = |\mathbf{a}|\,|\mathbf{b}| \cos \theta = (6)(5) \cos \frac{2\pi}{3} = 30\left(-\frac{1}{2}\right) = -15.$

5. $\mathbf{a} \cdot \mathbf{b} = \left\langle -2, \frac{1}{3} \right\rangle \cdot \langle -5, 12 \rangle = (-2)(-5) + \left(\frac{1}{3}\right)(12) = 10 + 4 = 14$

7. $\mathbf{a} \cdot \mathbf{b} = \left\langle 4, 1, \frac{1}{4} \right\rangle \cdot \langle 6, -3, -8 \rangle = (4)(6) + (1)(-3) + \left(\frac{1}{4}\right)(-8) = 19$

9. $\mathbf{a} \cdot \mathbf{b} = (2\,\mathbf{i} + \mathbf{j}) \cdot (\mathbf{i} - \mathbf{j} + \mathbf{k}) = (2)(1) + (1)(-1) + (0)(1) = 1$

11. $\mathbf{u}$, $\mathbf{v}$, and $\mathbf{w}$ are all unit vectors, so the triangle is an equilateral triangle. Thus the angle between $\mathbf{u}$ and $\mathbf{v}$ is $60°$ and

$\mathbf{u} \cdot \mathbf{v} = |\mathbf{u}|\,|\mathbf{v}| \cos 60° = (1)(1)\left(\frac{1}{2}\right) = \frac{1}{2}$. If $\mathbf{w}$ is moved so it has the same initial point as $\mathbf{u}$, we can see that the angle

between them is $120°$ and we have $\mathbf{u} \cdot \mathbf{w} = |\mathbf{u}|\,|\mathbf{w}| \cos 120° = (1)(1)\left(-\frac{1}{2}\right) = -\frac{1}{2}.$

13. (a) $\mathbf{i} \cdot \mathbf{j} = \langle 1, 0, 0 \rangle \cdot \langle 0, 1, 0 \rangle = (1)(0) + (0)(1) + (0)(0) = 0$ Similarly, $\mathbf{j} \cdot \mathbf{k} = (0)(0) + (1)(0) + (0)(1) = 0$ and

$\mathbf{k} \cdot \mathbf{i} = (0)(1) + (0)(0) + (1)(0) = 0.$

Another method: Because $\mathbf{i}$, $\mathbf{j}$, and $\mathbf{k}$ are mutually perpendicular, the cosine factor in each dot product is $\cos \frac{\pi}{2} = 0.$

(b) By Property 1 of the dot product, $\mathbf{i} \cdot \mathbf{i} = |\mathbf{i}|^2 = 1^2 = 1$ since $\mathbf{i}$ is a unit vector. Similarly, $\mathbf{j} \cdot \mathbf{j} = |\mathbf{j}|^2 = 1$ and

$\mathbf{k} \cdot \mathbf{k} = |\mathbf{k}|^2 = 1.$

15. $|\mathbf{a}| = \sqrt{(-8)^2 + 6^2} = 10$, $|\mathbf{b}| = \sqrt{\left(\sqrt{7}\right)^2 + 3^2} = 4$, and $\mathbf{a} \cdot \mathbf{b} = (-8)\left(\sqrt{7}\right) + (6)(3) = 18 - 8\sqrt{7}$. From the

definition of the dot product, we have $\cos \theta = \dfrac{\mathbf{a} \cdot \mathbf{b}}{|\mathbf{a}|\,|\mathbf{b}|} = \dfrac{18 - 8\sqrt{7}}{10 \cdot 4} = \dfrac{9 - 4\sqrt{7}}{20}$. So the angle between $\mathbf{a}$ and $\mathbf{b}$ is

$\theta = \cos^{-1}\left(\dfrac{9 - 4\sqrt{7}}{20}\right) \approx 95°.$

17. $|\mathbf{a}| = \sqrt{0^2 + 1^2 + 1^2} = \sqrt{2}$, $|\mathbf{b}| = \sqrt{1^2 + 2^2 + (-3)^2} = \sqrt{14}$, and $\mathbf{a} \cdot \mathbf{b} = (0)(1) + (1)(2) + (1)(-3) = -1.$

Then $\cos \theta = \dfrac{\mathbf{a} \cdot \mathbf{b}}{|\mathbf{a}|\,|\mathbf{b}|} = \dfrac{-1}{\sqrt{2} \cdot \sqrt{14}} = \dfrac{-1}{2\sqrt{7}}$ and $\theta = \cos^{-1}\left(-\dfrac{1}{2\sqrt{7}}\right) \approx 101°.$

19. Let a, b, and c be the angles at vertices A, B, and C respectively.

Then a is the angle between vectors $\overrightarrow{AB}$ and $\overrightarrow{AC}$, b is the angle

between vectors $\overrightarrow{BA}$ and $\overrightarrow{BC}$, and c is the angle between vectors

$\overrightarrow{CA}$ and $\overrightarrow{CB}$.

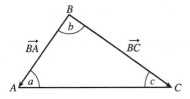

Thus $\cos a = \dfrac{\overrightarrow{AB} \cdot \overrightarrow{AC}}{\left|\overrightarrow{AB}\right|\left|\overrightarrow{AC}\right|} = \dfrac{\langle 2, 6 \rangle \cdot \langle -2, 4 \rangle}{\sqrt{2^2 + 6^2}\,\sqrt{(-2)^2 + 4^2}} = \dfrac{1}{\sqrt{40}\,\sqrt{20}}(-4 + 24) = \dfrac{20}{\sqrt{800}} = \dfrac{\sqrt{2}}{2}$ and

$a = \cos^{-1}\left(\dfrac{\sqrt{2}}{2}\right) = 45°$. Similarly, $\cos b = \dfrac{\overrightarrow{BA} \cdot \overrightarrow{BC}}{\left|\overrightarrow{BA}\right|\left|\overrightarrow{BC}\right|} = \dfrac{\langle -2, -6 \rangle \cdot \langle -4, -2 \rangle}{\sqrt{4 + 36}\,\sqrt{16 + 4}} = \dfrac{1}{\sqrt{40}\,\sqrt{20}}(8 + 12) = \dfrac{20}{\sqrt{800}} = \dfrac{\sqrt{2}}{2}$

so $b = \cos^{-1}\left(\dfrac{\sqrt{2}}{2}\right) = 45°$ and $c = 180° - (45° + 45°) = 90°.$

Alternate solution: Apply the Law of Cosines three times as follows: $\cos a = \dfrac{\left|\overrightarrow{BC}\right|^2 - \left|\overrightarrow{AB}\right|^2 - \left|\overrightarrow{AC}\right|^2}{2\left|\overrightarrow{AB}\right|\left|\overrightarrow{AC}\right|},$

$$\cos b = \frac{\left|\overrightarrow{AC}\right|^2 - \left|\overrightarrow{AB}\right|^2 - \left|\overrightarrow{BC}\right|^2}{2\left|\overrightarrow{AB}\right|\left|\overrightarrow{BC}\right|}, \text{ and } \cos c = \frac{\left|\overrightarrow{AB}\right|^2 - \left|\overrightarrow{AC}\right|^2 - \left|\overrightarrow{BC}\right|^2}{2\left|\overrightarrow{AC}\right|\left|\overrightarrow{BC}\right|}.$$

21. (a) $\mathbf{a} \cdot \mathbf{b} = (-5)(6) + (3)(-8) + (7)(2) = -40 \neq 0$, so $\mathbf{a}$ and $\mathbf{b}$ are not orthogonal. Also, since $\mathbf{a}$ is not a scalar multiple

of $\mathbf{b}$, $\mathbf{a}$ and $\mathbf{b}$ are not parallel.

(b) $\mathbf{a} \cdot \mathbf{b} = (4)(-3) + (6)(2) = 0$, so $\mathbf{a}$ and $\mathbf{b}$ are orthogonal (and not parallel).

(c) $\mathbf{a} \cdot \mathbf{b} = (-1)(3) + (2)(4) + (5)(-1) = 0$, so $\mathbf{a}$ and $\mathbf{b}$ are orthogonal (and not parallel).

(d) Because $\mathbf{a} = -\frac{2}{3}\,\mathbf{b}$, $\mathbf{a}$ and $\mathbf{b}$ are parallel.

23. $\overrightarrow{QP} = \langle -1, -3, 2 \rangle$, $\overrightarrow{QR} = \langle 4, -2, -1 \rangle$, and $\overrightarrow{QP} \cdot \overrightarrow{QR} = -4 + 6 - 2 = 0$. Thus $\overrightarrow{QP}$ and $\overrightarrow{QR}$ are orthogonal, so the angle of

the triangle at vertex Q is a right angle.

25. Let $\mathbf{a} = a_1\,\mathbf{i} + a_2\,\mathbf{j} + a_3\,\mathbf{k}$ be a vector orthogonal to both $\mathbf{i} + \mathbf{j}$ and $\mathbf{i} + \mathbf{k}$. Then $\mathbf{a} \cdot (\mathbf{i} + \mathbf{j}) = 0 \quad\Leftrightarrow\quad a_1 + a_2 = 0$ and

$\mathbf{a} \cdot (\mathbf{i} + \mathbf{k}) = 0 \quad\Leftrightarrow\quad a_1 + a_3 = 0$, so $a_1 = -a_2 = -a_3$. Furthermore $\mathbf{a}$ is to be a unit vector, so $1 = a_1^2 + a_2^2 + a_3^2 = 3a_1^2$

implies $a_1 = \pm\frac{1}{\sqrt{3}}$. Thus $\mathbf{a} = \frac{1}{\sqrt{3}}\,\mathbf{i} - \frac{1}{\sqrt{3}}\,\mathbf{j} - \frac{1}{\sqrt{3}}\,\mathbf{k}$ and $\mathbf{a} = -\frac{1}{\sqrt{3}}\,\mathbf{i} + \frac{1}{\sqrt{3}}\,\mathbf{j} + \frac{1}{\sqrt{3}}\,\mathbf{k}$ are two such unit vectors.

27. The line $2x - y = 3 \quad\Leftrightarrow\quad y = 2x - 3$ has slope 2, so a vector parallel to the line is $\mathbf{a} = \langle 1, 2 \rangle$. The line $3x + y = 7 \quad\Leftrightarrow$

$y = -3x + 7$ has slope -3, so a vector parallel to the line is $\mathbf{b} = \langle 1, -3 \rangle$. The angle between the lines is the same as the

angle θ between the vectors. Here we have $\mathbf{a} \cdot \mathbf{b} = (1)(1) + (2)(-3) = -5$, $|\mathbf{a}| = \sqrt{1^2 + 2^2} = \sqrt{5}$, and

$|\mathbf{b}| = \sqrt{1^2 + (-3)^2} = \sqrt{10}$, so $\cos\theta = \dfrac{\mathbf{a} \cdot \mathbf{b}}{|\mathbf{a}|\,|\mathbf{b}|} = \dfrac{-5}{\sqrt{5} \cdot \sqrt{10}} = \dfrac{-5}{5\sqrt{2}} = -\dfrac{1}{\sqrt{2}}$ or $\dfrac{\sqrt{2}}{2}$. Thus $\theta = 135°$, and the

acute angle between the lines is $180° - 135° = 45°$.

29. $|\mathbf{a}| = \sqrt{3^2 + (-4)^2} = 5$. The scalar projection of $\mathbf{b}$ onto $\mathbf{a}$ is $\text{comp}_{\mathbf{a}}\,\mathbf{b} = \dfrac{\mathbf{a} \cdot \mathbf{b}}{|\mathbf{a}|} = \dfrac{3 \cdot 5 + (-4) \cdot 0}{5} = 3$ and the vector

projection of $\mathbf{b}$ onto $\mathbf{a}$ is $\text{proj}_{\mathbf{a}}\,\mathbf{b} = \left(\dfrac{\mathbf{a} \cdot \mathbf{b}}{|\mathbf{a}|}\right)\dfrac{\mathbf{a}}{|\mathbf{a}|} = 3 \cdot \frac{1}{5}\langle 3, -4 \rangle = \langle \frac{9}{5}, -\frac{12}{5} \rangle$.

31. $|\mathbf{a}| = \sqrt{4 + 1 + 16} = \sqrt{21}$ so the scalar projection of $\mathbf{b}$ onto $\mathbf{a}$ is $\text{comp}_{\mathbf{a}}\,\mathbf{b} = \dfrac{\mathbf{a} \cdot \mathbf{b}}{|\mathbf{a}|} = \dfrac{0 - 1 + 2}{\sqrt{21}} = \dfrac{1}{\sqrt{21}}$ while the vector

projection of $\mathbf{b}$ onto $\mathbf{a}$ is $\text{proj}_{\mathbf{a}}\,\mathbf{b} = \dfrac{1}{\sqrt{21}}\dfrac{\mathbf{a}}{|\mathbf{a}|} = \dfrac{1}{\sqrt{21}} \cdot \dfrac{2\mathbf{i} - \mathbf{j} + 4\mathbf{k}}{\sqrt{21}} = \frac{1}{21}(2\mathbf{i} - \mathbf{j} + 4\mathbf{k}) = \frac{2}{21}\,\mathbf{i} - \frac{1}{21}\,\mathbf{j} + \frac{4}{21}\,\mathbf{k}$.

33. $(\text{orth}_{\mathbf{a}}\,\mathbf{b}) \cdot \mathbf{a} = (\mathbf{b} - \text{proj}_{\mathbf{a}}\,\mathbf{b}) \cdot \mathbf{a} = \mathbf{b} \cdot \mathbf{a} - (\text{proj}_{\mathbf{a}}\,\mathbf{b}) \cdot \mathbf{a} = \mathbf{b} \cdot \mathbf{a} - \dfrac{\mathbf{a} \cdot \mathbf{b}}{|\mathbf{a}|^2}\,\mathbf{a} \cdot \mathbf{a} = \mathbf{b} \cdot \mathbf{a} - \dfrac{\mathbf{a} \cdot \mathbf{b}}{|\mathbf{a}|^2}\,|\mathbf{a}|^2 = \mathbf{b} \cdot \mathbf{a} - \mathbf{a} \cdot \mathbf{b} = 0$.

So they are orthogonal by (2).

35. $\text{comp}_{\mathbf{a}}\,\mathbf{b} = \dfrac{\mathbf{a} \cdot \mathbf{b}}{|\mathbf{a}|} = 2 \quad\Leftrightarrow\quad \mathbf{a} \cdot \mathbf{b} = 2\,|\mathbf{a}| = 2\sqrt{10}$. If $\mathbf{b} = \langle b_1, b_2, b_3 \rangle$, then we need $3b_1 + 0b_2 - 1b_3 = 2\sqrt{10}$.

One possible solution is obtained by taking $b_1 = 0, b_2 = 0, b_3 = -2\sqrt{10}$. In general, $\mathbf{b} = \langle s, t, 3s - 2\sqrt{10}\,\rangle$, $s, t \in \mathbb{R}$.

37. The displacement vector is $\mathbf{D} = (6 - 0)\,\mathbf{i} + (12 - 10)\,\mathbf{j} + (20 - 8)\,\mathbf{k} = 6\,\mathbf{i} + 2\,\mathbf{j} + 12\,\mathbf{k}$ so, as in Example 2, the work done is

$W = \mathbf{F} \cdot \mathbf{D} = (8\,\mathbf{i} - 6\,\mathbf{j} + 9\,\mathbf{k}) \cdot (6\,\mathbf{i} + 2\,\mathbf{j} + 12\,\mathbf{k}) = 48 - 12 + 108 = 144$ joules.

39. Here $|\mathbf{D}| = 80$ ft, $|\mathbf{F}| = 30$ lb, and $\theta = 40°$. Thus

$$W = \mathbf{F} \cdot \mathbf{D} = |\mathbf{F}|\,|\mathbf{D}|\cos\theta = (30)(80)\cos 40° = 2400\cos 40° \approx 1839 \text{ ft-lb.}$$

41. First note that $\mathbf{n} = \langle a, b \rangle$ is perpendicular to the line, because if $Q_1 = (a_1, b_1)$ and $Q_2 = (a_2, b_2)$ lie on the line, then

$\mathbf{n} \cdot \overrightarrow{Q_1 Q_2} = aa_2 - aa_1 + bb_2 - bb_1 = 0$, since $aa_2 + bb_2 = -c = aa_1 + bb_1$ from the equation of the line.

Let $P_2 = (x_2, y_2)$ lie on the line. Then the distance from P_1 to the line is the absolute value of the scalar projection

of $\overrightarrow{P_1 P_2}$ onto $\mathbf{n}$. $\text{comp}_{\mathbf{n}}\left(\overrightarrow{P_1 P_2}\right) = \dfrac{|\mathbf{n} \cdot \langle x_2 - x_1, y_2 - y_1 \rangle|}{|\mathbf{n}|} = \dfrac{|ax_2 - ax_1 + by_2 - by_1|}{\sqrt{a^2 + b^2}} = \dfrac{|ax_1 + by_1 + c|}{\sqrt{a^2 + b^2}}$

since $ax_2 + by_2 = -c$. The required distance is $\dfrac{|(3)(-2) + (-4)(3) + 5|}{\sqrt{3^2 + (-4)^2}} = \dfrac{13}{5}$.

43. For convenience, consider the unit cube positioned so that its back left corner is at the origin, and its edges lie along the

coordinate axes. The diagonal of the cube that begins at the origin and ends at $(1, 1, 1)$ has vector representation $\langle 1, 1, 1 \rangle$.

The angle θ between this vector and the vector of the edge which also begins at the origin and runs along the x-axis [that is,

$\langle 1, 0, 0 \rangle$] is given by $\cos\theta = \dfrac{\langle 1, 1, 1 \rangle \cdot \langle 1, 0, 0 \rangle}{|\langle 1, 1, 1 \rangle|\,|\langle 1, 0, 0 \rangle|} = \dfrac{1}{\sqrt{3}} \quad \Rightarrow \quad \theta = \cos^{-1}\left(\frac{1}{\sqrt{3}}\right) \approx 55°$.

45. Consider the H—C—H combination consisting of the sole carbon atom and the two hydrogen atoms that are at $(1, 0, 0)$ and

$(0, 1, 0)$ (or any H—C—H combination, for that matter). Vector representations of the line segments emanating from the

carbon atom and extending to these two hydrogen atoms are $\langle 1 - \frac{1}{2}, 0 - \frac{1}{2}, 0 - \frac{1}{2} \rangle = \langle \frac{1}{2}, -\frac{1}{2}, -\frac{1}{2} \rangle$ and

$\langle 0 - \frac{1}{2}, 1 - \frac{1}{2}, 0 - \frac{1}{2} \rangle = \langle -\frac{1}{2}, \frac{1}{2}, -\frac{1}{2} \rangle$. The bond angle, θ, is therefore given by

$$\cos\theta = \dfrac{\langle \frac{1}{2}, -\frac{1}{2}, -\frac{1}{2} \rangle \cdot \langle -\frac{1}{2}, \frac{1}{2}, -\frac{1}{2} \rangle}{|\langle \frac{1}{2}, -\frac{1}{2}, -\frac{1}{2} \rangle|\,|\langle -\frac{1}{2}, \frac{1}{2}, -\frac{1}{2} \rangle|} = \dfrac{-\frac{1}{4} - \frac{1}{4} + \frac{1}{4}}{\sqrt{\frac{3}{4}}\sqrt{\frac{3}{4}}} = -\dfrac{1}{3} \quad \Rightarrow \quad \theta = \cos^{-1}\left(-\frac{1}{3}\right) \approx 109.5°.$$

47. If $c = 0$ then $c\mathbf{a} = \mathbf{0}$, so $(c\mathbf{a}) \cdot \mathbf{b} = \mathbf{0} \cdot \mathbf{b} = 0$ by Property 5. Similarly, $\mathbf{a} \cdot (c\mathbf{b}) = \mathbf{a} \cdot \mathbf{0} = 0$, and

$c(\mathbf{a} \cdot \mathbf{b}) = 0(|\mathbf{a}|\,|\mathbf{b}|\cos\theta) = 0$, thus $(c\mathbf{a}) \cdot \mathbf{b} = c(\mathbf{a} \cdot \mathbf{b}) = \mathbf{a} \cdot (c\mathbf{b})$. If $c > 0$, the angle θ between $\mathbf{a}$ and $\mathbf{b}$ coincides with the

angle between $c\mathbf{a}$ and $\mathbf{b}$, so by definition of the dot product, $(c\mathbf{a}) \cdot \mathbf{b} = |c\mathbf{a}|\,|\mathbf{b}|\cos\theta = |c|\,|\mathbf{a}|\,|\mathbf{b}|\cos\theta = c\,|\mathbf{a}|\,|\mathbf{b}|\cos\theta$.

Similarly, $\mathbf{a} \cdot (c\mathbf{b}) = |\mathbf{a}|\,|c\mathbf{b}|\cos\theta = |\mathbf{a}|\,|c|\,|\mathbf{b}|\cos\theta = c\,|\mathbf{a}|\,|\mathbf{b}|\cos\theta$, and $c(\mathbf{a} \cdot \mathbf{b}) = c\,|\mathbf{a}|\,|\mathbf{b}|\cos\theta$. Thus,

$(c\mathbf{a}) \cdot \mathbf{b} = c(\mathbf{a} \cdot \mathbf{b}) = \mathbf{a} \cdot (c\mathbf{b})$. The case for $c < 0$ is similar. Using components, let $\mathbf{a} = \langle a_1, a_2, a_3 \rangle$ and $\mathbf{b} = \langle b_1, b_2, b_3 \rangle$.

Then

$$(c\mathbf{a}) \cdot \mathbf{b} = \langle ca_1, ca_2, ca_3 \rangle \cdot \langle b_1, b_2, b_3 \rangle = (ca_1)b_1 + (ca_2)b_2 + (ca_3)b_3$$

$$= c(a_1 b_1 + a_2 b_2 + a_3 b_3) = c(\mathbf{a} \cdot \mathbf{b})$$

$$= a_1(cb_1) + a_2(cb_2) + a_3(cb_3) = \langle a_1, a_2, a_3 \rangle \cdot \langle cb_1, cb_2, cb_3 \rangle = \mathbf{a} \cdot (c\mathbf{b})$$

49. $|\mathbf{a} \cdot \mathbf{b}| = |\,|\mathbf{a}|\,|\mathbf{b}|\cos\theta\,| = |\mathbf{a}|\,|\mathbf{b}|\,|\cos\theta|$. Since $|\cos\theta| \leq 1$, $|\mathbf{a} \cdot \mathbf{b}| = |\mathbf{a}|\,|\mathbf{b}|\,|\cos\theta| \leq |\mathbf{a}|\,|\mathbf{b}|$.

Note: We have equality in the case of $\cos\theta = \pm 1$, so $\theta = 0$ or $\theta = \pi$, thus equality when $\mathbf{a}$ and $\mathbf{b}$ are parallel.

51. (a)

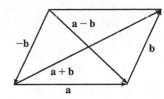

The Parallelogram Law states that the sum of the squares of the lengths of the diagonals of a parallelogram equals the sum of the squares of its (four) sides.

(b) $|\mathbf{a}+\mathbf{b}|^2 = (\mathbf{a}+\mathbf{b})\cdot(\mathbf{a}+\mathbf{b}) = |\mathbf{a}|^2 + 2(\mathbf{a}\cdot\mathbf{b}) + |\mathbf{b}|^2$ and $|\mathbf{a}-\mathbf{b}|^2 = (\mathbf{a}-\mathbf{b})\cdot(\mathbf{a}-\mathbf{b}) = |\mathbf{a}|^2 - 2(\mathbf{a}\cdot\mathbf{b}) + |\mathbf{b}|^2$.

Adding these two equations gives $|\mathbf{a}+\mathbf{b}|^2 + |\mathbf{a}-\mathbf{b}|^2 = 2\,|\mathbf{a}|^2 + 2\,|\mathbf{b}|^2$.

9.4   The Cross Product

1. (a) Since $\mathbf{b}\times\mathbf{c}$ is a vector, the dot product $\mathbf{a}\cdot(\mathbf{b}\times\mathbf{c})$ is meaningful and is a scalar.

(b) $\mathbf{b}\cdot\mathbf{c}$ is a scalar, so $\mathbf{a}\times(\mathbf{b}\cdot\mathbf{c})$ is meaningless, as the cross product is defined only for two *vectors*.

(c) Since $\mathbf{b}\times\mathbf{c}$ is a vector, the cross product $\mathbf{a}\times(\mathbf{b}\times\mathbf{c})$ is meaningful and results in another vector.

(d) $\mathbf{a}\cdot\mathbf{b}$ is a scalar, so the cross product $(\mathbf{a}\cdot\mathbf{b})\times\mathbf{c}$ is meaningless.

(e) Since $(\mathbf{a}\cdot\mathbf{b})$ and $(\mathbf{c}\cdot\mathbf{d})$ are both scalars, the cross product $(\mathbf{a}\cdot\mathbf{b})\times(\mathbf{c}\cdot\mathbf{d})$ is meaningless.

(f) $\mathbf{a}\times\mathbf{b}$ and $\mathbf{c}\times\mathbf{d}$ are both vectors, so the dot product $(\mathbf{a}\times\mathbf{b})\cdot(\mathbf{c}\times\mathbf{d})$ is meaningful and is a scalar.

3. If we sketch $\mathbf{u}$ and $\mathbf{v}$ starting from the same initial point, we see that the angle between them is $60°$, so

$$|\mathbf{u}\times\mathbf{v}| = |\mathbf{u}|\,|\mathbf{v}|\sin\theta = (12)(16)\sin 60° = 192\cdot\frac{\sqrt{3}}{2} = 96\sqrt{3}.$$

By the right-hand rule, $\mathbf{u}\times\mathbf{v}$ is directed into the page.

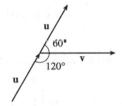

5. The magnitude of the torque is $|\tau| = |\mathbf{r}\times\mathbf{F}| = |\mathbf{r}|\,|\mathbf{F}|\sin\theta = (0.18\text{ m})(60\text{ N})\sin(70+10)° = 10.8\sin 80° \approx 10.6$ N·m.

7. $\mathbf{a}\times\mathbf{b} = \begin{vmatrix} \mathbf{i} & \mathbf{j} & \mathbf{k} \\ 6 & 0 & -2 \\ 0 & 8 & 0 \end{vmatrix} = \begin{vmatrix} 0 & -2 \\ 8 & 0 \end{vmatrix}\mathbf{i} - \begin{vmatrix} 6 & -2 \\ 0 & 0 \end{vmatrix}\mathbf{j} + \begin{vmatrix} 6 & 0 \\ 0 & 8 \end{vmatrix}\mathbf{k}$

$= [0-(-16)]\,\mathbf{i} - (0-0)\,\mathbf{j} + (48-0)\,\mathbf{k} = 16\,\mathbf{i} + 48\,\mathbf{k}$

Now $(\mathbf{a}\times\mathbf{b})\cdot\mathbf{a} = \langle 16,0,48\rangle\cdot\langle 6,0,-2\rangle = 96+0-96 = 0$ and $(\mathbf{a}\times\mathbf{b})\cdot\mathbf{b} = \langle 16,0,48\rangle\cdot\langle 0,8,0\rangle = 0+0+0 = 0$, so $\mathbf{a}\times\mathbf{b}$ is orthogonal to both $\mathbf{a}$ and $\mathbf{b}$.

9. $\mathbf{a}\times\mathbf{b} = \begin{vmatrix} \mathbf{i} & \mathbf{j} & \mathbf{k} \\ 1 & 3 & -2 \\ -1 & 0 & 5 \end{vmatrix} = \begin{vmatrix} 3 & -2 \\ 0 & 5 \end{vmatrix}\mathbf{i} - \begin{vmatrix} 1 & -2 \\ -1 & 5 \end{vmatrix}\mathbf{j} + \begin{vmatrix} 1 & 3 \\ -1 & 0 \end{vmatrix}\mathbf{k}$

$= (15-0)\,\mathbf{i} - (5-2)\,\mathbf{j} + [0-(-3)]\,\mathbf{k} = 15\,\mathbf{i} - 3\,\mathbf{j} + 3\,\mathbf{k}$

Since $(\mathbf{a}\times\mathbf{b})\cdot\mathbf{a} = (15\,\mathbf{i} - 3\,\mathbf{j} + 3\,\mathbf{k})\cdot(\mathbf{i} + 3\,\mathbf{j} - 2\,\mathbf{k}) = 15 - 9 - 6 = 0$, $\mathbf{a}\times\mathbf{b}$ is orthogonal to $\mathbf{a}$.

Since $(\mathbf{a}\times\mathbf{b})\cdot\mathbf{b} = (15\,\mathbf{i} - 3\,\mathbf{j} + 3\,\mathbf{k})\cdot(-\mathbf{i} + 5\,\mathbf{k}) = -15 + 0 + 15 = 0$, $\mathbf{a}\times\mathbf{b}$ is orthogonal to $\mathbf{b}$.

11. $\mathbf{a} \times \mathbf{b} = \begin{vmatrix} \mathbf{i} & \mathbf{j} & \mathbf{k} \\ 1 & -1 & -1 \\ \frac{1}{2} & 1 & \frac{1}{2} \end{vmatrix} = \begin{vmatrix} -1 & -1 \\ 1 & \frac{1}{2} \end{vmatrix} \mathbf{i} - \begin{vmatrix} 1 & -1 \\ \frac{1}{2} & \frac{1}{2} \end{vmatrix} \mathbf{j} + \begin{vmatrix} 1 & -1 \\ \frac{1}{2} & 1 \end{vmatrix} \mathbf{k}$

$\qquad = \left[-\frac{1}{2} - (-1) \right] \mathbf{i} - \left[\frac{1}{2} - (-\frac{1}{2}) \right] \mathbf{j} + \left[1 - (-\frac{1}{2}) \right] \mathbf{k} = \frac{1}{2} \mathbf{i} - \mathbf{j} + \frac{3}{2} \mathbf{k}$

Now $(\mathbf{a} \times \mathbf{b}) \cdot \mathbf{a} = \left(\frac{1}{2} \mathbf{i} - \mathbf{j} + \frac{3}{2} \mathbf{k} \right) \cdot (\mathbf{i} - \mathbf{j} - \mathbf{k}) = \frac{1}{2} + 1 - \frac{3}{2} = 0$ and

$(\mathbf{a} \times \mathbf{b}) \cdot \mathbf{b} = \left(\frac{1}{2} \mathbf{i} - \mathbf{j} + \frac{3}{2} \mathbf{k} \right) \cdot \left(\frac{1}{2} \mathbf{i} + \mathbf{j} + \frac{1}{2} \mathbf{k} \right) = \frac{1}{4} - 1 + \frac{3}{4} = 0$, so $\mathbf{a} \times \mathbf{b}$ is orthogonal to both $\mathbf{a}$ and $\mathbf{b}$.

13. $\mathbf{a} \times \mathbf{b} = \begin{vmatrix} \mathbf{i} & \mathbf{j} & \mathbf{k} \\ t & t^2 & t^3 \\ 1 & 2t & 3t^2 \end{vmatrix} = \begin{vmatrix} t^2 & t^3 \\ 2t & 3t^2 \end{vmatrix} \mathbf{i} - \begin{vmatrix} t & t^3 \\ 1 & 3t^2 \end{vmatrix} \mathbf{j} + \begin{vmatrix} t & t^2 \\ 1 & 2t \end{vmatrix} \mathbf{k}$

$\qquad = (3t^4 - 2t^4) \mathbf{i} - (3t^3 - t^3) \mathbf{j} + (2t^2 - t^2) \mathbf{k} = t^4 \mathbf{i} - 2t^3 \mathbf{j} + t^2 \mathbf{k}$

Since $(\mathbf{a} \times \mathbf{b}) \cdot \mathbf{a} = \langle t^4, -2t^3, t^2 \rangle \cdot \langle t, t^2, t^3 \rangle = t^5 - 2t^5 + t^5 = 0$, $\mathbf{a} \times \mathbf{b}$ is orthogonal to $\mathbf{a}$.

Since $(\mathbf{a} \times \mathbf{b}) \cdot \mathbf{b} = \langle t^4, -2t^3, t^2 \rangle \cdot \langle 1, 2t, 3t^2 \rangle = t^4 - 4t^4 + 3t^4 = 0$, $\mathbf{a} \times \mathbf{b}$ is orthogonal to $\mathbf{b}$.

15. By Example 2, $\mathbf{i} \times \mathbf{j} = \mathbf{k}$, so $(\mathbf{i} \times \mathbf{j}) \times \mathbf{k} = \mathbf{k} \times \mathbf{k} = \mathbf{0}$ [by the margin note on page 655].

17. $(\mathbf{j} - \mathbf{k}) \times (\mathbf{k} - \mathbf{i}) = (\mathbf{j} - \mathbf{k}) \times \mathbf{k} + (\mathbf{j} - \mathbf{k}) \times (-\mathbf{i})$ $\qquad\qquad$ by Property 3

$\qquad = \mathbf{j} \times \mathbf{k} + (-\mathbf{k}) \times \mathbf{k} + \mathbf{j} \times (-\mathbf{i}) + (-\mathbf{k}) \times (-\mathbf{i})$ $\qquad$ by Property 4

$\qquad = (\mathbf{j} \times \mathbf{k}) + (-1)(\mathbf{k} \times \mathbf{k}) + (-1)(\mathbf{j} \times \mathbf{i}) + (-1)^2 (\mathbf{k} \times \mathbf{i})$ $\qquad$ by Property 2

$\qquad = \mathbf{i} + (-1)\,\mathbf{0} + (-1)(-\mathbf{k}) + \mathbf{j} = \mathbf{i} + \mathbf{j} + \mathbf{k}$ $\qquad\qquad$ by Example 2 and
$\qquad\qquad\qquad\qquad\qquad\qquad\qquad\qquad\qquad\qquad\qquad\qquad\qquad\qquad$ the margin note on page 655

19. We know that the cross product of two vectors is orthogonal to both. So we calculate

$\langle 1, -1, 1 \rangle \times \langle 0, 4, 4 \rangle = \begin{vmatrix} \mathbf{i} & \mathbf{j} & \mathbf{k} \\ 1 & -1 & 1 \\ 0 & 4 & 4 \end{vmatrix} = \begin{vmatrix} -1 & 1 \\ 4 & 4 \end{vmatrix} \mathbf{i} - \begin{vmatrix} 1 & 1 \\ 0 & 4 \end{vmatrix} \mathbf{j} + \begin{vmatrix} 1 & -1 \\ 0 & 4 \end{vmatrix} \mathbf{k} = -8\,\mathbf{i} - 4\,\mathbf{j} + 4\,\mathbf{k}.$

So two unit vectors orthogonal to both are $\pm \dfrac{\langle -8, -4, 4 \rangle}{\sqrt{64 + 16 + 16}} = \pm \dfrac{\langle -8, -4, 4 \rangle}{4\sqrt{6}}$, that is, $\left\langle -\frac{2}{\sqrt{6}}, -\frac{1}{\sqrt{6}}, \frac{1}{\sqrt{6}} \right\rangle$

and $\left\langle \frac{2}{\sqrt{6}}, \frac{1}{\sqrt{6}}, -\frac{1}{\sqrt{6}} \right\rangle$.

21. By plotting the vertices, we can see that the parallelogram is determined by the

vectors $\overrightarrow{AB} = \langle 2, 3 \rangle$ and $\overrightarrow{AD} = \langle 4, -2 \rangle$. We know that the area of the parallelogram

determined by two vectors is equal to the length of the cross product of these vectors.

In order to compute the cross product, we consider the vector $\overrightarrow{AB}$ as the three-

dimensional vector $\langle 2, 3, 0 \rangle$ (and similarly for $\overrightarrow{AD}$), and then the area of

parallelogram $ABCD$ is

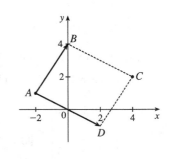

$\left| \overrightarrow{AB} \times \overrightarrow{AD} \right| = \left\| \begin{vmatrix} \mathbf{i} & \mathbf{j} & \mathbf{k} \\ 2 & 3 & 0 \\ 4 & -2 & 0 \end{vmatrix} \right\| = |(0)\,\mathbf{i} - (0)\,\mathbf{j} + (-4 - 12)\,\mathbf{k}| = |-16\,\mathbf{k}| = 16$

23. (a) $\overrightarrow{PQ} = \langle 4, 3, -2 \rangle$ and $\overrightarrow{PR} = \langle 5, 5, 1 \rangle$, so a vector orthogonal to the plane through P, Q, and R is

$$\overrightarrow{PQ} \times \overrightarrow{PR} = \langle (3)(1) - (-2)(5), (-2)(5) - (4)(1), (4)(5) - (3)(5) \rangle = \langle 13, -14, 5 \rangle \text{ [or any scalar mutiple thereof]}.$$

(b) The area of the parallelogram determined by $\overrightarrow{PQ}$ and $\overrightarrow{PR}$ is

$$\left| \overrightarrow{PQ} \times \overrightarrow{PR} \right| = |\langle 13, -14, 5 \rangle| = \sqrt{13^2 + (-14)^2 + 5^2} = \sqrt{390}, \text{ so the area of triangle } PQR \text{ is } \tfrac{1}{2}\sqrt{390}.$$

25. Using the notation of (1), $\mathbf{r} = \langle 0, 0.3, 0 \rangle$ and $\mathbf{F}$ has direction $\langle 0, 3, -4 \rangle$. The angle θ between them can be determined by

$$\cos\theta = \frac{\langle 0, 0.3, 0 \rangle \cdot \langle 0, 3, -4 \rangle}{|\langle 0, 0.3, 0 \rangle| \, |\langle 0, 3, -4 \rangle|} \;\Rightarrow\; \cos\theta = \frac{0.9}{(0.3)(5)} \;\Rightarrow\; \cos\theta = 0.6 \;\Rightarrow\; \theta \approx 53.1°. \text{ Then } |\boldsymbol{\tau}| = |\mathbf{r}| \, |\mathbf{F}| \sin\theta \;\Rightarrow$$

$$100 = 0.3 \, |\mathbf{F}| \sin 53.1° \;\Rightarrow\; |\mathbf{F}| \approx 417 \text{ N}.$$

27. We know that the volume of the parallelepiped determined by $\mathbf{a}$, $\mathbf{b}$, and $\mathbf{c}$ is the magnitude of their scalar triple product, which

$$\text{is } \mathbf{a} \cdot (\mathbf{b} \times \mathbf{c}) = \begin{vmatrix} 6 & 3 & -1 \\ 0 & 1 & 2 \\ 4 & -2 & 5 \end{vmatrix} = 6 \begin{vmatrix} 1 & 2 \\ -2 & 5 \end{vmatrix} - 3 \begin{vmatrix} 0 & 2 \\ 4 & 5 \end{vmatrix} + (-1) \begin{vmatrix} 0 & 1 \\ 4 & -2 \end{vmatrix} = 6(5 + 4) - 3(0 - 8) - (0 - 4) = 82.$$

Thus the volume of the parallelepiped is 82 cubic units.

29. $\mathbf{a} = \overrightarrow{PQ} = \langle 2, 1, 1 \rangle$, $\mathbf{b} = \overrightarrow{PR} = \langle 1, \ 1, 2 \rangle$, and $\mathbf{c} = \overrightarrow{PS} = \langle 0, -2, 3 \rangle$.

$$\mathbf{a} \cdot (\mathbf{b} \times \mathbf{c}) = \begin{vmatrix} 2 & 1 & 1 \\ 1 & -1 & 2 \\ 0 & -2 & 3 \end{vmatrix} = 2 \begin{vmatrix} -1 & 2 \\ -2 & 3 \end{vmatrix} - 1 \begin{vmatrix} 1 & 2 \\ 0 & 3 \end{vmatrix} + 1 \begin{vmatrix} 1 & -1 \\ 0 & -2 \end{vmatrix} = 2 - 3 - 2 = -3,$$

so the volume of the parallelepiped is 3 cubic units.

31. $\mathbf{u} \cdot (\mathbf{v} \times \mathbf{w}) = \begin{vmatrix} 1 & 5 & -2 \\ 3 & -1 & 0 \\ 5 & 9 & -4 \end{vmatrix} = 1 \begin{vmatrix} -1 & 0 \\ 9 & -4 \end{vmatrix} - 5 \begin{vmatrix} 3 & 0 \\ 5 & -4 \end{vmatrix} + (-2) \begin{vmatrix} 3 & -1 \\ 5 & 9 \end{vmatrix} = 4 + 60 - 64 = 0,$ which says that the volume

of the parallelepiped determined by $\mathbf{u}$, $\mathbf{v}$ and $\mathbf{w}$ is 0, and thus these three vectors are coplanar.

33. (a)

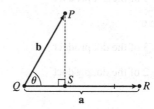

The distance between a point and a line is the length of the perpendicular from the point to the line, here $\left| \overrightarrow{PS} \right| = d$. But referring to triangle PQS,

$$d = \left| \overrightarrow{PS} \right| = \left| \overrightarrow{QP} \right| \sin\theta = |\mathbf{b}| \sin\theta. \text{ But } \theta \text{ is the angle between } \overrightarrow{QP} = \mathbf{b}$$

and $\overrightarrow{QR} = \mathbf{a}$. Thus by the definition of the cross product, $\sin\theta = \dfrac{|\mathbf{a} \times \mathbf{b}|}{|\mathbf{a}| \, |\mathbf{b}|}$

and so $d = |\mathbf{b}| \sin\theta = \dfrac{|\mathbf{b}| \, |\mathbf{a} \times \mathbf{b}|}{|\mathbf{a}| \, |\mathbf{b}|} = \dfrac{|\mathbf{a} \times \mathbf{b}|}{|\mathbf{a}|}.$

(b) $\mathbf{a} = \overrightarrow{QR} = \langle -1, -2, -1 \rangle$ and $\mathbf{b} = \overrightarrow{QP} = \langle 1, -5, -7 \rangle$. Then

$$\mathbf{a} \times \mathbf{b} = \langle (-2)(-7) - (-1)(-5), (-1)(1) - (-1)(-7), (-1)(-5) - (-2)(1) \rangle = \langle 9, -8, 7 \rangle.$$

Thus the distance is $d = \dfrac{|\mathbf{a} \times \mathbf{b}|}{|\mathbf{a}|} = \dfrac{1}{\sqrt{6}} \sqrt{81 + 64 + 49} = \sqrt{\tfrac{194}{6}} = \sqrt{\tfrac{97}{3}}.$

35. $(\mathbf{a} - \mathbf{b}) \times (\mathbf{a} + \mathbf{b}) = (\mathbf{a} - \mathbf{b}) \times \mathbf{a} + (\mathbf{a} - \mathbf{b}) \times \mathbf{b}$ by Property 3 of the cross product

$$= \mathbf{a} \times \mathbf{a} + (-\mathbf{b}) \times \mathbf{a} + \mathbf{a} \times \mathbf{b} + (-\mathbf{b}) \times \mathbf{b} \qquad \text{by Property 4}$$

$$= (\mathbf{a} \times \mathbf{a}) - (\mathbf{b} \times \mathbf{a}) + (\mathbf{a} \times \mathbf{b}) - (\mathbf{b} \times \mathbf{b}) \qquad \text{by Property 2 (with } c = -1)$$

$$= \mathbf{0} - (\mathbf{b} \times \mathbf{a}) + (\mathbf{a} \times \mathbf{b}) - \mathbf{0} \qquad \text{by the margin note on page 655}$$

$$= (\mathbf{a} \times \mathbf{b}) + (\mathbf{a} \times \mathbf{b}) \qquad \text{by Property 1}$$

$$= 2(\mathbf{a} \times \mathbf{b})$$

37. $\mathbf{a} \times (\mathbf{b} \times \mathbf{c}) + \mathbf{b} \times (\mathbf{c} \times \mathbf{a}) + \mathbf{c} \times (\mathbf{a} \times \mathbf{b})$

$$= [(\mathbf{a} \cdot \mathbf{c})\mathbf{b} - (\mathbf{a} \cdot \mathbf{b})\mathbf{c}] + [(\mathbf{b} \cdot \mathbf{a})\mathbf{c} - (\mathbf{b} \cdot \mathbf{c})\mathbf{a}] + [(\mathbf{c} \cdot \mathbf{b})\mathbf{a} - (\mathbf{c} \cdot \mathbf{a})\mathbf{b}] \qquad \text{by Exercise 36}$$

$$= (\mathbf{a} \cdot \mathbf{c})\mathbf{b} - (\mathbf{a} \cdot \mathbf{b})\mathbf{c} + (\mathbf{a} \cdot \mathbf{b})\mathbf{c} - (\mathbf{b} \cdot \mathbf{c})\mathbf{a} + (\mathbf{b} \cdot \mathbf{c})\mathbf{a} - (\mathbf{a} \cdot \mathbf{c})\mathbf{b} = \mathbf{0}$$

39. (a) No. If $\mathbf{a} \cdot \mathbf{b} = \mathbf{a} \cdot \mathbf{c}$, then $\mathbf{a} \cdot (\mathbf{b} - \mathbf{c}) = 0$, so $\mathbf{a}$ is perpendicular to $\mathbf{b} - \mathbf{c}$, which can happen if $\mathbf{b} \neq \mathbf{c}$. For example,

let $\mathbf{a} = \langle 1, 1, 1 \rangle$, $\mathbf{b} = \langle 1, 0, 0 \rangle$ and $\mathbf{c} = \langle 0, 1, 0 \rangle$.

(b) No. If $\mathbf{a} \times \mathbf{b} = \mathbf{a} \times \mathbf{c}$ then $\mathbf{a} \times (\mathbf{b} - \mathbf{c}) = \mathbf{0}$, which implies that $\mathbf{a}$ is parallel to $\mathbf{b} - \mathbf{c}$, which of course can happen

if $\mathbf{b} \neq \mathbf{c}$.

(c) Yes. Since $\mathbf{a} \cdot \mathbf{c} = \mathbf{a} \cdot \mathbf{b}$, $\mathbf{a}$ is perpendicular to $\mathbf{b} - \mathbf{c}$, by part (a). From part (b), $\mathbf{a}$ is also parallel to $\mathbf{b} - \mathbf{c}$. Thus since

$\mathbf{a} \neq \mathbf{0}$ but is both parallel and perpendicular to $\mathbf{b} - \mathbf{c}$, we have $\mathbf{b} - \mathbf{c} = \mathbf{0}$, so $\mathbf{b} = \mathbf{c}$.

41. (a) $\mathbf{u} \cdot \mathbf{r} = \mathbf{v} \cdot \mathbf{r} \;\Leftrightarrow\; \mathbf{u} \cdot \mathbf{r} - \mathbf{v} \cdot \mathbf{r} = 0 \;\Leftrightarrow\; (\mathbf{u} - \mathbf{v}) \cdot \mathbf{r} = 0$ [by Properties 2, 3, and 4 of the dot product]. This is true

for all vectors $\mathbf{r}$ so in particular it is true for $\mathbf{r} = \mathbf{u} - \mathbf{v}$ which gives $(\mathbf{u} - \mathbf{v}) \cdot (\mathbf{u} - \mathbf{v}) = 0 \;\Rightarrow\; |\mathbf{u} - \mathbf{v}|^2 = 0$

[by Property 1 of the dot product] $\;\Rightarrow\; \mathbf{u} - \mathbf{v} = \mathbf{0} \;\Rightarrow\; \mathbf{u} = \mathbf{v}$.

(b) Let $\mathbf{r}$ be any vector in V_3. Then

$$[\mathbf{a} \times (\mathbf{b} + \mathbf{c})] \cdot \mathbf{r} = \mathbf{r} \cdot [\mathbf{a} \times (\mathbf{b} + \mathbf{c})] \qquad \text{by Property 2 of the dot product}$$

$$= (\mathbf{r} \times \mathbf{a}) \cdot (\mathbf{b} + \mathbf{c}) \qquad \text{by Equation 6}$$

$$= (\mathbf{r} \times \mathbf{a}) \cdot \mathbf{b} + (\mathbf{r} \times \mathbf{a}) \cdot \mathbf{c} \qquad \text{by Property 3 of the dot product}$$

$$= \mathbf{r} \cdot (\mathbf{a} \times \mathbf{b}) + \mathbf{r} \cdot (\mathbf{a} \times \mathbf{c}) \qquad \text{by Equation 6}$$

$$= \mathbf{r} \cdot [(\mathbf{a} \times \mathbf{b}) + (\mathbf{a} \times \mathbf{c})] \qquad \text{by Property 3 of the dot product}$$

$$= [\mathbf{a} \times \mathbf{b} + \mathbf{a} \times \mathbf{c}] \cdot \mathbf{r} \qquad \text{by Property 2 of the dot product}$$

By part (a), we must have $\mathbf{a} \times (\mathbf{b} + \mathbf{c}) = \mathbf{a} \times \mathbf{b} + \mathbf{a} \times \mathbf{c}$.

9.5 Equations of Lines and Planes

1. (a) True; each of the first two lines has a direction vector parallel to the direction vector of the third line, so these vectors are

each scalar multiples of the third direction vector. Then the first two direction vectors are also scalar multiples of each

other, so these vectors, and hence the two lines, are parallel.

(b) False; for example, the x- and y-axes are both perpendicular to the z-axis, yet the x- and y-axes are not parallel.

(c) True; each of the first two planes has a normal vector parallel to the normal vector of the third plane, so these two normal vectors are parallel to each other and the planes are parallel.

(d) False; for example, the xy- and yz-planes are not parallel, yet they are both perpendicular to the xz-plane.

(e) False; the x- and y-axes are not parallel, yet they are both parallel to the plane $z = 1$.

(f) True; if each line is perpendicular to a plane, then the lines' direction vectors are both parallel to a normal vector for the plane. Thus, the direction vectors are parallel to each other and the lines are parallel.

(g) False; the planes $y = 1$ and $z = 1$ are not parallel, yet they are both parallel to the x-axis.

(h) True; if each plane is perpendicular to a line, then any normal vector for each plane is parallel to a direction vector for the line. Thus, the normal vectors are parallel to each other and the planes are parallel.

(i) True; see Figure 9 and the accompanying discussion.

(j) False; they can be skew, as in Example 3 .

(k) True. Consider any normal vector for the plane and any direction vector for the line. If the normal vector is perpendicular to the direction vector, the line and plane are parallel. Otherwise, the vectors meet at an angle θ, $0° \le \theta < 90°$, and the line will intersect the plane at an angle $90° - \theta$.

3. For this line, we have $\mathbf{r}_0 = 2\,\mathbf{i} + 2.4\,\mathbf{j} + 3.5\,\mathbf{k}$ and $\mathbf{v} = 3\,\mathbf{i} + 2\,\mathbf{j} - \mathbf{k}$, so a vector equation is
$\mathbf{r} = \mathbf{r}_0 + t\,\mathbf{v} = (2\,\mathbf{i} + 2.4\,\mathbf{j} + 3.5\,\mathbf{k}) + t(3\,\mathbf{i} + 2\,\mathbf{j} - \mathbf{k}) = (2 + 3t)\,\mathbf{i} + (2.4 + 2t)\,\mathbf{j} + (3.5 - t)\,\mathbf{k}$ and parametric equations are $x = 2 + 3t,\ y = 2.4 + 2t,\ z = 3.5 - t$.

5. A line perpendicular to the given plane has the same direction as a normal vector to the plane, such as $\mathbf{n} = \langle 1, 3, 1 \rangle$. So $\mathbf{r}_0 = \mathbf{i} + 6\,\mathbf{k}$, and we can take $\mathbf{v} = \mathbf{i} + 3\,\mathbf{j} + \mathbf{k}$. Then a vector equation is
$\mathbf{r} = (\mathbf{i} + 6\,\mathbf{k}) + t(\mathbf{i} + 3\,\mathbf{j} + \mathbf{k}) = (1 + t)\,\mathbf{i} + 3t\,\mathbf{j} + (6 + t)\,\mathbf{k}$, and parametric equations are $x = 1 + t,\ y = 3t,\ z = 6 + t$.

7. $\mathbf{v} = \langle 2 - 0, 1 - \frac{1}{2}, -3 - 1 \rangle = \langle 2, \frac{1}{2}, -4 \rangle$, and letting $P_0 = (2, 1, -3)$, parametric equations are $x = 2 + 2t,\ y = 1 + \frac{1}{2}t$, $z = -3 - 4t$, while symmetric equations are $\dfrac{x - 2}{2} = \dfrac{y - 1}{1/2} = \dfrac{z + 3}{-4}$ or $\dfrac{x - 2}{2} = 2y - 2 = \dfrac{z + 3}{-4}$.

9. The line has direction $\mathbf{v} = \langle 1, 2, 1 \rangle$. Letting $P_0 = (1, -1, 1)$, parametric equations are $x = 1 + t,\ y = -1 + 2t,\ z = 1 + t$
and symmetric equations are $x - 1 = \dfrac{y + 1}{2} = z - 1$.

11. Direction vectors of the lines are $\mathbf{v}_1 = \langle -2 - (-4), 0 - (-6), -3 - 1 \rangle = \langle 2, 6, -4 \rangle$ and
$\mathbf{v}_2 = \langle 5 - 10, 3 - 18, 14 - 4 \rangle = \langle -5, -15, 10 \rangle$, and since $\mathbf{v}_2 = -\frac{5}{2}\mathbf{v}_1$, the direction vectors and thus the lines are parallel.

13. (a) The line passes through the point $(1, -5, 6)$ and a direction vector for the line is $\langle -1, 2, -3 \rangle$, so symmetric equations for the line are $\dfrac{x - 1}{-1} = \dfrac{y + 5}{2} = \dfrac{z - 6}{-3}$.

(b) The line intersects the xy-plane when $z = 0$, so we need $\dfrac{x - 1}{-1} = \dfrac{y + 5}{2} = \dfrac{0 - 6}{-3}$ or $\dfrac{x - 1}{-1} = 2 \ \Rightarrow \ x = -1$,
$\dfrac{y + 5}{2} = 2 \ \Rightarrow \ y = -1$. Thus the point of intersection with the xy-plane is $(-1, -1, 0)$. Similarly for the yz-plane,
we need $x = 0 \ \Rightarrow \ 1 = \dfrac{y + 5}{2} = \dfrac{z - 6}{-3} \ \Rightarrow \ y = -3,\ z = 3$. Thus the line intersects the yz-plane at $(0, -3, 3)$. For

the xz-plane, we need $y = 0$ $\Rightarrow$ $\dfrac{x-1}{-1} = \dfrac{5}{2} = \dfrac{z-6}{-3}$ $\Rightarrow$ $x = -\frac{3}{2}, z = -\frac{3}{2}$. So the line intersects the xz-plane

at $\left(-\frac{3}{2}, 0, -\frac{3}{2}\right)$.

15. From Equation 4 , the line segment from $\mathbf{r}_0 = 2\,\mathbf{i} - \mathbf{j} + 4\,\mathbf{k}$ to $\mathbf{r}_1 = 4\,\mathbf{i} + 6\,\mathbf{j} + \mathbf{k}$ is

$\mathbf{r}(t) = (1-t)\,\mathbf{r}_0 + t\,\mathbf{r}_1 = (1-t)(2\,\mathbf{i} - \mathbf{j} + 4\,\mathbf{k}) + t(4\,\mathbf{i} + 6\,\mathbf{j} + \mathbf{k}) = (2\,\mathbf{i} - \mathbf{j} + 4\,\mathbf{k}) + t(2\,\mathbf{i} + 7\,\mathbf{j} - 3\,\mathbf{k}), 0 \le t \le 1.$

17. Since the direction vectors are $\mathbf{v}_1 = \langle -6, 9, -3 \rangle$ and $\mathbf{v}_2 = \langle 2, -3, 1 \rangle$, we have $\mathbf{v}_1 = -3\mathbf{v}_2$ so the lines are parallel.

19. Since the direction vectors $\langle 1, 2, 3 \rangle$ and $\langle -4, -3, 2 \rangle$ are not scalar multiples of each other, the lines are not parallel, so we

check to see if the lines intersect. The parametric equations of the lines are L_1: $x = t, y = 1 + 2t, z = 2 + 3t$ and L_2:

$x = 3 - 4s, y = 2 - 3s, z = 1 + 2s$. For the lines to intersect, we must be able to find one value of t and one value of s that

produce the same point from the respective parametric equations. Thus we need to satisfy the following three equations:

$t = 3 - 4s, 1 + 2t = 2 - 3s, 2 + 3t = 1 + 2s$. Solving the first two equations we get $t = -1$, $s = 1$ and checking, we see

that these values don't satisfy the third equation. Thus the lines aren't parallel and don't intersect, so they must be skew lines.

21. Since the plane is perpendicular to the vector $\langle -2, 1, 5 \rangle$, we can take $\langle -2, 1, 5 \rangle$ as a normal vector to the plane.

$(6, 3, 2)$ is a point on the plane, so setting $a = -2, b = 1, c = 5$ and $x_0 = 6, y_0 = 3, z_0 = 2$ in Equation 7 gives

$-2(x - 6) + 1(y - 3) + 5(z - 2) = 0$ or $-2x + y + 5z = 1$ to be an equation of the plane.

23. Since the two planes are parallel, they will have the same normal vectors. So we can take $\mathbf{n} = \langle 3, 0, -7 \rangle$, and an equation of

the plane is $3(x - 4) + 0[y - (-2)] - 7(z - 3) = 0$ or $3x - 7z = -9$.

25. Here the vectors $\mathbf{a} = \langle 1 - 0, 0 - 1, 1 - 1 \rangle = \langle 1, -1, 0 \rangle$ and $\mathbf{b} = \langle 1 - 0, 1 - 1, 0 - 1 \rangle = \langle 1, 0, -1 \rangle$ lie in the plane, so

$\mathbf{a} \times \mathbf{b}$ is a normal vector to the plane. Thus, we can take $\mathbf{n} = \mathbf{a} \times \mathbf{b} = \langle 1 - 0, 0 + 1, 0 + 1 \rangle = \langle 1, 1, 1 \rangle$. If P_0 is the point

$(0, 1, 1)$, an equation of the plane is $1(x - 0) + 1(y - 1) + 1(z - 1) = 0$ or $x + y + z = 2$.

27. If we first find two nonparallel vectors in the plane, their cross product will be a normal vector to the plane. Since the given

line lies in the plane, its direction vector $\mathbf{a} = \langle -2, 5, 4 \rangle$ is one vector in the plane. We can verify that the given point $(6, 0, -2)$

does not lie on this line, so to find another nonparallel vector $\mathbf{b}$ which lies in the plane, we can pick any point on the line and

find a vector connecting the points. If we put $t = 0$, we see that $(4, 3, 7)$ is on the line, so

$\mathbf{b} = \langle 6 - 4, 0 - 3, -2 - 7 \rangle = \langle 2, -3, -9 \rangle$ and $\mathbf{n} = \mathbf{a} \times \mathbf{b} = \langle -45 + 12, 8 - 18, 6 - 10 \rangle = \langle -33, -10, -4 \rangle$. Thus, an

equation of the plane is $-33(x - 6) - 10(y - 0) - 4[z - (-2)] = 0$ or $33x + 10y + 4z = 190$.

29. A direction vector for the line of intersection is $\mathbf{a} = \mathbf{n}_1 \times \mathbf{n}_2 = \langle 1, 1, -1 \rangle \times \langle 2, -1, 3 \rangle = \langle 2, -5, -3 \rangle$, and $\mathbf{a}$ is parallel to the

desired plane. Another vector parallel to the plane is the vector connecting any point on the line of intersection to the given

point $(-1, 2, 1)$ in the plane. Setting $x = 0$, the equations of the planes reduce to $y - z = 2$ and $-y + 3z = 1$ with

simultaneous solution $y = \frac{7}{2}$ and $z = \frac{3}{2}$. So a point on the line is $\left(0, \frac{7}{2}, \frac{3}{2}\right)$ and another vector parallel to the plane is

$\left\langle -1, -\frac{3}{2}, -\frac{1}{2} \right\rangle$. Then a normal vector to the plane is $\mathbf{n} = \langle 2, -5, -3 \rangle \times \left\langle -1, -\frac{3}{2}, -\frac{1}{2} \right\rangle = \langle -2, 4, -8 \rangle$ and an equation of

the plane is $-2(x + 1) + 4(y - 2) - 8(z - 1) = 0$ or $x - 2y + 4z = -1$.

31. If a plane is perpendicular to two other planes, its normal vector is perpendicular to the normal vectors of the other two planes. Thus $\langle 2, 1, -2 \rangle \times \langle 1, 0, 3 \rangle = \langle 3 - 0, -2 - 6, 0 - 1 \rangle = \langle 3, -8, -1 \rangle$ is a normal vector to the desired plane. The point $(1, 5, 1)$ lies on the plane, so an equation is $3(x - 1) - 8(y - 5) - (z - 1) = 0$ or $3x - 8y - z = -38$.

33. To find the x-intercept we set $y = z = 0$ in the equation $2x + 5y + z = 10$ and obtain $2x = 10 \implies x = 5$ so the x-intercept is $(5, 0, 0)$. When $x = z = 0$ we get $5y = 10 \implies y = 2$, so the y-intercept is $(0, 2, 0)$. Setting $x = y = 0$ gives $z = 10$, so the z-intercept is $(0, 0, 10)$ and we graph the portion of the plane that lies in the first octant.

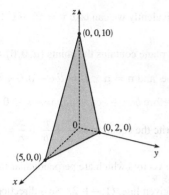

35. Setting $y = z = 0$ in the equation $6x - 3y + 4z = 6$ gives $6x = 6 \implies x = 1$, when $x = z = 0$ we have $-3y = 6 \implies y = -2$, and $x = y = 0$ implies $4z = 6 \implies z = \frac{3}{2}$, so the intercepts are $(1, 0, 0)$, $(0, -2, 0)$, and $(0, 0, \frac{3}{2})$. The figure shows the portion of the plane cut off by the coordinate planes.

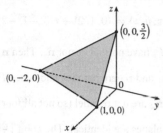

37. Substitute the parametric equations of the line into the equation of the plane: $(3 - t) - (2 + t) + 2(5t) = 9 \implies 8t = 8 \implies t = 1$. Therefore, the point of intersection of the line and the plane is given by $x = 3 - 1 = 2$, $y = 2 + 1 = 3$, and $z = 5(1) = 5$, that is, the point $(2, 3, 5)$.

39. Normal vectors for the planes are $\mathbf{n}_1 = \langle 1, 4, -3 \rangle$ and $\mathbf{n}_2 = \langle -3, 6, 7 \rangle$, so the normals (and thus the planes) aren't parallel. But $\mathbf{n}_1 \cdot \mathbf{n}_2 = -3 + 24 - 21 = 0$, so the normals (and thus the planes) are perpendicular.

41. Normal vectors for the planes are $\mathbf{n}_1 = \langle 1, 1, 1 \rangle$ and $\mathbf{n}_2 = \langle 1, -1, 1 \rangle$. The normals are not parallel, so neither are the planes. Furthermore, $\mathbf{n}_1 \cdot \mathbf{n}_2 = 1 - 1 + 1 = 1 \neq 0$, so the planes aren't perpendicular. The angle between them is given by

$$\cos \theta = \frac{\mathbf{n}_1 \cdot \mathbf{n}_2}{|\mathbf{n}_1|\, |\mathbf{n}_2|} = \frac{1}{\sqrt{3}\,\sqrt{3}} = \frac{1}{3} \implies \theta = \cos^{-1}\left(\tfrac{1}{3}\right) \approx 70.5°.$$

43. (a) To find a point on the line of intersection, set one of the variables equal to a constant, say $z = 0$. (This will fail if the line of intersection does not cross the xy-plane; in that case, try setting x or y equal to 0.) The equations of the two planes reduce to $x + y = 1$ and $x + 2y = 1$. Solving these two equations gives $x = 1$, $y = 0$. Thus a point on the line is $(1, 0, 0)$.

A vector $\mathbf{v}$ in the direction of this intersecting line is perpendicular to the normal vectors of both planes, so we can take $\mathbf{v} = \mathbf{n}_1 \times \mathbf{n}_2 = \langle 1, 1, 1 \rangle \times \langle 1, 2, 2 \rangle = \langle 2 - 2, 1 - 2, 2 - 1 \rangle = \langle 0, -1, 1 \rangle$. By Equations 2, parametric equations for the line are $x = 1$, $y = -t$, $z = t$.

(b) The angle between the planes satisfies $\cos \theta = \dfrac{\mathbf{n}_1 \cdot \mathbf{n}_2}{|\mathbf{n}_1|\,|\mathbf{n}_2|} = \dfrac{1 + 2 + 2}{\sqrt{3}\,\sqrt{9}} = \dfrac{5}{3\sqrt{3}}$. Therefore $\theta = \cos^{-1}\left(\dfrac{5}{3\sqrt{3}}\right) \approx 15.8°$.

45. Setting $z = 0$, the equations of the two planes become $5x - 2y = 1$ and $4x + y = 6$. Solving these two equations gives $x = 1$, $y = 2$ so a point on the line of intersection is $(1, 2, 0)$. A vector $\mathbf{v}$ in the direction of this intersecting line is perpendicular to the normal vectors of both planes. So we can use $\mathbf{v} = \mathbf{n}_1 \times \mathbf{n}_2 = \langle 5, -2, -2 \rangle \times \langle 4, 1, 1 \rangle = \langle 0, -13, 13 \rangle$ or equivalently we can take $\mathbf{v} = \langle 0, -1, 1 \rangle$, and symmetric equations for the line are $x = 1$, $\dfrac{y - 2}{-1} = \dfrac{z}{1}$ or $x = 1$, $y - 2 = -z$.

47. The plane contains the points $(a, 0, 0)$, $(0, b, 0)$ and $(0, 0, c)$. Thus the vectors $\mathbf{a} = \langle -a, b, 0 \rangle$ and $\mathbf{b} = \langle -a, 0, c \rangle$ lie in the plane, and $\mathbf{n} = \mathbf{a} \times \mathbf{b} = \langle bc - 0, 0 + ac, 0 + ab \rangle = \langle bc, ac, ab \rangle$ is a normal vector to the plane. The equation of the plane is therefore $bcx + acy + abz = abc + 0 + 0$ or $bcx + acy + abz = abc$. Notice that if $a \neq 0$, $b \neq 0$ and $c \neq 0$ then we can rewrite the equation as $\dfrac{x}{a} + \dfrac{y}{b} + \dfrac{z}{c} = 1$. This is a good equation to remember!

49. Two vectors which are perpendicular to the required line are the normal of the given plane, $\langle 1, 1, 1 \rangle$, and a direction vector for the given line, $\langle 1, -1, 2 \rangle$. So a direction vector for the required line is $\langle 1, 1, 1 \rangle \times \langle 1, -1, 2 \rangle = \langle 3, -1, -2 \rangle$. Thus L is given by $\langle x, y, z \rangle = \langle 0, 1, 2 \rangle + t \langle 3, -1, -2 \rangle$, or in parametric form, $x = 3t$, $y = 1 - t$, $z = 2 - 2t$.

51. Let P_i have normal vector $\mathbf{n}_i$. Then $\mathbf{n}_1 = \langle 3, 6, -3 \rangle$, $\mathbf{n}_2 = \langle 4, -12, 8 \rangle$, $\mathbf{n}_3 = \langle 3, -9, 6 \rangle$, $\mathbf{n}_4 = \langle 1, 2, -1 \rangle$. Now $\mathbf{n}_1 = 3\mathbf{n}_4$, so $\mathbf{n}_1$ and $\mathbf{n}_4$ are parallel, and hence P_1 and P_4 are parallel; similarly P_2 and P_3 are parallel because $\mathbf{n}_2 = \frac{4}{3}\mathbf{n}_3$. However, $\mathbf{n}_1$ and $\mathbf{n}_2$ are not parallel (so not all four planes are parallel). Notice that the point $(2, 0, 0)$ lies on both P_1 and on P_4, so these two planes are identical. The point $\left(\frac{5}{4}, 0, 0 \right)$ lies on P_2 but not on P_3, so these are different planes.

53. Let $Q = (1, 3, 4)$ and $R = (2, 1, 1)$, points on the line corresponding to $t = 0$ and $t = 1$. Let $P = (4, 1, -2)$. Then $\mathbf{a} = \overrightarrow{QR} = \langle 1, -2, -3 \rangle$, $\mathbf{b} = \overrightarrow{QP} = \langle 3, -2, -6 \rangle$. The distance is

$$d = \frac{|\mathbf{a} \times \mathbf{b}|}{|\mathbf{a}|} = \frac{|\langle 1, -2, -3 \rangle \times \langle 3, -2, -6 \rangle|}{|\langle 1, -2, -3 \rangle|} = \frac{|\langle 6, -3, 4 \rangle|}{|\langle 1, -2, -3 \rangle|} = \frac{\sqrt{6^2 + (-3)^2 + 4^2}}{\sqrt{1^2 + (-2)^2 + (-3)^2}} = \frac{\sqrt{61}}{\sqrt{14}} = \sqrt{\frac{61}{14}}.$$

55. By Equation 9, the distance is $D = \dfrac{|ax_1 + by_1 + cz_1 + d|}{\sqrt{a^2 + b^2 + c^2}} = \dfrac{|3(1) + 2(-2) + 6(4) - 5|}{\sqrt{3^2 + 2^2 + 6^2}} = \dfrac{|18|}{\sqrt{49}} = \dfrac{18}{7}$.

57. Put $y = z = 0$ in the equation of the first plane to get the point $(2, 0, 0)$ on the plane. Because the planes are parallel, the distance D between them is the distance from $(2, 0, 0)$ to the second plane. By Equation 9,

$$D = \frac{|4(2) - 6(0) + 2(0) - 3|}{\sqrt{4^2 + (-6)^2 + (2)^2}} = \frac{5}{\sqrt{56}} = \frac{5}{2\sqrt{14}} \text{ or } \frac{5\sqrt{14}}{28}.$$

59. The distance between two parallel planes is the same as the distance between a point on one of the planes and the other plane. Let $P_0 = (x_0, y_0, z_0)$ be a point on the plane given by $ax + by + cz + d_1 = 0$. Then $ax_0 + by_0 + cz_0 + d_1 = 0$ and the distance between P_0 and the plane given by $ax + by + cz + d_2 = 0$ is, from Equation 9,

$$D = \frac{|ax_0 + by_0 + cz_0 + d_2|}{\sqrt{a^2 + b^2 + c^2}} = \frac{|-d_1 + d_2|}{\sqrt{a^2 + b^2 + c^2}} = \frac{|d_1 - d_2|}{\sqrt{a^2 + b^2 + c^2}}.$$

61. L_1: $x = y = z$ $\Rightarrow$ $x = y$ **(1)**. L_2: $x + 1 = y/2 = z/3$ $\Rightarrow$ $x + 1 = y/2$ **(2)**. The solution of **(1)** and **(2)** is $x = y = -2$. However, when $x = -2$, $x = z$ $\Rightarrow$ $z = -2$, but $x + 1 = z/3$ $\Rightarrow$ $z = -3$, a contradiction. Hence the lines do not intersect. For L_1, $\mathbf{v}_1 = \langle 1, 1, 1 \rangle$, and for L_2, $\mathbf{v}_2 = \langle 1, 2, 3 \rangle$, so the lines are not parallel. Thus the lines are skew

lines. If two lines are skew, they can be viewed as lying in two parallel planes and so the distance between the skew lines

would be the same as the distance between these parallel planes. The common normal vector to the planes must be

perpendicular to both $\langle 1, 1, 1 \rangle$ and $\langle 1, 2, 3 \rangle$, the direction vectors of the two lines. So set

$\mathbf{n} = \langle 1, 1, 1 \rangle \times \langle 1, 2, 3 \rangle = \langle 3 - 2, -3 + 1, 2 - 1 \rangle = \langle 1, -2, 1 \rangle$. From above, we know that $(-2, -2, -2)$ and $(-2, -2, -3)$

are points of L_1 and L_2 respectively. So in the notation of Equation 8, $1(-2) - 2(-2) + 1(-2) + d_1 = 0 \quad \Rightarrow \quad d_1 = 0$ and

$1(-2) - 2(-2) + 1(-3) + d_2 = 0 \quad \Rightarrow \quad d_2 = 1$.

By Exercise 59, the distance between these two skew lines is $D = \dfrac{|0 - 1|}{\sqrt{1 + 4 + 1}} = \dfrac{1}{\sqrt{6}}$.

Alternate solution (without reference to planes): A vector which is perpendicular to both of the lines is

$\mathbf{n} = \langle 1, 1, 1 \rangle \times \langle 1, 2, 3 \rangle = \langle 1, -2, 1 \rangle$. Pick any point on each of the lines, say $(-2, -2, -2)$ and $(-2, -2, -3)$, and form the

vector $\mathbf{b} = \langle 0, 0, 1 \rangle$ connecting the two points. The distance between the two skew lines is the absolute value of the scalar

projection of $\mathbf{b}$ along $\mathbf{n}$, that is, $D = \dfrac{|\mathbf{n} \cdot \mathbf{b}|}{|\mathbf{n}|} = \dfrac{|1 \cdot 0 - 2 \cdot 0 + 1 \cdot 1|}{\sqrt{1 + 4 + 1}} = \dfrac{1}{\sqrt{6}}$.

63. If $a \neq 0$, then $ax + by + cz + d = 0 \quad \Rightarrow \quad a(x + d/a) + b(y - 0) + c(z - 0) = 0$ which by (7) is the scalar equation of the

plane through the point $(-d/a, 0, 0)$ with normal vector $\langle a, b, c \rangle$. Similarly, if $b \neq 0$ (or if $c \neq 0$) the equation of the plane can

be rewritten as $a(x - 0) + b(y + d/b) + c(z - 0) = 0$ [or as $a(x - 0) + b(y - 0) + c(z + d/c) = 0$] which by (7) is the

scalar equation of a plane through the point $(0, -d/b, 0)$ [or the point $(0, 0, -d/c)$] with normal vector $\langle a, b, c \rangle$.

9.6 Functions and Surfaces

1. (a) According to Table 1, $f(40, 15) = 25$, which means that if a 40-knot wind has been blowing in the open sea for 15 hours,

it will create waves with estimated heights of 25 feet.

(b) $h = f(30, t)$ means we fix v at 30 and allow t to vary, resulting in a function of one variable. Thus here, $h = f(30, t)$

gives the wave heights produced by 30-knot winds blowing for t hours. From the table (look at the row corresponding to

$v = 30$), the function increases but at a declining rate as t increases. In fact, the function values appear to be approaching a

limiting value of approximately 19, which suggests that 30-knot winds cannot produce waves higher than about 19 feet.

(c) $h = f(v, 30)$ means we fix t at 30, again giving a function of one variable. So, $h = f(v, 30)$ gives the wave heights

produced by winds of speed v blowing for 30 hours. From the table (look at the column corresponding to $t = 30$), the

function appears to increase at an increasing rate, with no apparent limiting value. This suggests that faster winds (lasting

30 hours) always create higher waves.

3. (a) $g(2, -1) = \cos(2 + 2(-1)) = \cos(0) = 1$

(b) $x + 2y$ is defined for all choices of values for x and y and the cosine function is defined for all input values, so the domain

of g is $\mathbb{R}^2$.

(c) The range of the cosine function is $[-1, 1]$ and $x + 2y$ generates all possible input values for the cosine function, so the

range of $\cos(x + 2y)$ is $[-1, 1]$.

5. $\sqrt{y - x^2}$ is defined only when $y - x^2 \geq 0$, or $y \geq x^2$.

In addition, f is not defined if $1 - x^2 = 0$ ⟺

$x = \pm 1$. Thus the domain of f is

$\{(x, y) \mid y \geq x^2, \ x \neq \pm 1\}$.

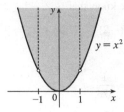

7. $\sqrt{1 - x^2}$ is defined only when $1 - x^2 \geq 0$, or

$x^2 \leq 1$ ⟺ $-1 \leq x \leq 1$, and $\sqrt{1 - y^2}$ is defined

only when $1 - y^2 \geq 0$, or $y^2 \leq 1$ ⟺ $-1 \leq y \leq 1$.

Thus the domain of f is

$\{(x, y) \mid -1 \leq x \leq 1, \ -1 \leq y \leq 1\}$.

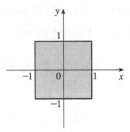

9. $z = 3$, a horizontal plane through the point $(0, 0, 3)$.

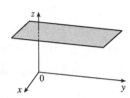

11. $z = 6 - 3x - 2y$ or $3x + 2y + z = 6$, a plane with

intercepts 2, 3, and 6.

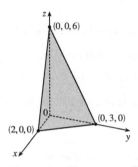

13. $z = y^2 + 1$, a parabolic cylinder

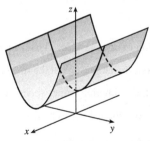

15. All six graphs have different traces in the planes $x = 0$ and $y = 0$, so we investigate these for each function.

(a) $f(x, y) = |x| + |y|$. The trace in $x = 0$ is $z = |y|$, and in $y = 0$ is $z = |x|$, so it must be graph VI.

(b) $f(x, y) = |xy|$. The trace in $x = 0$ is $z = 0$, and in $y = 0$ is $z = 0$, so it must be graph V.

(c) $f(x, y) = \dfrac{1}{1 + x^2 + y^2}$. The trace in $x = 0$ is $z = \dfrac{1}{1 + y^2}$, and in $y = 0$ is $z = \dfrac{1}{1 + x^2}$. In addition, we can see that f is

close to 0 for large values of x and y, so this is graph I.

(d) $f(x, y) = (x^2 - y^2)^2$. The trace in $x = 0$ is $z = y^4$, and in $y = 0$ is $z = x^4$. Both graph II and graph IV seem plausible;

notice the trace in $z = 0$ is $0 = (x^2 - y^2)^2$ ⟹ $y = \pm x$, so it must be graph IV.

(e) $f(x, y) = (x - y)^2$. The trace in $x = 0$ is $z - y^2$, and in $y = 0$ is $z = x^2$. Both graph II and graph IV seem plausible; notice the trace in $z = 0$ is $0 = (x - y)^2$ ⇒ $y = x$, so it must be graph II.

(f) $f(x, y) = \sin(|x| + |y|)$. The trace in $x = 0$ is $z = \sin|y|$, and in $y = 0$ is $z = \sin|x|$. In addition, notice that the oscillating nature of the graph is characteristic of trigonometric functions. So this is graph III.

17. The equation of the graph is $z = \sqrt{4x^2 + y^2}$ or equivalently $4x^2 + y^2 = z^2$, $z \geq 0$. Traces in $x = k$ are $z^2 - y^2 = 4k^2$, $z \geq 0$, a family of hyperbolas where we have only the upper branch. Traces in $y = k$ are $z^2 - 4x^2 = k^2$, $z \geq 0$, again a family of half-hyperbolas. Traces in $z = k$, $k \geq 0$, are $4x^2 + y^2 = k^2$ or $x^2 + \dfrac{y^2}{4} = \dfrac{k^2}{4}$, a family of ellipses. Note that the original equation can be written as $x^2 + \dfrac{y^2}{4} = \dfrac{z^2}{4}$, $z \geq 0$, which we recognize as the upper half of an elliptical cone.

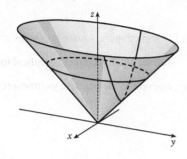

19. $y = z^2 - x^2$. The traces in $x = k$ are the parabolas $y = z^2 - k^2$; the traces in $y = k$ are $k = z^2 - x^2$, which are hyperbolas (note the hyperbolas are oriented differently for $k > 0$ than for $k < 0$); and the traces in $z = k$ are the parabolas $y = k^2 - x^2$. Thus, $\dfrac{y}{1} = \dfrac{z^2}{1^2} - \dfrac{x^2}{1^2}$ is a hyperbolic paraboloid.

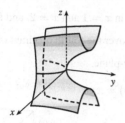

21. Completing squares in y and z gives $4x^2 + (y - 2)^2 + 4(z - 3)^2 = 4$ or $x^2 + \dfrac{(y - 2)^2}{4} + (z - 3)^2 = 1$, an ellipsoid with center $(0, 2, 3)$.

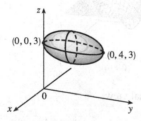

23. (a) In $\mathbb{R}^2$, $x^2 + y^2 = 1$ represents a circle of radius 1 centered at the origin.

(b) In $\mathbb{R}^3$, the equation doesn't involve z, which means that any horizontal plane $z = k$ intersects the surface in a circle $x^2 + y^2 = 1$, $z = k$. Thus the surface is a circular cylinder, made up of infinitely many shifted copies of the circle $x^2 + y^2 = 1$, with axis the z-axis.

(c) In $\mathbb{R}^3$, $x^2 + z^2 = 1$ also represents a circular cylinder of radius 1, this time with axis the y-axis.

25. (a) The traces of $x^2 + y^2 - z^2 = 1$ in $x = k$ are $y^2 - z^2 = 1 - k^2$, a family of hyperbolas. (Note that the hyperbolas are oriented differently for $-1 < k < 1$ than for $k < -1$ or $k > 1$.) The traces in $y = k$ are $x^2 - z^2 = 1 - k^2$, a similar family of hyperbolas. The traces in $z = k$ are $x^2 + y^2 = 1 + k^2$, a family of circles. For $k = 0$, the trace in the xy-plane, the circle is of radius 1. As $|k|$ increases, so does the radius of the circle. This behavior, combined with the hyperbolic vertical traces, gives the graph of the hyperboloid of one sheet in Table 2.

(b) The shape of the surface is unchanged, but the hyperboloid is rotated so that its axis is the y-axis. Traces in $y = k$ are circles, while traces in $x = k$ and $z = k$ are hyperbolas.

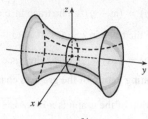

(c) Completing the square in y gives $x^2 + (y+1)^2 - z^2 = 1$. The surface is a hyperboloid identical to the one in part (a) but shifted one unit in the negative y-direction.

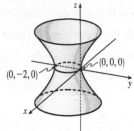

27. Graph III has these traces. One indication is found by noting that the higher z-values occur for negative values of y in the traces in $x = 1$ and $x = 2$, and for positive values of x in the traces in $y = -1$ and $y = -2$. Thus the graph should have a "hill" over the fourth quadrant of the xy-plane. Similarly, we should expect a "valley" corresponding to the second quadrant of the xy-plane.

29. $f(x,y) = xye^{x+2y-9x^2-9y^2}$

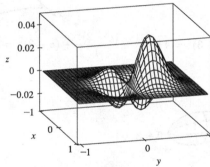

Three-dimensional view

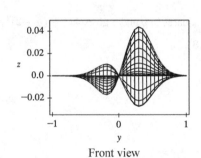

Front view

It does appear that the function has a maximum value, at the higher of the two "hilltops." From the front view graph, we can estimate the maximum value to be approximately 0.044. Both hilltops could be considered local maximum points, as the values of f there are larger than at the neighboring points. Similarly, the two "valley bottoms" visible in the graph can be considered local minimum points, as all the neighboring points give greater values of f. (And f achieves a minimum value at the lower valley dip.)

31.

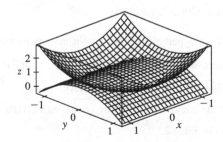

The curve of intersection looks like a bent ellipse. The projection of this curve onto the xy-plane is the set of points $(x, y, 0)$ which satisfy $x^2 + y^2 = 1 - y^2 \iff x^2 + 2y^2 = 1 \iff$

$x^2 + \dfrac{y^2}{\left(1/\sqrt{2}\right)^2} = 1$. This is an equation of an ellipse.

33. If (a, b, c) satisfies $z = y^2 - x^2$, then $c = b^2 - a^2$. L_1: $x = a + t$, $y = b + t$, $z = c + 2(b - a)t$,

L_2: $x = a + t$, $y = b - t$, $z = c - 2(b + a)t$. Substitute the parametric equations of L_1 into the equation

of the hyperbolic paraboloid in order to find the points of intersection: $z = y^2 - x^2$ ⇒

$c + 2(b - a)t = (b + t)^2 - (a + t)^2 = b^2 - a^2 + 2(b - a)t$ ⇒ $c = b^2 - a^2$. As this is true for all values of t,

L_1 lies on $z = y^2 - x^2$. Performing similar operations with L_2 gives: $z = y^2 - x^2$ ⇒

$c - 2(b + a)t = (b - t)^2 - (a + t)^2 = b^2 - a^2 - 2(b + a)t$ ⇒ $c = b^2 - a^2$. This tells us that all of L_2 also lies on

$z = y^2 - x^2$.

9.7 Cylindrical and Spherical Coordinates

1. See Figure 2 and the accompanying discussion on page 682; see the paragraph preceding Example 2 on page 683.

3. (a)

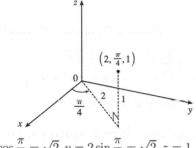

$x = 2\cos\dfrac{\pi}{4} = \sqrt{2}$, $y = 2\sin\dfrac{\pi}{4} = \sqrt{2}$, $z = 1$,

so the point is $(\sqrt{2}, \sqrt{2}, 1)$ in rectangular coordinates.

(b)

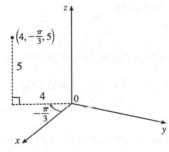

$x = 4\cos\left(-\dfrac{\pi}{3}\right) = 2$, $y = 4\sin\left(-\dfrac{\pi}{3}\right) = -2\sqrt{3}$,

and $z = 5$, so the point is $(2, -2\sqrt{3}, 5)$ in rectangular

coordinates.

5. (a) $r^2 = x^2 + y^2 = 1^2 + (-1)^2 = 2$ so $r = \sqrt{2}$; $\tan\theta = \dfrac{y}{x} = \dfrac{-1}{1} = -1$ and the point $(1, -1)$ is in the fourth quadrant of

the xy-plane, so $\theta = \dfrac{7\pi}{4} + 2n\pi$; $z = 4$. Thus, one set of cylindrical coordinates is $\left(\sqrt{2}, \dfrac{7\pi}{4}, 4\right)$.

(b) $r^2 = (-1)^2 + \left(-\sqrt{3}\right)^2 = 4$ so $r = 2$; $\tan\theta = \dfrac{-\sqrt{3}}{-1} = \sqrt{3}$ and the point $\left(-1, -\sqrt{3}\right)$ is in the third quadrant of the

xy-plane, so $\theta = \dfrac{4\pi}{3} + 2n\pi$; $z = 2$. Thus, one set of cylindrical coordinates is $\left(2, \dfrac{4\pi}{3}, 2\right)$.

7. (a)

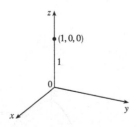

$x = \rho\sin\phi\cos\theta = (1)\sin 0\cos 0 = 0$,

$y = \rho\sin\phi\sin\theta = (1)\sin 0\sin 0 = 0$, and

$z = \rho\cos\phi = (1)\cos 0 = 1$ so the point is

$(0, 0, 1)$ in rectangular coordinates.

(b)

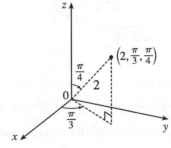

$x = 2\sin\dfrac{\pi}{4}\cos\dfrac{\pi}{3} = \dfrac{\sqrt{2}}{2}$, $y = 2\sin\dfrac{\pi}{4}\sin\dfrac{\pi}{3} = \dfrac{\sqrt{6}}{2}$,

$z = 2\cos\dfrac{\pi}{4} = \sqrt{2}$ so the point is $\left(\dfrac{\sqrt{2}}{2}, \dfrac{\sqrt{6}}{2}, \sqrt{2}\right)$ in

rectangular coordinates.

9. (a) $\rho = \sqrt{x^2 + y^2 + z^2} = \sqrt{1 + 3 + 12} = 4$, $\cos\phi = \dfrac{z}{\rho} = \dfrac{2\sqrt{3}}{4} = \dfrac{\sqrt{3}}{2}$ $\Rightarrow$ $\phi = \dfrac{\pi}{6}$, and

$\cos\theta = \dfrac{x}{\rho\sin\phi} = \dfrac{1}{4\sin(\pi/6)} = \dfrac{1}{2}$ $\Rightarrow$ $\theta = \dfrac{\pi}{3}$ [since $y > 0$]. Thus spherical coordinates are $\left(4, \dfrac{\pi}{3}, \dfrac{\pi}{6}\right)$.

(b) $\rho = \sqrt{0 + 1 + 1} = \sqrt{2}$, $\cos\phi = \dfrac{-1}{\sqrt{2}}$ $\Rightarrow$ $\phi = \dfrac{3\pi}{4}$, and $\cos\theta = \dfrac{0}{\sqrt{2}\sin(3\pi/4)} = 0$ $\Rightarrow$ $\theta = \dfrac{3\pi}{2}$ [since $y < 0$].

Thus spherical coordinates are $\left(\sqrt{2}, \dfrac{3\pi}{2}, \dfrac{3\pi}{4}\right)$.

11. Since $\theta = \frac{\pi}{4}$ but r and z may vary, the surface is a vertical half-plane including the z-axis and intersecting the xy-plane in the half-line $y = x$, $x \geq 0$.

13. Since $\phi = \frac{\pi}{3}$, the surface is the top half of the right circular cone with vertex at the origin and axis the positive z-axis.

15. $z = 4 - r^2 = 4 - (x^2 + y^2)$ or $4 - x^2 - y^2$, so the surface is a circular paraboloid with vertex $(0, 0, 4)$, axis the z-axis, and opening downward.

17. $r = 2\cos\theta$ $\Rightarrow$ $r^2 = x^2 + y^2 = 2r\cos\theta = 2x$ $\Leftrightarrow$ $(x-1)^2 + y^2 = 1$, which is the equation of a circular cylinder with radius 1, whose axis is the vertical line $x = 1$, $y = 0$, $z = z$.

19. $\rho = \sin\theta\sin\phi$ $\Rightarrow$ $\rho^2 = \rho\sin\theta\sin\phi$ $\Leftrightarrow$ $x^2 + y^2 + z^2 = y$ $\Leftrightarrow$ $x^2 + y^2 - y + \frac{1}{4} + z^2 = \frac{1}{4}$ $\Leftrightarrow$ $x^2 + (y - \frac{1}{2})^2 + z^2 = \frac{1}{4}$. Therefore, the surface is a sphere of radius $\frac{1}{2}$ centered at $(0, \frac{1}{2}, 0)$.

21. (a) Substituting $x^2 + y^2 = r^2$ and $y = r\sin\theta$, the equation $x^2 + y^2 = 2y$ becomes $r^2 = 2r\sin\theta$ or $r = 2\sin\theta$.

(b) $\rho^2\sin^2\phi(\cos^2\theta + \sin^2\theta) = 2\rho\sin\phi\sin\theta$ or $\rho\sin^2\phi = 2\sin\phi\sin\theta$ or $\rho\sin\phi = 2\sin\theta$.

23. (a) Substituting $x = r\cos\theta$ and $y = r\sin\theta$, the equation $3x + 2y + z = 6$ becomes $3r\cos\theta + 2r\sin\theta + z = 6$ or $z = 6 - r(3\cos\theta + 2\sin\theta)$.

(b) $x = \rho\sin\phi\cos\theta$, $y = \rho\sin\phi\sin\theta$, and $z = \rho\cos\phi$, so the equation becomes $3\rho\sin\phi\cos\theta + 2\rho\sin\phi\sin\theta + \rho\cos\phi = 6$ or $\rho(3\sin\phi\cos\theta + 2\sin\phi\sin\theta + \cos\phi) = 6$.

25.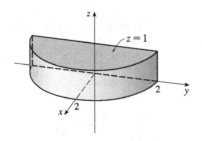

$0 \leq r \leq 2$ and $0 \leq z \leq 1$ describe a solid circular cylinder with radius 2, axis the z-axis, and height 1, but $-\pi/2 \leq \theta \leq \pi/2$ restricts the solid to the first and fourth quadrants of the xy-plane, so we have a half-cylinder.

27. $\rho = 2$ represents a sphere of radius 2, centered at the origin, so $\rho \leq 2$ is this sphere and its interior. $0 \leq \phi \leq \frac{\pi}{2}$ restricts the solid to that portion of the region that lies on or above the xy-plane, and $0 \leq \theta \leq \frac{\pi}{2}$ further restricts the solid to the first octant. Thus the solid is the portion in the first octant of the solid ball centered at the origin with radius 2.

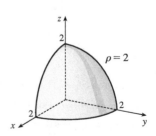

29. $\rho \leq 1$ represents the solid sphere of radius 1 centered at the origin.

$\frac{3\pi}{4} \leq \phi \leq \pi$ restricts the solid to that portion on or below the cone $\phi = \frac{3\pi}{4}$.

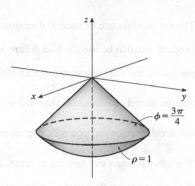

31. We can position the cylindrical shell vertically so that its axis coincides with the z-axis and its base lies in the xy-plane. If we

use centimeters as the unit of measurement, then cylindrical coordinates conveniently describe the shell as $6 \leq r \leq 7$,

$0 \leq \theta \leq 2\pi, 0 \leq z \leq 20$.

33. $z \geq \sqrt{x^2 + y^2}$ because the solid lies above the cone. Squaring both sides of this inequality gives $z^2 \geq x^2 + y^2 \Rightarrow$

$2z^2 \geq x^2 + y^2 + z^2 = \rho^2 \Rightarrow z^2 = \rho^2 \cos^2 \phi \geq \frac{1}{2}\rho^2 \Rightarrow \cos^2 \phi \geq \frac{1}{2}$. The cone opens upward so that the inequality is

$\cos \phi \geq \frac{1}{\sqrt{2}}$, or equivalently $0 < \phi \leq \frac{\pi}{4}$. In spherical coordinates the sphere $z = x^2 + y^2 + z^2$ is $\rho \cos \phi = \rho^2 \Rightarrow$

$\rho = \cos \phi$. $0 \leq \rho \leq \cos \phi$ because the solid lies below the sphere. The solid can therefore be described as the region in

spherical coordinates satisfying $0 \leq \rho \leq \cos \phi, 0 \leq \phi \leq \frac{\pi}{4}$.

35. In cylindrical coordinates, the equation of the cylinder is $r = 3, 0 \leq z \leq 10$.

The hemisphere is the upper part of the sphere radius 3, center $(0, 0, 10)$, equation

$r^2 + (z - 10)^2 = 3^2, z \geq 10$. In Maple, we can use the `coords=cylindrical` option

in a regular `plot3d` command. In Mathematica, we can use `RevolutionPlot3D` or

`ParametricPlot3D`.

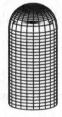

9 Review

CONCEPT CHECK

1. A scalar is a real number, while a vector is a quantity that has both a real-valued magnitude and a direction.

2. To add two vectors geometrically, we can use either the Triangle Law or the Parallelogram Law, as illustrated in Figures 3

and 4 in Section 9.2. Algebraically, we add the corresponding components of the vectors.

3. For $c > 0$, $c\mathbf{a}$ is a vector with the same direction as $\mathbf{a}$ and length c times the length of $\mathbf{a}$. If $c < 0$, $c\mathbf{a}$ points in the opposite

direction as $\mathbf{a}$ and has length $|c|$ times the length of $\mathbf{a}$. (See Figures 7 and 15 in Section 9.2.) Algebraically, to find $c\mathbf{a}$ we

multiply each component of $\mathbf{a}$ by c.

4. See (1) in Section 9.2.

5. See the definition on page 649 and the boxed equation on page 650.

6. The dot product can be used to determine the work done moving an object given the force and displacement vectors. The dot product can also be used to find the angle between two vectors and the scalar projection of one vector onto another. In particular, the dot product can determine if two vectors are orthogonal.

7. See the boxed equations on page 652 as well as Figures 5 and 6 and the accompanying discussion on pages 651–52.

8. See the definition on page 655; use either (2) or (4) in Section 9.4.

9. The cross product can be used to determine torque if the force and position vectors are known. In addition, the cross product can be used to create a vector orthogonal to two given vectors as well as to determine if two vectors are parallel. The cross product can also be used to find the area of a parallelogram determined by two vectors.

10. (a) The area of the parallelogram determined by $\mathbf{a}$ and $\mathbf{b}$ is the length of the cross product: $|\mathbf{a} \times \mathbf{b}|$.

    (b) The volume of the parallelepiped determined by $\mathbf{a}$, $\mathbf{b}$, and $\mathbf{c}$ is the magnitude of their scalar triple product: $|\mathbf{a} \cdot (\mathbf{b} \times \mathbf{c})|$.

11. If an equation of the plane is known, it can be written as $ax + by + cz + d = 0$. A normal vector, which is perpendicular to the plane, is $\langle a, b, c \rangle$ (or any scalar multiple of $\langle a, b, c \rangle$). If an equation is not known, we can use points on the plane to find two non-parallel vectors which lie in the plane. The cross product of these vectors is a vector perpendicular to the plane.

12. The angle between two intersecting planes is defined as the acute angle between their normal vectors. We can find this angle using the definition of the dot product on page 649.

13. See (1), (2), and (3) in Section 9.5.

14. See (5), (6), and (7) in Section 9.5.

15. (a) Two (nonzero) vectors are parallel if and only if one is a scalar multiple of the other. In addition, two nonzero vectors are parallel if and only if their cross product is $\mathbf{0}$.

    (b) Two vectors are perpendicular if and only if their dot product is 0.

    (c) Two planes are parallel if and only if their normal vectors are parallel.

16. (a) Determine the vectors $\overrightarrow{PQ} = \langle a_1, a_2, a_3 \rangle$ and $\overrightarrow{PR} = \langle b_1, b_2, b_3 \rangle$. If there is a scalar t such that $\langle a_1, a_2, a_3 \rangle = t \langle b_1, b_2, b_3 \rangle$, then the vectors are parallel and the points must all lie on the same line.

    Alternatively, if $\overrightarrow{PQ} \times \overrightarrow{PR} = \mathbf{0}$, then $\overrightarrow{PQ}$ and $\overrightarrow{PR}$ are parallel, so P, Q, and R are collinear.

    Thirdly, an algebraic method is to determine an equation of the line joining two of the points, and then check whether or not the third point satisfies this equation.

    (b) Find the vectors $\overrightarrow{PQ} = \mathbf{a}$, $\overrightarrow{PR} = \mathbf{b}$, $\overrightarrow{PS} = \mathbf{c}$. $\mathbf{a} \times \mathbf{b}$ is normal to the plane formed by P, Q and R, and so S lies on this plane if $\mathbf{a} \times \mathbf{b}$ and $\mathbf{c}$ are orthogonal, that is, if $(\mathbf{a} \times \mathbf{b}) \cdot \mathbf{c} = 0$. (Or use the reasoning in Example 6 in Section 9.4.) Alternatively, find an equation for the plane determined by three of the points and check whether or not the fourth point satisfies this equation.

17. (a) See Exercise 9.4.33.

(b) See Example 8 in Section 9.5.

(c) See Example 10 in Section 9.5.

18. One method of graphing a function of two variables is to first find traces (see Example 6 in Section 9.6 and the discussion preceding it).

19. See Table 2 in Section 9.6.

20. (a) See (1) and the discussion accompanying Figure 4 in Section 9.7.

(b) See (3) and Figures 7–9, and the accompanying discussion, in Section 9.7.

TRUE-FALSE QUIZ

1. True, by Property 2 of the dot product. (See page 651.)

3. True. If θ is the angle between $\mathbf{u}$ and $\mathbf{v}$, then by the definition of the cross product,

$|\mathbf{u} \times \mathbf{v}| = |\mathbf{u}|\,|\mathbf{v}|\sin\theta = |\mathbf{v}|\,|\mathbf{u}|\sin\theta = |\mathbf{v} \times \mathbf{u}|$.

(Or, by Properties 1 and 2 of the cross product, $|\mathbf{u} \times \mathbf{v}| = |-\mathbf{v} \times \mathbf{u}| = |-1|\,|\mathbf{v} \times \mathbf{u}| = |\mathbf{v} \times \mathbf{u}|$.)

5. Property 2 of the cross product tells us that this is true.

7. This is true by (6) in Section 9.4.

9. This is true because $\mathbf{u} \times \mathbf{v}$ is orthogonal to $\mathbf{u}$ (see page 655), and the dot product of two orthogonal vectors is 0.

11. If $|\mathbf{u}| = 1$, $|\mathbf{v}| = 1$ and θ is the angle between these two vectors (so $0 \le \theta \le \pi$), then by the definition of the cross product,

$|\mathbf{u} \times \mathbf{v}| = |\mathbf{u}|\,|\mathbf{v}|\sin\theta = \sin\theta$, which is equal to 1 if and only if $\theta = \frac{\pi}{2}$ (that is, if and only if the two vectors are orthogonal).

Therefore, the assertion that the cross product of two unit vectors is a unit vector is false.

13. This is false. In $\mathbb{R}^2$, $x^2 + y^2 = 1$ represents a circle, but $\{(x, y, z) \mid x^2 + y^2 = 1\}$ represents a *three-dimensional surface*, namely, a circular cylinder with axis the z-axis.

15. False. For example, $\mathbf{i} \cdot \mathbf{j} = 0$ but $\mathbf{i} \ne \mathbf{0}$ and $\mathbf{j} \ne \mathbf{0}$.

17. This is true. If $\mathbf{u}$ and $\mathbf{v}$ are both nonzero, then by (2) in Section 9.3, $\mathbf{u} \cdot \mathbf{v} = 0$ implies that $\mathbf{u}$ and $\mathbf{v}$ are orthogonal. But $\mathbf{u} \times \mathbf{v} = \mathbf{0}$ implies that $\mathbf{u}$ and $\mathbf{v}$ are parallel (see the boxed statement preceding Example 1 on page 655). Two nonzero vectors can't be both parallel and orthogonal, so at least one of $\mathbf{u}$, $\mathbf{v}$ must be $\mathbf{0}$.

EXERCISES

1. (a) The radius of the sphere is the distance between the points $(-1, 2, 1)$ and $(6, -2, 3)$, namely,

$\sqrt{[6 - (-1)]^2 + (-2 - 2)^2 + (3 - 1)^2} = \sqrt{69}$. By the formula for an equation of a sphere (see page 637), an equation of the sphere with center $(-1, 2, 1)$ and radius $\sqrt{69}$ is $(x + 1)^2 + (y - 2)^2 + (z - 1)^2 = 69$.

(b) The intersection of this sphere with the yz-plane is the set of points on the sphere whose x-coordinate is 0. Putting $x = 0$ into the equation, we have $(y-2)^2 + (z-1)^2 = 68, x = 0$ which represents a circle in the yz-plane with center $(0, 2, 1)$ and radius $\sqrt{68}$.

(c) Completing squares gives $(x-4)^2 + (y+1)^2 + (z+3)^2 = -1 + 16 + 1 + 9 = 25$. Thus the sphere is centered at $(4, -1, -3)$ and has radius 5.

3. $\mathbf{u} \cdot \mathbf{v} = |\mathbf{u}|\,|\mathbf{v}|\cos 45° = (2)(3)\frac{\sqrt{2}}{2} = 3\sqrt{2}$. $\quad |\mathbf{u} \times \mathbf{v}| = |\mathbf{u}|\,|\mathbf{v}|\sin 45° = (2)(3)\frac{\sqrt{2}}{2} = 3\sqrt{2}$.

   By the right-hand rule, $\mathbf{u} \times \mathbf{v}$ is directed out of the page.

5. For the two vectors to be orthogonal, we need $\langle 3, 2, x\rangle \cdot \langle 2x, 4, x\rangle = 0 \quad \Leftrightarrow \quad (3)(2x) + (2)(4) + (x)(x) = 0 \quad \Leftrightarrow$

   $x^2 + 6x + 8 = 0 \quad \Leftrightarrow \quad (x+2)(x+4) = 0 \quad \Leftrightarrow \quad x = -2$ or $x = -4$.

7. (a) $(\mathbf{u} \times \mathbf{v}) \cdot \mathbf{w} = \mathbf{u} \cdot (\mathbf{v} \times \mathbf{w}) = 2$

   (b) $\mathbf{u} \cdot (\mathbf{w} \times \mathbf{v}) = \mathbf{u} \cdot [-(\mathbf{v} \times \mathbf{w})] = -\mathbf{u} \cdot (\mathbf{v} \times \mathbf{w}) = -2$

   (c) $\mathbf{v} \cdot (\mathbf{u} \times \mathbf{w}) = (\mathbf{v} \times \mathbf{u}) \cdot \mathbf{w} = -(\mathbf{u} \times \mathbf{v}) \cdot \mathbf{w} = -2$

   (d) $(\mathbf{u} \times \mathbf{v}) \cdot \mathbf{v} = \mathbf{u} \cdot (\mathbf{v} \times \mathbf{v}) = \mathbf{u} \cdot \mathbf{0} = 0$

9. For simplicity, consider a unit cube positioned with its back left corner at the origin. Vector representations of the diagonals joining the points $(0, 0, 0)$ to $(1, 1, 1)$ and $(1, 0, 0)$ to $(0, 1, 1)$ are $\langle 1, 1, 1\rangle$ and $\langle -1, 1, 1\rangle$. Let θ be the angle between these two vectors. $\langle 1, 1, 1\rangle \cdot \langle -1, 1, 1\rangle = -1 + 1 + 1 = 1 = |\langle 1, 1, 1\rangle|\,|\langle -1, 1, 1\rangle|\cos\theta = 3\cos\theta \quad \Rightarrow \quad \cos\theta = \frac{1}{3} \quad \Rightarrow$

   $\theta = \cos^{-1}\left(\frac{1}{3}\right) \approx 71°$.

11. $\overrightarrow{AB} = \langle 1, 0, -1\rangle$, $\overrightarrow{AC} = \langle 0, 4, 3\rangle$, so

    (a) a vector perpendicular to the plane is $\overrightarrow{AB} \times \overrightarrow{AC} = \langle 0 + 4, -(3+0), 4 - 0\rangle = \langle 4, -3, 4\rangle$.

    (b) $\frac{1}{2}\left|\overrightarrow{AB} \times \overrightarrow{AC}\right| = \frac{1}{2}\sqrt{16 + 9 + 16} = \frac{\sqrt{41}}{2}$.

13. Let F_1 be the magnitude of the force directed 20° away from the direction of shore, and let F_2 be the magnitude of the other force. Separating these forces into components parallel to the direction of the resultant force and perpendicular to it gives

    $F_1\cos 20° + F_2\cos 30° = 255$ **(1)**, and $F_1\sin 20° - F_2\sin 30° = 0 \quad \Rightarrow \quad F_1 = F_2\dfrac{\sin 30°}{\sin 20°}$ **(2)**. Substituting **(2)**

    into **(1)** gives $F_2(\sin 30°\cot 20° + \cos 30°) = 255 \quad \Rightarrow \quad F_2 \approx 114$ N. Substituting this into **(2)** gives $F_1 \approx 166$ N.

15. The line has direction $\mathbf{v} = \langle -3, 2, 3\rangle$. Letting $P_0 = (4, -1, 2)$, parametric equations are

    $x = 4 - 3t, \; y = -1 + 2t, \; z = 2 + 3t$.

17. A direction vector for the line is a normal vector for the plane, $\mathbf{n} = \langle 2, -1, 5\rangle$, and parametric equations for the line are

    $x = -2 + 2t, \; y = 2 - t, \; z = 4 + 5t$.

19. Here the vectors $\mathbf{a} = \langle 4 - 3, 0 - (-1), 2 - 1\rangle = \langle 1, 1, 1\rangle$ and $\mathbf{b} = \langle 6 - 3, 3 - (-1), 1 - 1\rangle = \langle 3, 4, 0\rangle$ lie in the plane,

    so $\mathbf{n} = \mathbf{a} \times \mathbf{b} = \langle -4, 3, 1\rangle$ is a normal vector to the plane and an equation of the plane is

    $-4(x - 3) + 3(y - (-1)) + 1(z - 1) = 0$ or $-4x + 3y + z = -14$.

21. $\mathbf{n}_1 = \langle 1, 0, -1 \rangle$ and $\mathbf{n}_2 = \langle 0, 1, 2 \rangle$. Setting $z = 0$, it is easy to see that $(1, 3, 0)$ is a point on the line of intersection of $x - z = 1$ and $y + 2z = 3$. The direction of this line is $\mathbf{v}_1 = \mathbf{n}_1 \times \mathbf{n}_2 = \langle 1, -2, 1 \rangle$. A second vector parallel to the desired plane is $\mathbf{v}_2 = \langle 1, 1, -2 \rangle$, since it is perpendicular to $x + y - 2z = 1$. Therefore, the normal of the plane in question is $\mathbf{n} = \mathbf{v}_1 \times \mathbf{v}_2 = \langle 4 - 1, 1 + 2, 1 + 2 \rangle = 3\langle 1, 1, 1 \rangle$. Taking $(x_0, y_0, z_0) = (1, 3, 0)$, the equation we are looking for is $(x - 1) + (y - 3) + z = 0 \iff x + y + z = 4$.

23. Since the direction vectors $\langle 2, 3, 4 \rangle$ and $\langle 6, -1, 2 \rangle$ aren't parallel, neither are the lines. For the lines to intersect, the three equations $1 + 2t = -1 + 6s$, $2 + 3t = 3 - s$, $3 + 4t = -5 + 2s$ must be satisfied simultaneously. Solving the first two equations gives $t = \frac{1}{5}$, $s = \frac{2}{5}$ and checking we see these values don't satisfy the third equation. Thus the lines aren't parallel and they don't intersect, so they must be skew.

25. (a) By Exercise 9.5.59, $D = \dfrac{|-2 - (-24)|}{\sqrt{3^2 + 1^2 + (-4)^2}} = \dfrac{22}{\sqrt{26}}$.

(b) Use the formula proven in Exercise 9.4.33(a). In the notation used in that exercise, $\mathbf{a}$ is just the direction of the line; that is, $\mathbf{a} = \langle 1, -1, 2 \rangle$. A point on the line is $(1, 2, -1)$ (setting $t = 0$), and therefore $\mathbf{b} = \langle 1 - 0, 2 - 0, -1 - 0 \rangle = \langle 1, 2, -1 \rangle$.

Hence $d = \dfrac{|\mathbf{a} \times \mathbf{b}|}{|\mathbf{a}|} = \dfrac{|\langle 1, -1, 2 \rangle \times \langle 1, 2, -1 \rangle|}{\sqrt{1 + 1 + 4}} = \dfrac{|\langle -3, 3, 3 \rangle|}{\sqrt{6}} = \sqrt{\dfrac{27}{6}} = \dfrac{3}{\sqrt{2}}$.

27. $\ln(x - y^2)$ is defined only when $x - y^2 > 0$, or $x > y^2$, and x is defined for all real numbers, so the domain of the product $x \ln(x - y^2)$ is $\{(x, y) \mid x > y^2\}$.

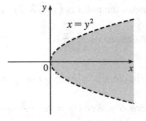

29. The graph is the plane $z = 6 - 2x - 3y \implies 2x + 3y + z = 6$. The intercepts with the coordinate axes are $(3, 0, 0)$, $(0, 2, 0)$, and $(0, 0, 6)$ which enable us to sketch the portion of the plane that lies in the first octant.

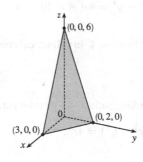

31. The equation is $z = 4 - x^2 - 4y^2$. The traces in $x = k$ are $z = 4 - k^2 - 4y^2$, a family of parabolas opening downward, as are the traces in $y = k$, $z = 4 - 4k^2 - x^2$. The traces in $z = k$ are $x^2 + 4y^2 = 4 - k$, a family of ellipses, so the surface is an elliptic paraboloid.

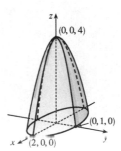

33. An equivalent equation is $\dfrac{x^2}{(1/2)^2} + y^2 + z^2 = 1$, an ellipsoid centered at

the origin with intercepts $\pm\frac{1}{2}$, ±1, and ±1.

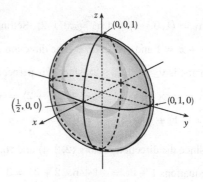

35. $y^2 + z^2 = 1$ is the equation of a circular cylinder with axis the x-axis.

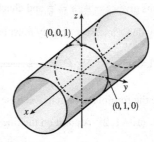

37. $x = r\cos\theta = 2\sqrt{3}\cos\frac{\pi}{3} = 2\sqrt{3}\cdot\frac{1}{2} = \sqrt{3}$, $y = r\sin\theta = 2\sqrt{3}\sin\frac{\pi}{3} = 2\sqrt{3}\cdot\frac{\sqrt{3}}{2} = 3$, $z = 2$, so in rectangular

coordinates the point is $\left(\sqrt{3},3,2\right)$. $\rho = \sqrt{r^2 + z^2} = \sqrt{12+4} = 4$, $\theta = \frac{\pi}{3}$, and $\cos\phi = \frac{z}{\rho} = \frac{1}{2}$, so $\phi = \frac{\pi}{3}$ and spherical

coordinates are $\left(4,\frac{\pi}{3},\frac{\pi}{3}\right)$.

39. $x = \rho\sin\phi\cos\theta = 8\sin\frac{\pi}{6}\cos\frac{\pi}{4} = 8\cdot\frac{1}{2}\cdot\frac{\sqrt{2}}{2} = 2\sqrt{2}$, $y = \rho\sin\phi\sin\theta = 8\sin\frac{\pi}{6}\sin\frac{\pi}{4} = 2\sqrt{2}$, and

$z = \rho\cos\phi = 8\cos\frac{\pi}{6} = 8\cdot\frac{\sqrt{3}}{2} = 4\sqrt{3}$. Thus rectangular coordinates for the point are $\left(2\sqrt{2},2\sqrt{2},4\sqrt{3}\right)$.

$r^2 = x^2 + y^2 = 8+8 = 16$ $\Rightarrow$ $r = 4$, $\theta = \frac{\pi}{4}$, and $z = 4\sqrt{3}$, so cylindrical coordinates are $\left(4,\frac{\pi}{4},4\sqrt{3}\right)$.

41. $x^2 + y^2 + z^2 = 4$. In cylindrical coordinates, this becomes $r^2 + z^2 = 4$. In spherical coordinates, it becomes $\rho^2 = 4$ or

$\rho = 2$.

43. The resulting surface is a circular paraboloid with equation $z = 4x^2 + 4y^2$. Changing to cylindrical coordinates we have

$z = 4\left(x^2 + y^2\right) = 4r^2$.

☐ FOCUS ON PROBLEM SOLVING

1. Since three-dimensional situations are often difficult to visualize and work with, let us first try to find an analogous problem in two dimensions. The analogue of a cube is a square and the analogue of a sphere is a circle. Thus a similar problem in two dimensions is the following: if five circles with the same radius r are contained in a square of side 1 m so that the circles touch each other and four of the circles touch two sides of the square, find r.

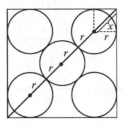

The diagonal of the square is $\sqrt{2}$. The diagonal is also $4r + 2x$. But x is the diagonal of a smaller square of side r. Therefore

$$x = \sqrt{2}\, r \quad \Rightarrow \quad \sqrt{2} = 4r + 2x = 4r + 2\sqrt{2}\, r = \left(4 + 2\sqrt{2}\right)r \quad \Rightarrow \quad r = \frac{\sqrt{2}}{4 + 2\sqrt{2}}.$$

Let's use these ideas to solve the original three-dimensional problem. The diagonal of the cube is $\sqrt{1^2 + 1^2 + 1^2} = \sqrt{3}$. The diagonal of the cube is also $4r + 2x$ where x is the diagonal of a smaller cube with edge r. Therefore

$$x = \sqrt{r^2 + r^2 + r^2} = \sqrt{3}\, r \quad \Rightarrow \quad \sqrt{3} = 4r + 2x = 4r + 2\sqrt{3}\, r = \left(4 + 2\sqrt{3}\right)r. \text{ Thus } r = \frac{\sqrt{3}}{4 + 2\sqrt{3}} = \frac{2\sqrt{3} - 3}{2}.$$

The radius of each ball is $\left(\sqrt{3} - \frac{3}{2}\right)$ m.

3. (a) We find the line of intersection L as in Example 9.5.7(b). Observe that the point $(-1, c, c)$ lies on both planes. Now since L lies in both planes, it is perpendicular to both of the normal vectors $\mathbf{n}_1$ and $\mathbf{n}_2$, and thus parallel to their cross product

$$\mathbf{n}_1 \times \mathbf{n}_2 = \begin{vmatrix} \mathbf{i} & \mathbf{j} & \mathbf{k} \\ c & 1 & 1 \\ 1 & -c & c \end{vmatrix} = \langle 2c, -c^2 + 1, -c^2 - 1 \rangle. \text{ So symmetric equations of } L \text{ can be written as}$$

$$\frac{x + 1}{-2c} = \frac{y - c}{c^2 - 1} = \frac{z - c}{c^2 + 1}, \text{ provided that } c \neq 0, \pm 1.$$

If $c = 0$, then the two planes are given by $y + z = 0$ and $x = -1$, so symmetric equations of L are $x = -1$, $y = -z$. If $c = -1$, then the two planes are given by $-x + y + z = -1$ and $x + y + z = -1$, and they intersect in the line $x = 0$, $y = -z - 1$. If $c = 1$, then the two planes are given by $x + y + z = 1$ and $x - y + z = 1$, and they intersect in the line $y = 0$, $x = 1 - z$.

(b) If we set $z = t$ in the symmetric equations and solve for x and y separately, we get $x + 1 = \dfrac{(t - c)(-2c)}{c^2 + 1}$,

$$y - c = \frac{(t - c)(c^2 - 1)}{c^2 + 1} \quad \Rightarrow \quad x = \frac{-2ct + (c^2 - 1)}{c^2 + 1}, \quad y = \frac{(c^2 - 1)t + 2c}{c^2 + 1}. \text{ Eliminating } c \text{ from these equations, we}$$

have $x^2 + y^2 = t^2 + 1$. So the curve traced out by L in the plane $z = t$ is a circle with center at $(0, 0, t)$ and radius $\sqrt{t^2 + 1}$.

79

(c) The area of a horizontal cross-section of the solid is $A(z) = \pi(z^2 + 1)$, so $V = \int_0^1 A(z)\,dz = \pi\left[\frac{1}{3}z^3 + z\right]_0^1 = \frac{4\pi}{3}$.

5. $\mathbf{v}_3 = \mathrm{proj}_{\mathbf{v}_1}\mathbf{v}_2 = \dfrac{\mathbf{v}_1 \cdot \mathbf{v}_2}{|\mathbf{v}_1|^2}\,\mathbf{v}_1 = \dfrac{5}{2^2}\,\mathbf{v}_1$ so $|\mathbf{v}_3| = \dfrac{5}{2^2}\,|\mathbf{v}_1| = \dfrac{5}{2}$,

$\mathbf{v}_4 = \mathrm{proj}_{\mathbf{v}_2}\mathbf{v}_3 = \dfrac{\mathbf{v}_2 \cdot \mathbf{v}_3}{|\mathbf{v}_2|^2}\,\mathbf{v}_2 = \dfrac{\mathbf{v}_2 \cdot \frac{5}{2^2}\mathbf{v}_1}{|\mathbf{v}_2|^2}\,\mathbf{v}_2 = \dfrac{5}{2^2 \cdot 3^2}(\mathbf{v}_1 \cdot \mathbf{v}_2)\,\mathbf{v}_2 = \dfrac{5^2}{2^2 \cdot 3^2}\,\mathbf{v}_2 \;\Rightarrow\; |\mathbf{v}_4| = \dfrac{5^2}{2^2 \cdot 3^2}\,|\mathbf{v}_2| = \dfrac{5^2}{2^2 \cdot 3}$,

$\mathbf{v}_5 = \mathrm{proj}_{\mathbf{v}_3}\mathbf{v}_4 = \dfrac{\mathbf{v}_3 \cdot \mathbf{v}_4}{|\mathbf{v}_3|^2}\,\mathbf{v}_3 = \dfrac{\frac{5}{2^2}\mathbf{v}_1 \cdot \frac{5^2}{2^2\,3^2}\mathbf{v}_2}{\left(\frac{5}{2}\right)^2}\left(\dfrac{5}{2^2}\,\mathbf{v}_1\right) = \dfrac{5^2}{2^4 \cdot 3^2}(\mathbf{v}_1 \cdot \mathbf{v}_2)\,\mathbf{v}_1 = \dfrac{5^3}{2^4 \cdot 3^2}\,\mathbf{v}_1 \;\Rightarrow$

$|\mathbf{v}_5| = \dfrac{5^3}{2^4 \cdot 3^2}\,|\mathbf{v}_1| = \dfrac{5^3}{2^3 \cdot 3^2}$. Similarly, $|\mathbf{v}_6| = \dfrac{5^4}{2^4 \cdot 3^3}$, $|\mathbf{v}_7| = \dfrac{5^5}{2^5 \cdot 3^4}$, and in general, $|\mathbf{v}_n| = \dfrac{5^{n-2}}{2^{n-2} \cdot 3^{n-3}} = 3\left(\dfrac{5}{6}\right)^{n-2}$.

Thus

$$\sum_{n=1}^{\infty} |\mathbf{v}_n| = |\mathbf{v}_1| + |\mathbf{v}_2| + \sum_{n=3}^{\infty} 3\left(\tfrac{5}{6}\right)^{n-2} = 2 + 3 + \sum_{n=1}^{\infty} 3\left(\tfrac{5}{6}\right)^{n}$$

$$= 5 + \sum_{n=1}^{\infty} \tfrac{5}{2}\left(\tfrac{5}{6}\right)^{n-1} = 5 + \dfrac{\frac{5}{2}}{1 - \frac{5}{6}} \quad \text{[sum of a geometric series]} \quad = 5 + 15 = 20$$

7. (a) When $\theta = \theta_s$, the block is not moving, so the sum of the forces on the block

must be $\mathbf{0}$, thus $\mathbf{N} + \mathbf{F} + \mathbf{W} = \mathbf{0}$. This relationship is illustrated

geometrically in the figure. Since the vectors form a right triangle, we have

$$\tan(\theta_s) = \dfrac{|\mathbf{F}|}{|\mathbf{N}|} = \dfrac{\mu_s n}{n} = \mu_s.$$

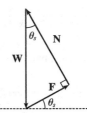

(b) We place the block at the origin and sketch the force vectors acting on the block, including the additional horizontal force

$\mathbf{H}$, with initial points at the origin. We then rotate this system so that $\mathbf{F}$ lies along the positive x-axis and the inclined plane

is parallel to the x-axis. (See the following figure.)

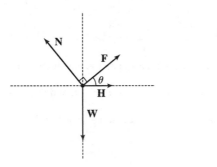 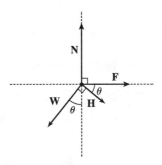

$|\mathbf{F}|$ is maximal, so $|\mathbf{F}| = \mu_s n$ for $\theta > \theta_s$. Then the vectors, in terms of components parallel and perpendicular to the

inclined plane, are

$$\mathbf{N} = n\,\mathbf{j} \qquad\qquad \mathbf{F} = (\mu_s n)\,\mathbf{i}$$

$$\mathbf{W} = (-mg\sin\theta)\,\mathbf{i} + (-mg\cos\theta)\,\mathbf{j} \qquad\qquad \mathbf{H} = (h_{\min}\cos\theta)\,\mathbf{i} + (-h_{\min}\sin\theta)\,\mathbf{j}$$

Equating components, we have

$$\mu_s n - mg\sin\theta + h_{min}\cos\theta = 0 \quad\Rightarrow\quad h_{min}\cos\theta + \mu_s n = mg\sin\theta \tag{1}$$

$$n - mg\cos\theta - h_{min}\sin\theta = 0 \quad\Rightarrow\quad h_{min}\sin\theta + mg\cos\theta = n \tag{2}$$

(c) Since **(2)** is solved for n, we substitute into **(1)**:

$$h_{min}\cos\theta + \mu_s(h_{min}\sin\theta + mg\cos\theta) = mg\sin\theta \quad\Rightarrow$$

$$h_{min}\cos\theta + h_{min}\mu_s\sin\theta = mg\sin\theta - mg\mu_s\cos\theta \quad\Rightarrow$$

$$h_{min} = mg\left(\frac{\sin\theta - \mu_s\cos\theta}{\cos\theta + \mu_s\sin\theta}\right) = mg\left(\frac{\tan\theta - \mu_s}{1 + \mu_s\tan\theta}\right)$$

From part (a) we know $\mu_s = \tan\theta_s$, so this becomes $h_{min} = mg\left(\dfrac{\tan\theta - \tan\theta_s}{1 + \tan\theta_s\tan\theta}\right)$ and using a trigonometric identity,

this is $mg\tan(\theta - \theta_s)$ as desired.

Note for $\theta = \theta_s$, $h_{min} = mg\tan 0 = 0$, which makes sense since the block is at rest for θ_s, thus no additional force **H** is necessary to prevent it from moving. As θ increases, the factor $\tan(\theta - \theta_s)$, and hence the value of h_{min}, increases slowly for small values of $\theta - \theta_s$ but much more rapidly as $\theta - \theta_s$ becomes significant. This seems reasonable, as the steeper the inclined plane, the less the horizontal components of the various forces affect the movement of the block, so we would need a much larger magnitude of horizontal force to keep the block motionless. If we allow $\theta \to 90°$, corresponding to the inclined plane being placed vertically, the value of h_{min} is quite large; this is to be expected, as it takes a great amount of horizontal force to keep an object from moving vertically. In fact, without friction (so $\theta_s = 0$), we would have $\theta \to 90° \quad\Rightarrow\quad h_{min} \to \infty$, and it would be impossible to keep the block from slipping.

(d) Since h_{max} is the largest value of h that keeps the block from slipping, the force of friction is keeping the block from moving *up* the inclined plane; thus, **F** is directed *down* the plane. Our system of forces is similar to that in part (b), then, except that we have $\mathbf{F} = -(\mu_s n)\,\mathbf{i}$. (Note that $|\mathbf{F}|$ is again maximal.) Following our procedure in parts (b) and (c), we equate components:

$$-\mu_s n - mg\sin\theta + h_{max}\cos\theta = 0 \quad\Rightarrow\quad h_{max}\cos\theta - \mu_s n = mg\sin\theta$$

$$n - mg\cos\theta - h_{max}\sin\theta = 0 \quad\Rightarrow\quad h_{max}\sin\theta + mg\cos\theta = n$$

Then substituting,

$$h_{max}\cos\theta - \mu_s(h_{max}\sin\theta + mg\cos\theta) = mg\sin\theta \quad\Rightarrow$$

$$h_{max}\cos\theta - h_{max}\mu_s\sin\theta = mg\sin\theta + mg\mu_s\cos\theta \quad\Rightarrow$$

$$h_{max} = mg\left(\frac{\sin\theta + \mu_s\cos\theta}{\cos\theta - \mu_s\sin\theta}\right) = mg\left(\frac{\tan\theta + \mu_s}{1 - \mu_s\tan\theta}\right)$$

$$= mg\left(\frac{\tan\theta + \tan\theta_s}{1 - \tan\theta_s\tan\theta}\right) = mg\tan(\theta + \theta_s)$$

We would expect $h_{\max}$ to increase as θ increases, with similar behavior as we established for $h_{\min}$, but with $h_{\max}$ values always larger than $h_{\min}$. We can see that this is the case if we graph $h_{\max}$ as a function of θ, as the curve is the graph of $h_{\min}$ translated $2\theta_s$ to the left, so the equation does seem reasonable. Notice that the equation predicts $h_{\max} \to \infty$ as $\theta \to (90° - \theta_s)$. In fact, as $h_{\max}$ increases, the normal force increases as well. When $(90° - \theta_s) \leq \theta \leq 90°$, the horizontal force is completely counteracted by the sum of the normal and frictional forces, so no part of the horizontal force contributes to moving the block up the plane no matter how large its magnitude.

10 ☐ VECTOR FUNCTIONS

10.1 Vector Functions and Space Curves

1. The component functions $\sqrt{4-t^2}$, e^{-3t}, and $\ln(t+1)$ are all defined when $4-t^2 \geq 0$ $\Rightarrow$ $-2 \leq t \leq 2$ and

$t+1 > 0$ $\Rightarrow$ $t > -1$, so the domain of $\mathbf{r}$ is $(-1, 2]$.

3. $\lim\limits_{t\to\infty} \dfrac{1+t^2}{1-t^2} = \lim\limits_{t\to\infty} \dfrac{(1/t^2)+1}{(1/t^2)-1} = \dfrac{0+1}{0-1} = -1$, $\lim\limits_{t\to\infty} \tan^{-1} t = \dfrac{\pi}{2}$, $\lim\limits_{t\to\infty} \dfrac{1-e^{-2t}}{t} = \lim\limits_{t\to\infty} \dfrac{1}{t} - \dfrac{1}{te^{2t}} = 0 - 0 = 0$. Thus

$\lim\limits_{t\to\infty} \left\langle \dfrac{1+t^2}{1-t^2}, \tan^{-1} t, \dfrac{1-e^{-2t}}{t} \right\rangle = \left\langle -1, \dfrac{\pi}{2}, 0 \right\rangle$.

5. The corresponding parametric equations for this curve are $x = \sin t$, $y = t$.

We can make a table of values, or we can eliminate the parameter: $t = y$ $\Rightarrow$

$x = \sin y$, with $y \in \mathbb{R}$. By comparing different values of t, we find the direction in

which t increases as indicated in the graph.

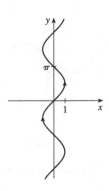

7. The corresponding parametric equations are $x = t$, $y = 2 - t$, $z = 2t$, which are

parametric equations of a line through the point $(0, 2, 0)$ and with direction vector

$\langle 1, -1, 2 \rangle$.

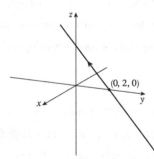

9. The corresponding parametric equations are $x = 1$, $y = \cos t$, $z = 2 \sin t$.

Eliminating the parameter in y and z gives $y^2 + (z/2)^2 = \cos^2 t + \sin^2 t = 1$

or $y^2 + z^2/4 = 1$. Since $x = 1$, the curve is an ellipse centered at $(1, 0, 0)$ in

the plane $x = 1$.

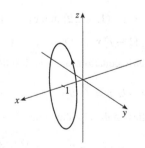

11. The parametric equations are $x = t^2$, $y = t^4$, $z = t^6$. These are positive

for $t \neq 0$ and 0 when $t = 0$. So the curve lies entirely in the first octant.

The projection of the graph onto the xy-plane is $y = x^2$, $y > 0$, a half parabola.

Onto the xz-plane $z = x^3$, $z > 0$, a half cubic, and the yz-plane, $y^3 = z^2$.

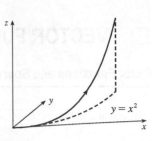

13. The projection of the curve onto the xy-plane is given by $\mathbf{r}(t) = \langle t, \sin t, 0 \rangle$ [we use 0 for the z-component] whose graph

is the curve $y = \sin x$, $z = 0$. Similarly, the projection onto the xz-plane is $\mathbf{r}(t) = \langle t, 0, 2\cos t \rangle$, whose graph is the cosine

wave $z = 2\cos x$, $y = 0$, and the projection onto the yz-plane is $\mathbf{r}(t) = \langle 0, \sin t, 2\cos t \rangle$ whose graph is the ellipse

$y^2 + \frac{1}{4}z^2 = 1$, $x = 0$.

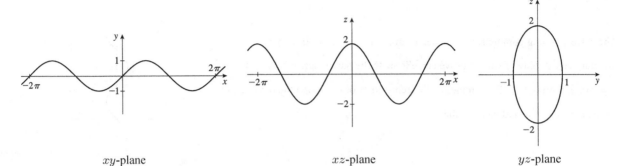

xy-plane xz-plane yz-plane

From the projection onto the yz-plane we see that the curve lies on an elliptical

cylinder with axis the x-axis. The other two projections show that the curve

oscillates both vertically and horizontally as we move in the x-direction,

suggesting that the curve is an elliptical helix that spirals along the cylinder.

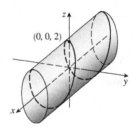

15. Taking $\mathbf{r}_0 = \langle 0, 0, 0 \rangle$ and $\mathbf{r}_1 = \langle 1, 2, 3 \rangle$, we have from Equation 9.5.4

$\mathbf{r}(t) = (1 - t)\,\mathbf{r}_0 + t\,\mathbf{r}_1 = (1 - t)\,\langle 0, 0, 0 \rangle + t\,\langle 1, 2, 3 \rangle$, $0 \le t \le 1$ or $\mathbf{r}(t) = \langle t, 2t, 3t \rangle$, $0 \le t \le 1$.

Parametric equations are $x = t$, $y = 2t$, $z = 3t$, $0 \le t \le 1$.

17. Taking $\mathbf{r}_0 = \langle 1, -1, 2 \rangle$ and $\mathbf{r}_1 = \langle 4, 1, 7 \rangle$, we have

$\mathbf{r}(t) = (1 - t)\,\mathbf{r}_0 + t\,\mathbf{r}_1 = (1 - t)\,\langle 1, -1, 2 \rangle + t\,\langle 4, 1, 7 \rangle$, $0 \le t \le 1$ or $\mathbf{r}(t) = \langle 1 + 3t, -1 + 2t, 2 + 5t \rangle$, $0 \le t \le 1$.

Parametric equations are $x = 1 + 3t$, $y = -1 + 2t$, $z = 2 + 5t$, $0 \le t \le 1$.

19. $x = t\cos t$, $y = t$, $z = t\sin t$, $t \ge 0$. At any point (x, y, z) on the curve, $x^2 + z^2 = t^2\cos^2 t + t^2\sin^2 t = t^2 = y^2$ so the

curve lies on the circular cone $x^2 + z^2 = y^2$ with axis the y-axis. Also notice that $y \ge 0$; the graph is II.

21. $x = t$, $y = 1/(1 + t^2)$, $z = t^2$. At any point on the curve we have $z = x^2$, so the curve lies on a parabolic cylinder parallel

to the y-axis. Notice that $0 < y \le 1$ and $z \ge 0$. Also the curve passes through $(0, 1, 0)$ when $t = 0$ and $y \to 0$, $z \to \infty$ as

$t \to \pm\infty$, so the graph must be V.

23. $x = \cos 8t$, $y = \sin 8t$, $z = e^{0.8t}$, $t > 0$. $x^2 + y^2 = \cos^2 8t + \sin^2 8t = 1$, so the curve lies on a circular cylinder with axis the z-axis. A point (x, y, z) on the curve lies directly above the point $(x, y, 0)$, which moves counterclockwise around the unit circle in the xy-plane as t increases. The curve starts at $(1, 0, 1)$, when $t = 0$, and $z \to \infty$ (at an increasing rate) as $t \to \infty$, so the graph is IV.

25. If $x = t \cos t$, $y = t \sin t$, $z = t$, then $x^2 + y^2 = t^2 \cos^2 t + t^2 \sin^2 t = t^2 = z^2$, so the curve lies on the cone $z^2 = x^2 + y^2$. Since $z = t$, the curve is a spiral on this cone.

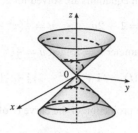

27. Parametric equations for the curve are $x = t$, $y = 0$, $z = 2t - t^2$. Substituting into the equation of the paraboloid gives $2t - t^2 = t^2 \;\Rightarrow\; 2t = 2t^2 \;\Rightarrow\; t = 0, 1$. Since $\mathbf{r}(0) = \mathbf{0}$ and $\mathbf{r}(1) = \mathbf{i} + \mathbf{k}$, the points of intersection are $(0, 0, 0)$ and $(1, 0, 1)$.

29. $\mathbf{r}(t) = \langle \cos t \sin 2t, \sin t \sin 2t, \cos 2t \rangle$.

We include both a regular plot and a plot showing a tube of radius 0.08 around the curve.

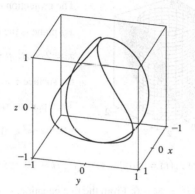
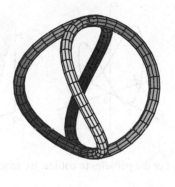

31. $\mathbf{r}(t) = \langle \cos 2t, \cos 3t, \cos 4t \rangle$

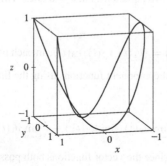

33.

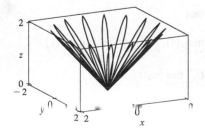

$x = (1 + \cos 16t) \cos t$, $y = (1 + \cos 16t) \sin t$, $z = 1 + \cos 16t$. At any point on the graph,

$x^2 + y^2 = (1 + \cos 16t)^2 \cos^2 t + (1 + \cos 16t)^2 \sin^2 t$

$= (1 + \cos 16t)^2 = z^2$, so the graph lies on the cone $x^2 + y^2 = z^2$.

From the graph at left, we see that this curve looks like the projection of a leaved two-dimensional curve onto a cone.

35. If $t = -1$, then $x = 1$, $y = 4$, $z = 0$, so the curve passes through the point $(1, 4, 0)$. If $t = 3$, then $x = 9$, $y = -8$, $z = 28$, so the curve passes through the point $(9, -8, 28)$. For the point $(4, 7, -6)$ to be on the curve, we require $y = 1 - 3t = 7 \Rightarrow t = -2$. But then $z = 1 + (-2)^3 = -7 \neq -6$, so $(4, 7, -6)$ is not on the curve.

37. Both equations are solved for z, so we can substitute to eliminate z: $\sqrt{x^2 + y^2} = 1 + y \Rightarrow x^2 + y^2 = 1 + 2y + y^2 \Rightarrow$ $x^2 = 1 + 2y \Rightarrow y = \frac{1}{2}(x^2 - 1)$. We can form parametric equations for the curve C of intersection by choosing a parameter $x = t$, then $y = \frac{1}{2}(t^2 - 1)$ and $z = 1 + y = 1 + \frac{1}{2}(t^2 - 1) = \frac{1}{2}(t^2 + 1)$. Thus a vector function representing C is $\mathbf{r}(t) = t\,\mathbf{i} + \frac{1}{2}(t^2 - 1)\,\mathbf{j} + \frac{1}{2}(t^2 + 1)\,\mathbf{k}$.

39. The projection of the curve C of intersection onto the xy-plane is the circle $x^2 + y^2 = 1$, $z = 0$, so we can write $x = \cos t$, $y = \sin t$, $0 \leq t \leq 2\pi$. Since C also lies on the surface $z = x^2 - y^2$, we have $z = x^2 - y^2 = \cos^2 t - \sin^2 t$ or $\cos 2t$. Thus parametric equations for C are $x = \cos t$, $y = \sin t$, $z = \cos 2t$, $0 \leq t \leq 2\pi$, and the corresponding vector function is $\mathbf{r}(t) = \cos t\,\mathbf{i} + \sin t\,\mathbf{j} + \cos 2t\,\mathbf{k}$, $0 \leq t \leq 2\pi$.

41.

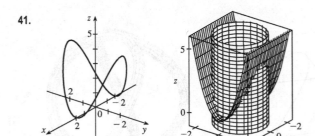

The projection of the curve C of intersection onto the xy-plane is the circle $x^2 + y^2 = 4$, $z = 0$. Then we can write $x = 2\cos t$, $y = 2\sin t$, $0 \leq t \leq 2\pi$. Since C also lies on the surface $z = x^2$, we have $z = x^2 = (2\cos t)^2 = 4\cos^2 t$. Then parametric equations for C are $x = 2\cos t$, $y = 2\sin t$, $z = 4\cos^2 t$, $0 \leq t \leq 2\pi$.

43. For the particles to collide, we require $\mathbf{r}_1(t) = \mathbf{r}_2(t) \Leftrightarrow \langle t^2, 7t - 12, t^2 \rangle = \langle 4t - 3, t^2, 5t - 6 \rangle$. Equating components gives $t^2 = 4t - 3$, $7t - 12 = t^2$, and $t^2 = 5t - 6$. From the first equation, $t^2 - 4t + 3 = 0 \Leftrightarrow (t - 3)(t - 1) = 0$ so $t = 1$ or $t = 3$. $t = 1$ does not satisfy the other two equations, but $t = 3$ does. The particles collide when $t = 3$, at the point $(9, 9, 9)$.

45. Let $\mathbf{u}(t) = \langle u_1(t), u_2(t), u_3(t) \rangle$ and $\mathbf{v}(t) = \langle v_1(t), v_2(t), v_3(t) \rangle$. In each part of this problem the basic procedure is to use Equation 1 and then analyze the individual component functions using the limit properties we have already developed for real-valued functions.

(a) $\lim\limits_{t \to a} \mathbf{u}(t) + \lim\limits_{t \to a} \mathbf{v}(t) = \left\langle \lim\limits_{t \to a} u_1(t), \lim\limits_{t \to a} u_2(t), \lim\limits_{t \to a} u_3(t) \right\rangle + \left\langle \lim\limits_{t \to a} v_1(t), \lim\limits_{t \to a} v_2(t), \lim\limits_{t \to a} v_3(t) \right\rangle$ and the limits of these component functions must each exist since the vector functions both possess limits as $t \to a$. Then adding the two vectors and using the addition property of limits for real-valued functions, we have that

$$\lim\limits_{t \to a} \mathbf{u}(t) + \lim\limits_{t \to a} \mathbf{v}(t) = \left\langle \lim\limits_{t \to a} u_1(t) + \lim\limits_{t \to a} v_1(t), \lim\limits_{t \to a} u_2(t) + \lim\limits_{t \to a} v_2(t), \lim\limits_{t \to a} u_3(t) + \lim\limits_{t \to a} v_3(t) \right\rangle$$

$$= \left\langle \lim\limits_{t \to a} [u_1(t) + v_1(t)], \lim\limits_{t \to a} [u_2(t) + v_2(t)], \lim\limits_{t \to a} [u_3(t) + v_3(t)] \right\rangle$$

$$= \lim\limits_{t \to a} \langle u_1(t) + v_1(t), u_2(t) + v_2(t), u_3(t) + v_3(t) \rangle \qquad \text{[using (1) backward]}$$

$$= \lim\limits_{t \to a} [\mathbf{u}(t) + \mathbf{v}(t)]$$

(b) $\displaystyle\lim_{t\to a} c\mathbf{u}(t) = \lim_{t\to a} \langle cu_1(t), cu_2(t), cu_3(t)\rangle = \left\langle \lim_{t\to a} cu_1(t), \lim_{t\to a} cu_2(t), \lim_{t\to a} cu_3(t)\right\rangle$

$\qquad\qquad = \left\langle c\lim_{t\to a} u_1(t), c\lim_{t\to a} u_2(t), c\lim_{t\to a} u_3(t)\right\rangle = c\left\langle \lim_{t\to a} u_1(t), \lim_{t\to a} u_2(t), \lim_{t\to a} u_3(t)\right\rangle$

$\qquad\qquad = c\lim_{t\to a} \langle u_1(t), u_2(t), u_3(t)\rangle = c\lim_{t\to a} \mathbf{u}(t)$

(c) $\displaystyle\lim_{t\to a} \mathbf{u}(t) \cdot \lim_{t\to a} \mathbf{v}(t) = \left\langle \lim_{t\to a} u_1(t), \lim_{t\to a} u_2(t), \lim_{t\to a} u_3(t)\right\rangle \cdot \left\langle \lim_{t\to a} v_1(t), \lim_{t\to a} v_2(t), \lim_{t\to a} v_3(t)\right\rangle$

$\qquad\qquad = \left[\lim_{t\to a} u_1(t)\right]\left[\lim_{t\to a} v_1(t)\right] + \left[\lim_{t\to a} u_2(t)\right]\left[\lim_{t\to a} v_2(t)\right] + \left[\lim_{t\to a} u_3(t)\right]\left[\lim_{t\to a} v_3(t)\right]$

$\qquad\qquad = \lim_{t\to a} u_1(t)v_1(t) + \lim_{t\to a} u_2(t)v_2(t) + \lim_{t\to a} u_3(t)v_3(t)$

$\qquad\qquad = \lim_{t\to a} [u_1(t)v_1(t) + u_2(t)v_2(t) + u_3(t)v_3(t)] = \lim_{t\to a} [\mathbf{u}(t)\cdot\mathbf{v}(t)]$

(d) $\displaystyle\lim_{t\to a} \mathbf{u}(t) \times \lim_{t\to a} \mathbf{v}(t) = \left\langle \lim_{t\to a} u_1(t), \lim_{t\to a} u_2(t), \lim_{t\to a} u_3(t)\right\rangle \times \left\langle \lim_{t\to a} v_1(t), \lim_{t\to a} v_2(t), \lim_{t\to a} v_3(t)\right\rangle$

$\qquad\qquad = \left\langle \left[\lim_{t\to a} u_2(t)\right]\left[\lim_{t\to a} v_3(t)\right] - \left[\lim_{t\to a} u_3(t)\right]\left[\lim_{t\to a} v_2(t)\right],\right.$

$\qquad\qquad\qquad \left[\lim_{t\to a} u_3(t)\right]\left[\lim_{t\to a} v_1(t)\right] - \left[\lim_{t\to a} u_1(t)\right]\left[\lim_{t\to a} v_3(t)\right],$

$\qquad\qquad\qquad \left.\left[\lim_{t\to a} u_1(t)\right]\left[\lim_{t\to a} v_2(t)\right] - \left[\lim_{t\to a} u_2(t)\right]\left[\lim_{t\to a} v_1(t)\right]\right\rangle$

$\qquad\qquad = \left\langle \lim_{t\to a} [u_2(t)v_3(t) - u_3(t)v_2(t)], \lim_{t\to a} [u_3(t)v_1(t) - u_1(t)v_3(t)],\right.$

$\qquad\qquad\qquad \left.\lim_{t\to a} [u_1(t)v_2(t) - u_2(t)v_1(t)]\right\rangle$

$\qquad\qquad = \lim_{t\to a} \langle u_2(t)v_3(t) - u_3(t)v_2(t), u_3(t)v_1(t) - u_1(t)v_3(t), u_1(t)v_2(t) - u_2(t)v_1(t)\rangle$

$\qquad\qquad = \lim_{t\to a} [\mathbf{u}(t) \times \mathbf{v}(t)]$

10.2 Derivatives and Integrals of Vector Functions

1. (a)

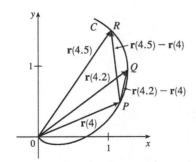

(b) $\dfrac{\mathbf{r}(4.5) - \mathbf{r}(4)}{0.5} = 2[\mathbf{r}(4.5) - \mathbf{r}(4)]$, so we draw a vector in the same

direction but with twice the length of the vector $\mathbf{r}(4.5) - \mathbf{r}(4)$.

$\dfrac{\mathbf{r}(4.2) - \mathbf{r}(4)}{0.2} = 5[\mathbf{r}(4.2) - \mathbf{r}(4)]$, so we draw a vector in the same

direction but with 5 times the length of the vector $\mathbf{r}(4.2) - \mathbf{r}(4)$.

(c) By Definition 1, $\mathbf{r}'(4) = \displaystyle\lim_{h\to 0} \dfrac{\mathbf{r}(4+h) - \mathbf{r}(4)}{h}$ $\quad \mathbf{T}(4) = \dfrac{\mathbf{r}'(4)}{|\mathbf{r}'(4)|}$

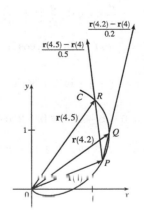

(d) $\mathbf{T}(4)$ is a unit vector in the same direction as $\mathbf{r}'(4)$, that is, parallel to the tangent line to the curve at $\mathbf{r}(4)$ with length 1.

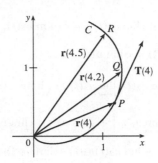

3. Since $(x+2)^2 = t^2 = y - 1 \;\Rightarrow$ (a), (c)

$y = (x+2)^2 - 1$, the curve is a

parabola.

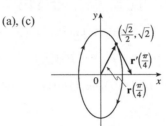

(b) $\mathbf{r}'(t) = \langle 1, 2t \rangle$,

    $\mathbf{r}'(-1) = \langle 1, -2 \rangle$

5. $x = \sin t, \;\; y = 2\cos t$ so   (a), (c)

$x^2 + (y/2)^2 = 1$ and the curve is

an ellipse.

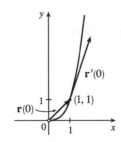

(b) $\mathbf{r}'(t) = \cos t\,\mathbf{i} - 2\sin t\,\mathbf{j}$,

    $\mathbf{r}'\!\left(\dfrac{\pi}{4}\right) = \dfrac{\sqrt{2}}{2}\,\mathbf{i} - \sqrt{2}\,\mathbf{j}$

7. Since $y = e^{3t} = (e^t)^3 = x^3$, the   (a), (c)

curve is part of a cubic cuve. Note

that here, $x > 0$.

(b) $\mathbf{r}'(t) = e^t\,\mathbf{i} + 3e^{3t}\,\mathbf{j}$,

    $\mathbf{r}'(0) = \mathbf{i} + 3\,\mathbf{j}$

9. $\mathbf{r}'(t) = \left\langle \dfrac{d}{dt}\,[t\sin t], \dfrac{d}{dt}\,[t^2], \dfrac{d}{dt}\,[t\cos 2t] \right\rangle = \langle t\cos t + \sin t, 2t, t(-\sin 2t)\cdot 2 + \cos 2t \rangle$

        $= \langle t\cos t + \sin t, 2t, \cos 2t - 2t\sin 2t \rangle$

11. $\mathbf{r}(t) = e^{t^2}\,\mathbf{i} - \mathbf{j} + \ln(1+3t)\,\mathbf{k} \;\;\Rightarrow\;\; \mathbf{r}'(t) = 2te^{t^2}\,\mathbf{i} + \dfrac{3}{1+3t}\,\mathbf{k}$

13. $\mathbf{r}'(t) = \mathbf{0} + \mathbf{b} + 2t\,\mathbf{c} = \mathbf{b} + 2t\,\mathbf{c}$ by Formulas 1 and 3 of Theorem 3.

15. $\mathbf{r}'(t) = \langle -te^{-t} + e^{-t}, 2/(1+t^2), 2e^t \rangle \;\;\Rightarrow\;\; \mathbf{r}'(0) = \langle 1, 2, 2 \rangle$. So $|\mathbf{r}'(0)| = \sqrt{1^2 + 2^2 + 2^2} = \sqrt{9} = 3$ and

    $\mathbf{T}(0) = \dfrac{\mathbf{r}'(0)}{|\mathbf{r}'(0)|} = \tfrac{1}{3}\,\langle 1, 2, 2 \rangle = \left\langle \tfrac{1}{3}, \tfrac{2}{3}, \tfrac{2}{3} \right\rangle$.

17. $\mathbf{r}'(t) = -\sin t\,\mathbf{i} + 3\,\mathbf{j} + 4\cos 2t\,\mathbf{k} \quad\Rightarrow\quad \mathbf{r}'(0) = 3\,\mathbf{j} + 4\,\mathbf{k}$. Thus

$$\mathbf{T}(0) = \frac{\mathbf{r}'(0)}{|\mathbf{r}'(0)|} = \frac{1}{\sqrt{0^2 + 3^2 + 4^2}}\,(3\,\mathbf{j} + 4\,\mathbf{k}) = \tfrac{1}{5}(3\,\mathbf{j} + 4\,\mathbf{k}) = \tfrac{3}{5}\,\mathbf{j} + \tfrac{4}{5}\,\mathbf{k}.$$

19. $\mathbf{r}(t) = \langle t, e^t, te^t \rangle \quad\Rightarrow\quad \mathbf{r}'(t) = \langle 1, e^t, (t+1)e^t \rangle$. Then $\mathbf{r}'(0) = \langle 1,1,1 \rangle$ and $|\mathbf{r}'(0)| = \sqrt{1^2 + 1^2 + 1^2} = \sqrt{3}$, so

$$\mathbf{T}(0) = \frac{\mathbf{r}'(0)}{|\mathbf{r}'(0)|} = \tfrac{1}{\sqrt{3}}\,\langle 1,1,1 \rangle = \left\langle \tfrac{1}{\sqrt{3}}, \tfrac{1}{\sqrt{3}}, \tfrac{1}{\sqrt{3}} \right\rangle. \quad \mathbf{r}''(t) = \langle 0, e^t, (t+2)e^t \rangle, \text{ so}$$

$$\mathbf{r}'(t) \cdot \mathbf{r}''(t) = \langle 1, e^t, (t+1)e^t \rangle \cdot \langle 0, e^t, (t+2)e^t \rangle = (1)(0) + (e^t)(e^t) + ((t+1)e^t)((t+2)e^t)$$

$$= 0 + e^{2t} + (t+1)(t+2)e^{2t} = (t^2 + 3t + 3)e^{2t}$$

21. The vector equation for the curve is $\mathbf{r}(t) = \langle 1 + 2\sqrt{t}, t^3 - t, t^3 + t \rangle$, so $\mathbf{r}'(t) = \langle 1/\sqrt{t}, 3t^2 - 1, 3t^2 + 1 \rangle$. The point $(3,0,2)$ corresponds to $t = 1$, so the tangent vector there is $\mathbf{r}'(1) = \langle 1, 2, 4 \rangle$. Thus, the tangent line goes through the point $(3,0,2)$ and is parallel to the vector $\langle 1, 2, 4 \rangle$. Parametric equations are $x = 3 + t$, $y = 2t$, $z = 2 + 4t$.

23. The vector equation for the curve is $\mathbf{r}(t) = \langle e^{-t}\cos t, e^{-t}\sin t, e^{-t} \rangle$, so

$$\mathbf{r}'(t) = \langle e^{-t}(-\sin t) + (\cos t)(-e^{-t}), e^{-t}\cos t + (\sin t)(-e^{-t}), (-e^{-t}) \rangle$$

$$= \langle -e^{-t}(\cos t + \sin t), e^{-t}(\cos t - \sin t), -e^{-t} \rangle$$

The point $(1,0,1)$ corresponds to $t = 0$, so the tangent vector there is

$\mathbf{r}'(0) = \langle -e^0(\cos 0 + \sin 0), e^0(\cos 0 - \sin 0), -e^0 \rangle = \langle -1, 1, -1 \rangle$. Thus, the tangent line is parallel to the vector $\langle -1, 1, -1 \rangle$ and parametric equations are $x = 1 + (-1)t = 1 - t$, $y = 0 + 1 \cdot t = t$, $z = 1 + (-1)t = 1 - t$.

25. First we parametrize the curve C of intersection. The projection of C onto the xy-plane is contained in the circle $x^2 + y^2 = 25$, $z = 0$, so we can write $x = 5\cos t$, $y = 5\sin t$. C also lies on the cylinder $y^2 + z^2 = 20$, and $z \ge 0$ near the point $(3,4,2)$, so we can write $z = \sqrt{20 - y^2} = \sqrt{20 - 25\sin^2 t}$. A vector equation then for C is

$$\mathbf{r}(t) = \left\langle 5\cos t, 5\sin t, \sqrt{20 - 25\sin^2 t} \right\rangle \quad\Rightarrow\quad \mathbf{r}'(t) = \left\langle -5\sin t, 5\cos t, \tfrac{1}{2}(20 - 25\sin^2 t)^{-1/2}(-50\sin t \cos t) \right\rangle.$$

The point $(3,4,2)$ corresponds to $t = \cos^{-1}\left(\tfrac{3}{5}\right)$, so the tangent vector there is

$$\mathbf{r}'\left(\cos^{-1}\left(\tfrac{3}{5}\right)\right) = \left\langle -5\left(\tfrac{4}{5}\right), 5\left(\tfrac{3}{5}\right), \tfrac{1}{2}\left(20 - 25\left(\tfrac{4}{5}\right)^2\right)^{-1/2}\left(-50\left(\tfrac{4}{5}\right)\left(\tfrac{3}{5}\right)\right) \right\rangle = \langle -4, 3, -6 \rangle.$$

The tangent line is parallel to this vector and passes through $(3,4,2)$, so a vector equation for the line is $\mathbf{r}(t) = (3 - 4t)\mathbf{i} + (4 + 3t)\mathbf{j} + (2 - 6t)\mathbf{k}$.

27. $\mathbf{r}(t) = \langle t, e^{-t}, 2t - t^2 \rangle \quad\Rightarrow\quad \mathbf{r}'(t) = \langle 1, -e^{-t}, 2 - 2t \rangle$. At $(0, 1, 0)$, $t = 0$ and $\mathbf{r}'(0) = \langle 1, -1, 2 \rangle$. Thus, parametric equations of the tangent line are $x = t$, $y = 1 - t$, $z = 2t$.

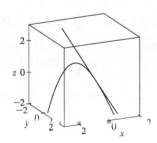

29. $\mathbf{r}(t) = \langle t \cos t, t, t \sin t \rangle \;\Rightarrow\; \mathbf{r}'(t) = \langle \cos t - t \sin t, 1, t \cos t + \sin t \rangle$.

At $(-\pi, \pi, 0)$, $t = \pi$ and $\mathbf{r}'(\pi) = \langle -1, 1, -\pi \rangle$. Thus, parametric equations

of the tangent line are $x = -\pi - t$, $y = \pi + t$, $z = -\pi t$.

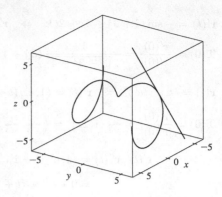

31. The angle of intersection of the two curves is the angle between the two tangent vectors to the curves at the point of

intersection. Since $\mathbf{r}_1'(t) = \langle 1, 2t, 3t^2 \rangle$ and $t = 0$ at $(0, 0, 0)$, $\mathbf{r}_1'(0) = \langle 1, 0, 0 \rangle$ is a tangent vector to $\mathbf{r}_1$ at $(0, 0, 0)$. Similarly,

$\mathbf{r}_2'(t) = \langle \cos t, 2 \cos 2t, 1 \rangle$ and since $\mathbf{r}_2(0) = \langle 0, 0, 0 \rangle$, $\mathbf{r}_2'(0) = \langle 1, 2, 1 \rangle$ is a tangent vector to $\mathbf{r}_2$ at $(0, 0, 0)$. If θ is the angle

between these two tangent vectors, then $\cos \theta = \frac{1}{\sqrt{1}\sqrt{6}} \langle 1, 0, 0 \rangle \cdot \langle 1, 2, 1 \rangle = \frac{1}{\sqrt{6}}$ and $\theta = \cos^{-1}\left(\frac{1}{\sqrt{6}}\right) \approx 66°$.

33. $\int_0^1 (16t^3 \,\mathbf{i} - 9t^2 \,\mathbf{j} + 25t^4 \,\mathbf{k}) \, dt = \left(\int_0^1 16t^3 \, dt\right)\mathbf{i} - \left(\int_0^1 9t^2 \, dt\right)\mathbf{j} + \left(\int_0^1 25t^4 \, dt\right)\mathbf{k}$

$$= \left[4t^4\right]_0^1 \mathbf{i} - \left[3t^3\right]_0^1 \mathbf{j} + \left[5t^5\right]_0^1 \mathbf{k} = 4\,\mathbf{i} - 3\,\mathbf{j} + 5\,\mathbf{k}$$

35. $\int_0^{\pi/2} (3 \sin^2 t \cos t \,\mathbf{i} + 3 \sin t \cos^2 t \,\mathbf{j} + 2 \sin t \cos t \,\mathbf{k}) \, dt$

$$= \left(\int_0^{\pi/2} 3 \sin^2 t \cos t \, dt\right)\mathbf{i} + \left(\int_0^{\pi/2} 3 \sin t \cos^2 t \, dt\right)\mathbf{j} + \left(\int_0^{\pi/2} 2 \sin t \cos t \, dt\right)\mathbf{k}$$

$$= \left[\sin^3 t\right]_0^{\pi/2} \mathbf{i} + \left[-\cos^3 t\right]_0^{\pi/2}\mathbf{j} + \left[\sin^2 t\right]_0^{\pi/2} \mathbf{k} = (1-0)\,\mathbf{i} + (0+1)\,\mathbf{j} + (1-0)\,\mathbf{k} = \mathbf{i} + \mathbf{j} + \mathbf{k}$$

37. $\int (\sec^2 t \,\mathbf{i} + t(t^2 + 1)^3 \,\mathbf{j} + t^2 \ln t \,\mathbf{k}) \, dt = \left(\int \sec^2 t \, dt\right)\mathbf{i} + \left(\int t(t^2 + 1)^3 \, dt\right)\mathbf{j} + \left(\int t^2 \ln t \, dt\right)\mathbf{k}$

$$= \tan t \,\mathbf{i} + \tfrac{1}{8}(t^2 + 1)^4 \,\mathbf{j} + \left(\tfrac{1}{3}t^3 \ln t - \tfrac{1}{9}t^3\right)\mathbf{k} + \mathbf{C},$$

where $\mathbf{C}$ is a vector constant of integration. [For the z-component, integrate by parts with $u = \ln t$, $dv = t^2 \, dt$.]

39. $\mathbf{r}'(t) = 2t\,\mathbf{i} + 3t^2\,\mathbf{j} + \sqrt{t}\,\mathbf{k} \;\Rightarrow\; \mathbf{r}(t) = t^2\,\mathbf{i} + t^3\,\mathbf{j} + \tfrac{2}{3}t^{3/2}\,\mathbf{k} + \mathbf{C}$, where $\mathbf{C}$ is a constant vector.

But $\mathbf{i} + \mathbf{j} = \mathbf{r}(1) = \mathbf{i} + \mathbf{j} + \tfrac{2}{3}\mathbf{k} + \mathbf{C}$. Thus $\mathbf{C} = -\tfrac{2}{3}\mathbf{k}$ and $\mathbf{r}(t) = t^2\,\mathbf{i} + t^3\,\mathbf{j} + \left(\tfrac{2}{3}t^{3/2} - \tfrac{2}{3}\right)\mathbf{k}$.

For Exercises 41–44, let $\mathbf{u}(t) = \langle u_1(t), u_2(t), u_3(t) \rangle$ and $\mathbf{v}(t) = \langle v_1(t), v_2(t), v_3(t) \rangle$. In each of these exercises, the procedure is to apply Theorem 2 so that the corresponding properties of derivatives of real-valued functions can be used.

41. $\dfrac{d}{dt}\,[\mathbf{u}(t) + \mathbf{v}(t)] = \dfrac{d}{dt}\,\langle u_1(t) + v_1(t), u_2(t) + v_2(t), u_3(t) + v_3(t) \rangle$

$$= \left\langle \dfrac{d}{dt}\,[u_1(t) + v_1(t)], \dfrac{d}{dt}\,[u_2(t) + v_2(t)], \dfrac{d}{dt}\,[u_3(t) + v_3(t)] \right\rangle$$

$$= \langle u_1'(t) + v_1'(t), u_2'(t) + v_2'(t), u_3'(t) + v_3'(t) \rangle$$

$$= \langle u_1'(t), u_2'(t), u_3'(t) \rangle + \langle v_1'(t), v_2'(t), v_3'(t) \rangle = \mathbf{u}'(t) + \mathbf{v}'(t)$$

43. $\dfrac{d}{dt}\left[\mathbf{u}(t)\times\mathbf{v}(t)\right] = \dfrac{d}{dt}\langle u_2(t)v_3(t)-u_3(t)v_2(t),\, u_3(t)v_1(t)-u_1(t)v_3(t),\, u_1(t)v_2(t)-u_2(t)v_1(t)\rangle$

$$= \langle u_2'(t)v_3(t)+u_2(t)v_3'(t)-u_3'(t)v_2(t)-u_3(t)v_2'(t),$$
$$u_3'(t)v_1(t)+u_3(t)v_1'(t)-u_1'(t)v_3(t)-u_1(t)v_3'(t),$$
$$u_1'(t)v_2(t)+u_1(t)v_2'(t)-u_2'(t)v_1(t)-u_2(t)v_1'(t)\rangle$$

$$= \langle u_2'(t)v_3(t)-u_3'(t)v_2(t),\, u_3'(t)v_1(t)-u_1'(t)v_3(t),\, u_1'(t)v_2(t)-u_2'(t)v_1(t)\rangle$$
$$+ \langle u_2(t)v_3'(t)-u_3(t)v_2'(t),\, u_3(t)v_1'(t)-u_1(t)v_3'(t),\, u_1(t)v_2'(t)-u_2(t)v_1'(t)\rangle$$

$$= \mathbf{u}'(t)\times\mathbf{v}(t)+\mathbf{u}(t)\times\mathbf{v}'(t)$$

Alternate solution: Let $\mathbf{r}(t)=\mathbf{u}(t)\times\mathbf{v}(t)$. Then

$$\mathbf{r}(t+h)-\mathbf{r}(t)=[\mathbf{u}(t+h)\times\mathbf{v}(t+h)]-[\mathbf{u}(t)\times\mathbf{v}(t)]$$
$$=[\mathbf{u}(t+h)\times\mathbf{v}(t+h)]-[\mathbf{u}(t)\times\mathbf{v}(t)]+[\mathbf{u}(t+h)\times\mathbf{v}(t)]-[\mathbf{u}(t+h)\times\mathbf{v}(t)]$$
$$=\mathbf{u}(t+h)\times[\mathbf{v}(t+h)-\mathbf{v}(t)]+[\mathbf{u}(t+h)-\mathbf{u}(t)]\times\mathbf{v}(t)$$

(Be careful of the order of the cross product.) Dividing through by h and taking the limit as $h\to 0$ we have

$$\mathbf{r}'(t)=\lim_{h\to 0}\frac{\mathbf{u}(t+h)\times[\mathbf{v}(t+h)-\mathbf{v}(t)]}{h}+\lim_{h\to 0}\frac{[\mathbf{u}(t+h)-\mathbf{u}(t)]\times\mathbf{v}(t)}{h}=\mathbf{u}(t)\times\mathbf{v}'(t)+\mathbf{u}'(t)\times\mathbf{v}(t)$$

by Exercise 10.1.45(a) and Definition 1.

45. $\dfrac{d}{dt}\left[\mathbf{u}(t)\cdot\mathbf{v}(t)\right]=\mathbf{u}'(t)\cdot\mathbf{v}(t)+\mathbf{u}(t)\cdot\mathbf{v}'(t)$ \quad [by Formula 4 of Theorem 3]

$$= \langle\cos t,-\sin t,1\rangle\cdot\langle t,\cos t,\sin t\rangle+\langle\sin t,\cos t,t\rangle\cdot\langle 1,-\sin t,\cos t\rangle$$
$$= t\cos t-\cos t\sin t+\sin t+\sin t-\cos t\sin t+t\cos t$$
$$= 2t\cos t+2\sin t-2\cos t\sin t$$

47. By Formula 4 of Theorem 3, $f'(t)=\mathbf{u}'(t)\cdot\mathbf{v}(t)+\mathbf{u}(t)\cdot\mathbf{v}'(t)$, and $\mathbf{v}'(t)=\langle 1,2t,3t^2\rangle$, so

$$f'(2)=\mathbf{u}'(2)\cdot\mathbf{v}(2)+\mathbf{u}(2)\cdot\mathbf{v}'(2)=\langle 3,0,4\rangle\cdot\langle 2,4,8\rangle+\langle 1,2,-1\rangle\cdot\langle 1,4,12\rangle=6+0+32+1+8-12=35.$$

49. $\dfrac{d}{dt}\left[\mathbf{r}(t)\times\mathbf{r}'(t)\right]=\mathbf{r}'(t)\times\mathbf{r}'(t)+\mathbf{r}(t)\times\mathbf{r}''(t)$ by Formula 5 of Theorem 3. But $\mathbf{r}'(t)\times\mathbf{r}'(t)=\mathbf{0}$ (by the margin note on

page 655). Thus, $\dfrac{d}{dt}\left[\mathbf{r}(t)\times\mathbf{r}'(t)\right]=\mathbf{r}(t)\times\mathbf{r}''(t).$

51. $\dfrac{d}{dt}|\mathbf{r}(t)|=\dfrac{d}{dt}[\mathbf{r}(t)\cdot\mathbf{r}(t)]^{1/2}=\tfrac{1}{2}[\mathbf{r}(t)\cdot\mathbf{r}(t)]^{-1/2}[2\mathbf{r}(t)\cdot\mathbf{r}'(t)]=\dfrac{1}{|\mathbf{r}(t)|}\mathbf{r}(t)\cdot\mathbf{r}'(t)$

53. Since $\mathbf{u}(t)=\mathbf{r}(t)\cdot[\mathbf{r}'(t)\times\mathbf{r}''(t)]$,

$$\mathbf{u}'(t)=\mathbf{r}'(t)\cdot[\mathbf{r}'(t)\times\mathbf{r}''(t)]+\mathbf{r}(t)\cdot\dfrac{d}{dt}[\mathbf{r}'(t)\times\mathbf{r}''(t)]$$
$$=0+\mathbf{r}(t)\cdot[\mathbf{r}''(t)\times\mathbf{r}''(t)+\mathbf{r}'(t)\times\mathbf{r}'''(t)]\qquad[\text{since }\mathbf{r}'(t)\perp\mathbf{r}'(t)\times\mathbf{r}''(t)]$$
$$=\mathbf{r}(t)\cdot[\mathbf{r}'(t)\times\mathbf{r}'''(t)]\qquad[\text{since }\mathbf{r}''(t)\times\mathbf{r}''(t)=\mathbf{0}]$$

10.3 Arc Length and Curvature

1. $\mathbf{r}(t) = \langle 2\sin t, 5t, 2\cos t \rangle \;\Rightarrow\; \mathbf{r}'(t) = \langle 2\cos t, 5, -2\sin t \rangle \;\Rightarrow\; |\mathbf{r}'(t)| = \sqrt{(2\cos t)^2 + 5^2 + (-2\sin t)^2} = \sqrt{29}$.

Then using Formula 3, we have $L = \int_{-10}^{10} |\mathbf{r}'(t)|\, dt = \int_{-10}^{10} \sqrt{29}\, dt = \sqrt{29}\, t\Big]_{-10}^{10} = 20\sqrt{29}$.

3. $\mathbf{r}(t) = \sqrt{2}\, t\,\mathbf{i} + e^t\mathbf{j} + e^{-t}\mathbf{k} \;\Rightarrow\; \mathbf{r}'(t) = \sqrt{2}\,\mathbf{i} + e^t\mathbf{j} - e^{-t}\mathbf{k} \;\Rightarrow$

$|\mathbf{r}'(t)| = \sqrt{\left(\sqrt{2}\right)^2 + (e^t)^2 + (-e^{-t})^2} = \sqrt{2 + e^{2t} + e^{-2t}} = \sqrt{(e^t + e^{-t})^2} = e^t + e^{-t}$ [since $e^t + e^{-t} > 0$].

Then $L = \int_0^1 |\mathbf{r}'(t)|\, dt = \int_0^1 (e^t + e^{-t})\, dt = \left[e^t - e^{-t}\right]_0^1 = e - e^{-1}$.

5. $\mathbf{r}(t) = \mathbf{i} + t^2\mathbf{j} + t^3\mathbf{k} \;\Rightarrow\; \mathbf{r}'(t) = 2t\mathbf{j} + 3t^2\mathbf{k} \;\Rightarrow\; |\mathbf{r}'(t)| = \sqrt{4t^2 + 9t^4} = t\sqrt{4 + 9t^2}$ [since $t \geq 0$].

Then $L = \int_0^1 |\mathbf{r}'(t)|\, dt = \int_0^1 t\sqrt{4 + 9t^2}\, dt = \frac{1}{18} \cdot \frac{2}{3}(4 + 9t^2)^{3/2}\Big]_0^1 = \frac{1}{27}(13^{3/2} - 4^{3/2}) = \frac{1}{27}(13^{3/2} - 8)$.

7. $\mathbf{r}(t) = \langle \sqrt{t}, t, t^2 \rangle \;\Rightarrow\; \mathbf{r}'(t) = \left\langle \dfrac{1}{2\sqrt{t}}, 1, 2t \right\rangle \;\Rightarrow\; |\mathbf{r}'(t)| = \sqrt{\left(\frac{1}{2\sqrt{t}}\right)^2 + 1^2 + (2t)^2} = \sqrt{\frac{1}{4t} + 1 + 4t^2}$, so

$L = \int_1^4 |\mathbf{r}'(t)|\, dt = \int_1^4 \sqrt{\frac{1}{4t} + 1 + 4t^2}\, dt \approx 15.3841$.

9. $\mathbf{r}(t) = \langle \sin t, \cos t, \tan t \rangle \;\Rightarrow\; \mathbf{r}'(t) = \langle \cos t, -\sin t, \sec^2 t \rangle \;\Rightarrow$

$|\mathbf{r}'(t)| = \sqrt{\cos^2 t + (-\sin t)^2 + (\sec^2 t)^2} = \sqrt{1 + \sec^4 t}$ and $L = \int_0^{\pi/4} |\mathbf{r}'(t)|\, dt = \int_0^{\pi/4} \sqrt{1 + \sec^4 t}\, dt \approx 1.2780$.

11. The projection of the curve C onto the xy-plane is the curve $x^2 = 2y$ or $y = \frac{1}{2}x^2$, $z = 0$. Then we can choose the parameter

$x = t \;\Rightarrow\; y = \frac{1}{2}t^2$. Since C also lies on the surface $3z = xy$, we have $z = \frac{1}{3}xy = \frac{1}{3}(t)(\frac{1}{2}t^2) = \frac{1}{6}t^3$. Then parametric

equations for C are $x = t$, $y = \frac{1}{2}t^2$, $z = \frac{1}{6}t^3$ and the corresponding vector equation is $\mathbf{r}(t) = \langle t, \frac{1}{2}t^2, \frac{1}{6}t^3 \rangle$. The origin

corresponds to $t = 0$ and the point $(6, 18, 36)$ corresponds to $t = 6$, so

$$L = \int_0^6 |\mathbf{r}'(t)|\, dt = \int_0^6 \left|\langle 1, t, \tfrac{1}{2}t^2 \rangle\right| dt = \int_0^6 \sqrt{1^2 + t^2 + \left(\tfrac{1}{2}t^2\right)^2}\, dt = \int_0^6 \sqrt{1 + t^2 + \tfrac{1}{4}t^4}\, dt$$

$$= \int_0^6 \sqrt{\left(1 + \tfrac{1}{2}t^2\right)^2}\, dt = \int_0^6 \left(1 + \tfrac{1}{2}t^2\right) dt = \left[t + \tfrac{1}{6}t^3\right]_0^6 = 6 + 36 = 42$$

13. $\mathbf{r}(t) = 2t\mathbf{i} + (1 - 3t)\mathbf{j} + (5 + 4t)\mathbf{k} \;\Rightarrow\; \mathbf{r}'(t) = 2\mathbf{i} - 3\mathbf{j} + 4\mathbf{k}$ and $\dfrac{ds}{dt} = |\mathbf{r}'(t)| = \sqrt{4 + 9 + 16} = \sqrt{29}$. Then

$s = s(t) = \int_0^t |\mathbf{r}'(u)|\, du = \int_0^t \sqrt{29}\, du = \sqrt{29}\, t$. Therefore, $t = \frac{1}{\sqrt{29}}\, s$, and substituting for t in the original equation, we

have $\mathbf{r}(t(s)) = \frac{2}{\sqrt{29}}s\,\mathbf{i} + \left(1 - \frac{3}{\sqrt{29}}s\right)\mathbf{j} + \left(5 + \frac{4}{\sqrt{29}}s\right)\mathbf{k}$.

15. Here $\mathbf{r}(t) = \langle 3\sin t, 4t, 3\cos t \rangle$, so $\mathbf{r}'(t) = \langle 3\cos t, 4, -3\sin t \rangle$ and $|\mathbf{r}'(t)| = \sqrt{9\cos^2 t + 16 + 9\sin^2 t} = \sqrt{25} = 5$.

The point $(0, 0, 3)$ corresponds to $t = 0$, so the arc length function beginning at $(0, 0, 3)$ and measuring in the positive

direction is given by $s(t) = \int_0^t |\mathbf{r}'(u)|\, du = \int_0^t 5\, du = 5t$. $s(t) = 5 \;\Rightarrow\; 5t = 5 \;\Rightarrow\; t = 1$, thus your location after

moving 5 units along the curve is $(3\sin 1, 4, 3\cos 1)$.

17. (a) $\mathbf{r}(t) = \langle 2\sin t, 5t, 2\cos t \rangle \;\Rightarrow\; \mathbf{r}'(t) = \langle 2\cos t, 5, -2\sin t \rangle \;\Rightarrow\; |\mathbf{r}'(t)| = \sqrt{4\cos^2 t + 25 + 4\sin^2 t} = \sqrt{29}.$

Then $\mathbf{T}(t) = \dfrac{\mathbf{r}'(t)}{|\mathbf{r}'(t)|} = \dfrac{1}{\sqrt{29}}\langle 2\cos t, 5, -2\sin t \rangle$ or $\left\langle \dfrac{2}{\sqrt{29}}\cos t, \dfrac{5}{\sqrt{29}}, -\dfrac{2}{\sqrt{29}}\sin t \right\rangle.$

$\mathbf{T}'(t) = \dfrac{1}{\sqrt{29}}\langle -2\sin t, 0, -2\cos t \rangle \;\Rightarrow\; |\mathbf{T}'(t)| = \dfrac{1}{\sqrt{29}}\sqrt{4\sin^2 t + 0 + 4\cos^2 t} = \dfrac{2}{\sqrt{29}}.$ Thus

$\mathbf{N}(t) = \dfrac{\mathbf{T}'(t)}{|\mathbf{T}'(t)|} = \dfrac{1/\sqrt{29}}{2/\sqrt{29}}\langle -2\sin t, 0, -2\cos t \rangle = \langle -\sin t, 0, -\cos t \rangle.$

(b) $\kappa(t) = \dfrac{|\mathbf{T}'(t)|}{|\mathbf{r}'(t)|} = \dfrac{2/\sqrt{29}}{\sqrt{29}} = \dfrac{2}{29}$

19. (a) $\mathbf{r}(t) = \langle \sqrt{2}\,t, e^t, e^{-t} \rangle \;\Rightarrow\; \mathbf{r}'(t) = \langle \sqrt{2}, e^t, -e^{-t} \rangle \;\Rightarrow\; |\mathbf{r}'(t)| = \sqrt{2 + e^{2t} + e^{-2t}} = \sqrt{(e^t + e^{-t})^2} = e^t + e^{-t}.$

Then

$\mathbf{T}(t) = \dfrac{\mathbf{r}'(t)}{|\mathbf{r}'(t)|} = \dfrac{1}{e^t + e^{-t}}\langle \sqrt{2}, e^t, -e^{-t} \rangle = \dfrac{1}{e^{2t} + 1}\langle \sqrt{2}\,e^t, e^{2t}, -1 \rangle \quad \left[\text{after multiplying by } \dfrac{e^t}{e^t} \right] \quad \text{and}$

$\mathbf{T}'(t) = \dfrac{1}{e^{2t} + 1}\langle \sqrt{2}\,e^t, 2e^{2t}, 0 \rangle - \dfrac{2e^{2t}}{(e^{2t} + 1)^2}\langle \sqrt{2}\,e^t, e^{2t}, -1 \rangle$

$= \dfrac{1}{(e^{2t} + 1)^2}\left[(e^{2t} + 1)\langle \sqrt{2}\,e^t, 2e^{2t}, 0 \rangle - 2e^{2t}\langle \sqrt{2}\,e^t, e^{2t}, -1 \rangle \right] = \dfrac{1}{(e^{2t} + 1)^2}\langle \sqrt{2}\,e^t\,(1 - e^{2t}), 2e^{2t}, 2e^{2t} \rangle$

Then

$|\mathbf{T}'(t)| = \dfrac{1}{(e^{2t} + 1)^2}\sqrt{2e^{2t}(1 - 2e^{2t} + e^{4t}) + 4e^{4t} + 4e^{4t}} = \dfrac{1}{(e^{2t} + 1)^2}\sqrt{2e^{2t}(1 + 2e^{2t} + e^{4t})}$

$= \dfrac{1}{(e^{2t} + 1)^2}\sqrt{2e^{2t}\,(1 + e^{2t})^2} = \dfrac{\sqrt{2}\,e^t(1 + e^{2t})}{(e^{2t} + 1)^2} = \dfrac{\sqrt{2}\,e^t}{e^{2t} + 1}$

Therefore

$\mathbf{N}(t) = \dfrac{\mathbf{T}'(t)}{|\mathbf{T}'(t)|} = \dfrac{e^{2t} + 1}{\sqrt{2}\,e^t}\cdot\dfrac{1}{(e^{2t} + 1)^2}\langle \sqrt{2}\,e^t(1 - e^{2t}), 2e^{2t}, 2e^{2t} \rangle$

$= \dfrac{1}{\sqrt{2}\,e^t(e^{2t} + 1)}\langle \sqrt{2}\,e^t(1 - e^{2t}), 2e^{2t}, 2e^{2t} \rangle = \dfrac{1}{e^{2t} + 1}\langle 1 - e^{2t}, \sqrt{2}\,e^t, \sqrt{2}\,e^t \rangle$

(b) $\kappa(t) = \dfrac{|\mathbf{T}'(t)|}{|\mathbf{r}'(t)|} = \dfrac{\sqrt{2}\,e^t}{e^{2t} + 1}\cdot\dfrac{1}{e^t + e^{-t}} = \dfrac{\sqrt{2}\,e^t}{e^{3t} + 2e^t + e^{-t}} = \dfrac{\sqrt{2}\,e^{2t}}{e^{4t} + 2e^{2t} + 1} = \dfrac{\sqrt{2}\,e^{2t}}{(e^{2t} + 1)^2}$

21. $\mathbf{r}(t) = t^3\mathbf{j} + t^2\mathbf{k} \;\Rightarrow\; \mathbf{r}'(t) = 3t^2\mathbf{j} + 2t\mathbf{k}, \quad \mathbf{r}''(t) = 6t\mathbf{j} + 2\mathbf{k}, \quad |\mathbf{r}'(t)| = \sqrt{0^2 + (3t^2)^2 + (2t)^2} = \sqrt{9t^4 + 4t^2},$

$\mathbf{r}'(t) \times \mathbf{r}''(t) = -6t^2\mathbf{i}, \quad |\mathbf{r}'(t) \times \mathbf{r}''(t)| = 6t^2.$ Then $\kappa(t) = \dfrac{|\mathbf{r}'(t) \times \mathbf{r}''(t)|}{|\mathbf{r}'(t)|^3} = \dfrac{6t^2}{\left(\sqrt{9t^4 + 4t^2}\right)^3} = \dfrac{6t^2}{(9t^4 + 4t^2)^{3/2}}.$

23. $\mathbf{r}(t) = 3t\mathbf{i} + 4\sin t\mathbf{j} + 4\cos t\mathbf{k} \;\Rightarrow\; \mathbf{r}'(t) = 3\mathbf{i} + 4\cos t\mathbf{j} - 4\sin t\mathbf{k}, \quad \mathbf{r}''(t) = -4\sin t\mathbf{j} - 4\cos t\mathbf{k},$

$|\mathbf{r}'(t)| = \sqrt{9 + 16\cos^2 t + 16\sin^2 t} = \sqrt{9 + 16} = 5, \quad \mathbf{r}'(t) \times \mathbf{r}''(t) = -16\mathbf{i} + 12\cos t\mathbf{j} - 12\sin t\mathbf{k},$

$|\mathbf{r}'(t) \times \mathbf{r}''(t)| = \sqrt{256 + 144\cos^2 t + 144\sin^2 t} = \sqrt{400} = 20.$ Then $\kappa(t) = \dfrac{|\mathbf{r}'(t) \times \mathbf{r}''(t)|}{|\mathbf{r}'(t)|^3} = \dfrac{20}{5^3} = \dfrac{4}{25}.$

25. $\mathbf{r}(t) = \langle t, t^2, t^3 \rangle$ $\Rightarrow$ $\mathbf{r}'(t) = \langle 1, 2t, 3t^2 \rangle$. The point $(1, 1, 1)$ corresponds to $t = 1$, and $\mathbf{r}'(1) = \langle 1, 2, 3 \rangle$ $\Rightarrow$

$|\mathbf{r}'(1)| = \sqrt{1 + 4 + 9} = \sqrt{14}$. $\mathbf{r}''(t) = \langle 0, 2, 6t \rangle$ $\Rightarrow$ $\mathbf{r}''(1) = \langle 0, 2, 6 \rangle$. $\mathbf{r}'(1) \times \mathbf{r}''(1) = \langle 6, -6, 2 \rangle$, so

$|\mathbf{r}'(1) \times \mathbf{r}''(1)| = \sqrt{36 + 36 + 4} = \sqrt{76}$. Then $\kappa(1) = \dfrac{|\mathbf{r}'(1) \times \mathbf{r}''(1)|}{|\mathbf{r}'(1)|^3} = \dfrac{\sqrt{76}}{\sqrt{14}^3} = \dfrac{1}{7}\sqrt{\dfrac{19}{14}}$.

27. $f(x) = x^4$, $f'(x) = 4x^3$, $f''(x) = 12x^2$, $\kappa(x) = \dfrac{|f''(x)|}{[1 + (f'(x))^2]^{3/2}} = \dfrac{|12x^2|}{[1 + (4x^3)^2]^{3/2}} = \dfrac{12x^2}{(1 + 16x^6)^{3/2}}$

29. $f(x) = xe^x$, $f'(x) = xe^x + e^x$, $f''(x) = xe^x + 2e^x$,

$\kappa(x) = \dfrac{|f''(x)|}{[1 + (f'(x))^2]^{3/2}} = \dfrac{|xe^x + 2e^x|}{[1 + (xe^x + e^x)^2]^{3/2}} = \dfrac{|x + 2|\, e^x}{[1 + (xe^x + e^x)^2]^{3/2}}$

31. Since $y' = y'' = e^x$, the curvature is $\kappa(x) = \dfrac{|y''(x)|}{[1 + (y'(x))^2]^{3/2}} = \dfrac{e^x}{(1 + e^{2x})^{3/2}} = e^x(1 + e^{2x})^{-3/2}$.

To find the maximum curvature, we first find the critical numbers of $\kappa(x)$:

$\kappa'(x) = e^x(1 + e^{2x})^{-3/2} + e^x\left(-\frac{3}{2}\right)(1 + e^{2x})^{-5/2}(2e^{2x}) = e^x\dfrac{1 + e^{2x} - 3e^{2x}}{(1 + e^{2x})^{5/2}} = e^x\dfrac{1 - 2e^{2x}}{(1 + e^{2x})^{5/2}}$.

$\kappa'(x) = 0$ when $1 - 2e^{2x} = 0$, so $e^{2x} = \frac{1}{2}$ or $x = -\frac{1}{2}\ln 2$. And since $1 - 2e^{2x} > 0$ for $x < -\frac{1}{2}\ln 2$ and $1 - 2e^{2x} < 0$

for $x > -\frac{1}{2}\ln 2$, the maximum curvature is attained at the point $\left(-\frac{1}{2}\ln 2, e^{(-\ln 2)/2}\right) = \left(-\frac{1}{2}\ln 2, \frac{1}{\sqrt{2}}\right)$.

Since $\lim\limits_{x \to \infty} e^x(1 + e^{2x})^{-3/2} = 0$, $\kappa(x)$ approaches 0 as $x \to \infty$.

33. (a) C appears to be changing direction more quickly at P than Q, so we would expect the curvature to be greater at P.

(b) First we sketch approximate osculating circles at P and Q. Using the

axes scale as a guide, we measure the radius of the osculating circle

at P to be approximately 0.8 units, thus $\rho = \dfrac{1}{\kappa}$ $\Rightarrow$

$\kappa = \dfrac{1}{\rho} \approx \dfrac{1}{0.8} \approx 1.3$. Similarly, we estimate the radius of the

osculating circle at Q to be 1.4 units, so $\kappa = \dfrac{1}{\rho} \approx \dfrac{1}{1.4} \approx 0.7$.

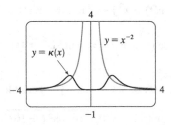

35. $y = x^{-2}$ $\Rightarrow$ $y' = -2x^{-3}$, $y'' = 6x^{-4}$, and

$\kappa(x) = \dfrac{|y''|}{[1 + (y')^2]^{3/2}} = \dfrac{|6x^{-4}|}{[1 + (-2x^{-3})^2]^{3/2}} = \dfrac{6}{x^4(1 + 4x^{-6})^{3/2}}$.

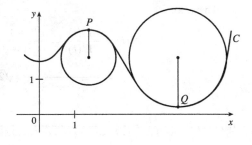

The appearance of the two humps in this graph is perhaps a little surprising, but it is

explained by the fact that $y = x^{-2}$ increases asymptotically at the origin from both

directions, and so its graph has very little bend there. [Note that $\kappa(0)$ is undefined.]

37. Notice that the curve b has two inflection points at which the graph appears almost straight. We would expect the curvature to be 0 or nearly 0 at these values, but the curve a isn't near 0 there. Thus, a must be the graph of $y = f(x)$ rather than the graph of curvature, and b is the graph of $y = \kappa(x)$.

39. Using a CAS, we find (after simplifying)

$$\kappa(t) = \frac{6\sqrt{4\cos^2 t - 12\cos t + 13}}{(17 - 12\cos t)^{3/2}}.$$ (To compute cross

products in Maple, use the `VectorCalculus` or

`LinearAlgebra` package and the `CrossProduct(a,b)`

command; in Mathematica, use `Cross[a,b]`.) Curvature is

largest at integer multiples of 2π.

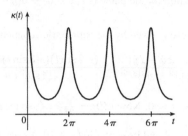

41. $x = t^2 \;\Rightarrow\; \dot{x} = 2t \;\Rightarrow\; \ddot{x} = 2, \quad y = t^3 \;\Rightarrow\; \dot{y} = 3t^2 \;\Rightarrow\; \ddot{y} = 6t.$

Then $\kappa(t) = \dfrac{|\dot{x}\ddot{y} - \dot{y}\ddot{x}|}{[\dot{x}^2 + \dot{y}^2]^{3/2}} = \dfrac{|(2t)(6t) - (3t^2)(2)|}{[(2t)^2 + (3t^2)^2]^{3/2}} = \dfrac{|12t^2 - 6t^2|}{(4t^2 + 9t^4)^{3/2}} = \dfrac{6t^2}{(4t^2 + 9t^4)^{3/2}}.$

43. $x = e^t\cos t \;\Rightarrow\; \dot{x} = e^t(\cos t - \sin t) \;\Rightarrow\; \ddot{x} = e^t(-\sin t - \cos t) + e^t(\cos t - \sin t) = -2e^t\sin t,$

$y = e^t\sin t \;\Rightarrow\; \dot{y} = e^t(\cos t + \sin t) \;\Rightarrow\; \ddot{y} = e^t(-\sin t + \cos t) + e^t(\cos t + \sin t) = 2e^t\cos t.$ Then

$\kappa(t) = \dfrac{|\dot{x}\ddot{y} - \dot{y}\ddot{x}|}{[\dot{x}^2 + \dot{y}^2]^{3/2}} = \dfrac{|e^t(\cos t - \sin t)(2e^t\cos t) - e^t(\cos t + \sin t)(-2e^t\sin t)|}{([e^t(\cos t - \sin t)]^2 + [e^t(\cos t + \sin t)]^2)^{3/2}}$

$= \dfrac{|2e^{2t}(\cos^2 t - \sin t\cos t + \sin t\cos t + \sin^2 t)|}{[e^{2t}(\cos^2 t - 2\cos t\sin t + \sin^2 t + \cos^2 t + 2\cos t\sin t + \sin^2 t)]^{3/2}} = \dfrac{|2e^{2t}(1)|}{[e^{2t}(1+1)]^{3/2}} = \dfrac{2e^{2t}}{e^{3t}(2)^{3/2}} = \dfrac{1}{\sqrt{2}\,e^t}$

45. $\left(1, \frac{2}{3}, 1\right)$ corresponds to $t = 1$. $\mathbf{T}(t) = \dfrac{\mathbf{r}'(t)}{|\mathbf{r}'(t)|} = \dfrac{\langle 2t, 2t^2, 1\rangle}{\sqrt{4t^2 + 4t^4 + 1}} = \dfrac{\langle 2t, 2t^2, 1\rangle}{2t^2 + 1}$, so $\mathbf{T}(1) = \left\langle \frac{2}{3}, \frac{2}{3}, \frac{1}{3}\right\rangle.$

$\mathbf{T}'(t) = -4t(2t^2 + 1)^{-2}\langle 2t, 2t^2, 1\rangle + (2t^2 + 1)^{-1}\langle 2, 4t, 0\rangle$ [by Formula 3 of Theorem 10.2.3]

$= (2t^2 + 1)^{-2}\langle -8t^2 + 4t^2 + 2, -8t^3 + 8t^3 + 4t, -4t\rangle = 2(2t^2 + 1)^{-2}\langle 1 - 2t^2, 2t, -2t\rangle$

$\mathbf{N}(t) = \dfrac{\mathbf{T}'(t)}{|\mathbf{T}'(t)|} = \dfrac{2(2t^2 + 1)^{-2}\langle 1 - 2t^2, 2t, -2t\rangle}{2(2t^2 + 1)^{-2}\sqrt{(1 - 2t^2)^2 + (2t)^2 + (-2t)^2}} = \dfrac{\langle 1 - 2t^2, 2t, -2t\rangle}{\sqrt{1 - 4t^2 + 4t^4 + 8t^2}} = \dfrac{\langle 1 - 2t^2, 2t, -2t\rangle}{1 + 2t^2}$

$\mathbf{N}(1) = \left\langle -\frac{1}{3}, \frac{2}{3}, -\frac{2}{3}\right\rangle$ and $\mathbf{B}(1) = \mathbf{T}(1) \times \mathbf{N}(1) = \left\langle -\frac{4}{9} - \frac{2}{9}, -\left(-\frac{4}{9} + \frac{1}{9}\right), \frac{4}{9} + \frac{2}{9}\right\rangle = \left\langle -\frac{2}{3}, \frac{1}{3}, \frac{2}{3}\right\rangle.$

47. $(0, \pi, -2)$ corresponds to $t = \pi$. $\mathbf{r}(t) = \langle 2\sin 3t, t, 2\cos 3t\rangle \;\Rightarrow$

$\mathbf{T}(t) = \dfrac{\mathbf{r}'(t)}{|\mathbf{r}'(t)|} = \dfrac{\langle 6\cos 3t, 1, -6\sin 3t\rangle}{\sqrt{36\cos^2 3t + 1 + 36\sin^2 3t}} = \dfrac{1}{\sqrt{37}}\langle 6\cos 3t, 1, -6\sin 3t\rangle.$

$\mathbf{T}(\pi) = \frac{1}{\sqrt{37}}\langle -6, 1, 0\rangle$ is a normal vector for the normal plane, and so $\langle -6, 1, 0\rangle$ is also normal. Thus an equation for the

plane is $-6(x - 0) + 1(y - \pi) + 0(z + 2) = 0$ or $y - 6x = \pi$.

$\mathbf{T}'(t) = \frac{1}{\sqrt{37}}\langle -18\sin 3t, 0, -18\cos 3t\rangle \;\Rightarrow\; |\mathbf{T}'(t)| = \dfrac{\sqrt{18^2\sin^2 3t + 18^2\cos^2 3t}}{\sqrt{37}} = \dfrac{18}{\sqrt{37}} \;\Rightarrow$

$$\mathbf{N}(t) = \frac{\mathbf{T}'(t)}{|\mathbf{T}'(t)|} = \langle -\sin 3t, 0, -\cos 3t \rangle. \text{ So } \mathbf{N}(\pi) = \langle 0, 0, 1 \rangle \text{ and } \mathbf{B}(\pi) = \tfrac{1}{\sqrt{37}}\langle -6, 1, 0 \rangle \times \langle 0, 0, 1 \rangle = \tfrac{1}{\sqrt{37}}\langle 1, 6, 0 \rangle.$$

Since $\mathbf{B}(\pi)$ is a normal to the osculating plane, so is $\langle 1, 6, 0 \rangle$.

An equation for the plane is $1(x - 0) + 6(y - \pi) + 0(z + 2) = 0$ or $x + 6y = 6\pi$.

49. The ellipse is given by the parametric equations $x = 2\cos t$, $y = 3\sin t$, so using the result from Exercise 40,

$$\kappa(t) = \frac{|\dot{x}\ddot{y} - \ddot{x}\dot{y}|}{[\dot{x}^2 + \dot{y}^2]^{3/2}} = \frac{|(-2\sin t)(-3\sin t) - (3\cos t)(-2\cos t)|}{(4\sin^2 t + 9\cos^2 t)^{3/2}} = \frac{6}{(4\sin^2 t + 9\cos^2 t)^{3/2}}.$$

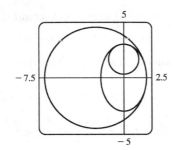

At $(2, 0)$, $t = 0$. Now $\kappa(0) = \tfrac{6}{27} = \tfrac{2}{9}$, so the radius of the osculating circle is

$1/\kappa(0) = \tfrac{9}{2}$ and its center is $\left(-\tfrac{5}{2}, 0\right)$. Its equation is therefore $\left(x + \tfrac{5}{2}\right)^2 + y^2 = \tfrac{81}{4}$.

At $(0, 3)$, $t = \tfrac{\pi}{2}$, and $\kappa\left(\tfrac{\pi}{2}\right) = \tfrac{6}{8} = \tfrac{3}{4}$. So the radius of the osculating circle is $\tfrac{4}{3}$ and

its center is $\left(0, \tfrac{5}{3}\right)$. Hence its equation is $x^2 + \left(y - \tfrac{5}{3}\right)^2 = \tfrac{16}{9}$.

51. The tangent vector is normal to the normal plane, and the vector $\langle 6, 6, -8 \rangle$ is normal to the given plane.

But $\mathbf{T}(t) \parallel \mathbf{r}'(t)$ and $\langle 6, 6, -8 \rangle \parallel \langle 3, 3, -4 \rangle$, so we need to find t such that $\mathbf{r}'(t) \parallel \langle 3, 3, -4 \rangle$.

$\mathbf{r}(t) = \langle t^3, 3t, t^4 \rangle \ \Rightarrow \ \mathbf{r}'(t) = \langle 3t^2, 3, 4t^3 \rangle \parallel \langle 3, 3, -4 \rangle$ when $t = -1$. So the planes are parallel at the point $(-1, -3, 1)$.

53. First we parametrize the curve of intersection. We can choose $y = t$; then $x = y^2 = t^2$ and $z = x^2 = t^4$, and the curve is

given by $\mathbf{r}(t) = \langle t^2, t, t^4 \rangle$. $\mathbf{r}'(t) = \langle 2t, 1, 4t^3 \rangle$ and the point $(1, 1, 1)$ corresponds to $t = 1$, so

$\mathbf{r}'(1) = \langle 2, 1, 4 \rangle$ is a normal vector for the normal plane. Thus an equation of the normal plane is

$$2(x - 1) + 1(y - 1) + 4(z - 1) = 0 \text{ or } 2x + y + 4z = 7. \quad \mathbf{T}(t) = \frac{\mathbf{r}'(t)}{|\mathbf{r}'(t)|} = \frac{1}{\sqrt{4t^2 + 1 + 16t^6}}\langle 2t, 1, 4t^3 \rangle \text{ and}$$

$\mathbf{T}'(t) = -\tfrac{1}{2}(4t^2 + 1 + 16t^6)^{-3/2}(8t + 96t^5)\langle 2t, 1, 4t^3 \rangle + (4t^2 + 1 + 16t^6)^{-1/2}\langle 2, 0, 12t^2 \rangle$. A normal vector for

the osculating plane is $\mathbf{B}(1) = \mathbf{T}(1) \times \mathbf{N}(1)$, but $\mathbf{r}'(1) = \langle 2, 1, 4 \rangle$ is parallel to $\mathbf{T}(1)$ and

$\mathbf{T}'(1) = -\tfrac{1}{2}(21)^{-3/2}(104)\langle 2, 1, 4 \rangle + (21)^{-1/2}\langle 2, 0, 12 \rangle = \tfrac{2}{21\sqrt{21}}\langle -31, -26, 22 \rangle$ is parallel to $\mathbf{N}(1)$ as is $\langle -31, -26, 22 \rangle$,

so $\langle 2, 1, 4 \rangle \times \langle -31, -26, 22 \rangle = \langle 126, -168, -21 \rangle$ is normal to the osculating plane. Thus an equation for the osculating

plane is $126(x - 1) - 168(y - 1) - 21(z - 1) = 0$ or $6x - 8y - z = -3$.

55. $\kappa = \left|\dfrac{d\mathbf{T}}{ds}\right| = \left|\dfrac{d\mathbf{T}/dt}{ds/dt}\right| = \dfrac{|d\mathbf{T}/dt|}{ds/dt}$ and $\mathbf{N} = \dfrac{d\mathbf{T}/dt}{|d\mathbf{T}/dt|}$, so $\kappa\mathbf{N} = \dfrac{\left|\dfrac{d\mathbf{T}}{dt}\right|\dfrac{d\mathbf{T}}{dt}}{\left|\dfrac{d\mathbf{T}}{dt}\right|\dfrac{ds}{dt}} = \dfrac{d\mathbf{T}/dt}{ds/dt} = \dfrac{d\mathbf{T}}{ds}$ by the Chain Rule.

57. (a) $|\mathbf{B}| = 1 \ \Rightarrow \ \mathbf{B} \cdot \mathbf{B} = 1 \ \Rightarrow \ \dfrac{d}{ds}(\mathbf{B} \cdot \mathbf{B}) = 0 \ \Rightarrow \ 2\dfrac{d\mathbf{B}}{ds} \cdot \mathbf{B} = 0 \ \Rightarrow \ \dfrac{d\mathbf{B}}{ds} \perp \mathbf{B}$

(b) $\mathbf{B} = \mathbf{T} \times \mathbf{N} \Rightarrow$

$$\frac{d\mathbf{B}}{ds} = \frac{d}{ds}(\mathbf{T} \times \mathbf{N}) = \frac{d}{dt}(\mathbf{T} \times \mathbf{N})\frac{1}{ds/dt} = \frac{d}{dt}(\mathbf{T} \times \mathbf{N})\frac{1}{|\mathbf{r}'(t)|} = [(\mathbf{T}' \times \mathbf{N}) + (\mathbf{T} \times \mathbf{N}')]\frac{1}{|\mathbf{r}'(t)|}$$

$$= \left[\left(\mathbf{T}' \times \frac{\mathbf{T}'}{|\mathbf{T}'|}\right) + (\mathbf{T} \times \mathbf{N}')\right]\frac{1}{|\mathbf{r}'(t)|} = \frac{\mathbf{T} \times \mathbf{N}'}{|\mathbf{r}'(t)|} \Rightarrow \frac{d\mathbf{B}}{ds} \perp \mathbf{T}$$

(c) $\mathbf{B} = \mathbf{T} \times \mathbf{N} \Rightarrow \mathbf{T} \perp \mathbf{N}, \mathbf{B} \perp \mathbf{T}$ and $\mathbf{B} \perp \mathbf{N}$. So $\mathbf{B}, \mathbf{T}$ and $\mathbf{N}$ form an orthogonal set of vectors in the three-dimensional space $\mathbb{R}^3$. From parts (a) and (b), $d\mathbf{B}/ds$ is perpendicular to both $\mathbf{B}$ and $\mathbf{T}$, so $d\mathbf{B}/ds$ is parallel to $\mathbf{N}$. Therefore, $d\mathbf{B}/ds = -\tau(s)\mathbf{N}$, where $\tau(s)$ is a scalar.

(d) Since $\mathbf{B} = \mathbf{T} \times \mathbf{N}, \mathbf{T} \perp \mathbf{N}$ and both $\mathbf{T}$ and $\mathbf{N}$ are unit vectors, $\mathbf{B}$ is a unit vector mutually perpendicular to both $\mathbf{T}$ and $\mathbf{N}$. For a plane curve, $\mathbf{T}$ and $\mathbf{N}$ always lie in the plane of the curve, so that $\mathbf{B}$ is a constant unit vector always perpendicular to the plane. Thus $d\mathbf{B}/ds = \mathbf{0}$, but $d\mathbf{B}/ds = -\tau(s)\mathbf{N}$ and $\mathbf{N} \neq \mathbf{0}$, so $\tau(s) = 0$.

59. (a) $\mathbf{r}' = s'\mathbf{T} \Rightarrow \mathbf{r}'' = s''\mathbf{T} + s'\mathbf{T}' = s''\mathbf{T} + s'\dfrac{d\mathbf{T}}{ds}s' = s''\mathbf{T} + \kappa(s')^2\mathbf{N}$ by the first Serret-Frenet formula.

(b) Using part (a), we have

$$\mathbf{r}' \times \mathbf{r}'' = (s'\mathbf{T}) \times [s''\mathbf{T} + \kappa(s')^2\mathbf{N}]$$

$$= [(s'\mathbf{T}) \times (s''\mathbf{T})] + [(s'\mathbf{T}) \times (\kappa(s')^2\mathbf{N})] \qquad \text{[by Property 3 of the cross product]}$$

$$= (s's'')(\mathbf{T} \times \mathbf{T}) + \kappa(s')^3(\mathbf{T} \times \mathbf{N}) = \mathbf{0} + \kappa(s')^3\mathbf{B} = \kappa(s')^3\mathbf{B}$$

(c) Using part (a), we have

$$\mathbf{r}''' = [s''\mathbf{T} + \kappa(s')^2\mathbf{N}]' = s'''\mathbf{T} + s''\mathbf{T}' + \kappa'(s')^2\mathbf{N} + 2\kappa s's''\mathbf{N} + \kappa(s')^2\mathbf{N}'$$

$$= s'''\mathbf{T} + s''\frac{d\mathbf{T}}{ds}s' + \kappa'(s')^2\mathbf{N} + 2\kappa s's''\mathbf{N} + \kappa(s')^2\frac{d\mathbf{N}}{ds}s'$$

$$= s'''\mathbf{T} + s''s'\kappa\mathbf{N} + \kappa'(s')^2\mathbf{N} + 2\kappa s's''\mathbf{N} + \kappa(s')^3(-\kappa\mathbf{T} + \tau\mathbf{B}) \qquad \text{[by the second formula]}$$

$$= [s''' - \kappa^2(s')^3]\mathbf{T} + [3\kappa s's'' + \kappa'(s')^2]\mathbf{N} + \kappa\tau(s')^3\mathbf{B}$$

(d) Using parts (b) and (c) and the facts that $\mathbf{B} \cdot \mathbf{T} = 0, \mathbf{B} \cdot \mathbf{N} = 0$, and $\mathbf{B} \cdot \mathbf{B} = 1$, we get

$$\frac{(\mathbf{r}' \times \mathbf{r}'') \cdot \mathbf{r}'''}{|\mathbf{r}' \times \mathbf{r}''|^2} = \frac{\kappa(s')^3\mathbf{B} \cdot \{[s''' - \kappa^2(s')^3]\mathbf{T} + [3\kappa s's'' + \kappa'(s')^2]\mathbf{N} + \kappa\tau(s')^3\mathbf{B}\}}{|\kappa(s')^3\mathbf{B}|^2} = \frac{\kappa(s')^3\kappa\tau(s')^3}{[\kappa(s')^3]^2} = \tau.$$

61. For one helix, the vector equation is $\mathbf{r}(t) = \langle 10\cos t, 10\sin t, 34t/(2\pi)\rangle$ (measuring in angstroms), because the radius of each helix is 10 angstroms, and z increases by 34 angstroms for each increase of 2π in t. Using the arc length formula, letting t go from 0 to $2.9 \times 10^8 \times 2\pi$, we find the approximate length of each helix to be

$$L = \int_0^{2.9 \times 10^8 \times 2\pi} |\mathbf{r}'(t)|\, dt = \int_0^{2.9 \times 10^8 \times 2\pi} \sqrt{(-10\sin t)^2 + (10\cos t)^2 + \left(\tfrac{34}{2\pi}\right)^2}\, dt = \sqrt{100 + \left(\tfrac{34}{2\pi}\right)^2}\, t\Bigg]_0^{2.9 \times 10^8 \times 2\pi}$$

$$2.9 \times 10^8 \times 2\pi \sqrt{100 + \left(\tfrac{34}{2\pi}\right)^2} \approx 2.07 \times 10^{10} \text{ Å} \text{ — more than two meters!}$$

10.4 Motion in Space: Velocity and Acceleration

1. (a) If $\mathbf{r}(t) = x(t)\,\mathbf{i} + y(t)\,\mathbf{j} + z(t)\,\mathbf{k}$ is the position vector of the particle at time t, then the average velocity over the time

interval $[0, 1]$ is

$$\mathbf{v}_{\text{ave}} = \frac{\mathbf{r}(1) - \mathbf{r}(0)}{1 - 0} = \frac{(4.5\,\mathbf{i} + 6.0\,\mathbf{j} + 3.0\,\mathbf{k}) - (2.7\,\mathbf{i} + 9.8\,\mathbf{j} + 3.7\,\mathbf{k})}{1} = 1.8\,\mathbf{i} - 3.8\,\mathbf{j} - 0.7\,\mathbf{k}.$$ Similarly, over the other

intervals we have

$$[0.5, 1]: \quad \mathbf{v}_{\text{ave}} = \frac{\mathbf{r}(1) - \mathbf{r}(0.5)}{1 - 0.5} = \frac{(4.5\,\mathbf{i} + 6.0\,\mathbf{j} + 3.0\,\mathbf{k}) - (3.5\,\mathbf{i} + 7.2\,\mathbf{j} + 3.3\,\mathbf{k})}{0.5} = 2.0\,\mathbf{i} - 2.4\,\mathbf{j} - 0.6\,\mathbf{k}$$

$$[1, 2]: \quad \mathbf{v}_{\text{ave}} = \frac{\mathbf{r}(2) - \mathbf{r}(1)}{2 - 1} = \frac{(7.3\,\mathbf{i} + 7.8\,\mathbf{j} + 2.7\,\mathbf{k}) - (4.5\,\mathbf{i} + 6.0\,\mathbf{j} + 3.0\,\mathbf{k})}{1} = 2.8\,\mathbf{i} + 1.8\,\mathbf{j} - 0.3\,\mathbf{k}$$

$$[1, 1.5]: \quad \mathbf{v}_{\text{ave}} = \frac{\mathbf{r}(1.5) - \mathbf{r}(1)}{1.5 - 1} = \frac{(5.9\,\mathbf{i} + 6.4\,\mathbf{j} + 2.8\,\mathbf{k}) - (4.5\,\mathbf{i} + 6.0\,\mathbf{j} + 3.0\,\mathbf{k})}{0.5} = 2.8\,\mathbf{i} + 0.8\,\mathbf{j} - 0.4\,\mathbf{k}$$

(b) We can estimate the velocity at $t = 1$ by averaging the average velocities over the time intervals $[0.5, 1]$ and $[1, 1.5]$:

$$\mathbf{v}(1) \approx \tfrac{1}{2}[(2\,\mathbf{i} - 2.4\,\mathbf{j} - 0.6\,\mathbf{k}) + (2.8\,\mathbf{i} + 0.8\,\mathbf{j} - 0.4\,\mathbf{k})] = 2.4\,\mathbf{i} - 0.8\,\mathbf{j} - 0.5\,\mathbf{k}.$$ Then the speed is

$$|\mathbf{v}(1)| \approx \sqrt{(2.4)^2 + (-0.8)^2 + (-0.5)^2} \approx 2.58.$$

3. $\mathbf{r}(t) = \left\langle -\tfrac{1}{2}t^2, t \right\rangle \quad \Rightarrow$ At $t = 2$:

$\mathbf{v}(t) = \mathbf{r}'(t) = \langle -t, 1 \rangle$ $\mathbf{v}(2) = \langle -2, 1 \rangle$

$\mathbf{a}(t) = \mathbf{r}''(t) = \langle -1, 0 \rangle$ $\mathbf{a}(2) = \langle -1, 0 \rangle$

$|\mathbf{v}(t)| = \sqrt{t^2 + 1}$

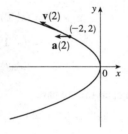

5. $(t) = 3\cos t\,\mathbf{i} + 2\sin t\,\mathbf{j} \quad \Rightarrow$ At $t = \pi/3$:

$\mathbf{v}(t) = -3\sin t\,\mathbf{i} + 2\cos t\,\mathbf{j}$ $\mathbf{v}\left(\frac{\pi}{3}\right) = -\frac{3\sqrt{3}}{2}\,\mathbf{i} + \mathbf{j}$

$\mathbf{a}(t) = -3\cos t\,\mathbf{i} - 2\sin t\,\mathbf{j}$ $\mathbf{a}\left(\frac{\pi}{3}\right) = -\frac{3}{2}\,\mathbf{i} - \sqrt{3}\,\mathbf{j}$

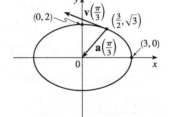

$|\mathbf{v}(t)| = \sqrt{9\sin^2 t + 4\cos^2 t} = \sqrt{4 + 5\sin^2 t}$

Notice that $x^2/9 + y^2/4 = \sin^2 t + \cos^2 t = 1$, so the path is an ellipse.

7. $\mathbf{r}(t) = t\,\mathbf{i} + t^2\,\mathbf{j} + 2\,\mathbf{k} \quad \Rightarrow$ At $t = 1$:

$\mathbf{v}(t) = \mathbf{i} + 2t\,\mathbf{j}$ $\mathbf{v}(1) = \mathbf{i} + 2\,\mathbf{j}$

$\mathbf{a}(t) = 2\,\mathbf{j}$ $\mathbf{a}(1) = 2\,\mathbf{j}$

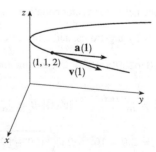

$|\mathbf{v}(t)| = \sqrt{1 + 4t^2}$

Here $x = t$, $y = t^2 \quad \Rightarrow \quad y = x^2$ and $z = 2$, so the path of the particle is a

parabola in the plane $z = 2$.

9. $\mathbf{r}(t) = \sqrt{2}\,t\,\mathbf{i} + e^t\,\mathbf{j} + e^{-t}\,\mathbf{k} \quad \Rightarrow \quad \mathbf{v}(t) = \mathbf{r}'(t) = \sqrt{2}\,\mathbf{i} + e^t\,\mathbf{j} - e^{-t}\,\mathbf{k}, \quad \mathbf{a}(t) = \mathbf{v}'(t) = e^t\,\mathbf{j} + e^{-t}\,\mathbf{k},$

$|\mathbf{v}(t)| = \sqrt{2 + e^{2t} + e^{-2t}} = \sqrt{(e^t + e^{-t})^2} = e^t + e^{-t}.$

11. $\mathbf{r}(t) = e^t\langle \cos t, \sin t, t\rangle \quad \Rightarrow$

$\mathbf{v}(t) = \mathbf{r}'(t) = e^t\langle \cos t, \sin t, t\rangle + e^t\langle -\sin t, \cos t, 1\rangle = e^t\langle \cos t - \sin t, \sin t + \cos t, t + 1\rangle$

$\mathbf{a}(t) = \mathbf{v}'(t) = e^t\langle \cos t - \sin t - \sin t - \cos t, \sin t + \cos t + \cos t - \sin t, t + 1 + 1\rangle$

$\qquad\quad = e^t\langle -2\sin t, 2\cos t, t + 2\rangle$

$|\mathbf{v}(t)| = e^t\sqrt{\cos^2 t + \sin^2 t - 2\cos t \sin t + \sin^2 t + \cos^2 t + 2\sin t \cos t + t^2 + 2t + 1}$

$\qquad\quad = e^t\sqrt{t^2 + 2t + 3}$

13. $\mathbf{a}(t) = \mathbf{i} + 2\mathbf{j} \quad \Rightarrow \quad \mathbf{v}(t) = \int \mathbf{a}(t)\,dt = \int(\mathbf{i} + 2\mathbf{j})\,dt = t\,\mathbf{i} + 2t\,\mathbf{j} + \mathbf{C}$ and $\mathbf{k} = \mathbf{v}(0) = \mathbf{C},$

so $\mathbf{C} = \mathbf{k}$ and $\mathbf{v}(t) = t\,\mathbf{i} + 2t\,\mathbf{j} + \mathbf{k}.$ $\mathbf{r}(t) = \int \mathbf{v}(t)\,dt = \int(t\,\mathbf{i} + 2t\,\mathbf{j} + \mathbf{k})\,dt = \frac{1}{2}t^2\,\mathbf{i} + t^2\,\mathbf{j} + t\,\mathbf{k} + \mathbf{D}.$

But $\mathbf{i} = \mathbf{r}(0) = \mathbf{D}$, so $\mathbf{D} = \mathbf{i}$ and $\mathbf{r}(t) = \left(\frac{1}{2}t^2 + 1\right)\mathbf{i} + t^2\,\mathbf{j} + t\,\mathbf{k}.$

15. (a) $\mathbf{a}(t) = 2t\,\mathbf{i} + \sin t\,\mathbf{j} + \cos 2t\,\mathbf{k} \quad \Rightarrow$ (b)

$\quad \mathbf{v}(t) = \int(2t\,\mathbf{i} + \sin t\,\mathbf{j} + \cos 2t\,\mathbf{k})\,dt = t^2\,\mathbf{i} - \cos t\,\mathbf{j} + \frac{1}{2}\sin 2t\,\mathbf{k} + \mathbf{C}$

$\quad$ and $\mathbf{i} = \mathbf{v}(0) = -\mathbf{j} + \mathbf{C}$, so $\mathbf{C} = \mathbf{i} + \mathbf{j}$

$\quad$ and $\mathbf{v}(t) = (t^2 + 1)\mathbf{i} + (1 - \cos t)\mathbf{j} + \frac{1}{2}\sin 2t\,\mathbf{k}.$

$\quad \mathbf{r}(t) = \int[(t^2 + 1)\mathbf{i} + (1 - \cos t)\mathbf{j} + \frac{1}{2}\sin 2t\,\mathbf{k}]\,dt$

$\qquad = \left(\frac{1}{3}t^3 + t\right)\mathbf{i} + (t - \sin t)\mathbf{j} - \frac{1}{4}\cos 2t\,\mathbf{k} + \mathbf{D}$

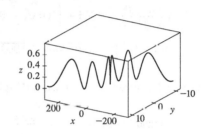

But $\mathbf{j} = \mathbf{r}(0) = -\frac{1}{4}\mathbf{k} + \mathbf{D}$, so $\mathbf{D} = \mathbf{j} + \frac{1}{4}\mathbf{k}$ and $\mathbf{r}(t) = \left(\frac{1}{3}t^3 + t\right)\mathbf{i} + (t - \sin t + 1)\mathbf{j} + \left(\frac{1}{4} - \frac{1}{4}\cos 2t\right)\mathbf{k}.$

17. $\mathbf{r}(t) = \langle t^2, 5t, t^2 - 16t\rangle \quad \Rightarrow \quad \mathbf{v}(t) = \langle 2t, 5, 2t - 16\rangle,\ |\mathbf{v}(t)| = \sqrt{4t^2 + 25 + 4t^2 - 64t + 256} = \sqrt{8t^2 - 64t + 281}$

and $\dfrac{d}{dt}\,|\mathbf{v}(t)| = \frac{1}{2}(8t^2 - 64t + 281)^{-1/2}(16t - 64)$. This is zero if and only if the numerator is zero, that is,

$16t - 64 = 0$ or $t = 4$. Since $\dfrac{d}{dt}\,|\mathbf{v}(t)| < 0$ for $t < 4$ and $\dfrac{d}{dt}\,|\mathbf{v}(t)| > 0$ for $t > 4$, the minimum speed of $\sqrt{153}$ is attained

at $t = 4$ units of time.

19. $|\mathbf{F}(t)| = 20$ N in the direction of the positive z-axis, so $\mathbf{F}(t) = 20\,\mathbf{k}$. Also $m = 4$ kg, $\mathbf{r}(0) = \mathbf{0}$ and $\mathbf{v}(0) = \mathbf{i} - \mathbf{j}.$

Since $20\mathbf{k} = \mathbf{F}(t) = 4\,\mathbf{a}(t)$, $\mathbf{a}(t) = 5\,\mathbf{k}$. Then $\mathbf{v}(t) = 5t\,\mathbf{k} + \mathbf{c}_1$ where $\mathbf{c}_1 = \mathbf{i} - \mathbf{j}$ so $\mathbf{v}(t) = \mathbf{i} - \mathbf{j} + 5t\,\mathbf{k}$ and the

speed is $|\mathbf{v}(t)| = \sqrt{1 + 1 + 25t^2} = \sqrt{25t^2 + 2}$. Also $\mathbf{r}(t) = t\,\mathbf{i} - t\,\mathbf{j} + \frac{5}{2}t^2\,\mathbf{k} + \mathbf{c}_2$ and $\mathbf{0} = \mathbf{r}(0)$, so $\mathbf{c}_2 = \mathbf{0}$

and $\mathbf{r}(t) = t\,\mathbf{i} - t\,\mathbf{j} + \frac{5}{2}t^2\,\mathbf{k}.$

21. $|\mathbf{v}(0)| = 200$ m/s and, since the angle of elevation is $60°$, a unit vector in the direction of the velocity is

$(\cos 60°)\mathbf{i} + (\sin 60°)\mathbf{j} = \frac{1}{2}\mathbf{i} + \frac{\sqrt{3}}{2}\mathbf{j}$. Thus $\mathbf{v}(0) = 200\left(\frac{1}{2}\mathbf{i} + \frac{\sqrt{3}}{2}\mathbf{j}\right) = 100\,\mathbf{i} + 100\sqrt{3}\,\mathbf{j}$ and if we set up the axes so that

the projectile starts at the origin, then $\mathbf{r}(0) = \mathbf{0}$. Ignoring air resistance, the only force is that due to gravity, so

$\mathbf{F}(t) = m\mathbf{a}(t) = -mg\,\mathbf{j}$ where $g \approx 9.8$ m/s^2. Thus $\mathbf{a}(t) = -9.8\,\mathbf{j}$ and, integrating, we have $\mathbf{v}(t) = -9.8t\,\mathbf{j} + \mathbf{C}$. But

$100\,\mathbf{i} + 100\,\sqrt{3}\,\mathbf{j} = \mathbf{v}(0) = \mathbf{C}$, so $\mathbf{v}(t) = 100\,\mathbf{i} + \left(100\,\sqrt{3} - 9.8t\right)\mathbf{j}$ and then (integrating again)

$\mathbf{r}(t) = 100\,t\,\mathbf{i} + \left(100\,\sqrt{3}\,t - 4.9t^2\right)\mathbf{j} + \mathbf{D}$ where $\mathbf{0} = \mathbf{r}(0) = \mathbf{D}$. Thus the position function of the projectile is

$\mathbf{r}(t) = 100\,t\,\mathbf{i} + \left(100\,\sqrt{3}\,t - 4.9t^2\right)\mathbf{j}$.

(a) Parametric equations for the projectile are $x(t) = 100t$, $y(t) = 100\,\sqrt{3}\,t - 4.9t^2$. The projectile reaches the ground when

$y(t) = 0$ (and $t > 0$) $\Rightarrow$ $100\,\sqrt{3}\,t - 4.9t^2 = t\left(100\,\sqrt{3} - 4.9t\right) = 0$ $\Rightarrow$ $t = \frac{100\sqrt{3}}{4.9} \approx 35.3$ s. So the range is

$x\left(\frac{100\sqrt{3}}{4.9}\right) = 100\left(\frac{100\sqrt{3}}{4.9}\right) \approx 3535$ m.

(b) The maximum height is reached when $y(t)$ has a critical number (or equivalently, when the vertical component

of velocity is 0): $y'(t) = 0$ $\Rightarrow$ $100\,\sqrt{3} - 9.8t = 0$ $\Rightarrow$ $t = \frac{100\sqrt{3}}{9.8} \approx 17.7$ s. Thus the maximum height is

$y\left(\frac{100\sqrt{3}}{9.8}\right) = 100\,\sqrt{3}\left(\frac{100\sqrt{3}}{9.8}\right) - 4.9\left(\frac{100\sqrt{3}}{9.8}\right)^2 \approx 1531$ m.

(c) From part (a), impact occurs at $t = \frac{100\sqrt{3}}{4.9}$ s. Thus, the velocity at impact is

$\mathbf{v}\left(\frac{100\sqrt{3}}{4.9}\right) = 100\,\mathbf{i} + \left[100\,\sqrt{3} - 9.8\left(\frac{100\sqrt{3}}{4.9}\right)\right]\mathbf{j} = 100\,\mathbf{i} - 100\,\sqrt{3}\,\mathbf{j}$ and the speed is

$\left|\mathbf{v}\left(\frac{100\sqrt{3}}{4.9}\right)\right| = \sqrt{10{,}000 + 30{,}000} = 200$ m/s.

23. As in Example 5, $\mathbf{r}(t) = (v_0 \cos 45°)t\,\mathbf{i} + \left[(v_0 \sin 45°)t - \frac{1}{2}gt^2\right]\mathbf{j} = \frac{1}{2}\left[v_0\sqrt{2}\,t\,\mathbf{i} + \left(v_0\sqrt{2}\,t - gt^2\right)\mathbf{j}\right]$. The ball lands when

$y = 0$ (and $t > 0$) $\Rightarrow$ $t = \frac{v_0\sqrt{2}}{g}$ s. Now since it lands 90 m away, $90 = x = \frac{1}{2}v_0\sqrt{2}\,\frac{v_0\sqrt{2}}{g}$ or $v_0^2 = 90g$ and the initial

velocity is $v_0 = \sqrt{90g} \approx 30$ m/s.

25. Let α be the angle of elevation. Then $v_0 = 150$ m/s and from Example 5, the horizontal distance traveled by the projectile is

$d = \frac{v_0^2 \sin 2\alpha}{g}$. Thus $\frac{150^2 \sin 2\alpha}{g} = 800$ $\Rightarrow$ $\sin 2\alpha = \frac{800g}{150^2} \approx 0.3484$ $\Rightarrow$ $2\alpha \approx 20.4°$ or $180 - 20.4 = 159.6°$.

Two angles of elevation then are $\alpha \approx 10.2°$ and $\alpha \approx 79.8°$.

27. Place the catapult at the origin and assume the catapult is 100 meters from the city, so the city lies between $(100, 0)$

and $(600, 0)$. The initial speed is $v_0 = 80$ m/s and let θ be the angle the catapult is set at. As in Example 5, the trajectory of

the catapulted rock is given by $\mathbf{r}(t) = (80 \cos \theta)t\,\mathbf{i} + \left[(80 \sin \theta)t - 4.9t^2\right]\mathbf{j}$. The top of the near city wall is at $(100, 15)$,

which the rock will hit when $(80 \cos \theta)\,t = 100$ $\Rightarrow$ $t = \frac{5}{4 \cos \theta}$ and $(80 \sin \theta)t - 4.9t^2 = 15$ $\Rightarrow$

$80 \sin \theta \cdot \frac{5}{4 \cos \theta} - 4.9\left(\frac{5}{4 \cos \theta}\right)^2 = 15$ $\Rightarrow$ $100 \tan \theta - 7.65625 \sec^2 \theta = 15$. Replacing $\sec^2 \theta$ with $\tan^2 \theta + 1$ gives

$7.65625 \tan^2 \theta - 100 \tan \theta + 22.62625 = 0$. Using the quadratic formula, we have $\tan \theta \approx 0.230324, 12.8309$ $\Rightarrow$

$\theta \approx 13.0°, 85.5°$. So for $13.0° < \theta < 85.5°$, the rock will land beyond the near city wall. The base of the far wall is located at $(600, 0)$ which the rock hits if $(80 \cos \theta)t = 600 \quad \Rightarrow \quad t = \dfrac{15}{2 \cos \theta}$ and $(80 \sin \theta)t - 4.9t^2 = 0 \quad \Rightarrow$

$80 \sin \theta \cdot \dfrac{15}{2 \cos \theta} - 4.9 \left(\dfrac{15}{2 \cos \theta} \right)^2 = 0 \quad \Rightarrow \quad 600 \tan \theta - 275.625 \sec^2 \theta = 0 \quad \Rightarrow$

$275.625 \tan^2 \theta - 600 \tan \theta + 275.625 = 0$. Solutions are $\tan \theta \approx 0.658678, 1.51819 \quad \Rightarrow \quad \theta \approx 33.4°, 56.6°$. Thus the

rock lands beyond the enclosed city ground for $33.4° < \theta < 56.6°$, and the angles that allow the rock to land on city ground

are $13.0° < \theta < 33.4°, 56.6° < \theta < 85.5°$. If you consider that the rock can hit the far wall and bounce back into the city, we

calculate the angles that cause the rock to hit the top of the wall at $(600, 15)$: $(80 \cos \theta)t = 600 \quad \Rightarrow \quad t = \dfrac{15}{2 \cos \theta}$ and

$(80 \sin \theta)t - 4.9t^2 = 15 \quad \Rightarrow \quad 600 \tan \theta - 275.625 \sec^2 \theta = 15 \quad \Rightarrow \quad 275.625 \tan^2 \theta - 600 \tan \theta + 290.625 = 0$.

Solutions are $\tan \theta \approx 0.727506, 1.44936 \quad \Rightarrow \quad \theta \approx 36.0°, 55.4°$, so the catapult should be set with angle θ where

$13.0° < \theta < 36.0°, 55.4° < \theta < 85.5°$.

29. (a) After t seconds, the boat will be $5t$ meters west of point A. The velocity

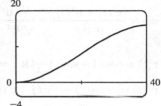

of the water at that location is $\frac{3}{400}(5t)(40 - 5t) \mathbf{j}$. The velocity of the

boat in still water is $5\mathbf{i}$, so the resultant velocity of the boat is

$\mathbf{v}(t) = 5\mathbf{i} + \frac{3}{400}(5t)(40 - 5t) \mathbf{j} = 5\mathbf{i} + \left(\frac{3}{2}t - \frac{3}{16}t^2 \right) \mathbf{j}$. Integrating, we obtain

$\mathbf{r}(t) = 5t\,\mathbf{i} + \left(\frac{3}{4}t^2 - \frac{1}{16}t^3 \right) \mathbf{j} + \mathbf{C}$. If we place the origin at A (and consider $\mathbf{j}$

to coincide with the northern direction) then $\mathbf{r}(0) = \mathbf{0} \quad \Rightarrow \quad \mathbf{C} = \mathbf{0}$ and we have $\mathbf{r}(t) = 5t\,\mathbf{i} + \left(\frac{3}{4}t^2 - \frac{1}{16}t^3 \right) \mathbf{j}$. The boat

reaches the east bank after 8 s, and it is located at $\mathbf{r}(8) = 5(8)\mathbf{i} + \left(\frac{3}{4}(8)^2 - \frac{1}{16}(8)^3 \right) \mathbf{j} = 40\mathbf{i} + 16\mathbf{j}$. Thus the boat is 16 m

downstream.

(b) Let α be the angle north of east that the boat heads. Then the velocity of the boat in still water is given by

$5(\cos \alpha) \mathbf{i} + 5(\sin \alpha) \mathbf{j}$. At t seconds, the boat is $5(\cos \alpha)t$ meters from the west bank, at which point the velocity

of the water is $\frac{3}{400}[5(\cos \alpha)t][40 - 5(\cos \alpha)t] \mathbf{j}$. The resultant velocity of the boat is given by

$\mathbf{v}(t) = 5(\cos \alpha)\mathbf{i} + \left[5 \sin \alpha + \frac{3}{400}(5t \cos \alpha)(40 - 5t \cos \alpha) \right] \mathbf{j} = (5 \cos \alpha)\mathbf{i} + \left(5 \sin \alpha + \frac{3}{2}t \cos \alpha - \frac{3}{16}t^2 \cos^2 \alpha \right) \mathbf{j}$.

Integrating, $\mathbf{r}(t) = (5t \cos \alpha)\mathbf{i} + \left(5t \sin \alpha + \frac{3}{4}t^2 \cos \alpha - \frac{1}{16}t^3 \cos^2 \alpha \right) \mathbf{j}$ (where we have again placed

the origin at A). The boat will reach the east bank when $5t \cos \alpha = 40 \quad \Rightarrow \quad t = \dfrac{40}{5 \cos \alpha} = \dfrac{8}{\cos \alpha}$.

In order to land at point $B(40, 0)$ we need $5t \sin \alpha + \frac{3}{4}t^2 \cos \alpha - \frac{1}{16}t^3 \cos^2 \alpha = 0 \quad \Rightarrow$

$5 \left(\dfrac{8}{\cos \alpha} \right) \sin \alpha + \frac{3}{4} \left(\dfrac{8}{\cos \alpha} \right)^2 \cos \alpha - \frac{1}{16} \left(\dfrac{8}{\cos \alpha} \right)^3 \cos^2 \alpha = 0 \quad \Rightarrow \quad \dfrac{1}{\cos \alpha} (40 \sin \alpha + 48 - 32) = 0 \quad \Rightarrow$

$40 \sin \alpha + 16 = 0 \quad \Rightarrow \quad \sin \alpha = -\frac{2}{5}$. Thus $\alpha = \sin^{-1} \left(-\frac{2}{5} \right) \approx -23.6°$, so the boat should head $23.6°$ south of

east (upstream). The path does seem realistic. The boat initially heads

upstream to counteract the effect of the current. Near the center of the river,

the current is stronger and the boat is pushed downstream. When the boat

nears the eastern bank, the current is slower and the boat is able to progress

upstream to arrive at point B.

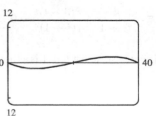

31. If $\mathbf{r}'(t) = \mathbf{c} \times \mathbf{r}(t)$ then $\mathbf{r}'(t)$ is perpendicular to both $\mathbf{c}$ and $\mathbf{r}(t)$. Remember that $\mathbf{r}'(t)$ points in the direction of motion, so if $\mathbf{r}'(t)$ is always perpendicular to $\mathbf{c}$, the path of the particle must lie in a plane perpendicular to $\mathbf{c}$. But $\mathbf{r}'(t)$ is also perpendicular to the position vector $\mathbf{r}(t)$ which confines the path to a sphere centered at the origin. Considering both restrictions, the path must be contained in a circle that lies in a plane perpendicular to $\mathbf{c}$, and the circle is centered on a line through the origin in the direction of $\mathbf{c}$.

33. $\mathbf{r}(t) = t^3\,\mathbf{i} + t^2\,\mathbf{j} \;\Rightarrow\; \mathbf{r}'(t) = 3t^2\,\mathbf{i} + 2t\,\mathbf{j}, \quad |\mathbf{r}'(t)| = \sqrt{(3t^2)^2 + (2t)^2} = \sqrt{9t^4 + 4t^2}$,

$\mathbf{r}''(t) = 6t\,\mathbf{i} + 2\,\mathbf{j}, \quad \mathbf{r}'(t) \times \mathbf{r}''(t) = -6t^2\,\mathbf{k}, \quad |\mathbf{r}'(t) \times \mathbf{r}''(t)| = 6t^2$. Then Equation 9 gives

$$a_T = \frac{\mathbf{r}'(t) \cdot \mathbf{r}''(t)}{|\mathbf{r}'(t)|} = \frac{(3t^2)(6t) + (2t)(2)}{\sqrt{9t^4 + 4t^2}} = \frac{18t^3 + 4t}{\sqrt{9t^4 + 4t^2}}$$

$\left[\text{or by Equation 8, } a_T = v' = \dfrac{d}{dt}\sqrt{9t^4 + 4t^2} = (18t^3 + 4t)/\sqrt{9t^4 + 4t^2}\right]$ and Equation 10 gives

$$a_N = \frac{|\mathbf{r}'(t) \times \mathbf{r}''(t)|}{|\mathbf{r}'(t)|} = \frac{6t^2}{\sqrt{9t^4 + 4t^2}}.$$

35. $\mathbf{r}(t) = \cos t\,\mathbf{i} + \sin t\,\mathbf{j} + t\,\mathbf{k} \;\Rightarrow\; \mathbf{r}'(t) = -\sin t\,\mathbf{i} + \cos t\,\mathbf{j} + \mathbf{k}, \quad |\mathbf{r}'(t)| = \sqrt{\sin^2 t + \cos^2 t + 1} = \sqrt{2}$,

$\mathbf{r}''(t) = -\cos t\,\mathbf{i} - \sin t\,\mathbf{j}, \quad \mathbf{r}'(t) \times \mathbf{r}''(t) = \sin t\,\mathbf{i} - \cos t\,\mathbf{j} + \mathbf{k}$.

Then $a_T = \dfrac{\mathbf{r}'(t) \cdot \mathbf{r}''(t)}{|\mathbf{r}'(t)|} = \dfrac{\sin t \cos t - \sin t \cos t}{\sqrt{2}} = 0$ and $a_N = \dfrac{|\mathbf{r}'(t) \times \mathbf{r}''(t)|}{|\mathbf{r}'(t)|} = \dfrac{\sqrt{\sin^2 t + \cos^2 t + 1}}{\sqrt{2}} = \dfrac{\sqrt{2}}{\sqrt{2}} = 1$.

37. The tangential component of $\mathbf{a}$ is the length of the projection of $\mathbf{a}$ onto $\mathbf{T}$, so we sketch the scalar projection of $\mathbf{a}$ in the tangential direction to the curve and estimate its length to be 4.5 (using the fact that $\mathbf{a}$ has length 10 as a guide). Similarly, the normal component of $\mathbf{a}$ is the length of the projection of $\mathbf{a}$ onto $\mathbf{N}$, so we sketch the scalar projection of $\mathbf{a}$ in the normal direction to the curve and estimate its length to be 9.0. Thus $a_T \approx 4.5$ cm/s^2 and $a_N \approx 9.0$ cm/s^2.

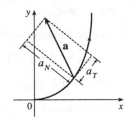

39. If the engines are turned off at time t, then the spacecraft will continue to travel in the direction of $\mathbf{v}(t)$, so we need a t such that for some scalar $s > 0$, $\mathbf{r}(t) + s\,\mathbf{v}(t) = \langle 6, 4, 9 \rangle$. $\quad \mathbf{v}(t) = \mathbf{r}'(t) = \mathbf{i} + \dfrac{1}{t}\,\mathbf{j} + \dfrac{8t}{(t^2 + 1)^2}\,\mathbf{k} \;\Rightarrow$

$$\mathbf{r}(t) + s\,\mathbf{v}(t) = \left\langle 3 + t + s,\; 2 + \ln t + \frac{s}{t},\; 7 - \frac{4}{t^2 + 1} + \frac{8st}{(t^2 + 1)^2} \right\rangle \;\Rightarrow\; 3 + t + s = 6 \;\Rightarrow\; s = 3 - t,$$

so $7 - \dfrac{4}{t^2 + 1} + \dfrac{8(3 - t)t}{(t^2 + 1)^2} = 9 \;\Leftrightarrow\; \dfrac{24t - 12t^2 - 4}{(t^2 + 1)^2} = 2 \;\Leftrightarrow\; t^4 + 8t^2 - 12t + 3 = 0$.

It is easily seen that $t = 1$ is a root of this polynomial. Also $2 + \ln 1 + \dfrac{3 - 1}{1} = 4$, so $t = 1$ is the desired solution.

10.5 Parametric Surfaces

1. $P(7, 10, 4)$ lies on the parametric surface $\mathbf{r}(u, v) = \langle 2u + 3v, 1 + 5u - v, 2 + u + v \rangle$ if and only if there are values for u

and v where $2u + 3v = 7$, $1 + 5u - v = 10$, and $2 + u + v = 4$. But solving the first two equations simultaneously gives

$u = 2$, $v = 1$ and these values do not satisfy the third equation, so P does not lie on the surface.

$Q(5, 22, 5)$ lies on the surface if $2u + 3v = 5$, $1 + 5u - v = 22$, and $2 + u + v = 5$ for some values of u and v. Solving the

first two equations simultaneously gives $u = 4$, $v = -1$ and these values satisfy the third equation, so Q lies on the surface.

3. $\mathbf{r}(u, v) = (u + v)\mathbf{i} + (3 - v)\mathbf{j} + (1 + 4u + 5v)\mathbf{k} = \langle 0, 3, 1 \rangle + u\langle 1, 0, 4 \rangle + v\langle 1, -1, 5 \rangle$. From Example 3, we recognize

this as a vector equation of a plane through the point $(0, 3, 1)$ and containing vectors $\mathbf{a} = \langle 1, 0, 4 \rangle$ and $\mathbf{b} = \langle 1, -1, 5 \rangle$. If we

wish to find a more conventional equation for the plane, a normal vector to the plane is $\mathbf{a} \times \mathbf{b} = \begin{vmatrix} \mathbf{i} & \mathbf{j} & \mathbf{k} \\ 1 & 0 & 4 \\ 1 & -1 & 5 \end{vmatrix} = 4\mathbf{i} - \mathbf{j} - \mathbf{k}$

and an equation of the plane is $4(x - 0) - (y - 3) - (z - 1) = 0$ or $4x - y - z = -4$.

5. $\mathbf{r}(s, t) = \langle s, t, t^2 - s^2 \rangle$, so the corresponding parametric equations for the surface are $x = s$, $y = t$, $z = t^2 - s^2$. For any

point (x, y, z) on the surface, we have $z = y^2 - x^2$. With no restrictions on the parameters, the surface is $z = y^2 - x^2$, which

we recognize as a hyperbolic paraboloid.

7. $\mathbf{r}(u, v) = \langle u^2 + 1, v^3 + 1, u + v \rangle$, $-1 \le u \le 1$, $-1 \le v \le 1$.

The surface has parametric equations $x = u^2 + 1$, $y = v^3 + 1$, $z = u + v$,

$-1 \le u \le 1$, $-1 \le v \le 1$. In Maple, the surface can be graphed by entering

`plot3d([u^2+1,v^3+1,u+v],u=-1..1,v=-1..1);`. In

Mathematica we use the `ParametricPlot3D` command. If we keep u

constant at u_0, $x = u_0^2 + 1$, a constant, so the corresponding grid curves must

be the curves parallel to the yz-plane. If v is constant, we have $y = v_0^3 + 1$,

a constant, so these grid curves are the curves parallel to the xz-plane.

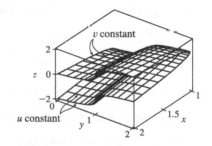

9. $\mathbf{r}(u, v) = \langle u \cos v, u \sin v, u^5 \rangle$.

The surface has parametric equations $x = u \cos v$, $y = u \sin v$,

$z = u^5$, $-1 \le u \le 1$, $0 \le v \le 2\pi$. Note that if $u = u_0$ is constant

then $z = u_0^5$ is constant and $x = u_0 \cos v$, $y = u_0 \sin v$ describe a

circle in x, y of radius $|u_0|$, so the corresponding grid curves are

circles parallel to the xy-plane. If $v = v_0$, a constant, the parametric

equations become $x = u \cos v_0$, $y = u \sin v_0$, $z = u^5$. Then

$y = (\tan v_0)x$, so these are the grid curves we see that lie in vertical

planes $y = kx$ through the z-axis.

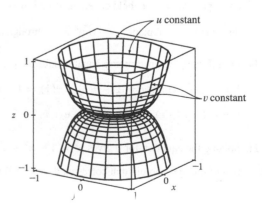

11. $x = \sin v$, $y = \cos u \sin 4v$, $z = \sin 2u \sin 4v$, $0 \le u \le 2\pi$, $-\frac{\pi}{2} \le v \le \frac{\pi}{2}$.

Note that if $v = v_0$ is constant, then $x = \sin v_0$ is constant, so the
corresponding grid curves must be parallel to the yz-plane. These
are the vertically oriented grid curves we see, each shaped like a
"figure-eight." When $u = u_0$ is held constant, the parametric
equations become $x = \sin v$, $y = \cos u_0 \sin 4v$,
$z = \sin 2u_0 \sin 4v$. Since z is a constant multiple of y, the
corresponding grid curves are the curves contained in planes
$z = ky$ that pass through the x-axis.

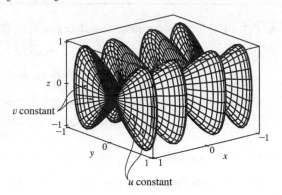

13. $\mathbf{r}(u, v) = u \cos v\, \mathbf{i} + u \sin v\, \mathbf{j} + v\, \mathbf{k}$. The parametric equations for the surface are $x = u \cos v$, $y = u \sin v$, $z = v$. We look at
the grid curves first; if we fix v, then x and y parametrize a straight line in the plane $z = v$ which intersects the z-axis. If u is
held constant, the projection onto the xy-plane is circular; with $z = v$, each grid curve is a helix. The surface is a spiraling
ramp, graph IV.

15. $\mathbf{r}(u, v) = \sin v\, \mathbf{i} + \cos u \sin 2v\, \mathbf{j} + \sin u \sin 2v\, \mathbf{k}$. Parametric equations for the surface are $x = \sin v$, $y = \cos u \sin 2v$,
$z = \sin u \sin 2v$. If $v = v_0$ is fixed, then $x = \sin v_0$ is constant, and $y = (\sin 2v_0) \cos u$ and $z = (\sin 2v_0) \sin u$ describe a
circle of radius $|\sin 2v_0|$, so each corresponding grid curve is a circle contained in the vertical plane $x = \sin v_0$ parallel to the
yz-plane. The only possible surface is graph II. The grid curves we see running lengthwise along the surface correspond to
holding u constant, in which case $y = (\cos u_0) \sin 2v$, $z = (\sin u_0) \sin 2v$ $\Rightarrow$ $z = (\tan u_0)y$, so each grid curve lies in a
plane $z = ky$ that includes the x-axis.

17. $x = \cos^3 u \cos^3 v$, $y = \sin^3 u \cos^3 v$, $z = \sin^3 v$. If $v = v_0$ is held constant then $z = \sin^3 v_0$ is constant, so the
corresponding grid curve lies in a horizontal plane. Several of the graphs exhibit horizontal grid curves, but the curves for this
surface are neither circles nor straight lines, so graph III is the only possibility. (In fact, the horizontal grid curves here are
members of the family $x = a \cos^3 u$, $y = a \sin^3 u$ and are called astroids.) The vertical grid curves we see on the surface
correspond to $u = u_0$ held constant, as then we have $x = \cos^3 u_0 \cos^3 v$, $y = \sin^3 u_0 \cos^3 v$ so the corresponding grid curve
lies in the vertical plane $y = (\tan^3 u_0)x$ through the z-axis.

19. From Example 3, parametric equations for the plane through the point $(1, 2, -3)$ that contains the vectors $\mathbf{a} = \langle 1, 1, -1 \rangle$ and
$\mathbf{b} = \langle 1, -1, 1 \rangle$ are $x = 1 + u(1) + v(1) = 1 + u + v$, $y = 2 + u(1) + v(-1) = 2 + u - v$,
$z = -3 + u(-1) + v(1) = -3 - u + v$.

21. Solving the equation for y gives $y^2 = 1 - x^2 + z^2$ $\Rightarrow$ $y = \sqrt{1 - x^2 + z^2}$. (We choose the positive root since we want the
part of the hyperboloid that corresponds to $y \ge 0$.) If we let x and z be the parameters, parametric equations are $x = x$, $z = z$,
$y = \sqrt{1 - x^2 + z^2}$.

23. Since the cone intersects the sphere in the circle $x^2 + y^2 = 2$, $z = \sqrt{2}$ and we want the portion of the sphere above this, we

can parametrize the surface as $x = x$, $y = y$, $z = \sqrt{4 - x^2 - y^2}$ where $x^2 + y^2 \le 2$.

Alternate solution: Using spherical coordinates, $x = 2\sin\phi\cos\theta$, $y = 2\sin\phi\sin\theta$, $z = 2\cos\phi$ where $0 \le \phi \le \frac{\pi}{4}$ and

$0 \le \theta \le 2\pi$.

25. Parametric equations are $x = x$, $y = 4\cos\theta$, $z = 4\sin\theta$, $0 \le x \le 5$, $0 \le \theta \le 2\pi$.

27. The surface appears to be a portion of a circular cylinder of radius 3 with axis the x-axis. An equation of the cylinder is

$y^2 + z^2 = 9$, and we can impose the restrictions $0 \le x \le 5$, $y \le 0$ to obtain the portion shown. To graph the surface on a

CAS, we can use parametric equations $x = u$, $y = 3\cos v$, $z = 3\sin v$ with the parameter domain $0 \le u \le 5$, $\frac{\pi}{2} \le v \le \frac{3\pi}{2}$.

Alternatively, we can regard x and z as parameters. Then parametric equations are $x = x$, $z = z$, $y = -\sqrt{9 - z^2}$, where

$0 \le x \le 5$ and $-3 \le z \le 3$.

29. Using Equations 3, we have the parametrization $x = x$, $y = e^{-x}\cos\theta$, $z = e^{-x}\sin\theta$, $0 \le x \le 3$, $0 \le \theta \le 2\pi$.

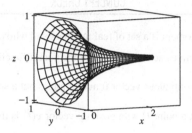

31. (a) $x = a\sin u\cos v$, $y = b\sin u\sin v$, $z = c\cos u$ $\Rightarrow$

(b)
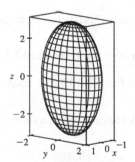

$$\frac{x^2}{a^2} + \frac{y^2}{b^2} + \frac{z^2}{c^2} = (\sin u\cos v)^2 + (\sin u\sin v)^2 + (\cos u)^2$$

$$= \sin^2 u + \cos^2 u = 1$$

and since the ranges of u and v are sufficient to generate the entire graph,

the parametric equations represent an ellipsoid.

33. (a) Replacing $\cos u$ by $\sin u$ and $\sin u$ by $\cos u$ gives parametric equations

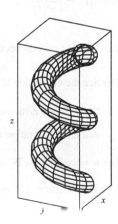

$x = (2 + \sin v)\sin u$, $y = (2 + \sin v)\cos u$, $z = u + \cos v$. From the graph, it

appears that the direction of the spiral is reversed. We can verify this observation by

noting that the projection of the spiral grid curves onto the xy-plane, given by

$x = (2 + \sin v)\sin u$, $y = (2 + \sin v)\cos u$, $z = 0$, draws a circle in the clockwise

direction for each value of v. The original equations, on the other hand, give circular

projections drawn in the counterclockwise direction. The equation for z is identical in

both surfaces, so as v increases, these grid curves spiral up in opposite directions for

the two surfaces.

(b) Replacing $\cos u$ by $\cos 2u$ and $\sin u$ by $\sin 2u$ gives parametric equations

$x = (2 + \sin v)\cos 2u$, $y = (2 + \sin v)\sin 2u$, $z = u + \cos v$. From the graph, it

appears that the number of coils in the surface doubles within the same parametric

domain. We can verify this observation by noting that the projection of the spiral grid

curves onto the xy-plane, given by $x = (2 + \sin v)\cos 2u$, $y = (2 + \sin v)\sin 2u$,

$z = 0$ (where v is constant), complete circular revolutions for $0 \leq u \leq \pi$ while the

original surface requires $0 \leq u \leq 2\pi$ for a complete revolution. Thus, the new

surface winds around twice as fast as the original surface, and since the equation for z

is identical in both surfaces, we observe twice as many circular coils in the same

z-interval.

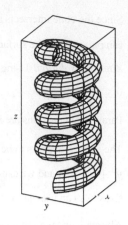

10 Review

CONCEPT CHECK

1. A vector function is a function whose domain is a set of real numbers and whose range is a set of vectors. To find the derivative
or integral, we can differentiate or integrate each component of the vector function.

2. The tip of the moving vector $\mathbf{r}(t)$ of a continuous vector function traces out a space curve.

3. The tangent vector to a smooth curve at a point P with position vector $\mathbf{r}(t)$ is the vector $\mathbf{r}'(t)$. The tangent line at P is the line

through P parallel to the tangent vector $\mathbf{r}'(t)$. The unit tangent vector is $\mathbf{T}(t) = \dfrac{\mathbf{r}'(t)}{|\mathbf{r}'(t)|}$.

4. (a)–(f) See Theorem 10.2.3.

5. Use Formula 10.3.2, or equivalently, 10.3.3.

6. (a) The curvature of a curve is $\kappa = \left| \dfrac{d\mathbf{T}}{ds} \right|$ where $\mathbf{T}$ is the unit tangent vector.

(b) $\kappa(t) = \left| \dfrac{\mathbf{T}'(t)}{\mathbf{r}'(t)} \right|$ (c) $\kappa(t) = \dfrac{|\mathbf{r}'(t) \times \mathbf{r}''(t)|}{|\mathbf{r}'(t)|^3}$ (d) $\kappa(x) = \dfrac{|f''(x)|}{[1 + (f'(x))^2]^{3/2}}$

7. (a) The unit normal vector: $\mathbf{N}(t) = \dfrac{\mathbf{T}'(t)}{|\mathbf{T}'(t)|}$.   The binormal vector: $\mathbf{B}(t) = \mathbf{T}(t) \times \mathbf{N}(t)$.

(b) See the discussion at the top of page 713.

8. (a) If $\mathbf{r}(t)$ is the position vector of the particle on the space curve, the velocity $\mathbf{v}(t) = \mathbf{r}'(t)$, the speed is given by $|\mathbf{v}(t)|$,
and the acceleration $\mathbf{a}(t) = \mathbf{v}'(t) = \mathbf{r}''(t)$.

(b) $\mathbf{a} = a_T\mathbf{T} + a_N\mathbf{N}$ where $a_T = v'$ and $a_N = \kappa v^2$.

9. See the statement of Kepler's Laws on page 722.

10. See the discussion on pages 727 and 728.

TRUE-FALSE QUIZ

1. True. If we reparametrize the curve by replacing $u = t^3$, we have $\mathbf{r}(u) = u\,\mathbf{i} + 2u\,\mathbf{j} + 3u\,\mathbf{k}$, which is a line through the origin with direction vector $\mathbf{i} + 2\,\mathbf{j} + 3\,\mathbf{k}$.

3. False. By Formula 5 of Theorem 10.2.3, $\dfrac{d}{dt}\,[\mathbf{u}(t) \times \mathbf{v}(t)] = \mathbf{u}'(t) \times \mathbf{v}(t) + \mathbf{u}(t) \times \mathbf{v}'(t)$.

5. False. κ is the magnitude of the rate of change of the unit tangent vector $\mathbf{T}$ with respect to arc length s, not with respect to t.

7. True. At an inflection point where f is twice continuously differentiable we must have $f''(x) = 0$, and by Equation 10.3.11, the curvature is 0 there.

9. False. If $\mathbf{r}(t)$ is the position of a moving particle at time t and $|\mathbf{r}(t)| = 1$ then the particle lies on the unit circle or the unit sphere, but this does not mean that the speed $|\mathbf{r}'(t)|$ must be constant. As a counterexample, let $\mathbf{r}(t) = \langle t, \sqrt{1 - t^2}\rangle$, then $\mathbf{r}'(t) = \langle 1, -t/\sqrt{1-t^2}\rangle$ and $|\mathbf{r}(t)| = \sqrt{t^2 + 1 - t^2} = 1$ but $|\mathbf{r}'(t)| = \sqrt{1 + t^2/(1-t^2)} = 1/\sqrt{1-t^2}$ which is not constant.

11. True. See the discussion at the top of page 713.

EXERCISES

1. (a) The corresponding parametric equations for the curve are $x = t$, $y = \cos \pi t$, $z = \sin \pi t$. Since $y^2 + z^2 = 1$, the curve is contained in a circular cylinder with axis the x-axis. Since $x = t$, the curve is a helix.

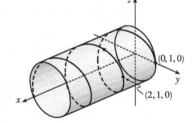

(b) $\mathbf{r}(t) = t\,\mathbf{i} + \cos \pi t\,\mathbf{j} + \sin \pi t\,\mathbf{k} \ \Rightarrow$

$\mathbf{r}'(t) = \mathbf{i} - \pi \sin \pi t\,\mathbf{j} + \pi \cos \pi t\,\mathbf{k} \ \Rightarrow$

$\mathbf{r}''(t) = -\pi^2 \cos \pi t\,\mathbf{j} - \pi^2 \sin \pi t\,\mathbf{k}$

3. The projection of the curve C of intersection onto the xy-plane is the circle $x^2 + y^2 = 16, z = 0$. So we can write $x = 4\cos t, \ y = 4\sin t, \ 0 \le t \le 2\pi$. From the equation of the plane, we have $z = 5 - x = 5 - 4\cos t$, so parametric equations for C are $x = 4\cos t, \ y = 4\sin t, \ z = 5 - 4\cos t, 0 \le t \le 2\pi$, and the corresponding vector function is $\mathbf{r}(t) = 4\cos t\,\mathbf{i} + 4\sin t\,\mathbf{j} + (5 - 4\cos t)\,\mathbf{k}, 0 \le t \le 2\pi$.

5. $\int_0^1 (t^2\,\mathbf{i} + t\cos \pi t\,\mathbf{j} + \sin \pi t\,\mathbf{k})\,dt = \left(\int_0^1 t^2\,dt\right)\mathbf{i} + \left(\int_0^1 t\cos \pi t\,dt\right)\mathbf{j} + \left(\int_0^1 \sin \pi t\,dt\right)\mathbf{k}$

$$= \left[\tfrac{1}{3}t^3\right]_0^1 \mathbf{i} + \left(\tfrac{t}{\pi}\sin \pi t\Big]_0^1 - \int_0^1 \tfrac{1}{\pi}\sin \pi t\,dt\right)\mathbf{j} + \left[-\tfrac{1}{\pi}\cos \pi t\right]_0^1 \mathbf{k}$$

$$= \tfrac{1}{3}\mathbf{i} + \left[\tfrac{1}{\pi^2}\cos \pi t\right]_0^1 \mathbf{j} + \tfrac{2}{\pi}\mathbf{k} = \tfrac{1}{3}\mathbf{i} - \tfrac{2}{\pi^2}\mathbf{j} + \tfrac{2}{\pi}\mathbf{k}$$

where we integrated by parts in the y-component.

7. $\mathbf{r}(t) = \langle t^2, t^3, t^4 \rangle$ $\Rightarrow$ $\mathbf{r}'(t) = \langle 2t, 3t^2, 4t^3 \rangle$ $\Rightarrow$ $|\mathbf{r}'(t)| = \sqrt{4t^2 + 9t^4 + 16t^6}$ and

$L = \int_0^3 |\mathbf{r}'(t)|\, dt = \int_0^3 \sqrt{4t^2 + 9t^4 + 16t^6}\, dt$. Using Simpson's Rule with $f(t) = \sqrt{4t^2 + 9t^4 + 16t^6}$ and $n = 6$ we

have $\Delta t = \frac{3-0}{6} = \frac{1}{2}$ and

$$L \approx \frac{\Delta t}{3}\left[f(0) + 4f\!\left(\tfrac{1}{2}\right) + 2f(1) + 4f\!\left(\tfrac{3}{2}\right) + 2f(2) + 4f\!\left(\tfrac{5}{2}\right) + f(3) \right]$$

$$= \tfrac{1}{6}\left[\sqrt{0 + 0 + 0} + 4 \cdot \sqrt{4\left(\tfrac{1}{2}\right)^2 + 9\left(\tfrac{1}{2}\right)^4 + 16\left(\tfrac{1}{2}\right)^6} + 2 \cdot \sqrt{4(1)^2 + 9(1)^4 + 16(1)^6} \right.$$

$$+ 4 \cdot \sqrt{4\left(\tfrac{3}{2}\right)^2 + 9\left(\tfrac{3}{2}\right)^4 + 16\left(\tfrac{3}{2}\right)^6} + 2 \cdot \sqrt{4(2)^2 + 9(2)^4 + 16(2)^6}$$

$$\left. + 4 \cdot \sqrt{4\left(\tfrac{5}{2}\right)^2 + 9\left(\tfrac{5}{2}\right)^4 + 16\left(\tfrac{5}{2}\right)^6} + \sqrt{4(3)^2 + 9(3)^4 + 16(3)^6} \right]$$

$$\approx 86.631$$

9. The angle of intersection of the two curves, θ, is the angle between their respective tangents at the point of intersection.

For both curves the point $(1, 0, 0)$ occurs when $t = 0$.

$\mathbf{r}_1'(t) = -\sin t\,\mathbf{i} + \cos t\,\mathbf{j} + \mathbf{k}$ $\Rightarrow$ $\mathbf{r}_1'(0) = \mathbf{j} + \mathbf{k}$ and $\mathbf{r}_2'(t) = \mathbf{i} + 2t\,\mathbf{j} + 3t^2\,\mathbf{k}$ $\Rightarrow$ $\mathbf{r}_2'(0) = \mathbf{i}$.

$\mathbf{r}_1'(0) \cdot \mathbf{r}_2'(0) = (\mathbf{j} + \mathbf{k}) \cdot \mathbf{i} = 0$. Therefore, the curves intersect in a right angle, that is, $\theta = \frac{\pi}{2}$.

11. (a) $\mathbf{T}(t) = \dfrac{\mathbf{r}'(t)}{|\mathbf{r}'(t)|} = \dfrac{\langle t^2, t, 1 \rangle}{|\langle t^2, t, 1 \rangle|} = \dfrac{\langle t^2, t, 1 \rangle}{\sqrt{t^4 + t^2 + 1}}$

(b) $\mathbf{T}'(t) = -\frac{1}{2}(t^4 + t^2 + 1)^{-3/2}(4t^3 + 2t)\langle t^2, t, 1 \rangle + (t^4 + t^2 + 1)^{-1/2}\langle 2t, 1, 0 \rangle$

$$= \dfrac{-2t^3 - t}{(t^4 + t^2 + 1)^{3/2}}\langle t^2, t, 1 \rangle + \dfrac{1}{(t^4 + t^2 + 1)^{1/2}}\langle 2t, 1, 0 \rangle$$

$$= \dfrac{\langle -2t^5 - t^3, -2t^4 - t^2, -2t^3 - t \rangle + \langle 2t^5 + 2t^3 + 2t, t^4 + t^2 + 1, 0 \rangle}{(t^4 + t^2 + 1)^{3/2}} = \dfrac{\langle 2t, -t^4 + 1, -2t^3 - t \rangle}{(t^4 + t^2 + 1)^{3/2}}$$

$|\mathbf{T}'(t)| = \dfrac{\sqrt{4t^2 + t^8 - 2t^4 + 1 + 4t^6 + 4t^4 + t^2}}{(t^4 + t^2 + 1)^{3/2}} = \dfrac{\sqrt{t^8 + 4t^6 + 2t^4 + 5t^2}}{(t^4 + t^2 + 1)^{3/2}}$ and $\mathbf{N}(t) = \dfrac{\langle 2t, 1 - t^4, -2t^3 - t \rangle}{\sqrt{t^8 + 4t^6 + 2t^4 + 5t^2}}$.

(c) $\kappa(t) = \dfrac{|\mathbf{T}'(t)|}{|\mathbf{r}'(t)|} = \dfrac{\sqrt{t^8 + 4t^6 + 2t^4 + 5t^2}}{(t^4 + t^2 + 1)^2}$

13. $y' = 4x^3$, $y'' = 12x^2$ and $\kappa(x) = \dfrac{|y''|}{[1 + (y')^2]^{3/2}} = \dfrac{|12x^2|}{(1 + 16x^6)^{3/2}}$, so $\kappa(1) = \dfrac{12}{17^{3/2}}$.

15. $\mathbf{r}(t) = \langle \sin 2t, t, \cos 2t \rangle$ $\Rightarrow$ $\mathbf{r}'(t) = \langle 2\cos 2t, 1, -2\sin 2t \rangle$ $\Rightarrow$ $\mathbf{T}(t) = \frac{1}{\sqrt{5}}\langle 2\cos 2t, 1, -2\sin 2t \rangle$ $\Rightarrow$

$\mathbf{T}'(t) = \frac{1}{\sqrt{5}}\langle -4\sin 2t, 0, -4\cos 2t \rangle$ $\Rightarrow$ $\mathbf{N}(t) = \langle -\sin 2t, 0, -\cos 2t \rangle$. So $\mathbf{N} = \mathbf{N}(\pi) = \langle 0, 0, -1 \rangle$ and

$\mathbf{B} = \mathbf{T} \times \mathbf{N} = \frac{1}{\sqrt{5}}\langle -1, 2, 0 \rangle$. So a normal to the osculating plane is $\langle -1, 2, 0 \rangle$ and an equation is

$-1(x - 0) + 2(y - \pi) + 0(z - 1) = 0$ or $x - 2y + 2\pi = 0$.

17. $\mathbf{r}(t) = t \ln t\,\mathbf{i} + t\,\mathbf{j} + e^{-t}\,\mathbf{k}$, $\quad \mathbf{v}(t) = \mathbf{r}'(t) = (1 + \ln t)\,\mathbf{i} + \mathbf{j} - e^{-t}\,\mathbf{k}$,

$|\mathbf{v}(t)| = \sqrt{(1 + \ln t)^2 + 1^2 + (-e^{-t})^2} = \sqrt{2 + 2\ln t + (\ln t)^2 + e^{-2t}}$, $\quad \mathbf{a}(t) = \mathbf{v}'(t) = \frac{1}{t}\mathbf{i} + e^{-t}\,\mathbf{k}$

19. We set up the axes so that the shot leaves the athlete's hand 7 ft above the origin. Then we are given $\mathbf{r}(0) = 7\mathbf{j}$,

$|\mathbf{v}(0)| = 43$ ft/s, and $\mathbf{v}(0)$ has direction given by a $45°$ angle of elevation. Then a unit vector in the direction of $\mathbf{v}(0)$ is

$\frac{1}{\sqrt{2}}(\mathbf{i}+\mathbf{j}) \Rightarrow \mathbf{v}(0) = \frac{43}{\sqrt{2}}(\mathbf{i}+\mathbf{j})$. Assuming air resistance is negligible, the only external force is due to gravity, so as in

Example 10.4.5 we have $\mathbf{a} = -g\mathbf{j}$ where here $g \approx 32$ ft/s^2. Since $\mathbf{v}'(t) = \mathbf{a}(t)$, we integrate, giving $\mathbf{v}(t) = -gt\mathbf{j} + \mathbf{C}$

where $\mathbf{C} = \mathbf{v}(0) = \frac{43}{\sqrt{2}}(\mathbf{i}+\mathbf{j}) \Rightarrow \mathbf{v}(t) = \frac{43}{\sqrt{2}}\mathbf{i} + \left(\frac{43}{\sqrt{2}} - gt\right)\mathbf{j}$. Since $\mathbf{r}'(t) = \mathbf{v}(t)$ we integrate again, so

$\mathbf{r}(t) = \frac{43}{\sqrt{2}}t\mathbf{i} + \left(\frac{43}{\sqrt{2}}t - \frac{1}{2}gt^2\right)\mathbf{j} + \mathbf{D}$. But $\mathbf{D} = \mathbf{r}(0) = 7\mathbf{j} \Rightarrow \mathbf{r}(t) = \frac{43}{\sqrt{2}}t\mathbf{i} + \left(\frac{43}{\sqrt{2}}t - \frac{1}{2}gt^2 + 7\right)\mathbf{j}$.

(a) At 2 seconds, the shot is at $\mathbf{r}(2) = \frac{43}{\sqrt{2}}(2)\mathbf{i} + \left(\frac{43}{\sqrt{2}}(2) - \frac{1}{2}g(2)^2 + 7\right)\mathbf{j} \approx 60.8\,\mathbf{i} + 3.8\,\mathbf{j}$, so the shot is about 3.8 ft above

the ground, at a horizontal distance of 60.8 ft from the athlete.

(b) The shot reaches its maximum height when the vertical component of velocity is 0: $\frac{43}{\sqrt{2}} - gt = 0 \Rightarrow$

$t = \dfrac{43}{\sqrt{2}\,g} \approx 0.95$ s. Then $\mathbf{r}(0.95) \approx 28.9\,\mathbf{i} + 21.4\,\mathbf{j}$, so the maximum height is approximately 21.4 ft.

(c) The shot hits the ground when the vertical component of $\mathbf{r}(t)$ is 0, so $\frac{43}{\sqrt{2}}t - \frac{1}{2}gt^2 + 7 = 0 \Rightarrow$

$-16t^2 + \frac{43}{\sqrt{2}}t + 7 = 0 \Rightarrow t \approx 2.11$ s. $\mathbf{r}(2.11) \approx 64.2\,\mathbf{i} - 0.08\,\mathbf{j}$, thus the shot lands approximately 64.2 ft from the

athlete.

21. From Example 4 in Section 10.5, a parametric representation of the sphere $x^2 + y^2 + z^2 = 4$ is $x = 2\sin\phi\cos\theta$,

$y = 2\sin\phi\sin\theta$, $z = 2\cos\phi$ with $0 \le \theta \le 2\pi$ and $0 \le \phi \le \pi$. We can restrict the surface to that portion between the planes

$z = 1$ and $z = -1$ by restricting $-1 \le z \le 1 \Rightarrow -1 \le 2\cos\phi \le 1 \Rightarrow \frac{\pi}{3} \le \phi \le \frac{2\pi}{3}$.

23. By the Fundamental Theorem of Calculus, $\mathbf{r}'(t) = \left\langle \sin\left(\frac{1}{2}\pi t^2\right), \cos\left(\frac{1}{2}\pi t^2\right)\right\rangle$, $|\mathbf{r}'(t)| = 1$ and so $\mathbf{T}(t) = \mathbf{r}'(t)$.

Thus $\mathbf{T}'(t) = \pi t \left\langle \cos\left(\frac{1}{2}\pi t^2\right), -\sin\left(\frac{1}{2}\pi t^2\right)\right\rangle$ and the curvature is $\kappa = |\mathbf{T}'(t)| = \sqrt{(\pi t)^2(1)} = \pi\,|t|$.

1. (a) $\mathbf{r}(t) = R\cos\omega t\,\mathbf{i} + R\sin\omega t\,\mathbf{j} \;\Rightarrow\; \mathbf{v} = \mathbf{r}'(t) = -\omega R\sin\omega t\,\mathbf{i} + \omega R\cos\omega t\,\mathbf{j}$, so $\mathbf{r} = R(\cos\omega t\,\mathbf{i} + \sin\omega t\,\mathbf{j})$ and

$\mathbf{v} = \omega R(-\sin\omega t\,\mathbf{i} + \cos\omega t\,\mathbf{j})$. $\mathbf{v}\cdot\mathbf{r} = \omega R^2(-\cos\omega t\sin\omega t + \sin\omega t\cos\omega t) = 0$, so $\mathbf{v}\perp\mathbf{r}$. Since $\mathbf{r}$ points along a

radius of the circle, and $\mathbf{v}\perp\mathbf{r}$, $\mathbf{v}$ is tangent to the circle. Because it is a velocity vector, $\mathbf{v}$ points in the direction of motion.

(b) In (a), we wrote $\mathbf{v}$ in the form $\omega R\,\mathbf{u}$, where $\mathbf{u}$ is the unit vector $-\sin\omega t\,\mathbf{i} + \cos\omega t\,\mathbf{j}$. Clearly $|\mathbf{v}| = \omega R|\mathbf{u}| = \omega R$. At

speed ωR, the particle completes one revolution, a distance $2\pi R$, in time $T = \dfrac{2\pi R}{\omega R} = \dfrac{2\pi}{\omega}$.

(c) $\mathbf{a} = \dfrac{d\mathbf{v}}{dt} = -\omega^2 R\cos\omega t\,\mathbf{i} - \omega^2 R\sin\omega t\,\mathbf{j} = -\omega^2 R(\cos\omega t\,\mathbf{i} + \sin\omega t\,\mathbf{j})$, so $\mathbf{a} = -\omega^2\mathbf{r}$. This shows that $\mathbf{a}$ is proportional

to $\mathbf{r}$ and points in the opposite direction (toward the origin). Also, $|\mathbf{a}| = \omega^2|\mathbf{r}| = \omega^2 R$.

(d) By Newton's Second Law (see Section 10.4), $\mathbf{F} = m\mathbf{a}$, so $|\mathbf{F}| = m|\mathbf{a}| = mR\omega^2 = \dfrac{m(\omega R)^2}{R} = \dfrac{m|\mathbf{v}|^2}{R}$.

3. (a) The projectile reaches maximum height when $0 = \dfrac{dy}{dt} = \dfrac{d}{dt}\left[(v_0\sin\alpha)t - \tfrac{1}{2}gt^2\right] = v_0\sin\alpha - gt$; that is, when

$t = \dfrac{v_0\sin\alpha}{g}$ and $y = (v_0\sin\alpha)\left(\dfrac{v_0\sin\alpha}{g}\right) - \dfrac{1}{2}g\left(\dfrac{v_0\sin\alpha}{g}\right)^2 = \dfrac{v_0^2\sin^2\alpha}{2g}$. This is the maximum height attained when

the projectile is fired with an angle of elevation α. This maximum height is largest when $\alpha = \tfrac{\pi}{2}$. In that case, $\sin\alpha = 1$

and the maximum height is $\dfrac{v_0^2}{2g}$.

(b) Let $R = v_0^2/g$. We are asked to consider the parabola $x^2 + 2Ry - R^2 = 0$ which can be rewritten as $y = -\dfrac{1}{2R}x^2 + \dfrac{R}{2}$.

The points on or inside this parabola are those for which $-R \le x \le R$ and $0 \le y \le \dfrac{-1}{2R}x^2 + \dfrac{R}{2}$. When the projectile is

fired at angle of elevation α, the points (x,y) along its path satisfy the relations $x = (v_0\cos\alpha)t$ and

$y = (v_0\sin\alpha)t - \tfrac{1}{2}gt^2$, where $0 \le t \le (2v_0\sin\alpha)/g$ (as in Example 10.4.5). Thus

$|x| \le \left|v_0\cos\alpha\left(\dfrac{2v_0\sin\alpha}{g}\right)\right| = \left|\dfrac{v_0^2}{g}\sin 2\alpha\right| \le \left|\dfrac{v_0^2}{g}\right| = |R|$. This shows that $-R \le x \le R$.

For t in the specified range, we also have $y = t\left(v_0\sin\alpha - \tfrac{1}{2}gt\right) = \tfrac{1}{2}gt\left(\dfrac{2v_0\sin\alpha}{g} - t\right) \ge 0$ and

$y = (v_0\sin\alpha)\dfrac{x}{v_0\cos\alpha} - \dfrac{g}{2}\left(\dfrac{x}{v_0\cos\alpha}\right)^2 = (\tan\alpha)x - \dfrac{g}{2v_0^2\cos^2\alpha}x^2 = -\dfrac{1}{2R\cos^2\alpha}x^2 + (\tan\alpha)x$. Thus

$$y - \left(\dfrac{-1}{2R}x^2 + \dfrac{R}{2}\right) = \dfrac{-1}{2R\cos^2\alpha}x^2 + \dfrac{1}{2R}x^2 + (\tan\alpha)x - \dfrac{R}{2}$$

$$= \dfrac{x^2}{2R}\left(1 - \dfrac{1}{\cos^2\alpha}\right) + (\tan\alpha)x - \dfrac{R}{2} = \dfrac{x^2(1 - \sec^2\alpha) + 2R(\tan\alpha)x - R^2}{2R}$$

$$= \dfrac{-(\tan^2\alpha)x^2 + 2R(\tan\alpha)x - R^2}{2R} = \dfrac{-[(\tan\alpha)x - R]^2}{2R} \le 0$$

We have shown that every target that can be hit by the projectile lies on or inside the parabola $y = -\dfrac{1}{2R} x^2 + \dfrac{R}{2}$.

Now let (a, b) be any point on or inside the parabola $y = -\dfrac{1}{2R} x^2 + \dfrac{R}{2}$. Then $-R \le a \le R$ and $0 \le b \le -\dfrac{1}{2R} a^2 + \dfrac{R}{2}$.

We seek an angle α such that (a, b) lies in the path of the projectile; that is, we wish to find an angle α such that

$b = -\dfrac{1}{2R \cos^2 \alpha} a^2 + (\tan \alpha) \, a$ or equivalently $b = \dfrac{-1}{2R} (\tan^2 \alpha + 1)a^2 + (\tan \alpha) \, a$. Rearranging this equation we get

$\dfrac{a^2}{2R} \tan^2 \alpha - a \tan \alpha + \left(\dfrac{a^2}{2R} + b \right) = 0$ or $a^2(\tan \alpha)^2 - 2aR(\tan \alpha) + (a^2 + 2bR) = 0$ $(*)$. This quadratic equation

for $\tan \alpha$ has real solutions exactly when the discriminant is nonnegative. Now $B^2 - 4AC \ge 0$ $\Leftrightarrow$

$(-2aR)^2 - 4a^2(a^2 + 2bR) \ge 0$ $\Leftrightarrow$ $4a^2(R^2 - a^2 - 2bR) \ge 0$ $\Leftrightarrow$ $-a^2 - 2bR + R^2 \ge 0$ $\Leftrightarrow$

$b \le \dfrac{1}{2R}(R^2 - a^2)$ $\Leftrightarrow$ $b \le \dfrac{-1}{2R} a^2 + \dfrac{R}{2}$. This condition is satisfied since (a, b) is on or inside the parabola

$y = -\dfrac{1}{2R} x^2 + \dfrac{R}{2}$. It follows that (a, b) lies in the path of the projectile when $\tan \alpha$ satisfies $(*)$, that is, when

$\tan \alpha = \dfrac{2aR \pm \sqrt{4a^2(R^2 - a^2 - 2bR)}}{2a^2} = \dfrac{R \pm \sqrt{R^2 - 2bR - a^2}}{a}$.

(c)

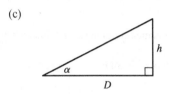

If the gun is pointed at a target with height h at a distance D downrange, then

$\tan \alpha = h/D$. When the projectile reaches a distance D downrange (remember

we are assuming that it doesn't hit the ground first), we have $D = x = (v_0 \cos \alpha)t$,

so $t = \dfrac{D}{v_0 \cos \alpha}$ and $y = (v_0 \sin \alpha)t - \tfrac{1}{2}gt^2 = D \tan \alpha - \dfrac{gD^2}{2v_0^2 \cos^2 \alpha}$.

Meanwhile, the target, whose x-coordinate is also D, has fallen from height h to height

$h - \tfrac{1}{2}gt^2 = D \tan \alpha - \dfrac{gD^2}{2v_0^2 \cos^2 \alpha}$. Thus the projectile hits the target.

5. (a) $\mathbf{a} = -g\mathbf{j}$ $\Rightarrow$ $\mathbf{v} = \mathbf{v}_0 - gt\mathbf{j} = 2\mathbf{i} - gt\mathbf{j}$ $\Rightarrow$ $\mathbf{s} = \mathbf{s}_0 + 2t\mathbf{i} - \tfrac{1}{2}gt^2\mathbf{j} = 3.5\mathbf{j} + 2t\mathbf{i} - \tfrac{1}{2}gt^2\mathbf{j}$ $\Rightarrow$

$\mathbf{s} = 2t\mathbf{i} + \left(3.5 - \tfrac{1}{2}gt^2\right)\mathbf{j}$. Therefore $y = 0$ when $t = \sqrt{7/g}$ seconds. At that instant, the ball is $2\sqrt{7/g} \approx 0.94$ ft to the

right of the table top. Its coordinates (relative to an origin on the floor directly under the table's edge) are $(0.94, 0)$. At

impact, the velocity is $\mathbf{v} = 2\mathbf{i} - \sqrt{7g}\,\mathbf{j}$, so the speed is $|\mathbf{v}| = \sqrt{4 + 7g} \approx 15$ ft/s.

(b) The slope of the curve when $t = \sqrt{\dfrac{7}{g}}$ is $\dfrac{dy}{dx} = \dfrac{dy/dt}{dx/dt} = \dfrac{-gt}{2} = \dfrac{-g\sqrt{7/g}}{2} = \dfrac{-\sqrt{7g}}{2}$. Thus $\cot \theta = \dfrac{\sqrt{7g}}{2}$

and $\theta \approx 7.6°$.

(c) From (a), $|\mathbf{v}| = \sqrt{4 + 7g}$. So the ball rebounds with speed $0.8\sqrt{4 + 7g} \approx 12.08$ ft/s at angle of inclination

$90° - \theta \approx 82.3886°$. By Example 10.4.5, the horizontal distance traveled between bounces is $d = \dfrac{v_0^2 \sin 2\alpha}{g}$, where

$v_0 \approx 12.08$ ft/s and $\alpha \approx 82.3886°$. Therefore, $d \approx 1.197$ ft. So the ball strikes the floor at about

$2\sqrt{7/g} + 1.197 \approx 2.13$ ft to the right of the table's edge.

7. The trajectory of the projectile is given by $\mathbf{r}(t) = (v\cos\alpha)t\,\mathbf{i} + \left[(v\sin\alpha)t - \frac{1}{2}gt^2\right]\mathbf{j}$, so

$\mathbf{v}(t) = \mathbf{r}'(t) = v\cos\alpha\,\mathbf{i} + (v\sin\alpha - gt)\,\mathbf{j}$ and

$$|\mathbf{v}(t)| = \sqrt{(v\cos\alpha)^2 + (v\sin\alpha - gt)^2} = \sqrt{v^2 - (2vg\sin\alpha)\,t + g^2t^2} = \sqrt{g^2\left(t^2 - \frac{2v}{g}(\sin\alpha)\,t + \frac{v^2}{g^2}\right)}$$

$$= g\sqrt{\left(t - \frac{v}{g}\sin\alpha\right)^2 + \frac{v^2}{g^2} - \frac{v^2}{g^2}\sin^2\alpha} = g\sqrt{\left(t - \frac{v}{g}\sin\alpha\right)^2 + \frac{v^2}{g^2}\cos^2\alpha}$$

The projectile hits the ground when $(v\sin\alpha)t - \frac{1}{2}gt^2 = 0 \;\Rightarrow\; t = \frac{2v}{g}\sin\alpha$, so the distance traveled by the projectile is

$$L(\alpha) = \int_0^{(2v/g)\sin\alpha} |\mathbf{v}(t)|\,dt = \int_0^{(2v/g)\sin\alpha} g\sqrt{\left(t - \frac{v}{g}\sin\alpha\right)^2 + \frac{v^2}{g^2}\cos^2\alpha}\,dt$$

$$= g\left[\frac{t - (v/g)\sin\alpha}{2}\sqrt{\left(t - \frac{v}{g}\sin\alpha\right)^2 + \left(\frac{v}{g}\cos\alpha\right)^2}\right.$$

$$\left. + \frac{[(v/g)\cos\alpha]^2}{2}\ln\left(t - \frac{v}{g}\sin\alpha + \sqrt{\left(t - \frac{v}{g}\sin\alpha\right)^2 + \left(\frac{v}{g}\cos\alpha\right)^2}\right)\right]_0^{(2v/g)\sin\alpha}$$

[using Formula 21 in the Table of Integrals]

$$= \frac{g}{2}\left[\frac{v}{g}\sin\alpha\sqrt{\left(\frac{v}{g}\sin\alpha\right)^2 + \left(\frac{v}{g}\cos\alpha\right)^2} + \left(\frac{v}{g}\cos\alpha\right)^2\ln\left(\frac{v}{g}\sin\alpha + \sqrt{\left(\frac{v}{g}\sin\alpha\right)^2 + \left(\frac{v}{g}\cos\alpha\right)^2}\right)\right.$$

$$\left. + \frac{v}{g}\sin\alpha\sqrt{\left(\frac{v}{g}\sin\alpha\right)^2 + \left(\frac{v}{g}\cos\alpha\right)^2} - \left(\frac{v}{g}\cos\alpha\right)^2\ln\left(-\frac{v}{g}\sin\alpha + \sqrt{\left(\frac{v}{g}\sin\alpha\right)^2 + \left(\frac{v}{g}\cos\alpha\right)^2}\right)\right]$$

$$= \frac{g}{2}\left[\frac{v}{g}\sin\alpha\cdot\frac{v}{g} + \frac{v^2}{g^2}\cos^2\alpha\ln\left(\frac{v}{g}\sin\alpha + \frac{v}{g}\right) + \frac{v}{g}\sin\alpha\cdot\frac{v}{g} - \frac{v^2}{g^2}\cos^2\alpha\ln\left(-\frac{v}{g}\sin\alpha + \frac{v}{g}\right)\right]$$

$$= \frac{v^2}{g}\sin\alpha + \frac{v^2}{2g}\cos^2\alpha\ln\left(\frac{(v/g)\sin\alpha + v/g}{-(v/g)\sin\alpha + v/g}\right) = \frac{v^2}{g}\sin\alpha + \frac{v^2}{2g}\cos^2\alpha\ln\left(\frac{1 + \sin\alpha}{1 - \sin\alpha}\right)$$

We want to maximize $L(\alpha)$ for $0 \le \alpha \le \pi/2$.

$$L'(\alpha) = \frac{v^2}{g}\cos\alpha + \frac{v^2}{2g}\left[\cos^2\alpha\cdot\frac{1 - \sin\alpha}{1 + \sin\alpha}\cdot\frac{2\cos\alpha}{(1 - \sin\alpha)^2} - 2\cos\alpha\sin\alpha\ln\left(\frac{1 + \sin\alpha}{1 - \sin\alpha}\right)\right]$$

$$= \frac{v^2}{g}\cos\alpha + \frac{v^2}{2g}\left[\cos^2\alpha\cdot\frac{2}{\cos\alpha} - 2\cos\alpha\sin\alpha\ln\left(\frac{1 + \sin\alpha}{1 - \sin\alpha}\right)\right]$$

$$= \frac{v^2}{g}\cos\alpha + \frac{v^2}{g}\cos\alpha\left[1 - \sin\alpha\ln\left(\frac{1 + \sin\alpha}{1 - \sin\alpha}\right)\right] = \frac{v^2}{g}\cos\alpha\left[2 - \sin\alpha\ln\left(\frac{1 + \sin\alpha}{1 - \sin\alpha}\right)\right]$$

$L(\alpha)$ has critical points for $0 < \alpha < \pi/2$ when $L'(\alpha) = 0 \;\Rightarrow\; 2 - \sin\alpha\ln\left(\frac{1 + \sin\alpha}{1 - \sin\alpha}\right) = 0$ [since $\cos\alpha \ne 0$].

Solving by graphing (or using a CAS) gives $\alpha \approx 0.9855$. Compare values at the critical point and the endpoints:

$L(0) = 0$, $L(\pi/2) = v^2/g$, and $L(0.9855) \approx 1.20v^2/g$. Thus the distance traveled by the projectile is maximized

for $\alpha \approx 0.9855$ or $\approx 56°$.

9. We can write the vector equation as $\mathbf{r}_1(t) = \mathbf{a}t^2 + \mathbf{b}t + \mathbf{c}$ where $\mathbf{a} = \langle a_1, a_2, a_3 \rangle$, $\mathbf{b} = \langle b_1, b_2, b_3 \rangle$, and $\mathbf{c} = \langle c_1, c_2, c_3 \rangle$.

We know from Example 3 in Section 10.5 that $\mathbf{r}_2(u, v) = \mathbf{r}_0 + u\mathbf{a} + v\mathbf{b}$ is the vector equation of a plane, and

$\mathbf{r}_1(t) = \mathbf{r}_2(t^2, t)$ when $\mathbf{r}_0 = \mathbf{c}$, so the curve lies in the plane $\mathbf{r}(u, v) = \mathbf{c} + u\mathbf{a} + v\mathbf{b}$. [Here we assume that $\mathbf{a}$ and $\mathbf{b}$ are

nonparallel. Otherwise, $\mathbf{r}_1(t)$ and $\mathbf{r}(u, v)$ are identical lines which lie in many planes.] We can find an equation in terms

of x, y, z for the plane by observing that $\mathbf{a}$ and $\mathbf{b}$ are parallel to the plane (and not to each other), so a normal vector for the

plane is $\mathbf{a} \times \mathbf{b} = \langle a_2 b_3 - a_3 b_2, a_3 b_1 - a_1 b_3, a_1 b_2 - a_2 b_1 \rangle$. The point (c_1, c_2, c_3) lies on the plane, so an equation of the

plane is

$$(a_2 b_3 - a_3 b_2)(x - c_1) + (a_3 b_1 - a_1 b_3)(y - c_2) + (a_1 b_2 - a_2 b_1)(z - c_3) = 0$$

or

$$(a_2 b_3 - a_3 b_2)x + (a_3 b_1 - a_1 b_3)y + (a_1 b_2 - a_2 b_1)z = a_2 b_3 c_1 - a_3 b_2 c_1 + a_3 b_1 c_2 - a_1 b_3 c_2 + a_1 b_2 c_3 - a_2 b_1 c_3$$

Note: Another approach is to show that the osculating plane at any point on the curve is the same and so the entire curve must

lie in that plane.

11 ☐ PARTIAL DERIVATIVES

11.1 Functions of Several Variables

1. (a) From Table 1, $f(-15, 40) = -27$, which means that if the temperature is $-15°C$ and the wind speed is 40 km/h, then the air would feel equivalent to approximately $-27°C$ without wind.

(b) The question is asking: when the temperature is $-20°C$, what wind speed gives a wind-chill index of $-30°C$? From Table 1, the speed is 20 km/h.

(c) The question is asking: when the wind speed is 20 km/h, what temperature gives a wind-chill index of $-49°C$? From Table 1, the temperature is $-35°C$.

(d) The function $W = f(-5, v)$ means that we fix T at -5 and allow v to vary, resulting in a function of one variable. In other words, the function gives wind-chill index values for different wind speeds when the temperature is $-5°C$. From Table 1 (look at the row corresponding to $T = -5$), the function decreases and appears to approach a constant value as v increases.

(e) The function $W = f(T, 50)$ means that we fix v at 50 and allow T to vary, again giving a function of one variable. In other words, the function gives wind-chill index values for different temperatures when the wind speed is 50 km/h . From Table 1 (look at the column corresponding to $v = 50$), the function increases almost linearly as T increases.

3. If the amounts of labor and capital are both doubled, we replace L, K in the function with $2L, 2K$, giving

$$P(2L, 2K) = 1.01(2L)^{0.75}(2K)^{0.25} = 1.01(2^{0.75})(2^{0.25})L^{0.75}K^{0.25} = (2^1)1.01L^{0.75}K^{0.25} = 2P(L, K)$$

Thus, the production is doubled. It is also true for the general case $P(L, K) = bL^\alpha K^{1-\alpha}$:

$$P(2L, 2K) = b(2L)^\alpha(2K)^{1-\alpha} = b(2^\alpha)(2^{1-\alpha})L^\alpha K^{1-\alpha} = (2^{\alpha+1-\alpha})bL^\alpha K^{1-\alpha} = 2P(L, K).$$

5. $\ln(9 - x^2 - 9y^2)$ is defined only when $9 - x^2 - 9y^2 > 0$, or $\frac{1}{9}x^2 + y^2 < 1$. So the domain of f is $\{(x, y) \mid \frac{1}{9}x^2 + y^2 < 1\}$, the interior of an ellipse.

For this domain, the range of $g(x, y) = 9 - x^2 - 9y^2$ is $(0, 9]$, so the range of $f(x, y) = \ln(g(x, y))$ is $(-\infty, \ln 9]$.

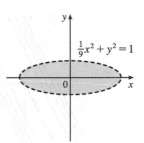

7. (a) $f(1, 1, 1) = \sqrt{1} + \sqrt{1} + \sqrt{1} + \ln(4 - 1^2 - 1^2 - 1^2) = 3 + \ln 1 = 3$

(b) $\sqrt{x}$, $\sqrt{y}$, $\sqrt{z}$ are defined only when $x \geq 0$, $y \geq 0$, $z \geq 0$, and $\ln(4 - x^2 - y^2 - z^2)$ is defined when

$$4 - x^2 - y^2 - z^2 > 0 \quad \Leftrightarrow \quad x^2 + y^2 + z^2 < 4, \text{ thus the domain is}$$

$\left\{ (x, y, z) \mid x^2 + y^2 + z^2 < 4, \ x \geq 0, \ y \geq 0, \ z \geq 0 \right\}$, the portion of the interior of a sphere of radius 2, centered at the

origin, that is in the first octant.

9. The point $(-3, 3)$ lies between the level curves with z-values 50 and 60. Since the point is a little closer to the level curve with

$z = 60$, we estimate that $f(-3, 3) \approx 56$. The point $(3, -2)$ appears to be just about halfway between the level curves with

z-values 30 and 40, so we estimate $f(3, -2) \approx 35$. The graph rises as we approach the origin, gradually from above, steeply

from below.

11. The point $(160, 10)$, corresponding to day 160 and a depth of 10 m, lies between the isothermals with temperature values

of 8 and $12°C$. Since the point appears to be located about three-fourths the distance from the $8°C$ isothermal to the $12°C$

isothermal, we estimate the temperature at that point to be approximately $11°C$. The point $(180, 5)$ lies between the 16 and

$20°C$ isothermals, very close to the $20°C$ level curve, so we estimate the temperature there to be about $19.5°C$.

13. Near A, the level curves are very close together, indicating that the terrain is quite steep. At B, the level curves are much

farther apart, so we would expect the terrain to be much less steep than near A, perhaps almost flat.

15.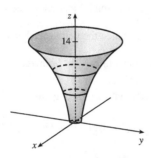

17.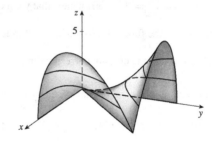

19. The level curves are $(y - 2x)^2 = k$ or $y = 2x \pm \sqrt{k}$,

$k \geq 0$, a family of pairs of parallel lines.

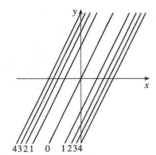

21. The level curves are $\sqrt{x} + y = k$ or $y = -\sqrt{x} + k$, a

family of vertical translations of the graph of the root

function $y = -\sqrt{x}$.

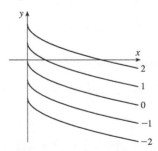

23. The level curves are $ye^x = k$ or $y = ke^{-x}$, a family of exponential curves.

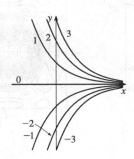

25. The level curves are $\sqrt{y^2 - x^2} = k$ or $y^2 - x^2 = k^2$, $k \geq 0$. When $k = 0$ the level curve is the pair of lines $y = \pm x$. For $k > 0$, the level curves are hyperbolas with axis the y-axis.

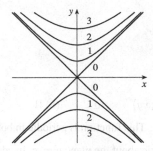

27. The contour map consists of the level curves $k = x^2 + 9y^2$, a family of ellipses with major axis the x-axis. (Or, if $k = 0$, the origin.)

The graph of $f(x, y)$ is the surface $z = x^2 + 9y^2$, an elliptic paraboloid.

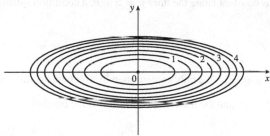

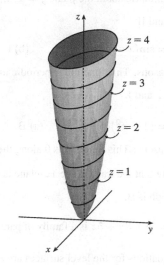

If we visualize lifting each ellipse $k = x^2 + 9y^2$ of the contour map to the plane $z = k$, we have horizontal traces that indicate the shape of the graph of f.

29. The isothermals are given by $k = 100/(1 + x^2 + 2y^2)$ or $x^2 + 2y^2 = (100 - k)/k$ $[0 < k \leq 100]$, a family of ellipses.

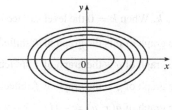

31. $f(x, y) = xy^2 - x^3$

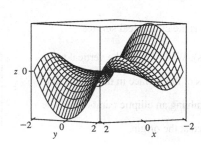

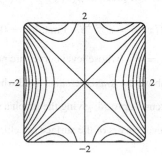

The traces parallel to the yz-plane (such as the left-front trace in the graph above) are parabolas; those parallel to the xz-plane (such as the right-front trace) are cubic curves. The surface is called a monkey saddle because a monkey sitting on the surface near the origin has places for both legs and tail to rest.

33. $f(x,y) = e^{-(x^2+y^2)/3}\left(\sin(x^2) + \cos(y^2)\right)$

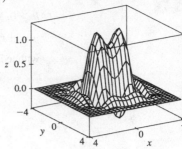

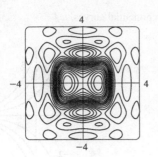

35. $z = \sin(xy)$ (a) C   (b) II

Reasons: This function is periodic in both x and y, and the function is the same when x is interchanged with y, so its graph is symmetric about the plane $y = x$. In addition, the function is 0 along the x- and y-axes. These conditions are satisfied only by C and II.

37. $z = \sin(x - y)$ (a) F   (b) I

Reasons: This function is periodic in both x and y but is constant along the lines $y = x + k$, a condition satisfied only by F and I.

39. $z = (1 - x^2)(1 - y^2)$ (a) B   (b) VI

Reasons: This function is 0 along the lines $x = \pm1$ and $y = \pm1$. The only contour map in which this could occur is VI. Also note that the trace in the xz-plane is the parabola $z = 1 - x^2$ and the trace in the yz-plane is the parabola $z = 1 - y^2$, so the graph is B.

41. $k = x + 3y + 5z$ is a family of parallel planes with normal vector $\langle 1, 3, 5 \rangle$.

43. Equations for the level surfaces are $k = y^2 + z^2$. For $k > 0$, we have a family of circular cylinders with axis the x-axis and radius $\sqrt{k}$. When $k = 0$ the level surface is the x-axis. (There are no level surfaces for $k < 0$.)

45. (a) The graph of g is the graph of f shifted upward 2 units.

(b) The graph of g is the graph of f stretched vertically by a factor of 2.

(c) The graph of g is the graph of f reflected about the xy-plane.

(d) The graph of $g(x, y) = -f(x, y) + 2$ is the graph of f reflected about the xy-plane and then shifted upward 2 units.

47. $f(x, y) = e^{cx^2+y^2}$. First, if $c = 0$, the graph is the cylindrical surface

$z = e^{y^2}$ (whose level curves are parallel lines). When $c > 0$, the vertical trace above the y-axis remains fixed while the sides of the surface in the x-direction "curl" upward, giving the graph a shape resembling an elliptic paraboloid. The level curves of the surface are ellipses centered at the origin.

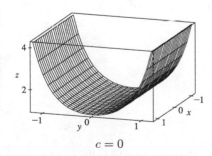

$c = 0$

For $0 < c < 1$, the ellipses have major axis the x-axis and the eccentricity increases as $c \to 0$.

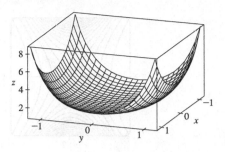
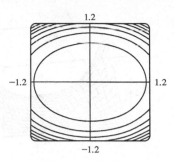

$c = 0.5$ (level curves in increments of 1)

For $c = 1$ the level curves are circles centered at the origin.

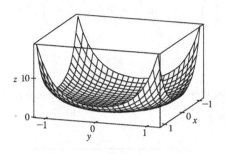
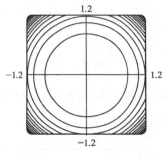

$c = 1$ (level curves in increments of 1)

When $c > 1$, the level curves are ellipses with major axis the y-axis, and the eccentricity increases as c increases.

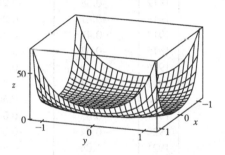
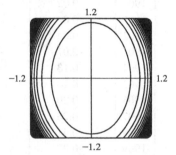

$c = 2$ (level curves in increments of 4)

For values of $c < 0$, the sides of the surface in the x-direction curl downward and approach the xy-plane (while the vertical trace $x = 0$ remains fixed), giving a saddle-shaped appearance to the graph near the point $(0, 0, 1)$. The level curves consist of a family of hyperbolas. As c decreases, the surface becomes flatter in the x-direction and the surface's approach to the curve in the trace $x = 0$ becomes steeper, as the graphs demonstrate.

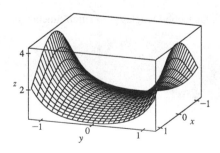
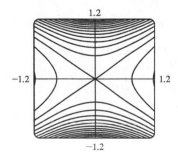

$c = -0.5$ (level curves in increments of 0.25)

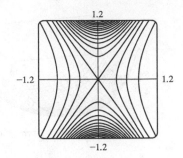

$$c = -2 \text{ (level curves in increments of } 0.25)$$

49. (a) $P = bL^\alpha K^{1-\alpha} \;\Rightarrow\; \dfrac{P}{K} = bL^\alpha K^{-\alpha} \;\Rightarrow\; \dfrac{P}{K} = b\left(\dfrac{L}{K}\right)^\alpha \;\Rightarrow\; \ln\dfrac{P}{K} = \ln\left(b\left(\dfrac{L}{K}\right)^\alpha\right) \;\Rightarrow\;$

$$\ln\frac{P}{K} = \ln b + \alpha \ln\left(\frac{L}{K}\right)$$

(b) We list the values for $\ln(L/K)$ and $\ln(P/K)$ for the years 1899–1922. (Historically, these values were rounded to 2 decimal places.)

Year	$x = \ln(L/K)$	$y = \ln(P/K)$	Year	$x = \ln(L/K)$	$y = \ln(P/K)$
1899	0	0	1911	−0.38	−0.34
1900	−0.02	−0.06	1912	−0.38	−0.24
1901	−0.04	−0.02	1913	−0.41	−0.25
1902	−0.04	0	1914	−0.47	−0.37
1903	−0.07	−0.05	1915	−0.53	−0.34
1904	−0.13	−0.12	1916	−0.49	−0.28
1905	−0.18	−0.04	1917	−0.53	−0.39
1906	−0.20	−0.07	1918	−0.60	−0.50
1907	−0.23	−0.15	1919	−0.68	−0.57
1908	−0.41	−0.38	1920	−0.74	−0.57
1909	−0.33	−0.24	1921	−1.05	−0.85
1910	−0.35	−0.27	1922	−0.98	−0.59

After entering the (x, y) pairs into a calculator or CAS, the resulting least squares regression line through the points is approximately $y = 0.75136x + 0.01053$, which we round to $y = 0.75x + 0.01$.

(c) Comparing the regression line from part (b) to the equation $y = \ln b + \alpha x$ with $x = \ln(L/K)$ and $y = \ln(P/K)$, we have $\alpha = 0.75$ and $\ln b = 0.01 \;\Rightarrow\; b = e^{0.01} \approx 1.01$. Thus, the Cobb-Douglas production function is

$$P = bL^\alpha K^{1-\alpha} = 1.01L^{0.75}K^{0.25}.$$

11.2   Limits and Continuity

1. In general, we can't say anything about $f(3,1)$! $\displaystyle\lim_{(x,y)\to(3,1)} f(x,y) = 6$ means that the values of $f(x,y)$ approach 6 as

(x,y) approaches, but is not equal to, $(3,1)$. If f is continuous, we know that $\displaystyle\lim_{(x,y)\to(a,b)} f(x,y) = f(a,b)$, so

$\displaystyle\lim_{(x,y)\to(3,1)} f(x,y) = f(3,1) = 6.$

3. We make a table of values of

$$f(x,y) = \frac{x^2 y^3 + x^3 y^2 - 5}{2 - xy} \text{ for a set}$$

of (x,y) points near the origin.

x \ y	−0.2	−0.1	−0.05	0	0.05	0.1	0.2
−0.2	−2.551	−2.525	−2.513	−2.500	−2.488	−2.475	−2.451
−0.1	−2.525	−2.513	−2.506	−2.500	−2.494	−2.488	−2.475
−0.05	−2.513	−2.506	−2.503	−2.500	−2.497	−2.494	−2.488
0	−2.500	−2.500	−2.500		−2.500	−2.500	−2.500
0.05	−2.488	−2.494	−2.497	−2.500	−2.503	−2.506	−2.513
0.1	−2.475	−2.488	−2.494	−2.500	−2.506	−2.513	−2.525
0.2	−2.451	−2.475	−2.488	−2.500	−2.513	−2.525	−2.551

As the table shows, the values of $f(x,y)$ seem to approach -2.5 as (x,y) approaches the origin from a variety of different

directions. This suggests that $\displaystyle\lim_{(x,y)\to(0,0)} f(x,y) = -2.5$. Since f is a rational function, it is continuous on its domain. f is

defined at $(0,0)$, so we can use direct substitution to establish that $\displaystyle\lim_{(x,y)\to(0,0)} f(x,y) = \frac{0^2 0^3 + 0^3 0^2 - 5}{2 - 0\cdot 0} = -\frac{5}{2}$, verifying

our guess.

5. $f(x,y) = 5x^3 - x^2 y^2$ is a polynomial, and hence continuous, so $\displaystyle\lim_{(x,y)\to(1,2)} f(x,y) = f(1,2) = 5(1)^3 - (1)^2(2)^2 = 1.$

7. $f(x,y) = y^4/(x^4 + 3y^4)$.   First approach $(0,0)$ along the x-axis. Then $f(x,0) = 0/x^4 = 0$ for $x \neq 0$, so $f(x,y) \to 0$.

Now approach $(0,0)$ along the y-axis. Then for $y \neq 0$, $f(0,y) = y^4/3y^4 = 1/3$, so $f(x,y) \to 1/3$. Since f has two different

limits along two different lines, the limit does not exist.

9. $f(x,y) = (xy \cos y)/(3x^2 + y^2)$.   On the x-axis, $f(x,0) = 0$ for $x \neq 0$, so $f(x,y) \to 0$ as $(x,y) \to (0,0)$ along the

x-axis. Approaching $(0,0)$ along the line $y = x$, $f(x,x) = (x^2 \cos x)/4x^2 = \frac{1}{4} \cos x$ for $x \neq 0$, so $f(x,y) \to \frac{1}{4}$ along this

line. Thus the limit does not exist.

11. $f(x,y) = \dfrac{xy}{\sqrt{x^2 + y^2}}$.   We can see that the limit along any line through $(0,0)$ is 0, as well as along other paths through

$(0,0)$ such as $x = y^2$ and $y = x^2$. So we suspect that the limit exists and equals 0; we use the Squeeze Theorem to prove our

assertion. $0 \leq \left| \dfrac{xy}{\sqrt{x^2 + y^2}} \right| \leq |x|$ since $|y| \leq \sqrt{x^2 + y^2}$, and $|x| \to 0$ as $(x,y) \to (0,0)$. So $\displaystyle\lim_{(x,y)\to(0,0)} f(x,y) = 0.$

13. Let $f(x, y) = \dfrac{x^2 y e^y}{x^4 + 4y^2}$. Then $f(x, 0) = 0$ for $x \neq 0$, so $f(x, y) \to 0$ as $(x, y) \to (0, 0)$ along the x-axis. Approaching

$(0, 0)$ along the y-axis or the line $y = x$ also gives a limit of 0. But $f(x, x^2) = \dfrac{x^2 x^2 e^{x^2}}{x^4 + 4(x^2)^2} = \dfrac{x^4 e^{x^2}}{5x^4} = \dfrac{e^{x^2}}{5}$ for $x \neq 0$, so

$f(x, y) \to e^0/5 = \frac{1}{5}$ as $(x, y) \to (0, 0)$ along the parabola $y = x^2$. Thus the limit doesn't exist.

15. $\displaystyle\lim_{(x,y)\to(0,0)} \dfrac{x^2 + y^2}{\sqrt{x^2 + y^2 + 1} - 1} = \lim_{(x,y)\to(0,0)} \dfrac{x^2 + y^2}{\sqrt{x^2 + y^2 + 1} - 1} \cdot \dfrac{\sqrt{x^2 + y^2 + 1} + 1}{\sqrt{x^2 + y^2 + 1} + 1}$

$\qquad\qquad = \displaystyle\lim_{(x,y)\to(0,0)} \dfrac{\left(x^2 + y^2\right)\left(\sqrt{x^2 + y^2 + 1} + 1\right)}{x^2 + y^2} = \lim_{(x,y)\to(0,0)} \left(\sqrt{x^2 + y^2 + 1} + 1\right) = 2$

17. e^{-xy} and $\sin(\pi z/2)$ are each compositions of continuous functions, and hence continuous, so their product

$f(x, y, z) = e^{-xy} \sin(\pi z/2)$ is a continuous function. Then

$\qquad \displaystyle\lim_{(x,y,z)\to(3,0,1)} f(x, y, z) = f(3, 0, 1) = e^{-(3)(0)} \sin(\pi \cdot 1/2) = 1.$

19. $f(x, y, z) = \dfrac{xy + yz^2 + xz^2}{x^2 + y^2 + z^4}$. Then $f(x, 0, 0) = 0/x^2 = 0$ for $x \neq 0$, so as $(x, y, z) \to (0, 0, 0)$ along the x-axis,

$f(x, y, z) \to 0$. But $f(x, x, 0) = x^2/(2x^2) = \frac{1}{2}$ for $x \neq 0$, so as $(x, y, z) \to (0, 0, 0)$ along the line $y = x$, $z = 0$,

$f(x, y, z) \to \frac{1}{2}$. Thus the limit doesn't exist.

21. 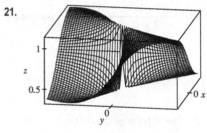 From the ridges on the graph, we see that as $(x, y) \to (0, 0)$ along the lines under the two ridges, $f(x, y)$ approaches different values. So the limit does not exist.

23. $h(x, y) = g(f(x, y)) = (2x + 3y - 6)^2 + \sqrt{2x + 3y - 6}$. Since f is a polynomial, it is continuous on $\mathbb{R}^2$ and g is

continuous on its domain $\{t \mid t \geq 0\}$. Thus h is continuous on its domain.

$D = \{(x, y) \mid 2x + 3y - 6 \geq 0\} = \{(x, y) \mid y \geq -\frac{2}{3}x + 2\}$, which consists of all points on or above the line $y = -\frac{2}{3}x + 2$.

25. 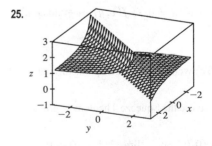 From the graph, it appears that f is discontinuous along the line $y = x$.

If we consider $f(x, y) = e^{1/(x-y)}$ as a composition of functions,

$g(x, y) = 1/(x - y)$ is a rational function and therefore continuous except

where $x - y = 0 \ \Rightarrow \ y = x$. Since the function $h(t) = e^t$ is continuous

everywhere, the composition $h(g(x, y)) = e^{1/(x-y)} = f(x, y)$ is

continuous except along the line $y = x$, as we suspected.

27. $F(x, y) = \arctan\left(x + \sqrt{y}\right) = g(f(x, y))$ where $f(x, y) = x + \sqrt{y}$, continuous on its domain $\{(x, y) \mid y \geq 0\}$, and

$g(t) = \arctan t$ is continuous everywhere. Thus F is continuous on its domain $\{(x, y) \mid y \geq 0\}$.

29. $G(x,y) = \ln(x^2 + y^2 - 4) = g(f(x,y))$ where $f(x,y) = x^2 + y^2 - 4$, continuous on $\mathbb{R}^2$, and $g(t) = \ln t$, continuous on its

domain $\{t \mid t > 0\}$. Thus G is continuous on its domain $\{(x,y) \mid x^2 + y^2 - 4 > 0\} = \{(x,y) \mid x^2 + y^2 > 4\}$, the exterior

of the circle $x^2 + y^2 = 4$.

31. $\sqrt{y}$ is continuous on its domain $\{y \mid y \geq 0\}$ and $x^2 - y^2 + z^2$ is continuous everywhere, so $f(x,y,z) = \dfrac{\sqrt{y}}{x^2 - y^2 + z^2}$ is

continuous for $y \geq 0$ and $x^2 - y^2 + z^2 \neq 0 \Rightarrow y^2 \neq x^2 + z^2$, that is, $\{(x,y,z) \mid y \geq 0, y \neq \sqrt{x^2 + z^2}\}$.

33. $f(x,y) = \begin{cases} \dfrac{x^2 y^3}{2x^2 + y^2} & \text{if } (x,y) \neq (0,0) \\ 1 & \text{if } (x,y) = (0,0) \end{cases}$ The first piece of f is a rational function defined everywhere except at the

origin, so f is continuous on $\mathbb{R}^2$ except possibly at the origin. Since $x^2 \leq 2x^2 + y^2$, we have $\left| x^2 y^3/(2x^2 + y^2) \right| \leq |y^3|$. We

know that $|y^3| \to 0$ as $(x,y) \to (0,0)$. So, by the Squeeze Theorem, $\displaystyle\lim_{(x,y)\to(0,0)} f(x,y) = \lim_{(x,y)\to(0,0)} \dfrac{x^2 y^3}{2x^2 + y^2} = 0$.

But $f(0,0) = 1$, so f is discontinuous at $(0,0)$. Therefore, f is continuous on the set $\{(x,y) \mid (x,y) \neq (0,0)\}$.

35. $\displaystyle\lim_{(x,y)\to(0,0)} \dfrac{x^3 + y^3}{x^2 + y^2} = \lim_{r\to 0^+} \dfrac{(r\cos\theta)^3 + (r\sin\theta)^3}{r^2} = \lim_{r\to 0^+} (r\cos^3\theta + r\sin^3\theta) = 0$

37. $\displaystyle\lim_{(x,y,z)\to(0,0,0)} \dfrac{xyz}{x^2 + y^2 + z^2} = \lim_{\rho\to 0^+} \dfrac{(\rho\sin\phi\cos\theta)(\rho\sin\phi\sin\theta)(\rho\cos\phi)}{\rho^2} = \lim_{\rho\to 0^+} (\rho\sin^2\phi\cos\phi\sin\theta\cos\theta) = 0$

39. $f(x,y) = \begin{cases} \dfrac{\sin(xy)}{xy} & \text{if } (x,y) \neq (0,0) \\ 1 & \text{if } (x,y) = (0,0) \end{cases}$

From the graph, it appears that f is continuous everywhere. We know

xy is continuous on $\mathbb{R}^2$ and $\sin t$ is continuous everywhere, so

$\sin(xy)$ is continuous on $\mathbb{R}^2$ and $\dfrac{\sin(xy)}{xy}$ is continuous on $\mathbb{R}^2$

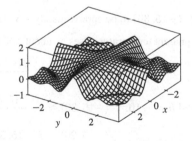

except possibly where $xy = 0$. To show that f is continuous at those points, consider any point (a,b) in $\mathbb{R}^2$ where $ab = 0$.

Because xy is continuous, $xy \to ab = 0$ as $(x,y) \to (a,b)$. If we let $t = xy$, then $t \to 0$ as $(x,y) \to (a,b)$ and

$\displaystyle\lim_{(x,y)\to(a,b)} \dfrac{\sin(xy)}{xy} = \lim_{t\to 0} \dfrac{\sin(t)}{t} = 1$ by Equation 3.3.2. Thus $\displaystyle\lim_{(x,y)\to(a,b)} f(x,y) = f(a,b)$ and f is continuous on $\mathbb{R}^2$.

11.3 Partial Derivatives

1. (a) $\partial T/\partial x$ represents the rate of change of T when we fix y and t and consider T as a function of the single variable x, which describes how quickly the temperature changes when longitude changes but latitude and time are constant. $\partial T/\partial y$ represents the rate of change of T when we fix x and t and consider T as a function of y, which describes how quickly the temperature changes when latitude changes but longitude and time are constant. $\partial T/\partial t$ represents the rate of change of T when we fix x and y and consider T as a function of t, which describes how quickly the temperature changes over time for a constant longitude and latitude.

(b) $f_x(158, 21, 9)$ represents the rate of change of temperature at longitude $158°$W, latitude $21°$N at 9:00 AM when only longitude varies. Since the air is warmer to the west than to the east, increasing longitude results in an increased air temperature, so we would expect $f_x(158, 21, 9)$ to be positive. $f_y(158, 21, 9)$ represents the rate of change of temperature at the same time and location when only latitude varies. Since the air is warmer to the south and cooler to the north, increasing latitude results in a decreased air temperature, so we would expect $f_y(158, 21, 9)$ to be negative. $f_t(158, 21, 9)$ represents the rate of change of temperature at the same time and location when only time varies. Since typically air temperature increases from the morning to the afternoon as the sun warms it, we would expect $f_t(158, 21, 9)$ to be positive.

3. (a) By Definition 4, $f_T(-15, 30) = \lim\limits_{h \to 0} \dfrac{f(-15 + h, 30) - f(-15, 30)}{h}$, which we can approximate by considering $h = 5$ and $h = -5$ and using the values given in the table:

$f_T(-15, 30) \approx \dfrac{f(-10, 30) - f(-15, 30)}{5} = \dfrac{-20 - (-26)}{5} = \dfrac{6}{5} = 1.2$,

$f_T(-15, 30) \approx \dfrac{f(-20, 30) - f(-15, 30)}{-5} = \dfrac{-33 - (-26)}{-5} = \dfrac{-7}{-5} = 1.4$. Averaging these values, we estimate $f_T(-15, 30)$ to be approximately 1.3. Thus, when the actual temperature is $-15°$C and the wind speed is 30 km/h, the apparent temperature rises by about $1.3°$C for every degree that the actual temperature rises.

Similarly, $f_v(-15, 30) = \lim\limits_{h \to 0} \dfrac{f(-15, 30 + h) - f(-15, 30)}{h}$ which we can approximate by considering $h = 10$

and $h = -10$: $f_v(-15, 30) \approx \dfrac{f(-15, 40) - f(-15, 30)}{10} = \dfrac{-27 - (-26)}{10} = \dfrac{-1}{10} = -0.1$,

$f_v(-15, 30) \approx \dfrac{f(-15, 20) - f(-15, 30)}{-10} = \dfrac{-24 - (-26)}{-10} = \dfrac{2}{-10} = -0.2$. Averaging these values, we estimate $f_v(-15, 30)$ to be approximately -0.15. Thus, when the actual temperature is $-15°$C and the wind speed is 30 km/h, the apparent temperature decreases by about $0.15°$C for every km/h that the wind speed increases.

(b) For a fixed wind speed v, the values of the wind-chill index W increase as temperature T increases (look at a column of the table), so $\dfrac{\partial W}{\partial T}$ is positive. For a fixed temperature T, the values of W decrease (or remain constant) as v increases (look at a row of the table), so $\dfrac{\partial W}{\partial v}$ is negative (or perhaps 0).

(c) For fixed values of T, the function values $f(T, v)$ appear to become constant (or nearly constant) as v increases, so the corresponding rate of change is 0 or near 0 as v increases. This suggests that $\lim\limits_{v \to \infty} (\partial W/\partial v) = 0$.

5. (a) If we start at $(1, 2)$ and move in the positive x-direction, the graph of f increases. Thus $f_x(1, 2)$ is positive.

(b) If we start at $(1, 2)$ and move in the positive y-direction, the graph of f decreases. Thus $f_y(1, 2)$ is negative.

7. (a) $f_{xx} = \frac{\partial}{\partial x}(f_x)$, so f_{xx} is the rate of change of f_x in the x-direction. f_x is negative at $(-1, 2)$ and if we move in the

positive x-direction, the surface becomes less steep. Thus the values of f_x are increasing and $f_{xx}(-1, 2)$ is positive.

(b) f_{yy} is the rate of change of f_y in the y-direction. f_y is negative at $(-1, 2)$ and if we move in the positive y-direction, the

surface becomes steeper. Thus the values of f_y are decreasing, and $f_{yy}(-1, 2)$ is negative.

9. First of all, if we start at the point $(3, -3)$ and move in the positive y-direction, we see that both b and c decrease, while a

increases. Both b and c have a low point at about $(3, -1.5)$, while a is 0 at this point. So a is definitely the graph of f_y, and

one of b and c is the graph of f. To see which is which, we start at the point $(-3, -1.5)$ and move in the positive x-direction.

b traces out a line with negative slope, while c traces out a parabola opening downward. This tells us that b is the x-derivative

of c. So c is the graph of f, b is the graph of f_x, and a is the graph of f_y.

11. $f(x, y) = 16 - 4x^2 - y^2 \;\Rightarrow\; f_x(x, y) = -8x$ and $f_y(x, y) = -2y \;\Rightarrow\; f_x(1, 2) = -8$ and $f_y(1, 2) = -4$. The graph

of f is the paraboloid $z = 16 - 4x^2 - y^2$ and the vertical plane $y = 2$ intersects it in the parabola $z = 12 - 4x^2$, $y = 2$

(the curve C_1 in the first figure). The slope of the tangent line
to this parabola at $(1, 2, 8)$ is $f_x(1, 2) = -8$. Similarly the
plane $x = 1$ intersects the paraboloid in the parabola
$z = 12 - y^2$, $x = 1$ (the curve C_2 in the second figure) and
the slope of the tangent line at $(1, 2, 8)$ is $f_y(1, 2) = -4$.

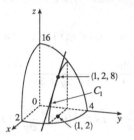
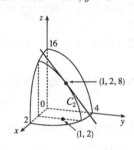

13. $f(x, y) = x^2 + y^2 + x^2y \;\Rightarrow\; f_x = 2x + 2xy, \quad f_y = 2y + x^2$

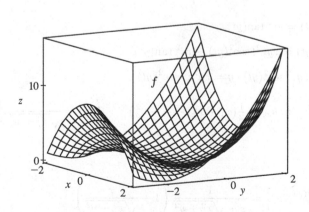

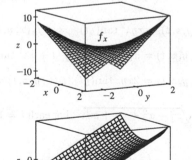

Note that the traces of f in planes parallel to the xz-plane are parabolas which open downward for $y < -1$ and upward for

$y > -1$, and the traces of f_x in these planes are straight lines, which have negative slopes for $y < -1$ and positive slopes for

$y > -1$. The traces of f in planes parallel to the yz-plane are parabolas which always open upward, and the traces of f_y in

these planes are straight lines with positive slopes.

15. $f(x,y) = y^5 - 3xy \Rightarrow f_x(x,y) = 0 - 3y = -3y, \ f_y(x,y) = 5y^4 - 3x$

17. $f(x,t) = e^{-t}\cos \pi x \Rightarrow f_x(x,t) = e^{-t}(-\sin \pi x)(\pi) = -\pi e^{-t}\sin \pi x, \ f_t(x,t) = e^{-t}(-1)\cos \pi x = -e^{-t}\cos \pi x$

19. $z = (2x+3y)^{10} \Rightarrow \dfrac{\partial z}{\partial x} = 10(2x+3y)^9 \cdot 2 = 20(2x+3y)^9, \ \dfrac{\partial z}{\partial y} = 10(2x+3y)^9 \cdot 3 = 30(2x+3y)^9$

21. $f(x,y) = \dfrac{x-y}{x+y} \Rightarrow f_x(x,y) = \dfrac{(1)(x+y) - (x-y)(1)}{(x+y)^2} = \dfrac{2y}{(x+y)^2}$,

$f_y(x,y) = \dfrac{(-1)(x+y) - (x-y)(1)}{(x+y)^2} = -\dfrac{2x}{(x+y)^2}$

23. $w = \sin \alpha \cos \beta \Rightarrow \dfrac{\partial w}{\partial \alpha} = \cos \alpha \cos \beta, \ \dfrac{\partial w}{\partial \beta} = -\sin \alpha \sin \beta$

25. $f(r,s) = r\ln(r^2 + s^2) \Rightarrow f_r(r,s) = r \cdot \dfrac{2r}{r^2 + s^2} + \ln(r^2 + s^2) \cdot 1 = \dfrac{2r^2}{r^2 + s^2} + \ln(r^2 + s^2)$,

$f_s(r,s) = r \cdot \dfrac{2s}{r^2 + s^2} + 0 = \dfrac{2rs}{r^2 + s^2}$

27. $u = te^{w/t} \Rightarrow \dfrac{\partial u}{\partial t} = t \cdot e^{w/t}(-wt^{-2}) + e^{w/t} \cdot 1 = e^{w/t} - \dfrac{w}{t}e^{w/t} = e^{w/t}\left(1 - \dfrac{w}{t}\right), \ \dfrac{\partial u}{\partial w} = te^{w/t} \cdot \dfrac{1}{t} = e^{w/t}$

29. $f(x,y,z) = xz - 5x^2y^3z^4 \Rightarrow f_x(x,y,z) = z - 10xy^3z^4, \ f_y(x,y,z) = -15x^2y^2z^4, \ f_z(x,y,z) = x - 20x^2y^3z^3$

31. $w = \ln(x + 2y + 3z) \Rightarrow \dfrac{\partial w}{\partial x} = \dfrac{1}{x + 2y + 3z}, \ \dfrac{\partial w}{\partial y} = \dfrac{2}{x + 2y + 3z}, \ \dfrac{\partial w}{\partial z} = \dfrac{3}{x + 2y + 3z}$

33. $u = xy\sin^{-1}(yz) \Rightarrow \dfrac{\partial u}{\partial x} = y\sin^{-1}(yz), \ \dfrac{\partial u}{\partial y} = xy \cdot \dfrac{1}{\sqrt{1-(yz)^2}}(z) + \sin^{-1}(yz) \cdot x = \dfrac{xyz}{\sqrt{1-y^2z^2}} + x\sin^{-1}(yz)$,

$\dfrac{\partial u}{\partial z} = xy \cdot \dfrac{1}{\sqrt{1-(yz)^2}}(y) = \dfrac{xy^2}{\sqrt{1-y^2z^2}}$

35. $f(x,y,z,t) = xyz^2\tan(yt) \Rightarrow f_x(x,y,z,t) = yz^2\tan(yt)$,

$f_y(x,y,z,t) = xyz^2 \cdot \sec^2(yt) \cdot t + xz^2\tan(yt) = xyz^2t\sec^2(yt) + xz^2\tan(yt)$,

$f_z(x,y,z,t) = 2xyz\tan(yt), \ f_t(x,y,z,t) = xyz^2\sec^2(yt) \cdot y = xy^2z^2\sec^2(yt)$

37. $u = \sqrt{x_1^2 + x_2^2 + \cdots + x_n^2}$. For each $i = 1, \ldots, n, \ u_{x_i} = \tfrac{1}{2}\left(x_1^2 + x_2^2 + \cdots + x_n^2\right)^{-1/2}(2x_i) = \dfrac{x_i}{\sqrt{x_1^2 + x_2^2 + \cdots + x_n^2}}.$

39. $f(x,y) = \ln\left(x + \sqrt{x^2 + y^2}\right) \Rightarrow$

$f_x(x,y) = \dfrac{1}{x + \sqrt{x^2 + y^2}}\left[1 + \tfrac{1}{2}(x^2 + y^2)^{-1/2}(2x)\right] = \dfrac{1}{x + \sqrt{x^2 + y^2}}\left(1 + \dfrac{x}{\sqrt{x^2 + y^2}}\right)$,

so $f_x(3,4) = \dfrac{1}{3 + \sqrt{3^2 + 4^2}}\left(1 + \dfrac{3}{\sqrt{3^2 + 4^2}}\right) = \tfrac{1}{8}\left(1 + \tfrac{3}{5}\right) = \tfrac{1}{5}.$

41. $f(x, y, z) = \dfrac{y}{x + y + z}$ $\Rightarrow$ $f_y(x, y, z) = \dfrac{1(x + y + z) - y(1)}{(x + y + z)^2} = \dfrac{x + z}{(x + y + z)^2}$,

so $f_y(2, 1, -1) = \dfrac{2 + (-1)}{(2 + 1 + (-1))^2} = \dfrac{1}{4}$.

43. $f(x, y) = xy^2 - x^3 y$ $\Rightarrow$

$$f_x(x, y) = \lim_{h \to 0} \frac{f(x + h, y) - f(x, y)}{h} = \lim_{h \to 0} \frac{(x + h)y^2 - (x + h)^3 y - (xy^2 - x^3 y)}{h}$$

$$= \lim_{h \to 0} \frac{h(y^2 - 3x^2 y - 3xyh - yh^2)}{h} = \lim_{h \to 0} (y^2 - 3x^2 y - 3xyh - yh^2) = y^2 - 3x^2 y$$

$$f_y(x, y) = \lim_{h \to 0} \frac{f(x, y + h) - f(x, y)}{h} = \lim_{h \to 0} \frac{x(y + h)^2 - x^3(y + h) - (xy^2 - x^3 y)}{h} = \lim_{h \to 0} \frac{h(2xy + xh - x^3)}{h}$$

$$= \lim_{h \to 0} (2xy + xh - x^3) = 2xy - x^3$$

45. $x^2 + y^2 + z^2 = 3xyz$ $\Rightarrow$ $\dfrac{\partial}{\partial x}(x^2 + y^2 + z^2) = \dfrac{\partial}{\partial x}(3xyz)$ $\Rightarrow$ $2x + 0 + 2z \dfrac{\partial z}{\partial x} = 3y\left(x \dfrac{\partial z}{\partial x} + z \cdot 1\right)$ $\Leftrightarrow$

$2z \dfrac{\partial z}{\partial x} - 3xy \dfrac{\partial z}{\partial x} = 3yz - 2x$ $\Leftrightarrow$ $(2z - 3xy) \dfrac{\partial z}{\partial x} = 3yz - 2x$, so $\dfrac{\partial z}{\partial x} = \dfrac{3yz - 2x}{2z - 3xy}$.

$\dfrac{\partial}{\partial y}(x^2 + y^2 + z^2) = \dfrac{\partial}{\partial y}(3xyz)$ $\Rightarrow$ $0 + 2y + 2z \dfrac{\partial z}{\partial y} = 3x\left(y \dfrac{\partial z}{\partial y} + z \cdot 1\right)$ $\Leftrightarrow$ $2z \dfrac{\partial z}{\partial y} - 3xy \dfrac{\partial z}{\partial y} = 3xz - 2y$ $\Leftrightarrow$

$(2z - 3xy) \dfrac{\partial z}{\partial y} = 3xz - 2y$, so $\dfrac{\partial z}{\partial y} = \dfrac{3xz - 2y}{2z - 3xy}$.

47. $x - z = \arctan(yz)$ $\Rightarrow$ $\dfrac{\partial}{\partial x}(x - z) = \dfrac{\partial}{\partial x}(\arctan(yz))$ $\Rightarrow$ $1 - \dfrac{\partial z}{\partial x} = \dfrac{1}{1 + (yz)^2} \cdot y \dfrac{\partial z}{\partial x}$ $\Leftrightarrow$

$1 = \left(\dfrac{y}{1 + y^2 z^2} + 1\right) \dfrac{\partial z}{\partial x}$ $\Leftrightarrow$ $1 = \left(\dfrac{y + 1 + y^2 z^2}{1 + y^2 z^2}\right) \dfrac{\partial z}{\partial x}$, so $\dfrac{\partial z}{\partial x} = \dfrac{1 + y^2 z^2}{1 + y + y^2 z^2}$.

$\dfrac{\partial}{\partial y}(x - z) = \dfrac{\partial}{\partial y}(\arctan(yz))$ $\Rightarrow$ $0 - \dfrac{\partial z}{\partial y} = \dfrac{1}{1 + (yz)^2} \cdot \left(y \dfrac{\partial z}{\partial y} + z \cdot 1\right)$ $\Leftrightarrow$

$-\dfrac{z}{1 + y^2 z^2} = \left(\dfrac{y}{1 + y^2 z^2} + 1\right) \dfrac{\partial z}{\partial y}$ $\Leftrightarrow$ $-\dfrac{z}{1 + y^2 z^2} = \left(\dfrac{y + 1 + y^2 z^2}{1 + y^2 z^2}\right) \dfrac{\partial z}{\partial y}$ $\Leftrightarrow$ $\dfrac{\partial z}{\partial y} = -\dfrac{z}{1 + y + y^2 z^2}$.

49. (a) $z = f(x) + g(y)$ $\Rightarrow$ $\dfrac{\partial z}{\partial x} = f'(x)$, $\dfrac{\partial z}{\partial y} = g'(y)$

(b) $z = f(x + y)$. Let $u = x + y$. Then $\dfrac{\partial z}{\partial x} = \dfrac{df}{du} \dfrac{\partial u}{\partial x} = \dfrac{df}{du}(1) = f'(u) = f'(x + y)$,

$\dfrac{\partial z}{\partial y} = \dfrac{df}{du} \dfrac{\partial u}{\partial y} = \dfrac{df}{du}(1) = f'(u) = f'(x + y)$.

51. $f(x, y) = x^3 y^5 + 2x^4 y$ $\Rightarrow$ $f_x(x, y) = 3x^2 y^5 + 8x^3 y$, $f_y(x, y) = 5x^3 y^4 + 2x^4$. Then $f_{xx}(x, y) = 6xy^5 + 24x^2 y$,

$f_{xy}(x, y) = 15x^2 y^4 + 8x^3$, $f_{yx}(x, y) = 15x^2 y^4 + 8x^3$, and $f_{yy}(x, y) = 20x^3 y^3$.

53. $w = \sqrt{u^2 + v^2}$ $\Rightarrow$ $w_u = \frac{1}{2}(u^2 + v^2)^{-1/2} \cdot 2u = \dfrac{u}{\sqrt{u^2 + v^2}}$, $w_v = \frac{1}{2}(u^2 + v^2)^{-1/2} \cdot 2v = \dfrac{v}{\sqrt{u^2 + v^2}}$. Then

$$w_{uu} = \frac{1 \cdot \sqrt{u^2 + v^2} - u \cdot \frac{1}{2}(u^2 + v^2)^{-1/2}(2u)}{\left(\sqrt{u^2 + v^2}\right)^2} = \frac{\sqrt{u^2 + v^2} - u^2/\sqrt{u^2 + v^2}}{u^2 + v^2} = \frac{u^2 + v^2 - u^2}{(u^2 + v^2)^{3/2}} = \frac{v^2}{(u^2 + v^2)^{3/2}},$$

$$w_{uv} = u\left(-\tfrac{1}{2}\right)\left(u^2 + v^2\right)^{-3/2}(2v) = -\frac{uv}{(u^2+v^2)^{3/2}}, \quad w_{vu} = v\left(-\tfrac{1}{2}\right)\left(u^2 + v^2\right)^{-3/2}(2u) = -\frac{uv}{(u^2+v^2)^{3/2}},$$

$$w_{vv} = \frac{1 \cdot \sqrt{u^2 + v^2} - v \cdot \frac{1}{2}(u^2 + v^2)^{-1/2}(2v)}{\left(\sqrt{u^2 + v^2}\right)^2} = \frac{\sqrt{u^2 + v^2} - v^2/\sqrt{u^2 + v^2}}{u^2 + v^2} = \frac{u^2 + v^2 - v^2}{(u^2 + v^2)^{3/2}} = \frac{u^2}{(u^2 + v^2)^{3/2}}.$$

55. $z = \arctan \dfrac{x+y}{1-xy}$ $\Rightarrow$

$$z_x = \frac{1}{1 + \left(\frac{x+y}{1-xy}\right)^2} \cdot \frac{(1)(1-xy) - (x+y)(-y)}{(1-xy)^2} = \frac{1+y^2}{(1-xy)^2 + (x+y)^2} = \frac{1+y^2}{1 + x^2 + y^2 + x^2y^2}$$

$$= \frac{1+y^2}{(1+x^2)(1+y^2)} = \frac{1}{1+x^2},$$

$$z_y = \frac{1}{1 + \left(\frac{x+y}{1-xy}\right)^2} \cdot \frac{(1)(1-xy) - (x+y)(-x)}{(1-xy)^2} = \frac{1+x^2}{(1-xy)^2 + (x+y)^2} = \frac{1+x^2}{(1+x^2)(1+y^2)} = \frac{1}{1+y^2}.$$

Then $z_{xx} = -(1+x^2)^{-2} \cdot 2x = -\dfrac{2x}{(1+x^2)^2}$, $z_{xy} = 0$, $z_{yx} = 0$, $z_{yy} = -(1+y^2)^{-2} \cdot 2y = -\dfrac{2y}{(1+y^2)^2}$.

57. $u = xe^{xy}$ $\Rightarrow$ $u_x = x \cdot ye^{xy} + e^{xy} \cdot 1 = (xy + 1)e^{xy}$, $u_{xy} = (xy + 1) \cdot xe^{xy} + e^{xy} \cdot x = (x^2y + 2x)e^{xy}$ and

$u_y = x(xe^{xy}) = x^2 e^{xy}$, $u_{yx} = x^2 \cdot ye^{xy} + e^{xy} \cdot 2x = (x^2 y + 2x)e^{xy}$. Thus $u_{xy} = u_{yx}$.

59. $f(x,y) = 3xy^4 + x^3 y^2$ $\Rightarrow$ $f_x = 3y^4 + 3x^2 y^2$, $f_{xx} = 6xy^2$, $f_{xxy} = 12xy$ and

$f_y = 12xy^3 + 2x^3 y$, $f_{yy} = 36xy^2 + 2x^3$, $f_{yyy} = 72xy$.

61. $f(x,y,z) = \cos(4x + 3y + 2z)$ $\Rightarrow$

$f_x = -\sin(4x + 3y + 2z)(4) = -4\sin(4x + 3y + 2z)$, $f_{xy} = -4\cos(4x + 3y + 2z)(3) = -12\cos(4x + 3y + 2z)$,

$f_{xyz} = -12(-\sin(4x + 3y + 2z))(2) = 24\sin(4x + 3y + 2z)$ and

$f_y = -\sin(4x + 3y + 2z)(3) = -3\sin(4x + 3y + 2z)$,

$f_{yz} = -3\cos(4x + 3y + 2z)(2) = -6\cos(4x + 3y + 2z)$, $f_{yzz} = -6(-\sin(4x + 3y + 2z))(2) = 12\sin(4x + 3y + 2z)$.

63. $u = e^{r\theta} \sin\theta$ $\Rightarrow$ $\dfrac{\partial u}{\partial \theta} = e^{r\theta}\cos\theta + \sin\theta \cdot e^{r\theta}(r) = e^{r\theta}(\cos\theta + r\sin\theta)$,

$\dfrac{\partial^2 u}{\partial r \, \partial \theta} = e^{r\theta}(\sin\theta) + (\cos\theta + r\sin\theta)e^{r\theta}(\theta) = e^{r\theta}(\sin\theta + \theta\cos\theta + r\theta\sin\theta)$,

$\dfrac{\partial^3 u}{\partial r^2 \, \partial \theta} = e^{r\theta}(\theta\sin\theta) + (\sin\theta + \theta\cos\theta + r\theta\sin\theta) \cdot e^{r\theta}(\theta) = \theta e^{r\theta}(2\sin\theta + \theta\cos\theta + r\theta\sin\theta)$.

65. Assuming that the third partial derivatives of f are continuous (easily verified), we can write $f_{xzy} = f_{yxz}$. Then

$f(x,y,z) = xy^2z^3 + \arcsin\left(x\sqrt{z}\right)$ $\Rightarrow$ $f_y = 2xyz^3 + 0$, $f_{yx} = 2yz^3$, and $f_{yxz} = 6yz^2 = f_{xzy}$.

67. By Definition 4, $f_x(3, 2) = \lim\limits_{h \to 0} \dfrac{f(3+h, 2) - f(3, 2)}{h}$ which we can approximate by considering $h = 0.5$ and $h = -0.5$:

$f_x(3, 2) \approx \dfrac{f(3.5, 2) - f(3, 2)}{0.5} = \dfrac{22.4 - 17.5}{0.5} = 9.8$, $f_x(3, 2) \approx \dfrac{f(2.5, 2) - f(3, 2)}{-0.5} = \dfrac{10.2 - 17.5}{-0.5} = 14.6$. Averaging

these values, we estimate $f_x(3, 2)$ to be approximately 12.2. Similarly, $f_x(3, 2.2) = \lim\limits_{h \to 0} \dfrac{f(3+h, 2.2) - f(3, 2.2)}{h}$ which

we can approximate by considering $h = 0.5$ and $h = -0.5$: $f_x(3, 2.2) \approx \dfrac{f(3.5, 2.2) - f(3, 2.2)}{0.5} = \dfrac{26.1 - 15.9}{0.5} = 20.4$,

$f_x(3, 2.2) \approx \dfrac{f(2.5, 2.2) - f(3, 2.2)}{-0.5} = \dfrac{9.3 - 15.9}{-0.5} = 13.2$. Averaging these values, we have $f_x(3, 2.2) \approx 16.8$.

To estimate $f_{xy}(3, 2)$, we first need an estimate for $f_x(3, 1.8)$:

$f_x(3, 1.8) \approx \dfrac{f(3.5, 1.8) - f(3, 1.8)}{0.5} = \dfrac{20.0 - 18.1}{0.5} = 3.8$, $f_x(3, 1.8) \approx \dfrac{f(2.5, 1.8) - f(3, 1.8)}{-0.5} = \dfrac{12.5 - 18.1}{-0.5} = 11.2$.

Averaging these values, we get $f_x(3, 1.8) \approx 7.5$. Now $f_{xy}(x, y) = \dfrac{\partial}{\partial y}[f_x(x, y)]$ and $f_x(x, y)$ is itself a function of two

variables, so Definition 4 says that $f_{xy}(x, y) = \dfrac{\partial}{\partial y}[f_x(x, y)] = \lim\limits_{h \to 0} \dfrac{f_x(x, y+h) - f_x(x, y)}{h} \Rightarrow$

$f_{xy}(3, 2) = \lim\limits_{h \to 0} \dfrac{f_x(3, 2+h) - f_x(3, 2)}{h}$. We can estimate this value using our previous work with $h = 0.2$ and $h = -0.2$:

$f_{xy}(3, 2) \approx \dfrac{f_x(3, 2.2) - f_x(3, 2)}{0.2} = \dfrac{16.8 - 12.2}{0.2} = 23$, $f_{xy}(3, 2) \approx \dfrac{f_x(3, 1.8) - f_x(3, 2)}{-0.2} = \dfrac{7.5 - 12.2}{-0.2} = 23.5$.

Averaging these values, we estimate $f_{xy}(3, 2)$ to be approximately 23.25.

69. $u = e^{-\alpha^2 k^2 t} \sin kx \;\Rightarrow\; u_x = k e^{-\alpha^2 k^2 t} \cos kx$, $u_{xx} = -k^2 e^{-\alpha^2 k^2 t} \sin kx$, and $u_t = -\alpha^2 k^2 e^{-\alpha^2 k^2 t} \sin kx$.

Thus $\alpha^2 u_{xx} = u_t$.

71. $u = \dfrac{1}{\sqrt{x^2 + y^2 + z^2}} \;\Rightarrow\; u_x = \left(-\tfrac{1}{2}\right)(x^2 + y^2 + z^2)^{-3/2}(2x) = -x(x^2 + y^2 + z^2)^{-3/2}$ and

$u_{xx} = -(x^2 + y^2 + z^2)^{-3/2} - x\left(-\tfrac{3}{2}\right)(x^2 + y^2 + z^2)^{-5/2}(2x) = \dfrac{2x^2 - y^2 - z^2}{(x^2 + y^2 + z^2)^{5/2}}$.

By symmetry, $u_{yy} = \dfrac{2y^2 - x^2 - z^2}{(x^2 + y^2 + z^2)^{5/2}}$ and $u_{zz} = \dfrac{2z^2 - x^2 - y^2}{(x^2 + y^2 + z^2)^{5/2}}$.

Thus $u_{xx} + u_{yy} + u_{zz} = \dfrac{2x^2 - y^2 - z^2 + 2y^2 - x^2 - z^2 + 2z^2 - x^2 - y^2}{(x^2 + y^2 + z^2)^{5/2}} = 0$.

73. Let $v = x + at$, $w = x - at$. Then $u_t = \dfrac{\partial[f(v) + g(w)]}{\partial t} = \dfrac{df(v)}{dv}\dfrac{\partial v}{\partial t} + \dfrac{dg(w)}{dw}\dfrac{\partial w}{\partial t} = af'(v) - ag'(w)$ and

$u_{tt} = \dfrac{\partial[af'(v) - ag'(w)]}{\partial t} = a[af''(v) + ag''(w)] = a^2[f''(v) + g''(w)]$. Similarly, by using the Chain Rule we have

$u_x = f'(v) + g'(w)$ and $u_{xx} = f''(v) + g''(w)$. Thus $u_{tt} = a^2 u_{xx}$.

75. $u = xe^y + ye^x$ $\Rightarrow$ $\dfrac{\partial u}{\partial x} = e^y + ye^x$, $\dfrac{\partial^2 u}{\partial x^2} = ye^x$, $\dfrac{\partial^3 u}{\partial x^3} = ye^x$, $\dfrac{\partial u}{\partial y} = xe^y + e^x$, $\dfrac{\partial^2 u}{\partial y^2} = xe^y$, $\dfrac{\partial^3 u}{\partial y^3} = xe^y$,

$\dfrac{\partial^3 u}{\partial x\, \partial y^2} = \dfrac{\partial}{\partial x}\left(\dfrac{\partial^2 u}{\partial y^2}\right) = \dfrac{\partial}{\partial x}(xe^y) = e^y$, $\dfrac{\partial^2 u}{\partial x\, \partial y} = e^y + e^x$ $\Rightarrow$ $\dfrac{\partial^3 u}{\partial x^2\, \partial y} = e^x$. Then

$$\dfrac{\partial^3 u}{\partial x^3} + \dfrac{\partial^3 u}{\partial y^3} = ye^x + xe^y = x\left(e^y\right) + y\left(e^x\right) = x\,\dfrac{\partial^3 u}{\partial x\, \partial y^2} + y\,\dfrac{\partial^3 u}{\partial x^2\, \partial y}$$

77. If we fix $K = K_0$, $P(L, K_0)$ is a function of a single variable L, and $\dfrac{dP}{dL} = \alpha\,\dfrac{P}{L}$ is a separable differential equation. Then

$\dfrac{dP}{P} = \alpha\,\dfrac{dL}{L}$ $\Rightarrow$ $\displaystyle\int \dfrac{dP}{P} = \int \alpha\,\dfrac{dL}{L}$ $\Rightarrow$ $\ln|P| = \alpha\ln|L| + C(K_0)$, where $C(K_0)$ can depend on K_0. Then

$|P| = e^{\alpha\ln|L| + C(K_0)}$, and since $P > 0$ and $L > 0$, we have $P = e^{\alpha\ln L}e^{C(K_0)} = e^{C(K_0)}e^{\ln L^\alpha} = C_1(K_0)L^\alpha$ where

$C_1(K_0) = e^{C(K_0)}$.

79. By the Chain Rule, taking the partial derivative of both sides with respect to R_1 gives

$\dfrac{\partial R^{-1}}{\partial R}\dfrac{\partial R}{\partial R_1} = \dfrac{\partial\left[(1/R_1) + (1/R_2) + (1/R_3)\right]}{\partial R_1}$ or $-R^{-2}\dfrac{\partial R}{\partial R_1} = -R_1^{-2}$. Thus $\dfrac{\partial R}{\partial R_1} = \dfrac{R^2}{R_1^2}$.

81. (a) $P = \dfrac{mRT}{V}$ so $\dfrac{\partial P}{\partial V} = \dfrac{-mRT}{V^2}$; $V = \dfrac{mRT}{P}$, so $\dfrac{\partial V}{\partial T} = \dfrac{mR}{P}$; $T = \dfrac{PV}{mR}$, so $\dfrac{\partial T}{\partial P} = \dfrac{V}{mR}$.

Thus $\dfrac{\partial P}{\partial V}\dfrac{\partial V}{\partial T}\dfrac{\partial T}{\partial P} = \dfrac{-mRT}{V^2}\dfrac{mR}{P}\dfrac{V}{mR} = \dfrac{-mRT}{PV} = -1$, since $PV = mRT$.

(b) By part (a), $PV = mRT$ $\Rightarrow$ $P = \dfrac{mRT}{V}$, so $\dfrac{\partial P}{\partial T} = \dfrac{mR}{V}$. Also, $PV = mRT$ $\Rightarrow$ $V = \dfrac{mRT}{P}$ and $\dfrac{\partial V}{\partial T} = \dfrac{mR}{P}$.

Since $T = \dfrac{PV}{mR}$, we have $T\dfrac{\partial P}{\partial T}\dfrac{\partial V}{\partial T} = \dfrac{PV}{mR}\cdot\dfrac{mR}{V}\cdot\dfrac{mR}{P} = mR$.

83. $\dfrac{\partial K}{\partial m} = \tfrac{1}{2}v^2$, $\dfrac{\partial K}{\partial v} = mv$, $\dfrac{\partial^2 K}{\partial v^2} = m$. Thus $\dfrac{\partial K}{\partial m}\cdot\dfrac{\partial^2 K}{\partial v^2} = \tfrac{1}{2}v^2 m = K$.

85. $f_x(x, y) = x + 4y$ $\Rightarrow$ $f_{xy}(x, y) = 4$ and $f_y(x, y) = 3x - y$ $\Rightarrow$ $f_{yx}(x, y) = 3$. Since f_{xy} and f_{yx} are continuous

everywhere but $f_{xy}(x, y) \neq f_{yx}(x, y)$, Clairaut's Theorem implies that such a function $f(x, y)$ does not exist.

87. By the geometry of partial derivatives, the slope of the tangent line is $f_x(1, 2)$. By implicit differentiation of

$4x^2 + 2y^2 + z^2 = 16$, we get $8x + 2z\,(\partial z/\partial x) = 0$ $\Rightarrow$ $\partial z/\partial x = -4x/z$, so when $x = 1$ and $z = 2$ we have

$\partial z/\partial x = -2$. So the slope is $f_x(1, 2) = -2$. Thus the tangent line is given by $z - 2 = -2(x - 1)$, $y = 2$. Taking the

parameter to be $t = x - 1$, we can write parametric equations for this line: $x = 1 + t$, $y = 2$, $z = 2 - 2t$.

89. Let $g(x) = f(x, 0) = x(x^2)^{-3/2}e^0 = x\,|x|^{-3}$. But we are using the point $(1, 0)$, so near $(1, 0)$, $g(x) = x^{-2}$. Then

$g'(x) = -2x^{-3}$ and $g'(1) = -2$, so using (1) we have $f_x(1, 0) = g'(1) = -2$.

91. (a)

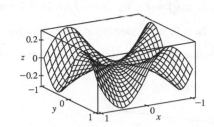

(b) For $(x, y) \neq (0, 0)$,

$$f_x(x, y) = \frac{(3x^2y - y^3)(x^2 + y^2) - (x^3y - xy^3)(2x)}{(x^2 + y^2)^2}$$

$$= \frac{x^4y + 4x^2y^3 - y^5}{(x^2 + y^2)^2}$$

and by symmetry $f_y(x, y) = \dfrac{x^5 - 4x^3y^2 - xy^4}{(x^2 + y^2)^2}$.

(c) $f_x(0, 0) = \lim\limits_{h \to 0} \dfrac{f(h, 0) - f(0, 0)}{h} = \lim\limits_{h \to 0} \dfrac{(0/h^2) - 0}{h} = 0$ and $f_y(0, 0) = \lim\limits_{h \to 0} \dfrac{f(0, h) - f(0, 0)}{h} = 0$.

(d) By (3), $f_{xy}(0, 0) = \dfrac{\partial f_x}{\partial y} = \lim\limits_{h \to 0} \dfrac{f_x(0, h) - f_x(0, 0)}{h} = \lim\limits_{h \to 0} \dfrac{(-h^5 - 0)/h^4}{h} = -1$ while by (2),

$$f_{yx}(0, 0) = \frac{\partial f_y}{\partial x} = \lim\limits_{h \to 0} \frac{f_y(h, 0) - f_y(0, 0)}{h} = \lim\limits_{h \to 0} \frac{h^5/h^4}{h} = 1.$$

(e) For $(x, y) \neq (0, 0)$, we use a CAS to compute

$$f_{xy}(x, y) = \frac{x^6 + 9x^4y^2 - 9x^2y^4 - y^6}{(x^2 + y^2)^3}$$

Now as $(x, y) \to (0, 0)$ along the x-axis, $f_{xy}(x, y) \to 1$ while as

$(x, y) \to (0, 0)$ along the y-axis, $f_{xy}(x, y) \to -1$. Thus f_{xy} isn't

continuous at $(0, 0)$ and Clairaut's Theorem doesn't apply, so there is

no contradiction. The graphs of f_{xy} and f_{yx} are identical except at the

origin, where we observe the discontinuity.

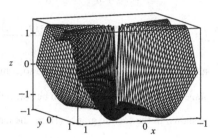

11.4 Tangent Planes and Linear Approximations

1. $z = f(x, y) = 3y^2 - 2x^2 + x \ \Rightarrow \ f_x(x, y) = -4x + 1, \ f_y(x, y) = 6y$, so $f_x(2, -1) = -7, \ f_y(2, -1) = -6$.

By Equation 2, an equation of the tangent plane is $z - (-3) = f_x(2, -1)(x - 2) + f_y(2, -1)[y - (-1)] \ \Rightarrow$

$z + 3 = -7(x - 2) - 6(y + 1)$ or $z = -7x - 6y + 5$.

3. $z = f(x, y) = \sqrt{xy} \ \Rightarrow \ f_x(x, y) = \frac{1}{2}(xy)^{-1/2} \cdot y = \frac{1}{2}\sqrt{y/x}, f_y(x, y) = \frac{1}{2}(xy)^{-1/2} \cdot x = \frac{1}{2}\sqrt{x/y}$, so $f_x(1, 1) = \frac{1}{2}$

and $f_y(1, 1) = \frac{1}{2}$. Thus an equation of the tangent plane is $z - 1 = f_x(1, 1)(x - 1) + f_y(1, 1)(y - 1) \ \Rightarrow$

$z - 1 = \frac{1}{2}(x - 1) + \frac{1}{2}(y - 1)$ or $x + y - 2z = 0$.

5. $z = f(x, y) = y\cos(x - y) \ \Rightarrow \ f_x = y(-\sin(x - y)(1)) = -y\sin(x - y)$,

$f_y = y(-\sin(x - y)(-1)) + \cos(x - y) = y\sin(x - y) + \cos(x - y)$, so $f_x(2, 2) = -2\sin(0) = 0$,

$f_y(2, 2) = 2\sin(0) + \cos(0) = 1$ and an equation of the tangent plane is $z - 2 = 0(x - 2) + 1(y - 2)$ or $z = y$.

7. $z = f(x,y) = x^2 + xy + 3y^2$, so $f_x(x,y) = 2x + y \Rightarrow f_x(1,1) = 3$, $f_y(x,y) = x + 6y \Rightarrow f_y(1,1) = 7$ and an

equation of the tangent plane is $z - 5 = 3(x - 1) + 7(y - 1)$ or $z = 3x + 7y - 5$. After zooming in, the surface and the

tangent plane become almost indistinguishable. (Here, the tangent plane is below the surface.) If we zoom in farther, the

surface and the tangent plane will appear to coincide.

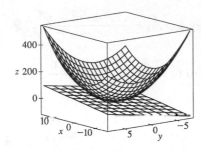
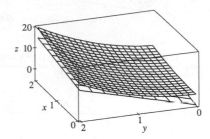

9. $f(x,y) = \dfrac{xy\sin(x-y)}{1 + x^2 + y^2}$. A CAS gives $f_x(x,y) = \dfrac{y\sin(x-y) + xy\cos(x-y)}{1 + x^2 + y^2} - \dfrac{2x^2 y\sin(x-y)}{(1 + x^2 + y^2)^2}$ and

$f_y(x,y) = \dfrac{x\sin(x-y) - xy\cos(x-y)}{1 + x^2 + y^2} - \dfrac{2xy^2\sin(x-y)}{(1 + x^2 + y^2)^2}$. We use the CAS to evaluate these at $(1,1)$, and then

substitute the results into Equation 2 to compute an equation of the tangent plane: $z = \frac{1}{3}x - \frac{1}{3}y$. The surface and tangent

plane are shown in the first graph below. After zooming in, the surface and the tangent plane become almost indistinguishable,

as shown in the second graph. (Here, the tangent plane is shown with fewer traces than the surface.) If we zoom in farther, the

surface and the tangent plane will appear to coincide.

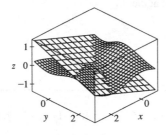
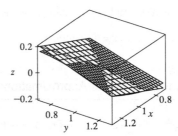

11. $f(x,y) = x\sqrt{y}$. The partial derivatives are $f_x(x,y) = \sqrt{y}$ and $f_y(x,y) = \dfrac{x}{2\sqrt{y}}$, so $f_x(1,4) = 2$ and $f_y(1,4) = \frac{1}{4}$. Both

f_x and f_y are continuous functions for $y > 0$, so by Theorem 8, f is differentiable at $(1,4)$. By Equation 3, the linearization of

f at $(1,4)$ is given by $L(x,y) = f(1,4) + f_x(1,4)(x - 1) + f_y(1,4)(y - 4) = 2 + 2(x - 1) + \frac{1}{4}(y - 4) = 2x + \frac{1}{4}y - 1$.

13. $f(x,y) = \dfrac{x}{x+y}$. The partial derivatives are $f_x(x,y) = \dfrac{1(x+y) - x(1)}{(x+y)^2} = y/(x+y)^2$ and

$f_y(x,y) = x(-1)(x+y)^{-2} \cdot 1 = -x/(x+y)^2$, so $f_x(2,1) = \frac{1}{9}$ and $f_y(2,1) = -\frac{2}{9}$. Both f_x and f_y are continuous

functions for $y \neq -x$, so f is differentiable at $(2,1)$ by Theorem 8. The linearization of f at $(2,1)$ is given by

$L(x,y) = f(2,1) + f_x(2,1)(x - 2) + f_y(2,1)(y - 1) = \frac{2}{3} + \frac{1}{9}(x - 2) - \frac{2}{9}(y - 1) = \frac{1}{9}x - \frac{2}{9}y + \frac{2}{3}$.

15. Let $f(x, y) = \dfrac{2x + 3}{4y + 1}$. Then $f_x(x, y) = \dfrac{2}{4y + 1}$ and $f_y(x, y) = (2x + 3)(-1)(4y + 1)^{-2}(4) = \dfrac{-8x - 12}{(4y + 1)^2}$. Both f_x and f_y

are continuous functions for $y \neq -\frac{1}{4}$, so by Theorem 8, f is differentiable at $(0, 0)$. We have $f_x(0, 0) = 2$, $f_y(0, 0) = -12$

and the linear approximation of f at $(0, 0)$ is $f(x, y) \approx f(0, 0) + f_x(0, 0)(x - 0) + f_y(0, 0)(y - 0) = 3 + 2x - 12y$.

17. We can estimate $f(2.2, 4.9)$ using a linear approximation of f at $(2, 5)$, given by

$f(x, y) \approx f(2, 5) + f_x(2, 5)(x - 2) + f_y(2, 5)(y - 5) = 6 + 1(x - 2) + (-1)(y - 5) = x - y + 9$. Thus

$f(2.2, 4.9) \approx 2.2 - 4.9 + 9 = 6.3$.

19. $f(x, y, z) = \sqrt{x^2 + y^2 + z^2} \;\Rightarrow\; f_x(x, y, z) = \dfrac{x}{\sqrt{x^2 + y^2 + z^2}}$, $f_y(x, y, z) = \dfrac{y}{\sqrt{x^2 + y^2 + z^2}}$, and

$f_z(x, y, z) = \dfrac{z}{\sqrt{x^2 + y^2 + z^2}}$, so $f_x(3, 2, 6) = \frac{3}{7}$, $f_y(3, 2, 6) = \frac{2}{7}$, $f_z(3, 2, 6) = \frac{6}{7}$. Then the linear approximation of f at

$(3, 2, 6)$ is given by

$$f(x, y, z) \approx f(3, 2, 6) + f_x(3, 2, 6)(x - 3) + f_y(3, 2, 6)(y - 2) + f_z(3, 2, 6)(z - 6)$$

$$= 7 + \tfrac{3}{7}(x - 3) + \tfrac{2}{7}(y - 2) + \tfrac{6}{7}(z - 6) = \tfrac{3}{7}x + \tfrac{2}{7}y + \tfrac{6}{7}z$$

Thus $\sqrt{(3.02)^2 + (1.97)^2 + (5.99)^2} = f(3.02, 1.97, 5.99) \approx \frac{3}{7}(3.02) + \frac{2}{7}(1.97) + \frac{6}{7}(5.99) \approx 6.9914$.

21. From the table, $f(94, 80) = 127$. To estimate $f_T(94, 80)$ and $f_H(94, 80)$ we follow the procedure used in Section 11.3. Since

$f_T(94, 80) = \lim\limits_{h \to 0} \dfrac{f(94 + h, 80) - f(94, 80)}{h}$, we approximate this quantity with $h = \pm 2$ and use the values given in the

table:

$$f_T(94, 80) \approx \frac{f(96, 80) - f(94, 80)}{2} = \frac{135 - 127}{2} = 4, \quad f_T(94, 80) \approx \frac{f(92, 80) - f(94, 80)}{-2} = \frac{119 - 127}{-2} = 4$$

Averaging these values gives $f_T(94, 80) \approx 4$. Similarly, $f_H(94, 80) = \lim\limits_{h \to 0} \dfrac{f(94, 80 + h) - f(94, 80)}{h}$, so we use $h = \pm 5$:

$$f_H(94, 80) \approx \frac{f(94, 85) - f(94, 80)}{5} = \frac{132 - 127}{5} = 1, \quad f_H(94, 80) \approx \frac{f(94, 75) - f(94, 80)}{-5} = \frac{122 - 127}{-5} = 1$$

Averaging these values gives $f_H(94, 80) \approx 1$. The linear approximation, then, is

$$f(T, H) \approx f(94, 80) + f_T(94, 80)(T - 94) + f_H(94, 80)(H - 80)$$

$$\approx 127 + 4(T - 94) + 1(H - 80) \qquad \text{[or } 4T + H - 329]$$

Thus when $T = 95$ and $H = 78$, $f(95, 78) \approx 127 + 4(95 - 94) + 1(78 - 80) = 129$, so we estimate the heat index to be

approximately $129°$F.

23. $z = x^3 \ln(y^2) \;\Rightarrow\; dz = \dfrac{\partial z}{\partial x} dx + \dfrac{\partial z}{\partial y} dy = 3x^2 \ln(y^2)\, dx + x^3 \cdot \dfrac{1}{y^2}(2y)\, dy = 3x^2 \ln(y^2)\, dx + \dfrac{2x^3}{y}\, dy$

25. $m = p^5 q^3 \;\Rightarrow\; dm = \dfrac{\partial m}{\partial n} dp + \dfrac{\partial m}{\partial q} dq = 5p^4 q^3\, dp + 3p^5 q^2\, dq$

27. $R = \alpha \beta^9 \cos\gamma \;\Rightarrow\; dR = \dfrac{\partial R}{\partial \alpha} d\alpha + \dfrac{\partial R}{\partial \beta} d\beta + \dfrac{\partial R}{\partial \gamma} d\gamma = \beta^9 \cos\gamma\, d\alpha + 2\alpha\beta \cos\gamma\, d\beta - \alpha\beta^2 \sin\gamma\, d\gamma$

29. $dx = \Delta x = 0.05$, $dy = \Delta y = 0.1$, $z = 5x^2 + y^2$, $z_x = 10x$, $z_y = 2y$. Thus when $x = 1$ and $y = 2$,

$dz = z_x(1, 2)\,dx + z_y(1, 2)\,dy = (10)(0.05) + (4)(0.1) = 0.9$ while

$\Delta z = f(1.05, 2.1) - f(1, 2) = 5(1.05)^2 + (2.1)^2 - 5 - 4 = 0.9225$.

31. $dA = \dfrac{\partial A}{\partial x}\,dx + \dfrac{\partial A}{\partial y}\,dy = y\,dx + x\,dy$ and $|\Delta x| \le 0.1$, $|\Delta y| \le 0.1$. We use $dx = 0.1$, $dy = 0.1$ with $x = 30$, $y = 24$; then

the maximum error in the area is about $dA = 24(0.1) + 30(0.1) = 5.4$ cm^2.

33. The volume of a can is $V = \pi r^2 h$ and $\Delta V \approx dV$ is an estimate of the amount of tin. Here $dV = 2\pi rh\,dr + \pi r^2\,dh$, so put

$dr = 0.04$, $dh = 0.08$ (0.04 on top, 0.04 on bottom) and then $\Delta V \approx dV = 2\pi(48)(0.04) + \pi(16)(0.08) \approx 16.08$ cm^3.

Thus the amount of tin is about 16 cm^3.

35. The errors in measurement are at most 2%, so $\left|\dfrac{\Delta w}{w}\right| \le 0.02$ and $\left|\dfrac{\Delta h}{h}\right| \le 0.02$. The relative error in the calculated surface

area is

$$\frac{\Delta S}{S} \approx \frac{dS}{S} = \frac{0.1091(0.425w^{0.425-1})h^{0.725}\,dw + 0.1091w^{0.425}(0.725h^{0.725-1})\,dh}{0.1091w^{0.425}h^{0.725}} = 0.425\frac{dw}{w} + 0.725\frac{dh}{h}$$

To estimate the maximum relative error, we use $\dfrac{dw}{w} = \left|\dfrac{\Delta w}{w}\right| = 0.02$ and $\dfrac{dh}{h} = \left|\dfrac{\Delta h}{h}\right| = 0.02 \quad\Rightarrow$

$\dfrac{dS}{S} = 0.425\,(0.02) + 0.725\,(0.02) = 0.023$. Thus the maximum percentage error is approximately 2.3%.

37. First we find $\dfrac{\partial R}{\partial R_1}$ implicitly by taking partial derivatives of both sides with respect to R_1:

$$\frac{\partial}{\partial R_1}\left(\frac{1}{R}\right) = \frac{\partial\,[(1/R_1) + (1/R_2) + (1/R_3)]}{\partial R_1} \quad\Rightarrow\quad -R^{-2}\frac{\partial R}{\partial R_1} = -R_1^{-2} \quad\Rightarrow\quad \frac{\partial R}{\partial R_1} = \frac{R^2}{R_1^2}.$$ Then by symmetry,

$\dfrac{\partial R}{\partial R_2} = \dfrac{R^2}{R_2^2}$, $\dfrac{\partial R}{\partial R_3} = \dfrac{R^2}{R_3^2}$. When $R_1 = 25$, $R_2 = 40$ and $R_3 = 50$, $\dfrac{1}{R} = \dfrac{17}{200} \iff R = \frac{200}{17}$ Ω. Since the possible error

for each R_i is 0.5%, the maximum error of R is attained by setting $\Delta R_i = 0.005R_i$. So

$$\Delta R \approx dR = \frac{\partial R}{\partial R_1}\,\Delta R_1 + \frac{\partial R}{\partial R_2}\,\Delta R_2 + \frac{\partial R}{\partial R_3}\,\Delta R_3 = (0.005)R^2\left(\frac{1}{R_1} + \frac{1}{R_2} + \frac{1}{R_3}\right) = (0.005)R = \tfrac{1}{17} \approx 0.059\ \Omega.$$

39. $\mathbf{r}(u, v) = (u + v)\,\mathbf{i} + 3u^2\,\mathbf{j} + (u - v)\,\mathbf{k}$.

$\mathbf{r}_u = \mathbf{i} + 6u\,\mathbf{j} + \mathbf{k}$ and $\mathbf{r}_v = \mathbf{i} - \mathbf{k}$, so $\mathbf{r}_u \times \mathbf{r}_v = -6u\,\mathbf{i} + 2\,\mathbf{j} - 6u\,\mathbf{k}$.

Since the point $(2, 3, 0)$ corresponds to $u = 1$, $v = 1$, a normal vector

to the surface at $(2, 3, 0)$ is $-6\,\mathbf{i} + 2\,\mathbf{j} - 6\,\mathbf{k}$, and an equation of the

tangent plane is $-6x + 2y - 6z = -6$ or $3x - y + 3z = 3$.

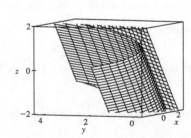

41. $\mathbf{r}(u, v) = u^2\,\mathbf{i} + 2u\sin v\,\mathbf{j} + u\cos v\,\mathbf{k} \;\Rightarrow\; \mathbf{r}(1, 0) = (1, 0, 1)$.

$\mathbf{r}_u = 2u\,\mathbf{i} + 2\sin v\,\mathbf{j} + \cos v\,\mathbf{k}$ and $\mathbf{r}_v = 2u\cos v\,\mathbf{j} - u\sin v\,\mathbf{k}$,

so a normal vector to the surface at the point $(1, 0, 1)$ is

$\mathbf{r}_u(1, 0) \times \mathbf{r}_v(1, 0) = (2\,\mathbf{i} + \mathbf{k}) \times (2\,\mathbf{j}) = -2\,\mathbf{i} + 4\,\mathbf{k}$.

Thus an equation of the tangent plane at $(1, 0, 1)$ is

$-2(x - 1) + 0(y - 0) + 4(z - 1) = 0$ or $-x + 2z = 1$.

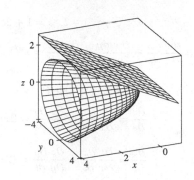

43. $\mathbf{r}(u, v) = u\,\mathbf{i} + \ln(uv)\,\mathbf{j} + v\,\mathbf{k} \;\Rightarrow\; \mathbf{r}_u(u, v) = \mathbf{i} + \frac{1}{u}\,\mathbf{j}$,

$\mathbf{r}_v(u, v) = \frac{1}{v}\,\mathbf{j} + \mathbf{k}$. $\mathbf{r}(1, 1) = \mathbf{i} + \mathbf{k}$, so the point corresponding to

$u = 1$, $v = 1$ is $(1, 0, 1)$. A normal vector for the tangent plane is

$\mathbf{r}_u(1, 1) \times \mathbf{r}_v(1, 1) = (\mathbf{i} + \mathbf{j}) \times (\mathbf{j} + \mathbf{k}) = \mathbf{i} - \mathbf{j} + \mathbf{k}$, so an equation

of the tangent plane is $(x - 1) - (y - 0) + (z - 1) = 0$

or $x - y + z = 2$.

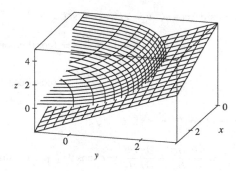

45. $\Delta z = f(a + \Delta x, b + \Delta y) - f(a, b) = (a + \Delta x)^2 + (b + \Delta y)^2 - (a^2 + b^2)$

$= a^2 + 2a\,\Delta x + (\Delta x)^2 + b^2 + 2b\,\Delta y + (\Delta y)^2 - a^2 - b^2 = 2a\,\Delta x + (\Delta x)^2 + 2b\,\Delta y + (\Delta y)^2$

But $f_x(a, b) = 2a$ and $f_y(a, b) = 2b$ and so $\Delta z = f_x(a, b)\,\Delta x + f_y(a, b)\,\Delta y + \Delta x\,\Delta x + \Delta y\,\Delta y$, which is Definition 7

with $\varepsilon_1 = \Delta x$ and $\varepsilon_2 = \Delta y$. Hence f is differentiable.

47. To show that f is continuous at (a, b) we need to show that $\displaystyle\lim_{(x,y)\to(a,b)} f(x, y) = f(a, b)$ or

equivalently $\displaystyle\lim_{(\Delta x, \Delta y)\to(0,0)} f(a + \Delta x, b + \Delta y) = f(a, b)$. Since f is differentiable at (a, b),

$f(a + \Delta x, b + \Delta y) - f(a, b) = \Delta z = f_x(a, b)\,\Delta x + f_y(a, b)\,\Delta y + \varepsilon_1\,\Delta x + \varepsilon_2\,\Delta y$, where ε_1 and $\varepsilon_2 \to 0$ as

$(\Delta x, \Delta y) \to (0, 0)$. Thus $f(a + \Delta x, b + \Delta y) = f(a, b) + f_x(a, b)\,\Delta x + f_y(a, b)\,\Delta y + \varepsilon_1\,\Delta x + \varepsilon_2\,\Delta y$. Taking the limit of

both sides as $(\Delta x, \Delta y) \to (0, 0)$ gives $\displaystyle\lim_{(\Delta x, \Delta y)\to(0,0)} f(a + \Delta x, b + \Delta y) = f(a, b)$. Thus f is continuous at (a, b).

11.5   The Chain Rule

1. $z = x^2 + y^2 + xy$, $x = \sin t$, $y = e^t \;\Rightarrow\; \dfrac{dz}{dt} = \dfrac{\partial z}{\partial x}\dfrac{dx}{dt} + \dfrac{\partial z}{\partial y}\dfrac{dy}{dt} = (2x + y)\cos t + (2y + x)e^t$

3. $z = \sqrt{1 + x^2 + y^2}$, $x = \ln t$, $y = \cos t \;\Rightarrow$

$\dfrac{dz}{dt} = \dfrac{\partial z}{\partial x}\dfrac{dx}{dt} + \dfrac{\partial z}{\partial y}\dfrac{dy}{dt} = \frac{1}{2}(1 + x^2 + y^2)^{-1/2}(2x) \cdot \dfrac{1}{t} + \frac{1}{2}(1 + x^2 + y^2)^{-1/2}(2y)(-\sin t) = \dfrac{1}{\sqrt{1 + x^2 + y^2}}\left(\dfrac{x}{t} - y\sin t\right)$

5. $w = xe^{y/z}$, $x = t^2$, $y = 1 - t$, $z = 1 + 2t$ $\Rightarrow$

$$\frac{dw}{dt} = \frac{\partial w}{\partial x}\frac{dx}{dt} + \frac{\partial w}{\partial y}\frac{dy}{dt} + \frac{\partial w}{\partial z}\frac{dz}{dt} = e^{y/z} \cdot 2t + xe^{y/z}\left(\frac{1}{z}\right) \cdot (-1) + xe^{y/z}\left(-\frac{y}{z^2}\right) \cdot 2 = e^{y/z}\left(2t - \frac{x}{z} - \frac{2xy}{z^2}\right)$$

7. $z = x^2 y^3$, $x = s\cos t$, $y = s\sin t$ $\Rightarrow$

$$\frac{\partial z}{\partial s} = \frac{\partial z}{\partial x}\frac{\partial x}{\partial s} + \frac{\partial z}{\partial y}\frac{\partial y}{\partial s} = 2xy^3\cos t + 3x^2 y^2\sin t$$

$$\frac{\partial z}{\partial t} = \frac{\partial z}{\partial x}\frac{\partial x}{\partial t} + \frac{\partial z}{\partial y}\frac{\partial y}{\partial t} = (2xy^3)(-s\sin t) + (3x^2 y^2)(s\cos t) = -2sxy^3\sin t + 3sx^2 y^2\cos t$$

9. $z = \sin\theta\cos\phi$, $\theta = st^2$, $\phi = s^2 t$ $\Rightarrow$

$$\frac{\partial z}{\partial s} = \frac{\partial z}{\partial\theta}\frac{\partial\theta}{\partial s} + \frac{\partial z}{\partial\phi}\frac{\partial\phi}{\partial s} = (\cos\theta\cos\phi)(t^2) + (-\sin\theta\sin\phi)(2st) = t^2\cos\theta\cos\phi - 2st\sin\theta\sin\phi$$

$$\frac{\partial z}{\partial t} = \frac{\partial z}{\partial\theta}\frac{\partial\theta}{\partial t} + \frac{\partial z}{\partial\phi}\frac{\partial\phi}{\partial t} = (\cos\theta\cos\phi)(2st) + (-\sin\theta\sin\phi)(s^2) = 2st\cos\theta\cos\phi - s^2\sin\theta\sin\phi$$

11. $z = e^r\cos\theta$, $r = st$, $\theta = \sqrt{s^2 + t^2}$ $\Rightarrow$

$$\frac{\partial z}{\partial s} = \frac{\partial z}{\partial r}\frac{\partial r}{\partial s} + \frac{\partial z}{\partial\theta}\frac{\partial\theta}{\partial s} = e^r\cos\theta \cdot t + e^r(-\sin\theta) \cdot \tfrac{1}{2}(s^2 + t^2)^{-1/2}(2s) = te^r\cos\theta - e^r\sin\theta \cdot \frac{s}{\sqrt{s^2 + t^2}}$$

$$= e^r\left(t\cos\theta - \frac{s}{\sqrt{s^2 + t^2}}\sin\theta\right)$$

$$\frac{\partial z}{\partial t} = \frac{\partial z}{\partial r}\frac{\partial r}{\partial t} + \frac{\partial z}{\partial\theta}\frac{\partial\theta}{\partial t} = e^r\cos\theta \cdot s + e^r(-\sin\theta) \cdot \tfrac{1}{2}(s^2 + t^2)^{-1/2}(2t) = se^r\cos\theta - e^r\sin\theta \cdot \frac{t}{\sqrt{s^2 + t^2}}$$

$$= e^r\left(s\cos\theta - \frac{t}{\sqrt{s^2 + t^2}}\sin\theta\right)$$

13. When $t = 3$, $x = g(3) = 2$ and $y = h(3) = 7$. By the Chain Rule (2),

$$\frac{dz}{dt} = \frac{\partial f}{\partial x}\frac{dx}{dt} + \frac{\partial f}{\partial y}\frac{dy}{dt} = f_x(2,7)g'(3) + f_y(2,7)h'(3) = (6)(5) + (-8)(-4) = 62.$$

15. $g(u,v) = f(x(u,v), y(u,v))$ where $x = e^u + \sin v$, $y = e^u + \cos v$ $\Rightarrow$

$\dfrac{\partial x}{\partial u} = e^u$, $\dfrac{\partial x}{\partial v} = \cos v$, $\dfrac{\partial y}{\partial u} = e^u$, $\dfrac{\partial y}{\partial v} = -\sin v$. By the Chain Rule (3), $\dfrac{\partial g}{\partial u} = \dfrac{\partial f}{\partial x}\dfrac{\partial x}{\partial u} + \dfrac{\partial f}{\partial y}\dfrac{\partial y}{\partial u}$. Then

$$g_u(0,0) = f_x(x(0,0), y(0,0))\,x_u(0,0) + f_y(x(0,0), y(0,0))\,y_u(0,0) = f_x(1,2)(e^0) + f_y(1,2)(e^0) = 2(1) + 5(1) = 7.$$

Similarly, $\dfrac{\partial g}{\partial v} = \dfrac{\partial f}{\partial x}\dfrac{\partial x}{\partial v} + \dfrac{\partial f}{\partial y}\dfrac{\partial y}{\partial v}$. Then

$$g_v(0,0) = f_x(x(0,0), y(0,0))\,x_v(0,0) + f_y(x(0,0), y(0,0))\,y_v(0,0) = f_x(1,2)(\cos 0) + f_y(1,2)(-\sin 0)$$
$$= 2(1) + 5(0) = 2$$

17.

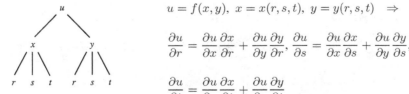

$u = f(x,y)$, $x = x(r,s,t)$, $y = y(r,s,t)$ $\Rightarrow$

$$\frac{\partial u}{\partial r} = \frac{\partial u}{\partial x}\frac{\partial x}{\partial r} + \frac{\partial u}{\partial y}\frac{\partial y}{\partial r}, \quad \frac{\partial u}{\partial s} = \frac{\partial u}{\partial x}\frac{\partial x}{\partial s} + \frac{\partial u}{\partial y}\frac{\partial y}{\partial s},$$

$$\frac{\partial u}{\partial t} = \frac{\partial u}{\partial x}\frac{\partial x}{\partial t} + \frac{\partial u}{\partial y}\frac{\partial y}{\partial t}$$

19.

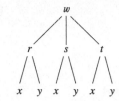

$$w = f(r,s,t), \quad r = r(x,y), \quad s = s(x,y), \quad t = t(x,y) \quad \Rightarrow$$

$$\frac{\partial w}{\partial x} = \frac{\partial w}{\partial r}\frac{\partial r}{\partial x} + \frac{\partial w}{\partial s}\frac{\partial s}{\partial x} + \frac{\partial w}{\partial t}\frac{\partial t}{\partial x}, \quad \frac{\partial w}{\partial y} = \frac{\partial w}{\partial r}\frac{\partial r}{\partial y} + \frac{\partial w}{\partial s}\frac{\partial s}{\partial y} + \frac{\partial w}{\partial t}\frac{\partial t}{\partial y}$$

21. $z = x^2 + xy^3, \; x = uv^2 + w^3, \; y = u + ve^w \;\Rightarrow\; \dfrac{\partial z}{\partial u} = \dfrac{\partial z}{\partial x}\dfrac{\partial x}{\partial u} + \dfrac{\partial z}{\partial y}\dfrac{\partial y}{\partial u} = (2x + y^3)(v^2) + (3xy^2)(1),$

$$\frac{\partial z}{\partial v} = \frac{\partial z}{\partial x}\frac{\partial x}{\partial v} + \frac{\partial z}{\partial y}\frac{\partial y}{\partial v} = (2x + y^3)(2uv) + (3xy^2)(e^w), \quad \frac{\partial z}{\partial w} = \frac{\partial z}{\partial x}\frac{\partial x}{\partial w} + \frac{\partial z}{\partial y}\frac{\partial y}{\partial w} = (2x + y^3)(3w^2) + (3xy^2)(ve^w).$$

When $u = 2$, $v = 1$, and $w = 0$, we have $x = 2$, $y = 3$, so $\dfrac{\partial z}{\partial u} = (31)(1) + (54)(1) = 85,$

$\dfrac{\partial z}{\partial v} = (31)(4) + (54)(1) = 178, \;\; \dfrac{\partial z}{\partial w} = (31)(0) + (54)(1) = 54.$

23. $R = \ln(u^2 + v^2 + w^2), \; u = x + 2y, \; v = 2x - y, \; w = 2xy \;\Rightarrow$

$$\frac{\partial R}{\partial x} = \frac{\partial R}{\partial u}\frac{\partial u}{\partial x} + \frac{\partial R}{\partial v}\frac{\partial v}{\partial x} + \frac{\partial R}{\partial w}\frac{\partial w}{\partial x} = \frac{2u}{u^2 + v^2 + w^2}\,(1) + \frac{2v}{u^2 + v^2 + w^2}\,(2) + \frac{2w}{u^2 + v^2 + w^2}\,(2y)$$

$$= \frac{2u + 4v + 4wy}{u^2 + v^2 + w^2},$$

$$\frac{\partial R}{\partial y} = \frac{\partial R}{\partial u}\frac{\partial u}{\partial y} + \frac{\partial R}{\partial v}\frac{\partial v}{\partial y} + \frac{\partial R}{\partial w}\frac{\partial w}{\partial y} = \frac{2u}{u^2 + v^2 + w^2}\,(2) + \frac{2v}{u^2 + v^2 + w^2}\,(-1) + \frac{2w}{u^2 + v^2 + w^2}\,(2x)$$

$$= \frac{4u - 2v + 4wx}{u^2 + v^2 + w^2}.$$

When $x = y = 1$ we have $u = 3$, $v = 1$, and $w = 2$, so $\dfrac{\partial R}{\partial x} = \dfrac{9}{7}$ and $\dfrac{\partial R}{\partial y} = \dfrac{9}{7}$.

25. $u = x^2 + yz, \; x = pr\cos\theta, \; y = pr\sin\theta, \; z = p + r \;\Rightarrow$

$$\frac{\partial u}{\partial p} = \frac{\partial u}{\partial x}\frac{\partial x}{\partial p} + \frac{\partial u}{\partial y}\frac{\partial y}{\partial p} + \frac{\partial u}{\partial z}\frac{\partial z}{\partial p} = (2x)(r\cos\theta) + (z)(r\sin\theta) + (y)(1) = 2xr\cos\theta + zr\sin\theta + y,$$

$$\frac{\partial u}{\partial r} = \frac{\partial u}{\partial x}\frac{\partial x}{\partial r} + \frac{\partial u}{\partial y}\frac{\partial y}{\partial r} + \frac{\partial u}{\partial z}\frac{\partial z}{\partial r} = (2x)(p\cos\theta) + (z)(p\sin\theta) + (y)(1) = 2xp\cos\theta + zp\sin\theta + y,$$

$$\frac{\partial u}{\partial \theta} = \frac{\partial u}{\partial x}\frac{\partial x}{\partial \theta} + \frac{\partial u}{\partial y}\frac{\partial y}{\partial \theta} + \frac{\partial u}{\partial z}\frac{\partial z}{\partial \theta} = (2x)(-pr\sin\theta) + (z)(pr\cos\theta) + (y)(0) = -2xpr\sin\theta + zpr\cos\theta.$$

When $p = 2$, $r = 3$, and $\theta = 0$ we have $x = 6$, $y = 0$, and $z = 5$, so $\dfrac{\partial u}{\partial p} = 36$, $\dfrac{\partial u}{\partial r} = 24$, and $\dfrac{\partial u}{\partial \theta} = 30$.

27. $\cos(x - y) = xe^y$, so let $F(x,y) = \cos(x - y) - xe^y = 0$.

Then $\dfrac{dy}{dx} = -\dfrac{F_x}{F_y} = -\dfrac{-\sin(x - y) - e^y}{-\sin(x - y)(-1) - xe^y} = \dfrac{\sin(x - y) + e^y}{\sin(x - y) - xe^y}.$

29. $x^2 + y^2 + z^2 = 3xyz$, so let $F(x,y,z) = x^2 + y^2 + z^2 - 3xyz = 0$. Then by Equations 7

$\dfrac{\partial z}{\partial x} = -\dfrac{F_x}{F_z} = -\dfrac{2x - 3yz}{2z - 3xy} = \dfrac{3yz - 2x}{2z - 3xy}$ and $\dfrac{\partial z}{\partial y} = -\dfrac{F_y}{F_z} = -\dfrac{2y - 3xz}{2z - 3xy} = \dfrac{3xz - 2y}{2z - 3xy}.$

31. $x - z = \arctan(yz)$, so let $F(x, y, z) = x - z - \arctan(yz) = 0$. Then

$$\frac{\partial z}{\partial x} = -\frac{F_x}{F_z} = -\frac{1}{-1 - \frac{1}{1 + (yz)^2}(y)} = \frac{1 + y^2 z^2}{1 + y + y^2 z^2} \text{ and}$$

$$\frac{\partial z}{\partial y} = -\frac{F_y}{F_z} = -\frac{-\frac{1}{1 + (yz)^2}(z)}{-1 - \frac{1}{1 + (yz)^2}(y)} = -\frac{\frac{z}{1 + y^2 z^2}}{\frac{1 + y^2 z^2 + y}{1 + y^2 z^2}} = -\frac{z}{1 + y + y^2 z^2}.$$

33. Since x and y are each functions of t, $T(x, y)$ is a function of t, so by the Chain Rule, $\dfrac{dT}{dt} = \dfrac{\partial T}{\partial x}\dfrac{dx}{dt} + \dfrac{\partial T}{\partial y}\dfrac{dy}{dt}$. After

3 seconds, $x - \sqrt{1 + t} = \sqrt{1 \mid 3} = 2$, $y - 2 + \frac{1}{3}t = 2 + \frac{1}{3}(3) = 3$, $\dfrac{dx}{dt} = \dfrac{1}{2\sqrt{1+t}} = \dfrac{1}{2\sqrt{1+3}} = \dfrac{1}{4}$, and $\dfrac{dy}{dt} = \dfrac{1}{3}$.

Then $\dfrac{dT}{dt} = T_x(2, 3)\dfrac{dx}{dt} + T_y(2, 3)\dfrac{dy}{dt} = 4\left(\frac{1}{4}\right) + 3\left(\frac{1}{3}\right) = 2$. Thus the temperature is rising at a rate of $2°\text{C/s}$.

35. $C = 1449.2 + 4.6T - 0.055T^2 + 0.00029T^3 + 0.016D$, so $\dfrac{\partial C}{\partial T} = 4.6 - 0.11T + 0.00087T^2$ and $\dfrac{\partial C}{\partial D} = 0.016$.

According to the graph, the diver is experiencing a temperature of approximately $12.5°\text{C}$ at $t = 20$ minutes, so

$\dfrac{\partial C}{\partial T} = 4.6 - 0.11(12.5) + 0.00087(12.5)^2 \approx 3.36$. By sketching tangent lines at $t = 20$ to the graphs given, we estimate

$\dfrac{dD}{dt} \approx \dfrac{1}{2}$ and $\dfrac{dT}{dt} \approx -\dfrac{1}{10}$. Then, by the Chain Rule, $\dfrac{dC}{dt} = \dfrac{\partial C}{\partial T}\dfrac{dT}{dt} + \dfrac{\partial C}{\partial D}\dfrac{dD}{dt} \approx (3.36)\left(-\frac{1}{10}\right) + (0.016)\left(\frac{1}{2}\right) \approx -0.33$.

Thus the speed of sound experienced by the diver is decreasing at a rate of approximately 0.33 m/s per minute.

37. (a) $V = \ell w h$, so by the Chain Rule,

$$\frac{dV}{dt} = \frac{\partial V}{\partial \ell}\frac{d\ell}{dt} + \frac{\partial V}{\partial w}\frac{dw}{dt} + \frac{\partial V}{\partial h}\frac{dh}{dt} = wh\frac{d\ell}{dt} + \ell h\frac{dw}{dt} + \ell w\frac{dh}{dt} = 2 \cdot 2 \cdot 2 + 1 \cdot 2 \cdot 2 + 1 \cdot 2 \cdot (-3) = 6 \text{ m}^3/\text{s}.$$

(b) $S = 2(\ell w + \ell h + wh)$, so by the Chain Rule,

$$\frac{dS}{dt} = \frac{\partial S}{\partial \ell}\frac{d\ell}{dt} + \frac{\partial S}{\partial w}\frac{dw}{dt} + \frac{\partial S}{\partial h}\frac{dh}{dt} = 2(w + h)\frac{d\ell}{dt} + 2(\ell + h)\frac{dw}{dt} + 2(\ell + w)\frac{dh}{dt}$$

$$= 2(2 + 2)2 + 2(1 + 2)2 + 2(1 + 2)(-3) = 10 \text{ m}^2/\text{s}$$

(c) $L^2 = \ell^2 + w^2 + h^2 \Rightarrow 2L\dfrac{dL}{dt} = 2\ell\dfrac{d\ell}{dt} + 2w\dfrac{dw}{dt} + 2h\dfrac{dh}{dt} = 2(1)(2) + 2(2)(2) + 2(2)(-3) = 0 \Rightarrow$

$dL/dt = 0 \text{ m/s}.$

39. $\dfrac{dP}{dt} = 0.05$, $\dfrac{dT}{dt} - 0.15$, $V = 8.31\dfrac{T}{P}$ and $\dfrac{dV}{dt} - \dfrac{8.31}{P}\dfrac{dT}{dt} - 8.31\dfrac{T}{P^2}\dfrac{dP}{dt}$. Thus when $P = 20$ and $T = 320$,

$$\frac{dV}{dt} = 8.31\left[\frac{0.15}{20} - \frac{(0.05)(320)}{400}\right] \approx -0.27 \text{ L/s}.$$

41. Let x be the length of the first side of the triangle and y the length of the second side. The area A of the triangle is given by

$A = \frac{1}{2}xy\sin\theta$ where θ is the angle between the two sides. Thus A is a function of x, y, and θ, and x, y, and θ are each in turn

functions of time t. We are given that $\dfrac{dx}{dt} = 3$, $\dfrac{dy}{dt} = -2$, and because A is constant, $\dfrac{dA}{dt} = 0$. By the Chain Rule,

$$\frac{dA}{dt} = \frac{\partial A}{\partial x}\frac{dx}{dt} + \frac{\partial A}{\partial y}\frac{dy}{dt} + \frac{\partial A}{\partial \theta}\frac{d\theta}{dt} \quad \Rightarrow \quad \frac{dA}{dt} = \tfrac{1}{2}y\sin\theta \cdot \frac{dx}{dt} + \tfrac{1}{2}x\sin\theta \cdot \frac{dy}{dt} + \tfrac{1}{2}xy\cos\theta \cdot \frac{d\theta}{dt}.$$ When $x = 20$, $y = 30$,

and $\theta = \pi/6$ we have

$$0 = \tfrac{1}{2}(30)\left(\sin\tfrac{\pi}{6}\right)(3) + \tfrac{1}{2}(20)\left(\sin\tfrac{\pi}{6}\right)(-2) + \tfrac{1}{2}(20)(30)\left(\cos\tfrac{\pi}{6}\right)\frac{d\theta}{dt}$$

$$= 45 \cdot \tfrac{1}{2} - 20 \cdot \tfrac{1}{2} + 300 \cdot \frac{\sqrt{3}}{2} \cdot \frac{d\theta}{dt} = \tfrac{25}{2} + 150\sqrt{3}\,\frac{d\theta}{dt}$$

Solving for $\dfrac{d\theta}{dt}$ gives $\dfrac{d\theta}{dt} = \dfrac{-25/2}{150\sqrt{3}} = -\dfrac{1}{12\sqrt{3}}$, so the angle between the sides is decreasing at a rate of

$1/(12\sqrt{3}) \approx 0.048$ rad/s.

43. (a) By the Chain Rule, $\dfrac{\partial z}{\partial r} = \dfrac{\partial z}{\partial x}\cos\theta + \dfrac{\partial z}{\partial y}\sin\theta$, $\dfrac{\partial z}{\partial \theta} = \dfrac{\partial z}{\partial x}(-r\sin\theta) + \dfrac{\partial z}{\partial y}r\cos\theta$.

(b) $\left(\dfrac{\partial z}{\partial r}\right)^2 = \left(\dfrac{\partial z}{\partial x}\right)^2\cos^2\theta + 2\dfrac{\partial z}{\partial x}\dfrac{\partial z}{\partial y}\cos\theta\sin\theta + \left(\dfrac{\partial z}{\partial y}\right)^2\sin^2\theta$,

$\left(\dfrac{\partial z}{\partial \theta}\right)^2 = \left(\dfrac{\partial z}{\partial x}\right)^2 r^2\sin^2\theta - 2\dfrac{\partial z}{\partial x}\dfrac{\partial z}{\partial y}r^2\cos\theta\sin\theta + \left(\dfrac{\partial z}{\partial y}\right)^2 r^2\cos^2\theta$. Thus

$\left(\dfrac{\partial z}{\partial r}\right)^2 + \dfrac{1}{r^2}\left(\dfrac{\partial z}{\partial \theta}\right)^2 = \left[\left(\dfrac{\partial z}{\partial x}\right)^2 + \left(\dfrac{\partial z}{\partial y}\right)^2\right](\cos^2\theta + \sin^2\theta) = \left(\dfrac{\partial z}{\partial x}\right)^2 + \left(\dfrac{\partial z}{\partial y}\right)^2.$

45. Let $u = x - y$. Then $\dfrac{\partial z}{\partial x} = \dfrac{dz}{du}\dfrac{\partial u}{\partial x} = \dfrac{dz}{du}$ and $\dfrac{\partial z}{\partial y} = \dfrac{dz}{du}(-1)$. Thus $\dfrac{\partial z}{\partial x} + \dfrac{\partial z}{\partial y} = 0$.

47. Let $u = x + at$, $v = x - at$. Then $z = f(u) + g(v)$, so $\partial z/\partial u = f'(u)$ and $\partial z/\partial v = g'(v)$.

Thus $\dfrac{\partial z}{\partial t} = \dfrac{\partial z}{\partial u}\dfrac{\partial u}{\partial t} + \dfrac{\partial z}{\partial v}\dfrac{\partial v}{\partial t} = af'(u) - ag'(v)$ and

$\dfrac{\partial^2 z}{\partial t^2} = a\dfrac{\partial}{\partial t}[f'(u) - g'(v)] = a\left(\dfrac{df'(u)}{du}\dfrac{\partial u}{\partial t} - \dfrac{dg'(v)}{dv}\dfrac{\partial v}{\partial t}\right) = a^2 f''(u) + a^2 g''(v).$

Similarly $\dfrac{\partial z}{\partial x} = f'(u) + g'(v)$ and $\dfrac{\partial^2 z}{\partial x^2} = f''(u) + g''(v)$. Thus $\dfrac{\partial^2 z}{\partial t^2} = a^2\dfrac{\partial^2 z}{\partial x^2}$.

49. $\dfrac{\partial z}{\partial s} = \dfrac{\partial z}{\partial x}2s + \dfrac{\partial z}{\partial y}2r$. Then

$$\frac{\partial^2 z}{\partial r\,\partial s} = \frac{\partial}{\partial r}\left(\frac{\partial z}{\partial x}2s\right) + \frac{\partial}{\partial r}\left(\frac{\partial z}{\partial y}2r\right)$$

$$= \frac{\partial^2 z}{\partial x^2}\frac{\partial x}{\partial r}2s + \frac{\partial}{\partial y}\left(\frac{\partial z}{\partial x}\right)\frac{\partial y}{\partial r}2s + \frac{\partial z}{\partial x}\frac{\partial}{\partial r}2s + \frac{\partial^2 z}{\partial y^2}\frac{\partial y}{\partial r}2r + \frac{\partial}{\partial x}\left(\frac{\partial z}{\partial y}\right)\frac{\partial x}{\partial r}2r + \frac{\partial z}{\partial y}2$$

$$= 4rs\frac{\partial^2 z}{\partial x^2} + \frac{\partial^2 z}{\partial y\,\partial x}4s^2 + 0 + 4rs\frac{\partial^2 z}{\partial y^2} + \frac{\partial^2 z}{\partial x\,\partial y}4r^2 + 2\frac{\partial z}{\partial y}$$

By the continuity of the partials, $\dfrac{\partial^2 z}{\partial r\,\partial s} = 4rs\dfrac{\partial^2 z}{\partial r^2} + 4rs\dfrac{\partial^2 z}{\partial u^2} + (4r^2 + 4s^2)\dfrac{\partial^2 z}{\partial x\,\partial y} + 2\dfrac{\partial z}{\partial y}$.

51. $\dfrac{\partial z}{\partial r} = \dfrac{\partial z}{\partial x}\cos\theta + \dfrac{\partial z}{\partial y}\sin\theta$ and $\dfrac{\partial z}{\partial\theta} = -\dfrac{\partial z}{\partial x}r\sin\theta + \dfrac{\partial z}{\partial y}r\cos\theta$. Then

$$\frac{\partial^2 z}{\partial r^2} = \cos\theta\left(\frac{\partial^2 z}{\partial x^2}\cos\theta + \frac{\partial^2 z}{\partial y\,\partial x}\sin\theta\right) + \sin\theta\left(\frac{\partial^2 z}{\partial y^2}\sin\theta + \frac{\partial^2 z}{\partial x\,\partial y}\cos\theta\right)$$

$$= \cos^2\theta\,\frac{\partial^2 z}{\partial x^2} + 2\cos\theta\,\sin\theta\,\frac{\partial^2 z}{\partial x\,\partial y} + \sin^2\theta\,\frac{\partial^2 z}{\partial y^2}$$

and

$$\frac{\partial^2 z}{\partial\theta^2} = -r\cos\theta\,\frac{\partial z}{\partial x} + (-r\sin\theta)\left(\frac{\partial^2 z}{\partial x^2}(-r\sin\theta) + \frac{\partial^2 z}{\partial y\,\partial x}r\cos\theta\right)$$

$$\qquad -r\sin\theta\,\frac{\partial z}{\partial y} + r\cos\theta\left(\frac{\partial^2 z}{\partial y^2}r\cos\theta + \frac{\partial^2 z}{\partial x\,\partial y}(-r\sin\theta)\right)$$

$$= -r\cos\theta\,\frac{\partial z}{\partial x} - r\sin\theta\,\frac{\partial z}{\partial y} + r^2\sin^2\theta\,\frac{\partial^2 z}{\partial x^2} - 2r^2\cos\theta\,\sin\theta\,\frac{\partial^2 z}{\partial x\,\partial y} + r^2\cos^2\theta\,\frac{\partial^2 z}{\partial y^2}$$

Thus

$$\frac{\partial^2 z}{\partial r^2} + \frac{1}{r^2}\frac{\partial^2 z}{\partial\theta^2} + \frac{1}{r}\frac{\partial z}{\partial r} = (\cos^2\theta + \sin^2\theta)\frac{\partial^2 z}{\partial x^2} + (\sin^2\theta + \cos^2\theta)\frac{\partial^2 z}{\partial y^2}$$

$$\qquad -\frac{1}{r}\cos\theta\,\frac{\partial z}{\partial x} - \frac{1}{r}\sin\theta\,\frac{\partial z}{\partial y} + \frac{1}{r}\left(\cos\theta\,\frac{\partial z}{\partial x} + \sin\theta\,\frac{\partial z}{\partial y}\right)$$

$$= \frac{\partial^2 z}{\partial x^2} + \frac{\partial^2 z}{\partial y^2} \text{ as desired.}$$

53. $F(x, y, z) = 0$ is assumed to define z as a function of x and y, that is, $z = f(x, y)$. So by (7), $\dfrac{\partial z}{\partial x} = -\dfrac{F_x}{F_z}$ since $F_z \neq 0$.

Similarly, it is assumed that $F(x, y, z) = 0$ defines x as a function of y and z, that is $x = h(x, z)$. Then $F(h(y, z), y, z) = 0$

and by the Chain Rule, $F_x\dfrac{\partial x}{\partial y} + F_y\dfrac{\partial y}{\partial y} + F_z\dfrac{\partial z}{\partial y} = 0$. But $\dfrac{\partial z}{\partial y} = 0$ and $\dfrac{\partial y}{\partial y} = 1$, so $F_x\dfrac{\partial x}{\partial y} + F_y = 0 \;\Rightarrow\; \dfrac{\partial x}{\partial y} = -\dfrac{F_y}{F_x}$.

A similar calculation shows that $\dfrac{\partial y}{\partial z} = -\dfrac{F_z}{F_y}$. Thus $\dfrac{\partial z}{\partial x}\dfrac{\partial x}{\partial y}\dfrac{\partial y}{\partial z} = \left(-\dfrac{F_x}{F_z}\right)\left(-\dfrac{F_y}{F_x}\right)\left(-\dfrac{F_z}{F_y}\right) = -1$.

11.6 Directional Derivatives and the Gradient Vector

1. We can approximate the directional derivative of the pressure function at K in the direction of S by the average rate of change of pressure between the points where the red line intersects the contour lines closest to K (extend the red line slightly at the left). In the direction of S, the pressure changes from 1000 millibars to 996 millibars and we estimate the distance between these two points to be approximately 50 km (using the fact that the distance from K to S is 300 km). Then the rate of change of pressure in the direction given is approximately $\frac{996 - 1000}{50} = -0.08$ millibar/km.

3. $D_{\mathbf{u}} f(-20, 30) = \nabla f(-20, 30) \cdot \mathbf{u} = f_T(-20, 30)\left(\frac{1}{\sqrt{2}}\right) + f_v(-20, 30)\left(\frac{1}{\sqrt{2}}\right)$.

$f_T(-20, 30) = \lim\limits_{h\to 0}\dfrac{f(-20 + h, 30) - f(-20, 30)}{h}$, so we can approximate $f_T(-20, 30)$ by considering $h = \pm 5$ and

using the values given in the table: $f_T(-20, 30) \approx \dfrac{f(-15, 30) - f(-20, 30)}{5} = \dfrac{-26 - (-33)}{5} = 1.4$,

$f_T(-20, 30) \approx \dfrac{f(-25, 30) - f(-20, 30)}{-5} = \dfrac{-39 - (-33)}{-5} = 1.2$. Averaging these values gives $f_T(-20, 30) \approx 1.3$.

Similarly, $f_v(-20, 30) = \lim\limits_{h \to 0} \dfrac{f(-20, 30 + h) - f(-20, 30)}{h}$, so we can approximate $f_v(-20, 30)$ with $h = \pm 10$:

$$f_v(-20, 30) \approx \frac{f(-20, 40) - f(-20, 30)}{10} = \frac{-34 - (-33)}{10} = -0.1,$$

$$f_v(-20, 30) \approx \frac{f(-20, 20) - f(-20, 30)}{-10} = \frac{-30 - (-33)}{-10} = -0.3.$$ Averaging these values gives $f_v(-20, 30) \approx -0.2$.

Then $D_{\mathbf{u}} f(-20, 30) \approx 1.3\left(\frac{1}{\sqrt{2}}\right) + (-0.2)\left(\frac{1}{\sqrt{2}}\right) \approx 0.778$.

5. $f(x, y) = ye^{-x} \;\Rightarrow\; f_x(x, y) = -ye^{-x}$ and $f_y(x, y) = e^{-x}$. If $\mathbf{u}$ is a unit vector in the direction of $\theta = 2\pi/3$, then

from Equation 6, $D_{\mathbf{u}} f(0, 4) = f_x(0, 4) \cos\left(\frac{2\pi}{3}\right) + f_y(0, 4) \sin\left(\frac{2\pi}{3}\right) = -4 \cdot \left(-\frac{1}{2}\right) + 1 \cdot \frac{\sqrt{3}}{2} = 2 + \frac{\sqrt{3}}{2}$.

7. $f(x, y) = \sin(2x + 3y)$

(a) $\nabla f(x, y) = \dfrac{\partial f}{\partial x}\mathbf{i} + \dfrac{\partial f}{\partial y}\mathbf{j} = [\cos(2x + 3y) \cdot 2]\mathbf{i} + [\cos(2x + 3y) \cdot 3]\mathbf{j} = 2\cos(2x + 3y)\mathbf{i} + 3\cos(2x + 3y)\mathbf{j}$

(b) $\nabla f(-6, 4) = (2\cos 0)\mathbf{i} + (3\cos 0)\mathbf{j} = 2\mathbf{i} + 3\mathbf{j}$

(c) By Equation 9, $D_{\mathbf{u}} f(-6, 4) = \nabla f(-6, 4) \cdot \mathbf{u} = (2\mathbf{i} + 3\mathbf{j}) \cdot \frac{1}{2}(\sqrt{3}\mathbf{i} - \mathbf{j}) = \frac{1}{2}(2\sqrt{3} - 3) = \sqrt{3} - \frac{3}{2}$.

9. $f(x, y, z) = xe^{2yz}$

(a) $\nabla f(x, y, z) = \langle f_x(x, y, z), f_y(x, y, z), f_z(x, y, z)\rangle = \langle e^{2yz}, 2xze^{2yz}, 2xye^{2yz}\rangle$

(b) $\nabla f(3, 0, 2) = \langle 1, 12, 0\rangle$

(c) By Equation 14, $D_{\mathbf{u}} f(3, 0, 2) = \nabla f(3, 0, 2) \cdot \mathbf{u} = \langle 1, 12, 0\rangle \cdot \langle \frac{2}{3}, -\frac{2}{3}, \frac{1}{3}\rangle = \frac{2}{3} - \frac{24}{3} + 0 = -\frac{22}{3}$.

11. $f(x, y) = 1 + 2x\sqrt{y} \;\Rightarrow\; \nabla f(x, y) = \langle 2\sqrt{y}, 2x \cdot \frac{1}{2}y^{-1/2}\rangle = \langle 2\sqrt{y}, x/\sqrt{y}\rangle$, $\nabla f(3, 4) = \langle 4, \frac{3}{2}\rangle$, and a unit vector in

the direction of $\mathbf{v}$ is $\mathbf{u} = \dfrac{1}{\sqrt{4^2 + (-3)^2}}\langle 4, -3\rangle = \langle \frac{4}{5}, -\frac{3}{5}\rangle$, so $D_{\mathbf{u}} f(3, 4) = \nabla f(3, 4) \cdot \mathbf{u} = \langle 4, \frac{3}{2}\rangle \cdot \langle \frac{4}{5}, -\frac{3}{5}\rangle = \frac{23}{10}$.

13. $g(p, q) = p^4 - p^2q^3 \;\Rightarrow\; \nabla g(p, q) = (4p^3 - 2pq^3)\mathbf{i} + (-3p^2q^2)\mathbf{j}$, $\nabla g(2, 1) = 28\mathbf{i} - 12\mathbf{j}$, and a unit

vector in the direction of $\mathbf{v}$ is $\mathbf{u} = \dfrac{1}{\sqrt{1^2 + 3^2}}(\mathbf{i} + 3\mathbf{j}) = \frac{1}{\sqrt{10}}(\mathbf{i} + 3\mathbf{j})$, so

$D_{\mathbf{u}} g(2, 1) = \nabla g(2, 1) \cdot \mathbf{u} = (28\mathbf{i} - 12\mathbf{j}) \cdot \frac{1}{\sqrt{10}}(\mathbf{i} + 3\mathbf{j}) = \frac{1}{\sqrt{10}}(28 - 36) = -\frac{8}{\sqrt{10}}$ or $-\frac{4\sqrt{10}}{5}$.

15. $f(x, y, z) = xe^y + ye^z + ze^x \;\Rightarrow\; \nabla f(x, y, z) = \langle e^y + ze^x, xe^y + e^z, ye^z + e^x\rangle$, $\nabla f(0, 0, 0) = \langle 1, 1, 1\rangle$, and a unit

vector in the direction of $\mathbf{v}$ is $\mathbf{u} = \dfrac{1}{\sqrt{25 + 1 + 4}}\langle 5, 1, -2\rangle = \frac{1}{\sqrt{30}}\langle 5, 1, -2\rangle$, so

$D_{\mathbf{u}} f(0, 0, 0) = \nabla f(0, 0, 0) \cdot \mathbf{u} = \langle 1, 1, 1\rangle \cdot \frac{1}{\sqrt{30}}\langle 5, 1, -2\rangle = \frac{4}{\sqrt{30}}$.

17. $g(x, y, z) = (x + 2y + 3z)^{3/2} \;\Rightarrow$

$\nabla g(x, y, z) = \langle \frac{3}{2}(x + 2y + 3z)^{1/2}(1), \frac{3}{2}(x + 2y + 3z)^{1/2}(2), \frac{3}{2}(x + 2y + 3z)^{1/2}(3)\rangle$

$\qquad = \langle \frac{3}{2}\sqrt{x + 2y + 3z}, 3\sqrt{x + 2y + 3z}, \frac{9}{2}\sqrt{x + 2y + 3z}\rangle$, $\nabla g(1, 1, 2) = \langle \frac{9}{2}, 9, \frac{27}{2}\rangle$,

and a unit vector in the direction of $\mathbf{v} = 2\mathbf{j} - \mathbf{k}$ is $\mathbf{u} = \frac{2}{\sqrt{5}}\mathbf{j} - \frac{1}{\sqrt{5}}\mathbf{k}$, so

$D_{\mathbf{u}} g(1, 1, 2) = \langle \frac{9}{2}, 9, \frac{27}{2}\rangle \cdot \langle 0, \frac{2}{\sqrt{5}}, \frac{1}{\sqrt{5}}\rangle = \frac{18}{\sqrt{5}} \quad \frac{27}{2\sqrt{5}} - \frac{9}{2\sqrt{5}}$

19. $f(x,y) = \sqrt{xy} \;\Rightarrow\; \nabla f(x,y) = \left\langle \frac{1}{2}(xy)^{-1/2}(y), \frac{1}{2}(xy)^{-1/2}(x)\right\rangle = \left\langle \frac{y}{2\sqrt{xy}}, \frac{x}{2\sqrt{xy}}\right\rangle$, so $\nabla f(2,8) = \left\langle 1, \frac{1}{4}\right\rangle$.

The unit vector in the direction of $\overrightarrow{PQ} = \langle 5-2, 4-8\rangle = \langle 3,-4\rangle$ is $\mathbf{u} = \left\langle \frac{3}{5}, -\frac{4}{5}\right\rangle$, so

$D_{\mathbf{u}} f(2,8) = \nabla f(2,8) \cdot \mathbf{u} = \left\langle 1, \frac{1}{4}\right\rangle \cdot \left\langle \frac{3}{5}, -\frac{4}{5}\right\rangle = \frac{2}{5}$.

21. $f(x,y) = \sin(xy) \;\Rightarrow\; \nabla f(x,y) = \langle y\cos(xy), x\cos(xy)\rangle$, $\nabla f(1,0) = \langle 0,1\rangle$. Thus the maximum rate of change is $|\nabla f(1,0)| = 1$ in the direction $\langle 0,1\rangle$.

23. $f(x,y,z) = \sqrt{x^2+y^2+z^2} \;\Rightarrow$

$\nabla f(x,y,z) = \left\langle \frac{1}{2}(x^2+y^2+z^2)^{-1/2}\cdot 2x, \frac{1}{2}(x^2+y^2+z^2)^{-1/2}\cdot 2y, \frac{1}{2}(x^2+y^2+z^2)^{-1/2}\cdot 2z\right\rangle$

$= \left\langle \frac{x}{\sqrt{x^2+y^2+z^2}}, \frac{y}{\sqrt{x^2+y^2+z^2}}, \frac{z}{\sqrt{x^2+y^2+z^2}}\right\rangle$,

$\nabla f(3,6,-2) = \left\langle \frac{3}{\sqrt{49}}, \frac{6}{\sqrt{49}}, \frac{-2}{\sqrt{49}}\right\rangle = \left\langle \frac{3}{7}, \frac{6}{7}, -\frac{2}{7}\right\rangle$. Thus the maximum rate of change is

$|\nabla f(3,6,-2)| = \sqrt{\left(\frac{3}{7}\right)^2 + \left(\frac{6}{7}\right)^2 + \left(-\frac{2}{7}\right)^2} = \sqrt{\frac{9+36+4}{49}} = 1$ in the direction $\left\langle \frac{3}{7}, \frac{6}{7}, -\frac{2}{7}\right\rangle$ or equivalently $\langle 3,6,-2\rangle$.

25. (a) As in the proof of Theorem 15, $D_{\mathbf{u}} f = |\nabla f| \cos\theta$. Since the minimum value of $\cos\theta$ is -1 occurring when $\theta = \pi$, the minimum value of $D_{\mathbf{u}} f$ is $-|\nabla f|$ occurring when $\theta = \pi$, that is when $\mathbf{u}$ is in the opposite direction of ∇f (assuming $\nabla f \neq \mathbf{0}$).

(b) $f(x,y) = x^4 y - x^2 y^3 \;\Rightarrow\; \nabla f(x,y) = \langle 4x^3 y - 2xy^3, x^4 - 3x^2 y^2\rangle$, so f decreases fastest at the point $(2,-3)$ in the direction $-\nabla f(2,-3) = -\langle 12,-92\rangle = \langle -12,92\rangle$.

27. The direction of fastest change is $\nabla f(x,y) = (2x-2)\mathbf{i} + (2y-4)\mathbf{j}$, so we need to find all points (x,y) where $\nabla f(x,y)$ is parallel to $\mathbf{i}+\mathbf{j} \;\Leftrightarrow\; (2x-2)\mathbf{i} + (2y-4)\mathbf{j} = k(\mathbf{i}+\mathbf{j}) \;\Leftrightarrow\; k = 2x-2$ and $k = 2y-4$. Then $2x-2 = 2y-4 \;\Rightarrow\; y = x+1$, so the direction of fastest change is $\mathbf{i}+\mathbf{j}$ at all points on the line $y = x+1$.

29. $T = \frac{k}{\sqrt{x^2+y^2+z^2}}$ and $120 = T(1,2,2) = \frac{k}{3}$ so $k = 360$.

(a) $\mathbf{u} = \frac{\langle 1,-1,1\rangle}{\sqrt{3}}$,

$D_{\mathbf{u}} T(1,2,2) = \nabla T(1,2,2) \cdot \mathbf{u} = \left[-360(x^2+y^2+z^2)^{-3/2}\langle x,y,z\rangle\right]_{(1,2,2)} \cdot \mathbf{u} = -\frac{40}{3}\langle 1,2,2\rangle \cdot \frac{1}{\sqrt{3}}\langle 1,-1,1\rangle = -\frac{40}{3\sqrt{3}}$

(b) From (a), $\nabla T = -360(x^2+y^2+z^2)^{-3/2}\langle x,y,z\rangle$, and since $\langle x,y,z\rangle$ is the position vector of the point (x,y,z), the vector $-\langle x,y,z\rangle$, and thus ∇T, always points toward the origin.

31. $\nabla V(x,y,z) = \langle 10x - 3y + yz, xz - 3x, xy\rangle$, $\nabla V(3,4,5) = \langle 38,6,12\rangle$

(a) $D_{\mathbf{u}} V(3,4,5) = \langle 38,6,12\rangle \cdot \frac{1}{\sqrt{3}}\langle 1,1,-1\rangle = \frac{32}{\sqrt{3}}$

(b) $\nabla V(3,4,5) = \langle 38,6,12\rangle$, or equivalently, $\langle 19,3,6\rangle$.

(c) $|\nabla V(3,4,5)| = \sqrt{38^2 + 6^2 + 12^2} = \sqrt{1624} = 2\sqrt{406}$

33. A unit vector in the direction of $\overrightarrow{AB}$ is $\mathbf{i}$ and a unit vector in the direction of $\overrightarrow{AC}$ is $\mathbf{j}$. Thus $D_{\overrightarrow{AB}} f(1,3) = f_x(1,3) = 3$ and

$D_{\overrightarrow{AC}} f(1,3) = f_y(1,3) = 26$. Therefore $\nabla f(1,3) = \langle f_x(1,3), f_y(1,3) \rangle = \langle 3, 26 \rangle$, and by definition,

$D_{\overrightarrow{AD}} f(1,3) = \nabla f \cdot \mathbf{u}$ where $\mathbf{u}$ is a unit vector in the direction of $\overrightarrow{AD}$, which is $\langle \frac{5}{13}, \frac{12}{13} \rangle$. Therefore,

$D_{\overrightarrow{AD}} f(1,3) = \langle 3, 26 \rangle \cdot \langle \frac{5}{13}, \frac{12}{13} \rangle = 3 \cdot \frac{5}{13} + 26 \cdot \frac{12}{13} = \frac{327}{13}$.

35. (a) $\nabla(au + bv) = \left\langle \dfrac{\partial(au+bv)}{\partial x}, \dfrac{\partial(au+bv)}{\partial y} \right\rangle = \left\langle a\dfrac{\partial u}{\partial x} + b\dfrac{\partial v}{\partial x}, a\dfrac{\partial u}{\partial y} + b\dfrac{\partial v}{\partial y} \right\rangle = a\left\langle \dfrac{\partial u}{\partial x}, \dfrac{\partial u}{\partial y} \right\rangle + b\left\langle \dfrac{\partial v}{\partial x}, \dfrac{\partial v}{\partial y} \right\rangle$

$= a\,\nabla u + b\,\nabla v$

(b) $\nabla(uv) = \left\langle v\dfrac{\partial u}{\partial x} + u\dfrac{\partial v}{\partial x}, v\dfrac{\partial u}{\partial y} + u\dfrac{\partial v}{\partial y} \right\rangle = v\left\langle \dfrac{\partial u}{\partial x}, \dfrac{\partial u}{\partial y} \right\rangle + u\left\langle \dfrac{\partial v}{\partial x}, \dfrac{\partial v}{\partial y} \right\rangle = v\,\nabla u + u\,\nabla v$

(c) $\nabla\left(\dfrac{u}{v}\right) = \left\langle \dfrac{v\dfrac{\partial u}{\partial x} - u\dfrac{\partial v}{\partial x}}{v^2}, \dfrac{v\dfrac{\partial u}{\partial y} - u\dfrac{\partial v}{\partial y}}{v^2} \right\rangle = \dfrac{v\left\langle \dfrac{\partial u}{\partial x}, \dfrac{\partial u}{\partial y} \right\rangle - u\left\langle \dfrac{\partial v}{\partial x}, \dfrac{\partial v}{\partial y} \right\rangle}{v^2} = \dfrac{v\,\nabla u - u\,\nabla v}{v^2}$

(d) $\nabla u^n = \left\langle \dfrac{\partial(u^n)}{\partial x}, \dfrac{\partial(u^n)}{\partial y} \right\rangle = \left\langle nu^{n-1}\dfrac{\partial u}{\partial x}, nu^{n-1}\dfrac{\partial u}{\partial y} \right\rangle = nu^{n-1}\,\nabla u$

37. $f(x,y) = x^3 + 5x^2 y + y^3 \quad \Rightarrow$

$D_{\mathbf{u}} f(x,y) = \nabla f(x,y) \cdot \mathbf{u} = \langle 3x^2 + 10xy, 5x^2 + 3y^2 \rangle \cdot \langle \frac{3}{5}, \frac{4}{5} \rangle = \frac{9}{5}x^2 + 6xy + 4x^2 + \frac{12}{5}y^2 = \frac{29}{5}x^2 + 6xy + \frac{12}{5}y^2$. Then

$D_{\mathbf{u}}^2 f(x,y) = D_{\mathbf{u}}[D_{\mathbf{u}} f(x,y)] = \nabla[D_{\mathbf{u}} f(x,y)] \cdot \mathbf{u} = \langle \frac{58}{5}x + 6y, 6x + \frac{24}{5}y \rangle \cdot \langle \frac{3}{5}, \frac{4}{5} \rangle$

$= \frac{174}{25}x + \frac{18}{5}y + \frac{24}{5}x + \frac{96}{25}y = \frac{294}{25}x + \frac{186}{25}y$

and $D_{\mathbf{u}}^2 f(2,1) = \frac{294}{25}(2) + \frac{186}{25}(1) = \frac{774}{25}$.

39. Let $F(x,y,z) = 2(x-2)^2 + (y-1)^2 + (z-3)^2$. Then $2(x-2)^2 + (y-1)^2 + (z-3)^2 = 10$ is a level surface of F.

$F_x(x,y,z) = 4(x-2) \quad \Rightarrow \quad F_x(3,3,5) = 4, F_y(x,y,z) = 2(y-1) \quad \Rightarrow \quad F_y(3,3,5) = 4$, and

$F_z(x,y,z) = 2(z-3) \quad \Rightarrow \quad F_z(3,3,5) = 4$.

(a) Equation 19 gives an equation of the tangent plane at $(3,3,5)$ as $4(x-3) + 4(y-3) + 4(z-5) = 0 \quad \Leftrightarrow$

$4x + 4y + 4z = 44$ or equivalently $x + y + z = 11$.

(b) By Equation 20, the normal line has symmetric equations $\dfrac{x-3}{4} = \dfrac{y-3}{4} = \dfrac{z-5}{4}$ or equivalently

$x - 3 = y - 3 = z - 5$. Corresponding parametric equations are $x = 3 + t, y = 3 + t, z = 5 + t$.

41. Let $F(x,y,z) = x^2 - 2y^2 + z^2 + yz$. Then $x^2 - 2y^2 + z^2 + yz = 2$ is a level surface of F

and $\nabla F(x,y,z) = \langle 2x, -4y + z, 2z + y \rangle$.

(a) $\nabla F(2,1,-1) = \langle 4, -5, -1 \rangle$ is a normal vector for the tangent plane at $(2,1,-1)$, so an equation of the tangent plane

is $4(x-2) - 5(y-1) - 1(z+1) = 0$ or $4x - 5y - z = 4$.

(b) The normal line has direction $\langle 4, -5, -1 \rangle$, so parametric equations are $x = 2 + 4t$, $y = 1 - 5t$, $z = -1 - t$, and

symmetric equations are $\dfrac{x-2}{4} = \dfrac{y-1}{-5} = \dfrac{z+1}{-1}$.

43. $F(x, y, z) = -z + xe^y \cos z \Rightarrow \nabla F(x, y, z) = \langle e^y \cos z, xe^y \cos z, -1 - xe^y \sin z \rangle$ and $\nabla F(1, 0, 0) = \langle 1, 1, -1 \rangle$.

(a) $1(x - 1) + 1(y - 0) - 1(z - 0) = 0$ or $x + y - z = 1$

(b) $x - 1 = y = -z$

45. $F(x, y, z) = xy + yz + zx$,

$\nabla F(x, y, z) = \langle y + z, x + z, y + x \rangle$,

$\nabla F(1, 1, 1) = \langle 2, 2, 2 \rangle$, so an equation of the tangent

plane is $2x + 2y + 2z = 6$ or $x + y + z = 3$, and the

normal line is given by $x - 1 = y - 1 = z - 1$ or

$x = y = z$. To graph the surface we solve for z:

$z = \dfrac{3 - xy}{x + y}$.

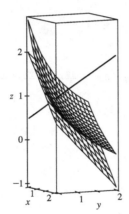

47. $f(x, y) = xy \Rightarrow \nabla f(x, y) = \langle y, x \rangle$,

$\nabla f(3, 2) = \langle 2, 3 \rangle$. $\nabla f(3, 2)$ is perpendicular to the

tangent line, so the tangent line has equation

$\nabla f(3, 2) \cdot \langle x - 3, y - 2 \rangle = 0 \Rightarrow$

$\langle 2, 3 \rangle \cdot \langle x - 3, x - 2 \rangle = 0 \Rightarrow$

$2(x - 3) + 3(y - 2) = 0$ or $2x + 3y = 12$.

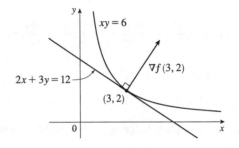

49. $\nabla F(x_0, y_0, z_0) = \left\langle \dfrac{2x_0}{a^2}, \dfrac{2y_0}{b^2}, \dfrac{2z_0}{c^2} \right\rangle$. Thus an equation of the tangent plane at (x_0, y_0, z_0) is

$\dfrac{2x_0}{a^2} x + \dfrac{2y_0}{b^2} y + \dfrac{2z_0}{c^2} z = 2\left(\dfrac{x_0^2}{a^2} + \dfrac{y_0^2}{b^2} + \dfrac{z_0^2}{c^2} \right) = 2(1) = 2$ since (x_0, y_0, z_0) is a point on the ellipsoid. Hence

$\dfrac{x_0}{a^2} x + \dfrac{y_0}{b^2} y + \dfrac{z_0}{c^2} z = 1$ is an equation of the tangent plane.

51. The hyperboloid $x^2 - y^2 - z^2 = 1$ is a level surface of $F(x, y, z) = x^2 - y^2 - z^2$ and $\nabla F(x, y, z) = \langle 2x, -2y, -2z \rangle$ is a

normal vector to the surface and hence a normal vector for the tangent plane at (x, y, z). The tangent plane is parallel to the

plane $z = x + y$ or $x + y - z = 0$ if and only if the corresponding normal vectors are parallel, so we need a point (x_0, y_0, z_0)

on the hyperboloid where $\langle 2x_0, -2y_0, -2z_0 \rangle = c \langle 1, 1, -1 \rangle$ or equivalently $\langle x_0, -y_0, -z_0 \rangle = k \langle 1, 1, -1 \rangle$ for some $k \neq 0$.

Then we must have $x_0 = k$, $y_0 = -k$, $z_0 = k$ and substituting into the equation of the hyperboloid gives

$k^2 - (-k)^2 - k^2 = 1 \iff -k^2 = 1$, an impossibility. Thus there is no such point on the hyperboloid.

53. Let (x_0, y_0, z_0) be a point on the cone [other than $(0, 0, 0)$]. The cone is a level surface of $F(x, y, z) = x^2 + y^2 - z^2$ and

$\nabla F(x, y, z) = \langle 2x, 2y, -2z \rangle$, so $\nabla F(x_0, y_0, z_0) = \langle 2x_0, 2y_0, -2z_0 \rangle$ is a normal vector to the cone at this point and an

equation of the tangent plane there is $2x_0 (x - x_0) + 2y_0 (y - y_0) - 2z_0 (z - z_0) = 0$ or $x_0 x + y_0 y - z_0 z = x_0^2 + y_0^2 - z_0^2$.

But $x_0^2 + y_0^2 = z_0^2$ so the tangent plane is given by $x_0 x + y_0 y - z_0 z = 0$, a plane which always contains the origin.

55. Let (x_0, y_0, z_0) be a point on the surface. Then an equation of the tangent plane at the point is

$\dfrac{x}{2\sqrt{x_0}} + \dfrac{y}{2\sqrt{y_0}} + \dfrac{z}{2\sqrt{z_0}} = \dfrac{\sqrt{x_0} + \sqrt{y_0} + \sqrt{z_0}}{2}$. But $\sqrt{x_0} + \sqrt{y_0} + \sqrt{z_0} = \sqrt{c}$, so the equation is

$\dfrac{x}{\sqrt{x_0}} + \dfrac{y}{\sqrt{y_0}} + \dfrac{z}{\sqrt{z_0}} = \sqrt{c}$. The x-, y-, and z-intercepts are $\sqrt{cx_0}$, $\sqrt{cy_0}$ and $\sqrt{cz_0}$ respectively. (The x-intercept is found by

setting $y = z = 0$ and solving the resulting equation for x, and the y- and z-intercepts are found similarly.) So the sum of the

intercepts is $\sqrt{c}(\sqrt{x_0} + \sqrt{y_0} + \sqrt{z_0}) = c$, a constant.

57. If $f(x, y, z) = z - x^2 - y^2$ and $g(x, y, z) = 4x^2 + y^2 + z^2$, then the tangent line is perpendicular to both ∇f and ∇g

at $(-1, 1, 2)$. The vector $\mathbf{v} = \nabla f \times \nabla g$ will therefore be parallel to the tangent line.

We have $\nabla f(x, y, z) = \langle -2x, -2y, 1 \rangle$ $\Rightarrow$ $\nabla f(-1, 1, 2) = \langle 2, -2, 1 \rangle$, and $\nabla g(x, y, z) = \langle 8x, 2y, 2z \rangle$ $\Rightarrow$

$\nabla g(-1, 1, 2) = \langle -8, 2, 4 \rangle$. Hence $\mathbf{v} = \nabla f \times \nabla g = \begin{vmatrix} \mathbf{i} & \mathbf{j} & \mathbf{k} \\ 2 & -2 & 1 \\ -8 & 2 & 4 \end{vmatrix} = -10\,\mathbf{i} - 16\,\mathbf{j} - 12\,\mathbf{k}$.

Parametric equations are: $x = -1 - 10t$, $y = 1 - 16t$, $z = 2 - 12t$.

59. (a) The direction of the normal line of F is given by ∇F, and that of G by ∇G. Assuming that

$\nabla F \neq 0 \neq \nabla G$, the two normal lines are perpendicular at P if $\nabla F \cdot \nabla G = 0$ at P $\Leftrightarrow$

$\langle \partial F/\partial x, \partial F/\partial y, \partial F/\partial z \rangle \cdot \langle \partial G/\partial x, \partial G/\partial y, \partial G/\partial z \rangle = 0$ at P $\Leftrightarrow$ $F_x G_x + F_y G_y + F_z G_z = 0$ at P.

(b) Here $F = x^2 + y^2 - z^2$ and $G = x^2 + y^2 + z^2 - r^2$, so

$\nabla F \cdot \nabla G = \langle 2x, 2y, -2z \rangle \cdot \langle 2x, 2y, 2z \rangle = 4x^2 + 4y^2 - 4z^2 = 4F - 0$, since the point (x, y, z) lies on the graph of

$F = 0$. To see that this is true without using calculus, note that $G = 0$ is the equation of a sphere centered at the origin and

$F = 0$ is the equation of a right circular cone with vertex at the origin (which is generated by lines through the origin). At

any point of intersection, the sphere's normal line (which passes through the origin) lies on the cone, and thus is

perpendicular to the cone's normal line. So the surfaces with equations $F = 0$ and $G = 0$ are everywhere orthogonal.

61. Let $\mathbf{u} = \langle a, b \rangle$ and $\mathbf{v} = \langle c, d \rangle$. Then we know that at the given point, $D_{\mathbf{u}} f = \nabla f \cdot \mathbf{u} = af_x + bf_y$ and

$D_{\mathbf{v}} f = \nabla f \cdot \mathbf{v} = cf_x + df_y$. But these are just two linear equations in the two unknowns f_x and f_y, and since $\mathbf{u}$ and $\mathbf{v}$ are

not parallel, we can solve the equations to find $\nabla f = \langle f_x, f_y \rangle$ at the given point. In fact,

$\nabla f = \left\langle \dfrac{d\,D_{\mathbf{u}} f - b\,D_{\mathbf{v}} f}{ad - bc}, \dfrac{a\,D_{\mathbf{v}} f - c\,D_{\mathbf{u}} f}{ad - bc} \right\rangle$.

11.7 Maximum and Minimum Values

1. (a) First we compute $D(1,1) = f_{xx}(1,1)\, f_{yy}(1,1) - [f_{xy}(1,1)]^2 = (4)(2) - (1)^2 = 7$. Since $D(1,1) > 0$ and

$f_{xx}(1,1) > 0$, f has a local minimum at $(1,1)$ by the Second Derivatives Test.

(b) $D(1,1) = f_{xx}(1,1)\, f_{yy}(1,1) - [f_{xy}(1,1)]^2 = (4)(2) - (3)^2 = -1$. Since $D(1,1) < 0$, f has a saddle point at $(1,1)$ by

the Second Derivatives Test.

3. In the figure, a point at approximately $(1,1)$ is enclosed by level curves which are oval in shape and indicate that as we move

away from the point in any direction the values of f are increasing. Hence we would expect a local minimum at or near $(1,1)$.

The level curves near $(0,0)$ resemble hyperbolas, and as we move away from the origin, the values of f increase in some

directions and decrease in others, so we would expect to find a saddle point there.

To verify our predictions, we have $f(x,y) = 4 + x^3 + y^3 - 3xy$ $\Rightarrow$ $f_x(x,y) = 3x^2 - 3y$, $f_y(x,y) = 3y^2 - 3x$. We

have critical points where these partial derivatives are equal to 0: $3x^2 - 3y = 0$, $3y^2 - 3x = 0$. Substituting $y = x^2$ from the

first equation into the second equation gives $3(x^2)^2 - 3x = 0$ $\Rightarrow$ $3x(x^3 - 1) = 0$ $\Rightarrow$ $x = 0$ or $x = 1$. Then we have

two critical points, $(0,0)$ and $(1,1)$. The second partial derivatives are $f_{xx}(x,y) = 6x$, $f_{xy}(x,y) = -3$, and $f_{yy}(x,y) = 6y$,

so $D(x,y) = f_{xx}(x,y)\, f_{yy}(x,y) - [f_{xy}(x,y)]^2 = (6x)(6y) - (-3)^2 = 36xy - 9$. Then $D(0,0) = 36(0)(0) - 9 = -9$,

and $D(1,1) = 36(1)(1) - 9 = 27$. Since $D(0,0) < 0$, f has a saddle point at $(0,0)$ by the Second Derivatives Test. Since

$D(1,1) > 0$ and $f_{xx}(1,1) > 0$, f has a local minimum at $(1,1)$.

5. $f(x,y) = x^2 + xy + y^2 + y$ $\Rightarrow$ $f_x = 2x + y$, $f_y = x + 2y + 1$, $f_{xx} = 2$, $f_{xy} = 1$, $f_{yy} = 2$. Then $f_x = 0$ implies

$y = -2x$, and substitution into $f_y = x + 2y + 1 = 0$ gives $x + 2(-2x) + 1 = 0$ $\Rightarrow$ $-3x = -1$ $\Rightarrow$ $x = \frac{1}{3}$.

Then $y = -\frac{2}{3}$ and the only critical point is $\left(\frac{1}{3}, -\frac{2}{3}\right)$. $D(x,y) = f_{xx} f_{yy} - (f_{xy})^2 = (2)(2) - (1)^2 = 3$, and since

$D\left(\frac{1}{3}, -\frac{2}{3}\right) = 3 > 0$ and $f_{xx}\left(\frac{1}{3}, -\frac{2}{3}\right) = 2 > 0$, $f\left(\frac{1}{3}, -\frac{2}{3}\right) = -\frac{1}{3}$ is a local minimum by the Second Derivatives Test.

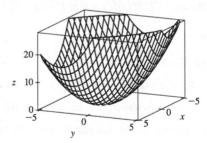

7. $f(x,y) = x^4 + y^4 - 4xy + 2$ $\Rightarrow$ $f_x = 4x^3 - 4y$, $f_y = 4y^3 - 4x$,

$f_{xx} = 12x^2$, $f_{xy} = -4$, $f_{yy} = 12y^2$. Then $f_x = 0$ implies $y = x^3$,

and substitution into $f_y = 0$ $\Rightarrow$ $x = y^3$ gives $x^9 - x = 0$ $\Rightarrow$

$x(x^8 - 1) = 0$ $\Rightarrow$ $x = 0$ or $x = \pm 1$. Thus the critical points are $(0,0)$,

$(1,1)$, and $(-1,-1)$. Now $D(0,0) = 0 \cdot 0 - (-4)^2 = -16 < 0$,

so $(0,0)$ is a saddle point. $D(1,1) = (12)(12) - (-4)^2 > 0$ and

$f_{xx}(1,1) = 12 > 0$, so $f(1,1) = 0$ is a local minimum. $D(-1,-1) = (12)(12) - (-4)^2 > 0$ and

$f_{xx} = (-1,-1) = 12 > 0$, so $f(-1,-1) = 0$ is also a local minimum.

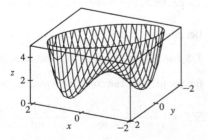

9. $f(x, y) = x^3 - 12xy + 8y^3 \;\Rightarrow\; f_x = 3x^2 - 12y,\; f_y = -12x + 24y^2,$

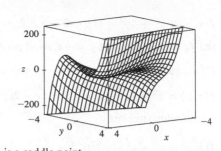

$f_{xx} = 6x,\; f_{xy} = -12,\; f_{yy} = 48y.$ Then $f_x = 0$ implies $x^2 = 4y$ and

$f_y = 0$ implies $x = 2y^2$. Substituting the second equation into the first

gives $(2y^2)^2 = 4y \;\Rightarrow\; 4y^4 = 4y \;\Rightarrow\; 4y(y^3 - 1) = 0 \;\Rightarrow\; y = 0$ or

$y = 1$. If $y = 0$ then $x = 0$ and if $y = 1$ then $x = 2$, so the critical points

are $(0, 0)$ and $(2, 1)$. $D(0, 0) = (0)(0) - (-12)^2 = -144 < 0$, so $(0, 0)$ is a saddle point.

$D(2, 1) = (12)(48) - (-12)^2 = 432 > 0$ and $f_{xx}(2, 1) = 12 > 0$ so $f(2, 1) = -8$ is a local minimum.

11. $f(x, y) = e^x \cos y \;\Rightarrow\; f_x = e^x \cos y,\; f_y = -e^x \sin y.$

Now $f_x = 0$ implies $\cos y = 0$ or $y = \frac{\pi}{2} + n\pi$ for n an integer.

But $\sin\left(\frac{\pi}{2} + n\pi\right) \neq 0$, so there are no critical points.

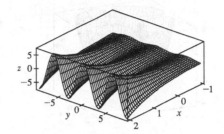

13. $f(x, y) = (x^2 + y^2)e^{y^2 - x^2} \;\Rightarrow$

$f_x = (x^2 + y^2)e^{y^2 - x^2}(-2x) + 2xe^{y^2 - x^2} = 2xe^{y^2 - x^2}(1 - x^2 - y^2),$

$f_y = (x^2 + y^2)e^{y^2 - x^2}(2y) + 2ye^{y^2 - x^2} = 2ye^{y^2 - x^2}(1 + x^2 + y^2),$

$f_{xx} = 2xe^{y^2 - x^2}(-2x) + (1 - x^2 - y^2)\left(2x\left(-2xe^{y^2 - x^2}\right) + 2e^{y^2 - x^2}\right) = 2e^{y^2 - x^2}((1 - x^2 - y^2)(1 - 2x^2) - 2x^2),$

$f_{xy} = 2xe^{y^2 - x^2}(-2y) + 2x(2y)e^{y^2 - x^2}(1 - x^2 - y^2) = -4xye^{y^2 - x^2}(x^2 + y^2),$

$f_{yy} = 2ye^{y^2 - x^2}(2y) + (1 + x^2 + y^2)\left(2y\left(2ye^{y^2 - x^2}\right) + 2e^{y^2 - x^2}\right) = 2e^{y^2 - x^2}((1 + x^2 + y^2)(1 + 2y^2) + 2y^2).$

$f_y = 0$ implies $y = 0$, and substituting into $f_x = 0$ gives

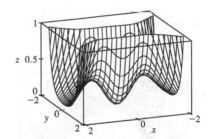

$2xe^{-x^2}(1 - x^2) = 0 \;\Rightarrow\; x = 0$ or $x = \pm 1$. Thus the critical points are

$(0, 0)$ and $(\pm 1, 0)$. Now $D(0, 0) = (2)(2) - 0 > 0$ and $f_{xx}(0, 0) = 2 > 0$,

so $f(0, 0) = 0$ is a local minimum. $D(\pm 1, 0) = (-4e^{-1})(4e^{-1}) - 0 < 0$

so $(\pm 1, 0)$ are saddle points.

15. $f(x, y) = y^2 - 2y \cos x \;\Rightarrow\; f_x = 2y \sin x,\; f_y = 2y - 2\cos x,$

$f_{xx} = 2y \cos x,\; f_{xy} = 2 \sin x,\; f_{yy} = 2.$ Then $f_x = 0$ implies $y = 0$ or

$\sin x = 0 \;\Rightarrow\; x = 0,\; \pi,\; \text{or } 2\pi$ for $-1 \le x \le 7$. Substituting $y = 0$ into

$f_y = 0$ gives $\cos x = 0 \;\Rightarrow\; x = \frac{\pi}{2}$ or $\frac{3\pi}{2}$, substituting $x = 0$ or $x = 2\pi$

into $f_y = 0$ gives $y = 1$, and substituting $x = \pi$ into $f_y = 0$ gives $y = -1$.

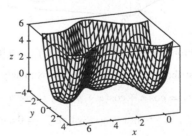

Thus the critical points are $(0, 1)$, $\left(\frac{\pi}{2}, 0\right)$, $(\pi, -1)$, $\left(\frac{3\pi}{2}, 0\right)$, and $(2\pi, 1)$.

$D\left(\frac{\pi}{2}, 0\right) = D\left(\frac{3\pi}{2}, 0\right) = -4 < 0$ so $\left(\frac{\pi}{2}, 0\right)$ and $\left(\frac{3\pi}{2}, 0\right)$ are saddle points. $D(0, 1) = D(\pi, -1) = D(2\pi, 1) = 4 > 0$ and

$f_{xx}(0, 1) = f_{xx}(\pi, -1) = f_{xx}(2\pi, 1) = 2 > 0$, so $f(0, 1) = f(\pi, -1) = f(2\pi, 1) = -1$ are local minima.

17. $f(x,y) = x^2 + 4y^2 - 4xy + 2$ $\Rightarrow$ $f_x = 2x - 4y$, $f_y = 8y - 4x$, $f_{xx} = 2$, $f_{xy} = -4$, $f_{yy} = 8$. Then $f_x = 0$

and $f_y = 0$ each implies $y = \frac{1}{2}x$, so all points of the form $\left(x_0, \frac{1}{2}x_0\right)$ are critical points and for each of these we have

$D\left(x_0, \frac{1}{2}x_0\right) = (2)(8) - (-4)^2 = 0$. The Second Derivatives Test gives no information, but

$f(x,y) = x^2 + 4y^2 - 4xy + 2 = (x - 2y)^2 + 2 \geq 2$ with equality if and only if $y = \frac{1}{2}x$. Thus $f\left(x_0, \frac{1}{2}x_0\right) = 2$ are all local

(and absolute) minima.

19. $f(x,y) = x^2 + y^2 + x^{-2}y^{-2}$

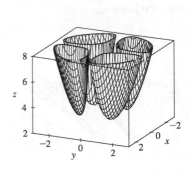 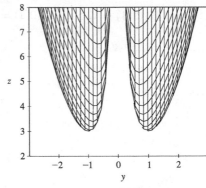 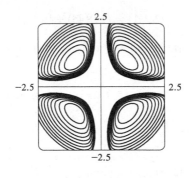

From the graphs, there appear to be local minima of about $f(1, \pm 1) = f(-1, \pm 1) \approx 3$ (and no local maxima or saddle

points). $f_x = 2x - 2x^{-3}y^{-2}$, $f_y = 2y - 2x^{-2}y^{-3}$, $f_{xx} = 2 + 6x^{-4}y^{-2}$, $f_{xy} = 4x^{-3}y^{-3}$, $f_{yy} = 2 + 6x^{-2}y^{-4}$. Then

$f_x = 0$ implies $2x^4y^2 - 2 = 0$ or $x^4y^2 = 1$ or $y^2 = x^{-4}$. Note that neither x nor y can be zero. Now $f_y = 0$ implies

$2x^2y^4 - 2 = 0$, and with $y^2 = x^{-4}$ this implies $2x^{-6} - 2 = 0$ or $x^6 = 1$. Thus $x = \pm 1$ and if $x = 1$, $y = \pm 1$; if $x = -1$,

$y = \pm 1$. So the critical points are $(1,1)$, $(1,-1)$, $(-1,1)$ and $(-1,-1)$. Now $D(1, \pm 1) = D(-1, \pm 1) = 64 - 16 > 0$ and

$f_{xx} > 0$ always, so $f(1, \pm 1) = f(-1, \pm 1) = 3$ are local minima.

21. $f(x,y) = \sin x + \sin y + \sin(x + y)$, $0 \leq x \leq 2\pi$, $0 \leq y \leq 2\pi$

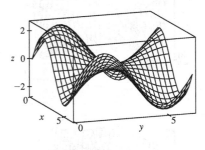 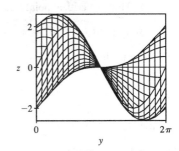 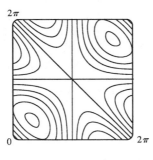

From the graphs it appears that f has a local maximum at about $(1,1)$ with value approximately 2.6, a local minimum

at about $(5,5)$ with value approximately -2.6, and a saddle point at about $(3,3)$.

$f_x = \cos x + \cos(x + y)$, $f_y = \cos y + \cos(x + y)$, $f_{xx} = -\sin x - \sin(x + y)$, $f_{yy} = -\sin y - \sin(x + y)$,

$f_{xy} = -\sin(x + y)$. Setting $f_x = 0$ and $f_y = 0$ and subtracting gives $\cos x - \cos y = 0$ or $\cos x = \cos y$. Thus $x = y$

or $x = 2\pi - y$. If $x = y$, $f_x = 0$ becomes $\cos x + \cos 2x = 0$ or $2\cos^2 x + \cos x - 1 = 0$, a quadratic in $\cos x$. Thus

$\cos x = -1$ or $\frac{1}{2}$ and $x = \pi$, $\frac{\pi}{3}$, or $\frac{5\pi}{3}$, giving the critical points (π, π), $\left(\frac{\pi}{3}, \frac{\pi}{3}\right)$ and $\left(\frac{5\pi}{3}, \frac{5\pi}{3}\right)$. Similarly if

$x = 2\pi - y$, $f_x = 0$ becomes $(\cos x) + 1 = 0$ and the resulting critical point is (π, π). Now

$D(x, y) = \sin x \, \sin y + \sin x \, \sin(x + y) + \sin y \, \sin(x + y)$. So $D(\pi, \pi) = 0$ and the Second Derivatives Test doesn't apply.

However, along the line $y = x$ we have $f(x, x) = 2 \sin x + \sin 2x = 2 \sin x + 2 \sin x \cos x = 2 \sin x (1 + \cos x)$, and

$f(x, x) > 0$ for $0 < x < \pi$ while $f(x, x) < 0$ for $\pi < x < 2\pi$. Thus every disk with center (π, π) contains points where f is

positive as well as points where f is negative, so the graph crosses its tangent plane ($z = 0$) there and (π, π) is a saddle point.

$D\left(\frac{\pi}{3}, \frac{\pi}{3}\right) = \frac{9}{4} > 0$ and $f_{xx}\left(\frac{\pi}{3}, \frac{\pi}{3}\right) < 0$ so $f\left(\frac{\pi}{3}, \frac{\pi}{3}\right) = \frac{3\sqrt{3}}{2}$ is a local maximum while $D\left(\frac{5\pi}{3}, \frac{5\pi}{3}\right) = \frac{9}{4} > 0$ and

$f_{xx}\left(\frac{5\pi}{3}, \frac{5\pi}{3}\right) > 0$, so $f\left(\frac{5\pi}{3}, \frac{5\pi}{3}\right) = -\frac{3\sqrt{3}}{2}$ is a local minimum.

23. $f(x, y) = x^4 - 5x^2 + y^2 + 3x + 2$ $\Rightarrow$ $f_x(x, y) = 4x^3 - 10x + 3$ and $f_y(x, y) = 2y$. $f_y = 0$ $\Rightarrow$ $y = 0$, and the graph

of f_x shows that the roots of $f_x = 0$ are approximately $x = -1.714, 0.312$ and 1.402. (Alternatively, we could have used a

calculator or a CAS to find these roots.) So to three decimal places, the critical points are $(-1.714, 0)$, $(1.402, 0)$, and

$(0.312, 0)$. Now since $f_{xx} = 12x^2 - 10$, $f_{xy} = 0$, $f_{yy} = 2$, and $D = 24x^2 - 20$, we have $D(-1.714, 0) > 0$,

$f_{xx}(-1.714, 0) > 0$, $D(1.402, 0) > 0$, $f_{xx}(1.402, 0) > 0$, and $D(0.312, 0) < 0$. Therefore $f(-1.714, 0) \approx -9.200$ and

$f(1.402, 0) \approx 0.242$ are local minima, and $(0.312, 0)$ is a saddle point. The lowest point on the graph is approximately

$(-1.714, 0, -9.200)$.

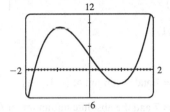
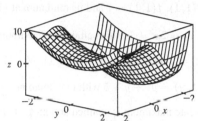

25. $f(x, y) = 2x + 4x^2 - y^2 + 2xy^2 - x^4 - y^4$ $\Rightarrow$ $f_x(x, y) = 2 + 8x + 2y^2 - 4x^3$, $f_y(x, y) = -2y + 4xy - 4y^3$.

Now $f_y = 0$ $\Leftrightarrow$ $2y(2y^2 - 2x + 1) = 0$ $\Leftrightarrow$ $y = 0$ or $y^2 = x - \frac{1}{2}$. The first of these implies that $f_x = -4x^3 + 8x + 2$,

and the second implies that $f_x = 2 + 8x + 2\left(x - \frac{1}{2}\right) - 4x^3 = -4x^3 + 10x + 1$. From the graphs, we see that the first

possibility for f_x has roots at approximately $-1.267, -0.259$, and 1.526, and the second has a root at

approximately 1.629 (the negative roots do not give critical points, since $y^2 = x - \frac{1}{2}$ must be positive). So to three decimal

places, f has critical points at $(-1.267, 0)$, $(-0.259, 0)$, $(1.526, 0)$, and $(1.629, \pm 1.063)$. Now since $f_{xx} = 8 - 12x^2$,

$f_{xy} = 4y$, $f_{yy} = 4x - 12y^2$, and $D = (8 - 12x^2)(4x - 12y^2) - 16y^2$, we have $D(-1.267, 0) > 0$, $f_{xx}(-1.267, 0) > 0$,

$D(-0.259, 0) < 0$, $D(1.526, 0) < 0$, $D(1.629, \pm 1.063) > 0$, and $f_{xx}(1.629, \pm 1.063) < 0$. Therefore, to three decimal

places, $f(-1.267, 0) \approx 1.310$ and $f(1.629, \pm 1.063) \approx 8.105$ are local maxima, and $(-0.259, 0)$ and $(1.526, 0)$ are saddle

points. The highest points on the graph are approximately $(1.629, \pm 1.063, 8.105)$.

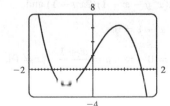
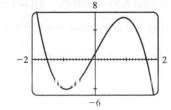
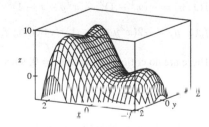

27. Since f is a polynomial it is continuous on D, so an absolute maximum and minimum exist. Here $f_x = 4$, $f_y = -5$ so there are no critical points inside D. Thus the absolute extrema must both occur on the boundary. Along L_1: $x = 0$ and $f(0, y) = 1 - 5y$ for $0 \le y \le 3$, a decreasing function in y, so the maximum value is $f(0, 0) = 1$ and the minimum value is $f(0, 3) = -14$. Along L_2: $y = 0$ and $f(x, 0) = 1 + 4x$ for $0 \le x \le 2$, an increasing function in x, so the minimum value is $f(0, 0) = 1$ and the maximum value is $f(2, 0) = 9$. Along L_3: $y = -\frac{3}{2}x + 3$ and $f\left(x, -\frac{3}{2}x + 3\right) = \frac{23}{2}x - 14$ for $0 \le x \le 2$, an increasing function in x, so the minimum value is $f(0, 3) = -14$ and the maximum value is $f(2, 0) = 9$. Thus the absolute maximum of f on D is $f(2, 0) = 9$ and the absolute minimum is $f(0, 3) = -14$.

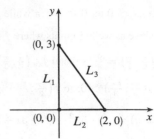

29. $f_x(x, y) = 2x + 2xy$, $f_y(x, y) = 2y + x^2$, and setting $f_x = f_y = 0$ gives $(0, 0)$ as the only critical point in D, with $f(0, 0) = 4$.

On L_1: $y = -1$, $f(x, -1) = 5$, a constant.

On L_2: $x = 1$, $f(1, y) = y^2 + y + 5$, a quadratic in y which attains its maximum at $(1, 1)$, $f(1, 1) = 7$ and its minimum at $\left(1, -\frac{1}{2}\right)$, $f\left(1, -\frac{1}{2}\right) = \frac{19}{4}$.

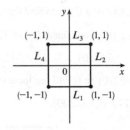

On L_3: $f(x, 1) = 2x^2 + 5$ which attains its maximum at $(-1, 1)$ and $(1, 1)$ with $f(\pm 1, 1) = 7$ and its minimum at $(0, 1)$, $f(0, 1) = 5$.

On L_4: $f(-1, y) = y^2 + y + 5$ with maximum at $(-1, 1)$, $f(-1, 1) = 7$ and minimum at $\left(-1, -\frac{1}{2}\right)$, $f\left(-1, -\frac{1}{2}\right) = \frac{19}{4}$.

Thus the absolute maximum is attained at both $(\pm 1, 1)$ with $f(\pm 1, 1) = 7$ and the absolute minimum on D is attained at $(0, 0)$ with $f(0, 0) = 4$.

31. $f_x(x, y) = 6x^2$ and $f_y(x, y) = 4y^3$. And so $f_x = 0$ and $f_y = 0$ only occur when $x = y = 0$. Hence, the only critical point inside the disk is at $x = y = 0$ where $f(0, 0) = 0$. Now on the circle $x^2 + y^2 = 1$, $y^2 = 1 - x^2$ so let

$$g(x) = f(x, y) = 2x^3 + (1 - x^2)^2 = x^4 + 2x^3 - 2x^2 + 1, -1 \le x \le 1. \text{ Then } g'(x) = 4x^3 + 6x^2 - 4x = 0 \quad \Rightarrow \quad x = 0,$$

-2, or $\frac{1}{2}$. $f(0, \pm 1) = g(0) = 1$, $f\left(\frac{1}{2}, \pm\frac{\sqrt{3}}{2}\right) = g\left(\frac{1}{2}\right) = \frac{13}{16}$, and $(-2, -3)$ is not in D. Checking the endpoints, we get

$f(-1, 0) = g(-1) = -2$ and $f(1, 0) = g(1) = 2$. Thus the absolute maximum and minimum of f on D are $f(1, 0) = 2$ and $f(-1, 0) = -2$.

Another method: On the boundary $x^2 + y^2 = 1$ we can write $x = \cos\theta$, $y = \sin\theta$, so $f(\cos\theta, \sin\theta) = 2\cos^3\theta + \sin^4\theta$, $0 \le \theta \le 2\pi$.

33. $f(x, y) = -(x^2 - 1)^2 - (x^2 y - x - 1)^2 \quad \Rightarrow \quad f_x(x, y) = -2(x^2 - 1)(2x) - 2(x^2 y - x - 1)(2xy - 1)$ and $f_y(x, y) = -2(x^2 y - x - 1)x^2$. Setting $f_y(x, y) = 0$ gives either $x = 0$ or $x^2 y - x - 1 = 0$.

There are no critical points for $x = 0$, since $f_x(0, y) = -2$, so we set $x^2 y - x - 1 = 0 \quad \Leftrightarrow \quad y = \dfrac{x + 1}{x^2}$ $[x \ne 0]$,

so $f_x\left(x, \dfrac{x + 1}{x^2}\right) = -2(x^2 - 1)(2x) - 2\left(x^2 \dfrac{x + 1}{x^2} - x - 1\right)\left(2x \dfrac{x + 1}{x^2} - 1\right) = -4x(x^2 - 1)$. Therefore

$f_x(x, y) = f_y(x, y) = 0$ at the points $(1, 2)$ and $(-1, 0)$. To classify these critical points, we calculate

$f_{xx}(x, y) = -12x^2 - 12x^2y^2 + 12xy + 4y + 2$, $f_{yy}(x, y) = -2x^4$,

and $f_{xy}(x, y) = -8x^3y + 6x^2 + 4x$. In order to use the Second Derivatives

Test we calculate

$D(-1, 0) = f_{xx}(-1, 0) f_{yy}(-1, 0) - [f_{xy}(-1, 0)]^2 = 16 > 0$,

$f_{xx}(-1, 0) = -10 < 0$, $D(1, 2) = 16 > 0$, and $f_{xx}(1, 2) = -26 < 0$, so

both $(-1, 0)$ and $(1, 2)$ give local maxima.

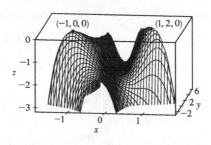

35. Let d be the distance from $(2, 1, -1)$ to any point (x, y, z) on the plane $x + y - z = 1$, so

$d = \sqrt{(x - 2)^2 + (y - 1)^2 + (z + 1)^2}$ where $z = x + y - 1$, and we minimize

$d^2 = f(x, y) = (x - 2)^2 + (y - 1)^2 + (x + y)^2$. Then $f_x(x, y) = 2(x - 2) + 2(x + y) = 4x + 2y - 4$,

$f_y(x, y) = 2(y - 1) + 2(x + y) = 2x + 4y - 2$. Solving $4x + 2y - 4 = 0$ and $2x + 4y - 2 = 0$ simultaneously gives $x = 1$,

$y = 0$. An absolute minimum exists (since there is a minimum distance from the point to the plane) and it must occur at a

critical point, so the shortest distance occurs for $x = 1$, $y = 0$ for which $d = \sqrt{(1 - 2)^2 + (0 - 1)^2 + (0 + 1)^2} = \sqrt{3}$.

37. Let d be the distance from the point $(4, 2, 0)$ to any point (x, y, z) on the cone, so $d = \sqrt{(x - 4)^2 + (y - 2)^2 + z^2}$ where

$z^2 = x^2 + y^2$, and we minimize $d^2 = (x - 4)^2 + (y - 2)^2 + x^2 + y^2 = f(x, y)$. Then

$f_x(x, y) = 2(x - 4) + 2x = 4x - 8$, $f_y(x, y) = 2(y - 2) + 2y = 4y - 4$, and the critical points occur when

$f_x = 0 \;\; \Rightarrow \;\; x = 2$, $f_y = 0 \;\; \Rightarrow \;\; y = 1$. Thus the only critical point is $(2, 1)$. An absolute minimum exists (since there

is a minimum distance from the cone to the point) which must occur at a critical point, so the points on the cone closest

to $(4, 2, 0)$ are $(2, 1, \pm\sqrt{5})$.

39. $x + y + z = 100$, so maximize $f(x, y) = xy(100 - x - y)$. $f_x = 100y - 2xy - y^2$, $f_y = 100x - x^2 - 2xy$,

$f_{xx} = -2y$, $f_{yy} = -2x$, $f_{xy} = 100 - 2x - 2y$. Then $f_x = 0$ implies $y = 0$ or $y = 100 - 2x$. Substituting $y = 0$ into

$f_y = 0$ gives $x = 0$ or $x = 100$ and substituting $y = 100 - 2x$ into $f_y = 0$ gives $3x^2 - 100x = 0$ so $x = 0$ or $\frac{100}{3}$.

Thus the critical points are $(0, 0)$, $(100, 0)$, $(0, 100)$ and $\left(\frac{100}{3}, \frac{100}{3}\right)$.

$D(0, 0) = D(100, 0) = D(0, 100) = -10{,}000$ while $D\left(\frac{100}{3}, \frac{100}{3}\right) = \frac{10{,}000}{3}$ and $f_{xx}\left(\frac{100}{3}, \frac{100}{3}\right) = -\frac{200}{3} < 0$. Thus $(0, 0)$,

$(100, 0)$ and $(0, 100)$ are saddle points whereas $f\left(\frac{100}{3}, \frac{100}{3}\right)$ is a local maximum. Thus the numbers are $x = y = z = \frac{100}{3}$.

41. Center the sphere at the origin so that its equation is $x^2 + y^2 + z^2 = r^2$, and orient the inscribed rectangular box so that its

edges are parallel to the coordinate axes. Any vertex of the box satisfies $x^2 + y^2 + z^2 = r^2$, so take (x, y, z) to be the vertex

in the first octant. Then the box has length $2x$, width $2y$, and height $2z = 2\sqrt{r^2 - x^2 - y^2}$ with volume given by

$V(x, y) = (2x)(2y)\left(2\sqrt{r^2 - x^2 - y^2}\right) = 8xy\sqrt{r^2 - x^2 - y^2}$ for $0 < x < r$, $0 < y < r$. Then

$V_x = (8xy) \cdot \frac{1}{2}(r^2 - x^2 - y^2)^{-1/2}(-2x) + \sqrt{r^2 - x^2 - y^2} \cdot 8y = \dfrac{8y(r^2 - 2x^2 - y^2)}{\sqrt{r^2 - x^2 - y^2}}$ and $V_y = \dfrac{8x(r^2 - x^2 - 2y^2)}{\sqrt{r^2 - x^2 - y^2}}$

Setting $V_x = 0$ gives $y = 0$ or $2x^2 + y^2 = r^2$, but $y > 0$ so only the latter solution applies. Similarly, $V_y = 0$ with $x > 0$ implies $x^2 + 2y^2 = r^2$. Substituting, we have $2x^2 + y^2 = x^2 + 2y^2 \Rightarrow x^2 = y^2 \Rightarrow y = x$. Then $x^2 + 2y^2 = r^2 \Rightarrow 3x^2 = r^2 \Rightarrow x = \sqrt{r^2/3} = r/\sqrt{3} = y$. Thus the only critical point is $(r/\sqrt{3}, r/\sqrt{3})$. There must be a maximum volume and here it must occur at a critical point, so the maximum volume occurs when $x = y = r/\sqrt{3}$ and the maximum

volume is $V\left(\frac{r}{\sqrt{3}}, \frac{r}{\sqrt{3}}\right) = 8\left(\frac{r}{\sqrt{3}}\right)\left(\frac{r}{\sqrt{3}}\right) \sqrt{r^2 - \left(\frac{r}{\sqrt{3}}\right)^2 - \left(\frac{r}{\sqrt{3}}\right)^2} = \frac{8}{3\sqrt{3}} r^3$.

43. Maximize $f(x, y) = \dfrac{xy}{3} (6 - x - 2y)$, then the maximum volume is $V = xyz$.

$f_x = \frac{1}{3}(6y - 2xy - y^2) = \frac{1}{3}y(6 - 2x - 2y)$ and $f_y = \frac{1}{3}x(6 - x - 4y)$. Setting $f_x = 0$ and $f_y = 0$ gives the critical point $(2, 1)$ which geometrically must give a maximum. Thus the volume of the largest such box is $V = (2)(1)\left(\frac{2}{3}\right) = \frac{4}{3}$.

45. Let the dimensions be x, y, and z; then $4x + 4y + 4z = c$ and the volume is

$V = xyz = xy\left(\frac{1}{4}c - x - y\right) = \frac{1}{4}cxy - x^2y - xy^2$, $x > 0$, $y > 0$. Then $V_x = \frac{1}{4}cy - 2xy - y^2$ and $V_y = \frac{1}{4}cx - x^2 - 2xy$, so $V_x = 0 = V_y$ when $2x + y = \frac{1}{4}c$ and $x + 2y = \frac{1}{4}c$. Solving, we get $x = \frac{1}{12}c$, $y = \frac{1}{12}c$ and $z = \frac{1}{4}c - x - y = \frac{1}{12}c$. From the geometrical nature of the problem, this critical point must give an absolute maximum. Thus the box is a cube with edge length $\frac{1}{12}c$.

47. Let the dimensions be x, y and z, then minimize $xy + 2(xz + yz)$ if $xyz = 32{,}000$ cm^3. Then

$f(x, y) = xy + [64{,}000(x + y)/xy] = xy + 64{,}000(x^{-1} + y^{-1})$, $f_x = y - 64{,}000x^{-2}$, $f_y = x - 64{,}000y^{-2}$.
And $f_x = 0$ implies $y = 64{,}000/x^2$; substituting into $f_y = 0$ implies $x^3 = 64{,}000$ or $x = 40$ and then $y = 40$. Now $D(x, y) = [(2)(64{,}000)]^2 x^{-3}y^{-3} - 1 > 0$ for $(40, 40)$ and $f_{xx}(40, 40) > 0$ so this is indeed a minimum. Thus the dimensions of the box are $x = y = 40$ cm, $z = 20$ cm.

49. Let x, y, z be the dimensions of the rectangular box. Then the volume of the box is xyz and

$L = \sqrt{x^2 + y^2 + z^2} \Rightarrow L^2 = x^2 + y^2 + z^2 \Rightarrow z = \sqrt{L^2 - x^2 - y^2}$.
Substituting, we have volume $V(x, y) = xy\sqrt{L^2 - x^2 - y^2}$ $(x, y > 0)$.

$V_x = xy \cdot \frac{1}{2}(L^2 - x^2 - y^2)^{-1/2}(-2x) + y\sqrt{L^2 - x^2 - y^2} = y\sqrt{L^2 - x^2 - y^2} - \dfrac{x^2y}{\sqrt{L^2 - x^2 - y^2}}$,

$V_y = x\sqrt{L^2 - x^2 - y^2} - \dfrac{xy^2}{\sqrt{L^2 - x^2 - y^2}}$. $V_x = 0$ implies $y(L^2 - x^2 - y^2) = x^2y \Rightarrow y(L^2 - 2x^2 - y^2) = 0 \Rightarrow$

$2x^2 + y^2 = L^2$ (since $y > 0$), and $V_y = 0$ implies $x(L^2 - x^2 - y^2) = xy^2 \Rightarrow x(L^2 - x^2 - 2y^2) = 0 \Rightarrow$

$x^2 + 2y^2 = L^2$ (since $x > 0$). Substituting $y^2 = L^2 - 2x^2$ into $x^2 + 2y^2 = L^2$ gives $x^2 + 2L^2 - 4x^2 = L^2 \Rightarrow$

$3x^2 = L^2 \Rightarrow x = L/\sqrt{3}$ (since $x > 0$) and then $y = \sqrt{L^2 - 2(L/\sqrt{3})^2} = L/\sqrt{3}$.

So the only critical point is $(L/\sqrt{3}, L/\sqrt{3})$ which, from the geometrical nature of the problem, must give an absolute

maximum. Thus the maximum volume is $V(L/\sqrt{3}, L/\sqrt{3}) = (L/\sqrt{3})^2 \sqrt{L^2 - (L/\sqrt{3})^2 - (L/\sqrt{3})^2} = L^3/(3\sqrt{3})$

cubic units.

51. Note that here the variables are m and b, and $f(m,b) = \sum_{i=1}^{n} [y_i - (mx_i + b)]^2$. Then $f_m = \sum_{i=1}^{n} 2x_i[y_i - (mx_i + b)] = 0$

implies $\sum_{i=1}^{n} (x_iy_i - mx_i^2 - bx_i) = 0$ or $\sum_{i=1}^{n} x_iy_i = m \sum_{i=1}^{n} x_i^2 + b \sum_{i=1}^{n} x_i$ and $f_b = \sum_{i=1}^{n} -2[y_i - (mx_i + b)] = 0$ implies

$\sum_{i=1}^{n} y_i = m \sum_{i=1}^{n} x_i + \sum_{i=1}^{n} b = m \left(\sum_{i=1}^{n} x_i \right) + nb$. Thus we have the two desired equations.

Now $f_{mm} = \sum_{i=1}^{n} 2x_i^2$, $f_{bb} = \sum_{i=1}^{n} 2 = 2n$ and $f_{mb} = \sum_{i=1}^{n} 2x_i$. And $f_{mm}(m,b) > 0$ always and

$D(m,b) = 4n \left(\sum_{i=1}^{n} x_i^2 \right) - 4 \left(\sum_{i=1}^{n} x_i \right)^2 = 4 \left[n \left(\sum_{i=1}^{n} x_i^2 \right) - \left(\sum_{i=1}^{n} x_i \right)^2 \right] > 0$ always so the solutions of these two

equations do indeed minimize $\sum_{i=1}^{n} d_i^2$.

11.8 Lagrange Multipliers

1. At the extreme values of f, the level curves of f just touch the curve $g(x,y) = 8$ with a common tangent line. (See Figure 1
and the accompanying discussion.) We can observe several such occurrences on the contour map, but the level curve
$f(x,y) = c$ with the largest value of c which still intersects the curve $g(x,y) = 8$ is approximately $c = 59$, and the smallest
value of c corresponding to a level curve which intersects $g(x,y) = 8$ appears to be $c = 30$. Thus we estimate the maximum
value of f subject to the constraint $g(x,y) = 8$ to be about 59 and the minimum to be 30.

3. $f(x,y) = x^2 + y^2$, $g(x,y) = xy = 1$, and $\nabla f = \lambda \nabla g \Rightarrow \langle 2x, 2y \rangle = \langle \lambda y, \lambda x \rangle$, so $2x = \lambda y$, $2y = \lambda x$, and $xy = 1$.
From the last equation, $x \neq 0$ and $y \neq 0$, so $2x = \lambda y \Rightarrow \lambda = 2x/y$. Substituting, we have $2y = (2x/y)x \Rightarrow$
$y^2 = x^2 \Rightarrow y = \pm x$. But $xy = 1$, so $x = y = \pm 1$ and the possible points for the extreme values of f are $(1,1)$ and
$(-1,-1)$. Here there is no maximum value, since the constraint $xy = 1$ allows x or y to become arbitrarily large, and hence
$f(x,y) = x^2 + y^2$ can be made arbitrarily large. The minimum value is $f(1,1) = f(-1,-1) = 2$.

5. $f(x,y) = x^2y$, $g(x,y) = x^2 + 2y^2 = 6 \Rightarrow \nabla f = \langle 2xy, x^2 \rangle$, $\lambda \nabla g = \langle 2\lambda x, 4\lambda y \rangle$. Then $2xy = 2\lambda x$ implies $x = 0$
or $\lambda = y$. If $x = 0$, then $x^2 = 4\lambda y$ implies $\lambda = 0$ or $y = 0$. However, if $y = 0$ then $g(x,y) = 0$, a contradiction.
So $\lambda = 0$ and then $g(x,y) = 6 \Rightarrow y = \pm\sqrt{3}$. If $\lambda = y$, then $x^2 = 4\lambda y$ implies $x^2 = 4y^2$, and so $g(x,y) = 6 \Rightarrow$
$4y^2 + 2y^2 = 6 \Rightarrow y^2 = 1 \Rightarrow y = \pm 1$. Thus f has possible extreme values at the points $(0, \pm\sqrt{3})$, $(\pm 2, 1)$, and
$(\pm 2, -1)$. After evaluating f at these points, we find the maximum value to be $f(\pm 2, 1) = 4$ and the minimum to be
$f(\pm 2, -1) = -4$.

7. $f(x,y,z) = 2x + 6y + 10z$, $g(x,y,z) = x^2 + y^2 + z^2 = 35 \Rightarrow \nabla f = \langle 2, 6, 10 \rangle$, $\lambda \nabla g = \langle 2\lambda x, 2\lambda y, 2\lambda z \rangle$. Then
$2\lambda x = 2$, $2\lambda y = 6$, $2\lambda z = 10$ imply $x = \dfrac{1}{\lambda}$, $y = \dfrac{3}{\lambda}$, and $z = \dfrac{5}{\lambda}$. But $35 = x^2 + y^2 + z^2 = \left(\dfrac{1}{\lambda} \right)^2 + \left(\dfrac{3}{\lambda} \right)^2 + \left(\dfrac{5}{\lambda} \right)^2 \Rightarrow$
$35 = \dfrac{35}{\lambda^2} \Rightarrow \lambda = \pm 1$, so f has possible extreme values at the points $(1,3,5)$, $(-1,-3,-5)$. The maximum value of f on
$x^2 + y^2 + z^2 = 35$ is $f(1,3,5) = 70$, and the minimum is $f(-1,-3,-5) = -70$.

9. $f(x, y, z) = xyz$, $g(x, y, z) = x^2 + 2y^2 + 3z^2 = 6$. $\nabla f = \lambda \nabla g \Rightarrow \langle yz, xz, xy \rangle = \lambda \langle 2x, 4y, 6z \rangle$. If any of x, y, or z is zero then $x = y = z = 0$ which contradicts $x^2 + 2y^2 + 3z^2 = 6$. Then $\lambda = (yz)/(2x) = (xz)/(4y) = (xy)/(6z)$ or $x^2 = 2y^2$ and $z^2 = \frac{2}{3}y^2$. Thus $x^2 + 2y^2 + 3z^2 = 6$ implies $6y^2 = 6$ or $y = \pm 1$. Then the possible points are $\left(\sqrt{2}, \pm 1, \sqrt{\frac{2}{3}} \right)$, $\left(\sqrt{2}, \pm 1, -\sqrt{\frac{2}{3}} \right)$, $\left(-\sqrt{2}, \pm 1, \sqrt{\frac{2}{3}} \right)$, $\left(-\sqrt{2}, \pm 1, -\sqrt{\frac{2}{3}} \right)$. The maximum value of f on the ellipsoid is $\frac{2}{\sqrt{3}}$, occurring when all coordinates are positive or exactly two are negative and the minimum is $-\frac{2}{\sqrt{3}}$ occurring when 1 or 3 of the coordinates are negative.

11. $f(x, y, z) = x^2 + y^2 + z^2$, $g(x, y, z) = x^4 + y^4 + z^4 = 1 \Rightarrow \nabla f = \langle 2x, 2y, 2z \rangle$, $\lambda \nabla g = \langle 4\lambda x^3, 4\lambda y^3, 4\lambda z^3 \rangle$.

Case 1: If $x \neq 0$, $y \neq 0$ and $z \neq 0$, then $\nabla f = \lambda \nabla g$ implies $\lambda = 1/(2x^2) = 1/(2y^2) = 1/(2z^2)$ or $x^2 = y^2 = z^2$ and $3x^4 = 1$ or $x = \pm \frac{1}{\sqrt[4]{3}}$ giving the points $\left(\pm \frac{1}{\sqrt[4]{3}}, \frac{1}{\sqrt[4]{3}}, \frac{1}{\sqrt[4]{3}} \right)$, $\left(\pm \frac{1}{\sqrt[4]{3}}, -\frac{1}{\sqrt[4]{3}}, \frac{1}{\sqrt[4]{3}} \right)$, $\left(\pm \frac{1}{\sqrt[4]{3}}, \frac{1}{\sqrt[4]{3}}, -\frac{1}{\sqrt[4]{3}} \right)$, $\left(\pm \frac{1}{\sqrt[4]{3}}, -\frac{1}{\sqrt[4]{3}}, -\frac{1}{\sqrt[4]{3}} \right)$ all with an f-value of $\sqrt{3}$.

Case 2: If one of the variables equals zero and the other two are not zero, then the squares of the two nonzero coordinates are equal with common value $\frac{1}{\sqrt{2}}$ and corresponding f value of $\sqrt{2}$.

Case 3: If exactly two of the variables are zero, then the third variable has value ± 1 with the corresponding f value of 1. Thus on $x^4 + y^4 + z^4 = 1$, the maximum value of f is $\sqrt{3}$ and the minimum value is 1.

13. $f(x, y, z, t) = x + y + z + t$, $g(x, y, z, t) = x^2 + y^2 + z^2 + t^2 = 1 \Rightarrow \langle 1, 1, 1, 1 \rangle = \langle 2\lambda x, 2\lambda y, 2\lambda z, 2\lambda t \rangle$, so $\lambda = 1/(2x) = 1/(2y) = 1/(2z) = 1/(2t)$ and $x = y = z = t$. But $x^2 + y^2 + z^2 + t^2 = 1$, so the possible points are $\left(\pm \frac{1}{2}, \pm \frac{1}{2}, \pm \frac{1}{2}, \pm \frac{1}{2} \right)$. Thus the maximum value of f is $f \left(\frac{1}{2}, \frac{1}{2}, \frac{1}{2}, \frac{1}{2} \right) = 2$ and the minimum value is $f \left(-\frac{1}{2}, -\frac{1}{2}, -\frac{1}{2}, -\frac{1}{2} \right) = -2$.

15. $f(x, y, z) = x + 2y$, $g(x, y, z) = x + y + z = 1$, $h(x, y, z) = y^2 + z^2 = 4 \Rightarrow \nabla f = \langle 1, 2, 0 \rangle$, $\lambda \nabla g = \langle \lambda, \lambda, \lambda \rangle$ and $\mu \nabla h = \langle 0, 2\mu y, 2\mu z \rangle$. Then $1 = \lambda$, $2 = \lambda + 2\mu y$ and $0 = \lambda + 2\mu z$ so $\mu y = \frac{1}{2} = -\mu z$ or $y = 1/(2\mu)$, $z = -1/(2\mu)$. Thus $x + y + z = 1$ implies $x = 1$ and $y^2 + z^2 = 4$ implies $\mu = \pm \frac{1}{2\sqrt{2}}$. Then the possible points are $\left(1, \pm \sqrt{2}, \mp \sqrt{2} \right)$ and the maximum value is $f \left(1, \sqrt{2}, -\sqrt{2} \right) = 1 + 2\sqrt{2}$ and the minimum value is $f \left(1, -\sqrt{2}, \sqrt{2} \right) = 1 - 2\sqrt{2}$.

17. $f(x, y, z) = yz + xy$, $g(x, y, z) = xy = 1$, $h(x, y, z) = y^2 + z^2 = 1 \Rightarrow \nabla f = \langle y, x + z, y \rangle$, $\lambda \nabla g = \langle \lambda y, \lambda x, 0 \rangle$, $\mu \nabla h = \langle 0, 2\mu y, 2\mu z \rangle$. Then $y = \lambda y$ implies $\lambda = 1$ [$y \neq 0$ since $g(x, y, z) = 1$], $x + z = \lambda x + 2\mu y$ and $y = 2\mu z$. Thus $\mu = z/(2y) = y/(2y)$ or $y^2 = z^2$, and so $y^2 + z^2 = 1$ implies $y = \pm \frac{1}{\sqrt{2}}$, $z = \pm \frac{1}{\sqrt{2}}$. Then $xy = 1$ implies $x = \pm \sqrt{2}$ and the possible points are $\left(\pm \sqrt{2}, \pm \frac{1}{\sqrt{2}}, \frac{1}{\sqrt{2}} \right)$, $\left(\pm \sqrt{2}, \pm \frac{1}{\sqrt{2}}, -\frac{1}{\sqrt{2}} \right)$. Hence the maximum of f subject to the constraints is $f \left(\pm \sqrt{2}, \pm \frac{1}{\sqrt{2}}, \pm \frac{1}{\sqrt{2}} \right) = \frac{3}{2}$ and the minimum is $f \left(\pm \sqrt{2}, \pm \frac{1}{\sqrt{2}}, \mp \frac{1}{\sqrt{2}} \right) = \frac{1}{2}$.

Note: Since $xy = 1$ is one of the constraints we could have solved the problem by solving $f(y, z) = yz + 1$ subject to $y^2 + z^2 = 1$.

19. $f(x, y) = e^{-xy}$.   For the interior of the region, we find the critical points: $f_x = -ye^{-xy}$, $f_y = -xe^{-xy}$, so the only

critical point is $(0, 0)$, and $f(0, 0) = 1$. For the boundary, we use Lagrange multipliers. $g(x, y) = x^2 + 4y^2 = 1$ $\Rightarrow$

$\lambda \nabla g = \langle 2\lambda x, 8\lambda y \rangle$, so setting $\nabla f = \lambda \nabla g$ we get $-ye^{-xy} = 2\lambda x$ and $-xe^{-xy} = 8\lambda y$. The first of these gives

$e^{-xy} = -2\lambda x / y$, and then the second gives $-x(-2\lambda x / y) = 8\lambda y$ $\Rightarrow$ $x^2 = 4y^2$. Solving this last equation with the

constraint $x^2 + 4y^2 = 1$ gives $x = \pm\frac{1}{\sqrt{2}}$ and $y = \pm\frac{1}{2\sqrt{2}}$. Now $f\left(\pm\frac{1}{\sqrt{2}}, \mp\frac{1}{2\sqrt{2}}\right) = e^{1/4} \approx 1.284$ and

$f\left(\pm\frac{1}{\sqrt{2}}, \pm\frac{1}{2\sqrt{2}}\right) = e^{-1/4} \approx 0.779$. The former are the maxima on the region and the latter are the minima.

21. (a) $f(x, y) = x$, $g(x, y) = y^2 + x^4 - x^3 = 0$ $\Rightarrow$ $\nabla f = \langle 1, 0 \rangle = \lambda \nabla g = \lambda \langle 4x^3 - 3x^2, 2y \rangle$. Then

$1 = \lambda(4x^3 - 3x^2)$ **(1)** and $0 = 2\lambda y$ **(2)**. We have $\lambda \neq 0$ from **(1)**, so **(2)** gives $y = 0$. Then, from the constraint equation,

$x^4 - x^3 = 0$ $\Rightarrow$ $x^3(x - 1) = 0$ $\Rightarrow$ $x = 0$ or $x = 1$. But $x = 0$ contradicts **(1)**, so the only possible extreme value

subject to the constraint is $f(1, 0) = 1$. (The question remains whether this is indeed the minimum of f.)

(b) The constraint is $y^2 + x^4 - x^3 = 0$ $\Leftrightarrow$ $y^2 = x^3 - x^4$. The left side is non-negative, so we must have $x^3 - x^4 \geq 0$

which is true only for $0 \leq x \leq 1$. Therefore the minimum possible value for $f(x, y) = x$ is 0 which occurs for $x = y = 0$.

However, $\lambda \nabla g(0, 0) = \lambda \langle 0 - 0, 0 \rangle = \langle 0, 0 \rangle$ and $\nabla f(0, 0) = \langle 1, 0 \rangle$, so $\nabla f(0, 0) \neq \lambda \nabla g(0, 0)$ for all values of λ.

(c) Here $\nabla g(0, 0) = \mathbf{0}$ but the method of Lagrange multipliers requires that $\nabla g \neq \mathbf{0}$ everywhere on the constraint curve.

23. $P(L, K) = bL^\alpha K^{1-\alpha}$, $g(L, K) = mL + nK = p$ $\Rightarrow$ $\nabla P = \langle \alpha b L^{\alpha-1} K^{1-\alpha}, (1-\alpha) b L^\alpha K^{-\alpha} \rangle$, $\lambda \nabla g = \langle \lambda m, \lambda n \rangle$.

Then $\alpha b (K/L)^{1-\alpha} = \lambda m$ and $(1-\alpha) b (L/K)^\alpha = \lambda n$ and $mL + nK = p$, so $\alpha b (K/L)^{1-\alpha} / m = (1-\alpha) b (L/K)^\alpha / n$ or

$n\alpha / [m(1-\alpha)] = (L/K)^\alpha (L/K)^{1-\alpha}$ or $L = Kn\alpha / [m(1-\alpha)]$. Substituting into $mL + nK = p$ gives $K = (1-\alpha)p/n$

and $L = \alpha p/m$ for the maximum production.

25. Let the sides of the rectangle be x and y. Then $f(x, y) = xy$, $g(x, y) = 2x + 2y = p$ $\Rightarrow$ $\nabla f(x, y) = \langle y, x \rangle$,

$\lambda \nabla g = \langle 2\lambda, 2\lambda \rangle$. Then $\lambda = \frac{1}{2}y = \frac{1}{2}x$ implies $x = y$ and the rectangle with maximum area is a square with side length $\frac{1}{4}p$.

27. Let $f(x, y, z) = d^2 = (x - 2)^2 + (y - 1)^2 + (z + 1)^2$, then we want to minimize f subject to the constraint

$g(x, y, z) = x + y - z = 1$. $\nabla f = \lambda \nabla g$ $\Rightarrow$ $\langle 2(x - 2), 2(y - 1), 2(z + 1) \rangle = \lambda \langle 1, 1, -1 \rangle$, so $x = (\lambda + 4)/2$,

$y = (\lambda + 2)/2$, $z = -(\lambda + 2)/2$. Substituting into the constraint equation gives $\dfrac{\lambda + 4}{2} + \dfrac{\lambda + 2}{2} + \dfrac{\lambda + 2}{2} = 1$ $\Rightarrow$

$3\lambda + 8 = 2$ $\Rightarrow$ $\lambda = -2$, so $x = 1$, $y = 0$, and $z = 0$. This must correspond to a minimum, so the shortest distance is

$d = \sqrt{(1 - 2)^2 + (0 - 1)^2 + (0 + 1)^2} = \sqrt{3}$.

29. Let $f(x, y, z) = d^2 = (x - 4)^2 + (y - 2)^2 + z^2$. Then we want to minimize f subject to the constraint

$g(x, y, z) = x^2 + y^2 - z^2 = 0$. $\nabla f = \lambda \nabla g$ $\Rightarrow$ $\langle 2(x - 4), 2(y - 2), 2z \rangle = \langle 2\lambda x, 2\lambda y, -2\lambda z \rangle$, so $x - 4 = \lambda x$,

$y - 2 = \lambda y$, and $z = -\lambda z$. From the last equation we have $z + \lambda z = 0$ $\Rightarrow$ $z(1 + \lambda) = 0$, so either $z = 0$ or $\lambda = -1$.

But from the constraint equation we have $z = 0$ $\Rightarrow$ $x^2 + y^2 = 0$ $\Rightarrow$ $x = y = 0$ which is not possible from the first

two equations. So $\lambda = -1$ and $x - 4 = \lambda x$ $\Rightarrow$ $x = 2$, $y - 2 = \lambda y$ $\Rightarrow$ $y = 1$, and $x^2 + y^2 - z^2 = 0$ $\Rightarrow$

$4 + 1 - z^2 = 0$ $\Rightarrow$ $z = \pm\sqrt{5}$. This must correspond to a minimum, so the points on the cone closest to $(4, 2, 0)$

are $\left(2, 1, \pm\sqrt{5}\right)$.

31. $f(x, y, z) = xyz$, $g(x, y, z) = x + y + z = 100 \Rightarrow \nabla f = \langle yz, xz, xy \rangle = \lambda \nabla g = \langle \lambda, \lambda, \lambda \rangle$. Then $\lambda = yz = xz = xy$

implies $x = y = z = \frac{100}{3}$.

33. If the dimensions are $2x$, $2y$, and $2z$, then maximize $f(x, y, z) = (2x)(2y)(2z) = 8xyz$ subject to

$g(x, y, z) = x^2 + y^2 + z^2 = r^2$ ($x > 0$, $y > 0$, $z > 0$). Then $\nabla f = \lambda \nabla g \Rightarrow \langle 8yz, 8xz, 8xy \rangle = \lambda \langle 2x, 2y, 2z \rangle \Rightarrow$

$8yz = 2\lambda x$, $8xz = 2\lambda y$, and $8xy = 2\lambda z$, so $\lambda = \dfrac{4yz}{x} = \dfrac{4xz}{y} = \dfrac{4xy}{z}$. This gives $x^2 z = y^2 z \Rightarrow x^2 = y^2$ (since $z \neq 0$)

and $xy^2 = xz^2 \Rightarrow z^2 = y^2$, so $x^2 = y^2 = z^2 \Rightarrow x = y = z$, and substituting into the constraint

equation gives $3x^2 = r^2 \Rightarrow x = r/\sqrt{3} = y = z$. Thus the largest volume of such a box is

$$ f\left(\frac{r}{\sqrt{3}}, \frac{r}{\sqrt{3}}, \frac{r}{\sqrt{3}} \right) = 8 \left(\frac{r}{\sqrt{3}} \right) \left(\frac{r}{\sqrt{3}} \right) \left(\frac{r}{\sqrt{3}} \right) = \frac{8}{3\sqrt{3}} r^3. $$

35. $f(x, y, z) = xyz$, $g(x, y, z) = x + 2y + 3z = 6 \Rightarrow \nabla f = \langle yz, xz, xy \rangle = \lambda \nabla g = \langle \lambda, 2\lambda, 3\lambda \rangle$.

Then $\lambda = yz = \frac{1}{2}xz = \frac{1}{3}xy$ implies $x = 2y$, $z = \frac{2}{3}y$. But $2y + 2y + 2y = 6$ so $y = 1$, $x = 2$, $z = \frac{2}{3}$ and the volume

is $V = \frac{4}{3}$.

37. $f(x, y, z) = xyz$, $g(x, y, z) = 4(x + y + z) = c \Rightarrow \nabla f = \langle yz, xz, xy \rangle$, $\lambda \nabla g = \langle 4\lambda, 4\lambda, 4\lambda \rangle$. Thus

$4\lambda = yz = xz = xy$ or $x = y = z = \frac{1}{12}c$ are the dimensions giving the maximum volume.

39. If the dimensions of the box are given by x, y, and z, then we need to find the maximum value of $f(x, y, z) = xyz$

$[x, y, z > 0]$ subject to the constraint $L = \sqrt{x^2 + y^2 + z^2}$ or $g(x, y, z) = x^2 + y^2 + z^2 = L^2$. $\nabla f = \lambda \nabla g \Rightarrow$

$\langle yz, xz, xy \rangle = \lambda \langle 2x, 2y, 2z \rangle$, so $yz = 2\lambda x \Rightarrow \lambda = \dfrac{yz}{2x}$, $xz = 2\lambda y \Rightarrow \lambda = \dfrac{xz}{2y}$, and $xy = 2\lambda z \Rightarrow \lambda = \dfrac{xy}{2z}$.

Thus $\lambda = \dfrac{yz}{2x} = \dfrac{xz}{2y} \Rightarrow x^2 = y^2$ [since $z \neq 0$] $\Rightarrow x = y$ and $\lambda = \dfrac{yz}{2x} = \dfrac{xy}{2z} \Rightarrow x = z$ [since $y \neq 0$].

Substituting into the constraint equation gives $x^2 + x^2 + x^2 = L^2 \Rightarrow x^2 = L^2/3 \Rightarrow x = L/\sqrt{3} = y = z$ and the

maximum volume is $\left(L/\sqrt{3} \right)^3 = L^3/\left(3\sqrt{3} \right)$.

41. We need to find the extreme values of $f(x, y, z) = x^2 + y^2 + z^2$ subject to the two constraints $g(x, y, z) = x + y + 2z = 2$

and $h(x, y, z) = x^2 + y^2 - z = 0$. $\nabla f = \langle 2x, 2y, 2z \rangle$, $\lambda \nabla g = \langle \lambda, \lambda, 2\lambda \rangle$ and $\mu \nabla h = \langle 2\mu x, 2\mu y, -\mu \rangle$. Thus we need

$2x = \lambda + 2\mu x$ **(1)**, $2y = \lambda + 2\mu y$ **(2)**, $2z = 2\lambda - \mu$ **(3)**, $x + y + 2z = 2$ **(4)**, and $x^2 + y^2 - z = 0$ **(5)**.

From **(1)** and **(2)**, $2(x - y) = 2\mu(x - y)$, so if $x \neq y$, $\mu = 1$. Putting this in **(3)** gives $2z = 2\lambda - 1$ or $\lambda = z + \frac{1}{2}$, but putting

$\mu = 1$ into **(1)** says $\lambda = 0$. Hence $z + \frac{1}{2} = 0$ or $z = -\frac{1}{2}$. Then **(4)** and **(5)** become $x + y - 3 = 0$ and $x^2 + y^2 + \frac{1}{2} = 0$. The

last equation cannot be true, so this case gives no solution. So we must have $x = y$. Then **(4)** and **(5)** become $2x + 2z = 2$ and

$2x^2 - z = 0$ which imply $z = 1 - x$ and $z = 2x^2$. Thus $2x^2 = 1 - x$ or $2x^2 + x - 1 = (2x - 1)(x + 1) = 0$ so $x = \frac{1}{2}$ or

$x = -1$. The two points to check are $\left(\frac{1}{2}, \frac{1}{2}, \frac{1}{2} \right)$ and $(-1, -1, 2)$: $f\left(\frac{1}{2}, \frac{1}{2}, \frac{1}{2} \right) = \frac{3}{4}$ and $f(-1, -1, 2) = 6$. Thus $\left(\frac{1}{2}, \frac{1}{2}, \frac{1}{2} \right)$ is

the point on the ellipse nearest the origin and $(-1, -1, 2)$ is the one farthest from the origin.

43. $f(x, y, z) = ye^{x-z}$, $g(x, y, z) = 9x^2 + 4y^2 + 36z^2 = 36$, $h(x, y, z) = xy + yz = 1$. $\nabla f = \lambda \nabla g + \mu \nabla h$ ⟹

$\langle ye^{x-z}, e^{x-z}, -ye^{x-z} \rangle = \lambda \langle 18x, 8y, 72z \rangle + \mu \langle y, x + z, y \rangle$, so $ye^{x-z} = 18\lambda x + \mu y$, $e^{x-z} = 8\lambda y + \mu(x + z)$,

$-ye^{x-z} = 72\lambda z + \mu y$, $9x^2 + 4y^2 + 36z^2 = 36$, $xy + yz = 1$. Using a CAS to solve these 5 equations simultaneously for x,

y, z, λ, and μ (in Maple, use the `allvalues` command), we get 4 real-valued solutions:

$$x \approx 0.222444, \quad y \approx -2.157012, \quad z \approx -0.686049, \quad \lambda \approx -0.200401, \quad \mu \approx 2.108584$$

$$x \approx -1.951921, \quad y \approx -0.545867, \quad z \approx 0.119973, \quad \lambda \approx 0.003141, \quad \mu \approx -0.076238$$

$$x \approx 0.155142, \quad y \approx 0.904622, \quad z \approx 0.950293, \quad \lambda \approx -0.012447, \quad \mu \approx 0.489938$$

$$x \approx 1.138731, \quad y \approx 1.768057, \quad z \approx -0.573138, \quad \lambda \approx 0.317141, \quad \mu \approx 1.862675$$

Substituting these values into f gives $f(0.222444, -2.157012, -0.686049) \approx -5.3506$,

$f(-1.951921, -0.545867, 0.119973) \approx -0.0688$, $f(0.155142, 0.904622, 0.950293) \approx 0.4084$,

$f(1.138731, 1.768057, -0.573138) \approx 9.7938$. Thus the maximum is approximately 9.7938, and the mininum is

approximately -5.3506.

45. (a) We wish to maximize $f(x_1, x_2, \ldots, x_n) = \sqrt[n]{x_1 x_2 \cdots x_n}$ subject to

$g(x_1, x_2, \ldots, x_n) = x_1 + x_2 + \cdots + x_n = c$ and $x_i > 0$.

$\nabla f = \left\langle \frac{1}{n}(x_1 x_2 \cdots x_n)^{\frac{1}{n}-1}(x_2 \cdots x_n), \frac{1}{n}(x_1 x_2 \cdots x_n)^{\frac{1}{n}-1}(x_1 x_3 \cdots x_n), \ldots, \frac{1}{n}(x_1 x_2 \cdots x_n)^{\frac{1}{n}-1}(x_1 \cdots x_{n-1}) \right\rangle$

and $\lambda \nabla g = \langle \lambda, \lambda, \ldots, \lambda \rangle$, so we need to solve the system of equations

$$\frac{1}{n}(x_1 x_2 \cdots x_n)^{\frac{1}{n}-1}(x_2 \cdots x_n) = \lambda \quad \Rightarrow \quad x_1^{1/n} x_2^{1/n} \cdots x_n^{1/n} = n\lambda x_1$$

$$\frac{1}{n}(x_1 x_2 \cdots x_n)^{\frac{1}{n}-1}(x_1 x_3 \cdots x_n) = \lambda \quad \Rightarrow \quad x_1^{1/n} x_2^{1/n} \cdots x_n^{1/n} = n\lambda x_2$$

$$\vdots$$

$$\frac{1}{n}(x_1 x_2 \cdots x_n)^{\frac{1}{n}-1}(x_1 \cdots x_{n-1}) = \lambda \quad \Rightarrow \quad x_1^{1/n} x_2^{1/n} \cdots x_n^{1/n} = n\lambda x_n$$

This implies $n\lambda x_1 = n\lambda x_2 = \cdots = n\lambda x_n$. Note $\lambda \neq 0$, otherwise we can't have all $x_i > 0$. Thus $x_1 = x_2 = \cdots = x_n$.

But $x_1 + x_2 + \cdots + x_n = c$ ⟹ $nx_1 = c$ ⟹ $x_1 = \dfrac{c}{n} = x_2 = x_3 = \cdots = x_n$. Then the only point where f can

have an extreme value is $\left(\dfrac{c}{n}, \dfrac{c}{n}, \ldots, \dfrac{c}{n} \right)$. Since we can choose values for $(x_1, x_2, \ldots, x_n)$ that make f as close to

zero (but not equal) as we like, f has no minimum value. Thus the maximum value is

$$f\left(\frac{c}{n}, \frac{c}{n}, \ldots, \frac{c}{n} \right) = \sqrt[n]{\frac{c}{n} \cdot \frac{c}{n} \cdot \cdots \cdot \frac{c}{n}} = \frac{c}{n}.$$

(b) From part (a), $\dfrac{c}{n}$ is the maximum value of f. Thus $f(x_1, x_2, \ldots, x_n) = \sqrt[n]{x_1 x_2 \cdots x_n} \leq \dfrac{c}{n}$. But

$x_1 + x_2 + \cdots + x_n = c$, so $\sqrt[n]{x_1 x_2 \cdots x_n} \leq \dfrac{x_1 + x_2 + \cdots + x_n}{n}$. These two means are equal when f attains its

maximum value $\dfrac{c}{n}$, but this can occur only at the point $\left(\dfrac{c}{n}, \dfrac{c}{n}, \ldots, \dfrac{c}{n} \right)$ we found in part (a). So the means are equal only

when $x_1 = x_2 = x_3 = \cdots = x_n = \dfrac{c}{n}$.

11 Review

CONCEPT CHECK

1. (a) A function f of two variables is a rule that assigns to each ordered pair (x, y) of real numbers in its domain a unique real number denoted by $f(x, y)$.

   (b) One way to visualize a function of two variables is by graphing it, resulting in the surface $z = f(x, y)$. Another method for visualizing a function of two variables is a contour map. The contour map consists of level curves of the function which are horizontal traces of the graph of the function projected onto the xy-plane.

2. A function f of three variables is a rule that assigns to each ordered triple (x, y, z) in its domain a unique real number $f(x, y, z)$. We can visualize a function of three variables by examining its level surfaces $f(x, y, z) = k$, where k is a constant.

3. $\lim\limits_{(x,y) \to (a,b)} f(x, y) = L$ means the values of $f(x, y)$ approach the number L as the point (x, y) approaches the point (a, b) along any path that is within the domain of f. We can show that a limit at a point does not exist by finding two different paths approaching the point along which $f(x, y)$ has different limits.

4. (a) See Definition 11.2.3.

   (b) If f is continuous on $\mathbb{R}^2$, its graph will appear as a surface without holes or breaks.

5. (a) See (2) and (3) in Section 11.3.

   (b) See "Interpretations of Partial Derivatives" on page 759.

   (c) To find f_x, regard y as a constant and differentiate $f(x, y)$ with respect to x. To find f_y, regard x as a constant and differentiate $f(x, y)$ with respect to y.

6. See the statement of Clairaut's Theorem on page 763.

7. (a) See (2) in Section 11.4

   (b) See (19) and the preceding discussion in Section 11.6.

   (c) See "Tangent Planes to Parametric Surfaces" on page 777.

8. See (3) and (4) and the accompanying discussion in Section 11.4. We can interpret the linearization of f at (a, b) geometrically as the linear function whose graph is the tangent plane to the graph of f at (a, b). Thus it is the linear function which best approximates f near (a, b).

9. (a) See Definition 11.4.7.

   (b) Use Theorem 11.4.8.

10. See (10) and the associated discussion in Section 11.4.

11. See (2) and (3) in Section 11.5.

12. See (7) and the preceding discussion in Section 11.5.

13. (a) See Definition 11.6.2. We can interpret it as the rate of change of f at (x_0, y_0) in the direction of $\mathbf{u}$. Geometrically, if P is the point $(x_0, y_0, f(x_0, y_0))$ on the graph of f and C is the curve of intersection of the graph of f with the vertical plane that passes through P in the direction $\mathbf{u}$, the directional derivative of f at (x_0, y_0) in the direction of $\mathbf{u}$ is the slope of the tangent line to C at P. (See Figure 5 in Section 11.6.)

(b) See Theorem 11.6.3.

14. (a) See (8) and (13) in Section 11.6.

(b) $D_{\mathbf{u}} f(x, y) = \nabla f(x, y) \cdot \mathbf{u}$ or $D_{\mathbf{u}} f(x, y, z) = \nabla f(x, y, z) \cdot \mathbf{u}$

(c) The gradient vector of a function points in the direction of maximum rate of increase of the function. On a graph of the function, the gradient points in the direction of steepest ascent.

15. (a) f has a local maximum at (a, b) if $f(x, y) \leq f(a, b)$ when (x, y) is near (a, b).

(b) f has an absolute maximum at (a, b) if $f(x, y) \leq f(a, b)$ for all points (x, y) in the domain of f.

(c) f has a local minimum at (a, b) if $f(x, y) \geq f(a, b)$ when (x, y) is near (a, b).

(d) f has an absolute minimum at (a, b) if $f(x, y) \geq f(a, b)$ for all points (x, y) in the domain of f.

(e) f has a saddle point at (a, b) if $f(a, b)$ is a local maximum in one direction but a local minimum in another.

16. (a) By Theorem 11.7.2, if f has a local maximum at (a, b) and the first-order partial derivatives of f exist there, then
$$f_x(a, b) = 0 \text{ and } f_y(a, b) = 0.$$

(b) A critical point of f is a point (a, b) such that $f_x(a, b) = 0$ and $f_y(a, b) = 0$ or one of these partial derivatives does not exist.

17. See (3) in Section 11.7.

18. (a) See Figure 11 and the accompanying discussion in Section 11.7.

(b) See Theorem 11.7.8.

(c) See the procedure outlined in (9) in Section 11.7.

19. See the discussion beginning on page 813; see "Two Constraints" on page 817.

TRUE-FALSE QUIZ

1. True. $f_y(a, b) = \lim\limits_{h \to 0} \dfrac{f(a, b + h) - f(a, b)}{h}$ from Equation 11.3.3. Let $h = y - b$. As $h \to 0$, $y \to b$. Then by substituting, we get $f_y(a, b) = \lim\limits_{y \to b} \dfrac{f(a, y) - f(a, b)}{y - b}$.

3. False. $f_{xy} = \dfrac{\partial^2 f}{\partial y\, \partial x}$.

5. False. See Example 11.2.3.

7. True. If f has a local minimum and f is differentiable at (a, b) then by Theorem 11.7.2, $f_x(a, b) = 0$ and $f_y(a, b) = 0$, so
$$\nabla f(a, b) = \langle f_x(a, b), f_y(a, b) \rangle = \langle 0, 0 \rangle = \mathbf{0}.$$

9. False. $\nabla f(x, y) = \langle 0, 1/y \rangle$.

11. True. $\nabla f = \langle \cos x, \cos y \rangle$, so $|\nabla f| = \sqrt{\cos^2 x + \cos^2 y}$. But $|\cos \theta| \leq 1$, so $|\nabla f| \leq \sqrt{2}$. Now
$$D_\mathbf{u} f(x, y) = \nabla f \cdot \mathbf{u} = |\nabla f|\,|\mathbf{u}| \cos \theta, \text{ but } \mathbf{u} \text{ is a unit vector, so } |D_\mathbf{u} f(x, y)| \leq \sqrt{2} \cdot 1 \cdot 1 = \sqrt{2}.$$

EXERCISES

1. $\ln(x + y + 1)$ is defined only when $x + y + 1 > 0 \quad \Leftrightarrow \quad y > -x - 1$,
so the domain of f is $\{(x, y) \mid y > -x - 1\}$, all those points above the
line $y = -x - 1$.

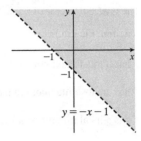

3. $z = f(x, y) = 1 - y^2$, a
parabolic cylinder

5. The level curves are $\sqrt{4x^2 + y^2} = k$ or
$4x^2 + y^2 = k^2$, $k \geq 0$, a family of ellipses.

7.

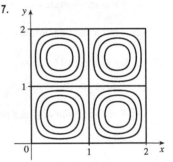

9. f is a rational function, so it is continuous on its domain. Since f is defined at $(1, 1)$, we use direct substitution to evaluate the
limit: $\displaystyle\lim_{(x,y)\to(1,1)} \frac{2xy}{x^2 + 2y^2} = \frac{2(1)(1)}{1^2 + 2(1)^2} = \frac{2}{3}$.

11. (a) $T_x(6, 4) = \displaystyle\lim_{h\to 0} \frac{T(6 + h, 4) - T(6, 4)}{h}$, so we can approximate $T_x(6, 4)$ by considering $h = \pm 2$ and

using the values given in the table: $T_x(6, 4) \approx \dfrac{T(8, 4) - T(6, 4)}{2} = \dfrac{86 - 80}{2} = 3$,

$T_x(6, 4) \approx \dfrac{T(4, 4) - T(6, 4)}{-2} = \dfrac{72 - 80}{-2} = 4$. Averaging these values, we estimate $T_x(6, 4)$ to be approximately

$3.5°C/m$. Similarly, $T_y(6, 4) = \displaystyle\lim_{h\to 0} \frac{T(6, 4 + h) - T(6, 4)}{h}$, which we can approximate with $h = \pm 2$:

$T_y(6, 4) \approx \dfrac{T(6, 6) - T(6, 4)}{2} = \dfrac{75 - 80}{2} = -2.5$, $T_y(6, 4) \approx \dfrac{T(6, 2) - T(6, 4)}{-2} = \dfrac{87 - 80}{-2} = -3.5$. Averaging these

values, we estimate $T_y(6, 4)$ to be approximately $-3.0°C/m$.

(b) Here $\mathbf{u} = \left\langle \frac{1}{\sqrt{2}}, \frac{1}{\sqrt{2}} \right\rangle$, so by Equation 11.6.9, $D_{\mathbf{u}} T(6, 4) = \nabla T(6, 4) \cdot \mathbf{u} = T_x(6, 4) \frac{1}{\sqrt{2}} + T_y(6, 4) \frac{1}{\sqrt{2}}$. Using our

estimates from part (a), we have $D_{\mathbf{u}} T(6, 4) \approx (3.5) \frac{1}{\sqrt{2}} + (-3.0) \frac{1}{\sqrt{2}} = \frac{1}{2\sqrt{2}} \approx 0.35$. This means that as we move

through the point $(6, 4)$ in the direction of $\mathbf{u}$, the temperature increases at a rate of approximately $0.35°\,\text{C/m}$.

Alternatively, we can use Definition 11.6.2: $D_{\mathbf{u}} T(6, 4) = \lim\limits_{h \to 0} \dfrac{T\left(6 + h\frac{1}{\sqrt{2}}, 4 + h\frac{1}{\sqrt{2}}\right) - T(6, 4)}{h}$,

which we can estimate with $h = \pm 2\sqrt{2}$. Then $D_{\mathbf{u}} T(6, 4) \approx \dfrac{T(8, 6) - T(6, 4)}{2\sqrt{2}} = \dfrac{80 - 80}{2\sqrt{2}} = 0$,

$D_{\mathbf{u}} T(6, 4) \approx \dfrac{T(4, 2) - T(6, 4)}{-2\sqrt{2}} = \dfrac{74 - 80}{-2\sqrt{2}} = \dfrac{3}{\sqrt{2}}$. Averaging these values, we have $D_{\mathbf{u}} T(6, 4) \approx \frac{3}{2\sqrt{2}} \approx 1.1°\,\text{C/m}$.

(c) $T_{xy}(x, y) = \dfrac{\partial}{\partial y} [T_x(x, y)] = \lim\limits_{h \to 0} \dfrac{T_x(x, y + h) - T_x(x, y)}{h}$, so $T_{xy}(6, 4) = \lim\limits_{h \to 0} \dfrac{T_x(6, 4 + h) - T_x(6, 4)}{h}$ which we can

estimate with $h = \pm 2$. We have $T_x(6, 4) \approx 3.5$ from part (a), but we will also need values for $T_x(6, 6)$ and $T_x(6, 2)$. If we

use $h = \pm 2$ and the values given in the table, we have

$T_x(6, 6) \approx \dfrac{T(8, 6) - T(6, 6)}{2} = \dfrac{80 - 75}{2} = 2.5$, $T_x(6, 6) \approx \dfrac{T(4, 6) - T(6, 6)}{-2} = \dfrac{68 - 75}{-2} = 3.5$.

Averaging these values, we estimate $T_x(6, 6) \approx 3.0$. Similarly,

$T_x(6, 2) \approx \dfrac{T(8, 2) - T_x(6, 2)}{2} = \dfrac{90 - 87}{2} = 1.5$, $T_x(6, 2) \approx \dfrac{T(4, 2) - T(6, 2)}{-2} = \dfrac{74 - 87}{-2} = 6.5$.

Averaging these values, we estimate $T_x(6, 2) \approx 4.0$. Finally, we estimate $T_{xy}(6, 4)$:

$T_{xy}(6, 4) \approx \dfrac{T_x(6, 6) - T_x(6, 4)}{2} = \dfrac{3.0 - 3.5}{2} = -0.25$, $T_{xy}(6, 4) \approx \dfrac{T_x(6, 2) - T_x(6, 4)}{-2} = \dfrac{4.0 - 3.5}{-2} = -0.25$.

Averaging these values, we have $T_{xy}(6, 4) \approx -0.25$.

13. $f(x, y) = \sqrt{2x + y^2} \;\Rightarrow\; f_x = \frac{1}{2}(2x + y^2)^{-1/2}(2) = \dfrac{1}{\sqrt{2x + y^2}}$, $f_y = \frac{1}{2}(2x + y^2)^{-1/2}(2y) = \dfrac{y}{\sqrt{2x + y^2}}$

15. $g(u, v) = u \tan^{-1} v \;\Rightarrow\; g_u = \tan^{-1} v$, $g_v = \dfrac{u}{1 + v^2}$

17. $T(p, q, r) = p \ln(q + e^r) \;\Rightarrow\; T_p = \ln(q + e^r)$, $T_q = \dfrac{p}{q + e^r}$, $T_r = \dfrac{pe^r}{q + e^r}$

19. $f(x, y) = 4x^3 - xy^2 \;\Rightarrow\; f_x = 12x^2 - y^2$, $f_y = -2xy$, $f_{xx} = 24x$, $f_{yy} = -2x$, $f_{xy} = f_{yx} = -2y$

21. $f(x, y, z) = x^k y^l z^m \;\Rightarrow\; f_x = kx^{k-1} y^l z^m$, $f_y = lx^k y^{l-1} z^m$, $f_z = mx^k y^l z^{m-1}$, $f_{xx} = k(k - 1)x^{k-2} y^l z^m$,

$f_{yy} = l(l - 1)x^k y^{l-2} z^m$, $f_{zz} = m(m - 1)x^k y^l z^{m-2}$, $f_{xy} = f_{yx} = klx^{k-1} y^{l-1} z^m$, $f_{xz} = f_{zx} = kmx^{k-1} y^l z^{m-1}$,

$f_{yz} = f_{zy} = lmx^k y^{l-1} z^{m-1}$

23. $z = xy + xe^{y/x} \;\Rightarrow\; \dfrac{\partial z}{\partial x} = y - \dfrac{y}{x}e^{y/x} + e^{y/x}$, $\dfrac{\partial z}{\partial y} = x + e^{y/x}$ and

$x\dfrac{\partial z}{\partial x} + y\dfrac{\partial z}{\partial y} = x\left(y - \dfrac{y}{x}e^{y/x} + e^{y/x}\right) + y\left(x + e^{y/x}\right) = xy - ye^{y/x} + xe^{y/x} + xy + ye^{y/x} = xy + xy + xe^{y/x} = xy + z$.

25. (a) $z_x = 6x + 2 \;\Rightarrow\; z_x(1, -2) = 8$ and $z_y = -2y \;\to\; z_y(1, -2) = 4$, so an equation of the tangent plane is

$z - 1 = 8(x - 1) + 4(y + 2)$ or $z = 8x + 4y + 1$

(b) A normal vector to the tangent plane (and the surface) at $(1, -2, 1)$ is $\langle 8, 4, -1 \rangle$. Then parametric equations for the normal

line there are $x = 1 + 8t$, $y = -2 + 4t$, $z = 1 - t$, and symmetric equations are $\dfrac{x-1}{8} = \dfrac{y+2}{4} = \dfrac{z-1}{-1}$.

27. (a) Let $F(x, y, z) = x^2 + 2y^2 - 3z^2$. Then $F_x = 2x$, $F_y = 4y$, $F_z = -6z$, so $F_x(2, -1, 1) = 4$, $F_y(2, -1, 1) = -4$,

$F_z(2, -1, 1) = -6$. From Equation 11.6.19, an equation of the tangent plane is $4(x - 2) - 4(y + 1) - 6(z - 1) = 0$

or, equivalently, $2x - 2y - 3z = 3$.

(b) From Equations 11.6.20, symmetric equations for the normal line are $\dfrac{x-2}{4} = \dfrac{y+1}{-4} = \dfrac{z-1}{-6}$.

29. (a) $\mathbf{r}(u, v) = (u + v)\mathbf{i} + u^2\mathbf{j} + v^2\mathbf{k}$ and the point $(3, 4, 1)$ corresponds to $u = 2$, $v = 1$. Then $\mathbf{r}_u = \mathbf{i} + 2u\mathbf{j}$ $\Rightarrow$

$\mathbf{r}_u(2, 1) = \mathbf{i} + 4\mathbf{j}$ and $\mathbf{r}_v = \mathbf{i} + 2v\mathbf{k}$ $\Rightarrow$ $\mathbf{r}_v(2, 1) = \mathbf{i} + 2\mathbf{j}$. A normal vector to the surface at $(3, 4, 1)$ is

$\mathbf{r}_u \times \mathbf{r}_v = 8\mathbf{i} - 2\mathbf{j} - 4\mathbf{k}$, so an equation of the tangent plane there is $8(x - 3) - 2(y - 4) - 4(z - 1) = 0$ or equivalently

$4x - y - 2z = 6$.

(b) A direction vector for the normal line through $(3, 4, 1)$ is $8\mathbf{i} - 2\mathbf{j} - 4\mathbf{k}$, so a vector equation is

$\mathbf{r}(t) = (3\mathbf{i} + 4\mathbf{j} + \mathbf{k}) + t(8\mathbf{i} - 2\mathbf{j} - 4\mathbf{k})$, and the corresponding parametric equations are $x = 3 + 8t$, $y = 4 - 2t$,

$z = 1 - 4t$.

31. The hyperboloid is a level surface of the function $F(x, y, z) = x^2 + 4y^2 - z^2$, so a normal vector to the surface at (x_0, y_0, z_0)

is $\nabla F(x_0, y_0, z_0) = \langle 2x_0, 8y_0, -2z_0 \rangle$. A normal vector for the plane $2x + 2y + z = 5$ is $\langle 2, 2, 1 \rangle$. For the planes to be

parallel, we need the normal vectors to be parallel, so $\langle 2x_0, 8y_0, -2z_0 \rangle = k\langle 2, 2, 1 \rangle$, or $x_0 = k$, $y_0 = \frac{1}{4}k$, and $z_0 = -\frac{1}{2}k$.

But $x_0^2 + 4y_0^2 - z_0^2 = 4$ $\Rightarrow$ $k^2 + \frac{1}{4}k^2 - \frac{1}{4}k^2 = 4$ $\Rightarrow$ $k^2 = 4$ $\Rightarrow$ $k = \pm 2$. So there are two such points:

$(2, \frac{1}{2}, -1)$ and $(-2, -\frac{1}{2}, 1)$.

33. $f(x, y, z) = x^3\sqrt{y^2 + z^2}$ $\Rightarrow$ $f_x(x, y, z) = 3x^2\sqrt{y^2 + z^2}$, $f_y(x, y, z) = \dfrac{yx^3}{\sqrt{y^2 + z^2}}$, $f_z(x, y, z) = \dfrac{zx^3}{\sqrt{y^2 + z^2}}$,

so $f(2, 3, 4) = 8(5) = 40$, $f_x(2, 3, 4) = 3(4)\sqrt{25} = 60$, $f_y(2, 3, 4) = \dfrac{3(8)}{\sqrt{25}} = \dfrac{24}{5}$, and $f_z(2, 3, 4) = \dfrac{4(8)}{\sqrt{25}} = \dfrac{32}{5}$. Then the

linear approximation of f at $(2, 3, 4)$ is

$$f(x, y, z) \approx f(2, 3, 4) + f_x(2, 3, 4)(x - 2) + f_y(2, 3, 4)(y - 3) + f_z(2, 3, 4)(z - 4)$$
$$= 40 + 60(x - 2) + \tfrac{24}{5}(y - 3) + \tfrac{32}{5}(z - 4) = 60x + \tfrac{24}{5}y + \tfrac{32}{5}z - 120$$

Then $(1.98)^3\sqrt{(3.01)^2 + (3.97)^2} = f(1.98, 3.01, 3.97) \approx 60(1.98) + \tfrac{24}{5}(3.01) + \tfrac{32}{5}(3.97) - 120 = 38.656$.

35. $\dfrac{du}{dp} = \dfrac{\partial u}{\partial x}\dfrac{dx}{dp} + \dfrac{\partial u}{\partial y}\dfrac{dy}{dp} + \dfrac{\partial u}{\partial z}\dfrac{dz}{dp} = 2xy^3(1 + 6p) + 3x^2y^2(pe^p + e^p) + 4z^3(p\cos p + \sin p)$

37. By the Chain Rule, $\dfrac{\partial z}{\partial s} = \dfrac{\partial z}{\partial x}\dfrac{\partial x}{\partial s} + \dfrac{\partial z}{\partial y}\dfrac{\partial y}{\partial s}$. When $s = 1$ and $t = 2$, $x = g(1, 2) = 3$ and $y = h(1, 2) = 6$, so

$\dfrac{\partial z}{\partial s} = f_x(3, 6)g_s(1, 2) + f_y(3, 6)h_s(1, 2) = (7)(-1) + (8)(-5) = -47$. Similarly, $\dfrac{\partial z}{\partial t} = \dfrac{\partial z}{\partial x}\dfrac{\partial x}{\partial t} + \dfrac{\partial z}{\partial y}\dfrac{\partial y}{\partial t}$, so

$\dfrac{\partial z}{\partial t} = f_x(3, 6)g_t(1, 2) + f_y(3, 6)h_t(1, 2) = (7)(4) + (8)(10) = 108$.

39. $\dfrac{\partial z}{\partial x} = 2xf'(x^2 - y^2), \quad \dfrac{\partial z}{\partial y} = 1 - 2yf'(x^2 - y^2) \quad \left[\text{where } f' = \dfrac{df}{d(x^2 - y^2)}\right].$ Then

$$y\frac{\partial z}{\partial x} + x\frac{\partial z}{\partial y} = 2xyf'(x^2 - y^2) + x - 2xyf'(x^2 - y^2) = x.$$

41. $\dfrac{\partial z}{\partial x} = \dfrac{\partial z}{\partial u}\,y + \dfrac{\partial z}{\partial v}\dfrac{-y}{x^2}$ and

$$\frac{\partial^2 z}{\partial x^2} = y\frac{\partial}{\partial x}\left(\frac{\partial z}{\partial u}\right) + \frac{2y}{x^3}\frac{\partial z}{\partial v} + \frac{-y}{x^2}\frac{\partial}{\partial x}\left(\frac{\partial z}{\partial v}\right) = \frac{2y}{x^3}\frac{\partial z}{\partial v} + y\left(\frac{\partial^2 z}{\partial u^2}y + \frac{\partial^2 z}{\partial v\,\partial u}\frac{-y}{x^2}\right) + \frac{-y}{x^2}\left(\frac{\partial^2 z}{\partial v^2}\frac{-y}{x^2} + \frac{\partial^2 z}{\partial u\,\partial v}y\right)$$

$$= \frac{2y}{x^3}\frac{\partial z}{\partial v} + y^2\frac{\partial^2 z}{\partial u^2} - \frac{2y^2}{x^2}\frac{\partial^2 z}{\partial u\,\partial v} + \frac{y^2}{x^4}\frac{\partial^2 z}{\partial v^2}$$

Also $\dfrac{\partial z}{\partial y} = x\dfrac{\partial z}{\partial u} + \dfrac{1}{x}\dfrac{\partial z}{\partial v}$ and

$$\frac{\partial^2 z}{\partial y^2} = x\frac{\partial}{\partial y}\left(\frac{\partial z}{\partial u}\right) + \frac{1}{x}\frac{\partial}{\partial y}\left(\frac{\partial z}{\partial v}\right) = x\left(\frac{\partial^2 z}{\partial u^2}x + \frac{\partial^2 z}{\partial v\,\partial u}\frac{1}{x}\right) + \frac{1}{x}\left(\frac{\partial^2 z}{\partial v^2}\frac{1}{x} + \frac{\partial^2 z}{\partial u\,\partial v}x\right) = x^2\frac{\partial^2 z}{\partial u^2} + 2\frac{\partial^2 z}{\partial u\,\partial v} + \frac{1}{x^2}\frac{\partial^2 z}{\partial v^2}$$

Thus

$$x^2\frac{\partial^2 z}{\partial x^2} - y^2\frac{\partial^2 z}{\partial y^2} = \frac{2y}{x}\frac{\partial z}{\partial v} + x^2y^2\frac{\partial^2 z}{\partial u^2} - 2y^2\frac{\partial^2 z}{\partial u\,\partial v} + \frac{y^2}{x^2}\frac{\partial^2 z}{\partial v^2} - x^2y^2\frac{\partial^2 z}{\partial u^2} - 2y^2\frac{\partial^2 z}{\partial u\,\partial v} - \frac{y^2}{x^2}\frac{\partial^2 z}{\partial v^2}$$

$$= \frac{2y}{x}\frac{\partial z}{\partial v} - 4y^2\frac{\partial^2 z}{\partial u\,\partial v} = 2v\frac{\partial z}{\partial v} - 4uv\frac{\partial^2 z}{\partial u\,\partial v}$$

since $y = xv = \dfrac{uv}{y}$ or $y^2 = uv$.

43. $f(x, y, z) = x^2 e^{yz^2} \quad \Rightarrow \quad \nabla f = \langle f_x, f_y, f_z\rangle = \left\langle 2xe^{yz^2}, x^2 e^{yz^2}\cdot z^2, x^2 e^{yz^2}\cdot 2yz\right\rangle = \left\langle 2xe^{yz^2}, x^2 z^2 e^{yz^2}, 2x^2 yz e^{yz^2}\right\rangle$

45. $f(x, y) = x^2 e^{-y} \quad \Rightarrow \quad \nabla f = \langle 2xe^{-y}, -x^2 e^{-y}\rangle, \ \nabla f(-2, 0) = \langle -4, -4\rangle.$ The direction is given by $\langle 4, -3\rangle$, so

$\mathbf{u} = \dfrac{1}{\sqrt{4^2+(-3)^2}}\langle 4, -3\rangle = \frac{1}{5}\langle 4, -3\rangle$ and $D_{\mathbf{u}}f(-2, 0) = \nabla f(-2, 0)\cdot\mathbf{u} = \langle -4, -4\rangle\cdot\frac{1}{5}\langle 4, -3\rangle = \frac{1}{5}(-16 + 12) = -\frac{4}{5}.$

47. $\nabla f = \left\langle 2xy, x^2 + 1/(2\sqrt{y})\right\rangle, \ |\nabla f(2, 1)| = \left|\langle 4, \frac{9}{2}\rangle\right|.$ Thus the maximum rate of change of f at $(2, 1)$ is $\frac{\sqrt{145}}{2}$ in the

direction $\langle 4, \frac{9}{2}\rangle.$

49. First we draw a line passing through Homestead and the eye of the hurricane. We can approximate the directional derivative at Homestead in the direction of the eye of the hurricane by the average rate of change of wind speed between the points where this line intersects the contour lines closest to Homestead. In the direction of the eye of the hurricane, the wind speed changes from 45 to 50 knots. We estimate the distance between these two points to be approximately 8 miles, so the rate of change of wind speed in the direction given is approximately $\frac{50 - 45}{8} = \frac{5}{8} = 0.625$ knot/mi.

51. $f(x, y) = x^2 - xy + y^2 + 9x - 6y + 10 \quad \Rightarrow \quad f_x = 2x - y + 9,$

$f_y = -x + 2y - 6, \ f_{xx} = 2 = f_{yy}, \ f_{xy} = -1.$ Then $f_x = 0$ and $f_y = 0$ imply

$y = 1, x = -4.$ Thus the only critical point is $(-4, 1)$ and $f_{xx}(-4, 1) > 0,$

$D(-4, 1) = 3 > 0,$ so $f(-4, 1) = -11$ is a local minimum.

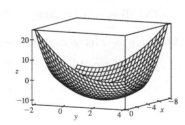

53. $f(x, y) = 3xy - x^2y - xy^2 \Rightarrow f_x = 3y - 2xy - y^2$, $f_y = 3x - x^2 - 2xy$,

$f_{xx} = -2y$, $f_{yy} = -2x$, $f_{xy} = 3 - 2x - 2y$. Then $f_x = 0$ implies

$y(3 - 2x - y) = 0$ so $y = 0$ or $y = 3 - 2x$. Substituting into $f_y = 0$ implies

$x(3 - x) = 0$ or $3x(-1 + x) = 0$. Hence the critical points are $(0, 0)$, $(3, 0)$,

$(0, 3)$ and $(1, 1)$. $D(0, 0) = D(3, 0) = D(0, 3) = -9 < 0$ so $(0, 0)$, $(3, 0)$, and

$(0, 3)$ are saddle points. $D(1, 1) = 3 > 0$ and $f_{xx}(1, 1) = -2 < 0$, so

$f(1, 1) = 1$ is a local maximum.

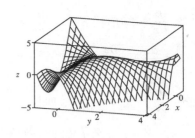

55. First solve inside D. Here $f_x = 4y^2 - 2xy^2 - y^3$, $f_y = 8xy - 2x^2y - 3xy^2$.

Then $f_x = 0$ implies $y = 0$ or $y = 4 - 2x$, but $y = 0$ isn't inside D. Substituting

$y = 4 - 2x$ into $f_y = 0$ implies $x = 0$, $x = 2$ or $x = 1$, but $x = 0$ isn't inside D,

and when $x = 2$, $y = 0$ but $(2, 0)$ isn't inside D. Thus the only critical point inside

D is $(1, 2)$ and $f(1, 2) = 4$. Secondly we consider the boundary of D.

On L_1: $f(x, 0) = 0$ and so $f = 0$ on L_1. On L_2: $x = -y + 6$ and

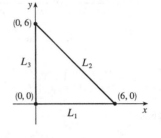

$f(-y + 6, y) = y^2(6 - y)(-2) = -2(6y^2 - y^3)$ which has critical points

at $y = 0$ and $y = 4$. Then $f(6, 0) = 0$ while $f(2, 4) = -64$. On L_3: $f(0, y) = 0$, so $f = 0$ on L_3. Thus on D the absolute

maximum of f is $f(1, 2) = 4$ while the absolute minimum is $f(2, 4) = -64$.

57. $f(x, y) = x^3 - 3x + y^4 - 2y^2$

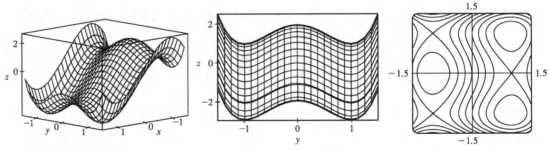

From the graphs, it appears that f has a local maximum $f(-1, 0) \approx 2$, local minima $f(1, \pm 1) \approx -3$, and saddle points at

$(-1, \pm 1)$ and $(1, 0)$.

To find the exact quantities, we calculate $f_x = 3x^2 - 3 = 0 \Leftrightarrow x = \pm 1$ and $f_y = 4y^3 - 4y = 0 \Leftrightarrow$

$y = 0, \pm 1$, giving the critical points estimated above. Also $f_{xx} = 6x$, $f_{xy} = 0$, $f_{yy} = 12y^2 - 4$, so using the Second

Derivatives Test, $D(-1, 0) = 24 > 0$ and $f_{xx}(-1, 0) = -6 < 0$ indicating a local maximum $f(-1, 0) = 2$;

$D(1, \pm 1) = 48 > 0$ and $f_{xx}(1, \pm 1) = 6 > 0$ indicating local minima $f(1, \pm 1) = -3$; and $D(-1, \pm 1) = -48$ and

$D(1, 0) = -24$, indicating saddle points.

59. $f(x, y) = x^2y$, $g(x, y) = x^2 + y^2 = 1 \Rightarrow \nabla f = \langle 2xy, x^2 \rangle = \lambda \nabla g = \langle 2\lambda x, 2\lambda y \rangle$. Then $2xy = 2\lambda x$ implies $x = 0$ or

$y = \lambda$. If $x = 0$ then $x^2 + y^2 = 1$ gives $y = \pm 1$ and we have possible points $(0, \pm 1)$ where $f(0, \pm 1) = 0$. If $y = \lambda$ then

$x^2 = 2\lambda y$ implies $x^2 = 2y^2$ and substitution into $x^2 + y^2 = 1$ gives $3y^2 = 1 \Rightarrow y = \pm \frac{1}{\sqrt{3}}$ and $x = \pm \sqrt{\frac{2}{3}}$. The

corresponding possible points are $\left(\pm \sqrt{\frac{2}{3}}, \pm \frac{1}{\sqrt{3}} \right)$. The absolute maximum is $f\left(\pm \sqrt{\frac{2}{3}}, \frac{1}{\sqrt{3}} \right) = \frac{2}{3\sqrt{3}}$ while the absolute

minimum is $f\left(\pm \sqrt{\frac{2}{3}}, -\frac{1}{\sqrt{3}} \right) = -\frac{2}{3\sqrt{3}}$.

61. $f(x,y,z) = xyz$, $g(x,y,z) = x^2 + y^2 + z^2 = 3$. $\nabla f = \lambda \nabla g \Rightarrow \langle yz, xz, xy \rangle = \lambda \langle 2x, 2y, 2z \rangle$. If any of x, y, or z is

zero, then $x = y = z = 0$ which contradicts $x^2 + y^2 + z^2 = 3$. Then $\lambda = \dfrac{yz}{2x} = \dfrac{xz}{2y} = \dfrac{xy}{2z} \Rightarrow 2y^2z = 2x^2z \Rightarrow$

$y^2 = x^2$, and similarly $2yz^2 = 2x^2y \Rightarrow z^2 = x^2$. Substituting into the constraint equation gives $x^2 + x^2 + x^2 = 3 \Rightarrow$

$x^2 = 1 = y^2 = z^2$. Thus the possible points are $(1,1,\pm1)$, $(1,-1,\pm1)$, $(-1,1,\pm1)$, $(-1,-1,\pm1)$. The absolute maximum

is $f(1,1,1) = f(1,-1,-1) = f(-1,1,-1) = f(-1,-1,1) = 1$ and the absolute

minimum is $f(1,1,-1) = f(1,-1,1) = f(-1,1,1) = f(-1,-1,-1) = -1$.

63. $f(x,y,z) = x^2 + y^2 + z^2$, $g(x,y,z) = xy^2z^3 = 2 \Rightarrow \nabla f = \langle 2x, 2y, 2z \rangle = \lambda \nabla g = \langle \lambda y^2z^3, 2\lambda xyz^3, 3\lambda xy^2z^2 \rangle$.

Since $xy^2z^3 = 2$, $x \neq 0$, $y \neq 0$ and $z \neq 0$, so $2x = \lambda y^2z^3$ **(1)**, $1 = \lambda xz^3$ **(2)**, $2 = 3\lambda xy^2z$ **(3)**. Then **(2)** and **(3)** imply

$\dfrac{1}{xz^3} = \dfrac{2}{3xy^2z}$ or $y^2 = \tfrac{2}{3}z^2$ so $y = \pm z\sqrt{\tfrac{2}{3}}$. Similarly **(1)** and **(3)** imply $\dfrac{2x}{y^2z^3} = \dfrac{2}{3xy^2z}$ or $3x^2 = z^2$ so $x = \pm\tfrac{1}{\sqrt{3}}z$. But

$xy^2z^3 = 2$ so x and z must have the same sign, that is, $x = \dfrac{1}{\sqrt{3}}z$. Thus $g(x,y,z) = 2$ implies $\dfrac{1}{\sqrt{3}}z\left(\tfrac{2}{3}z^2\right)z^3 = 2$ or

$z = \pm3^{1/4}$ and the possible points are $(\pm3^{-1/4}, 3^{-1/4}\sqrt{2}, \pm3^{1/4})$, $(\pm3^{-1/4}, -3^{-1/4}\sqrt{2}, \pm3^{1/4})$. However at each of these

points f takes on the same value, $2\sqrt{3}$. But $(2,1,1)$ also satisfies $g(x,y,z) = 2$ and $f(2,1,1) = 6 > 2\sqrt{3}$. Thus f has an

absolute minimum value of $2\sqrt{3}$ and no absolute maximum subject to the constraint $xy^2z^3 = 2$.

Alternate solution: $g(x,y,z) = xy^2z^3 = 2$ implies $y^2 = \dfrac{2}{xz^3}$, so minimize $f(x,z) = x^2 + \dfrac{2}{xz^3} + z^2$. Then

$f_x = 2x - \dfrac{2}{x^2z^3}$, $f_z = -\dfrac{6}{xz^4} + 2z$, $f_{xx} = 2 + \dfrac{4}{x^3z^3}$, $f_{zz} = \dfrac{24}{xz^5} + 2$ and $f_{xz} = \dfrac{6}{x^2z^4}$. Now $f_x = 0$ implies

$2x^3z^3 - 2 = 0$ or $z = 1/x$. Substituting into $f_y = 0$ implies $-6x^3 + 2x^{-1} = 0$ or $x = \dfrac{1}{\sqrt[4]{3}}$, so the two critical points are

$\left(\pm\dfrac{1}{\sqrt[4]{3}}, \pm\sqrt[4]{3}\right)$. Then $D\left(\pm\dfrac{1}{\sqrt[4]{3}}, \pm\sqrt[4]{3}\right) = (2+4)\left(2 + \tfrac{24}{3}\right) - \left(\dfrac{6}{\sqrt{3}}\right)^2 > 0$ and $f_{xx}\left(\pm\dfrac{1}{\sqrt[4]{3}}, \pm\sqrt[4]{3}\right) = 6 > 0$, so each point

is a minimum. Finally, $y^2 = \dfrac{2}{xz^3}$, so the four points closest to the origin are $\left(\pm\dfrac{1}{\sqrt[4]{3}}, \dfrac{\sqrt{2}}{\sqrt[4]{3}}, \pm\sqrt[4]{3}\right)$, $\left(\pm\dfrac{1}{\sqrt[4]{3}}, -\dfrac{\sqrt{2}}{\sqrt[4]{3}}, \pm\sqrt[4]{3}\right)$.

65.

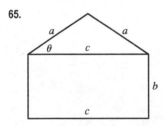

The area of the triangle is $\tfrac{1}{2}ca\sin\theta$ and the area of the rectangle is bc. Thus,

the area of the whole object is $f(a,b,c) = \tfrac{1}{2}ca\sin\theta + bc$. The perimeter of

the object is $g(a,b,c) = 2a + 2b + c = P$. To simplify $\sin\theta$ in terms of a, b,

and c notice that $a^2\sin^2\theta + \left(\tfrac{1}{2}c\right)^2 = a^2 \Rightarrow \sin\theta = \dfrac{1}{2a}\sqrt{4a^2 - c^2}$.

Thus $f(a,b,c) = \dfrac{c}{4}\sqrt{4a^2 - c^2} + bc$. (Instead of using θ, we could just have

used the Pythagorean Theorem.) As a result, by Lagrange's method, we must find a, b, c, and λ by solving $\nabla f = \lambda \nabla g$ which

gives the following equations: $ca(4a^2 - c^2)^{-1/2} = 2\lambda$ **(1)**, $c = 2\lambda$ **(2)**, $\tfrac{1}{4}(4a^2 - c^2)^{1/2} - \tfrac{1}{4}c^2(4a^2 - c^2)^{-1/2} + b = \lambda$

(3), and $2a + 2b + c = P$ **(4)**. From **(2)**, $\lambda = \tfrac{1}{2}c$ and so **(1)** produces $ca(4a^2 - c^2)^{-1/2} = c \Rightarrow (4a^2 - c^2)^{1/2} = a \Rightarrow$

$4a^2 - c^2 = a^2 \Rightarrow c = \sqrt{3}\,a$ **(5)**. Similarly, since $(4a^2 - c^2)^{1/2} = a$ and $\lambda = \tfrac{1}{2}c$, **(3)** gives $\dfrac{a}{4} - \dfrac{c^2}{4a} + b = \dfrac{c}{2}$, so from

(5), $\dfrac{a}{4} - \dfrac{3a}{4} + b = \dfrac{\sqrt{3}\,a}{2} \Rightarrow -\dfrac{a}{2} - \dfrac{\sqrt{3}\,a}{2} = -b \Rightarrow b = \dfrac{a}{2}\left(1 + \sqrt{3}\right)$ **(6)**. Substituting **(5)** and **(6)** into **(4)** we get:

$2a + a\left(1 + \sqrt{3}\right) + \sqrt{3}\,a = P \Rightarrow 3a + 2\sqrt{3}\,a = P \Rightarrow a = \dfrac{P}{3 + 2\sqrt{3}} = \dfrac{2\sqrt{3} - 3}{3}P$ and thus

$b = \dfrac{\left(2\sqrt{3} - 3\right)\left(1 + \sqrt{3}\right)}{6}P = \dfrac{3 - \sqrt{3}}{6}P$ and $c = \left(2 - \sqrt{3}\right)P$.

☐ FOCUS ON PROBLEM SOLVING

1. The areas of the smaller rectangles are $A_1 = xy$, $A_2 = (L-x)y$,

   $A_3 = (L-x)(W-y)$, $A_4 = x(W-y)$. For $0 \le x \le L$, $0 \le y \le W$, let

   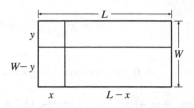

   $$f(x,y) = A_1^2 + A_2^2 + A_3^2 + A_4^2$$
   $$= x^2 y^2 + (L-x)^2 y^2 + (L-x)^2 (W-y)^2 + x^2 (W-y)^2$$
   $$= [x^2 + (L-x)^2][y^2 + (W-y)^2]$$

   Then we need to find the maximum and minimum values of $f(x,y)$. Here

   $f_x(x,y) = [2x - 2(L-x)][y^2 + (W-y)^2] = 0 \Rightarrow 4x - 2L = 0$ or $x = \frac{1}{2}L$, and

   $f_y(x,y) = [x^2 + (L-x)^2][2y - 2(W-y)] = 0 \Rightarrow 4y - 2W = 0$ or $y = W/2$. Also

   $f_{xx} = 4[y^2 + (W-y)^2]$, $f_{yy} = 4[x^2 + (L-x)^2]$, and $f_{xy} = (4x - 2L)(4y - 2W)$. Then

   $D = 16[y^2 + (W-y)^2][x^2 + (L-x)^2] - (4x - 2L)^2(4y - 2W)^2$. Thus when $x = \frac{1}{2}L$ and $y = \frac{1}{2}W$, $D > 0$ and

   $f_{xx} = 2W^2 > 0$. Thus a minimum of f occurs at $\left(\frac{1}{2}L, \frac{1}{2}W\right)$ and this minimum value is $f\left(\frac{1}{2}L, \frac{1}{2}W\right) = \frac{1}{4}L^2 W^2$.

   There are no other critical points, so the maximum must occur on the boundary. Now along the width of the rectangle let

   $g(y) = f(0,y) = f(L,y) = L^2[y^2 + (W-y)^2]$, $0 \le y \le W$. Then $g'(y) = L^2[2y - 2(W-y)] = 0 \Leftrightarrow y = \frac{1}{2}W$.

   And $g\left(\frac{1}{2}\right) = \frac{1}{2}L^2 W^2$. Checking the endpoints, we get $g(0) = g(W) = L^2 W^2$. Along the length of the rectangle let

   $h(x) = f(x,0) = f(x,W) = W^2[x^2 + (L-x)^2]$, $0 \le x \le L$. By symmetry $h'(x) = 0 \Leftrightarrow x = \frac{1}{2}L$ and

   $h\left(\frac{1}{2}L\right) = \frac{1}{2}L^2 W^2$. At the endpoints we have $h(0) = h(L) = L^2 W^2$. Therefore $L^2 W^2$ is the maximum value of f.

   This maximum value of f occurs when the "cutting" lines correspond to sides of the rectangle.

3. (a) The area of a trapezoid is $\frac{1}{2}h(b_1 + b_2)$, where h is the height (the distance between the two parallel sides) and b_1, b_2 are

   the lengths of the bases (the parallel sides). From the figure in the text, we see that $h = x \sin\theta$, $b_1 = w - 2x$, and

   $b_2 = w - 2x + 2x \cos\theta$. Therefore the cross-sectional area of the rain gutter is

   $$A(x,\theta) = \frac{1}{2}x \sin\theta \left[(w - 2x) + (w - 2x + 2x \cos\theta)\right] = (x \sin\theta)(w - 2x + x \cos\theta)$$
   $$= wx \sin\theta - 2x^2 \sin\theta + x^2 \sin\theta \cos\theta, \quad 0 < x \le \frac{1}{2}w, 0 < \theta \le \frac{\pi}{2}$$

   We look for the critical points of A: $\partial A/\partial x = w \sin\theta - 4x \sin\theta + 2x \sin\theta \cos\theta$ and

   $\partial A/\partial \theta = wx \cos\theta - 2x^2 \cos\theta + x^2 (\cos^2\theta - \sin^2\theta)$, so $\partial A/\partial x = 0 \Leftrightarrow \sin\theta (w - 4x + 2x \cos\theta) = 0 \Leftrightarrow$

   $\cos\theta = \dfrac{4x - w}{2x} = 2 - \dfrac{w}{2x} \quad (0 < \theta < \frac{\pi}{2} \Rightarrow \sin\theta > 0)$. If, in addition, $\partial A/\partial \theta = 0$, then

$$0 = wx\cos\theta - 2x^2\cos\theta + x^2(2\cos^2\theta - 1)$$

$$= wx\left(2 - \frac{w}{2x}\right) - 2x^2\left(2 - \frac{w}{2x}\right) + x^2\left[2\left(2 - \frac{w}{2x}\right)^2 - 1\right]$$

$$= 2wx - \tfrac{1}{2}w^2 - 4x^2 + wx + x^2\left[8 - \frac{4w}{x} + \frac{w^2}{2x^2} - 1\right] = -wx + 3x^2 = x(3x - w)$$

Since $x > 0$, we must have $x = \tfrac{1}{3}w$, in which case $\cos\theta = \tfrac{1}{2}$, so $\theta = \tfrac{\pi}{3}$, $\sin\theta = \tfrac{\sqrt{3}}{2}$, $k = \tfrac{\sqrt{3}}{6}w$, $b_1 = \tfrac{1}{3}w$, $b_2 = \tfrac{2}{3}w$,

and $A = \tfrac{\sqrt{3}}{12}w^2$. As in Example 11.7.6, we can argue from the physical nature of this problem that we have found a local

maximum of A. Now checking the boundary of A, let

$$y(\theta) = A(w/2, \theta) = \tfrac{1}{2}w^2\sin\theta - \tfrac{1}{2}w^2\sin\theta + \tfrac{1}{4}w^2\sin\theta\cos\theta = \tfrac{1}{8}w^2\sin 2\theta, \; 0 < \theta \le \tfrac{\pi}{2}.$$ Clearly g is maximized when

$\sin 2\theta = 1$ in which case $A = \tfrac{1}{8}w^2$. Also along the line $\theta = \tfrac{\pi}{2}$, let $h(x) = A\left(x, \tfrac{\pi}{2}\right) = wx - 2x^2$, $0 < x < \tfrac{1}{2}w \;\Rightarrow\;$

$h'(x) = w - 4x = 0 \;\Leftrightarrow\; x = \tfrac{1}{4}w$, and $h\left(\tfrac{1}{4}w\right) = w\left(\tfrac{1}{4}w\right) - 2\left(\tfrac{1}{4}w\right)^2 = \tfrac{1}{8}w^2$. Since $\tfrac{1}{8}w^2 < \tfrac{\sqrt{3}}{12}w^2$, we conclude that

the local maximum found earlier was an absolute maximum.

(b) If the metal were bent into a semi-circular gutter of radius r, we would have $w = \pi r$ and $A = \tfrac{1}{2}\pi r^2 = \tfrac{1}{2}\pi\left(\tfrac{w}{\pi}\right)^2 = \tfrac{w^2}{2\pi}$.

Since $\dfrac{w^2}{2\pi} > \dfrac{\sqrt{3}\,w^2}{12}$, it *would* be better to bend the metal into a gutter with a semicircular cross-section.

5. Let $g(x, y) = xf\left(\dfrac{y}{x}\right)$. Then $g_x(x, y) = f\left(\dfrac{y}{x}\right) + xf'\left(\dfrac{y}{x}\right)\left(-\dfrac{y}{x^2}\right) = f\left(\dfrac{y}{x}\right) - \dfrac{y}{x}f'\left(\dfrac{y}{x}\right)$ and

$g_y(x, y) = xf'\left(\dfrac{y}{x}\right)\left(\dfrac{1}{x}\right) = f'\left(\dfrac{y}{x}\right)$. Thus the tangent plane at (x_0, y_0, z_0) on the surface has equation

$$z - x_0 f\left(\dfrac{y_0}{x_0}\right) = \left[f\left(\dfrac{y_0}{x_0}\right) - y_0 x_0^{-1} f'\left(\dfrac{y_0}{x_0}\right)\right](x - x_0) + f'\left(\dfrac{y_0}{x_0}\right)(y - y_0) \;\Rightarrow\;$$

$$\left[f\left(\dfrac{y_0}{x_0}\right) - y_0 x_0^{-1} f'\left(\dfrac{y_0}{x_0}\right)\right]x + \left[f'\left(\dfrac{y_0}{x_0}\right)\right]y - z = 0.$$ But any plane whose equation is of the form $ax + by + cz = 0$

passes through the origin. Thus the origin is the common point of intersection.

7. (a) $x = r\cos\theta$, $y = r\sin\theta$, $z = z$. Then $\dfrac{\partial u}{\partial r} = \dfrac{\partial u}{\partial x}\dfrac{\partial x}{\partial r} + \dfrac{\partial u}{\partial y}\dfrac{\partial y}{\partial r} + \dfrac{\partial u}{\partial z}\dfrac{\partial z}{\partial r} = \dfrac{\partial u}{\partial x}\cos\theta + \dfrac{\partial u}{\partial y}\sin\theta$ and

$$\dfrac{\partial^2 u}{\partial r^2} = \cos\theta\left[\dfrac{\partial^2 u}{\partial x^2}\dfrac{\partial x}{\partial r} + \dfrac{\partial^2 u}{\partial y\,\partial x}\dfrac{\partial y}{\partial r} + \dfrac{\partial^2 u}{\partial z\,\partial x}\dfrac{\partial z}{\partial r}\right] + \sin\theta\left[\dfrac{\partial^2 u}{\partial y^2}\dfrac{\partial y}{\partial r} + \dfrac{\partial^2 u}{\partial x\,\partial y}\dfrac{\partial x}{\partial r} + \dfrac{\partial^2 u}{\partial z\,\partial y}\dfrac{\partial z}{\partial r}\right]$$

$$= \dfrac{\partial^2 u}{\partial x^2}\cos^2\theta + \dfrac{\partial^2 u}{\partial y^2}\sin^2\theta + 2\dfrac{\partial^2 u}{\partial y\,\partial x}\cos\theta\sin\theta$$

Similarly $\dfrac{\partial u}{\partial \theta} = -\dfrac{\partial u}{\partial x}r\sin\theta + \dfrac{\partial u}{\partial y}r\cos\theta$ and

$$\frac{\partial^2 u}{\partial \theta^2} = \frac{\partial^2 u}{\partial x^2} r^2 \sin^2 \theta + \frac{\partial^2 u}{\partial y^2} r^2 \cos^2 \theta - 2 \frac{\partial^2 u}{\partial y \, \partial x} r^2 \sin \theta \cos \theta - \frac{\partial u}{\partial x} r \cos \theta - \frac{\partial u}{\partial y} r \sin \theta. \text{ So}$$

$$\frac{\partial^2 u}{\partial r^2} + \frac{1}{r} \frac{\partial u}{\partial r} + \frac{1}{r^2} \frac{\partial^2 u}{\partial \theta^2} + \frac{\partial^2 u}{\partial z^2} = \frac{\partial^2 u}{\partial x^2} \cos^2 \theta + \frac{\partial^2 u}{\partial y^2} \sin^2 \theta + 2 \frac{\partial^2 u}{\partial y \, \partial x} \cos \theta \sin \theta + \frac{\partial u}{\partial x} \frac{\cos \theta}{r} + \frac{\partial u}{\partial y} \frac{\sin \theta}{r}$$

$$+ \frac{\partial^2 u}{\partial x^2} \sin^2 \theta + \frac{\partial^2 u}{\partial y^2} \cos^2 \theta - 2 \frac{\partial^2 u}{\partial y \, \partial x} \sin \theta \cos \theta$$

$$- \frac{\partial u}{\partial x} \frac{\cos \theta}{r} - \frac{\partial u}{\partial y} \frac{\sin \theta}{r} + \frac{\partial^2 u}{\partial z^2}$$

$$= \frac{\partial^2 u}{\partial x^2} + \frac{\partial^2 u}{\partial y^2} + \frac{\partial^2 u}{\partial z^2}$$

(b) $x = \rho \sin \phi \cos \theta$, $y = \rho \sin \phi \sin \theta$, $z = \rho \cos \phi$. Then

$$\frac{\partial u}{\partial \rho} = \frac{\partial u}{\partial x} \frac{\partial x}{\partial \rho} + \frac{\partial u}{\partial y} \frac{\partial y}{\partial \rho} + \frac{\partial u}{\partial z} \frac{\partial z}{\partial \rho} = \frac{\partial u}{\partial x} \sin \phi \cos \theta + \frac{\partial u}{\partial y} \sin \phi \sin \theta + \frac{\partial u}{\partial z} \cos \phi, \text{ and}$$

$$\frac{\partial^2 u}{\partial \rho^2} = \sin \phi \cos \theta \left[\frac{\partial^2 u}{\partial x^2} \frac{\partial x}{\partial \rho} + \frac{\partial^2 u}{\partial y \, \partial x} \frac{\partial y}{\partial \rho} + \frac{\partial^2 u}{\partial z \, \partial x} \frac{\partial z}{\partial \rho} \right]$$

$$+ \sin \phi \sin \theta \left[\frac{\partial^2 u}{\partial y^2} \frac{\partial y}{\partial \rho} + \frac{\partial^2 u}{\partial x \, \partial y} \frac{\partial x}{\partial \rho} + \frac{\partial^2 u}{\partial z \, \partial y} \frac{\partial z}{\partial \rho} \right]$$

$$+ \cos \phi \left[\frac{\partial^2 u}{\partial z^2} \frac{\partial z}{\partial \rho} + \frac{\partial^2 u}{\partial x \, \partial z} \frac{\partial x}{\partial \rho} + \frac{\partial^2 u}{\partial y \, \partial z} \frac{\partial y}{\partial \rho} \right]$$

$$= 2 \frac{\partial^2 u}{\partial y \, \partial x} \sin^2 \phi \sin \theta \cos \theta + 2 \frac{\partial^2 u}{\partial z \, \partial x} \sin \phi \cos \phi \cos \theta + 2 \frac{\partial^2 u}{\partial y \, \partial z} \sin \phi \cos \phi \sin \theta$$

$$+ \frac{\partial^2 u}{\partial x^2} \sin^2 \phi \cos^2 \theta + \frac{\partial^2 u}{\partial y^2} \sin^2 \phi \sin^2 \theta + \frac{\partial^2 u}{\partial z^2} \cos^2 \phi$$

Similarly $\dfrac{\partial u}{\partial \phi} = \dfrac{\partial u}{\partial x} \rho \cos \phi \cos \theta + \dfrac{\partial u}{\partial y} \rho \cos \phi \sin \theta - \dfrac{\partial u}{\partial z} \rho \sin \phi$, and

$$\frac{\partial^2 u}{\partial \phi^2} = 2 \frac{\partial^2 u}{\partial y \, \partial x} \rho^2 \cos^2 \phi \sin \theta \cos \theta - 2 \frac{\partial^2 u}{\partial x \, \partial z} \rho^2 \sin \phi \cos \phi \cos \theta$$

$$- 2 \frac{\partial^2 u}{\partial y \, \partial z} \rho^2 \sin \phi \cos \phi \sin \theta + \frac{\partial^2 u}{\partial x^2} \rho^2 \cos^2 \phi \cos^2 \theta + \frac{\partial^2 u}{\partial y^2} \rho^2 \cos^2 \phi \sin^2 \theta$$

$$+ \frac{\partial^2 u}{\partial z^2} \rho^2 \sin^2 \phi - \frac{\partial u}{\partial x} \rho \sin \phi \cos \theta - \frac{\partial u}{\partial y} \rho \sin \phi \sin \theta - \frac{\partial u}{\partial z} \rho \cos \phi$$

And $\dfrac{\partial u}{\partial \theta} = -\dfrac{\partial u}{\partial x} \rho \sin \phi \sin \theta + \dfrac{\partial u}{\partial y} \rho \sin \phi \cos \theta$, while

$$\frac{\partial^2 u}{\partial \theta^2} = -2 \frac{\partial^2 u}{\partial y \, \partial x} \rho^2 \sin^2 \phi \cos \theta \sin \theta + \frac{\partial^2 u}{\partial x^2} \rho^2 \sin^2 \phi \sin^2 \theta$$

$$+ \frac{\partial^2 u}{\partial y^2} \rho^2 \sin^2 \phi \cos^2 \theta - \frac{\partial u}{\partial x} \rho \sin \phi \cos \theta - \frac{\partial u}{\partial y} \rho \sin \phi \sin \theta$$

[continued]

Therefore

$$\frac{\partial^2 u}{\partial \rho^2} + \frac{2}{\rho}\frac{\partial u}{\partial \rho} + \frac{\cot\phi}{\rho^2}\frac{\partial u}{\partial \phi} + \frac{1}{\rho^2}\frac{\partial^2 u}{\partial \phi^2} + \frac{1}{\rho^2 \sin^2\phi}\frac{\partial^2 u}{\partial \theta^2}$$

$$= \frac{\partial^2 u}{\partial x^2}\left[(\sin^2\phi\,\cos^2\theta) + (\cos^2\phi\,\cos^2\theta) + \sin^2\theta\right]$$

$$+ \frac{\partial^2 u}{\partial y^2}\left[(\sin^2\phi\,\sin^2\theta) + (\cos^2\phi\,\sin^2\theta) + \cos^2\theta\right] + \frac{\partial^2 u}{\partial z^2}\left[\cos^2\phi + \sin^2\phi\right]$$

$$+ \frac{\partial u}{\partial x}\left[\frac{2\sin^2\phi\,\cos\theta + \cos^2\phi\,\cos\theta - \sin^2\phi\,\cos\theta - \cos\theta}{\rho\sin\phi}\right]$$

$$+ \frac{\partial u}{\partial y}\left[\frac{2\sin^2\phi\,\sin\theta + \cos^2\phi\,\sin\theta - \sin^2\phi\,\sin\theta - \sin\theta}{\rho\sin\phi}\right]$$

But $2\sin^2\phi\,\cos\theta + \cos^2\phi\,\cos\theta - \sin^2\phi\,\cos\theta - \cos\theta = (\sin^2\phi + \cos^2\phi - 1)\cos\theta = 0$ and similarly the coefficient of

$\partial u/\partial y$ is 0. Also $\sin^2\phi\,\cos^2\theta + \cos^2\phi\,\cos^2\theta + \sin^2\theta = \cos^2\theta\,(\sin^2\phi + \cos^2\phi) + \sin^2\theta = 1$, and similarly the

coefficient of $\partial^2 u/\partial y^2$ is 1. So Laplace's Equation in spherical coordinates is as stated.

9. Since we are minimizing the area of the ellipse, and the circle lies above the x-axis,

the ellipse will intersect the circle for only one value of y. This y-value must

satisfy both the equation of the circle and the equation of the ellipse. Now

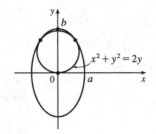

$\dfrac{x^2}{a^2} + \dfrac{y^2}{b^2} = 1 \;\Rightarrow\; x^2 = \dfrac{a^2}{b^2}\left(b^2 - y^2\right)$. Substituting into the equation of the

circle gives $\dfrac{a^2}{b^2}\left(b^2 - y^2\right) + y^2 - 2y = 0 \;\Rightarrow\; \left(\dfrac{b^2 - a^2}{b^2}\right)y^2 - 2y + a^2 = 0.$

In order for there to be only one solution to this quadratic equation, the discriminant must be 0, so $4 - 4a^2\,\dfrac{b^2 - a^2}{b^2} = 0 \;\Rightarrow$

$b^2 - a^2 b^2 + a^4 = 0$. The area of the ellipse is $A(a, b) = \pi ab$, and we minimize this function subject to the constraint

$g(a, b) = b^2 - a^2 b^2 + a^4 = 0.$

Now $\nabla A = \lambda \nabla g \;\Leftrightarrow\; \pi b = \lambda(4a^3 - 2ab^2),\; \pi a = \lambda(2b - 2ba^2) \;\Rightarrow\; \lambda = \dfrac{\pi b}{2a(2a^2 - b^2)}$ **(1)**,

$\lambda = \dfrac{\pi a}{2b(1 - a^2)}$ **(2)**, $b^2 - a^2 b^2 + a^4 = 0$ **(3)**. Comparing **(1)** and **(2)** gives $\dfrac{\pi b}{2a(2a^2 - b^2)} = \dfrac{\pi a}{2b(1 - a^2)} \;\Rightarrow$

$2\pi b^2 = 4\pi a^4 \;\Leftrightarrow\; a^2 = \frac{1}{\sqrt{2}}b$. Substitute this into **(3)** to get $b = \frac{3}{\sqrt{2}} \;\Rightarrow\; a - \sqrt{\frac{3}{2}}.$

12 □ MULTIPLE INTEGRALS

12.1 Double Integrals over Rectangles

1. (a) The subrectangles are shown in the figure.

The surface is the graph of $f(x,y) = xy$ and $\Delta A = 4$, so we estimate

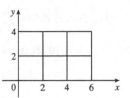

$$V \approx \sum_{i=1}^{3} \sum_{j=1}^{2} f(x_i, y_j)\, \Delta A$$

$$= f(2,2)\,\Delta A + f(2,4)\,\Delta A + f(4,2)\,\Delta A + f(4,4)\,\Delta A + f(6,2)\,\Delta A + f(6,4)\,\Delta A$$

$$= 4(4) + 8(4) + 8(4) + 16(4) + 12(4) + 24(4) = 288$$

(b) $V \approx \displaystyle\sum_{i=1}^{3} \sum_{j=1}^{2} f(\overline{x}_i, \overline{y}_j)\, \Delta A = f(1,1)\,\Delta A + f(1,3)\,\Delta A + f(3,1)\,\Delta A + f(3,3)\,\Delta A + f(5,1)\,\Delta A + f(5,3)\,\Delta A$

$$= 1(4) + 3(4) + 3(4) + 9(4) + 5(4) + 15(4) = 144$$

3. (a) The subrectangles are shown in the figure. Since $\Delta A = \pi^2/4$, we estimate

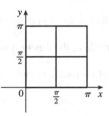

$$\iint_R \sin(x+y)\, dA \approx \sum_{i=1}^{2} \sum_{j=1}^{2} f(x_{ij}^*, y_{ij}^*)\, \Delta A$$

$$= f(0,0)\,\Delta A + f\left(0, \tfrac{\pi}{2}\right)\Delta A + f\left(\tfrac{\pi}{2}, 0\right)\Delta A + f\left(\tfrac{\pi}{2}, \tfrac{\pi}{2}\right)\Delta A$$

$$= 0\left(\tfrac{\pi^2}{4}\right) + 1\left(\tfrac{\pi^2}{4}\right) + 1\left(\tfrac{\pi^2}{4}\right) + 0\left(\tfrac{\pi^2}{4}\right) = \tfrac{\pi^2}{2} \approx 4.935$$

(b) $\iint_R \sin(x+y)\, dA \approx \displaystyle\sum_{i=1}^{2} \sum_{j=1}^{2} f(\overline{x}_i, \overline{y}_j)\, \Delta A$

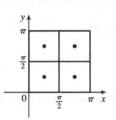

$$= f\left(\tfrac{\pi}{4}, \tfrac{\pi}{4}\right)\Delta A + f\left(\tfrac{\pi}{4}, \tfrac{3\pi}{4}\right)\Delta A + f\left(\tfrac{3\pi}{4}, \tfrac{\pi}{4}\right)\Delta A + f\left(\tfrac{3\pi}{4}, \tfrac{3\pi}{4}\right)\Delta A$$

$$= 1\left(\tfrac{\pi^2}{4}\right) + 0\left(\tfrac{\pi^2}{4}\right) + 0\left(\tfrac{\pi^2}{4}\right) + (-1)\left(\tfrac{\pi^2}{4}\right) = 0$$

5. (a) Each subrectangle and its midpoint are shown in the figure.

The area of each subrectangle is $\Delta A = 2$, so we evaluate f
at each midpoint and estimate

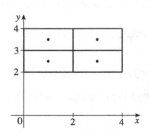

$$\iint_R f(x,y)\, dA \approx \sum_{i=1}^{2} \sum_{j=1}^{2} f(\overline{x}_i, \overline{y}_j)\, \Delta A$$

$$= f(1, 2.5)\,\Delta A + f(1, 3.5)\,\Delta A$$

$$\qquad + f(3, 2.5)\,\Delta A + f(3, 3.5)\,\Delta A$$

$$= -2(2) + (-1)(2) + 2(2) + 3(2) = 4$$

171

(b) The subrectangles are shown in the figure.

In each subrectangle, the sample point closest to the origin

is the lower left corner, and the area of each subrectangle is $\Delta A = \frac{1}{2}$.

Thus we estimate

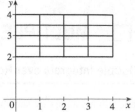

$$\iint_R f(x,y)\, dA \approx \sum_{i=1}^{4}\sum_{j=1}^{4} f\left(x_{ij}^*, y_{ij}^*\right)\Delta A$$

$$= f(0,2)\,\Delta A + f(0,2.5)\,\Delta A + f(0,3)\,\Delta A + f(0,3.5)\,\Delta A$$

$$+ f(1,2)\,\Delta A + f(1,2.5)\,\Delta A + f(1,3)\,\Delta A + f(1,3.5)\,\Delta A$$

$$+ f(2,2)\,\Delta A + f(2,2.5)\,\Delta A + f(2,3)\,\Delta A + f(2,3.5)\,\Delta A$$

$$+ f(3,2)\,\Delta A + f(3,2.5)\,\Delta A + f(3,3)\,\Delta A + f(3,3.5)\,\Delta A$$

$$= -3\left(\tfrac{1}{2}\right) + (-5)\left(\tfrac{1}{2}\right) + (-6)\left(\tfrac{1}{2}\right) + (-4)\left(\tfrac{1}{2}\right) + (-1)\left(\tfrac{1}{2}\right) + (-2)\left(\tfrac{1}{2}\right) + (-3)\left(\tfrac{1}{2}\right) + (-1)\left(\tfrac{1}{2}\right)$$

$$+ 1\left(\tfrac{1}{2}\right) + 0\left(\tfrac{1}{2}\right) + (-1)\left(\tfrac{1}{2}\right) + 1\left(\tfrac{1}{2}\right) + 2\left(\tfrac{1}{2}\right) + 2\left(\tfrac{1}{2}\right) + 1\left(\tfrac{1}{2}\right) + 3\left(\tfrac{1}{2}\right)$$

$$= -8$$

7. The values of $f(x,y) = \sqrt{52 - x^2 - y^2}$ get smaller as we move farther from the origin, so on any of the subrectangles in the

problem, the function will have its largest value at the lower left corner of the subrectangle and its smallest value at the upper

right corner, and any other value will lie between these two. So using these subrectangles we have $U < V < L$. (Note that this

is true no matter how R is divided into subrectangles.)

9. (a) With $m = n = 2$, we have $\Delta A = 4$. Using the contour map to estimate the value of f at the center of each subrectangle,

we have

$$\iint_R f(x,y)\, dA \approx \sum_{i=1}^{2}\sum_{j=1}^{2} f\left(\overline{x}_i, \overline{y}_j\right)\Delta A = \Delta A[f(1,1) + f(1,3) + f(3,1) + f(3,3)] \approx 4(27 + 4 + 14 + 17) = 248$$

(b) $f_{\text{ave}} = \frac{1}{A(R)}\iint_R f(x,y)\, dA \approx \frac{1}{16}(248) = 15.5$

11. $z = 3 > 0$, so we can interpret the integral as the volume of the solid S that lies below the plane $z = 3$ and above the

rectangle $[-2,2] \times [1,6]$. S is a rectangular solid, thus $\iint_R 3\, dA = 4 \cdot 5 \cdot 3 = 60$.

13. $z = f(x,y) = 4 - 2y \geq 0$ for $0 \leq y \leq 1$. Thus the integral represents the volume of that

part of the rectangular solid $[0,1] \times [0,1] \times [0,4]$ which lies below the plane $z = 4 - 2y$.

So

$$\iint_R(4 - 2y)\, dA = (1)(1)(2) + \tfrac{1}{2}(1)(1)(2) = 3$$

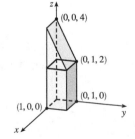

15. To calculate the estimates using a programmable calculator, we can use an algorithm similar to that of Exercise 5.1.7. In Maple, we can define the function $f(x, y) = \sqrt{1 + xe^{-y}}$ (calling it f), load the student package, and then use the command

```
middlesum(middlesum(f,x=0..1,m),
                y=0..1,m);
```

to get the estimate with $n = m^2$ squares of equal size. Mathematica has no special Riemann sum command, but we can define f and then use nested Sum commands to calculate the estimates.

n	estimate
1	1.141606
4	1.143191
16	1.143535
64	1.143617
256	1.143637
1024	1.143642

17. If we divide R into mn subrectangles, $\iint_R k\, dA \approx \sum\limits_{i=1}^{m} \sum\limits_{j=1}^{n} f\left(x_{ij}^*, y_{ij}^*\right) \Delta A$ for any choice of sample points $\left(x_{ij}^*, y_{ij}^*\right)$.

But $f\left(x_{ij}^*, y_{ij}^*\right) = k$ always and $\sum\limits_{i=1}^{m} \sum\limits_{j=1}^{n} \Delta A = $ area of $R = (b-a)(d-c)$. Thus, no matter how we choose the sample

points, $\sum\limits_{i=1}^{m} \sum\limits_{j=1}^{n} f\left(x_{ij}^*, y_{ij}^*\right) \Delta A = k \sum\limits_{i=1}^{m} \sum\limits_{j=1}^{n} \Delta A = k(b-a)(d-c)$ and so

$$\iint_R k\, dA = \lim_{m,n\to\infty} \sum_{i=1}^{m} \sum_{j=1}^{n} f\left(x_{ij}^*, y_{ij}^*\right) \Delta A = \lim_{m,n\to\infty} k \sum_{i=1}^{m} \sum_{j=1}^{n} \Delta A = \lim_{m,n\to\infty} k(b-a)(d-c) = k(b-a)(d-c).$$

12.2 Iterated Integrals

1. $\int_0^5 12x^2 y^3\, dx = \left[12\dfrac{x^3}{3}\, y^3\right]_{x=0}^{x=5} = 4x^3 y^3\Big]_{x=0}^{x=5} = 4(5)^3\, y^3 - 4(0)^3\, y^3 = 500y^3$,

$\int_0^1 12x^2 y^3\, dy = \left[12x^2\, \dfrac{y^4}{4}\right]_{y=0}^{y=1} = 3x^2 y^4\Big]_{y=0}^{y=1} = 3x^2 (1)^4 - 3x^2 (0)^4 = 3x^2$

3. $\int_1^3 \int_0^1 (1 + 4xy)\, dx\, dy = \int_1^3 \left[x + 2x^2 y\right]_{x=0}^{x=1} dy = \int_1^3 (1 + 2y)\, dy = \left[y + y^2\right]_1^3 = (3 + 9) - (1 + 1) = 10$

5. $\int_0^2 \int_0^{\pi/2} x \sin y\, dy\, dx = \int_0^2 x\, dx \int_0^{\pi/2} \sin y\, dy$ [as in Example 5] $= \left[\dfrac{x^2}{2}\right]_0^2 \left[-\cos y\right]_0^{\pi/2} = (2 - 0)(0 + 1) = 2$

7. $\int_0^2 \int_0^1 (2x + y)^8\, dx\, dy = \int_0^2 \left[\dfrac{1}{2}\dfrac{(2x + y)^9}{9}\right]_{x=0}^{x=1} dy$ [substitute $u = 2x + y \Rightarrow dx = \frac{1}{2}\, du$]

$= \dfrac{1}{18}\int_0^2 [(2 + y)^9 - (0 + y)^9]\, dy = \dfrac{1}{18}\left[\dfrac{(2 + y)^{10}}{10} - \dfrac{y^{10}}{10}\right]_0^2$

$= \dfrac{1}{180}[(4^{10} - 2^{10}) - (2^{10} - 0^{10})] = \dfrac{1,046,528}{180} = \dfrac{261,632}{45}$

9. $\int_1^4 \int_1^2 \left(\dfrac{x}{y} + \dfrac{y}{x}\right) dy\, dx = \int_1^4 \left[x \ln|y| + \dfrac{1}{x}\cdot\dfrac{1}{2} y^2\right]_{y=1}^{y=2} dx = \int_1^4 \left(x \ln 2 + \dfrac{3}{2x}\right) dx = \left[\tfrac{1}{2} x^2 \ln 2 + \tfrac{3}{2} \ln|x|\right]_1^4$

$= 8\ln 2 + \tfrac{3}{2}\ln 4 - \tfrac{1}{2}\ln 2 = \tfrac{15}{2}\ln 2 + 3\ln 4 - \tfrac{3}{2}\ln 2$

11. $\int_0^1 \int_0^1 (u-v)^5 \, du \, dv = \int_0^1 \left[\frac{1}{6}(u-v)^6 \right]_{u=0}^{u=1} dv = \frac{1}{6} \int_0^1 \left[(1-v)^6 - (0-v)^6 \right] dv$

$\qquad = \frac{1}{6} \int_0^1 \left[(1-v)^6 - v^6 \right] dv = \frac{1}{6} \left[-\frac{1}{7}(1-v)^7 - \frac{1}{7}v^7 \right]_0^1$

$\qquad = -\frac{1}{42} \left[(0+1) - (1+0) \right] = 0$

13. $\int_0^2 \int_0^\pi r \sin^2 \theta \, d\theta \, dr = \int_0^2 r \, dr \int_0^\pi \sin^2 \theta \, d\theta \quad \text{[as in Example 5]} = \int_0^2 r \, dr \int_0^\pi \frac{1}{2}(1 - \cos 2\theta) \, d\theta$

$\qquad = \left[\frac{1}{2}r^2 \right]_0^2 \cdot \frac{1}{2} \left[\theta - \frac{1}{2}\sin 2\theta \right]_0^\pi = (2-0) \cdot \frac{1}{2} \left[\left(\pi - \frac{1}{2}\sin 2\pi \right) - \left(0 - \frac{1}{2}\sin 0 \right) \right]$

$\qquad = 2 \cdot \frac{1}{2} \left[(\pi - 0) - (0 - 0) \right] = \pi$

15. $\iint_R (6x^2 y^3 - 5y^4) \, dA = \int_0^3 \int_0^1 (6x^2 y^3 - 5y^4) \, dy \, dx = \int_0^3 \left[\frac{3}{2}x^2 y^4 - y^5 \right]_{y=0}^{y=1} dx = \int_0^3 \left(\frac{3}{2}x^2 - 1 \right) dx$

$\qquad = \left[\frac{1}{2}x^3 - x \right]_0^3 = \frac{27}{2} - 3 = \frac{21}{2}$

17. $\iint_R \frac{xy^2}{x^2 + 1} \, dA = \int_0^1 \int_{-3}^3 \frac{xy^2}{x^2 + 1} \, dy \, dx = \int_0^1 \frac{x}{x^2 + 1} \, dx \int_{-3}^3 y^2 \, dy = \left[\frac{1}{2}\ln(x^2 + 1) \right]_0^1 \left[\frac{1}{3}y^3 \right]_{-3}^3$

$\qquad = \frac{1}{2}(\ln 2 - \ln 1) \cdot \frac{1}{3}(27 + 27) = 9\ln 2$

19. $\int_0^{\pi/6} \int_0^{\pi/3} x \sin(x+y) \, dy \, dx$

$\qquad = \int_0^{\pi/6} \left[-x\cos(x+y) \right]_{y=0}^{y=\pi/3} dx = \int_0^{\pi/6} \left[x\cos x - x\cos\left(x + \frac{\pi}{3} \right) \right] dx$

$\qquad = x \left[\sin x - \sin\left(x + \frac{\pi}{3} \right) \right]_0^{\pi/6} - \int_0^{\pi/6} \left[\sin x - \sin\left(x + \frac{\pi}{3} \right) \right] dx \qquad \text{[by integrating by parts separately for each term]}$

$\qquad = \frac{\pi}{6} \left[\frac{1}{2} - 1 \right] - \left[-\cos x + \cos\left(x + \frac{\pi}{3} \right) \right]_0^{\pi/6} = -\frac{\pi}{12} - \left[-\frac{\sqrt{3}}{2} + 0 - \left(-1 + \frac{1}{2} \right) \right] = \frac{\sqrt{3}-1}{2} - \frac{\pi}{12}$

21. $\iint_R xye^{x^2 y} \, dA = \int_0^2 \int_0^1 xye^{x^2 y} \, dx \, dy = \int_0^2 \left[\frac{1}{2}e^{x^2 y} \right]_{x=0}^{x=1} dy = \frac{1}{2} \int_0^2 (e^y - 1) \, dy = \frac{1}{2} \left[e^y - y \right]_0^2$

$\qquad = \frac{1}{2} \left[(e^2 - 2) - (1 - 0) \right] = \frac{1}{2}(e^2 - 3)$

23. $z = f(x,y) = 4 - x - 2y \geq 0$ for $0 \leq x \leq 1$ and $0 \leq y \leq 1$. So the solid

is the region in the first octant which lies below the plane $z = 4 - x - 2y$

and above $[0,1] \times [0,1]$.

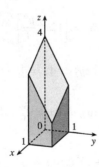

25. $V = \iint_R (12 - 3x - 2y) \, dA = \int_{-2}^3 \int_0^1 (12 - 3x - 2y) \, dx \, dy = \int_{-2}^3 \left[12x - \frac{3}{2}x^2 - 2xy \right]_{x=0}^{x=1} dy$

$\qquad = \int_{-2}^3 \left(\frac{21}{2} - 2y \right) dy = \left[\frac{21}{2}y - y^2 \right]_{-2}^3 = \frac{95}{2}$

27. $V = \int_{-2}^2 \int_{-1}^1 \left(1 - \frac{1}{4}x^2 - \frac{1}{9}y^2 \right) dx \, dy = 4 \int_0^2 \int_0^1 \left(1 - \frac{1}{4}x^2 - \frac{1}{9}y^2 \right) dx \, dy$

$\qquad = 4 \int_0^2 \left[x - \frac{1}{12}x^3 - \frac{1}{9}y^2 x \right]_{x=0}^{x=1} dy = 4 \int_0^2 \left(\frac{11}{12} - \frac{1}{9}y^2 \right) dy = 4 \left[\frac{11}{12}y - \frac{1}{27}y^3 \right]_0^2 = 4 \cdot \frac{83}{54} = \frac{166}{27}$

29. Here we need the volume of the solid lying under the surface $z = x \sec^2 y$ and above the rectangle $R = [0, 2] \times [0, \pi/4]$ in the xy-plane.

$$V = \int_0^2 \int_0^{\pi/4} x \sec^2 y \, dy \, dx = \int_0^2 x \, dx \int_0^{\pi/4} \sec^2 y \, dy = \left[\tfrac{1}{2}x^2\right]_0^2 \left[\tan y\right]_0^{\pi/4}$$

$$= (2 - 0)(\tan \tfrac{\pi}{4} - \tan 0) = 2(1 - 0) = 2$$

31. The solid lies below the surface $z = 2 + x^2 + (y - 2)^2$ and above the plane $z = 1$ for $-1 \le x \le 1$, $0 \le y \le 4$. The volume of the solid is the difference in volumes between the solid that lies under $z = 2 + x^2 + (y - 2)^2$ over the rectangle $R = [-1, 1] \times [0, 4]$ and the solid that lies under $z = 1$ over R.

$$V = \int_0^4 \int_{-1}^1 [2 + x^2 + (y - 2)^2] \, dx \, dy - \int_0^4 \int_{-1}^1 (1) \, dx \, dy = \int_0^4 \left[2x + \tfrac{1}{3}x^3 + x(y - 2)^2\right]_{x=-1}^{x=1} dy - \int_{-1}^1 dx \int_0^4 dy$$

$$= \int_0^4 \left[(2 + \tfrac{1}{3} + (y - 2)^2) - (-2 - \tfrac{1}{3} - (y - 2)^2)\right] dy - [x]_{-1}^1 \, [y]_0^4$$

$$= \int_0^4 \left[\tfrac{14}{3} + 2(y - 2)^2\right] dy - [1 - (-1)][4 - 0] = \left[\tfrac{14}{3}y + \tfrac{2}{3}(y - 2)^3\right]_0^4 - (2)(4)$$

$$= \left[\left(\tfrac{56}{3} + \tfrac{16}{3}\right) - \left(0 - \tfrac{16}{3}\right)\right] - 8 = \tfrac{88}{3} - 8 = \tfrac{64}{3}$$

33. In Maple, we can calculate the integral by defining the integrand as `f` and then using the command `int(int(f,x=0..1),y=0..1);`.
In Mathematica, we can use the command

`Integrate[f,{x,0,1},{y,0,1}]`

We find that $\iint_R x^5 y^3 e^{xy} \, dA = 21e - 57 \approx 0.0839$. We can use `plot3d` (in Maple) or `Plot3D` (in Mathematica) to graph the function.

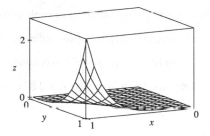

35. R is the rectangle $[-1, 1] \times [0, 5]$. Thus, $A(R) = 2 \cdot 5 = 10$ and

$$f_{\text{ave}} = \frac{1}{A(R)} \iint_R f(x, y) \, dA = \tfrac{1}{10} \int_0^5 \int_{-1}^1 x^2 y \, dx \, dy = \tfrac{1}{10} \int_0^5 \left[\tfrac{1}{3}x^3 y\right]_{x=-1}^{x=1} dy = \tfrac{1}{10} \int_0^5 \tfrac{2}{3} y \, dy = \tfrac{1}{10} \left[\tfrac{1}{3}y^2\right]_0^5 = \tfrac{5}{6}.$$

37. $\displaystyle \iint_R \frac{xy}{1 + x^4} \, dA = \int_{-1}^1 \int_0^1 \frac{xy}{1 + x^4} \, dy \, dx = \int_{-1}^1 \frac{x}{1 + x^4} \, dx \int_0^1 y \, dy$ [by Equation 5] but $f(x) = \dfrac{x}{1 + x^4}$ is an odd

function so $\displaystyle \int_{-1}^1 f(x) \, dx = 0$ by (6) in Section 5.5. Thus $\displaystyle \iint_R \frac{xy}{1 + x^4} \, dA = 0 \cdot \int_0^1 y \, dy = 0.$

39. Let $f(x, y) = \dfrac{x - y}{(x + y)^3}$. Then a CAS gives $\int_0^1 \int_0^1 f(x, y) \, dy \, dx = \tfrac{1}{2}$ and $\int_0^1 \int_0^1 f(x, y) \, dx \, dy = -\tfrac{1}{2}$.

To explain the seeming violation of Fubini's Theorem, note that f has an infinite discontinuity at $(0, 0)$ and thus does not satisfy the conditions of Fubini's Theorem. In fact, both iterated integrals involve improper integrals which diverge at their lower limits of integration.

12.3 Double Integrals over General Regions

1. $\int_0^4 \int_0^{\sqrt{y}} xy^2 \, dx \, dy = \int_0^4 \left[\frac{1}{2} x^2 y^2 \right]_{x=0}^{x=\sqrt{y}} dy = \int_0^4 \frac{1}{2} y^2 [(\sqrt{y})^2 - 0^2] dy = \frac{1}{2} \int_0^4 y^3 \, dy = \frac{1}{2} \left[\frac{1}{4} y^4 \right]_0^4 = \frac{1}{2}(64 - 0) = 32$

3. $\int_0^1 \int_{x^2}^x (1 + 2y) dy \, dx = \int_0^1 \left[y + y^2 \right]_{y=x^2}^{y=x} dx = \int_0^1 \left[x + x^2 - x^2 - (x^2)^2 \right] dx$

$\qquad = \int_0^1 (x - x^4) dx = \left[\frac{1}{2} x^2 - \frac{1}{5} x^5 \right]_0^1 = \frac{1}{2} - \frac{1}{5} - 0 + 0 = \frac{3}{10}$

5. $\int_0^{\pi/2} \int_0^{\cos \theta} e^{\sin \theta} dr \, d\theta = \int_0^{\pi/2} \left[r e^{\sin \theta} \right]_{r=0}^{r=\cos \theta} d\theta = \int_0^{\pi/2} (\cos \theta) \, e^{\sin \theta} d\theta = e^{\sin \theta} \Big]_0^{\pi/2} = e^{\sin(\pi/2)} - e^0 = e - 1$

7. $\iint_D y^2 \, dA = \int_{-1}^1 \int_{-y-2}^y y^2 \, dx \, dy = \int_{-1}^1 \left[xy^2 \right]_{x=-y-2}^{x=y} dy = \int_{-1}^1 y^2 \left[y - (-y - 2) \right] dy$

$\qquad = \int_{-1}^1 (2y^3 + 2y^2) dy = \left[\frac{1}{2} y^4 + \frac{2}{3} y^3 \right]_{-1}^1 = \frac{1}{2} + \frac{2}{3} - \frac{1}{2} + \frac{2}{3} = \frac{4}{3}$

9. $\iint_D x \, dA = \int_0^\pi \int_0^{\sin x} x \, dy \, dx = \int_0^\pi [xy]_{y=0}^{y=\sin x} dx = \int_0^\pi x \sin x \, dx \quad \left[\begin{array}{c} \text{integrate by parts} \\ \text{with } u = x, \, dv = \sin x \, dx \end{array} \right]$

$\qquad = \left[-x \cos x + \sin x \right]_0^\pi = -\pi \cos \pi + \sin \pi + 0 - \sin 0 = \pi$

11. (a) At the right we sketch an example of a region D that can be described as lying between the graphs of two continuous functions of x (a type I region) but not as lying between graphs of two continuous functions of y (a type II region). The regions shown in Figures 6 and 8 in the text are additional examples.

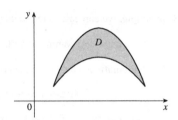

(b) Now we sketch an example of a region D that can be described as lying between the graphs of two continuous functions of y but not as lying between graphs of two continuous functions of x. The first region shown in Figure 7 is another example.

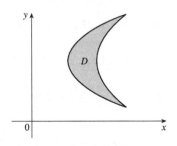

13.

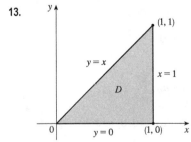

As a type I region, D lies between the lower boundary $y = 0$ and the upper boundary $y = x$ for $0 \le x \le 1$, so $D = \{(x, y) \mid 0 \le x \le 1, 0 \le y \le x\}$. If we describe D as a type II region, D lies between the left boundary $x = y$ and the right boundary $x = 1$ for $0 \le y \le 1$, so $D = \{(x, y) \mid 0 \le y \le 1, y \le x \le 1\}$.

Thus $\iint_D x \, dA = \int_0^1 \int_0^x x \, dy \, dx = \int_0^1 [xy]_{y=0}^{y=x} dx = \int_0^1 x^2 \, dx = \frac{1}{3} x^3 \Big]_0^1 = \frac{1}{3}(1 - 0) = \frac{1}{3}$ or

$\iint_D x \, dA = \int_0^1 \int_y^1 x \, dx \, dy = \int_0^1 \left[\frac{1}{2} x^2 \right]_{x=y}^{x=1} dy = \frac{1}{2} \int_0^1 (1 - y^2) \, dy = \frac{1}{2} \left[y - \frac{1}{3} y^3 \right]_0^1 = \frac{1}{2} \left[(1 - \frac{1}{3}) - 0 \right] = \frac{1}{3}$.

15.

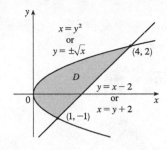

The curves $y = x - 2$ or $x = y + 2$ and $x = y^2$ intersect when $y + 2 = y^2$ ⇔ $y^2 - y - 2 = 0$ ⇔ $(y - 2)(y + 1) = 0$ ⇔ $y = -1, y = 2$, so the points of intersection are $(1, -1)$ and $(4, 2)$. If we describe D as a type I region, the upper boundary curve is $y = \sqrt{x}$ but the lower boundary curve consists of two parts,

$$y = -\sqrt{x} \text{ for } 0 \le x \le 1 \text{ and } y = x - 2 \text{ for } 1 \le x \le 4.$$

Thus $D = \{(x, y) \mid 0 \le x \le 1, \ -\sqrt{x} \le y \le \sqrt{x}\} \cup \{(x, y) \mid 1 \le x \le 4, x - 2 \le y \le \sqrt{x}\}$ and

$\iint_D y \, dA = \int_0^1 \int_{-\sqrt{x}}^{\sqrt{x}} y \, dy \, dx + \int_1^4 \int_{x-2}^{\sqrt{x}} y \, dy \, dx$. If we describe D as a type II region, D is enclosed by the left boundary

$x = y^2$ and the right boundary $x = y + 2$ for $-1 \le y \le 2$, so $D = \{(x, y) \mid -1 \le y \le 2, y^2 \le x \le y + 2\}$ and

$\iint_D y \, dA = \int_{-1}^2 \int_{y^2}^{y+2} y \, dx \, dy$. In either case, the resulting iterated integrals are not difficult to evaluate but the region D is

more simply described as a type II region, giving one iterated integral rather than a sum of two, so we evaluate the latter

integral:

$$\iint_D y \, dA = \int_{-1}^2 \int_{y^2}^{y+2} y \, dx \, dy = \int_{-1}^2 \left[xy \right]_{x=y^2}^{x=y+2} dy = \int_{-1}^2 (y + 2 - y^2) y \, dy = \int_{-1}^2 (y^2 + 2y - y^3) \, dy$$

$$= \left[\tfrac{1}{3} y^3 + y^2 - \tfrac{1}{4} y^4 \right]_{-1}^2 = \left(\tfrac{8}{3} + 4 - 4 \right) - \left(-\tfrac{1}{3} + 1 - \tfrac{1}{4} \right) = \tfrac{9}{4}$$

17. $\int_0^1 \int_0^{x^2} x \cos y \, dy \, dx = \int_0^1 \left[x \sin y \right]_{y=0}^{y=x^2} dx = \int_0^1 x \sin x^2 \, dx = -\tfrac{1}{2} \cos x^2 \Big]_0^1 = \tfrac{1}{2} (1 - \cos 1)$

19.

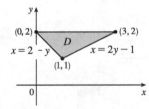

$$\int_1^2 \int_{2-y}^{2y-1} y^3 \, dx \, dy = \int_1^2 \left[xy^3 \right]_{x=2-y}^{x=2y-1} dy = \int_1^2 [(2y - 1) - (2 - y)] y^3 \, dy$$

$$= \int_1^2 (3y^4 - 3y^3) \, dy = \left[\tfrac{3}{5} y^5 - \tfrac{3}{4} y^4 \right]_1^2$$

$$= \tfrac{96}{5} - 12 - \tfrac{3}{5} + \tfrac{3}{4} = \tfrac{147}{20}$$

21.

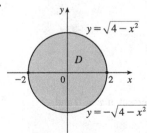

$$\int_{-2}^2 \int_{-\sqrt{4-x^2}}^{\sqrt{4-x^2}} (2x - y) \, dy \, dx$$

$$= \int_{-2}^2 \left[2xy - \tfrac{1}{2} y^2 \right]_{y=-\sqrt{4-x^2}}^{y=\sqrt{4-x^2}} dx$$

$$= \int_{-2}^2 \left[2x \sqrt{4 - x^2} - \tfrac{1}{2} (4 - x^2) + 2x \sqrt{4 - x^2} + \tfrac{1}{2} (4 - x^2) \right] dx$$

$$= \int_{-2}^2 4x \sqrt{4 - x^2} \, dx = -\tfrac{4}{3} (4 - x^2)^{3/2} \Big]_{-2}^2 = 0$$

[Or, note that $4x \sqrt{4 - x^2}$ is an odd function, so $\int_{-2}^2 4x \sqrt{4 - x^2} \, dx = 0$.]

23.

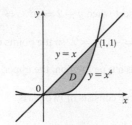

$V = \int_0^1 \int_{x^4}^x (x + 2y)\,dy\,dx$

$= \int_0^1 \left[xy + y^2 \right]_{y=x^4}^{y=x} dx = \int_0^1 (2x^2 - x^5 - x^8)\,dx$

$= \left[\frac{2}{3}x^3 - \frac{1}{6}x^6 - \frac{1}{9}x^9 \right]_0^1 = \frac{2}{3} - \frac{1}{6} - \frac{1}{9} = \frac{7}{18}$

25.

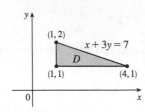

$V = \int_1^2 \int_1^{7-3y} xy\,dx\,dy = \int_1^2 \left[\frac{1}{2}x^2 y \right]_{x=1}^{x=7-3y} dy$

$= \frac{1}{2}\int_1^2 (48y - 42y^2 + 9y^3)\,dy$

$= \frac{1}{2}\left[24y^2 - 14y^3 + \frac{9}{4}y^4 \right]_1^2 = \frac{31}{8}$

27.

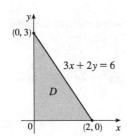

$V = \int_0^2 \int_0^{3 - \frac{3}{2}x} (6 - 3x - 2y)\,dy\,dx$

$= \int_0^2 \left[6y - 3xy - y^2 \right]_{y=0}^{y=3-\frac{3}{2}x} dx$

$= \int_0^2 \left[6(3 - \frac{3}{2}x) - 3x(3 - \frac{3}{2}x) - (3 - \frac{3}{2}x)^2 \right] dx$

$= \int_0^2 \left(\frac{9}{4}x^2 - 9x + 9 \right) dx = \left[\frac{3}{4}x^3 - \frac{9}{2}x^2 + 9x \right]_0^2 = 6 - 0 = 6$

29.

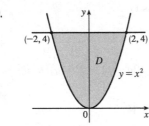

$V = \int_{-2}^2 \int_{x^2}^4 x^2\,dy\,dx$

$= \int_{-2}^2 x^2 \left[y \right]_{y=x^2}^{y=4} dx = \int_{-2}^2 (4x^2 - x^4)\,dx$

$= \left[\frac{4}{3}x^3 - \frac{1}{5}x^5 \right]_{-2}^2 = \frac{32}{3} - \frac{32}{5} + \frac{32}{3} - \frac{32}{5} = \frac{128}{15}$

31.

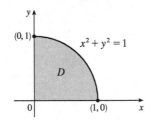

$V = \int_0^1 \int_0^{\sqrt{1-x^2}} y\,dy\,dx = \int_0^1 \left[\frac{y^2}{2} \right]_{y=0}^{y=\sqrt{1-x^2}} dx$

$= \int_0^1 \frac{1-x^2}{2}\,dx = \frac{1}{2}\left[x - \frac{1}{3}x^3 \right]_0^1 = \frac{1}{3}$

33.

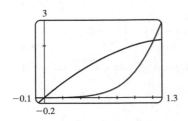

From the graph, it appears that the two curves intersect at $x = 0$ and at $x \approx 1.213$. Thus the desired integral is

$\iint_D x\,dA \approx \int_0^{1.213} \int_{x^4}^{3x - x^2} x\,dy\,dx = \int_0^{1.213} \left[xy \right]_{y=x^4}^{y=3x-x^2} dx$

$= \int_0^{1.213} (3x^2 - x^3 - x^5)\,dx = \left[x^3 - \frac{1}{4}x^4 - \frac{1}{6}x^6 \right]_0^{1.213}$

≈ 0.713

35. The two bounding curves $y = 1 - x^2$ and $y = x^2 - 1$ intersect at $(\pm 1, 0)$ with $1 - x^2 \geq x^2 - 1$ on $[-1, 1]$. Within this

region, the plane $z = 2x + 2y + 10$ is above the plane $z = 2 - x - y$, so

$$V = \int_{-1}^{1} \int_{x^2-1}^{1-x^2} (2x + 2y + 10) \, dy \, dx - \int_{-1}^{1} \int_{x^2-1}^{1-x^2} (2 - x - y) \, dy \, dx$$

$$= \int_{-1}^{1} \int_{x^2-1}^{1-x^2} (2x + 2y + 10 - (2 - x - y)) \, dy \, dx$$

$$= \int_{-1}^{1} \int_{x^2-1}^{1-x^2} (3x + 3y + 8) \, dy \, dx = \int_{-1}^{1} \left[3xy + \tfrac{3}{2}y^2 + 8y \right]_{y=x^2-1}^{y=1-x^2} dx$$

$$= \int_{-1}^{1} \left[3x(1 - x^2) + \tfrac{3}{2}(1 - x^2)^2 + 8(1 - x^2) - 3x(x^2 - 1) - \tfrac{3}{2}(x^2 - 1)^2 - 8(x^2 - 1) \right] dx$$

$$= \int_{-1}^{1} (-6x^3 - 16x^2 + 6x + 16) \, dx = \left[-\tfrac{3}{2}x^4 - \tfrac{16}{3}x^3 + 3x^2 + 16x \right]_{-1}^{1}$$

$$= -\tfrac{3}{2} - \tfrac{16}{3} + 3 + 16 + \tfrac{3}{2} - \tfrac{16}{3} - 3 + 16 = \tfrac{64}{3}$$

37. The solid lies below the plane $z = 1 - x - y$

or $x + y + z = 1$ and above the region

$D = \{(x, y) \mid 0 \leq x \leq 1, 0 \leq y \leq 1 - x\}$

in the xy-plane. The solid is a tetrahedron.

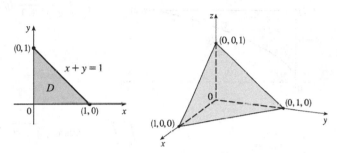

39. The two bounding curves $y = x^3 - x$ and $y = x^2 + x$ intersect at the origin and at $x = 2$, with $x^2 + x > x^3 - x$ on $(0, 2)$.

Using a CAS, we find that the volume is

$$V = \int_0^2 \int_{x^3-x}^{x^2+x} z \, dy \, dx = \int_0^2 \int_{x^3-x}^{x^2+x} (x^3 y^4 + xy^2) \, dy \, dx = \frac{13{,}984{,}735{,}616}{14{,}549{,}535}$$

41.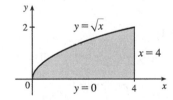

Because the region of integration is

$D = \{(x, y) \mid 0 \leq y \leq \sqrt{x}, 0 \leq x \leq 4\} = \{(x, y) \mid y^2 \leq x \leq 4, 0 \leq y \leq 2\}$

we have $\int_0^4 \int_0^{\sqrt{x}} f(x, y) \, dy \, dx = \iint_D f(x, y) \, dA = \int_0^2 \int_{y^2}^4 f(x, y) \, dx \, dy$.

43.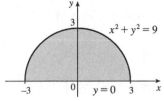

Because the region of integration is

$$D = \left\{(x, y) \mid -\sqrt{9 - y^2} \leq x \leq \sqrt{9 - y^2}, 0 \leq y \leq 3\right\}$$

$$= \left\{(x, y) \mid 0 \leq y \leq \sqrt{9 - x^2}, -3 \leq x \leq 3\right\}$$

we have

$$\int_0^3 \int_{-\sqrt{9-y^2}}^{\sqrt{9-y^2}} f(x, y) \, dx \, dy = \iint_D f(x, y) \, dA$$

$$= \int_{-3}^{3} \int_0^{\sqrt{9-x^2}} f(x, y) \, dy \, dx$$

45.

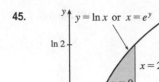

Because the region of integration is

$$D = \{(x,y) \mid 0 \leq y \leq \ln x, \, 1 \leq x \leq 2\} = \{(x,y) \mid e^y \leq x \leq 2, \, 0 \leq y \leq \ln 2\}$$

we have

$$\int_1^2 \int_0^{\ln x} f(x,y)\,dy\,dx = \iint_D f(x,y)\,dA = \int_0^{\ln 2} \int_{e^y}^2 f(x,y)\,dx\,dy$$

47.

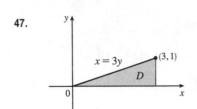

$$\int_0^1 \int_{3y}^3 e^{x^2}\,dx\,dy = \int_0^3 \int_0^{x/3} e^{x^2}\,dy\,dx = \int_0^3 \left[e^{x^2} y \right]_{y=0}^{y=x/3}\,dx$$

$$= \int_0^3 \left(\frac{x}{3}\right) e^{x^2}\,dx = \tfrac{1}{6} e^{x^2} \Big]_0^3 = \frac{e^9 - 1}{6}$$

49.

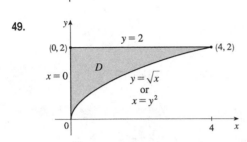

$$\int_0^4 \int_{\sqrt{x}}^2 \frac{1}{y^3 + 1}\,dy\,dx = \int_0^2 \int_0^{y^2} \frac{1}{y^3 + 1}\,dx\,dy$$

$$= \int_0^2 \frac{1}{y^3 + 1} \left[x \right]_{x=0}^{x=y^2}\,dy = \int_0^2 \frac{y^2}{y^3 + 1}\,dy$$

$$= \tfrac{1}{3} \ln |y^3 + 1| \Big]_0^2 = \tfrac{1}{3}(\ln 9 - \ln 1) = \tfrac{1}{3}\ln 9$$

51.

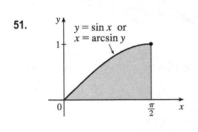

$$\int_0^1 \int_{\arcsin y}^{\pi/2} \cos x \sqrt{1 + \cos^2 x}\,dx\,dy$$

$$= \int_0^{\pi/2} \int_0^{\sin x} \cos x \sqrt{1 + \cos^2 x}\,dy\,dx$$

$$= \int_0^{\pi/2} \cos x \sqrt{1 + \cos^2 x} \left[y \right]_{y=0}^{y=\sin x}\,dx$$

$$= \int_0^{\pi/2} \cos x \sqrt{1 + \cos^2 x}\,\sin x\,dx \qquad \left[\begin{array}{l} \text{Let } u = \cos x, \, du = -\sin x\,dx, \\ dx = du/(-\sin x) \end{array} \right]$$

$$= \int_1^0 -u \sqrt{1 + u^2}\,du = -\tfrac{1}{3}\left(1 + u^2\right)^{3/2} \Big]_1^0$$

$$= \tfrac{1}{3}\left(\sqrt{8} - 1\right) = \tfrac{1}{3}\left(2\sqrt{2} - 1\right)$$

53. $D = \{(x,y) \mid 0 \leq x \leq 1, \, -x + 1 \leq y \leq 1\} \cup \{(x,y) \mid -1 \leq x \leq 0, \, x + 1 \leq y \leq 1\}$

$$\cup \{(x,y) \mid 0 \leq x \leq 1, \, -1 \leq y \leq x - 1\} \cup \{(x,y) \mid -1 \leq x \leq 0, \, -1 \leq y \leq -x - 1\}, \quad \text{all type I.}$$

$$\iint_D x^2\,dA = \int_0^1 \int_{1-x}^1 x^2\,dy\,dx + \int_{-1}^0 \int_{x+1}^1 x^2\,dy\,dx + \int_0^1 \int_{-1}^{x-1} x^2\,dy\,dx + \int_{-1}^0 \int_{-1}^{-x-1} x^2\,dy\,dx$$

$$= 4 \int_0^1 \int_{1-x}^1 x^2\,dy\,dx \qquad \text{[by symmetry of the regions and because } f(x,y) = x^2 \geq 0]$$

$$= 4 \int_0^1 x^3\,dx = 4\left[\tfrac{1}{4}x^4\right]_0^1 = 1$$

55. Here $Q = \left\{(x,y) \mid x^2 + y^2 \leq \tfrac{1}{4}, \, x \geq 0, \, y \geq 0\right\}$, and $0 \leq (x^2 + y^2)^2 \leq \left(\tfrac{1}{4}\right)^2 \Rightarrow -\tfrac{1}{16} \leq -(x^2 + y^2)^2 \leq 0$ so

$e^{-1/16} \leq e^{-(x^2+y^2)^2} \leq e^0 = 1$ since e^t is an increasing function. We have $A(Q) = \tfrac{1}{4}\pi \left(\tfrac{1}{2}\right)^2 = \tfrac{\pi}{16}$, so by Property 11,

$e^{-1/16} A(Q) \le \iint_Q e^{-(x^2+y^2)^2} dA \le 1 \cdot A(Q) \quad \Rightarrow \quad \frac{\pi}{16} e^{-1/16} \le \iint_Q e^{-(x^2+y^2)^2} dA \le \frac{\pi}{16}$ or we can say

$0.1844 < \iint_Q e^{-(x^2+y^2)^2} dA < 0.1964$. (We have rounded the lower bound down and the upper bound up to preserve the inequalities.)

57. The average value of a function f of two variables defined on a rectangle R was

defined in Section 12.1 as $f_{\text{ave}} = \frac{1}{A(R)} \iint_R f(x,y)dA$. Extending this definition

to general regions D, we have $f_{\text{ave}} = \frac{1}{A(D)} \iint_D f(x,y)dA$.

Here $D = \{(x,y) \mid 0 \le x \le 1, 0 \le y \le 3x\}$, so $A(D) = \frac{1}{2}(1)(3) = \frac{3}{2}$ and

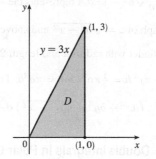

$$f_{\text{ave}} = \frac{1}{A(D)} \iint_D f(x,y)dA = \frac{1}{3/2} \int_0^1 \int_0^{3x} xy \, dy \, dx$$

$$= \frac{2}{3} \int_0^1 \left[\frac{1}{2}xy^2\right]_{y=0}^{y=3x} dx = \frac{1}{3} \int_0^1 9x^3 \, dx = \frac{3}{4}x^4\Big]_0^1 = \frac{3}{4}$$

59. Since $m \le f(x,y) \le M$, $\iint_D m \, dA \le \iint_D f(x,y) \, dA \le \iint_D M \, dA$ by (8) $\Rightarrow$

$m \iint_D 1 \, dA \le \iint_D f(x,y) \, dA \le M \iint_D 1 \, dA$ by (7) $\Rightarrow$ $mA(D) \le \iint_D f(x,y) \, dA \le MA(D)$ by (10).

61.

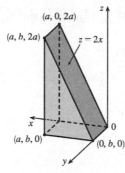

First we can write $\iint_D (x+2) \, dA = \iint_D x \, dA + \iint_D 2 \, dA$. But $f(x,y) = x$ is

an odd function with respect to x [that is, $f(-x,y) = -f(x,y)$] and D is

symmetric with respect to x. Consequently, the volume above D and below the

graph of f is the same as the volume below D and above the graph of f, so

$\iint_D x \, dA = 0$. Also, $\iint_D 2 \, dA = 2 \cdot A(D) = 2 \cdot \frac{1}{2}\pi(3)^2 = 9\pi$ since D is a half

disk of radius 3. Thus $\iint_D (x+2) \, dA = 0 + 9\pi = 9\pi$.

63. We can write $\iint_D (2x + 3y) \, dA = \iint_D 2x \, dA + \iint_D 3y \, dA$. $\iint_D 2x \, dA$ represents the volume of the solid lying under the

plane $z = 2x$ and above the rectangle D. This solid region is a triangular cylinder with length b and whose cross-section is a

triangle with width a and height $2a$. (See the first figure.)

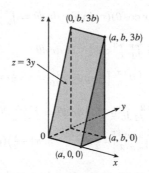

Thus its volume is $\frac{1}{2} \cdot a \cdot 2a \cdot b = a^2 b$. Similarly, $\iint_D 3y \, dA$ represents the volume of a triangular cylinder with length a,

triangular cross-section with width b and height $3b$, and volume $\frac{1}{2} \cdot b \cdot 3b \cdot a = \frac{3}{2}ab^2$. (See the second figure.) Thus

$$\iint_D (2x + 3y) \, dA = a^2 b + \frac{3}{2}ab^2$$

65. $\iint_D \left(ax^3 + by^3 + \sqrt{a^2 - x^2}\right) dA = \iint_D ax^3 \, dA + \iint_D by^3 \, dA + \iint_D \sqrt{a^2 - x^2} \, dA.$ Now ax^3 is odd with respect

to x and by^3 is odd with respect to y, and the region of integration is symmetric with respect to both x and y,

so $\iint_D ax^3 \, dA = \iint_D by^3 \, dA = 0.$

$\iint_D \sqrt{a^2 - x^2} \, dA$ represents the volume of the solid region under the

graph of $z = \sqrt{a^2 - x^2}$ and above the rectangle D, namely a half circular

cylinder with radius a and length $2b$ (see the figure) whose volume is

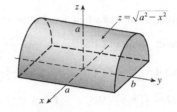

$\frac{1}{2} \cdot \pi r^2 h = \frac{1}{2}\pi a^2 (2b) = \pi a^2 b.$ Thus

$\iint_D \left(ax^3 + by^3 + \sqrt{a^2 - x^2}\right) dA = 0 + 0 + \pi a^2 b = \pi a^2 b.$

12.4   Double Integrals in Polar Coordinates

1. The region R is more easily described by polar coordinates: $R = \left\{(r, \theta) \mid 0 \le r \le 4, 0 \le \theta \le \frac{3\pi}{2}\right\}.$

Thus $\iint_R f(x, y) \, dA = \int_0^{3\pi/2} \int_0^4 f(r\cos\theta, r\sin\theta) \, r \, dr \, d\theta.$

3. The region R is more easily described by rectangular coordinates: $R = \left\{(x, y) \mid -1 \le x \le 1, 0 \le y \le \frac{1}{2}x + \frac{1}{2}\right\}.$

Thus $\iint_R f(x, y) \, dA = \int_{-1}^{1} \int_0^{(x+1)/2} f(x, y) \, dy \, dx.$

5. The integral $\int_\pi^{2\pi} \int_4^7 r \, dr \, d\theta$ represents the area of the region

$R = \{(r, \theta) \mid 4 \le r \le 7, \pi \le \theta \le 2\pi\}$, the lower half of a ring.

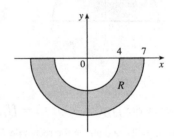

$\int_\pi^{2\pi} \int_4^7 r \, dr \, d\theta = \int_\pi^{2\pi} d\theta \int_4^7 r \, dr$

$= \left[\theta\right]_\pi^{2\pi} \left[\frac{1}{2}r^2\right]_4^7 = \pi \cdot \frac{1}{2}(49 - 16) = \frac{33\pi}{2}$

7. The disk D can be described in polar coordinates as $D = \{(r, \theta) \mid 0 \le r \le 3, 0 \le \theta \le 2\pi\}.$ Then

$\iint_D xy \, dA = \int_0^{2\pi} \int_0^3 (r\cos\theta)(r\sin\theta) \, r \, dr \, d\theta = \int_0^{2\pi} \sin\theta \cos\theta \, d\theta \int_0^3 r^3 \, dr = \left[\frac{1}{2}\sin^2\theta\right]_0^{2\pi} \left[\frac{1}{4}r^4\right]_0^3 = 0.$

9. $\iint_R \cos(x^2 + y^2) \, dA = \int_0^\pi \int_0^3 \cos(r^2) \, r \, dr \, d\theta = \int_0^\pi d\theta \int_0^3 r\cos(r^2) \, dr$

$= \left[\theta\right]_0^\pi \left[\frac{1}{2}\sin(r^2)\right]_0^3 = \pi \cdot \frac{1}{2}(\sin 9 - \sin 0) = \frac{\pi}{2}\sin 9$

11. $\iint_D e^{-x^2 - y^2} \, dA = \int_{-\pi/2}^{\pi/2} \int_0^2 e^{-r^2} r \, dr \, d\theta = \int_{-\pi/2}^{\pi/2} d\theta \int_0^2 r e^{-r^2} \, dr$

$= \left[\theta\right]_{-\pi/2}^{\pi/2} \left[-\frac{1}{2}e^{-r^2}\right]_0^2 = \pi\left(-\frac{1}{2}\right)(e^{-4} - e^0) = \frac{\pi}{2}(1 - e^{-4})$

13. R is the region shown in the figure, and can be described

by $R = \{(r, \theta) \mid 0 \le \theta \le \pi/4, 1 \le r \le 2\}.$ Thus

$\iint_R \arctan(y/x) \, dA = \int_0^{\pi/4} \int_1^2 \arctan(\tan\theta) \, r \, dr \, d\theta$ since $y/x = \tan\theta.$

Also, $\arctan(\tan\theta) = \theta$ for $0 \le \theta \le \pi/4$, so the integral becomes

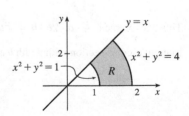

$\int_0^{\pi/4} \int_1^2 \theta r \, dr \, d\theta = \int_0^{\pi/4} \theta \, d\theta \int_1^2 r \, dr = \left[\frac{1}{2}\theta^2\right]_0^{\pi/4} \left[\frac{1}{2}r^2\right]_1^2 = \frac{\pi^2}{32} \cdot \frac{3}{2} = \frac{3}{64}\pi^2.$

15. $V = \iint_{x^2 + y^2 \leq 4} \sqrt{x^2 + y^2}\, dA = \int_0^{2\pi} \int_0^2 \sqrt{r^2}\, r\, dr\, d\theta = \int_0^{2\pi} d\theta \int_0^2 r^2\, dr = \left[\theta\right]_0^{2\pi} \left[\frac{1}{3}r^3\right]_0^2 = 2\pi\left(\frac{8}{3}\right) = \frac{16}{3}\pi$

17. The hyperboloid of two sheets $-x^2 - y^2 + z^2 = 1$ intersects the plane $z = 2$ when $-x^2 - y^2 + 4 = 1$ or $x^2 + y^2 = 3$. So the solid region lies above the surface $z = \sqrt{1 + x^2 + y^2}$ and below the plane $z = 2$ for $x^2 + y^2 \leq 3$, and its volume is

$$V = \iint_{x^2 + y^2 \leq 3} \left(2 - \sqrt{1 + x^2 + y^2}\right) dA = \int_0^{2\pi} \int_0^{\sqrt{3}} \left(2 - \sqrt{1 + r^2}\right) r\, dr\, d\theta$$

$$= \int_0^{2\pi} d\theta \int_0^{\sqrt{3}} \left(2r - r\sqrt{1 + r^2}\right) dr = \left[\theta\right]_0^{2\pi} \left[r^2 - \frac{1}{3}(1 + r^2)^{3/2}\right]_0^{\sqrt{3}}$$

$$= 2\pi\left(3 - \frac{8}{3} - 0 + \frac{1}{3}\right) = \frac{4}{3}\pi$$

19. By symmetry,

$$V = 2 \iint_{x^2 + y^2 \leq a^2} \sqrt{a^2 - x^2 - y^2}\, dA = 2\int_0^{2\pi} \int_0^a \sqrt{a^2 - r^2}\, r\, dr\, d\theta = 2\int_0^{2\pi} d\theta \int_0^a r\sqrt{a^2 - r^2}\, dr$$

$$= 2\left[\theta\right]_0^{2\pi} \left[-\frac{1}{3}(a^2 - r^2)^{3/2}\right]_0^a = 2(2\pi)\left(0 + \frac{1}{3}a^3\right) = \frac{4\pi}{3}a^3$$

21. The cone $z = \sqrt{x^2 + y^2}$ intersects the sphere $x^2 + y^2 + z^2 = 1$ when $x^2 + y^2 + \left(\sqrt{x^2 + y^2}\right)^2 = 1$ or $x^2 + y^2 = \frac{1}{2}$. So

$$V = \iint_{x^2 + y^2 \leq 1/2} \left(\sqrt{1 - x^2 - y^2} - \sqrt{x^2 + y^2}\right) dA = \int_0^{2\pi} \int_0^{1/\sqrt{2}} \left(\sqrt{1 - r^2} - r\right) r\, dr\, d\theta$$

$$= \int_0^{2\pi} d\theta \int_0^{1/\sqrt{2}} \left(r\sqrt{1 - r^2} - r^2\right) dr = \left[\theta\right]_0^{2\pi} \left[-\frac{1}{3}(1 - r^2)^{3/2} - \frac{1}{3}r^3\right]_0^{1/\sqrt{2}} = 2\pi\left(-\frac{1}{3}\right)\left(\frac{1}{\sqrt{2}} - 1\right) = \frac{\pi}{3}\left(2 - \sqrt{2}\right)$$

23. The given solid is the region inside the cylinder $x^2 + y^2 = 4$ between the surfaces $z = \sqrt{64 - 4x^2 - 4y^2}$ and $z = -\sqrt{64 - 4x^2 - 4y^2}$. So

$$V = \iint_{x^2 + y^2 \leq 4} \left[\sqrt{64 - 4x^2 - 4y^2} - \left(-\sqrt{64 - 4x^2 - 4y^2}\right)\right] dA = \iint_{x^2 + y^2 \leq 4} 2\sqrt{64 - 4x^2 - 4y^2}\, dA$$

$$= 4\int_0^{2\pi} \int_0^2 \sqrt{16 - r^2}\, r\, dr\, d\theta = 4\int_0^{2\pi} d\theta \int_0^2 r\sqrt{16 - r^2}\, dr = 4\left[\theta\right]_0^{2\pi} \left[-\frac{1}{3}(16 - r^2)^{3/2}\right]_0^2$$

$$= 8\pi\left(-\frac{1}{3}\right)(12^{3/2} - 16^{2/3}) = \frac{8\pi}{3}\left(64 - 24\sqrt{3}\right)$$

25. One loop is given by the region

$D = \{(r, \theta)\,|\,-\pi/6 \leq \theta \leq \pi/6,\, 0 \leq r \leq \cos 3\theta\}$, so the area is

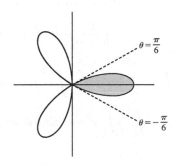

$$\iint_D dA = \int_{-\pi/6}^{\pi/6} \int_0^{\cos 3\theta} r\, dr\, d\theta = \int_{-\pi/6}^{\pi/6} \left[\frac{1}{2}r^2\right]_{r=0}^{r=\cos 3\theta} d\theta$$

$$= \int_{-\pi/6}^{\pi/6} \frac{1}{2}\cos^2 3\theta\, d\theta = 2\int_0^{\pi/6} \frac{1}{2}\left(\frac{1 + \cos 6\theta}{2}\right) d\theta$$

$$= \frac{1}{2}\left[\theta + \frac{1}{6}\sin 6\theta\right]_0^{\pi/6} = \frac{\pi}{12}$$

27.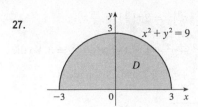

$$\int_{-3}^{3}\int_{0}^{\sqrt{9-x^2}} \sin(x^2+y^2)\,dy\,dx = \int_{0}^{\pi}\int_{0}^{3} \sin\left(r^2\right) r\,dr\,d\theta$$

$$= \int_{0}^{\pi} d\theta \int_{0}^{3} r \sin\left(r^2\right)dr = [\theta]_{0}^{\pi}\left[-\tfrac{1}{2}\cos\left(r^2\right)\right]_{0}^{3}$$

$$= \pi\left(-\tfrac{1}{2}\right)(\cos 9 - 1) = \tfrac{\pi}{2}(1-\cos 9)$$

29.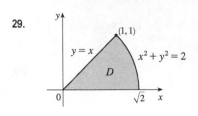

$$\int_{0}^{\pi/4}\int_{0}^{\sqrt{2}} (r\cos\theta + r\sin\theta) r\,dr\,d\theta = \int_{0}^{\pi/4}(\cos\theta + \sin\theta)\,d\theta \int_{0}^{\sqrt{2}} r^2\,dr$$

$$= [\sin\theta - \cos\theta]_{0}^{\pi/4}\left[\tfrac{1}{3}r^3\right]_{0}^{\sqrt{2}}$$

$$= \left[\tfrac{\sqrt{2}}{2} - \tfrac{\sqrt{2}}{2} - 0 + 1\right]\cdot\tfrac{1}{3}\left(2\sqrt{2} - 0\right) = \tfrac{2\sqrt{2}}{3}$$

31. The surface of the water in the pool is a circular disk D with radius 20 ft. If we place D on coordinate axes with the origin at the center of D and define $f(x,y)$ to be the depth of the water at (x,y), then the volume of water in the pool is the volume of the solid that lies above $D = \{(x,y) \mid x^2 + y^2 \le 400\}$ and below the graph of $f(x,y)$. We can associate north with the positive y-direction, so we are given that the depth is constant in the x-direction and the depth increases linearly in the y-direction from $f(0,-20) = 2$ to $f(0,20) = 7$. The trace in the yz-plane is a line segment from $(0,-20,2)$ to $(0,20,7)$. The slope of this line is $\frac{7-2}{20-(-20)} = \tfrac{1}{8}$, so an equation of the line is $z - 7 = \tfrac{1}{8}(y-20)$ $\Rightarrow$ $z = \tfrac{1}{8}y + \tfrac{9}{2}$. Since $f(x,y)$ is independent of x, $f(x,y) = \tfrac{1}{8}y + \tfrac{9}{2}$. Thus the volume is given by $\iint_D f(x,y)\,dA$, which is most conveniently evaluated using polar coordinates. Then $D = \{(r,\theta) \mid 0 \le r \le 20, 0 \le \theta \le 2\pi\}$ and substituting $x = r\cos\theta$, $y = r\sin\theta$ the integral becomes

$$\int_{0}^{2\pi}\int_{0}^{20}\left(\tfrac{1}{8}r\sin\theta + \tfrac{9}{2}\right) r\,dr\,d\theta = \int_{0}^{2\pi}\left[\tfrac{1}{24}r^3\sin\theta + \tfrac{9}{4}r^2\right]_{r=0}^{r=20}d\theta = \int_{0}^{2\pi}\left(\tfrac{1000}{3}\sin\theta + 900\right)d\theta$$

$$= \left[-\tfrac{1000}{3}\cos\theta + 900\theta\right]_{0}^{2\pi} = 1800\pi$$

Thus the pool contains $1800\pi \approx 5655$ ft^3 of water.

33. As in Exercise 12.3.57, $f_{\text{ave}} = \frac{1}{A(D)}\iint_D f(x,y)\,dA$. Here $D = \{(r,\theta) \mid a \le r \le b, 0 \le \theta \le 2\pi\}$,

so $A(D) = \pi b^2 - \pi a^2 = \pi(b^2 - a^2)$ and

$$f_{\text{ave}} = \frac{1}{A(D)}\iint_D \frac{1}{\sqrt{x^2+y^2}}\,dA = \frac{1}{\pi(b^2-a^2)}\int_{0}^{2\pi}\int_{a}^{b}\frac{1}{\sqrt{r^2}} r\,dr\,d\theta = \frac{1}{\pi(b^2-a^2)}\int_{0}^{2\pi}d\theta\int_{a}^{b}dr$$

$$= \frac{1}{\pi(b^2-a^2)}[\theta]_{0}^{2\pi}[r]_{a}^{b} = \frac{1}{\pi(b^2-a^2)}(2\pi)(b-a) = \frac{2(b-a)}{(b+a)(b-a)} = \frac{2}{a+b}$$

35.
$$\int_{1/\sqrt{2}}^{1}\int_{\sqrt{1-x^2}}^{x} xy\,dy\,dx + \int_{1}^{\sqrt{2}}\int_{0}^{x} xy\,dy\,dx + \int_{\sqrt{2}}^{2}\int_{0}^{\sqrt{4-x^2}} xy\,dy\,dx$$

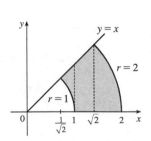

$$= \int_{0}^{\pi/4}\int_{1}^{2} r^3\cos\theta\sin\theta\,dr\,d\theta = \int_{0}^{\pi/4}\left[\frac{r^4}{4}\cos\theta\sin\theta\right]_{r=1}^{r=2}d\theta$$

$$= \frac{15}{4}\int_{0}^{\pi/4}\sin\theta\cos\theta\,d\theta = \frac{15}{4}\left[\frac{\sin^2\theta}{2}\right]_{0}^{\pi/4} = \frac{15}{16}$$

37. (a) We integrate by parts with $u = x$ and $dv = xe^{-x^2}\, dx$. Then $du = dx$ and $v = -\frac{1}{2}e^{-x^2}$, so

$$\int_0^\infty x^2 e^{-x^2}\, dx = \lim_{t\to\infty} \int_0^t x^2 e^{-x^2}\, dx = \lim_{t\to\infty} \left(-\tfrac{1}{2}xe^{-x^2}\Big]_0^t + \int_0^t \tfrac{1}{2}e^{-x^2}\, dx \right)$$

$$= \lim_{t\to\infty} \left(-\tfrac{1}{2}te^{-t^2} \right) + \tfrac{1}{2}\int_0^\infty e^{-x^2}\, dx = 0 + \tfrac{1}{2}\int_0^\infty e^{-x^2}\, dx \qquad \text{[by l'Hospital's Rule]}$$

$$= \tfrac{1}{4}\int_{-\infty}^\infty e^{-x^2}\, dx \qquad \text{[since } e^{-x^2} \text{ is an even function]}$$

$$= \tfrac{1}{4}\sqrt{\pi} \qquad \text{[by Exercise 36(c)]}$$

(b) Let $u = \sqrt{x}$. Then $u^2 = x \;\Rightarrow\; dx = 2u\, du \;\Rightarrow$

$$\int_0^\infty \sqrt{x}e^{-x}\, dx = \lim_{t\to\infty} \int_0^t \sqrt{x}\,e^{-x}\, dx = \lim_{t\to\infty} \int_0^{\sqrt{t}} ue^{-u^2}\, 2u\, du = 2\int_0^\infty u^2 e^{-u^2}\, du = 2\left(\tfrac{1}{4}\sqrt{\pi}\right) \quad \text{[by part(a)]} = \tfrac{1}{2}\sqrt{\pi}.$$

12.5 Applications of Double Integrals

1. $Q = \iint_D \sigma(x,y)\, dA = \int_1^3 \int_0^2 (2xy + y^2)\, dy\, dx = \int_1^3 \left[xy^2 + \tfrac{1}{3}y^3 \right]_{y=0}^{y=2} dx$

$= \int_1^3 \left(4x + \tfrac{8}{3} \right) dx = \left[2x^2 + \tfrac{8}{3}x \right]_1^3 = 16 + \tfrac{16}{3} = \tfrac{64}{3}$ C

3. $m = \iint_D \rho(x,y)\, dA = \int_0^2 \int_{-1}^1 xy^2\, dy\, dx = \int_0^2 x\, dx \int_{-1}^1 y^2\, dy = \left[\tfrac{1}{2}x^2\right]_0^2 \left[\tfrac{1}{3}y^3\right]_{-1}^1 = 2 \cdot \tfrac{2}{3} = \tfrac{4}{3}$,

$\bar{x} = \tfrac{1}{m}\iint_D x\rho(x,y)\, dA = \tfrac{3}{4}\int_0^2 \int_{-1}^1 x^2 y^2\, dy\, dx = \tfrac{3}{4}\int_0^2 x^2\, dx \int_{-1}^1 y^2\, dy = \tfrac{3}{4}\left[\tfrac{1}{3}x^3\right]_0^2 \left[\tfrac{1}{3}y^3\right]_{-1}^1 = \tfrac{3}{4}\cdot\tfrac{8}{3}\cdot\tfrac{2}{3} = \tfrac{4}{3}$,

$\bar{y} = \tfrac{1}{m}\iint_D y\rho(x,y)\, dA = \tfrac{3}{4}\int_0^2 \int_{-1}^1 xy^3\, dy\, dx = \tfrac{3}{4}\int_0^2 x\, dx \int_{-1}^1 y^3\, dy = \tfrac{3}{4}\left[\tfrac{1}{2}x^2\right]_0^2 \left[\tfrac{1}{4}y^4\right]_{-1}^1 = \tfrac{3}{4}\cdot 2 \cdot 0 = 0.$

Hence, $(\bar{x}, \bar{y}) = \left(\tfrac{4}{3}, 0\right)$.

5. $m = \int_0^2 \int_{x/2}^{3-x} (x + y)\, dy\, dx = \int_0^2 \left[xy + \tfrac{1}{2}y^2 \right]_{y=x/2}^{y=3-x} dx = \int_0^2 \left[x(3 - \tfrac{3}{2}x) + \tfrac{1}{2}(3 - x)^2 - \tfrac{1}{8}x^2 \right] dx$

$= \int_0^2 \left(-\tfrac{9}{8}x^2 + \tfrac{9}{2} \right) dx = \left[-\tfrac{9}{8}\left(\tfrac{1}{3}x^3\right) + \tfrac{9}{2}x \right]_0^2 = 6,$

$M_y = \int_0^2 \int_{x/2}^{3-x} (x^2 + xy)\, dy\, dx = \int_0^2 \left[x^2 y + \tfrac{1}{2}xy^2 \right]_{y=x/2}^{y=3-x} dx = \int_0^2 \left(\tfrac{9}{2}x - \tfrac{9}{8}x^3 \right) dx = \tfrac{9}{2},$

$M_x = \int_0^2 \int_{x/2}^{3-y} (xy + y^2)\, dy\, dx = \int_0^2 \left[\tfrac{1}{2}xy^2 + \tfrac{1}{3}y^3 \right]_{y=x/2}^{y=3-x} dx = \int_0^2 \left(9 - \tfrac{9}{2}x \right) dx = 9.$

Hence $m = 6$, $(\bar{x}, \bar{y}) = \left(\dfrac{M_y}{m}, \dfrac{M_x}{m} \right) = \left(\dfrac{3}{4}, \dfrac{3}{2} \right).$

7. $m = \int_0^1 \int_0^{e^x} y\, dy\, dx = \int_0^1 \left[\tfrac{1}{2}y^2\right]_{y=0}^{y=e^x} dx = \tfrac{1}{2}\int_0^1 e^{2x}\, dx = \tfrac{1}{4}e^{2x}\Big]_0^1 = \tfrac{1}{4}(e^2 - 1),$

$M_y = \int_0^1 \int_0^{e^x} xy\, dy\, dx = \tfrac{1}{2}\int_0^1 xe^{2x}\, dx = \tfrac{1}{2}\left[\tfrac{1}{2}xe^{2x} - \tfrac{1}{4}e^{2x}\right]_0^1 = \tfrac{1}{8}(e^2 + 1),$

$M_x = \int_0^1 \int_0^{e^x} y^2\, dy\, dx = \int_0^1 \left[\tfrac{1}{3}y^3\right]_{y=0}^{y=e^x} dx = \tfrac{1}{3}\int_0^1 e^{3x}\, dx = \tfrac{1}{3}\left[\tfrac{1}{3}e^{3x}\right]_0^1 = \tfrac{1}{9}(e^3 - 1).$

Hence $m = \tfrac{1}{4}(e^2 - 1)$, $(\bar{x}, \bar{y}) = \left(\dfrac{\tfrac{1}{8}(e^2+1)}{\tfrac{1}{4}(e^2-1)}, \dfrac{\tfrac{1}{9}(e^3-1)}{\tfrac{1}{4}(e^2-1)} \right) = \left(\dfrac{e^2+1}{2(e^2-1)}, \dfrac{4(e^3-1)}{9(e^2-1)} \right)$

9. Note that $\sin(\pi x/L) \geq 0$ for $0 \leq x \leq L$.

$$m = \int_0^L \int_0^{\sin(\pi x/L)} y \, dy \, dx = \int_0^L \tfrac{1}{2} \sin^2(\pi x/L) \, dx = \tfrac{1}{2} \left[\tfrac{1}{2}x - \tfrac{L}{4\pi} \sin(2\pi x/L) \right]_0^L = \tfrac{1}{4}L,$$

$$M_y = \int_0^L \int_0^{\sin(\pi x/L)} x \cdot y \, dy \, dx = \tfrac{1}{2} \int_0^L x \sin^2(\pi x/L) \, dx \qquad \left[\begin{array}{c} \text{integrate by parts with} \\ u = x, \, dv = \sin^2(\pi x/L) \, dx \end{array} \right]$$

$$= \tfrac{1}{2} \cdot x \left(\tfrac{1}{2}x - \tfrac{L}{4\pi} \sin(2\pi x/L) \right) \Big]_0^L - \tfrac{1}{2} \int_0^L \left[\tfrac{1}{2}x - \tfrac{L}{4\pi} \sin(2\pi x/L) \right] dx$$

$$= \tfrac{1}{4}L^2 - \tfrac{1}{2} \left[\tfrac{1}{4}x^2 + \tfrac{L^2}{4\pi^2} \cos(2\pi x/L) \right]_0^L = \tfrac{1}{4}L^2 - \tfrac{1}{2} \left(\tfrac{1}{4}L^2 + \tfrac{L^2}{4\pi^2} - \tfrac{L^2}{4\pi^2} \right) = \tfrac{1}{8}L^2,$$

$$M_x = \int_0^L \int_0^{\sin(\pi x/L)} y \cdot y \, dy \, dx = \int_0^L \tfrac{1}{3} \sin^3(\pi x/L) \, dx = \tfrac{1}{3} \int_0^L \left[1 - \cos^2(\pi x/L) \right] \sin(\pi x/L) \, dx$$

$$\left[\text{substitute } u = \cos(\pi x/L) \quad \Rightarrow \quad du = -\tfrac{\pi}{L} \sin(\pi x/L) \right]$$

$$= \tfrac{1}{3}\left(-\tfrac{L}{\pi} \right) \left[\cos(\pi x/L) - \tfrac{1}{3} \cos^3(\pi x/L) \right]_0^L = -\tfrac{L}{3\pi} \left(-1 + \tfrac{1}{3} - 1 + \tfrac{1}{3} \right) = \tfrac{4}{9\pi}L.$$

Hence $m = \dfrac{L}{4}$, $(\bar{x}, \bar{y}) = \left(\dfrac{L^2/8}{L/4}, \dfrac{4L/(9\pi)}{L/4} \right) = \left(\dfrac{L}{2}, \dfrac{16}{9\pi} \right)$.

11. $\rho(x, y) = ky = kr \sin\theta$, $m = \int_0^{\pi/2} \int_0^1 kr^2 \sin\theta \, dr \, d\theta = \tfrac{1}{3}k \int_0^{\pi/2} \sin\theta \, d\theta = \tfrac{1}{3}k \left[-\cos\theta \right]_0^{\pi/2} = \tfrac{1}{3}k$,

$$M_y = \int_0^{\pi/2} \int_0^1 kr^3 \sin\theta \cos\theta \, dr \, d\theta = \tfrac{1}{4}k \int_0^{\pi/2} \sin\theta \cos\theta \, d\theta = \tfrac{1}{8}k \left[-\cos 2\theta \right]_0^{\pi/2} = \tfrac{1}{8}k,$$

$$M_x = \int_0^{\pi/2} \int_0^1 kr^3 \sin^2\theta \, dr \, d\theta = \tfrac{1}{4}k \int_0^{\pi/2} \sin^2\theta \, d\theta = \tfrac{1}{8}k \left[\theta + \sin 2\theta \right]_0^{\pi/2} = \tfrac{\pi}{16}k.$$

Hence $(\bar{x}, \bar{y}) = \left(\tfrac{3}{8}, \tfrac{3\pi}{16} \right)$.

13.

$$\rho(x, y) = k\sqrt{x^2 + y^2} = kr,$$

$$m = \iint_D \rho(x, y) \, dA = \int_0^\pi \int_1^2 kr \cdot r \, dr \, d\theta$$

$$= k \int_0^\pi d\theta \int_1^2 r^2 \, dr = k(\pi) \left[\tfrac{1}{3}r^3 \right]_1^2 = \tfrac{7}{3}\pi k,$$

$$M_y = \iint_D x\rho(x, y) \, dA = \int_0^\pi \int_1^2 (r\cos\theta)(kr) \, r \, dr \, d\theta = k \int_0^\pi \cos\theta \, d\theta \int_1^2 r^3 \, dr$$

$$= k \left[\sin\theta \right]_0^\pi \left[\tfrac{1}{4}r^4 \right]_1^2 = k(0) \left(\tfrac{15}{4} \right) = 0 \qquad \begin{array}{l} \text{[this is to be expected as the region and density} \\ \text{function are symmetric about the } y\text{-axis]} \end{array}$$

$$M_x = \iint_D y\rho(x, y) \, dA = \int_0^\pi \int_1^2 (r\sin\theta)(kr) \, r \, dr \, d\theta = k \int_0^\pi \sin\theta \, d\theta \int_1^2 r^3 \, dr$$

$$= k \left[-\cos\theta \right]_0^\pi \left[\tfrac{1}{4}r^4 \right]_1^2 = k(1+1) \left(\tfrac{15}{4} \right) = \tfrac{15}{2}k.$$

Hence $(\bar{x}, \bar{y}) = \left(0, \dfrac{15k/2}{7\pi k/3} \right) = \left(0, \dfrac{45}{14\pi} \right)$.

15. Placing the vertex opposite the hypotenuse at $(0, 0)$, $\rho(x, y) = k(x^2 + y^2)$. Then

$$m = \int_0^a \int_0^{a-x} k(x^2 + y^2) \, dy \, dx = k \int_0^a \left[ax^2 - x^3 + \tfrac{1}{3}(a-x)^3 \right] dx = k \left[\tfrac{1}{3}ax^3 - \tfrac{1}{4}x^4 - \tfrac{1}{12}(a-x)^4 \right]_0^a = \tfrac{1}{6}ka^4.$$

By symmetry,

$$M_y = M_x = \int_0^a \int_0^{a-x} ky(x^2 + y^2) \, dy \, dx = k \int_0^a \left[\tfrac{1}{2}(a-x)^2 x^2 + \tfrac{1}{4}(a-x)^4 \right] dx$$

$$= k \left[\tfrac{1}{6}a^2 x^3 - \tfrac{1}{4}ax^4 + \tfrac{1}{10}x^5 - \tfrac{1}{20}(a-x)^5 \right]_0^a = \tfrac{1}{15}ka^5$$

Hence $(\bar{x}, \bar{y}) = \left(\tfrac{2}{5}a, \tfrac{2}{5}a \right)$.

17. $I_x = \iint_D y^2 \rho(x,y) dA = \int_0^1 \int_0^{e^x} y^2 \cdot y \, dy \, dx = \int_0^1 \left[\frac{1}{4}y^4\right]_{y=0}^{y=e^x} dx = \frac{1}{4}\int_0^1 e^{4x} \, dx = \frac{1}{4}\left[\frac{1}{4}e^{4x}\right]_0^1 = \frac{1}{16}(e^4 - 1),$

$I_y = \iint_D x^2 \rho(x,y)\, dA = \int_0^1 \int_0^{e^x} x^2 y \, dy \, dx = \int_0^1 x^2 \left[\frac{1}{2}y^2\right]_{y=0}^{y=e^x} dx = \frac{1}{2}\int_0^1 x^2 e^{2x} \, dx$

$\quad = \frac{1}{2}\left[\left(\frac{1}{2}x^2 - \frac{1}{2}x + \frac{1}{4}\right)e^{2x}\right]_0^1 \quad \text{[integrate by parts twice]} \quad = \frac{1}{8}(e^2 - 1),$

and $I_0 = I_x + I_y = \frac{1}{16}(e^4 - 1) + \frac{1}{8}(e^2 - 1) = \frac{1}{16}(e^4 + 2e^2 - 3).$

19. As in Exercise 15, we place the vertex opposite the hypotenuse at $(0,0)$ and the equal sides along the positive axes.

$I_x = \int_0^a \int_0^{a-x} y^2 k(x^2 + y^2) \, dy \, dx = k\int_0^a \int_0^{a-x}(x^2 y^2 + y^4) \, dy \, dx = k\int_0^a \left[\frac{1}{3}x^2 y^3 + \frac{1}{5}y^5\right]_{y=0}^{y=a-x} dx$

$\quad = k\int_0^a \left[\frac{1}{3}x^2(a-x)^3 + \frac{1}{5}(a-x)^5\right] dx = k\left[\frac{1}{3}\left(\frac{1}{3}a^3 x^3 - \frac{3}{4}a^2 x^4 + \frac{3}{5}ax^5 - \frac{1}{6}x^6\right) - \frac{1}{30}(a-x)^6\right]_0^a = \frac{7}{180}ka^6,$

$I_y = \int_0^a \int_0^{a-x} x^2 k(x^2 + y^2) \, dy \, dx = k\int_0^a \int_0^{a-x}(x^4 + x^2 y^2) \, dy \, dx = k\int_0^a \left[x^4 y + \frac{1}{3}x^2 y^3\right]_{y=0}^{y=a-x} dx$

$\quad = k\int_0^a \left[x^4(a-x) + \frac{1}{3}x^2(a-x)^3\right] dx = k\left[\frac{1}{5}ax^5 - \frac{1}{6}x^6 + \frac{1}{3}\left(\frac{1}{3}a^3 x^3 - \frac{3}{4}a^2 x^4 + \frac{3}{5}ax^5 - \frac{1}{6}x^6\right)\right]_0^a = \frac{7}{180}ka^6,$

and $I_0 = I_x + I_y = \frac{7}{90}ka^6.$

21. Using a CAS, we find $m = \iint_D \rho(x,y) \, dA = \int_0^\pi \int_0^{\sin x} xy \, dy \, dx = \dfrac{\pi^2}{8}.$ Then

$\bar{x} = \dfrac{1}{m}\iint_D x\rho(x,y) \, dA = \dfrac{8}{\pi^2}\int_0^\pi \int_0^{\sin x} x^2 y \, dy \, dx = \dfrac{2\pi}{3} - \dfrac{1}{\pi}$ and

$\bar{y} = \dfrac{1}{m}\iint_D y\rho(x,y) \, dA = \dfrac{8}{\pi^2}\int_0^\pi \int_0^{\sin x} xy^2 \, dy \, dx = \dfrac{16}{9\pi},$ so $(\bar{x}, \bar{y}) = \left(\dfrac{2\pi}{3} - \dfrac{1}{\pi}, \dfrac{16}{9\pi}\right).$

The moments of inertia are $I_x = \iint_D y^2 \rho(x,y) \, dA = \int_0^\pi \int_0^{\sin x} xy^3 \, dy \, dx = \dfrac{3\pi^2}{64},$

$I_y = \iint_D x^2 \rho(x,y) \, dA = \int_0^\pi \int_0^{\sin x} x^3 y \, dy \, dx = \dfrac{\pi^2}{16}(\pi^2 - 3),$ and $I_0 = I_x + I_y = \dfrac{\pi^2}{64}(4\pi^2 - 9).$

23. (a) $f(x,y)$ is a joint density function, so we know $\iint_{\mathbb{R}^2} f(x,y) \, dA = 1.$ Since $f(x,y) = 0$ outside the rectangle $[0,1] \times [0,2]$, we can say

$$\iint_{\mathbb{R}^2} f(x,y) \, dA = \int_{-\infty}^\infty \int_{-\infty}^\infty f(x,y) \, dy \, dx = \int_0^1 \int_0^2 Cx(1+y) \, dy \, dx$$

$$= C\int_0^1 x\left[y + \frac{1}{2}y^2\right]_{y=0}^{y=2} dx = C\int_0^1 4x \, dx = C\left[2x^2\right]_0^1 = 2C$$

Then $2C = 1 \Rightarrow C = \frac{1}{2}.$

(b) $P(X \leq 1, Y \leq 1) = \int_{-\infty}^1 \int_{-\infty}^1 f(x,y) \, dy \, dx = \int_0^1 \int_0^1 \frac{1}{2}x(1+y) \, dy \, dx$

$\quad = \int_0^1 \frac{1}{2}x\left[y + \frac{1}{2}y^2\right]_{y=0}^{y=1} dx = \int_0^1 \frac{1}{2}x\left(\frac{3}{2}\right) dx = \frac{3}{4}\left[\frac{1}{2}x^2\right]_0^1 = \frac{3}{8}$ or 0.375

(c) $P(X + Y \leq 1) = P((X,Y) \in D)$ where D is the triangular region shown in

the figure. Thus

$P(X + Y \leq 1) = \iint_D f(x,y) \, dA = \int_0^1 \int_0^{1-x} \frac{1}{2}x(1+y) \, dy \, dx$

$\quad = \int_0^1 \frac{1}{2}x\left[y + \frac{1}{2}y^2\right]_{y=0}^{y=1-x} dx = \int_0^1 \frac{1}{2}x\left(\frac{1}{2}x^2 - 2x + \frac{3}{2}\right) dx$

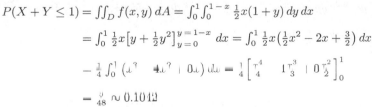

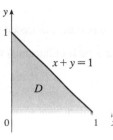

$x + y = 1$

D

$\quad = \frac{1}{4}\int_0^1 (x^3 - 4x^2 + 3x) \, dx = \frac{1}{4}\left[\frac{x^4}{4} - \frac{4x^3}{3} + \frac{3x^2}{2}\right]_0^1$

$\quad = \frac{5}{48} \approx 0.1042$

25. (a) $f(x,y) \geq 0$, so f is a joint density function if $\iint_{\mathbb{R}^2} f(x,y)\,dA = 1$. Here, $f(x,y) = 0$ outside the first quadrant, so

$$\iint_{\mathbb{R}^2} f(x,y)\,dA = \int_0^\infty \int_0^\infty 0.1e^{-(0.5x+0.2y)}\,dy\,dx = 0.1\int_0^\infty \int_0^\infty e^{-0.5x}e^{-0.2y}\,dy\,dx = 0.1\int_0^\infty e^{-0.5x}\,dx\int_0^\infty e^{-0.2y}\,dy$$

$$= 0.1\lim_{t\to\infty}\int_0^t e^{-0.5x}\,dx\lim_{t\to\infty}\int_0^t e^{-0.2y}\,dy = 0.1\lim_{t\to\infty}\left[-2e^{-0.5x}\right]_0^t\lim_{t\to\infty}\left[-5e^{-0.2y}\right]_0^t$$

$$= 0.1\lim_{t\to\infty}\left[-2(e^{-0.5t}-1)\right]\lim_{t\to\infty}\left[-5(e^{-0.2t}-1)\right] = (0.1)\cdot(-2)(0-1)\cdot(-5)(0-1) = 1$$

Thus $f(x,y)$ is a joint density function.

(b) (i) No restriction is placed on X, so

$$P(Y \geq 1) = \int_{-\infty}^\infty \int_1^\infty f(x,y)\,dy\,dx = \int_0^\infty \int_1^\infty 0.1e^{-(0.5x+0.2y)}\,dy\,dx$$

$$= 0.1\int_0^\infty e^{-0.5x}\,dx\int_1^\infty e^{-0.2y}\,dy = 0.1\lim_{t\to\infty}\int_0^t e^{-0.5x}\,dx\lim_{t\to\infty}\int_1^t e^{-0.2y}\,dy$$

$$= 0.1\lim_{t\to\infty}\left[-2e^{-0.5x}\right]_0^t\lim_{t\to\infty}\left[-5e^{-0.2y}\right]_1^t = 0.1\lim_{t\to\infty}\left[-2(e^{-0.5t}-1)\right]\lim_{t\to\infty}\left[-5(e^{-0.2t}-e^{-0.2})\right]$$

$$(0.1)\cdot(-2)(0-1)\cdot(-5)(0-e^{-0.2}) = e^{-0.2} \approx 0.8187$$

(ii) $P(X \leq 2, Y \leq 4) = \int_{-\infty}^2 \int_{-\infty}^4 f(x,y)\,dy\,dx = \int_0^2 \int_0^4 0.1e^{-(0.5x+0.2y)}\,dy\,dx$

$$= 0.1\int_0^2 e^{-0.5x}\,dx\int_0^4 e^{-0.2y}\,dy = 0.1\left[-2e^{-0.5x}\right]_0^2\left[-5e^{-0.2y}\right]_0^4$$

$$= (0.1)\cdot(-2)(e^{-1}-1)\cdot(-5)(e^{-0.8}-1)$$

$$= (e^{-1}-1)(e^{-0.8}-1) = 1 + e^{-1.8} - e^{-0.8} - e^{-1} \approx 0.3481$$

(c) The expected value of X is given by

$$\mu_1 = \iint_{\mathbb{R}^2} x\,f(x,y)\,dA = \int_0^\infty \int_0^\infty x\left[0.1e^{-(0.5x+0.2y)}\right]dy\,dx$$

$$= 0.1\int_0^\infty xe^{-0.5x}\,dx\int_0^\infty e^{-0.2y}\,dy = 0.1\lim_{t\to\infty}\int_0^t xe^{-0.5x}\,dx\lim_{t\to\infty}\int_0^t e^{-0.2y}\,dy$$

To evaluate the first integral, we integrate by parts with $u = x$ and $dv = e^{-0.5x}\,dx$ (or we can use Formula 96 in the Table of Integrals): $\int xe^{-0.5x}\,dx = -2xe^{-0.5x} - \int -2e^{-0.5x}\,dx = -2xe^{-0.5x} - 4e^{-0.5x} = -2(x+2)e^{-0.5x}$.

Thus

$$\mu_1 = 0.1\lim_{t\to\infty}\left[-2(x+2)e^{-0.5x}\right]_0^t\lim_{t\to\infty}\left[-5e^{-0.2y}\right]_0^t$$

$$= 0.1\lim_{t\to\infty}(-2)\left[(t+2)e^{-0.5t}-2\right]\lim_{t\to\infty}(-5)\left[e^{-0.2t}-1\right]$$

$$= 0.1(-2)\left(\lim_{t\to\infty}\frac{t+2}{e^{0.5t}}-2\right)(-5)(-1) = 2 \qquad \text{[by l'Hospital's Rule]}$$

The expected value of Y is given by

$$\mu_2 = \iint_{\mathbb{R}^2} y\,f(x,y)\,dA = \int_0^\infty \int_0^\infty y\left[0.1e^{-(0.5+0.2y)}\right]dy\,dx$$

$$= 0.1\int_0^\infty e^{-0.5x}\,dx\int_0^\infty ye^{-0.2y}\,dy = 0.1\lim_{t\to\infty}\int_0^t e^{-0.5x}\,dx\lim_{t\to\infty}\int_0^t ye^{-0.2y}\,dy$$

To evaluate the second integral, we integrate by parts with $u = y$ and $dv = e^{-0.2y}\,dy$ (or again we can use Formula 96 in the Table of Integrals) which gives $\int ye^{-0.2y}\,dy = -5ye^{-0.2y} + \int 5e^{-0.2y}\,dy = -5(y+5)e^{-0.2y}$. Then

$$\mu_2 = 0.1\lim_{t\to\infty}\left[-2e^{-0.5x}\right]_0^t\lim_{t\to\infty}\left[-5(y+5)e^{-0.2y}\right]_0^t$$

$$= 0.1\lim_{t\to\infty}\left[-2(e^{-0.5t}-1)\right]\lim_{t\to\infty}\left(-5\left[(t+5)e^{-0.2t}-5\right]\right)$$

$$= 0.1(-2)(-1)\cdot(-5)\left(\lim_{t\to\infty}\frac{t+5}{e^{0.2t}}-5\right) = 5 \qquad \text{[by l'Hospital's Rule]}$$

27. (a) The random variables X and Y are normally distributed with $\mu_1 = 45$, $\mu_2 = 20$, $\sigma_1 = 0.5$, and $\sigma_2 = 0.1$.

The individual density functions for X and Y, then, are $f_1(x) = \dfrac{1}{0.5\sqrt{2\pi}}\, e^{-(x-45)^2/0.5}$ and

$f_2(y) = \dfrac{1}{0.1\sqrt{2\pi}}\, e^{-(y-20)^2/0.02}$. Since X and Y are independent, the joint density function is the product

$f(x,y) = f_1(x)f_2(y) = \dfrac{1}{0.5\sqrt{2\pi}}\, e^{-(x-45)^2/0.5}\, \dfrac{1}{0.1\sqrt{2\pi}}\, e^{-(y-20)^2/0.02} = \dfrac{10}{\pi}\, e^{-2(x-45)^2 - 50(y-20)^2}$.

Then $P(40 \le X \le 50,\ 20 \le Y \le 25) = \int_{40}^{50}\int_{20}^{25} f(x,y)\,dy\,dx = \dfrac{10}{\pi}\int_{40}^{50}\int_{20}^{25} e^{-2(x-45)^2 - 50(y-20)^2}\,dy\,dx$.

Using a CAS or calculator to evaluate the integral, we get $P(40 \le X \le 50,\ 20 \le Y \le 25) \approx 0.500$.

(b) $P(4(X-45)^2 + 100(Y-20)^2 \le 2) = \iint_D \dfrac{10}{\pi}\, e^{-2(x-45)^2 - 50(y-20)^2}\,dA$, where D is the region enclosed by the ellipse

$4(x-45)^2 + 100(y-20)^2 = 2$. Solving for y gives $y = 20 \pm \frac{1}{10}\sqrt{2 - 4(x-45)^2}$, the upper and lower halves of the

ellipse, and these two halves meet where $y = 20$ [since the ellipse is centered at $(45, 20)$] $\Rightarrow 4(x-45)^2 = 2 \Rightarrow$

$x = 45 \pm \frac{1}{\sqrt{2}}$. Thus

$$\iint_D \frac{10}{\pi}\, e^{-2(x-45)^2 - 50(y-20)^2}\,dA = \frac{10}{\pi}\int_{45-1/\sqrt{2}}^{45+1/\sqrt{2}}\int_{20-\frac{1}{10}\sqrt{2-4(x-45)^2}}^{20+\frac{1}{10}\sqrt{2-4(x-45)^2}} e^{-2(x-45)^2 - 50(y-20)^2}\,dy\,dx.$$

Using a CAS or calculator to evaluate the integral, we get $P(4(X-45)^2 + 100(Y-20)^2 \le 2) \approx 0.632$.

29. (a) If $f(P, A)$ is the probability that an individual at A will be infected by an individual at P, and $k\,dA$ is the number of
infected individuals in an element of area dA, then $f(P, A)k\,dA$ is the number of infections that should result from
exposure of the individual at A to infected people in the element of area dA. Integration over D gives the number of
infections of the person at A due to all the infected people in D. In rectangular coordinates (with the origin at the city's
center), the exposure of a person at A is

$$E = \iint_D k f(P, A)\,dA = k\iint_D \frac{1}{20}\,[20 - d(P, A)]\,dA = k\iint_D \left[1 - \frac{1}{20}\sqrt{(x - x_0)^2 + (y - y_0)^2}\right]dA$$

(b) If $A = (0, 0)$, then

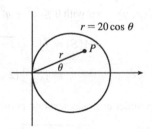

$r = 20\cos\theta$

$$E = k\iint_D \left[1 - \frac{1}{20}\sqrt{x^2 + y^2}\right]dA$$

$$= k\int_0^{2\pi}\int_0^{10}\left(1 - \frac{1}{20}r\right) r\,dr\,d\theta = 2\pi k\left[\frac{1}{2}r^2 - \frac{1}{60}r^3\right]_0^{10}$$

$$= 2\pi k\left(50 - \frac{50}{3}\right) = \frac{200}{3}\pi k \approx 209k$$

For A at the edge of the city, it is convenient to use a polar coordinate system centered at A. Then the polar equation for
the circular boundary of the city becomes $r = 20\cos\theta$ instead of $r = 10$, and the distance from A to a point P in the city
is again r (see the figure). So

$$E = k\int_{-\pi/2}^{\pi/2}\int_0^{20\cos\theta}\left(1 - \frac{1}{20}r\right) r\,dr\,d\theta = k\int_{-\pi/2}^{\pi/2}\left[\frac{1}{2}r^2 - \frac{1}{60}r^3\right]_{r=0}^{r=20\cos\theta}d\theta$$

$$= k\int_{-\pi/2}^{\pi/2}\left(200\cos^2\theta - \frac{400}{3}\cos^3\theta\right)d\theta = 200k\int_{-\pi/2}^{\pi/2}\left[\frac{1}{2} + \frac{1}{2}\cos 2\theta - \frac{2}{3}(1 - \sin^2\theta)\cos\theta\right]d\theta$$

$$= 200k\left[\frac{1}{2}\theta + \frac{1}{4}\sin 2\theta - \frac{2}{3}\sin\theta + \frac{2}{3}\cdot\frac{1}{3}\sin^3\theta\right]_{-\pi/2}^{\pi/2} = 200k\left[\frac{\pi}{4} + 0 - \frac{2}{3} + \frac{2}{9} + \frac{\pi}{4} + 0 - \frac{2}{3} + \frac{2}{9}\right]$$

$$= 200k\left(\frac{\pi}{2} - \frac{8}{9}\right) \approx 136k.$$

Therefore the risk of infection is much lower at the edge of the city than in the middle, so it is better to live at the edge.

12.6 Surface Area

1. Here we can write $z = f(x, y) = \frac{1}{3} - \frac{1}{3}x - \frac{2}{3}y$ and D is the disk $x^2 + y^2 \le 3$, so by Formula 6 the area of the surface is

$$A(S) = \iint_D \sqrt{1 + \left(\frac{\partial z}{\partial x}\right)^2 + \left(\frac{\partial z}{\partial y}\right)^2}\, dA = \iint_D \sqrt{1 + \left(-\frac{1}{3}\right)^2 + \left(-\frac{2}{3}\right)^2}\, dA = \frac{\sqrt{14}}{3} \iint_D dA$$

$$= \frac{\sqrt{14}}{3} A(D) = \frac{\sqrt{14}}{3} \cdot \pi \left(\sqrt{3}\right)^2 = \sqrt{14}\,\pi$$

3. The surface S is given by $z = f(x, y) = 6 - 3x - 2y$ which intersects the xy-plane in the line $3x + 2y = 6$, so D is the triangular region given by $\{(x, y) \mid 0 \le x \le 2, 0 \le y \le 3 - \frac{3}{2}x\}$. By Formula 6, the surface area of S is

$$A(S) = \iint_D \sqrt{1 + \left(\frac{\partial z}{\partial x}\right)^2 + \left(\frac{\partial z}{\partial y}\right)^2}\, dA$$

$$= \iint_D \sqrt{1 + (-3)^2 + (-2)^2}\, dA = \sqrt{14} \iint_D dA = \sqrt{14}\, A(D) = \sqrt{14} \left(\frac{1}{2} \cdot 2 \cdot 3\right) = 3\sqrt{14}.$$

5. $z = f(x, y) = \sqrt{x^2 + y^2} \quad \Rightarrow \quad \dfrac{\partial z}{\partial x} = \dfrac{1}{2}\left(x^2 + y^2\right)^{-1/2} \cdot 2x = \dfrac{x}{\sqrt{x^2 + y^2}}, \quad \dfrac{\partial z}{\partial y} = \dfrac{y}{\sqrt{x^2 + y^2}}$, and

$$\sqrt{1 + \left(\frac{\partial z}{\partial x}\right)^2 + \left(\frac{\partial z}{\partial y}\right)^2} = \sqrt{1 + \frac{x^2}{x^2 + y^2} + \frac{y^2}{x^2 + y^2}} = \sqrt{1 + \frac{x^2 + y^2}{x^2 + y^2}} = \sqrt{2}$$

Here D is given by $\{(x, y) \mid 0 \le x \le 1, x^2 \le y \le x\}$, so by Formula 6 the surface area of S is

$$A(S) = \iint_D \sqrt{2}\, dA = \int_0^1 \int_{x^2}^x \sqrt{2}\, dy\, dx = \sqrt{2} \int_0^1 (x - x^2)\, dx = \sqrt{2}\left[\tfrac{1}{2}x^2 - \tfrac{1}{3}x^3\right]_0^1 = \sqrt{2}\left(\tfrac{1}{2} - \tfrac{1}{3}\right) = \frac{\sqrt{2}}{6}$$

7. $\mathbf{r}_u = \langle 2u, v, 0\rangle$, $\mathbf{r}_v = \langle 0, u, v\rangle$, and $\mathbf{r}_u \times \mathbf{r}_v = \langle v^2, -2uv, 2u^2\rangle$. Then

$$A(S) = \iint_D |\mathbf{r}_u \times \mathbf{r}_v|\, dA = \int_0^1 \int_0^2 \sqrt{v^4 + 4u^2 v^2 + 4u^4}\, dv\, du = \int_0^1 \int_0^2 \sqrt{(v^2 + 2u^2)^2}\, dv\, du$$

$$= \int_0^1 \int_0^2 (v^2 + 2u^2)\, dv\, du = \int_0^1 \left[\tfrac{1}{3}v^3 + 2u^2 v\right]_{v=0}^{v=2}\, du = \int_0^1 \left(\tfrac{8}{3} + 4u^2\right) du = \left[\tfrac{8}{3}u + \tfrac{4}{3}u^3\right]_0^1 = 4$$

9. $z = f(x, y) = xy$ with $0 \le x^2 + y^2 \le 1$, so $f_x = y$, $f_y = x \quad \Rightarrow$

$$A(S) = \iint_D \sqrt{1 + y^2 + x^2}\, dA = \int_0^{2\pi} \int_0^1 \sqrt{r^2 + 1}\, r\, dr\, d\theta = \int_0^{2\pi} \left[\tfrac{1}{3}(r^2 + 1)^{3/2}\right]_{r=0}^{r=1}\, d\theta$$

$$= \int_0^{2\pi} \tfrac{1}{3}(2\sqrt{2} - 1)\, d\theta = \tfrac{2\pi}{3}(2\sqrt{2} - 1)$$

11. The cylinder encloses separate portions of the sphere in the upper and lower halves. The top half of the sphere is $z = f(x, y) = \sqrt{b^2 - x^2 - y^2}$ and D is given by $\{(x, y) \mid x^2 + y^2 \le a^2\}$. By Formula 6, the surface area of the upper enclosed portion is

$$A = \iint_D \sqrt{1 + \left(\frac{-x}{\sqrt{b^2 - x^2 - y^2}}\right)^2 + \left(\frac{-y}{\sqrt{b^2 - x^2 - y^2}}\right)^2}\, dA = \iint_D \sqrt{1 + \frac{x^2 + y^2}{b^2 - x^2 - y^2}}\, dA$$

$$= \iint_D \sqrt{\frac{b^2}{b^2 - x^2 - y^2}}\, dA = \int_0^{2\pi} \int_0^a \frac{b}{\sqrt{b^2 - r^2}}\, r\, dr\, d\theta = b \int_0^{2\pi} d\theta \int_0^a \frac{r}{\sqrt{b^2 - r^2}}\, dr$$

$$= b\,[\theta]_0^{2\pi} \left[-\sqrt{b^2 - r^2}\right]_0^a = 2\pi b\left(-\sqrt{b^2 - a^2} + \sqrt{b^2 - 0}\right) = 2\pi b\left(b - \sqrt{b^2 - a^2}\right)$$

The lower portion of the sphere enclosed by the cylinder has identical shape, so the total area is $2A = 4\pi b\left(b - \sqrt{b^2 - a^2}\right)$.

13. $z = f(x,y) = e^{-x^2-y^2}$, $f_x = -2xe^{-x^2-y^2}$, $f_y = -2ye^{-x^2-y^2}$. Then

$$A(S) = \iint\limits_{x^2+y^2\leq 4} \sqrt{1+(-2xe^{-x^2-y^2})^2+(-2ye^{-x^2-y^2})^2}\,dA = \iint\limits_{x^2+y^2\leq 4} \sqrt{1+4(x^2+y^2)e^{-2(x^2+y^2)}}\,dA.$$

Converting to polar coordinates we have

$$A(S) = \int_0^{2\pi}\int_0^2 \sqrt{1+4r^2e^{-2r^2}}\,r\,dr\,d\theta = \int_0^{2\pi}d\theta \int_0^2 r\sqrt{1+4r^2e^{-2r^2}}\,dr$$

$$= 2\pi\int_0^2 r\sqrt{1+4r^2e^{-2r^2}}\,dr \approx 13.9783 \text{ using a calculator.}$$

15. (a) $A(S) = \iint\limits_D \sqrt{1+\left(\frac{\partial z}{\partial x}\right)^2+\left(\frac{\partial z}{\partial y}\right)^2}\,dA = \int_0^6\int_0^4 \sqrt{1+\dfrac{4x^2+4y^2}{(1+x^2+y^2)^4}}\,dy\,dx.$

Using the Midpoint Rule with $f(x,y) = \sqrt{1+\dfrac{4x^2+4y^2}{(1+x^2+y^2)^4}}$, $m=3$, $n=2$ we have

$$A(S) \approx \sum_{i=1}^3\sum_{j=1}^2 f(\overline{x}_i,\overline{y}_j)\,\Delta A = 4\left[f(1,1)+f(1,3)+f(3,1)+f(3,3)+f(5,1)+f(5,3)\right] \approx 24.2055$$

(b) Using a CAS we have $A(S) = \int_0^6\int_0^4 \sqrt{1+\dfrac{4x^2+4y^2}{(1+x^2+y^2)^4}}\,dy\,dx \approx 24.2476$. This agrees with the estimate in part (a)

to the first decimal place.

17. $\mathbf{r}(u,v) = \langle\cos^3 u\cos^3 v, \sin^3 u\cos^3 v, \sin^3 v\rangle$, so $\mathbf{r}_u = \langle -3\cos^2 u\sin u\cos^3 v, 3\sin^2 u\cos u\cos^3 v, 0\rangle$,

$\mathbf{r}_v = \langle -3\cos^3 u\cos^2 v\sin v, -3\sin^3 u\cos^2 v\sin v, 3\sin^2 v\cos v\rangle$, and

$\mathbf{r}_u \times \mathbf{r}_v = \langle 9\cos u\sin^2 u\cos^4 v\sin^2 v, 9\cos^2 u\sin u\cos^4 v\sin^2 v, 9\cos^2 u\sin^2 u\cos^5 v\sin v\rangle$. Then

$$|\mathbf{r}_u \times \mathbf{r}_v| = 9\sqrt{\cos^2 u\sin^4 u\cos^8 v\sin^4 v + \cos^4 u\sin^2 u\cos^8 v\sin^4 v + \cos^4 u\sin^4 u\cos^{10} v\sin^2 v}$$

$$= 9\sqrt{\cos^2 u\sin^2 u\cos^8 v\sin^2 v\,(\sin^2 v + \cos^2 u\sin^2 u\cos^2 v)}$$

$$= 9\cos^4 v\,|\cos u\sin u\sin v|\sqrt{\sin^2 v + \cos^2 u\sin^2 u\cos^2 v}$$

Using a CAS, we have $A(S) = \int_0^\pi\int_0^{2\pi} 9\cos^4 v\,|\cos u\sin u\sin v|\sqrt{\sin^2 v + \cos^2 u\sin^2 u\cos^2 v}\,dv\,du \approx 4.4506$.

19. $z = 1+2x+3y+4y^2$, so

$$A(S) = \iint\limits_D \sqrt{1+\left(\frac{\partial z}{\partial x}\right)^2+\left(\frac{\partial z}{\partial y}\right)^2}\,dA = \int_1^4\int_0^1 \sqrt{1+4+(3+8y)^2}\,dy\,dx = \int_1^4\int_0^1 \sqrt{14+48y+64y^2}\,dy\,dx.$$

Using a CAS, we have

$$\int_1^4\int_0^1 \sqrt{14+48y+64y^2}\,dy\,dx = \frac{45}{8}\sqrt{14}+\frac{15}{16}\ln\left(11\sqrt{5}+3\sqrt{14}\sqrt{5}\right)-\frac{15}{16}\ln\left(3\sqrt{5}+\sqrt{14}\sqrt{5}\right)$$

or $\frac{45}{8}\sqrt{14}+\frac{15}{16}\ln\dfrac{11\sqrt{5}+3\sqrt{70}}{3\sqrt{5}+\sqrt{70}}$.

21. (a) $x = a\sin u\cos v$, $y = b\sin u\sin v$, $z = c\cos u \Rightarrow$

$$\frac{x^2}{a^2}+\frac{y^2}{b^2}+\frac{z^2}{c^2} = (\sin u\cos v)^2+(\sin u\sin v)^2+(\cos u)^2$$

$$\sin^2 u + \cos^2 u = 1$$

and since the ranges of u and v are sufficient to generate the entire graph, the parametric equations represent an ellipsoid.

(b)

(c) From the parametric equations (with $a = 1$, $b = 2$, and $c = 3$),

we calculate $\mathbf{r}_u = \cos u \cos v \, \mathbf{i} + 2 \cos u \sin v \, \mathbf{j} - 3 \sin u \, \mathbf{k}$ and

$\mathbf{r}_v = -\sin u \sin v \, \mathbf{i} + 2 \sin u \cos v \, \mathbf{j}$. So

$\mathbf{r}_u \times \mathbf{r}_v = 6 \sin^2 u \cos v \, \mathbf{i} + 3 \sin^2 u \sin v \, \mathbf{j} + 2 \sin u \cos u \, \mathbf{k}$,

and the surface area is given by

$$A(S) = \int_0^{2\pi} \int_0^{\pi} |\mathbf{r}_u \times \mathbf{r}_v| \, du \, dv$$

$$= \int_0^{2\pi} \int_0^{\pi} \sqrt{36 \sin^4 u \cos^2 v + 9 \sin^4 u \sin^2 v + 4 \cos^2 u \sin^2 u} \, du \, dv$$

23. If we revolve the curve $y = f(x)$, $a \le x \le b$ about the x-axis, where $f(x) \ge 0$, then from Equations 10.5.3 we know we can

parametrize the surface using $x = x$, $y = f(x) \cos \theta$, and $z = f(x) \sin \theta$, where $a \le x \le b$ and $0 \le \theta \le 2\pi$. Thus we can

say the surface is represented by $\mathbf{r}(x, \theta) = x \, \mathbf{i} + f(x) \cos \theta \, \mathbf{j} + f(x) \sin \theta \, \mathbf{k}$, with $a \le x \le b$ and $0 \le \theta \le 2\pi$. Then by (4),

the surface area is given by $A(S) = \iint_D |\mathbf{r}_x \times \mathbf{r}_\theta| \, dA$ where D is the rectangular parameter region $[a, b] \times [0, 2\pi]$. Here,

$\mathbf{r}_x(x, \theta) = \mathbf{i} + f'(x) \cos \theta \, \mathbf{j} + f'(x) \sin \theta \, \mathbf{k}$ and $\mathbf{r}_\theta(x) = -f(x) \sin \theta \, \mathbf{j} + f(x) \cos \theta \, \mathbf{k}$. So

$$\mathbf{r}_x \times \mathbf{r}_\theta = \begin{vmatrix} \mathbf{i} & \mathbf{j} & \mathbf{k} \\ 1 & f'(x) \cos \theta & f'(x) \sin \theta \\ 0 & -f(x) \sin \theta & f(x) \cos \theta \end{vmatrix} = [f(x)f'(x) \cos^2 \theta + f(x)f'(x) \sin^2 \theta] \, \mathbf{i} - f(x) \cos \theta \, \mathbf{j} - f(x) \sin \theta \, \mathbf{k}$$

$$= f(x)f'(x) \mathbf{i} - f(x) \cos \theta \, \mathbf{j} - f(x) \sin \theta \, \mathbf{k} \text{ and}$$

$$|\mathbf{r}_x \times \mathbf{r}_\theta| = \sqrt{[f(x)f'(x)]^2 + [f(x)]^2 \cos^2 \theta + [f(x)]^2 \sin^2 \theta}$$

$$= \sqrt{[f(x)]^2 ([f'(x)]^2 + 1)} = f(x)\sqrt{1 + [f'(x)]^2} \text{ [since } f(x) \ge 0]. \text{ Thus}$$

$$A(S) = \iint_D |\mathbf{r}_x \times \mathbf{r}_\theta| \, dA = \int_a^b \int_0^{2\pi} f(x)\sqrt{1 + [f'(x)]^2} \, d\theta \, dx$$

$$= \int_a^b f(x)\sqrt{1 + [f'(x)]^2} \, [\theta]_0^{2\pi} \, dx = 2\pi \int_a^b f(x)\sqrt{1 + [f'(x)]^2} \, dx$$

25. $y = f(x) = \sqrt{1 + 4x} \Rightarrow f'(x) = \frac{1}{2}(1 + 4x)^{-1/2} \cdot 4 = 2/\sqrt{1 + 4x}$. Then by Formula 7,

$$A = 2\pi \int_1^5 f(x) \sqrt{1 + [f'(x)]^2} \, dx = 2\pi \int_1^5 \sqrt{1 + 4x} \sqrt{1 + \left(2/\sqrt{1 + 4x}\right)^2} \, dx$$

$$= 2\pi \int_1^5 \sqrt{1 + 4x} \sqrt{\frac{5 + 4x}{1 + 4x}} \, dx = 2\pi \int_1^5 \sqrt{5 + 4x} \, dx = 2\pi \left[\frac{1}{6}(5 + 4x)^{3/2}\right]_1^5$$

$$= \frac{\pi}{3}(25^{3/2} - 9^{3/2}) = \frac{\pi}{3}(125 - 27) = \frac{98}{3}\pi$$

27. To find the region D: $z = x^2 + y^2$ implies $z + z^2 = 4z$ or $z^2 - 3z = 0$. Thus $z = 0$ or $z = 3$ are the planes where the

surfaces intersect. But $x^2 + y^2 + z^2 = 4z$ implies $x^2 + y^2 + (z - 2)^2 = 4$, so $z = 3$ intersects the upper hemisphere.

Thus $(z-2)^2 = 4 - x^2 - y^2$ or $z = 2 + \sqrt{4 - x^2 - y^2}$. Therefore D is the region inside the circle $x^2 + y^2 + (3-2)^2 = 4$,

that is, $D = \{(x,y) \mid x^2 + y^2 \le 3\}$.

$$A(S) = \iint_D \sqrt{1 + [(-x)(4 - x^2 - y^2)^{-1/2}]^2 + [(-y)(4 - x^2 - y^2)^{-1/2}]^2}\, dA$$

$$= \int_0^{2\pi} \int_0^{\sqrt{3}} \sqrt{1 + \frac{r^2}{4 - r^2}}\, r\, dr\, d\theta = \int_0^{2\pi} \int_0^{\sqrt{3}} \frac{2r\, dr}{\sqrt{4 - r^2}}\, d\theta = \int_0^{2\pi} \left[-2(4 - r^2)^{1/2}\right]_{r=0}^{r=\sqrt{3}} d\theta$$

$$= \int_0^{2\pi}(-2 + 4)\, d\theta = 2\theta\Big]_0^{2\pi} = 4\pi$$

12.7 Triple Integrals

1. $\iiint_B xyz^2\, dV = \int_0^1 \int_0^3 \int_{-1}^2 xyz^2\, dy\, dz\, dx = \int_0^1 \int_0^3 \left[\frac{1}{2}xy^2z^2\right]_{y=-1}^{y=2} dz\, dx = \int_0^1 \int_0^3 \frac{3}{2}xz^2\, dz\, dx$

$$= \int_0^1 \left[\frac{1}{2}xz^3\right]_{z=0}^{z=3} dx = \int_0^1 \frac{27}{2}x\, dx = \frac{27}{4}x^2\Big]_0^1 = \frac{27}{4}$$

3. $\int_0^1 \int_0^z \int_0^{x+z} 6xz\, dy\, dx\, dz = \int_0^1 \int_0^z \left[6xyz\right]_{y=0}^{y=x+z} dx\, dz = \int_0^1 \int_0^z 6xz(x+z)\, dx\, dz$

$$= \int_0^1 \left[2x^3z + 3x^2z^2\right]_{x=0}^{x=z} dz = \int_0^1 (2z^4 + 3z^4)\, dz = \int_0^1 5z^4\, dz = z^5\Big]_0^1 = 1$$

5. $\int_0^3 \int_0^1 \int_0^{\sqrt{1-z^2}} ze^y\, dx\, dz\, dy = \int_0^3 \int_0^1 \left[xze^y\right]_{x=0}^{x=\sqrt{1-z^2}} dz\, dy = \int_0^3 \int_0^1 ze^y \sqrt{1-z^2}\, dz\, dy$

$$= \int_0^3 \left[-\frac{1}{3}(1-z^2)^{3/2}e^y\right]_{z=0}^{z=1} dy = \int_0^3 \frac{1}{3}e^y\, dy = \frac{1}{3}e^y\Big]_0^3 = \frac{1}{3}(e^3 - 1)$$

7. $\int_0^{\pi/2} \int_0^y \int_0^x \cos(x+y+z)\, dz\, dx\, dy = \int_0^{\pi/2} \int_0^y \left[\sin(x+y+z)\right]_{z=0}^{z=x} dx\, dy$

$$= \int_0^{\pi/2} \int_0^y \left[\sin(2x+y) - \sin(x+y)\right] dx\, dy$$

$$= \int_0^{\pi/2} \left[-\frac{1}{2}\cos(2x+y) + \cos(x+y)\right]_{x=0}^{x=y} dy$$

$$= \int_0^{\pi/2} \left[-\frac{1}{2}\cos 3y + \cos 2y + \frac{1}{2}\cos y - \cos y\right] dy$$

$$= \left[-\frac{1}{6}\sin 3y + \frac{1}{2}\sin 2y - \frac{1}{2}\sin y\right]_0^{\pi/2} = \frac{1}{6} - \frac{1}{2} = -\frac{1}{3}$$

9. $\iiint_E 2x\, dV = \int_0^2 \int_0^{\sqrt{4-y^2}} \int_0^y 2x\, dz\, dx\, dy = \int_0^2 \int_0^{\sqrt{4-y^2}} \left[2xz\right]_{z=0}^{z=y} dx\, dy = \int_0^2 \int_0^{\sqrt{4-y^2}} 2xy\, dx\, dy$

$$= \int_0^2 \left[x^2 y\right]_{x=0}^{x=\sqrt{4-y^2}} dy = \int_0^2 (4 - y^2)y\, dy = \left[2y^2 - \frac{1}{4}y^4\right]_0^2 = 4$$

11. Here $E = \{(x,y,z) \mid 0 \le x \le 1, 0 \le y \le \sqrt{x}, 0 \le z \le 1 + x + y\}$, so

$$\iiint_E 6xy\, dV = \int_0^1 \int_0^{\sqrt{x}} \int_0^{1+x+y} 6xy\, dz\, dy\, dx = \int_0^1 \int_0^{\sqrt{x}} \left[6xyz\right]_{z=0}^{z=1+x+y} dy\, dx = \int_0^1 \int_0^{\sqrt{x}} 6xy(1 + x + y)\, dy\, dx$$

$$= \int_0^1 \left[3xy^2 + 3x^2y^2 + 2xy^3\right]_{y=0}^{y=\sqrt{x}} dx = \int_0^1 (3x^2 + 3x^3 + 2x^{5/2})\, dx = \left[x^3 + \frac{3}{4}x^4 + \frac{4}{7}x^{7/2}\right]_0^1 = \frac{65}{28}$$

13.

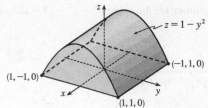

E is the region below the parabolic cylinder $z = 1 - y^2$ and above the square $[-1, 1] \times [-1, 1]$ in the xy-plane.

$$\iiint_E x^2 e^y \, dV = \int_{-1}^1 \int_{-1}^1 \int_0^{1-y^2} x^2 e^y \, dz \, dy \, dx$$

$$= \int_{-1}^1 \int_{-1}^1 x^2 e^y (1 - y^2) \, dy \, dx$$

$$= \int_{-1}^1 x^2 \, dx \int_{-1}^1 (e^y - y^2 e^y) \, dy$$

$$= \left[\tfrac{1}{3} x^3 \right]_{-1}^1 \left[e^y - (y^2 - 2y + 2) e^y \right]_{-1}^1 \qquad \begin{bmatrix} \text{integrate by} \\ \text{parts twice} \end{bmatrix}$$

$$= \tfrac{1}{3} (2)[e - e - e^{-1} + 5e^{-1}] = \tfrac{8}{3e}$$

15.

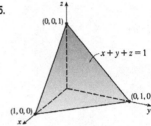

Here $T = \{(x, y, z) \mid 0 \le x \le 1, 0 \le y \le 1 - x, 0 \le z \le 1 - x - y\}$, so

$$\iiint_T x^2 \, dV = \int_0^1 \int_0^{1-x} \int_0^{1-x-y} x^2 \, dz \, dy \, dx = \int_0^1 \int_0^{1-x} x^2 (1 - x - y) \, dy \, dx$$

$$= \int_0^1 \int_0^{1-x} (x^2 - x^3 - x^2 y) \, dy \, dx = \int_0^1 \left[x^2 y - x^3 y - \tfrac{1}{2} x^2 y^2 \right]_{y=0}^{y=1-x} dx$$

$$= \int_0^1 \left[x^2 (1 - x) - x^3 (1 - x) - \tfrac{1}{2} x^2 (1 - x)^2 \right] dx$$

$$= \int_0^1 \left(\tfrac{1}{2} x^4 - x^3 + \tfrac{1}{2} x^2 \right) dx = \left[\tfrac{1}{10} x^5 - \tfrac{1}{4} x^4 + \tfrac{1}{6} x^3 \right]_0^1$$

$$= \tfrac{1}{10} - \tfrac{1}{4} + \tfrac{1}{6} = \tfrac{1}{60}$$

17.

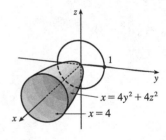

The projection E on the yz-plane is the disk $y^2 + z^2 \le 1$. Using polar coordinates $y = r \cos \theta$ and $z = r \sin \theta$, we get

$$\iiint_E x \, dV = \iint_D \left[\int_{4y^2 + 4z^2}^4 x \, dx \right] dA = \tfrac{1}{2} \iint_D \left[4^2 - (4y^2 + 4z^2)^2 \right] dA$$

$$= 8 \int_0^{2\pi} \int_0^1 (1 - r^4) r \, dr \, d\theta = 8 \int_0^{2\pi} d\theta \int_0^1 (r - r^5) \, dr$$

$$= 8(2\pi) \left[\tfrac{1}{2} r^2 - \tfrac{1}{6} r^6 \right]_0^1 = \tfrac{16\pi}{3}$$

19. The plane $2x + y + z = 4$ intersects the xy-plane when

$$2x + y + 0 = 4 \quad \Rightarrow \quad y = 4 - 2x, \text{ so}$$

$$E = \{(x, y, z) \mid 0 \le x \le 2, 0 \le y \le 4 - 2x, 0 \le z \le 4 - 2x - y\} \text{ and}$$

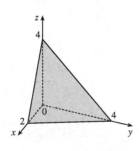

$$V = \int_0^2 \int_0^{4-2x} \int_0^{4-2x-y} dz \, dy \, dx = \int_0^2 \int_0^{4-2x} (4 - 2x - y) \, dy \, dx$$

$$= \int_0^2 \left[4y - 2xy - \tfrac{1}{2} y^2 \right]_{y=0}^{y=4-2x} dx$$

$$= \int_0^2 \left[4(4 - 2x) - 2x(4 - 2x) - \tfrac{1}{2} (4 - 2x)^2 \right] dx$$

$$= \int_0^2 (2x^2 - 8x + 8) \, dx = \left[\tfrac{2}{3} x^3 - 4x^2 + 8x \right]_0^2 = \tfrac{16}{3}$$

21. $V = \int_{-3}^{3} \int_{-\sqrt{9-x^2}}^{\sqrt{9-x^2}} \int_{1}^{5-y} dz\, dy\, dx = \int_{-3}^{3} \int_{-\sqrt{9-x^2}}^{\sqrt{9-x^2}} (5 - y - 1)\, dy\, dx = \int_{-3}^{3} \left[4y - \tfrac{1}{2} y^2 \right]_{y=-\sqrt{9-x^2}}^{y=\sqrt{9-x^2}} dx$

$= \int_{-3}^{3} 8\sqrt{9 - x^2}\, dx = 8 \left[\tfrac{x}{2} \sqrt{9 - x^2} + \tfrac{9}{2} \sin^{-1}\left(\tfrac{x}{3}\right) \right]_{-3}^{3}$ $\quad\left[\begin{array}{l} \text{using trigonometric substitution or} \\ \text{Formula 30 in the Table of Integrals} \end{array} \right]$

$= 8 \left[\tfrac{9}{2} \sin^{-1}(1) - \tfrac{9}{2} \sin^{-1}(-1) \right] = 36\left(\tfrac{\pi}{2} - \left(-\tfrac{\pi}{2}\right)\right) = 36\pi$

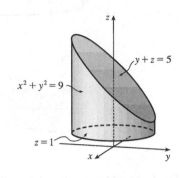

Alternatively, use polar coordinates to evaluate the double integral:

$\int_{-3}^{3} \int_{-\sqrt{9-x^2}}^{\sqrt{9-x^2}} (4 - y)\, dy\, dx = \int_{0}^{2\pi} \int_{0}^{3} (4 - r\sin\theta)\, r\, dr\, d\theta$

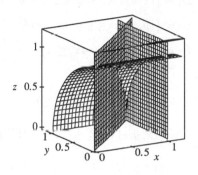

$= \int_{0}^{2\pi} \left[2r^2 - \tfrac{1}{3} r^3 \sin\theta \right]_{r=0}^{r=3} d\theta$

$= \int_{0}^{2\pi} (18 - 9\sin\theta)\, d\theta$

$= 18\theta + 9\cos\theta \Big]_{0}^{2\pi} = 36\pi$

23. (a) The wedge can be described as the region

$D = \left\{ (x, y, z) \mid y^2 + z^2 \le 1, 0 \le x \le 1, 0 \le y \le x \right\}$

$= \left\{ (x, y, z) \mid 0 \le x \le 1, 0 \le y \le x, 0 \le z \le \sqrt{1 - y^2} \right\}$

So the integral expressing the volume of the wedge is

$\iiint_{D} dV = \int_{0}^{1} \int_{0}^{x} \int_{0}^{\sqrt{1-y^2}} dz\, dy\, dx.$

(b) A CAS gives $\int_{0}^{1} \int_{0}^{x} \int_{0}^{\sqrt{1-y^2}} dz\, dy\, dx = \tfrac{\pi}{4} - \tfrac{1}{3}.$

(Or use Formulas 30 and 87 from the Table of Integrals.)

25. Here $f(x, y, z) = \dfrac{1}{\ln(1 + x + y + z)}$ and $\Delta V = 2 \cdot 4 \cdot 2 = 16$, so the Midpoint Rule gives

$\iiint_{B} f(x, y, z)\, dV \approx \sum_{i=1}^{l} \sum_{j=1}^{m} \sum_{k=1}^{n} f(\overline{x}_i, \overline{y}_j, \overline{z}_k)\, \Delta V$

$= 16[f(1, 2, 1) + f(1, 2, 3) + f(1, 6, 1) + f(1, 6, 3)$

$+ f(3, 2, 1) + f(3, 2, 3) + f(3, 6, 1) + f(3, 6, 3)]$

$= 16\left[\tfrac{1}{\ln 5} + \tfrac{1}{\ln 7} + \tfrac{1}{\ln 9} + \tfrac{1}{\ln 11} + \tfrac{1}{\ln 7} + \tfrac{1}{\ln 9} + \tfrac{1}{\ln 11} + \tfrac{1}{\ln 13} \right] \approx 60.533$

27. $E = \{(x, y, z) \mid 0 \le x \le 1, 0 \le z \le 1 - x, 0 \le y \le 2 - 2z\}$,

the solid bounded by the three coordinate planes and the planes

$z = 1 - x,\ y = 2 - 2z.$

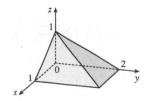

29.

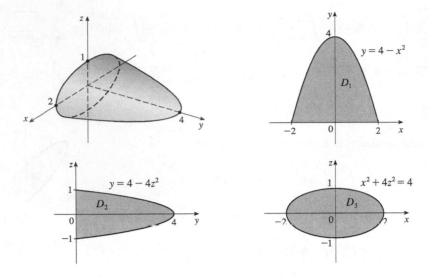

If D_1, D_2, D_3 are the projections of E on the xy-, yz-, and xz-planes, then

$$D_1 = \left\{(x,y) \mid -2 \le x \le 2, 0 \le y \le 4 - x^2\right\} = \left\{(x,y) \mid 0 \le y \le 4, -\sqrt{4-y} \le x \le \sqrt{4-y}\right\}$$

$$D_2 = \left\{(y,z) \mid 0 \le y \le 4, -\tfrac{1}{2}\sqrt{4-y} \le z \le \tfrac{1}{2}\sqrt{4-y}\right\} = \left\{(y,z) \mid -1 \le z \le 1, 0 \le y \le 4 - 4z^2\right\}$$

$$D_3 = \left\{(x,z) \mid x^2 + 4z^2 \le 4\right\}$$

Therefore

$$E = \left\{(x,y,z) \mid -2 \le x \le 2, 0 \le y \le 4 - x^2, -\tfrac{1}{2}\sqrt{4 - x^2 - y} \le z \le \tfrac{1}{2}\sqrt{4 - x^2 - y}\right\}$$

$$= \left\{(x,y,z) \mid 0 \le y \le 4, -\sqrt{4-y} \le x \le \sqrt{4-y}, -\tfrac{1}{2}\sqrt{4 - x^2 - y} \le z \le \tfrac{1}{2}\sqrt{4 - x^2 - y}\right\}$$

$$= \left\{(x,y,z) \mid -1 \le z \le 1, 0 \le y \le 4 - 4z^2, -\sqrt{4 - y - 4z^2} \le x \le \sqrt{4 - y - 4z^2}\right\}$$

$$= \left\{(x,y,z) \mid 0 \le y \le 4, -\tfrac{1}{2}\sqrt{4-y} \le z \le \tfrac{1}{2}\sqrt{4-y}, -\sqrt{4 - y - 4z^2} \le x \le \sqrt{4 - y - 4z^2}\right\}$$

$$= \left\{(x,y,z) \mid -2 \le x \le 2, -\tfrac{1}{2}\sqrt{4 - x^2} \le z \le \tfrac{1}{2}\sqrt{4 - x^2}, 0 \le y \le 4 - x^2 - 4z^2\right\}$$

$$= \left\{(x,y,z) \mid -1 \le z \le 1, -\sqrt{4 - 4z^2} \le x \le \sqrt{4 - 4z^2}, 0 \le y \le 4 - x^2 - 4z^2\right\}$$

Then

$$\iiint_E f(x,y,z)\,dV = \int_{-2}^{2}\int_{0}^{4-x^2}\int_{-\sqrt{4-x^2-y}/2}^{\sqrt{4-x^2-y}/2} f(x,y,z)\,dz\,dy\,dx = \int_{0}^{4}\int_{-\sqrt{4-y}}^{\sqrt{4-y}}\int_{-\sqrt{4-x^2-y}/2}^{\sqrt{4-x^2-y}/2} f(x,y,z)\,dz\,dx\,dy$$

$$= \int_{-1}^{1}\int_{0}^{4-4z^2}\int_{-\sqrt{4-y-4z^2}}^{\sqrt{4-y-4z^2}} f(x,y,z)\,dx\,dy\,dz = \int_{0}^{4}\int_{-\sqrt{4-y}/2}^{\sqrt{4-y}/2}\int_{-\sqrt{4-y-4z^2}}^{\sqrt{4-y-4z^2}} f(x,y,z)\,dx\,dz\,dy$$

$$= \int_{-2}^{2}\int_{-\sqrt{4-x^2}/2}^{\sqrt{4-x^2}/2}\int_{0}^{4-x^2-4z^2} f(x,y,z)\,dy\,dz\,dx = \int_{-1}^{1}\int_{-\sqrt{4-4z^2}}^{\sqrt{4-4z^2}}\int_{0}^{4-x^2-4z^2} f(x,y,z)\,dy\,dx\,dz$$

31.

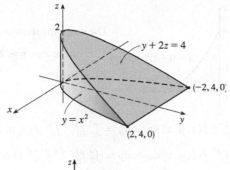

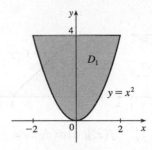

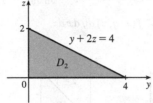

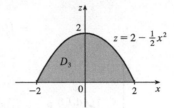

If D_1, D_2, and D_3 are the projections of E on the xy-, yz-, and xz-planes, then

$$D_1 = \left\{ (x,y) \mid -2 \leq x \leq 2, x^2 \leq y \leq 4 \right\} = \left\{ (x,y) \mid 0 \leq y \leq 4, -\sqrt{y} \leq x \leq \sqrt{y} \right\},$$

$$D_2 = \left\{ (y,z) \mid 0 \leq y \leq 4, 0 \leq z \leq 2 - \tfrac{1}{2}y \right\} = \left\{ (y,z) \mid 0 \leq z \leq 2, 0 \leq y \leq 4 - 2z \right\}, \text{ and}$$

$$D_3 = \left\{ (x,z) \mid -2 \leq x \leq 2, 0 \leq z \leq 2 - \tfrac{1}{2}x^2 \right\} = \left\{ (x,z) \mid 0 \leq z \leq 2, -\sqrt{4-2z} \leq x \leq \sqrt{4-2z} \right\}$$

Therefore

$$E = \left\{ (x,y,z) \mid -2 \leq x \leq 2, x^2 \leq y \leq 4, 0 \leq z \leq 2 - \tfrac{1}{2}y \right\}$$

$$= \left\{ (x,y,z) \mid 0 \leq y \leq 4, -\sqrt{y} \leq x \leq \sqrt{y}, 0 \leq z \leq 2 - \tfrac{1}{2}y \right\}$$

$$= \left\{ (x,y,z) \mid 0 \leq y \leq 4, 0 \leq z \leq 2 - \tfrac{1}{2}y, -\sqrt{y} \leq x \leq \sqrt{y} \right\}$$

$$= \left\{ (x,y,z) \mid 0 \leq z \leq 2, 0 \leq y \leq 4 - 2z, -\sqrt{y} \leq x \leq \sqrt{y} \right\}$$

$$= \left\{ (x,y,z) \mid -2 \leq x \leq 2, 0 \leq z \leq 2 - \tfrac{1}{2}x^2, x^2 \leq y \leq 4 - 2z \right\}$$

$$= \left\{ (x,y,z) \mid 0 \leq z \leq 2, -\sqrt{4-2z} \leq x \leq \sqrt{4-2z}, x^2 \leq y \leq 4 - 2z \right\}$$

Then

$$\iiint_E f(x,y,z)\,dV = \int_{-2}^{2} \int_{x^2}^{4} \int_{0}^{2-y/2} f(x,y,z)\,dz\,dy\,dx = \int_{0}^{4} \int_{-\sqrt{y}}^{\sqrt{y}} \int_{0}^{2-y/2} f(x,y,z)\,dz\,dx\,dy$$

$$= \int_{0}^{4} \int_{0}^{2-y/2} \int_{-\sqrt{y}}^{\sqrt{y}} f(x,y,z)\,dx\,dz\,dy = \int_{0}^{2} \int_{0}^{4-2z} \int_{-\sqrt{y}}^{\sqrt{y}} f(x,y,z)\,dx\,dy\,dz$$

$$= \int_{-2}^{2} \int_{0}^{2-x^2/2} \int_{x^2}^{4-2z} f(x,y,z)\,dy\,dz\,dx = \int_{0}^{2} \int_{-\sqrt{4-2z}}^{\sqrt{4-2z}} \int_{x^2}^{4-2z} f(x,y,z)\,dy\,dx\,dz$$

33.

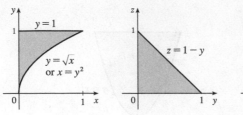

The diagrams show the projections of E on the xy-, yz-, and xz-planes. Therefore

$$\int_0^1 \int_{\sqrt{x}}^1 \int_0^{1-y} f(x,y,z)\, dz\, dy\, dx = \int_0^1 \int_0^{y^2} \int_0^{1-y} f(x,y,z)\, dz\, dx\, dy = \int_0^1 \int_0^{1-z} \int_0^{y^2} f(x,y,z)\, dx\, dy\, dz$$

$$= \int_0^1 \int_0^{1-y} \int_0^{y^2} f(x,y,z)\, dx\, dz\, dy = \int_0^1 \int_0^{1-\sqrt{x}} \int_{\sqrt{x}}^{1-z} f(x,y,z)\, dy\, dz\, dx$$

$$= \int_0^1 \int_0^{(1-z)^2} \int_{\sqrt{x}}^{1-z} f(x,y,z)\, dy\, dx\, dz$$

35.

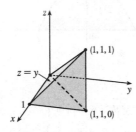 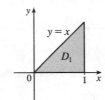 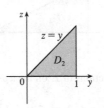 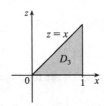

$\int_0^1 \int_y^1 \int_0^y f(x,y,z)\, dz\, dx\, dy = \iiint_E f(x,y,z)\, dV$ where $E = \{(x,y,z) \mid 0 \le z \le y, y \le x \le 1, 0 \le y \le 1\}$.

If D_1, D_2, and D_3 are the projections of E on the xy-, yz- and xz-planes then

$$D_1 = \{(x,y) \mid 0 \le y \le 1, y \le x \le 1\} = \{(x,y) \mid 0 \le x \le 1, 0 \le y \le x\},$$

$$D_2 = \{(y,z) \mid 0 \le y \le 1, 0 \le z \le y\} = \{(y,z) \mid 0 \le z \le 1, z \le y \le 1\}, \text{ and}$$

$$D_3 = \{(x,z) \mid 0 \le x \le 1, 0 \le z \le x\} = \{(x,z) \mid 0 \le z \le 1, z \le x \le 1\}.$$

Thus we also have

$$E = \{(x,y,z) \mid 0 \le x \le 1, 0 \le y \le x, 0 \le z \le y\} = \{(x,y,z) \mid 0 \le y \le 1, 0 \le z \le y, y \le x \le 1\}$$

$$= \{(x,y,z) \mid 0 \le z \le 1, z \le y \le 1, y \le x \le 1\} = \{(x,y,z) \mid 0 \le x \le 1, 0 \le z \le x, z \le y \le x\}$$

$$= \{(x,y,z) \mid 0 \le z \le 1, z \le x \le 1, z \le y \le x\}.$$

Then

$$\int_0^1 \int_y^1 \int_0^y f(x,y,z)\, dz\, dx\, dy = \int_0^1 \int_0^x \int_0^y f(x,y,z)\, dz\, dy\, dx = \int_0^1 \int_0^y \int_y^1 f(x,y,z)\, dx\, dz\, dy$$

$$= \int_0^1 \int_z^1 \int_y^1 f(x,y,z)\, dx\, dy\, dz = \int_0^1 \int_0^x \int_z^x f(x,y,z)\, dy\, dz\, dx$$

$$= \int_0^1 \int_z^1 \int_z^x f(x,y,z)\, dy\, dx\, dz$$

37. $m = \iiint_E \rho(x,y,z)\, dV = \int_0^1 \int_0^{\sqrt{x}} \int_0^{1+x+y} 2\, dz\, dy\, dx = \int_0^1 \int_0^{\sqrt{x}} 2(1+x+y)\, dy\, dx$

$= \int_0^1 \left[2y + 2xy + y^2 \right]_{y=0}^{y=\sqrt{x}} dx = \int_0^1 \left(2\sqrt{x} + 2x^{3/2} + x \right) dx = \left[\frac{4}{3}x^{3/2} + \frac{4}{5}x^{5/2} + \frac{1}{2}x^2 \right]_0^1 = \frac{79}{30}$

$M_{yz} = \iiint_E x\rho(x,y,z)\,dV = \int_0^1 \int_0^{\sqrt{x}} \int_0^{1+x+y} 2x\,dz\,dy\,dx = \int_0^1 \int_0^{\sqrt{x}} 2x(1+x+y)\,dy\,dx$

$= \int_0^1 \left[2xy + 2x^2y + xy^2\right]_{y=0}^{y=\sqrt{x}}\,dx = \int_0^1 (2x^{3/2} + 2x^{5/2} + x^2)\,dx = \left[\frac{4}{5}x^{5/2} + \frac{4}{7}x^{7/2} + \frac{1}{3}x^3\right]_0^1 = \frac{179}{105}$

$M_{xz} = \iiint_E y\rho(x,y,z)\,dV = \int_0^1 \int_0^{\sqrt{x}} \int_0^{1+x+y} 2y\,dz\,dy\,dx = \int_0^1 \int_0^{\sqrt{x}} 2y(1+x+y)\,dy\,dx$

$= \int_0^1 \left[y^2 + xy^2 + \frac{2}{3}y^3\right]_{y=0}^{y=\sqrt{x}}\,dx = \int_0^1 \left(x + x^2 + \frac{2}{3}x^{3/2}\right)\,dx = \left[\frac{1}{2}x^2 + \frac{1}{3}x^3 + \frac{4}{15}x^{5/2}\right]_0^1 = \frac{11}{10}$

$M_{xy} = \iiint_E z\rho(x,y,z)\,dV = \int_0^1 \int_0^{\sqrt{x}} \int_0^{1+x+y} 2z\,dz\,dy\,dx = \int_0^1 \int_0^{\sqrt{x}} \left[z^2\right]_{z=0}^{z=1+x+y}\,dy\,dx = \int_0^1 \int_0^{\sqrt{x}} (1+x+y)^2\,dy\,dx$

$= \int_0^1 \int_0^{\sqrt{x}} (1 + 2x + 2y + 2xy + x^2 + y^2)\,dy\,dx = \int_0^1 \left[y + 2xy + y^2 + xy^2 + x^2y + \frac{1}{3}y^3\right]_{y=0}^{y=\sqrt{x}}\,dx$

$= \int_0^1 \left(\sqrt{x} + \frac{7}{3}x^{3/2} + x + x^2 + x^{5/2}\right)\,dx = \left[\frac{2}{3}x^{3/2} + \frac{14}{15}x^{5/2} + \frac{1}{2}x^2 + \frac{1}{3}x^3 + \frac{2}{7}x^{7/2}\right]_0^1 = \frac{571}{210}$

Thus the mass is $\frac{79}{30}$ and the center of mass is $(\overline{x}, \overline{y}, \overline{z}) = \left(\dfrac{M_{yz}}{m}, \dfrac{M_{xz}}{m}, \dfrac{M_{xy}}{m}\right) = \left(\dfrac{358}{553}, \dfrac{33}{79}, \dfrac{571}{553}\right)$.

39. $m = \int_0^a \int_0^a \int_0^a (x^2 + y^2 + z^2)\,dx\,dy\,dz = \int_0^a \int_0^a \left[\frac{1}{3}x^3 + xy^2 + xz^2\right]_{x=0}^{x=a}\,dy\,dz = \int_0^a \int_0^a \left(\frac{1}{3}a^3 + ay^2 + az^2\right)\,dy\,dz$

$= \int_0^a \left[\frac{1}{3}a^3y + \frac{1}{3}ay^3 + ayz^2\right]_{y=0}^{y=a}\,dz = \int_0^a \left(\frac{2}{3}a^4 + a^2z^2\right)\,dz = \left[\frac{2}{3}a^4z + \frac{1}{3}a^2z^3\right]_0^a = \frac{2}{3}a^5 + \frac{1}{3}a^5 = a^5$

$M_{yz} = \int_0^a \int_0^a \int_0^a \left[x^3 + x(y^2 + z^2)\right]\,dx\,dy\,dz = \int_0^a \int_0^a \left[\frac{1}{4}a^4 + \frac{1}{2}a^2(y^2 + z^2)\right]\,dy\,dz$

$= \int_0^a \left(\frac{1}{4}a^5 + \frac{1}{6}a^5 + \frac{1}{2}a^3z^2\right)\,dz = \frac{1}{4}a^6 + \frac{1}{6}a^6 = \frac{7}{12}a^6 = M_{xz} = M_{xy}$ by symmetry of E and $\rho(x,y,z)$

Hence $(\overline{x}, \overline{y}, \overline{z}) = \left(\frac{7}{12}a, \frac{7}{12}a, \frac{7}{12}a\right)$.

41. $I_x = \int_0^L \int_0^L \int_0^L k(y^2 + z^2)\,dz\,dy\,dx = k\int_0^L \int_0^L \left(Ly^2 + \frac{1}{3}L^3\right)\,dy\,dx = k\int_0^L \frac{2}{3}L^4\,dx = \frac{2}{3}kL^5$.

By symmetry, $I_x = I_y = I_z = \frac{2}{3}kL^5$.

43. $I_z = \iiint_E (x^2 + y^2)\rho(x,y,z)\,dV = \iint\limits_{x^2+y^2\le a^2} \left[\int_0^h k(x^2+y^2)\,dz\right]\,dA = \iint\limits_{x^2+y^2\le a^2} k(x^2+y^2)h\,dA$

$= kh \int_0^{2\pi} \int_0^a (r^2)\,r\,dr\,d\theta = kh\int_0^{2\pi}\,d\theta \int_0^a r^3\,dr = kh(2\pi)\left[\frac{1}{4}r^4\right]_0^a = 2\pi kh \cdot \frac{1}{4}a^4 = \frac{1}{2}\pi kha^4$

45. (a) $m = \int_{-3}^3 \int_{-\sqrt{9-x^2}}^{\sqrt{9-x^2}} \int_1^{5-y} \sqrt{x^2+y^2}\,dz\,dy\,dx$

(b) $(\overline{x}, \overline{y}, \overline{z}) = \left(\dfrac{M_{yz}}{m}, \dfrac{M_{xz}}{m}, \dfrac{M_{xy}}{m}\right)$ where

$M_{yz} = \int_{-3}^3 \int_{-\sqrt{9-x^2}}^{\sqrt{9-x^2}} \int_1^{5-y} x\sqrt{x^2+y^2}\,dz\,dy\,dx$, $M_{xz} = \int_{-3}^3 \int_{-\sqrt{9-x^2}}^{\sqrt{9-x^2}} \int_1^{5-y} y\sqrt{x^2+y^2}\,dz\,dy\,dx$, and

$M_{xy} = \int_{-3}^3 \int_{-\sqrt{9-x^2}}^{\sqrt{9-x^2}} \int_1^{5-y} z\sqrt{x^2+y^2}\,dz\,dy\,dx$.

(c) $I_z = \int_{-3}^3 \int_{-\sqrt{9-x^2}}^{\sqrt{9-x^2}} \int_1^{5-y} (x^2+y^2)\sqrt{x^2+y^2}\,dz\,dy\,dx = \int_{-3}^3 \int_{-\sqrt{9-x^2}}^{\sqrt{9-x^2}} \int_1^{5-y} (x^2+y^2)^{3/2}\,dz\,dy\,dx$

47. (a) $m = \int_0^1 \int_0^{\sqrt{1-x^2}} \int_0^y (1+x+y+z)\, dz\, dy\, dx = \frac{3\pi}{32} + \frac{11}{24}$

(b) $(\bar{x}, \bar{y}, \bar{z}) = \left(m^{-1} \int_0^1 \int_0^{\sqrt{1-x^2}} \int_0^y x(1+x+y+z)\, dz\, dy\, dx, \right.$

$$m^{-1} \int_0^1 \int_0^{\sqrt{1-x^2}} \int_0^y y(1+x+y+z)\, dz\, dy\, dx,$$

$$\left. m^{-1} \int_0^1 \int_0^{\sqrt{1-x^2}} \int_0^y z(1+x+y+z)\, dz\, dy\, dx \right)$$

$$= \left(\frac{28}{9\pi + 44}, \frac{30\pi + 128}{45\pi + 220}, \frac{45\pi + 208}{135\pi + 660} \right)$$

(c) $I_z = \int_0^1 \int_0^{\sqrt{1-x^2}} \int_0^y (x^2 + y^2)(1+x+y+z)\, dz\, dy\, dx = \dfrac{68 + 15\pi}{240}$

49. (a) $f(x,y,z)$ is a joint density function, so we know $\iiint_{\mathbb{R}^3} f(x,y,z)\, dV = 1$. Here we have

$$\iiint_{\mathbb{R}^3} f(x,y,z)\, dV = \int_{-\infty}^{\infty} \int_{-\infty}^{\infty} \int_{-\infty}^{\infty} f(x,y,z)\, dz\, dy\, dx = \int_0^2 \int_0^2 \int_0^2 Cxyz\, dz\, dy\, dx$$

$$= C \int_0^2 x\, dx \int_0^2 y\, dy \int_0^2 z\, dz = C \left[\tfrac{1}{2}x^2\right]_0^2 \left[\tfrac{1}{2}y^2\right]_0^2 \left[\tfrac{1}{2}z^2\right]_0^2 = 8C$$

Then we must have $8C = 1 \;\Rightarrow\; C = \tfrac{1}{8}$.

(b) $P(X \le 1, Y \le 1, Z \le 1) = \int_{-\infty}^1 \int_{-\infty}^1 \int_{-\infty}^1 f(x,y,z)\, dz\, dy\, dx = \int_0^1 \int_0^1 \int_0^1 \tfrac{1}{8}xyz\, dz\, dy\, dx$

$$= \tfrac{1}{8} \int_0^1 x\, dx \int_0^1 y\, dy \int_0^1 z\, dz = \tfrac{1}{8} \left[\tfrac{1}{2}x^2\right]_0^1 \left[\tfrac{1}{2}y^2\right]_0^1 \left[\tfrac{1}{2}z^2\right]_0^1 = \tfrac{1}{8}\left(\tfrac{1}{2}\right)^3 = \tfrac{1}{64}$$

(c) $P(X+Y+Z \le 1) = P((X,Y,Z) \in E)$ where E is the solid region in the first octant bounded by the coordinate planes

and the plane $x+y+z = 1$. The plane $x+y+z = 1$ meets the xy-plane in the line $x+y = 1$, so we have

$$P(X+Y+Z \le 1) = \iiint_E f(x,y,z)\, dV = \int_0^1 \int_0^{1-x} \int_0^{1-x-y} \tfrac{1}{8}xyz\, dz\, dy\, dx$$

$$= \tfrac{1}{8} \int_0^1 \int_0^{1-x} xy\left[\tfrac{1}{2}z^2\right]_{z=0}^{z=1-x-y} dy\, dx = \tfrac{1}{16} \int_0^1 \int_0^{1-x} xy(1-x-y)^2\, dy\, dx$$

$$= \tfrac{1}{16} \int_0^1 \int_0^{1-x} \left[(x^3 - 2x^2 + x)y + (2x^2 - 2x)y^2 + xy^3\right] dy\, dx$$

$$= \tfrac{1}{16} \int_0^1 \left[(x^3 - 2x^2 + x)\tfrac{1}{2}y^2 + (2x^2 - 2x)\tfrac{1}{3}y^3 + x\left(\tfrac{1}{4}y^4\right)\right]_{y=0}^{y=1-x} dx$$

$$= \tfrac{1}{192} \int_0^1 (x - 4x^2 + 6x^3 - 4x^4 + x^5)\, dx = \tfrac{1}{192}\left(\tfrac{1}{30}\right) = \tfrac{1}{5760}$$

51. $V(E) = L^3 \;\Rightarrow\; f_{ave} = \dfrac{1}{L^3} \int_0^L \int_0^L \int_0^L xyz\, dx\, dy\, dz = \dfrac{1}{L^3} \int_0^L x\, dx \int_0^L y\, dy \int_0^L z\, dz$

$$= \dfrac{1}{L^3} \left[\dfrac{x^2}{2}\right]_0^L \left[\dfrac{y^2}{2}\right]_0^L \left[\dfrac{z^2}{2}\right]_0^L = \dfrac{1}{L^3} \dfrac{L^2}{2} \dfrac{L^2}{2} \dfrac{L^2}{2} = \dfrac{L^3}{8}$$

53. (a) The triple integral will attain its maximum when the integrand $1 - x^2 - 2y^2 - 3z^2$ is positive in the region E and negative

everywhere else. For if E contains some region F where the integrand is negative, the integral could be increased by

excluding F from E, and if E fails to contain some part G of the region where the integrand is positive, the integral could be increased by including G in E. So we require that $x^2 + 2y^2 + 3z^2 \le 1$. This describes the region bounded by the ellipsoid $x^2 + 2y^2 + 3z^2 = 1$.

(b) The maximum value of $\iiint_E (1 - x^2 - 2y^2 - 3z^2)\, dV$ occurs when E is the solid region bounded by the ellipsoid $x^2 + 2y^2 + 3z^2 = 1$. The projection of E on the xy-plane is the planar region bounded by the ellipse $x^2 + 2y^2 = 1$, so

$$E = \left\{ (x, y, z) \mid -1 \le x \le 1, -\sqrt{\tfrac{1}{2}(1 - x^2)} \le y \le \sqrt{\tfrac{1}{2}(1 - x^2)}, -\sqrt{\tfrac{1}{3}(1 - x^2 - 2y^2)} \le z \le \sqrt{\tfrac{1}{3}(1 - x^2 - 2y^2)} \right\}$$

and

$$\iiint_E (1 - x^2 - 2y^2 - 3z^2)\, dV = \int_{-1}^{1} \int_{-\sqrt{\frac{1}{2}(1-x^2)}}^{\sqrt{\frac{1}{2}(1-x^2)}} \int_{-\sqrt{\frac{1}{3}(1-x^2-2y^2)}}^{\sqrt{\frac{1}{3}(1-x^2-2y^2)}} (1 - x^2 - 2y^2 - 3z^2)\, dz\, dy\, dx = \frac{4\sqrt{6}}{45}\pi$$

using a CAS.

12.8 Triple Integrals in Cylindrical and Spherical Coordinates

1.

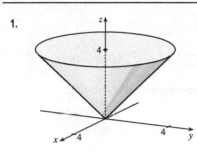

The region of integration is given in cylindrical coordinates by $E = \{(r, \theta, z) \mid 0 \le \theta \le 2\pi, 0 \le r \le 4, r \le z \le 4\}$. This represents the solid region bounded below by the cone $z = r$ and above by the horizontal plane $z = 4$.

$$\int_0^4 \int_0^{2\pi} \int_r^4 r\, dz\, d\theta\, dr = \int_0^4 \int_0^{2\pi} [rz]_{z=r}^{z=4}\, d\theta\, dr = \int_0^4 \int_0^{2\pi} r(4 - r)\, d\theta\, dr$$

$$= \int_0^4 (4r - r^2)\, dr \int_0^{2\pi} d\theta = \left[2r^2 - \tfrac{1}{3}r^3\right]_0^4 \left[\theta\right]_0^{2\pi}$$

$$= \left(32 - \tfrac{64}{3}\right)(2\pi) = \tfrac{64\pi}{3}$$

3.

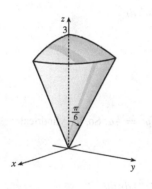

The region of integration is given in spherical coordinates by $E = \{(\rho, \theta, \phi) \mid 0 \le \rho \le 3, 0 \le \theta \le \pi/2, 0 \le \phi \le \pi/6\}$. This represents the solid region in the first octant bounded above by the sphere $\rho = 3$ and below by the cone $\phi = \pi/6$.

$$\int_0^{\pi/6} \int_0^{\pi/2} \int_0^3 \rho^2 \sin\phi\, d\rho\, d\theta\, d\phi = \int_0^{\pi/6} \sin\phi\, d\phi \int_0^{\pi/2} d\theta \int_0^3 \rho^2\, d\rho$$

$$= \left[-\cos\phi\right]_0^{\pi/6} \left[\theta\right]_0^{\pi/2} \left[\tfrac{1}{3}\rho^3\right]_0^3$$

$$= \left(1 - \frac{\sqrt{3}}{2}\right)\left(\frac{\pi}{2}\right)(9) = \frac{9\pi}{4}\left(2 - \sqrt{3}\right)$$

5. The solid E is most conveniently described if we use cylindrical coordinates:

$E = \left\{(r, \theta, z) \mid 0 \le \theta \le \frac{\pi}{2}, 0 \le r \le 3, 0 \le z \le 2\right\}$. Then

$\iiint_E f(x, y, z)\, dV = \int_0^{\pi/2} \int_0^3 \int_0^2 f(r\cos\theta, r\sin\theta, z)\, r\, dz\, dr\, d\theta$.

7. In cylindrical coordinates, E is given by $\{(r, \theta, z) \mid 0 \le \theta \le 2\pi, 0 \le r \le 4, -5 \le z \le 4\}$. So

$$\iiint_E \sqrt{x^2 + y^2}\, dV = \int_0^{2\pi} \int_0^4 \int_{-5}^4 \sqrt{r^2}\, r\, dz\, dr\, d\theta = \int_0^{2\pi} d\theta \int_0^4 r^2\, dr \int_{-5}^4 dz$$

$$= \left[\theta\right]_0^{2\pi} \left[\tfrac{1}{3}r^3\right]_0^4 \left[z\right]_{-5}^4 = (2\pi)\left(\tfrac{64}{3}\right)(9) = 384\pi$$

9. In cylindrical coordinates E is bounded by the paraboloid $z = 1 + r^2$, the cylinder $r^2 = 5$ or $r = \sqrt{5}$, and the xy-plane, so E is given by $\{(r, \theta, z) \mid 0 \le \theta \le 2\pi, 0 \le r \le \sqrt{5}, 0 \le z \le 1 + r^2\}$. Thus

$$\iiint_E e^z \, dV = \int_0^{2\pi} \int_0^{\sqrt{5}} \int_0^{1+r^2} e^z \, r \, dz \, dr \, d\theta = \int_0^{2\pi} \int_0^{\sqrt{5}} r \left[e^z \right]_{z=0}^{z=1+r^2} dr \, d\theta = \int_0^{2\pi} \int_0^{\sqrt{5}} r(e^{1+r^2} - 1) \, dr \, d\theta$$

$$= \int_0^{2\pi} d\theta \int_0^{\sqrt{5}} \left(re^{1+r^2} - r \right) dr = 2\pi \left[\tfrac{1}{2} e^{1+r^2} - \tfrac{1}{2} r^2 \right]_0^{\sqrt{5}} = \pi(e^6 - e - 5)$$

11. In cylindrical coordinates, E is bounded by the cylinder $r = 1$, the plane $z = 0$, and the cone $z = 2r$. So $E = \{(r, \theta, z) \mid 0 \le \theta \le 2\pi, 0 \le r \le 1, 0 \le z \le 2r\}$ and

$$\iiint_E x^2 \, dV = \int_0^{2\pi} \int_0^1 \int_0^{2r} r^2 \cos^2 \theta \, r \, dz \, dr \, d\theta = \int_0^{2\pi} \int_0^1 \left[r^3 \cos^2 \theta \, z \right]_{z=0}^{z=2r} dr \, d\theta = \int_0^{2\pi} \int_0^1 2r^4 \cos^2 \theta \, dr \, d\theta$$

$$= \int_0^{2\pi} \left[\tfrac{2}{5} r^5 \cos^2 \theta \right]_{r=0}^{r=1} d\theta = \tfrac{2}{5} \int_0^{2\pi} \cos^2 \theta \, d\theta = \tfrac{2}{5} \int_0^{2\pi} \tfrac{1}{2} (1 + \cos 2\theta) \, d\theta = \tfrac{1}{5} \left[\theta + \tfrac{1}{2} \sin 2\theta \right]_0^{2\pi} = \tfrac{2\pi}{5}$$

13. (a) The paraboloids intersect when $x^2 + y^2 = 36 - 3x^2 - 3y^2 \;\Rightarrow\; x^2 + y^2 = 9$, so the region of integration is $D = \{(x, y) \mid x^2 + y^2 \le 9\}$. Then, in cylindrical coordinates,

$E = \{(r, \theta, z) \mid r^2 \le z \le 36 - 3r^2, 0 \le r \le 3, 0 \le \theta \le 2\pi\}$ and

$$V = \int_0^{2\pi} \int_0^3 \int_{r^2}^{36-3r^2} r \, dz \, dr \, d\theta = \int_0^{2\pi} \int_0^3 (36r - 4r^3) \, dr \, d\theta = \int_0^{2\pi} \left[18r^2 - r^4 \right]_{r=0}^{r=3} d\theta = \int_0^{2\pi} 81 \, d\theta = 162\pi.$$

(b) For constant density K, $m = KV = 162\pi K$ from part (a). Since the region is homogeneous and symmetric, $M_{yz} = M_{xz} = 0$ and

$$M_{xy} = \int_0^{2\pi} \int_0^3 \int_{r^2}^{36-3r^2} (zK) \, r \, dz \, dr \, d\theta = K \int_0^{2\pi} \int_0^3 r \left[\tfrac{1}{2} z^2 \right]_{z=r^2}^{z=36-3r^2} dr \, d\theta$$

$$= \tfrac{K}{2} \int_0^{2\pi} \int_0^3 r((36 - 3r^2)^2 - r^4) \, dr \, d\theta = \tfrac{K}{2} \int_0^{2\pi} d\theta \int_0^3 (8r^5 - 216r^3 + 1296r) \, dr$$

$$= \tfrac{K}{2} (2\pi) \left[\tfrac{8}{6} r^6 - \tfrac{216}{4} r^4 + \tfrac{1296}{2} r^2 \right]_0^3 = \pi K (2430) = 2430\pi K$$

Thus $(\overline{x}, \overline{y}, \overline{z}) = \left(\dfrac{M_{yz}}{m}, \dfrac{M_{xz}}{m}, \dfrac{M_{xy}}{m} \right) = \left(0, 0, \dfrac{2430\pi K}{162\pi K} \right) = (0, 0, 15)$.

15. The paraboloid $z = 4x^2 + 4y^2$ intersects the plane $z = a$ when $a = 4x^2 + 4y^2$ or $x^2 + y^2 = \tfrac{1}{4} a$. So, in cylindrical coordinates, $E = \{(r, \theta, z) \mid 0 \le r \le \tfrac{1}{2} \sqrt{a}, 0 \le \theta \le 2\pi, 4r^2 \le z \le a\}$. Thus

$$m = \int_0^{2\pi} \int_0^{\sqrt{a}/2} \int_{4r^2}^{a} Kr \, dz \, dr \, d\theta = K \int_0^{2\pi} \int_0^{\sqrt{a}/2} (ar - 4r^3) \, dr \, d\theta$$

$$= K \int_0^{2\pi} \left[\tfrac{1}{2} ar^2 - r^4 \right]_{r=0}^{r=\sqrt{a}/2} d\theta = K \int_0^{2\pi} \tfrac{1}{16} a^2 \, d\theta = \tfrac{1}{8} a^2 \pi K$$

Since the region is homogeneous and symmetric, $M_{yz} = M_{xz} = 0$ and

$$M_{xy} = \int_0^{2\pi} \int_0^{\sqrt{a}/2} \int_{4r^2}^{a} Krz \, dz \, dr \, d\theta = K \int_0^{2\pi} \int_0^{\sqrt{a}/2} \left(\tfrac{1}{2} a^2 r - 8r^5 \right) dr \, d\theta$$

$$= K \int_0^{2\pi} \left[\tfrac{1}{4} a^2 r^2 - \tfrac{4}{3} r^6 \right]_{r=0}^{r=\sqrt{a}/2} d\theta = K \int_0^{2\pi} \tfrac{1}{24} a^3 \, d\theta = \tfrac{1}{12} a^3 \pi K$$

Hence $(\overline{x}, \overline{y}, \overline{z}) = \left(0, 0, \tfrac{2}{3} a \right)$.

17. In spherical coordinates, B is represented by $\{(\rho, \theta, \phi) \mid 0 \le \rho \le 5, 0 \le \theta \le 2\pi, 0 \le \phi \le \pi\}$. Thus

$$\iiint_B (x^2 + y^2 + z^2)^2 \, dV = \int_0^\pi \int_0^{2\pi} \int_0^5 (\rho^2)^2 \rho^2 \sin\phi \, d\rho \, d\theta \, d\phi = \int_0^\pi \sin\phi \, d\phi \int_0^{2\pi} d\theta \int_0^5 \rho^6 \, d\rho$$

$$= \left[-\cos\phi\right]_0^\pi \left[\theta\right]_0^{2\pi} \left[\tfrac{1}{7}\rho^7\right]_0^5 = (2)(2\pi)\left(\tfrac{78,125}{7}\right)$$

$$= \tfrac{312,500}{7}\pi \approx 140,249.7$$

19. In spherical coordinates, E is represented by $\{(\rho, \theta, \phi) \mid 1 \le \rho \le 2, 0 \le \theta \le \frac{\pi}{2}, 0 \le \phi \le \frac{\pi}{2}\}$. Thus

$$\iiint_E z \, dV = \int_0^{\pi/2} \int_0^{\pi/2} \int_1^2 (\rho\cos\phi)\,\rho^2 \sin\phi \, d\rho \, d\theta \, d\phi = \int_0^{\pi/2} \cos\phi\sin\phi \, d\phi \int_0^{\pi/2} d\theta \int_1^2 \rho^3 \, d\rho$$

$$= \left[\tfrac{1}{2}\sin^2\phi\right]_0^{\pi/2} \left[\theta\right]_0^{\pi/2} \left[\tfrac{1}{4}\rho^4\right]_1^2 = \left(\tfrac{1}{2}\right)\left(\tfrac{\pi}{2}\right)\left(\tfrac{15}{4}\right) = \tfrac{15\pi}{16}$$

21. $\iiint_E x^2 \, dV = \int_0^\pi \int_0^\pi \int_3^4 (\rho\sin\phi\cos\theta)^2 \rho^2 \sin\phi \, d\rho \, d\phi \, d\theta = \int_0^\pi \cos^2\theta \, d\theta \int_0^\pi \sin^3\phi \, d\phi \int_3^4 \rho^4 \, d\rho$

$$= \left[\tfrac{1}{2}\theta + \tfrac{1}{4}\sin 2\theta\right]_0^\pi \left[-\tfrac{1}{3}(2 + \sin^2\phi)\cos\phi\right]_0^\pi \left[\tfrac{1}{5}\rho^5\right]_3^4 = \left(\tfrac{\pi}{2}\right)\left(\tfrac{2}{3} + \tfrac{2}{3}\right)\tfrac{1}{5}(4^5 - 3^5) = \tfrac{1562}{15}\pi$$

23. The solid region is given by $E = \{(\rho, \theta, \phi) \mid 0 \le \rho \le a, 0 \le \theta \le 2\pi, \frac{\pi}{6} \le \phi \le \frac{\pi}{3}\}$ and its volume is

$$V = \iiint_E dV = \int_{\pi/6}^{\pi/3} \int_0^{2\pi} \int_0^a \rho^2 \sin\phi \, d\rho \, d\theta \, d\phi = \int_{\pi/6}^{\pi/3} \sin\phi \, d\phi \int_0^{2\pi} d\theta \int_0^a \rho^2 \, d\rho$$

$$= \left[-\cos\phi\right]_{\pi/6}^{\pi/3} \left[\theta\right]_0^{2\pi} \left[\tfrac{1}{3}\rho^3\right]_0^a = \left(-\tfrac{1}{2} + \tfrac{\sqrt{3}}{2}\right)(2\pi)\left(\tfrac{1}{3}a^3\right) = \tfrac{\sqrt{3}-1}{3}\pi a^3$$

25. (a) Since $\rho = 4\cos\phi$ implies $\rho^2 = 4\rho\cos\phi$, the equation is that of a sphere of radius 2 with center at $(0, 0, 2)$. Thus

$$V = \int_0^{2\pi} \int_0^{\pi/3} \int_0^{4\cos\phi} \rho^2 \sin\phi \, d\rho \, d\phi \, d\theta = \int_0^{2\pi} \int_0^{\pi/3} \left[\tfrac{1}{3}\rho^3\right]_{\rho=0}^{\rho=4\cos\phi} \sin\phi \, d\phi \, d\theta = \int_0^{2\pi} \int_0^{\pi/3} \left(\tfrac{64}{3}\cos^3\phi\right)\sin\phi \, d\phi \, d\theta$$

$$= \int_0^{2\pi} \left[-\tfrac{16}{3}\cos^4\phi\right]_{\phi=0}^{\phi=\pi/3} d\theta = \int_0^{2\pi} -\tfrac{16}{3}\left(\tfrac{1}{16} - 1\right) d\theta = 5\theta\Big]_0^{2\pi} = 10\pi$$

(b) By the symmetry of the problem $M_{yz} = M_{xz} = 0$. Then

$$M_{xy} = \int_0^{2\pi} \int_0^{\pi/3} \int_0^{4\cos\phi} \rho^3 \cos\phi\sin\phi \, d\rho \, d\phi \, d\theta = \int_0^{2\pi} \int_0^{\pi/3} \cos\phi\sin\phi \left(64\cos^4\phi\right) d\phi \, d\theta$$

$$= \int_0^{2\pi} 64 \left[-\tfrac{1}{6}\cos^6\phi\right]_{\phi=0}^{\phi=\pi/3} d\theta = \int_0^{2\pi} \tfrac{21}{2} \, d\theta = 21\pi$$

Hence $(\overline{x}, \overline{y}, \overline{z}) = (0, 0, 2.1)$.

27. By the symmetry of the region, $M_{xy} = 0$ and $M_{yz} = 0$. Assuming constant density K,

$$m = \iiint_E K \, dV = K \int_0^\pi \int_0^\pi \int_3^4 \rho^2 \sin\phi \, d\rho \, d\phi \, d\theta = K \int_0^\pi d\theta \int_0^\pi \sin\phi \, d\phi \int_3^4 \rho^2 \, d\rho$$

$$= K\pi \left[-\cos\phi\right]_0^\pi \left[\tfrac{1}{3}\rho^3\right]_3^4 = 2K\pi \cdot \tfrac{37}{3} = \tfrac{74}{3}\pi K$$

and $M_{xz} = \iiint_E y K \, dV = K \int_0^\pi \int_0^\pi \int_3^4 (\rho\sin\phi\sin\theta)\,\rho^2 \sin\phi \, d\rho \, d\phi \, d\theta = K \int_0^\pi \sin\theta \, d\theta \int_0^\pi \sin^2\phi \, d\phi \int_3^4 \rho^3 \, d\rho$

$$= K\left[-\cos\theta\right]_0^\pi \left[\tfrac{1}{2}\phi - \tfrac{1}{4}\sin 2\phi\right]_0^\pi \left[\tfrac{1}{4}\rho^4\right]_3^4 = K(2)\left(\tfrac{\pi}{2}\right)\tfrac{1}{4}(256 - 81) = \tfrac{175}{4}\pi K$$

Thus the centroid is $(\overline{x}, \overline{y}, \overline{z}) = \left(\dfrac{M_{yz}}{m}, \dfrac{M_{xz}}{m}, \dfrac{M_{xy}}{m}\right) = \left(0, \dfrac{175\pi K/4}{74\pi K/3}, 0\right) = \left(0, \tfrac{525}{296}, 0\right)$.

29. (a) The density function is $\rho(x, y, z) = K$, a constant, and by the symmetry of the problem $M_{xz} = M_{yz} = 0$. Then

$$M_{xy} = \int_0^{2\pi} \int_0^{\pi/2} \int_0^a K\rho^3 \sin\phi \cos\phi \, d\rho \, d\phi \, d\theta = \frac{1}{2}\pi K a^4 \int_0^{\pi/2} \sin\phi \cos\phi \, d\phi = \frac{1}{8}\pi K a^4.$$ But the mass is K(volume of

the hemisphere) $= \frac{2}{3}\pi K a^3$, so the centroid is $\left(0, 0, \frac{3}{8}a\right)$.

(b) Place the center of the base at $(0, 0, 0)$; the density function is $\rho(x, y, z) = K$. By symmetry, the moments of inertia about

any two such diameters will be equal, so we just need to find I_x:

$$I_x = \int_0^{2\pi} \int_0^{\pi/2} \int_0^a (K\rho^2 \sin\phi) \rho^2 (\sin^2\phi \sin^2\theta + \cos^2\phi) \, d\rho \, d\phi \, d\theta$$

$$= K \int_0^{2\pi} \int_0^{\pi/2} (\sin^3\phi \sin^2\theta + \sin\phi \cos^2\phi)\left(\frac{1}{5}a^5\right) d\phi \, d\theta$$

$$= \frac{1}{5}Ka^5 \int_0^{2\pi} \left[\sin^2\theta \left(-\cos\phi + \frac{1}{3}\cos^3\phi\right) + \left(-\frac{1}{3}\cos^3\phi\right)\right]_{\phi=0}^{\phi=\pi/2} d\theta = \frac{1}{5}Ka^5 \int_0^{2\pi} \left[\frac{2}{3}\sin^2\theta + \frac{1}{3}\right] d\theta$$

$$= \frac{1}{5}Ka^5 \left[\frac{2}{3}\left(\frac{1}{2}\theta - \frac{1}{4}\sin 2\theta\right) + \frac{1}{3}\theta\right]_0^{2\pi} = \frac{1}{5}Ka^5 \left[\frac{2}{3}(\pi - 0) + \frac{1}{3}(2\pi - 0)\right] = \frac{4}{15}Ka^5\pi$$

31. In spherical coordinates $z = \sqrt{x^2 + y^2}$ becomes $\cos\phi = \sin\phi$ or $\phi = \frac{\pi}{4}$. Then

$$V = \int_0^{2\pi} \int_0^{\pi/4} \int_0^1 \rho^2 \sin\phi \, d\rho \, d\phi \, d\theta = \int_0^{2\pi} d\theta \int_0^{\pi/4} \sin\phi \, d\phi \int_0^1 \rho^2 \, d\rho = 2\pi\left(-\frac{\sqrt{2}}{2} + 1\right)\left(\frac{1}{3}\right) = \frac{1}{3}\pi(2 - \sqrt{2}),$$

$$M_{xy} = \int_0^{2\pi} \int_0^{\pi/4} \int_0^1 \rho^3 \sin\phi \cos\phi \, d\rho \, d\phi \, d\theta = 2\pi\left[-\frac{1}{4}\cos 2\phi\right]_0^{\pi/4}\left(\frac{1}{4}\right) = \frac{\pi}{8}$$ and by symmetry $M_{yz} = M_{xz} = 0$.

Hence $(\overline{x}, \overline{y}, \overline{z}) = \left(0, 0, \dfrac{3}{8(2 - \sqrt{2})}\right)$.

33. In cylindrical coordinates the paraboloid is given by $z = r^2$ and the plane by $z = 2r\sin\theta$ and they intersect in the circle

$r = 2\sin\theta$. Then $\iiint_E z \, dV = \int_0^\pi \int_0^{2\sin\theta} \int_{r^2}^{2r\sin\theta} rz \, dz \, dr \, d\theta = \frac{5\pi}{6}$ [using a CAS].

35. The region of integration is the region above the cone $z = \sqrt{x^2 + y^2}$, or $z = r$, and below the plane $z = 2$. Also, we have

$-2 \le y \le 2$ with $-\sqrt{4 - y^2} \le x \le \sqrt{4 - y^2}$ which describes a circle of radius 2 in the xy-plane centered at $(0, 0)$. Thus,

$$\int_{-2}^{2} \int_{-\sqrt{4-y^2}}^{\sqrt{4-y^2}} \int_{\sqrt{x^2+y^2}}^{2} xz \, dz \, dx \, dy = \int_0^{2\pi} \int_0^2 \int_r^2 (r\cos\theta) zr \, dz \, dr \, d\theta = \int_0^{2\pi} \int_0^2 \int_r^2 r^2 (\cos\theta) z \, dz \, dr \, d\theta$$

$$= \int_0^{2\pi} \int_0^2 r^2 (\cos\theta) \left[\frac{1}{2}z^2\right]_{z=r}^{z=2} dr \, d\theta = \frac{1}{2}\int_0^{2\pi} \int_0^2 r^2 (\cos\theta)\left(4 - r^2\right) dr \, d\theta$$

$$= \frac{1}{2}\int_0^{2\pi} \cos\theta \, d\theta \int_0^2 \left(4r^2 - r^4\right) dr = \frac{1}{2}[\sin\theta]_0^{2\pi} \left[\frac{4}{3}r^3 - \frac{1}{5}r^5\right]_0^2 = 0$$

37. The region E of integration is the region above the cone $z = \sqrt{x^2 + y^2}$ and below the sphere $x^2 + y^2 + z^2 = 2$ in the first

octant. Because E is in the first octant we have $0 \le \theta \le \frac{\pi}{2}$. The cone has equation $\phi = \frac{\pi}{4}$ (as in Example 4), so $0 \le \phi \le \frac{\pi}{4}$,

and $0 \le \rho \le \sqrt{2}$. So the integral becomes

$$\int_0^{\pi/4} \int_0^{\pi/2} \int_0^{\sqrt{2}} (\rho\sin\phi\cos\theta)(\rho\sin\phi\sin\theta) \rho^2 \sin\phi \, d\rho \, d\theta \, d\phi$$

$$= \int_0^{\pi/4} \sin^3\phi \, d\phi \int_0^{\pi/2} \sin\theta\cos\theta \, d\theta \int_0^{\sqrt{2}} \rho^4 \, d\rho = \left(\int_0^{\pi/4} (1 - \cos^2\phi)\sin\phi \, d\phi\right) \left[\frac{1}{2}\sin^2\theta\right]_0^{\pi/2} \left[\frac{1}{5}\rho^5\right]_0^{\sqrt{2}}$$

$$= \left[\frac{1}{3}\cos^3\phi - \cos\phi\right]_0^{\pi/4} \cdot \frac{1}{2} \cdot \frac{1}{5}\left(\sqrt{2}\right)^5 = \left[\frac{\sqrt{2}}{12} - \frac{\sqrt{2}}{2} - \left(\frac{1}{3} - 1\right)\right] \cdot \frac{2\sqrt{2}}{5} = \frac{4\sqrt{2} - 5}{15}$$

39. If E is the solid enclosed by the surface $\rho = 1 + \frac{1}{5}\sin 6\theta \sin 5\phi$, it can be described in spherical coordinates as

$E = \left\{ (\rho, \theta, \phi) \mid 0 \le \rho \le 1 + \frac{1}{5}\sin 6\theta \sin 5\phi, 0 \le \theta \le 2\pi, 0 \le \phi \le \pi \right\}$. Its volume is given by

$V(E) = \iiint_E dV = \int_0^\pi \int_0^{2\pi} \int_0^{1 + (\sin 6\theta \sin 5\phi)/5} \rho^2 \sin\phi \, d\rho \, d\theta \, d\phi = \frac{136\pi}{99}$ [using a CAS].

41. (a) The mountain comprises a solid conical region C. The work done in lifting a small volume of material ΔV with density

$g(P)$ to a height $h(P)$ above sea level is $h(P)g(P)\,\Delta V$. Summing over the whole mountain we get

$W = \iiint_C h(P)g(P)\,dV$.

(b) Here C is a solid right circular cone with radius $R = 62{,}000$ ft, height $H = 12{,}400$ ft,

and density $g(P) = 200$ lb/ft^3 at all points P in C. We use cylindrical coordinates:

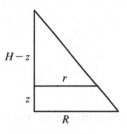

$W = \int_0^{2\pi} \int_0^H \int_0^{R(1-z/H)} z \cdot 200r \, dr \, dz \, d\theta = 2\pi \int_0^H 200z \left[\frac{1}{2}r^2 \right]_{r=0}^{r=R(1-z/H)} dz$

$= 400\pi \int_0^H z \frac{R^2}{2} \left(1 - \frac{z}{H} \right)^2 dz = 200\pi R^2 \int_0^H \left(z - \frac{2z^2}{H} + \frac{z^3}{H^2} \right) dz$

$= 200\pi R^2 \left[\frac{z^2}{2} - \frac{2z^3}{3H} + \frac{z^4}{4H^2} \right]_0^H = 200\pi R^2 \left(\frac{H^2}{2} - \frac{2H^2}{3} + \frac{H^2}{4} \right)$

$= \frac{50}{3}\pi R^2 H^2 = \frac{50}{3}\pi (62{,}000)^2 (12{,}400)^2 \approx 3.1 \times 10^{19}$ ft-lb

$\frac{r}{R} = \frac{H-z}{H} = 1 - \frac{z}{H}$

12.9   Change of Variables in Multiple Integrals

1. $x = 5u - v, \ y = u + 3v$.

The Jacobian is $\dfrac{\partial(x,y)}{\partial(u,v)} = \begin{vmatrix} \partial x/\partial u & \partial x/\partial v \\ \partial y/\partial u & \partial y/\partial v \end{vmatrix} = \begin{vmatrix} 5 & -1 \\ 1 & 3 \end{vmatrix} = 5(3) - (-1)(1) = 16.$

3. $x = e^{-r}\sin\theta, \ y = e^r\cos\theta$.

$\dfrac{\partial(x,y)}{\partial(r,\theta)} = \begin{vmatrix} \partial x/\partial r & \partial x/\partial\theta \\ \partial y/\partial r & \partial y/\partial\theta \end{vmatrix} = \begin{vmatrix} -e^{-r}\sin\theta & e^{-r}\cos\theta \\ e^r\cos\theta & -e^r\sin\theta \end{vmatrix} = e^{-r}e^r\sin^2\theta - e^{-r}e^r\cos^2\theta = \sin^2\theta - \cos^2\theta$ or $-\cos 2\theta$

5. $x = u/v, \ y = v/w, \ z = w/u$.

$\dfrac{\partial(x,y,z)}{\partial(u,v,w)} = \begin{vmatrix} \partial x/\partial u & \partial x/\partial v & \partial x/\partial w \\ \partial y/\partial u & \partial y/\partial v & \partial y/\partial w \\ \partial z/\partial u & \partial z/\partial v & \partial z/\partial w \end{vmatrix} = \begin{vmatrix} 1/v & -u/v^2 & 0 \\ 0 & 1/w & -v/w^2 \\ -w/u^2 & 0 & 1/u \end{vmatrix}$

$= \dfrac{1}{v}\begin{vmatrix} 1/w & -v/w^2 \\ 0 & 1/u \end{vmatrix} - \left(-\dfrac{u}{v^2} \right)\begin{vmatrix} 0 & -v/w^2 \\ -w/u^2 & 1/u \end{vmatrix} + 0\begin{vmatrix} 0 & 1/w \\ -w/u^2 & 0 \end{vmatrix}$

$= \dfrac{1}{v}\left(\dfrac{1}{uw} - 0 \right) + \dfrac{u}{v^2}\left(0 - \dfrac{v}{u^2 w} \right) + 0 = \dfrac{1}{uvw} - \dfrac{1}{uvw} = 0$

7. The transformation maps the boundary of S to the boundary of the image R, so we first look at side S_1 in the uv-plane. S_1 is

described by $v = 0, 0 \le u \le 3$, so $x = 2u + 3v = 2u$ and $y = u - v = u$. Eliminating u, we have $x = 2y, 0 \le x \le 6$. S_2 is

the line segment $u = 3, 0 \le v \le 2$, so $x = 6 + 3v$ and $y = 3 - v$. Then $v = 3 - y \Rightarrow x = 6 + 3(3 - y) = 15 - 3y$,

$6 \le x \le 12$. S_3 is the line segment $v = 2, 0 \le u \le 3$, so $x = 2u + 6$ and $y = u - 2$, giving $u = y + 2 \Rightarrow x = 2y + 10$,

$6 \le x \le 12$. Finally, S_4 is the segment $u = 0, 0 \le v \le 2$, so $x = 3v$ and $y = -v \Rightarrow x = -3y, 0 \le x \le 6$. The image of

set S is the region R shown in the xy-plane, a parallelogram bounded by these four segments.

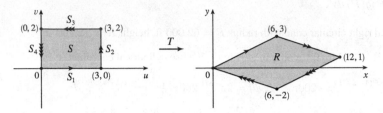

9. S_1 is the line segment $u = v, 0 \le u \le 1$, so $y = v = u$ and $x = u^2 = y^2$. Since $0 \le u \le 1$, the image is the portion of the

parabola $x = y^2, 0 \le y \le 1$. S_2 is the segment $v = 1, 0 \le u \le 1$, thus $y = v = 1$ and $x = u^2$, so $0 \le x \le 1$. The image is

the line segment $y = 1, 0 \le x \le 1$. S_3 is the segment $u = 0, 0 \le v \le 1$, so $x = u^2 = 0$ and $y = v \Rightarrow 0 \le y \le 1$. The

image is the segment $x = 0, 0 \le y \le 1$. Thus, the image of S is the region R in the first quadrant bounded by the parabola

$x = y^2$, the y-axis, and the line $y = 1$.

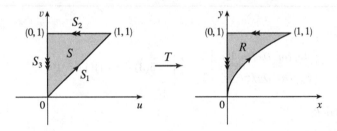

11. R is a parallelogram enclosed by the parallel lines $y = 2x - 1, y = 2x + 1$ and the parallel lines $y = 1 - x, y = 3 - x$. The

first pair of equations can be written as $y - 2x = -1, y - 2x = 1$. If we let $u = y - 2x$ then these lines are mapped to the

vertical lines $u = -1, u = 1$ in the uv-plane. Similarly, the second pair of equations can be written as $x + y = 1, x + y = 3$,

and setting $v = x + y$ maps these lines to the horizontal lines $v = 1, v = 3$ in the uv-plane. Boundary curves are mapped to

boundary curves under a transformation, so here the equations $u = y - 2x, v = x + y$ define a transformation T^{-1} that

maps R in the xy-plane to the square S enclosed by the lines $u = -1, u = 1, v = 1, v = 3$ in the uv-plane. To find the

transformation T that maps S to R we solve $u = y - 2x, v = x + y$ for x, y: Subtracting the first equation from the second

gives $v - u = 3x \Rightarrow x = \frac{1}{3}(v - u)$ and adding twice the second equation to the first gives $u + 2v = 3y \Rightarrow$

$y = \frac{1}{3}(u + 2v)$. Thus one possible transformation T (there are many) is given by $x = \frac{1}{3}(v - u), y = \frac{1}{3}(u + 2v)$.

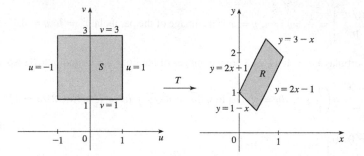

13. R is a portion of an annular region (see the figure) that is easily described in polar coordinates as

$R = \{(r,\theta) \mid 1 \le r \le \sqrt{2}, 0 \le \theta \le \pi/2\}$. If we converted a double integral over R to polar coordinates the resulting region

of integration is a rectangle (in the $r\theta$-plane), so we can create a transformation T here by letting u play the role of r and v the

role of θ. Thus T is defined by $x = u\cos v,\, y = u\sin v$ and T maps the rectangle $S = \{(u,v) \mid 1 \le u \le \sqrt{2}, 0 \le v \le \pi/2\}$

in the uv-plane to R in the xy-plane.

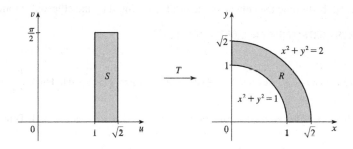

15. $\dfrac{\partial(x,y)}{\partial(u,v)} = \begin{vmatrix} 2 & 1 \\ 1 & 2 \end{vmatrix} = 3$ and $x - 3y = (2u+v) - 3(u+2v) = -u - 5v$. To find the region S in the uv-plane that

corresponds to R we first find the corresponding boundary under the given transformation. The line through $(0,0)$ and $(2,1)$ is

$y = \frac{1}{2}x$ which is the image of $u + 2v = \frac{1}{2}(2u + v) \;\Rightarrow\; v = 0$; the line through $(2,1)$ and $(1,2)$ is $x + y = 3$ which is the

image of $(2u + v) + (u + 2v) = 3 \;\Rightarrow\; u + v = 1$; the line through $(0,0)$ and $(1,2)$ is $y = 2x$ which is the image of

$u + 2v = 2(2u + v) \;\Rightarrow\; u = 0$. Thus S is the triangle $0 \le v \le 1 - u,\, 0 \le u \le 1$ in the uv-plane and

$$\iint_R (x - 3y)\, dA = \int_0^1 \int_0^{1-u} (-u - 5v)\, |3|\, dv\, du = -3 \int_0^1 \left[uv + \tfrac{5}{2}v^2 \right]_{v=0}^{v=1-u} du$$

$$= -3 \int_0^1 \left(u - u^2 + \tfrac{5}{2}(1-u)^2 \right) du = -3 \left[\tfrac{1}{2}u^2 - \tfrac{1}{3}u^3 - \tfrac{5}{6}(1-u)^3 \right]_0^1 = -3\left(\tfrac{1}{2} - \tfrac{1}{3} + \tfrac{5}{6} \right) = -3$$

17. $\dfrac{\partial(x,y)}{\partial(u,v)} = \begin{vmatrix} 2 & 0 \\ 0 & 3 \end{vmatrix} = 6$, $x^2 = 4u^2$ and the planar ellipse $9x^2 + 4y^2 \le 36$ is the image of the disk $u^2 + v^2 \le 1$. Thus

$$\iint_R x^2\, dA = \iint_{u^2+v^2\le 1} (4u^2)(6)\, du\, dv = \int_0^{2\pi} \int_0^1 (24r^2 \cos^2 \theta)\, r\, dr\, d\theta = 24 \int_0^{2\pi} \cos^2 \theta\, d\theta \int_0^1 r^3\, dr$$

$$= 24 \left[\tfrac{1}{2}x + \tfrac{1}{4}\sin 2x \right]_0^{2\pi} \left[\tfrac{1}{4}r^4 \right]_0^1 = 24(\pi)\left(\tfrac{1}{4}\right) = 6\pi$$

19. $\dfrac{\partial(x,y)}{\partial(u,v)} = \begin{vmatrix} 1/v & -u/v^2 \\ 0 & 1 \end{vmatrix} = \dfrac{1}{v}$, $xy = u$, $y = x$ is the image of the parabola $v^2 = u$, $y = 3x$ is the image of the parabola

$v^2 = 3u$, and the hyperbolas $xy = 1$, $xy = 3$ are the images of the lines $u = 1$ and $u = 3$ respectively. Thus

$$\iint_R xy\,dA = \int_1^3 \int_{\sqrt{u}}^{\sqrt{3u}} u\left(\dfrac{1}{v}\right) dv\,du = \int_1^3 u\left(\ln\sqrt{3u} - \ln\sqrt{u}\right) du = \int_1^3 u\ln\sqrt{3}\,du = 4\ln\sqrt{3} = 2\ln 3.$$

21. (a) $\dfrac{\partial(x,y,z)}{\partial(u,v,w)} = \begin{vmatrix} a & 0 & 0 \\ 0 & b & 0 \\ 0 & 0 & c \end{vmatrix} = abc$ and since $u = \dfrac{x}{a}$, $v = \dfrac{y}{b}$, $w = \dfrac{z}{c}$ the solid enclosed by the ellipsoid is the image of the

ball $u^2 + v^2 + w^2 \le 1$. So

$$\iiint_E dV = \iiint_{u^2+v^2+w^2\le 1} abc\,du\,dv\,dw = (abc)(\text{volume of the ball}) = \tfrac{4}{3}\pi abc$$

(b) If we approximate the surface of the earth by the ellipsoid $\dfrac{x^2}{6378^2} + \dfrac{y^2}{6378^2} + \dfrac{z^2}{6356^2} = 1$, then we can estimate

the volume of the earth by finding the volume of the solid E enclosed by the ellipsoid. From part (a), this is

$\iiint_E dV = \tfrac{4}{3}\pi(6378)(6378)(6356) \approx 1.083 \times 10^{12}$ km^3.

23. Letting $u = x - 2y$ and $v = 3x - y$, we have $x = \tfrac{1}{5}(2v - u)$ and $y = \tfrac{1}{5}(v - 3u)$. Then $\dfrac{\partial(x,y)}{\partial(u,v)} = \begin{vmatrix} -1/5 & 2/5 \\ -3/5 & 1/5 \end{vmatrix} = \dfrac{1}{5}$

and R is the image of the rectangle enclosed by the lines $u = 0$, $u = 4$, $v = 1$, and $v = 8$. Thus

$$\iint_R \dfrac{x-2y}{3x-y}\,dA = \int_0^4 \int_1^8 \dfrac{u}{v}\left|\dfrac{1}{5}\right| dv\,du = \dfrac{1}{5}\int_0^4 u\,du \int_1^8 \dfrac{1}{v}\,dv = \tfrac{1}{5}\left[\tfrac{1}{2}u^2\right]_0^4 \left[\ln|v|\right]_1^8 = \tfrac{8}{5}\ln 8.$$

25. Letting $u = y - x$, $v = y + x$, we have $y = \tfrac{1}{2}(u + v)$, $x = \tfrac{1}{2}(v - u)$. Then $\dfrac{\partial(x,y)}{\partial(u,v)} = \begin{vmatrix} -1/2 & 1/2 \\ 1/2 & 1/2 \end{vmatrix} = -\dfrac{1}{2}$ and R is the

image of the trapezoidal region with vertices $(-1,1)$, $(-2,2)$, $(2,2)$, and $(1,1)$. Thus

$$\iint_R \cos\dfrac{y-x}{y+x}\,dA = \int_1^2 \int_{-v}^v \cos\dfrac{u}{v}\left|-\dfrac{1}{2}\right| du\,dv = \dfrac{1}{2}\int_1^2 \left[v\sin\dfrac{u}{v}\right]_{u=-v}^{u=v} dv = \dfrac{1}{2}\int_1^2 2v\sin(1)\,dv = \tfrac{3}{2}\sin 1$$

27. Let $u = x + y$ and $v = -x + y$. Then $u + v = 2y \;\Rightarrow\; y = \tfrac{1}{2}(u + v)$ and $u - v = 2x \;\Rightarrow\; x = \tfrac{1}{2}(u - v)$.

$\dfrac{\partial(x,y)}{\partial(u,v)} = \begin{vmatrix} 1/2 & -1/2 \\ 1/2 & 1/2 \end{vmatrix} = \dfrac{1}{2}$. Now $|u| = |x + y| \le |x| + |y| \le 1 \;\Rightarrow\; -1 \le u \le 1$, and

$|v| = |-x + y| \le |x| + |y| \le 1 \;\Rightarrow\; -1 \le v \le 1$. R is the image of the square

region with vertices $(1,1)$, $(1,-1)$, $(-1,-1)$, and $(-1,1)$.

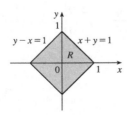

So $\iint_R e^{x+y}\,dA = \tfrac{1}{2}\int_{-1}^1 \int_{-1}^1 e^u\,du\,dv = \tfrac{1}{2}\left[e^u\right]_{-1}^1 \left[v\right]_{-1}^1 = e - e^{-1}$.

12 Review

CONCEPT CHECK

1. (a) A double Riemann sum of f is $\sum_{i=1}^{m} \sum_{j=1}^{n} f(x_{ij}^*, y_{ij}^*) \, \Delta A$, where ΔA is the area of each subrectangle and (x_{ij}^*, y_{ij}^*) is a sample point in each subrectangle. If $f(x,y) \geq 0$, this sum represents an approximation to the volume of the solid that lies above the rectangle R and below the graph of f.

(b) $\iint_R f(x,y) \, dA = \lim_{m,n \to \infty} \sum_{i=1}^{m} \sum_{j=1}^{n} f(x_{ij}^*, y_{ij}^*) \, \Delta A$

(c) If $f(x,y) \geq 0$, $\iint_R f(x,y) \, dA$ represents the volume of the solid that lies above the rectangle R and below the surface $z = f(x,y)$. If f takes on both positive and negative values, $\iint_R f(x,y) \, dA$ is the difference of the volume above R but below the surface $z = f(x,y)$ and the volume below R but above the surface $z = f(x,y)$.

(d) We usually evaluate $\iint_R f(x,y) \, dA$ as an iterated integral according to Fubini's Theorem (see Theorem 12.2.4).

(e) The Midpoint Rule for Double Integrals says that we approximate the double integral $\iint_R f(x,y) \, dA$ by the double Riemann sum $\sum_{i=1}^{m} \sum_{j=1}^{n} f(\overline{x}_i, \overline{y}_j) \, \Delta A$ where the sample points $(\overline{x}_i, \overline{y}_j)$ are the centers of the subrectangles.

(f) $f_{ave} = \dfrac{1}{A(R)} \iint_R f(x,y) \, dA$ where $A(R)$ is the area of R.

2. (a) See (1) and (2) and the accompanying discussion in Section 12.3.

(b) See (3) and the accompanying discussion in Section 12.3.

(c) See (5) and the preceding discussion in Section 12.3.

(d) See (6)–(11) in Section 12.3.

3. We may want to change from rectangular to polar coordinates in a double integral if the region R of integration is more easily described in polar coordinates. To accomplish this, we use $\iint_R f(x,y) \, dA = \int_\alpha^\beta \int_a^b f(r\cos\theta, r\sin\theta) \, r \, dr \, d\theta$ where R is given by $0 \leq a \leq r \leq b, \alpha \leq \theta \leq \beta$.

4. (a) $m = \iint_D \rho(x,y) \, dA$

(b) $M_x = \iint_D y\rho(x,y) \, dA$, $M_y = \iint_D x\rho(x,y) \, dA$

(c) The center of mass is $(\overline{x}, \overline{y})$ where $\overline{x} = \dfrac{M_y}{m}$ and $\overline{y} = \dfrac{M_x}{m}$.

(d) $I_x = \iint_D y^2 \rho(x,y) \, dA$, $I_y = \iint_D x^2 \rho(x,y) \, dA$, $I_0 = \iint_D (x^2 + y^2)\rho(x,y) \, dA$

5. (a) $P(a \leq X \leq b, c \leq Y \leq d) = \int_a^b \int_c^d f(x,y) \, dy \, dx$

(b) $f(x,y) \geq 0$ and $\iint_{\mathbb{R}^2} f(x,y) \, dA = 1$.

(c) The expected value of X is $\mu_1 = \iint_{\mathbb{R}^2} x f(x,y) \, dA$; the expected value of Y is $\mu_2 = \iint_{\mathbb{R}^2} y f(x,y) \, dA$.

6. (a) $A(S) = \iint_D |\mathbf{r}_u \times \mathbf{r}_v|\, dA$

(b) $A(S) = \iint_D \sqrt{1 + \left(\dfrac{\partial z}{\partial x}\right)^2 + \left(\dfrac{\partial z}{\partial y}\right)^2}\, dA$

(c) $A(S) = 2\pi \int_a^b f(x)\sqrt{1 + [f'(x)]^2}\, dx$

7. (a) $\iiint_B f(x,y,z)\, dV = \lim\limits_{l,m,n \to \infty} \sum\limits_{i=1}^{l} \sum\limits_{j=1}^{m} \sum\limits_{k=1}^{n} f\left(x_{ijk}^*, y_{ijk}^*, z_{ijk}^*\right) \Delta V$

(b) We usually evaluate $\iiint_B f(x,y,z)\, dV$ as an iterated integral according to Fubini's Theorem for Triple Integrals (see Theorem 12.7.4).

(c) See the paragraph following Example 12.7.1.

(d) See (5) and (6) and the accompanying discussion in Section 12.7.

(e) See (10) and the accompanying discussion in Section 12.7.

(f) See (11) and the preceding discussion in Section 12.7.

8. (a) $m = \iiint_E \rho(x,y,z)\, dV$

(b) $M_{yz} = \iiint_E x\rho(x,y,z)\, dV$, $\;M_{xz} = \iiint_E y\rho(x,y,z)\, dV$, $\;M_{xy} = \iiint_E z\rho(x,y,z)\, dV$.

(c) The center of mass is $(\overline{x}, \overline{y}, \overline{z})$ where $\overline{x} = \dfrac{M_{yz}}{m}$, $\overline{y} = \dfrac{M_{xz}}{m}$, and $\overline{z} = \dfrac{M_{xy}}{m}$.

(d) $I_x = \iiint_E (y^2 + z^2)\rho(x,y,z)\, dV$, $\;I_y = \iiint_E (x^2 + z^2)\rho(x,y,z)\, dV$, $\;I_z = \iiint_E (x^2 + y^2)\rho(x,y,z)\, dV$.

9. (a) See Formula 12.8.2 and the accompanying discussion.

(b) See Formula 12.8.4 and the accompanying discussion.

(c) We may want to change from rectangular to cylindrical or spherical coordinates in a triple integral if the region E of integration is more easily described in cylindrical or spherical coordinates or if the triple integral is easier to evaluate using cylindrical or spherical coordinates.

10. (a) $\dfrac{\partial(x,y)}{\partial(u,v)} = \begin{vmatrix} \partial x/\partial u & \partial x/\partial v \\ \partial y/\partial u & \partial y/\partial v \end{vmatrix} = \dfrac{\partial x}{\partial u}\dfrac{\partial y}{\partial v} - \dfrac{\partial x}{\partial v}\dfrac{\partial y}{\partial u}$

(b) See (9) and the accompanying discussion in Section 12.9.

(c) See (13) and the accompanying discussion in Section 12.9.

TRUE-FALSE QUIZ

1. This is true by Fubini's Theorem.

3. True. See the discussion following Example 4 on page 842.

5. True. By Equation 12.2.5 we can write $\int_0^1 \int_0^1 f(x)\,f(y)\,dy\,dx = \int_0^1 f(x)\,dx \int_0^1 f(y)\,dy$. But $\int_0^1 f(y)\,dy = \int_0^1 f(x)\,dx$ so

this becomes $\int_0^1 f(x)\,dx \int_0^1 f(x)\,dx = \left[\int_0^1 f(x)\,dx\right]^2$.

7. True: $\quad \iint_D \sqrt{4 - x^2 - y^2}\,dA = $ the volume under the surface $x^2 + y^2 + z^2 = 4$ and above the xy-plane

$$= \tfrac{1}{2} \left(\text{the volume of the sphere } x^2 + y^2 + z^2 = 4\right) = \tfrac{1}{2} \cdot \tfrac{4}{3}\pi(2)^3 = \tfrac{16}{3}\pi$$

9. The volume enclosed by the cone $z = \sqrt{x^2 + y^2}$ and the plane $z = 2$ is, in cylindrical coordinates,

$V = \int_0^{2\pi} \int_0^2 \int_r^2 r\,dz\,dr\,d\theta \neq \int_0^{2\pi} \int_0^2 \int_r^2 dz\,dr\,d\theta$, so the assertion is false.

EXERCISES

1. As shown in the contour map, we divide R into 9 equally sized subsquares, each with area $\Delta A = 1$. Then we approximate

$\iint_R f(x, y)\,dA$ by a Riemann sum with $m = n = 3$ and the sample points the upper right corners of each square, so

$$\iint_R f(x, y)\,dA \approx \sum_{i=1}^{3} \sum_{j=1}^{3} f(x_i, y_j)\,\Delta A$$

$$= \Delta A\left[f(1, 1) + f(1, 2) + f(1, 3) + f(2, 1) + f(2, 2) + f(2, 3) + f(3, 1) + f(3, 2) + f(3, 3)\right]$$

Using the contour lines to estimate the function values, we have

$$\iint_R f(x, y)\,dA \approx 1[2.7 + 4.7 + 8.0 + 4.7 + 6.7 + 10.0 + 6.7 + 8.6 + 11.9] \approx 64.0$$

3. $\int_1^2 \int_0^2 (y + 2xe^y)\,dx\,dy = \int_1^2 \left[xy + x^2 e^y\right]_{x=0}^{x=2} dy = \int_1^2 (2y + 4e^y)\,dy = \left[y^2 + 4e^y\right]_1^2$

$$= 4 + 4e^2 - 1 - 4e = 4e^2 - 4e + 3$$

5. $\int_0^1 \int_0^x \cos(x^2)\,dy\,dx = \int_0^1 \left[\cos(x^2)y\right]_{y=0}^{y=x} dx = \int_0^1 x\cos(x^2)\,dx = \tfrac{1}{2}\sin(x^2)\Big]_0^1 = \tfrac{1}{2}\sin 1$

7. $\int_0^\pi \int_0^1 \int_0^{\sqrt{1-y^2}} y\sin x\,dz\,dy\,dx = \int_0^\pi \int_0^1 \left[(y\sin x)z\right]_{z=0}^{z=\sqrt{1-y^2}} dy\,dx = \int_0^\pi \int_0^1 y\sqrt{1-y^2}\sin x\,dy\,dx$

$$= \int_0^\pi \left[-\tfrac{1}{3}(1-y^2)^{3/2}\sin x\right]_{y=0}^{y=1} dx = \int_0^\pi \tfrac{1}{3}\sin x\,dx = -\tfrac{1}{3}\cos x\Big]_0^\pi = \tfrac{2}{3}$$

9. The region R is more easily described by polar coordinates: $R = \{(r, \theta) \mid 2 \le r \le 4, 0 \le \theta \le \pi\}$. Thus

$\iint_R f(x, y)\,dA = \int_0^\pi \int_2^4 f(r\cos\theta, r\sin\theta)\,r\,dr\,d\theta$.

11.

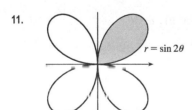

$r = \sin 2\theta$

The region whose area is given by $\int_0^{\pi/2} \int_0^{\sin 2\theta} r\,dr\,d\theta$ is

$\{(r, \theta) \mid 0 \le \theta \le \tfrac{\pi}{2}, 0 \le r \le \sin 2\theta\}$, which is the region contained in the

loop in the first quadrant of the four-leaved rose $r = \sin 2\theta$.

13.

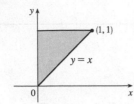

$$\int_0^1 \int_x^1 \cos(y^2)\, dy\, dx = \int_0^1 \int_0^y \cos(y^2)\, dx\, dy$$

$$= \int_0^1 \cos(y^2) \left[x \right]_{x=0}^{x=y} dy = \int_0^1 y \cos(y^2)\, dy$$

$$= \left[\tfrac{1}{2} \sin(y^2) \right]_0^1 = \tfrac{1}{2} \sin 1$$

15. $\iint_R y e^{xy}\, dA = \int_0^3 \int_0^2 y e^{xy}\, dx\, dy = \int_0^3 \left[e^{xy} \right]_{x=0}^{x=2} dy = \int_0^3 (e^{2y} - 1)\, dy = \left[\tfrac{1}{2} e^{2y} - y \right]_0^3 = \tfrac{1}{2} e^6 - 3 - \tfrac{1}{2} = \tfrac{1}{2} e^6 - \tfrac{7}{2}$

17.

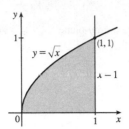

$$\iint_D \frac{y}{1+x^2}\, dA = \int_0^1 \int_0^{\sqrt{x}} \frac{y}{1+x^2}\, dy\, dx = \int_0^1 \frac{1}{1+x^2} \left[\tfrac{1}{2} y^2 \right]_{y=0}^{y=\sqrt{x}} dx$$

$$= \tfrac{1}{2} \int_0^1 \frac{x}{1+x^2}\, dx = \left[\tfrac{1}{4} \ln(1+x^2) \right]_0^1 = \tfrac{1}{4} \ln 2$$

19.

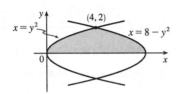

$$\iint_D y\, dA = \int_0^2 \int_{y^2}^{8-y^2} y\, dx\, dy$$

$$= \int_0^2 y \left[x \right]_{x=y^2}^{x=8-y^2} dy = \int_0^2 y(8 - y^2 - y^2)\, dy$$

$$= \int_0^2 (8y - 2y^3)\, dy = \left[4y^2 - \tfrac{1}{2} y^4 \right]_0^2 = 8$$

21.

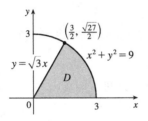

$$\iint_D (x^2 + y^2)^{3/2}\, dA = \int_0^{\pi/3} \int_0^3 (r^2)^{3/2} r\, dr\, d\theta$$

$$= \int_0^{\pi/3} d\theta \int_0^3 r^4\, dr = \left[\theta \right]_0^{\pi/3} \left[\tfrac{1}{5} r^5 \right]_0^3$$

$$= \frac{\pi}{3} \frac{3^5}{5} = \frac{81\pi}{5}$$

23. $\iiint_E xy\, dV = \int_0^3 \int_0^x \int_0^{x+y} xy\, dz\, dy\, dx = \int_0^3 \int_0^x xy \left[z \right]_{z=0}^{z=x+y} dy\, dx = \int_0^3 \int_0^x xy(x+y)\, dy\, dx$

$$= \int_0^3 \int_0^x (x^2 y + xy^2)\, dy\, dx = \int_0^3 \left[\tfrac{1}{2} x^2 y^2 + \tfrac{1}{3} xy^3 \right]_{y=0}^{y=x} dx = \int_0^3 \left(\tfrac{1}{2} x^4 + \tfrac{1}{3} x^4 \right) dx$$

$$= \tfrac{5}{6} \int_0^3 x^4\, dx = \left[\tfrac{1}{6} x^5 \right]_0^3 = \tfrac{81}{2} = 40.5$$

25. $\iiint_E y^2 z^2\, dV = \int_{-1}^1 \int_{-\sqrt{1-y^2}}^{\sqrt{1-y^2}} \int_0^{1-y^2-z^2} y^2 z^2\, dx\, dz\, dy = \int_{-1}^1 \int_{-\sqrt{1-y^2}}^{\sqrt{1-y^2}} y^2 z^2 (1 - y^2 - z^2)\, dz\, dy$

$$= \int_0^{2\pi} \int_0^1 (r^2 \cos^2 \theta)(r^2 \sin^2 \theta)(1 - r^2) r\, dr\, d\theta = \int_0^{2\pi} \int_0^1 \tfrac{1}{4} \sin^2 2\theta (r^5 - r^7)\, dr\, d\theta$$

$$= \int_0^{2\pi} \tfrac{1}{8} (1 - \cos 4\theta) \left[\tfrac{1}{6} r^6 - \tfrac{1}{8} r^8 \right]_{r=0}^{r=1} d\theta = \tfrac{1}{192} \left[\theta - \tfrac{1}{4} \sin 4\theta \right]_0^{2\pi} = \tfrac{2\pi}{192} = \tfrac{\pi}{96}$$

27. $\iiint_E yz\, dV = \int_{-2}^2 \int_0^{\sqrt{4-x^2}} \int_0^y yz\, dz\, dy\, dx = \int_{-2}^2 \int_0^{\sqrt{4-x^2}} \tfrac{1}{2} y^3\, dy\, dx = \int_0^\pi \int_0^2 \tfrac{1}{2} r^3 (\sin^3 \theta)\, r\, dr\, d\theta$

$$= \tfrac{16}{5} \int_0^\pi \sin^3 \theta\, d\theta = \tfrac{16}{5} \left[-\cos \theta + \tfrac{1}{3} \cos^3 \theta \right]_0^\pi = \tfrac{64}{15}$$

29. $V = \int_0^2 \int_1^4 (x^2 + 4y^2)\, dy\, dx = \int_0^2 \left[x^2 y + \tfrac{4}{3} y^3 \right]_{y=1}^{y=4} dx = \int_0^2 (3x^2 + 84)\, dx = 176$

31.

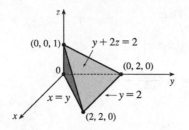

$$V = \int_0^2 \int_0^y \int_0^{(2-y)/2} dz\, dx\, dy = \int_0^2 \int_0^y \left(1 - \tfrac{1}{2}y\right) dx\, dy$$

$$= \int_0^2 \left(y - \tfrac{1}{2}y^2\right) dy = \tfrac{2}{3}$$

33. Using the wedge above the plane $z = 0$ and below the plane $z = mx$ and noting that we have the same volume for $m < 0$ as

for $m > 0$ (so use $m > 0$), we have

$$V = 2\int_0^{a/3} \int_0^{\sqrt{a^2-9y^2}} mx\, dx\, dy = 2\int_0^{a/3} \tfrac{1}{2}m(a^2 - 9y^2)\, dy = m\left[a^2 y - 3y^3\right]_0^{a/3} = m\left(\tfrac{1}{3}a^3 - \tfrac{1}{9}a^3\right) = \tfrac{2}{9}ma^3.$$

35. (a) $m = \int_0^1 \int_0^{1-y^2} y\, dx\, dy = \int_0^1 (y - y^3)\, dy = \tfrac{1}{2} - \tfrac{1}{4} = \tfrac{1}{4}$

(b) $M_y = \int_0^1 \int_0^{1-y^2} xy\, dx\, dy = \int_0^1 \tfrac{1}{2}y(1 - y^2)^2\, dy = -\tfrac{1}{12}(1 - y^2)^3\big]_0^1 = \tfrac{1}{12}$,

$M_x = \int_0^1 \int_0^{1-y^2} y^2\, dx\, dy = \int_0^1 (y^2 - y^4)\, dy = \tfrac{2}{15}$. Hence $(\overline{x}, \overline{y}) = \left(\tfrac{1}{3}, \tfrac{8}{15}\right)$.

(c) $I_x = \int_0^1 \int_0^{1-y^2} y^3\, dx\, dy = \int_0^1 (y^3 - y^5)\, dy = \tfrac{1}{12}$,

$I_y = \int_0^1 \int_0^{1-y^2} yx^2\, dx\, dy = \int_0^1 \tfrac{1}{3}y(1 - y^2)^3\, dy = -\tfrac{1}{24}(1 - y^2)^4\big]_0^1 = \tfrac{1}{24}$, $I_0 = I_x + I_y = \tfrac{1}{8}$

37. (a) The equation of the cone with the suggested orientation is $(h - z) = \tfrac{h}{a}\sqrt{x^2 + y^2}, 0 \le z \le h$. Then $V = \tfrac{1}{3}\pi a^2 h$ is the

volume of one frustum of a cone; by symmetry $M_{yz} = M_{xz} = 0$; and

$$M_{xy} = \iint\limits_{x^2 + y^2 \le a^2} \int_0^{h-(h/a)\sqrt{x^2+y^2}} z\, dz\, dA = \int_0^{2\pi} \int_0^a \int_0^{(h/a)(a-r)} rz\, dz\, dr\, d\theta = \pi \int_0^a r\frac{h^2}{a^2}(a - r)^2\, dr$$

$$= \frac{\pi h^2}{a^2} \int_0^a (a^2 r - 2ar^2 + r^3)\, dr = \frac{\pi h^2}{a^2}\left(\frac{a^4}{2} - \frac{2a^4}{3} + \frac{a^4}{4}\right) = \frac{\pi h^2 a^2}{12}$$

Hence the centroid is $(\overline{x}, \overline{y}, \overline{z}) = \left(0, 0, \tfrac{1}{4}h\right)$.

(b) $I_z = \int_0^{2\pi} \int_0^a \int_0^{(h/a)(a-r)} r^3\, dz\, dr\, d\theta = 2\pi \int_0^a \frac{h}{a}(ar^3 - r^4)\, dr = \frac{2\pi h}{a}\left(\frac{a^5}{4} - \frac{a^5}{5}\right) = \frac{\pi a^4 h}{10}$

39. Let D represent the given triangle; then D can be described as the area enclosed by the x- and y-axes and the line $y = 2 - 2x$,

or equivalently $D = \{(x, y) \mid 0 \le x \le 1, 0 \le y \le 2 - 2x\}$. We want to find the surface area of the part of the graph of

$z = x^2 + y$ that lies over D, so using Equation 12.6.6 we have

$$A(S) = \iint_D \sqrt{1 + \left(\frac{\partial z}{\partial x}\right)^2 + \left(\frac{\partial z}{\partial y}\right)^2}\, dA = \iint_D \sqrt{1 + (2x)^2 + (1)^2}\, dA = \int_0^1 \int_0^{2-2x} \sqrt{2 + 4x^2}\, dy\, dx$$

$$= \int_0^1 \sqrt{2 + 4x^2}\, [y]_{y=0}^{y=2-2x}\, dx = \int_0^1 (2 - 2x)\sqrt{2 + 4x^2}\, dx = \int_0^1 2\sqrt{2 + 4x^2}\, dx - \int_0^1 2x\sqrt{2 + 4x^2}\, dx$$

Using Formula 21 in the Table of Integrals with $a = \sqrt{2}$, $u = 2x$, and $du = 2\, dx$, we have

$\int 2\sqrt{2 + 4x^2}\, dx = x\sqrt{2 + 4x^2} + \ln\left(2x + \sqrt{2 + 4x^2}\right)$ If we substitute $u = 2 + 4x^2$ in the second integral, then

$du = 8x\,dx$ and $\int 2x\sqrt{2+4x^2}\,dx = \frac{1}{4}\int \sqrt{u}\,du = \frac{1}{4}\cdot\frac{2}{3}u^{3/2} = \frac{1}{6}(2+4x^2)^{3/2}$. Thus

$$A(S) = \left[x\sqrt{2+4x^2} + \ln\left(2x+\sqrt{2+4x^2}\right) - \frac{1}{6}(2+4x^2)^{3/2}\right]_0^1$$

$$= \sqrt{6} + \ln\left(2+\sqrt{6}\right) - \frac{1}{6}(6)^{3/2} - \ln\sqrt{2} + \frac{\sqrt{2}}{3} = \ln\frac{2+\sqrt{6}}{\sqrt{2}} + \frac{\sqrt{2}}{3}$$

$$= \ln\left(\sqrt{2}+\sqrt{3}\right) + \frac{\sqrt{2}}{3} \approx 1.6176$$

41.

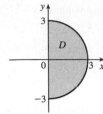

$$\int_0^3 \int_{-\sqrt{9-x^2}}^{\sqrt{9-x^2}} (x^3 + xy^2)\,dy\,dx = \int_0^3 \int_{-\sqrt{9-x^2}}^{\sqrt{9-x^2}} x(x^2+y^2)\,dy\,dx$$

$$= \int_{-\pi/2}^{\pi/2} \int_0^3 (r\cos\theta)(r^2)\,r\,dr\,d\theta$$

$$= \int_{-\pi/2}^{\pi/2} \cos\theta\,d\theta \int_0^3 r^4\,dr$$

$$= \left[\sin\theta\right]_{-\pi/2}^{\pi/2} \left[\frac{1}{5}r^5\right]_0^3 = 2\cdot\frac{1}{5}(243) = \frac{486}{5} = 97.2$$

43. From the graph, it appears that $1 - x^2 = e^x$ at $x \approx -0.71$ and at

$x = 0$, with $1 - x^2 > e^x$ on $(-0.71, 0)$. So the desired integral is

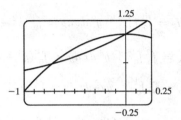

$$\iint_D y^2\,dA \approx \int_{-0.71}^0 \int_{e^x}^{1-x^2} y^2\,dy\,dx$$

$$= \frac{1}{3}\int_{-0.71}^0 \left[(1-x^2)^3 - e^{3x}\right]dx$$

$$= \frac{1}{3}\left[x - x^3 + \frac{3}{5}x^5 - \frac{1}{7}x^7 - \frac{1}{3}e^{3x}\right]_{-0.71}^0 \approx 0.0512$$

45. (a) $f(x,y)$ is a joint density function, so we know that $\iint_{\mathbb{R}^2} f(x,y)\,dA = 1$. Since $f(x,y) = 0$ outside the rectangle

$[0,3]\times[0,2]$, we can say

$$\iint_{\mathbb{R}^2} f(x,y)\,dA = \int_{-\infty}^{\infty}\int_{-\infty}^{\infty} f(x,y)\,dy\,dx = \int_0^3\int_0^2 C(x+y)\,dy\,dx$$

$$= C\int_0^3 \left[xy + \frac{1}{2}y^2\right]_{y=0}^{y=2} dx = C\int_0^3 (2x+2)\,dx = C\left[x^2+2x\right]_0^3 = 15C$$

Then $15C = 1 \;\Rightarrow\; C = \frac{1}{15}$.

(b) $P(X \le 2, Y \ge 1) = \int_{-\infty}^2 \int_1^{\infty} f(x,y)\,dy\,dx = \int_0^2\int_1^2 \frac{1}{15}(x,y)\,dy\,dx = \frac{1}{15}\int_0^2 \left[xy + \frac{1}{2}y^2\right]_{y=1}^{y=2} dx$

$= \frac{1}{15}\int_0^2 \left(x + \frac{3}{2}\right)dx = \frac{1}{15}\left[\frac{1}{2}x^2 + \frac{3}{2}x\right]_0^2 = \frac{1}{3}$

(c) $P(X+Y \le 1) = P((X,Y) \in D)$ where D is the triangular region shown in

the figure. Thus

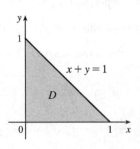

$$P(X+Y \le 1) = \iint_D f(x,y)\,dA = \int_0^1\int_0^{1-x} \frac{1}{15}(x+y)\,dy\,dx$$

$$= \frac{1}{15}\int_0^1 \left[xy + \frac{1}{2}y^2\right]_{y=0}^{y=1-x} dx$$

$$= \frac{1}{15}\int_0^1 \left[x(1-x) + \frac{1}{2}(1-x)^2\right]dx$$

$$= \frac{1}{30}\int_0^1 (1-x^2)\,dx = \frac{1}{30}\left[x - \frac{1}{3}x^3\right]_0^1 = \frac{1}{45}$$

47.

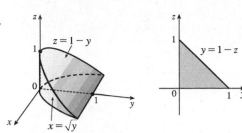

$$\int_{-1}^{1}\int_{x^2}^{1}\int_{0}^{1-y} f(x,y,z)\,dz\,dy\,dx = \int_{0}^{1}\int_{0}^{1-z}\int_{-\sqrt{y}}^{\sqrt{y}} f(x,y,z)\,dx\,dy\,dz$$

49. Since $u = x - y$ and $v = x + y$, $x = \frac{1}{2}(u + v)$ and $y = \frac{1}{2}(v - u)$.

Thus $\dfrac{\partial(x,y)}{\partial(u,v)} = \begin{vmatrix} 1/2 & 1/2 \\ -1/2 & 1/2 \end{vmatrix} = \dfrac{1}{2}$ and $\displaystyle\iint_R \dfrac{x-y}{x+y}\,dA = \int_2^4\int_{-2}^{0} \dfrac{u}{v}\left(\dfrac{1}{2}\right)\,du\,dv = -\int_2^4 \dfrac{dv}{v} = -\ln 2.$

51. Let $u = y - x$ and $v = y + x$ so $x = y - u = (v - x) - u \;\Rightarrow\; x = \frac{1}{2}(v - u)$ and $y = v - \frac{1}{2}(v - u) = \frac{1}{2}(v + u)$.

$\left|\dfrac{\partial(x,y)}{\partial(u,v)}\right| = \left|\dfrac{\partial x}{\partial u}\dfrac{\partial y}{\partial v} - \dfrac{\partial x}{\partial v}\dfrac{\partial y}{\partial u}\right| = \left|-\frac{1}{2}\left(\frac{1}{2}\right) - \frac{1}{2}\left(\frac{1}{2}\right)\right| = \left|-\frac{1}{2}\right| = \frac{1}{2}.$ R is the image under this transformation of the square

with vertices $(u, v) = (0, 0), (-2, 0), (0, 2),$ and $(-2, 2)$. So

$$\iint_R xy\,dA = \int_0^2\int_{-2}^{0} \dfrac{v^2 - u^2}{4}\left(\dfrac{1}{2}\right)\,du\,dv = \tfrac{1}{8}\int_0^2 \left[v^2 u - \tfrac{1}{3}u^3\right]_{u=-2}^{u=0}\,dv = \tfrac{1}{8}\int_0^2 \left(2v^2 - \tfrac{8}{3}\right)\,dv = \tfrac{1}{8}\left[\tfrac{2}{3}v^3 - \tfrac{8}{3}v\right]_0^2 = 0$$

This result could have been anticipated by symmetry, since the integrand is an odd function of y and R is symmetric about

the x-axis.

☐ FOCUS ON PROBLEM SOLVING

1. Let $R = \bigcup_{i=1}^{5} R_i$, where

$$R_i = \{(x,y) \mid x + y \geq i + 2, x + y < i + 3, 1 \leq x \leq 3, 2 \leq y \leq 5\}.$$

$$\iint_R [\![x + y]\!]\, dA = \sum_{i=1}^{5} \iint_{R_i} [\![x + y]\!]\, dA = \sum_{i=1}^{5} [\![x + y]\!] \iint_{R_i} dA, \text{ since}$$

$[\![x + y]\!] = \text{constant} = i + 2$ for $(x, y) \in R_i$. Therefore

$$\iint_R [\![x + y]\!]\, dA = \sum_{i=1}^{5} (i + 2)\,[A(R_i)]$$
$$= 3A(R_1) + 4A(R_2) + 5A(R_3) + 6A(R_4) + 7A(R_5)$$
$$= 3\left(\tfrac{1}{2}\right) + 4\left(\tfrac{3}{2}\right) + 5(2) + 6\left(\tfrac{3}{2}\right) + 7\left(\tfrac{1}{2}\right) = 30$$

3. $f_{\text{ave}} = \dfrac{1}{b-a} \displaystyle\int_a^b f(x)\, dx = \dfrac{1}{1-0} \int_0^1 \left[\int_x^1 \cos(t^2)\, dt \right] dx$

$= \int_0^1 \int_x^1 \cos(t^2)\, dt\, dx = \int_0^1 \int_0^t \cos(t^2)\, dx\, dt$ [changing the order of integration]

$= \int_0^1 t \cos(t^2)\, dt = \tfrac{1}{2} \sin(t^2)\big]_0^1 = \tfrac{1}{2} \sin 1$

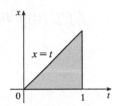

5. Since $|xy| < 1$, except at $(1,1)$, the formula for the sum of a geometric series gives $\dfrac{1}{1 - xy} = \displaystyle\sum_{n=0}^{\infty} (xy)^n$, so

$$\int_0^1 \int_0^1 \tfrac{1}{1-xy}\, dx\, dy = \int_0^1 \int_0^1 \sum_{n=0}^{\infty} (xy)^n\, dx\, dy = \sum_{n=0}^{\infty} \int_0^1 \int_0^1 (xy)^n\, dx\, dy = \sum_{n=0}^{\infty} \left[\int_0^1 x^n\, dx \right]\left[\int_0^1 y^n\, dy \right]$$

$$= \sum_{n=0}^{\infty} \tfrac{1}{n+1} \cdot \tfrac{1}{n+1} = \sum_{n=0}^{\infty} \tfrac{1}{(n+1)^2} = \tfrac{1}{1^2} + \tfrac{1}{2^2} + \tfrac{1}{3^2} + \cdots = \sum_{n=1}^{\infty} \tfrac{1}{n^2}$$

7. (a) Since $|xyz| < 1$ except at $(1,1,1)$, the formula for the sum of a geometric series gives $\dfrac{1}{1 - xyz} = \displaystyle\sum_{n=0}^{\infty} (xyz)^n$, so

$$\int_0^1 \int_0^1 \int_0^1 \tfrac{1}{1-xyz}\, dx\, dy\, dz = \int_0^1 \int_0^1 \int_0^1 \sum_{n=0}^{\infty} (xyz)^n\, dx\, dy\, dz = \sum_{n=0}^{\infty} \int_0^1 \int_0^1 \int_0^1 (xyz)^n\, dx\, dy\, dz$$

$$= \sum_{n=0}^{\infty} \left[\int_0^1 x^n\, dx \right]\left[\int_0^1 y^n\, dy \right]\left[\int_0^1 z^n\, dz \right] = \sum_{n=0}^{\infty} \tfrac{1}{n+1} \cdot \tfrac{1}{n+1} \cdot \tfrac{1}{n+1}$$

$$= \sum_{n=0}^{\infty} \tfrac{1}{(n+1)^3} = \tfrac{1}{1^3} + \tfrac{1}{2^3} + \tfrac{1}{3^3} + \cdots = \sum_{n=1}^{\infty} \tfrac{1}{n^3}$$

(b) Since $|-xyz| < 1$, except at $(1,1,1)$, the formula for the sum of a geometric series gives $\dfrac{1}{1 + xyz} = \displaystyle\sum_{n=0}^{\infty} (-xyz)^n$, so

$$\int_0^1 \int_0^1 \int_0^1 \tfrac{1}{1+xyz}\, dx\, dy\, dz = \int_0^1 \int_0^1 \int_0^1 \sum_{n=0}^{\infty} (-xyz)^n\, dx\, dy\, dz = \sum_{n=0}^{\infty} \int_0^1 \int_0^1 \int_0^1 (-xyz)^n\, dx\, dy\, dz$$

$$= \sum_{n=0}^{\infty} (-1)^n \left[\int_0^1 x^n\, dx \right]\left[\int_0^1 y^n\, dy \right]\left[\int_0^1 z^n\, dz \right] = \sum_{n=0}^{\infty} (-1)^n \tfrac{1}{n+1} \cdot \tfrac{1}{n+1} \cdot \tfrac{1}{n+1}$$

$$= \sum_{n=0}^{\infty} \tfrac{(-1)^n}{(n+1)^3} = \tfrac{1}{1^3} - \tfrac{1}{2^3} + \tfrac{1}{3^3} - \cdots = \sum_{n=0}^{\infty} \tfrac{(-1)^{n-1}}{n^3}$$

To evaluate this sum, we first write out a few terms: $s = 1 - \dfrac{1}{2^3} + \dfrac{1}{3^3} - \dfrac{1}{4^3} + \dfrac{1}{5^3} - \dfrac{1}{6^3} \approx 0.8998$. Notice that

$a_7 = \dfrac{1}{7^3} < 0.003$. By the Alternating Series Estimation Theorem from Section 8.4, we have $|s - s_6| \le a_7 < 0.003$. This

error of 0.003 will not affect the second decimal place, so we have $s \approx 0.90$.

9. $\int_0^x \int_0^y \int_0^z f(t)\, dt\, dz\, dy = \iiint_E f(t)\, dV$, where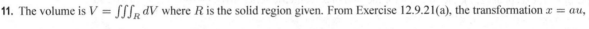

$E = \{(t, z, y) \mid 0 \le t \le z, 0 \le z \le y, 0 \le y \le x\}$.

If we let D be the projection of E on the yt-plane then

$D = \{(y, t) \mid 0 \le t \le x, t \le y \le x\}$. And we see from the diagram

that $E - \{(t, z, y) \mid t \le z \le y, t \le y \le x, 0 \le t \le x\}$. So

$$\int_0^x \int_0^y \int_0^z f(t)\, dt\, dz\, dy = \int_0^x \int_t^x \int_t^y f(t)\, dz\, dy\, dt = \int_0^x \left[\int_t^x (y - t) f(t)\, dy \right] dt$$

$$= \int_0^x \left[\left(\tfrac{1}{2} y^2 - ty \right) f(t) \right]_{y=t}^{y=x} dt = \int_0^x \left[\tfrac{1}{2} x^2 - tx - \tfrac{1}{2} t^2 + t^2 \right] f(t)\, dt$$

$$= \int_0^x \left[\tfrac{1}{2} x^2 - tx + \tfrac{1}{2} t^2 \right] f(t)\, dt = \int_0^x \left(\tfrac{1}{2} x^2 - 2tx + t^2 \right) f(t)\, dt$$

$$= \tfrac{1}{2} \int_0^x (x - t)^2 f(t)\, dt$$

11. The volume is $V = \iiint_R dV$ where R is the solid region given. From Exercise 12.9.21(a), the transformation $x = au$,

$y = bv$, $z = cw$ maps the unit ball $u^2 + v^2 + w^2 \le 1$ to the solid ellipsoid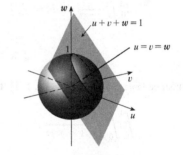

$\dfrac{x^2}{a^2} + \dfrac{y^2}{b^2} + \dfrac{z^2}{c^2} \le 1$ with $\dfrac{\partial(x, y, z)}{\partial(u, v, w)} = abc$. The same transformation maps the

plane $u + v + w = 1$ to $\dfrac{x}{a} + \dfrac{y}{b} + \dfrac{z}{c} = 1$. Thus the region R in xyz-space

corresponds to the region S in uvw-space consisting of the smaller piece of the

unit ball cut off by the plane $u + v + w = 1$, a "cap of a sphere" (see the figure).

We will need to compute the volume of S, but first consider the general case

where a horizontal plane slices the upper portion of a sphere of radius r to produce

a cap of height h. We use spherical coordinates. From the figure, a line at angle ϕ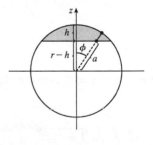

from the z-axis intersects the plane when $\cos \phi = (r - h)/a \;\Rightarrow$

$a = (r - h)/\cos \phi$, and the line passes through the outer rim of the cap when

$a = r \;\Rightarrow\; \cos \phi = (r - h)/r \;\Rightarrow\; \phi = \cos^{-1}((r - h)/r)$. Thus the cap

is described by $\{(\rho, \theta, \phi) \mid (r - h)/\cos \phi \le \rho \le r, 0 \le \theta \le 2\pi, 0 \le \phi \le \cos^{-1}((r - h)/r)\}$ and its volume is

$$V - \int_0^{2\pi} \int_0^{\cos^{-1}((r-h)/r)} \int_{(r-h)/\cos\phi}^r \rho^2 \sin\phi \, d\rho \, d\phi \, d\theta$$

$$= \int_0^{2\pi} \int_0^{\cos^{-1}((r-h)/r)} \left[\tfrac{1}{3}\rho^3 \sin\phi\right]_{\rho=(r-h)/\cos\phi}^{\rho=r} d\phi \, d\theta$$

$$= \frac{1}{3} \int_0^{2\pi} \int_0^{\cos^{-1}((r-h)/r)} \left[r^3 \sin\phi - \frac{(r-h)^3}{\cos^3\phi} \sin\phi\right] d\phi \, d\theta$$

$$= \tfrac{1}{3} \int_0^{2\pi} \left[-r^3 \cos\phi - \tfrac{1}{2}(r-h)^3 \cos^{-2}\phi\right]_{\phi=0}^{\phi=\cos^{-1}((r-h)/r)} d\theta$$

$$= \frac{1}{3} \int_0^{2\pi} \left[-r^3 \left(\frac{r-h}{r}\right) - \frac{1}{2}(r-h)^3 \left(\frac{r-h}{r}\right)^{-2} + r^3 + \frac{1}{2}(r-h)^3\right] d\theta$$

$$= \tfrac{1}{3} \int_0^{2\pi} (\tfrac{3}{2}rh^2 - \tfrac{1}{2}h^3) \, d\theta = \tfrac{1}{3}(\tfrac{3}{2}rh^2 - \tfrac{1}{2}h^3)(2\pi) = \pi h^2(r - \tfrac{1}{3}h)$$

(This volume can also be computed by treating the cap as a solid of revolution and using the single variable disk method; see Exercise 6.2.33.)

To determine the height h of the cap cut from the unit ball by the plane $u + v + w = 1$, note that the line $u = v = w$ passes through the origin with direction vector $\langle 1, 1, 1 \rangle$ which is perpendicular to the plane. Therefore this line coincides with a radius of the sphere that passes through the center of the cap and h is measured along this line. The line intersects the plane at $\left(\tfrac{1}{3}, \tfrac{1}{3}, \tfrac{1}{3}\right)$ and the sphere at $\left(\tfrac{1}{\sqrt{3}}, \tfrac{1}{\sqrt{3}}, \tfrac{1}{\sqrt{3}}\right)$. (See the figure.)

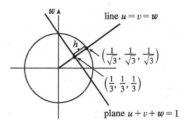

The distance between these points is $h = \sqrt{3 \left(\tfrac{1}{\sqrt{3}} - \tfrac{1}{3}\right)^2} = \sqrt{3}\left(\tfrac{1}{\sqrt{3}} - \tfrac{1}{3}\right) = 1 - \tfrac{1}{\sqrt{3}}$. Thus the volume of R is

$$V = \iiint_R dV = \iiint_S \left|\frac{\partial(x, y, z)}{\partial(u, v, w)}\right| dV = abc \iiint_S dV = abc \, V(S)$$

$$= abc \cdot \pi h^2 (r - \tfrac{1}{3}h) = abc \cdot \pi\left(1 - \tfrac{1}{\sqrt{3}}\right)^2 \left[1 - \tfrac{1}{3}\left(1 - \tfrac{1}{\sqrt{3}}\right)\right]$$

$$= abc\pi \left(\tfrac{4}{3} - \tfrac{2}{\sqrt{3}}\right)\left(\tfrac{2}{3} + \tfrac{1}{3\sqrt{3}}\right) = abc\pi \left(\tfrac{2}{3} - \tfrac{8}{9\sqrt{3}}\right) \approx 0.482abc$$

13 ☐ VECTOR CALCULUS

13.1 Vector Fields

1. $\mathbf{F}(x,y) = 0.3\,\mathbf{i} - 0.4\,\mathbf{j}$

All vectors in this field are identical, with length 0.5 and

parallel to $\langle 3, -4 \rangle$.

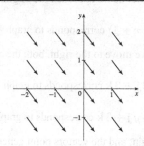

3. $\mathbf{F}(x,y) = y\,\mathbf{i} + \frac{1}{2}\,\mathbf{j}$

The length of the vector $y\,\mathbf{i} + \frac{1}{2}\,\mathbf{j}$ is $\sqrt{y^2 + \frac{1}{4}}$. Vectors

are tangent to parabolas opening about the x-axis.

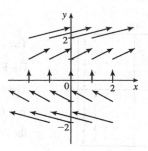

5. $\mathbf{F}(x,y) = \dfrac{y\,\mathbf{i} + x\,\mathbf{j}}{\sqrt{x^2 + y^2}}$

The length of the vector $\dfrac{y\,\mathbf{i} + x\,\mathbf{j}}{\sqrt{x^2 + y^2}}$ is 1.

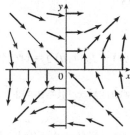

7. $\mathbf{F}(x,y,z) = \mathbf{k}$

All vectors in this field are parallel to the z-axis and have

length 1.

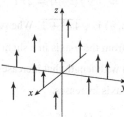

9. $\mathbf{F}(x,y,z) = x\,\mathbf{k}$

At each point (x,y,z), $\mathbf{F}(x,y,z)$ is a vector of length $|x|$.

For $x > 0$, all point in the direction of the positive z-axis,

while for $x < 0$, all are in the direction of the negative

z-axis. In each plane $x = k$, all the vectors are identical.

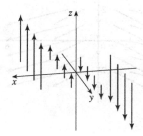

11. $\mathbf{F}(x, y) = \langle y, x \rangle$ corresponds to graph II. In the first quadrant all the vectors have positive x- and y-components, in the second quadrant all vectors have positive x-components and negative y-components, in the third quadrant all vectors have negative x- and y-components, and in the fourth quadrant all vectors have negative x-components and positive y-components. In addition, the vectors get shorter as we approach the origin.

13. $\mathbf{F}(x, y) = \langle x - 2, x + 1 \rangle$ corresponds to graph I since the vectors are independent of y (vectors along vertical lines are identical) and, as we move to the right, both the x- and the y-components get larger.

15. $\mathbf{F}(x, y, z) = \mathbf{i} + 2\mathbf{j} + 3\mathbf{k}$ corresponds to graph IV, since all vectors have identical length and direction.

17. $\mathbf{F}(x, y, z) = x\mathbf{i} + y\mathbf{j} + 3\mathbf{k}$ corresponds to graph III; the projection of each vector onto the xy-plane is $x\mathbf{i} + y\mathbf{j}$, which points away from the origin, and the vectors point generally upward because their z-components are all 3.

19.

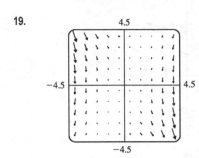

The vector field seems to have very short vectors near the line $y = 2x$.

For $\mathbf{F}(x, y) = \langle 0, 0 \rangle$ we must have $y^2 - 2xy = 0$ and $3xy - 6x^2 = 0$.

The first equation holds if $y = 0$ or $y = 2x$, and the second holds if $x = 0$ or $y = 2x$. So both equations hold [and thus $\mathbf{F}(x, y) = \mathbf{0}$] along the line $y = 2x$.

21. $f(x, y) = xe^{xy}$ $\Rightarrow$

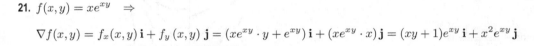

$\nabla f(x, y) = f_x(x, y)\,\mathbf{i} + f_y(x, y)\,\mathbf{j} = (xe^{xy} \cdot y + e^{xy})\,\mathbf{i} + (xe^{xy} \cdot x)\,\mathbf{j} = (xy + 1)e^{xy}\,\mathbf{i} + x^2 e^{xy}\,\mathbf{j}$

23. $\nabla f(x, y, z) = f_x(x, y, z)\,\mathbf{i} + f_y(x, y, z)\,\mathbf{j} + f_z(x, y, z)\,\mathbf{k} = \dfrac{x}{\sqrt{x^2 + y^2 + z^2}}\,\mathbf{i} + \dfrac{y}{\sqrt{x^2 + y^2 + z^2}}\,\mathbf{j} + \dfrac{z}{\sqrt{x^2 + y^2 + z^2}}\,\mathbf{k}$

25. $f(x, y) = x^2 - y$ $\Rightarrow$ $\nabla f(x, y) = 2x\,\mathbf{i} - \mathbf{j}$.

The length of $\nabla f(x, y)$ is $\sqrt{4x^2 + 1}$. When $x \neq 0$, the vectors point away from the y-axis in a slightly downward direction with length that increases as the distance from the y-axis increases.

27. We graph ∇f along with a contour map of f.

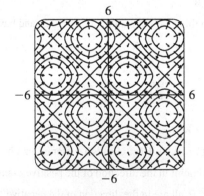

The graph shows that the gradient vectors are perpendicular to the level curves. Also, the gradient vectors point in the direction in which f is increasing and are longer where the level curves are closer together.

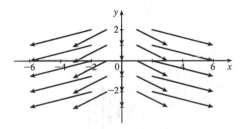

29. $f(x, y) = x^2 + y^2 \;\Rightarrow\; \nabla f(x, y) = 2x\,\mathbf{i} + 2y\,\mathbf{j}$. Thus, each vector $\nabla f(x, y)$ has the same direction and twice the length of the position vector of the point (x, y), so the vectors all point directly away from the origin and their lengths increase as we move away from the origin. Hence, ∇f is graph III.

31. $f(x, y) = (x + y)^2 \;\Rightarrow\; \nabla f(x, y) = 2(x + y)\,\mathbf{i} + 2(x + y)\,\mathbf{j}$. The x- and y-components of each vector are equal, so all vectors are parallel to the line $y = x$. The vectors are $\mathbf{0}$ along the line $y = -x$ and their length increases as the distance from this line increases. Thus, ∇f is graph II.

33. At $t = 3$ the particle is at $(2, 1)$ so its velocity is $\mathbf{V}(2, 1) = \langle 4, 3 \rangle$. After 0.01 units of time, the particle's change in location should be approximately $0.01\,\mathbf{V}(2, 1) = 0.01\,\langle 4, 3 \rangle = \langle 0.04, 0.03 \rangle$, so the particle should be approximately at the point $(2.04, 1.03)$.

35. (a) We sketch the vector field $\mathbf{F}(x, y) = x\,\mathbf{i} - y\,\mathbf{j}$ along with several approximate flow lines. The flow lines appear to be hyperbolas with shape similar to the graph of $y = \pm 1/x$, so we might guess that the flow lines have equations $y = C/x$.

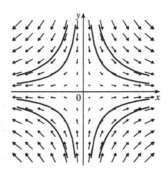

(b) If $x = x(t)$ and $y = y(t)$ are parametric equations of a flow line, then the velocity vector of the flow line at the point (x, y) is $x'(t)\,\mathbf{i} + y'(t)\,\mathbf{j}$. Since the velocity vectors coincide with the vectors in the vector field, we have

$x'(t)\,\mathbf{i} + y'(t)\,\mathbf{j} = x\,\mathbf{i} - y\,\mathbf{j} \;\Rightarrow\; dx/dt = x,\, dy/dt = -y$. To solve these differential equations, we know

$dx/dt = x \;\Rightarrow\; dx/x = dt \;\Rightarrow\; \ln|x| = t + C \;\Rightarrow\; x = \pm e^{t+C} = Ae^t$ for some constant A, and

$dy/dt = -y \;\Rightarrow\; dy/y = -dt \;\Rightarrow\; \ln|y| = -t + K \;\Rightarrow\; y = \pm e^{-t+K} = Be^{-t}$ for some constant B. Therefore

$xy = Ae^t Be^{-t} = AB = $ constant. If the flow line passes through $(1, 1)$ then $(1)(1) = $ constant $= 1 \;\Rightarrow\; xy = 1 \;\Rightarrow\; y = 1/x, x > 0$.

13.2   Line Integrals

1. $x = t^3$ and $y = t$, $0 \le t \le 2$, so by Formula 3

$$\int_C y^3\, ds = \int_0^2 t^3 \sqrt{\left(\frac{dx}{dt}\right)^2 + \left(\frac{dy}{dt}\right)^2}\, dt = \int_0^2 t^3 \sqrt{(3t^2)^2 + (1)^2}\, dt = \int_0^2 t^3 \sqrt{9t^4 + 1}\, dt$$

$$= \tfrac{1}{36} \cdot \tfrac{2}{3}\left(9t^4 + 1\right)^{3/2}\Big]_0^2 = \tfrac{1}{54}(145^{3/2} - 1) \text{ or } \tfrac{1}{54}\left(145\sqrt{145} - 1\right)$$

3. Parametric equations for C are $x = 4\cos t$, $y = 4\sin t$, $-\frac{\pi}{2} \le t \le \frac{\pi}{2}$. Then

$$\int_C xy^4\, ds = \int_{-\pi/2}^{\pi/2}(4\cos t)(4\sin t)^4 \sqrt{(-4\sin t)^2 + (4\cos t)^2}\, dt = \int_{-\pi/2}^{\pi/2} 4^5 \cos t \, \sin^4 t \sqrt{16(\sin^2 t + \cos^2 t)}\, dt$$

$$= 4^5 \int_{-\pi/2}^{\pi/2}(\sin^4 t \cos t)(4)\, dt = (4)^6 \left[\tfrac{1}{5}\sin^5 t\right]_{-\pi/2}^{\pi/2} = \tfrac{2 \cdot 4^6}{5} = 1638.4$$

5. If we choose x as the parameter, parametric equations for C are $x = x$, $y = \sqrt{x}$ for $1 \le x \le 4$ and

$$\int_C \left(x^2 y^3 - \sqrt{x}\right) dy = \int_1^4 \left[x^2 \cdot (\sqrt{x})^3 - \sqrt{x}\right] \frac{1}{2\sqrt{x}} dx = \frac{1}{2} \int_1^4 \left(x^3 - 1\right) dx$$

$$= \frac{1}{2}\left[\frac{1}{4}x^4 - x\right]_1^4 = \frac{1}{2}\left(64 - 4 - \frac{1}{4} + 1\right) = \frac{243}{8}$$

7.

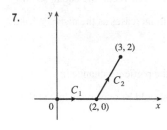

$C = C_1 + C_2$

On C_1: $x = x, y = 0 \Rightarrow dy = 0\,dx, \ 0 \le x \le 2$.

On C_2: $x = x, y = 2x - 4 \Rightarrow dy = 2\,dx, \ 2 \le x \le 3$.

Then

$$\int_C xy\,dx + (x - y)\,dy = \int_{C_1} xy\,dx + (x - y)\,dy + \int_{C_2} xy\,dx + (x - y)\,dy$$

$$= \int_0^2 (0 + 0)\,dx + \int_2^3 \left[(2x^2 - 4x) + (-x + 4)(2)\right] dx$$

$$= \int_2^3 \left(2x^2 - 6x + 8\right) dx = \frac{17}{3}$$

9. $x = 2\sin t$, $y = t$, $z = -2\cos t$, $0 \le t \le \pi$. Then by Formula 9,

$$\int_C xyz\,ds = \int_0^\pi (2\sin t)(t)(-2\cos t)\sqrt{\left(\frac{dx}{dt}\right)^2 + \left(\frac{dy}{dt}\right)^2 + \left(\frac{dz}{dt}\right)^2}\,dt$$

$$= \int_0^\pi -4t\sin t\cos t\,\sqrt{(2\cos t)^2 + (1)^2 + (2\sin t)^2}\,dt = \int_0^\pi -2t\sin 2t\,\sqrt{4(\cos^2 t + \sin^2 t) + 1}\,dt$$

$$= -2\sqrt{5}\int_0^\pi t\sin 2t\,dt = -2\sqrt{5}\left[-\frac{1}{2}t\cos 2t + \frac{1}{4}\sin 2t\right]_0^\pi \qquad \left[\begin{array}{l}\text{integrate by parts with}\\ u = t,\,dv = \sin 2t\,dt\end{array}\right]$$

$$= -2\sqrt{5}\left(-\frac{\pi}{2} - 0\right) = \sqrt{5}\,\pi$$

11. Parametric equations for C are $x = t$, $y = 2t$, $z = 3t$, $0 \le t \le 1$. Then

$$\int_C xe^{yz}\,ds = \int_0^1 te^{(2t)(3t)}\sqrt{1^2 + 2^2 + 3^2}\,dt = \sqrt{14}\int_0^1 te^{6t^2}\,dt = \sqrt{14}\left[\frac{1}{12}e^{6t^2}\right]_0^1 = \frac{\sqrt{14}}{12}(e^6 - 1).$$

13. $\int_C x^2 y\sqrt{z}\,dz = \int_0^1 (t^3)^2(t)\sqrt{t^2}\cdot 2t\,dt = \int_0^1 2t^9\,dt = \frac{1}{5}t^{10}\Big]_0^1 = \frac{1}{5}$

15.

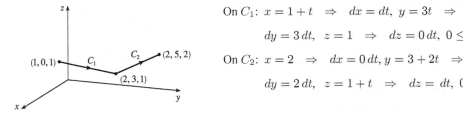

On C_1: $x = 1 + t \Rightarrow dx = dt$, $y = 3t \Rightarrow$

$dy = 3\,dt$, $z = 1 \Rightarrow dz = 0\,dt$, $0 \le t \le 1$.

On C_2: $x = 2 \Rightarrow dx = 0\,dt$, $y = 3 + 2t \Rightarrow$

$dy = 2\,dt$, $z = 1 + t \Rightarrow dz = dt$, $0 \le t \le 1$.

Then

$$\int_C (x + yz)\,dx + 2x\,dy + xyz\,dz$$

$$= \int_{C_1} (x + yz)\,dx + 2x\,dy + xyz\,dz + \int_{C_2} (x + yz)\,dx + 2x\,dy + xyz\,dz$$

$$= \int_0^1 (1 + t + (3t)(1))\,dt + 2(1 + t)\cdot 3\,dt + (1 + t)(3t)(1)\cdot 0\,dt$$

$$\quad + \int_0^1 (2 + (3 + 2t)(1 + t))\cdot 0\,dt + 2(2)\cdot 2\,dt + (2)(3 + 2t)(1 + t)\,dt$$

$$= \int_0^1 (10t + 7)\,dt + \int_0^1 (4t^2 + 10t + 14)\,dt = \left[5t^2 + 7t\right]_0^1 + \left[\frac{4}{3}t^3 + 5t^2 + 14t\right]_0^1 = 12 + \frac{61}{3} = \frac{97}{3}$$

17. (a) Along the line $x = -3$, the vectors of $\mathbf{F}$ have positive y-components, so since the path goes upward, the integrand $\mathbf{F} \cdot \mathbf{T}$ is always positive. Therefore $\int_{C_1} \mathbf{F} \cdot d\mathbf{r} = \int_{C_1} \mathbf{F} \cdot \mathbf{T}\, ds$ is positive.

(b) All of the (nonzero) field vectors along the circle with radius 3 are pointed in the clockwise direction, that is, opposite the direction to the path. So $\mathbf{F} \cdot \mathbf{T}$ is negative, and therefore $\int_{C_2} \mathbf{F} \cdot d\mathbf{r} = \int_{C_2} \mathbf{F} \cdot \mathbf{T}\, ds$ is negative.

19. $\mathbf{r}(t) = 11t^4\,\mathbf{i} + t^3\,\mathbf{j}$, so $\mathbf{F}(\mathbf{r}(t)) = (11t^4)(t^3)\,\mathbf{i} + 3(t^3)^2\,\mathbf{j} = 11t^7\,\mathbf{i} + 3t^6\,\mathbf{j}$ and $\mathbf{r}'(t) = 44t^3\,\mathbf{i} + 3t^2\,\mathbf{j}$. Then

$\int_C \mathbf{F} \cdot d\mathbf{r} = \int_0^1 \mathbf{F}(\mathbf{r}(t)) \cdot \mathbf{r}'(t)\, dt = \int_0^1 (11t^7 \cdot 44t^3 + 3t^6 \cdot 3t^2)\, dt = \int_0^1 (484t^{10} + 9t^8)\, dt = \left[44t^{11} + t^9 \right]_0^1 = 45.$

21. $\int_C \mathbf{F} \cdot d\mathbf{r} = \int_0^1 \langle \sin t^3, \cos(-t^2), t^4 \rangle \cdot \langle 3t^2, -2t, 1 \rangle\, dt$

$= \int_0^1 (3t^2 \sin t^3 - 2t \cos t^2 + t^4)\, dt = \left[-\cos t^3 - \sin t^2 + \tfrac{1}{5}t^5 \right]_0^1 = \tfrac{6}{5} - \cos 1 - \sin 1$

23. $\mathbf{F}(\mathbf{r}(t)) = (e^t)\left(e^{-t^2}\right)\mathbf{i} + \sin\left(e^{-t^2}\right)\mathbf{j} = e^{t-t^2}\,\mathbf{i} + \sin\left(e^{-t^2}\right)\mathbf{j}$, $\mathbf{r}'(t) = e^t\,\mathbf{i} - 2te^{-t^2}\,\mathbf{j}$. Then

$$\int_C \mathbf{F} \cdot d\mathbf{r} = \int_1^2 \mathbf{F}(\mathbf{r}(t)) \cdot \mathbf{r}'(t)\, dt = \int_1^2 \left[e^{t-t^2}e^t + \sin\left(e^{-t^2}\right) \cdot \left(-2te^{-t^2}\right) \right] dt$$

$$= \int_1^2 \left[e^{2t-t^2} - 2te^{-t^2} \sin\left(e^{-t^2}\right) \right] dt \approx 1.9633$$

25. $x = t^2$, $y = t^3$, $z = t^4$ so by Formula 9,

$$\int_C x \sin(y+z)\, ds = \int_0^5 (t^2) \sin(t^3 + t^4)\sqrt{(2t)^2 + (3t^2)^2 + (4t^3)^2}\, dt$$

$$= \int_0^5 t^2 \sin(t^3 + t^4)\sqrt{4t^2 + 9t^4 + 16t^6}\, dt \approx 15.0074$$

27. We graph $\mathbf{F}(x, y) = (x - y)\,\mathbf{i} + xy\,\mathbf{j}$ and the curve C. We see that most of the vectors starting on C point in roughly the same direction as C, so for these portions of C the tangential component $\mathbf{F} \cdot \mathbf{T}$ is positive. Although some vectors in the third quadrant which start on C point in roughly the opposite direction, and hence give negative tangential components, it seems reasonable that the effect of these portions of C is outweighed by the positive tangential components. Thus, we would expect $\int_C \mathbf{F} \cdot d\mathbf{r} = \int_C \mathbf{F} \cdot \mathbf{T}\, ds$ to be positive.

To verify, we evaluate $\int_C \mathbf{F} \cdot d\mathbf{r}$. The curve C can be represented by $\mathbf{r}(t) = 2\cos t\,\mathbf{i} + 2\sin t\,\mathbf{j}$, $0 \le t \le \frac{3\pi}{2}$, so $\mathbf{F}(\mathbf{r}(t)) = (2\cos t - 2\sin t)\,\mathbf{i} + 4\cos t \sin t\,\mathbf{j}$ and $\mathbf{r}'(t) = -2\sin t\,\mathbf{i} + 2\cos t\,\mathbf{j}$. Then

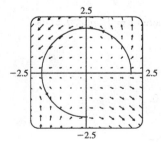

$\int_C \mathbf{F} \cdot d\mathbf{r} = \int_0^{3\pi/2} \mathbf{F}(\mathbf{r}(t)) \cdot \mathbf{r}'(t)\, dt$

$= \int_0^{3\pi/2}[-2\sin t(2\cos t - 2\sin t) + 2\cos t(4\cos t \sin t)]\, dt$

$= 4\int_0^{3\pi/2}(\sin^2 t - \sin t \cos t + 2\sin t \cos^2 t)\, dt$

$= 3\pi + \tfrac{2}{3}$ [using a CAS]

29. (a) $\int_C \mathbf{F} \cdot d\mathbf{r} = \int_0^1 \left\langle e^{t^2-1}, t^5 \right\rangle \cdot \langle 2t, 3t^2 \rangle\, dt = \int_0^1 \left(2te^{t^2-1} + 3t^7 \right) dt = \left[e^{t^2-1} + \tfrac{3}{8}t^8 \right]_0^1 = \tfrac{11}{8} - 1/e$

(b) $\mathbf{r}(0) = \mathbf{0}$, $\mathbf{F}(\mathbf{r}(0)) = \langle e^{-1}, 0 \rangle$;

$\mathbf{r}\left(\frac{1}{\sqrt{2}}\right) = \left\langle \frac{1}{2}, \frac{1}{2\sqrt{2}} \right\rangle$, $\mathbf{F}\left(\mathbf{r}\left(\frac{1}{\sqrt{2}}\right)\right) = \left\langle e^{-1/2}, \frac{1}{4\sqrt{2}} \right\rangle$;

$\mathbf{r}(1) = \langle 1, 1 \rangle$, $\mathbf{F}(\mathbf{r}(1)) = \langle 1, 1 \rangle$.

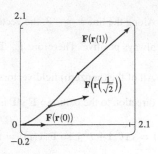

In order to generate the graph with Maple, we use the `line` command in

the `plottools` package to define each of the vectors. For example,

$$\texttt{v1:=line([0,0],[exp(-1),0]):}$$

generates the vector from the vector field at the point $(0,0)$ (but without an arrowhead) and gives it the name `v1`. To show

everything on the same screen, we use the `display` command. In Mathematica, we use `ListPlot` (with the

`PlotJoined -> True` option) to generate the vectors, and then `Show` to show everything on the same screen.

31. $x = e^{-t}\cos 4t$, $y = e^{-t}\sin 4t$, $z = e^{-t}$, $0 \le t \le 2\pi$.

Then $\dfrac{dx}{dt} = e^{-t}(-\sin 4t)(4) - e^{-t}\cos 4t = -e^{-t}(4\sin 4t + \cos 4t)$,

$\dfrac{dy}{dt} = e^{-t}(\cos 4t)(4) - e^{-t}\sin 4t = -e^{-t}(-4\cos 4t + \sin 4t)$, and $\dfrac{dz}{dt} = -e^{-t}$, so

$$\sqrt{\left(\frac{dx}{dt}\right)^2 + \left(\frac{dy}{dt}\right)^2 + \left(\frac{dz}{dt}\right)^2} = \sqrt{(-e^{-t})^2[(4\sin 4t + \cos 4t)^2 + (-4\cos 4t + \sin 4t)^2 + 1]}$$

$$= e^{-t}\sqrt{16(\sin^2 4t + \cos^2 4t) + \sin^2 4t + \cos^2 4t + 1} = 3\sqrt{2}\,e^{-t}$$

Therefore $\int_C x^3 y^2 z \, ds = \int_0^{2\pi} (e^{-t}\cos 4t)^3 (e^{-t}\sin 4t)^2 (e^{-t})(3\sqrt{2}\,e^{-t})\,dt$

$$= \int_0^{2\pi} 3\sqrt{2}\,e^{-7t}\cos^3 4t \sin^2 4t\,dt = \tfrac{172{,}704}{5{,}632{,}705}\sqrt{2}\,(1 - e^{-14\pi})$$

33. We use the parametrization $x = 2\cos t$, $y = 2\sin t$, $-\frac{\pi}{2} \le t \le \frac{\pi}{2}$. Then

$ds = \sqrt{\left(\frac{dx}{dt}\right)^2 + \left(\frac{dy}{dt}\right)^2}\,dt = \sqrt{(-2\sin t)^2 + (2\cos t)^2}\,dt = 2\,dt$, so $m = \int_C k\,ds = 2k\int_{-\pi/2}^{\pi/2} dt = 2k(\pi)$,

$\bar{x} = \frac{1}{2\pi k}\int_C xk\,ds = \frac{1}{2\pi}\int_{-\pi/2}^{\pi/2}(2\cos t)2\,dt = \frac{1}{2\pi}\left[4\sin t\right]_{-\pi/2}^{\pi/2} = \frac{4}{\pi}$, $\bar{y} = \frac{1}{2\pi k}\int_C yk\,ds = \frac{1}{2\pi}\int_{-\pi/2}^{\pi/2}(2\sin t)2\,dt = 0$.

Hence $(\bar{x}, \bar{y}) = \left(\frac{4}{\pi}, 0\right)$.

35. (a) $\bar{x} = \dfrac{1}{m}\displaystyle\int_C x\rho(x,y,z)\,ds$, $\bar{y} = \dfrac{1}{m}\displaystyle\int_C y\rho(x,y,z)\,ds$, $\bar{z} = \dfrac{1}{m}\displaystyle\int_C z\rho(x,y,z)\,ds$ where $m = \int_C \rho(x,y,z)\,ds$.

(b) $m = \int_C k\,ds = k\int_0^{2\pi}\sqrt{4\sin^2 t + 4\cos^2 t + 9}\,dt = k\sqrt{13}\int_0^{2\pi} dt = 2\pi k\sqrt{13}$,

$\bar{x} = \dfrac{1}{2\pi k\sqrt{13}}\displaystyle\int_0^{2\pi} 2k\sqrt{13}\sin t\,dt = 0$, $\bar{y} = \dfrac{1}{2\pi k\sqrt{13}}\displaystyle\int_0^{2\pi} 2k\sqrt{13}\cos t\,dt = 0$,

$\bar{z} = \dfrac{1}{2\pi k\sqrt{13}}\displaystyle\int_0^{2\pi}\left(k\sqrt{13}\right)(3t)\,dt = \dfrac{3}{2\pi}(2\pi^2) = 3\pi$. Hence $(\bar{x}, \bar{y}, \bar{z}) = (0, 0, 3\pi)$.

37. From Example 3, $\rho(x,y) = k(1-y)$, $\ x = \cos t$, $y = \sin t$, and $ds = dt$, $0 \le t \le \pi \ \Rightarrow$

$$I_x = \int_C y^2 \rho(x,y)\,ds = \int_0^\pi \sin^2 t\,[k(1-\sin t)]\,dt = k\int_0^\pi (\sin^2 t - \sin^3 t)\,dt$$

$$= \tfrac{1}{2}k\int_0^\pi (1-\cos 2t)\,dt - k\int_0^\pi (1-\cos^2 t)\sin t\,dt \quad \begin{bmatrix} \text{Let } u = \cos t,\ du = -\sin t\,dt \\ \text{in the second integral} \end{bmatrix}$$

$$= k\left[\tfrac{\pi}{2} + \int_1^{-1}(1-u^2)\,du\right] = k\left(\tfrac{\pi}{2} - \tfrac{4}{3}\right)$$

$$I_y = \int_C x^2 \rho(x,y)\,ds = k\int_0^\pi \cos^2 t\,(1-\sin t)\,dt = \tfrac{k}{2}\int_0^\pi (1+\cos 2t)\,dt - k\int_0^\pi \cos^2 t \sin t\,dt$$

$$= k\left(\tfrac{\pi}{2} - \tfrac{2}{3}\right), \text{ using the same substitution as above.}$$

39. $W = \int_C \mathbf{F}\cdot d\mathbf{r} = \int_0^{2\pi} \langle t - \sin t, 3 - \cos t\rangle \cdot \langle 1 - \cos t, \sin t\rangle\,dt$

$$= \int_0^{2\pi}(t - t\cos t - \sin t + \sin t\cos t + 3\sin t - \sin t\cos t)\,dt$$

$$= \int_0^{2\pi}(t - t\cos t + 2\sin t)\,dt = \left[\tfrac{1}{2}t^2 - (t\sin t + \cos t) - 2\cos t\right]_0^{2\pi} \quad \begin{bmatrix} \text{integrate by parts} \\ \text{in the second term} \end{bmatrix}$$

$$= 2\pi^2$$

41. $\mathbf{r}(t) = \langle 1 + 2t, 4t, 2t\rangle$, $\ 0 \le t \le 1$,

$$W = \int_C \mathbf{F}\cdot d\mathbf{r} = \int_0^1 \langle 6t, 1+4t, 1+6t\rangle \cdot \langle 2,4,2\rangle\,dt = \int_0^1 (12t + 4(1+4t) + 2(1+6t))\,dt$$

$$= \int_0^1 (40t + 6)\,dt = \left[20t^2 + 6t\right]_0^1 = 26$$

43. Let $\mathbf{F} = 185\,\mathbf{k}$. To parametrize the staircase, let $x = 20\cos t$, $\ y = 20\sin t$, $\ z = \tfrac{90}{6\pi}t = \tfrac{15}{\pi}t$, $\ 0 \le t \le 6\pi \ \Rightarrow$

$$W = \int_C \mathbf{F}\cdot d\mathbf{r} = \int_0^{6\pi} \langle 0,0,185\rangle \cdot \langle -20\sin t, 20\cos t, \tfrac{15}{\pi}\rangle\,dt = (185)\tfrac{15}{\pi}\int_0^{6\pi} dt = (185)(90) \approx 1.67 \times 10^4 \text{ ft-lb}$$

45. (a) $\mathbf{r}(t) = \langle \cos t, \sin t\rangle$, $\ 0 \le t \le 2\pi$, and let $\mathbf{F} = \langle a, b\rangle$. Then

$$W = \int_C \mathbf{F}\cdot d\mathbf{r} = \int_0^{2\pi} \langle a,b\rangle \cdot \langle -\sin t, \cos t\rangle\,dt = \int_0^{2\pi}(-a\sin t + b\cos t)\,dt = \left[a\cos t + b\sin t\right]_0^{2\pi}$$

$$= a + 0 - a + 0 = 0$$

(b) Yes. $\mathbf{F}(x,y) = k\,\mathbf{x} = \langle kx, ky\rangle$ and

$$W = \int_C \mathbf{F}\cdot d\mathbf{r} = \int_0^{2\pi} \langle k\cos t, k\sin t\rangle \cdot \langle -\sin t, \cos t\rangle\,dt = \int_0^{2\pi}(-k\sin t\,\cos t + k\sin t\,\cos t)\,dt = \int_0^{2\pi} 0\,dt = 0.$$

47. The work done in moving the object is $\int_C \mathbf{F}\cdot d\mathbf{r} = \int_C \mathbf{F}\cdot \mathbf{T}\,ds$. We can approximate this integral by dividing C into

7 segments of equal length $\Delta s = 2$ and approximating $\mathbf{F}\cdot \mathbf{T}$, that is, the tangential component of force, at a point (x_i^*, y_i^*) on

each segment. Since C is composed of straight line segments, $\mathbf{F}\cdot \mathbf{T}$ is the scalar projection of each force vector onto C.

If we choose (x_i^*, y_i^*) to be the point on the segment closest to the origin, then the work done is

$$\int_C \mathbf{F}\cdot \mathbf{T}\,ds \approx \sum_{i=1}^{7} [\mathbf{F}(x_i^*, y_i^*)\cdot \mathbf{T}(x_i^*, y_i^*)]\,\Delta s = [2+2+2+2+1+1+1](2) = 22. \text{ Thus, we estimate the work done to}$$

be approximately 22 J.

13.3 The Fundamental Theorem for Line Integrals

1. C appears to be a smooth curve, and since ∇f is continuous, we know f is differentiable. Then Theorem 2 says that the value of $\int_C \nabla f \cdot d\mathbf{r}$ is simply the difference of the values of f at the terminal and initial points of C. From the graph, this is $50 - 10 = 40$.

3. $\partial(2x - 3y)/\partial y = -3 = \partial(-3x + 4y - 8)/\partial x$ and the domain of $\mathbf{F}$ is $\mathbb{R}^2$ which is open and simply-connected, so by Theorem 6 $\mathbf{F}$ is conservative. Thus, there exists a function f such that $\nabla f = \mathbf{F}$, that is, $f_x(x, y) = 2x - 3y$ and $f_y(x, y) = -3x + 4y - 8$. But $f_x(x, y) = 2x - 3y$ implies $f(x, y) = x^2 - 3xy + g(y)$ and differentiating both sides of this equation with respect to y gives $f_y(x, y) = -3x + g'(y)$. Thus $-3x + 4y - 8 = -3x + g'(y)$ so $g'(y) = 4y - 8$ and $g(y) = 2y^2 - 8y + K$ where K is a constant. Hence $f(x, y) = x^2 - 3xy + 2y^2 - 8y + K$ is a potential function for $\mathbf{F}$.

5. $\partial(e^x \cos y)/\partial y = -e^x \sin y$, $\partial(e^x \sin y)/\partial x = e^x \sin y$. Since these are not equal, $\mathbf{F}$ is not conservative.

7. $\partial(ye^x + \sin y)/\partial y = e^x + \cos y = \partial(e^x + x \cos y)/\partial x$ and the domain of $\mathbf{F}$ is $\mathbb{R}^2$. Hence $\mathbf{F}$ is conservative so there exists a function f such that $\nabla f = \mathbf{F}$. Then $f_x(x, y) = ye^x + \sin y$ implies $f(x, y) = ye^x + x \sin y + g(y)$ and $f_y(x, y) = e^x + x \cos y + g'(y)$. But $f_y(x, y) = e^x + x \cos y$ so $g(y) = K$ and $f(x, y) = ye^x + x \sin y + K$ is a potential function for $\mathbf{F}$.

9. $\partial(\ln y + 2xy^3)/\partial y = 1/y + 6xy^2 = \partial(3x^2y^2 + x/y)/\partial x$ and the domain of $\mathbf{F}$ is $\{(x, y) \mid y > 0\}$ which is open and simply connected. Hence $\mathbf{F}$ is conservative so there exists a function f such that $\nabla f = \mathbf{F}$. Then $f_x(x, y) = \ln y + 2xy^3$ implies $f(x, y) = x \ln y + x^2y^3 + g(y)$ and $f_y(x, y) = x/y + 3x^2y^2 + g'(y)$. But $f_y(x, y) = 3x^2y^2 + x/y$ so $g'(y) = 0 \Rightarrow g(y) = K$ and $f(x, y) = x \ln y + x^2y^3 + K$ is a potential function for $\mathbf{F}$.

11. (a) $\mathbf{F}$ has continuous first-order partial derivatives and $\dfrac{\partial}{\partial y} 2xy = 2x = \dfrac{\partial}{\partial x}(x^2)$ on $\mathbb{R}^2$, which is open and simply-connected.

Thus, $\mathbf{F}$ is conservative by Theorem 6. Then we know that the line integral of $\mathbf{F}$ is independent of path; in particular, the value of $\int_C \mathbf{F} \cdot d\mathbf{r}$ depends only on the endpoints of C. Since all three curves have the same initial and terminal points, $\int_C \mathbf{F} \cdot d\mathbf{r}$ will have the same value for each curve.

(b) We first find a potential function f, so that $\nabla f = \mathbf{F}$. We know $f_x(x, y) = 2xy$ and $f_y(x, y) = x^2$. Integrating $f_x(x, y)$ with respect to x, we have $f(x, y) = x^2y + g(y)$. Differentiating both sides with respect to y gives $f_y(x, y) = x^2 + g'(y)$, so we must have $x^2 + g'(y) = x^2 \Rightarrow g'(y) = 0 \Rightarrow g(y) = K$, a constant. Thus $f(x, y) = x^2y + K$. All three curves start at $(1, 2)$ and end at $(3, 2)$, so by Theorem 2, $\int_C \mathbf{F} \cdot d\mathbf{r} = f(3, 2) - f(1, 2) = 18 - 2 = 16$ for each curve.

13. (a) $f_x(x, y) = xy^2$ implies $f(x, y) = \frac{1}{2}x^2y^2 + g(y)$ and $f_y(x, y) = x^2y + g'(y)$. But $f_y(x, y) = x^2y$ so $g'(y) = 0 \Rightarrow g(y) = K$, a constant. We can take $K = 0$, so $f(x, y) = \frac{1}{2}x^2y^2$.

(b) The initial point of C is $\mathbf{r}(0) = (0, 1)$ and the terminal point is $\mathbf{r}(1) = (2, 1)$, so $\int_C \mathbf{F} \cdot d\mathbf{r} = f(2, 1) - f(0, 1) = 2 - 0 = 2$.

15. (a) $f_x(x, y, z) = yz$ implies $f(x, y, z) = xyz + g(y, z)$ and so $f_y(x, y, z) = xz + g_y(y, z)$. But $f_y(x, y, z) = xz$ so

$g_y(y, z) = 0 \implies g(y, z) = h(z)$. Thus $f(x, y, z) = xyz + h(z)$ and $f_z(x, y, z) = xy + h'(z)$. But

$f_z(x, y, z) = xy + 2z$, so $h'(z) = 2z \implies h(z) = z^2 + K$. Hence $f(x, y, z) = xyz + z^2$ (taking $K = 0$).

(b) $\int_C \mathbf{F} \cdot d\mathbf{r} = f(4, 6, 3) - f(1, 0, -2) = 81 - 4 = 77$.

17. (a) $f_x(x, y, z) = y^2 \cos z$ implies $f(x, y, z) = xy^2 \cos z + g(y, z)$ and so $f_y(x, y, z) = 2xy \cos z + g_y(y, z)$. But

$f_y(x, y, z) = 2xy \cos z$ so $g_y(y, z) = 0 \implies g(y, z) = h(z)$. Thus $f(x, y, z) = xy^2 \cos z + h(z)$ and

$f_z(x, y, z) = -xy^2 \sin z + h'(z)$. But $f_z(x, y, z) = -xy^2 \sin z$, so $h'(z) = 0 \implies h(z) = K$. Hence

$f(x, y, z) = xy^2 \cos z$ (taking $K = 0$).

(b) $\mathbf{r}(0) = \langle 0, 0, 0 \rangle$, $\mathbf{r}(\pi) = \langle \pi^2, 0, \pi \rangle$ so $\int_C \mathbf{F} \cdot d\mathbf{r} = f(\pi^2, 0, \pi) - f(0, 0, 0) = 0 - 0 = 0$.

19. Here $\mathbf{F}(x, y) = \tan y \, \mathbf{i} + x \sec^2 y \, \mathbf{j}$. Then $f(x, y) = x \tan y$ is a potential function for $\mathbf{F}$, that is, $\nabla f = \mathbf{F}$ so

$\mathbf{F}$ is conservative and thus its line integral is independent of path. Hence

$\int_C \tan y \, dx + x \sec^2 y \, dy = \int_C \mathbf{F} \cdot d\mathbf{r} = f\left(2, \frac{\pi}{4}\right) - f(1, 0) = 2 \tan \frac{\pi}{4} - \tan 0 = 2$.

21. If $\mathbf{F}$ is conservative, then $\int_C \mathbf{F} \cdot d\mathbf{r}$ is independent of path. This means that the work done along all piecewise-smooth curves

that have the described initial and terminal points is the same. Your reply: It doesn't matter which curve is chosen.

23. $\mathbf{F}(x, y) = 2y^{3/2} \, \mathbf{i} + 3x \sqrt{y} \, \mathbf{j}$, $W = \int_C \mathbf{F} \cdot d\mathbf{r}$. Since $\partial(2y^{3/2})/\partial y = 3\sqrt{y} = \partial(3x\sqrt{y})/\partial x$, there exists a function f

such that $\nabla f = \mathbf{F}$. In fact, $f_x(x, y) = 2y^{3/2} \implies f(x, y) = 2xy^{3/2} + g(y) \implies f_y(x, y) = 3xy^{1/2} + g'(y)$. But

$f_y(x, y) = 3x\sqrt{y}$ so $g'(y) = 0$ or $g(y) = K$. We can take $K = 0 \implies f(x, y) = 2xy^{3/2}$. Thus

$W = \int_C \mathbf{F} \cdot d\mathbf{r} = f(2, 4) - f(1, 1) = 2(2)(8) - 2(1) = 30$.

25. We know that if the vector field (call it $\mathbf{F}$) is conservative, then around any closed path C, $\int_C \mathbf{F} \cdot d\mathbf{r} = 0$. But take C to be a

circle centered at the origin, oriented counterclockwise. All of the field vectors that start on C are roughly in the direction of

motion along C, so the integral around C will be positive. Therefore the field is not conservative.

27.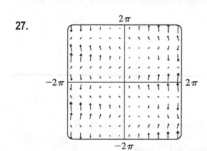

From the graph, it appears that $\mathbf{F}$ is conservative, since around all closed

paths, the number and size of the field vectors pointing in directions similar

to that of the path seem to be roughly the same as the number and size of the

vectors pointing in the opposite direction. To check, we calculate

$\frac{\partial}{\partial y}(\sin y) = \cos y = \frac{\partial}{\partial x}(1 + x \cos y)$. Thus $\mathbf{F}$ is conservative, by

Theorem 6.

29. Since $\mathbf{F}$ is conservative, there exists a function f such that $\mathbf{F} = \nabla f$, that is, $P = f_x$, $Q = f_y$, and $R = f_z$. Since P,

Q, and R have continuous first order partial derivatives, Clairaut's Theorem says that $\partial P/\partial y = f_{xy} = f_{yx} = \partial Q/\partial x$,

$\partial P/\partial z = f_{xz} = f_{zx} = \partial R/\partial x$, and $\partial Q/\partial z = f_{yz} = f_{zy} = \partial R/\partial y$.

31. $D = \{(x,y) \mid 0 < y < 3\}$ consists of those points between, but not
on, the horizontal lines $y = 0$ and $y = 3$.

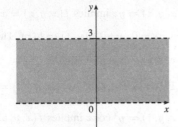

(a) Since D does not include any of its boundary points, it is open. More
formally, at any point in D there is a disk centered at that point that
lies entirely in D.

(b) Any two points chosen in D can always be joined by a path that lies
entirely in D, so D is connected. (D consists of just one "piece.")

(c) D is connected and it has no holes, so it's simply-connected. (Every simple closed curve in D encloses only points that are
in D.)

33. $D = \{(x,y) \mid 1 \le x^2 + y^2 \le 4,\ y \ge 0\}$ is the semiannular region
in the upper half-plane between circles centered at the origin of radii
1 and 2 (including all boundary points).

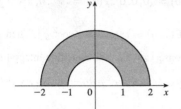

(a) D includes boundary points, so it is not open. [Note that at any
boundary point, $(1,0)$ for instance, any disk centered there cannot lie
entirely in D.]

(b) The region consists of one piece, so it's connected.

(c) D is connected and has no holes, so it's simply-connected.

35. (a) $P = -\dfrac{y}{x^2+y^2}$, $\dfrac{\partial P}{\partial y} = \dfrac{y^2-x^2}{(x^2+y^2)^2}$ and $Q = \dfrac{x}{x^2+y^2}$, $\dfrac{\partial Q}{\partial x} = \dfrac{y^2-x^2}{(x^2+y^2)^2}$. Thus $\dfrac{\partial P}{\partial y} = \dfrac{\partial Q}{\partial x}$.

(b) C_1: $x = \cos t$, $y = \sin t$, $0 \le t \le \pi$, C_2: $x = \cos t$, $y = \sin t$, $t = 2\pi$ to $t = \pi$. Then

$$\int_{C_1} \mathbf{F} \cdot d\mathbf{r} = \int_0^\pi \frac{(-\sin t)(-\sin t) + (\cos t)(\cos t)}{\cos^2 t + \sin^2 t}\, dt = \int_0^\pi dt = \pi \text{ and } \int_{C_2} \mathbf{F} \cdot d\mathbf{r} = \int_{2\pi}^\pi dt = -\pi$$

Since these aren't equal, the line integral of $\mathbf{F}$ isn't independent of path. (Or notice that $\int_{C_3} \mathbf{F} \cdot d\mathbf{r} = \int_0^{2\pi} dt = 2\pi$ where
C_3 is the circle $x^2 + y^2 = 1$, and apply the contrapositive of Theorem 3.) This doesn't contradict Theorem 6, since the
domain of $\mathbf{F}$, which is $\mathbb{R}^2$ except the origin, isn't simply-connected.

13.4 Green's Theorem

1. (a) Parametric equations for C are $x = 2\cos t$, $y = 2\sin t$, $0 \le t \le 2\pi$. Then

$$\oint_C (x-y)\, dx + (x+y)\, dy = \int_0^{2\pi} [(2\cos t - 2\sin t)(-2\sin t) + (2\cos t + 2\sin t)(2\cos t)]\, dt$$

$$= \int_0^{2\pi}(4\sin^2 t + 4\cos^2 t)\, dt = \int_0^{2\pi} 4\, dt = 4t\Big]_0^{2\pi} = 8\pi$$

(b) Note that C as given in part (a) is a positively oriented, smooth, simple closed curve. Then by Green's Theorem,

$$\oint_C (x-y)\, dx + (x+y)\, dy = \iint_D \left[\frac{\partial}{\partial x}(x+y) - \frac{\partial}{\partial y}(x-y) \right] dA = \iint_D [1 - (-1)]\, dA = 2 \iint_D dA$$

$$= 2A(D) = 2\pi(2)^2 = 8\pi$$

3. (a)

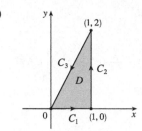

$C_1: x = t \Rightarrow dx = dt, \ y = 0 \Rightarrow dy = 0 \, dt, \ 0 \le t \le 1.$

$C_2: x = 1 \Rightarrow dx = 0 \, dt, \ y = t \Rightarrow dy = dt, \ 0 \le t \le 2.$

$C_3: x = 1 - t \Rightarrow dx = -dt, \ y = 2 - 2t \Rightarrow dy = -2 \, dt, \ 0 \le t \le 1.$

Thus
$$\oint_C xy \, dx + x^2 y^3 \, dy = \oint_{C_1 + C_2 + C_3} xy \, dx + x^2 y^3 \, dy$$

$$= \int_0^1 0 \, dt + \int_0^2 t^3 \, dt + \int_0^1 \left[-(1-t)(2-2t) - 2(1-t)^2(2-2t)^3\right] dt$$

$$= 0 + \left[\tfrac{1}{4}t^4\right]_0^2 + \left[\tfrac{2}{3}(1-t)^3 + \tfrac{8}{3}(1-t)^6\right]_0^1 = 4 - \tfrac{10}{3} = \tfrac{2}{3}$$

(b) $\oint_C xy \, dx + x^2 y^3 \, dy = \iint_D \left[\frac{\partial}{\partial x}(x^2 y^3) - \frac{\partial}{\partial y}(xy)\right] dA = \int_0^1 \int_0^{2x} (2xy^3 - x) \, dy \, dx$

$$= \int_0^1 \left[\tfrac{1}{2}xy^4 - xy\right]_{y=0}^{y=2x} dx = \int_0^1 (8x^5 - 2x^2) \, dx = \tfrac{4}{3} - \tfrac{2}{3} = \tfrac{2}{3}$$

5.

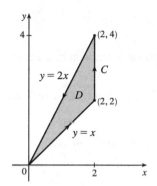

The region D enclosed by C is given by $\{(x,y) \mid 0 \le x \le 2, x \le y \le 2x\}$, so

$$\int_C xy^2 \, dx + 2x^2 y \, dy = \iint_D \left[\frac{\partial}{\partial x}(2x^2 y) - \frac{\partial}{\partial y}(xy^2)\right] dA$$

$$= \int_0^2 \int_x^{2x} (4xy - 2xy) \, dy \, dx$$

$$= \int_0^2 \left[xy^2\right]_{y=x}^{y=2x} dx$$

$$= \int_0^2 3x^3 \, dx = \tfrac{3}{4}x^4\Big]_0^2 = 12$$

7. $\int_C \left(y + e^{\sqrt{x}}\right) dx + (2x + \cos y^2) \, dy = \iint_D \left[\frac{\partial}{\partial x}(2x + \cos y^2) - \frac{\partial}{\partial y}\left(y + e^{\sqrt{x}}\right)\right] dA$

$$= \int_0^1 \int_{y^2}^{\sqrt{y}} (2 - 1) \, dx \, dy = \int_0^1 (y^{1/2} - y^2) \, dy = \tfrac{1}{3}$$

9. $\int_C y^3 \, dx - x^3 \, dy = \iint_D \left[\frac{\partial}{\partial x}(-x^3) - \frac{\partial}{\partial y}(y^3)\right] dA = \iint_D (-3x^2 - 3y^2) \, dA = \int_0^{2\pi} \int_0^2 (-3r^2) \, r \, dr \, d\theta$

$$= -3 \int_0^{2\pi} d\theta \int_0^2 r^3 \, dr = -3(2\pi)(4) = -24\pi$$

11. $\mathbf{F}(x,y) = \left\langle \sqrt{x} + y^3, \ x^2 + \sqrt{y} \right\rangle$ and the region D enclosed by C is given by $\{(x,y) \mid 0 \le x \le \pi, 0 \le y \le \sin x\}$.

C is traversed clockwise, so $-C$ gives the positive orientation.

$$\int_C \mathbf{F} \cdot d\mathbf{r} = - \int_{-C} \left(\sqrt{x} + y^3\right) dx + \left(x^2 + \sqrt{y}\right) dy = - \iint_D \left[\frac{\partial}{\partial x}\left(x^2 + \sqrt{y}\right) - \frac{\partial}{\partial y}\left(\sqrt{x} + y^3\right)\right] dA$$

$$= - \int_0^\pi \int_0^{\sin x} (2x - 3y^2) \, dy \, dx = - \int_0^\pi \left[2xy - y^3\right]_{y=0}^{y=\sin x} dx$$

$$= - \int_0^\pi (2x \sin x - \sin^3 x) \, dx = - \int_0^\pi (2x \sin x - (1 - \cos^2 x) \sin x) \, dx$$

$$= - \left[2 \sin x - 2x \cos x + \cos x - \tfrac{1}{3}\cos^3 x\right]_0^\pi \qquad \text{[integrate by parts in the first term]}$$

$$= - \left(2\pi - 2 + \tfrac{4}{3}\right) = \tfrac{4}{3} - 2\pi$$

13. $\mathbf{F}(x,y) = \langle e^x + x^2 y, e^y - xy^2 \rangle$ and the region D enclosed by C is the disk $x^2 + y^2 \le 25$.

C is traversed clockwise, so $-C$ gives the positive orientation.

$$\int_C \mathbf{F} \cdot d\mathbf{r} = -\int_{-C}(e^x + x^2 y)\, dx + (e^y - xy^2)\, dy = -\iint_D \left[\frac{\partial}{\partial x}(e^y - xy^2) - \frac{\partial}{\partial y}(e^x + x^2 y) \right] dA$$

$$= -\iint_D (-y^2 - x^2)\, dA = \iint_D (x^2 + y^2)\, dA = \int_0^{2\pi} \int_0^5 (r^2)\, r\, dr\, d\theta$$

$$= \int_0^{2\pi} d\theta \int_0^5 r^3\, dr = 2\pi \left[\tfrac{1}{4} r^4 \right]_0^5 = \frac{625}{2}\pi$$

15. Here $C = C_1 + C_2$ where

C_1 can be parametrized as $x = t$, $y = 1$, $-1 \le t \le 1$, and

C_2 is given by $x = -t$, $y = 2 - t^2$, $-1 \le t \le 1$.

Then the line integral is

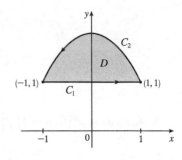

$$\oint_{C_1 + C_2} y^2 e^x\, dx + x^2 e^y\, dy = \int_{-1}^1 [1 \cdot e^t + t^2 e \cdot 0]\, dt$$

$$+ \int_{-1}^1 [(2 - t^2)^2 e^{-t}(-1) + (-t)^2 e^{2-t^2}(-2t)]\, dt$$

$$= \int_{-1}^1 [e^t - (2 - t^2)^2 e^{-t} - 2t^3 e^{2-t^2}]\, dt = -8e + 48e^{-1}$$

according to a CAS. The double integral is

$$\iint_D \left(\frac{\partial Q}{\partial x} - \frac{\partial P}{\partial y} \right) dA = \int_{-1}^1 \int_1^{2-x^2} (2xe^y - 2ye^x)\, dy\, dx = -8e + 48e^{-1}, \text{ verifying Green's Theorem in this case.}$$

17. By Green's Theorem, $W = \int_C \mathbf{F} \cdot d\mathbf{r} = \int_C x(x+y)\, dx + xy^2\, dy = \iint_D (y^2 - x)\, dA$ where C is the path described in the question and D is the triangle bounded by C. So

$$W = \int_0^1 \int_0^{1-x}(y^2 - x)\, dy\, dx = \int_0^1 \left[\tfrac{1}{3} y^3 - xy \right]_{y=0}^{y=1-x} dx = \int_0^1 \left(\tfrac{1}{3}(1-x)^3 - x(1-x) \right) dx$$

$$= \left[-\tfrac{1}{12}(1-x)^4 - \tfrac{1}{2}x^2 + \tfrac{1}{3}x^3 \right]_0^1 = \left(-\tfrac{1}{2} + \tfrac{1}{3} \right) - \left(-\tfrac{1}{12} \right) = -\tfrac{1}{12}$$

19. Let C_1 be the arch of the cycloid from $(0,0)$ to $(2\pi, 0)$, which corresponds to $0 \le t \le 2\pi$, and let C_2 be the segment from $(2\pi, 0)$ to $(0,0)$, so C_2 is given by $x = 2\pi - t$, $y = 0$, $0 \le t \le 2\pi$. Then $C = C_1 \cup C_2$ is traversed clockwise, so $-C$ is oriented positively. Thus $-C$ encloses the area under one arch of the cycloid and from (5) we have

$$A = -\oint_{-C} y\, dx = \int_{C_1} y\, dx + \int_{C_2} y\, dx = \int_0^{2\pi}(1 - \cos t)(1 - \cos t)\, dt + \int_0^{2\pi} 0\,(-dt)$$

$$= \int_0^{2\pi}(1 - 2\cos t + \cos^2 t)\, dt + 0 = \left[t - 2\sin t + \tfrac{1}{2}t + \tfrac{1}{4}\sin 2t \right]_0^{2\pi} = 3\pi$$

21. (a) Using Equation 13.2.8, we write parametric equations of the line segment as $x = (1-t)x_1 + tx_2$, $y = (1-t)y_1 + ty_2$, $0 \le t \le 1$. Then $dx = (x_2 - x_1)\, dt$ and $dy = (y_2 - y_1)\, dt$, so

$$\int_C x\, dy - y\, dx = \int_0^1 [(1-t)x_1 + tx_2](y_2 - y_1)\, dt + [(1-t)y_1 + ty_2](x_2 - x_1)\, dt$$

$$= \int_0^1 (x_1(y_2 - y_1) - y_1(x_2 - x_1) + t[(y_2 - y_1)(x_2 - x_1) - (x_2 - x_1)(y_2 - y_1)])\, dt$$

$$= \int_0^1 (x_1 y_2 - x_2 y_1)\, dt = x_1 y_2 - x_2 y_1$$

(b) We apply Green's Theorem to the path $C = C_1 \cup C_2 \cup \cdots \cup C_n$, where C_i is the line segment that joins (x_i, y_i) to (x_{i+1}, y_{i+1}) for $i = 1, 2, \ldots, n-1$, and C_n is the line segment that joins (x_n, y_n) to (x_1, y_1). From (5),

$\tfrac{1}{2} \int_C x\, dy - y\, dx = \iint_D dA$, where D is the polygon bounded by C. Therefore

$$\text{area of polygon} = A(D) = \iint_D dA = \tfrac{1}{2}\oint_C x\,dy - y\,dx$$
$$= \tfrac{1}{2}\left(\int_{C_1} x\,dy - y\,dx + \int_{C_2} x\,dy - y\,dx + \cdots + \int_{C_{n-1}} x\,dy - y\,dx + \int_{C_n} x\,dy - y\,dx\right)$$

To evaluate these integrals we use the formula from (a) to get

$$A(D) = \tfrac{1}{2}[(x_1y_2 - x_2y_1) + (x_2y_3 - x_3y_2) + \cdots + (x_{n-1}y_n - x_ny_{n-1}) + (x_ny_1 - x_1y_n)].$$

(c) $A = \tfrac{1}{2}[(0 \cdot 1 - 2 \cdot 0) + (2 \cdot 3 - 1 \cdot 1) + (1 \cdot 2 - 0 \cdot 3) + (0 \cdot 1 - (-1) \cdot 2) + (-1 \cdot 0 - 0 \cdot 1)]$

$\qquad = \tfrac{1}{2}(0 + 5 + 2 + 2) = \tfrac{9}{2}$

23. We orient the quarter-circular region as shown in the figure.

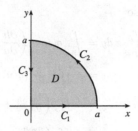

$A = \tfrac{1}{4}\pi a^2$ so $\overline{x} = \dfrac{1}{\pi a^2/2}\oint_C x^2\,dy$ and $\overline{y} = -\dfrac{1}{\pi a^2/2}\oint_C y^2\,dx.$

Here $C = C_1 + C_2 + C_3$ where $C_1\colon x = t,\ \ y = 0,\ \ 0 \le t \le a$;

$C_2\colon x = a\cos t,\ \ y = a\sin t,\ \ 0 \le t \le \tfrac{\pi}{2}$; and

$C_3\colon x = 0,\ y = a - t,\ 0 \le t \le a.$ Then

$\oint_C x^2\,dy = \int_{C_1} x^2\,dy + \int_{C_2} x^2\,dy + \int_{C_3} x^2\,dy = \int_0^a 0\,dt + \int_0^{\pi/2}(a\cos t)^2(a\cos t)\,dt + \int_0^a 0\,dt$

$\qquad = \int_0^{\pi/2} a^3 \cos^3 t\,dt = a^3\int_0^{\pi/2}(1 - \sin^2 t)\cos t\,dt = a^3\left[\sin t - \tfrac{1}{3}\sin^3 t\right]_0^{\pi/2} = \tfrac{2}{3}a^3$

so $\overline{x} = \dfrac{1}{\pi a^2/2}\oint_C x^2\,dy - \dfrac{4a}{3\pi}.$

$\oint_C y^2\,dx = \int_{C_1} y^2\,dx + \int_{C_2} y^2\,dx + \int_{C_3} y^2\,dx = \int_0^a 0\,dt + \int_0^{\pi/2}(a\sin t)^2(-a\sin t)\,dt + \int_0^a 0\,dt$

$\qquad = \int_0^{\pi/2}(-a^3\sin^3 t)\,dt = -a^3\int_0^{\pi/2}(1 - \cos^2 t)\sin t\,dt = -a^3\left[\tfrac{1}{3}\cos^3 t - \cos t\right]_0^{\pi/2} = -\tfrac{2}{3}a^3,$

so $\overline{y} = -\dfrac{1}{\pi a^2/2}\oint_C y^2\,dx = \dfrac{4a}{3\pi}.$ Thus $(\overline{x}, \overline{y}) = \left(\dfrac{4a}{3\pi}, \dfrac{4a}{3\pi}\right).$

25. By Green's Theorem, $-\tfrac{1}{3}\rho\oint_C y^3\,dx = -\tfrac{1}{3}\rho\iint_D(-3y^2)\,dA = \iint_D y^2\rho\,dA = I_x$ and

$\tfrac{1}{3}\rho\oint_C x^3\,dy = \tfrac{1}{3}\rho\iint_D(3x^2)\,dA = \iint_D x^2\rho\,dA = I_y.$

27. As in Example 5, let C' be a counterclockwise-oriented circle with center the origin and radius a, where a is chosen to

be small enough so that C' lies inside C, and D the region bounded by C and C'. Here

$P = \dfrac{2xy}{(x^2+y^2)^2} \quad \Rightarrow \quad \dfrac{\partial P}{\partial y} = \dfrac{2x(x^2+y^2)^2 - 2xy \cdot 2(x^2+y^2) \cdot 2y}{(x^2+y^2)^4} = \dfrac{2x^3 - 6xy^2}{(x^2+y^2)^3}$ and

$Q = \dfrac{y^2 - x^2}{(x^2+y^2)^2} \quad \Rightarrow \quad \dfrac{\partial Q}{\partial x} = \dfrac{-2x(x^2+y^2)^2 - (y^2-x^2) \cdot 2(x^2+y^2) \cdot 2x}{(x^2+y^2)^4} = \dfrac{2x^3 - 6xy^2}{(x^2+y^2)^3}.$ Thus, as in the example,

$$\int_C P\,dx + Q\,dy + \int_{-C'} P\,dx + Q\,dy = \iint_D\left(\dfrac{\partial Q}{\partial x} - \dfrac{\partial P}{\partial y}\right)dA = \iint_D 0\,dA = 0$$

and $\int_C \mathbf{F} \cdot d\mathbf{r} = \int_{C'} \mathbf{F} \cdot d\mathbf{r}.$ We parametrize C' as $\mathbf{r}(t) = a\cos t\,\mathbf{i} + a\sin t\,\mathbf{j}, 0 \le t \le 2\pi.$ Then

$$\int_C \mathbf{F} \cdot d\mathbf{r} = \int_{C'} \mathbf{F} \cdot d\mathbf{r} = \int_0^{2\pi} \dfrac{2\,(a\cos t)\,(a\sin t)\,\mathbf{i} + \left(a^2\sin^2 t - a^2\cos^2 t\right)\mathbf{j}}{\left(a^2\cos^2 t + a^2\sin^2 t\right)^2} \cdot \left(-a\sin t\,\mathbf{i} + a\cos t\,\mathbf{j}\right)dt$$

$$= \dfrac{1}{a}\int_0^{2\pi}\left(-\cos t\sin^2 t - \cos^3 t\right)dt = \dfrac{1}{a}\int_0^{2\pi}\left(-\cos t\sin^2 t - \cos t\left(1 - \sin^2 t\right)\right)dt$$

$$= \dfrac{1}{a}\int_0^{2\pi} \cos t\,dt = \dfrac{1}{a}\sin t\Big]_0^{2\pi} = 0$$

29. Since C is a simple closed path which doesn't pass through or enclose the origin, there exists an open region that doesn't contain the origin but does contain D. Thus $P = -y/(x^2 + y^2)$ and $Q = x/(x^2 + y^2)$ have continuous partial derivatives on this open region containing D and we can apply Green's Theorem. But by Exercise 13.3.35(a), $\partial P/\partial y = \partial Q/\partial x$, so

$$\oint_C \mathbf{F} \cdot d\mathbf{r} = \iint_D 0\, dA = 0.$$

31. Using the first part of (5), we have that $\iint_R dx\, dy = A(R) = \int_{\partial R} x\, dy$. But $x = g(u, v)$, and $dy = \dfrac{\partial h}{\partial u}\, du + \dfrac{\partial h}{\partial v}\, dv$, and we orient ∂S by taking the positive direction to be that which corresponds, under the mapping, to the positive direction along ∂R, so

$$\int_{\partial R} x\, dy = \int_{\partial S} g(u, v)\left(\frac{\partial h}{\partial u}\, du + \frac{\partial h}{\partial v}\, dv \right) = \int_{\partial S} g(u, v) \frac{\partial h}{\partial u}\, du + g(u, v) \frac{\partial h}{\partial v}\, dv$$

$$= \pm \iint_S \left[\frac{\partial}{\partial u}\left(g(u, v) \frac{\partial h}{\partial v} \right) - \frac{\partial}{\partial v}\left(g(u, v) \frac{\partial h}{\partial u} \right) \right] dA \qquad \text{[using Green's Theorem in the } uv\text{-plane]}$$

$$= \pm \iint_S \left(\frac{\partial g}{\partial u} \frac{\partial h}{\partial v} + g(u, v) \frac{\partial^2 h}{\partial u\, \partial v} - \frac{\partial g}{\partial v} \frac{\partial h}{\partial u} - g(u, v) \frac{\partial^2 h}{\partial v\, \partial u} \right) dA \qquad \text{[using the Chain Rule]}$$

$$= \pm \iint_S \left(\frac{\partial x}{\partial u} \frac{\partial y}{\partial v} - \frac{\partial x}{\partial v} \frac{\partial y}{\partial u} \right) dA \quad \text{[by the equality of mixed partials]} \quad = \pm \iint_S \frac{\partial(x, y)}{\partial(u, v)}\, du\, dv$$

The sign is chosen to be positive if the orientation that we gave to ∂S corresponds to the usual positive orientation, and it is negative otherwise. In either case, since $A(R)$ is positive, the sign chosen must be the same as the sign of $\dfrac{\partial(x, y)}{\partial(u, v)}$.

Therefore $A(R) = \displaystyle\iint_R dx\, dy = \iint_S \left| \frac{\partial(x, y)}{\partial(u, v)} \right| du\, dv.$

13.5 Curl and Divergence

1. (a) $\operatorname{curl} \mathbf{F} = \nabla \times \mathbf{F} = \begin{vmatrix} \mathbf{i} & \mathbf{j} & \mathbf{k} \\ \partial/\partial x & \partial/\partial y & \partial/\partial z \\ xyz & 0 & -x^2 y \end{vmatrix} = (-x^2 - 0)\,\mathbf{i} - (-2xy - xy)\,\mathbf{j} + (0 - xz)\,\mathbf{k}$

$\qquad = -x^2\,\mathbf{i} + 3xy\,\mathbf{j} - xz\,\mathbf{k}$

(b) $\operatorname{div} \mathbf{F} = \nabla \cdot \mathbf{F} = \dfrac{\partial}{\partial x}(xyz) + \dfrac{\partial}{\partial y}(0) + \dfrac{\partial}{\partial z}(-x^2 y) = yz + 0 + 0 = yz$

3. (a) $\operatorname{curl} \mathbf{F} = \nabla \times \mathbf{F} = \begin{vmatrix} \mathbf{i} & \mathbf{j} & \mathbf{k} \\ \partial/\partial x & \partial/\partial y & \partial/\partial z \\ xye^z & 0 & yze^x \end{vmatrix} = (ze^x - 0)\,\mathbf{i} - (yze^x - xye^z)\,\mathbf{j} + (0 - xe^z)\,\mathbf{k}$

$\qquad = ze^x\,\mathbf{i} + (xye^z - yze^x)\,\mathbf{j} - xe^z\,\mathbf{k}$

(b) $\operatorname{div} \mathbf{F} = \nabla \cdot \mathbf{F} = \dfrac{\partial}{\partial x}(xye^z) + \dfrac{\partial}{\partial y}(0) + \dfrac{\partial}{\partial z}(yze^x) = ye^z + 0 + ye^x = y(e^z + e^x)$

5. (a) $\operatorname{curl} \mathbf{F} = \nabla \times \mathbf{F} = \begin{vmatrix} \mathbf{i} & \mathbf{j} & \mathbf{k} \\ \partial/\partial x & \partial/\partial y & \partial/\partial z \\ \dfrac{x}{\sqrt{x^2 + y^2 + z^2}} & \dfrac{y}{\sqrt{x^2 + y^2 + z^2}} & \dfrac{z}{\sqrt{x^2 + y^2 + z^2}} \end{vmatrix}$

$\qquad = \dfrac{1}{(x^2 + y^2 + z^2)^{3/2}}\left[(-yz + yz)\,\mathbf{i} - (-xz + xz)\,\mathbf{j} + (-xy + xy)\,\mathbf{k} \right] = \mathbf{0}$

(b) $\operatorname{div} \mathbf{F} = \nabla \cdot \mathbf{F} = \dfrac{\partial}{\partial x}\left(\dfrac{x}{\sqrt{x^2+y^2+z^2}}\right) + \dfrac{\partial}{\partial y}\left(\dfrac{y}{\sqrt{x^2+y^2+z^2}}\right) + \dfrac{\partial}{\partial z}\left(\dfrac{z}{\sqrt{x^2+y^2+z^2}}\right)$

$= \dfrac{x^2+y^2+z^2-x^2}{(x^2+y^2+z^2)^{3/2}} + \dfrac{x^2+y^2+z^2-y^2}{(x^2+y^2+z^2)^{3/2}} + \dfrac{x^2+y^2+z^2-z^2}{(x^2+y^2+z^2)^{3/2}} = \dfrac{2x^2+2y^2+2z^2}{(x^2+y^2+z^2)^{3/2}} = \dfrac{2}{\sqrt{x^2+y^2+z^2}}$

7. (a) $\operatorname{curl} \mathbf{F} = \nabla \times \mathbf{F} = \begin{vmatrix} \mathbf{i} & \mathbf{j} & \mathbf{k} \\ \partial/\partial x & \partial/\partial y & \partial/\partial z \\ \ln x & \ln(xy) & \ln(xyz) \end{vmatrix} = \left(\dfrac{xz}{xyz}-0\right)\mathbf{i} - \left(\dfrac{yz}{xyz}-0\right)\mathbf{j} + \left(\dfrac{y}{xy}-0\right)\mathbf{k} = \left\langle \dfrac{1}{y}, -\dfrac{1}{x}, \dfrac{1}{x}\right\rangle$

(b) $\operatorname{div} \mathbf{F} = \nabla \cdot \mathbf{F} = \dfrac{\partial}{\partial x}(\ln x) + \dfrac{\partial}{\partial y}(\ln(xy)) + \dfrac{\partial}{\partial z}(\ln(xyz)) = \dfrac{1}{x} + \dfrac{x}{xy} + \dfrac{xy}{xyz} = \dfrac{1}{x} + \dfrac{1}{y} + \dfrac{1}{z}$

9. If the vector field is $\mathbf{F} = P\mathbf{i} + Q\mathbf{j} + R\mathbf{k}$, then we know $R = 0$. In addition, the x-component of each vector of $\mathbf{F}$ is 0, so

$P = 0$, hence $\dfrac{\partial P}{\partial x} = \dfrac{\partial P}{\partial y} = \dfrac{\partial P}{\partial z} = \dfrac{\partial R}{\partial x} = \dfrac{\partial R}{\partial y} = \dfrac{\partial R}{\partial z} = 0$. Q decreases as y increases, so $\dfrac{\partial Q}{\partial y} < 0$, but Q doesn't change

in the x- or z-directions, so $\dfrac{\partial Q}{\partial x} = \dfrac{\partial Q}{\partial z} = 0$.

(a) $\operatorname{div} \mathbf{F} = \dfrac{\partial P}{\partial x} + \dfrac{\partial Q}{\partial y} + \dfrac{\partial R}{\partial z} = 0 + \dfrac{\partial Q}{\partial y} + 0 < 0$

(b) $\operatorname{curl} \mathbf{F} - \left(\dfrac{\partial R}{\partial y} - \dfrac{\partial Q}{\partial z}\right)\mathbf{i} + \left(\dfrac{\partial P}{\partial z} - \dfrac{\partial R}{\partial x}\right)\mathbf{j} + \left(\dfrac{\partial Q}{\partial x} - \dfrac{\partial P}{\partial y}\right)\mathbf{k} = (0-0)\mathbf{i} + (0-0)\mathbf{j} + (0-0)\mathbf{k} = \mathbf{0}$

11. If the vector field is $\mathbf{F} = P\mathbf{i} + Q\mathbf{j} + R\mathbf{k}$, then we know $R = 0$. In addition, the y-component of each vector of $\mathbf{F}$ is 0, so

$Q = 0$, hence $\dfrac{\partial Q}{\partial x} = \dfrac{\partial Q}{\partial y} = \dfrac{\partial Q}{\partial z} - \dfrac{\partial R}{\partial x} - \dfrac{\partial R}{\partial y} = \dfrac{\partial R}{\partial z} = 0$. P increases as y increases, so $\dfrac{\partial P}{\partial y} > 0$, but P doesn't change in

the x- or z-directions, so $\dfrac{\partial P}{\partial x} = \dfrac{\partial P}{\partial z} = 0$.

(a) $\operatorname{div} \mathbf{F} = \dfrac{\partial P}{\partial x} + \dfrac{\partial Q}{\partial y} + \dfrac{\partial R}{\partial z} = 0 + 0 + 0 = 0$

(b) $\operatorname{curl} \mathbf{F} = \left(\dfrac{\partial R}{\partial y} - \dfrac{\partial Q}{\partial z}\right)\mathbf{i} + \left(\dfrac{\partial P}{\partial z} - \dfrac{\partial R}{\partial x}\right)\mathbf{j} + \left(\dfrac{\partial Q}{\partial x} - \dfrac{\partial P}{\partial y}\right)\mathbf{k} = (0-0)\mathbf{i} + (0-0)\mathbf{j} + \left(0 - \dfrac{\partial P}{\partial y}\right)\mathbf{k} = -\dfrac{\partial P}{\partial y}\mathbf{k}$

Since $\dfrac{\partial P}{\partial y} > 0$, $-\dfrac{\partial P}{\partial y}\mathbf{k}$ is a vector pointing in the negative z-direction.

13. $\operatorname{curl} \mathbf{F} = \nabla \times \mathbf{F} = \begin{vmatrix} \mathbf{i} & \mathbf{j} & \mathbf{k} \\ \partial/\partial x & \partial/\partial y & \partial/\partial z \\ y^2 z^3 & 2xyz^3 & 3xy^2 z^2 \end{vmatrix} = (6xyz^2 - 6xyz^2)\mathbf{i} - (3y^2 z^2 - 3y^2 z^2)\mathbf{j} + (2yz^3 - 2yz^3)\mathbf{k} = \mathbf{0}$

and $\mathbf{F}$ is defined on all of $\mathbb{R}^3$ with component functions which have continuous partial derivatives, so by Theorem 4,

$\mathbf{F}$ is conservative. Thus, there exists a function f such that $\mathbf{F} = \nabla f$. Then $f_x(x,y,z) = y^2 z^3$ implies

$f(x,y,z) = xy^2 z^3 + g(y,z)$ and $f_y(x,y,z) = 2xyz^3 + g_y(y,z)$. But $f_y(x,y,z) = 2xyz^3$, so $g(y,z) = h(z)$ and

$f(x,y,z) = xy^2 z^3 + h(z)$. Thus $f_z(x,y,z) = 3xy^2 z^2 + h'(z)$ but $f_z(x,y,z) = 3xy^2 z^2$ so $h(z) = K$, a constant.

Hence a potential function for $\mathbf{F}$ is $f(x,y,z) = xy^2 z^3 + K$.

15. $\operatorname{curl}\mathbf{F} = \nabla \times \mathbf{F} = \begin{vmatrix} \mathbf{i} & \mathbf{j} & \mathbf{k} \\ \partial/\partial x & \partial/\partial y & \partial/\partial z \\ 2xy & x^2 + 2yz & y^2 \end{vmatrix} = (2y - 2y)\,\mathbf{i} - (0 - 0)\,\mathbf{j} + (2x - 2x)\,\mathbf{k} = \mathbf{0}$, $\mathbf{F}$ is defined on all of $\mathbb{R}^3$,

and the partial derivatives of the component functions are continuous, so $\mathbf{F}$ is conservative. Thus there exists a function f

such that $\nabla f = \mathbf{F}$. Then $f_x(x,y,z) = 2xy$ implies $f(x,y,z) = x^2y + g(y,z)$ and $f_y(x,y,z) = x^2 + g_y(y,z)$. But

$f_y(x,y,z) = x^2 + 2yz$, so $g(y,z) = y^2z + h(z)$ and $f(x,y,z) = x^2y + y^2z + h(z)$. Thus $f_z(x,y,z) = y^2 + h'(z)$ but

$f_z(x,y,z) = y^2$ so $h(z) = K$ and $f(x,y,z) = x^2y + y^2z + K$.

17. $\operatorname{curl}\mathbf{F} = \nabla \times \mathbf{F} = \begin{vmatrix} \mathbf{i} & \mathbf{j} & \mathbf{k} \\ \partial/\partial x & \partial/\partial y & \partial/\partial z \\ ye^{-x} & e^{-x} & 2z \end{vmatrix} = (0 - 0)\,\mathbf{i} - (0 - 0)\,\mathbf{j} + (-e^{-x} - e^{-x})\,\mathbf{k} = -2e^{-x}\,\mathbf{k} \neq \mathbf{0}$,

so $\mathbf{F}$ is not conservative.

19. No. Assume there is such a $\mathbf{G}$. Then $\operatorname{div}(\operatorname{curl}\mathbf{G}) = \dfrac{\partial}{\partial x}(x\sin y) + \dfrac{\partial}{\partial y}(\cos y) + \dfrac{\partial}{\partial z}(z - xy) = \sin y - \sin y + 1 \neq 0$,

which contradicts Theorem 11.

21. $\operatorname{curl}\mathbf{F} = \begin{vmatrix} \mathbf{i} & \mathbf{j} & \mathbf{k} \\ \partial/\partial x & \partial/\partial y & \partial/\partial z \\ f(x) & g(y) & h(z) \end{vmatrix} = (0 - 0)\,\mathbf{i} + (0 - 0)\,\mathbf{j} + (0 - 0)\,\mathbf{k} = \mathbf{0}$. Hence $\mathbf{F} = f(x)\,\mathbf{i} + g(y)\,\mathbf{j} + h(z)\,\mathbf{k}$

is irrotational.

For Exercises 23–29, let $\mathbf{F}(x,y,z) = P_1\,\mathbf{i} + Q_1\,\mathbf{j} + R_1\,\mathbf{k}$ and $\mathbf{G}(x,y,z) = P_2\,\mathbf{i} + Q_2\,\mathbf{j} + R_2\,\mathbf{k}$.

23. $\operatorname{div}(\mathbf{F} + \mathbf{G}) = \operatorname{div}\langle P_1 + P_2, Q_1 + Q_2, R_1 + R_2 \rangle = \dfrac{\partial(P_1 + P_2)}{\partial x} + \dfrac{\partial(Q_1 + Q_2)}{\partial y} + \dfrac{\partial(R_1 + R_2)}{\partial z}$

$= \dfrac{\partial P_1}{\partial x} + \dfrac{\partial P_2}{\partial x} + \dfrac{\partial Q_1}{\partial y} + \dfrac{\partial Q_2}{\partial y} + \dfrac{\partial R_1}{\partial z} + \dfrac{\partial R_2}{\partial z} = \left(\dfrac{\partial P_1}{\partial x} + \dfrac{\partial Q_1}{\partial y} + \dfrac{\partial R_1}{\partial z} \right) + \left(\dfrac{\partial P_2}{\partial x} + \dfrac{\partial Q_2}{\partial y} + \dfrac{\partial R_2}{\partial z} \right)$

$= \operatorname{div}\langle P_1, Q_1, R_1 \rangle + \operatorname{div}\langle P_2, Q_2, R_2 \rangle = \operatorname{div}\mathbf{F} + \operatorname{div}\mathbf{G}$

25. $\operatorname{div}(f\mathbf{F}) = \operatorname{div}(f\langle P_1, Q_1, R_1 \rangle) = \operatorname{div}\langle fP_1, fQ_1, fR_1 \rangle = \dfrac{\partial(fP_1)}{\partial x} + \dfrac{\partial(fQ_1)}{\partial y} + \dfrac{\partial(fR_1)}{\partial z}$

$= \left(f\dfrac{\partial P_1}{\partial x} + P_1\dfrac{\partial f}{\partial x} \right) + \left(f\dfrac{\partial Q_1}{\partial y} + Q_1\dfrac{\partial f}{\partial y} \right) + \left(f\dfrac{\partial R_1}{\partial z} + R_1\dfrac{\partial f}{\partial z} \right)$

$= f\left(\dfrac{\partial P_1}{\partial x} + \dfrac{\partial Q_1}{\partial y} + \dfrac{\partial R_1}{\partial z} \right) + \langle P_1, Q_1, R_1 \rangle \cdot \left\langle \dfrac{\partial f}{\partial x}, \dfrac{\partial f}{\partial y}, \dfrac{\partial f}{\partial z} \right\rangle = f\operatorname{div}\mathbf{F} + \mathbf{F}\cdot\nabla f$

27. $\text{div}(\mathbf{F} \times \mathbf{G}) = \nabla \cdot (\mathbf{F} \times \mathbf{G}) = \begin{vmatrix} \partial/\partial x & \partial/\partial y & \partial/\partial z \\ P_1 & Q_1 & R_1 \\ P_2 & Q_2 & R_2 \end{vmatrix} = \dfrac{\partial}{\partial x}\begin{vmatrix} Q_1 & R_1 \\ Q_2 & R_2 \end{vmatrix} - \dfrac{\partial}{\partial y}\begin{vmatrix} P_1 & R_1 \\ P_2 & R_2 \end{vmatrix} + \dfrac{\partial}{\partial z}\begin{vmatrix} P_1 & Q_1 \\ P_2 & Q_2 \end{vmatrix}$

$$= \left[Q_1 \frac{\partial R_2}{\partial x} + R_2 \frac{\partial Q_1}{\partial x} - Q_2 \frac{\partial R_1}{\partial x} - R_1 \frac{\partial Q_2}{\partial x} \right] - \left[P_1 \frac{\partial R_2}{\partial y} + R_2 \frac{\partial P_1}{\partial y} - P_2 \frac{\partial R_1}{\partial y} - R_1 \frac{\partial P_2}{\partial y} \right]$$

$$+ \left[P_1 \frac{\partial Q_2}{\partial z} + Q_2 \frac{\partial P_1}{\partial z} - P_2 \frac{\partial Q_1}{\partial z} - Q_1 \frac{\partial P_2}{\partial z} \right]$$

$$= \left[P_2 \left(\frac{\partial R_1}{\partial y} - \frac{\partial Q_1}{\partial z} \right) + Q_2 \left(\frac{\partial P_1}{\partial z} - \frac{\partial R_1}{\partial x} \right) + R_2 \left(\frac{\partial Q_1}{\partial x} - \frac{\partial P_1}{\partial y} \right) \right]$$

$$- \left[P_1 \left(\frac{\partial R_2}{\partial y} - \frac{\partial Q_2}{\partial z} \right) + Q_1 \left(\frac{\partial P_2}{\partial z} - \frac{\partial R_2}{\partial x} \right) + R_1 \left(\frac{\partial Q_2}{\partial x} - \frac{\partial P_2}{\partial y} \right) \right]$$

$$= \mathbf{G} \cdot \text{curl}\,\mathbf{F} - \mathbf{F} \cdot \text{curl}\,\mathbf{G}$$

29. $\text{curl}(\text{curl}\,\mathbf{F}) = \nabla \times (\nabla \times \mathbf{F}) = \begin{vmatrix} \mathbf{i} & \mathbf{j} & \mathbf{k} \\ \partial/\partial x & \partial/\partial y & \partial/\partial z \\ \partial R_1/\partial y - \partial Q_1/\partial z & \partial P_1/\partial z - \partial R_1/\partial x & \partial Q_1/\partial x - \partial P_1/\partial y \end{vmatrix}$

$$= \left(\frac{\partial^2 Q_1}{\partial y \partial x} - \frac{\partial^2 P_1}{\partial y^2} - \frac{\partial^2 P_1}{\partial z^2} + \frac{\partial^2 R_1}{\partial z \partial x} \right) \mathbf{i} + \left(\frac{\partial^2 R_1}{\partial z \partial y} - \frac{\partial^2 Q_1}{\partial z^2} - \frac{\partial^2 Q_1}{\partial x^2} + \frac{\partial^2 P_1}{\partial x \partial y} \right) \mathbf{j}$$

$$+ \left(\frac{\partial^2 P_1}{\partial x \partial z} - \frac{\partial^2 R_1}{\partial x^2} - \frac{\partial^2 R_1}{\partial y^2} + \frac{\partial^2 Q_1}{\partial y \partial z} \right) \mathbf{k}$$

Now let's consider $\text{grad}(\text{div}\,\mathbf{F}) - \nabla^2 \mathbf{F}$ and compare with the above.

(Note that $\nabla^2 \mathbf{F}$ is defined on page 945.)

$$\text{grad}(\text{div}\,\mathbf{F}) - \nabla^2 \mathbf{F} = \left[\left(\frac{\partial^2 P_1}{\partial x^2} + \frac{\partial^2 Q_1}{\partial x \partial y} + \frac{\partial^2 R_1}{\partial x \partial z} \right) \mathbf{i} + \left(\frac{\partial^2 P_1}{\partial y \partial x} + \frac{\partial^2 Q_1}{\partial y^2} + \frac{\partial^2 R_1}{\partial y \partial z} \right) \mathbf{j} + \left(\frac{\partial^2 P_1}{\partial z \partial x} + \frac{\partial^2 Q_1}{\partial z \partial y} + \frac{\partial^2 R_1}{\partial z^2} \right) \mathbf{k} \right]$$

$$- \left[\left(\frac{\partial^2 P_1}{\partial x^2} + \frac{\partial^2 P_1}{\partial y^2} + \frac{\partial^2 P_1}{\partial z^2} \right) \mathbf{i} + \left(\frac{\partial^2 Q_1}{\partial x^2} + \frac{\partial^2 Q_1}{\partial y^2} + \frac{\partial^2 Q_1}{\partial z^2} \right) \mathbf{j} \right.$$

$$\left. + \left(\frac{\partial^2 R_1}{\partial x^2} + \frac{\partial^2 R_1}{\partial y^2} + \frac{\partial^2 R_1}{\partial z^2} \right) \mathbf{k} \right]$$

$$= \left(\frac{\partial^2 Q_1}{\partial x \partial y} + \frac{\partial^2 R_1}{\partial x \partial z} - \frac{\partial^2 P_1}{\partial y^2} - \frac{\partial^2 P_1}{\partial z^2} \right) \mathbf{i} + \left(\frac{\partial^2 P_1}{\partial y \partial x} + \frac{\partial^2 R_1}{\partial y \partial z} - \frac{\partial^2 Q_1}{\partial x^2} - \frac{\partial^2 Q_1}{\partial z^2} \right) \mathbf{j}$$

$$+ \left(\frac{\partial^2 P_1}{\partial z \partial x} + \frac{\partial^2 Q_1}{\partial z \partial y} - \frac{\partial^2 R_1}{\partial x^2} - \frac{\partial^2 R_2}{\partial y^2} \right) \mathbf{k}$$

Then applying Clairaut's Theorem to reverse the order of differentiation in the second partial derivatives as needed and comparing, we have $\text{curl}\,\text{curl}\,\mathbf{F} = \text{grad}\,\text{div}\,\mathbf{F} - \nabla^2 \mathbf{F}$ as desired.

31. (a) $\nabla r = \nabla \sqrt{x^2 + y^2 + z^2} = \dfrac{x}{\sqrt{x^2 + y^2 + z^2}} \mathbf{i} + \dfrac{y}{\sqrt{x^2 + y^2 + z^2}} \mathbf{j} + \dfrac{z}{\sqrt{x^2 + y^2 + z^2}} \mathbf{k} = \dfrac{x\mathbf{i} + y\mathbf{j} + z\mathbf{k}}{\sqrt{x^2 + y^2 + z^2}} = \dfrac{\mathbf{r}}{r}$

(b) $\nabla \times \mathbf{r} = \begin{vmatrix} \mathbf{i} & \mathbf{j} & \mathbf{k} \\ \dfrac{\partial}{\partial x} & \dfrac{\partial}{\partial y} & \dfrac{\partial}{\partial z} \\ x & y & z \end{vmatrix} = \left[\dfrac{\partial}{\partial y}(z) - \dfrac{\partial}{\partial z}(y) \right] \mathbf{i} + \left[\dfrac{\partial}{\partial z}(x) - \dfrac{\partial}{\partial x}(z) \right] \mathbf{j} + \left[\dfrac{\partial}{\partial x}(y) - \dfrac{\partial}{\partial y}(x) \right] \mathbf{k} = \mathbf{0}$

(c) $\nabla \left(\dfrac{1}{r} \right) = \nabla \left(\dfrac{1}{\sqrt{x^2 + y^2 + z^2}} \right)$

$= \dfrac{-\dfrac{1}{2\sqrt{x^2 + y^2 + z^2}}(2x)}{x^2 + y^2 + z^2} \mathbf{i} - \dfrac{\dfrac{1}{2\sqrt{x^2 + y^2 + z^2}}(2y)}{x^2 + y^2 + z^2} \mathbf{j} - \dfrac{\dfrac{1}{2\sqrt{x^2 + y^2 + z^2}}(2z)}{x^2 + y^2 + z^2} \mathbf{k}$

$= -\dfrac{x\mathbf{i} + y\mathbf{j} + z\mathbf{k}}{(x^2 + y^2 + z^2)^{3/2}} = -\dfrac{\mathbf{r}}{r^3}$

(d) $\nabla \ln r = \nabla \ln (x^2 + y^2 + z^2)^{1/2} = \tfrac{1}{2} \nabla \ln (x^2 + y^2 + z^2)$

$= \dfrac{x}{x^2 + y^2 + z^2} \mathbf{i} + \dfrac{y}{x^2 + y^2 + z^2} \mathbf{j} + \dfrac{z}{x^2 + y^2 + z^2} \mathbf{k} = \dfrac{x\mathbf{i} + y\mathbf{j} + z\mathbf{k}}{x^2 + y^2 + z^2} = \dfrac{\mathbf{r}}{r^2}$

33. By (13), $\oint_C f(\nabla g) \cdot \mathbf{n}\, ds = \iint_D \text{div}(f\nabla g)\, dA = \iint_D [f\, \text{div}(\nabla g) + \nabla g \cdot \nabla f]\, dA$ by Exercise 25. But $\text{div}(\nabla g) = \nabla^2 g$.

Hence $\iint_D f\nabla^2 g\, dA = \oint_C f(\nabla g) \cdot \mathbf{n}\, ds - \iint_D \nabla g \cdot \nabla f\, dA$.

35. Let $f(x,y) = 1$. Then $\nabla f = \mathbf{0}$ and Green's first identity (see Exercise 33) says

$\iint_D \nabla^2 g\, dA = \oint_C (\nabla g) \cdot \mathbf{n}\, ds - \iint_D \mathbf{0} \cdot \nabla g\, dA \;\Rightarrow\; \iint_D \nabla^2 g\, dA = \oint_C \nabla g \cdot \mathbf{n}\, ds$. But g is harmonic on D, so

$\nabla^2 g = 0 \;\Rightarrow\; \oint_C \nabla g \cdot \mathbf{n}\, ds = 0$ and $\oint_C D_\mathbf{n} g\, ds = \oint_C (\nabla g \cdot \mathbf{n})\, ds = 0$.

37. (a) We know that $\omega = v/d$, and from the diagram $\sin \theta = d/r \;\Rightarrow\; v = d\omega = (\sin \theta) r\omega = |\mathbf{w} \times \mathbf{r}|$. But $\mathbf{v}$ is perpendicular to both $\mathbf{w}$ and $\mathbf{r}$, so that $\mathbf{v} = \mathbf{w} \times \mathbf{r}$.

(b) From (a), $\mathbf{v} = \mathbf{w} \times \mathbf{r} = \begin{vmatrix} \mathbf{i} & \mathbf{j} & \mathbf{k} \\ 0 & 0 & \omega \\ x & y & z \end{vmatrix} = (0 \cdot z - \omega y)\mathbf{i} + (\omega x - 0 \cdot z)\mathbf{j} + (0 \cdot y - x \cdot 0)\mathbf{k} = -\omega y\, \mathbf{i} + \omega x\, \mathbf{j}$

(c) $\text{curl}\, \mathbf{v} = \nabla \times \mathbf{v} = \begin{vmatrix} \mathbf{i} & \mathbf{j} & \mathbf{k} \\ \partial/\partial x & \partial/\partial y & \partial/\partial z \\ -\omega y & \omega x & 0 \end{vmatrix}$

$= \left[\dfrac{\partial}{\partial y}(0) - \dfrac{\partial}{\partial z}(\omega x) \right] \mathbf{i} + \left[\dfrac{\partial}{\partial z}(-\omega y) - \dfrac{\partial}{\partial x}(0) \right] \mathbf{j} + \left[\dfrac{\partial}{\partial x}(\omega x) - \dfrac{\partial}{\partial y}(-\omega y) \right] \mathbf{k}$

$= [\omega - (-\omega)]\, \mathbf{k} = 2\omega\, \mathbf{k} = 2\mathbf{w}$

39. For any continuous function f on $\mathbb{R}^3$, define a vector field $\mathbf{G}(x,y,z) = \langle g(x,y,z), 0, 0 \rangle$ where $g(x,y,z) = \int_0^x f(t,y,z)\, dt$.

Then $\text{div}\, \mathbf{G} = \dfrac{\partial}{\partial x}(g(x,y,z)) + \dfrac{\partial}{\partial y}(0) + \dfrac{\partial}{\partial z}(0) = \dfrac{\partial}{\partial x} \int_0^x f(t,y,z)\, dt = f(x,y,z)$ by the Fundamental Theorem of

Calculus. Thus every continuous function f on $\mathbb{R}^3$ is the divergence of some vector field.

13.6 Surface Integrals

1. The faces of the box in the planes $x = 0$ and $x = 2$ have surface area 24 and centers $(0, 2, 3)$, $(2, 2, 3)$. The faces in $y = 0$ and $y = 4$ have surface area 12 and centers $(1, 0, 3)$, $(1, 4, 3)$, and the faces in $z = 0$ and $z = 6$ have area 8 and centers $(1, 2, 0)$, $(1, 2, 6)$. For each face we take the point P_{ij}^* to be the center of the face and $f(x, y, z) = e^{-0.1(x+y+z)}$, so by Definition 1,

$$\iint_S f(x, y, z)\, dS \approx [f(0, 2, 3)](24) + [f(2, 2, 3)](24) + [f(1, 0, 3)](12)$$
$$+ [f(1, 4, 3)](12) + [f(1, 2, 0)](8) + [f(1, 2, 6)](8)$$
$$= 24(e^{-0.5} + e^{-0.7}) + 12(e^{-0.4} + e^{-0.8}) + 8(e^{-0.3} + e^{-0.9}) \approx 49.09$$

3. We can use the xz- and yz-planes to divide H into four patches of equal size, each with surface area equal to $\frac{1}{8}$ the surface area of a sphere with radius $\sqrt{50}$, so $\Delta S = \frac{1}{8}(4)\pi\left(\sqrt{50}\right)^2 = 25\pi$. Then $(\pm 3, \pm 4, 5)$ are sample points in the four patches, and using a Riemann sum as in Definition 1, we have

$$\iint_H f(x, y, z)\, dS \approx f(3, 4, 5)\,\Delta S + f(3, -4, 5)\,\Delta S + f(-3, 4, 5)\,\Delta S + f(-3, -4, 5)\,\Delta S$$
$$= (7 + 8 + 9 + 12)(25\pi) = 900\pi \approx 2827$$

5. $\mathbf{r}(u, v) = (u + v)\,\mathbf{i} + (u - v)\,\mathbf{j} + (1 + 2u + v)\,\mathbf{k}$, $0 \le u \le 2$, $0 \le v \le 1$ and

$\mathbf{r}_u \times \mathbf{r}_v = (\mathbf{i} + \mathbf{j} + 2\,\mathbf{k}) \times (\mathbf{i} - \mathbf{j} + \mathbf{k}) = 3\,\mathbf{i} \mid \mathbf{j} - 2\,\mathbf{k} \quad \Rightarrow \quad |\mathbf{r}_u \times \mathbf{r}_v| = \sqrt{3^2 + 1^2 + (-2)^2} = \sqrt{14}$. Then by Formula 2,

$$\iint_S (x + y + z)\, dS = \iint_D (u + v + u - v + 1 + 2u + v)\,|\mathbf{r}_u \times \mathbf{r}_v|\, dA = \int_0^1 \int_0^2 (4u + v + 1) \cdot \sqrt{14}\, du\, dv$$
$$= \sqrt{14} \int_0^1 \left[2u^2 + uv + u\right]_{u=0}^{u=2} dv = \sqrt{14} \int_0^1 (2v + 10)\, dv = \sqrt{14}\left[v^2 + 10v\right]_0^1 = 11\sqrt{14}$$

7. $\mathbf{r}(u, v) = \langle u\cos v, u\sin v, v \rangle$, $0 \le u \le 1$, $0 \le v \le \pi$ and

$\mathbf{r}_u \times \mathbf{r}_v = \langle \cos v, \sin v, 0 \rangle \times \langle -u\sin v, u\cos v, 1 \rangle = \langle \sin v, -\cos v, u \rangle \quad \Rightarrow$

$|\mathbf{r}_u \times \mathbf{r}_v| = \sqrt{\sin^2 v + \cos^2 v + u^2} = \sqrt{u^2 + 1}$. Then

$$\iint_S y\, dS = \iint_D (u\sin v)\,|\mathbf{r}_u \times \mathbf{r}_v|\, dA = \int_0^1 \int_0^\pi (u\sin v) \cdot \sqrt{u^2 + 1}\, dv\, du = \int_0^1 u\sqrt{u^2 + 1}\, du \int_0^\pi \sin v\, dv$$
$$= \left[\tfrac{1}{3}(u^2 + 1)^{3/2}\right]_0^1 [-\cos v]_0^\pi = \tfrac{1}{3}(2^{3/2} - 1) \cdot 2 = \tfrac{2}{3}(2\sqrt{2} - 1)$$

9. $z = 1 + 2x + 3y$ so $\dfrac{\partial z}{\partial x} = 2$ and $\dfrac{\partial z}{\partial y} = 3$. Then by Formula 4,

$$\iint_S x^2 yz\, dS = \iint_D x^2 yz \sqrt{\left(\frac{\partial z}{\partial x}\right)^2 + \left(\frac{\partial z}{\partial y}\right)^2 + 1}\, dA = \int_0^3 \int_0^2 x^2 y(1 + 2x + 3y)\sqrt{4 + 9 + 1}\, dy\, dx$$
$$= \sqrt{14} \int_0^3 \int_0^2 (x^2 y + 2x^3 y + 3x^2 y^2)\, dy\, dx = \sqrt{14} \int_0^3 \left[\tfrac{1}{2}x^2 y^2 + x^3 y^2 + x^2 y^3\right]_{y=0}^{y=2} dx$$
$$= \sqrt{14} \int_0^3 (10x^2 + 4x^3)\, dx = \sqrt{14}\left[\tfrac{10}{3}x^3 + x^4\right]_0^3 = 171\sqrt{14}$$

11. S is the part of the plane $z = 1 - x - y$ over the region $D = \{(x, y) \mid 0 \le x \le 1, 0 \le y \le 1 - x\}$. Thus

$$\iint_S yz\, dS = \iint_D y(1 - x - y)\sqrt{(-1)^2 + (-1)^2 + 1}\, dA = \sqrt{3} \int_0^1 \int_0^{1-x} (y - xy - y^2)\, dy\, dx$$
$$= \sqrt{3} \int_0^1 \left[\tfrac{1}{2}y^2 - \tfrac{1}{2}xy^2 - \tfrac{1}{3}y^3\right]_{y=0}^{y=1-x} dx = \sqrt{3} \int_0^1 \tfrac{1}{6}(1 - x)^3\, dx = -\tfrac{\sqrt{3}}{24}(1 - x)^4\Big|_0^1 = \tfrac{\sqrt{3}}{24}$$

13. S is the portion of the cone $z^2 = x^2 + y^2$ for $1 \le z \le 3$, or equivalently, S is the part of the surface $z = \sqrt{x^2 + y^2}$ over the region $D = \{(x, y) \mid 1 \le x^2 + y^2 \le 9\}$. Thus

$$\iint_S x^2 z^2 \, dS = \iint_D x^2(x^2 + y^2)\sqrt{\left(\frac{x}{\sqrt{x^2+y^2}}\right)^2 + \left(\frac{y}{\sqrt{x^2+y^2}}\right)^2 + 1}\, dA$$

$$= \iint_D x^2(x^2 + y^2)\sqrt{\frac{x^2+y^2}{x^2+y^2} + 1}\, dA = \iint_D \sqrt{2}\, x^2(x^2 + y^2)\, dA = \sqrt{2}\int_0^{2\pi}\int_1^3 (r\cos\theta)^2(r^2)\, r\, dr\, d\theta$$

$$= \sqrt{2}\int_0^{2\pi} \cos^2\theta\, d\theta \int_1^3 r^5\, dr = \sqrt{2}\left[\tfrac{1}{2}\theta + \tfrac{1}{4}\sin 2\theta\right]_0^{2\pi}\left[\tfrac{1}{6}r^6\right]_1^3 = \sqrt{2}\,(\pi)\cdot\tfrac{1}{6}(3^6 - 1) = \frac{364\sqrt{2}}{3}\,\pi$$

15. Using x and z as parameters, we have $\mathbf{r}(x, z) = x\,\mathbf{i} + (x^2 + z^2)\,\mathbf{j} + z\,\mathbf{k}$, $x^2 + z^2 \le 4$. Then

$\mathbf{r}_x \times \mathbf{r}_z = (\mathbf{i} + 2x\,\mathbf{j}) \times (2z\,\mathbf{j} + \mathbf{k}) = 2x\,\mathbf{i} - \mathbf{j} + 2z\,\mathbf{k}$ and $|\mathbf{r}_x \times \mathbf{r}_z| = \sqrt{4x^2 + 1 + 4z^2} = \sqrt{1 + 4(x^2 + z^2)}$. Thus

$$\iint_S y\, dS = \iint_{x^2+z^2\le 4}(x^2 + z^2)\sqrt{1 + 4(x^2 + z^2)}\, dA = \int_0^{2\pi}\int_0^2 r^2\sqrt{1 + 4r^2}\, r\, dr\, d\theta = \int_0^{2\pi} d\theta \int_0^2 r^2\sqrt{1 + 4r^2}\, r\, dr$$

$$= 2\pi\int_0^2 r^2\sqrt{1 + 4r^2}\, r\, dr \qquad \left[\text{let } u = 1 + 4r^2 \;\Rightarrow\; r^2 = \tfrac{1}{4}(u - 1) \text{ and } \tfrac{1}{8}du = r\, dr\right]$$

$$= 2\pi\int_1^{17}\tfrac{1}{4}(u - 1)\sqrt{u}\cdot\tfrac{1}{8}du = \tfrac{1}{16}\pi\int_1^{17}(u^{3/2} - u^{1/2})\, du$$

$$= \tfrac{1}{16}\pi\left[\tfrac{2}{5}u^{5/2} - \tfrac{2}{3}u^{3/2}\right]_1^{17} = \tfrac{1}{16}\pi\left[\tfrac{2}{5}(17)^{5/2} - \tfrac{2}{3}(17)^{3/2} - \tfrac{2}{5} + \tfrac{2}{3}\right] = \frac{\pi}{60}\left(391\sqrt{17} + 1\right)$$

17. Using spherical coordinates and Example 12.6.1 we have $\mathbf{r}(\phi, \theta) = 2\sin\phi\cos\theta\,\mathbf{i} + 2\sin\phi\sin\theta\,\mathbf{j} + 2\cos\phi\,\mathbf{k}$ and $|\mathbf{r}_\phi \times \mathbf{r}_\theta| = 4\sin\phi$. Then $\iint_S (x^2 z + y^2 z)\, dS = \int_0^{2\pi}\int_0^{\pi/2}(4\sin^2\phi)(2\cos\phi)(4\sin\phi)\, d\phi\, d\theta = 16\pi\sin^4\phi\big]_0^{\pi/2} = 16\pi$.

19. S is given by $\mathbf{r}(u, v) = u\,\mathbf{i} + \cos v\,\mathbf{j} + \sin v\,\mathbf{k}$, $0 \le u \le 3$, $0 \le v \le \pi/2$. Then

$\mathbf{r}_u \times \mathbf{r}_v = \mathbf{i} \times (-\sin v\,\mathbf{j} + \cos v\,\mathbf{k}) = -\cos v\,\mathbf{j} - \sin v\,\mathbf{k}$ and $|\mathbf{r}_u \times \mathbf{r}_v| = \sqrt{\cos^2 v + \sin^2 v} = 1$, so

$$\iint_S(z + x^2 y)\, dS = \int_0^{\pi/2}\int_0^3 (\sin v + u^2\cos v)(1)\, du\, dv = \int_0^{\pi/2}(3\sin v + 9\cos v)\, dv$$

$$= [-3\cos v + 9\sin v]_0^{\pi/2} = 0 + 9 + 3 - 0 = 12$$

21. $\mathbf{F}(x, y, z) = xy\,\mathbf{i} + yz\,\mathbf{j} + zx\,\mathbf{k}$, $z = g(x, y) = 4 - x^2 - y^2$, and D is the square $[0, 1] \times [0, 1]$, so by Equation 10

$$\iint_S \mathbf{F}\cdot d\mathbf{S} = \iint_D[-xy(-2x) - yz(-2y) + zx]\, dA = \int_0^1\int_0^1[2x^2 y + 2y^2(4 - x^2 - y^2) + x(4 - x^2 - y^2)]\, dy\, dx$$

$$= \int_0^1\left(\tfrac{1}{3}x^2 + \tfrac{11}{3}x - x^3 + \tfrac{34}{15}\right)dx = \tfrac{713}{180}$$

23. $\mathbf{F}(x, y, z) = xze^y\,\mathbf{i} - xze^y\,\mathbf{j} + z\,\mathbf{k}$, $z = g(x, y) = 1 - x - y$, and $D = \{(x, y) \mid 0 \le x \le 1, 0 \le y \le 1 - x\}$. Since S has downward orientation, we have

$$\iint_S \mathbf{F}\cdot d\mathbf{S} = -\iint_D[-xze^y(-1) - (-xze^y)(-1) + z]\, dA = -\int_0^1\int_0^{1-x}(1 - x - y)\, dy\, dx$$

$$= -\int_0^1\left(\tfrac{1}{2}x^2 - x + \tfrac{1}{2}\right)dx = -\tfrac{1}{6}$$

25. $\mathbf{F}(x, y, z) = x\,\mathbf{i} - z\,\mathbf{j} + y\,\mathbf{k}$, $z = g(x, y) = \sqrt{4 - x^2 - y^2}$ and D is the quarter disk $\{(x, y) \mid 0 \le x \le 2, 0 \le y \le \sqrt{4 - x^2}\}$. S has downward orientation, so by Formula 10,

$$\iint_S \mathbf{F} \cdot d\mathbf{S} = -\iint_D \left[-x \cdot \tfrac{1}{2}(4 - x^2 - y^2)^{-1/2}(-2x) - (-z) \cdot \tfrac{1}{2}(4 - x^2 - y^2)^{-1/2}(-2y) + y \right] dA$$

$$= -\iint_D \left(\frac{x^2}{\sqrt{4 - x^2 - y^2}} - \sqrt{4 - x^2 - y^2} \cdot \frac{y}{\sqrt{4 - x^2 - y^2}} + y \right) dA$$

$$= -\iint_D x^2 (4 - (x^2 + y^2))^{-1/2}\, dA = -\int_0^{\pi/2} \int_0^2 (r\cos\theta)^2 (4 - r^2)^{-1/2}\, r\, dr\, d\theta$$

$$= -\int_0^{\pi/2} \cos^2\theta\, d\theta \int_0^2 r^3 (4 - r^2)^{-1/2}\, dr \qquad \left[\text{let } u = 4 - r^2 \ \Rightarrow \ r^2 = 4 - u \text{ and } -\tfrac{1}{2}\, du = r\, dr \right]$$

$$= -\int_0^{\pi/2} \left(\tfrac{1}{2} + \tfrac{1}{2}\cos 2\theta \right) d\theta \int_4^0 -\tfrac{1}{2}(4 - u)(u)^{-1/2}\, du$$

$$= -\left[\tfrac{1}{2}\theta + \tfrac{1}{4}\sin 2\theta \right]_0^{\pi/2} \left(-\tfrac{1}{2}\right) \left[8\sqrt{u} - \tfrac{2}{3}u^{3/2} \right]_4^0 = -\tfrac{\pi}{4}\left(-\tfrac{1}{2}\right)\left(-16 + \tfrac{16}{3}\right) = -\tfrac{4}{3}\pi$$

27. Let S_1 be the paraboloid $y = x^2 + z^2$, $0 \le y \le 1$ and S_2 the disk $x^2 + z^2 \le 1$, $y = 1$. Since S is a closed surface, we use the outward orientation.

On S_1: $\mathbf{F}(\mathbf{r}(x, z)) = (x^2 + z^2)\mathbf{j} - z\mathbf{k}$ and $\mathbf{r}_x \times \mathbf{r}_z = 2x\,\mathbf{i} - \mathbf{j} + 2z\,\mathbf{k}$ (since the $\mathbf{j}$-component must be negative on S_1). Then

$$\iint_{S_1} \mathbf{F} \cdot d\mathbf{S} = \iint_{x^2 + z^2 \le 1} [-(x^2 + z^2) - 2z^2]\, dA = -\int_0^{2\pi} \int_0^1 (r^2 + 2r^2 \cos^2\theta)\, r\, dr\, d\theta$$

$$= -\int_0^{2\pi} \tfrac{1}{4}(1 + 2\cos^2\theta)\, d\theta = -\left(\tfrac{\pi}{2} + \tfrac{\pi}{2} \right) = -\pi$$

On S_2: $\mathbf{F}(\mathbf{r}(x, z)) = \mathbf{j} - z\mathbf{k}$ and $\mathbf{r}_z \times \mathbf{r}_x = \mathbf{j}$. Then $\iint_{S_2} \mathbf{F} \cdot d\mathbf{S} = \iint_{x^2 + z^2 \le 1} (1)\, dA = \pi$.

Hence $\iint_S \mathbf{F} \cdot d\mathbf{S} = -\pi + \pi = 0$.

29. Here S consists of the six faces of the cube as labeled in the figure. On S_1:

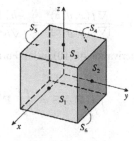

$\mathbf{F} = \mathbf{i} + 2y\mathbf{j} + 3z\mathbf{k}$, $\mathbf{r}_y \times \mathbf{r}_z = \mathbf{i}$ and $\iint_{S_1} \mathbf{F} \cdot d\mathbf{S} = \int_{-1}^1 \int_{-1}^1 dy\, dz = 4$;

S_2: $\mathbf{F} = x\mathbf{i} + 2\mathbf{j} + 3z\mathbf{k}$, $\mathbf{r}_z \times \mathbf{r}_x = \mathbf{j}$ and $\iint_{S_2} \mathbf{F} \cdot d\mathbf{S} = \int_{-1}^1 \int_{-1}^1 2\, dx\, dz = 8$;

S_3: $\mathbf{F} = x\mathbf{i} + 2y\mathbf{j} + 3\mathbf{k}$, $\mathbf{r}_x \times \mathbf{r}_y = \mathbf{k}$ and $\iint_{S_3} \mathbf{F} \cdot d\mathbf{S} = \int_{-1}^1 \int_{-1}^1 3\, dx\, dy = 12$;

S_4: $\mathbf{F} = -\mathbf{i} + 2y\mathbf{j} + 3z\mathbf{k}$, $\mathbf{r}_z \times \mathbf{r}_y = -\mathbf{i}$ and $\iint_{S_4} \mathbf{F} \cdot d\mathbf{S} = 4$;

S_5: $\mathbf{F} = x\mathbf{i} - 2\mathbf{j} + 3z\mathbf{k}$, $\mathbf{r}_x \times \mathbf{r}_z = -\mathbf{j}$ and $\iint_{S_5} \mathbf{F} \cdot d\mathbf{S} = 8$;

S_6: $\mathbf{F} = x\mathbf{i} + 2y\mathbf{j} - 3\mathbf{k}$, $\mathbf{r}_y \times \mathbf{r}_x = -\mathbf{k}$ and $\iint_{S_6} \mathbf{F} \cdot d\mathbf{S} = \int_{-1}^1 \int_{-1}^1 3\, dx\, dy = 12$.

Hence $\iint_S \mathbf{F} \cdot d\mathbf{S} = \sum_{i=1}^6 \iint_{S_i} \mathbf{F} \cdot d\mathbf{S} = 48$.

31. Here S consists of four surfaces: S_1, the top surface (a portion of the circular cylinder $y^2 + z^2 = 1$); S_2, the bottom surface (a portion of the xy-plane); S_3, the front half-disk in the plane $x = 2$, and S_4, the back half-disk in the plane $x = 0$.

On S_1: The surface is $z = \sqrt{1 - y^2}$ for $0 \le x \le 2$, $-1 \le y \le 1$ with upward orientation, so

$$\iint_{S_1} \mathbf{F} \cdot d\mathbf{S} = \int_0^2 \int_{-1}^1 \left[-x^2 (0) - y^2 \left(-\frac{y}{\sqrt{1 - y^2}} \right) + z^2 \right] dy\, dx = \int_0^2 \int_{-1}^1 \left(\frac{y^3}{\sqrt{1 - y^2}} + 1 - y^2 \right) dy\, dx$$

$$= \int_0^2 \left[-\sqrt{1 - y^2} + \tfrac{1}{3}(1 - y^2)^{3/2} + y - \tfrac{1}{3}y^3 \right]_{y=-1}^{y=1} dx = \int_0^2 \tfrac{4}{3}\, dx = \tfrac{8}{3}$$

On S_2: The surface is $z = 0$ with downward orientation, so

$$\iint_{S_2} \mathbf{F} \cdot d\mathbf{S} = \int_0^2 \int_{-1}^1 \left(-z^2\right) dy\, dx = \int_0^2 \int_{-1}^1 (0)\, dy\, dx = 0$$

On S_3: The surface is $x = 2$ for $-1 \le y \le 1$, $0 \le z \le \sqrt{1 - y^2}$, oriented in the positive x-direction. Regarding y and z as parameters, we have $\mathbf{r}_y \times \mathbf{r}_z = \mathbf{i}$ and

$$\iint_{S_3} \mathbf{F} \cdot d\mathbf{S} = \int_{-1}^1 \int_0^{\sqrt{1-y^2}} x^2\, dz\, dy = \int_{-1}^1 \int_0^{\sqrt{1-y^2}} 4\, dz\, dy = 4A\left(S_3\right) = 2\pi$$

On S_4: The surface is $x = 0$ for $-1 \le y \le 1$, $0 \le z \le \sqrt{1 - y^2}$, oriented in the negative x-direction. Regarding y and z as parameters, we use $-\left(\mathbf{r}_y \times \mathbf{r}_z\right) = -\mathbf{i}$ and

$$\iint_{S_4} \mathbf{F} \cdot d\mathbf{S} = \int_{-1}^1 \int_0^{\sqrt{1-y^2}} x^2\, dz\, dy = \int_{-1}^1 \int_0^{\sqrt{1-y^2}} (0)\, dz\, dy = 0$$

Thus $\iint_S \mathbf{F} \cdot d\mathbf{S} = \frac{8}{3} + 0 + 2\pi + 0 = 2\pi + \frac{8}{3}$.

33. We use Formula 4 with $z = 3 - 2x^2 - y^2 \;\Rightarrow\; \partial z/\partial x = -4x$, $\partial z/\partial y = -2y$. The boundaries of the region

$3 - 2x^2 - y^2 \ge 0$ are $-\sqrt{\frac{3}{2}} \le x \le \sqrt{\frac{3}{2}}$ and $-\sqrt{3 - 2x^2} \le y \le \sqrt{3 - 2x^2}$, so we use a CAS (with precision reduced to

seven or fewer digits; otherwise the calculation may take a long time) to calculate

$$\iint_S x^2 y^2 z^2\, dS = \int_{-\sqrt{3/2}}^{\sqrt{3/2}} \int_{-\sqrt{3 - 2x^2}}^{\sqrt{3 - 2x^2}} x^2 y^2 (3 - 2x^2 - y^2)^2 \sqrt{16x^2 + 4y^2 + 1}\, dy\, dx \approx 3.4895$$

35. If S is given by $y = h(x, z)$, then S is also the level surface $f(x, y, z) = y - h(x, z) = 0$.

$$\mathbf{n} = \frac{\nabla f(x, y, z)}{|\nabla f(x, y, z)|} = \frac{-h_x \mathbf{i} + \mathbf{j} - h_z \mathbf{k}}{\sqrt{h_x^2 + 1 + h_z^2}},\ \text{and } -\mathbf{n} \text{ is the unit normal that points to the left. Now we proceed as in the}$$

derivation of (10), using Formula 4 to evaluate

$$\iint_S \mathbf{F} \cdot d\mathbf{S} = \iint_S \mathbf{F} \cdot \mathbf{n}\, dS = \iint_D (P\mathbf{i} + Q\mathbf{j} + R\mathbf{k}) \frac{\dfrac{\partial h}{\partial x}\mathbf{i} - \mathbf{j} + \dfrac{\partial h}{\partial z}\mathbf{k}}{\sqrt{\left(\dfrac{\partial h}{\partial x}\right)^2 + 1 + \left(\dfrac{\partial h}{\partial z}\right)^2}} \sqrt{\left(\dfrac{\partial h}{\partial x}\right)^2 + 1 + \left(\dfrac{\partial h}{\partial z}\right)^2}\, dA$$

where D is the projection of S onto the xz-plane. Therefore $\displaystyle\iint_S \mathbf{F} \cdot d\mathbf{S} = \iint_D \left(P\frac{\partial h}{\partial x} - Q + R\frac{\partial h}{\partial z}\right) dA$.

37. $m = \iint_S K\, dS = K \cdot 4\pi\left(\frac{1}{2}a^2\right) = 2\pi a^2 K$; by symmetry $M_{xz} = M_{yz} = 0$, and

$M_{xy} = \iint_S zK\, dS = K \int_0^{2\pi} \int_0^{\pi/2} (a\cos\phi)(a^2 \sin\phi)\, d\phi\, d\theta = 2\pi K a^3 \left[-\frac{1}{4}\cos 2\phi\right]_0^{\pi/2} = \pi K a^3$.

Hence $(\bar{x}, \bar{y}, \bar{z}) = \left(0, 0, \frac{1}{2}a\right)$.

39. (a) $I_z = \iint_S (x^2 + y^2)\rho(x, y, z)\, dS$

(b) $I_z = \iint_S (x^2 + y^2)\left(10 - \sqrt{x^2 + y^2}\right) dS = \iint\limits_{1 \le x^2 + y^2 \le 16} (x^2 + y^2)\left(10 - \sqrt{x^2 + y^2}\right)\sqrt{2}\, dA$

$= \int_0^{2\pi} \int_1^4 \sqrt{2}\,(10r^3 - r^4)\, dr\, d\theta = 2\sqrt{2}\,\pi\left(\frac{4329}{10}\right) = \frac{4329}{5}\sqrt{2}\,\pi$

41. The rate of flow through the cylinder is the flux $\iint_S \rho\mathbf{v} \cdot \mathbf{n}\, dS = \iint_S \rho\mathbf{v} \cdot d\mathbf{S}$. We use the parametric representation

$\mathbf{r}(u,v) = 2\cos u\, \mathbf{i} + 2\sin u\, \mathbf{j} + v\, \mathbf{k}$ for S, where $0 \le u \le 2\pi$, $0 \le v \le 1$, so $\mathbf{r}_u = -2\sin u\, \mathbf{i} + 2\cos u\, \mathbf{j}$, $\mathbf{r}_v = \mathbf{k}$, and the

outward orientation is given by $\mathbf{r}_u \times \mathbf{r}_v = 2\cos u\, \mathbf{i} + 2\sin u\, \mathbf{j}$. Then

$$\iint_S \rho\mathbf{v} \cdot d\mathbf{S} = \rho \int_0^{2\pi} \int_0^1 \left(v\, \mathbf{i} + 4\sin^2 u\, \mathbf{j} + 4\cos^2 u\, \mathbf{k} \right) \cdot (2\cos u\, \mathbf{i} + 2\sin u\, \mathbf{j})\, dv\, du$$

$$= \rho \int_0^{2\pi} \int_0^1 \left(2v\cos u + 8\sin^3 u \right) dv\, du = \rho \int_0^{2\pi} \left(\cos u + 8\sin^3 u \right) du$$

$$= \rho\left[\sin u + 8\left(-\tfrac{1}{3}\right)(2 + \sin^2 u)\cos u \right]_0^{2\pi} = 0\ \text{kg/s}$$

43. S consists of the hemisphere S_1 given by $z = \sqrt{a^2 - x^2 - y^2}$ and the disk S_2 given by $0 \le x^2 + y^2 \le a^2$, $z = 0$.

On S_1: $\mathbf{E} = a\sin\phi\cos\theta\, \mathbf{i} + a\sin\phi\sin\theta\, \mathbf{j} + 2a\cos\phi\, \mathbf{k}$,

$\mathbf{T}_\phi \times \mathbf{T}_\theta = a^2\sin^2\phi\cos\theta\, \mathbf{i} + a^2\sin^2\phi\sin\theta\, \mathbf{j} + a^2\sin\phi\cos\phi\, \mathbf{k}$. Thus

$$\iint_{S_1} \mathbf{E} \cdot d\mathbf{S} = \int_0^{2\pi} \int_0^{\pi/2} (a^3\sin^3\phi + 2a^3\sin\phi\cos^2\phi)\, d\phi\, d\theta$$

$$= \int_0^{2\pi} \int_0^{\pi/2} (a^3\sin\phi + a^3\sin\phi\cos^2\phi)\, d\phi\, d\theta = (2\pi)a^3\left(1 + \tfrac{1}{3}\right) = \tfrac{8}{3}\pi a^3$$

On S_2: $\mathbf{E} = x\, \mathbf{i} + y\, \mathbf{j}$, and $\mathbf{r}_y \times \mathbf{r}_x = -\mathbf{k}$ so $\iint_{S_2} \mathbf{E} \cdot d\mathbf{S} = 0$. Hence the total charge is $q = \varepsilon_0 \iint_S \mathbf{E} \cdot d\mathbf{S} = \tfrac{8}{3}\pi a^3 \varepsilon_0$.

45. $K\nabla u = 6.5(4y\, \mathbf{j} + 4z\, \mathbf{k})$. S is given by $\mathbf{r}(x,\theta) = x\, \mathbf{i} + \sqrt{6}\cos\theta\, \mathbf{j} + \sqrt{6}\sin\theta\, \mathbf{k}$ and since we want the inward heat flow, we

use $\mathbf{r}_x \times \mathbf{r}_\theta = -\sqrt{6}\cos\theta\, \mathbf{j} - \sqrt{6}\sin\theta\, \mathbf{k}$. Then the rate of heat flow inward is given by

$$\iint_S (-K\nabla u) \cdot d\mathbf{S} = \int_0^{2\pi} \int_0^4 -(6.5)(-24)\, dx\, d\theta = (2\pi)(156)(4) = 1248\pi.$$

47. Let S be a sphere of radius a centered at the origin. Then $|\mathbf{r}| = a$ and $\mathbf{F}(\mathbf{r}) = c\mathbf{r}/|\mathbf{r}|^3 = (c/a^3)(x\, \mathbf{i} + y\, \mathbf{j} + z\, \mathbf{k})$. A

parametric representation for S is $\mathbf{r}(\phi,\theta) = a\sin\phi\cos\theta\, \mathbf{i} + a\sin\phi\sin\theta\, \mathbf{j} + a\cos\phi\, \mathbf{k}$, $0 \le \phi \le \pi$, $0 \le \theta \le 2\pi$. Then

$\mathbf{r}_\phi = a\cos\phi\cos\theta\, \mathbf{i} + a\cos\phi\sin\theta\, \mathbf{j} - a\sin\phi\, \mathbf{k}$, $\mathbf{r}_\theta = -a\sin\phi\sin\theta\, \mathbf{i} + a\sin\phi\cos\theta\, \mathbf{j}$, and the outward orientation is given

by $\mathbf{r}_\phi \times \mathbf{r}_\theta = a^2\sin^2\phi\cos\theta\, \mathbf{i} + a^2\sin^2\phi\sin\theta\, \mathbf{j} + a^2\sin\phi\cos\phi\, \mathbf{k}$. The flux of $\mathbf{F}$ across S is

$$\iint_S \mathbf{F} \cdot d\mathbf{S} = \int_0^\pi \int_0^{2\pi} \frac{c}{a^3} (a\sin\phi\cos\theta\, \mathbf{i} + a\sin\phi\sin\theta\, \mathbf{j} + a\cos\phi\, \mathbf{k})$$

$$\cdot (a^2\sin^2\phi\cos\theta\, \mathbf{i} + a^2\sin^2\phi\sin\theta\, \mathbf{j} + a^2\sin\phi\cos\phi\, \mathbf{k})\, d\theta\, d\phi$$

$$= \frac{c}{a^3} \int_0^\pi \int_0^{2\pi} a^3 \left(\sin^3\phi + \sin\phi\cos^2\phi \right) d\theta\, d\phi = c \int_0^\pi \int_0^{2\pi} \sin\phi\, d\theta\, d\phi = 4\pi c$$

Thus the flux does not depend on the radius a.

13.7 Stokes' Theorem

1. Both H and P are oriented piecewise-smooth surfaces that are bounded by the simple, closed, smooth curve $x^2 + y^2 = 4$,

$z = 0$ (which we can take to be oriented positively for both surfaces). Then H and P satisfy the hypotheses of Stokes'

Theorem, so by (3) we know $\iint_H \text{curl}\, \mathbf{F} \cdot d\mathbf{S} = \int_C \mathbf{F} \cdot d\mathbf{r} = \iint_P \text{curl}\, \mathbf{F} \cdot d\mathbf{S}$ (where C is the boundary curve).

3. The paraboloid $z = x^2 + y^2$ intersects the cylinder $x^2 + y^2 = 4$ in the circle $x^2 + y^2 = 4$, $z = 4$. This boundary curve C

should be oriented in the counterclockwise direction when viewed from above, so a vector equation of C is

$\mathbf{r}(t) = 2\cos t\,\mathbf{i} + 2\sin t\,\mathbf{j} + 4\,\mathbf{k}$, $0 \le t \le 2\pi$. Then $\mathbf{r}'(t) = -2\sin t\,\mathbf{i} + 2\cos t\,\mathbf{j}$,

$$\mathbf{F}(\mathbf{r}(t)) = (4\cos^2 t)(16)\,\mathbf{i} + (4\sin^2 t)(16)\,\mathbf{j} + (2\cos t)(2\sin t)(4)\,\mathbf{k} = 64\cos^2 t\,\mathbf{i} + 64\sin^2 t\,\mathbf{j} + 16\sin t\,\cos t\,\mathbf{k},$$

and by Stokes' Theorem,

$$\iint_S \text{curl}\, \mathbf{F} \cdot d\mathbf{S} = \int_C \mathbf{F} \cdot d\mathbf{r} = \int_0^{2\pi} \mathbf{F}(\mathbf{r}(t)) \cdot \mathbf{r}'(t)\, dt = \int_0^{2\pi} (-128\cos^2 t\,\sin t + 128\sin^2 t\,\cos t + 0)\, dt$$

$$= 128\left[\tfrac{1}{3}\cos^3 t + \tfrac{1}{3}\sin^3 t\right]_0^{2\pi} = 0$$

5. C is the square in the plane $z = -1$. By (3), $\iint_{S_1} \text{curl}\, \mathbf{F} \cdot d\mathbf{S} = \oint_C \mathbf{F} \cdot d\mathbf{r} = \iint_{S_2} \text{curl}\, \mathbf{F} \cdot d\mathbf{S}$ where S_1 is the original cube

without the bottom and S_2 is the bottom face of the cube. $\text{curl}\, \mathbf{F} = x^2 z\,\mathbf{i} + (xy - 2xyz)\,\mathbf{j} + (y - xz)\,\mathbf{k}$. For S_2, we choose

$\mathbf{n} = \mathbf{k}$ so that C has the same orientation for both surfaces. Then $\text{curl}\, \mathbf{F} \cdot \mathbf{n} = y - xz = x + y$ on S_2, where $z = -1$. Thus

$\iint_{S_2} \text{curl}\, \mathbf{F} \cdot d\mathbf{S} = \int_{-1}^{1} \int_{-1}^{1} (x + y)\, dx\, dy = 0$ so $\iint_{S_1} \text{curl}\, \mathbf{F} \cdot d\mathbf{S} = 0$.

7. $\text{curl}\, \mathbf{F} = -2z\,\mathbf{i} - 2x\,\mathbf{j} - 2y\,\mathbf{k}$ and we take the surface S to be the planar region enclosed by C, so S is the portion of the plane

$x + y + z = 1$ over $D = \{(x, y) \mid 0 \le x \le 1, 0 \le y \le 1 - x\}$. Since C is oriented counterclockwise, we orient S upward.

Using Equation 13.6.10, we have $z = g(x, y) = 1 - x - y$, $P = -2z$, $Q = -2x$, $R = -2y$, and

$$\int_C \mathbf{F} \cdot d\mathbf{r} = \iint_S \text{curl}\, \mathbf{F} \cdot d\mathbf{S} = \iint_D [-(-2z)(-1) - (-2x)(-1) + (-2y)]\, dA$$

$$= \int_0^1 \int_0^{1-x} (-2)\, dy\, dx = -2\int_0^1 (1 - x)\, dx = -1$$

9. $\text{curl}\, \mathbf{F} = (xe^{xy} - 2x)\,\mathbf{i} - (ye^{xy} - y)\,\mathbf{j} + (2z - z)\,\mathbf{k}$ and we take S to be the disk $x^2 + y^2 \le 16$, $z = 5$. Since C is oriented

counterclockwise (from above), we orient S upward. Then $\mathbf{n} = \mathbf{k}$ and $\text{curl}\, \mathbf{F} \cdot \mathbf{n} = 2z - z$ on S, where $z = 5$. Thus

$$\oint_C \mathbf{F} \cdot d\mathbf{r} = \iint_S \text{curl}\, \mathbf{F} \cdot \mathbf{n}\, dS = \iint_S (2z - z)\, dS = \iint_S (10 - 5)\, dS = 5(\text{area of } S) = 5(\pi \cdot 4^2) = 80\pi$$

11. (a) The curve of intersection is an ellipse in the plane $x + y + z = 1$ with unit normal $\mathbf{n} = \frac{1}{\sqrt{3}}(\mathbf{i} + \mathbf{j} + \mathbf{k})$,

$\text{curl}\, \mathbf{F} = x^2\,\mathbf{j} + y^2\,\mathbf{k}$, and $\text{curl}\, \mathbf{F} \cdot \mathbf{n} = \frac{1}{\sqrt{3}}(x^2 + y^2)$. Then

$$\oint_C \mathbf{F} \cdot d\mathbf{r} = \iint_S \frac{1}{\sqrt{3}}(x^2 + y^2)\, dS = \iint_{x^2 + y^2 \le 9} (x^2 + y^2)\, dx\, dy = \int_0^{2\pi} \int_0^3 r^3\, dr\, d\theta = 2\pi\left(\tfrac{81}{4}\right) = \tfrac{81\pi}{2}$$

(b)

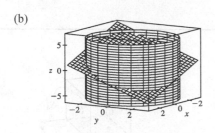

(c) One possible parametrization is $x = 3\cos t$, $y = 3\sin t$,
$z = 1 - 3\cos t - 3\sin t$, $0 \le t \le 2\pi$.

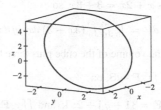

13. The boundary curve C is the circle $x^2 + y^2 = 16$, $z = 4$ oriented in the clockwise direction as viewed from above (since S is

oriented downward). We can parametrize C by $\mathbf{r}(t) = 4\cos t\,\mathbf{i} - 4\sin t\,\mathbf{j} + 4\,\mathbf{k}$, $0 \le t \le 2\pi$, and then

$\mathbf{r}'(t) = -4\sin t\,\mathbf{i} - 4\cos t\,\mathbf{j}$. Thus $\mathbf{F}(\mathbf{r}(t)) = 4\sin t\,\mathbf{i} + 4\cos t\,\mathbf{j} - 2\,\mathbf{k}$, $\mathbf{F}(\mathbf{r}(t)) \cdot \mathbf{r}'(t) = -16\sin^2 t - 16\cos^2 t = -16$, and

$$\oint_C \mathbf{F} \cdot d\mathbf{r} = \int_0^{2\pi} \mathbf{F}(\mathbf{r}(t)) \cdot \mathbf{r}'(t)\, dt = \int_0^{2\pi} (-16)\, dt = -16\,(2\pi) = -32\pi$$

Now curl $\mathbf{F} = 2\,\mathbf{k}$, and the projection D of S on the xy-plane is the disk $x^2 + y^2 \le 16$, so by Equation 13.6.10 with

$z = g(x,y) = \sqrt{x^2 + y^2}$ [and multiplying by -1 for the downward orientation] we have

$$\iint_S \operatorname{curl}\mathbf{F} \cdot d\mathbf{S} = -\iint_D (-0 - 0 + 2)\, dA = -2 \cdot A(D) = -2 \cdot \pi(4^2) = -32\pi$$

15. The boundary curve C is the circle $x^2 + z^2 = 1$, $y = 0$ oriented in the counterclockwise direction as viewed from the positive

y-axis. Then C can be described by $\mathbf{r}(t) = \cos t\,\mathbf{i} - \sin t\,\mathbf{k}$, $0 \le t \le 2\pi$, and $\mathbf{r}'(t) = -\sin t\,\mathbf{i} - \cos t\,\mathbf{k}$. Thus

$\mathbf{F}(\mathbf{r}(t)) = -\sin t\,\mathbf{j} + \cos t\,\mathbf{k}$, $\mathbf{F}(\mathbf{r}(t)) \cdot \mathbf{r}'(t) = -\cos^2 t$, and $\oint_C \mathbf{F} \cdot d\mathbf{r} = \int_0^{2\pi} (-\cos^2 t)\, dt = \left[-\tfrac{1}{2}t - \tfrac{1}{4}\sin 2t\right]_0^{2\pi} = -\pi$.

Now curl $\mathbf{F} = -\mathbf{i} - \mathbf{j} - \mathbf{k}$, and S can be parametrized (see Example 12.6.1) by

$\mathbf{r}(\phi, \theta) = \sin\phi\,\cos\theta\,\mathbf{i} + \sin\phi\,\sin\theta\,\mathbf{j} + \cos\phi\,\mathbf{k}$, $0 \le \theta \le \pi$, $0 \le \phi \le \pi$. Then

$\mathbf{r}_\phi \times \mathbf{r}_\theta = \sin^2\phi\,\cos\theta\,\mathbf{i} + \sin^2\phi\,\sin\theta\,\mathbf{j} + \sin\phi\,\cos\phi\,\mathbf{k}$ and

$$\iint_S \operatorname{curl}\mathbf{F} \cdot d\mathbf{S} = \iint_{x^2+z^2\le 1} \operatorname{curl}\mathbf{F} \cdot (\mathbf{r}_\phi \times \mathbf{r}_\theta)\, dA = \int_0^\pi \int_0^\pi (-\sin^2\phi\,\cos\theta - \sin^2\phi\,\sin\theta - \sin\phi\,\cos\phi)\, d\theta\, d\phi$$

$$= \int_0^\pi (-2\sin^2\phi - \pi\sin\phi\,\cos\phi)\, d\phi = \left[\tfrac{1}{2}\sin 2\phi - \phi - \tfrac{\pi}{2}\sin^2\phi\right]_0^\pi = -\pi$$

17. It is easier to use Stokes' Theorem than to compute the work directly. Let S be the planar region enclosed by the path of the

particle, so S is the portion of the plane $z = \tfrac{1}{2}y$ for $0 \le x \le 1$, $0 \le y \le 2$, with upward orientation.

curl $\mathbf{F} = 8y\,\mathbf{i} + 2z\,\mathbf{j} + 2y\,\mathbf{k}$ and

$$\oint_C \mathbf{F} \cdot d\mathbf{r} = \iint_S \operatorname{curl}\mathbf{F} \cdot d\mathbf{S} = \iint_D \left[-8y\,(0) - 2z\left(\tfrac{1}{2}\right) + 2y\right] dA = \int_0^1 \int_0^2 \left(2y - \tfrac{1}{2}y\right) dy\, dx$$

$$= \int_0^1 \int_0^2 \tfrac{3}{2}y\, dy\, dx = \int_0^1 \left[\tfrac{3}{4}y^2\right]_{y=0}^{y=2} dx = \int_0^1 3\, dx = 3$$

19. Assume S is centered at the origin with radius a and let H_1 and H_2 be the upper and lower hemispheres, respectively, of S.

Then $\iint_S \operatorname{curl}\mathbf{F} \cdot d\mathbf{S} = \iint_{H_1} \operatorname{curl}\mathbf{F} \cdot d\mathbf{S} + \iint_{H_2} \operatorname{curl}\mathbf{F} \cdot d\mathbf{S} = \oint_{C_1} \mathbf{F} \cdot d\mathbf{r} + \oint_{C_2} \mathbf{F} \cdot d\mathbf{r}$ by Stokes' Theorem. But C_1 is the

circle $x^2 + y^2 = a^2$ oriented in the counterclockwise direction while C_2 is the same circle oriented in the clockwise direction.

Hence $\oint_{C_2} \mathbf{F} \cdot d\mathbf{r} = -\oint_{C_1} \mathbf{F} \cdot d\mathbf{r}$ so $\iint_S \operatorname{curl}\mathbf{F} \cdot d\mathbf{S} = 0$ as desired.

13.8 The Divergence Theorem

1. div $\mathbf{F} = 3 + x + 2x = 3 + 3x$, so

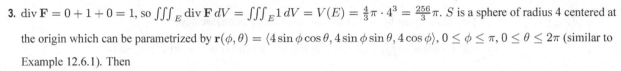

$\iiint_E \text{div}\,\mathbf{F}\,dV = \int_0^1 \int_0^1 \int_0^1 (3x+3)\,dx\,dy\,dz = \frac{9}{2}$ (notice the triple integral is

three times the volume of the cube plus three times $\overline{x}$).

To compute $\iint_S \mathbf{F} \cdot d\mathbf{S}$, on

S_1: $\mathbf{n} = \mathbf{i}$, $\mathbf{F} = 3\mathbf{i} + y\mathbf{j} + 2z\mathbf{k}$, and $\iint_{S_1} \mathbf{F} \cdot d\mathbf{S} = \iint_{S_1} 3\,dS = 3$;

S_2: $\mathbf{F} = 3x\mathbf{i} + x\mathbf{j} + 2xz\mathbf{k}$, $\mathbf{n} = \mathbf{j}$ and $\iint_{S_2} \mathbf{F} \cdot d\mathbf{S} = \iint_{S_2} x\,dS = \frac{1}{2}$;

S_3: $\mathbf{F} = 3x\mathbf{i} + xy\mathbf{j} + 2x\mathbf{k}$, $\mathbf{n} = \mathbf{k}$ and $\iint_{S_3} \mathbf{F} \cdot d\mathbf{S} = \iint_{S_3} 2x\,dS - 1$;

S_4: $\mathbf{F} = \mathbf{0}$, $\iint_{S_4} \mathbf{F} \cdot d\mathbf{S} = 0$; S_5: $\mathbf{F} = 3x\mathbf{i} + 2x\mathbf{k}$, $\mathbf{n} = -\mathbf{j}$ and $\iint_{S_5} \mathbf{F} \cdot d\mathbf{S} = \iint_{S_5} 0\,dS = 0$;

S_6: $\mathbf{F} = 3x\mathbf{i} + xy\mathbf{j}$, $\mathbf{n} = -\mathbf{k}$ and $\iint_{S_6} \mathbf{F} \cdot d\mathbf{S} = \iint_{S_6} 0\,dS = 0$. Thus $\iint_S \mathbf{F} \cdot d\mathbf{S} = \frac{9}{2}$.

3. div $\mathbf{F} = 0 + 1 + 0 = 1$, so $\iiint_E \text{div}\,\mathbf{F}\,dV = \iiint_E 1\,dV = V(E) = \frac{4}{3}\pi \cdot 4^3 = \frac{256}{3}\pi$. S is a sphere of radius 4 centered at

the origin which can be parametrized by $\mathbf{r}(\phi, \theta) = \langle 4\sin\phi\cos\theta, 4\sin\phi\sin\theta, 4\cos\phi \rangle$, $0 \le \phi \le \pi$, $0 \le \theta \le 2\pi$ (similar to

Example 12.6.1). Then

$$\mathbf{r}_\phi \times \mathbf{r}_\theta = \langle 4\cos\phi\cos\theta, 4\cos\phi\sin\theta, -4\sin\phi \rangle \times \langle -4\sin\phi\sin\theta, 4\sin\phi\cos\theta, 0 \rangle$$

$$= \langle 16\sin^2\phi\cos\theta, 16\sin^2\phi\sin\theta, 16\cos\phi\sin\phi \rangle$$

and $\mathbf{F}(\mathbf{r}(\phi, \theta)) = \langle 4\cos\phi, 4\sin\phi\sin\theta, 4\sin\phi\cos\theta \rangle$. Thus

$\mathbf{F} \cdot (\mathbf{r}_\phi \times \mathbf{r}_\theta) = 64\cos\phi\sin^2\phi\cos\theta + 64\sin^3\phi\sin^2\theta + 64\cos\phi\sin^2\phi\cos\theta = 128\cos\phi\sin^2\phi\cos\theta + 64\sin^3\phi\sin^2\theta$

and

$$\iint_S \mathbf{F} \cdot d\mathbf{S} = \iint_D \mathbf{F} \cdot (\mathbf{r}_\phi \times \mathbf{r}_\theta)\,dA = \int_0^{2\pi} \int_0^\pi (128\cos\phi\sin^2\phi\cos\theta + 64\sin^3\phi\sin^2\theta)\,d\phi\,d\theta$$

$$= \int_0^{2\pi} \left[\frac{128}{3}\sin^3\phi\cos\theta + 64\left(-\frac{1}{3}(2 + \sin^2\phi)\cos\phi\right)\sin^2\theta \right]_{\phi=0}^{\phi=\pi} d\theta$$

$$= \int_0^{2\pi} \frac{256}{3}\sin^2\theta\,d\theta = \frac{256}{3}\left[\frac{1}{2}\theta - \frac{1}{4}\sin 2\theta\right]_0^{2\pi} = \frac{256}{3}\pi$$

5. div $\mathbf{F} = \frac{\partial}{\partial x}(xye^z) + \frac{\partial}{\partial y}(xy^2z^3) + \frac{\partial}{\partial z}(-ye^z) = ye^z + 2xyz^3 - ye^z = 2xyz^3$, so by the Divergence Theorem,

$$\iint_S \mathbf{F} \cdot d\mathbf{S} = \iiint_E \text{div}\,\mathbf{F}\,dV = \int_0^3 \int_0^2 \int_0^1 2xyz^3\,dz\,dy\,dx = 2\int_0^3 x\,dx \int_0^2 y\,dy \int_0^1 z^3\,dz$$

$$= 2\left[\frac{1}{2}x^2\right]_0^3 \left[\frac{1}{2}y^2\right]_0^2 \left[\frac{1}{4}z^4\right]_0^1 = 2\left(\frac{9}{2}\right)(2)\left(\frac{1}{4}\right) = \frac{9}{2}$$

7. div $\mathbf{F} = 3y^2 + 0 + 3z^2$, so using cylindrical coordinates with $y = r\cos\theta$, $z = r\sin\theta$, $x = x$ we have

$$\iint_S \mathbf{F} \cdot d\mathbf{S} = \iiint_E (3y^2 + 3z^2)\,dV = \int_0^{2\pi} \int_0^1 \int_{-1}^2 (3r^2\cos^2\theta + 3r^2\sin^2\theta)\,r\,dx\,dr\,d\theta$$

$$= 3\int_0^{2\pi} d\theta \int_0^1 r^3\,dr \int_{-1}^2 dx = 3(2\pi)\left(\frac{1}{4}\right)(3) = \frac{9\pi}{2}$$

9. div $\mathbf{F} = 2x\sin y - x\sin y - x\sin y = 0$, so by the Divergence Theorem, $\iint_S \mathbf{F} \cdot d\mathbf{S} = \iiint_E 0\,dV = 0$.

11. div $\mathbf{F} = y^2 + 0 + x^2 = x^2 + y^2$ so

$$\iint_S \mathbf{F} \cdot d\mathbf{S} = \iiint_E (x^2 + y^2)\, dV = \int_0^{2\pi} \int_0^2 \int_{r^2}^4 r^2 \cdot r\, dz\, dr\, d\theta = \int_0^{2\pi} \int_0^2 r^3 (4 - r^2)\, dr\, d\theta$$

$$= \int_0^{2\pi} d\theta \int_0^2 (4r^3 - r^5)\, dr = 2\pi \left[r^4 - \tfrac{1}{6} r^6\right]_0^2 = \tfrac{32}{3} \pi$$

13. div $\mathbf{F} = 12x^2 z + 12y^2 z + 12z^3$ so

$$\iint_S \mathbf{F} \cdot d\mathbf{S} = \iiint_E 12z(x^2 + y^2 + z^2)\, dV = \int_0^{2\pi} \int_0^\pi \int_0^R 12(\rho \cos\phi)(\rho^2)\rho^2 \sin\phi\, d\rho\, d\phi\, d\theta$$

$$= 12 \int_0^{2\pi} d\theta \int_0^\pi \sin\phi \cos\phi\, d\phi \int_0^R \rho^5\, d\rho = 12(2\pi) \left[\tfrac{1}{2} \sin^2 \phi\right]_0^\pi \left[\tfrac{1}{6} \rho^6\right]_0^R = 0$$

15. $\iint_S \mathbf{F} \cdot d\mathbf{S} = \iiint_E \sqrt{3 - x^2}\, dV = \int_{-1}^1 \int_{-1}^1 \int_0^{2 - x^4 - y^4} \sqrt{3 - x^2}\, dz\, dy\, dx = \tfrac{341}{60} \sqrt{2} + \tfrac{81}{20} \sin^{-1}\left(\tfrac{\sqrt{3}}{3}\right)$

17. For S_1 we have $\mathbf{n} = -\mathbf{k}$, so $\mathbf{F} \cdot \mathbf{n} = \mathbf{F} \cdot (-\mathbf{k}) = -x^2 z - y^2 = -y^2$ (since $z = 0$ on S_1). So if D is the unit disk, we get

$$\iint_{S_1} \mathbf{F} \cdot d\mathbf{S} = \iint_{S_1} \mathbf{F} \cdot \mathbf{n}\, dS = \iint_D (-y^2)\, dA = -\int_0^{2\pi} \int_0^1 r^2 (\sin^2 \theta)\, r\, dr\, d\theta = -\tfrac{1}{4}\pi.$$ Now since S_2 is closed, we can use

the Divergence Theorem. Since div $\mathbf{F} = \tfrac{\partial}{\partial x}(z^2 x) + \tfrac{\partial}{\partial y}\left(\tfrac{1}{3} y^3 + \tan z\right) + \tfrac{\partial}{\partial z}(x^2 z + y^2) = z^2 + y^2 + x^2$, we use spherical

coordinates to get $\iint_{S_2} \mathbf{F} \cdot d\mathbf{S} = \iiint_E \text{div}\, \mathbf{F}\, dV = \int_0^{2\pi} \int_0^{\pi/2} \int_0^1 \rho^2 \cdot \rho^2 \sin\phi\, d\rho\, d\phi\, d\theta = \tfrac{2}{5}\pi.$ Finally

$$\iint_S \mathbf{F} \cdot d\mathbf{S} = \iint_{S_2} \mathbf{F} \cdot d\mathbf{S} - \iint_{S_1} \mathbf{F} \cdot d\mathbf{S} = \tfrac{2}{5}\pi - \left(-\tfrac{1}{4}\pi\right) = \tfrac{13}{20}\pi.$$

19. The vectors that end near P_1 are longer than the vectors that start near P_1, so the net flow is inward near P_1 and div $\mathbf{F}(P_1)$ is negative. The vectors that end near P_2 are shorter than the vectors that start near P_2, so the net flow is outward near P_2 and div $\mathbf{F}(P_2)$ is positive.

21.
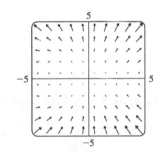

From the graph it appears that for points above the x-axis, vectors starting near a particular point are longer than vectors ending there, so divergence is positive. The opposite is true at points below the x-axis, where divergence is negative.

$\mathbf{F}(x, y) = \langle xy, x + y^2 \rangle \quad \Rightarrow \quad \text{div}\, \mathbf{F} = \tfrac{\partial}{\partial x}(xy) + \tfrac{\partial}{\partial y}(x + y^2) = y + 2y = 3y.$

Thus div $\mathbf{F} > 0$ for $y > 0$, and div $\mathbf{F} < 0$ for $y < 0$.

23. Since $\dfrac{\mathbf{x}}{|\mathbf{x}|^3} = \dfrac{x\mathbf{i} + y\mathbf{j} + z\mathbf{k}}{(x^2 + y^2 + z^2)^{3/2}}$ and $\dfrac{\partial}{\partial x}\left(\dfrac{x}{(x^2 + y^2 + z^2)^{3/2}}\right) = \dfrac{(x^2 + y^2 + z^2) - 3x^2}{(x^2 + y^2 + z^2)^{5/2}}$ with similar expressions

for $\dfrac{\partial}{\partial y}\left(\dfrac{y}{(x^2 + y^2 + z^2)^{3/2}}\right)$ and $\dfrac{\partial}{\partial z}\left(\dfrac{z}{(x^2 + y^2 + z^2)^{3/2}}\right)$, we have

$$\text{div}\left(\dfrac{\mathbf{x}}{|\mathbf{x}|^3}\right) = \dfrac{3(x^2 + y^2 + z^2) - 3(x^2 + y^2 + z^2)}{(x^2 + y^2 + z^2)^{5/2}} = 0, \text{ except at } (0, 0, 0) \text{ where it is undefined.}$$

25. $\iint_S \mathbf{a} \cdot \mathbf{n}\, dS = \iiint_E \text{div}\, \mathbf{a}\, dV = 0$ since div $\mathbf{a} = 0$.

27. $\iint_S \text{curl}\, \mathbf{F} \cdot d\mathbf{S} = \iiint_E \text{div}(\text{curl}\, \mathbf{F})\, dV = 0$ by Theorem 13.5.11.

29. $\iint_S (f\nabla g) \cdot \mathbf{n}\, dS = \iiint_E \text{div}(f\nabla g)\, dV = \iiint_D (f\nabla^2 g + \nabla g \cdot \nabla f)\, dV$ by Exercise 13.5.25.

31. If $\mathbf{c} = c_1\mathbf{i} + c_2\mathbf{j} + c_3\mathbf{k}$ is an arbitrary constant vector, we define $\mathbf{F} = f\mathbf{c} = fc_1\mathbf{i} + fc_2\mathbf{j} + fc_3\mathbf{k}$. Then

$$\operatorname{div}\mathbf{F} = \operatorname{div} f\mathbf{c} = \frac{\partial f}{\partial x}c_1 + \frac{\partial f}{\partial y}c_2 + \frac{\partial f}{\partial z}c_3 = \nabla f \cdot \mathbf{c} \text{ and the Divergence Theorem says } \iint_S \mathbf{F} \cdot d\mathbf{S} = \iiint_E \operatorname{div}\mathbf{F}\,dV \quad\Rightarrow$$

$$\iint_S \mathbf{F} \cdot \mathbf{n}\,dS = \iiint_E \nabla f \cdot \mathbf{c}\,dV. \text{ In particular, if } \mathbf{c} = \mathbf{i} \text{ then } \iint_S f\mathbf{i} \cdot \mathbf{n}\,dS = \iiint_E \nabla f \cdot \mathbf{i}\,dV \quad\Rightarrow$$

$$\iint_S f n_1\,dS = \iiint_E \frac{\partial f}{\partial x}\,dV \text{ (where } \mathbf{n} = n_1\mathbf{i} + n_2\mathbf{j} + n_3\mathbf{k}\text{). Similarly, if } \mathbf{c} = \mathbf{j} \text{ we have } \iint_S f n_2\,dS = \iiint_E \frac{\partial f}{\partial y}\,dV,$$

and $\mathbf{c} = \mathbf{k}$ gives $\displaystyle\iint_S f n_3\,dS = \iiint_E \frac{\partial f}{\partial z}\,dV.$ Then

$$\iint_S f\mathbf{n}\,dS = \left(\iint_S f n_1\,dS\right)\mathbf{i} + \left(\iint_S f n_2\,dS\right)\mathbf{j} + \left(\iint_S f n_3\,dS\right)\mathbf{k}$$

$$= \left(\iiint_E \frac{\partial f}{\partial x}\,dV\right)\mathbf{i} + \left(\iiint_E \frac{\partial f}{\partial y}\,dV\right)\mathbf{j} + \left(\iiint_E \frac{\partial f}{\partial z}\,dV\right)\mathbf{k} = \iiint_E \left(\frac{\partial f}{\partial x}\mathbf{i} + \frac{\partial f}{\partial y}\mathbf{j} + \frac{\partial f}{\partial z}\mathbf{k}\right)dV$$

$$= \iiint_E \nabla f\,dV \quad \text{as desired.}$$

13 Review

CONCEPT CHECK

1. See Definitions 1 and 2 in Section 13.1. A vector field can represent, for example, the wind velocity at any location in space, the speed and direction of the ocean current at any location, or the force vectors of Earth's gravitational field at a location in space.

2. (a) A conservative vector field $\mathbf{F}$ is a vector field which is the gradient of some scalar function f.

   (b) The function f in part (a) is called a potential function for $\mathbf{F}$, that is, $\mathbf{F} = \nabla f$.

3. (a) See Definition 13.2.2.

   (b) We normally evaluate the line integral using Formula 13.2.3.

   (c) The mass is $m = \int_C \rho(x,y)\,ds$, and the center of mass is $(\bar{x},\bar{y})$ where $\bar{x} = \frac{1}{m}\int_C x\rho(x,y)\,ds$, $\bar{y} = \frac{1}{m}\int_C y\rho(x,y)\,ds$.

   (d) See (5) and (6) in Section 13.2 for plane curves; we have similar definitions when C is a space curve
   [see the equation preceding (10) in Section 13.2].

   (e) For plane curves, see Equations 13.2.7. We have similar results for space curves
   [see the equation preceding (10) in Section 13.2].

4. (a) See Definition 13.2.13.

   (b) If $\mathbf{F}$ is a force field, $\int_C \mathbf{F} \cdot d\mathbf{r}$ represents the work done by $\mathbf{F}$ in moving a particle along the curve C.

   (c) $\int_C \mathbf{F} \cdot d\mathbf{r} = \int_C P\,dx + Q\,dy + R\,dz$

5. See Theorem 13.3.2.

6. (a) $\int_C \mathbf{F} \cdot d\mathbf{r}$ is independent of path if the line integral has the same value for any two curves that have the same initial and terminal points.

   (b) See Theorem 13.3.4.

7. See the statement of Green's Theorem on page 934.

8. See Equations 13.4.5.

9. (a) $\operatorname{curl} \mathbf{F} = \left(\dfrac{\partial R}{\partial y} - \dfrac{\partial Q}{\partial z} \right) \mathbf{i} + \left(\dfrac{\partial P}{\partial z} - \dfrac{\partial R}{\partial x} \right) \mathbf{j} + \left(\dfrac{\partial Q}{\partial x} - \dfrac{\partial P}{\partial y} \right) \mathbf{k} = \nabla \times \mathbf{F}$

(b) $\operatorname{div} \mathbf{F} = \dfrac{\partial P}{\partial x} + \dfrac{\partial Q}{\partial y} + \dfrac{\partial R}{\partial z} = \nabla \cdot \mathbf{F}$

(c) For curl $\mathbf{F}$, see the discussion accompanying Figure 1 on page 944 as well as Figure 6 and the accompanying discussion on page 964. For div $\mathbf{F}$, see the discussion following Example 5 on page 945 as well as the discussion preceding (8) on page 971.

10. See Theorem 13.3.6; see Theorem 13.5.4.

11. (a) See (1) in Section 13.6.

(b) We normally evaluate the surface integral using Formula 13.6.2.

(c) See Formula 13.6.4.

(d) The mass is $m = \iint_S \rho(x, y, z) \, dS$ and the center of mass is $(\bar{x}, \bar{y}, \bar{z})$ where $\bar{x} = \frac{1}{m} \iint_S x\rho(x, y, z) \, dS$, $\bar{y} = \frac{1}{m} \iint_S y\rho(x, y, z) \, dS$, $\bar{z} = \frac{1}{m} \iint_S z\rho(x, y, z) \, dS$.

12. (a) See Figures 6 and 7 and the accompanying discussion in Section 13.6. A Möbius strip is a nonorientable surface; see Figures 4 and 5 and the accompanying discussion on page 953.

(b) See Definition 13.6.8.

(c) See Formula 13.6.9.

(d) See Formula 13.6.10.

13. See the statement of Stokes' Theorem on page 961.

14. See the statement of the Divergence Theorem on page 967.

15. In each theorem, we have an integral of a "derivative" over a region on the left side, while the right side involves the values of the original function only on the boundary of the region.

TRUE-FALSE QUIZ

1. False; div $\mathbf{F}$ is a scalar field.

3. True, by Theorem 13.5.3 and the fact that div $\mathbf{0} = 0$.

5. False. See Exercise 13.3.35. (But the assertion is true if D is simply-connected; see Theorem 13.3.6.)

7. True. Apply the Divergence Theorem and use the fact that div $\mathbf{F} = 0$.

EXERCISES

1. (a) Vectors starting on C point in roughly the direction opposite to C, so the tangential component $\mathbf{F} \cdot \mathbf{T}$ is negative.
Thus $\int_C \mathbf{F} \cdot d\mathbf{r} = \int_C \mathbf{F} \cdot \mathbf{T}\, ds$ is negative.

(b) The vectors that end near P are shorter than the vectors that start near P, so the net flow is outward near P and $\operatorname{div} \mathbf{F}(P)$ is positive.

3. $\int_C yz \cos x \, ds = \int_0^\pi (3\cos t)(3\sin t) \cos t \sqrt{(1)^2 + (-3\sin t)^2 + (3\cos t)^2}\, dt = \int_0^\pi (9\cos^2 t \,\sin t)\sqrt{10}\, dt$

$$= 9\sqrt{10}\left(-\tfrac{1}{3}\cos^3 t\right)\Big]_0^\pi = -3\sqrt{10}\,(-2) = 6\sqrt{10}$$

5. $\int_C y^3\, dx + x^2\, dy = \int_{-1}^1 \left[y^3(-2y) + (1-y^2)^2\right] dy = \int_{-1}^1 (-y^4 - 2y^2 + 1)\, dy$

$$= \left[-\tfrac{1}{5}y^5 - \tfrac{2}{3}y^3 + y\right]_{-1}^1 = -\tfrac{1}{5} - \tfrac{2}{3} + 1 - \tfrac{1}{5} - \tfrac{2}{3} + 1 = \tfrac{4}{15}$$

7. $C\colon\; x = 1 + 2t \;\Rightarrow\; dx = 2\, dt,\, y = 4t \;\Rightarrow\; dy = 4\, dt,\, z = -1 + 3t \;\Rightarrow\; dz = 3\, dt,\, 0 \le t \le 1.$

$$\int_C xy\, dx + y^2\, dy + yz\, dz = \int_0^1 \left[(1+2t)(4t)(2) + (4t)^2(4) + (4t)(-1+3t)(3)\right] dt$$

$$= \int_0^1 (116t^2 - 4t)\, dt = \left[\tfrac{116}{3}t^3 - 2t^2\right]_0^1 = \tfrac{116}{3} - 2 = \tfrac{110}{3}$$

9. $\mathbf{F}(\mathbf{r}(t)) = e^{-t}\mathbf{i} + t^2(-t)\mathbf{j} + (t^2 + t^3)\,\mathbf{k},\; \mathbf{r}'(t) = 2t\,\mathbf{i} + 3t^2\,\mathbf{j} - \mathbf{k}$ and

$$\int_C \mathbf{F} \cdot d\mathbf{r} = \int_0^1 \left(2te^{-t} - 3t^5 - (t^2 + t^3)\right) dt = \left[-2te^{-t} - 2e^{-t} - \tfrac{1}{2}t^6 - \tfrac{1}{3}t^3 - \tfrac{1}{4}t^4\right]_0^1 = \tfrac{11}{12} - \tfrac{4}{e}.$$

11. $\frac{\partial}{\partial y}\left[(1+xy)e^{xy}\right] = 2xe^{xy} + x^2ye^{xy} = \frac{\partial}{\partial x}\left[e^y + x^2e^{xy}\right]$ and the domain of $\mathbf{F}$ is $\mathbb{R}^2$, so $\mathbf{F}$ is conservative. Thus there exists a function f such that $\mathbf{F} = \nabla f$. Then $f_y(x, y) = e^y + x^2e^{xy}$ implies $f(x, y) = e^y + xe^{xy} + g(x)$ and then $f_x(x, y) = xye^{xy} + e^{xy} + g'(x) = (1 + xy)e^{xy} + g'(x)$. But $f_x(x, y) = (1 + xy)e^{xy}$, so $g'(x) = 0 \;\Rightarrow\; g(x) = K$. Thus $f(x, y) = e^y + xe^{xy} + K$ is a potential function for $\mathbf{F}$.

13. Since $\frac{\partial}{\partial y}\left(4x^3y^2 - 2xy^3\right) = 8x^3y - 6xy^2 = \frac{\partial}{\partial x}\left(2x^4y - 3x^2y^2 + 4y^3\right)$ and the domain of $\mathbf{F}$ is $\mathbb{R}^2$, $\mathbf{F}$ is conservative. Furthermore $f(x, y) = x^4y^2 - x^2y^3 + y^4$ is a potential function for $\mathbf{F}$. $t = 0$ corresponds to the point $(0, 1)$ and $t = 1$ corresponds to $(1, 1)$, so $\int_C \mathbf{F} \cdot d\mathbf{r} = f(1, 1) - f(0, 1) = 1 - 1 = 0.$

15. $C_1\colon \mathbf{r}(t) = t\,\mathbf{i} + t^2\,\mathbf{j},\, -1 \le t \le 1;$

$C_2\colon \mathbf{r}(t) = -t\,\mathbf{i} + \mathbf{j},\, -1 \le t \le 1.$

Then

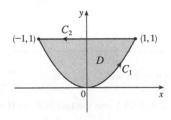

$$\int_C xy^2\, dx - x^2y\, dy = \int_{-1}^1 (t^5 - 2t^5)\, dt + \int_{-1}^1 t\, dt$$

$$= \left[-\tfrac{1}{6}t^6\right]_{-1}^1 + \left[\tfrac{1}{2}t^2\right]_{-1}^1 = 0$$

Using Green's Theorem, we have

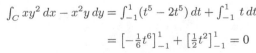

$$\int_C xy^2\, dx - x^2y\, dy = \iint_D \left[\frac{\partial}{\partial x}(-x^2y) - \frac{\partial}{\partial y}(xy^2)\right] dA = \iint_D (-2xy - 2xy)\, dA = \int_{-1}^1 \int_{x^2}^1 -4xy\, dy\, dx$$

$$= \int_{-1}^1 \left[-2xy^2\right]_{y=x^2}^{y=1}\, dx = \int_{-1}^1 (2x^5 - 2x)\, dx = \left[\tfrac{1}{3}x^6 - x^2\right]_{-1}^1 = 0$$

17. $\int_C x^2 y\, dx - xy^2\, dy = \iint\limits_{x^2+y^2\le 4} \left[\frac{\partial}{\partial x}(-xy^2) - \frac{\partial}{\partial y}(x^2 y) \right] dA = \iint\limits_{x^2+y^2\le 4} (-y^2 - x^2)\, dA = -\int_0^{2\pi}\int_0^2 r^3\, dr\, d\theta = -8\pi$

19. If we assume there is such a vector field $\mathbf{G}$, then $\operatorname{div}(\operatorname{curl} \mathbf{G}) = 2 + 3z - 2xz$. But $\operatorname{div}(\operatorname{curl} \mathbf{F}) = 0$ for all vector fields $\mathbf{F}$.

Thus such a $\mathbf{G}$ cannot exist.

21. For any piecewise-smooth simple closed plane curve C bounding a region D, we can apply Green's Theorem to

$\mathbf{F}(x, y) = f(x)\, \mathbf{i} + g(y)\, \mathbf{j}$ to get $\int_C f(x)\, dx + g(y)\, dy = \iint_D \left[\frac{\partial}{\partial x} g(y) - \frac{\partial}{\partial y} f(x) \right] dA = \iint_D 0\, dA = 0.$

23. $\nabla^2 f = 0$ means that $\dfrac{\partial^2 f}{\partial x^2} + \dfrac{\partial^2 f}{\partial y^2} = 0$. Now if $\mathbf{F} = f_y\, \mathbf{i} - f_x\, \mathbf{j}$ and C is any closed path in D, then applying Green's

Theorem, we get

$$\int_C \mathbf{F} \cdot d\mathbf{r} = \int_C f_y\, dx - f_x\, dy = \iint_D \left[\frac{\partial}{\partial x}(-f_x) - \frac{\partial}{\partial y}(f_y) \right] dA$$

$$= -\iint_D (f_{xx} + f_{yy})\, dA = -\iint_D 0\, dA = 0$$

Therefore the line integral is independent of path, by Theorem 13.3.3.

25. $z = f(x, y) = x^2 + y^2$ with $0 \le x^2 + y^2 \le 4$ so $\mathbf{r}_x \times \mathbf{r}_y = -2x\, \mathbf{i} - 2y\, \mathbf{j} + \mathbf{k}$ (using upward orientation). Then

$$\iint_S z\, dS = \iint\limits_{x^2+y^2\le 4} (x^2 + y^2) \sqrt{4x^2 + 4y^2 + 1}\, dA$$

$$= \int_0^{2\pi}\int_0^2 r^3 \sqrt{1 + 4r^2}\, dr\, d\theta = \tfrac{1}{60}\pi \left(391\sqrt{17} + 1 \right)$$

(Substitute $u = 1 + 4r^2$ and use tables.)

27. Since the sphere bounds a simple solid region, the Divergence Theorem applies and

$$\iint_S \mathbf{F} \cdot d\mathbf{S} = \iiint_E \operatorname{div} \mathbf{F}\, dV = \iiint_E (z - 2)\, dV = \iiint_E z\, dV - 2\iiint_E dV$$

$$= 0 \begin{bmatrix} \text{odd function in } z \\ \text{and } E \text{ is symmetric} \end{bmatrix} - 2 \cdot V(E) = -2 \cdot \tfrac{4}{3}\pi(2)^3 = -\tfrac{64}{3}\pi$$

Alternate solution: $\mathbf{F}(\mathbf{r}(\phi, \theta)) = 4\sin\phi\,\cos\theta\,\cos\phi\,\mathbf{i} - 4\sin\phi\,\sin\theta\,\mathbf{j} + 6\sin\phi\,\cos\theta\,\mathbf{k}$,

$\mathbf{r}_\phi \times \mathbf{r}_\theta = 4\sin^2\phi\,\cos\theta\,\mathbf{i} + 4\sin^2\phi\,\sin\theta\,\mathbf{j} + 4\sin\phi\,\cos\phi\,\mathbf{k}$, and

$\mathbf{F} \cdot (\mathbf{r}_\phi \times \mathbf{r}_\theta) = 16\sin^3\phi\,\cos^2\theta\,\cos\phi - 16\sin^3\phi\,\sin^2\theta + 24\sin^2\phi\,\cos\phi\,\cos\theta.$ Then

$$\iint_S \mathbf{F} \cdot d\mathbf{S} = \int_0^{2\pi}\int_0^\pi (16\sin^3\phi\,\cos\phi\,\cos^2\theta - 16\sin^3\phi\,\sin^2\theta + 24\sin^2\phi\,\cos\phi\,\cos\theta)\, d\phi\, d\theta$$

$$= \int_0^{2\pi} \tfrac{4}{3}(-16\sin^2\theta)\, d\theta = -\tfrac{64}{3}\pi$$

29. Since $\operatorname{curl} \mathbf{F} = 0$, $\iint_S (\operatorname{curl} \mathbf{F}) \cdot d\mathbf{S} = 0$. We parametrize C: $\mathbf{r}(t) = \cos t\, \mathbf{i} + \sin t\, \mathbf{j}$, $0 \le t \le 2\pi$ and

$\oint_C \mathbf{F} \cdot d\mathbf{r} = \int_0^{2\pi} (-\cos^2 t\,\sin t + \sin^2 t\,\cos t)\, dt = \left[\tfrac{1}{3}\cos^3 t + \tfrac{1}{3}\sin^3 t \right]_0^{2\pi} = 0.$

31. The surface is given by $x + y + z = 1$ or $z = 1 - x - y$, $0 \le x \le 1$, $0 \le y \le 1 - x$ and $\mathbf{r}_x \times \mathbf{r}_y = \mathbf{i} + \mathbf{j} + \mathbf{k}$. Then

$\oint_C \mathbf{F} \cdot d\mathbf{r} = \iint_S \operatorname{curl} \mathbf{F} \cdot d\mathbf{S} = \iint_D (-y\, \mathbf{i} - z\, \mathbf{j} - x\, \mathbf{k}) \cdot (\mathbf{i} + \mathbf{j} + \mathbf{k})\, dA = \iint_D (-1)\, dA = -(\text{area of } D) = -\tfrac{1}{2}.$

33. $\iiint_E \operatorname{div} \mathbf{F} \, dV = \iiint\limits_{x^2 + y^2 + z^2 \le 1} 3 \, dV = 3(\text{volume of sphere}) = 4\pi$. Then

$\mathbf{F}(\mathbf{r}(\phi, \theta)) \cdot (\mathbf{r}_\phi \times \mathbf{r}_\theta) = \sin^3 \phi \cos^2 \theta + \sin^3 \phi \sin^2 \theta + \sin \phi \cos^2 \phi = \sin \phi$ and

$\iint_S \mathbf{F} \cdot d\mathbf{S} = \int_0^{2\pi} \int_0^\pi \sin \phi \, d\phi \, d\theta = (2\pi)(2) = 4\pi$.

35. Because $\operatorname{curl} \mathbf{F} = \mathbf{0}$, $\mathbf{F}$ is conservative, so there exists a function f such that $\nabla f = \mathbf{F}$. Then $f_x(x, y, z) = 3x^2 yz - 3y$

implies $f(x, y, z) = x^3 yz - 3xy + g(y, z) \;\Rightarrow\; f_y(x, y, z) = x^3 z - 3x + g_y(y, z)$. But $f_y(x, y, z) = x^3 z - 3x$, so

$g(y, z) = h(z)$ and $f(x, y, z) = x^3 yz - 3xy + h(z)$. Then $f_z(x, y, z) = x^3 y + h'(z)$ but $f_z(x, y, z) = x^3 y + 2z$,

so $h(z) = z^2 + K$ and a potential function for $\mathbf{F}$ is $f(x, y, z) = x^3 yz - 3xy + z^2$. Hence

$\int_C \mathbf{F} \cdot d\mathbf{r} = \int_C \nabla f \cdot d\mathbf{r} = f(0, 3, 0) - f(0, 0, 2) = 0 - 4 = -4$.

37. By the Divergence Theorem, $\iint_S \mathbf{F} \cdot \mathbf{n} \, dS = \iiint_E \operatorname{div} \mathbf{F} \, dV = 3(\text{volume of } E) = 3(8 - 1) = 21$.

1. Let S_1 be the portion of $\Omega(S)$ between $S(a)$ and S, and let ∂S_1 be its boundary. Also let S_L be the lateral surface of S_1 [that is, the surface of S_1 except S and $S(a)$]. Applying the Divergence Theorem we have $\displaystyle\iint_{\partial S_1} \frac{\mathbf{r}\cdot\mathbf{n}}{r^3}\,dS = \iiint_{S_1} \nabla\cdot\frac{\mathbf{r}}{r^3}\,dV.$

But

$$\nabla\cdot\frac{\mathbf{r}}{r^3} = \left\langle \frac{\partial}{\partial x}, \frac{\partial}{\partial y}, \frac{\partial}{\partial z}\right\rangle \cdot \left\langle \frac{x}{(x^2+y^2+z^2)^{3/2}}, \frac{y}{(x^2+y^2+z^2)^{3/2}}, \frac{z}{(x^2+y^2+z^2)^{3/2}}\right\rangle$$

$$= \frac{(x^2+y^2+z^2-3x^2)+(x^2+y^2+z^2-3y^2)+(x^2+y^2+z^2-3z^2)}{(x^2+y^2+z^2)^{5/2}} = 0$$

$\Rightarrow \displaystyle\iint_{\partial S_1} \frac{\mathbf{r}\cdot\mathbf{n}}{r^3}\,dS = \iiint_{S_1} 0\,dV = 0.$ On the other hand, notice that for the surfaces of ∂S_1 other than $S(a)$ and S,

$\mathbf{r}\cdot\mathbf{n} = 0 \Rightarrow$

$$0 = \iint_{\partial S_1} \frac{\mathbf{r}\cdot\mathbf{n}}{r^3}\,dS = \iint_S \frac{\mathbf{r}\cdot\mathbf{n}}{r^3}\,dS + \iint_{S(a)} \frac{\mathbf{r}\cdot\mathbf{n}}{r^3}\,dS + \iint_{S_L} \frac{\mathbf{r}\cdot\mathbf{n}}{r^3}\,dS = \iint_S \frac{\mathbf{r}\cdot\mathbf{n}}{r^3}\,dS + \iint_{S(a)} \frac{\mathbf{r}\cdot\mathbf{n}}{r^3}\,dS \Rightarrow$$

$\displaystyle\iint_S \frac{\mathbf{r}\cdot\mathbf{n}}{r^3}\,dS = -\iint_{S(a)} \frac{\mathbf{r}\cdot\mathbf{n}}{r^3}\,dS.$ Notice that on $S(a)$, $r = a \Rightarrow \mathbf{n} = -\dfrac{\mathbf{r}}{r} = -\dfrac{\mathbf{r}}{a}$ and $\mathbf{r}\cdot\mathbf{r} = r^2 = a^2$, so

that $-\displaystyle\iint_{S(a)} \frac{\mathbf{r}\cdot\mathbf{n}}{r^3}\,dS = \iint_{S(a)} \frac{\mathbf{r}\cdot\mathbf{r}}{a^4}\,dS = \iint_{S(a)} \frac{a^2}{a^4}\,dS = \frac{1}{a^2}\iint_{S(a)}\,dS = \frac{\text{area of } S(a)}{a^2} = |\Omega(S)|.$

Therefore $|\Omega(S)| = \displaystyle\iint_S \frac{\mathbf{r}\cdot\mathbf{n}}{r^3}\,dS.$

3. Let $\mathbf{F} = \mathbf{a}\times\mathbf{r} = \langle a_1, a_2, a_3\rangle \times \langle x, y, z\rangle = \langle a_2 z - a_3 y, a_3 x - a_1 z, a_1 y - a_2 x\rangle.$ Then curl $\mathbf{F} = \langle 2a_1, 2a_2, 2a_3\rangle = 2\mathbf{a}$, and $\iint_S 2\mathbf{a}\cdot d\mathbf{S} = \iint_S \text{curl }\mathbf{F}\cdot d\mathbf{S} = \int_C \mathbf{F}\cdot d\mathbf{r} = \int_C (\mathbf{a}\times\mathbf{r})\cdot d\mathbf{r}$ by Stokes' Theorem.

5. The given line integral $\frac{1}{2}\int_C (bz - cy)\,dx + (cx - az)\,dy + (ay - bx)\,dz$ can be expressed as $\int_C \mathbf{F}\cdot d\mathbf{r}$ if we define the vector field $\mathbf{F}$ by $\mathbf{F}(x,y,z) = P\mathbf{i} + Q\mathbf{j} + R\mathbf{k} = \frac{1}{2}(bz - cy)\mathbf{i} + \frac{1}{2}(cx - az)\mathbf{j} + \frac{1}{2}(ay - bx)\mathbf{k}.$ Then define S to be the planar interior of C, so S is an oriented, smooth surface. Stokes' Theorem says $\int_C \mathbf{F}\cdot d\mathbf{r} = \iint_S \text{curl }\mathbf{F}\cdot d\mathbf{S} = \iint_S \text{curl }\mathbf{F}\cdot\mathbf{n}\,dS.$ Now

$$\text{curl }\mathbf{F} = \left(\frac{\partial R}{\partial y} - \frac{\partial Q}{\partial z}\right)\mathbf{i} + \left(\frac{\partial P}{\partial z} - \frac{\partial R}{\partial x}\right)\mathbf{j} + \left(\frac{\partial Q}{\partial x} - \frac{\partial P}{\partial y}\right)\mathbf{k}$$

$$= \left(\tfrac{1}{2}a + \tfrac{1}{2}a\right)\mathbf{i} + \left(\tfrac{1}{2}b + \tfrac{1}{2}b\right)\mathbf{j} + \left(\tfrac{1}{2}c + \tfrac{1}{2}c\right)\mathbf{k} = a\mathbf{i} + b\mathbf{j} + c\mathbf{k} = \mathbf{n}$$

so curl $\mathbf{F}\cdot\mathbf{n} = \mathbf{n}\cdot\mathbf{n} = |\mathbf{n}|^2 = 1$, hence $\iint_S \text{curl }\mathbf{F}\cdot\mathbf{n}\,dS = \iint_S\,dS$ which is simply the surface area of S. Thus, $\int_C \mathbf{F}\cdot d\mathbf{r} = \frac{1}{2}\int_C (bz - cy)\,dx + (cx - az)\,dy + (ay - bx)\,dz$ is the plane area enclosed by C.